Let's share our passion
for the greatest game of all

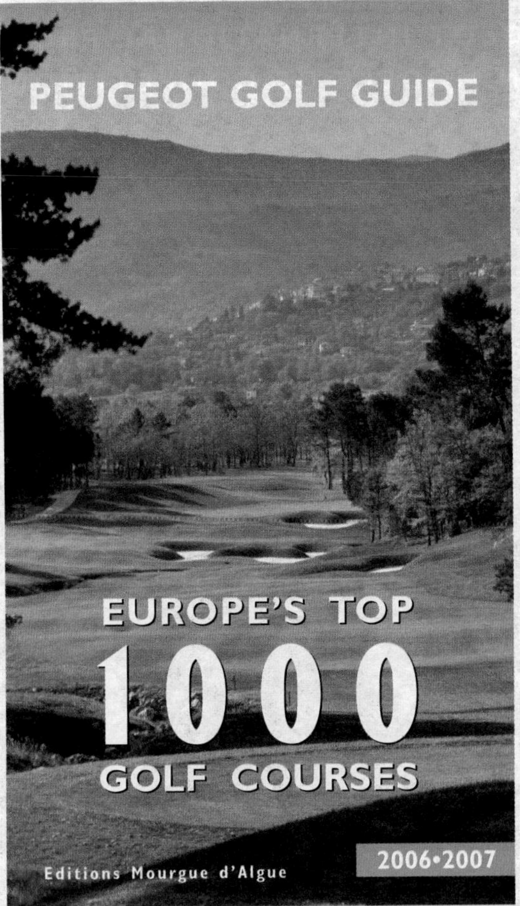

Picture acknowledgement for the cover/Photo de couverture :
Four Seasons at Terre Blanche/Brian Morgan

Founder/Fondateur : Dominique Motte
General Coordination for Inspection Teams/Coordinateur Rédactionnel : Denys Lémery

Editions MOURGUE d'ALGUE
Golf Européen Holding: 16, chemin du golf, F-78860 Saint-Nom-la-Bretèche,
www.peugeotgolfguide.com

Prices in the Guide as of end 2005, for guidance only.
Les Tarifs indiqués dans le Guide sont à fin 2005, et restent purements indicatifs.

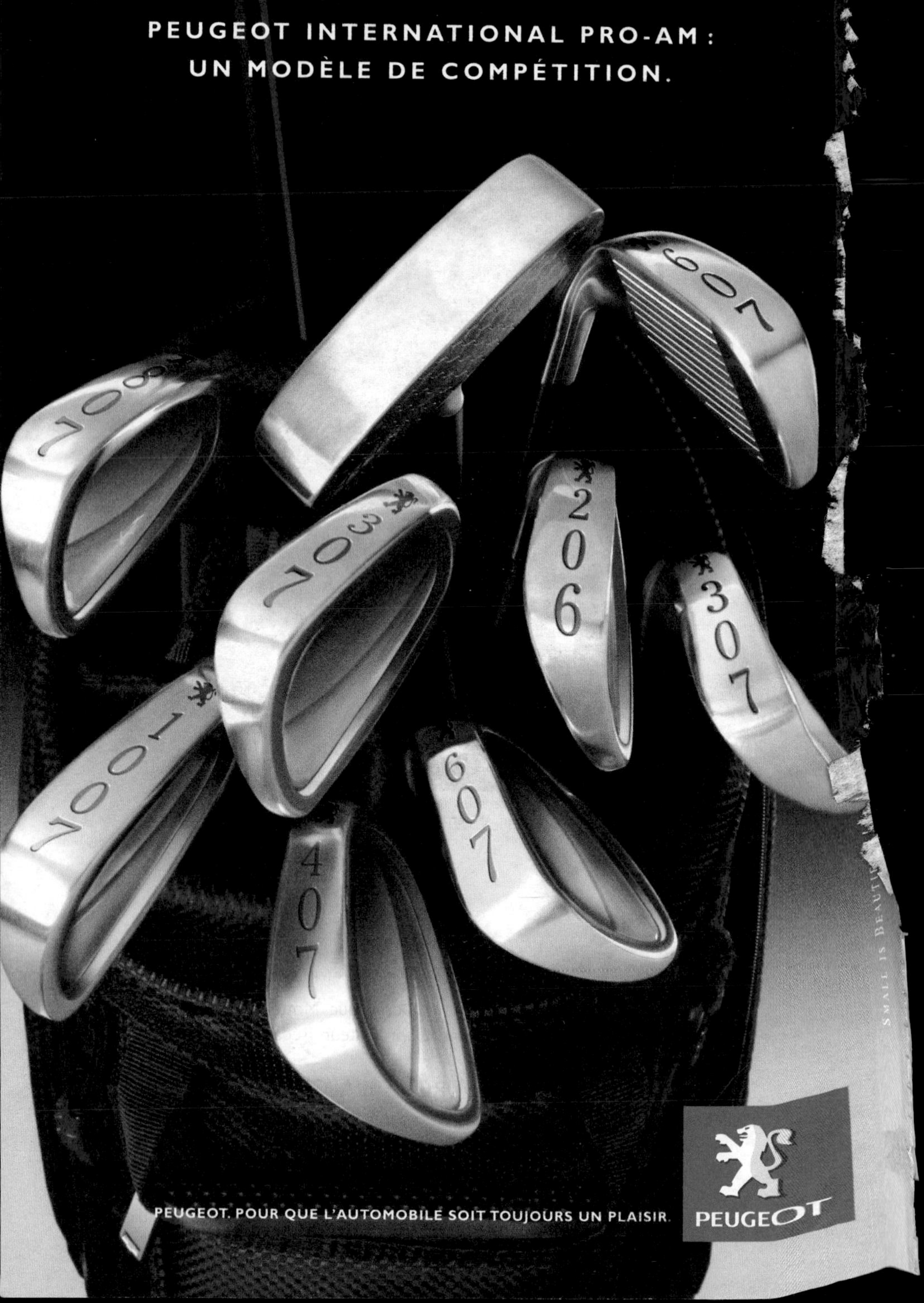

PEUGEOT INTERNATIONAL PRO-AM :
UN MODÈLE DE COMPÉTITION.

PEUGEOT. POUR QUE L'AUTOMOBILE SOIT TOUJOURS UN PLAISIR.

Since the building of the first corporate golf course by Jean-Pierre Peugeot in 1929, Automobiles Peugeot has constantly extended its commitment to the world of golf. The sponsor of the Peugeot French Open for 14 years, an official sponsor of the Lancôme Trophy up until 2003 and, since 2004, the organizer of the Peugeot International Pro-Am, Peugeot has, for the past 20 years and more, been involved with amateur golfers from around the world with the Peugeot Challenge Cup, which today is played in more than 30 countries.
To share its passion for golf still further, Peugeot proposes this guide to the best European golf courses which, I hope, will help you have a fabulous time golfing around Europe.
Happy reading.

Depuis la création du premier golf d'entreprise par Jean-Pierre Peugeot en 1929, Automobiles Peugeot n'a cessé d'accroître son engagement dans le milieu golfique. Parrain du Peugeot Open de France pendant 14 années, partenaire officiel du Trophée Lancôme jusqu'en 2003 et organisateur depuis 2004 du Peugeot International Pro Am à Paris, Peugeot part depuis plus de 20 ans à la rencontre des amateurs du monde entier avec la Peugeot Challenge Cup, qui se joue aujourd'hui dans plus de 30 pays.
Et pour encore mieux partager sa passion du golf, Peugeot vous propose ce guide des meilleurs golfs d'Europe qui, je l'espère, vous permettra de fouler de fabuleux greens !
Bonne lecture.

Seit Jean-Pierre Peugeot im Jahre 1929 den ersten Firmengolfplatz erbauen ließ, ist das Engagement von Peugeot in der Welt des Golf ständig gewachsen. 14 Jahre lang war Peugeot Hauptsponsor der Peugeot French Open, bis 2003 unterstützte der Automobilhersteller die Lancôme Trophy und seit 2004 nun das Peugeot International Pro-Am. In den vergangenen 20 Jahren haben Amateurgolfer in aller Welt am Peugeot Challenge Cup, der heute in mehr als dreißig Ländern ausgetragen wird, teilgenommen. Dieser Führer ist ein weiterer Beleg für die Golfleidenschaft des Hauses Peugeot und ich hoffe unser Guide hilft Ihnen, großartige Stunden auf Europas besten Plätzen zu erleben.

Sedan Jean-Pierre Peugeot 1929 byggde den allra första företagsbanan har Automobiles Peugeot hela tiden utökat sitt engagemang inom golfen. Man har varit sponsor för Peugeot French Open i 14 år, sponsrat Lancôme Trophy fram till 2003 och sedan 2004 har man arrangerat Peugeot International Pro-Am. Med Peugeot Challenge Cup, som i dag spelas i över 30 länder, har Peugeot engagerat sig för amatörgolfen.
För att ytterligare dela med oss av vår passion för golfsporten presenterar Peugeot här de bästa banorna i Europa. Jag hoppas guiden kommer att bidra till att ge dig många fantastiska stunder på Europas golfbanor.
Trevlig läsning!

Desde que Jean Pierre Peugeot decidió en 1929 la construcción del primer campo de golf corporativo, el compromiso de «Automobiles Peugeot» con el mundo del golf ha estado en progresión constante. Patrocinador exclusivo del Open de Francia Peugeot durante 14 años, patrocinador oficial del Trofeo Lancôme hasta 2003 y, desde 2004, organizador del «Peugeot International Pro-Am», la firma Peugeot ha patrocinado asimismo el Abierto de España Peugeot entre 1986 y 2000, además sostiene desde 2001 el Circuito profesional español con el Peugeot Tour de Golf, y lleva más de 20 años fomentando el golf amateur por todo el mundo con la Peugeot Challenge Cup, que se juega en más de 30 países.
Para seguir compartiendo aún más nuestra pasión por el golf, Peugeot ofrece esta guía de los mejores campos de golf de Europa, que espero pueda proporcionar a sus lectores grandes satisfacciones en tantos recorridos europeos excepcionales.
Buena lectura.

Dopo la realizzazione del primo campo di golf aziendale, voluto da Jean-Pierre Peugeot nel 1929, la Automobili Peugeot ha costantemente ampliato il proprio impegno nel mondo del golf. E' stata title sponsor dell'Open di Francia per 14 anni, sponsor ufficiale del Trofeo Lancôme sino al 2003 e dal 2004 organizzatrice del Peugeot International Pro-Am. Inoltre è impegnata da più di 20 anni con la Peugeot Challenge Cup, circuito di gare per dilettanti che si gioca in più di 30 paesi nel mondo.
Per condividere ancora di più la sua passione per il golf, Peugeot propone questa guida ai migliori campi in Europa che, mi auguro, vi farà trascorrere giornate di golf indimenticabili.
Buon divertimento.

Christian Peugeot
Directeur Marketing et Client

PEUGEOT

René Lacoste 1927

LACOSTE

www.lacoste.com

COMMENT UTILISER LE PEUGEOT GOLF GUIDE

17	6	5		
1 → 20	1 → 10	1 → 10		
Score for the course	**Score for the club house**	**Score for hotel facilities**	**Recommended golfing stay**	**Recommended holidays**
Note du parcours	Note du club house et annexes	Note de l'environnement hotelier	Séjour de golf recommandé	Vacances recommandées

Moliets 17 | 6 | 5

Ce parcours remarquable et généralement bien entretenu a été réalisé dans la forêt de pins des Landes (treize trous), et en bord de mer (cinq trous). L'architecte Robert Trent Jones l'a signé par son esthétique, mais aussi par des enjeux techniques et stratégiques très variés dénotant une connaissance profonde du golf : si les joueurs de haut niveau y trouveront un "challenge" difficile, partir des départs avancés permet davantage d'erreurs. Visuellement, ses fameux bunkers dentelés défendent remarquablement les greens aux surfaces modelées sans excès, dont trois sont pratiquement aveugles. Les larges fairways favorisent le rythme de jeu, et le sol sablonneux permet de jouer facilement toute l'année : quelques drainages nécessaires ont ainsi été effectués (notamment au 4). Il n'est pas trop fatigant, mais les distances entre les trous sont très importantes... Un bon 9 trous occupe les débutants de la famille, et un centre d'entraînement très complet permet de se perfectionner. Un regret, l'immobilier trop proche des trous.

This remarkable and well-maintained course was laid out in the pine forests of Les Landes and along the coast (five holes). Welcome to a typical Robert Trent Jones design, where detail to style and the very varied technical and strategic challenges reflect an in-depth knowledge of golf. While the more proficient golfer will find this a tough challenge, playing from the forward tees is, funnily enough, often more conducive to error. The famous jagged bunkers are a remarkable form of defence for the green, and the putting surfaces are neatly but never excessively contoured. The wide fairways help speed up the game and the sandy sub-soil keeps the course easily playable all year. This is not a tiring course but distances between holes are very long, so be warned. A good adjoining 9 hole course is ideal for beginners in the family and a very comprehensive training centre is just the job for getting that handicap down. The one regret is the property scheme, sometimes too close for comfort.

Golf de Moliets 1989
Rue Mathieu Desbieys
F - 40660 MOLIETS

Office	Secrétariat	(33) 05 58 48 54 65
Pro shop	Pro-shop	(33) 05 58 48 54 65
Fax	Fax	(33) 05 58 48 54 88
Web		www.golfmoliets.com
Situation	Situation	Dax 35 km - Bayonne 40 km
Annual closure	Fermeture annuelle	no

1 week at end of 03 and of 09 (1 semaine fin 03 et fin 09)

Weekly closure Fermeture hebdomadaire — no

Fees main season Tarifs haute saison — 18 holes

	Week days Semaine	We/Bank holidays We/Férié
Individual Individuel	€ 57,20	€ 57,20
Couple Couple	€ 114,20	€ 114,20

Juniors and students (under 24): € 28,6

Caddie Caddie no — **Electric Trolley** Chariot électrique no

Buggy Voiturette yes — **Clubs** Clubs yes

Credit cards Cartes de crédit
VISA - CB - Eurocard - MasterCard

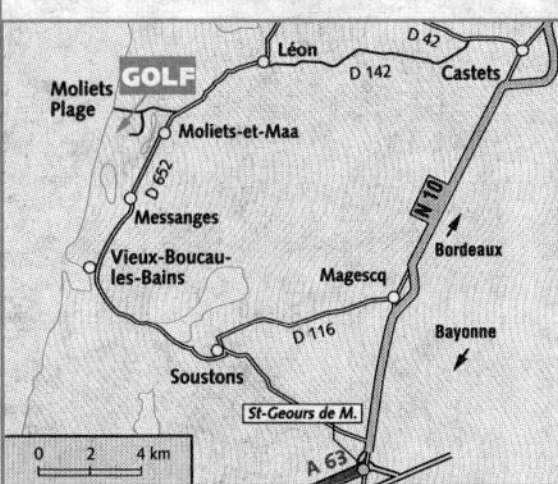

Access Accès : • Bordeaux, N10 → Castets. D142 → Léon, Moliets • Bayonne, N10 → Magescq, D116 → Soustons, D652 → Vieux-Boucau-les-Bains, Moliets
Map 12 on page 182 Carte 12 Page 182

GOLF COURSE — PARCOURS 17/20

Site	Site	
Maintenance	Entretien	
Architect	Architecte	Robert Trent Jones
Type	Type	forest, links
Relief	Relief	
Water in play	Eau en jeu	
Exp. to wind	Exposé au vent	
Trees in play	Arbres en jeu	

Scorecard Carte de score	**Chp.** Chp.	**Mens** Mess.	**Ladies** Da.
Length Long.	6173	5504	4653
Par	72	72	72
Slope system	133	128	126

Advised golfing ability Niveau de jeu recommandé — 0 12 24 36
Hcp required Handicap exigé — 36

293

CLUB HOUSE & AMENITIES — CLUB HOUSE ET ANNEXES 6/10

Pro shop Pro-shop
Driving range Practice
Sheltered couvert 10 mats - On grass sur herbe no - 20 mats open air - Putting-green putting-green yes
Pitching-green pitching green yes

HOTEL FACILITIES — ENVIRONNEMENT HOTELIER 5/10

HOTELS HÔTELS
Hôtel du Golf - 40 rooms, D € 1069 (7 days) - on site
Tel (33) 05 58 49 16 00, Fax (33) 05 58 49 16 29
Relais de la Poste - 17 rooms, D € 175 - Magescq 20 km
Tel (33) 05 58 47 70 25, Fax (33) 05 58 47 76 17
Côte d'Argent - 36 rooms, D € 50 - Vieux-Boucau 10 km
Tel (33) 05 58 48 13 17, Fax (33) 05 58 48 01 15

RESTAURANTS RESTAURANTS
Cabanon et Grange aux Canards - Magescq 21 km
Tel (33) 05 58 47 71 51
Relais de la Poste - Magescq 20 km - Tel (33) 05 58 47 70 25
Marinero - Vieux-Boucau 10 km - Tel (33) 05 58 48 14 15

PEUGEOT GOLF GUIDE 2006/2007

Scale from 0 to 10
Echelle de valeur de 0 à 10

Dreadful / Exécrable
Excellent / Parfait
Little / Peu
Much / Beaucoup
0 12 24 36
Advised golfing ability (HCP)
Niveau de jeu recommandé

Reference to Michelin maps
Renvoi aux cartes Michelin

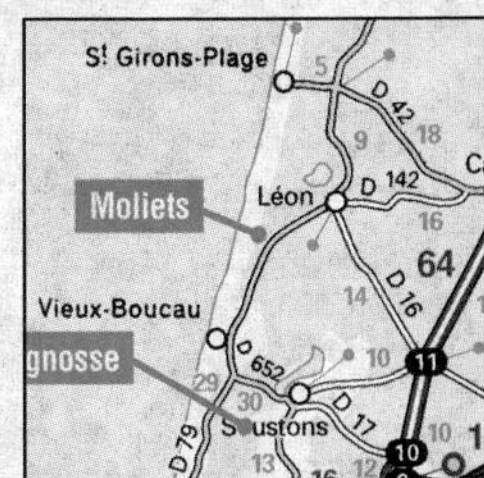

WIE DER PEUGEOT GOLF GUIDE BENUTZ WIRD

SÅ HÄR ANVÄNDER DU PEUGEOT GOLF GUIDE

16	8	7		
1 → 20	1 → 10	1 → 10		
Benotung des Golfplatzes	**Benotung des Klubhauses**	**Benotung des Hotelangebots**	**Empfohlener Golf Aufenthalt**	**Empfohlener Ferienort**
Rangning av golfbanan	Rangning av klubhus	Rangning av hotel	Rekommenderad golfvistelse	Rekommenderad semesterort

Båstad *Old Course* 16 | 8 | 7

Banan designades på 30-talet av Hawtree och Taylor, och smälter på ett fint sätt in i landskapet. Den rankas regelbundet bland de 20 bästa i Sverige. Initialt finansierades den av Ludvig Nobel (Alfreds brorson) för att attrahera engelska affärsmän. Banan är belägen på en halvö och har ett gammalt och mycket charmigt klubbhus. Den är ordentligt kuperad, vilket ger dig många intressanta lägen under din vandring. Detta gör bara layouten ännu bättre. Medelhandicaparen kommer att lära sig mycket under rundans gång, han behöver dock inte oroa sig över att bli av med särskilt många bollar. Största svårigheten är de ofta starkt ondulerade greenerna som tenderar att vara mycket snabba. Är du inte vän med din putter kan det stå dig riktigt dyrt. Flera av greenerna är också upphöjda, vilket kräver höga slag in mot dem. Varje hål är minnesvärt och skiljer sig från det föregående utan att harmonin störs. Den andra 18-hålsslingan på Båstad är inte lika charmig men är desto mer utmanande och kräver riktigt långa slag. Ett pittoreskt hotell bara några meter från första tee gör bilden komplett.

The natural-looking "Old Course" is regularly ranked in the country's top golf courses. It was financed by Ludvig Nobel (the nephew of Alfred) with the purpose of attracting British golfers. Located on a peninsula with an old-style club-house, all 18 holes involve a lot of climbing and provide all sorts of situations from where to play. This makes the layout all the more interesting... and instructive for mid-handicappers, who shouldn't have too much trouble with lost balls. One of the main difficulties lies with the greens, which are steeply contoured and often very slick. More, as some of the putting surfaces are elevated, high approach shots are the order of the day. Each hole is different and memorable, but this does nothing to deter from the overall impression of harmony and the measured layout of difficulties. The second course has not quite the same charm but is even more challenging, whence the need for some long-hitting. A beautiful hotel close to hole N°1 completes the picture.

Båstad Golfklubb 1930
Boarp, Box 1037
S - 269 21 BÅSTAD

Office	Sekretariat	(46) 0431 - 783 70
Pro shop	Pro shop	(46) 0431 - 732 81
Fax	Fax	(46) 0431 - 733 31
Web	www.bgk.se	
Situation	Läge	Båstad, 4 km
Annual closure	Årlig stängning	no
Weekly closure	Daglig stängning	no
Fees main season	Tariff hög säsong	Full day

	Week days Veckodag	We/Bank holidays Lör/Söndag/Helgdag
Individual Individuellt	SKr 500	SKr 500
Couple Par	SKr 1000	SKr 1000

Juniors: SKr 200 / Full week: SKr 2600

Caddie Caddie no — **Electric Trolley** El vagn no
Buggy Golfbil yes — **Clubs** Klubbor yes
Credit cards Kredit kort
VISA - Eurocard - MasterCard - AMEX - DC

1222

Access Tillfart : E6. Båstad → Torekov. → Golf.
Map 1 on page 1212 Karta 1 se sid: 1212

GOLF COURSE — BANA 16/20

Site	Läge	
Maintenance	Underhåll	
Architect	Arkitekt	Hawtree & Taylor
Type	Karaktär	parkland
Relief	Nivåskillnader	
Water in play	Vatten på spelfältet	
Exp. to wind	Vindutsatt	
Trees in play	Träd på spelfältet	

Scorecard Scorekort	Chp. Back tees	Mens Herrtee	Ladies Damtee
Length Längd	5632	5526	4787
Par	71	71	71
Slope system	—	121	118

Advised golfing ability Rekommenderad spelnivå — 0 12 24 36
Hcp required Hcp erfordrad — 36

CLUB HOUSE & AMENITIES — KLUBBHUS OCH OMGIVNING 8/10

Pro shop Pro shop
Driving range Träningsbana
Sheltered tak 4 mats - On grass på gräs no, 20 mats open air - Putting-green putting-green yes - Pitching-green pitching-green yes

HOTEL FACILITIES — HOTELL OMGIVNING 7/10

HOTELS HOTELL
Clarencegården - 8 rooms, D SKr 1400 - on site
Tel (46) 0431 - 73 840
Skansen Hotell - Båstad 12 km
112 rooms, D SKr 1360
Tel (46) 0431 - 558 100, Fax (46) 0431 - 558 110
Kattegatt - Torekov 12 km
11 rooms, D SKr 1695
Tel (46) 0431 - 363 002, Fax (46) 0431 - 363 003

RESTAURANTS RESTAURANGER
Kattegatt - Båstad 8 km - Tel (46) 0431 - 363 002
Margretetorp - Båstad 11 km - Tel (46) 0431 - 454 450
Enehall - Båstad 10 km - Tel (46) 0431 - 750 15

PEUGEOT GOLF GUIDE 2006/2007

Wertungen von 1 bis 10

Skala frän 0 till 10

Entselzlich/ Dålig

Mittelmässig / Förträfflig

Wenig / Få

Viel/ Manga

0 12 24 36

Empfohlene Spielstärke
Rekommenderad Spelnivå

Siehe Michelin-Karte
Se Michelin Kartor

COME USARE LA VOSTRA PEUGEOT GOLF GUIDE

16	8	8		
1 → 20	1 → 10	1 → 10		
Nota del campo	**Nota del Club House**	**Nota del complejo hotelero**	**Estancia de golf recomendada**	**Sitio de vacaciones recomendado**
Giudizio sul percorso	Giudizio sul Club House	Giudizio su offerta alberghiera	Soggiorno golfitistico raccomandato	Località di vacanze raccomandata

Islantilla *Verde/Azul* 16 8 8

Con 27 hoyos y una bonita casa club de estilo andaluz, el conjunto de este ambicioso proyecto de 300 has. domina el Atlántico desde un parque de frondosos pinos. El campo nació con tres recorridos de 9 hoyos con la expresa voluntad de combinarlos por sus diferentes características, aunque el Verde y el Azul se han ido imponiendo como la combinación más frecuente. El azul puede considerarse el más difícil, un desafío para los handicaps medios y bajos ya que hay que pegar largo y recto y los contornos de los greenes piden a gritos un juego corto sensible. El recorrido verde es el más largo de los tres, no es tan exigente en cuanto a la línea del golpe porque sus calles se pueden llamar anchas y abiertas, pero el diseño de los hoyos vuelve a invitar al jugador a pensar los golpes y la estrategia mejor para cubrir el a veces glorioso camino de tee a green. Además de los numerosos bunkers bien diseñados y de un cierto número de obstáculos de agua, greenes ondulados y a menudo en alto hacen muy técnico el recorrido. Si al gusto de jugar se añade el placer de las vistas sobre el Océano, Islantilla es una buena razón para acercarse al límite suroeste de España.

The 27 holes and attractive Andalusian style clubhouse of this ambitious complex overlook the Atlantic Ocean from a huge and very thick pine forest. The club started out with three 9-hole courses with the idea of combining them any way you like. Actually, the Verde and Azul form the best pairing. The Azul course is considered to be the most difficult, a real challenge for good players because you have to hit it long and straight and have a sharp short game. The Verde is the longest of the three but hardly the most challenging as the fairways are wide open. However, the design of holes calls for careful thought over the best strategy to reach the greens. Many well-designed bunkers, several water hazards and undulating greens make this a course for the artist. If you combine the pleasure of playing and the surrounding view (notably over the ocean on hole No 12), Islantilla is an excellent reason to drive on to the extreme limits of south-west Spain.

Islantilla Golf Club 1991
Paseo Barranco del Moro s/n.
E - 21416 ISLANTILLA – ISLA CRISTINA (Huelva - Andalucía)

Office	Secretaría	(34) 959 - 486 039
Pro shop	Pro-shop	(34) 959 - 486 049
Fax	Fax	(34) 959 - 486 104
Web	www.islantillagolfresort.com	
Situation	Situación	Sevilla, 147 km

Huelva (pop. 144 579), 40 km

Annual closure	Cierre anual	no
Weekly closure	Cierre semanal	no
Fees main season	Precios tempor. alta	18 holes

	Week days Semana	We/Bank holidays Fin de sem./fiestas
Individual Individual	€ 63	€ 63
Couple Pareja	€ 126	€ 126

Caddie Caddie no — **Electric Trolley** Carro eléctrico yes
Buggy Coche yes — **Clubs** Palos yes
Credit cards Tarjetas de crédito
VISA - AMEX - DC

Huelva
Lepe
El Empalme
Pozo del Camino
La Rendondela
Isla Cristina
La Antilla
GOLF
km 0 2,5 5

Access Acceso : A-49 (Sevilla-Huelva), Exit (salida) Ayamonte. At Lepe → La Antilla. In Urbanización Islantilla, at Isla Cristina.
Map 8 on page 1100 Plano 8 Página 1100

GOLF COURSE RECORRIDO 16/20

Site	Emplazamiento	
Maintenance	Mantenimiento	
Architect	Arquitecto	Enrique Canales, Luis Recasens
Type	Tipo	seaside course, forest
Relief	Relieve	
Water in play	Agua	
Exp. to wind	Exp. al viento	
Trees in play	Arboles	

Scorecard Tarjeta	**Chp.** Campeonato	**Mens** Caballeros	**Ladies** Damas
Length Longitud	6142	5697	4945
Par	72	72	72
Slope system	123	120	118

Advised golfing ability Nivel de juego aconsejado — 0 12 24 36
Hcp required Handicap exigido — 28 Men, 36 Ladies

CLUB HOUSE & AMENITIES CLUB HOUSE Y DEPENDENCIAS 8/10

Pro shop Pro-shop
Driving range Campo de prácticas
Sheltered cubierto no - On grass sobre hierba yes - Putting-green putting-green yes - Pitching-green pitching-green yes

HOTEL FACILITIES HOTELES CERCANOS 8/10

HOTELS HOTELES
Islantilla Golf Resort - on site
204 rooms, D € 190
Tel (34) 959 - 486 377, Fax (34) 959 - 486 203

Confortel Islantilla - Islantilla 1 km
344 rooms, D € 176
Tel (34) 959 - 486 017, Fax (34) 959 - 486 070

Oasis - 475 rooms, D € 201 - Islantilla 5 km
Tel (34) 959 - 486 422, Fax (34) 959 - 486 450

RESTAURANTS RESTAURANTES
El Coral - La Antilla 2 km - Tel (34) 959 - 481 406
Meson La Isla - Isla Cristina 5 km - Tel (34) 959 - 343 018

1140

PEUGEOT GOLF GUIDE 2006/2007

Escala de 0 a 10
Scala da 0 a 10

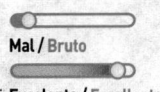

Mal / Bruto

Excelente / Eccellente

Poco / Poco

Mucho / Molto

0 12 24 36

Handicap exigido
Handicap richiesto

Consular los mapas Michelin
Consultate le carte Michelin

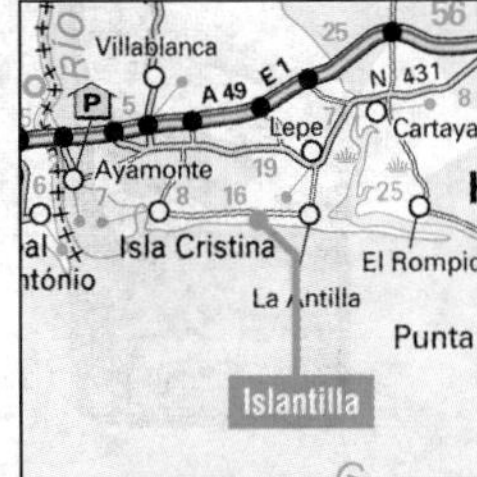

CONTENTS

CONTENTS

CONTENTS

PIDF.com, plan your day in Paris Ile-de-France

www.pidf.com, the official tourist website of Paris Ile-de-France

Dear Reader,

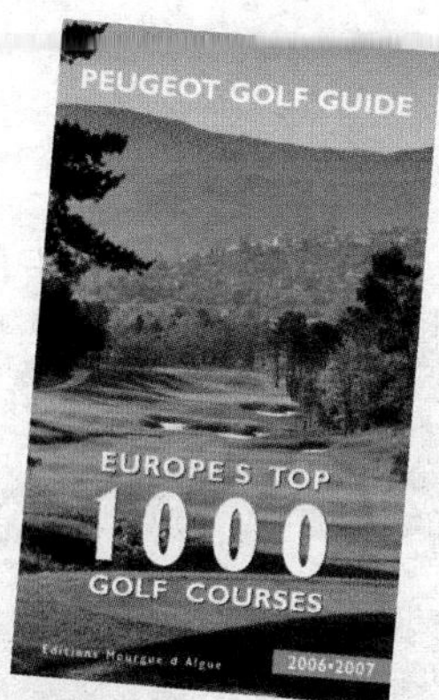

The first edition of the Peugeot Golf Guide was published in 1995 with a selection of the best golf courses in France, exactly 178 in all. Spurred by its initial success, the Guide gradually grew to include other European countries to the point where, in the 2000/2001 edition, readers were given the run-down on "Europe's top 1,000 golf courses".

Today it is our very great pleasure to present the brand new 2006/2007 edition. Our team of course inspectors, composed of professional golfers, top-level international amateurs, journalists, recognized golfers and many others captured by the spirit of this magic game, "ghosted" its way across Europe for months on end to discover recently opened or modernized courses, and to tirelessly check on those included in our previous editions.

As a result, 63 courses appear in the Peugeot Golf Guide 2006/2007 for the first time, and some are back with us after a few years of omission. As our numbers are limited to 1,000, the choices we had to make were often close-calls after lengthy discussions with our Editorial Committee.

Last but not least, please remember that we do take on board the opinions of our readers. Your views are of very special interest to us in order to continue to improve the book. So please feel free to write or get in touch.

We wish you all many years of happy golfing.

Editions Mourgue d'Algue

16 Chemin du Golf F-78860 Saint-Nom-La-Breteche

www.peugeotgolfguide.com

The PEUGEOT GOLF GUIDE commitments:

- ✓ **Ghost visits** to all European golf courses by our team of inspectors who stringently apply a standard method of assessment.
- ✓ **Total independence** a key factor for our Editorial Committee
- ✓ **Comprehensive updating** every two years*
- ✓ **A selection of the top European golf courses** irrespective of golfing proficiency or price of admission, because playing a great course is always a moment to be cherished.

* The prices shown in this Guide were valid when going to print at the end of 2005. They are given for purposes of guidance only, as courses and hotels reserve the right to subsequently alter their rates.

Cher Lecteur,

La première édition de Peugeot Golf Guide a vu le jour en 1995 avec une sélection des 178 meilleurs parcours en France. Devant son succès, le Guide s'est progressivement élargi à d'autres pays européens et c'est à partir de l'édition 2000/2001, qu'il a proposé à ses lecteurs les "1.000 meilleurs parcours d'Europe".

Aujourd'hui, nous avons le plaisir de vous présenter la toute nouvelle édition 2006/2007. Notre équipe d'inspecteurs, composée de joueurs et joueuses professionnels, d'amateurs de haut niveau ayant représenté leur pays, de journalistes, golfeurs reconnus, et de bien d'autres encore animés par l'esprit de ce merveilleux jeu, a sillonné toute l'Europe pendant des mois, découvrant les parcours récemment créés ou modernisés, et vérifiant sans cesse ceux inclus dans les éditions précédentes.

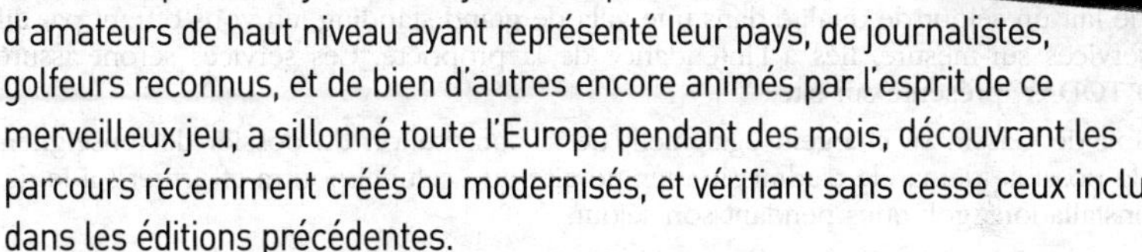

Ainsi 63 golfs font leur entrée dans le Peugeot Golf Guide 2006/2007, certains reviennent aussi après quelques saisons d'absence. Notre nombre étant limité à 1.000, les choix ont été souvent difficiles à faire au cours de longues discussions au sein de notre Comité de Rédaction.

Sachez enfin que nous prenons en compte les avis de nos lecteurs, qui nous intéressent tout particulièrement pour continuer à améliorer cet ouvrage. N'hésitez donc pas à nous écrire ou à nous contacter.

Nous vous souhaitons de belles années de golf.

Editions Mourgue d'Algue

16 Chemin du Golf F-78860 Saint-Nom-La-Breteche
www.peugeotgolfguide.com

Les engagements du PEUGEOT GOLF GUIDE

- ✓ **Visite anonyme** de tous les golfs européens par notre équipe d'inspecteurs qui applique avec rigueur une méthode homogène
- ✓ **Indépendance totale** de notre Comité de Rédaction
- ✓ **Mise à jour complète** tous les deux ans*
- ✓ **Sélection des meilleurs golfs européens** quels que soient le niveau de jeu ou les tarifs d'accès, parce que jouer au golf sur un grand parcours est toujours un moment de plaisir

* Les tarifs indiqués dans ce Guide sont à date d'impression, fin 2005, ils restent purement indicatifs, les golfs et hôtels se réservant le droit de les modifier ultérieurement.

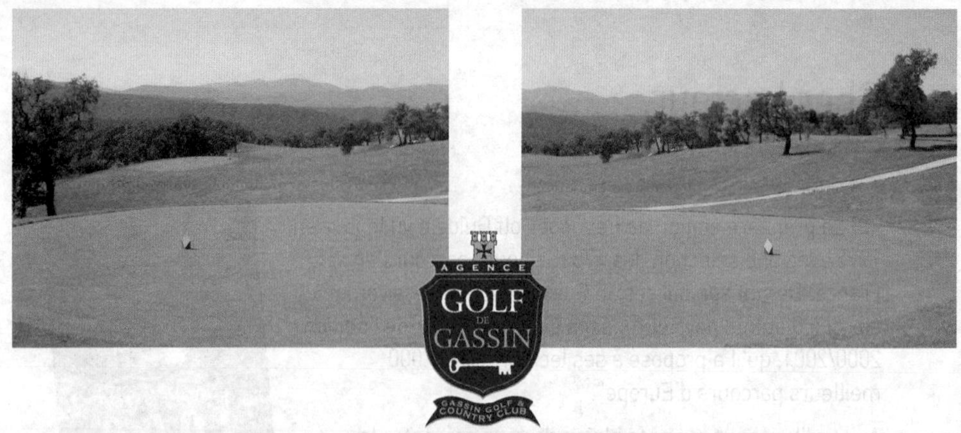

L'agence du Golf de Gassin vous propose à la location et à la vente, un certain nombre de maisons de golfeur et de villas individuelles sur le Domaine du Gassin Golf & Country Club.

L'agence, ayant une parfaite connaissance des biens du Domaine immobilier et des installations golfiques, vous assurera de fait un séjour de qualité dans une villa de grand standing, en vous offrant par ailleurs un ensemble de services sur-mesure, liés à l'intendance de la propriété. Ces services seront assurés par la société TO DO TODAY, présente sur site.

L'Agence du Golf de Gassin se chargera également de la constitution du dossier de renseignements du locataire et de la possible demande d'admission temporaire que celui-ci pourra effectuer s'il le désire, afin d'accéder aux installations golfiques pendant son séjour.

La réception de notre clientèle s'effectuera sur rendez-vous uniquement.

Pour toute information complémentaire,
veuillez contacter le 04 94 54 23 04 ou http://www.agencedugolfdegassin.com

The agency of the Golf de Gassin proposes rentals and sales of townhouses or villas located in The Domain of Gassin Golf & Country Club.

The agency has a perfect knowledge of every detail of the real estate and golf operations. It ensures a stay in a high quality townhouse or villa with home management services. These services will be taken care of by a company called TO DO TODAY which has on site office.

The Golf de Gassin Agency, when considering applications by tenants, will also seek temporary admission to the golf facilities if desired.

Please note we'll receive our clients by appointment only.

For further information,
please contact 04 94 54 23 04 or http://www.agencedugolfdegassin.com

Lieber Leser,

Die erste Ausgabe des Peugeot Golf Guide erschien 1995. Sie enthielt die besten Plätze in Frankreich, 178 an der Zahl. Angespornt durch den Erfolg der ersten Ausgabe wurde der Führer ständig erweitert und immer mehr Länder kamen hinzu. In der Ausgabe 2000/2001 wurde dem Leser erstmals ein kompletter Überblick über die„Besten 1.000 Plätze Europas" gegeben.

Heute freuen wir uns, Ihnen die brandneue Ausgaben 2006/2007 zu präsentieren. Unser Team von Inspektoren besteht aus Pros, Amateuren, die bei hochrangigen internationalen Turnieren Erfahrungen sammelten, aus Journalisten und vielen anderen, die vom Geist dieses magischen Spiels erfasst, sind. Diese Inspektoren sind kreuz und quer durch Europa gereist, haben anonym kürzlich eröffnete oder modernisierte Plätze getestet und die Anlagen inspiziert, die bereits in früheren Ausgaben enthalten waren.

Nach dem Ergebnis dieser unermüdlichen Recherchen vor Ort wurden insgesamt 63 Plätze erstmals in den Peugeot Golf Guide 2006/2007 aufgenommen und einige sind nach einigen Jahren der Abwesenheit zurückgekehrt. Da wir aber uns auf die Zahl 1.000 beschränken, gab es im Kreis unseres Redaktions-Komitees heftige und lange Diskussionen. Einige Plätze verfehlten nur ganz knapp die Aufnahme oder das Verbleiben in dieser Ausgabe.

Zu guter Letzt möchten wir Sie ermuntern, uns Ihre Meinung zu den Plätzen des Führers oder Anlagen, die Ihrer Meinung nicht fehlen dürfen, mitzuteilen. Wir legen auf Ihr Urteil viel wert! Sie helfen uns damit, die Qualität des Führers weiter zu steigern. Deshalb unsere Bitte: Kontaktieren Sie uns!

Wir wünschen Ihnen viele Jahre guten Golfs.

Editions Mourgue d'Algue

16 Chemin du Golf F-78860 Saint-Nom-La-Breteche

www.peugeotgolfguide.com

Der PEUGEOT GOLF GUIDE verpflichtet sich zu folgenden Leistungen und Richtlinien:

- ✓ **Anonyme Besuche** auf allen europäischen Plätzen durch unser Team von Inspektoren, die jeden Platz nach einem Standard-Verfahren und – Fragebogen genauesten bewerten.
- ✓ **Vollkommene Unabhängigkeit** unseres Redaktions-Komitees von jeglichen kommerziellen Interessen.
- ✓ **Umfangreiche Aktualisierung** alle zwei Jahre*
- ✓ **Die Auswahl der europäischen Spitzenplätze** erfolgt unabhängig vom erforderlichen golferischen Können oder dem Greenfee. Denn selbst wenn das Greenfee hoch und der Platz an diesem Tag für Sie zu schwer war, das Spiel auf einem großartigen Platz ist immer ein Genuss.

*Die Preise in diesem Führer waren gültig bei Drucklegung Ende 2005. Alle Preise sollten nur als Richtlinie gelten, zumal sich Golfplätze und Hotels vorbehalten, die Preise jederzeit zu ändern.

Kära läsare!

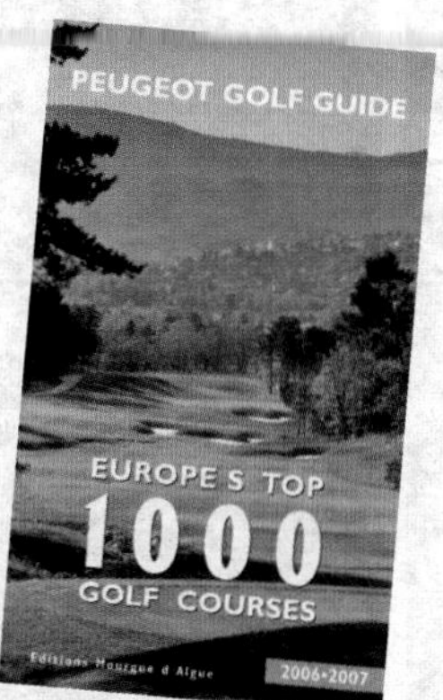

Den första upplagan av Peugeot Golf Guide publicerades 1995 och innehöll då 178 banor, vilket var ett urval av Frankrikes bästa banor. Sporrad av de första framgångarna växte guiden snabbt till att även inkludera andra europeiska länder i upplagan 2000/2001, i vilken läsarna fick möta "Europas 1.000 bästa golfbanor".

I dag är vi stolta över att kunna presentera en rykande färsk Guide, 2006/2007-års upplaga. Vårt team av baninspektörer – golfproffs, skickliga amatörspelare, journalister och många andra som har fångats av detta magiska spel – har i månader färdats inkognito genom Europa för att testa nya banor, och för att kontrollera tidigare banor inkluderade i Guiden.

Som ett resultat av detta har 63 helt nya banor inkluderats i Peugeot Golf Guide 2006/2007 för allra första gången, och du kommer även att finna andra banor som har tagits till nåder efter några års bortvaro. Eftersom vi inte ha ska ha fler än 1.000 banor har det ofta varit tuffa val, som föregåtts av långa diskussioner med vår redaktionskommitté.

Sist men inte minst, vi vill naturligtvis veta vad våra läsare tycker. Dina synpunkter är viktiga för att vi hela tiden ska kunna förbättra boken. Så tveka inte att ta kontakt.

Vi önskar er alla många underbara golfår!

Editions Mourgue d'Algue
16 Chemin du Golf F-78860 Saint-Nom-La-Breteche
www.peugeotgolfguide.com

Så här arbetar PEUGEOT GOLF GUIDE:

- ✓ **Våra baninspektörer,** som inkognito besöker Europas alla banor, arbetar med en gemensam metod.
- ✓ **Total självständighet** är en självklarhet för vårt redaktionsråd.
- ✓ **Vartannat år sker** en uppdatering av all fakta.
- ✓ **Vi har valt banorna oavsett vilken spelskicklighet** som krävs eller pris för att få tillträde: att spela en riktigt bra bana är ett ögonblick som ska vårdas.

* Priserna som du finner i Guiden var de aktuella när vi gick i tryck i slutet av 2005. De ska enbart ses som vägledande, då banor och hotell reserverar sig rätten att ändra sina priser.

Querido lector:

La primera edición de la Guía de golf Peugeot fue publicada en 1995 con una selección de los mejores campos de golf de Francia, concretamente 178. Estimulada por el éxito que tuvo desde el primer momento, ha ido ampliándose con campos de otros países europeos hasta el punto de que en la edición 2000-2001 alcanzaba el hito de publicar "los mejores 1.000 campos de golf de Europa".

Hoy tenemos la inmensa satisfacción de presentarles la nueva edición 2006/2007. Nuestro equipo de inspectores de campos compuesto por jugadores profesionales, amateurs de nivel internacional, periodistas, jugadores de prestigio y otros muchos cautivados por el espíritu de este deporte mágico, han atravesado silenciosamente Europa durante meses con el fin de descubrir los campos que se acaban de abrir al juego y los que se han modernizado además de comprobar incansablemente la calidad y los servicios de los campos incluidos en ediciones anteriores.

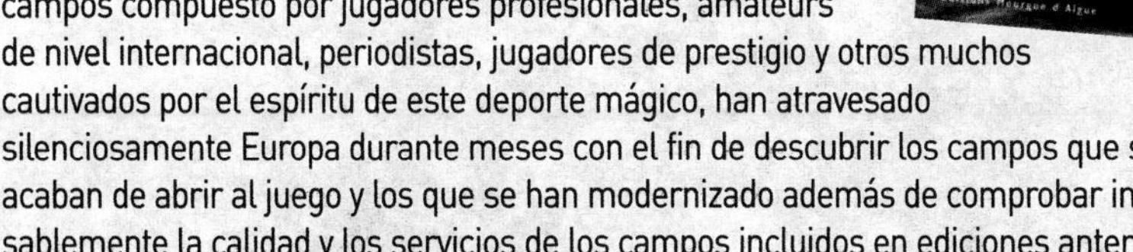

Así, en la Guía de Golf Peugeot 2006/2007 aparecen 63 campos nuevos y reaparecen otros pocos que se habían omitido unos años. Como la edición está limitada al millar de entradas, algunas inclusiones y algunos descartes han requerido largas y reñidas discusiones del comité editorial.

Teniendo siempre muy presente que nuestro objetivo es brindar el mejor servicio a nuestros lectores, les reiteramos que sus opiniones y apreciaciones nos ayudan a mejorar constantemente este libro de consulta. Por lo tanto, les agradeceremos siempre las sugerencias que nos hagan llegar cuando lo consideren oportuno.

A todos les deseamos que se diviertan con el golf durante muchos años.

Editions Mourgue d'Algue

16 Chemin du Golf F-78860 Saint-Nom-La-Breteche

www.peugeotgolfguide.com

Los principios de LA GUÍA DE GOLF PEUGEOT:

- ✓ **Visitas anónimas** a todos los campos europeos de nuestro equipo de inspectores, que aplica un riguroso método de valoración.
- ✓ Nuestro comité editorial se mueve con un criterio de **absoluta independencia.**
- ✓ **Renovación total** cada dos años*.
- ✓ **Una selección de los mejores campos de golf de Europa,** al margen de la categoría de los jugadores o de los precios de admisión, porque jugar en un gran campo siempre es un motivo de satisfacción.

* Los precios que recoge esta Guía están actualizados a finales de 2005, fecha de impresión de esta edición. Por lo tanto, son eminentemente indicativos, teniendo además en cuenta que tanto los campos como los hoteles se reservan el derecho de modificarlos en cualquier momento.

Caro Lettore,

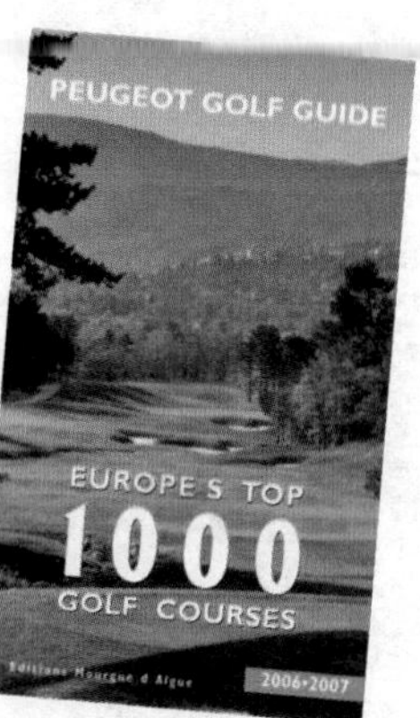

La prima edizione della Peugeot Golf Guide è stata pubblicata nel 1995 con una selezione dei migliori percorsi francesi, esattamente 178 in totale. Forte dell'immediato successo, la Guida ha iniziato a crescere gradualmente includendo i migliori campi di altre nazioni europee sino ad arrivare nell'edizione 2000/2001 ai "1.000 migliori golf club in Europa".

Oggi è nostro grande piacere presentare la nuova edizione 2006/2007. La nostra squadra di ispettori, che è composta da giocatori professionisti, dilettanti di alto livello, giornalisti e golfisti famosi ha girato in incognita l'Europa per mesi per scoprire percorsi nuovissimi, rimodernati o soltanto per confermare la validità di tutti quelli inseriti nelle precedenti edizioni.

Alla fine sono 63 i campi che appaiono nella Peugeot Golf Guide 2006/2007 per la prima volta e altri ritornano dopo qualche anno di assenza. Siccome abbiamo stabilito in 1.000 il numero dei percorsi, le scelte che dobbiamo fare non sono mai facili e vengono prese dopo lunghe riunioni con il nostro Comitato Editoriale

Desideriamo inoltre sottolineare che teniamo in grande considerazione l'opinione dei nostri lettori. Non esitate quindi a contattarci perché il vostro punto di vista ci interessa molto ed è importantissimo per continuare a migliorarci.

Un augurio a tutti voi per trascorrere molti anni felici sui campi da golf.

Editions Mourgue d'Algue

16 Chemin du Golf F-78860 Saint-Nom-La-Breteche

www.peugeotgolfguide.com

Le regole della PEUGEOT GOLF GUIDE:

- ✓ **Visite in incognita** in tutti i campi di golf europei da parte della nostra squadra di ispettori che applica rigorosamente un metodo uniforme di valutazione
- ✓ **Totale indipendenza** del nostro Comitato Editoriale
- ✓ **Aggiornamento completo** dei dati ogni due anni*
- ✓ **Una selezione dei migliori campi europei** che non è condizionata dalla difficoltà del percorso o dalle quote di ammissione al circolo, perché giocare su un bel campo è un fattore importante.

* I prezzi indicati nella Guida sono aggiornati al momento della stampa a fine 2005. Lo scopo è quello di essere un riferimento, perché sia i campi che gli alberghi si riservano il diritto di modificare successivamente le proprie tariffe.

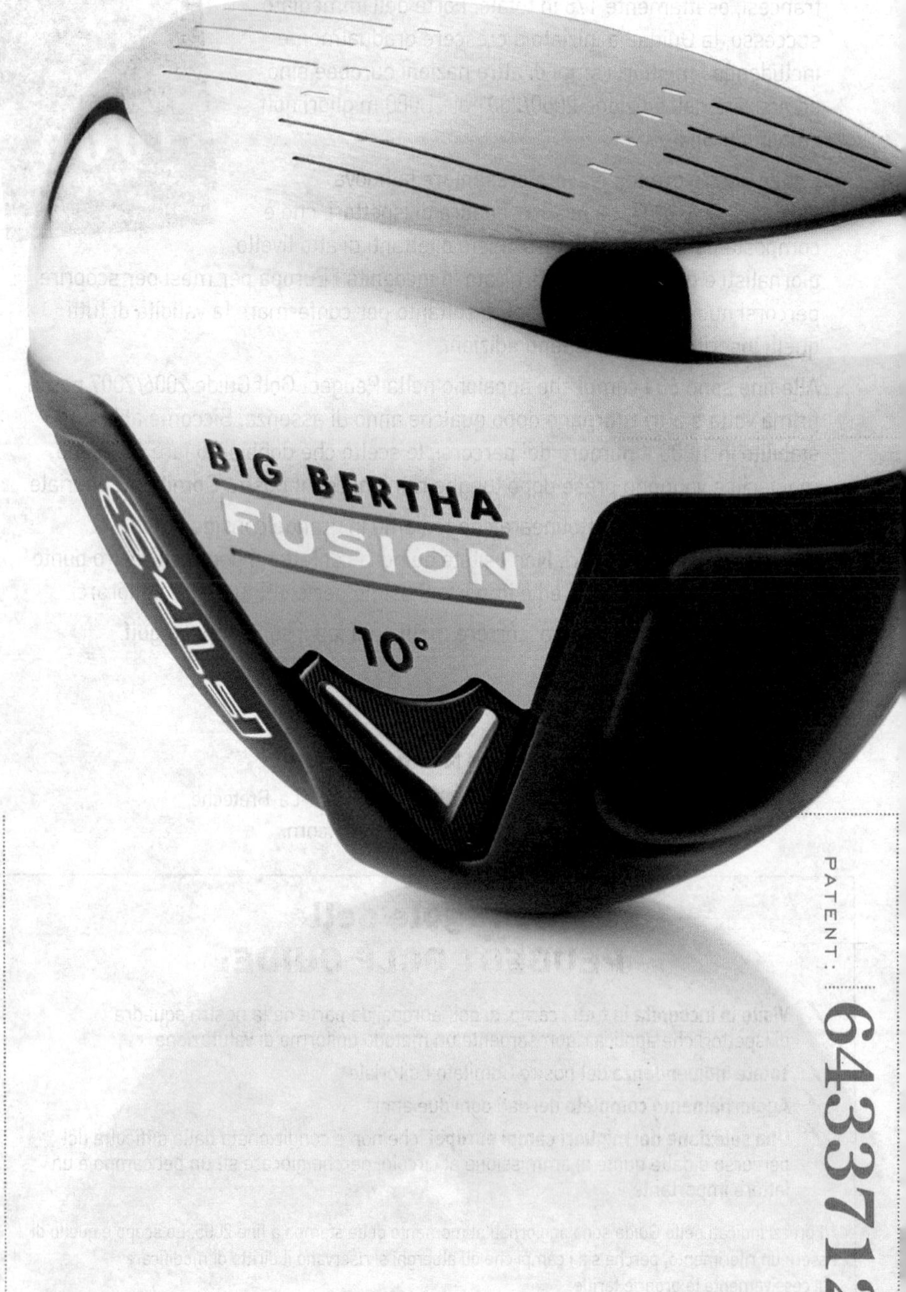
BIG BERTHA
FUSION
10°
PATENT: 6433712

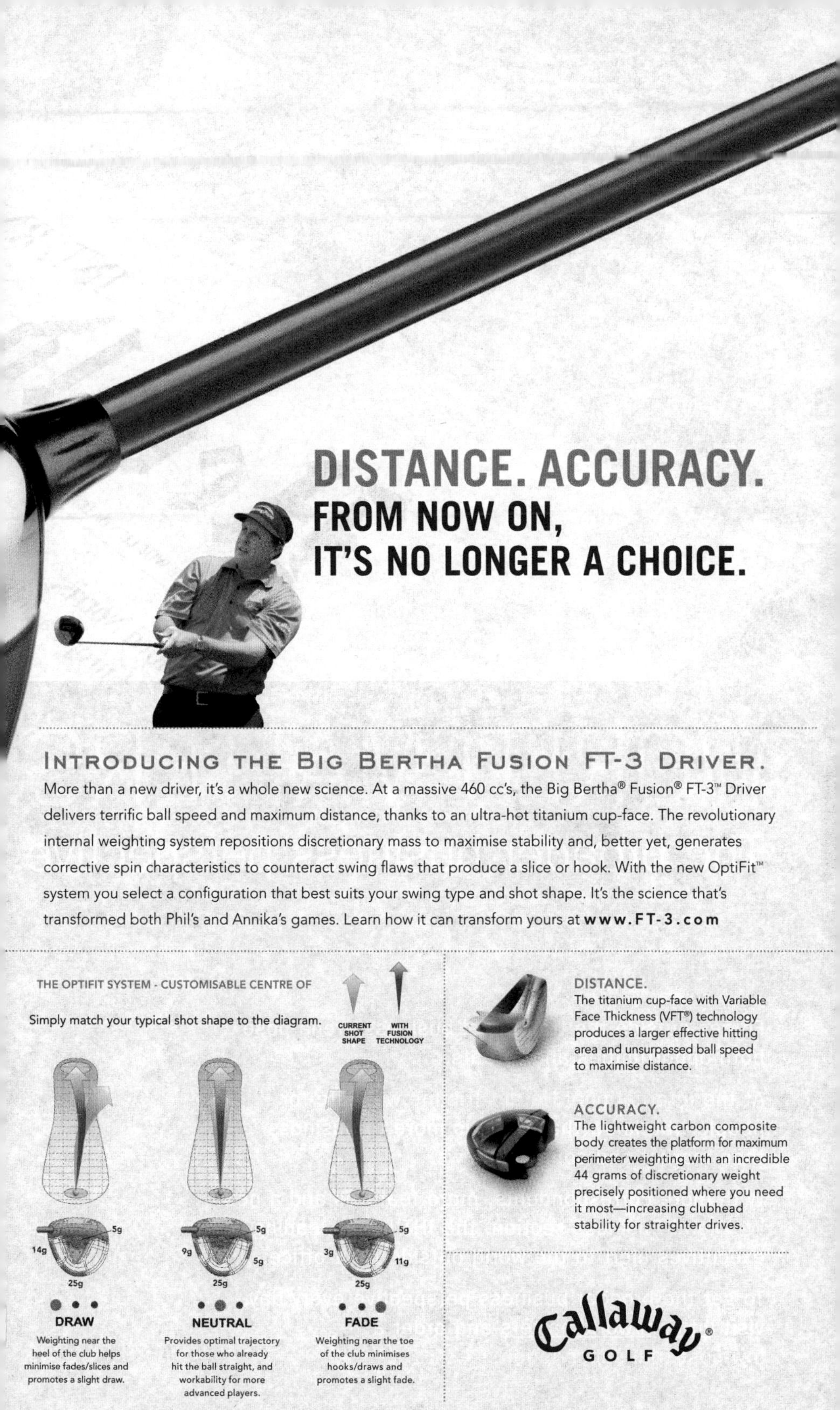

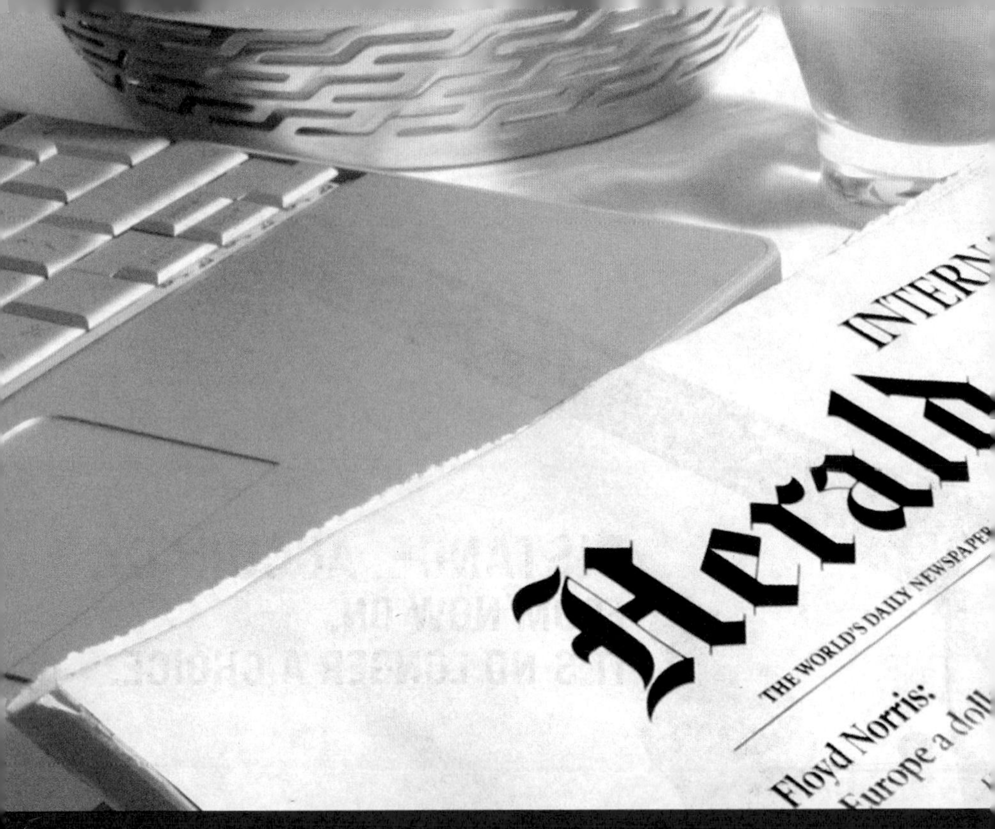
Herald
THE WORLD'S DAILY NEWSPAPER
Floyd Norris:

THE 63 NEWLY-PROMOTED GOLF COURSES

Les 63 nouveaux parcours
Die 63 neuen Plätze
63 nya golfbanor
Los 63 campos incorporados a esta guía
I 63 nuovi percorsi promossi

Kytäjä (Finland)

LASSI PEKKA TILANDER

AUSTRIA

The Country Club (Tullnerfeld) p.87

BELGIUM

Château de la Tournette p.98

DENMARK

Nordvestjysk p.131

FINLAND

Kytäjä p.146

FRANCE

Béthemont p.216
Four Seasons (Le Château) p.263
Four Seasons (Le Riou) p.264
La Domangère p.251

GERMANY

Bad Griesbach (Beckenbauer) p.370
Golfpark Gut Häusern p.383
Green Eagle p.394
Hardenberg (Niedersachsen course) p.404
Jura (Am Hamsberg) p.411
WinstonGolf p.464

ENGLAND

Bamburgh Castle p.503
Bovey Castle p.512
Cavendish p.528
Copt Heath p. 532
Hanbury Manor p.552
King's Lynn p.569
Luffenham Heath p.576
New Zealand p.587
Northamptonshire p.590
Old Thorns p.592
Reddish Vale p.601
Saunton (West Course) p.621
Tadmarton Heath p.640
Woodsome Hall p. 670

THE 63 NEWLY-PROMOTED GOLF COURSES

SCOTLAND

Cochrane Castle p.694
Dundonald p.705

IRELAND

Castleknock p.830
Druids Heath p.845
The Heritage p.857
Irish PGA National p.873
Killarney (Lackabane) p.862
Powerscourt (West Course) p.878
Rathcore p.879
Roganstown p.882
Rosapenna
(Sandy Hill Links) p.884

ITALY

Acaya p.934
Paradiso p.969
San Domenico p.978

THE NETHERLANDS

Drente p.998

NORWAY

Moss & Rygge p.1036

PORTUGAL

Estela p.1055
Ribagolfe Blue p.1071
Ribagolfe Green p.1072
Vilamoura (Victoria) p.1081

SPAIN

Alcanada p.1108
El Prat Amarillo p.1128
El Prat Rosa p.1129
El Puerto p.1130
La Reserva p.1152
San Roque New Course p.1189
Sherry Golf p.1194

SUEDE

Degeberga p.1227
Grönhögen p.1237
Hills p.1240
Knistad p.1245
Vidbynäs p.1270

SWITZERLAND

Engadin (Zuoz Madulain) p.1286
Vuissens p.1299

TURKEY

Antalya GC (Sultan) p.1312

CLASSIFICATION OF GOLF COURSES

Classement des parcours
Einteilung der golfplätze
Rankning av banor
Clasificación de los recorridos
Classifica dei percorsi

A Austria - **B** Belgium - **CH** Switzerland - **CYP** Cyprus - **Cz** Czech Republic - **D** Germany - **DK** Denmark - **E** Spain
Eng England - **F** France - **FIN** Finland - **I** Italy - **IRL** Republic of Ireland - **L** Luxembourg - **N** Norway - **NIR** Northern Ireland
NL Nederland - **P** Portugal - **RU** Russia - **S** Sweden - **SCO** Scotland - **SLO** Slovenia - **TR** Turkey - **WAL** Wales

Within each score, the ranking is purely alphabetical

19	7	6	**Ballybunion Old Course**	IRL	820
19	8	6	**Les Bordes**	F	221
19	5	6	**Carnoustie Championship**	SCO	693
19	8	5	**Ganton**	ENG	548
19	8	7	**Kingsbarns**	SCO	724
19	7	6	**Muirfield**	SCO	739
19	7	7	**Nairn**	SCO	742
19	7	8	**Portmarnock**	IRL	874
19	9	7	**Royal Birkdale**	ENG	604
19	6	7	**Royal County Down**	NIR	914
19	7	7	**Royal Dornoch Championship**	SCO	755
19	7	6	**Royal Porthcawl**	WAL	799
19	7	7	**Royal Portrush Dunluce Links**	NIR	915
19	7	5	**Royal St George's**	ENG	613
19	7	7	**Royal Troon Old Course**	SCO	757
19	9	7	**Turnberry Ailsa Course**	SCO	771
19	8	8	**Valderrama**	E	1202
19	7	8	**Woodhall Spa Hotchkin**	ENG	669

CLASSIFICATION OF GOLF COURSES

18	7	7	Alwoodley	ENG	501
18	8	6	Barsebäck Masters Course	S	1221
18	7	7	Biella - Le Betulle	I	941
18	8	6	Blairgowrie Rosemount	SCO	684
18	7	6	Burnham & Berrow	ENG	521
18	8	8	Castelconturbia Giallo + Blu	I	945
18	6	8	Castletown	ENG	527
18	7	6	Chantilly Vineuil	F	236
18	8	6	Chart Hills	ENG	529
18	5	6	County Louth	IRL	835
18	7	6	Cruden Bay	SCO	697
18	8	6	Domaine Impérial	CH	1285
18	3	5	Doonbeg	IRL	842
18	8	7	Dundonald	SCO	705
18	8	7	East Sussex National East Course	ENG	539
18	8	7	Eindhoven	NL	1000
18	6	8	El Saler	E	1131
18	5	6	The European	IRL	849
18	6	7	Falkenstein	D	385
18	8	5	Falsterbo	S	1230
18	7	6	Formby	ENG	545
18	8	7	Gleneagles King's	SCO	715
18	7	8	Haagsche	NL	1005
18	8	8	Halmstad	S	1238
18	9	8	The Heritage	IRL	857
18	8	6	Hills	S	1240
18	7	7	Hillside	ENG	560
18	8	6	Kempferhof	F	283
18	8	8	Kennemer	NL	1010
18	8	8	Las Brisas	E	1156
18	6	6	Lindrick	ENG	572
18	7	5	Ljunghusen	S	1251
18	8	6	Loch Lomond	SCO	730
18	6	4	Machrihanish	SCO	735
18	7	6	Médoc Les Châteaux	F	291
18	8	7	Miklagard	N	1035
18	7	7	Moortown	ENG	585
18	6	6	Morfontaine	F	297
18	9	6	Mount Juliet	IRL	869
18	6	6	National L'Albatros	F	298
18	7	8	Noordwijk	NL	1012
18	6	7	North Berwick	SCO	745
18	6	6	Notts (Hollinwell)	ENG	591
18	7	7	PGA de Catalunya	E	1181
18	6	7	Prestwick	SCO	750
18	8	5	Prince de Provence (Vidauban)	F	310
18	8	9	Puerta de Hierro Abajo	E	1183
18	7	5	Quinta de Cima	P	1066
18	7	7	Real Sociedad Club de Campo Norte	E	1186
18	8	7	Rethmar	D	432
18	7	8	Royal Aberdeen Balgownie Links	SCO	753
18	8	7	Royal Liverpool (Hoylake)	ENG	609
18	8	8	Royal Lytham & St Anne's	ENG	610
18	6	5	Royal St David's	WAL	800
18	7	5	Royal West Norfolk (Brancaster)	ENG	614
18	6	6	Rye	ENG	617
18	8	8	San Roque New Course	E	1188
18	7	4	Saunton East Course	ENG	620
18	9	7	Seddiner See Südplatz	D	445
18	7	4	Silloth-on-Solway	ENG	629
18	8	8	Sotogrande	E	1198
18	6	4	Southerness	SCO	760
18	7	5	Spérone	F	331
18	8	7	Sporting-Club Berlin Nick Faldo	D	449
18	8	8	St Andrews Old Course	SCO	764
18	7	4	St Enodoc Church Course	ENG	632
18	7	7	St George's Hill	ENG	633
18	8	8	Sunningdale New Course	ENG	637
18	8	8	Sunningdale Old Course	ENG	638
18	8	9	The Grove	ENG	643
18	7	6	Tralee	IRL	894
18	7	7	Vilamoura Victoria	P	1081
18	7	7	Walton Heath Old Course	ENG	651
18	6	7	Waterville	IRL	897
18	8	7	Wentworth West Course	ENG	654
18	7	5	West Sussex	ENG	660

17	7	7	Aberdovey	WAL	779
17	8	8	Alcanada	E	1108
17	7	8	Aloha	E	1113
17	7	7	Antalya GC Sultan	TR	1312
17	7	7	Antwerp	B	96
17	7	7	Aphrodite Hills	CYP	1306
17	9	9	Bad Griesbach Beckenbauer	D	370
17	9	9	Bad Griesbach Brunnwies	D	371
17	7	5	Ballyliffin Glashedy Links	IRL	822
17	7	6	Barbaroux	F	213
17	8	7	Berkshire Blue Course	ENG	507
17	8	7	Berkshire Red Course	ENG	508
17	7	6	Beuerberg	D	376
17	8	7	Bogogno Bonora	I	942
17	8	7	Bogogno Del Conte	I	943
17	6	6	Bowood G&CC	ENG	514
17	7	6	Bro-Bålsta	S	1226
17	7	7	Broadstone	ENG	517
17	8	7	Buckinghamshire	ENG	519
17	8	8	Carden Park Nicklaus Course	ENG	525
17	7	8	Cardrona	SCO	690
17	9	7	Celtic Manor Roman Road	WAL	784
17	6	5	Club zur Vahr (Garlstedt)	D	379
17	6	4	County Sligo	IRL	836
17	7	3	Courson Vert + Noir	F	246
17	8	8	Dalmahoy East Course	SCO	698
17	6	7	Downfield	SCO	699
17	6	7	East Devon	ENG	538
17	8	8	Eichenheim	A	78
17	7	6	Emporda Links	E	1132
17	8	6	Enniscrone	IRL	847
17	7	7	Ferndown Old Course	ENG	542
17	8	8	Fleesensee Schloss	D	387
17	7	7	Fontainebleau	F	259
17	7	7	Fontanals	E	1134
17	6	7	Forest Pines Forest + Pines	ENG	544

CLASSIFICATION OF GOLF COURSES

17	9	8	Four Seasons Provence Le Château	F	263
17	7	8	Frankfurter GC	D	388
17	7	8	Genève	CH	1288
17	8	7	Gleneagles PGA Centenary	SCO	716
17	7	6	Gullane No 1	SCO	720
17	7	7	Gut Altentann	A	81
17	9	7	Gut Lärchenhof	D	397
17	7	7	Gütersloh (Westfälischer GC)	D	400
17	6	6	Hankley Common	ENG	553
17	8	7	Hayling	ENG	556
17	8	6	Hubbelrath	D	408
17	7	6	Hunstanton	ENG	563
17	7	7	I Roveri	I	954
17	7	6	Ilkley	ENG	565
17	3	6	Is Arenas	I	955
17	7	8	Is Molas	I	956
17	8	7	Jura Golf Park Am Habsberg	D	411
17	8	8	K Club North Course	IRL	859
17	8	8	K Club South Course	IRL	860
17	6	7	Kilmarnock (Barassie)	SCO	723
17	6	8	Klagenfurt-Seltenheim	A	82
17	6	7	Köln (Refrath)	D	412
17	7	7	Krefelder	D	413
17	7	7	Kristianstad	S	1246
17	8	6	Kungsängen (European Tour Club)	S	1248
17	7	3	Kytäjä East Course	FIN	146
17	7	8	La Cala Norte	E	1142
17	7	8	La Moye	ENG	570
17	7	5	Ladybank	SCO	726
17	7	7	Lage Vuursche	NL	1011
17	6	6	Lahinch	IRL	864
17	8	5	Larvik	N	1032
17	8	7	Le Querce	I	958
17	7	6	Lerma	E	1159
17	6	6	Limère	F	287
17	7	6	Liphook	ENG	573
17	7	8	Little Aston	ENG	574
17	8	8	Lübeck-Travemünder	D	417
17	7	6	Lunds Akademiska	S	1252
17	7	5	Machrie	SCO	734
17	6	5	Moliets	F	293
17	6	6	Monifieth	SCO	736
17	8	8	Montecastillo	E	1171
17	5	6	Montrose	SCO	737
17	5	6	Moray Old	SCO	738
17	7	6	Moscow	RU	1310
17	7	6	Moss & Rygge	N	1036
17	8	6	Motzener See	D	422
17	7	7	National GC	TR	1314
17	7	7	Neguri	E	1173
17	7	6	Nîmes-Campagne	F	299
17	6	5	Oberfranken	D	426
17	8	7	Oitavos	P	1057
17	7	6	Örebro	S	1254
17	6	5	Panmure	SCO	746
17	6	6	Pennard	WAL	796
17	8	8	Pevero	I	971
17	7	5	Pléneuf-Val-André	F	304
17	7	8	Portmarnock Links	IRL	875
17	7	7	Powerscourt West Course	IRL	878
17	6	6	Praia d'El Rey	P	1063
17	7	5	Quinta da Ria	P	1065
17	7	7	Real Sociedad Club de Campo Sur	E	1187
17	8	6	Robinson	TR	1315
17	8	7	The Roxburghe	SCO	752
17	6	5	Royal Cinque Ports	ENG	605
17	6	6	Royal North Devon (Westward Ho!)	ENG	612
17	7	7	Royal Zoute	B	110
17	8	7	Rungsted	DK	133
17	8	7	Ruuhikoski	FIN	150
17	5	7	S. Lourenço	P	1073
17	7	7	Saint-Germain	F	320
17	8	8	Saint-Nom-la-Bretèche Rouge	F	324
17	8	8	San Roque Old Course	E	1189
17	7	5	Schloss Wilkendorf	D	443
17	8	6	Schwanhof	D	444
17	7	4	Seacroft	ENG	622
17	5	4	Seascale	ENG	623
17	7	5	Seaton Carew	ENG	624
17	7	7	Seignosse	F	328
17	7	8	Sevilla	E	1193
17	7	6	Sherwood Forest	ENG	628
17	5	5	Shiskine (Blackwaterfoot)	SCO	759
17	7	7	Skövde Södra Banan	S	1259
17	8	7	Slaley Hall Hunting Course	ENG	630
17	7	4	Soufflenheim	F	330
17	7	7	Spa (Les Fagnes)	B	112
17	8	7	Sporting-Club Berlin Arnold Palmer	D	448
17	8	8	St Andrews New Course	SCO	763
17	7	8	St Andrews Bay Devlin Course	SCO	765
17	9	6	St Mellion Nicklaus Course	ENG	634
17	7	6	St. Dionys	D	451
17	9	7	St. Leon-Rot St Leon Course	D	454
17	7	8	Stenungsund	S	1261
17	8	8	Stoke Park Golf Club	ENG	635
17	8	7	Svartinge	S	1263
17	6	8	Swinley Forest	ENG	639
17	6	6	Tain	SCO	768
17	7	6	Tenby	WAL	802
17	7	7	Trevose Championship	ENG	648
17	5	4	Troia	P	1075
17	8	6	Ullna	S	1266
17	7	6	Varberg Västra	S	1267
17	8	6	Vidbynäs	S	1270
17	7	7	Vilamoura Old Course	P	1079
17	8	7	Wentworth East Course	ENG	653
17	5	7	Western Gailes	SCO	774
17	7	7	Woburn Duke's Course	ENG	664
17	7	7	Woburn Marquess	ENG	665
17	6	6	Woking	ENG	666
17	7	6	Worplesdon	ENG	671

16	5	4	Aisses (Les) Rouge + Blanc	F	203
16	6	6	Albi	F	204
16	9	8	Am Alten Fliess Rot + Weiss	D	367
16	6	5	Ashburnham	WAL	780
16	7	6	Ashridge	ENG	502
16	6	5	Åtvidaberg	S	1220
16	5	7	Ayr (Belleisle)	SCO	679
16	7	6	Ballybunion Cashen (New Course)	IRL	819
16	7	5	Ballyliffin Old Course	IRL	823
16	8	7	Båstad Old Course	S	1222

MICHELIN
Une meilleure façon d'avancer

16	7	7	Beau Desert	ENG	505
16	6	5	Belle-Dune	F	215
16	7	7	Bergamo - L'Albenza Blu + Giallo	I	940
16	7	7	Bergisch Land Wuppertal	D	374
16	8	8	Berlin-Wannsee	D	375
16	6	5	Blackmoor	ENG	510
16	7	7	Bokskogen	S	1223
16	7	7	Bondues Blanc	F	219
16	8	7	Bonmont	E	1116
16	7	6	Brampton	ENG	515
16	7	7	Bråviken	S	1225
16	7	6	La Bresse	F	223
16	7	6	Buxtehude	D	378
16	7	7	Caldy	ENG	522
16	6	6	Camberley Heath	ENG	523
16	7	7	Carlisle	ENG	526
16	6	7	Carlow	IRL	827
16	4	8	Carton House The Montgomerie	IRL	828
16	7	7	Castillo de Gorraiz	E	1119
16	3	8	Castleknock	IRL	830
16	6	6	Castlerock	NIR	905
16	6	6	Charmeil	F	237
16	5	6	Château de la Chouette	F	238
16	6	8	Chiberta	F	242
16	7	7	Clitheroe	ENG	530
16	8	8	Club de Campo Negro	E	1121
16	7	7	Cochrane Castle	SCO	694
16	8	8	Colony Club Gutenhof West	A	76
16	7	7	Conwy	WAL	785
16	6	6	Copt Heath	ENG	532
16	8	7	Costa Ballena	E	1122
16	7	3	Courson Lilas + Orange	F	245
16	8	5	Cromstrijen	NL	996
16	7	6	Cumberwell Park	ENG	534
16	8	7	De Pan	NL	997
16	7	5	Degeberga-Widtsköfle	S	1227
16	6	7	Delamere Forest	ENG	536
16	7	8	Disneyland Paris Rouge + Bleu	F	249
16	5	5	La Domangère	F	251
16	7	6	Donegal (Murvagh)	IRL	840
16	9	7	Druids Glen Druids Glen	IRL	844
16	5	6	Dunbar	SCO	704
16	8	5	Efteling	NL	999
16	6	5	El Bosque	E	1126
16	5	8	El Cortijo	E	1127
16	8	8	El Prat Amarillo	E	1128
16	8	8	El Prat Rosa	E	1129
16	7	6	Espoo	FIN	144
16	9	5	Fågelbro	S	1229
16	7	8	Fairhaven	ENG	540
16	7	6	Feldafing	D	386
16	7	5	Flommen	S	1232
16	8	7	Fontana	A	79
16	7	4	Forsbacka	S	1233
16	6	5	Fortrose & Rosemarkie	SCO	713
16	8	6	Fota Island	IRL	851
16	9	8	Four Seasons Provence Le Riou	F	264
16	7	7	Frégate	F	265
16	8	6	Frösåker	S	1234
16	7	8	Fulford	ENG	547
16	7	8	Fürstlicher GC Bad Waldsee	D	390
16	7	7	Glasson	IRL	853
16	7	8	Gleidingen Grün + Blau	D	392
16	7	8	Golf del Sur	E	1136
16	8	7	Golfpark Gut Häusern	D	393
16	8	6	Golfresort Haugschlag Waldviertel	A	80
16	6	6	La Grande Bastide	F	270
16	6	4	La Grande-Motte Les Flamants Roses	F	271
16	5	8	Grange	IRL	855
16	7	6	Grenoble Bresson	F	273
16	7	5	Grönhögen	S	1237
16	7	6	Gut Grambek	D	395
16	7	5	Gut Thailing	D	399
16	8	7	Hamburg-Ahrensburg	D	401
16	6	6	Hanau-Wilhelmsbad	D	402
16	8	8	Hanbury Manor	ENG	552
16	8	6	Haninge	S	1239
16	7	7	Hannover	D	403
16	6	6	Hardelot Les Pins	F	275
16	7	8	Hardenberg Niedersachsen	D	404
16	7	8	Helsinki	FIN	145
16	7	6	Herkenbosch	NL	1006
16	6	7	High Post	ENG	559
16	7	7	Hilversum	NL	1007
16	8	6	Himmerland New Course	DK	126
16	6	5	Holstebro	DK	127
16	7	5	Holyhead	WAL	787
16	7	6	Hossegor	F	277
16	8	8	Houtrak	NL	1009
16	7	6	Iffeldorf	D	409
16	7	7	Inverness	SCO	722
16	8	8	Islantilla Verde + Azul	E	1140
16	7	5	L'Isle Adam	F	279
16	7	6	Isle of Purbeck	ENG	567
16	6	7	Jönköping	S	1241
16	8	7	Joyenval Marly	F	281
16	8	7	Joyenval Retz	F	282
16	7	7	Kikuoka	L	117
16	7	7	København Eremitagen	DK	128
16	7	8	La Cala Sur	E	1143
16	8	8	La Moraleja La Moraleja 2	E	1150
16	8	8	La Reserva	E	1152
16	6	5	Lanark	SCO	727
16	7	8	Las Américas	E	1155
16	8	5	Læsø Seaside	DK	129
16	7	7	Lausanne	CH	1291
16	6	5	Leven	SCO	729
16	7	5	Limburg BF	B	102
16	8	5	Linden Hall	ENG	571
16	5	7	Llandudno (Maesdu)	WAL	789
16	7	7	Los Naranjos	E	1161
16	4	6	Luffness New	SCO	732
16	7	7	Lundin	SCO	733
16	7	7	Manchester	ENG	577
16	8	6	Mannings Heath Waterfall Course	ENG	578
16	7	7	Masia Bach	E	1164
16	7	8	Maspalomas	E	1165
16	7	5	Massane-Montpellier	F	290
16	7	6	Mediterraneo	E	1166
16	7	6	Médoc Les Vignes	F	292
16	7	5	Meland	N	1034
16	6	7	Mijas Los Lagos	E	1167
16	9	8	Milano	I	963
16	7	7	Mittelrheinischer	D	421
16	7	5	Mölle	S	1253
16	8	7	Montenmedio	E	1172
16	8	7	Moor Park High Course	ENG	584
16	7	7	München-Riedhof	D	423
16	7	5	Nefyn & District	WAL	792
16	6	6	Neusiedlersee-Donnerskirchen	A	83
16	6	7	New Zealand	ENG	587
16	7	3	Nordcenter Benz Course	FIN	148

CLASSIFICATION OF GOLF COURSES

16	5	5	Nordvestjysk	DK	131
16	7	6	North Hants	ENG	589
16	6	8	North Wales (Llandudno)	WAL	794
16	6	6	Northamptonshire	ENG	590
16	7	7	Novo Sancti Petri	E	1174
16	7	6	Old Head	IRL	872
16	8	6	Olgiata	I	967
16	6	6	Österåker Västerled	S	1255
16	6	7	Pals (Platja de Pals)	E	1177
16	6	7	Pannal	ENG	594
16	7	5	Paris International	F	302
16	7	8	Parkstone	ENG	595
16	6	6	Pedreña	E	1179
16	6	9	Penha Longa	P	1060
16	8	6	Pleasington	ENG	597
16	7	6	Pont Royal	F	306
16	5	5	Portsalon	IRL	876
16	7	6	Portstewart Strand Course	NIR	912
16	6	4	Powfoot	SCO	749
16	8	7	Prestbury	ENG	599
16	6	7	Prestwick St Nicholas	SCO	751
16	8	9	Puerta de Hierro Arriba	E	1184
16	7	5	Pyle & Kenfig	WAL	797
16	6	7	Quinta do Lago Sul (B + C)	P	1069
16	8	8	Ravenstein Old Course	B	106
16	6	6	Rebetz	F	312
16	5	7	Reddish Vale	ENG	601
16	7	7	Reichswald-Nürnberg	D	431
16	8	6	Rheine/Mesum	D	433
16	6	5	The Rolls of Monmouth	WAL	798
16	8	9	Roma - Acquasanta	I	977
16	7	6	Rosapenna Old Tom Morris	IRL	883
16	7	6	Royal Ashdown Forest	ENG	603
16	7	8	Royal Burgess	SCO	754
16	8	7	Royal Dublin	IRL	886
16	7	8	Royal Jersey	ENG	608
16	8	8	Royal Mougins	F	315
16	8	7	Royal Musselburgh	SCO	756
16	7	4	Sablé-Solesmes La Forêt + La Rivière	F	316
16	7	8	Saint Donat	F	318
16	8	8	Saint-Nom-la-Bretèche Bleu	F	323
16	7	6	Saltsjöbaden	S	1257
16	7	7	San Domenico	I	978
16	5	7	Sandiway	ENG	619
16	6	5	Santo da Serra	P	1074
16	8	7	Sarfvik New Course	FIN	151
16	7	7	Sart-Tilman	B	111
16	7	7	Schloss Braunfels	D	436
16	8	6	Schloss Ebreichsdorf	A	82
16	8	5	Schloss Langenstein	D	439
16	7	7	Schloss Myllendonk	D	441
16	8	7	Schloss Nippenburg	D	442
16	6	6	Scotscraig	SCO	758
16	8	7	Semlin am See	D	446
16	8	7	Sempachersee West + Ost	CH	1298
16	8	7	Senne	D	447
16	7	6	Sheringham	ENG	627
16	8	8	Son Antem Oeste	E	1195
16	8	9	Son Muntaner	E	1196
16	7	7	Southerndown	WAL	801
16	7	7	Southport & Ainsdale	ENG	631
16	8	7	Sporting-Club Berlin Stan Eby	D	450
16	8	8	St Andrews Jubilee Course	SCO	762
16	7	7	St Margaret's	IRL	892
16	7	6	St. Eurach	D	452
16	9	7	St. Leon-Rot Rot	D	453
16	6	7	Stavanger	N	1039
16	8	7	Steiermärkischer Murhof	A	86
16	7	7	Stolper Heide	D	455
16	5	5	Stuttgarter Solitude	D	456
16	7	7	Täby	S	1264
16	9	8	The Belfry Brabazon	ENG	641
16	8	7	The Country Club (Tullnerfeld) Diamond	A	87
16	8	7	Torino - La Mandria Percorso Blu	I	979
16	5	7	Le Touquet La Mer	F	336
16	9	7	Turnberry Kintyre Course	SCO	772
16	6	6	Ulzama	E	1201
16	8	7	Vale Hotel, Golf & Spa(Vale of Glamorgan) Wales National	WAL	803
16	5	6	Valle del Este	E	1203
16	7	7	Vasatorp	S	1269
16	7	9	Venezia	I	981
16	9	8	Villa d'Este	I	983
16	7	6	Villamartin	E	1204
16	7	5	Villette d'Anthon Les Sangliers	F	340
16	7	5	Visby	S	1271
16	1	6	Vuissens	CH	1299
16	7	6	Walddörfer	D	460
16	7	7	Wallasey	ENG	649
16	7	7	Walton Heath New Course	ENG	650
16	6	6	Wantzenau (La)	F	342
16	8	7	Waterloo La Marache	B	114
16	8	7	Waterloo Le Lion	B	115
16	7	6	Wendlohe A-Kurs + B-Kurs	D	462
16	7	6	West Cornwall	ENG	656
16	6	6	West Hill	ENG	657
16	7	6	West Kilbride	SCO	773
16	7	7	West Lancashire	ENG	658
16	6	7	Whittington Heath	ENG	662
16	7	6	WinstonGolf	D	464
16	7	6	Wittelsbacher	D	465
16	7	6	Woodenbridge	IRL	900
16	7	6	Zaudín	E	1205

15	6	7	Adare	IRL	817
15	6	5	L'Ailette	F	202
15	8	8	Alicante	E	1110
15	7	5	Alloa	SCO	677
15	8	8	Almenara	E	1111
15	7	7	Amarilla	E	1114
15	7	7	Amsterdam	NL	992
15	6	6	Ängelholm	S	1218
15	7	6	Ängsö	S	1219
15	8	6	Apremont	F	206
15	8	8	Arcangues	F	208
15	7	5	Arendal	N	1030
15	9	8	Arzaga	I	937
15	7	7	Ascona	CH	1280
15	7	7	Bad Abbach-Deutenhof	D	368
15	5	7	Bad Bevensen	D	369
15	9	9	Bad Griesbach-Sagmühle Sagmühle	D	372
15	7	7	Bâle-Hagenthal	F	212

- *a. Coteaux de Chiroubles (Beaujolais) ?*
- *b. Vignoble des Riceys (Champagne) ?*
- *c. Riquewihr et son vignoble (Alsace) ?*

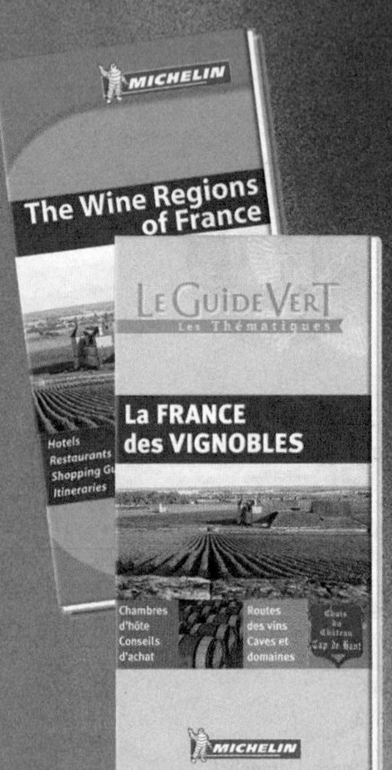

Vous ne savez pas quelle case cocher?

Alors plongez-vous dans le Guide Vert Michelin !

- tout ce qu'il faut voir et faire sur place
- les meilleurs itinéraires
- de nombreux conseils pratiques
- toutes les bonnes adresses

Le Guide Vert Michelin, l'esprit de découverte

15	7	6	Lichtenau-Weickershof	D	414
15	7	6	Limerick County	IRL	866
15	7	8	Lindau-Bad Schachen	D	415
15	7	6	Lisburn	NIR	909
15	9	7	London Golf Club International	ENG	575
15	8	7	Losby	N	1033
15	7	8	Lugano	CH	1293
15	7	7	Luttrellstown	IRL	867
15	6	8	Makila Golf Club	F	289
15	8	7	Manor House (Castle Combe)	ENG	579
15	7	8	Marbella	E	1163
15	8	8	Marco Simone	I	961
15	8	7	Marriott St Pierre Old Course	WAL	791
15	7	7	Master Master	FIN	147
15	7	7	Mere	ENG	582
15	7	7	Møn	DK	130
15	8	7	Monticello Rosso	I	966
15	6	6	Montreux	CH	1295
15	5	5	Mullingar	IRL	871
15	5	5	Mullion	ENG	586
15	6	7	Münchner-Strasslach	D	424
15	6	6	Murcar	SCO	740
15	7	7	Nairn Dunbar	SCO	743
15	6	7	Newport	WAL	793
15	9	6	Northop Country Park	WAL	795
15	6	6	Oberschwaben Bad Waldsee	D	427
15	7	7	Oostende	B	104
15	7	7	Oosterhout	NL	1014
15	7	6	Orchardleigh	ENG	593
15	7	7	Öschberghof	D	428
15	7	9	Oslo	N	1037
15	7	8	Paradiso del Garda	I	969
15	7	8	Penina	P	1061
15	7	7	Peralada	E	1180
15	6	6	Perranporth	ENG	596
15	5	6	PGA National	IRL	873
15	8	5	Pickala Seaside Course	FIN	149
15	7	9	Pineda	E	1182
15	7	7	Poggio dei Medici	I	972
15	6	6	Pornic	F	308
15	8	7	Portal Championship	ENG	598
15	6	6	Portpatrick (Dunskey)	SCO	748
15	7	7	Powerscourt East Course	IRL	877
15	6	7	Praha Karlstejn	CZ	1309
15	6	4	Prince's Himalayas-Shore	ENG	600
15	5	4	Quinta do Brinçal	P	1067
15	6	7	Quinta do Lago Norte (A + D)	P	1068
15	7	5	Quinta do Peru	P	1070
15	7	7	Rathcore	IRL	879
15	6	4	Ribagolfe Blue	P	1071
15	6	4	Ribagolfe Green	P	1072
15	7	7	Ring of Kerry	IRL	881
15	8	7	Rittergut Birkhof	D	435
15	7	7	Roncemay	F	314
15	7	6	Rosapenna Sandy Hill Links	IRL	884
15	7	7	Rosendael	NL	1017
15	7	7	Royal Belfast	NIR	913
15	7	6	Royal Cromer	ENG	606
15	7	7	Royal Guernsey	ENG	607
15	8	6	Royal Latem	B	109
15	7	4	Royal Oak	DK	132
15	7	8	Royal Wimbledon	ENG	615
15	7	8	Rya	S	1256
15	7	4	Saint-Endréol	F	319
15	6	5	Saint-Jean-de-Monts	F	321
15	4	7	Samsø	DK	134

15	7	7	Sand Moor	ENG	618
15	7	4	Saunton West Course	ENG	621
15	7	7	Schloss Egmating	D	437
15	6	6	Schloss Klingenburg	D	438
15	7	6	Schloss Lüdersburg Old Course	D	440
15	8	7	Schloss Schönborn	A	85
15	5	6	Sct. Knuds	DK	135
15	6	6	Seapoint	IRL	888
15	7	6	Shanklin & Sandown	ENG	625
15	6	6	Sherborne	ENG	626
15	7	7	Simon's	DK	136
15	7	5	Sint Nicolaasga	NL	1018
15	8	5	Slieve Russell	IRL	889
15	7	5	Söderåsen	S	1260
15	6	3	Sorknes	N	1038
15	7	8	St Andrews Bay Torrance Course	SCO	766
15	8	9	Stockholm	S	1262
15	7	8	Stoneham	ENG	636
15	7	7	Strasbourg Illkirch Jaune + Rouge	F	332
15	6	6	Strathaven	SCO	767
15	6	6	Sybrook	NL	1019
15	6	8	Sylt	D	457
15	8	6	Talma	FIN	152
15	7	4	Taulane	F	333
15	9	8	The Belfry PGA National	ENG	642
15	7	7	The Island	IRL	893
15	7	4	Thetford	ENG	644
15	7	6	Thorndon Park	ENG	645
15	6	5	Thornhill	SCO	770
15	6	5	Thurlestone	ENG	647
15	7	7	Torekov	S	1265
15	7	5	Toulouse Palmola	F	334
15	7	6	Toulouse-Seilh Rouge	F	335
15	7	6	Tulfarris	IRL	895
15	7	6	Tutzing	D	459
15	7	6	Twente	NL	1021
15	7	8	Vale do Lobo Royal Golf Course	P	1077
15	7	7	Vilamoura Laguna	P	1080
15	7	8	Warwickshire	ENG	652
15	7	7	Wasserburg Anholt	D	461
15	7	7	West Berkshire	ENG	655
15	7	6	West Surrey	ENG	659
15	6	7	Weston-Super-Mare	ENG	661
15	7	7	Westport	IRL	898
15	6	6	Whitekirk	SCO	775
15	7	6	Wilmslow	ENG	663
15	8	7	Winnerod	D	463
15	7	7	Woodbridge	ENG	667
15	7	6	Woodbrook	IRL	899
15	9	6	Woodbury Park The Oaks	ENG	668
15	7	6	Wouwse Plantage	NL	1022
15	7	6	Zumikon	CH	1301

14	7	6	A 6	S	1217
14	7	6	Abenberg	D	366
14	6	5	Aboyne	SCO	676
14	7	7	Acaya	I	934

14	8	8	Albarella	I	935
14	6	7	Alcaidesa	E	1107
14	6	7	Aldeburgh	ENG	500
14	7	6	Alhaurín	E	1109
14	7	7	Almerimar	E	1112
14	6	5	Alyth	SCO	678
14	7	8	L'Amirauté	F	205
14	7	6	Anderstein	NL	993
14	6	4	Ardglass	NIR	901
14	6	5	Aroeira Aroeira II	P	1052
14	6	6	Arras	F	209
14	6	8	Baberton	SCO	680
14	6	5	Baden	F	211
14	7	6	Ballykisteen	IRL	821
14	5	5	Bamburgh Castle	ENG	503
14	7	7	Banchory	SCO	682
14	6	5	Bangor	NIR	902
14	8	7	Barlassina	I	939
14	6	9	Bath	ENG	504
14	7	7	Bearna	IRL	824
14	7	7	Bélesbat	F	214
14	7	7	Bercuit	B	97
14	5	6	Béthemont	F	216
14	6	8	Biarritz-le-Phare	F	217
14	6	5	Bitche	F	218
14	6	6	Boat of Garten	SCO	685
14	7	6	Bonalba	E	1115
14	7	6	Bosjökloster	S	1224
14	7	6	Brest Iroise	F	224
14	7	6	Brigode	F	226
14	6	6	Buchanan Castle	SCO	688
14	6	6	Burntisland	SCO	689
14	5	6	Came Down	ENG	524
14	7	6	Campoamor	E	1117
14	7	8	Cannes Mandelieu Old Course	F	227
14	6	8	Cardiff	WAL	781
14	6	5	Cardigan	WAL	782
14	6	4	Cardross	SCO	691
14	7	4	Carmarthen	WAL	783
14	5	6	Carnoustie Burnside	SCO	692
14	4	8	Carton House The O'Meara	IRL	829
14	6	6	Carvoeiro Vale da Pinta + Gramacho	P	1054
14	8	7	Castello di Tolcinasco Giallo + Blu	I	947
14	5	7	Cerdaña	E	1120
14	8	6	Château de Chailly	F	231
14	5	7	Chambon-sur-Lignon	F	232
14	6	3	Champ de Bataille	F	234
14	7	7	Chantaco	F	235
14	6	4	Chaumont-en-Vexin	F	240
14	7	6	Cheverny	F	241
14	6	7	Cosmopolitan	I	949
14	7	7	Costa Brava	E	1123
14	5	5	Courtown	IRL	838
14	7	8	Crans-sur-Sierre	CH	1284
14	6	5	Dieppe-Pourville	F	247
14	6	7	Divonne	F	250
14	7	7	Domtal-Mommenheim	D	381
14	8	5	Drente	NL	998
14	7	8	Dromoland Castle	IRL	843
14	9	7	Druids Glen Druids Heath	IRL	845
14	6	3	Edzell	SCO	708
14	7	7	Ekerum Långe Jan	S	1228
14	7	7	Elfrather Mühle	D	383
14	6	6	Esker Hills	IRL	848
14	7	5	Falnuée	B	99
14	6	6	Felixstowe Ferry Martello Course	ENG	541
14	7	6	Five Nations	B	100

14	6	6	Fontcaude	F	260
14	7	5	Fontenailles Jaune + Blanc	F	261
14	5	4	Forfar	SCO	712
14	7	8	Franciacorta	I	951
14	7	5	Fränkische Schweiz	D	389
14	7	6	Galway Bay	IRL	852
14	7	8	Garlenda	I	953
14	6	7	Garmisch-Partenkirchen	D	391
14	5	5	Gelpenberg	NL	1001
14	7	7	Glamorganshire	WAL	786
14	7	6	Glen	SCO	714
14	7	5	Golf Parc Nantilly	F	268
14	5	4	Golspie	SCO	718
14	6	7	Granada	E	1137
14	6	7	Grand Ducal de Luxembourg	L	116
14	6	5	Grantown on Spey	SCO	719
14	4	4	Granville Le Links	F	272
14	7	6	La Gruyère	CH	1289
14	7	6	Guadalhorce	E	1138
14	6	5	Haut-Poitou	F	276
14	6	6	Hechingen-Hohenzollern	D	405
14	8	7	Hever	ENG	558
14	6	6	Interlaken	CH	1290
14	7	6	Jakobsberg	D	410
14	6	6	Karlshamn Gamla Banan	S	1243
14	7	8	Killarney Lackabane	IRL	862
14	7	6	La Dehesa	E	1144
14	8	8	La Quinta	E	1151
14	7	7	Langland Bay	WAL	788
14	8	8	Las Palmas	E	1157
14	7	7	Lauro	E	1158
14	7	5	Laval-Changé La Chabossière	F	286
14	8	8	Le Pavoniere	I	957
14	7	7	Lignano	I	960
14	8	8	Lindenhof	D	416
14	6	4	Llanymynech	WAL	790
14	7	5	Longniddry	SCO	731
14	6	7	Los Arqueros	E	1160
14	6	5	Luffenham Heath	ENG	576
14	7	7	Main-Taunus	D	418
14	8	5	Maison Blanche	F	288
14	7	8	Malahide Red + Blue + Yellow	IRL	868
14	7	6	Mariánské Lázne	CZ	1308
14	7	6	Märkischer Potsdam	D	419
14	5	6	Massereene	NIR	911
14	6	6	Memmingen Gut Westerhart	D	420
14	5	6	Mendip	ENG	580
14	8	7	Meon Valley Meon Course	ENG	581
14	7	4	Montanya	E	1169
14	6	7	Monte Carlo (Mont Agel)	F	295
14	6	7	Moor Allerton	ENG	583
14	7	7	Morgado do Reguengo	P	1056
14	7	7	Murrayshall	SCO	741
14	8	6	Nahetal	D	425
14	7	7	Neuchâtel	CH	1296
14	7	7	Newbury & Crookham	ENG	588
14	5	5	Newtonmore	SCO	744
14	7	6	Nunspeet North + East	NL	1013
14	7	7	Old Thorns	ENG	592
14	6	7	Oliva Nova	E	1175
14	7	5	Omaha Beach La Mer + Le Bocage	F	300
14	6	5	Oudenaarde Abdij + Anker	B	105
14	8	8	Padova Blue + Yellow	I	968
14	7	7	Palheiro	P	1058
14	5	6	Palmares	P	1059
14	6	4	Panoramica	E	1178
14	7	8	Parco di Roma	I	970

14	8	7	Pinheiros Altos	P	1062
14	6	6	Pinnau	D	429
14	6	6	Pitlochry	SCO	747
14	7	6	Ploemeur Océan	F	305
14	6	4	La Porcelaine	F	307
14	7	5	Le Prieuré Ouest	F	309
14	6	8	Punta Ala	I	973
14	8	7	Purmerend	NL	1015
14	6	7	Quinta da Marinha	P	1064
14	7	5	Château de Raray La Licorne	F	311
14	7	4	Rathsallagh	IRL	880
14	6	7	Reichsstadt Bad Windsheim	D	430
14	8	7	Rheinhessen	D	434
14	7	6	Rigenée	B	107
14	6	7	Rijk van Nijmegen Nijmeegse Baan	NL	1016
14	6	6	Rinkven Red + White	B	108
14	6	4	Rochefort	F	313
14	7	7	Roganstown	IRL	882
14	5	6	Ross-on-Wye	ENG	602
14	8	8	Royal Mid-Surrey Outer	ENG	611
14	8	7	Rudding Park	ENG	616
14	8	7	Saint-Cloud Vert	F	317
14	7	5	Saint-Laurent	F	322
14	7	6	La Sainte-Baume	F	325
14	6	6	San Sebastián	E	1190
14	6	7	Santa Ponsa Santa Ponsa I	E	1192
14	5	4	Savenay	F	327
14	7	6	Schönenberg	CH	1297
14	7	7	Seafield	IRL	887
14	7	7	Sherry Golf	E	1194
14	6	5	Skellefteå	S	1258
14	6	9	Son Vida	E	1197
14	7	8	South County	IRL	890
14	7	8	Spiegelven	B	113
14	8	8	St Andrews Eden Course	SCO	761
14	6	6	St Helen's Bay	IRL	891
14	6	5	Tadmarton Heath	ENG	640
14	7	6	Tawast	FIN	153
14	7	8	Tegernseer Bad Wiessee	D	458
14	7	7	Thorpeness	ENG	646
14	7	7	Torrequebrada	E	1200
14	7	6	Toxandria	NL	1020
14	7	5	Val de Sorne	F	337
14	6	5	Val Queven	F	338
14	6	8	Vale do Lobo Ocean Course	P	1076
14	8	7	Varese	I	980
14	7	5	Värnamo	S	1268
14	7	4	La Vaucouleurs Les Vallons	F	339
14	7	7	Vejle Blue + Red	DK	137
14	6	7	Vila Sol	P	1078
14	6	5	Les Volcans	F	341
14	5	6	Waterford Castle	IRL	896
14	7	6	Woodsome Hall	ENG	670
14	7	6	Wylihof	CH	1300
14	7	8	Zuid Limburg	NL	1023

13	6	4	Ableiges Les Etangs	F	201
13	7	7	Ambrosiano	I	936
13	6	6	Arcachon	F	207
13	7	7	Asolo Giallo + Verde	I	938
13	6	6	Athlone	IRL	818
13	6	4	Augerville	F	210
13	7	6	Bad Ragaz	CH	1281
13	7	7	Bologna	I	944
13	7	6	Breitenloo	CH	1283
13	6	7	Bundoran	IRL	826
13	6	5	Cairndhu	NIR	904
13	6	6	Cervia	I	948
13	6	6	Charleville	IRL	831
13	6	8	Citywest	IRL	832
13	8	6	Claux Amic	F	243
13	7	5	Cognac	F	244
13	6	6	Costa Dorada	E	1124
13	6	7	Dinard	F	248
13	7	6	Ennetsee-Holzhäusern	CH	1287
13	8	7	Escorpion Azul	E	1133
13	5	6	Etretat	F	255
13	7	7	Faithlegg	IRL	850
13	5	7	Falkirk Tryst	SCO	711
13	8	9	Firenze - Ugolino	I	950
13	6	4	Les Fontenelles	F	262
13	6	7	Glen of the Downs	IRL	854
13	7	6	Jarama R.A.C.E.	E	1141
13	6	6	Lacanau	F	284
13	7	6	Lee Valley	IRL	865
13	6	7	Luzern	CH	1294
13	4	6	Málaga	E	1162
13	6	6	Malone	NIR	910
13	7	7	Margara	I	962
13	6	7	Mijas Los Olivos	E	1168
13	7	7	Modena	I	964
13	7	6	Mont-Garni	B	103
13	5	5	Monte Mayor	E	1170
13	8	8	Montecchia	I	965
13	6	5	Mount Wolseley	IRL	870
13	7	5	Ozoir-la-Ferrière Château + Monthéty	F	301
13	6	8	Pau	F	303
13	6	5	Pula	E	1185
13	8	8	Rapallo	I	974
13	6	8	Rimini	I	975
13	7	7	Riva dei Tessali	I	976
13	5	6	Rosslare	IRL	885
13	7	7	Royal Portrush Valley	NIR	916
13	7	8	Sainte-Maxime	F	326
13	6	5	Sant Cugat	E	1191
13	5	7	Servanes	F	329
13	4	6	Taymouth Castle	SCO	769
13	7	7	Torremirona	E	1199
13	7	8	Verona	I	982
13	6	4	Warrenpoint	NIR	917
13	4	5	Wimereux	F	343

Architectes et parcours
Architekten und golfplätze
Arkitekter och golfbanor
Arquitectos y recorridos
Architettetti e percorsi

James Braid, M. Cowper
Shanklin & Sandown 625
James Braid, G. Duncan
Mere 582
James Braid, George Duncan Sandy Herd, Tom Simpson
Wilmslow 663
James Braid, George Fernie
Hunstanton 563
James Braid, Willie Fernie
Cardross 691
James Braid, Alister Mackenzie
Blairgowrie Rosemount 684
James Braid, Tom Morris
Alyth 678, Carnoustie Championship 693, Forfar 712, Lanark 727, Nairn 742, Royal Burgess 754, West Kilbride 773
James Braid, Tom Morris, Harry Vardon
Rosapenna Old Tom Morris 883
James Braid, Tom Morris, J.H. Taylor, Hawtree
Wallasey 649
James Braid, Mungo Park
Royal Musselburgh 756
James Braid, Willie Park
Parkstone 595
James Braid, Archie Simpson
Murcar 740
James Braid, Bob Simpson
Royal Aberdeen Balgownie 753
Crieff Ferntower Course 696
James Braid, Jim Steer
Fairhaven 540
James Braid, J.H. Taylor
Nefyn & District 792
James Braid, A.C. Brown, Willie Park
Grantown-on-Spey 719
James Braid, F. Pennink, D. Steel
Berwick-upon-Tweed 509

Declan Brannigan, Des Smyth
Ballykisteen 821, Seapoint 888, Waterford Castle 896

Douglas Brasier
Bosjökloster 1224, Ljunghusen 1251, Saltsjöbaden 1257
Douglas Brasier, R. Victorsson
Karlshamn Gamla Banan 1243
Douglas Brasier, Peter Nordwall
Åtvidaberg 1220
Douglas Brasier, T. Nordström
Kristianstad 1246

F.W. Brewster
Royal Jersey 608

Olivier Brizon
Aisses (Les) Rouge/Blanc 203

A.C. Brown, Willie Park, J. Braid
Grantown on Spey 719

R.J. Browne
Bearna 824

Ture Bruce
Bärseback 1220, Mölle 1253, Vasatorp 1269, Söderåsen 1260
Ture Bruce, åke Persson
Landskrona 1250

A.C. Brown, James Braid, Willie Park
Grantown-on-Spey 719

Yves Bureau
Baden 211, Fontenelles (Les) 262, Omaha Beach 300, Saint-Jean-de-Monts 321, Val Queven 338

Burrows, Del C. van Krimpen
Hilversum 1007

C

Sir Guy Campbell
Killarney Mahony's Point 863
Sir Guy Campbell, Tom Dunn
Royal Cinque Ports 605
Sir G. Campbell, C.K. Hutchinson
West Sussex 660, Wimereux 343
Sir G. Campbell, C.K. Hutchinson, Hotchkin
Ashridge 502
Sir Guy Campbell, John Morrison
Prince's 600

Willie Campbell
Seascale 623
Willie Campbell, Donald Steel
Machrie 734

Enrique Canales, L. Recasens
Islantilla Verde/Azul 1140

José Canales
Valle del Este 1203

Joe Carr, Eddie Hackett, Ron Kirby, Patrick Merrigan
Old Head 872

Doug Carrick, Hans Erhard
Fontana 71

Jim Cassidy, Andrew Gilbert
Kilkea Castle 861

Giulio Cavalsani
Punta Ala 973
G. Cavalsani, Biratti, Fazio, Dassú
Monticello Rosso 966

M. Chantepie, D. Fruchet
Etretat 255

Hubert Chesneau, Robert von Hagge
National L'Albatros 298

Clive Clark, Peter Alliss
Manor House 579, Alcaidesa 1107

Clive Clark, Peter Alliss, R. McMurray, Alex Hay
Woburn Marquess 665

Neil Coles, Angel Gallardo
PGA de Catalunya 1181

Harry S. Colt
Bath 504, Belvoir Park 903, Blackmoor 510, Brancepeth Castle 516, Brokenhurst Manor 518, Camberley Heath 523, Cannes Mandelieu Old Course 227, Chantaco 235, Denham 537, De Pan 997, East Devon 538, Eindhoven 1000, Frankfurter GC 388, Isle of Purbeck 567, Kennemer 1010, Manchester 577, Moor Park High Course 584, Northamptonshire 590, Pedreña 1179, Prestbury 599, Pyle & Kenfig 797, Royal Belfast 913, Royal Cromer 606, Royal Dublin 886, Royal Portrush Dunluce Links 915, Royal Wimbledon 615, Rye 617, Saint-Cloud Vert 317 Saint-Germain 320, Sant Cugat 1191, Sherwood Forest 628, St Andrews Eden Course 761, St George's Hill 633, Stoke Park 635, Sunningdale 637/638, Swinley Forest 639, Thorndon Park 645, Thurlestone 647, Trevose Championship 648, Wentworth East Course 653, Wentworth West Course 654, Whittington Heath 662
Harry S. Colt, Charles Alison,
County Sligo 836, Haagsche 1005
H.S. Colt, C. Alison, M. Hawtree
Granville Le Links 272
H.S. Colt, C. Alison, A. Mackenzie
Knock 908
H. S. Colt, C. Alison, J. Morrison
Falkenstein 385
H. S. Colt, James Braid
Sherwood Forest 628
H. S. Colt, J. Braid, H.Fowler
Aberdovey 779
H. S. Colt, J. Braid, D. Ross
Longniddry 731
H. S. Colt, T. Dunn
Broadstone 517
H.S. Colt, T. Dunn H. Vardon, C.K. Cotton
Ganton 548
H.S. Colt, Herbert Fowler T. Simpson, C.K. Cotton
Royal Lytham & St Anne's 610
H. S. Colt, A. Mackenzie
The Alwoodley 501, Ilkley 565

H. S. Colt, Tom Morris
Muirfield, 739
H. S. Colt, John Morrison
Prestbury 599
H. S. Colt, W. Park, Frank Pennink, Donald Steel
Formby 545
H. S. Colt, Tom Simpson
Málaga 1162
H. S. Colt, J.H. Taylor
Royal Cromer 606,
Le Touquet La Mer 336
H. S. Colt, Harry Vardon, Hotchkin
Woodhall Spa Hotchkin 669

E. Connaughton
Charleville 831

Bill Coore
Médoc Les Châteaux 291

Jean-Claude Cornillot
Arras 209

Cornish & Silva
Ambrosiano 936

C.K. Cotton
Ascona 1280, Downfield 699,
Marriott St Pierre Old Course 791,
Olgiata 967, Ross-on-Wye 602,
West Lancashire 658
C.K. Cotton, Cruikshank, M. Croze
Venezia 981
C.K. Cotton, James Braid
Pennard 796
C.K. Cotton, Herbert Fowler, H.S. Colt, T. Simpson
Royal Lytham & St Anne's 610
C.K. Cotton, T. Dunn, H.S. Colt, H. Vardon
Ganton 548
C.K. Cotton, John Harris
Bologna 944, Padova 968,
Verona 982
C.K. Cotton & Sutton
Bergamo L'Albenza 940
C.K. Cotton, Dreyer
Sct. Knuds 135
C.K. Cotton, F. Pennink, P. Mancinelli
Is Molas 956
C.K. Cotton, F. Pennink, D. Steel
Gardagolf 952

Henry Cotton
Penina 1061
Henry Cotton, Tom Dunn
Felixstowe Ferry 541
Henry Cotton, Rocky Roquemore
Vale do Lobo 1076/1077
Henry Cotton, Piero Mancinelli
Olgiata 967
Henry Cotton, Tom Simpson
Golf Barrière Deauville 266

M. Cowper, James Braid
Shanklin & Sandown 625

Tom Craddock, Pat Ruddy
Ballyliffin Glashedy Links 822,
Druids Glen Druids Glen 844,
St Margaret's 892

Arthur Croome
Liphook 57

Marco Croze
Cervia 948, Lignano 960,
Riva dei Tessali 976
M. Croze, C.K. Cotton, Cruikshank
Venezia 981
M. Croze, Pete Dye
Franciacorta 951
Jon Harris, Marco Croze
Albarella 935

Juan de la Cuadra, J. M. Olazábal
La Sella 1153

Robert E. Cupp
East Sussex National East 539

Brian Curley
Vidbynäs 1270

D

Baldovino Dassù, A. Rossi Fioravanti
Poggio dei Medici 972
Dassú, Biratti, Cavalsani, Fazio
Monticello Rosso 966

P. De Jong, F. Pennink
Noordwijk 1012

Christophe Descampe, P.Rolin
Rigenée 107

DeutscheGolfConsult
Öschberghof 428
Deutsche Golf Consult, Rainer Preismann
Bad Abbach-Deutenhof 368

Bruce Devlin
St Andrews Bay Devlin 765

Olivier Dongradi
Augerville 210
O. Dongradi, Peter Harradine
Maison Blanche 288

Frederik Dreyer
Esbjerg 124
F. Dreyer, C.K. Cotton
Sct. Knuds 135

B. Ducwing
Pau 303

Johan Dudok van Heel
Oosterhout 1014,
Wittelsbacher 465
J. Dudok van Heel, B. Steensels
Herkenbosch 1006
J. Dudok van Heel, D. Steel. G. Jol
Anderstein 993

George Duncan, James Braid
Mere 582

George Duncan, James Braid, Sandy Herd, Tom Simpson
Wilmslow 663

Mr Dunlop
Fanø 125

Tom Dunn
Bude & North Cornwall 520,
Seacroft 622, Sheringham 627,
Weston-super-Mare 661,
Woking 666
Tom Dunn, Sir Guy Campbell
Royal Cinque Ports 605
Tom Dunn, H. S. Colt
Broadstone 517
T. Dunn, H.S. Colt, H. Vardon, C.K. Cotton
Ganton 548
Tom Dunn, Henry Cotton
Felixstowe Ferry 541
Tom Dunn, W. Park, H. Fowler
Lindrick 572
Tom Dunn, J.H. Taylor
Came Down 524

Willie Dunn
Biarritz Le Phare 217, Dinard 248

P.B. Dye
Parco di Roma 970
P.B. Dye, Pete Dye
Barbaroux 213

Perry Dye
San Roque New Course 1188

Pete Dye
Domaine Impérial 1285
Klagenfurt-Seltenheim 74
Pete Dye, M. Croze
Franciacorta 951
Pete Dye, P.B. Dye
Barbaroux 213

Frank Dyer
Jönköping 1241

E F

Stan Eby
Sporting-Club Berlin Eby 450
Fleesensee 387

Jim Eremko, Les Furber
Praha Karlstejn 1309

Hans G. Erhard, Doug Carrick
Fontana 71
Hans G. Erhard, Kurt Rossknecht
Neusiedlersee-Donnerskirchen 75,

Björn Eriksson
Fågelbro 1229

Eschauzier & Thate
Graafschap 1004

Ramón Espinosa
Bonalba 1115, Fontanals 1134,
Mediterraneo 1166,
Golf d'Aro (Mas Nou) 1135

Euro Golf Projekt, C. Städler
Rheine/Mesum 433

Nick Faldo
Sporting-Club Berlin Faldo 449
Nick Faldo, Steve Smyers
Chart Hills 529

Faldo, Lawrie, Pennink, Hackett, Hopkins
Ballyliffin Old Course 823

Jim Fazio
Le Querce 958, Marco Simone 961
Paradiso del Garda 969
Fazio, Dassú, Biratti, Cavalsani
Monticello Rosso 966

Tom Fazio, J.A. Mulcahy, Eddie Hackett
Waterville 897

David Feherty, David Jones
National GC 1314

Heinz Fehring
München-Riedhof 423

Michael Fenn
Brest Iroise 224, Toulouse Palmola 334, Saint-Laurent 322

George Fernie, James Braid
Hunstanton 563

Willie Fernie
Dumfries & County 703, Pitlochry 747, Royal Troon Old Course 757, Shiskine 759, Southerndown 801, Thornhill 770
Willie Fernie, J.R. Stutt
Strathaven 767
Willie Fernie, James Braid
Cardross 691

Mel Flanagan
Rathcore 879

M. Flera
Örebro 1254

Anders Forsbrand
Kungsängen (European Tour Club) 1248

Jean-Pascal Fourès
Rebetz 312, Laval-Changé La Chabossière 286, Claux Amic 243

Herbert Fowler
Beau Desert 505, The Berkshire 507/508, Delamere Forest 536, Saunton East Course 620
Walton Heath 650/651
West Surrey 659
Herbert Fowler, Harry S. Colt, James Braid
Aberdovey 779
Herbert Fowler, H.S. Colt T. Simpson, C.K. Cotton
Royal Lytham & St Anne's 610
H. Fowler, Tom Dunn, W. Park
Lindrick 572

Ronald Fream
Arcangues 208, Cap d'Agde 229, Carvoeiro 1054, Pinheiros Altos 1062, Disneyland Paris 249, Frégate 265, L'Isle Adam 279, Massane-Montpellier 290, Montreux 1295
Ronald Fream, Robert Hersant
Golf Parc Nantilly 268

Patrick Fromanger, Mark Adam
Bélesbat 214, Bitche 218, Cély 230

Didier Fruchet, George Will
Gouverneur (Le) Le Breuil 269
D. Fruchet, M. Chantepie
Etretat 255

Pierre Fulke
Grönhögen 1237

Les Furber
Engadin Zuoz Madulain 1286
Les Furber, Jim Eremko
Praha Karlstejn 1309

G

Angel Gallardo, Neil Coles
PGA de Catalunya 1181

José Gancedo
Canyamel 1118, Costa Dorada 1124, Golf del Sur 1136, La Finca 1145, Lerma 1159, Monte Mayor 1170, Torrequebrada 1200
José Gancedo, Folco Nardi
Santa Ponsa Santa Ponsa I 1192

Peter Gannon
Villa d'Este 983
Peter Gannon, Cecil R. Blandford
Firenze–Ugolino 950, Milano 963, Varese 980

Jean Garaialde
La Porcelaine 307, Cognac 244
J. Garaialde, Jeremy Pern
Ableiges 201, Albi 204, Charmeil 237, La Largue 285, Toulouse-Seilh Rouge 335, La Wantzenau 342

Antonio Garrido, Manuel Piñero
La Quinta 1151

Carmelo García, Gregorio Sanz
Campoamor 1117

Jonathan Gaunt
Castleknock 830 - Linden Hall 571

Michel Gayon
L'Ailette 202, Esery 252, Le Chambon-sur-Lignon 232, La Domangère 251, Etiolles Colonial 254, Fontenailles 261, Gloria Golf 1313, Sablé-Solesmes 316, Saint-Endréol 319, Savenay 327, La Vaucouleurs 339

Michel Gayon, J. Lebreton
Golf Barrière La Baule Bleu 267, Pornic 308

Charles Gibson
Royal Porthcawl 799

Des Giffin, Willie Park Jr.
Portstewart Strand Course 912

Andrew Gilbert, Jim Cassidy
Kilkea Castle 861

Golden Bear Design
La Moraleja La Moraleja 2 1150
Golden Bear Design, Ron Kirby
London Golf Club International 575

G.H. Gowring
Berkhamsted 506

I.E. Grant, Hawtree & Son
Cardigan 782

Harald Gratenau
St. Dionys 451

Karl F. Grohs
Bitburger Land 377, Lübeck-Travemünder 417
Karl F. Grohs, F. Pennink
Gut Kaden A+B 396

Eddie Hackett
Belmullet (Carne Golf Links) 825, Connemara 833, Donegal (Murvagh) 840, Dooks 841, Enniscrone 847, Malahide 868
Ring of Kerry 881
E. Hackett, Fred Hawtree
The Island 893
Eddie Hackett, Ron Kirby, Patrick Merrigan, Joe Carr
Old Head 872
E. Hackett, N. Faldo, Lawrie, Pennink, Hopkins
Ballyliffin Old Course 823
E. Hackett, J.A. Mulcahy, Tom Fazio
Waterville 897
E.Hackett, C. O'Connor Jr.
Dingle Links (Ceann Sibeal) 839

W. Hall Blyth, Tom Morris
St Andrews New 763

Andy Haggar
San Domenico 978

Robert von Hagge
Les Bordes (Les) 221, Bogogno 942/943, Courson 245/246, Emporda 1132, Is Arenas 955, Kempferhof (Le) 283
Real Sociedad Club de Campo 1186/1187, Royal Mougins 315, Seignosse 328
Robert von Hagge, H. Chesneau
National L'Albatros 298

J. Hamilton Stutt
Costa Brava 1123, Murrayshall 741
Meon Valley Meon Course 581
Woodbury Park The Oaks 668

Donald Harradine
Bad Ragaz 1281, Beuerberg 376, Bled 1311, Chaumont-en-Vexin 240, Düsseldorfer 382, Interlaken 1290, Neuchâtel 1296, Schloss Klingenburg 438, Schloss Myllendonk 441, Schönenberg 1297, St. Eurach 452, Strasbourg Illkirch Jaune + Rouge 332, Sylt 457, Tegernseer Bad Wiessee 458, Zumikon 1301
D. Harradine, Ronald Fream
Montreux 1295
D. Harradine, P. Harradine
Sainte-Maxime 326
D. Harradine, L. Morandi
Nîmes-Campagne 299
D. Harradine, M. Nakowsky
Divonne 250
D. Harradine, F. Pennink
Breitenloo 1283
D. Harradine, C. B. Robinson
Lugano 1293
D. Harradine, B. von Limburger
Oberfranken 426
D. Harradine, F. Pennink
Breitenloo 1283

Peter Harradine
Golfpark Gut Häusern 383
Peter Harradine, O. Dongradi
Maison Blanche 288

F.A. Harris
Berlin-Wannsee 375

Harris & Associates
Courtown 838

John Harris
Garlenda 953, Lacanau 284
John Harris, Marco Croze
Albarella 935
John Harris, C.K. Cotton
Bologna 944, Padova 968, Verona 982
John Harris, Tom Simpson
Puerta de Hierro Arriba 1184

Fred Hawtree
Bondues Jaune 220, Gog Magog Old Course 549, Hillside 560, John O'Gaunt 568, Limburg 102, Lisburn 909, Malone 910, Massereene 911, Pals (Platja de Pals) 1177, Le Prieuré Ouest 309
Rochefort 313, Royal Latem 109, Saint-Nom-la-Bretèche 323/324, Son Vida 1197, Westport 898, Waterloo La Marache 114, Woodbridge 667
Zuid Limburg 1023

Fred Hawtree, E. Hackett
The Island 893
F. Hawtree, J. McAllister
Athlone 818
Hawtree & Son, I.E. Grant
Cardigan 782
F. Hawtree, J.H. Taylor
Royal Birkdale 604
F. Hawtree & Taylor
Båstad Old Course 1222, High Post 559, Rosslare 885

Martin Hawtree
Rudding Park 616, Simon's 136
M. Hawtree, C. Alison, H. S. Colt
Granville Le Links 272
M. Hawtree, T. Simpson
Oostende 104

Siegfried Heinz
Domtal-Mommenheim 381

Rolf Henning-Jensen
Møn 130

Sandy Herd
Harrogate 554
Sandy Herd, George Duncan, James Braid, Tom Simpson
Wilmslow 663
Sandy Herd, George Low
Pleasington 597
Sandy Herd, Charles Mackenzie
Pannal 594

H. Hertzberger, Donald Steel
Goes 1003

E.D. Hess
Wendlohe A-Kurs + B-Kurs 462

L. Hewson, Tom Simpson
Ballybunion Old Course 820

Reijo Hillberg
Pickala Seaside Course 149, Tawast 153

Arthur Hills
Hills 1240 – Oitavos 1057

Harold Hilton
Ferndown Old Course 542

Thomas Himmel, Carlo Knauss
Fürstlicher Bad Wadsee 390

Pierre Hirigoyen
San Sebastián 1190
P. Hirigoyen, Cecil R. Blandford
Arcachon 207

Karl-Heinz Hoffmann
Mittelrheinischer 421

Hotchkin, Sir G. Campbell, C.K. Hutchinson
Ashridge 502

Colonel S.V. Hotchkin, Harry S. Colt, Harry Vardon,
Woodhall Spa Hotchkin 669

Jeff Howes, Seve Ballesteros
The Heritage 857
Jeff Howes, Peter McEvoy, Ch. O'Connor Jr
Fota Island 851

Thierry Huau, Robin Nelson
Champ de Bataille 234

Brian Huggett
Orchardleigh 593
Brian Huggett, Knott, Bridge
Bowood (Cornwall) 513

Åke Hultström
Ängsö 1219

Bob Hunt, PGA Management
Meland 1034

C.W. Hunter
Portpatrick (Dunskey) 748

Charles Hunter
Cochrane Castle 694
Charles Hunter, James Allan
Prestwick St Nicholas 751

C.K. Hutchinson, Sir G. Campbell
West Sussex 660, Wimereux 343
C.K. Hutchinson, Sir G. Campbell, Hotchkin,
Ashridge 502

Horace Hutchinson, H. Ingleby
Royal W. Norfolk (Brancaster) 614

IJ

Ibergolf
Granada 1137

Holcombe Ingleby, H. Hutchinson
Royal West Norfolk (Brancaster) 614

Tony Jacklin, Dave Thomas
San Roque Old Course 1189

John Jacobs
Apremont 206 ,
The Buckinghamshire 519, Northop Country Park 795
John Jacobs, Golf associates
Las Américas 1155

Henrik Jacobsen
Samsø 134
Henrik Jacobsen, L. Andreasson
Læsø Seaside 129

Wolfgang Jersombek
Jakobsberg 410

Peter Johnson
Vale Hotel, Golf & Spa 803

Gérard Jol
Houtrak 1009, Drente 998
Gérard Jol, Frank Pennink
Broekpolder 995
G. Jol, J. Dudok van Heel, D. Steel
Anderstein 993

Peter McEvoy, Ch. O'Connor Jr.
Rathsallagh 880
P. McEvoy, C. O'Connor Jr, J. Howes
Fota Island 851

M. McKenna
Hermitage 858

David McLay Kidd
Powerscourt West Course 878

Patrick Merrigan
Faithlegg 850, Slieve Russell 889, Tulfarris 895, Woodenbridge 900
Patrick Merrigan, Ron Kirby, Joe Carr, Eddie Hackett
Old Head 872

David Mezzacane
Acaya 934, Cosmopolitan 949

Johnny Miller
Collingtree Park 531

William Mitchell
Quinta do Lago Sul 1069
William Mitchell, R. Roquemore
Quinta do Lago Norte 1068

Colin Montgomerie
Carton House Montgomerie 828

Theodore Moon
Kilmarnock (Barassie) 723

Léonard Morandi, D. Harradine
Nîmes-Campagne 299

John Morgan
Forest Pines Forest + Pines 544

Jack Morris
Royal Liverpool (Hoylake) 609

John Morris, Donald Steel
Caldy 522

Tom Morris
Dunbar 704, Luffness New 732, Machrihanish 735, Ladybank 726, Moray Old 738, North Devon (Westward Ho!) 612, Royal County Down 914, Royal Crail Balcomie Links 695, Tain 768
Tom Morris, Auchterlonie, John Angus, Donald Steel
St Andrews Jubilee Course 762
Tom Morris, James Braid
Alyth 678, Nairn 742, Carnoustie Championship 693, Forfar 712, Lanark 727, Royal Burgess 754, West Kilbride 773
Tom Morris, James Braid, Harry Vardon
Rosapenna Old Tom Morris 883
Tom Morris, James Braid, J.H. Taylor, Hawtree
Wallasey 64
Tom Morris, H. S. Colt
Muirfield, 739

Tom Morris, W. Hall Blyth
St Andrews New 763
Tom Morris, A. Mackenzie
Lahinch 864
Tom Morris, Donald Ross
Royal Dornoch 755

Jay Morrish, Tom Weiskopf
Loch Lomond 730

John Morrison
Biella Le Betulle 941, Torino, La Mandria Percorso Blu 979, Barlassina 939
Toxandria 1020
J.Morrison, C. Alison, H. S. Colt
Falkenstein 385
John Morrison, S. Böstrom
Lunds Akademiska 1252
John Morrison, Sir Guy Campbell
Prince's 600
John Morrison, H. S. Colt
Prestbury 599
John Morrison, M. Nicholson
Stockholm 1262

Tim Morrison
Cairndhu 904, Hossegor 277

Léonard Morandi
Nîmes-Campagne 299

Desmond Muirhead, J. Nicklaus
La Moraleja La Moraleja 1149

John A. Mulcahy, Tom Fazio, E. Hackett
Waterville 897

N

M. Nakowsky, D. Harradine
Divonne 250

Narbel, Jeremy Pern
Lausanne 1291

Folco Nardi
Lauro 1158
Folco Nardi, José Gancedo
Santa Ponsa Santa Ponsa I 1192

Peter Nicholson
Hever 558

M. Nicholson, Seve Ballesteros
Crans-sur-Sierre 1284
M. Nicholson, John Morrison
Stockholm 1262

Jack Nicklaus
Gleneagles PGA Centenary 716, Gut Altentann 73, Le Robinie 959, Gut Lärchenhof 397, Mount Juliet 869, Montecastillo 1171, Paris International 302
St Mellion Nicklaus Course 634
Jack Nicklaus, D. Muirhead
La Moraleja La Moraleja 1149

Jack Nicklaus, Steve Nicklaus
Carden Park Nicklaus Course 525

Jack Nicklaus JR.
Arzaga 937

Steve Nicklaus, Jack Nicklaus
Carden Park Nicklaus Course 525

Nicklaus design
The Hertfordshire 557

Tommy Nordström
Varberg Västra 1267, Borre 1031
Tommy Nordström, D. Brasier
Kristianstad 1246

Peter Nordwall
A 6 1217, Bro-Bålsta 1226, Ekerum Långe Jan 1228, Gränna 1236, Losby 1033, Skövde Södra Banan 1259, Stenungsund 1261, Svartinge 1263
Peter Nordwall, Douglas Brasier
Åtvidaberg 1220
Peter Nordwall, Nils Sköld
Visby 1271, Skellefteå 1258

Greg Norman
Doonbeg 842, El Prat 1128/1129

C. Noskowski
Karlovy Vary 1307

O P

Christy O'Connor Jr.
Citywest 832, Esker Hills 848, Galway Bay 852, Glasson 853, Headfort New Course 856, Lee Valley 865, Mount Wolseley 870, PGA National 873
E.Hackett, C. O'Connor Jr.
Dingle Links (Ceann Sibeal) 839
Ch. O'Connor Jr. Peter McEvoy
Rathsallagh 880
Ch. O'Connor Jr. Jeff Howes, Peter McEvoy,
Fota Island 851

José Maria Olazábal
Costa Ballena 1122
Masia Bach 1164, Sevilla 1193
J. M. Olazábal, J. de la Cuadra,
La Sella 1153

Mark O'Meara
Carton House The O'Meara 829

Arnold Palmer
Castello di Tolcinasco Giallo + Blu 947, K Club North 859, Tralee 894, Le Pavoniere 957, Sporting-Club Berlin Palmer 448, Vilamoura Victoria 1081
Arnold Palmer, Ed Seay
Rethmar 432
Arnold Palmer Design Company
K Club South Course 860

Arnold Palmer, R.D. Puttman, Dave Thomas
La Manga Sur 1148

Mungo Park, James Braid
Royal Musselburgh 756

Willie Park
Baberton 680, Burntisland 689, Duddingston 700, Huntercombe 564, Monte-Carlo (Mt Agel) 295, Silloth-on-Solway 629, Stoneham 636, Sunningdale Old 638,

Willie Park, James Braid
Parkstone 595

Willie Park, J. Braid, A.C. Brown,
Grantown-on-Spey 719

W. Park, H. Fowler, Tom Dunn
Lindrick 572

Willie Park, A. Mackenzie
Bruntsfield 687

W. Park, H. S. Colt, Frank Pennink, Donald Steel
Formby 545

Willie Park, Jack White
West Hill 657

Willie Park Jr.
Notts (Hollinwell) 591, Montrose 737, Dieppe-Pourville 247

Willie Park Jr, Des Giffin
Portstewart Strand Course 912

Willie Park Jr, Tom Simpson
Antwerp 96

Jerry Pate, R. Weishaupt
Schwanhof 444

Frank Pennink
Gelpenberg 1001, Kungsbacka 1249 Palmares 1059, Saunton West 621 Vilamoura Old 1079

F. Pennink, James Braid, D. Steel
Berwick-upon-Tweed 509

Frank Pennink, W. Park, H. S. Colt, Donald Steel
Formby 545

F. Pennink, C.K. Cotton
Is Molas 956

F. Pennink, Karl F. Grohs
Gut Kaden 396

F. Pennink, D. Harradine
Breitenloo 1283

F. Pennink, P. de Jong
Noordwijk 1012

F. Pennink, C.K. Cotton, D. Steel
Gardagolf 952

F. Pennink, Donald Steel
Gelpenberg 1001, Hoge Kleij 1008

Pennink, Hackett, Faldo, Lawrie, Hopkins
Ballyliffin Old Course 823

Frank Pennink, Gérard Jol
Broekpolder 995

F. Pennink, Del C. van Krimpen
Rosendael 1017

F. Pennink, Harry Vardon
Mendip 500

Jeremy Pern
La Bresse 223, Dartmouth 535 La Gruyère 1289, Les Bois 1292, Roncemay 314, The Country Club Diamond 79, Vuissens 1299,

Jeremy Pern, J. Garaialde
Ableiges 201, Albi 204, Charmeil 237, La Largue 285, Toulouse-Seilh Rouge 335, La Wantzenau 342

Jeremy Pern, Narbel
Lausanne 1291

Andrew Person
Göteborg 1235

Åke Persson, Ture Bruce
Landskrona 1250

Malling Petersen
Vejle Blå + Rød 137

Kyle Phillips
Kingsbarns 724, Dundonald 705, The Grove 643, Eichenheim 70

K. Phillips, R. Trent Jones Jr.
Lage Vuursche 1011

W.C. Pickeman, George Ross
Portmarnock 874

Manuel Piñero
El Puerto 1130, La Dehesa 1144,

Manuel Piñero, A. Garrido
La Quinta 1151

Michael Pinner
Winnerod 463

B. von Limburger, M. Pinner
Steiermärkischer Murhof 78

Chris Pittman
Fontcaude 260

Gary Player
Five Nations 100, Taulane 333, Zaudín 1205

Gary Player, Ron Kirby
Almerimar 1112

Jean-Marie Poellot
Feucherolles 258

P. Postel
Iffeldorf 409

Alain Prat
Pléneuf-Val-André 304, Gujan-Mestras 274

Rainer Preismann, Deutsche Golf Consult
Bad Abbach-Deutenhof 368

Keith Preston
Schloss Ebreichsdorf 76

Dr W. Laidlaw Purves
Royal St George's 613

John Putman
Villamartin 1204

Robert Dean Puttman
La Manga Norte 1147

R.D. Puttman, Arnold Palmer, Dave Thomas
La Manga Sur 1148

QR

Quenouille & MacAuley
Ploemeur Océan 305

Ted Ray
Sandiway 619

Agostino Reale
Margara 962

L. Recasens, R.& F. M. Benjumea
Pineda 1182

L. Recasens, Enrique Canales
Islantilla Verde/Azul 1140

Holger Rengstorf
WinstonGolf 464

Alan Rijks
Batouwe 994 , Gendersteyn 1002

A. Rijks, Paul Rolin
Sybrook 1019, St Nicolaasga 1018

Cabell B. Robinson
Aphrodite Hills 1306, Castillo de Gorraiz 1119, Evian 257, La Grande Bastide 270, La Cala Norte 1142/1143, La Reserva 1152, Limère 287, Palheiro 1058, Praia d'El Rey 1063

C. B. Robinson, D. Harradine
Lugano 1293

W.R. Robinson
Clandeboye Dufferin 906

George Rochester
Bamburgh Castle 503

Erik Röhs
Fjällbacka 1231

Paul Rolin
Nunspeet 1013 Rijk van Nijmegen Nijmeegse 1016, Rinkven Red - White 108

Paul Rolin, C. Descampe
Rigenée 107

Paul Rolin, Gérard Jol
Amsterdam 992

P. Rolin, European Golf Design
Waterloo Le Lion 115

Paul Rolin, A. Rijks
Sybrook 1019, St Nicolaasga 1018

Paul Rolin, Donald Steel
Wouwse Plantage 1022

Rocky Roquemore
Belas 1053, Makila 289, Quinta De Cima 1064, Quinta da Ria 1065, Quinta do Brinçal 1066, Quinta do Peru 1070

R. Roquemore, H. Cotton
Vale do Lobo 1076/1077
Rocky Roquemore, Joseph Lee
Vilamoura III (Laguna) 1080
R. Roquemore, William Mitchell
Quinta do Lago Norte 1068

Donald Ross, Tom Morris
Royal Dornoch 755
D. Ross, James Braid, H. S. Colt
Longniddry 731

George Ross, W.C. Pickeman
Portmarnock 874

Mackenzie Ross
Turnberry Ailsa Course 771
Castletown 527, Southerness 760, Maspalomas 1165, Glen 714
Mackenzie Ross, J. Dominguez
Las Palmas 1157
Mackenzie Ross, Tom Simpson
Carlisle 526
Mackenzie Ross, Donald Steel
Turnberry Kintyre Course 772

Jean-Manuel Rossi
Belle-Dune 215

A. Rossi Fioravanti, B. Dassù
Poggio dei Medici 972

Kurt Rossknecht
Am Alten Fliess 367, Bad Griesbach Sagmühle 372, Gut Ludwigsberg 398, Gut Thailing 399, Hof Trages 406, Hohenpähl 407, Rittergut Birkhof 435 Motzener See 422, Sempachersee 1298, Schloss Egmating 437, Schloss Schönborn 77, Son Muntaner 1196
Kurt Rossknecht, Hans G. Erhard
Colony Club Gutenhof 68, Neusiedlersee-Donnerskirchen 75
Kurt Rossknecht, B. Langer
Bad Griesbach Beckenbauer 370, Stolper Heide 455

Lucien Roux
Volcans (Les) 341

Pat Ruddy
Druids Glen Druids Heath 845, European (The) 849, Rosapenna Sandy Hill Links 884,
Pat Ruddy, Tom Craddock
Ballyliffin Glashedy Links 822, Druids Glen Druids Glen 844, St Margaret's 892

S

Gregorio Sanz, Carmelo García
Campoamor 1117

Ben Sayers
Castlerock 905

Ulrich Schmidt
Bad Bevensen 368

Erik Schnack
Holstebro 127, Nordvestjysk 131

Hannes Schreiner
St. Leon-Rot Rot Course 453

Archdeacon Scott
Royal Ashdown Forest 603

Jan Sederholm
Ängelholm 1218
Espoo 144, Haninge 1239, Himmerland New 126, Larvik 1032, Sarfvik New 151,
Jan Sederholm, Anders Amilon
Bokskogen 1223
Jan Sederholm, Sven Tumba
Österåker Västerled 1255

Brian Silva
Rimini 975

Archie Simpson
Aboyne 676
Archie Simpson, James Braid
Murcar 740,

Bob Simpson
Edzell 708
Bob Simpson, James Braid
Royal Aberdeen Balgownie 753
Crieff Ferntower Course 696

Tom Simpson
Carlow 827, Chantilly Vineuil 236, Chiberta 242, County Louth 835, Cruden Bay 697, Fontainebleau 259, Hainaut 101, Hardelot Les Pins 275, ICL Chantilly Les Chênes 278, Morfontaine 297, Ravenstein 106, Sart-Tilman 111, Spa (Les Fagnes) 112
Tom Simpson, Harry S. Colt
Málaga 1162
Tom Simpson, George Duncan, James Braid, Sandy Herd
Wilmslow 663
Tom Simpson, C.K. Cotton, Herbert Fowler, H.S. Colt
Royal Lytham & St Anne's 610
Tom Simpson, Henry Cotton
Golf Barrière Deauville 266
Tom Simpson, John Harris
Puerta de Hierro Arriba 1184
T. Simpson, M. Hawtree
Oostende 104
Tom Simpson, L. Hewson
Ballybunion Old Course 820
Tom Simpson, Willie Park Jr
Antwerp 96
Tom Simpson, Mackenzie Ross
Carlisle 526
Tom Simpson, J.H. Taylor
Hayling 556

Cameron Sinclair
Whitekirk 775

Nils Sköld
Forsbacka 1233, Täby 1264, Torekov 1265, Värnamo 1268
Nils Sköld, Sune Linde
Karlstad 1244
Nils Sköld, Sune Linde, Rafael Sundblom, Gierdsjö
Kalmar 1242
Nils Sköld, Peter Nordwall
Visby 1271, Skellefteå 1258
Nils Sköld, Rafael Sundblom
Drottningholm 1247

Fred Smith
Slavanger 1039

G.K. Smith, Donald Steel
Letham Grange Old Course 728

Steve Smyers, Nick Faldo
Chart Hills 529

Des Smyth
Limerick County 866
Des Smyth, Declan Brannigan
Ballykisteen 821, Seapoint 888, Waterford Castle 896

Juul Søgaard
Sorknes 1038

Jorge Soler
Peralada 1180

Duarte SottoMayor
Estela 1055

john souter
Banchory 682

Thierry Sprecher, G. Watine
Château de Chailly 231, Servanes 329

Christoph Stâdler
Semlin am See 446, Senne 447
Märkischer Potsdam 419
C. Städler, Euro Golf Projekt
Rheine/Mesum 433

John Stagg
West Berkshire 655

Donald Steel
Amarilla 1114, Aroeira II 1052, Efteling 999, Forest of Arden 543
Killarney Lackabane 862, Portal 598, Vila Sol 1078, Wouwse Plantage 1022
Donald Steel,John Angus, Auchterlonie, Old Tom Morris
St Andrews Jubilee Course 762
F. Pennink, James Braid, D. Steel
Berwick-upon-Tweed 509
Donald Steel, H. S. Colt, Frank Pennink, W. Park,
Formby 545
D. Steel, G. Jol, J. Dudok van Heel
Anderstein 993
D. Steel, H. Hertzberger
Goes 1003

Donald Steel, F. Pennink
Oelpenberg 1001, Hoge Kleij 1000
Donald Steel, GK. Smith
Letham Grange Old Course 728
D. Steel, C.K. Cotton, F. Pennink
Gardagolf 952
Donald Steel, Willie Campbell
Machrie 734
Donald Steel, Mackenzie Ross
Turnberry Kintyre Course 772
Donald Steel, C.H. Mayo
Thetford 644
Donald Steel, John Morris
Caldy 522
Donald Steel, Paul Rolin
Wouwse Plantage 1022
Bruno Steensels, T. MacAuley
Purmerend 1015
B. Steensels, J. Dudok van Heel
Herkenbosch 1006

Jim Steer, James Braid
Fairhaven 540

Blake Sterling
Sherry Golf 1194
Blake Sterling, Marco Martín
El Cortijo 1127

Adrian Stiff
Cumberwell Park 534

J.R. Stutt, Willie Fernie
Strathaven 767

Rafael Sundblom
Halmstad 1238, Rya 1256
Rafael Sundblom, Gierdsjö, Nils Sköld, Sune Linde
Kalmar 1242
Rafael Sundblom, Nils Sköld
Drottningholm 1247

T

Russell Talley, European Golf Design
Morgado do Reguengo 1056

J.H. Taylor
Carmarthen 783, Frilford Heath Red Course 546, Hindhead 561
Royal Mid-Surrey Outer 611
J.H. Taylor, James Braid, Tom Morris, Hawtree
Wallasey 649
J.H. Taylor, James Braid
Nefyn & District 792
J.H. Taylor, Harry S. Colt
Royal Cromer 606, Le Touquet La Mer 336
J.H. Taylor, Tom Dunn
Came Down 524
J.H. Taylor, Fred Hawtree
Royal Birkdale 604
J.H. Taylor, Tom Simpson
Hayling 556

Dave Thomas
Almenara 1111,
The Belfry PGA National 642,
Bowood G&CC 514, Cardrona 690,
Four Seasons Provence 263/264,
Robinson 1315,
The Roxburghe 752,
St. Leon-Rot St Leon Course 454,
Slaley Hall Hunting Course 630,
Dave Thomas, Peter Alliss
Blairgowrie Lansdowne 683,
Cannes-Mougins 228,
King's Lynn 569, Old Thorns 592,
The Belfry Brabazon 641
Dave Thomas, Tony Jacklin
San Roque Old Course 1189
Dave Thomas, R.D. Puttman, Arnold Palmer
La Manga Sur 1148

David Thomas
Montanya 1169

John Thompson
Aldeburgh 500

Peter Thomson
Duke's St Andrews 702

Mr Thompson
Portsalon 876

Peter Townsend
Ribagolfe Blue 1072

Robert Trent Jones
Adare 817, Ballybunion Cashen 819
Bercuit 97, Bondues Blanc 219,
Castelconturbia Giallo + Blu 945,
Castelgandolfo 946
Chamonix 233, El Bosque 1126,
Estérel 253, Genève 1288,
La Grande-Motte 271,
I Roveri 954, Joyenval 281/282,
Las Brisas 1156, Los Naranjos 1161, Marbella 1163, Moor Allerton 583, Mijas 1167/1168,
Moliets 293, Pevero 971,
Quinta da Marinha 1064,
Ruuhikoski 150, Spérone 331,
Santo da Serra 1074, Sotogrande 1198, Troia 1075,
Valderrama 1202,
R. Trent Jones, R. Trent Jones Jr.
Prince de Provence 310

Robert Trent Jones Jr.
Alcanada 1108, Bonmont 1116,
Celtic Manor Roman Road 784,
Château de la Chouette 238,
Grenoble Bresson 273,
Miklagard 1035, Moscow 1310,
Penha Longa 1060,
Puerta de Hierro Abajo 1183
Saint Donat 318,
Seddiner See Südplatz 445
R. Trent Jones Jr., K. Phillips
Lage Vuursche 1011

Sven Tumba, Jan Sederholm
Österåker Västerled 1255

Jeremy Turner
Moss & Rygge 1036
Knistad 1245

J.H. Turner
Newbury & Crookham 588

Reverend Tyack, Vicar of Lelant
West Cornwall 656

UVW

Iwao Uematsu
Kikuoka 117

Olivier van der Vynckt
Cheverny 241

Harry Vardon
Bundoran 826, Copt Heath 532,
Hanbury Manor 552,
Kingussie 725, Little Aston 574,
Tadmarton Heath 640 ,
H. Vardon , T. Morris, J. Braid
Rosapenna Old Tom Morris 883
Harry Vardon, H. S. Colt, Hotchkin
Woodhall Spa Hotchkin 669
H. Vardon, C.K. Cotton, T. Dunn, H.S. Colt
Ganton 548
Harry Vardon, F. Pennink
Mendip 580

Mario Verdieri
Ennetsee-Holzhäusern 1287

Robert Walker
Cardiff 781

Henrik Wartiainen
Talma 152

Philip Walton
County Tipperary 837
St Helen's Bay 891

Géry Watine, T. Sprecher
Château de Chailly 231,
Servanes 329

Reinhold Weishaupt, Jerry Pate
Schwanhof 444

Tom Weiskopf, Jay Morrish
Loch Lomond 730

Jack White, Willie Park
West Hill 657

Rod Whitman
Médoc Les Vignes 292

George Will, Didier Fruchet
Le Gouverneur Le Breuil 269

WEATHER IN EUROPE

Le temps en Europe

Temperatures (° C) (minimum/maximum)

Sun (Hours/day)

Average rainfall per month

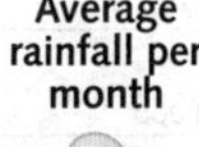

- 25 mm

- 50 mm

- 75 mm

- 100 mm

+ 100 mm

Snow

Snow

Denmark

	01	04	07	10
Temperatures	– 2/2	3/10	14/22	7/12
Sun	1 h	5 h	8 h	3 h

England/Wales

	01	04	07	10
Temperatures	2/7	6/13	13/21	8/14
Sun	2 h	5 h	6 h	3 h

Scotland

	01	04	07	10
Temperatures	1/6	4/11	11/20	7/12
Sun	2 h	5 h	6 h	3 h

Ireland

	01	04	07	10
Temperatures	1/8	4/13	11/20	7/14
Sun	2 h	5 h	6 h	3 h

Netherlands

	01	04	07	10
Temperatures	– 1/4	4/13	13/22	7/14
Sun	2 h	5 h	8 h	3 h

France

	01	04	07	10
Temperatures	0/6	5/15	14/25	9/17
Sun	2 h	6 h	8 h	4 h

Belgium/Luxemburg

	01	04	07	10
Temperatures	-1/5	5/14	11/23	10/20
Sun	2 h	6 h	7 h	4 h

France

Portugal

	01	04	07	10
Temperatures	8/15	10/20	20/28	15/22
Sun	5 h	9 h	11 h	7 h

Portugal

Spain

Spain

	01	04	07	10
Temperatures	5/15	11/24	18/30	12/25
Sun	6 h	8 h	12 h	7 h

Switzerland

	01	04	07	10
Temperatures	– 4/4	3/15	14/24	7/14
Sun	2 h	6 h	8 h	4 h

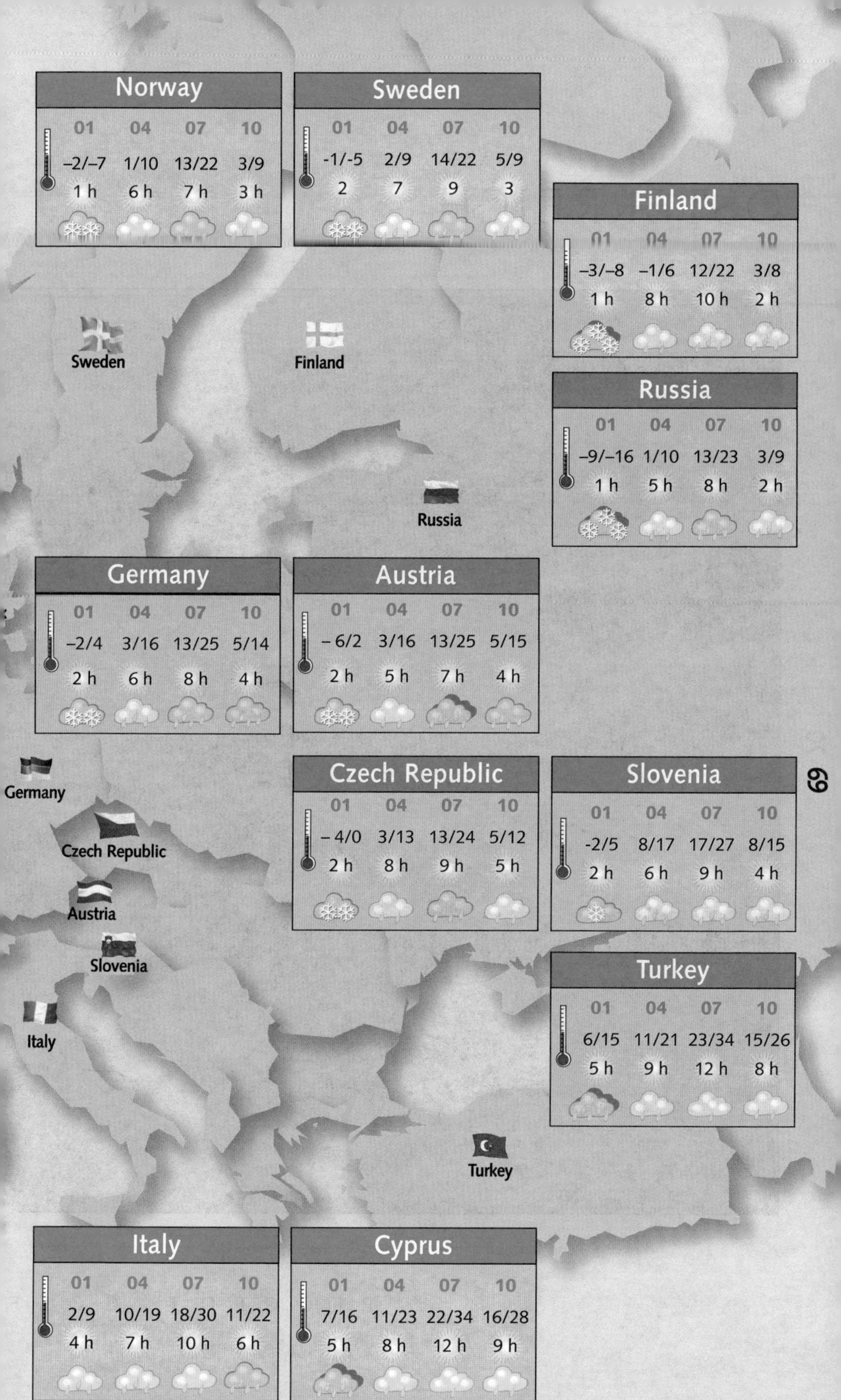

Norway

	01	04	07	10
🌡	–2/–7	1/10	13/22	3/9
	1 h	6 h	7 h	3 h

Sweden

	01	04	07	10
🌡	-1/-5	2/9	14/22	5/9
	2	7	9	3

Finland

	01	04	07	10
🌡	–3/–8	–1/6	12/22	3/8
	1 h	8 h	10 h	2 h

Russia

	01	04	07	10
🌡	–9/–16	1/10	13/23	3/9
	1 h	5 h	8 h	2 h

Germany

	01	04	07	10
🌡	–2/4	3/16	13/25	5/14
	2 h	6 h	8 h	4 h

Austria

	01	04	07	10
🌡	– 6/2	3/16	13/25	5/15
	2 h	5 h	7 h	4 h

Czech Republic

	01	04	07	10
🌡	– 4/0	3/13	13/24	5/12
	2 h	8 h	9 h	5 h

Slovenia

	01	04	07	10
🌡	-2/5	8/17	17/27	8/15
	2 h	6 h	9 h	4 h

Turkey

	01	04	07	10
🌡	6/15	11/21	23/34	15/26
	5 h	9 h	12 h	8 h

Italy

	01	04	07	10
🌡	2/9	10/19	18/30	11/22
	4 h	7 h	10 h	6 h

Cyprus

	01	04	07	10
🌡	7/16	11/23	22/34	16/28
	5 h	8 h	12 h	9 h

ÖSTERREICH

AUSTRIA

Gut Altentann

AUSTRIA

Austria, a land of mountains, has quickly built up a number of golf courses which are the ideal complement to the country's many skiing resorts. There are now more than 135 courses for almost 90,000 golfers. Naturally, golf here is a real sport and walking a tradition; and despite the harsh winters, producing a course in good shape is a question of honour. Often located in idyllic natural settings, the picture postcard appearance of most courses is a joy to behold for foreign visitors. Whether here for a golfing holiday or for a quick round in between other delightful holiday activities, you are in for some great surprises and hospitality typical of a country unlike any other.

ÖSTERREICH

In Österreich, dem Land der Berge, sind in den letzten Jahren viele Golfplätze enststanden. So sind viele Wintersportorte auch beliebte Sommerreiseziele. In Österreich findet man derzeit fast 135 Plätze, auf denen 90.000 einheimische Golfer die Schläger schwingen. Golf in Österreich ist ein Sport, auf den meisten Plätzen geht man zu Fuß. Obwohl die Winter in der Alpenrepublik streng sind, setzen die Greenkeeper allen Ehrgeiz daran, einen perfekt gepflegten Platz zu präsentieren. Die meisten Plätze liegen idyllisch, das herrliche Alpenpanorama wird Besucher beeindrucken. Ob Sie in Österreich einen Golfurlaub verbringen oder nur mal eben zwischendurch eine Runde Golf spielen: Es wird ein angenehme Überraschung werden, zumal die österreichische Gastfreundschaft und das einzigartige Land Sie faszienieren wird.

CLASSIFICATION OF GOLF COURSES
EINTEILUNG DER GOLFPLÄTZE

This classification gives priority consideration to the score awarded to the actual course.

Diese Einteilung berücksichtigt in erster Linie die dem Golfplatz erteilte Note.

Within each score, the ranking is purely alphabetical

Course score / Note für den Golfplatz — Page / Seite

				Page
17	8	8	Eichenheim	78
17	7	7	Gut Altentann	81
17	6	8	Klagenfurt-Seltenheim	82
16	8	8	Colony Club Gutenhof West	76
16	8	7	Fontana	79
16	8	6	Golfresort Haugschlag Waldviertel	80
16	6	6	Neusiedlersee-Donnerskirchen	83
16	8	6	Schloss Ebreichsdorf	84
16	8	7	Steiermärkischer Murhof	86
16	8	7	The Country Club (Tullnerfeld) Diamond	87
15	8	7	Dellach	77
	8	7	Schloss Schönborn	85

HOTEL FACILITIES
EINTEILUNG DES HOTELANGEBOTS DER UMGEBUNG

This classification gives priority consideration to the score awarded to the hotel facilities.

Diese Klassifikation berücksichtigt in erster Linie die Bewertung für das Hotelangebot.

Hotel facility score / Note für das Hotelangebot der Umgebung — Page / Seite

		Hotel score	Course	Page
16	8	**8**	Colony Club Gutenhof West	76
17	8	**8**	Eichenheim	78
17	6	**8**	Klagenfurt-Seltenheim	82
15	8	**7**	Dellach	77
16	8	**7**	Fontana	79
17	7	**7**	Gut Altentann	81
15	8	**7**	Schloss Schönborn	85
16	8	**7**	Steiermärkischer Murhof	86
16	8	**7**	The Country Club (Tullnerfeld) Diamond	87
16	8	**6**	Golfresort Haugschlag Waldviertel	80
16	6	**6**	Neusiedlersee-Donnerskirchen	83
16	8	**6**	Schloss Ebreichsdorf	84

RECOMMENDED GOLFING STAY
EMPFOHLENER GOLF AUFENTHALT

Course				Page
Colony Club Gutenhof West	**16**	8	8	76
Golfresort Haugschlag	**16**	8	6	80
The Country Club (Tullnerfeld)	**16**	8	7	87

RECOMMENDED HOLIDAYS
EMPFOHLENER FERIENORT

Course				Page
Dellach	**15**	8	7	77
Steiermärkischer Murhof	**16**	8	7	86
Klagenfurt-Seltenheim	**17**	6	8	82

Map No 1
Karte 1
km
0 10 20
Bad-Griesbach (D)
Bad Griesbach-Sagmühle (D)
Gut Altentann
Eichenheim
SALZBURG
LINZ
České Budějovice
Passau
Straubing
Deggendorf
Wels
Steyr
Gmunden
Bad Ischl
Bad Reichenhall
Berchtesgaden
Kitzbühel
Zell am See
Bad Gastein
Lienz
Villach
Velden
Spittal
Braunau
Burghausen
Ried
Vöcklabruck
Schärding
Liezen
Schladming
Radstadt
Bischofshofen
Hallein
Traunstein
Kufstein
Cortina d'Ampezzo
Jesenice
O B E R Ö S T E R R E I C H
S A L Z B U R G
K Ä R N T E N
O S T T I R O L
H O H E T A U E R N
MICHELIN

Haugschlag-Waldviertel
Schloss Schönborn
Country Club Tullnerfeld
Colony Golf Club
Schloss Ebreichsdorf
Fontana
Neusiedlersee Donnerskirchen
Steiermärkischer
Klagenfurt Seltenheim
Kärtner Dellach
Bled (Slovenia)
WIEN
GRAZ
LINZ
Klagenfurt
Maribor
České Budějovice
N I E D E R Ö S T E R R E I C H
S T E I E R M A R K
B U R G E N L A N D
MICHELIN
d'après base de données au 1/1 000 000 - édition 2005.
Autorisation n°0501023.

Colony Club Gutenhof *West*

16	8	8

Dieses ist das modernste Resort im Grossraum Wien, ausreichend stadtnah, um der Runde Golf einen Abend in der Staatsoper oder in einem der typischen Heurigen-Lokale folgen zu lassen. Der Colony Club verfügt über zwei 18-Loch-Plätze, die beide von Rossknecht und Erhart entworfen wurden und sich daher im Stil ähneln. Uns gefällt der West-Kurs besser, beide aber fügen sich sehr gut in die Landschaft ein. Alle Hindernisse sind vom Abschlag deutlich zu sehen, so dass einem die Spielstrategie nicht zu viele Kopfzerbrechen machen sollte. Die beiden Designer haben mit sechs Abschlägen pro Loch Golfer aller Spielstärken berücksichtigt. Rund 50 Fairway-Bunker erfordern akkurates Spielen und noch einmal so viele fordern noch mehr Präzision je mehr man sich den gut gestalteten und teilweise noch besser verteidigten Grüns nähert. Nimmt man die üppige Vegetation, dazu noch etliche Wasserhindernisse und das moderne Platzdesign, so ergibt das in der Summe einen modernen Resort Course und einen veritablen Test der golferischen Fertigkeit.

This is the most modern golf resort in the region of Vienna, at good driving distance from an evening out at the Staatsoper or a "Heurigen", one of those open-air restaurants where you drink new wines. With two 18-hole courses to play, we might have hoped for contrasting styles of architecture but the club preferred to employ Rossknecht and Erhart for both layouts, of which the West course gets our vote. Both blend in well with their surroundings and hazards are pretty clear to see so you don't have to think too long or hard about strategy. About fifty fairway bunkers call for unwavering accuracy, especially since more of the same awaits you as you get closer to well-designed greens with some impressive lines of defence. If we then add vegetation that is sometimes very much to the fore plus a number of threatening water hazards, you will have guessed that this is a challenging modern design, or what you might call an exacting trial of strength.

Colony Club Gutenhof Himberg — 1989

Gutenhof
A - 2325 HIMBERG

Office	Sekretariat	(43) 02235 87055 0
Pro shop	Pro shop	(43) 02235 87055 0
Fax	Fax	(43) 02235 8705514
Web		www.colonygolf.com
Situation	Lage	Wien, 10 km
Annual closure	Jährliche Schliessung	no
Weekly closure	Wöchentliche Schliessung	no

Restaurant closed in winter

Fees main season Preisliste hochsaison	Week days Woche	We/Bank holidays We/Feiertag
	18 holes	
Individual Individuell	€ 50	€ 80
Couple Ehepaar	€ 100	€ 160

Juniors & Students: – 50%

Caddie Caddie no — Electric Trolley Elektrokarren no
Buggy Elektrischer Wagen yes — Clubs Leihschläger yes
Credit cards Kreditkarten
VISA - MasterCard - AMEX - DC

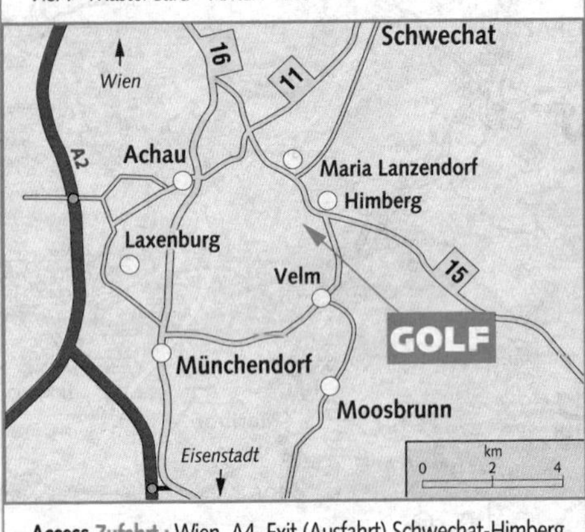

Access Zufahrt : Wien, A4. Exit (Ausfahrt) Schwechat-Himberg. → Moosbrunn. 2 km S. of Himberg, → Golfplatz
Map 1 on page 75 Karte 1 Seite 75

GOLF COURSE — PLATZ — 16/20

Site	Lage	
Maintenance	Instandhaltung	
Architect	Architekt	Kurt Rossknecht Hans G. Erhardt
Type	Typ	parkland, open country
Relief	Begehbarkeit	
Water in play	Platz mit Wasser	
Exp. to wind	Wind ausgesetzt	
Trees in play	Platz mit Bäumen	

Scorecard Scorekarte	Chp. Chp.	Mens Herren	Ladies Damen
Length Länge	6483	6193	5461
Par	73	73	73
Slope system	132	131	132

Advised golfing ability Empfohlene Spielstärke — 0 12 24 36
Hcp required Min. Handicap — 36

CLUB HOUSE & AMENITIES — KLUBHAUS UND NEBENGEBÄUDE — 8/10

Pro shop — Pro shop
Driving range — Übungsplatz
Sheltered überdacht 10 mats - On grass auf Rasen yes
Putting-green Putting-grün yes - Pitching-green Pitching-grün yes

HOTEL FACILITIES — HOTEL BESCHREIBUNG — 8/10

HOTELS HOTELS

Hotel Sacher - 118 rooms, D € 350 - Wien 18 km
Tel (43) 01 514 560, Fax (43) 01 514 568 10

Hotel im Palais Schwarzenberg - Wien 16 km
48 rooms, D € 330
Tel (43) 01 798 45 15, Fax (43) 01 798 47 14

Zum Guten Hirten - 12 rooms, D € 90 - Himberg 500 m
Tel (43) 02235 875 82, Fax (43) 02235 87582-27

RESTAURANTS RESTAURANTS

Hanner - Mayerling 10 km - Tel (43) 02258 23 78
Novelli - Wien 15 km - Tel (43) 01513 4200
Zum Guten Hirten - Himberg 500 m - Tel (43) 02235 875 82

Dellach

15	8	7

Die Natur hat rund um den Wörthersee eine wunderschöne Urlaubsregion geschaffen. Klagenfurt, die Hauptstadt von Kärnten, liegt im Westen, Velden im Osten. Und in Maria Wörth findet man die Kirche mit den Zwillingstürmen und Spuren der Römer. Wenn man ein wenig weiter fährt, kommt man nach Slowenien, wo man vorzüglich in Bled spielen kann (am Ende dieses Golfführers beschrieben). Der Platz von Dellach ist mehr als 60 Jahre alt, aber erst in den fünfziger Jahren wurde er auf 18 Löcher erweitert. Das Layout erinnert an Hamburg-Falkenstein, allerdings ist das Gelände weitaus hügeliger (ein Golfcart oder E-Trolley wird empfohlen) mit einigen steilen Anstiegen. Die Topografie und etliche blinde Löcher machen die Schlägerwahl schwierig. Die Grüns sind klein und besonders für hohe Handicaps nicht leicht zu treffen. Trotzdem werden auch schwächere Spieler den Spaziergang und die Blicke über den Wörthersee geniessen – vielleicht die schönsten Aussichten eines Golfplatzes in Österreich.

Only Mother Nature could have created a site as beautiful as Wörthersee in this superb region of Carinthia. Klagenfurt lies to the west, the resort of Velden to the east and here you are at Maria Wörth with a twin-towered church and Roman vestiges where Gothic style mixes with later influences. If you drive on a little further you end up in Slovenia where you can play Bled for example (cf. end of this volume). This Dellach course is more than 60 years old but the full 18 holes were opened only in the 1950s. The layout is reminiscent of Falkenstein although the terrain is much hillier (buggy recommended) with some sometimes steep slopes to climb. Whence a few blind holes and trickier-than-usual club selection. In addition, the greens are small and may be more than a handful for high-handicappers. Having said that, they will still enjoy the walk and vista over the lake, and views on a golf course don't get much better than this.

Kärtner Golf-Club Dellach — 1927

Golfstrasse 3
A - 9082 MARIA WÖRTH

Office	Sekretariat	(43) 04273 - 2515
Pro shop	Pro shop	(43) 04273 - 2515
Fax	Fax	(43) 04273 - 2515 20
Web	www.kgcdellach.at	
Situation	Lage	Klagenfurt, 12 km
Annual closure	Jährliche Schliessung	no
Weekly closure	Wöchentliche Schliessung	no

Fees main season Preisliste hochsaison		18 holes
	Week days Woche	We/Bank holidays We/Feiertag
Individual Individuell	€ 65	€ 65
Couple Ehepaar	€ 130	€ 130

– 18: € 32 / – 27: € 45

Caddie Caddie no — **Electric Trolley** Elektrokarren yes

Buggy Elektrischer Wagen yes — **Clubs** Leihschläger on request

Credit cards Kreditkarten
VISA - Eurocard - MasterCard - DC - AMEX

Access Zufahrt : Klagenfurt, → Velden, golf on the left bank of Wörthersee
Map 1 on page 75 Karte 1 Seite 75

GOLF COURSE — PLATZ — 15/20

Site	Lage	
Maintenance	Instandhaltung	
Architect	Architekt	unknown
Type	Typ	forest, parkland
Relief	Begehbarkeit	
Water in play	Platz mit Wasser	
Exp. to wind	Wind ausgesetzt	
Trees in play	Platz mit Bäumen	

Scorecard Scorekarte	Chp. Chp.	Mens Herren	Ladies Damen
Length Länge	5609	5301	4765
Par	71	71	71
Slope system	134	128	125

Advised golfing ability Empfohlene Spielstärke — 0 12 24 36
Hcp required Min. Handicap — 36

CLUB HOUSE & AMENITIES — KLUBHAUS UND NEBENGEBÄUDE — 8/10

Pro shop Pro shop
Driving range Übungsplatz
Sheltered überdacht 4 mats - On grass auf Rasen yes - Putting-green Putting-grün yes - Pitching-green Pitching-grün yes

HOTEL FACILITIES — HOTEL BESCHREIBUNG — 7/10

HOTELS HOTELS

Lamplhof - 29 rooms, D € 125 - on site
Tel (43) 04273 250 30, Fax (43) 04273 250 366

Hotel Wörth - 33 rooms, D € 158 - Maria Wörth 2 km
Tel (43) 04273 227 60, Fax (43) 04273 227 657

See- & Golfhotel Linde - 30 rooms, D € 200 - Maria Wörth 3 km
Tel (43) 04273 22 78, Fax (43) 04273 25 01

Seewirt - 26 rooms - Dellach, close
Tel (43) 04273 22 57, Fax (43) 04273 28 052

RESTAURANTS RESTAURANTS

Gasthaus Kaufhaus Lex - Dellach 100 m - Tel (43) 04273 25 43
Seewirt - Dellach 100 m - Tel (43) 04273 2257

Eichenheim

17	8	8

Mit dem neuesten Platz in Tirol ist Kitzbühel auch zu einem der Golfzentren des Landes aufgestiegen. Wie auch im Winter präsentiert sich Kitzbühel als eleganter Ferienort. Das Greenfee mag hoch erscheinen, aber dafür spielt man auf einem der vielversprechendsten Plätze Österreichs. Man sollte sich vor der Runde die Zeit nehmen, den Wilden Kaiser, diesen rauen, mit tiefen Schluchten durchzogenen Berg zu bewundern. Der Platz fordert einem spielerisch und körperlich alles ab, so dass man sich den Luxus eines Golfcarts gönnen sollte. Der Pflegezustand wie auch das Design von Kyle Phillips, einem der neuen Sterne am Himmel der Golfplatzdesigner (bekannt z.B. durch Kingsbarns und Dundonald) sind vorzüglich. Der Amerikaner integrierte geschickt die Steigungen und Abhänge ins Spiel, so dass man bei der ersten Runde nie weiss, welchen Schläger man wählen sollte. Es gibt viele Bäume und einige riesige Bunker, trotzdem hat man den Eindruck eines weit offenen Platzes. Der Platz ist nicht zu lang, sehr offen und unbedingt zu empfehlen.

With this recent course in Tyrolia, Kitzbühel has become one of the country's major golfing centres in sporting terms and for the same slightly worldly elegance it enjoys as a skiing resort. The green fee may certainly seem a little high but this is the price you pay for playing one of Austria's most promising golf courses. Take time out to admire the Wilden Kaiser, a rugged mountain with deep gorges, before setting out on a what is a physically rather demanding course where a buggy is anything but a luxury. Maintenance is on a par with the layout of Kyle Phillips, who is decidedly one of the great revelations for course design in recent years, notably with Kingsbarns and Dundonald in Scotland. He cleverly brings slopes and topography well into play and this implies some rather awkward club selection. There are also a lot of trees and some huge bunkers, but the overall impression is one of wide open space. Not very long but very open, this is a highly recommendable course.

Golfclub Eichenheim — 2000

Eichenheim 8
A - 6370 KITZBÜHEL

Office	Sekretariat	(43) 05356 666 15
Pro shop	Pro shop	(43) 05356 666 1517
Fax	Fax	(43) 05356 666 1515
Web	www.eichenheim.at	
Situation	Lage	Kitzbühel, 3 km
Annual closure	Jährliche Schliessung	1/11→31/3
Weekly closure	Wöchentliche Schliessung	

Fees main season Preisliste hochsaison	Week days Woche	We/Bank holidays We/Feiertag
		18 holes
Individual Individuell	€ 80	€ 80
Couple Ehepaar	€ 160	€ 160

Caddie Caddie no — Electric Trolley Elektrokarren yes
Buggy Elektrischer Wagen yes — Clubs Leihschläger yes

Credit cards Kreditkarten
VISA - Eurocard - MasterCard - DC - AMEX

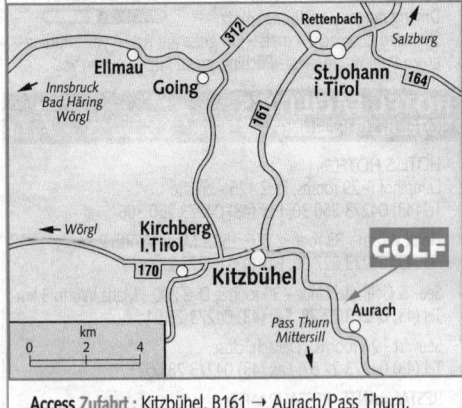

Access Zufahrt : Kitzbühel, B161 → Aurach/Pass Thurn. In Aurach, turn left → golf.
Map 1 on page 74 Karte 1 Seite 74

GOLF COURSE PLATZ — 17/20

Site	Lage	
Maintenance	Instandhaltung	
Architect	Architekt	Kyle Phillips
Type	Typ	mountain
Relief	Begehbarkeit	
Water in play	Platz mit Wasser	
Exp. to wind	Wind ausgesetzt	
Trees in play	Platz mit Bäumen	

Scorecard Scorekarte	Chp. Chp.	Mens Herren	Ladies Damen
Length Länge	6057	5605	4585
Par	71	71	71
Slope system	126	123	122

Advised golfing ability / Empfohlene Spielstärke: 0 12 24 36
Hcp required / Min. Handicap: 36

CLUB HOUSE & AMENITIES KLUBHAUS UND NEBENGEBÄUDE — 8/10

Pro shop — Pro shop
Driving range — Übungsplatz
Sheltered überdacht 10 mats - On grass auf Rasen yes - Putting-green Putting-grün yes - Pitching-green Pitching-grün yes

HOTEL FACILITIES HOTEL BESCHREIBUNG — 8/10

HOTELS HOTELS

Golfhotel Rasmushof - 59 rooms, D € 305 - Kitzbühel 3 km
Tel (43) 05356 652 520, Fax (43) 05356 652 5249

Sporthotel Bichlhof - 50 rooms, D € 215 - Kitzbühel 3 km
Tel (43) 05356 640 22, Fax (43) 05356 636 34

Romantik Hotel Tennerhof - Kitzbühel 3 km
60 rooms, D € 295
Tel (43) 05356 631 81, Fax (43) 05356 631 81 70

RESTAURANTS RESTAURANTS

Goldener Greif - Kitzbühel - Tel (43) 05356 643 11
Wirtshaus zum Rehkitz - Kitzbühel - Tel (43) 05356 661
Hallerwirt - Aurach 1 km - Tel (43) 05356 - 645 02

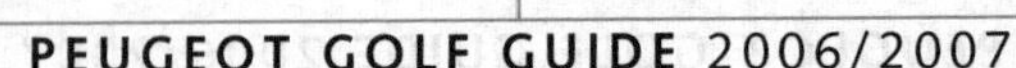

Fontana

16	8	7

Dieser Platz in dem reizvollen Städtchen Baden bei Wien gehört dem österreichisch-kanadischen Milliardär Frank Stronach. Beim Bau wurde zunächst ein zwanzig Hektar groSSer künstlicher See mit einem Sandstrand angelegt, dazu Felsen und ein beeindruckendes Clubhaus mit einem Dutzend Tennisplätze. Fast alle Löcher werden durch Wasser und durch Felsen verteidigt. Das verlangt nach präzisem Spiel, denn wenn man Wasser oder Felsen trifft, kann man seinen Golfball meist abschreiben. Im Prinzip kommt auf allen Löcher Wasser irgendwie ins Spiel und die Felsen erinnern Formationen, die man eher aus Kalifornien kennt. Anders ausgedrückt: Dieser Platz wirkt viel mehr amerikanisch denn österreichisch. Das Anspielen der Grüns ist gefährlich; man benötigt sauber getroffene, hohe Eisenschläge - eine Aufgabe, die durch den oft über das Gelände pfeifenden Wind erschwert wird. "Schutz" findet man in den bis zu fünf Meter tiefen Bunkern. Es gibt Bestrebungen, den Platz ein wenig zu modifizieren, denn der Club möchte Austragungsort einiger wichtiger Profi-Turniere werden.

This course was created by the Austrian Canadian billionaire Frank Stronach on the uplands of the delightful town of Baden bei Wien. They firstly dug an artificial lake of some 20 hectares, then an artificial sandy beach, rocks, an impressive club-house, a dozen tennis courts. All this water is used not only for swimming in but also for playing havoc with miscued golf balls. Virtually all the holes here are more or less protected by water and the rocks are re-creations of similar formations in California. In other words you can expect a course that is more American than Austrian in style. Playing to the greens is a somewhat hazardous occupation and calls for cleanly hit high iron shots, a feat made more complicated by the frequent wind that sweeps across this wide open space. One form of shelter is to make a visit to one of the dozen or so bunkers, some of which are up to 15 feet deep! There are some projects of modifications, the club wanting to be the site of important professional tournaments.

Golf & Sportclub Fontana — 1997

Fontana Allee 1
A - 2522 OBERWALTERSDORF

Office Sekretariat (43) 02253 606 401
Pro shop Pro shop (43) 02253 606 412
Fax Fax (43) 02253 606 403
Web www.fontana.at
Situation Lage Wien, 35 km
Annual closure Jährliche Schliessung no
Weekly closure Wöchentliche Schliessung no

Fees main season Preisliste hochsaison	18 holes	
	Week days Woche	**We/Bank holidays** We/Feiertag
Individual Individuell	€ 98	€ 125
Couple Ehepaar	€ 196	€ 250

–18: –50 % / –25: – 30 %

Caddie Caddie no **Electric Trolley** Elektrokarren yes

Buggy Elektrischer Wagen yes **Clubs** Leihschläger yes

Credit cards Kreditkarten
VISA - Eurocard - MasterCard - AMEX

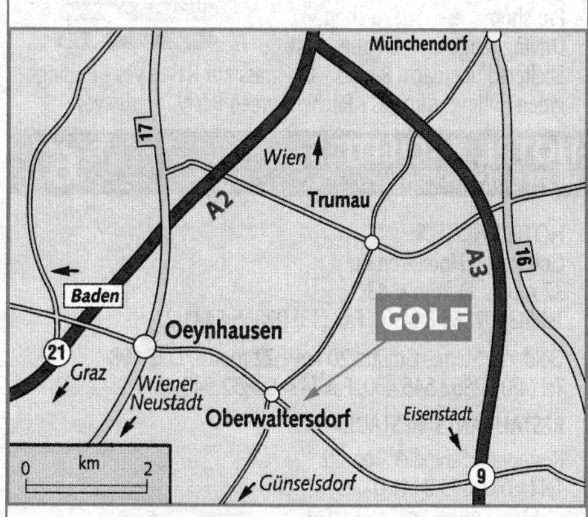

Access Zufahrt : Wien A2 → Graz. Exit (Ausfahrt) Baden. 210 to Oberwatersdorf.
Map 1 on page 75 Karte 1 Seite 75

GOLF COURSE — PLATZ 16/20

Site Lage
Maintenance Instandhaltung
Architect Architekt Doug Carrick, Hans Erhard
Type Typ inland, residential
Relief Begehbarkeit
Water in play Platz mit Wasser
Exp. to wind Wind ausgesetzt
Trees in play Platz mit Bäumen

Scorecard Scorekarte	**Chp.** Chp.	**Mens** Herren	**Ladies** Damen
Length Länge	6436	6021	4943
Par	72	72	72
Slope system	139	134	128

Advised golfing ability Empfohlene Spielstärke 0 12 24 36
Hcp required Min. Handicap 36

CLUB HOUSE & AMENITIES — KLUBHAUS UND NEBENGEBÄUDE 8/10

Pro shop Pro shop
Driving range Übungsplatz
Sheltered überdacht no - On grass auf Rasen yes - Putting-green Putting-grün yes - Pitching-green Pitching-grün yes

HOTEL FACILITIES — HOTEL BESCHREIBUNG 7/10

HOTELS HOTELS
Grand Hotel Sauerhof - Baden bei Wien 5 km
91 rooms, D € 205
Tel (43) 02252 412 51, Fax (43) 02252 480 47

Dorint Biedermeier - 203 rooms, D € 220 - Wien 35 km
Tel (43) 0171 - 6710, Fax (43) 0171 - 6715 03

Caruso - 75 rooms, D € 170 - Baden bei Wien 5 km
Tel (43) 02252 886 620, Fax (43) 02252 886 62504

RESTAURANTS RESTAURANTS
Steirereck - Wien 35 km - Tel (43) 017 133 168
Drei Husaren - Wien 35 km - Tel (43) 01512 109 20
Mörwald - Wien 35 km - Tel (43) 01961 611 61

Golfresort Haugschlag *Waldviertel*

16	8	6

Dieser Platz liegt nahe der tschechischen Grenze, und die Landschaft dieser Gegend erinnert schon an Böhmen mit seinen romantischen Wäldern, Seen und Bauernhöfen. Der Platz wurde auf leicht hügeligem Gelände zwischen Wäldern und Sümpfen angelegt. Trotzdem kommen Bäume nur an einem halben Dutzend Löcher gefährlich ins Spiel, ganz besonders am trickreichen Loch 4. Die Architekten meinten es gut mit hohen Handicaps, aber wiederum auch nicht gut genug, um den Spitznamen "Heimat der Birdies" zu rechtfertigen. Die Austrian Open wurde hier einige Male ausgetragen und die Pros lieferten reihenweise niedrige Ergebnisse ab. Auch Damen fühlen sich auf diesem Platz wohl. Als zweiter Platz wurde gerade der "Championship Course Haugschlag" in diesem angenehmem Resort esröffnet: sehr gute 18 Löcher, designt von Max Lamberg. Mit Längen von 5078 bis 6400 Metern ergänzt er sehr gut den vorhandenen Kurs.

This course, lying very close to the Czech frontier, is even closer to the landscapes of nearby Bohemia, a land of romantic forests, lakes and farms which mark the whole of northern Austria. It was laid out over just slightly hilly landscape in a setting of woods and marshland, but trees are only really dangerous on half a dozen holes or so (including the very tricky hole N° 4). In fact the architects have been rather kind to high-handicappers, but perhaps not kind enough to fully warrant the nickname of "Home of Birdies". Having said that, the Austrian Open has been held here on several occasions and players have produced an array of low scores. The ladies also willingly admit to feeling rather comfortable on this course, and you do not always hear them say that. A second course ("Haugschlag") has recently been opened in this very pleasant resort, a very good 18-hole designed by Max Lamberg. Stretching from 5078 to 6400 metres, it complements very well the present course.

Golfresort Haugschlag-Waldviertel — 1990

A - 3874 HAUGSCHLAG

Office	Sekretariat	(43) 02865 8441 0
Pro shop	Pro shop	(43) 02865 8441 0
Fax	Fax	(43) 02865 8441 22
Web	www.golfresort.at	
Situation	Lage	Gmünd, 24 km
Annual closure	Jährliche Schliessung	no
Weekly closure	Wöchentliche Schliessung	no

Fees main season Preisliste hochsaison	Week days Woche	We/Bank holidays We/Feiertag
		18 holes
Individual Individuell	€ 53	€ 67
Couple Ehepaar	€ 106	€ 134

Hotel Guests: € 32 and € 44 (We)

Caddie Caddie on request **Electric Trolley** Elektrokarren yes

Buggy Elektrischer Wagen yes **Clubs** Leihschläger yes

Credit cards Kreditkarten
VISA - Eurocard - MasterCard - DC - AMEX

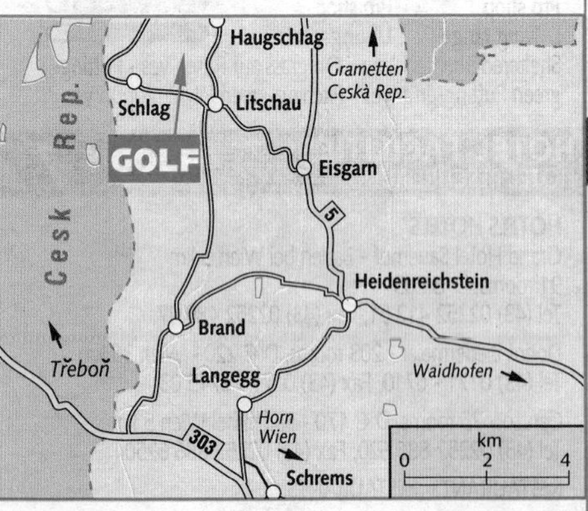

Access Zufahrt : • Wien, A22, E49 → Horn, Schrems, Gmünd
• Linz, E14 B38, B41 to Gmünd.
• Then, B30, B5 to Einsgarn, → Litschau, Haugschlag.
Map 1 on page 75 Karte 1 Seite 75

GOLF COURSE — PLATZ — 16/20

Site	Lage	
Maintenance	Instandhaltung	
Architect	Architekt	Austrogolf
Type	Typ	inland, forest
Relief	Begehbarkeit	
Water in play	Platz mit Wasser	
Exp. to wind	Wind ausgesetzt	
Trees in play	Platz mit Bäumen	

Scorecard Scorekarte	Chp. Chp.	Mens Herren	Ladies Damen
Length Länge	6262	5994	5030
Par	72	72	72
Slope system	125	119	118

Advised golfing ability Empfohlene Spielstärke: 0 12 24 36

Hcp required Min. Handicap 36

CLUB HOUSE & AMENITIES — KLUBHAUS UND NEBENGEBÄUDE — 8/10

Pro shop Pro shop
Driving range Übungsplatz
Sheltered überdacht 8 mats - On grass auf Rasen yes - Putting-green Putting-grün yes - Pitching-green Pitching-grün yes

HOTEL FACILITIES — HOTEL BESCHREIBUNG — 6/10

HOTELS HOTELS
Golf Resort Hotel - on site
37 rooms, D from € 130
Tel (43) 02865 8441 0, Fax (43) 02865 8441 22

Goldener Stern - Gmünd 20 km - 22 rooms, D € 108
Tel (43) 02852 545 450, Fax (43) 02852 545 48

RESTAURANTS RESTAURANTS
Restaurant Schindler - on site
Tel (43) 02865 8441 0
Goldener Stern - Gmünd 6 km
Tel (43) 02852 545 450

Gut Altentann

17	7	7

Salzburg ist die Heimatstadt von Mozart und eine Touristenattraktion. Die Architektur von Jack Nicklaus erinnert – um einen musikalischen Vergleich zu bemühen – eher an Wagner als an die subtile Inspiration von Mozart. Gut Altentann war der erste Platz, den Nicklaus in Europa entwarf. Es ist ein schwerer Platz mit vielen Hindernissen. Das Gelände wurde für Golf modelliert, man findet Bäume, aber auch weit offene Spielbahnen mit sanften Anstiegen und Gefällen und exzellente Grüns. Natürlich hat Nicklaus auch hier seine Vorlieben ausgelebt: So ist es in Altentann von Vorteil, wenn man die Grüns mit einem Fade anspielen kann, ganz so wie es die Golflegende als Spieler selbst tat. Die Schwierigkeiten des Platzes bestehen aus zwei Seen, weiteren Wasserhindernissen, Sümpfen und bestens konturierten Bunkern. Leider entspricht die Drainage auf dem Platz nicht dem hohen Design-Standard, so dass man den Platz nach heftigen Regenfällen meiden sollte.

Salzburg is Mozart's home town and an historical landmark bathed in light. The architectural style of Jack Nicklaus, though, is closer to Wagner than the brilliant inspiration and sprightliness of Mozart. Gut Altentann was the very first course designed by Nicklaus in Europe, a tough layout with spectacular continuity in terms of holes and hazards. The terrain was made for golf, sometimes full of trees, other times very open but always perfectly landscaped with gentle slopes and well-designed greens. Nicklaus has laid emphasis on the need to play intelligently and to think through each shot, and here again you will find some of his distinctive preferences, like having to fade approach shots into the greens. Hazards are basically two lakes, other water hazards and marshes, together with well-contoured bunkers, one of the hallmarks of the great man's architectural style. A class course but a little more in the way of the Baroque would have been more than welcome in Salzburg. Unfortunately the drainage is not up to the standard of the design. So beware of the condition after heavy rain.

Golf & Country Club Gut Altentann — 1989

Hof 54
A - 5302 HENNDORF AM WALLERSEE

Office	Sekretariat	(43) 06214 602 60
Pro shop	Pro shop	(43) 06214 602 612
Fax	Fax	(43) 06214 6105 81
Web	www.gutaltentann.com	
Situation	Lage	Salzburg, 15 km
Annual closure	Jährliche Schliessung	1/11→31/3
Weekly closure	Wöchentliche Schliessung	no

Fees main season Preisliste hochsaison	18 holes	
	Week days Woche	We/Bank holidays We/Feiertag
Individual Individuell	€ 60	€ 90
Couple Ehepaar	€ 120	€ 180

Softspikes only / Under 18: – 50%

Caddie Caddie on request **Electric Trolley** Elektrokarren yes

Buggy Elektrischer Wagen yes **Clubs** Leihschläger yes

Credit cards Kreditkarten
VISA - Eurocard - MasterCard

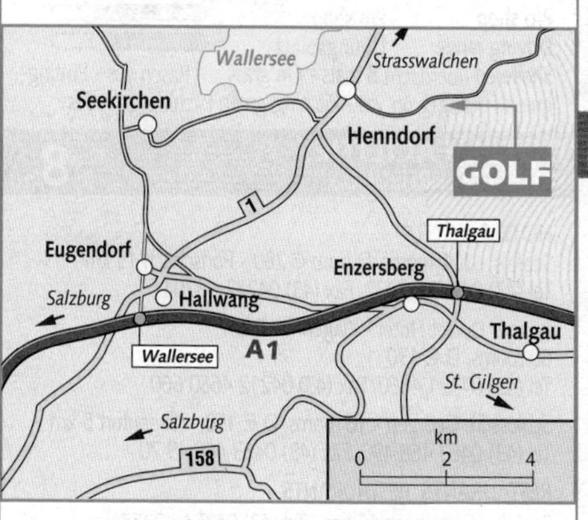

Access Zufahrt : Salzburg, 1 → Strasswalchen.
In Henndorf, turn right → Altentann, → Golfplatz.
Map 1 on page 74 Karte 1 Seite 74

GOLF COURSE — PLATZ — 17/20

Site	Lage	
Maintenance	Instandhaltung	
Architect	Architekt	Jack Nicklaus
Type	Typ	parkland, open country
Relief	Begehbarkeit	
Water in play	Platz mit Wasser	
Exp. to wind	Wind ausgesetzt	
Trees in play	Platz mit Bäumen	

Scorecard Scorekarte	Chp. Chp.	Mens Herren	Ladies Damen
Length Länge	6103	5652	4587
Par	72	72	72
Slope system	132	129	119

Advised golfing ability Empfohlene Spielstärke: 0 12 24 36

Hcp required Min. Handicap 36

CLUB HOUSE & AMENITIES — KLUBHAUS UND NEBENGEBÄUDE — 7/10

Pro shop	Pro shop	
Driving range	Übungsplatz	

Sheltered überdacht 10 mats - On grass auf Rasen yes - Putting-green Putting-grün yes - Pitching-green Pitching-grün yes

HOTEL FACILITIES — HOTEL BESCHREIBUNG — 7/10

HOTELS HOTELS

Sheraton Salzburg - 172 rooms, D € 345 - Salzburg 15 km
Tel (43) 0662 889 990, Fax (43) 0662 881 776

Sacher - 121 rooms, D € 330 - Salzburg 15 km
Tel (43) 0662 889 77, Fax (43) 0662 889 77 551

Goldener Hirsch - 73 rooms, D € 260 - Salzburg 14 km
Tel (43) 0662 808 40, Fax (43) 0662 843 349

RESTAURANTS RESTAURANTS

Alt Salzburg - Salzburg 15 km - Tel (43) 0662 841 476

Brandstätter - Salzburg-Liefering 18 km - Tel (43) 0662 434 535

Bei Bruno im Ratsherrnkeller - Salzburg 15 km
Tel (43) 0662 878 417

Pfefferschiff - Hallwang-Söllheim 10 km - Tel (43) 0662 661 242

Klagenfurt-Seltenheim

17 | 6 | 8

Die Stadt Klagenfurt blickt auf über 800 Jahre Geschichte zurück. In der pulsierenden Landeshauptstadt von Kärnten lässt es sich leben, zumal sie direkt am Ufer des Wörthersees liegt, einem der Lieblingsplätze von Brahms und Mahler. Auch wenn Golfplatz-Architektur eine Kunstform ist, fühlt man auf diesem klassischen Pete-Dye-Platz eine ganz andere Art von Inspiration. In dieses relativ flache Gelände legte Dye visuell reizvolle Hindernisse – immer genau an die richtige Stelle. Mit den vielen Wasserhindernissen wirkt der Platz amerikanisch, aber das nimmt man gerne in Kauf. Mit je sechs Abschlägen auf jeder Bahn bietet er jedem Golfer eine der Spielstärke angemessene Herausforderung. Mit Gesamtlängen von unter 5000 m bis zu rund 6300 m bietet der dem hohen Handicapper ebenso viel Spielvergnügen wie dem einstelligen Spieler. Das 18. Loch fordert beide gleichermaSSen, und kann zur nervenaufreibende Aufgabe werden, wenn die Clubhaus-Terrasse mit Zuschauern gefüllt ist.

The town of Klagenfurt bears the traces of a long history and you can spend many a pleasant moment in the bustling old town, not to mention the banks of the Wörthersee, a favourite spot for both Brahms and Mahler. But even though golf course architecture is also an art form, the inspiration you feel on this classy Pete Dye course is of a different nature. Starting off with rather flat terrain, he has developed an array of well-designed and visually attractive hazards, particularly the contours of the water hazards. This gives the layout a very American look, but no matter. The course is intelligent with no fewer than six tee-boxes per hole to give yardage ranging from less than 5,000 to almost 6,300 metres. If you cannot find the course to match your game, then you must be desperate, because even high handicappers can enjoy this almost as much as their single-figure counterparts, at least as far as the 18th hole, a nerve-wracking ordeal when the club-house terrace is crowded with onlookers.

Golfclub Klagenfurt-Seltenheim — 1996

Seltenheimerstrasse 137
A - 9061 KLAGENFURT- WÖLFNITZ

Office	Sekretariat	(43) 0463 40 223
Pro shop	Pro shop	(43) 0463 499 333
Fax	Fax	(43) 0463 402 2320
Web	www.golfktn.at	
Situation	Lage	Klagenfurt, 5 km
Annual closure	Jährliche Schliessung	30/11→31/3
Weekly closure	Wöchentliche Schliessung	no
Fees main season	Preisliste hochsaison	18 holes

	Week days Woche	We/Bank holidays We/Feiertag
Individual Individuell	€ 65	€ 65
Couple Ehepaar	€ 130	€ 130

Juniors: € 33 / 38 (We)

Caddie Caddie no — **Electric Trolley** Elektrokarren no

Buggy Elektrischer Wagen yes — **Clubs** Leihschläger yes

Credit cards Kreditkarten
VISA - Eurocard - MasterCard - DC - AMEX

Access Zufahrt : Klagenfurt B95 → Feldkirchen.
Exit (Ausfahrt) Lendorf, then turn left in Seltenheimerstrasse
Map 1 on page 75 Karte 1 Seite 75

GOLF COURSE — PLATZ — 17/20

Site	Lage	
Maintenance	Instandhaltung	
Architect	Architekt	Pete Dye
Type	Typ	open country
Relief	Begehbarkeit	
Water in play	Platz mit Wasser	
Exp. to wind	Wind ausgesetzt	
Trees in play	Platz mit Bäumen	

Scorecard Scorekarte	Chp. Chp.	Mens Herren	Ladies Damen
Length Länge	6286	5888	4957
Par	72	72	72
Slope system	122	123	116

Advised golfing ability Empfohlene Spielstärke — 0 12 24 36

Hcp required Min. Handicap 45

CLUB HOUSE & AMENITIES — KLUBHAUS UND NEBENGEBÄUDE — 6/10

Pro shop Pro shop
Driving range Übungsplatz
Sheltered überdacht 8 mats - On grass auf Rasen yes - Putting-green Putting-grün yes - Pitching-green Pitching-grün yes

HOTEL FACILITIES — HOTEL BESCHREIBUNG — 8/10

HOTELS HOTELS

Seefels - 101 rooms, D from € 280 - Pörtschach 15 km
Tel (43) 04272 - 2377, Fax (43) 04272 - 3704

Rogner Dorint Hotel - Klagenfurt 5 km
60 rooms, D € 130
Tel (43) 04121 4660, Fax (43) 04212 4660 660

Schloss St. Georgen - 16 rooms, D € 150 - Klagenfurt 5 km
Tel (43) 0463 468 490, Fax (43) 0463 468 49 70

RESTAURANTS RESTAURANTS

Seefels - Pörtschach 15 km - Tel (43) 04272 - 2377
Restaurant Knes - Lendorf 5 km - Tel (43) 0463 - 491 47
Dolce Vita - Klagenfurt 6 km - Tel (43) 0463 544 99

Neusiedlersee-Donnerskirchen 16 6 6

Dieser Platz liegt in der ländlichen Umgebung des Neusiedler Sees. Ganz in der Nähe liegt das pittoreske Städtchen Mörbisch, das ebenso einen Besuch lohnt wie der benachbarte Weinort Donnerskirchen. Doch auf dem Platz muss man sich mehr mit Wasser als mit Wein auseinandersetzen. Die wenigen Bäume kommen anders als die vielen Wasserhindernisse kaum ins Spiel, dafür kann der Wind an manchen Löchern, ähnlich einem Links Course, ganz schön kräftig wehen. Wer einen „Bump 'n run"-Schlag beherrscht, ist im Vorteil. Lochspiel Freunde werden diesen Platz lieben, da er was die strategischen Optionen angeht zu den besten des Landes gehört. Der Durchschnittsspieler mag beim Anblick von im Wasser versinkenden Bällen daran denken, dass der Platz nicht zu tückisch ist, solange man ihn mit ein wenig Taktik und Demut spielt. Anfänger werden ihn eher als schwierig empfinden. Alles in allem ein interessanter, abwechslungsreicher Platz, auf dem alle Hindernisse klar erkennbar sind und gute Schläge belohnt werden.

Nearby, the little town of Mörbisch, a real picture postcard if ever there was one, is worth a visit as is the wine production centre in the village of Donnerskirchen. But you will be more concerned with water when playing this course, as hazards abound. By contrast, the trees are seldom in play in what is a very open space where certain links course features came naturally and look the part when there is wind around. The bump 'n run shot will come in handy on occasions. Match-play experts will love this layout, which is one of the country's finest courses in terms of strategic and tactical options. The average hacker can rest assured though, because even if golf-balls tend to sink from view as much in Austria as elsewhere, they won't find the course too spiteful as long as they don't try to be too clever. Beginners will certainly find it more of a handful. A constantly entertaining and interesting course where trouble is clearly visible and flighters of the ball often well rewarded.

Golfclub Neusiedlersee-Donnerskirchen 1990

A - 7082 DONNERSKIRCHEN

Office	Sekretariat	(43) 02683 8171
Pro shop	Pro shop	(43) 02683 8171
Fax	Fax	(43) 02683 8172
Web	www.clubdanube.com	
Situation	Lage	Wien, 50 km
Annual closure	Jährliche Schliessung	no
Weekly closure	Wöchentliche Schliessung	no

Fees main season Preisliste hochsaison	Week days Woche	We/Bank holidays We/Feiertag
		18 holes
Individual Individuell	€ 47	€ 60
Couple Ehepaar	€ 94	€ 120

Caddie Caddie no **Electric Trolley** Elektrokarren no

Buggy Elektrischer Wagen yes **Clubs** Leihschläger yes

Credit cards Kreditkarten
VISA - MasterCard - DC

Access Zufahrt : Wien, A4 → Parndorf, Györ. Exit (Ausfahrt) Parndorf, 50/s31 → Einsiedeln. Donnerskirchen → Golfplatz.
Map 1 on page 75 Karte 1 Seite 75

GOLF COURSE — PLATZ 16/20

Site	Lage	
Maintenance	Instandhaltung	
Architect	Architekt	Kurt Rossknecht Hans G. Erhardt
Type	Typ	open country, links
Relief	Begehbarkeit	
Water in play	Platz mit Wasser	
Exp. to wind	Wind ausgesetzt	
Trees in play	Platz mit Bäumen	

Scorecard Scorekarte	Chp. Chp.	Mens Herren	Ladies Damen
Length Länge	6163	5957	5285
Par	72	72	72
Slope system	131	129	126

Advised golfing ability Empfohlene Spielstärke 0 12 24 36

Hcp required Min. Handicap 45

CLUB HOUSE & AMENITIES — KLUBHAUS UND NEBENGEBÄUDE 6/10

Pro shop Pro shop
Driving range Übungsplatz
Sheltered überdacht 5 mats - On grass auf Rasen yes - Putting-green Putting-grün yes - Pitching-green Pitching-grün yes

HOTEL FACILITIES — HOTEL BESCHREIBUNG 6/10

HOTELS HOTELS

Am Spitz - Purbach 5 km - 15 rooms, D € 90
Tel (43) 02683 5519, Fax (43) 02683 5519 20

Hotel Burgenland - Eisenstadt 11 km - 94 rooms, D € 130
Tel (43) 02682 6960, Fax (43) 02682 655 31

Seehotel Rust - Rust 10 km - 110 rooms, D € 154
Tel (43) 02685 3810, Fax (43) 02685 381 419

Hotel Wende - Neusiedl am See 25 km - 104 rooms, D € 120
Tel (43) 02167 8111, Fax (43) 02167 8111 649

RESTAURANTS RESTAURANTS

Kloster am Spitz - Purbach 5 km - Tel (43) 02683 551 90
Taubenkobel - Schützen 5 km - Tel (43) 02684 229 70

Schloss Ebreichsdorf

16 | 8 | 6

Wo man in Österreich auch hinkommt, Spuren von Komponisten finden sich überall. Unweit des Platzes liegt zunächst Eisenstadt, wo Haydn am Hof der Esterhazys musizierte. Ganz in der Nähe ist auch Baden, das Tor zum Wienerwald mit seinen herrlichen Wäldern, die bis nach Wien führen. Beethoven lebte hier, Mozart, Schubert und später die Walzerkönige kamen hierher oft zu Besuch. Kurstädte und Golf passen gut zuammen, wie der 15 Kilometer entfernte Platz belegt. Keith Preston hat auf Sandboden und ohne grosse Eingriffe in die Naturlandschaft einen angenehmen Parkland-Course entworfen. Er baute einige Doglegs ein, an denen man den Ball mit Fade oder Draw spielen muss. Wenn jedoch der Fade zum Slice und der Draw zum Hook ausartet, wird man sein Handicap nicht spielen können. Die hohen Bäume machen etliche der Fairways relativ eng. Diesen Platz muss man einige Male spielen, bevor man mit ihm vertraut ist.

Wherever you go in Austria, you always find the mark of at least one musician. Not far from here, there is firstly Eisenstadt, where Haydn entertained the Court of the Esterhazy (see their castle). Then there is Baden, the gateway to the Wienerwald, a magnificent forest which leads to Vienna. Beethoven used to live in this pretty spa town, also often visited by Mozart, Schubert and later on the kings of Waltz. Spas and golf go well together and this course was laid out about fifteen kilometres down the road. It is parkland with very pleasant sandy soil where Keith Preston has designed a fine layout without too much disruption to the natural site. He has designed in a few dog-legs where you will need to gently flight the ball, but overdo it and you are in trouble. If you can keep that hook or slice under control, you can probably play to your handicap here, even though the now "mature" trees make some of the fairways a little tight. A course that is well worth getting to know, to be played several times if you want to make any real impression.

Golfclub Schloss Ebreichsdorf — 1988

Schlossallee 1
A - 2483 EBREICHSDORF

Office	Sekretariat	(43) 02254 73 888
Pro shop	Pro shop	(43) 02254 73 888
Fax	Fax	(43) 02254 738 8813
Web	www.gcebreichsdorf.at	
Situation	Lage	Wien, 25 km
Annual closure	Jährliche Schliessung	no
Weekly closure	Wöchentliche Schliessung	no

Fees main season Preisliste hochsaison	Week days Woche	We/Bank holidays We/Feiertag
	18 holes	
Individual Individuell	€ 50	€ 70
Couple Ehepaar	€ 100	€ 140

– 26: – 50%

Caddie Caddie on request Electric Trolley Elektrokarren no

Buggy Elektrischer Wagen yes Clubs Leihschläger yes

Credit cards Kreditkarten
VISA - Eurocard - MasterCard - DC

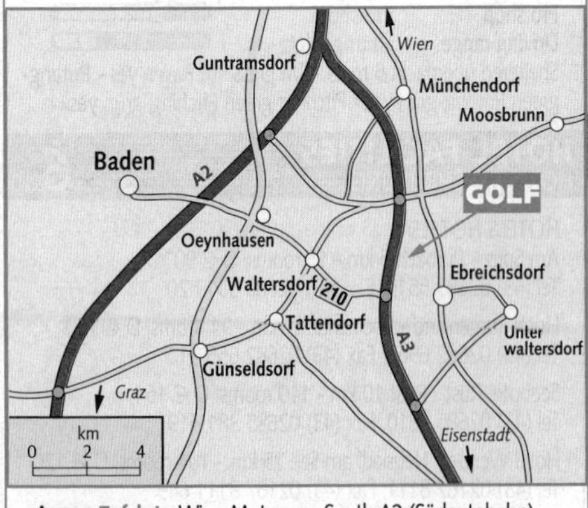

Access Zufahrt : Wien Motorway South A2 (Südautobahn) → Graz, then A3 → Eisenstadt.
Exit (Ausfahrt) Ebreichsdorf-Nord. → Golf
Map 1 on page 75 Karte 1 Seite 75

GOLF COURSE — PLATZ 16/20

Site	Lage	
Maintenance	Instandhaltung	
Architect	Architekt	Keith Preston
Type	Typ	parkland
Relief	Begehbarkeit	
Water in play	Platz mit Wasser	
Exp. to wind	Wind ausgesetzt	
Trees in play	Platz mit Bäumen	

Scorecard Scorekarte	Chp. Chp.	Mens Herren	Ladies Damen
Length Länge	6161	5960	5310
Par	72	72	72
Slope system	125	122	124

Advised golfing ability Empfohlene Spielstärke: 0 12 24 36

Hcp required Min. Handicap 36

CLUB HOUSE & AMENITIES — KLUBHAUS UND NEBENGEBÄUDE 8/10

Pro shop Pro shop
Driving range Übungsplatz
Sheltered überdacht 8 mats - On grass auf Rasen yes - Putting-green Putting-grün yes - Pitching-green Pitching-grün yes

HOTEL FACILITIES — HOTEL BESCHREIBUNG 6/10

HOTELS HOTELS

Domino - 40 rooms, D € 180 - Ebreichsdorf 500 m
Tel (43) 2254 749 87, Fax (43) 2254 749 87

Sacher - 113 rooms, D from € 250 - Wien 25 km
Tel (43) 0151 - 4560, Fax (43) 0151 - 456 810

König von Ungarn - 33 rooms, D € 192 - Wien 25 km
Tel (43) 0151 5840, Fax (43) 0151 5848

RESTAURANTS RESTAURANTS

Breughelhof - Ebreichsdorf 2 km - Tel (43) 02254 723 38

Altwienerhof - Wien (Schönbrunn) 25 km
Tel (43) 01 892 6000

Korso bei der Oper - Wien 25 km - Tel (43) 01 5151 6546

Schloss Schönborn

15	8	7

In diesem wundervollen Gut findet man 27 Löcher, von denen der Rote Platz für Meisterschaften genutzt wird. Obwohl der Architekt Kurt Rossknecht dem Platz deutlich seinen Stempel aufgedrückt hat, musste er sich auf Grund der vielen Bäume in diesem Park ein wenig in seiner gestalterischen Freiheit beschränken. Deshalb konnte er nicht allzu viele Doglegs einbauen, obwohl manchmal Bäume den geraden Weg zum Loch verstellen. Aber der alte Baumbestand ist auch charakteristisch für den Platz. Das Design wirkt britisch, denn (Wasser-)Hindernisse sind recht sparsam über den Platz verteilt, was das Spiel für alle erleichtert. Man muss den Platz nicht wieder und wieder spielen, um zu erkennen, welche Schläge und Taktik für einen guten Score wichtig sind. Der Platz ist bei Mitgliedern und Gästen gleichermassen beliebt, ganz besonders am Wochenende. Dies ist nur allzu verständlich, denn neben dem angenehmen Platz sind auch die anderen Einrichtungen, vor allem das Clubhaus, vorzüglich - eben dem Komfort des Wiener Lebensstil angepasst.

27 holes have been laid out in this magnificent estate. While Kurt Rossknecht has clearly left his mark in some wide open spaces, he has also had to curb his enthusiasm somewhat in a park full of trees, a feature that adds to the course's style. He has refrained from overdoing the dog-leg, even though well placed trees sometimes threaten the straightest line to the pin. The overall style is British, for example in the more limited numbers of hazards and more moderate use of water, thereby making life a little easier for all concerned. The design of this course is immediately clear to see and you don't need to play over and over again to understand what needs to be done to card a decent score. This is probably all for the better as the course is very busy with members especially on week-ends. Their being so many is understandable, as the pleasant course and the club-house are excellent, given the ever-present concern for comfort and quality of life that is so much a part of Viennese civilisation.

Golf Club Schloss Schönborn 1989

A - 2013 SCHÖNBORN 4

Office Sekretariat (43) 02267 2879
Pro shop Pro shop (43) 02267 2685
Fax Fax (43) 02267 2879-19
Web www.gcschoenborn.com
Situation Lage Wien, 30 km
Annual closure Jährliche Schliessung no
Weekly closure Wöchentliche Schliessung Monday
(Montag): Restaurant closed

Fees main season Preisliste hochsaison 18 holes

	Week days Woche	We/Bank holidays We/Feiertag
Individual Individuell	€ 55	€ 70
Couple Ehepaar	€ 110	€ 140

We: Hcp 28 (Men) and 36 (Ladies)

Caddie Caddie no **Electric Trolley** Elektrokarren no
Buggy Elektrischer Wagen yes **Clubs** Leihschläger yes
Credit cards Kreditkarten
VISA - MasterCard - AMEX - DC

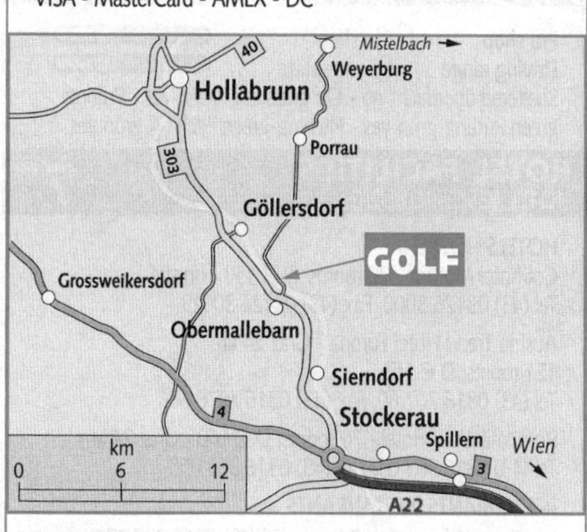

Access Zufahrt : Wien, A 22 → Stockerau, S 3 → Hollabrunn, Exit (Ausfahrt) Obermallebarn.
Map 1 on page 75 Karte 1 Seite 75

GOLF COURSE PLATZ 15/20

Site Lage
Maintenance Instandhaltung
Architect Architekt Kurt Rossknecht
Type Typ parkland
Relief Begehbarkeit
Water in play Platz mit Wasser
Exp. to wind Wind ausgesetzt
Trees in play Platz mit Bäumen

Scorecard Scorekarte	Chp. Chp.	Mens Herren	Ladies Damen
Length Länge	6387	6160	5449
Par	73	73	73
Slope system	131	134	127

Advised golfing ability Empfohlene Spielstärke 0 12 24 36
Hcp required Min. Handicap no (week days)

CLUB HOUSE & AMENITIES KLUBHAUS UND NEBENGEBÄUDE 8/10

Pro shop Pro shop
Driving range Übungsplatz
Sheltered überdacht 6 mats - On grass auf Rasen yes - Putting-green Putting-grün yes - Pitching-green Pitching-grün yes

HOTEL FACILITIES HOTEL BESCHREIBUNG 7/10

HOTELS HOTELS
InterContinental - 514 rooms, D € 310 - Wien 30 km
Tel (43) 01 - 711 220, Fax (43) 01 - 713 4489

Dreikönigs Hof - 39 rooms, D € 120 - Stockerau 17 km
Tel (43) 0266 627 880, Fax (43) 0266 627 886

Hotel de France - 208 rooms, D € 290 - Wien 30 km
Tel (43) 01 - 313 680, Fax (43) 01 - 319 5969

RESTAURANTS RESTAURANTS
Heurig'er Doppler - Sierndorf 4 km - Tel (43) 02267 3478
Gasthof zur Weissen Rose - Göllersdorf 5 km
Tel (43) 02267 2229
Club Restaurant - on site - Tel (43) 02267 2683

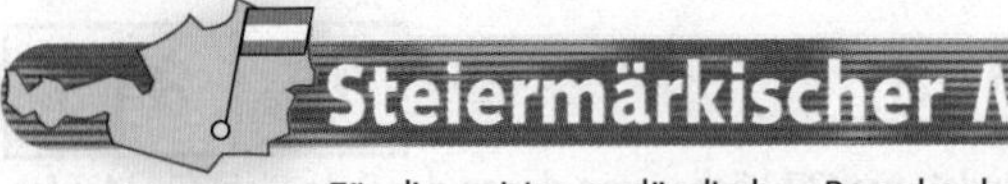

Steiermärkischer Murhof

16	8	7

Für die meisten ausländischen Besucher besteht Österreich aus Wien und Salzburg. Dabei hat Graz, ein Weltkulturerbe der Unesco, viel zu bieten. Der Platz des Steiermärkischen Golf Clubs wurde 1993 erbaut und liegt im Norden der Stadt. Damals gehörte zum Golfplatzbau in der Steiermark Pioniergeist, heute ist der Platz einer der Topplätze des Landes. Die alten Stallungen wurden zum Clubhaus mit Restaurant und zu einem Hotel im steirischen Stil umgebaut. Dieser Platz ist am besten von Frühlingsende bis Herbst zu bespielen, allerdings werden die Fairways nach langen Trockenperioden sehr hart. Im Sommer sind die Abschlagzeiten oft lange im Voraus gebucht, deshalb sollte man rechtzeitig reservieren. Im Gegensatz zu vielen anderen österreichischen Plätzen ist der Murhof, der von einem Fluss begrenzt wird, vollkommen flach. Viele Bäume sorgen für eine angenehme Umgebung, sind aber Strafe für verzogene Schläge. Das Design des bekannten Golfplatzarchitekten Dr. Bernhard von Limburger verlangt trotz des offenen Eindrucks genaue Drives, als Voraussetzung für einen guten Score.

For most foreign visitors, Austria is Vienna and Salzburg, but it would be a pity to overlook Graz, whose old town enjoys world heritage listing by Unesco. The present course was built to the north of the town, a rather bold venture at the time as no-one in Styria was really interested in golf back then. Today it is one of the country's most prestigious courses where former stables have been transformed into a club-house with restaurant and hotel resort in traditional style. This mid-altitude course plays at its best between the end of spring and autumn, but without a watering system for the fairways the course gets hard after long dry spells. You might expect some steep topography, as found on many Austrian courses, but in fact Steiermärkischer is virtually flat, flanked by a river and home to very many trees which provide at once a pleasant setting and real threat for wayward drives. The design is perfectly open, another reason to "drive carefully". A good score is anything but guaranteed.

Steiermärkischer Golf-Club Murhof — 1963

Adriach 53
A - 8130 FROHNLEITEN-MURHOF

Office	Sekretariat	(43) 03126 3010
Pro shop	Pro shop	(43) 03126 3010
Fax	Fax	(43) 03126 300 029
Web	www.murhof.at	
Situation	Lage	Graz, 20 km
Annual closure	Jährliche Schliessung	1/11→31/3
Weekly closure	Wöchentliche Schliessung	no

Fees main season Preisliste hochsaison	18 holes	
	Week days Woche	**We/Bank holidays** We/Feiertag
Individual Individuell	€ 58	€ 68
Couple Ehepaar	€ 116	€ 136

We: with members (nur in Mitgliederbegleitung)
Hotel guests: – 50% / Juniors:

Caddie Caddie no — **Electric Trolley** Elektrokarren no

Buggy Elektrischer Wagen yes — **Clubs** Leihschläger no

Credit cards Kreditkarten
VISA - Eurocard - Mastercard

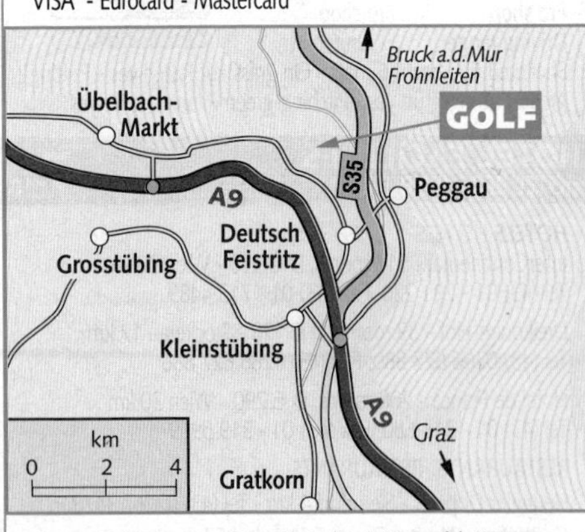

Access Zufahrt : Graz A9, S35. 2nd exit (2. Ausfahrt) Peggau. → Murhof, Golfplatz.
Map 1 on page 75 Karte 1 Seite 75

GOLF COURSE — PLATZ — 16/20

Site	Lage	
Maintenance	Instandhaltung	
Architect	Architekt	B. von Limburger, Michael Pinner
Type	Typ	parkland
Relief	Begehbarkeit	
Water in play	Platz mit Wasser	
Exp. to wind	Wind ausgesetzt	
Trees in play	Platz mit Bäumen	

Scorecard Scorekarte	**Chp.** Chp.	**Mens** Herren	**Ladies** Damen
Length Länge	6274	5924	5305
Par	72	72	72
Slope system	127	127	128

Advised golfing ability Empfohlene Spielstärke — 0 12 24 36

Hcp required Min. Handicap — 36

CLUB HOUSE & AMENITIES — KLUBHAUS UND NEBENGEBÄUDE — 8/10

Pro shop Pro shop
Driving range Übungsplatz
Sheltered überdacht no - On grass auf Rasen yes - Putting-green Putting-grün yes - Pitching-green Pitching-grün yes

HOTEL FACILITIES — HOTEL BESCHREIBUNG — 7/10

HOTELS HOTELS

Golfhotel Murhof - 20 rooms, D € 150 - on site
Tel (43) 03126 3000, Fax (43) 03126 30029

Austria Trend Hotel Europa - Graz 24 km
121 rooms, D € 155
Tel (43) 0316 707 60, Fax (43) 0316 7076 606

Romantik Park Hotel - 70 rooms, D € 160 - Graz 24 km
Tel (43) 0316 363 00, Fax (43) 0316 363 050

RESTAURANTS RESTAURANTS

Landhaus Keller - Graz 24 km - Tel (43) 0316 830 276
Krebsenkeller - Graz 24 km - Tel (43) 0316 829 377
Johan - Graz 24 km - Tel (43) 0316 821 312

The Country Club *Diamond* 16 | 8 | 7

The Country Club Tullnerfeld, Mitglied der GC 2000 Clubs, ist dem Zirkel ehrgeiziger Clubs in der Region um Wien beigetreten. Zweimal 18 Loch gestaltete der englische Golfplatzarchitekt Jeremy Pern: den „Gold Course", einen jede Spielstärke fordernden Par-65-Platz ohne Wasserhindernisse, dafür aber mit Bunkern und vielen Bäumen, und den „Diamond Course", der schon aufgrund seiner Länge anspruchsvoll ist, zudem liegen 9 Löcher direkt am Wasser. Die restlichen Spielbahnen der bewegten hügeligen Landschaft, in die auch grünverteidigende Bunker eingebaut sind, säumen die für die Donaulandschaft typischen Wienerwald, die einst schon Johann Strauss so rühmte. Dieser hervorragend angelegte Platz erfordert Präzision im Schlag aufs Grün und auch im Lesen derselben. Verfehlt man sie, hat man die Wahl zwischen hohen Schlägen oder flachen Annäherungen, je nach Terrain vor dem Grün. Sollte einen der Kurs gar zu sehr beuteln, findet man Trost in den Malereien von Egon Schiele im benachbarten Tulln. Denken Sie daran, es gibt immer jemanden den es härter trifft...

A newcomer in the clan of ambitious golf-clubs in Vienna. The "Gold Course" is a par-65 free of water hazards but with bunkers and trees a-plenty as part of the learning process. This "Diamond" is more demanding through its yardage, water in play on eight holes, bunkers neatly accommodated into sand-hills guarding and forming the greens, and large clumps of trees which add character to pleasantly rolling countryside, something of a local speciality between the Danube valley and the Viennese forest much vaunted by Johann Strauss. Very well designed and varied in lay-out, this course requires accuracy to hit putting surfaces that need some careful reading. Should you miss them, you can choose between lofted shots or daisy-cutters, depending on the surrounds in front of the green. If this course leaves you battered and bruised, you can always find some solace in the tormented faces painted by Egon Schiele in neighbouring Tulln. There is always someone worse off than yourself…

The Country Club — 2002

Am Golfplatz 1
A - 3452 ATZENBRUGG

Office	Sekretariat	(43) 02275 - 200 85
Pro shop	Pro shop	(43) 02275 - 200 85
Fax	Fax	(43) 02275 - 200 859
Web	www.countryclub.at	
Situation	Lage	Wien, 38 km
Annual closure	Jährliche Schliessung	1/12→15/2
Weekly closure	Wöchentliche Schliessung	no

Fees main season Preisliste hochsaison — 18 holes

	Week days / Woche	We/Bank holidays / We/Feiertag
Individual Individuell	€ 50	€ 70
Couple Ehepaar	€ 100	€ 140

Caddie Caddie no — **Electric Trolley** Elektrokarren no

Buggy Elektrischer Wagen yes — **Clubs** Leihschläger yes

Credit cards Kreditkarten
VISA - Eurocard - MasterCard - AMEX - DC

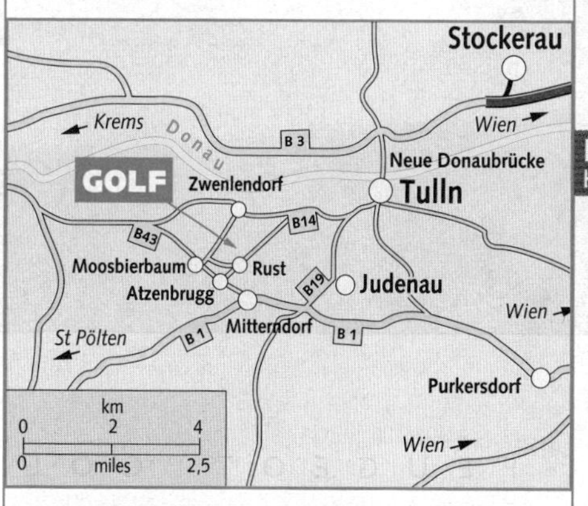

Access Zufahrt : Wien, B1 → St Pollten
Map 1 on page 75 Karte 1 Seite 75

GOLF COURSE — PLATZ — 16/20

Site	Lage	
Maintenance	Instandhaltung	
Architect	Architekt	Jeremy Pern
Type	Typ	parkland
Relief	Begehbarkeit	
Water in play	Platz mit Wasser	
Exp. to wind	Wind ausgesetzt	
Trees in play	Platz mit Bäumen	

Scorecard / Scorekarte	Chp. / Chp.	Mens / Herren	Ladies / Damen
Length Länge	6450	5949	4995
Par	72	72	72
Slope system	124	123	120

Advised golfing ability Empfohlene Spielstärke — 0 12 24 36
Hcp required Min. Handicap — no

CLUB HOUSE & AMENITIES — KLUBHAUS UND NEBENGEBÄUDE — 8/10

Pro shop Pro shop
Driving range Übungsplatz
Sheltered überdacht yes - On grass auf Rasen yes - Putting-green Putting-grün yes - Pitching-green Pitching-grün yes

HOTEL FACILITIES — HOTEL BESCHREIBUNG — 7/10

HOTELS HOTELS

Tee Room - 10 rooms, D € 80 - on site
Tel (43) 02275 - 200 85, Fax (43) 02275 - 200 859

Kaiserhof - 74 rooms, D € 155 - Wien 38 km
Tel (43) 01 - 505 1701, Fax (43) 01 - 5058 87588

K + K Palais Hotel - Wien 38 km
66 rooms, D € 215
Tel (43) 01 - 533 13 53, Fax (43) 01 - 533 135370

RESTAURANTS RESTAURANTS

Hütt - Michelhausen 4 km - Tel (43) 02275 - 52 54
Sodoma - Tulln 6 km - Tel (43) 02272 - 646 16
Steirer Stub'n - Wien 38 km - Tel (43) 01 - 544 43 49

BELGIQUE BELGIË LUXEMBOURG

BELGIUM
LUXEMBURG

Royal Golf Club des Fagnes (Spa)

BELGIUM LUXEMBURG

Belgium has more than 45,000 golfers (Luxembourg, 3,600) playing on around 50 eighteen-hole courses. All golf courses presented in this Guide are open to the public. Some may be difficult to play on week-ends owing to the number of members, but travelling green-feers should often be able to play during the week. Carrying a letter of introduction from your club may be a help, both for Belgian and foreign players.

BELGIQUE LUXEMBOURG

La Belgique compte près de 45.000 joueurs de golf (Luxembourg 3.600) pour 50 parcours de 18 trous environ. Les golfs présentés ici sont ouverts au public. Certes, une partie d'entre eux peut être difficile d'accès en week-end, en raison de leur grand nombre de membres, mais les voyageurs ont souvent la possibilité d'y jouer en semaine. Pour les joueurs belges comme pour les étrangers, le fait d'être muni d'une lettre d'introduction de leur propre club peut cependant faciliter les choses.

BELGIË LUXEMBURGO

België heeft meer dan 45.000 spelers (Luxembourg 3.600) op ongeveer 50 banen 18-holesbanen. De meeste golfclubs in Peugeot Golf Guide zijn vrij toegankelijk voor het publiek. In sommige raakt men wel moeilijker binnen tijdens het week-end, wegens hun groot aantal leden, maar 'reizigers' bevinden zich meestal gemakkelijker in de mogelijkheid om tijdens de week te spelen. Voor Belgische en buitenlandse spelers is een introductiebrief van de eigen club vaak een goed idee, om de zaken eenvoudiger te maken.

Map No 1
Carte 1
Auto Kaart blz 1
km
0 10 20
Goes (NL)
Wouwse Plantage (NL)
Royal Zoute
Rinkven
Royal Antwerp
Oostende
Royal Latem
Ravenstein
Oudenaarde
Waterloo
Bondues (F)
Hainaut
Mont-Garni
Rigenée
Brigode (F)
Château de la Tournette
Arras (F)
Ailette (L') (F)
Kingston upon Hull
Zierikzee
Middelburg
Vlissingen
Bergen op Zoom
Knokke-Heist
Blankenberge
Oostende (Ostende)
BRUGGE (BRUGES)
GENT (GAND)
ANTWERPEN (ANVERS)
St.-Niklaas
Kortrijk (Courtrai)
Ieper (Ypres)
Roeselare (Roulers)
Oudenaarde
Aalst (Alost)
BRUXELLES BRUSSEL
Tournai (Doornik)
Mons (Bergen)
Tourcoing
Roubaix
LILLE
Béthune
Lens
Douai
Valenciennes
Maubeuge
Cambrai
Arras
St Quentin
Laon
Soissons
Compiègne
Noyon
Péronne
Albert
Rethel
Charleroi
ZEELAND
WEST-VLAANDEREN
OOST-VLAANDEREN
HAINAUT
NORD
AISNE
MICHELIN

Toxandria (NL)
Gendersteyn (NL)
Eindhoven
Elfrather Mühle (D)
Schloss Myllendonk (D)
Krefelder (D)
Herkenbosch (NL)
Limburg
Zuid Limburgse (NL)
Spiegelven
Bercuit
Falnuée
Sart-Tilman
Spa (Les Fagnes)
Five Nations
Bitburger Land (D)
Grand Duc de Luxemb
EINDHOVEN
Tilburg
Breda
Turnhout
Helmond
Venray
Mönchengladbach
Roermond
Duisburg
Moers
Neuss
Krefeld
Hasselt
Genk
Maastricht
AACHEN
Heerlen
LIÈGE (LUIK)
Namur
Huy
Dinant
Verviers
Spa
Malmédy
Düren
Eupen
Tongeren
St.-Truiden
Tienen
Bastogne
Arlon
LUXEMBOURG
Charleville-Mézières
Sedan
Bouillon
Neufchâteau
Marche-en-Famenne
Rochefort
la Roche-en-A.
Houffalize
Clervaux
Wiltz
Diekirch
Echternach
Prüm
Bitburg
St-Vith
Longwy
Montmédy
Virton
Givet
Fumay
Revin
LIMBURG
LUXEMBOURG
NAMUR
LIÈGE
93
MICHELIN
d'après base de données au 1/1 000 000 - édition 20
Autorisation n°0501023.

CLASSIFICATION OF GOLF COURSES

CLASSEMENT DES PARCOURS — RANKSCHIKKING VAN DE BANEN

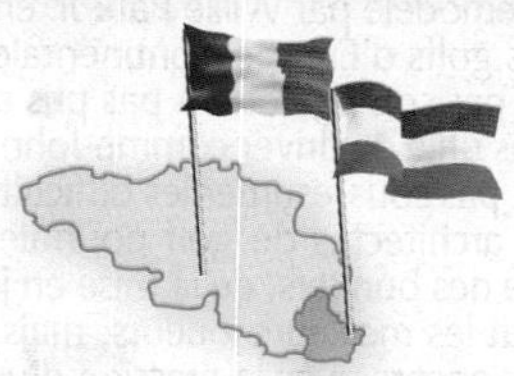

This classification gives priority consideration to the score awarded to the actual course.
Ce classement donne priorité à la note attribuée au parcours.
Deze rangschikking heeft voorang op de score toegekend aan de actuele.

Within each score, the ranking is purely alphabetical

B Belgium - **L** Luxembourg

Course score – Note du parcours / Cijfer van het terrein					Page / Blz
17	7	7	Antwerp	B	96
17	7	7	Royal Zoute	B	110
17	7	7	Spa (Les Fagnes)	B	112
16	7	7	Kikuoka	L	117
16	7	5	Limburg BF	B	102
16	8	8	Ravenstein Old Course	B	106
16	7	7	Sart-Tilman	B	111
16	8	7	Waterloo La Marache	B	114
16	8	7	Waterloo Le Lion	B	115
15	7	6	Château de la Tournette American	B	98
15	7	6	Hainaut Bruyere-Quesnoy-Etangs	B	101
15	7	7	Oostende	B	104
15	8	6	Royal Latem	B	109
14	7	7	Bercuit	B	97
14	7	5	Falnuée	B	99
14	7	6	Five Nations	B	100
14	6	7	Grand Ducal de Luxembourg	L	116
14	6	5	Oudenaarde Abdij/Anker	B	105
14	7	6	Rigenée	B	107
14	6	6	Rinkven Red - White	B	108
14	7	8	Spiegelven	B	113
13	7	6	Mont-Garni	B	103

HOTEL FACILITIES

ENVIRONNEMENT HOTELIER — CIJFER VAN HOTELS IN OMGEVING

This classification gives priority consideration to the score awarded to the hotel facilities.
Ce classement donne priorité à la note attribuée à l'environnement hôtelier.
Deze classificatie heeft voorang op de score van voor de hotel accommodatie.

		Hotel facility score / Note de l'environnement hotelier / Cijfer van hotels in omgeving			Page / Pagina
16	8	**8**	Ravenstein Old Course	B	106
14	7	**8**	Spiegelven	B	113
17	7	**7**	Antwerp	B	96
14	7	**7**	Bercuit	B	97
14	6	**7**	Grand Ducal de Luxembourg	L	116
16	7	**7**	Kikuoka	L	117
15	7	**7**	Oostende	B	104
17	7	**7**	Royal Zoute	B	110
16	7	**7**	Sart-Tilman	B	111
17	7	**7**	Spa (Les Fagnes)	B	112
16	8	**7**	Waterloo La Marache	B	114
16	8	**7**	Waterloo Le Lion	B	115
15	7	**6**	Château de la Tournette American	B	98
14	7	**6**	Five Nations	B	100
15	7	**6**	Hainaut Bruyere-Quesnoy-Etangs	B	101
13	7	**6**	Mont-Garni	B	103
14	7	**6**	Rigenée	B	107
14	6	**6**	Rinkven Red - White	B	108
15	8	**6**	Royal Latem	B	109
14	7	**5**	Falnuée	B	99
16	7	**5**	Limburg BF	B	102
14	6	**5**	Oudenaarde Abdij/Anker	B	105

Antwerp

17	7	7

Créé en 1888, remodelé par Willie Park Jr. en 1913 et Tom Simpson en 1930, c'est l'un des plus anciens golfs d'Europe Continentale et le plus ancien golf de Belgique, mais il ne fait toujours pas son âge et n'a pas pris une ride. Comme il a résolument conservé son caractère "old-style", il n'est pas utile de driver comme John Daly, ni d'avoir le toucher au putting d'un Corey Pavin. Mais il ne faut surtout pas sous-estimer les difficultés du tracé, ce parcours a une main de fer dans un gant de velours. Tous les architectes de golf pourraient d'ailleurs s'inspirer de l'intelligence du tracé, du placement très stratégique des bunkers, de la mise en jeu des arbres et de la bruyère. Ici, les principales difficultés concernent surtout les meilleurs joueurs, mais le parcours est une inspiration pour tous. Jouer ici est un vrai bonheur, et plus encore avec la pression d'une compétition. Et le charme visuel du lieu ajoute encore au plaisir.

Created in 1888 then redesigned by Willie Park in 1913 and Tom Simpson in 1930, this is Belgium's oldest club, although it looks as young as ever. Having the privilege of being an old-style course, its length doesn't mean having to drive à la John Daly and the subtle greens hardly require the putting touch of a Corey Pavin. But the trouble in store should never be under-estimated, as this is an iron hand in a velvet glove. The remarkably intelligent layout, highly strategic bunkering and the presence and use of trees and heather are an example for all modern designers. Here, the main difficulties have cleverly been reserved for the better players, but the general layout is an inspiration for us all. Playing here is a real pleasure, and playing with the pressure of a tournament even more so. The site adds visual charm to the enjoyment of golfing.

Royal Antwerp Golf Club — 1888/1930

Torenlei 1A
B - 2950 KAPELLEN

Office	Secrétariat	(32) 03 - 666 84 56
Pro shop	Pro-shop	(32) 03 - 666 46 87
Fax	Fax	(32) 03 - 666 44 37
Web	www.ragc.be	
Situation	Situation	Antwerpen / Anvers, 15 km
Annual closure	Fermeture annuelle	no
Weekly closure	Fermeture hebdomadaire	no

Monday (lundi), pro shop closed

Fees main season Tarifs haute saison — 18 holes

	Week days Semaine	We/Bank holidays We/Férié
Individual Individuel	€ 70	*
Couple Couple	€ 140	*

Juniors: – 50% / * We: members & guests only

Caddie Caddie no — **Electric Trolley** Chariot électrique yes

Buggy Voiturette yes — **Clubs** Clubs no

Credit cards Cartes de crédit
VISA - Eurocard - AMEX - DC

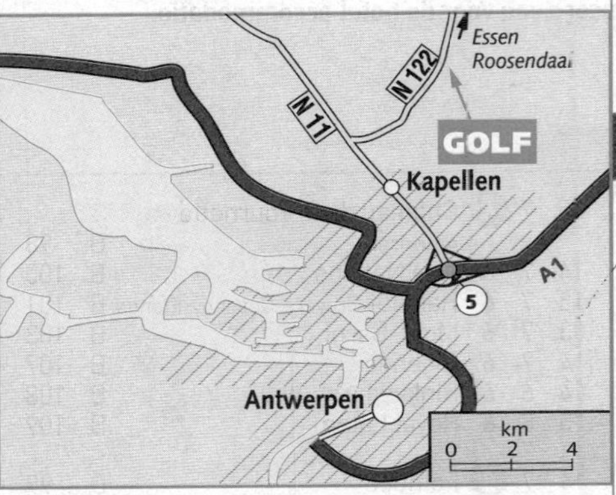

Access Accès : E19 Anvers → Breda, Exit 5 → N11
Map 1 on page 92 Carte 1 Page 92

GOLF COURSE — PARCOURS — 17/20

Site	Site	
Maintenance	Entretien	
Architect	Architecte	Willie Park Jr. Tom Simpson
Type	Type	parkland
Relief	Relief	
Water in play	Eau en jeu	
Exp. to wind	Exposé au vent	
Trees in play	Arbres en jeu	

Scorecard Carte de score	Chp. Chp.	Mens Mess.	Ladies Da.
Length Long.	6274	6200	5448
Par	73	73	73
Slope system	126	125	115

Advised golfing ability Niveau de jeu recommandé — 0 12 24 36

Hcp required Handicap exigé — 24 Men/28 Ladies

CLUB HOUSE & AMENITIES — CLUB HOUSE ET ANNEXES — 7/10

Pro shop Pro-shop
Driving range Practice

Sheltered couvert 4 mats - On grass sur herbe yes - Putting-green putting-green yes - Pitching-green pitching green yes

HOTEL FACILITIES — ENVIRONNEMENT HOTELIER — 7/10

HOTELS HÔTELS

Hilton - 211 rooms, D € 300 - Antwerpen 15 km
Tel (32) 03 - 204 12 12, Fax (32) 03 - 204 12 13

Alfa Theater - 127 rooms, D € 200 - Antwerpen 15 km
Tel (32) 03 - 203 54 10, Fax (32) 03 - 233 88 58

Rubens - 36 rooms, D € 185 - Antwerpen 15 km
Tel (32) 03 - 222 48 48, Fax (32) 03 - 225 19 40

RESTAURANTS RESTAURANTS

De Bellefleur - Kapellen 1 km - Tel (32) 03 - 664 67 19
't Fornuis - Antwerpen 15 km - Tel (32) 03 - 233 62 70
De Mangerie - Ekeren 5 km - Tel (32) 03 - 605 26 26

Bercuit

14	7	7

De son propre aveu, Robert Trent Jones n'a pas pu exprimer tout son talent, on ne retrouve notamment pas ici son dessin si caractéristique de bunkers. Autant le savoir, certains trous sont assez fatigants et "tricky", mais d'autres valent le déplacement. Le relief très mouvementé interdit de quitter les fairways, et les frappeurs se sentiront souvent privés de leur liberté d'expression, du moins s'ils souhaitent absolument jouer leur driver. L'arrosage des fairways a néanmoins rendu plus facile le choix des zones de réception des balles. Les greens, souvent rapides, bien défendus aux contours trompeurs proposent un sérieux challenge au putting. Après avoir joué plusieurs fois ce parcours, on en comprend mieux les pièges, mais il ne perdra pas complètement son caractère hasardeux. Un conseil : jouer au soleil et en voiturette, pour mieux profiter du décor arboré et des superbes panoramas sur le Brabant wallon.

You won't find here the bunkers that have come to typify Robert Trent Jones, and he readily admits that this is not one of his best courses. A number of holes are tiring and tricky but others are probably good enough to make you feel it was all worthwhile. The hilly terrain means you are best advised to keep it in the fairway, so big-hitters, if they insist on using the driver, might easily run into trouble. More optimistically, fairway sprinklers have made the choice of landing area a little easier. The greens, well-guarded, often slick but not always as receptive as they might be, are a stiff challenge to the best putter. After several rounds you will begin to understand the traps a little better but the course is never completely risk-free. One piece of advice: play in sunny weather and with a buggy to make the most of the tree-covered landscape and wonderful views over the Walloon Brabant.

Golf de Bercuit — 1965

Domaine de Bercuit, Les Gottes, 3
B - 1390 GREZ-DOICEAU

Office Secrétariat (32) 010 - 84 15 01
Pro shop Pro-shop (32) 010 - 84 15 01
Fax Fax (32) 010 - 84 55 95
Web www.golfdubercuit.be
Situation Situation Bruxelles / Brussel, 30 km
Annual closure Fermeture annuelle no
Weekly closure Fermeture hebdomadaire no
Fees main season Tarifs haute saison 18 holes

	Week days / Semaine	We/Bank holidays / We/Férié
Individual Individuel	€ 65	€ 85
Couple Couple	€ 130	€ 170

Juniors: – 50%

Caddie Caddie no — **Electric Trolley** Chariot électrique yes
Buggy Voiturette yes — **Clubs** Clubs yes
Credit cards Cartes de crédit
VISA - Eurocard - MasterCard

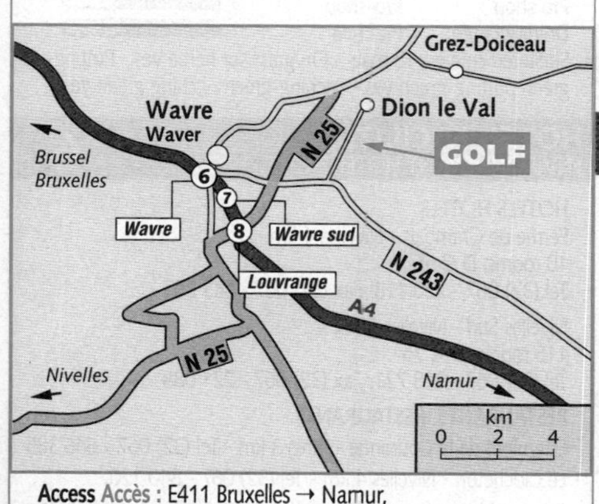

Access Accès : E411 Bruxelles → Namur, Exit (Sortie) 8 → Grez Doiceau, turn right on N243, 2 km on left hand side → Dion le Val
Map 1 on page 93 Carte 1 Page 93

GOLF COURSE — PARCOURS 14/20

Site	Site	
Maintenance	Entretien	
Architect	Architecte	Robert Trent Jones
Type	Type	forest
Relief	Relief	
Water in play	Eau en jeu	
Exp. to wind	Exposé au vent	
Trees in play	Arbres en jeu	

Scorecard / Carte de score	Chp. / Chp.	Mens / Mess.	Ladies / Da.
Length Long.	5961	5573	5208
Par	72	72	72
Slope system	136	129	128

Advised golfing ability / Niveau de jeu recommandé: 0 12 24 36
Hcp required Handicap exigé: 32 Men, 36 Ladies

CLUB HOUSE & AMENITIES — CLUB HOUSE ET ANNEXES 7/10

Pro shop Pro-shop
Driving range Practice
Sheltered couvert 10 mats - On grass sur herbe no - Putting-green putting-green yes - Pitching-green pitching green yes

HOTEL FACILITIES — ENVIRONNEMENT HOTELIER 7/10

HOTELS HÔTELS
Château du Lac - 121 rooms, D € 300 - Genval 11 km
Tel (32) 02 - 655 71 11, Fax (32) 02 - 655 74 44

Novotel - 102 rooms, D € 130- Wavre 5 km
Tel (32) 010 - 41 13 63, Fax (32) 010 - 41 19 22

At Home - 18 rooms, D € 80 - Wavre 5 km
Tel (32) 010 - 22 83 83, Fax (32) 010 - 81 69 39

Manoir du Lac - 13 rooms, D € 250 - Genval 11 km
Tel (32) 02 - 655 63 11, Fax (32) 02 - 655 64 55

RESTAURANTS RESTAURANTS
La Table du Marché - Wavre 5 km - Tel (32) 010 - 88 13 50
Carte Blanche - Wavre 5 km - Tel (32) 010 - 24 23 63
Le Bateau Ivre - Wavre 5 km - Tel (32) 010 - 24 37 64

Château de la Tournette *American* | 15 | 7 | 6

Le golf du Château de la Tournette dispose de deux parcours, dont "l'Américain" présente des mouvements de terre abondants, d'énormes bunkers, de grands greens et des obstacles d'eau sur 8 trous. Il est aussi plus physique, plus fatigant et plus scénique que "L'Anglais" (dessiné par Martin Hawtree), qui se déroule dans la plaine vallonnée typique de cette région du Brabant wallon. Dessiné par Bill Amick en 1988 et modifié par Clive Clark et Peter Alliss en 1991, avec les derniers travaux d'allongement en 2005. Les meilleurs trous sont les pars 3, même si le 16 possède un green trop pentu. Côté spectacle, le 15 est très certainement le plus scénique des 18 trous avec, entre de beaux grands arbres, une vue plongeante vers le green. Avec ses ambitions d'accueillir de grandes épreuves, mais aussi de s'imposer parmi les grands clubs "bruxellois", le club aura à cœur de maintenir la qualité d'entretien indispensable.

This club boasts two courses. The first, "L'Américain", has involved a huge amount of earth-shifting and is lined with enormous bunkers, large greens and water hazards on 8 holes. It is also hillier, more tiring and more panoramic than the other course, "L'Anglais" (designed by Martin Hawtree), which unwinds over a rolling plain that is typical of the Walloon Brabant region. "L'Américain" was designed by Bill Amick in 1988 then altered by Clive Clark and Peter Alliss in 1991 and has needed time to mellow. But in the wake of the latest work to lengthen the course in 2005, it seems to have matured nicely. The finest holes are the par 3s, even though the 16th plays to an excessively sloping green. Visually speaking, the 15th is definitely the most spectacular of the 18 holes with a plunging view down to the green between some magnificent large trees. Given the club's ambitions to host major events and also to become established as one of the great clubs around Brussels, indispensable excellence in green-keeping must, is and will be a top priority.

Château de la Tournette — 1988

Chemin de Beaudemont 21
B - 1400 NIVELLES

Office	Secrétariat	(32) 067 - 894 266
Pro shop	Pro-shop	(32) 067 - 894 272
Fax	Fax	(32) 067 - 219 517
Web	www.tournette.com	
Situation	Situation	Bruxelles, 35 km

Nivelles/Nijvel, 2 km

Annual closure	Fermeture annuelle	no
Weekly closure	Fermeture hebdomadaire	no
Fees main season	Tarifs haute saison	18 holes

	Week days / Semaine	We/Bank holidays / We/Férié
Individual Individuel	€ 47	€ 75
Couple Couple	€ 94	€ 150

Caddie Caddie no — **Electric Trolley** Chariot électrique no
Buggy Voiturette yes — **Clubs** Clubs yes
Credit cards Cartes de crédit
VISA - Eurocard - MasterCard - AMEX - DC

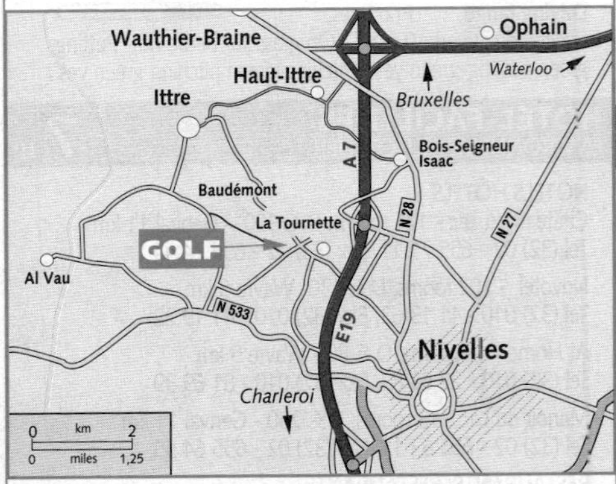

Access Accès : Bruxelles, E19 → Mons/Charleroi/Paris, Exit 18 Nivelles Nord
Map 1 on page 92 Carte 1 Page 92

GOLF COURSE — PARCOURS 15/20

Site	Site	
Maintenance	Entretien	
Architect	Architecte	William Amick
Type	Type	parkland
Relief	Relief	
Water in play	Eau en jeu	
Exp. to wind	Exposé au vent	
Trees in play	Arbres en jeu	

Scorecard Carte de score	Chp. Chp.	Mens Mess.	Ladies Da.
Length Long.	6031	5621	4643
Par	72	72	72
Slope system	—	—	—

Advised golfing ability Niveau de jeu recommandé: 0 12 24 36
Hcp required Handicap exigé: 36

CLUB HOUSE & AMENITIES — CLUB HOUSE ET ANNEXES 7/10

Pro shop Pro-shop
Driving range Practice
Sheltered couvert 18 mats - On grass sur herbe yes - Putting-green putting-green yes - Pitching-green pitching green yes

HOTEL FACILITIES — ENVIRONNEMENT HOTELIER 6/10

HOTELS HÔTELS

Ferme de Grambais - Nivelles 4 km
10 rooms, D € 55
Tel (32) 067 - 220 118, Fax (32) 067 - 841 307

Nivelles Sud - Nivelles 5 km
115 rooms, D € 75
Tel (32) 067 - 218 721, Fax (32) 067 - 221 088

RESTAURANTS RESTAURANTS

Estaminet de la Couronne - Ittres 3 km - Tel (32) 067 - 646 385
Le Clocheton - Nivelles 4 km - Tel (32) 067 - 840 120
Jacques Marit - Braine l'Alleud 10 km - Tel (32) 02 - 353 0246
Le Chabichou - Ophain 7 km - Tel (32) 02 - 385 0776

Falnuée

14 | 7 | 5

Un joli Club, avec son club-house dans les anciennes écuries voûtées remontant au Moyen-Age, le charme d'un paysage vallonné, la présence de deux rivières. Les puristes pourront certes relever une rupture avec la tradition, avec cinq par 3 (dont quatre au retour) et trois par 5, mais la longueur est réduite pour un par 70. La grande difficulté présentée par ce tracé consiste à tenir compte des dénivellations pour choisir les clubs, et aussi pour placer les drives: il suffit de quelques secondes d'inattention pour que les obstacles soient soudain très en jeu, ou manquer quelques greens surélevés qu'il autrait mieux valu rejoindre directement. Jean Jottrand a produit un dessin agréable, bien qu'un peu rustique, mais si l'on regrette une imagination un peu timide, Falnuée reste accessible à tous niveaux. On conseillera plutôt de jouer ici entre amis, pour le plaisir, sans vouloir chercher d'émotions visuelles et golfiques très violentes.

A pretty golf club, with a club-house in former vaulted stables dating from the Middle Ages, rolling landscape and two rivers. The purists will point to the break from tradition, as this short course is a par 70 with five par 3s (four of which are on the back 9) and three par 5s. The major difficulty is assessing the slopes and hills before choosing your club, and positioning the tee-shot. A momentary lapse of concentration can take you straight into the hazards and result in missing some of the elevated greens, which you are well advised to pitch directly. Jean Jottrand has produced a pleasant layout, perhaps a little on the rustic side, but despite the regrettable lack of imagination the course is playable by golfers of all levels. Your best bet here is a round with friends, just for fun, without looking for true visual or golfing excitement.

Golf de Falnuée — 1987

55, rue Emile Pirson
B - 5032 MAZY

Office	Secrétariat	(32) 081 - 63 30 90
Pro shop	Pro-shop	(32) 081 - 63 92 10
Fax	Fax	(32) 081 - 63 37 64
Web	www.falnuee.be	
Situation	Situation	Namur, 15 km
Annual closure	Fermeture annuelle	no
Weekly closure	Fermeture hebdomadaire	monday (lundi)

Fees main season Tarifs haute saison — 18 holes

	Week days Semaine	We/Bank holidays We/Férié
Individual Individuel	€ 35	€ 50
Couple Couple	€ 70	€ 100

Juniors: € 10

Caddie Caddie no — **Electric Trolley** Chariot électrique yes

Buggy Voiturette yes — **Clubs** Clubs yes

Credit cards Cartes de crédit
VISA - Eurocard - AMEX - DC

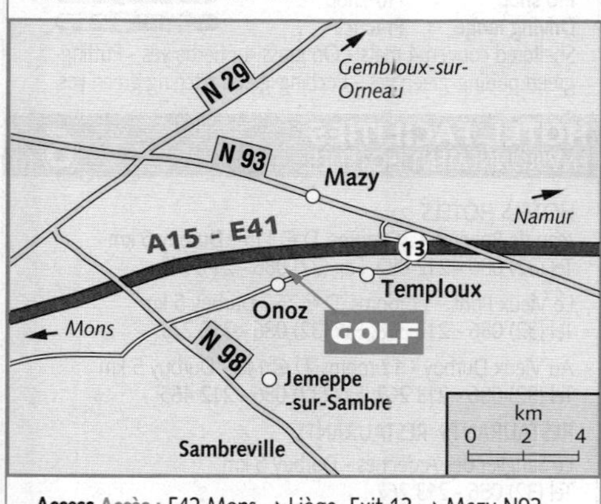

Access Accès : E42 Mons → Liège, Exit 13 → Mazy N93
Map 1 on page 93 Carte 1 Page 93

GOLF COURSE — PARCOURS — 14/20

Site	Site	
Maintenance	Entretien	
Architect	Architecte	Jean Jottrand
Type	Type	country, forest
Relief	Relief	
Water in play	Eau en jeu	
Exp. to wind	Exposé au vent	
Trees in play	Arbres en jeu	

Scorecard Carte de score	Chp. Chp.	Mens Mess.	Ladies Da.
Length Long.	5590	5590	4711
Par	70	70	70
Slope system	123	119	120

Advised golfing ability Niveau de jeu recommandé — 0 12 24 36

Hcp required Handicap exigé 36

CLUB HOUSE & AMENITIES — CLUB HOUSE ET ANNEXES — 7/10

Pro shop Pro-shop
Driving range Practice
Sheltered couvert 6 mats - On grass sur herbe no, 14 mats open air - Putting-green putting-green yes - Pitching-green pitching green yes

HOTEL FACILITIES — ENVIRONNEMENT HOTELIER — 5/10

HOTELS HÔTELS

Les Tanneurs - 29 rooms, D € 120 - Namur 15 km
Tel (32) 081 - 24 00 24, Fax (32) 081 - 24 00 25

Château de Namur - 30 rooms, D € 160 - Namur 15 km
Tel (32) 081 - 72 99 00, Fax (32) 081 - 72 99 99

Beauregard - 47 rooms, D € 110 - Namur 15 km
Tel (32) 081 - 23 00 28, Fax (32) 081 - 24 12 09

RESTAURANTS RESTAURANTS

L'Essentiel - Temploux 2 km - Tel
Biétrumé Picar - Namur 15 km - Tel (32) 081 - 23 07 39
L'Espièglerie - Namur 15 km - Tel (32) 081 - 24 00 24
La Bergerie - Lives-sur-Meuse 20 km - Tel (32) 081 - 58 06 13

Five Nations

14 | 7 | 6

Le site accidenté et l'importance des dénivelés imposent pratiquement la voiturette si l'on veut garder des forces pour jouer dans cette superbe région à l'orée des Ardennes. Au bénéfice de cette configuration de terrain, quelques belles perspectives, mais aussi des trous spectaculaires comme le 2 et le 13, avec une mention pour l'utilisation intelligente de l'espace, car la plupart des trous sont en légère montée ou en descente. A côté de trous très ouverts, l'étroitesse de certains fairways oblige à la précision, et impose une stratégie stricte, comme souvent chez l'architecte Gary Player, qui offre peu d'options de jeu différentes. Cela dit, sa connaissance des joueurs est évidente dans la répartition des difficultés d'un trou à l'autre, le souci de préserver des plages de repos entre les trous difficiles, ou encore la façon de provoquer les longs frappeurs avec de petits par 4 qu'ils seront tentés de driver directement. La qualité du club-house installé dans une grande et vieille ferme ajoute à l'agrément de cette réalisation.

Hilly terrain and sharp differences in altitude make a buggy almost a necessity if you want to keep any strength to play golf in this superb region on the edge of the Ardennes. On the upside the topography of the course gives a few fine vistas and some spectacular holes like the 2nd and 13th, with a special word for the intelligent use of space given that most holes are slightly uphill or downhill. Alongside a number of very open holes, the tightness of some fairways calls for extreme accuracy and obvious game strategy, as is often the case with architect Gary Player, who likes to offer very few playing options. Having said that, he obviously knows a thing or two about golfers in the way he spreads trouble from one hole to the next, slips in an easier hole between tougher propositions and adds the occasional short par-4 to tempt big hitters to go for the green off the tee. The pleasure of playing here is enhanced by the excellent club-house in a large old farmhouse.

Five Nations Golf Club — 1993

Château-Ferme du Grand Scley
B - 5372 MEAN (Havelange)

Office	Secrétariat	(32) 086 - 323 232
Pro shop	Pro-shop	(32) 086 - 323 232
Fax	Fax	(32) 086 - 323 011
Web	www.fivenations.be	
Situation	Situation	Namur, 40 km, Liège, 40 km
Annual closure	Fermeture annuelle	no
Weekly closure	Fermeture hebdomadaire	no

Restaurant closed (11 → 03)

Fees main season Tarifs haute saison	18 holes	
	Week days Semaine	**We/Bank holidays** We/Férié
Individual Individuel	€ 45	€ 55
Couple Couple	€ 90	€ 110

Friday: € 50

Caddie Caddie no — **Electric Trolley** Chariot électrique yes
Buggy Voiturette yes — **Clubs** Clubs yes
Credit cards Cartes de crédit
VISA - Eurocard - Mastercard

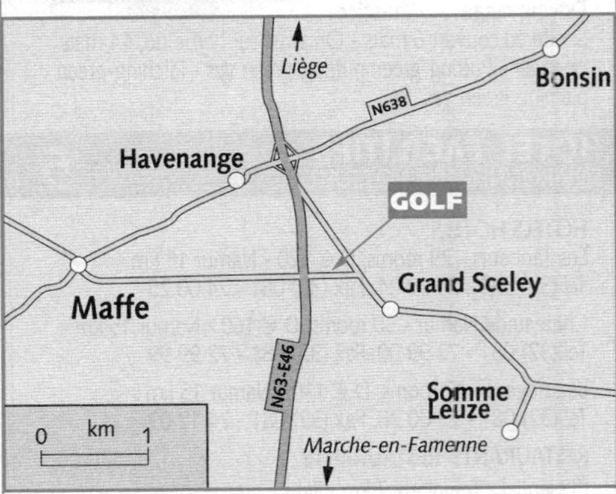

Access Accès : E411 Bruxelles-Namur. Exit (sortie) 18 → Marche. N4 to Marche. Direction N63 → Liège. Exit Mean.
Map 1 on page 93 Carte 1 Page 93

GOLF COURSE — PARCOURS — 14/20

Site	Site	
Maintenance	Entretien	
Architect	Architecte	Gary Player
Type	Type	parkland
Relief	Relief	
Water in play	Eau en jeu	
Exp. to wind	Exposé au vent	
Trees in play	Arbres en jeu	

Scorecard Carte de score	**Chp.** Chp.	**Mens** Mess.	**Ladies** Da.
Length Long.	6038	5623	4700
Par	72	72	72
Slope system	130	124	123

Advised golfing ability Niveau de jeu recommandé — 0 12 24 36
Hcp required Handicap exigé — 36

CLUB HOUSE & AMENITIES — CLUB HOUSE ET ANNEXES — 7/10

Pro shop Pro-shop
Driving range Practice
Sheltered couvert 4 mats - On grass sur herbe yes - Putting-green putting-green yes - Pitching-green pitching green yes

HOTEL FACILITIES — ENVIRONNEMENT HOTELIER — 6/10

HOTELS HÔTELS
Jean de Bohême - 26 rooms, D € 115 - Durbuy 5 km
Tel (32) 086 - 212 882, Fax (32) 086 - 211 168

Le Vieux Pont - 13 rooms, D € 75 - Durbuy 5 km
Tel (32) 086 - 212 808, Fax (32) 086 - 218 273

Au Vieux Durbuy - 12 rooms, D € 140 - Durbuy 5 km
Tel (32) 086 - 213 262, Fax (32) 086 - 212 465

RESTAURANTS RESTAURANTS
Le Sanglier des Ardennes - Durbuy 5 km
Tel (32) 086 - 213 262
Le Moulin - Durbuy 5 km - Tel (32) 086 - 212 970
Clos des Récollets - Durbuy 5 km - Tel (32) 081 - 212 969

Hainaut *Bruyère-Quesnoy*

15	7	6

Pour le 18 trous traditionnel (Bruyères et Quesnoy), voici une architecture très classique de Tom Simpson, sur un terrain sablonneux jouable toute l'année. Les obstacles sont bien visibles, stratégiquement bien placés, notamment les bunkers de fairway, s'ajoutant aux nombreux arbres du parcours (certains bois devraient être éclaircis), qui donnent un sentiment de calme et de charme tout à fait plaisants. Mais c'est un aspect trompeur, car les greens bien défendus sont accessibles après des drives bien placés et de bons coups de fers. Pour bien scorer, il faut maîtriser les balles levées, avec assez d'effet quand les greens sont rapides. Ce parcours au caractère britannique réserve de grandes satisfactions, avec un petit parfum d'autrefois très agréable. "Les Etangs" (9 trous) complètent cet équipement, avec beaucoup de trous en dog-leg, mais pas vraiment le même esprit. Très scénique et plus "moderne", il exige un jeu très long et précis, au milieu des pins.

The traditional 18-hole course is a very classic design by Tom Simpson on sandy soil that is playable all year. The hazards are clearly visible and strategically well located, especially the fairway bunkers, adding to the many trees on the course which give a pleasing impression of tranquillity and charm (though some of them should be thinned). But appearances can be deceptive, and here the well-defended greens, always perfectly in line with well-placed drives, call for some pretty sharp ironwork. Good scores need tight pitch and lob shots and backspin too when the greens are fast. The course has a pleasant British flavour and can give immense satisfaction with its very pleasant "olde worlde" charm. The 9-hole course ("Les Etangs") completes the picture in another style and includes a lot of dog-legs. Now mature, very scenic and more "modern" (i.e. lots of water), it demands both length and precision through the pine-trees.

Royal Golf Club du Hainaut — 1933

2, rue de la Verrerie
B - 7050 ERBISOEUL

Office Secrétariat (32) 065 - 22 02 00
Pro shop Pro-shop (32) 065 - 22 05 40
Fax Fax (32) 065 - 22 02 09
Web www.golf.be/hainaut
Situation Situation Bruxelles / Brussel, 60 km
Annual closure Fermeture annuelle no
Weekly closure Fermeture hebdomadaire no
Fees main season Tarifs haute saison 18 holes

	Week days / Semaine	We/Bank holidays / We/Férié
Individual Individuel	€ 55	€ 70
Couple Couple	€ 110	€ 140

Caddie Caddie no — **Electric Trolley** Chariot électrique no
Buggy Voiturette yes — **Clubs** Clubs yes
Credit cards Cartes de crédit
VISA - Eurocard - Mastercard - DC - AMEX

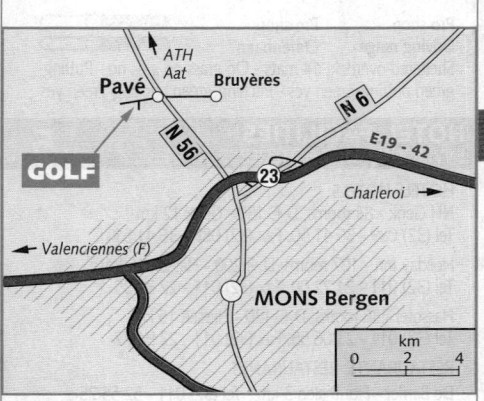

Access Accès : E42 Paris-Bruxelles, Exit (Sortie) 23, N6 → Mons, N56 → Ath
Map 1 on page 92 Carte 1 Page 92

GOLF COURSE — PARCOURS 15/20

Site	Site	
Maintenance	Entretien	
Architect	Architecte	Tom Simpson
Type	Type	forest, hilly
Relief	Relief	
Water in play	Eau en jeu	
Exp. to wind	Exposé au vent	
Trees in play	Arbres en jeu	

Scorecard / Carte de score	Chp. / Chp.	Mens / Mess.	Ladies / Da.
Length Long.	6113	6042	5318
Par	72	72	72
Slope system	123	120	124

Advised golfing ability Niveau de jeu recommandé 0 12 24 36
Hcp required Handicap exigé 36

CLUB HOUSE & AMENITIES — CLUB HOUSE ET ANNEXES 7/10

Pro shop — Pro-shop
Driving range — Practice
Sheltered couvert yes - On grass sur herbe no, mats open air - Putting-green putting-green yes - Pitching-green pitching green yes

HOTEL FACILITIES — ENVIRONNEMENT HOTELIER 6/10

HOTELS HÔTELS
Novotel - 51 rooms, D € 110- Nimy 4 km
Tel (32) 065 - 72 36 85, Fax (32) 065 - 72 41 44

Lido - 73 rooms, D € 150 - Mons 6 km
Tel (32) 065 - 32 78 00, Fax (32) 065 - 84 37 22

Saint James - 21 rooms, D € 95 - Mons 6 km
Tel (32) 065 - 72 48 24, Fax (32) 065 - 72 48 11

RESTAURANTS RESTAURANTS
Devos - Mons 6 km - Tel (32) 065 - 35 13 35
Chez John - Mons 6 km - Tel (32) 065 - 33 51 21
L'Assiette au Beurre - Frameries (Mons) 10 km
Tel (32) 065 - 67 76 73

Limburg *BF*

16 | 7 | 5

Midden in een natuurreservaat en een landschap van sparren en berken, typerend voor de Kempen, wordt dit licht golvend terrein een ware streling voor het oog als de heide in bloei staat, op het einde van de zomer en in de herfst. Het is het stroke-play parcours bij uitstek, met een harmonisch speelritme, enkele moeilijke pieken die gespreksstof vormen voor achteraf (sommige par 4 zijn hardnekkig), zeer mooie par 5 en een juweeltje, de 8, een kleine technische par 4 zoals men er geen meer durft ontwerpen. Het design van Fred Hawtree is van een op en top Brits classicisme, het ontwerp ziet eruit alsof de natuur zelf het zo gewild heeft, mooi gelegen tussen de heide en het bos, en het heeft een zeer "intelligente" bunkering. Daar het terrein zeer goed uitgebalanceerd is, met werkelijke verschillen tussen de champion tees en de andere, is het er zeer aangenaam spelen op elk niveau, en keert men met plezier nog eens terug. Onderhoud is nu zeer goed.

Set in a nature reserve of pine and birch that are typical of the Campine region (and somewhat reminiscent of a British inland course), this slightly rolling layout is a beautiful sight when the heather is in full bloom in late summer and in autumn. It is an excellent course for stroke-play, neatly balanced with a few memorable tough moments on the back nine (some par 4s are really hard going), some fabulous par 5s and a gem of a hole, the 8th, which is a short but very technical 4-par, the likes of which are hardly ever found these days. Fred Hawtree's layout is a pure British classic, winding its way almost naturally between heather and wood with particularly intelligent bunkering. Because it is so well balanced, with real differences between the tournament and hacker tees, it is pleasant tc play Limburg again and again whatever your level. Maintenance is now very good.

Limburg Golf & Country Club — 1967

Golfstraat 1
B - 3530 HOUTHALEN

Office Secretariaat (32) 089 - 38 35 43
Pro shop Pro shop (32) 089 - 84 32 04
Fax Fax (32) 089 - 84 12 08
Web www.golf.be/limburg
Situation Locatie Hasselt, 15 km
Annual closure Jaarlijkse sluiting no
Weekly closure Wekelijkse sluitingsdag no

Fees main season Hoogseizoen tarieven	**Week days** Weekdagen	**We/Bank holidays** We/Feestdagen
	18 holes	
Individual Individueel	€ 50	€ 60
Couple Paar	€ 100	€ 120

Juniors: € 10 / € 15 (We)

Caddie Caddie no — **Electric Trolley** Electrische trolley no
Buggy Buggy yes — **Clubs** Clubs no

Credit cards Creditcards
VISA - Eurocard - Mastercard - DC - AMEX

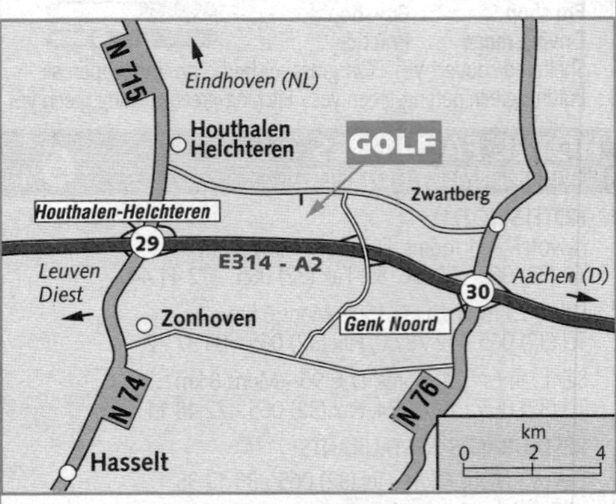

Access Toegang : E314 Brussel → Aix-la-Chapelle, Exit 29. N715 → Eindhoven, Houthalen, → Golf
Map 1 on page 93 Auto kaart 1 Blz 93

GOLF COURSE — BAAN 16/20

Site Terrein
Maintenance Onderhoud
Architect Architect Fred Hawtree
Type Type baan forest, heathland
Relief Reliëf
Water in play Waterhazards
Exp. to wind Windgevoelig
Trees in play Bomen

Scorecard Scorekaart	**Chp.** Back tees	**Mens** Heren	**Ladies** Damen
Length Lengte	6128	5750	5156
Par	72	72	72
Slope system	132	129	132

Advised golfing ability Aanbevolen golfvaardigheid 0 12 24 36
Hcp required Vereiste hcp W/E: 32 Men, 36 Ladies

CLUB HOUSE & AMENITIES — CLUB HOUSE EN ANNEXEN 7/10

Pro shop Pro shop
Driving range Oefenbaan
Sheltered overdekt 14 mats - On grass op gras no - Putting-green putting-green yes - Pitching-green pitching-green yes

HOTEL FACILITIES — ENVIRONNEMENT HOTELIER 5/10

HOTELS HOTELS
NH Genk - 83 rooms, D € 150 - Genk 12 km
Tel (32) 089 - 36 41 50, Fax (32) 089 - 36 41 51

Holiday Inn - 107 rooms, D € 200 - Hasselt 15 km
Tel (32) 011 - 24 22 00, Fax (32) 011 - 22 39 35

Hassotel - 36 rooms, D € 130 - Hasselt 15 km
Tel (32) 011 - 23 06 55, Fax (32) 011 - 22 94 77

RESTAURANTS RESTAURANTS
De Barrier - Houthalen 3 km - Tel (32) 011 - 52 55 25
De Postkoets - Houthalen 3 km - Tel (32) 089 - 38 20 79
't Konijntje - Genk 12 km - Tel (32) 089 - 35 26 45

Mont-Garni

13	7	6

Avec quelques arbres en moins (2, 13, 14, 17) qui empiètent sur la bonne ligne de jeu, l'élagage de certaines branches et un plus large nettoyage des sous-bois, Mont-Garni donnerait plus encore de plaisir aux golfeurs, rendrait plus évidente la stratégie de jeu et ne punirait vraiment que les coups lâchés. En revanche, le challenge est réel, beaucoup de trous sont intéressants, même si les pars 3 sont plus longs que vraiment subtils (leurs départs sont mal orientés). Il faut constamment se méfier des arbres et des étangs, qui rendent cependant le site assez séduisant : sur ce parcours qui demande pas mal de précision, on ne conseillera les départs arrière qu'aux joueurs de très bon niveau, les autres s'y amuseront beaucoup des départs "normaux" en match-play, en famille ou entre amis de niveau équivalent. Ce parcours a évolué de manière intéressante, et les non-golfeurs peuvent profiter du centre équestre sur place au lieu de porter les sacs une fois de plus...

With fewer trees right in the line of fire (on the 2nd, 13th, 14th and 17th holes), the trimming of a few branches and more extensive clearing of undergrowth, Mont-Garni would be even more enjoyable to play, would make game strategy more obvious and would punish only the really wayward shot. However, the challenge here hits you in the eye with a lot of interesting holes, even though the par 3s are longer than they are subtle. You have to be constantly on the outlook to avoid the trees and lakes, which at the same time add to the course's appeal. On a course like this, which demands precision play, we would recommend the back-tees only for the better players; the others can move forward and have fun with the family or friends with a round of match-play. The course has matured very attractively but rather than lug golf bags around, non-golfers may prefer the riding stables next door.

Golf du Mont-Garni — 1990

Rue du Mont-Garni, 3
B - 7331 BAUDOUR

Office	Secrétariat	(32) 065 - 52 94 10
Pro shop	Pro-shop	(32) 065 - 62 27 19
Fax	Fax	(32) 065 - 62 34 10
Web	www.golfmontgarni.be	
Situation	Situation	Mons / Bergen, 7 km
Annual closure	Fermeture annuelle	no
Weekly closure	Fermeture hebdomadaire	no

Fees main season / Tarifs haute saison	18 holes	
	Week days / Semaine	We/Bank holidays / We/Férié
Individual Individuel	€ 40	€ 60
Couple Couple	€ 80	€ 120

Juniors: – 50%

Caddie Caddie no — Electric Trolley Chariot électrique no

Buggy Voiturette yes — Clubs Clubs yes

Credit cards Cartes de crédit
VISA - Eurocard - Mastercard

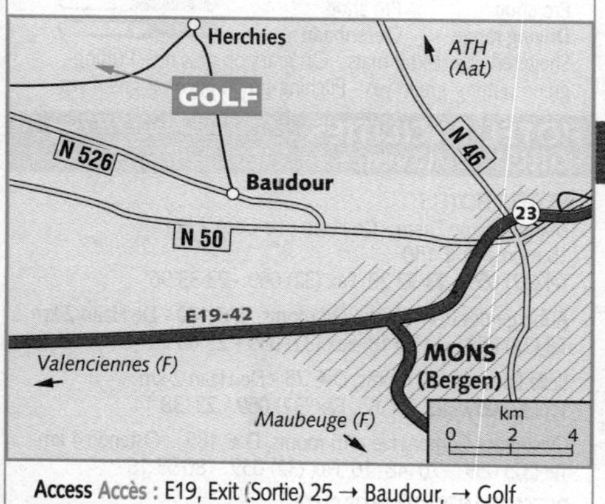

Access Accès : E19, Exit (Sortie) 25 → Baudour, → Golf
Map 1 on page 92 Carte 1 Page 92

GOLF COURSE — PARCOURS — 13/20

Site	Site	
Maintenance	Entretien	
Architect	Architecte	Tom MacAuley
Type	Type	forest, open country
Relief	Relief	
Water in play	Eau en jeu	
Exp. to wind	Exposé au vent	
Trees in play	Arbres en jeu	

Scorecard / Carte de score	Chp. / Chp.	Mens / Mess.	Ladies / Da.
Length Long.	6373	6047	5135
Par	74	74	74
Slope system	128	124	128

Advised golfing ability / Niveau de jeu recommandé: 0 12 24 36
Hcp required / Handicap exigé: 36

CLUB HOUSE & AMENITIES — CLUB HOUSE ET ANNEXES — 7/10

Pro shop — Pro-shop
Driving range — Practice
Sheltered couvert 8 mats - On grass sur herbe yes - Putting-green putting-green yes - Pitching-green pitching green yes

HOTEL FACILITIES — ENVIRONNEMENT HOTELIER — 6/10

HOTELS HÔTELS

Novotel - 51 rooms, D € 110 - Nimy 10 km
Tel (32) 065 - 72 36 85, Fax (32) 065 - 72 41 44

Casteau Resort - Casteau 12 km
73 rooms, D € 130
Tel (32) 065 - 32 04 00, Fax (32) 065 - 72 87 44

RESTAURANTS RESTAURANTS

Le Faitout - Baudour 1 km - Tel (32) 065 - 64 48 57
Devos - Mons 7 km - Tel (32) 065 - 35 13 35
La 5e Saison - Mons 7 km - Tel (32) 065 - 72 82 62
La Coquille Saint-Jacques - Mons 7 km
Tel (32) 065 - 84 36 53

Oostende

15 | 7 | 7

Het is nu bekend dat de originele design van de hand van Seymour Dunn en Tom Simpson. Het is een feit dat moderne aanpassingen niet steeds even succesvol zijn; daarom heft Martin Hawtree het effect van de links willen respecteren en waren zijn hervormingen slechts miniem. The holes langs de zee (van 5 tot 10) blijven indrukwekkend met hun zeer nadrukkelijk links-design. Eigenlijk ontbreken we daar 20 hectaren duinen! Het parcours blijft een serieuze fysieke inspanning vergen, vooral als er wind staat, en het is zeker een goede test voor spelers, die het lage balspel willen oefenen. Maar bij mooi weer is Oostende een parcours voor alle niveaus. De waterhindernissen die op het parcoursplan getekend staan, vormen niet echt een moeilijkheid, want de voornaamste problemen schuilen in de bunkers, het struikgewas en de rough. Eenmaal op de green aanbeland, bent u veilig: ze zijn mooi vlak en gemakkelijk bespeelbaar.

The original architects were Seymour Dunn and Tom Simpson, and even though modern restyling operations are not always as successful as they are supposed to be, Martin Hawtree set out to respect the feel of this links course and made only slight changes. The seaside holes (5 to 10) are as remarkable as ever with a very distinct links flavour. In fact, what is missing here is about 50 acres of sand-dunes, although the course that crosses the dunes is a good physical exercise when the wind blows and a stiff test as to a player's ability to hit low shots. In fine weather, Oostende is a course for all golfers: the few water hazards shown on the course map are not really in play and the main problems are the very many bunkers, bushes and the rough. Once on the greens, you are almost home and dry as the putting surfaces are flat and easy to read.

Royal Ostend Golf Club — 1903

Koninklijke Baan 2
B - 8420 DE HAAN

Office	Secretariaat	(32) 059 - 23 32 83
Pro shop	Pro shop	(32) 059 - 23 54 07
Fax	Fax	(32) 059 - 23 37 49
Web	www.golfoostende.be	
Situation	Locatie	close to Oostende
Annual closure	Jaarlijkse sluiting	no
Weekly closure	Wekelijkse sluitingsdag	no

Tuesday (diensdag): restaurant closed

Fees main season / Hoogseizoen tarieven	18 holes	
	Week days / Weekdagen	We/Bank holidays / We/Feestdagen
Individual Individueel	€ 60	€ 75
Couple Paar	€ 120	€ 150

Juniors: – 50%

Caddie Caddie no — Electric Trolley Electrische trolley no

Buggy Buggy yes — Clubs Clubs no

Credit cards Creditcards
VISA - Mastercard – also Amex - DC at the Pro shop

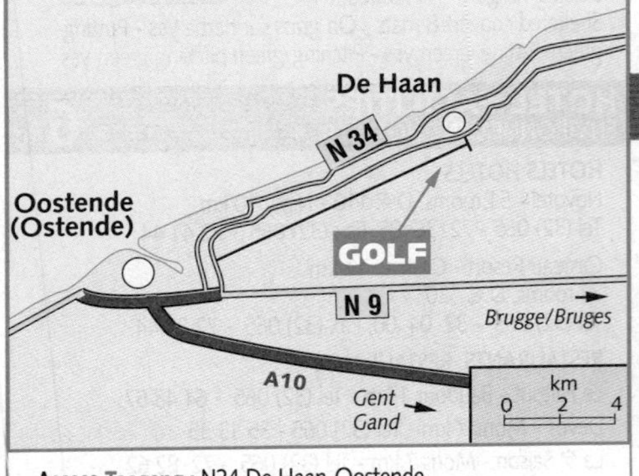

Access Toegang : N34 De Haan-Oostende
Map 1 on page 92 Auto kaart 1 Blz 92

GOLF COURSE BAAN — 15/20

Site	Terrein	
Maintenance	Onderhoud	
Architect	Architect	S. Dunn., T. Simpson Martin Hawtree,1990
Type	Type baan	seaside course, links
Relief	Reliëf	
Water in play	Waterhazards	
Exp. to wind	Windgevoelig	
Trees in play	Bomen	

Scorecard Scorekaart	Chp. Back tees	Mens Heren	Ladies Damen
Length Lengte	5618	5265	4642
Par	70	70	70
Slope system	123	118	121

Advised golfing ability / Aanbevolen golfvaardigheid: 0 12 24 36
Hcp required / Vereiste hcp: 34, 28 (We)

CLUB HOUSE & AMENITIES CLUB HOUSE EN ANNEXEN — 7/10

Pro shop — Pro shop
Driving range — Oefenbaan
Sheltered overdekt 9 mats - On grass op gras no - Putting-green putting-green yes - Pitching-green pitching-green yes

HOTEL FACILITIES HOTELS IN OMGEVING — 7/10

HOTELS HOTELS

Manoir Carpe Diem - De Haan (Le Coq) 2 km
15 rooms, D € 150
Tel (32) 059 - 23 32 20, Fax (32) 059 - 23 33 96

Auberge des Rois-Beach - 24 rooms, D € 140 - De Haan 2 km
Tel (32) 059 - 23 30 18, Fax (32) 059 - 23 60 78

Belle Epoque - 19 rooms, D € 75 - De Haan 2 km
Tel (32) 059 - 23 34 65, Fax (32) 059 - 23 38 14

Oostendse Compagnie - 15 rooms, D € 185 - Ostende 4 km
Tel (32) 059 - 70 48 16, Fax (32) 059 - 80 53 16

RESTAURANTS RESTAURANTS

Villa Maritza - Oostende 4 km - Tel (32) 059 - 50 88 08
't Vistrapje - Oostende 4 km - Tel (32) 059 - 80 23 82

Oudenaarde *Abdij + Anker*

14	6	5

Om een mooie wandeling te maken in een uitgestrekt park (prachtige beuken) met nadien een drankje in een club-house, dat ingericht is in een kasteel van de XIXe eeuw, is men in Oudenaarde aan het juiste adres. Als men echter een golfparcours "van sterke emoties" zoekt, dat een grote sportieve uitdaging vormt, kan men al beter van de back tees vertrekken. Hier heeft men vooral aan het genoegen van de leden gedacht! Het parcours van Oudenaarde heeft onlangs enkele wijzigingen ondergaan, die niet al te gelukkig zijn uitgevallen, omdat er enkele "goeie ouwe holes" werden geïntegreerd in een nieuw circuit van 9 holes. De nieuwe holes, die de oude verdwenen holes op het bestaande parcours vervangen, vergen wel enige athletische vastberadenheid, maar missen de charme van echt leuke golf. Het oude parcours, als het vanaf de back tees wordt gespeeld, biedt mede dankzij de talrijke hindernissen een niet te onderschatten uitdaging, zowel qua lengte als qua precisie. De greens zijn goed zichtbaar en niet te erg door bunkers omzoomd. De 9 holes die in 1991 werd aangelegd is korter. Naast de grote "monumenten" in de golfwereld, moeten er ook terreinen zoals dit zijn...

Personal assessment here depends on what you expect from a golf course. If you are looking primarily for a pleasant stroll through a large estate (with some beautiful beech trees) between Escaut and Vieil Escaut before returning and relaxing in a club-house converted from a mid-19th century castle, then Oudenaarde is for you. But if you are looking for exciting golf and a real sporting challenge, then drive on. Emphasis here is on pleasing members, most of whom are only average golfers. The main course (18 holes since 1976) is not very long and offers no great originality. The hazards are of no great danger and the greens are clearly in view with few bunkers. The 9-hole course built in 1991 is even shorter. But alongside the giant courses of this world, we also need courses like this...

Golf & Country-Club Oudenaarde — 1976

Kortrijkstraat 52
B - 9790 WORTEGEM-PETEGEM

Office	Secretariaat	(32) 055 - 33 41 61
Pro shop	Pro shop	(32) 055 - 33 41 63
Fax	Fax	(32) 055 - 31 98 49
Web	www.golfoudenaarde.be	
Situation	Locatie	Oudenaarde, 3 km

Gent / Gand, 25 km

Annual closure	Jaarlijkse sluiting	no
Weekly closure	Wekelijkse sluitingsdag	no
Fees main season	Hoogseizoen tarieven	18 holes
	Week days Weekdagen	**We/Bank holidays** We/Feestdagen
Individual Individueel	€ 50	€ 65
Couple Paar	€ 100	€ 130

Caddie Caddie no — **Electric Trolley** Electrische trolley yes
Buggy Buggy yes — **Clubs** Clubs no
Credit cards Creditcards
VISA - DC - AMEX

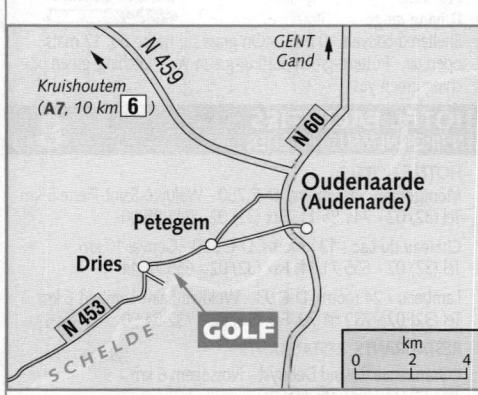

Access Toegang : E17 Kortrijk-Gent, Exit 8 De Pinte, N60 → Ronse, N453 → Kortrijk
Map 1 on page 92 Auto kaart 1 Blz 92

GOLF COURSE — BAAN — 14/20

Site	Terrein	
Maintenance	Onderhoud	
Architect	Architect	Harold (Bill) Baker
Type	Type baan	parkland
Relief	Reliëf	
Water in play	Waterhazards	
Exp. to wind	Windgevoelig	
Trees in play	Bomen	

Scorecard Scorekaart	**Chp.** Back tees	**Mens** Heren	**Ladies** Damen
Length Lengte	6172	5774	4983
Par	72	72	72
Slope system	132	128	130

Advised golfing ability Aanbevolen golfvaardigheid — 0 12 24 36
Hcp required Vereiste hcp — 36

CLUB HOUSE & AMENITIES — CLUB HOUSE EN ANNEXEN — 6/10

Pro shop Pro shop
Driving range Oefenbaan
Sheltered overdekt 12 mats - On grass op gras no, 6 mats open air - Putting-green putting-green yes - Pitching-green pitching-green yes

HOTEL FACILITIES — ENVIRONNEMENT HOTELIER — 5/10

HOTELS HOTELS

Le Shamrock - 5 rooms, D € 180 - Ronse 12 km
Tel (32) 055 - 21 55 29, Fax (32) 055 - 21 56 83

Cesar - 9 rooms, D € 85 - Oudenaarde 3 km
Tel (32) 055 - 30 13 81, Fax (32) 055 - 30 13 81

De Rantere - 19 rooms, D € 105 - Oudenaarde 3 km
Tel (32) 055 - 31 89 88, Fax (32) 055 - 33 01 11

RESTAURANTS RESTAURANTS

't Craeneveldt - Oudenaarde 5 km - Tel (32) 055 - 31 72 91
Le Shamrock - Ronse 12 km - Tel (32) 055 - 21 55 29
Wine, Dine, Café - Oudenaarde 3 km
Tel (32) 055 - 23 96 97

Ravenstein *Old Course*

16	8	8

Passionné par le golf, le Roi Léopold II a été notamment à l'origine d'Ostende et du Ravenstein. Le club fit appel à un architecte "royal", Tom Simpson, dont le dessin semble avoir été assez bien préservé, de même que la végétation, d'une beauté impressionnante. Chênes, bouleaux, cèdres bleus, ormes et saules offrent un spectacle qui ferait oublier le parcours, si celui-ci n'était d'une si évidente qualité. Il offre des drives sans gros problèmes (sauf aux 2, 4, 11 et 17), mais les attaques de green sont d'autant plus passionnantes que le putting ne sera pas ensuite évident. Les greens ne sont pas très ondulés, mais leurs surfaces sont plus difficiles à lire qu'il n'y paraît. Le Ravenstein peut être joué à tous les niveaux, mais les meilleurs y trouveront quelques défis de premier ordre, alors que sa longueur reste modérée, selon les exigences modernes en tout cas. Un "must". Plusieurs trous ont été "modernisés" par Martin Hawtree, en reculant les greens aux 14 et 18, et aussi (c'est moins convaincant) avec des buttes au 8 et des bunkers au 9.

King Leopold II was the instigator of the courses at Oostende and Ravenstein. The club called in a "royal" architect, the great Tom Simpson, whose design has remained largely unscathed. The same goes for the extremely beautiful vegetation. The impressive oak, birch, blue cedar, elm and willow trees could almost make you forget the course if it wasn't such an excellent layout. The tee shot is never a problem (except on 2nd, 4th, 11th and 17th holes) but the approach shots are all the more exciting in that putting here is an equally challenging proposition. These are hardly what you would call undulating greens but the putting surface is harder to read than you might think. Ravenstein can be played by golfers of all abilities but the most proficient will find a number of challenges, even though by modern standards the course posts only moderate yardage. Several holes have been "modernised" by Martin Hawtree, holes 14 and 18 have been lengthened (the greens pushed back).

Royal Golf Club de Belgique — 1905

Château de Ravenstein
B - 3080 TERVUREN

Office	Secrétariat	(32) 02 - 767 58 01
Pro shop	Pro-shop	(32) 02 - 767 55 60
Fax	Fax	(32) 02 - 767 28 41
Web	www.ravenstein.be	
Situation	Situation	Bruxelles / Brussel, 6 km
Annual closure	Fermeture annuelle	no
Weekly closure	Fermeture hebdomadaire	Monday (lundi)

Fees main season Tarifs haute saison	18 holes	
	Week days Semaine	We/Bank holidays We/Férié
Individual Individuel	€ 90	*
Couple Couple	€ 180	*

* Members guests only

Caddie Caddie on request **Electric Trolley** Chariot électrique no

Buggy Voiturette no **Clubs** Clubs no

Credit cards Cartes de crédit
VISA - DC - AMEX

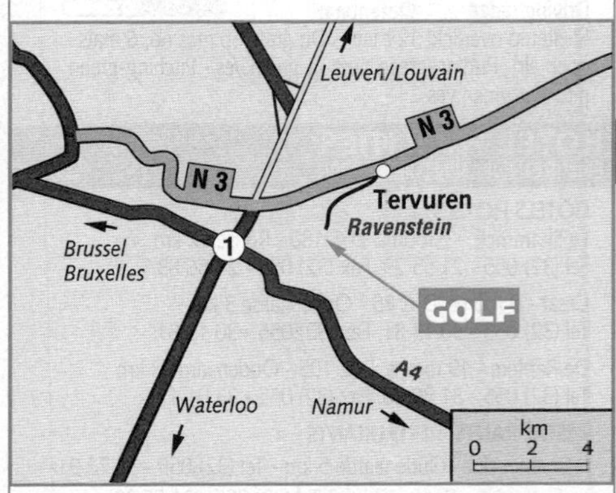

Access Accès : In Bruxelles, Avenue de Tervuren → Tervuren, go through Les Quatre Bras, → Golf
Map 1 on page 92 Carte 1 Page 92

GOLF COURSE — PARCOURS — 16/20

Site	Site	
Maintenance	Entretien	
Architect	Architecte	Tom Simpson
Type	Type	parkland, forest
Relief	Relief	
Water in play	Eau en jeu	
Exp. to wind	Exposé au vent	
Trees in play	Arbres en jeu	

Scorecard Carte de score	Chp. Chp.	Mens Mess.	Ladies Da.
Length Long.	6033	5775	5088
Par	72	72	72
Slope system	130	127	126

Advised golfing ability Niveau de jeu recommandé — 0 12 24 36

Hcp required Handicap exigé — 20 Men, 24 Ladies

CLUB HOUSE & AMENITIES — CLUB HOUSE ET ANNEXES — 8/10

Pro shop Pro-shop
Driving range Practice

Sheltered couvert 10 mats - On grass sur herbe no, 12 mats open air - Putting-green putting-green yes - Pitching-green pitching green yes

HOTEL FACILITIES — ENVIRONNEMENT HOTELIER — 8/10

HOTELS HÔTELS

Montgomery - 63 rooms, D € 280 - Woluwé-Saint-Pierre 5 km
Tel (32) 02 - 741 85 11, Fax (32) 02 - 741 85 00

Château du Lac - 121 rooms, D € 300 - Genval 10 km
Tel (32) 02 - 655 71 11, Fax (32) 02 - 655 74 44

Lambeau - 24 rooms, D € 93 - Woluwé-Saint-Lambert 6 km
Tel (32) 02 - 732 51 70, Fax (32) 02 - 732 54 90

RESTAURANTS RESTAURANTS

L'Orangeraie Roland Debuyst - Nossegem 6 km
Tel (32) 02 - 757 05 59

Les Deux Maisons - Woluwé-Saint-Pierre 5 km
Tel (32) 02 - 771 14 47

De Linde - Tervuren 1 km - Tel (32) 02 - 767 87 42

Rigenée

14 | 7 | 6

Très ouvert et peu arboré, c'est un parcours délicat quand le vent souffle. Les défauts originels du dessin ont été peu à peu gommés par Christophe Descampe, frère de l'excellente joueuse belge Florence Descampe. De nouveaux plans d'eau et des plantations devraient continuer à faire progresser cette réalisation dont l'entretien est de très bonne qualité. Ici, c'est une affaire de famille et cela se sent. Les trous sont assez bien équilibrés et imposent un rythme de jeu agréable, mais on notera surtout la qualité technique des par 5. Les roughs sont bien en jeu, les greens assez vastes et moyennement modelés sont bien défendus, ce qui impose un jeu précis. Assez naturel au départ, et sans prétendre au titre de chef-d'oeuvre, Rigenée progresse dans le bon sens. L'ambiance y est très amicale et sportive, c'est un point à souligner.

This very open and almost treeless course is a tricky proposition when the wind blows. The original flaws have been gradually designed out by Christophe Descampe, the brother of the excellent Belgian player Florence Descampe. New stretches of water and plantation programmes should keep the course moving in the right direction, helped by excellent maintenance. The holes are well balanced for a pleasant playing rhythm but most notable is the technical excellence of the par 5s. The rough is very much in play and the rather large and averagely contoured greens are well defended, thus calling for some precision play. A natural layout at the outset and with no pretence to the masterpiece label, Rigenée is improving all the time. The atmosphere is one of family entertainment and sport, an important point that deserves a special mention.

Golf de Rigenée — 1981

Rue du Châtelet, 62
B - 1495 VILLERS-LA-VILLE

Office Secrétariat (32) 071 - 87 77 65
Pro shop Pro-shop (32) 071 - 87 73 29
Fax Fax (32) 071 - 87 77 83
Web www.rigenee.be
Situation Situation Bruxelles /Brussel, 35 km
Nivelles (pop. 21 883), 15 km
Annual closure Fermeture annuelle no
Weekly closure Fermeture hebdomadaire Monday (lundi)

Fees main season Tarifs haute saison	18 holes	
	Week days Semaine	**We/Bank holidays** We/Férié
Individual Individuel	€ 40	€ 65
Couple Couple	€ 80	€ 130

We: € 55 before 10.00 / Juniors: € 15, € 20 (We)

Caddie Caddie no — **Electric Trolley** Chariot électrique no
Buggy Voiturette yes — **Clubs** Clubs yes
Credit cards Cartes de crédit VISA - Eurocard - Mastercard
Access Accès : N93 Nivelles → Namur,

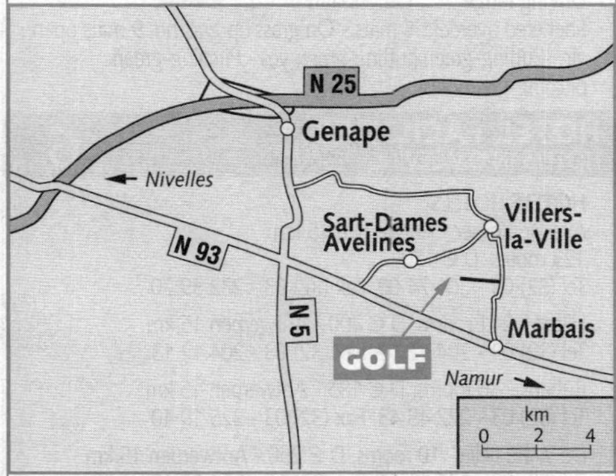

Marbais → Villers-la-Ville, Golf 2 km
Map 1 on page 92 Carte 1 Page 92

GOLF COURSE — PARCOURS — 14/20

Site Site
Maintenance Entretien
Architect Architecte Paul Rolin, C. Descampe
Type Type open country
Relief Relief
Water in play Eau en jeu
Exp. to wind Exposé au vent
Trees in play Arbres en jeu

Scorecard Carte de score	**Chp.** Chp.	**Mens** Mess.	**Ladies** Da.
Length Long.	6062	5661	5131
Par	73	73	73
Slope system	134	129	128

Advised golfing ability Niveau de jeu recommandé 0 12 24 36
Hcp required Handicap exigé 30 Men, 36 Ladies

CLUB HOUSE & AMENITIES — CLUB HOUSE ET ANNEXES — 7/10

Pro shop Pro-shop
Driving range Practice
Sheltered couvert 12 mats - On grass sur herbe yes (summer) - Putting-green putting-green yes - Pitching-green pitching green yes

HOTEL FACILITIES — ENVIRONNEMENT HOTELIER — 6/10

HOTELS HÔTELS

Château de Limelette - 88 rooms, D € 250 - Limelette 18 km
Tel (32) 010 - 42 19 99, Fax (32) 010 - 41 57 59

Ferme de Grambais - 10 rooms, D € 55 - Nivelles 17 km
Tel (32) 067 - 220 118, Fax (32) 067 - 841 307

Grand Hôtel de Waterloo - Waterloo 15 km
79 rooms, D € 250
Tel (32) 02 - 352 18 15, Fax (32) 02 - 352 18 88

RESTAURANTS RESTAURANTS

Le Cigalon - Villers-la-Ville 2 km - Tel (32) 071 - 87 85 54
La Cuisine au Vert - Waterloo 12 km - Tel (32) 02 - 357 34 94
Le Clocheton - Nivelles 17 km - Tel (32) 067 - 840 120

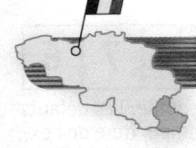

Rinkven *Red + White*

14	6	6

Na een mooie toegangsweg door de bossen, valt direct het professionalisme van de club op, door de kwaliteit van de installaties en het onderhoud van het terrein. Dit laatste bestaat nu uit 4 combineerbare 9-holes, met als uitblinker de blauwe 9 holes parcours aangelegd in 2005 met zeer spectaculaire waterhazards. Met als hoogtepunt de aanleg van 9 nieuwe holes, wordt Rinkven dé "grote" club van de metropool, met 36 holes en meer dan 1500 leden. Dit sterkt tevens de motivatie om een plan op lange termijn uit te werken voor het "updaten" van de moeilijkheden van het parcours naar een meer actuele stijl. Intussen mag u zeker niet aarzelen om volop van deze site te komen genieten, want hier biedt men u de best onderhouden greens van het Koninkrijk en een uiterst interessante natuur en fauna.

After a pleasant drive through the woods, you can tell the club's professionalism by the standard of facilities and course maintenance. There are now four combinable 9-hole courses with the addition of the 2005 Blue course, a modern design with spectacular water hazards, which adds some spices to the existing 27 holes lacking a bit of personality and style, and offering the same level of difficulty and similar-looking greens that are often narrow and elevated. The opening of those 9 new holes makes Rinkven the biggest club of Antwerp with 36 holes and more than 1,500 members. This status has also prompted the introduction of a long-term plan in order to update the difficulties around the course. In between time, don't hesitate to enjoy this site which very often boasts the best maintained greens in the kingdom and eye-catching flora and fauna to keep you company.

Rinkven Golf Club — 1981

Sint-Jobsteenweg, 120
B - 2970 SCHILDE

Office	Secretariaat	(32) 03 - 380 12 80
Pro shop	Pro shop	(32) 03 - 385 82 13
Fax	Fax	(32) 03 - 384 29 33
Web	www.golf.be/rinkven	
Situation	Locatie	Antwerpen/Anvers, 15 km
Annual closure	Jaarlijkse sluiting	no
Weekly closure	Wekelijkse sluitingsdag	no

Fees main season Hoogseizoen tarieven	Week days Weekdagen	We/Bank holidays We/Feestdagen
	18 holes	
Individual Individueel	€ 55	€ 75
Couple Paar	€ 110	€ 150

Juniors: € 16

Caddie Caddie no — **Electric Trolley** Electrische trolley yes
Buggy Buggy yes — **Clubs** Clubs no
Credit cards Creditcards
VISA - Mastercard - AMEX

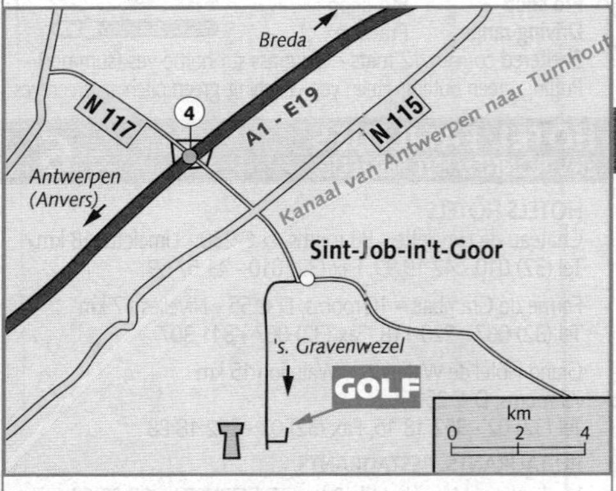

Access Toegang : E19 Anvers → Breda,
Exit (Sortie) St-Job-in-'t Goor → 's Gravenwesel → Golf
Map 1 on page 92 Auto kaart 1 Blz 92

GOLF COURSE — BAAN — 14/20

Site	Terrein	
Maintenance	Onderhoud	
Architect	Architect	Paul Rolin
Type	Type baan	forest
Relief	Reliëf	
Water in play	Waterhazards	
Exp. to wind	Windgevoelig	
Trees in play	Bomen	

Scorecard Scorekaart	Chp. Back tees	Mens Heren	Ladies Damen
Length Lengte	6177	6000	5371
Par	73	73	73
Slope system	139	137	134

Advised golfing ability Aanbevolen golfvaardigheid: 0 12 24 36
Hcp required Vereiste hcp: 36

CLUB HOUSE & AMENITIES — CLUB HOUSE EN ANNEXEN — 6/10

Pro shop Pro shop
Driving range Oefenbaan
Sheltered overdekt 6 mats - On grass op gras no, 9 mats open air - Putting-green putting-green yes - Pitching-green pitching-green yes

HOTEL FACILITIES — HOTELS IN OMGEVING — 6/10

HOTELS HOTELS
Alfa De Keyser - Antwerpen 15 km
123 rooms, D € 170
Tel (32) 03 - 206 74 60, Fax (32) 03 - 232 39 70

Hilton - 211 rooms, D € 300 - Antwerpen 15 km
Tel (32) 03 - 204 12 12, Fax (32) 03 - 204 12 13

Rubens - 36 rooms, D € 185 - Antwerpen 15 km
Tel (32) 03 - 222 48 48, Fax (32) 03 - 225 19 40

De Witte Lelie - 10 rooms, D € 250 - Antwerpen 15 km
Tel (32) 03 - 226 19 66, Fax (32) 03 - 234 00 19

RESTAURANTS RESTAURANTS
De Bellefleur - Kapellen 12 km - Tel (32) 03 - 664 67 19
't Fornuis - Antwerpen 15 km - Tel (32) 03 - 233 62 70

Royal Latem

15	8	6

Greens en bunkers werden in de jaren '50 hertekend door Hawtree. Het gebrek aan ruimte brengt ook een beperking in afstand met zich mee, en "out of bounds" op de helft van de holes. Het grote park is aangeplant met prachtige bomen, eiken, dennen, en beuken van meer dan 200 jaar oud, wat voor een zeer aantrekkelijke omgeving zorgt. De hindernissen zijn hoofdzakelijk bunkers, maar ook enkele vijvers en grachten, niet echt moeilijk. Het design is tamelijk eenvoudig, en de strategie voor de hand liggend, behalve op de 6 en de 18, met blinde drives. De strategie om de greens te bereiken, is niet ingewikkeld te noemen, zelfs niet de keuze van de club, behalve voor de approach van vijf ervan, die verhoogd zijn. Dankzij een afwisselend design, een matig reliëf en een opvallende charme en volkomenheid, kan Latem een parcours bieden, dat voor elk spelersniveau een plezier betekent. De zanderige bodem en de volledige irrigatie maken het mogelijk in alle seizoenen te spelen. Sinds 2005, twee nieuwe greens te ontdekken op de par 3's 14 en 16!

Opened back in 1909, this course has been redesigned by Hawtree in the 1950s. Lack of space has resulted in a shortish course and out-of-bounds on at least half of the holes. The estate is covered with some beautiful trees often more than 200 years old and makes for a very attractive setting. The main hazards are the bunkers but there are a number of ponds and ditches awaiting the mis-hit shot. The layout is clear and strategy obvious except on the 6th and 18th holes where the drive is blind. Approach shots are not too complex, either, and choice of club is more or less straightforward, except for the five elevated greens. This varied layout is not made for the very best players but the rest will have fun. Sandy soil and comprehensive irrigation facilities make this course playable virtually all year. Since 2005, two new greens at par 3s 14 and 16 have to be discovered!

Royal Latem Golf Club — 1909

Latemstraat 120
B - 9380 ST-MARTENS-LATEM

Office Secretariaat (32) 09 - 282 54 11
Pro shop Pro shop (32) 09 - 282 57 65
Fax Fax (32) 09 - 282 90 19
Web www.golf.be/latem
Situation Locatie Gent/Gand, 10 km
Annual closure Jaarlijkse sluiting no
Weekly closure Wekelijkse sluitingsdag no
Monday (maandag): restaurant closed

Fees main season Hoogseizoen tarieven	18 holes	
	Week days Weekdagen	We/Bank holidays We/Feestdagen
Individual Individueel	€ 60	€ 70
Couple Paar	€ 120	€ 140

Juniors: – 50%

Caddie Caddie no — **Electric Trolley** Electrische trolley no
Buggy Buggy yes — **Clubs** Clubs no
Credit cards Creditcards
VISA - Eurocard - Mastercard

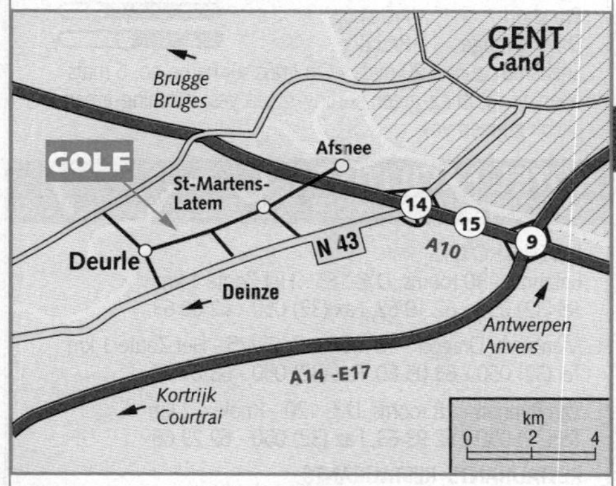

Access Toegang : E40 Brussel-Oostende,
Exit (Sortie) 14, N43 → Kortrijk, → Golf
Map 1 on page 92 Auto kaart 1 Blz 92

GOLF COURSE — BAAN — 15/20

Site Terrein
Maintenance Onderhoud
Architect Architect Fred Hawtree
Type Type baan forest, residential
Relief Reliëf
Water in play Waterhazards
Exp. to wind Windgevoelig
Trees in play Bomen

Scorecard Scorekaart	Chp. Back tees	Mens Heren	Ladies Damen
Length Lengte	5767	5767	5143
Par	72	72	72
Slope system	123	123	123

Advised golfing ability Aanbevolen golfvaardigheid 0 12 24 36
Hcp required Vereiste hcp 36 weekdays, 28 We

CLUB HOUSE & AMENITIES — CLUB HOUSE EN ANNEXEN — 8/10

Pro shop Pro shop
Driving range Oefenbaan
Sheltered overdekt 14 mats - On grass op gras no - Putting-green putting-green yes - Pitching-green pitching-green yes

HOTEL FACILITIES — HOTELS IN OMGEVING — 6/10

HOTELS HOTELS
Auberge du Pêcheur - Sint-Martens 1,5 km
32 rooms, D € 140
Tel (32) 09 - 282 31 44, Fax (32) 09 - 282 90 58

Novotel Centrum - 114 rooms, D € 145 - Gent 10 km
Tel (32) 09 - 224 22 30, Fax (32) 09 - 224 32 95

Chamade - 45 rooms, D € 125 - Gent 10 km
Tel (32) 09 - 220 15 15, Fax (32) 09 - 221 97 66

RESTAURANTS RESTAURANTS
Auberge du Pêcheur - Sint-Martens 1,5 km
Tel (32) 09 - 282 31 44
Jan van den Bon - Gent 10 km - Tel (32) 09 - 221 90 85
De 3 Biggetjes - Gent 10 km - Tel (32) 09 - 224 46 48

Royal Zoute

17	7	7

Royal Zoute est un club centenaire, mais son parcours a subi bien des vicissitudes, devant être entièrement reconstruit après la seconde Guerre Mondiale. Si la signature d'Harry Colt n'est plus vraiment flagrante, les auteurs en ont évidemment subi l'influence, et la qualité du tracé est peu contestable. En apparence, Royal Zoute n'est pas trop difficile, en tout cas lorsque le haut rough n'est pas trop proche, mais c'est un formidable défi quand le vent se met à souffler. Les difficultés ne sont jamais cachées, comme c'est parfois le cas avec les links, on saura ainsi où placer son départ pour mieux préparer le coup suivant. Les greens sont généralement rapides et bien modelés, défendus avec intelligence et subtilité. Le chemin le plus direct est clairement défini entre les dunes et les arbres, mais ne prenez pas trop vite confiance en vous, les fairways roulants peuvent réserver des positions de balle inconfortables. Un parcours d'un grand classicisme.

Royal Zoute is a venerable age-old golf club but the actual course has had an eventful career and was even completely rebuilt after World War II. While the Harry Colt trademark has faded somewhat, the more recent architects were obviously under his influence and the quality of this layout is unquestionable. Royal Zoute does not look too difficult on the outside, at least when the tall rough is some distance away, but it is a tremendous challenge when the wind blows. The difficulties are never hidden away, as is sometimes the case with links courses, so you know where to place the drive for an easier second shot. The greens are by and large slick and well contoured and the way their defence is a lesson in subtlety and intelligence. The quickest way home is clearly outlined between the dunes and trees, but whatever you do don't get over-confident; these fast-rolling fairways can leave your ball lying in some rather awkward positions. All things considered, a classic course.

Royal Zoute Golf Club — 1945

Caddiespad 14
B - 8300 KNOKKE-ZOUTE

Office	Secrétariat	(32) 050 - 60 12 27
Pro shop	Pro-shop	(32) 050 - 60 19 60
Fax	Fax	(32) 050 - 62 30 29
Web	www.zoute.be	
Situation	Situation	close to Knokke-Heist
Annual closure	Fermeture annuelle	no
Weekly closure	Fermeture hebdomadaire	no
Fees main season	Tarifs haute saison	18 holes

	Week days Semaine	We/Bank holidays We/Férié
Individual Individuel	€ 95	€ 95
Couple Couple	€ 190	€ 190

Juniors: – 50%

Caddie Caddie yes — **Electric Trolley** Chariot électrique yes
Buggy Voiturette yes — **Clubs** Clubs yes
Credit cards Cartes de crédit no

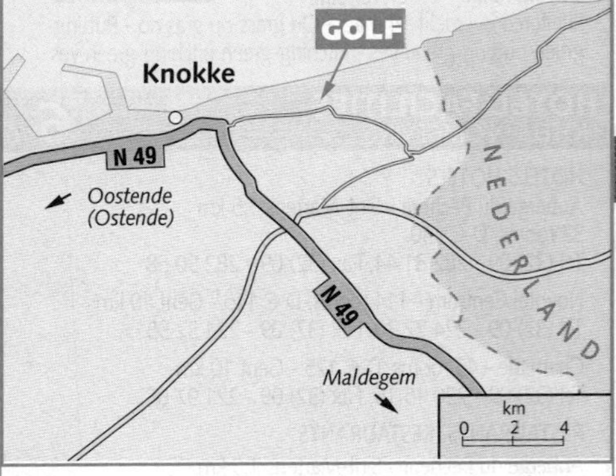

Access Accès : Knokke-Heist (Knokke-le-Zoute)
Map 1 on page 92 Carte 1 Page 92

GOLF COURSE — PARCOURS — 17/20

Site	Site	
Maintenance	Entretien	
Architect	Architecte	unknown
Type	Type	links
Relief	Relief	
Water in play	Eau en jeu	
Exp. to wind	Exposé au vent	
Trees in play	Arbres en jeu	

Scorecard Carte de score	Chp. Chp.	Mens Mess.	Ladies Da.
Length Long.	6172	6172	5292
Par	72	72	72
Slope system	132	132	130

Advised golfing ability Niveau de jeu recommandé — 0 12 24 36
Hcp required Handicap exigé — 20 Men, 24 Ladies

CLUB HOUSE & AMENITIES — CLUB HOUSE ET ANNEXES — 7/10

Pro shop Pro-shop
Driving range Practice
Sheltered couvert 20 mats - On grass sur herbe no, 6 mats open air - Putting-green putting-green yes - Pitching-green pitching green yes

HOTEL FACILITIES — ENVIRONNEMENT HOTELIER — 7/10

HOTELS HÔTELS

Britannia - 30 rooms, D € 165 - Het Zoute 1 km
Tel (32) 050 - 62 10 62, Fax (32) 050 - 62 00 63

Manoir du Dragon - 16 rooms, D € 275 - Het Zoute 1 km
Tel (32) 050 - 63 05 80, Fax (32) 050 - 63 05 90

Van Bunnen - 18 rooms, D € 120 - Knokke 2 km
Tel (32) 050 - 62 93 63, Fax (32) 050 - 62 29 66

RESTAURANTS RESTAURANTS

Esmeralda - Albertstrand 4 km - Tel (32) 050 - 60 33 66
De Oosthoek - Het Zoute 1 km - Tel (32) 050 - 62 23 33
De Savoye - Knokke 2 km - Tel (32) 050 - 62 23 61

Sart-Tilman

16 | 7 | 7

Il y a des parcours de golf qui paraissent mieux adaptés que d'autres à certaines formules de jeu. Ainsi, celui-ci est l'un des meilleurs parcours de match-play de Belgique. La longueur de certains trous (dont quelques terribles par 4), leur relief raisonnable et naturel, la présence insistante des arbres, et des greens diaboliques le rendent difficile à scorer, notamment pour les joueurs de moins de 12 de handicap, qui pourront vraiment y tester leur jeu. Il faut établir sa stratégie dès le départ en fonction des positions de drapeau. Son relief mesuré, son excellent rythme, son honnêteté et la beauté du site traduisent bien le génie de son architecte Tom Simpson. Le lac du 14, qui cassait l'harmonie du dessin a été heureusement supprimé. La qualité de l'entretien ajoute encore au plaisir : Le Royal Sart-Tilman mérite un large détour pour sa franchise, son intérêt, son absence de "vices cachés", son confort général et son ambiance chaleureuse.

This is one of Belgium's finest match-play courses. The length of some holes (some pretty challenging par 4s), the measured, natural relief, the looming presence of trees and devilishly tricky greens make scoring a tough business, especially for players with a handicap under 12, who will find this a real test. Game strategy must be set before starting out and be geared to pin positions. The measured relief and excellent balance, plus the course's fairness and the beauty of the site are a good reflection on the genius of architect Tom Simpson. The lake on the 14th, which broke the harmony of the layout, has been filled in. The standard of maintenance only enhances the enjoyment of playing here. Royal Sart-Tilman is well worth the time and journey for its openness, appeal, absence of hidden vices, general pleasantness and warm atmosphere.

Royal Golf Club du Sart-Tilman — 1939

Route du Condroz, 541
B - 4031 ANGLEUR-LIEGE

Office Secrétariat (32) 04 - 336 20 21
Pro shop Pro-shop (32) 04 - 336 58 00
Fax Fax (32) 04 - 337 20 26
Web www.golf.be/sarttilman
Situation Situation Liège/Luik, 5 km
Annual closure Fermeture annuelle no
Weekly closure Fermeture hebdomadaire no
Monday (lundi): Pro-shop closed

Fees main season Tarifs haute saison — 18 holes

	Week days Semaine	We/Bank holidays We/Férié
Individual Individuel	€ 45	€ 60
Couple Couple	€ 90	€ 120

Caddie Caddie no — **Electric Trolley** Chariot électrique no
Buggy Voiturette yes — **Clubs** Clubs no
Credit cards Cartes de crédit
VISA - Eurocard - Mastercard - AMEX - DC

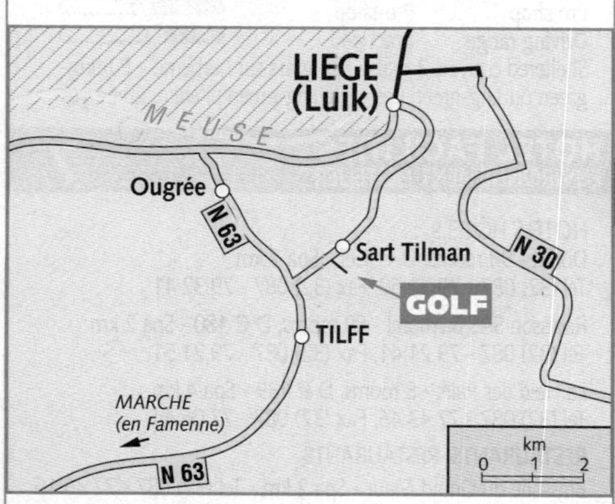

Access Accès : N63 Liège - Marche
Map 1 on page 93 Carte 1 Page 93

GOLF COURSE — PARCOURS — 16/20

Site Site
Maintenance Entretien
Architect Architecte Tom Simpson
Type Type parkland, hilly
Relief Relief
Water in play Eau en jeu
Exp. to wind Exposé au vent
Trees in play Arbres en jeu

Scorecard Carte de score	Chp. Chp.	Mens Mess.	Ladies Da.
Length Long.	5994	5687	4891
Par	72	72	72
Slope system	125	121	122

Advised golfing ability Niveau de jeu recommandé 0 12 24 36
Hcp required Handicap exigé 36

CLUB HOUSE & AMENITIES — CLUB HOUSE ET ANNEXES — 7/10

Pro shop Pro-shop
Driving range Practice
Sheltered couvert 10 mats - On grass sur herbe no, 7 mats open air - Putting-green putting-green yes - Pitching-green pitching green yes

HOTEL FACILITIES — ENVIRONNEMENT HOTELIER — 7/10

HOTELS HÔTELS
Mercure - 105 rooms, D € 175 - Liège 5 km
Tel (32) 04 - 221 77 11, Fax (32) 04 - 221 77 01

Bedford- 149 rooms, D € 235 - Liège 5 km
Tel (32) 04 - 228 81 11, Fax (32) 04 - 227 45 75

Holiday Inn - 219 rooms, D € 205 - Liège 5 km
Tel (32) 04 - 349 20 00, Fax (32) 04 - 343 48 10

RESTAURANTS RESTAURANTS
Max - Liège 5 km - Tel (32) 04 - 222 08 59
La Ciboulette - Flemalle 6 km - Tel (32) 04 - 275 19 65
La Petite Table - Rocourt 7 km - Tel (32) 04 - 239 19 00

Spa (Les Fagnes)

17 | 7 | 7

La signature de Tom Simpson est une garantie de parcours technique et stratégique. De relief modéré, c'est un des bons exemples d'architecture classique "inland", où il faut maîtriser l'ensemble de son jeu pour éviter les bois, les roughs et autres bunkers, admirablement disposés. Le placement du drive est essentiel, notamment sur quatre longs par 4, mais le travail ne s'arrête pas là, car les greens sont bien défendus, leurs surfaces assez subtiles à lire. Dans un site d'une parfaite tranquillité, on a l'impression de prendre une retraite pour méditer non seulement sur le golf, mais aussi sur l'intelligente sobriété de l'architecture, révélant une connaissance parfaite des joueurs de tous niveaux, mais sans jamais dissimuler les pièges. Exigeant, ce parcours donne un plaisir que l'on souhaite retrouver très souvent. Les 12 (par 5), 7 et 15 (par 4) sont de pures merveilles. Et l'arrosage automatique a nettement amélioré l'ensemble.

The Tom Simpson label is the guarantee of a technical and strategic course. This moderately hilly layout is one of the classic examples of inland architecture where every part of your game has to be in shape to avoid the woods, rough and admirably located bunkers. Placing the tee-shot is essential, especially on the four long par 4s, but the job doesn't stop there because the greens are well defended and the putting surfaces tricky to read. On a site of perfect tranquility, you get the impression of being in a sanctuary from where to meditate not only about the course but also about the smart discretion of a layout which reveals good insight into every golfing ability but never conceals the traps. It is a demanding course but an enjoyable one, too. The type you like to come back and play again and again. The 7th, 12th and 15th holes are architectural masterpieces. And the automatic watering system has made the course even better.

Royal Golf Club des Fagnes — 1930

Avenue de l'Hippodrome, 1
B - 4900 SPA

Office	Secrétariat	(32) 087 - 79 30 30
Pro shop	Pro-shop	(32) 087 - 79 30 32
Fax	Fax	(32) 087 - 79 30 39
Web	www.golf.be/fagnes	
Situation	Situation	Spa (pop. 9 953), 2 km
Annual closure	Fermeture annuelle	no
Weekly closure	Fermeture hebdomadaire	no

Fees main season Tarifs haute saison	18 holes	
	Week days Semaine	**We/Bank holidays** We/Férié
Individual Individuel	€ 60	€ 67
Couple Couple	€ 120	€ 134

Caddie Caddie no — **Electric Trolley** Chariot électrique no
Buggy Voiturette yes — **Clubs** Clubs no
Credit cards Cartes de crédit
VISA - Eurocard - Mastercard

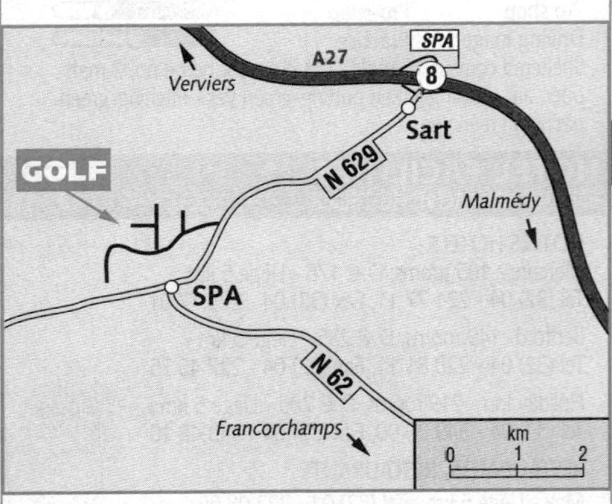

Access Accès : Autoroute des Ardennes,
Exit (Sortie) Spa → Golf
Map 1 on page 93 Carte 1 Page 93

GOLF COURSE — PARCOURS — 17/20

Site	Site	
Maintenance	Entretien	
Architect	Architecte	Tom Simpson
Type	Type	parkland, hilly
Relief	Relief	
Water in play	Eau en jeu	
Exp. to wind	Exposé au vent	
Trees in play	Arbres en jeu	

Scorecard Carte de score	**Chp.** Chp.	**Mens** Mess.	**Ladies** Da.
Length Long.	6040	5671	4858
Par	72	72	72
Slope system	130	126	119

Advised golfing ability Niveau de jeu recommandé: 0 12 24 36
Hcp required Handicap exigé: 36

CLUB HOUSE & AMENITIES — CLUB HOUSE ET ANNEXES — 7/10

Pro shop Pro-shop
Driving range Practice
Sheltered couvert 2 mats - On grass sur herbe no - Putting-green putting-green yes - Pitching-green pitching green yes

HOTEL FACILITIES — ENVIRONNEMENT HOTELIER — 7/10

HOTELS HÔTELS

Dorint - 98 rooms, D € 195 - Spa 2 km
Tel (32) 087 - 79 32 50, Fax (32) 087 - 79 32 41

Radisson SAS Balmoral - 89 rooms, D € 180 - Spa 2 km
Tel (32) 087 - 79 21 41, Fax (32) 087 - 79 21 51

La Heid des Pairs - 8 rooms, D € 139 - Spa 4 km
Tel (32) 087 - 77 43 46, Fax (32) 087 - 77 06 44

RESTAURANTS RESTAURANTS

Brasserie du Grand Maur - Spa 2 km - Tel (32) 087 - 77 36 16
Le Petit Normand - Sart 6 km - Tel (32) 087 - 47 49 04
L'Art de Vivre - Spa 2 km - Tel (32) 087 - 77 04 44
Les Santons - Sart 6 km - Tel (32) 087 - 47 43 15

Spiegelven

14 | 7 | 8

Een terrein dat een juist uitgebalanceerd spel vraagt. De eerste 9 holes, in de bossen, eisen veel nauwkeurigheid en aandacht bij het plaatsen van de drives. De laatste 9 liggen temidden van de heide, en zijn ook langer, meer bepaald drie van de par 4. De moeilijkheden, fairway bunkers en waterhindernissen, zijn goed zichtbaar en op een slimme manier gesitueerd; de architect, Ron Kirby, had een goed inzicht in de mogelijkheden van de spelers, en dit op verschillende niveaus. Hij heeft tegelijk echter ook zoveel mogelijk het natuurlijke uitzicht van het terrein proberen te bewaren, en het prachtig geïntegreerd. De perfecte uitdunning van het onderhout is opmerkelijk. De greens zijn mooi ontworpen, niet te golvend, maar de speler moet, bij het bepalen van zijn strategie, rekening houden met de plaatsing van de vlaggen. Het terrein is tamelijk heuvelachtig, maar kan gemakkelijk te voet worden gespeeld. Geplaatst op een voormalige stortplaats, heeft dit terrein zeer vlug een plaats verworven onder de goede, recente realisaties, die waar men herinneringen aan overhoudt, behalve van de 7 de hole.

A course that demands a solid all-round game. The front nine in the woods call for precision in the extreme and a lot of care when placing the tee-shot. The back nine are in the heather and are longer, particularly three of the par 4s. The difficulties, fairway bunkers and water hazards are clear to see and astutely located, revealing designer Ron Kirby's insight when it comes to understanding golfers of differing abilities. At the same time, he has preserved the course's natural look as far as possible and the way it blends in with its surroundings is exemplary. The undergrowth has been conveniently cleared to avoid penalising players too heavily, the greens are well designed and slope quite a bit, but the pin positions must be watched carefully if you want to establish an effective game strategy. The site is hilly but easily walkable.

Spiegelven Golf Club Genk — 1988

Wiemesmeerstraat 109
B - 3600 GENK

Office Secretariaat (32) 089 - 35 96 16
Pro shop Pro shop (32) 089 - 36 20 60
Fax Fax (32) 089 - 36 41 84
Web www.golf.be/spiegelven
Situation Locatie Genk, 10 km
Hasselt (pop. 64 722), 20 km
Annual closure Jaarlijkse sluiting no
Weekly closure Wekelijkse sluitingsdag no

Fees main season Hoogseizoen tarieven	18 holes	
	Week days Weekdagen	**We/Bank holidays** We/Feestdagen
Individual Individueel	€ 45	€ 55
Couple Paar	€ 90	€ 110

Juniors: – 50%

Caddie Caddie no — **Electric Trolley** Electrische trolley no
Buggy Buggy yes — **Clubs** Clubs yes
Credit cards Creditcards
Only in Pro shop & Club house. Club house : DC - AMEX

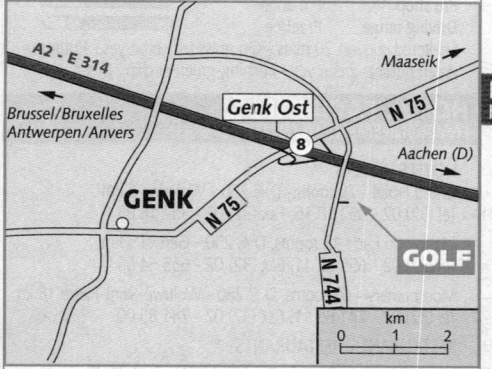

Access Toegang : E314, Exit 32, N744 → Zutendal, Golf
Map 1 on page 93 Auto kaart 1 Blz 93

GOLF COURSE — BAAN — 14/20

Site Terrein
Maintenance Onderhoud
Architect Architect — Ron Kirby
Type Type baan — forest
Relief Reliëf
Water in play Waterhazards
Exp. to wind Windgevoelig
Trees in play Bomen

Scorecard Scorekaart	**Chp.** Back tees	**Mens** Heren	**Ladies** Damen
Length Lengte	6098	5732	4978
Par	72	72	72
Slope system	133	130	125

Advised golfing ability Aanbevolen golfvaardigheid — 0 12 24 36
Hcp required Vereiste hcp — 36

CLUB HOUSE & AMENITIES — CLUB HOUSE EN ANNEXEN — 7/10

Pro shop Pro shop
Driving range Oefenbaan
Sheltered overdekt 9 mats - On grass op gras yes - Putting-green putting-green yes - Pitching-green pitching-green yes

HOTEL FACILITIES — HOTELS IN OMGEVING — 8/10

HOTELS HOTELS
Golfhotel La Résidence - on site
70 rooms, D € 85
Tel (32) 089 - 35 58 28, Fax (32) 089 - 35 58 03

NH Genk - 83 rooms, D € 150 - Genk 3 km
Tel (32) 089 - 36 41 50, Fax (32) 089 - 36 41 51

Atlantis - Genk 5 km
24 rooms, D € 125
Tel (32) 089 - 35 65 51, Fax (32) 089 - 35 35 29

RESTAURANTS RESTAURANTS
Da Vinci - Genk 5 km - Tel (32) 089 - 30 60 59
't Konijntje - Genk 5 km - Tel (32) 089 - 35 26 45
St Maarten - Genk 5 km - Tel (32) 089 - 35 26 57

Waterloo *La Marache*

16	8	7

Les Français ne trouveront guère que Waterloo soit une "morne plaine" (le retour est assez vallonné), et le parcours de "La Marache", plus ancien parcours du "Lion" voisin, doit être abordé avec prudence et sagesse. Très bon exemple de l'architecture de Fred Hawtree du début des années 60, le tracé vient d'être complètement revu par son fils, Martin, pour apporter plus de modernité et donc plus de difficulté aux zones de greens. Celle-ci ont été complètement "reliftées" de façon à rendre les seconds coups plus intéressants, plus longs et donc plus complexes. Les contours de greens obligent à présent à posséder un petit jeu à toute épreuve. Pour le reste, l'environnement boisé et vallonné est toujours aussi plaisant. Les bons et longs drivers pourront cependant s'exprimer, sans trop de souci des tragédies bien plus graves dont Waterloo a été le cadre autrefois ! Ce complexe s'étend au total sur 150 hectares, et ses équipements sont dignes de ces dimensions. La Marache est à nouveau redevenu un terrain de championnat !

Even the French would now hardly describe Waterloo as the "cheerless plain" it was once said to be (the back 9 are laid out over rolling terrain) and "La Marache" should be approached with caution and common sense. A fine example of Hawtree architecture from the 1960s, the course has been completely restyled by his son Martin, updating the whole layout and making the greens much tougher in the process. They have been completely restyled in such a way as to make the second shot more interesting, longer and so more complicated. Nowadays you need a really hot short game on and around the putting surfaces here. For the rest, the woody rolling landscape is as pleasant as ever. Good drivers of the ball can let rip without too much to worry about, and anyway Waterloo has seen worst disasters (for some) than wayward tee-shots! The full complex stretches over 370 acres and facilities are excellent. The Marache has regained its status of championship course.

Royal Waterloo Golf Club — 1960

Vieux Chemin de Wavre 50
B - 1380 OHAIN

Office	Secrétariat	(32) 02 - 633 18 50
Pro shop	Pro-shop	(32) 02 - 633 43 16
Fax	Fax	(32) 02 - 633 28 66
Web	www.royalwaterloogolfclub.be	
Situation	Situation	Bruxelles/Brussel, 20 km
Annual closure	Fermeture annuelle	no
Weekly closure	Fermeture hebdomadaire	no

Monday (lundi): restaurant closed

Fees main season / Tarifs haute saison	18 holes	
	Week days / Semaine	We/Bank holidays / We/Férié
Individual Individuel	€ 90	*
Couple Couple	€ 180	*

* We, members only / Juniors: € 20

Caddie Caddie on request **Electric Trolley** Chariot électrique yes

Buggy Voiturette yes (on request) **Clubs** Clubs yes

Credit cards Cartes de crédit
VISA - Eurocard - Mastercard

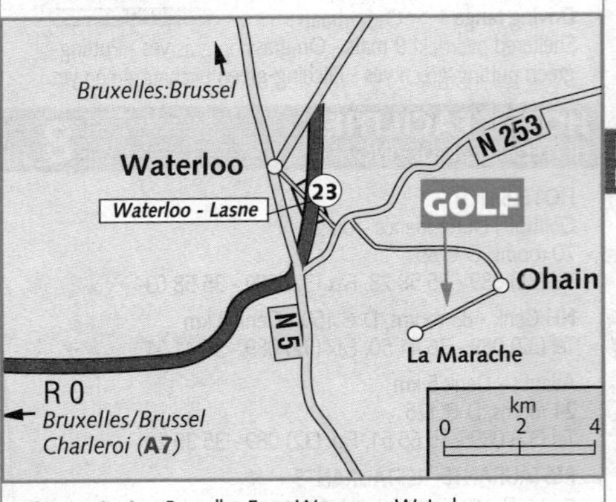

Access Accès : Bruxelles E, → Wavre, → Waterloo
Map 1 on page 92 Carte 1 Page 92

GOLF COURSE — PARCOURS 16/20

Site	Site	
Maintenance	Entretien	
Architect	Architecte	Fred Hawtree Martin Hawtree
Type	Type	country, parkland
Relief	Relief	
Water in play	Eau en jeu	
Exp. to wind	Exposé au vent	
Trees in play	Arbres en jeu	

Scorecard / Carte de score	Chp. / Chp.	Mens / Mess.	Ladies / Da.
Length Long.	6235	5887	5277
Par	72	72	72
Slope system	128	125	127

Advised golfing ability / Niveau de jeu recommandé: 0 12 24 36
Hcp required / Handicap exigé: 24

CLUB HOUSE & AMENITIES — CLUB HOUSE ET ANNEXES 8/10

Pro shop — Pro-shop
Driving range — Practice
Sheltered couvert 20 mats - On grass sur herbe yes - Putting-green putting-green yes - Pitching-green pitching green yes

HOTEL FACILITIES — ENVIRONNEMENT HOTELIER 7/10

HOTELS HÔTELS

Grand Hôtel - 79 rooms, D € 250 - Waterloo 6 km
Tel (32) 02 - 352 18 15, Fax (32) 02 - 352 18 88

Manoir du Lac - 13 rooms, D € 250 - Genval 5 km
Tel (32) 02 - 655 63 11, Fax (32) 02 - 655 64 55

Montgomery - 63 rooms, D € 280 - Woluwé-Saint-Pierre 18 km
Tel (32) 02 - 741 85 11, Fax (32) 02 - 741 85 00

RESTAURANTS RESTAURANTS

Le Dernier Tri - Ohain 3 km - Tel (32) 02 - 633 34 20
Auberge de la Roseraie - Ohain 3 km - Tel (32) 02 - 633 13 74
Rêve Richelle - Waterloo 6 km - Tel (32) 02 - 354 82 84
Yves Lemercier - Waterloo 6 km - Tel (32) 02 - 387 17 78

Waterloo *Le Lion*

16	8	7

Le Royal Waterloo est l'un des grands clubs du continent, avec un joli site naturel au charme typique du Brabant Wallon, et un fameux nom ! Son parcours du "Lion" manquait passablement de mordant, mais les interventions décisives d'European Golf Design en ont rehaussé considérablement la qualité. On peut toujours souhaiter une refonte plus décisive des départs et une révision du 14, mais ce sont des détails par rapport au plaisir éprouvé à jouer ici. Joliment paysagé, très bien équilibré dans son déroulement comme dans la répartition des obstacles, exigeant techniquement pour qui cherche à scorer,en particulier depuis les départs arrière, c'est aussi un parcours tout à fait jouable pour les moins ambitieux. La qualité de l'entretien ajoute encore à l'agrément du site. Si le visiteur est assez pressé pour ne passer qu'une journée ici, on lui conseillera le début de l'été, en mettant les deux parcours de Waterloo à son programme.

Royal Waterloo is one of the great continental golf courses stretching over a pretty and natural site which drains well and sports a famous name. This "Lion" course had become a little tame until a number of decisive measures taken by European Golf Design considerably enhanced overall standards. We would perhaps like to see some of the tee areas re-designed and maybe a re-styling of the 14th hole but these are mere details when compared to the pleasure of playing here. The course is prettily landscaped and very well balanced in lay-out and for the placing of hazards. Although technically challenging for golfers looking to card a good score, especially when playing from the back tees, it is still perfectly playable for the less skilled golfer. The excellence of maintenance also does much to enhance the course's overall appeal. If you are passing through and have just one day to spare, come here in early summer and plan on playing both courses at Waterloo.

Royal Waterloo Golf Club 1985

Vieux Chemin de Wavre 50
B - 1380 OHAIN

Office	Secrétariat	(32) 02 - 633 18 50
Pro shop	Pro-shop	(32) 02 - 633 43 16
Fax	Fax	(32) 02 - 633 28 66
Web	www.royalwaterloogolfclub.be	
Situation	Situation	Bruxelles/Brussel, 20 km
Annual closure	Fermeture annuelle	no
Weekly closure	Fermeture hebdomadaire	no

Monday (lundi): restaurant closed

Fees main season Tarifs haute saison	Week days Semaine	We/Bank holidays We/Férié
Individual Individuel	€ 90	*
Couple Couple	€ 180	*

18 holes

* We, members only / Juniors: € 20

Caddie Caddie on request **Electric Trolley** Chariot électrique yes

Buggy Voiturette yes (on request) **Clubs** Clubs yes

Credit cards Cartes de crédit
VISA - Eurocard - Mastercard

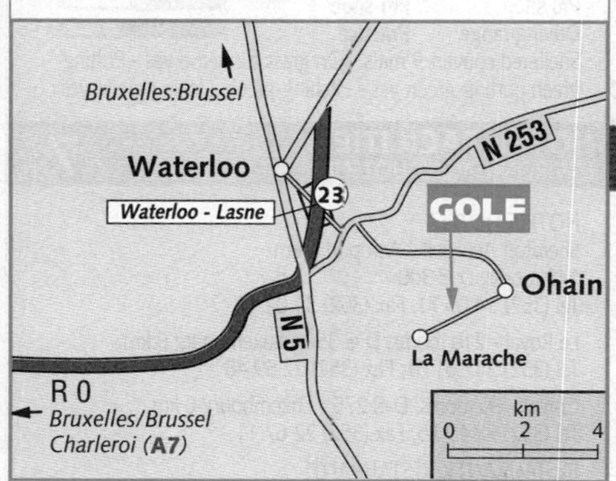

Access Accès : Bruxelles E, → Wavre, → Waterloo

Map 1 on page 92 Carte 1 Page 92

GOLF COURSE
PARCOURS — 16/20

Site	Site	
Maintenance	Entretien	
Architect	Architecte	Paul Rolin European Golf Design
Type	Type	inland
Relief	Relief	
Water in play	Eau en jeu	
Exp. to wind	Exposé au vent	
Trees in play	Arbres en jeu	

Scorecard / Carte de score	Chp. / Chp.	Mens / Mess.	Ladies / Da.
Length Long.	6215	5823	5006
Par	72	72	72
Slope system	128	125	130

Advised golfing ability / Niveau de jeu recommandé: 0 12 24 36

Hcp required Handicap exigé 24

CLUB HOUSE & AMENITIES
CLUB HOUSE ET ANNEXES — 8/10

Pro shop Pro-shop

Driving range Practice

Sheltered couvert 20 mats - On grass sur herbe yes - Putting-green putting-green yes - Pitching-green pitching green yes

HOTEL FACILITIES
ENVIRONNEMENT HOTELIER — 7/10

HOTELS HÔTELS

Grand Hôtel - 79 rooms, D € 250 - Waterloo 6 km
Tel (32) 02 - 352 18 15, Fax (32) 02 - 352 18 88

Manoir du Lac - 13 rooms, D € 250 - Genval 5 km
Tel (32) 02 - 655 63 11, Fax (32) 02 - 655 64 55

Montgomery - 63 rooms, D € 280 - Woluwé-Saint-Pierre 18 km
Tel (32) 02 - 741 85 11, Fax (32) 02 - 741 85 00

RESTAURANTS RESTAURANTS

Le Dernier Tri - Ohain 3 km - Tel (32) 02 - 633 34 20
Auberge de la Roseraie - Ohain 3 km - Tel (32) 02 - 633 13 74
Rêve Richelle - Waterloo 6 km - Tel (32) 02 - 354 82 84
Yves Lemercier - Waterloo 6 km - Tel (32) 02 - 387 17 78

Grand Ducal de Luxembourg

14	6	7

La faible longueur du "Grand Ducal" plaira à la grande majorité des joueurs de tous niveaux. Mais que les bons frappeurs se méfient, les arbres sont très beaux, mais les éviter constitue la difficulté essentielle d'un parcours dont l'esthétique très britannique (quelques "cross-bunkers") coïncide de bien avec les traditions golfiques cultivées ici. Les bunkers sont assez nombreux, mais défendent les greens sans méchanceté aucune. Ceux-ci sont de dimensions très raisonnables, mais leurs pentes exigent de l'attention avant de jouer. Le vallonnement du terrain reste modéré, il intervient surtout au 6, un long par 4 en montée, et seul trou vraiment difficile. En revanche, le 18, un par 5, laissera une bonne impression, car il présente une bonne occasion de birdie. En résumé, un parcours où le driver n'est pas indispensable, généralement en bon état, et très agréable quand on visite le pays. Cependant, les avions de l'aéroport tout proche manquent parfois de respect au golf...

The short yardage of the "Grand Ducal" will appeal to the vast majority of golfers of all levels. Yet the big-hitters should beware: the trees might look a pretty picture but avoiding them is one of the main difficulties on a course whose very attractive and very British style (with a few cross-bunkers to boot) perfectly reflects the golfing traditions nurtured in this part of the world. There are a lot of bunkers which defend the greens but are never unduly spiteful. The greens themselves are very reasonably sized but their slopes call for careful reading at all times. This is a moderately hilly course but is especially steep on the 6th, a long uphill 4-par and the only really tough hole. In contrast, the 18th, a par 5, should leave you liking the course because the birdie here is a definite possibility. In short, this is a course where the driver can easily stay in the bag. It is in good condition and very pleasant to play when you visit the "Grand Duché". Unfortunately, the planes from the neighbouring airport don't always respect the game of golf...

Golf Club Grand Ducal — 1936

Route de Trèves, 1
L - 2633 SENNINGERBERG

Office	Secrétariat	(352) 34 00 90-1
Pro shop	Pro-shop	(352) 34 83 94
Fax	Fax	(352) 34 83 91
Web	www.golfgrandducal.net	
Situation	Situation	Luxembourg, 6 km
Annual closure	Fermeture annuelle	no
Weekly closure	Fermeture hebdomadaire	no

Fees main season Tarifs haute saison		18 holes
	Week days Semaine	We/Bank holidays We/Férié
Individual Individuel	€ 50	*
Couple Couple	€ 100	*

* We: Members only

Caddie Caddie no — Electric Trolley Chariot électrique no
Buggy Voiturette no — Clubs Clubs yes
Credit cards Cartes de crédit no

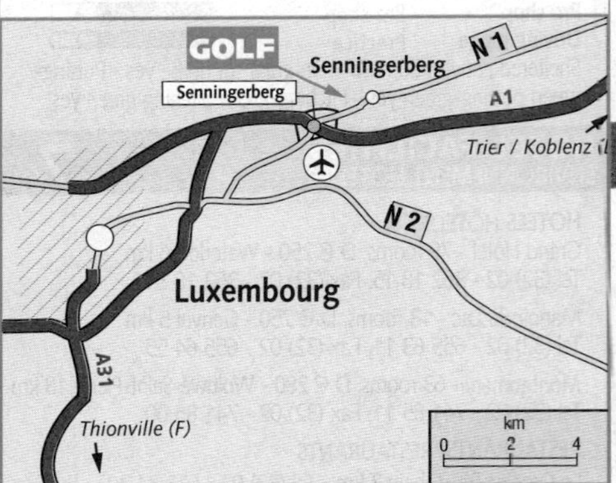

Access Accès : N1 Luxembourg → Airport (Aéroport)
Map 1 on page 93 Carte 1 Page 93

GOLF COURSE PARCOUR — 14/20

Site	Site	
Maintenance	Entretien	
Architect	Architecte	Tom Simpson
Type	Type	parkland
Relief	Relief	
Water in play	Eau en jeu	
Exp. to wind	Exposé au vent	
Trees in play	Arbres en jeu	

Scorecard Carte de score	Chp. Chp.	Mens Mess.	Ladies Da.
Length Long.	5782	5782	4870
Par	71	71	71
Slope system	129	125	127

Advised golfing ability Niveau de jeu recommandé: 0 12 24 36
Hcp required Handicap exigé: 28 Men, 32 Ladies

CLUB HOUSE & AMENITIES CLUB HOUSE ET ANNEXES — 6/10

Pro shop Pro-shop
Driving range Practice
Sheltered couvert 9 mats - On grass sur herbe yes - Putting-green putting-green yes - Pitching-green pitching green yes

HOTEL FACILITIES ENVIRONNEMENT HOTELIER — 7/10

HOTELS HÔTELS

Sheraton Aérogolf - Aéroport 1 km
148 rooms, D € 300
Tel (352) 34 05 71, Fax (352) 34 02 17

Le Royal - 210 rooms, D € 350 - Luxembourg 6 km
Tel (352) 241 61 61, Fax (352) 22 59 48

Cravat - 60 rooms, D € 275 - Luxembourg 6 km
Tel (352) 22 19 75, Fax (352) 22 67 11

RESTAURANTS RESTAURANTS

Clairefontaine - Luxembourg 6 km - Tel (352) 46 22 11
Le Grimpereau - Senningerberg 1 km - Tel (352) 43 67 87
Mosconi - Luxembourg 6 km - Tel (352) 54 69 94

Kikuoka

16	7	7

Sans atteindre des sommets, ce parcours créé en 1991 ne déçoit jamais. D'ailleurs, les joueurs professionnels du "Challenge Tour" en ont apprécié à la fois le "challenge" et la franchise. Sur chaque départ, on sait exactement où jouer, et les différences visuelles d'un trou à l'autre renouvellent constamment l'intérêt du jeu. Sans être sublime, le site est agréablement boisé et vallonné (facile à jouer à pied), souvent à flanc de côteau, et l'architecte en a utilisé habilement les contours. En l'absence d'arbres, quelques mouvements de terrain ont été créés, mais sans le côté spectaculaire qu'un von Hagge aurait pu donner à cet espace très ouvert. Les principaux obstacles sont les bunkers, qui sont près d'une centaine, certains de grande taille, et placés autant pour capter les balles égarées que pour définir les trous. De fait, le crayon d'Iwao Uematsu a subi des influences américaines, en particulier pour la forte défense des greens et les formes de ceux-ci. L'hôtel sur place ne peut que faire mieux connaître ce parcours.

Although not what you would call a top-flight course, this 1991 layout is great golfing every time. The pros on the Challenge Tour appreciated both the challenge and the openness of the course, as from each tee-box you know exactly where to play and the visual differences from one hole to the next keep it constantly interesting. The site is pleasantly wooded over lightly rolling terrain (easily walkable) often on the side of a hill, and the architect very cleverly used the natural topography. Where there are no trees he shifted a little earth, but without going to the lengths you might have found if someone like von Hagge had been let loose here. The main hazards are bunkers, almost a hundred in all, some of which are huge and placed to both snap up mis-hit shots and define the holes. As a result, the design of Iwao Uematsu has undergone a definite American influence, particularly concerning the well-guarded greens and the shape of the putting surfaces.

Kikuoka Country Club — 1991
Scheierhaff
L - 5412 CANACH

Office	Secrétariat	(352) 35 61 35
Pro shop	Pro-shop	(352) 35 61 35
Fax	Fax	(352) 35 74 50
Web	www.kikuoka.lu	
Situation	Situation	Luxembourg, 17 km
Annual closure	Fermeture annuelle	no
Weekly closure	Fermeture hebdomadaire	no

Fees main season Tarifs haute saison	18 holes	
	Week days / Semaine	We/Bank holidays / We/Férié
Individual Individuel	€ 55	€ 70
Couple Couple	€ 110	€ 140

Caddie Caddie on request **Electric Trolley** Chariot électrique no
Buggy Voiturette yes **Clubs** Clubs yes
Credit cards Cartes de crédit
VISA - Eurocard - MasterCard - AMEX - DC

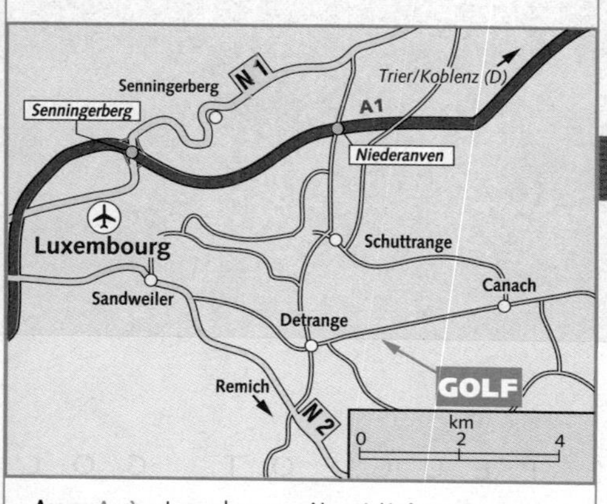

Access Accès : Luxembourg → Airport (Aréoport). E29 → Saarbrücken. At Sandweiler, N28 and CR 144 → Wormeldange, Golf on right hand side
Map 1 on page 93 Carte 1 Page 93

GOLF COURSE — PARCOUR 16/20

Site	Site	
Maintenance	Entretien	
Architect	Architecte	Iwao Uematsu
Type	Type	open country
Relief	Relief	
Water in play	Eau en jeu	
Exp. to wind	Exposé au vent	
Trees in play	Arbres en jeu	

Scorecard Carte de score	Chp. Chp.	Mens Mess.	Ladies Da.
Length Long.	6404	5896	5480
Par	72	72	72
Slope system	128	122	123

Advised golfing ability Niveau de jeu recommandé — 0 12 24 36
Hcp required Handicap exigé 35

CLUB HOUSE & AMENITIES — CLUB HOUSE ET ANNEXES 7/10

Pro shop Pro-shop
Driving range Practice
Sheltered couvert yes - On grass sur herbe yes - Putting-green putting-green yes - Pitching-green pitching green yes

HOTEL FACILITIES — ENVIRONNEMENT HOTELIER 7/10

HOTELS HÔTELS
Mercure Hotel - 74 rooms, D € 130 - on site
Tel (352) 26 35 41, Fax (352) 26 35 44 44

Hôtel des Vignes - 24 rooms, D € 98 - Remich 12 km
Tel (352) 69 91 49, Fax (352) 69 84 63

Bamberg's - 12 rooms, D € 90 - Ehnen 9 km
Tel (352) 76 00 22, Fax (352) 76 00 56

RESTAURANTS RESTAURANTS
Le Bouquet Garni - Luxembourg 17 km
Tel (352) 26 20 06 20

Speltz - Luxembourg 17 km - Tel (352) 47 49 50

Simmer - Ehnen 9 km - Tel (352) 76 00 30

DANMARK

DENMARK

Royal Oak

DENMARK

Denmark is the southernmost Scandinavian country and climate-wise is also the mildest. Having said that, the North and Baltic Seas are never far away and it can sometimes be very wet in this part of the world, with enough rain to ensure lush landscapes and thick grass. This is, of course, ideal for golf, a sport played by 131,000 Danes on 141 18-hole courses. Denmark boasts both inland and coastal courses, sometimes nestling on the country's many islands, or again close to seaside resorts. Anyone from southern Europe would need a lot of prompting to bathe in these cold waters, but the Danes are a hardy bunch and have produced some top world golfers, the best known of whom being Thomas Björn, Anders Hansen or Iben Tinning.

DANMARK

Danmark er det sydligste af de Skandisnaviske lande og kilmaet er det mildeste. Man skal imidlertid ikke ignorere at Vesterhavet og Østersøen aldrig er langt væk og vejret kan i denne del af verden tit være meget fugtig. Her falder nok regn til at landskabeter grønt og græsset er tæt og frodigt. Det er naturligtvis ideelt for golf, en sport som har 131,000 danske udøvere og her er ca. 141 18 huls golfbaner. Danmark har både inland og kyst golfbaner, links, og til tider er banen kreeret på en af de mange øer eller tæt på et af badestæderne. I Danmark er man aldrig mere end 30 km fra havet. Det kan være svært at få en sydeuropæer til at bade på disse kanter, men danskerne er robuste og flere top spillere i verdensklasse kommer herfra. Den bedst kendte er naturligtvis Thomas Bjørn, Anders Hansen, Iben Tinning.

CLASSIFICATION OF GOLF COURSES
KLASSIFICATION AF GOLFBANER

This classification gives priority consideration to the score awarded to the actual course.
Denne klassifikation giver prioritet til bedømmelsen af banens standard.

Within each score, the ranking is purely alphabetical

Course score / Klassifikation af golfbaner				Page / Side
17	8	7	Rungsted	133
16	8	6	Himmerland New Course	126
16	6	5	Holstebro	127
16	7	7	København Eremitagen	128
16	8	5	Læsø Seaside	129
16	5	5	Nordvestjysk	131
15	6	5	Esbjerg	124
15	4	7	Fanø	125
15	7	7	Møn	130
15	7	4	Royal Oak	132
15	4	7	Samsø	134
15	5	6	Sct. Knuds	135
15	7	7	Simon's	136
14	7	7	Vejle Blue + Red Slings	137

HOTEL FACILITIES
ENVIRONNEMENT HOTELIER
EINTEILUNG DES HOTELANGEBOTS DER UMGEBUNG

This classification gives priority consideration to the score awarded to the actual course.
Denne klassifikation giver prioritet til bedømmelsen af hotellets faciliteter.

		Hotel facility score / Hotel klassifikation		Page / Side
15	4	**7**	Fanø	125
16	7	**7**	København Eremitagen	128
15	7	**7**	Møn	130
17	8	**7**	Rungsted	133
15	4	**7**	Samsø	134
15	7	**7**	Simon's	136
14	7	**7**	Vejle Blue + Red Slings	137
16	8	**6**	Himmerland New Course	126
15	5	**6**	Sct. Knuds	135
15	6	**5**	Esbjerg	124
16	6	**5**	Holstebro	127
16	8	**5**	Læsø Seaside	129
16	5	**5**	Nordvestjysk	131
15	7	**4**	Royal Oak	132

RECOMMENDED GOLFING STAY
AMBELOVEN GOLF VACANTIE

Himmerland New Course	**16**	8	6	126
Holstebro	**16**	6	5	127
Rungsted	**17**	8	7	133

RECOMMENDED HOLIDAYS
AMBELOVEN VACANTIE-OORD

Esbjerg	**15**	6	5	124
Fanø	**15**	4	7	125
Læsø Seaside	**16**	8	5	129
Rungsted	**17**	8	7	133

Map No 1
Kort 1
km
0 10 20
NORDSØEN
(MER DU NORD)
Egersund
Bergen
Tórshavn
Hanstholm
Nordvestjysk
Frøstrup
Fierritslev
Nørre Vorupør
Thy
Thisted
Feggesund
Løgstør
Himmerland
Mors
Nykøbing M
Hurup
Thyborøn
Nissum Bredning
Hvidbjerg
Salling
Hvalpsund
Farsø
Rødding
Skive
Lemvig
Struer
Vinderup
Sahl
Torsminde
Nissum Fjord
Holstebro
Ulfborg
Avlum
Karup
JYLLAND
Ringkøbing
Herning
Ikast
Silkeborg
Hvide Sande
Videbæk
Ringkøbing Fjord
Holmslands Klit
Skjern
Tarm
Omme Å
S. Felding
Brande
Nørre Nebel
Ølgod
Give
Tørring
Grindsted
Jelling
Oksbøl
Billund
Vejle
Esbjerg
Varde
Oksby
Agerbæk
Egtved
Vejle
Fanø
Nordby
Holsted
Bramming
Vejen
Kolding
Harwich
Ribe
Rødding
Fanø Bugt
Royal Oak
Gram
Christiansfeld
Brøns
Rømø
Vojens
Toftlund
Haderslev
Skærbæk
Skrydstrup
Havneby
Sylt (D)
Løgumkloster
Sylt
List
Åbenrå
Rødekro
Højer
Tønder
Bylderup-Bov
Wester and
Tinglev
Gråsten
Klanxbüll
Kruså
Broager
Hörnum
Föhr
Niebüll
Glücksburg
Dagebüll
Leck
Flensburg
Amrum
Wyk
Nordfriesische Inseln
Wittdün
Tarp
Süderbrarup
Bredstedt
Nordstrand
Silberstedt
Husum
Schleswig
Treene
Kropp
Tönning
MICHELIN

123
Hjørring
Frederikshavn
Læsø Seaside
Göteborg (Sv)
Kungsbacka (Sv)
Kungsbacka
Varberg
Varberg (Sv)
Falkenberg
KATTEGAT
Anholt
Halmstad (Sv)
Halmstad
Båstad (Sv)
Torekov (Sv)
Mölle (Sv)
Höganäs
Vasatorp (Sv)
Simon's
Rya (Sv)
Helsingborg
Rungsted
Landskrona (Sv)
København
KØBENHAVN
Flommen (Sv)
Falsterbo (Sv)
Ljunghusen (Sv)
MALMÖ
Møn
Brønderslev
Vendsyssel
ÅLBORG
Ålborg Bugt
Himmerland
Hobro
Randers
Grenå
Djursland
ÅRHUS
Ebeltoft
Skanderborg
Horsens
Odder
Samsø
Kalundborg
Holbæk
Roskilde
Hillerød
Helsingør
Fredericia
Middelfart
ODENSE
Nyborg
Sct. Knuds
Svendborg
Langeland
Ærøskøbing
Slagelse
Sorø
Ringsted
Køge
Næstved
Vordingborg
Nakskov
Lolland
Maribo
Rødbyhavn
Puttgarden
Kieler Bucht
DANMARK
SJÆLLAND
FYN
Storebælt
Øresund
MICHELIN
d'après base de données au 1/1 500 000 - édition 2005.
Autorisation n°0501023.

Esbjerg

15	6	5

Vestjyllands marsk, sandklitter og strande langs Vesterhavet er ikke Danmarks golfmekka. Synd, for de baner, området byder på, er temmelig gode. Som nu for eksempel Esbjergs fine gamle mesterskabsbane, der som den altid er det, især når det blæser – ved DM i 1999 var en skrap test for de bedste spillere. Her bliver ikke lavet stribevis af 5 under par-runder! Banen er uden egentlige vand-hazarder, og der er heller ikke mange træer. Dens hovedforhindringer er en række meget velplacerede bunkers, især på de sidste ni huller, og så den altid tilstedeværende vind. Læg dertil, at hullerne er meget flade, og man kunne få det indtryk, at de er meget ens. Javist, men mere naturlig bane i så barske omgivelser skal man lede længe efter, i hvert fald i Danmark. Den er indbegrebet af underspillet charme, og man føler sig virkelig i pagt med naturen på runden. Ni relativt nye huller er med til at gøre et besøg mere varieret.

The west coast of Jutland is not the most popular area of Denmark for tourists, but it certainly has its share of romance with infinite stretches of moor-land which seem to merge with the sand dunes alongside the North Sea. The first good reason for coming here is the pretty medieval town of Ribe, a major trading centre and port from the Viking era. Another reason is this golf course, the only real seaside course in a country where you are never far from the sea. Strangely enough, there are no water hazards on this pretty layout. There are not many trees, either, and the main difficulties lie with some excellent bunkering, particularly in the fairways on the back 9, and the ever present wind. Should we add that the holes are very flat, you might get the impression that they are all much the same. In actual fact, what is a very natural course in a rather rough setting is a picture of subtlety and charm, helped by the impression of isolation you get when playing here. An extra 9 holes enhance these qualities still further.

Esbjerg Golfklub — 1964

Sønderhedevej 11
DK - 6710 ESBJERG V

Office	Sekretariat	(45) 75 26 92 19
Pro shop	Pro-shop	(45) 75 26 92 72
Fax	Fax	(45) 75 26 94 19
Web	www.esbjerg-golfklub.dk	
Situation	Sted	Esbjerg, 15 km
Annual closure	Årlig lukkeperiode	no
Weekly closure	Ugentlig lukketid	no

Fees main season Priser i højsæson	Week days Hverdage	We/Bank holidays Helligdage
		Full day
Individual Individuelt	DKr 350	DKr 350
Couple Par	DKr 700	DKr 700

Juniors: DKr 150

Caddie Caddie no — Electric Trolley Elektrisk golfvogn yes
Buggy Golf car yes — Clubs Koeller yes
Credit cards Kreditkord
VISA - Eurocard - DC

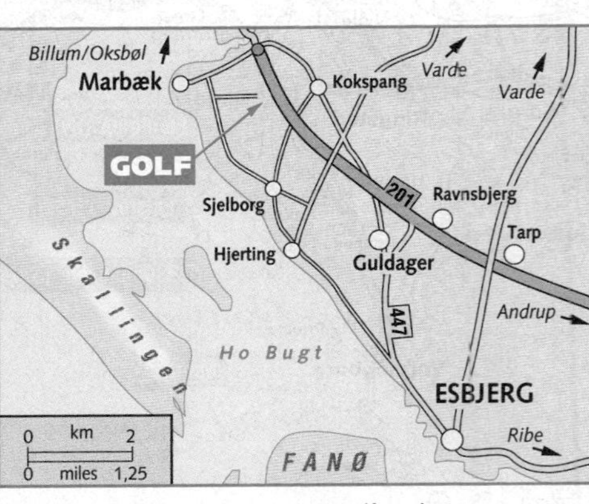

Access Adgang : E20, Exit → 463 → Blåvand. → Marbæk/Golf
Map 1 on page 122 Kort 1 på side 122

GOLF COURSE 15/20
GOLF BANE

Site	Sted	
Maintenance	Vedligeholdelse	
Architect	Arkitekt	Frederik Dreyer
Type	Type	seaside course
Relief	Lettelse	
Water in play	Vand i spil	
Exp. to wind	Udsat for vind	
Trees in play	Træer i spil	

Scorecard Skorekort	Chp. Back tee	Mens Herre tee	Ladies Dame tee
Length Længde	6317	5638	4858
Par	71	71	71
Slope system	—	124	121

Advised golfing ability / Anbefalet golf niveau: 0 12 24 36
Hcp required / Max. handicap: 36

CLUB HOUSE & AMENITIES 6/10
KLUBHUSET OG FACILITETER

Pro shop — Pro-shop
Driving range — Driving range
Sheltered Ly 5 mats - On grass på græs yes (04 →10) - Putting-green Putting-green yes - Pitching-green Indspilsgreen yes

HOTEL FACILITIES 5/10
HOTEL FACILITETERNE

HOTELS HOTEL
Britannia - Esbjerg 15 km
85 rooms, D DKr 1050
Tel (45) 75 13 01 11, Fax (45) 75 45 20 85

Hjerting - Esbjerg 15 km
48 rooms, D from DKr 825
Tel (45) 75 11 70 00

RESTAURANTS RESTAURANTER
Pakhuset - Esbjerg 15 km - Tel (45) 75 12 74 55
Henne Kirkeby Kro - Henne 30 km - Tel (45) 75 25 54 00

Fanø

15 | 4 | 7

Ti minutter med færgen fra Esbjerg – og man er i helt andre omgivelser på Fanø. Et kig indenfor i banens "kontor" med efterfølgende spil på banen, og man kunne tilføje: I en helt anden tidsalder. Fanø er Danmarks ældste bane, fra før verden gik af lave. Den åbnede i 1901, og tre af hullerne samt én green, den 16., fra det originale hulforløb eksisterer den dag i dag. Hullerne løber ikke helt ud til vandet, men der er ikke desto mindre tale om Danmarks eneste links-bane udlagt blandt de for linksbaner karakteristiske sandklitter. Disse er banens fornemste forhindringer. Dels fordi de ikke er rare at stifte bekendtskab med for éns bold, dels fordi de resulterer i mange mere eller mindre blinde slag, både fra tee og ind til green. Det kræver adskillige runder at finde ud af, hvordan banens spidsfindigheder skal tackles. Til banens 100 års jubilæum byggede man et regulært klubhus og forlængede banen. Den fik to nye par 5-huller og færre par 3-huller, så par nu er 70.

This course, located on the island of Fanø, is just opposite the town of Esbjerg, which is also well worth a visit via a 10-minute boat-trip. The crossing only adds to the change of surroundings. Only a few houses here and there are able to counter the sensation of travelling through time on a course opened in 1901 and doubtless designed by a Brit, judging by the style (the green on hole N° 16 is most original). Although not exactly by the sea, this is a real links course where the dunes, and of course the wind, are the main obstacles. The tall rough is omnipresent but the dunes carefully conceal a number of greens and fairways, resulting in a number of blind shots and blind greens. You will need several rounds to size up the layout and understand its more subtle features. For the centenary year, a club-house was built and the course lengthened with two new par 5s and fewer par 3s. The overall par is now 70.

Fanø Golf Links — 1901

Golfvej 5
DK - 6720 NORDBY

Office	Sekretariat	(45) 76 66 00 77
Pro shop	Pro-shop	(45) 76 66 00 77
Fax	Fax	(45) 76 66 00 44
Web	www.fanoe-golf-links.dk	
Situation	Sted	Esbjerg, 12 mn (Ferry)
Annual closure	Årlig lukkeperiode	no
Weekly closure	Ugentlig lukketid	no
Fees main season	Priser i højsæson	Full day

	Week days Hverdage	We/Bank holidays Helligdage
Individual Individuelt	DKr 280	DKr 280
Couple Par	DKr 560	DKr 560

Junior: – 50%

Caddie Caddie no — **Electric Trolley** Elektrisk golfvogn no

Buggy Golf car yes — **Clubs** Koeller yes

Credit cards Kreditkord
VISA - DC

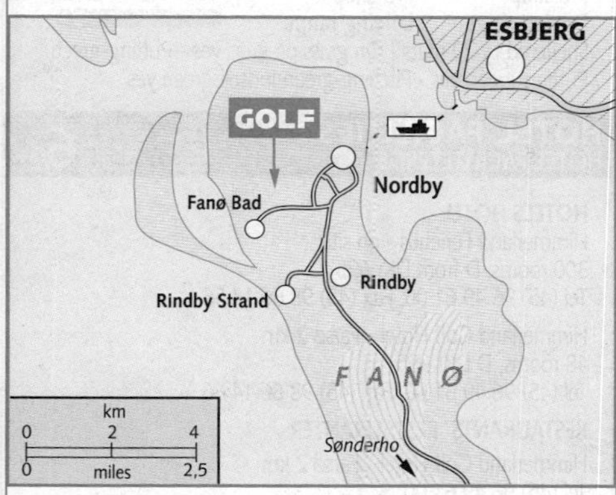

Access Adgang : Esbjerg, Ferry. → Rindby.
Map 1 on page 122 Kort 1 på side 122

GOLF COURSE — GOLF BANE — 15/20

Site	Sted	
Maintenance	Vedligeholdelse	
Architect	Arkitekt	Mr Dunlop
Type	Type	links
Relief	Lettelse	
Water in play	Vand i spil	
Exp. to wind	Udsat for vind	
Trees in play	Træer i spil	

Scorecard Skorekort	Chp. Back tee	Mens Herre tee	Ladies Dame tee
Length Længde	5080	5080	4314
Par	70	70	70
Slope system	119	119	116

Advised golfing ability Anbefalet golf niveau: 0 12 24 36

Hcp required Max. handicap 36

CLUB HOUSE & AMENITIES — KLUBHUSET OG FACILITETER — 4/10

Pro shop Pro-shop
Driving range Driving range

Sheltered Ly no - On grass på græs no - Putting-green Putting-green yes - Pitching-green Indspilsgreen no

HOTEL FACILITIES — HOTEL FACILITETERNE — 7/10

HOTELS HOTEL

Fanø Badeland - Rindby 100 m
126 rooms, D DKr 800
Tel (45) 75 16 60 00, Fax (45) 75 16 60 11

Sønderhø Kro - Sønderho 5 km
18 rooms, D DKr 1200
Tel (45) 75 16 40 09, Fax (45) 75 16 43 85

RESTAURANTS RESTAURANTER

Sønderho Kro - Sønderho 5 km
Tel (45) 75 16 40 09

Nørdby Kro - Nordby 2 km
Tel (45) 75 16 35 89

Himmerland *New Course*

16 | 8 | 6

Den gamle vikingebegravelsesplads Lindholm samt Rold Skov, Danmarks største, er blandt seværdig- hederne i nærheden af Himmerland. Selv på dette 36-hullers anlæg er der andet at tage sig til end at spille golf, stå på vandski på Gatten sø, fx. Banerne kaldes Old Course og New Course. Den sidste er tegnet Jan Sederholm, og det bærer greens som altid præg af: De er udlagt, så greenkeeperen har mulighed for meget forskellige flagplaceringer. Området er relativt fladt og åbent. Vand-hazarder her og der giver nærmest indtryk af amerikansk parkbane, og det samme gør de i visse tilfælde meget store fairwaybunkers. 18. hul er en glimrende afslutning – lige op til klubhuset, hvor man kan sidde og følge dristige spilleres forsøg på at skære hjørnet af den sø, der æder sig ind i fairway på det kun godt 300 m lange hul. New Course er en krævende bane, også fordi den er temmelig lang, og det skyldes blandt andet et af golfverdenens meget sjældne par 6-huller – i dette tilfælde det 10., som er hele 610 m. Bedre egnet til spillere på alle niveauer er den 700 m kortere Old Course.

Travelling from one side of Denmark to the other never involves any more than a few hours of driving, but the eastern region of Jutland is more protected from oceanic influences than the west coast and the landscapes are more lush with alternating meadows and forests. After a visit to Ålborg, Europe's cleanest city, don't miss Lindholm Høje, an age-old Viking cemetery kept in perfect condition. The same goes for Rold Skov, the country's largest forest, before reaching Himmerland. This 36-hole resort comprises the New Course designed by Jan Sederholm, whose greens most connoisseurs would recognize, always laid out in the true spirit of the game. In relatively flat and clear open space, the large fairway bunkers and the scattering of a few hazards gives a slightly American flavour. Well designed and demanding, this layout is probably difficult for inexperienced players, but they will find another course here. A curiosity is the par-6 10th... reachable in 3 by the longer hitters.

Himmerland Golf Klub — 1993

Centervej 1 - Gatten
DK - 9640 FARSØ

Office	Sekretariat	(45) 96 49 61 00
Pro shop	Pro-shop	(45) 96 49 61 09
Fax	Fax	(45) 98 66 14 56
Web	www.himmerlandgolf.dk	
Situation	Sted	Aalborg, 50 km
Annual closure	Årlig lukkeperiode	no
Weekly closure	Ugentlig lukketid	no
Fees main season	Priser i højsæson	Full day

	Week days Hverdage	We/Bank holidays Helligdage
Individual Individuelt	DKr 450	DKr 600
Couple Par	DKr 900	DKr 1200

Juniors: – 50%

Caddie Caddie no — Electric Trolley Elektrisk golfvogn no

Buggy Golf car yes — Clubs Koeller yes

Credit cards Kreditkord
VISA - Eurocard - DC

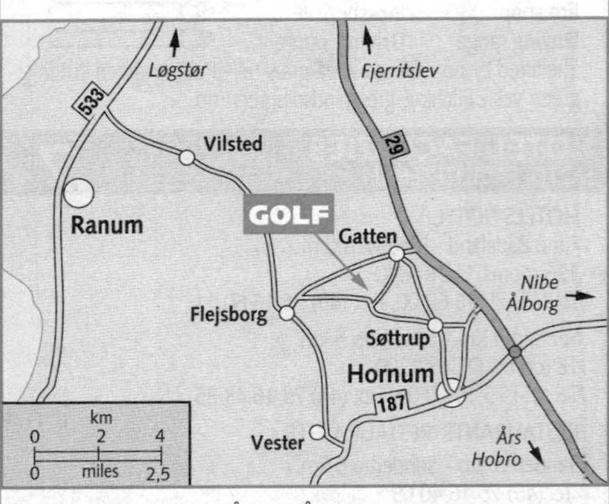

Access Adgang : E 45 Århus - Ålborg. Exit (Frakørsel) 33, 535 → Aars. 29 → Løgstør.

Map 1 on page 122 Kort 1 på side 122

GOLF COURSE — GOLF BANE — 16/20

Site	Sted	
Maintenance	Vedligeholdelse	
Architect	Arkitekt	Jan Sederholm
Type	Type	open country
Relief	Lettelse	
Water in play	Vand i spil	
Exp. to wind	Udsat for vind	
Trees in play	Træer i spil	

Scorecard Skorekort	Chp. Back tee	Mens Herre tee	Ladies Dame tee
Length Længde	6371	6102	5347
Par	73	73	73
Slope system	133	129	129

Advised golfing ability / Anbefalet golf niveau: 0 12 24 36

Hcp required — Max. handicap — 35

CLUB HOUSE & AMENITIES — KLUBHUSET OG FACILITETER — 8/10

Pro shop — Pro-shop
Driving range — Driving range
Sheltered Ly 20 mats - On grass på græs yes - Putting-green Putting-green yes - Pitching-green Indspilsgreen yes

HOTEL FACILITIES — HOTEL FACILITETERNE — 6/10

HOTELS HOTEL

Himmerland Feriehus - on site
300 rooms, D from DKr 695
Tel (45) 96 49 61 00, Fax (45) 98 66 14 56

Himmerland Golf Hotel - Farsø 2 km
48 rooms, D DKr 995
Tel (45) 96 49 61 00, Fax (45) 98 66 14 66

RESTAURANTS RESTAURANTER

Himmerland Golf Hotel - Farsø 2 km
Tel (45) 96 49 61 00

Holstebro

16 | 6 | 5

Denne bane er næsten altid at finde på danske golferes top 3. Den ligger i et tidligere plantageområde og må om nogen betegnes som en skovbane. Fairways er forholdsvis brede, men kommer du først uden for fairway, kan der være problemer med overhovedet at finde den igen. Det er ingen overdrivelse, men forholdet mellem brede fairways og straffende skov er helt rigtigt, og det forklarer, hvorfor banen kun har ganske få bunkers. Træerne – mellem hvilke man går i storladen isolation – er sammen med en række vand-hazarder alt rigeligt til at holde selv den bedste spiller i ørerne. Men Holstebro er også en åben og ærlig bane. Spilleplanen for hvert hul er klar. Kun på dogleg-huller kan man ikke se green fra teestedet. Greens er veldesignede uden de store ondulationer. Banen ER svær – men så byder Holstebros anlæg også på en ni-hullers bane for de lidt mindre skrappe.

This course is regularly ranked amongst the country's top three, even by those people who have never played here. That's what reputation can do for you. It is located in a former plantation, which explains the very many trees. The fairways are wide, but if you spray the ball left or right you might end up not actually knowing how to get back onto the "short stuff". That's no exaggeration. It all gives a marvellous sensation of isolation and explains why there are few green-side bunkers and just a single fairway bunker; the trees and water hazards are enough to keep most players on their toes. With this said, Holstebro is a very forthright course: game strategy is immediately clear, there are no blind greens (except on the dog-legs) and greens are well designed without any excessively steep slopes. Spectacular for its forest setting, very pleasant for its peace and quiet but a little tough for high-handicappers. Holstebro is worth a visit. What's more, there is another shortish 9 hole course, which is perfect for all the family.

Holstebro Golfklub — 1970

Brandsbjergvet 4
DK - 7570 VEMB

Office	Sekretariat	(45) 97 48 51 55
Pro shop	Pro-shop	(45) 96 12 62 01
Fax	Fax	(45) 97 48 51 11
Web	www.hosterbro-golfklub.dk	
Situation	Sted	Århus, 100 km

Holstebro, 15 km

Annual closure	Årlig lukkeperiode	no
Weekly closure	Ugentlig lukketid	no
Fees main season	Priser i højsæson	Full day

	Week days Hverdage	We/Bank holidays Helligdage
Individual Individuelt	DKr 300	DKr 350
Couple Par	DKr 600	DKr 700

Juniors: – 50%

Caddie Caddie no — **Electric Trolley** Elektrisk golfvogn no

Buggy Golf car yes — **Clubs** Koeller yes

Credit cards Kreditkord
VISA - Eurocard - DC

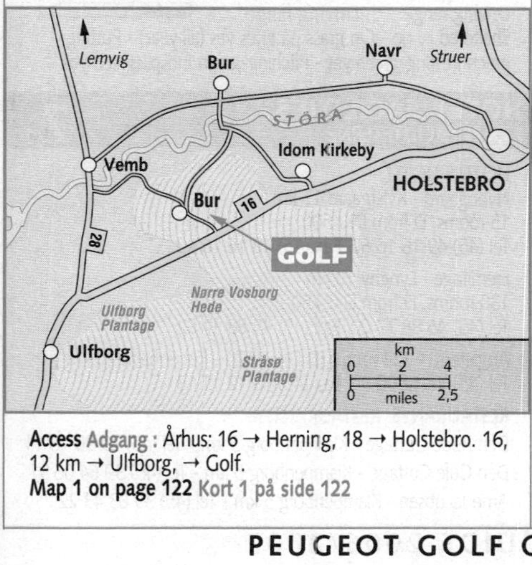

Access Adgang : Århus: 16 → Herning, 18 → Holstebro. 16, 12 km → Ulfborg, → Golf.

Map 1 on page 122 Kort 1 på side 122

GOLF COURSE — GOLF BANE — 16/20

Site	Sted	
Maintenance	Vedligeholdelse	
Architect	Arkitekt	Erik Schnack
Type	Type	forest, parkland
Relief	Lettelse	
Water in play	Vand i spil	
Exp. to wind	Udsat for vind	
Trees in play	Træer i spil	

Scorecard Skorekort	**Chp.** Back tee	**Mens** Herre tee	**Ladies** Dame tee
Length Længde	6221	5856	5055
Par	72	72	72
Slope system	136	131	128

Advised golfing ability Anbefalet golf niveau — 0 12 24 36

Hcp required Max. handicap — 42

CLUB HOUSE & AMENITIES — KLUBHUSET OG FACILITETER — 6/10

Pro shop Pro-shop

Driving range Driving range

Sheltered Ly no - **On grass** på græs yes (04 → 10) - **Putting-green** Putting-green yes - **Pitching-green** Indspilsgreen yes

HOTEL FACILITIES — HOTEL FACILITETERNE — 5/10

HOTELS HOTEL

Schaumburg - Holstebro 15 km
80 rooms, D DKr 1245
Tel (45) 97 42 31 11, Fax (45) 97 42 72 82

Royal Holstebro - Holstebro 15 km
65 rooms, D from DKr 795
Tel (45) 97 40 23 33, Fax (45) 97 40 30 87

RESTAURANTS RESTAURANTER

NR. Wosborg - Vemb 8 km
Tel (45) 97 48 17 40

Sevel Kro - Sevel 20 km
Tel (45) 97 44 80 11

København *Eremitagen*

16 | 7 | 7

Det er ikke kun vindens susen, man mærker på de åbne vidder, når man spiller Københavns Golf Klubs bane kun 20 km nord for Københavns centrum. Også historiens vingesus presser sig på: Klubben er Skandinaviens ældste, fra 1899, der har været spillet golf i området siden 1901, og den nuværende bane er fra 1928. Dansk golfs grand old man, Frederik Dreyer, har siden bidraget til flere af hullernes nuværende udformning. Banens oprindelige arkitekt kendes ikke. Dreyer har prøvet at finde ham, men det er (endnu) ikke lykkes. Førnævnte vind kan sammen med sensommerens meget høje rough gøre banen til en ordentlig mundfuld. Men man går også på en bane af stor skønhed. Man kan ikke undgå at se nogle af de flere tusind rådyr, der går frit i området. Det flere kilometer lange skovparti, som løber i højre side af fem, seks huller og afgrænser banen mod nord, er uendelig smukt, især om efteråret. Og i tilgift kommer man på 16. hul helt tæt på et ægte barokslot, Eremitage-slottet, som har givet banen dens daglige tilnavn, "Eremitagen".

While you are playing at Københavns Golf Klub, 20 kilometers north of the Danish capital, you will instantly notice two things: 1. The sizzling wind that playfully runs through the landscape. 2. The great impact that the history has on this place: the golf club, founded in 1899 is the oldest in Scandinavia, and the first balls were hit two years later. The existing course of today is from 1928. Mr Golf in Denmark, Frederik Dreyer, has thereafter contributed with a few new layout solutions. The original architect is unknown, despite some intensive research. The wind in combination with the thick rough makes the course a rather difficult test. But don't bother, the great beauty of the landscape will soon make you forget a lost ball or two. You will also notice the roe deers, there are thousands of them. Six of the holes runs through a deep forrest, but the most memorable hole is the 16th, close to an old barock castle, Eremitage-slottet, that also has given the course it's nickname, "Eremitagen".

Københavns Golf Klub — 1928

Dyrehaven 2
DK - 2800 KONGENS LYNGBY

Office	Sekretariat	(45) 39 63 04 83
Pro shop	Pro-shop	(45) 39 63 02 83
Fax	Fax	(45) 39 63 46 83
Web	www.kgkgolf.dk	
Situation	Sted	København, 20 km
Annual closure	Årlig lukkeperiode	no
Weekly closure	Ugentlig lukketid	no

Fees main season Priser i højsæson	18 holes	
	Week days Hverdage	We/Bank holidays Helligdage
Individual Individuelt	DKr 350	DKr 450
Couple Par	DKr 700	DKr 900

No booking in advance / W/E: members only before 12:00
Juniors: – 50%

Caddie Caddie no — **Electric Trolley** Elektrisk golfvogn no
Buggy Golf car no — **Clubs** Koeller yes
Credit cards Kreditkord
VISA - DC

Access Adgang : From København, E47 → Helsingør. Exit Strandvejen Nord → Taarbæk. Follow signs to "Københavns Golf Klub"
Map 1 on page 123 Kort 1 på side 123

GOLF COURSE — GOLF BANE — 16/20

Site	Sted	
Maintenance	Vedligeholdelse	
Architect	Arkitekt	unknown
Type	Type	inland, open country
Relief	Lettelse	
Water in play	Vand i spil	
Exp. to wind	Udsat for vind	
Trees in play	Træer i spil	

Scorecard Skorekort	Chp. Back tee	Mens Herre tee	Ladies Dame tee
Length Længde	6031	5761	5026
Par	71	71	71
Slope system	—	134	126

Advised golfing ability Anbefalet golf niveau — 0 12 24 36
Hcp required Max. handicap — 32

CLUB HOUSE & AMENITIES — KLUBHUSET OG FACILITETER — 7/10

Pro shop Pro-shop
Driving range Driving range
Sheltered Ly no - On grass på græs yes (all year) - Putting-green Putting-green yes - Pitching-green Indspilsgreen yes

HOTEL FACILITIES — HOTEL FACILITETERNE — 7/10

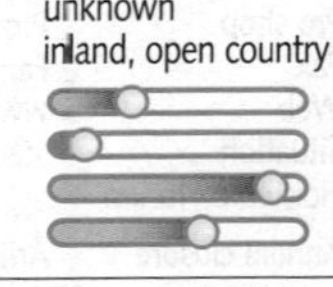

HOTELS HOTEL
Nybogaard - Kvistgaard 15 km
15 rooms, D from DKr 500
Tel (45) 49 16 16 60, Fax (45) 49 16 16 80

Eremitage - Lyngby 10 km
130 rooms, D from DKr 750
Tel (45) 45 88 77 00, Fax (45) 45 88 17 82

Angleterre - 123 rooms, D DKr 2170 - København 20 km
Tel (45) 33 12 00 95, Fax (45) 33 12 11 18

RESTAURANTS RESTAURANTER
Den Røde Cottage - Klampenborg 5 km - Tel (45) 39 90 46 14
Den Gule Cottage - Klampenborg 5 km - Tel (45) 39 64 06 91
Arne Jacobsen - Klampenborg 5 km - Tel (45) 39 63 43 22

Læsø Seaside

16	8	5

Med 90 minutters sejltur fra Frederikshavn eller en lille times taxi-flyning fra Roskilde er saltsydningens, krebsenes og biernes ø Læsø ikke et sted, man sådan lige lægger vejen forbi. Men er du allerede i Nordjylland for at spille golf, bør du gøre turen ud til øens naturskønne, varierede og svære bane. Svær, fordi man på kun ét af dens 15 lange huller hiver driveren op af bagen uden at betænke sig. På de resterende 14 er landingsområderne enten meget smalle, eller også er hullet dogleg, så der kræves den helt rigtige længde på slaget, for at bolden kommer til at ligge rigtigt. Slår man skævt, straffes man hårdt af træer med dertil hørende tyk underskov. Eller af høj rough som den, der på det prægtige par 5 afslutningshul klemmer fairway til maks. 25 meter. Vand-hazarder, der ikke alle er lige tydelige, gør ikke banen nemmere. Til gengæld er der ikke mange bunkers – men det havde næsten også været for meget. Læsø er banen for folk, der har mange slag i bagen, og har du ikke det, første gang du besøger banen, så glem din score, og nyd i stedet, hvor naturligt det kan lade sig gøre at udlægge en golbane.

With a 90 minute ferry trip, you don't come here without a purpose. You can also hit your wayward shots without too many people watching in a tranquil setting made to feel even more isolated by the thick trees and rough. You won't have much opportunity to use the driver, either, because the fairways are narrow or because the turn of the dog-legs are too close, or the water hazards are too. Fortunately, there are few bunkers. In fact, this is a course designed for seasoned golfers who can quickly adjust their game The first time out, you might be put off by the demands of the course; in this case, focus on discovering the course. You will understand the course better the next time out. Over an area naturally suited to golf, the architect didn't have to move much earth, and this is noticeable in the already "mature" feel to the whole complex.

Læsø Seaside Golfklub — 1995

Prof. Johansensvej 2
DK - 9940 Læso

Office	Sekretariat	(45) 98 49 84 00
Pro shop	Pro-shop	(45) 98 49 84 00
Fax	Fax	—
Web	www.laesoe-golf.dk	
Situation	Sted	Frederikshavn, 90 mn (Ferry)
Annual closure	Årlig lukkeperiode	no
Weekly closure	Ugentlig lukketid	no

Fees main season Priser i højsæson — Full day

	Week days / Hverdage	We/Bank holidays / Helligdage
Individual Individuelt	DKr 300	DKr 300
Couple Par	DKr 600	DKr 600

Juniors: - 50%

Caddie Caddie no — **Electric Trolley** Elektrisk golfvogn no

Buggy Golf car no — **Clubs** Koeller yes

Credit cards Kreditkord
VISA - Eurocard - DC

Access Adgang : Frederikshavn, 90 mn Ferry.
Vesterø → Østerby

Map 1 on page 123 Kort 1 på side 123

GOLF COURSE — GOLF BANE — 16/20

Site	Sted	
Maintenance	Vedligeholdelse	
Architect	Arkitekt	Lars Andreasson, Henrik Jacobsen
Type	Type	seaside course, forest
Relief	Lettelse	
Water in play	Vand i spil	
Exp. to wind	Udsat for vind	
Trees in play	Træer i spil	

Scorecard Skorekort	Chp. Back tee	Mens Herre tee	Ladies Dame tee
Length Længde	6577	6053	5174
Par	74	74	74
Slope system	—	125	116

Advised golfing ability Anbefalet golf niveau — 0 12 24 36

Hcp required Max. handicap — 36

CLUB HOUSE & AMENITIES — KLUBHUSET OG FACILITETER — 8/10

Pro shop Pro-shop
Driving range Driving range
Sheltered Ly - - On grass på græs no, 8 mats open air - Putting-green Putting-green yes - Pitching-green Indspilsgreen no

HOTEL FACILITIES — HOTEL FACILITETERNE — 5/10

HOTELS HOTEL
Læsø Seaside Hotel - 24 rooms, D DKr 800 - Læsø 1 km
Tel (45) 48 99 88 90, Fax (45) 98 49 88 00

Hotel Nyggard - 18 rooms, D DKr 750 - Østerby, close
Tel (45) 98 49 16 66, Fax (45) 98 49 16 68

RESTAURANTS RESTAURANTER
Hotel Nygaard - Østerby 5 km - Tel (45) 98 49 16 66
Delikaten - Vesterø 10 km - Tel (45) 98 49 99 01
Restaurant Bakken - Tel (45) 98 49 11 20 - Byrum, close

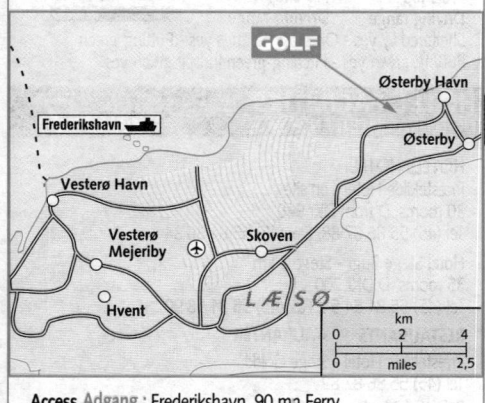

Møn

15	7	7

Begynd gerne en udflugt til golfbanen på Møn med at køre for langt. Fortsætter du forbi banen, der ligger umiddelbart øst for Stege, ender du nemlig helt ude på øens østkyst, og her er det et helt fantastisk syn at opleve morgensolens stråler ramme de majestætiske hvide klinter. En anden af øens attraktioner er de fine middelalderlige kalkmalerier, der kan ses i flere kirker ikke langt fra banen. Den forholdsvis nye bane, der i hesteskoform strækker sig rundt om inderste del af Stege Nor, er i glimrende stand, og man lægger straks mærke til de fine fairways. Det begynder blødt med forholdsvis åbne huller, men strammer til på de sidste ni, hvor vand-hazarder og især rough straffer den, der slår skævt. 14. hul, et langt par 4, er strålende i al sin enkelhed: Lidt op ad bakke zigzagger fairwayen sig mellem den bølgende rough op til greenen, hvor en enkel bunker står vagt. Alt i alt en ærlig og ikke alt for kuperet bane, hvor golfere på alle niveauer kan være med. Som på Korsør leder 9. hul ikke ind til det i øvrigt perfekt placerede klubhus, fra hvis terrasse man har udsigt ned over Stege Nor.

Møn is hardly the best known of the many islands in Denmark and as a result has retained unspoiled many of its natural treasures, huge white beaches, dunes, forests and amazing white chalk cliffs. This golf course is two km from the little town of Stege, surrounded by ramparts. Art-loving golfers will not want to miss visiting the three churches here, decorated with Middle Age frescos. On the course, these same golfers will want to know how to sometimes bend the ball when they stray off the excellent fairways on holes lined with trees, although there are enough more open holes to make up for poor accuracy. Caution is required however, as the tall rough is a very dangerous proposition on about half a dozen holes and often more so than water, which really comes into play on 3 holes. This is an honest course, relatively playable by golfers of all abilities and sufficiently steep in places to recommend a buggy for unfit golfers. If you didn't know already, not all of Denmark is flat...

Møn Golfklub — 1994

Klintevej 118
DK - 4780 STEGE

Office	Sekretariat	(45) 55 81 32 60
Pro shop	Pro-shop	(45) 55 81 39 69
Fax	Fax	(45) 55 81 32 60
Web	www.mgc.golfin.dk	
Situation	Sted	Vordingborg, 20 km
Annual closure	Årlig lukkeperiode	no
Weekly closure	Ugentlig lukketid	no

Fees main season / Priser i højsæson	Week days / Hverdage	We/Bank holidays / Helligdage
18 holes		
Individual Individuelt	DKr 250	DKr 300
Couple Par	DKr 500	DKr 600

Juniors: – 50%

Caddie Caddie no — Electric Trolley Elektrisk golfvogn no

Buggy Golf car yes — Clubs Koeller yes

Credit cards Kreditkord
VISA - Eurocard - DC

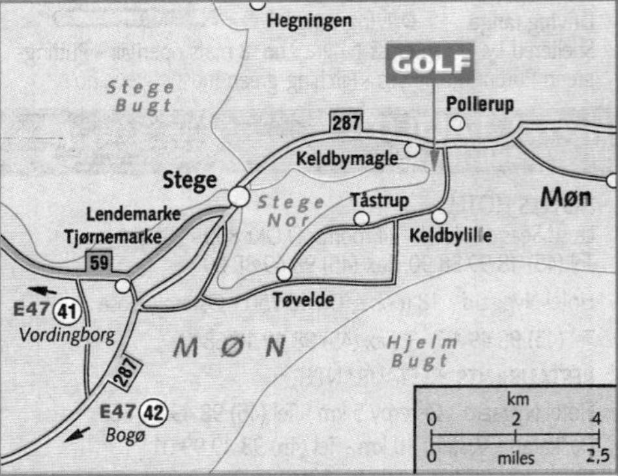

Access Adgang : København, E47/E55 → Vordingborg. → Stege.

Map 1 on page 123 Kort 1 på side 123

GOLF COURSE / GOLF BANE — 15/20

Site	Sted	
Maintenance	Vedligeholdelse	
Architect	Arkitekt	Rolf Henning-Jensen
Type	Type	country, hilly
Relief	Lettelse	
Water in play	Vand i spil	
Exp. to wind	Udsat for vind	
Trees in play	Træer i spil	

Scorecard / Skorekort	Chp. / Back tee	Mens / Herre tee	Ladies / Dame tee
Length Længde	5917	5917	4974
Par	72	72	72
Slope system	—	121	121

Advised golfing ability / Anbefalet golf niveau: 0 12 24 36

Hcp required — Max. handicap: 48

CLUB HOUSE & AMENITIES / KLUBHUSET OG FACILITETER — 7/10

Pro shop — Pro-shop
Driving range — Driving range
Sheltered Ly yes - On grass på græs yes - Putting-green Putting-green yes - Pitching-green Indspilsgreen yes

HOTEL FACILITIES / HOTEL FACILITETERNE — 7/10

HOTELS HOTEL

Præstekilde Hotel - on site
30 rooms, D from DKr 940
Tel (45) 55 86 87 88, Fax (45) 55 81 36 34

Hotel Stege Bugt - Stege 2 km
35 rooms, D DKr 700
Tel (45) 55 81 54 54, Fax (45) 55 81 58 90

RESTAURANTS RESTAURANTER

Præstekilde Hotel - Stege Golfkl
Tel (45) 55 86 87 88

Babette - Vordingborg 20 km - Tel (45) 55 34 30 30

Skipperkrøn - Præstø 30 km - Tel (45) 55 99 22 00

Nordvestjysk

16 | 5 | 5

Nordvestjysk Golfklubs bane i Nystrup Plantage byder på dramatisk natur i et omfang, som ingen anden dansk bane kan matche. Alle hullerne ligger i en klitplantage, og jorden er derfor meget sandet. Men derudover udmærker hullerne 2.-8. samt 13. og 14. sig ved to ting, man normalt ikke finder på en bane, der er skåret ud blandt træerne. Dels er hullerne meget kuperede, og dels har fairways linkskarakter i den forstand at de som tagrender er lidt dybere på midten end ude i siderne. Kombinationen af disse ting er yderst sjælden og meget smuk. Dertil kommer en fabelagtig udsigt på adskillige af hullerne. De resterende huller fejler heller ikke noget. Det er glimrende skovhuller, men fordi de er flade, savner de dramatikken. De mange træer er stort set banens eneste forhindringer bortset fra greenbunkers. Et par vandhuller og et par fairwaybunkers er i spil, det er det hele. Hele banen fremstår ekstremt naturlig. Naturoplevelsen er helt i top, for man ser kun det hul, man spiller. Banens eneste minus er, at den ligger i et yderområde af Danmark, men når man har spillet banen, er turen derop for intet at regne, og man kan ikke vente med at komme til at spille den igen.

Nordvestjysk treats you to an amount of naturally dramatic nature that no other Danish course can match. Half the holes (2-8, 13 and 14), are characterized by two things not normally found on a Danish course cut out inbetween the trees. The holes are very hilly but somewhat like holes on a links course in that fairways are slightly lower in the middle than along the sides. A rare and beautiful combination, with astonishing views of the surrounding landscape. There's nothing wrong with the remaining nine holes, but because they lack this drama. Trees are Nordvestjysk's only hazards besides greenbunkers and two water hazards in play. The course comes across as extremely natural. Only drawback is that the course is situated on the outskirts of Denmark, but once you've played it, the time spent going there seems short, and you can't wait to play it again.

Nordvestjysk Golfklub — 1973

Nystrupvej 19
DK - 7700 THISTED

Office Sekretariat (45) 97 97 41 41
Pro shop Pro-shop (45) 97 97 41 01
Fax Fax (45) 97 97 41 41
Web www.nvgolf.dk
Situation Sted Thisted, 15 km
Annual closure Årlig lukkeperiode no
Weekly closure Ugentlig lukketid no

Fees main season / Priser i højsæson	Week days / Hverdage	We/Bank holidays / Helligdage
Individual Individuelt	DKr 250	DKr 300
Couple Par	DKr 500	DKr 600

Full day

Juniors: - 50%

Caddie Caddie no — **Electric Trolley** Elektrisk golfvogn no
Buggy Golf car yes — **Clubs** Koeller yes
Credit cards Kreditkord
VISA - Eurocard - MasterCard

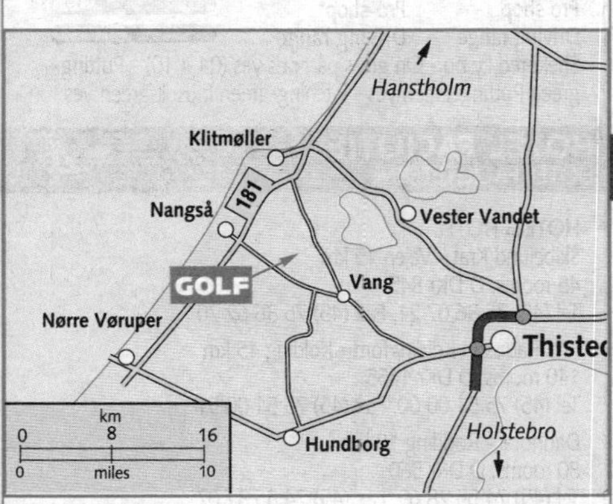

Access Adgang : Arhus, E45 to Hobro. Route 29 → Fjerritslev. 29 → Hanstholm. 101 → Klitmøller. After Klitmøller, turn left → Vang. Follow signs to golf.
Map 1 on page 122 Kort 1 på side 122

GOLF COURSE — GOLF BANE — 16/20

Site Sted
Maintenance Vedligeholdelse
Architect Arkitekt Erik Schnack, Henrik Jacobsen
Type Type forest, hilly
Relief Lettelse
Water in play Vand i spil
Exp. to wind Udsat for vind
Trees in play Træer i spil

Scorecard / Skorekort	Chp. / Back tee	Mens / Herre tee	Ladies / Dame tee
Length Længde	5646	5646	4877
Par	72	72	72
Slope system	130	130	125

Advised golfing ability Anbefalet golf niveau 0 12 24 36
Hcp required Max. handicap 40

CLUB HOUSE & AMENITIES — KLUBHUSET OG FACILITETER — 5/10

Pro shop Pro-shop
Driving range Driving range
Sheltered Ly no - On grass på græs yes - Putting-green Putting-green yes - Pitching-green Indspilsgreen yes

HOTEL FACILITIES — HOTEL FACILITETERNE — 5/10

HOTELS HOTEL
Hotel Thisted - Thisted 15 km
25 rooms, D DKr 850
Tel (45) 97 92 52 00, Fax (45) 97 92 61 23

Klitmøller Gl. Kro - Klitmøller 3 km
20 rooms, D DKr 590 - Tel (45) 97 97 55 22

Hotel Hanstholm - Hanstholm 15 km
76 rooms, D DKr 925
Tel (45) 97 96 10 44

RESTAURANTS RESTAURANTER
Hotel Thisted - Thisted 15 km
Tel (45) 97 92 52 00

Svinkløv Badehotel - Svinkløv 50 km - Tel (45) 98 21 70 02

Royal Oak

15	7	4

Ved bredden af Jels Sø ligger Royal Oak, opkaldt efter det egetræ, hvor kongen engang gjorde holdt, og som stadig står. Træer af mere moderat størrelse er i spil flere steder på denne fine bane, der åbnede i 1992, og med bunkers og vand-hazarder spredt tilsvarende ud er problemerne ligeligt fordelt og samtidig tydelige for enhver. Den mest imponerende vand-hazard er dog selve Jels Sø, der gør flere af hullerne på de første ni ualmindelig smukke. Trods sin ærlige karakter kan banen være svær at score på, især hvis størrelsen på de veldesignede, hurtige greens udnyttes til at stille flagene svært. Banen har sammen med Simon's ry for at være den mest velplejede i Danmark, og det gør den a tid til en fornøjelse at spille.

On the shores of lake Jels, the Royal Oak takes its name from the oak tree under which the king and his son rested when on the road to Vejen. It is not, however, the only tree on this course, first opened in 1992 on an estate located in the middle of Jylland. Many others are clearly in play, giving this course the look of a fabulous park, especially beautiful for the holes along the lake. With bunkers and water hazards, difficulties are evenly spread around the course and are clearly visible to allow the golfer to immediately feel at ease. Despite the visual simplicity, you need several rounds here to collect any sort of score, which will also particularly depend on the pin positions on rather large, well designed and often very fast greens. Generally speaking, green-keeping and maintenance here are first rate, resulting as always in more enjoyable golf. Rather spectacular while retaining its naturalness, this is a quality course, which is obviously much appreciated for its peaceful location and impressive landscape.

Royal Oak Golf Club — 1992

Golfvej, Jels
DK - 6630 RØDDING

Office	Sekretariat	(45) 74 55 32 94
Pro shop	Pro-shop	(45) 74 55 32 94
Fax	Fax	(45) 74 55 32 95
Web	www.royal-oak.dk	
Situation	Sted	Vejen, 15 km
Annual closure	Årlig lukkeperiode	no
Weekly closure	Ugentlig lukketid	no
Fees main season	Priser i højsæson	Full day

	Week days Hverdage	We/Bank holidays Helligdage
Individual Individuelt	DKr 360	DKr 400
Couple Par	DKr 720	DKr 800

Juniors: – 50%

Caddie Caddie no — **Electric Trolley** Elektrisk golfvogn yes

Buggy Golf car yes — **Clubs** Koeller yes

Credit cards Kreditkord
VISA - Eurocard - DC

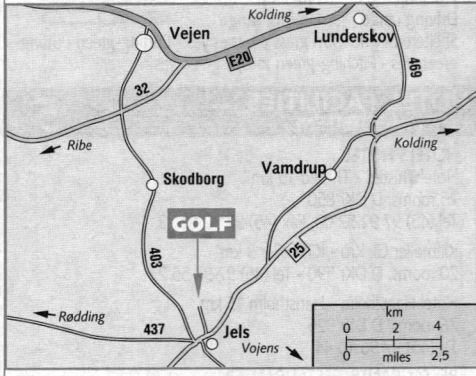

Access Adgang : E45. Exit → Kolding Syd. 403. → Jels, → Golf.

Map 1 on page 122 Kort 1 på side 122

GOLF COURSE — GOLF BANE — 15/20

Site	Sted	
Maintenance	Vedligeholdelse	
Architect	Arkitekt	Malling/Gundtoft
Type	Type	parkland
Relief	Lettelse	
Water in play	Vand i spil	
Exp. to wind	Udsat for vind	
Trees in play	Træer i spil	

Scorecard Skorekort	Chp. Back tee	Mens Herre tee	Ladies Dame tee
Length Længde	6374	5967	4995
Par	72	72	72
Slope system	—	129	122

Advised golfing ability Anbefalet golf niveau — 0 12 24 36

Hcp required Max. handicap — 32

CLUB HOUSE & AMENITIES — KLUBHUSET OG FACILITETER — 7/10

Pro shop Pro-shop
Driving range Driving range
Sheltered Ly no - On grass på græs yes (04 # 10) - Putting-green Putting-green yes - Pitching-green Indspilsgreen yes

HOTEL FACILITIES — HOTEL FACILITETERNE — 4/10

HOTELS HOTEL

Skibelund Krat - Vejen 15 km
45 rooms, D DKr 845
Tel (45) 75 36 07 21, Fax (45) 75 36 62 70

SAS Radisson Koldingford - Kolding 45 km
140 rooms, D DKr 1455
Tel (45) 75 51 00 00, Fax (45) 75 51 00 51

Danhotel - Rødding 10 km
80 rooms, D DKr 560
Tel (45) 74 55 28 69, Fax (45) 74 55 31 07

Rungsted

17 | 8 | 7

En meget berømt bane – ikke kun fordi den er fra 1936 og således en af landets ældste, men fordi dens originale layout skyldes C.A. MacKenzie, bror til ingen ringere end Augusta-skaberen Alister MacKenzie. I det nordsjællandske Strandvejsområde, der domineres af marinaer og millionvillaer – og ikke langt fra Karen Blixens fødested, Rungstedlund, der i dag fungerer som Blixen-museum – ligger en af Danmarks bedste baner. Den er udlagt blandt masser af store træer, der taler deres tydelige sprog om banens alder. Få, men velplacerede bunkers og ikke mindst et vandløb, der krydser ikke færre end syv huller, sørger for, at den ikke specielt lange bane alligevel er svær at score på. Banen er ikke særlig kuperet. Der står en aura af diskret afmålthed omkring banen. Alting er i balance. Og så har banen flere karakteristisk smukke og egenartede huller: Det ubrudte skovparti langs højre side af det lange 4. hul. Den grydeagtige green nede mellem træerne på det korte 6. hul. De store rododen- dronbuske bag 15. green. Rungsted er en bane, man husker.

This is one of Denmark's most famous courses... because it dates back to 1936 and was one of the country's first layouts, because it was designed by C.A. Mackenzie (brother of Alister, designer of Augusta) and because it is situated in a magnificent region. Starting out from the capital Copenhagen and heading north towards Sjælland, the coast road reveals some superb villas, a number of small harbours with marinas, and a view of Sweden on the other side of the Øresund straits. Rungsted is also the birthplace of the writer Karen Blixen. The golf course was laid out in a huge park, only slightly scarred by a railway line, where huge trees and very well designed bunkers testify to the art of a designer in a class of his own. Water hazards are cleverly used and well in play without ever looking artificial, and greens are well-guarded without the need for massive protection. There is a sense of measure to everything about this well-balanced course, which fairly rewards good and well shaped shots.

Rungsted Golf Klub — 1936

Vestre Stationsvej 16
DK - 2960 RUNGSTED KYST

Office Sekretariat (45) 45 86 34 44
Pro shop Pro-shop (45) 45 86 34 14
Fax Fax (45) 45 86 57 70
Web www.rungstedgolfklub.dk
Situation Sted København, 25 km
Annual closure Årlig lukkeperiode no
Weekly closure Ugentlig lukketid no

Fees main season Priser i højsæson — 18 holes

	Week days Hverdage	We/Bank holidays Helligdage
Individual Individuelt	DKr 525	DKr 575
Couple Par	DKr 1050	DKr 1150

Juniors: DKr 240

Caddie Caddie no — **Electric Trolley** Elektrisk golfvogn no
Buggy Golf car yes — **Clubs** Koeller yes
Credit cards Kreditkord
VISA - Eurocard - MasterCard - DC

Access Adgang : E47, Exit Hørsholm C. → Rungsted, → Golf.
Map 1 on page 123 Kort 1 på side 123

GOLF COURSE — GOLF BANE — 17/20

Site Sted
Maintenance Vedligeholdelse
Architect Arkitekt — C.A. MacKenzie
Type Type — forest, parkland
Relief Lettelse
Water in play Vand i spil
Exp. to wind Udsat for vind
Trees in play Træer i spil

Scorecard Skorekort	Chp. Back tee	Mens Herre tee	Ladies Dame tee
Length Længde	5950	5681	5107
Par	72	72	72
Slope system	131	128	129

Advised golfing ability Anbefalet golf niveau — 0 12 24 36
Hcp required Max. handicap — 21 Men, 26 Ladies

CLUB HOUSE & AMENITIES — KLUBHUSET OG FACILITETER — 8/10

Pro shop Pro-shop
Driving range Driving range
Sheltered Ly no - On grass på græs yes (04 → 10) - Putting-green Putting-green yes - Pitching-green Indspilsgreen yes

HOTEL FACILITIES — HOTEL FACILITETERNE — 7/10

HOTELS HOTEL
Store Kro - Fredensborg 10 km
40 rooms, D from DKr 1500
Tel (45) 48 40 01 11, Fax (45) 48 48 45 61

Nybogaard - 15 rooms, D from DKr 500 - Kvistgaard 5 km
Tel (45) 49 16 16 60, Fax (45) 49 16 16 80

Scanticon Borupgaard - Snekkersten 18 km
45 rooms, D DKr 1100
Tel (45) 49 22 03 33, Fax (45) 49 22 03 99

RESTAURANTS RESTAURANTER
Nokken - Rungsted 5 km - Tel (45) 45 57 13 14
Søllerød Kro - Søllerød 10 km - Tel (45) 45 80 25 05
Taarbæk Kro - Taarbæk 15 km - Tel (45) 39 63 00 96

Samsø

15	4	7

Nogle af Danmarks bedste baner synes at spille kostbare i den forstand, at de ikke er sådan lige at komme til. Det gælder Læsø Seaside, og det gælder banen på Samsø, Strisserens ø midt i Danmark. Det tager mindst en time at sejle med færge fra Jylland eller Sjælland, men tiden er godt givet ud, for Samsøbanen er måske den smukkest beliggende i Danmark. På to tredjedele af de 18 huller går man med udsigt over Kattegat. Som helhed er banen nænsomt og stort set uden planering af jord udlagt i terræn, der for det meste skråner ned mod havet. Lidt bunkers, lidt vand-hazarder, lidt træer – alt er i balance. Og som altid, når Henrik Jacobsen har designet en bane, ligger forhindringerne, hvor de skal. Helt ned til vandet kommer man på 8. hul, et par 3, der har Kattegat som uendeligt bagtæppe, og på 16. hul, der løber langs med og kun en lille meter oven for selve stranden. Eneste anke ved banen er, at den er relativt kort.

Some of the best courses in Denmark seem to enjoy playing hard-to-get, or rather hard-to-get-to, being situated on islands and involving a few hours of travel. Samsø can be reached by ferry from Kalundborg (Sjælland) or Hov (Jutland) but it really is worth the trouble and the wait. The terrain made available to Henrik Jacobsen was ideal. Laudable concern for blending the course into the landscape, a few cleverly placed bunkers and a number of water hazards have produced a great layout. The successful outcome also required a lot of good taste and insight into the game, and there are often several solutions for reaching the medium-sized but well designed greens. From the many holes that stick in the mind, the signature hole is the most memorable, the par-3 8th hole whose green is backed by the ocean. A very pleasant course for all golfing abilities, where the only criticism might be lack of yardage (except when the wind blows) and hilly contours for senior players, but the latter is simply an excuse to stop, catch your breath and admire the scenery.

Samsø Golf Club — 1992

Besser Kirkevej 24
DK - 8305 Samsø

Office	Sekretariat	(45) 86 59 22 18
Pro shop	Pro-shop	(45) 86 59 22 18
Fax	Fax	(45) 86 59 22 21
Web	www.samsoegolfklub.dk	
Situation	Sted	on Samsø Island
Annual closure	Årlig lukkeperiode	no
Weekly closure	Ugentlig lukketid	no
Fees main season	Priser i højsæson	Full day

	Week days Hverdage	We/Bank holidays Helligdage
Individual Individuelt	DKr 220	DKr 275
Couple Par	DKr 440	DKr 550

Juniors: DKr 100

Caddie Caddie no — **Electric Trolley** Elektrisk golfvogn no

Buggy Golf car yes — **Clubs** Koeller yes

Credit cards Kreditkord
VISA - Eurocard - DC

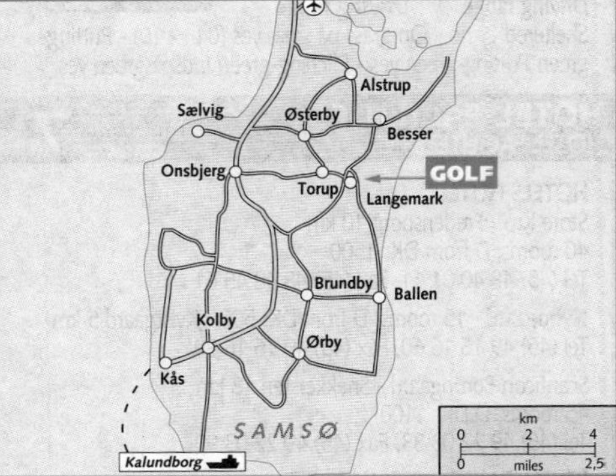

Access Adgang : Kalundborg, Ferry → Samsø - Hov (Jutland), Ferry → Sælvig

Map 1 on page 123 Kort 1 på side 123

GOLF COURSE — GOLF BANE — 15/20

Site	Sted	
Maintenance	Vedligeholdelse	
Architect	Arkitekt	Henrik Jacobsen
Type	Type	seaside course, country
Relief	Lettelse	
Water in play	Vand i spil	
Exp. to wind	Udsat for vind	
Trees in play	Træer i spil	

Scorecard Skorekort	Chp. Back tee	Mens Herre tee	Ladies Dame tee
Length Længde	5615	5615	4885
Par	72	72	72
Slope system	—	131	127

Advised golfing ability Anbefalet golf niveau: 0 12 24 36

Hcp required Max. handicap 54

CLUB HOUSE & AMENITIES — KLUBHUSET OG FACILITETER — 4/10

Pro shop Pro-shop
Driving range Driving range

Sheltered Ly no - On grass på græs yes (04 → 10) - Putting-green Putting-green yes - Pitching-green Indspilsgreen yes

HOTEL FACILITIES — HOTEL FACILITETERNE — 7/10

HOTELS HOTEL

Flinch's Hotel - Tranebjerg 5 km
25 rooms, D DKr 710
Tel (45) 86 59 17 22, Fax (45) 86 59 35 50

Ballen Badehotel - Ballen 5 km
30 rooms, D DKr 750
Tel (45) 86 59 17 99, Fax (45) 86 59 06 59

Motel Sølyst - 20 rooms, D DKr 640 - Vesterløkken 5 km
Tel (45) 86 59 16 59, Fax (45) 86 59 16 99

RESTAURANTS RESTAURANTER

Ved Kæret - Nordby 20 km - Tel (45) 86 59 61 22
Skipperly - Ballen 5 km - Tel (45) 86 59 10 18
Ballen Badehotel - Ballen 5 km - Tel (45) 86 59 17 99

Sct. Knuds

15	5	6

Måske den nemmeste bane at finde i hele Danmark, fordi man ser ned på den fra motorvejen mellem Nyborg og Storebæltsbroen. Alligevel virker støjen kun generende på et par huller. Resten af runden går man dybt inde blandt træerne eller nede ved vandet. Egentlige vand-hazarder er der kun ganske få af. Dén på det 450 meter lange 16. hul er til gengæld imponerende: Det er selve Storebælt, man kan forsøge at skære så meget af i sit drive, som man tør. Ellers sørger især de tydeligvis gamle træer og også bunkers for problemerne på den næsten helt flade bane. Sct. Knuds mangler de tekniske raffinementer, der skal til for at udfordre den dygtige spiller, men kan så til gengæld spilles uden problemer af folk med højt handicap.

Here is an easy-to-find course: the motorway that crosses the three major regions of Denmark (Sjælland, Fyn and Jutland) runs along about 6 or 7 holes but is only really a nuisance on holes 10 and 11. If you can forget it is there, this well-wooded and very varied site is most pleasant. On the clearer sections of the course, the trees give way to the Storebælt, particularly on the 16th, a magnificent short par 5. This belt of sea is moreover the only water hazard on the course, the other hazards being more classical and typically British in the form of trees (sometimes very much in play) and the standard bunkers. All this gives a very open course, which hides none of its difficulties. For the more demanding player, though, it probably lacks a little technical subtlety to be played too often. With that said, you will have fun golfing here with all the family or with friends, even with widely differing abilities.

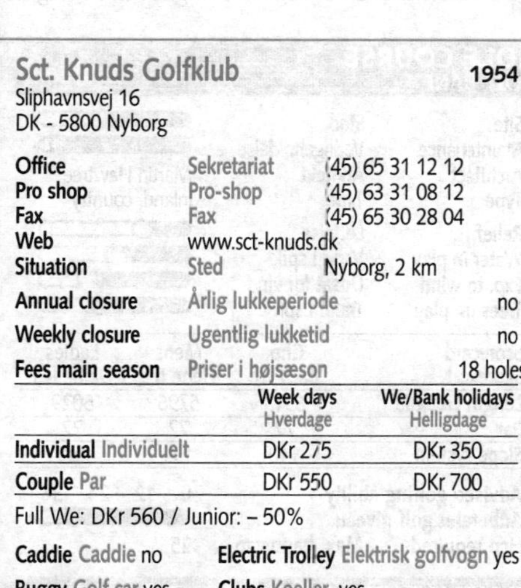

Sct. Knuds Golfklub **1954**

Sliphavnsvej 16
DK - 5800 Nyborg

Office	Sekretariat	(45) 65 31 12 12
Pro shop	Pro-shop	(45) 63 31 08 12
Fax	Fax	(45) 65 30 28 04
Web	www.sct-knuds.dk	
Situation	Sted	Nyborg, 2 km
Annual closure	Årlig lukkeperiode	no
Weekly closure	Ugentlig lukketid	no
Fees main season	Priser i højsæson	18 holes

	Week days / Hverdage	We/Bank holidays / Helligdage
Individual Individuelt	DKr 275	DKr 350
Couple Par	DKr 550	DKr 700

Full We: DKr 560 / Junior: – 50%

Caddie Caddie no — **Electric Trolley** Elektrisk golfvogn yes

Buggy Golf car yes — **Clubs** Koeller yes

Credit cards Kreditkord
VISA - Eurocard - DC

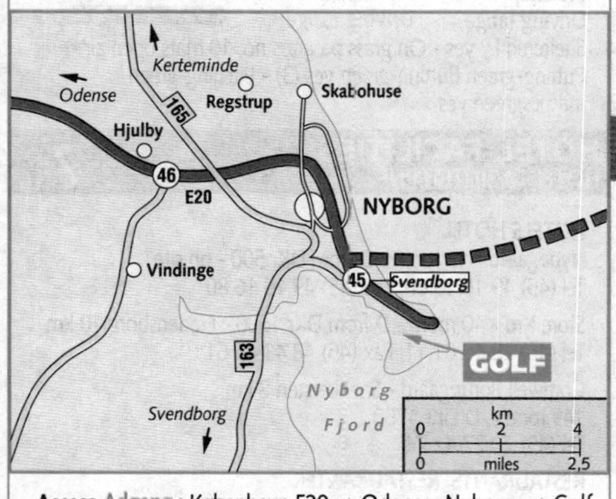

Access Adgang : København E20 → Odense. Nyborg, → Golf.
Map 1 on page 123 Kort 1 på side 123

GOLF COURSE
GOLF BANE — **15**/20

Site	Sted	
Maintenance	Vedligeholdelse	
Architect	Arkitekt	C.K. Cotton, Dreyer
Type	Type	forest, open country
Relief	Lettelse	
Water in play	Vand i spil	
Exp. to wind	Udsat for vind	
Trees in play	Træer i spil	

Scorecard Skorekort	Chp. Back tee	Mens Herre tee	Ladies Dame tee
Length Længde	5994	5729	4853
Par	72	72	72
Slope system	129	126	122

Advised golfing ability Anbefalet golf niveau: 0 12 24 36

Hcp required Max. handicap 36

CLUB HOUSE & AMENITIES
KLUBHUSET OG FACILITETER — **5**/10

Pro shop Pro-shop
Driving range Driving range
Sheltered Ly no - On grass på græs yes (03 → 11) - Putting-green Putting-green yes - Pitching-green Indspilsgreen yes

HOTEL FACILITIES
HOTEL FACILITETERNE — **6**/10

HOTELS HOTEL
Hesselet - Nyborg 2 km
43 rooms, D DKr 1680
Tel (45) 65 31 30 29, Fax (45) 65 31 29 58

Nyborg Strand - Nyborg 3 km
284 rooms, D DKr 1000
Tel (45) 65 31 31 31, Fax (45) 65 31 37 01

RESTAURANTS RESTAURANTER
Hos Svend - Svendborg 30 km
Tel (45) 62 22 07 95

Hesselet - Nyborg 2 km
Tel (45) 65 31 30 29

Sognegården - Millinge 40 km - Tel (45) 62 68 11 11

Simon's

15	7	7

Med sin placering kun få kilometer ned ad motorvejen fra Helsingør er Simon's en bane, svenskere gerne betaler de temmelig mange penge, det koster at spille den. For de ved, at de – ligesom alle andre – får noget for pengene. Fremragende stand, først og fremmest – banen regnes sammen med Royal Oak for Danmarks bedst holdte. Og en bane, der er sværere, end den ser ud til – ikke mindst på grund af dens meget store, ondulerede og efter danske forhold lynhurtige greens samt de små græstuer, der flankerer mange af dem på tre sider. Banen har været vært for adskillige turneringer på Challenge-touren, og det ses på fairways, de er ikke specielt brede. En stor sø dominerer det korte 10. hul, hvor man skal slå over for at komme på green, og det 18., hvis 460 meter lange venstre side ER søen. Banen er ikke specielt kuperet, men byder alligevel på en del blinde slag og skjulte forhindringer. Især approach-slaget til den højtliggende 3. green er svært.

A few miles from here, don't miss Helsingør and make sure you visit the castle of Kronborg on a foggy night; this is the castle of Elsenor, the setting for Shakespeare's Hamlet. The old houses in town are worth visiting as much as the castle, which in fact is more Renaissance than medieval in style. The course was opened only very recently on a pleasant site, despite the closeness of the motorway. A large lake is in play on the 10th and the 18th, a now classic par 5 edged by water up the whole of the left side. The course is not hilly but five of the greens and several hazards are almost blind, which does not help things first time out on the course. Likewise, you will need to concentrate over the whole round, not necessarily a good thing for pace of play and relaxation. Simon's is well worth a visit, even though we might have imagined a more "dramatic" course in this part of the world...

Simon's Golf Klub — 1993

Nybovej 5
DK - 3490 KVISTGAARD

Office	Sekretariat	(45) 49 19 14 78
Pro shop	Pro-shop	(45) 49 19 16 74
Fax	Fax	(45) 49 19 14 70
Web	www.simonsgolf.dk	
Situation	Sted	København, 30 km
Annual closure	Årlig lukkeperiode	no
Weekly closure	Ugentlig lukketid	no

Fees main season Priser i højsæson — 18 holes

	Week days / Hverdage	We/Bank holidays / Helligdage
Individual Individuelt	DKr 450	DKr 600
Couple Par	DKr 900	DKr 1200

Juniors: – 50%

Caddie Caddie no — **Electric Trolley** Elektrisk golfvogn no

Buggy Golf car yes — **Clubs** Koeller yes

Credit cards Kreditkord
VISA - Eurocard - DC

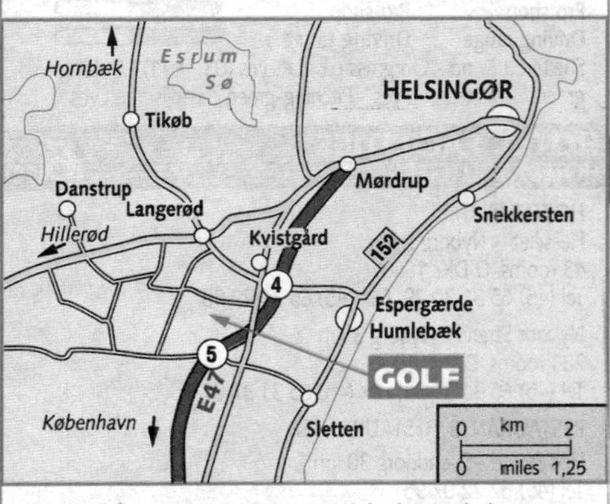

Access Adgang : E47 Exit 5 → Humlebæk. Hørsholmvej, → Golf.

Map 1 on page 123 Kort 1 på side 123

GOLF COURSE — GOLF BANE — 15/20

Site	Sted	
Maintenance	Vedligeholdelse	
Architect	Arkitekt	Martin Hawtree
Type	Type	inland, country
Relief	Lettelse	
Water in play	Vand i spil	
Exp. to wind	Udsat for vind	
Trees in play	Træer i spil	

Scorecard / Skorekort	Chp. / Back tee	Mens / Herre tee	Ladies / Dame tee
Length Længde	6313	5796	5029
Par	72	72	72
Slope system	140	134	131

Advised golfing ability Anbefalet golf niveau — 0 12 24 36

Hcp required Max. handicap — 25

CLUB HOUSE & AMENITIES — KLUBHUSET OG FACILITETER — 7/10

Pro shop Pro-shop
Driving range Driving range
Sheltered Ly yes - On grass på græs no, 10 mats open air - Putting-green Putting-green yes (3) - Pitching-green Indspilsgreen yes

HOTEL FACILITIES — HOTEL FACILITETERNE — 7/10

HOTELS HOTEL
Nybogaard - 15 rooms, D from DKr 500 - on site
Tel (45) 49 16 16 60, Fax (45) 49 16 16 80

Store Kro - 40 rooms, D from DKr 1500 - Fredensborg 10 km
Tel (45) 48 40 01 11, Fax (45) 48 48 45 61

Comwell Borupgaard - Snekkersten 8 km
149 rooms, D DKr 1750
Tel (45) 70 27 42 74

RESTAURANTS RESTAURANTER
Nokken - Rungsted 10 km - Tel (45) 45 57 13 14
Jan Hurtigkarl - Ålsgårde 5 km - Tel (45) 49 70 90 03
Taarbæk Kro - Taarbæk 20 km - Tel (45) 39 63 00 96

Vejle *Blå + Rød Slings*

14	7	7

Legoland ligger lige i nærheden, i Billund, dér er alt i miniatureformat. På Vejle-banen er der ikke miniature over hverken banens niveau eller dens træer. Tværtimod. Storladen er det ord, der bedst beskriver træerne, højdeforskellene og isolationen på den såkaldte blå banes ni huller. Det 4. hul er helt fantastisk. Når man står på teestedet og ser de store træer og de høje klippesider, skulle man ikke tro, at man befinder sig i en dansk skov. Vejles anlæg består også af en rød og en gul bane, i alt 27 huller, der byder på meget stor variation. Anlægget har flere gange lagt huller til Danish Open på damernes Europa-tour. Kombinationen blå/rød bane hører med en course slope på 139 til blandt de allersværeste 18 huller i Danmark. Ikke specielt lang, men smal og med svære dogleg-huller. De ni gule huller kom til i 1994. De er længere og af mere åben karakter. Kombinationen rød-gul bane er banen for den mindre øvede spiller.

When you are in this region, you simply have to drive a few miles west towards Billund... a little town of no special interest except Legoland, an incredible miniature world built with the famous plastic cubes that are a favourite toy for children all over the world. And since there is a child in every golfer, find a little inspiration to get to grips with the 27 holes at Vejle, of which the "Blue" 9-hole course (Blå) is without a doubt the hardest test of golf in Denmark. What it lacks in yardage it makes up for with some devilish dog-legs, the tremendous challenge of the forest and some disconcerting, sometimes even excessive, differences in level and altitude. The "Red" course (Rød), a 9-holer which originally completed the Blue course, is hardly any easier for wayward hitters, whereas the Yellow course, opened in 1994, is both more open and forthright, despite the number of small water hazards. For mid-handicappers and inexperienced players, we would recommend a "Red/Yellow" mix. At once spectacular, tricky and very natural, Vejle will leave some sort of mark on every golfer...

Vejle Golf Club — 1972

Ibækvej 46
DK - 7100 VEJLE

Office	Sekretariat	(45) 75 85 81 85
Pro shop	Pro-shop	(45) 75 85 81 43
Fax	Fax	(45) 75 85 83 01
Web	www.vejlegolfclub.dk	
Situation	Sted	Vejle, 5 km
Annual closure	Årlig lukkeperiode	no
Weekly closure	Ugentlig lukketid	no

Fees main season Priser i højsæson	Full day	
	Week days Hverdage	**We/Bank holidays** Helligdage
Individual Individuelt	DKr 300	DKr 350
Couple Par	DKr 600	DKr 700

Juniors: – 50%

Caddie Caddie no — **Electric Trolley** Elektrisk golfvogn no

Buggy Golf car yes — **Clubs** Koeller yes

Credit cards Kreditkord
VISA - Eurocard - DC

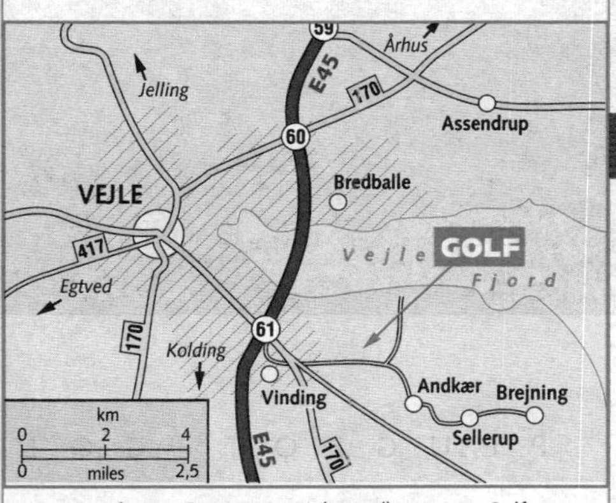

Access Adgang : E45 Exit 61. Vejle, Andkjærvej, → Golf.
Map 1 on page 122 Kort 1 på side 122

GOLF COURSE — GOLF BANE — 14/20

Site	Sted	
Maintenance	Vedligeholdelse	
Architect	Arkitekt	Malling Petersen
Type	Type	forest, hilly
Relief	Lettelse	
Water in play	Vand i spil	
Exp. to wind	Udsat for vind	
Trees in play	Træer i spil	

Scorecard Skorekort	**Chp.** Back tee	**Mens** Herre tee	**Ladies** Dame tee
Length Længde	5575	5575	4693
Par	72	72	72
Slope system	—	140	130

Advised golfing ability Anbefalet golf niveau — 0 12 24 36

Hcp required Max. handicap 36

CLUB HOUSE & AMENITIES — KLUBHUSET OG FACILITETER — 7/10

Pro shop Pro-shop

Driving range Driving range

Sheltered Ly no - On grass på græs yes (04 → 10) - Putting-green Putting-green yes - Pitching-green Indspilsgreen yes

HOTEL FACILITIES — HOTEL FACILITETERNE — 7/10

HOTELS HOTEL

Munkebjerg - Vejle 300 m
150 rooms, D DKr 1775
Tel (45) 76 42 85 00, Fax (45) 75 72 08 86

Park Inn - Vejle 5 km
135 rooms, D DKr 1145
Tel (45) 76 43 67 00, Fax (45) 76 43 67 01

RESTAURANTS RESTAURANTER

Munkjeberg Hotel Restaurant - Vejle 300 m
Tel (45) 76 42 85 00

Merlot - Vejle 5 km
Tel (45) 75 83 88 44

Da Franco - Vejle 5 km - Tel (45) 75 82 57 67

SUOMI

FINLAND

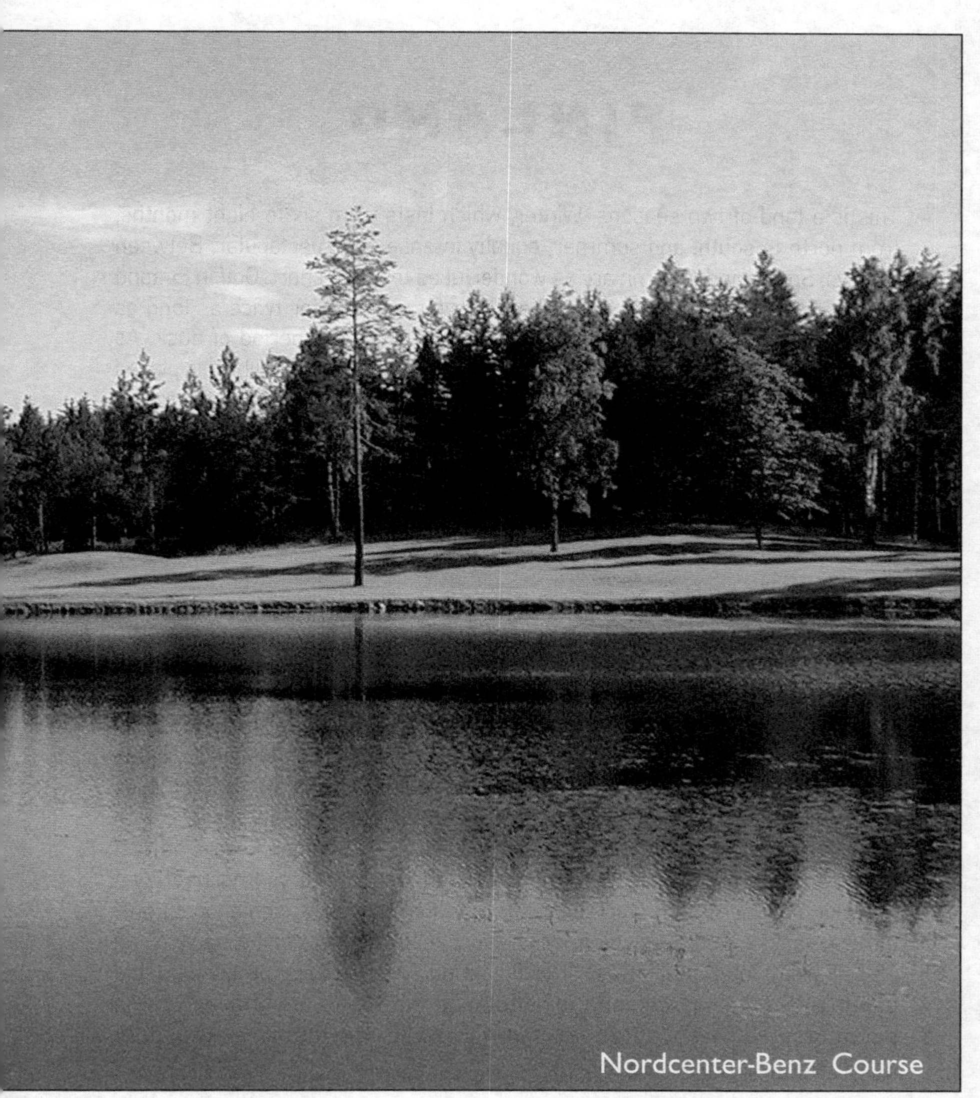

Nordcenter-Benz Course

FINLAND

This is a land of two seasons. Winter, which lasts from six to eight months, from north to south, and summer, equally intense and spectacular. Between the two, Spring and Autumn are as wonderful as they are short. Golf in Finland is played from May to late September, but you can play for twice as long as anywhere else. In the summer, night-time is just a brief period of dusk. As inveterate nature lovers, the Finns have naturally taken to golf, which is played as soon as the ice has thawed until the first winter snowfall. Today, there are 106 courses open (more than 65 eighteen-holers) catering to 105,000 golfers, and they include new layouts like the very impressive Kytäjä resort. And as here golf is a real sport, there are already enough good players for Finland to have produced many a good performance in the world team championships.

SUOMI

Suomi on kahden vuodenajan maa. Kuusi, jopa kahdeksankin kuukautta pitkä talvi, pohjoisesta etelään asti, ja kesä, yhtä intensiivinen ja loistelias. Niiden väliin jäävät kesä ja syksy ovat yhtä ihmeelliset kuin lyhyetkin. Golfia Suomessa pelataan toukokuusta syyskuun loppupuolelle, mutta täällä voi silti pelata kaksin verroin kauemmin kuin missään muualla, sillä Suomen kesäyö on vain lyhyt hämärän hetki. Parantumattomina luonnonystävinä suomalaiset ovat tietenkin ryhtyneet harrastamaan golfia, jota he pelaavat lumenlähdöstä ensi lumeen saakka. Suomessa on nykyisin avoinna 106 golfkenttää (joista yli 65 on 18-reikäisiä), jotka huolehtivat 105.000:sta golfin pelaajasta. Ja koska golfia pidetään Suomessa oikeana urheilulajina, on täällä jo riittävästi hyviä pelaajia,jotka ovat antaneet monta hyvää näytöstä joukkueiden maailmanmestaruuskisoissa.

CLASSIFICATION OF GOLF COURSES
GOLFIKENTTIEN LUOKITUS

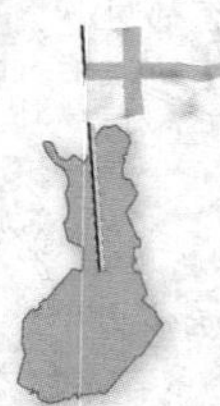

This classification gives priority consideration to the score awarded to the actual course.
Tämä luokitus perustuu ensisijaisesti kentän saamiin pisteisiin.

Within each score, the ranking is purely alphabetical

Course score / Golfikenttien luokitus				Page / Sivulla
17	7	3	Kytäjä South-East Course	146
17	8	7	Ruuhikoski	150
16	7	6	Espoo	144
16	7	8	Helsinki	145
16	7	3	Nordcenter Benz Course	148
16	8	7	Sarfvik New Course	151
15	7	7	Master Master	147
15	8	5	Pickala Seaside Course	149
15	8	6	Talma	152
14	7	6	Tawast	153

HOTEL FACILITIES
HOTELLIEN LUOKITUS

This classification gives priority consideration to the score awarded to the hotel facilities.
Tämä luokitus perustuu ensisijaisesti hotellin saamiin pisteisiin.

		Hotel facility score / Hotellien luokitus		Page / Sivulla
16	7	**8**	Helsinki	145
15	7	**7**	Master Master	147
17	8	**7**	Ruuhikoski	150
16	8	**7**	Sarfvik New Course	151
16	7	**6**	Espoo	144
15	8	**6**	Talma	152
14	7	**6**	Tawast	153
15	8	**5**	Pickala Seaside Course	149
17	7	**3**	Kytäjä South-East Course	146
16	7	**3**	Nordcenter Benz Course	148

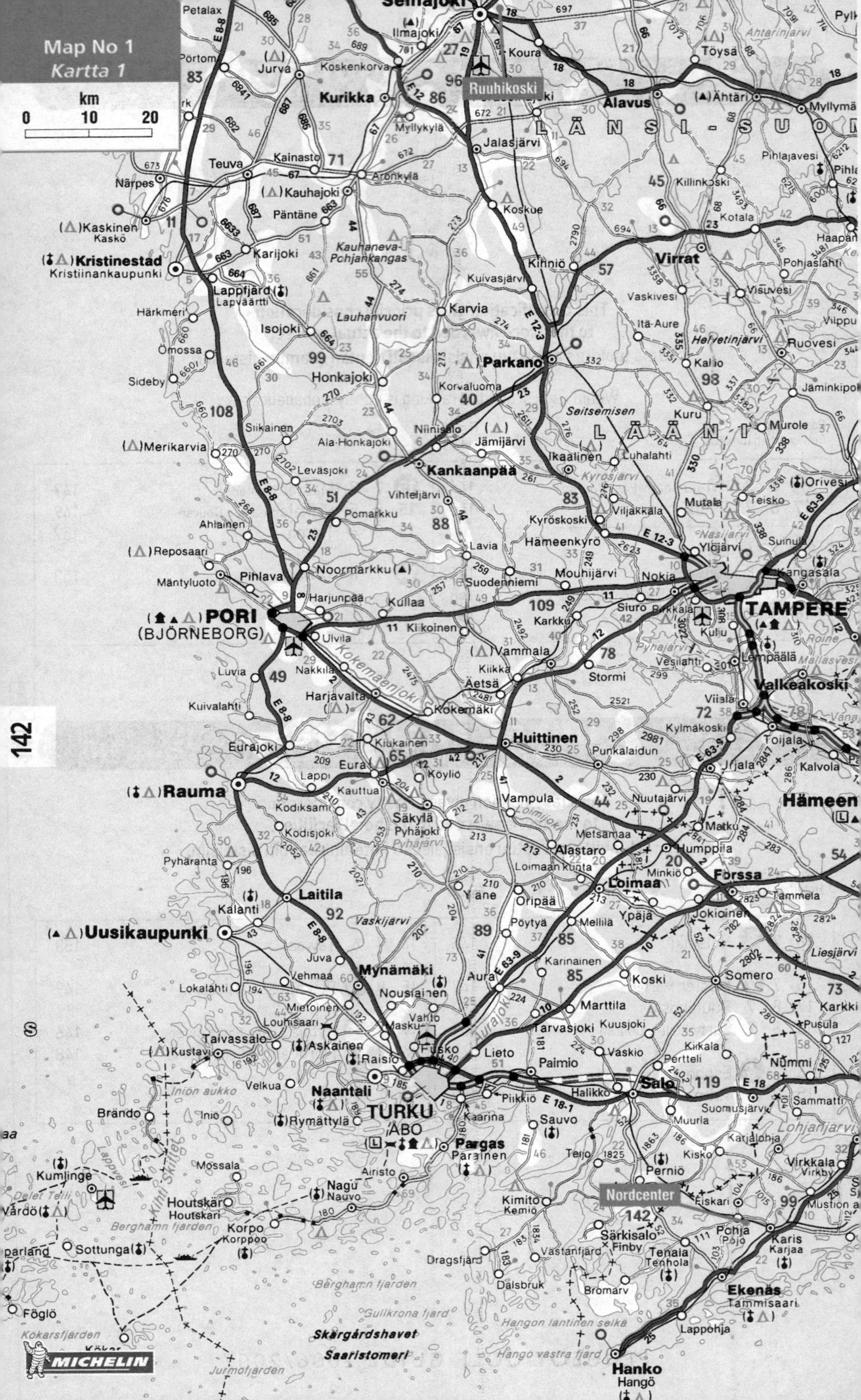
Map No 1
Kartta 1
km
0 10 20
142
Seinäjoki
Ilmajoki
Koura
Ruuhikoski
Töysä
Ähtärinjärvi
Ähtäri
Myllymäki
Alavus
Kurikka
Koskenkorva
Jurva
Petalax
Pörtom
Myllykylä
Jalasjärvi
LÄNSI - SUOMEN LÄÄNI
Teuva
Kainasto
Närpes
Aronkylä
Kauhajoki
Pihlajavesi
Killinkoski
Kaskinen
Kaskö
Päntäne
Koskue
Kotala
Haapamäki
Kristinestad
Kristiinankaupunki
Karijoki
Kauhaneva-Pohjankangas
Kihniö
Virrat
Pohjaslahti
Lappfjärd
Lapväärtti
Kuivasjärvi
Vaskivesi
Visuvesi
Härkmeri
Karvia
Lauhanvuori
Isojoki
Itä-Aure
Helvetinjärvi
Ruovesi
Vilppula
Ömossa
Parkano
Kallio
Sideby
Honkajoki
Korvaluoma
Jäminkipohja
Seitsemisen
Kuru
Siikainen
Niinisalo
Jämijärvi
Murole
Merikarvia
Ala-Honkajoki
Ikaalinen
Luhalahti
Leväsjoki
Kankaanpää
Kyrösjärvi
Orivesi
Vihteljärvi
Mutala
Teisko
Ahlainen
Pomarkku
Viljakkala
Kyröskoski
Näsijärvi
Suinula
Reposaari
Lavia
Hämeenkyrö
Ylöjärvi
Kangasala
Noormarkku
Mäntyluoto
Pihlava
Suodenniemi
Mouhijärvi
Nokia
Harjunpää
Kullaa
Siuro
Pirkkala
TAMPERE
PORI
(BJÖRNEBORG)
Ulvila
Kiikoinen
Karkku
Kuru
Roine
Vammala
Pyhäjärvi
Lempäälä
Mallasvesi
Kokemäenjoki
Luvia
Nakkila
Kiikka
Vesilahti
Valkeakoski
Äetsä
Stormi
Harjavalta
Kuivalahti
Kokemäki
Viiala
Kylmäkoski
Eurajoki
Kiukainen
Huittinen
Punkalaidun
Toijala
Eura
Köyliö
Kalvola
Rauma
Lappi
Urjala
Kauttua
Vampula
Nuutajärvi
Hämeen
Kodiksami
Säkylä
Pyhäjoki
Loimijoki
Matku
Kodisjoki
Metsämaa
Humppila
Pyhäranta
Alastaro
Loimaan kunta
Minkiö
Forssa
Laitila
Yläne
Oripää
Loimaa
Tammela
Kalanti
Vaskijärvi
Pöytyä
Mellilä
Ypäjä
Jokioinen
Uusikaupunki
Liesjärvi
Juva
Karinainen
Somero
Mynämäki
Vehmaa
Aura
Koski
Lokalahti
Nousiainen
Marttila
Karkkila
Mietoinen
Louhisaari
Vahto
Masku
Tarvasjoki
Kuusjoki
Pusula
Taivassalo
Askainen
Kiikala
Kustavi
Rusko
Lieto
Vaskio
Raisio
Paimio
Perttelli
Nummi
Velkua
Salo
Iniön aukko
Naantali
Piikkiö
Halikko
Sammatti
TURKU
ÅBO
Kaarina
Suomusjärvi
Brändö
Iniö
Rymättylä
Sauvo
Muurla
Lohjanjärvi
Pargas
Parainen
Karjalohja
Teijo
Kisko
Mossala
Perniö
Virkkala
Virkby
Kumlinge
Airisto
Nagu
Nauvo
Nordcenter
Fiskari
Delet Teili
Vårdö
Houtskär
Houtskari
Kimito
Kemiö
Mustio
Berghamn fjärden
Korpo
Korppoo
Särkisalo
Finby
Pohja
Pojo
Karis
Karjaa
Sottunga
Vastanfjärd
Tenala
Tenhola
Dragsfjärd
Dalsbruk
Bromarv
Ekenäs
Tammisaari
Föglö
Gullkrona fjärd
Hangon läntinen selkä
Lappohja
Kökar
Kokarsfjärden
Skärgårdshavet
Saaristomeri
Hango västra fjärd
Jurmofjärden
Hanko
Hangö
MICHELIN

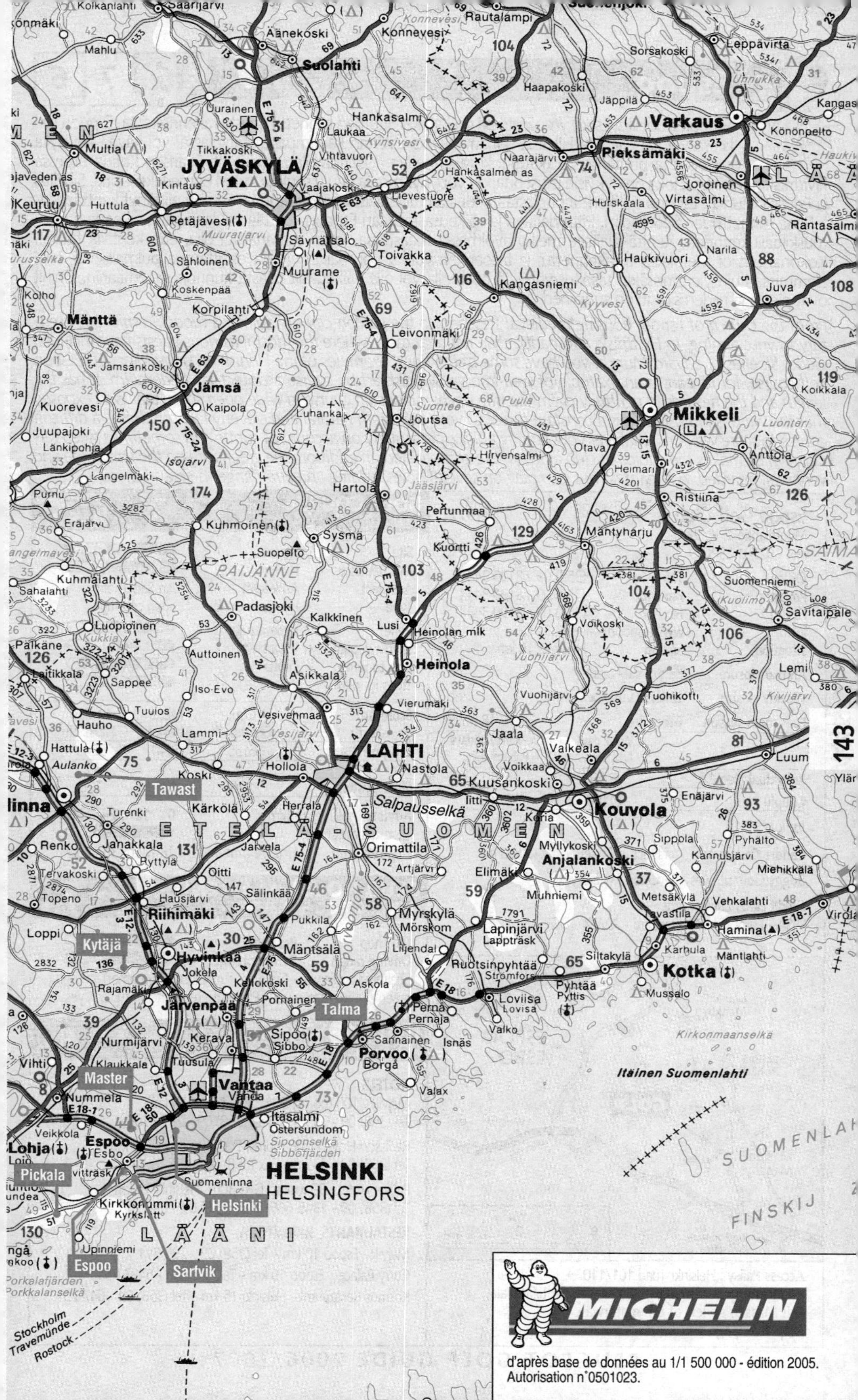
Kolkanlahti
Saarijärvi
Konnevesi
Rautalampi
Suonenjoki
Leppävirta
Äänekoski
Suolahti
Sorsakoski
Haapakoski
Unnukka
Mahlu
Uurainen
Hankasalmi
Jäppilä
Varkaus
Kangas
Könönpelto
Laukaa
Multia
Tikkakoski
Vihtavuori
Kynsivesi
Naarajärvi
Pieksämäki
Joroinen
JYVÄSKYLÄ
Hankasalmen as
Kintaus
Vaajakoski
Lievestuore
Keuruu
Huttula
Petäjävesi
Hurskaala
Virtasalmi
Rantasalmi
Muuratjärvi
Säynätsalo
Toivakka
Haukivuori
Narila
Sahloinen
Muurame
Kangasniemi
Juva
Kolho
Koskenpää
Kyyvesi
Korpilahti
Mänttä
Leivonmäki
Jamsankoski
Jämsä
Koikkala
Kuorevesi
Kaipola
Luhanka
Puula
Suontee
Mikkeli
Juupajoki
Länkipohja
Joutsa
Luonteri
Otava
Anttola
Isojärvi
Hirvensalmi
Heimari
Langelmäki
Jääsjärvi
Ristiina
Purnu
Hartola
Pertunmaa
Eräjärvi
Kuhmoinen
Mäntyharju
Sysmä
Kuortti
Suopelto
SAIMAA
PÄIJÄNNE
Kuhmalahti
Suomenniemi
Sahalahti
Padasjoki
Kuolimo
Savitaipale
Luopioinen
Kalkkinen
Lusi
Heinolan mlk
Voikoski
Kukkia
Palkäne
Auttoinen
Heinola
Vuohijärvi
Laitikkala
Asikkala
Lemi
Sappee
Iso-Evo
Vuohijärvi
Tuohikotti
Kiviljärvi
Tuulos
Vierumäki
Vesivehmaa
Hauho
Lammi
Vesijärvi
Jaala
Hattula
Valkeala
Aulanko
LAHTI
Hollola
Nastola
Voikkaa
Luum
Koski
Kuusankoski
Tawast
Iitti
Enäjärvi
Turenki
Kärkölä
Herrala
Salpausselkä
Koria
Kouvola
Hämeenlinna
ETELÄ-SUOMEN LÄÄNI
Renko
Janakkala
Järvelä
Orimattila
Myllykoski
Sippola
Pyhältö
Ryttylä
Artjärvi
Anjalankoski
Kannusjärvi
Tervakoski
Oitti
Elimäki
Miehikkälä
Topeno
Hausjärvi
Sälinkää
Muhniemi
Metsäkylä
Vehkalahti
Riihimäki
Pukkila
Myrskylä
Mörskom
Tavastila
Loppi
Kytäjä
Lapinjärvi
Lappträsk
Hamina
Virolahti
Hyvinkää
Mäntsälä
Liljendal
Siltakylä
Karhula
Mäntlahti
Jokela
Porvoonjoki
Ruotsinpyhtää
Strömfors
Kotka
Rajamäki
Kellokoski
Askola
Pyhtää
Pyttis
Mussalo
Järvenpää
Pornainen
Talma
Perna
Pernaja
Loviisa
Lovisa
Valko
Nurmijärvi
Kerava
Sipoo
Sibbo
Sannainen
Isnäs
Kirkonmaanselkä
Klaukkala
Tuusula
Porvoo
Borgå
Vihti
Master
Vantaa
Vanda
Itäinen Suomenlahti
Nummela
Valax
Veikkola
Itäsalmi
Östersundom
Lohja
Lojo
Espoo
Esbo
Sipoonselkä
Sibbofjärden
SUOMENLAHTI
Pickala
Vittträsk
Suomenlinna
HELSINKI
HELSINGFORS
Kirkkonummi
Kyrkslätt
Helsinki
FINSKIJ
Upinniemi
Espoo
Sarfvik
Porkalafjärden
Porkkalanselkä
Stockholm
Travemünde
Rostock
143
MICHELIN
d'après base de données au 1/1 500 000 - édition 2005.
Autorisation n°0501023.

Espoo

16 | 7 | 6

Espoon (ruotsiksi Esbo) ympäristössä on joitakin Suomen tunnetuimmista rakennuksista. Espoon kirkossa voi katsella keskiaikaisia seinämaalauksia.Vähän kauempana, Tapiolassa, voi käydä kävelyllä puistoissa ja puutarhoissa (kaupunki rakennettiin 1950-luvulla). Arkkitehti Saarisen kotina olleessa Hvitträskin huvilassa, joka on nykyisin museona, on yöpynyt monia kuuluisuuksia,kuten esimerkiksi Gorki, Sibelius ja Edvard Munch. Espoon golfkenttä puolestaan edustaa ruotsalaista arkkitehtuuria. Sen on piirtänyt kenttäarkkitehtinä tunnettu Jan Sederholm. Pituudeltaan ja vaikeusasteeltaan Espoon kenttää voidaan pitää oikeana mestaruuskilpailukenttänä. Kenttä sijaitsee melko avoimessa maastossa, joten vaarana voi olla, että kentällä tuulee. Kokonaisuus on nerokkaasti rakennettu, ja tasoerojen vuoksi voi mailan valinta osoittautua pulmalliseksi. Niin alemmissa kuin ylemmissäkin tasoitusryhmissä pelaavilla voi olla vaikeuksia päästä kunnon pistemääriin. Griinit ovat pieniä ja niiden sijainti on suojainen.

From the church of Espoo, housing medieval frescoes, to the garden city of Tapiola, a model in mid-20th century town-planning, to Hvitträsk, a romantic style national castle where the most illustrious guests have included Gorki, Sibelius or Edvard Munch, you have some of the finest examples of the Finnish art of building. The Espoo golf course, for its part, is an example of well-known Swedish art by course architect Jan Sederholm. It has the length and the hazards to rightfully claim the title of championship course in wide open space that is so exposed that the wind is almost always a constant threat to your ball. Both natural and cleverly laid out, this is a difficult course to score well on, whatever your golfing ability, particularly on account of subtle and sometimes steep terrain, which makes the choice of club a little more complicated. In addition, the greens are on the small side and very well guarded. A stream comes into play on several holes, adding an extra danger here and there.

Espoo Golf Club — 1977

Mynttiläntie 1, PL 26
FIN - 02781 ESPOO

Office	Toimisto	(358) 09 - 8190 3444
Pro shop	Pro shop	(358) 09 - 8190 3444
Fax	Fax	(358) 09 - 8190 3434
Web	www.espoongolfseura.fi	
Situation	Sijainti	Helsinki, 15 km
Annual closure	Kenttä suljetaan	no
Weekly closure	Suljetan viikolla	no

Fees main season Green fee	18 holes	
	Week days Arkipäivisin	**We/Bank holidays** Pyhäpäivisin
Individual Henkilö	€ 50	€ 50
Couple Pari	€ 100	€ 100

Juniors: € 10

Caddie Caddie no — **Electric Trolley** Sähkörattaat no
Buggy Golfauto yes — **Clubs** Mailat yes
Credit cards Luottokortit
VISA - Eurocard - MasterCard - AMEX - DC

Access Pääsy : Helsinki, road 101/110 → Kauniainen/Grankulla, E18/50 → Kauklahti/Masala. Exit Masala, go left of the motorway.
Map 1 on page 143 Kartta 1 sivulla : 143

GOLF COURSE — 16/20
BAN

Site	Sijainti	
Maintenance	Hoito	
Architect	Arkkitehti	Jan Sederholm
Type	Kentän luonne	open country
Relief	Vapautuminen	
Water in play	Vesiesteitä	
Exp. to wind	Tuulta	
Trees in play	Puita	

Scorecard Tuloskortti	**Chp.** Champ. tii	**Mens** Miest. tii	**Ladies** Naist. tii
Length Pituus	6155	5940	5245
Par	72	72	72
Slope system	126	124	126

Advised golfing ability Tasoitusvaatimus — 0 12 24 36
Hcp required Hcp-vaatimus — 28 Men, 36 Ladies

CLUB HOUSE & AMENITIES — 7/10
KLUBHUSET OG FACILITETER

Pro shop Pro shop
Driving range Driving range
Sheltered suoja yes - On grass ruoholla yes (Summer) - Putting-green putting-green yes - Pitching-green pitching-green yes

HOTEL FACILITIES — 6/10
HOTEL FACILITETERNE

HOTELS
Majvik - 100 rooms, D € 130 - Espoo 10 km
Tel (358) 09 - 295 511, Fax (358) 09 - 297 6306

Radisson Hotel - 208 rooms, D € 90 - Espoo 10 km
Tel (358) 09 - 435 80, Fax (358) 09 - 466 693

Palace Hotel - 39 rooms, D € 300 - Helsinki 15 km
Tel (358) 09 - 1345 6661, Fax (358) 09 - 654 736

RESTAURANTS RAVINTOLA
Majvik - Espoo 10 km - Tel (358) 09 - 295 511
Curry Palace - Espoo 10 km - Tel (358) 09 - 5483 751
Kosmos Restaurant - Helsinki 15 km - Tel (358) 09 - 647 255

Helsinki

16 | 7 | 8

Helsingissä (ruotsiksi Helsingfors) tuntuu voimakkaasti 1900 luvun suurien arkkitehtien Eliel Saarinen ja Alvar Aallon vaikutus. Jos haluaa nähdä vanhoja, perinteisiä rakennuksia, on Seurasaaren ulkomuseo, joka sijaitsee vain lyhyen bussimatkan päässä kaupungista, käymisen arvoinen. Kaupunkia on kutsuttu Itämeren tyttäreksi, ja Seurasaari (Fölisön) on vain yksi sitä ympäröivistä saarista. Vaikka Suomen ilmasto asettaakin rajoituksensa on golf saanut nopeasti jalansijaa urheilulajina. Helsingin Golfklubin kenttä on Suomen vanhin ja se sijaitsee lähellä keskustaa. Kerho on järjestänyt monia suuria amatöörikilpailuja. Lauri Arkkolan kauniiseen lehtomaisemaan suunnittelemalla kentällä on ilmiselviä brittiläisiä esikuvia. Kenttää kehystävät jättimäiset puut, maasto on tasaista ja väylät erinomaiset. Vesiesteitä on vain muutama, kolmen reiän kohdalla on kuitenkin otettava huomioon joki. Kenttä on houkuttelevan avoin ja liikkuminen on helppoa, mutta täällä on kuitenkin vaikea päästä hyviin pistelukemiin. Reikien pituus vaihtelee, joten on viisasta pitää mukanaan kaikki 14 mailaa.

Many isles and peninsulas spread around Helsinki, known as "the daughter of the Baltic". In a country where nature commands so much respect, the game of golf has quickly gained a foothold despite the sometimes harsh climate. The Helsinki golf club is the oldest of them all and the course, virtually within the city limits, has hosted a number of top amateur events. Designed by Lauri Arkkola with a very definite British influence, this is a magnificent park with some wonderful trees, virtually flat terrain and great fairways. There are not many water hazards, just a stream that only really comes into play on three holes, on a course which is very forthright, easy to play on foot but much harder to come to terms with and card a good score. Despite this course being on the shortish side, holes come in all lengths so pack the full 14 clubs.

Helsinki Golf Club — 1932

Talin Kartano
FIN - 00350 HELSINKI

Office	Toimisto	(358) 09 - 2252 370
Pro shop	Pro shop	(358) 09 - 2252 3714
Fax	Fax	(358) 09 - 2252 3737
Web	www.helsingingolfklubi.fi	
Situation	Sijainti	within Helsinki
Annual closure	Kenttä suljetaan	no
Weekly closure	Suljetan viikolla	no

Fees main season Green fee	Week days Arkipäivisin	We/Bank holidays Pyhäpäivisin
		18 holes
Individual Henkilö	€ 50	€ 50
Couple Pari	€ 100	€ 100

Juniors: - 50%

Caddie Caddie no — Electric Trolley Sähkörattaat no
Buggy Golfauto no — Clubs Mailat yes
Credit cards Luottokortit no

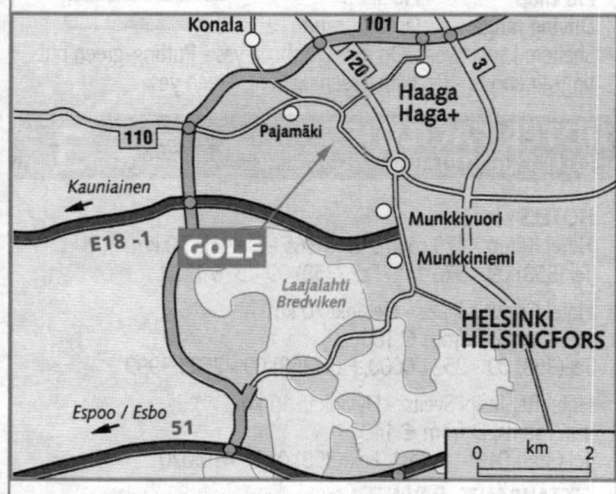

Access Pääsy : In Helsinki, → Haaga then Pajamäki
Map 1 on page 143 Kartta 1 sivulla : 143

GOLF COURSE — BAN — 16/20

Site	Sijainti	
Maintenance	Hoito	
Architect	Arkkitehti	Lauri Arkkola
Type	Kentän luonne	parkland
Relief	Vapautuminen	
Water in play	Vesiesteitä	
Exp. to wind	Tuulta	
Trees in play	Puita	

Scorecard Tuloskortti	Chp. Champ. tii	Mens Miest. tii	Ladies Naist. tii
Length Pituus	5829	5486	4782
Par	71	71	71
Slope system	134	131	126

Advised golfing ability Tasoitusvaatimus: 0 12 24 36
Hcp required Hcp-vaatimus: 24 Men, 30 Ladies

CLUB HOUSE & AMENITIES — KLUBHUSET OG FACILITETER — 7/10

Pro shop — Pro shop
Driving range — Driving range
Sheltered suoja yes - On grass ruoholla yes (Summer) - Putting-green putting-green yes - Pitching-green pitching-green yes

HOTEL FACILITIES — HOTEL FACILITETERNE — 8/10

HOTELS

Hotel Kämp - 179 rooms, D € 380 - Helsinki 3 km
Tel (358) 09 - 576 111, Fax (358) 09 - 576 1122

Rivoli Jardin - 55 rooms, D € 305 - Helsinki 5 km
Tel (358) 09 - 681 500, Fax (358) 09 - 656 988

Hilton Hotel Kalastajatorppa - Helsinki 4 km
238 rooms, D € 300
Tel (358) 09 - 458 11, Fax (358) 09 - 4581 2211

RESTAURANTS RAVINTOLA

Ravintola Sipuli - Helsinki 3 km - Tel (358) 09 - 179 900
Havis Amanda - Helsinki 5 km - Tel (358) 09 - 666 882
Savoy - Helsinki 5 km - Tel (358) 09 -4684 4020
Chez Dominique - Helsinki 5 km - Tel (358) 09 -612 7393

Kytäjä South East Course

17 | 7 | 3

Yksityisen golfkeskuksen rakentaminen suurelle maatilalle noin neljänkymmenen kilometrin päähän Helsingistä on yksi Pohjois-Euroopan kunnianhimoisimmista ja vaikuttavimmista hankkeista. Alueelle on tarkoitus rakentaa hotelli, ja se käsittää valmistuttuaan kolme 18 reiän golfkenttää. South-East-kenttä avattiin vuonna 2002. Tämän jälkeen valmistui North-East-kenttä ja North-West-kentän on tarkoitus valmistua vuoden 2006 aikana. South-East on maisemallisesti kaunein kenttä. Yhdeksän ensimmäistä reikää sijaitsee metsäisessä maastossa, jossa on runsaasti korkeuseroja. Yhdeksällä viimeisellä reiällä maasto on tasaisempaa, ja reiät sijaitsevat romanttisen järven välittömässä läheisyydessä. Maisema tuo mieleen postikorteissa kuvatun suomalaismaiseman. Koko seutu voi olla ylpeä kauniisti suunnitteluista golfkentistä, rinteiden juurella sijaitsevista mahtavista hiekkaesteistä ja haastavista viheriöistä, joita kuulee usein kehuttavan. North-East-kentän korkeuserot näyttävät hieman pienemmiltä, mutta vaikutelman ei pidä antaa hämätä itseään.

This is one of the most ambitious and impressive projects in Northern Europe over a huge estate forty kilometres down the road from Helsinki. A private resort course with plans for a hotel, the site will eventually comprise three 18-hole courses. The South-East was opened in 2002, followed by the North-East, and the North-West is scheduled for 2006. These three championship courses have been laid out by the Canadian Tom McBroom. The South-East is the most panoramic with nine holes running through a lot of trees and over hilly terrain, then a further nine playing over flatter land alongside a wonderfully romantic lake, all to a backdrop of the Finnish landscape you see on picture postcards. The beautiful styling of these courses does the whole site proud with some deep, majestic bunkers beneath steep slopes and very tricky greens that are often elevated. Green-keeping is top-rate and the greens as fast as you could wish for.

Kytäjä Golf Oy — 2002

Kytäjäntie 1265
FIN - 05720 HYVINNKÄÄ

Office Toimisto (358) 019 - 456 5700
Pro shop Pro shop (358) 019 - 456 5714
Fax Fax (358) 019 - 456 5750
Web www.kytajagolf.fi
Situation Sijainti Helsinki, 70 km
Hyvinkää, 15 km
Annual closure Kenttä suljetaan 15/10→15/5
Weekly closure Suljetan viikolla no
Fees main season Green fee 18 holes

	Week days Arkipäivisin	We/Bank holidays Pyhäpäivisin
Individual Henkilö	€ 70	€ 70
Couple Pari	€ 140	€ 140

Juniors under 21: € 25 / Full day: € 105
Caddie Caddie no — **Electric Trolley** Sähkörattaat no
Buggy Golfauto yes — **Clubs** Mailat yes
Credit cards Luottokortit
VISA - Eurocard - MasterCard - AMEX - DC

Access Pääsy : Helsinki, E12 → Tampere. Exit Hyvinkää
Map 1 on page 143 Kartta 1 sivulla : 143

GOLF COURSE — BAN — 17/20

Site	Sijainti	
Maintenance	Hoito	
Architect	Arkkitehti	Thomas McBroom
Type	Kentän luonne	parkland, forest
Relief	Vapautuminen	
Water in play	Vesiesteitä	
Exp. to wind	Tuulta	
Trees in play	Puita	

Scorecard Tuloskortti	Chp. Champ. tii	Mens Miest. tii	Ladies Naist. tii
Length Pituus	6369	5923	4874
Par	71	71	71
Slope system	141	136	129

Advised golfing ability Tasoitusvaatimus 0 12 24 36
Hcp required Hcp-vaatimus 36 Men, 45 Ladies

CLUB HOUSE & AMENITIES — KLUBHUSET OG FACILITETER — 7/10

Pro shop Pro shop
Driving range Driving range
Sheltered suoja yes - On grass ruoholla yes - Putting-green putting-green yes - Pitching-green pitching-green yes

HOTEL FACILITIES — HOTEL FACILITETERNE — 3/10

HOTELS

Hotel Kämp - 179 rooms, D € 365 - Helsinki 70 km
Tel (358) 09 - 576 111, Fax (358) 09 - 576 1122

Hotel Crowne Plaza - Helsinki 70 km
496 rooms, D from € 160
Tel (358) 09 - 2521 0000, Fax (358) 09 - 2521 3999

Hotel Rantasipi Sveitsi - Hyvinkää 15 km
196 rooms, D from € 140
Tel (358) 019 - 45 881, Fax (358) 019 - 419 020

RESTAURANTS RAVINTOLA
G.W. Sundmans - Helsinki 70 km - Tel (358) 09 - 622 6410
Nokka - Helsinki 70 km - Tel (358) 09 - 687 7330

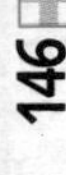

Master *Master*

15 | 7 | 7

Espoo (ruotsiksi Esbo) on Helsingin rajanaapuri ja yksi Suomen suurimmista kaupungeista. Lähes 90 prosenttia rakennuksista on rakennettu vuoden 1960 jälkeen, mutta alue oli aikaisemmin tunnettu monista kartanoistaan, jotka sijaitsivat vanhan rantatien tuntumassa. Master Golf klubin kaksi 18-reikäistä kenttää on rakennettu tähän näyttävään ympäristöön. Forest-kenttä kaikkine puineen on saanut varsin osuvan nimen. Laajassa puistomaisemassa sijaitseva Master-kenttä on vielä parempi. Ensimmäiset seitsemän reikää ovat avoimia, mutta kierroksen loppuosassa on paljon vettä, mukaan luettuna lampi, joka on otettava huomioon etenkin viimeisten yhdeksän reiän kohdalla. Kenttä on erittäin tasapainoinen ja soveltuu kaikenlaisille pelaajille. Master-kenttä onkin suomalaisten golfinpelaajien suosiossa ammattitaitoisen palvelun ja kenttien erinomaisen kunnon ansiosta.

Espoo/Esbo is one of the largest cities in Finland and today virtually adjoins Helsinki. While almost 90% of the housing dates from the 1960s and thereafter, this used to be a region of a extensive properties not far from the old coast road. This grand golf club, with two 18-hole courses, is laid out on one such former estate. The first course, "the Forest", has the name it deserves and boasts any number of age-old trees. The second, "the Master", is even better and sprawls over a huge park. While the first seven holes are laid out over wide open space, the rest of the course features a lot of water, including a lake which spectacularly comes into play on half the holes, especially on the back nine. Well-balanced overall, open and adapting to players of all abilities, the "Master" is a very popular course with Finnish golfers, a fact equally explained to some extent by very professional administration and excellent maintenance.

Master Golf Club — 1988

Bodominkuja 7
FIN - 02940 ESPOO

Office	Toimisto	(358) 09 - 849 2300
Pro shop	Pro shop	(358) 09 - 8492 3060
Fax	Fax	(358) 09 - 8492 3011
Web	www.mastergolf.fi	
Situation	Sijainti	Helsinki, 15 km
Annual closure	Kenttä suljetaan	no
Weekly closure	Suljetan viikolla	no

Fees main season Green fee — 18 holes

	Week days Arkipäivisin	We/Bank holidays Pyhäpäivisin
Individual Henkilö	€ 55	€ 65*
Couple Pari	€ 110	€ 130*

* With members only / Juniors: € 15

Caddie Caddie no — **Electric Trolley** Sähkörattaat no
Buggy Golfauto yes — **Clubs** Mailat yes
Credit cards Luottokortit
VISA - Eurocard - MasterCard - AMEX - DC

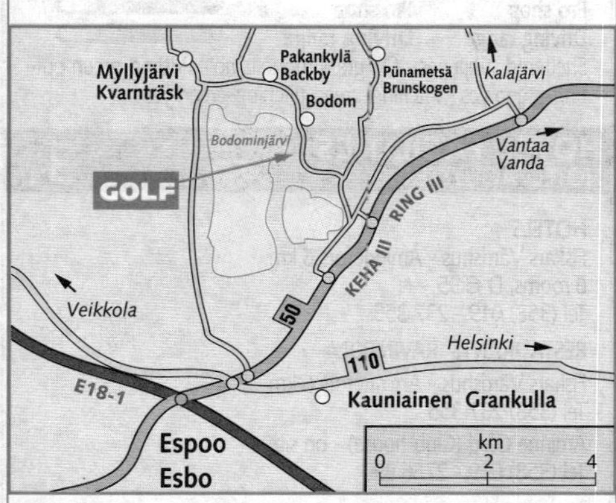

Access Pääsy : Helsinki, take 50/E18, Exit Bodominjärvi/Bodom, go left towards the lake.
Map 1 on page 143 Kartta 1 sivulla : 143

GOLF COURSE — BAN — 15/20

Site	Sijainti	
Maintenance	Hoito	
Architect	Arkkitehti	Kosti Kuronen
Type	Kentän luonne	parkland
Relief	Vapautuminen	
Water in play	Vesiesteitä	
Exp. to wind	Tuulta	
Trees in play	Puita	

Scorecard Tuloskortti	Chp. Champ. tii	Mens Miest. tii	Ladies Naist. tii
Length Pituus	6083	5708	4799
Par	72	72	72
Slope system	131	136	125

Advised golfing ability Tasoitusvaatimus — 0 12 24 36
Hcp required Hcp-vaatimus — 30 Men, 36 Ladies

CLUB HOUSE & AMENITIES — KLUBHUSET OG FACILITETER — 7/10

Pro shop Pro shop
Driving range Driving range
Sheltered suoja yes - On grass ruoholla yes (Summer) - Putting-green putting-green yes - Pitching-green pitching-green yes

HOTEL FACILITIES — HOTEL FACILITETERNE — 7/10

HOTELS

Kaisankoti - 80 rooms, D € 100 - Espoo 3 km
Tel (358) 09 - 887 191, Fax (358) 09 - 855 2979

Radisson Hotel - 208 rooms, D € 90 - Espoo 10 km
Tel (358) 09 - 435 80, Fax (358) 09 - 466 693

Radisson SAS Hesperia Hotel - Helsinki 15 km
364 rooms, D € 220
Tel (358) 09 - 69 360, Fax (358) 09 - 693 2123

RESTAURANTS RAVINTOLA

Kaisankoti - Espoo 3 km - Tel (358) 09 - 887 191
Kellarikrouvi - Helsinki 15 km - Tel (358) 09 - 686 0730
König - Helsinki 15 km - Tel (358) 09 - 6844 0713

Nordcenter *Benz Course*

16	7	3

Vain 75 kilometrin päässä Helsingistä sijaitsee Nordcenter, joka on 36-reikäinen kenttä kuten lähellä olevat Pickalan ja Sarfvikin kentätkin. Lohjanjärven rannalle rakennettu Nordcenter on kahden amerikkalaisen suunnittelema, varsin eksklusiivinen kenttä, joka ei varmaankaan oudoksuta niitä, jotka ovat pelanneet golfia USA:ssa. Ronald Freamin suunnittelema kenttä on avoin ja maaston korkeuserot ovat suuret (suosittelemme golfauton käyttöä). Neljä reikää pelataan vedenrajassa. Nordcenterissä suosittelemme korkeuseroiltaan helpompaa Benz kenttää, jolla liikkuminen ei ole yhtä rasittavaa kuin Fream kentällä. Tämän kentän on piirtänyt Bradford Benz, ja metsineen ja vesistöineen se tuntuu paljon "suomalaisemmalta". Vesi ja puut tulevat mukaan peliin kymmenen reiän kohdalla. Väylät ovat leveitä ja pieleen menneistä lyönneistä voi täällä pelastautua: varomattomuudesta ei sakoteta. Takatiiltä ei kuitenkaan kannata pelata, vaikka kenttä onkin avoin eikä sisällä salattuja vaikeuksia. Riittää kun lyö klubitiiltä. Nordcenter on täydellinen "resort"-kenttä.

Like the Master Golf Club, Pickala or Sarfvik, here is another 36-hole resort just 75 km from Helsinki in a setting that overlooks the lake of Lohjanjarvi. This also happens to be a very exclusive club, which called on the services of two American architects to design the courses on which any American would feel very much at home. The course designed by Ronald Fream is very open and very hilly (buggy recommended) where four holes run along the shores of the lake. We would recommend the less hilly and so more easily walkable course designed by Bradford Benz, which is more specifically Finnish in its landscape of wood and water, both of which are very much in play on about ten holes. The fairways are wide, so the less accurate or less cautious golfers should get by without too much damage to their card. Don't think twice about opting for the front tees (men and ladies), at least to get to know the layout, even though the course is very open and hides nothing. A great golfing resort.

Nordcenter Golf & Country Club — 1993

FIN - 10410 ÅMINNEFORS

Office	Toimisto	(358) 019 - 276 6850
Pro shop	Pro shop	(358) 019 - 276 6850
Fax	Fax	(358) 019 - 238 861
Web	www.golfpiste.com/kentat/ngcc/	
Situation	Sijainti	Helsinki, 75 km
Annual closure	Kenttä suljetaan	no
Weekly closure	Suljetan viikolla	no

Fees main season Green fee	18 holes	
	Week days Arkipäivisin	**We/Bank holidays** Pyhäpäivisin
Individual Henkilö	€ 75	€ 100
Couple Pari	€ 150	€ 200

Juniors: € 25

Caddie Caddie no — **Electric Trolley** Sähköratttaat yes

Buggy Golfauto yes — **Clubs** Mailat yes

Credit cards Luottokortit
VISA - Eurocard - MasterCard - AMEX - DC

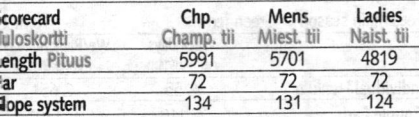

Access Pääsy : Helsinki, E18, them road 25 → Lohja/Karis, → Pohja, turn left → Åminnefors

Map 1 on page 142 Kartta 1 sivulla: 142

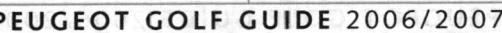

GOLF COURSE — BAN — 16/20

Site	Sijainti	
Maintenance	Hoito	
Architect	Arkkitehti	Bradford Benz
Type	Kentän luonne	forest
Relief	Vapautuminen	
Water in play	Vesiesteitä	
Exp. to wind	Tuulta	
Trees in play	Puita	

Scorecard Tuloskortti	**Chp.** Champ. tii	**Mens** Miest. tii	**Ladies** Naist. tii
Length Pituus	5991	5701	4819
Par	72	72	72
Slope system	134	131	124

Advised golfing ability Tasoitusvaatimus — 0 12 24 36

Hcp required Hcp-vaatimus — 30 Men, 36 Ladies

CLUB HOUSE & AMENITIES — KLUBHUSET OG FACILITETER — 7/10

Pro shop Pro shop
Driving range Driving range
Sheltered suoja yes - On grass ruoholla no - Putting-green putting-green yes - Pitching-green pitching-green yes

HOTEL FACILITIES — HOTEL FACILITETERNE — 3/10

HOTELS
Fiskars Värdshus - Åminnefors 6 km
6 rooms, D € 95
Tel (358) 019 - 237 355

RESTAURANTS RAVINTOLA
Fiskars Värdshus - Åminnefors 6 km
Tel (358) 237 355
Åminne Gård (Club-house) - on site
Tel (358) 019 - 2766 890

Pickala *Seaside Course*

15 | 8 | 5

Pickalan Golfclubiin kuuluu suuri urheilulaitos tenniskenttineen ja hevostalleineen, ja täällä voi purjehtia sekä pelata golfia kahdella kentällä. Sijainti Itämeren rannalla on upea, ja toinen, kentistä kapeampi, onkin saanut nimekseen Seaside. Leveämpi kenttä on nimeltään Park. Seaside-kenttään kuuluu vähemmän puita, mutta sitäkin enemmän vesiesteitä, patoja ja lammikoita, joita yhdistää pieni joki. Vesi on mukana pelissä kahdentoista reiän kohdalla, mikä asettaa suuria vaatimuksia aloituslyönnille ja rankaisee epäonnistuneista jatkolyönneistä. Griinien ympärillä on bunkkerointeja, harvemmin vettä. Jos kyseessä on vain harjoituskierros, sopii kenttä hyvin kaikenlaisille pelaajille: ensiksi vaaratekijöiden arviointi, seuraavaksi aloituslyönti, ja sitten voikin vain toivoa parasta. Hyvänä uutisena mainittakoon, että Seaside ei sisällä todella pitkiä reikiä. Tuuli sen sijaan on aina otettava huomioon. Park-kenttä on myös erittäin hyvä ja kerhotalo, ravintola ja alueen vuokramökit ovat erinomaiset.

The Pickala golf club is a huge sporting complex which features tennis courts, horse-riding, sailing and two golf courses. The location is quite magnificent, on the Baltic coastline, which, as the name suggests, serves as a backdrop for the "Seaside" course. Tighter than the "Park Course", "Seaside" has very few trees but a lot of water in the shape of ponds and small lakes, linked by a small river. Water actually comes into play on about a dozen holes as frontal or lateral hazards and is more dangerous for the drive or wayward second shot than when really attacking the greens, where the bunkers take over. In practice, players of all abilities can play here, calculate the risks they are willing to take and hope for the best. Last but not least, there are no excessively long holes here, good news for big-hitters, who will nonetheless have to reckon with the wind. The second course has much to be said for it, as do the club-house, restaurant and chalets for rent on site.

Pickala Golf Club — 1986

Golfkuja 5
FIN - 02580 SIUNTIO

Office	Toimisto	(358) 09 - 221 90844
Pro shop	Pro shop	(358) 09 - 221 90844
Fax	Fax	(358) 09 - 221 90899
Web	www.pickalagolf.fi	
Situation	Sijainti	Helsinki, 45 km
Annual closure	Kenttä suljetaan	no
Weekly closure	Suljetan viikolla	no

Fees main season Green fee	18 holes	
	Week days Arkipäivisin	**We/Bank holidays** Pyhäpäivisin
Individual Henkilö	€ 45	€ 65
Couple Pari	€ 90	€ 130

Juniors: € 20

Caddie Caddie no — **Electric Trolley** Sähkörattaat no
Buggy Golfauto yes — **Clubs** Mailat yes
Credit cards Luottokortit
VISA - Eurocard - MasterCard - AMEX - DC

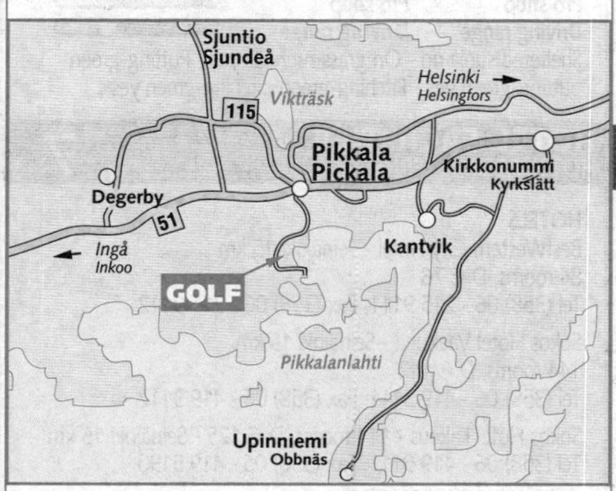

Access Pääsy : Helsinki, road 51 → Kirkkonummi/Kyrkslatt, in Pikkala/Pickala → Golf
Map 1 on page 143 Kartta 1 sivulla : 143

GOLF COURSE — 15/20
BAN

Site	Sijainti	
Maintenance	Hoito	
Architect	Arkkitehti	Reijo Hillberg
Type	Kentän luonne	seaside course, links
Relief	Vapautuminen	
Water in play	Vesiesteitä	
Exp. to wind	Tuulta	
Trees in play	Puita	

Scorecard Tuloskortti	**Chp.** Champ. tii	**Mens** Miest. tii	**Ladies** Naist. tii
Length Pituus	6118	5745	4871
Par	71	71	71
Slope system	131	127	118

Advised golfing ability Tasoitusvaatimus — 0 12 24 36
Hcp required Hcp-vaatimus — 30 Men, 36 Ladies

CLUB HOUSE & AMENITIES — 8/10
KLUBHUSET OG FACILITETER

Pro shop Pro shop
Driving range Driving range
Sheltered suoja yes - On grass ruoholla yes (Summer) - Putting-green putting-green yes - Pitching-green pitching-green yes

HOTEL FACILITIES — 5/10
HOTEL FACILITETERNE

HOTELS

Majvik - 100 rooms, D € 130 - Espoo 25 km
Tel (358) 09 - 295 511, Fax (358) 09 - 297 6306

Radisson Hotel - 208 rooms, D € 90 - Espoo 25 km
Tel (358) 09 - 435 80, Fax (358) 09 - 466 693

RESTAURANTS RAVINTOLA

Majvik - Espoo 25 km - Tel (358) 09 - 295 511
Curry Palace - Espoo 25 km - Tel (358) 09 - 5483 751

Ruuhikoski

17 | 8 | 7

1900-luvun maailman huippuihin lukeutuvan arkkitehti Alvar Aallon suunnitteleman Seinäjoen kaupungin arvovaltainen kaupungintalo se soo keskellä Pohjanmaan suuria lakeuksia. Toinen johtava hahmo, tällä kertaa golfin arkkitehtuurissa, on Robert Trent Jones Jr. ja hänen suunnittelemansa pieni mestariteos, joka on vehreää kumpuilevaa maastoa puineen ja vesiesteineen (ensimmäiset 9 reikää).Pienet greenit ja esteiden suuri lukumäärä tekevät pelaamisesta haastavan. Esteistä ei ole puutetta, sillä jokainen väylä on pieni osa suurta kokonaisuutta, jota hallitsee kentän kaukainen ja rauhallinen sijainti. Jokaisella väylällä on oma luonteensa, mikä tekee pelaamisesta jopa hauskaa. Klubipelaajille arkkitehti on ollut ystävällinen, mutta tosi pelaajille se näyttää todelliset hampaansa. Kesä-heinäkuussa starttiajat eivät lopu kesken, koska aurinko ei laske lainkaan. Ruuhikoski on paranturut jatkuvasti Suomen ilmastosta huolimatta. Mikäli mietit seuraavaa pelikohdettasi Suomessa - valitse Ruuhikoski.

In the middle of the plain of Ostrobotnia, the town of Seinäjoki boasts an administrative building designed by one of the top XXth century architects, Alva Aalto. Another leading figure, this time in golf architecture, Robert Trent Jones Jr., has produced what looks to be a small masterpiece over friendly rolling terrain dotted with woods and water (for 9 holes). There is no shortage of hazards, which are all the more in play in that the greens are not really large. Each hole has its own character, making this even more fun to play, but everything fits into a sort of harmony that probably owes much to the tranquillity of this remote site. The architect has been kind here, because the course is accessible and fair from the "human" tees with wide open fairways (defended by huge bunkers) but tends to bare its teeth to players looking for the steepest challenge. They will have the time to discover its secrets as here in June and July the sun never sets. A must to play as soon as you can.

Ruuhikoski Golf — 1992

Isokoskentie 533
FIN - 60550 NURMO

Office	Toimisto	(358) 06 - 423 4545
Pro shop	Pro shop	(358) 06 - 423 4545
Fax	Fax	(358) 06 - 423 4547
Web		www.ruuhikoskigolf.fi
Situation	Sijainti	15 km from Seinäjoki
Annual closure	Kenttä suljetaan	no
Weekly closure	Suljetan viikolla	no
Fees main season	Green fee	18 holes

	Week days Arkipäivisin	We/Bank holidays Pyhäpäivisin
Individual Henkilö	€ 50	€ 50
Couple Pari	€ 100	€ 100

Caddie Caddie no — **Electric Trolley** Sähkörattaat no
Buggy Golfauto yes — **Clubs** Mailat yes

Credit cards Luottokortit
VISA - Eurocard - MasterCard - AMEX - DC

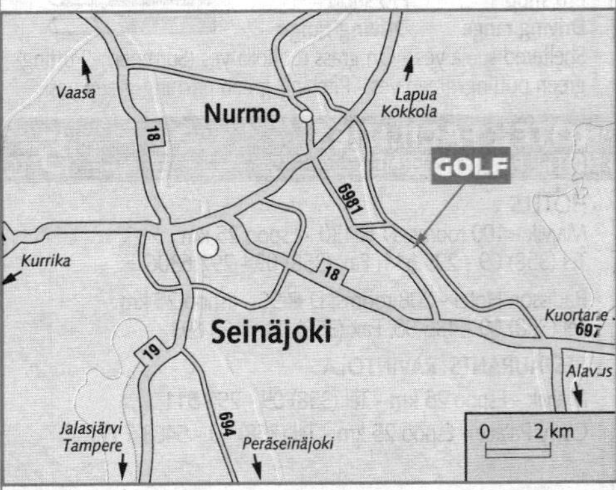

Access Pääsy :
Map 1 on page 142 Kartta 1 sivulla : 142

GOLF COURSE — 17/20
BAN

Site	Sijainti	
Maintenance	Hoito	
Architect	Arkkitehti	Robert Trent Jones Jr.
Type	Kentän luonne	forest, open country
Relief	Vapautuminen	
Water in play	Vesiesteitä	
Exp. to wind	Tuulta	
Trees in play	Puita	

Scorecard Tuloskortti	Chp. Champ. tii	Mens Miest. tii	Ladies Naist. tii
Length Pituus	6187	5806	4691
Par	72	72	72
Slope system	—	—	—

Advised golfing ability Tasoitusvaatimus — 0 12 24 36
Hcp required Hcp-vaatimus — 36

CLUB HOUSE & AMENITIES — 8/10
KLUBHUSET OG FACILITETER

Pro shop Pro shop
Driving range Driving range
Sheltered suoja no - On grass ruoholla yes - Putting-green putting-green yes - Pitching-green pitching-green yes

HOTEL FACILITIES — 7/10
HOTEL FACILITETERNE

HOTELS
BestWestern City Hotel - Seinäjoki 15 km
84 rooms, D € 76
Tel (358) 06 - 215 9111, Fax (358) 06 - 215 9112

Sokos Hotel Vaakuna - Seinäjoki 15 km
144 rooms, D € 142
Tel (358) 06 - 419 3111, Fax (358) 06 - 419 3112

Sokos Hotel Lakeus - 114 rooms, D € 125 - Seinäjoki 15 km
Tel (358) 06 - 419 5111, Fax (358) 06 - 419 5190

RESTAURANTS RAVINTOLA
Restaurant Rosso - Seinäjoki 15 km - Tel (358) 06 - 425 7900
Herkku Vintti - Seinäjoki 15 km - Tel (358) 06 - 423 5880

Sarfvik New Course

16 | 8 | 7

Sarfvik Golfklubista on kehittynyt kaikkien tavoittelema, Suomen eksklusiivisin ja kallein kerho. Vaikka kenttiä on kaksi, voi täällä pelata greenfee-vieraana ainoastaan viikonloppuisin ja silloinkin vain jonkun kerhonjäsenen seurassa. Molempien kenttien suunnittelusta vastaa Jan Sederholm, joka on yksi Ruotsin tuotteliaimpia arkkitehtejä. Pelaaminen on nautinnollista molemmilla kentillä, vaikkakin eri syistä: Old Course on tasainen, avoin puistokenttä kun taas New Course on mäkinen ja kiemurtelee metsän läpi. Jälkimmäinen on kentistä haastavampi, koska tasoerot vaikeuttavat oikean mailan valintaa. Tämän lisäksi on palloa välillä taivutettava, ellei halua päätyä puiden sekaan. Samanaikaisesti metsä luo miellyttävän erillisyyden ja rauhan tunteen. Muutama vesieste luo elävyyttä kaiken vihreyden keskellä, ja griinibunkkerit, joita ei ole kovin monta, on erittäin hyvin sijoitettu. New Course on erittäin hyvä kenttä, joka vaatii pelaajaltaan keskittäytymistä, jos haluaa pelata taitoaan vastaavasti. Täällä pelaamiseen voi varata pitkän kesäpäivän ja pelata molemmat kentät.

It is one of Finland's most exclusive and most expensive golf club. And even though there are two courses, you can only play here on week-ends if accompanied by a member. Both courses were laid out by Jan Sederholm, one of Sweden's most prolific architects, and both are very enjoyable in their very different ways. The "Old Course" is flat like a park with wide open space, while the "New Course" is hilly and runs through a forest. The latter is the most challenging of the two, as the steep topography adds to the difficulty of club selection and players need to be able to bend the ball to keep out of the trees. At the same time, the forest landscape gives a great feeling of isolation and tranquillity, while a few water hazards give visual variety to all the shades of green around you, not forgetting the few but well located sand traps by the greens. A very fine complex where you need to concentrate long and hard to play to your handicap. Play both courses on one long summer's day.

Sarfvik Golf Club — 1984

Finnbyntie 30
FIN - 02430 MASALA

Office	Toimisto	(358) 09 - 221 9000
Pro shop	Pro shop	(358) 09 - 221 9000
Fax	Fax	(358) 09 - 297 7134
Web		www.golfsarfvik.fi
Situation	Sijainti	Helsinki, 15 km
Annual closure	Kenttä suljetaan	no
Weekly closure	Suljetan viikolla	no

Fees main season Green fee	Week days Arkipäivisin	We/Bank holidays Pyhäpäivisin
18 holes		
Individual Henkilö	€ 85	€ 85
Couple Pari	€ 170	€ 170

Juniors: € 35

Caddie Caddie no **Electric Trolley** Sähkörattaat no

Buggy Golfauto yes **Clubs** Mailat yes

Credit cards Luottokortit
VISA - Eurocard - MasterCard - AMEX - DC

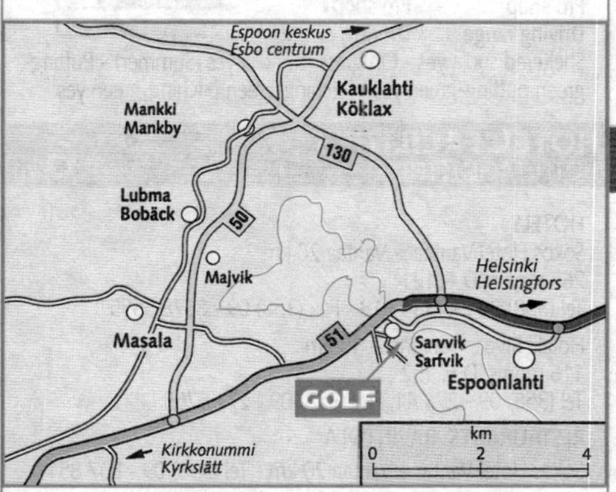

Access Pääsy : Helsinki, 51 → Kirkkonummi/Kyrkslatt. After Espoonlahti and bridge, turn left → Sarfvik

Map 1 on page 143 Kartta 1 sivulla : 143

GOLF COURSE — BAN — 16/20

Site	Sijainti	
Maintenance	Hoito	
Architect	Arkkitehti	Jan Sederholm
Type	Kentän luonne	forest
Relief	Vapautuminen	
Water in play	Vesiesteitä	
Exp. to wind	Tuulta	
Trees in play	Puita	

Scorecard Tuloskortti	Chp. Champ. tii	Mens Miest. tii	Ladies Naist. tii
Length Pituus	5854	5688	4696
Par	72	72	72
Slope system	135	133	125

Advised golfing ability Tasoitusvaatimus — 0 12 24 36

Hcp required Hcp-vaatimus — 24 Men, 30 Ladies

CLUB HOUSE & AMENITIES — KLUBHUSET OG FACILITETER — 8/10

Pro shop — Pro shop
Driving range — Driving range
Sheltered suoja 5 mats - On grass ruoholla yes (Summer) - Putting-green putting-green yes - Pitching-green pitching-green yes

HOTEL FACILITIES — HOTEL FACILITETERNE — 7/10

HOTELS

Majvik - 100 rooms, D € 130 - Espoo 25 km
Tel (358) 09 - 295 511, Fax (358) 09 - 297 6306

Radisson Hotel - Espoo 25 km
208 rooms, D € 90
Tel (358) 09 - 435 80, Fax (358) 09 - 466 693

Palace Hotel - 39 rooms, D € 300 - Helsinki 15 km
Tel (358) 09 - 1345 6661, Fax (358) 09 - 654 786

RESTAURANTS RAVINTOLA

Majvik - Espoo 9 km - Tel (358) 09 - 295 511
Curry Palace - Espoo 9 km - Tel (358) 09 - 5483 751
Kosmos Restaurant - Helsinki 15 km - Tel (358) 09 - 647 255

Talma

15	8	6

Musiikista kiinnostunut pelaaja jatkaa kentältä Tuusulanjärven rannalla sijaitsevaan Ainolaan, missä säveltäjä Jean Sibelius asui suurimman osan elämästään. Lähistöllä on myös Gauguinin oppilaana olleen taidemaalari Pekka Halonen talo. Niin Halosen kuin Sibeliuksenkin inspiraation lähteitä olivat Suomen kansa, luonto ja legendat. Golf Talman klubitalo on rakennettu suomalaisten taide- ja suunnitteluperinteiden hengessä. 27-reikäisen kentänkin luulisi silloin olevan erikoisemman, mutta kokonaisuus on varsin hillitty, ja maisema sisältää niin metsäosuuksia kuin puistomaisempiakin alueita. Jos pelaa vain 18 reikää, ovat A- ja B-väylä golfteknisesti vaikein osuus. Muutoin erot eivät ole suuria. Erityistä kiitosta ansaitsevat erinomaiset harjoitusmahdollisudet, jotka kohottavat kokonaisvaikutelmaa.

Music-lovers will want to push a little further north-west from this course as far as Ainola on the shores of lake Tuusula. This is where the composer Jean Sibelius spent most of his life. A little further still and you can visit the house and studio of the painter Pekka Halonen, a student with Gauguin. The two men were inspired by the Finnish people, their legends and nature. The club-house here follows the country's tradition of art and design, and as such might leave you expecting a more exceptional and stylish course than is actually the case. As it happens, the 27 holes here are rather more sedate in a calm setting between parkland and forest. If you play only 18 holes, the combination of the two nine-hole A and B courses is perhaps the most difficult golf-wise, but there is little difference between the three. The whole complex is enhanced by the excellence of the practice facilities.

Golf Talma 1989

Nygårdintie
FIN - 04240 TALMA

Office	Toimisto	(358) 9 - 274 6540
Pro shop	Pro shop	(358) 050 - 566 7167
Fax	Fax	(358) 9 - 2746 5432
Web	www.golftalma.fi	
Situation	Sijainti	Helsinki, 30 km
Annual closure	Kenttä suljetaan	no
Weekly closure	Suljetan viikolla	no

Fees main season Green fee		18 holes
	Week days Arkipäivisin	**We/Bank holidays** Pyhäpäivisin
Individual Henkilö	€ 50	€ 60
Couple Pari	€ 100	€ 120

Juniors: – 50 %

Caddie Caddie no **Electric Trolley** Sähkörattaat no

Buggy Golfauto yes **Clubs** Mailat yes

Credit cards Luottokortit
VISA - Eurocard - MasterCard - AMEX - DC

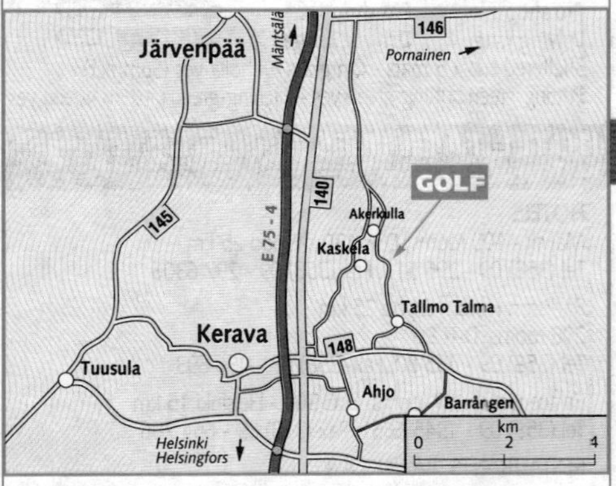

Access Pääsy : Helsinki, road 4/E75 → Järvenpää. Exit Kerava, turn right on road 148 → Sibbo, then left on 140, then right → Talma/Tallmo → Golf

Map 1 on page 143 Kartta 1 sivulla : 143

GOLF COURSE 15/20
BAN

Site	Sijainti	
Maintenance	Hoito	
Architect	Arkkitehti	Henrik Wartiainen
Type	Kentän luonne	forest, parkland
Relief	Vapautuminen	
Water in play	Vesiesteitä	
Exp. to wind	Tuulta	
Trees in play	Puita	

Scorecard Tuloskortti	**Chp.** Champ. tii	**Mens** Miest. tii	**Ladies** Naist. tii
Length Pituus	6114	5809	4971
Par	72	72	72
Slope system	132	128	123

Advised golfing ability Tasoitusvaatimus 0 12 24 36

Hcp required Hcp-vaatimus 36

CLUB HOUSE & AMENITIES 8/10
KLUBHUSET OG FACILITETER

Pro shop	Pro shop
Driving range	Driving range

Sheltered suoja yes - On grass ruoholla yes (Summer) - Putting-green putting-green yes - Pitching-green pitching-green yes

HOTEL FACILITIES 6/10
HOTEL FACILITETERNE

HOTELS

Sokos Hotel Vantaa - Vantaa 20 km
265 rooms, D € 121
Tel (358) 020 - 1234 618 - Fax (358) 09 - 8578 5555

Hotelli Rivoli - Järvanpää 15 km
116 rooms, D € 152
Tel (358) 09 - 271 41, Fax (358) 09 - 271 5755

RESTAURANTS RAVINTOLA

Sokos Hotel Vantaa - Vantaa 20 km - Tel (358) 09 - 857 851

Chique - Vantaa 20 km - Tel (358) 09 - 8234 832

Tawast

14 | 7 | 6

Hämeenlinnan (ruotsiksi Tavastehus) Tawast-kenttä sijaitsee upeassa rantamaisemassa. Metsät rikkovat vain harvakseltaan alueen rikkaita vesistöjä, joilla voi tehdä laivamatkoja järveltä toiselle. Alue on yksi Suomen suurimmista turistikeskuksista, ja suurimmat kaupungit ovat nimeltään Tampere (Tammerfors) ja Savonlinna (Nyslott). Tawastin kenttä sijaitsee Katumajärven rannalla, puistomaisemassa, ja arkkitehdillä on ollut siinä määrin mieltymys dog leg – välien käyttöön, että pelaaja yllättyy, kun par 3 – reiät ovatkin suoria. Tawastin kokonaisuus on kuitenkin erittäin mielenkiintoinen, joskin kenttä on lyhyenlainen monien Suomen kenttien tapaan. Arkkitehdit hemmottelevat kuntoilijagolfareita! Tawast vaatii keskittymistä monien esteiden selvittämiseksi. Pelaajalta vaaditaan erilaisten lyöntien hallintaa tasoerojen aiheuttamien tilanteiden hallitsemiseksi. Vanhan kartanon talliin rakennettu kerhotalo on erittäin viihtyisä ja tyylikäs.

Hämeenlinna (Tavastehus) is one of the gateways to the wonderful region of lakes, interrupted only occasionally by forests, where you can set out on almost endless water cruises across lakes that are often inter-linked by stretches of water. This is one of the country's major tourist areas, around the two centres of Tampere and Savonlinna. The Tawast course lies along one of these superb lakes in a wood-covered parkland landscape where the architect seems to have been hell-bent on producing nothing but dog-legs. It's a wonder he did not curve the par 3s as well. Having said that, this is an interesting layout, albeit not very long (like most courses in Finland), where the designers had a lot of thought for mid-handicappers. Every golfer here will have to negotiate all types of hazard, try every shot in the book and cope with a number of different situations owing to the topology. Facilities are good, including a very pleasant and stylish club-house in the old stables of a former lordly estate.

Tawast Golf & Country Club — 1987

Tawastintie 48
FIN - 13270 HÄMEENLINNA

Office Toimisto (358) 03 - 630 610
Pro shop Pro shop (358) 03 - 506 2977
Fax Fax (358) 03 - 630 6120
Web www.tawastgolf.fi
Situation Sijainti Helsinki, 75 km
Annual closure Kenttä suljetaan no
Weekly closure Suljetan viikolla no

Fees main season Green fee	Week days Arkipäivisin	We/Bank holidays Pyhäpäivisin
	18 holes	
Individual Henkilö	€ 40	€ 40
Couple Pari	€ 80	€ 80

Juniors: - 50 %

Caddie Caddie no — **Electric Trolley** Sähkörattaat no
Buggy Golfauto yes — **Clubs** Mailat yes
Credit cards Luottokortit
VISA - Eurocard - MasterCard - AMEX - DC

Access Pääsy : Helsinki, E12 → Tampere. Exit Hämeenlinna.
Map 1 on page 143 Kartta 1 sivulla : 143

GOLF COURSE — 14/20
BAN

Site	Sijainti	
Maintenance	Hoito	
Architect	Arkkitehti	Reijo Hillberg
Type	Kentän luonne	forest, inland
Relief	Vapautuminen	
Water in play	Vesiesteitä	
Exp. to wind	Tuulta	
Trees in play	Puita	

Scorecard Tuloskortti	Chp. Champ. tii	Mens Miest. tii	Ladies Naist. tii
Length Pituus	6063	5741	5019
Par	72	72	72
Slope system	137	132	127

Advised golfing ability Tasoitusvaatimus 0 12 24 36
Hcp required Hcp-vaatimus 30

CLUB HOUSE & AMENITIES — 7/10
KLUBHUSET OG FACILITETER

Pro shop Pro shop
Driving range Driving range
Sheltered suoja yes - On grass ruoholla yes (Summer) - Putting-green putting-green yes - Pitching-green pitching-green yes

HOTEL FACILITIES — 6/10
HOTEL FACILITETERNE

HOTELS

Vanajanlinna Castle Hotel - Hämeenlinna 3 km
50 rooms, D € 120
Tel (358) 03 - 61 020, Fax (358) 03 - 610 2210

Rantasipi Aulanko - Hämeenlinna 5 km
246 rooms, D € 160
Tel (358) 03 - 658 801, Fax (358) 03 - 682 1922

RESTAURANTS RAVINTOLA

Vanajanlinna - Hämesnlinna 3 km - Tel (358) 03 - 619 6565
Pipparkakkutalo - Hämeenlinna 5 km - Tel (358) 03 - 648 040

FRANCE

FRANCE

Seignosse

FRANCE

Although France can point to a long history of golf – the first course built on the continent of Europe was in Pau back in 1856 – the game only really took off here in the 1980s. Great course architects like Willie Dunn considered that France, with its amazing variety of landscapes, was the ideal country for developing golf. Today it has more than 360,000 registered players for around 550 courses, of which almost 400 are 18-hole layouts, and there is still a lot of room for golf-trotters, at least on week days. Although now the world's leading tourist destination, France has never really been considered a country for golfing but it does have an awful lot going for it.

In this Guide you will basically find the best courses open to the public. The traditional top courses – often to be found around the larger cities – sometimes admit visitors especially during the week and in the summer but they never really advertise the fact. With a letter of introduction from your club and sometimes, too, a decent handicap, you can try your luck at some of the most highly reputed courses like Chantilly, Saint-Germain, Fontainebleau, Saint-Nom-la-Bretèche, Paris International, Joyenval and La Boulie, which all feature in this Guide. In the last edition we included two very exclusive courses – Morfontaine and Prince de Provence in Vidauban – because you might have been hoping to become a member there, or because you would like to be a member there, or because a member there might invite you for a round, or quite simply to find out how we assess these little gems in our French and European ranking systems. Naturally we have retained them in this latest edition.

After years of some quite hectic expansion, golf course promoters are much quieter these days. A point of saturation has been reached in several regions and only two courses make a first appearance this year. These are the two 18-hole courses at the Four Seasons Provence (Terre Blanche), which have established new standards of excellence for golf resorts. Two other courses are back with us: Béthemont, now in new hands, and La Domangère, whose beautiful layout had suffered for too long from poor green-keeping. Once again, this summer's drought has severely hampered the work of green-keepers, particularly in France. As the damage caused is often erased in the space of a few weeks, we saw no point in taking any account of the temporary effects of this in our reports when judging the standard of course maintenance.

FRENCH GOLF
HOLIDAYS

IAGTO

ABTA

GolfPlanet
HOLIDAYS

FRANCE

Bien que son histoire soit longue, et que le premier golf du continent y ait été construit dès 1856 (à Pau), de grands architectes comme Willie Dunn estimaient que c'était le pays idéal pour développer le golf, avec sa diversité de paysages. Mais le golf en France ne s'est vraiment développé qu'à partir des années 1980. Il compte aujourd'hui plus de 360.000 golfeurs pour environ 550 parcours, dont près de 400 de 18 trous. Il reste encore beaucoup de place pour les visiteurs, en tout cas en semaine ! Premier pays du monde pour le tourisme, la France n'a jamais vraiment été considérée comme une destination golfique, alors que ses arguments en la matière ne manquent pas.

Dans ce Guide, vous trouverez essentiellement les meilleurs parcours ouverts au public. Certes, les grands golfs privés traditionnels – souvent situés aux alentours des grandes métropoles – acceptent parfois les visiteurs en semaine notamment, et en été, mais ils ne font pas vraiment de publicité à ce sujet. Avec une lettre d'introduction de votre club, parfois aussi avec un bon handicap, vous pouvez tenter votre chance auprès des plus réputés: par exemple Chantilly, Saint-Germain, Fontainebleau, Saint-Nom-la-Bretèche, le Paris International, Joyenval, La Boulie, qui tous figurent dans ce Guide... Quant aux deux golfs les plus exclusifs, Morfontaine, et le Prince de Provence à Vidauban, ils avaient été inclus parce que vous avez peut-être espéré en devenir membre, ou parce que vous aimeriez l'être, ou parce qu'un membre peut vous y inviter, ou tout simplement pour connaître notre évaluation de ces petits bijoux dans la hiérarchie française et européenne, nous les avons conservés ici, bien sûr.

Les promoteurs s'étaient nettement calmés en France après des années d'euphorie, on atteint à présent la saturation dans plusieurs régions, mais seuls deux nouveaux parcours font leur apparition cette année, les deux 18 trous de Four Seasons Provence (Terre Blanche), qui ont imposé un nouveau standard de qualité de resort. Deux autres parcours font leur retour, Béthemont qui a changé de propriétaire, et La Domangère, dont le beau tracé avait longtemps souffert d'un entretien médiocre. Une fois encore, la sécheresse de l'été a beaucoup gêné le travail des green-keepers, en France particulièrement. Nous n'avons pas voulu tenir compte des effets ponctuels de cet état de fait pour juger de l'entretien des parcours, car les effets peuvent être rapidement gommés.

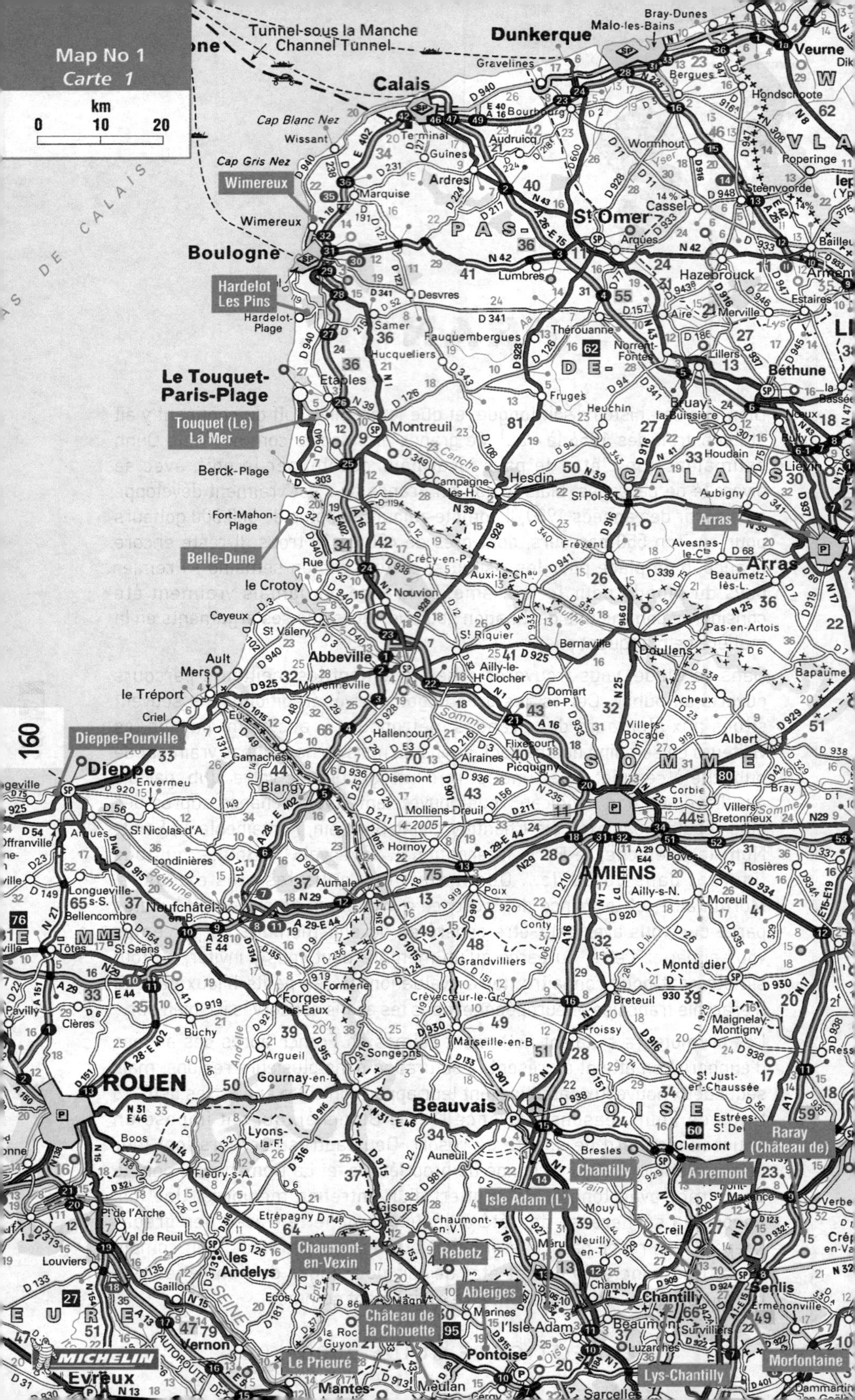

Map No 1
Carte 1
km
0 10 20
Tunnel-sous la Manche
Channel Tunnel
Dunkerque
Bray-Dunes
Malo-les-Bains
Veurne
Gravelines
Calais
Cap Blanc Nez
Wissant
Cap Gris Nez
Wimereux
Marquise
Guines
Ardres
Audruicq
Bourbourg
Bergues
Hondschoote
Wormhout
Poperinge
Steenvoorde
Cassel
St Omer
Arques
Boulogne
Hardelot
Les Pins
Hardelot-Plage
Desvres
Lumbres
Hazebrouck
Aire
Merville
Estaires
Samer
Hucqueliers
Fauquembergues
Thérouanne
Norrent-Fontes
Lillers
Béthune
Le Touquet-Paris-Plage
Touquet (Le)
La Mer
Etaples
Montreuil
Fruges
Heuchin
Bruay-la-Buissière
Houdain
Berck-Plage
Campagne-les-H.
Hesdin
St Pol-s-T.
Aubigny
Fort-Mahon-Plage
Belle-Dune
Arras
Rue
Crécy-en-P.
Auxi-le-Chau
Frévent
Avesnes-le-Cte
Beaumetz-lès-L.
le Crotoy
Nouvion
Cayeux
St Valery
St Riquier
Bernaville
Doullens
Pas-en-Artois
Ault
Mers
le Tréport
Criel
Abbeville
Ailly-le-Ht Clocher
Domart-en-P.
Bapaume
Acheux
Albert
Dieppe-Pourville
Dieppe
Envermeu
Gamaches
Hallencourt
Airaines
Flixecourt
Picquigny
Villers-Bocage
Corbie
Bray
Villers-Bretonneux
Blangy
Oisemont
Molliens-Dreuil
Offranville
Arques
St Nicolas-d'A.
Londinières
Hornoy
AMIENS
Boves
Rosières
Longueville-s-S.
Bellencombre
Neufchâtel-en-B.
Aumale
Poix
Ailly-s-N.
Moreuil
Tôtes
St Saëns
Conty
Grandvilliers
Montdidier
Formerie
Forges-les-Eaux
Crèvecoeur-le-Gd
Breteuil
Pavilly
Clères
Buchy
Maignelay-Montigny
Argueil
Songeons
Marseille-en-B
Froissy
ROUEN
Gournay-en-B
St Just-en-Chaussée
Beauvais
Estrées-St Denis
Clermont
Raray
(Château de)
Boos
Lyons-la-F.
Auneuil
Bresles
Chantilly
Aremont
Fleury-s-A.
Mouy
Pt de l'Arche
Isle Adam (L')
Val de Reuil
Etrépagny
Gisors
Chaumont-en-V.
Creil
Pont-St Maxence
Verberie
Crépy-en-Valois
Louviers
les Andelys
Chaumont-en-Vexin
Rebetz
Méru
Neuilly-en-T.
Senlis
Gaillon
Chambly
Ablèges
Chantilly
Ermenonville
Ecos
Magny
Marines
Beaumont
Surviliers
Château de la Chouette
l'Isle-Adam
Luzarches
Vernon
la Roche-Guyon
Pontoise
Le Prieuré
Lys-Chantilly
Morfontaine
MICHELIN
Evreux
Mantes-
Meulan
Sarcelles
Dammartin
PAS-DE-CALAIS
SOMME
OISE
EURE

160

161
GENT (GAND)
Torhout
Tielt
Deinze
Zele
Dendermonde
Willebroek
(Malines) Mechelen
Aarschot
Keerbergen
Wetteren
(Alost) Aalst
Roeselare (Roulers)
Ingelmunster
Izegem
Harelbeke
Waregem
OOST-VLAANDEREN
VLAAMS
Asse
Vilvoorde
Kortrijk (Courtrai)
Oudenaarde
BRUXELLES
BRUSSEL
Ninove
Tervuren
Overijse
Menen
Wervik
Comines
Halluin
Tourcoing
Mouscron
Roubaix
Geraardsbergen
Lessines
Enghien
Halle
Wavre
Tournai (Doornik)
V. d'Ascq
Haubourdin
Seclin
Cysoing
Ath
Leuze
Beloeil
Braine-le-Comte
Soignies
Nivelles
Genappe
Louvain-la-Neuve
Villers-la-V
Gembloux
Carvin
Pont-à-Marcq
Péruwelz
HAINAUT
St Amand-les-Eaux
Orchies
Condé
Fleurus
La Louvière
Gosselies
Namur
Hénin-Beaumont
Marchiennes
Bruay-s-l'E.
Mons (Bergen)
Anderlues
Binche
Châtelet
Fosses
Douai
Quiévrain
Valenciennes
Thuin
Charleroi
Profondeville
Denain
NORD
Scarpe
Aniche
Vitry-en-A.
Maubeuge
Jeumont
Sambre
Bouchain
Bavay
Hautmont
le Quesnoy
Berlaimont
Aulnoye-Aymeries
Beaumont
Florennes
Philippeville
Hastière
Givet
Marquion
Cambrai
Solesmes
Solre-le-Château
Sars-Poteries
Landrecies
Avesnes
Sains-du-N.
Caudry
le Cateau
Vireux-Wallerand
Trélon
Chimay
Couvin
le Nouvion-en-T.
Wassigny
Fourmies
le Catelet
Bohain-en-V.
la Capelle
Revin
Roisel
Hirson
St Michel
Rocroi
Péronne
Mon Idée
Renwez
Guise
Oise
St Quentin
Vermand
Origny-Ste Benoîte
Aubenton
Rumigny
Vervins
Sains-Richaumont
Ribemont
Ham
Nesle
Marle
Rozoy
Crécy
la Fère
Montcornet
Signy-l'Abbaye
Guiscard
Tergnier
AISNE
Poix-Terron
Chauny
Novion-Porcien
Noyon
St Gobain
Laon
Sissonne
ARDENNE
Blérancourt
Anizy-le-Château
Château-Porcien
Rethel
Attigny
Ribécourt
Coucy-le-Château-Auffrique
Ailette (L')
Craonne
Asfeld
Compiègne
Neufchâtel
Vic
Vailly
Mazagran
Vouziers
Soissons
Aisne
Juniville
Machault
Pierrefonds
Braine
Pontfaverger-Moronvilliers
Villers-Cotterêts
Fismes
Vesle
REIMS
La Ferté-Milon
Oulchy-le-Château
Fère-en-T.
Ourcq
Ville-en-T.
Betz
Neuilly-St Front
Châtillon-s-M.
Dormans
Château-Thierry
Epernay
Royal Latem (B)
Ravenstein (B)
Bondues
Oudenaarde (B)
Hainaut (B)
Waterloo (B)
Bercuit (B)
Mont-Garni (B)
Rigenée (B)
Brigode
Château de la Tournette (B)
Falnuée (B)
MICHELIN
d'après bases de données au 1/200 000
et 1/1 000 000 - édition 2005.
Autorisation n°0501023.

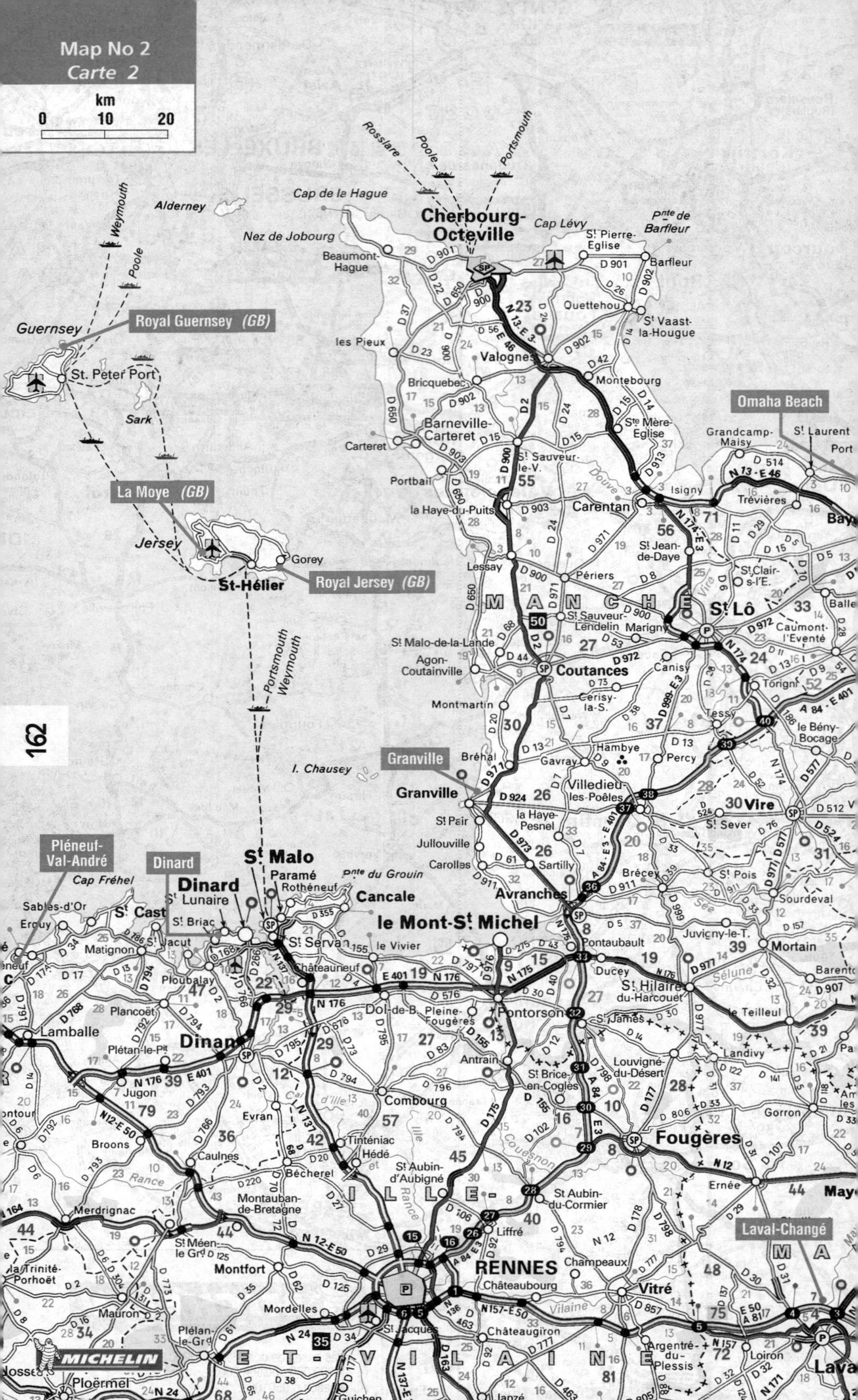

Map No 2
Carte 2
km
0 10 20
Royal Guernsey (GB)
La Moye (GB)
Royal Jersey (GB)
Omaha Beach
Granville
Pléneuf-Val-André
Dinard
Laval-Changé
Alderney
Guernsey
St. Peter Port
Sark
Jersey
St-Hélier
Gorey
Weymouth
Poole
Rosslare
Portsmouth
Cap de la Hague
Nez de Jobourg
Cherbourg-Octeville
Cap Lévy
Pnte de Barfleur
Barfleur
Beaumont-Hague
St Pierre-Eglise
Quettehou
St Vaast-la-Hougue
les Pieux
Valognes
Bricquebec
Montebourg
Barneville-Carteret
Carteret
Ste Mère-Eglise
St Sauveur-le-V.
Portbail
Carentan
Isigny
la Haye-du-Puits
Lessay
Périers
St Jean-de-Daye
Grandcamp-Maisy
St Laurent
Port
Trévières
St Clair-s-l'E.
MANCHE
St Lô
St Sauveur-Lendelin
Marigny
Caumont-l'Eventé
St Malo-de-la-Lande
Agon-Coutainville
Coutances
Canisy
Torigni
Cerisy-la-S.
Montmartin
Tessy
le Bény-Bocage
Hambye
Bréhal
Gavray
Percy
I. Chausey
Villedieu-les-Poêles
Vire
St Sever
la Haye-Pesnel
St Pair
Jullouville
Carolles
Sartilly
Brécey
St Pois
Avranches
Sourdeval
Juvigny-le-T.
Mortain
St Malo
Paramé
Rothéneuf
Pnte du Grouin
Cancale
Cap Fréhel
Dinard
St Lunaire
St Briac
St Cast
Sables-d'Or
Erquy
Matignon
St Jacut
St Servan
le Mont-St Michel
le Vivier
Pontaubault
Ducey
St Hilaire-du-Harcouët
Châteauneuf
Ploubalay
Dol-de-B.
Pleine-Fougères
Pontorson
St James
le Teilleul
Plancoët
Lamballe
Dinan
Plélan-le-Pt
Jugon
Antrain
Louvigné-du-Désert
Landivy
St Brice-en-Coglès
Combourg
Evran
Broons
Caulnes
Tinténiac
Hédé
Bécherel
Fougères
Gorron
St Aubin-d'Aubigné
Montauban-de-Bretagne
Ernée
St Aubin-du-Cormier
Merdrignac
Liffré
St Méen-le-Grd
ILLE-ET-VILAINE
RENNES
Champeaux
Montfort
la Trinité-Porhoët
Châteaubourg
Vitré
Mauron
Mordelles
St Jacques
Châteaugiron
Argentré-du-Plessis
Loiron
Plélan-le-Grd
Ploërmel
Guichen
Janzé
Laval
MICHELIN

162

Dieppe-Pourville
Dieppe
Varengeville
Veules-les-Roses
St Valery-en-Caux
Veulettes
Offranville
Cany-Barville
Fontaine-le-Dun
Bacqueville
Etretat
Fécamp
Yport
Étretat
Valmont
Ourville
Doudeville
Yerville
Tôtes
Criquetot-l'Esneval
Goderville
Fauville
Yvetot
Bolbec
Pavilly
Portsmouth
Montivilliers
Ste Adresse
Caudebec
Barentin
St Romain-de-C.
Lillebonne
St Wandrille
LE HAVRE
Duclair
P. de Tancarville
Quillebeuf
New Golf de Deauville
Villerville
Honfleur
Trouville
Deauville
Jumièges
Bessin
St Aubin
Langrune
Arromanches
Courseulles
Luc
Blonville
Villers
Ouistreham
Lion
Houlgate
Beuzeville
Grd Couronne
Cabourg
Dives
Pont-Audemer
Bourg-Achard
Bourgtheroulde
Creully
Douvres-la-D.
Merville
Pont-l'Évêque
Montfort-s-R.
Elbeuf
Cormeilles
le Bec-Hellouin
Amirauté (L')
Champ de Bataille
Tilly-s-S.
Lieurey
Louviers
Brionne
CAEN
Troarn
Cambremer
Thiberville
le Neubourg
Villers-Bocage
Evrecy
Moult
Mézidon-Canon
Lisieux
la Rivière-Thibouville
Bernay
CALVADOS
Aunay-s-O
Thury-Harcourt
St Pierre-s-Dives
Orbec
Beaumont-le-Roger
Livarot
Broglie
Beaumesnil
Potigny
Vimoutiers
Conches
Clécy
Condé-s-Noireau
Falaise
Fin 2005
la Neuve-Lyre
Pont-d'Ouilly
Trun
Damville
Flers
la Ferté-Frênel
Gacé
Rugles
Breteuil
Tillières
Putanges
Exmes
l'Aigle
Messei
Ecouché
Argentan
Verneuil
Nonant-le-Pin
Briouze
le Merlerault
Moulins-la-Marche
Brezolles
ORNE
Avre
Domfront
Mortrée
Courtomer
la Ferté-Mace
Sées
la Ferté-Vidame
Bagnoles-de-l'Orne
Carrouges
Tourouvre
Senonches
Juvigny-s/s-A.
Bazoches-s-H.
Longny
Couptrain
Mortagne-au-Perche
le Mêle
Lassay
Pré-en-Pail
Alençon
la Loupe
M! des Avaloirs
Javron
Pervenchères
Rémalard
Bellême
Villaines-la-Juhel
Mamers
Thiron-Gardais
Nogent-le-Rotrou
Fresnay-s-S.
le Theil
Bais
Beaumont-s-S.
Marolles-les-Braults
Sillé-le-Guillaume
Bonnétable
la Ferté-Bernard
Authon
Montsûrs
Evron
Ballon
Ste Suzanne
Corlie
Tuffé
Montmirail
St Denis-d'Orques
Connerré
Vaiges
Vibraye
LE MANS
Droué
MICHELIN

Map No 3
Carte 3
km
0 10 20
Raray (Château de)
Apremont
Isle Adam (L')
Chantilly
Morfontaine
Chaumont-en Vexin
Rebetz
Ableiges
Château de la Chouette
Lys-Chantilly
Voir carte 15
Le Prieuré
Vaucouleurs (La) Les Vallons
Golf Parc Nantilly
Rochefort
Courson
Belesbat
Cély
Fontainebleau
Augerville
Bordes (Les)
Limère
Aisses (Les)
Cheverny
PARIS
VERSAILLES
ORLÉANS
Chartres
Evreux
Dreux
Blois
Beauvais
MICHELIN

Compiègne
Vic
Soissons
Pierrefonds
Villers-Cotterêts
la Ferté-Milon
Oulchy-le-Château
Betz
Nanteuil-le-H.
Neuilly-St Front
Vailly
Aisne
Braine
Fismes
Vesle
Fère-en-T.
Ourcq
Ville-en-Tardenois
Châtillon-s-M.
Dormans
Château-Thierry
Condé-en-Brie
Lizy
Charly-s-Marne
la Ferté-s/s-Jouarre
Jouarre
Marne
Disneyland Paris
Coulommiers
Rebais
la Ferté-Gaucher
Montmirail
Esternay
Sézanne
Rozay-en-Brie
Guignes
Fontenailles
Mormant
Nangis
Provins
Villiers-St Georges
Villenauxe-la-Grde
Nogent-s-S.
Romilly
Donnemarie-Dontilly
Bray
Montereau-Fault-Yonne
Moret
Seine
Yonne
Pont-s-Y.
Lorrez-le-Bocage
Chéroy
Sens
Ferrières-en-Gâtinais
Courtenay
Villeneuve-s-Y.
St Julien-du-S.
Joigny
Cerisiers
Villeneuve-l'Archevêque
Marcilly-le-Hayer
Marigny-le-Châtel
Neufchâtel
Juniville
Machault
Mazagran
Pontfaverger-Moronvilliers
REIMS
Verzy
Mourmelon-le-Grd
Suippes
Ay
Epernay
Avize
Montmort
Vertus
MARNE
Châlons-en-Champagne
l'Epine
Fère-Champenoise
Sommesous
Vitry-le-François
Mailly-le-Camp
Anglure
Aube
Méry
Arcis
AUBE
Brienne-le-Château
Piney
Lac du Temple
Lac d'Orient
Vendeuvre
TROYES
Lusigny
Estissac
Aix-en-Othe
Bouilly
Bar-s-Seine
Chaource
Essoyes
les Riceys
Mussy
Ervy
St Florentin
Brienon
Migennes
Flogny
Armançon
Pontigny
Seignelay
Ligny-le-Châtel
Tonnerre
Tanlay
Laignes
Chablis
Ancy-le-Franc
Noyers
Montargis
Château-Renard
Sépeaux
Charny
Aillant
Châtillon-Coligny
Roncemay
Auxerre
YONNE
Toucy
Bléneau
Loing
St Fargeau
St Sauveur-en-Puisaye
St Amand-en-Puisaye
Coulanges-la V.
Courson-les-C.
Coulanges
Vermenton
Nitry
l'Isle-s-S.
Montbard
Fontenay
Venarey-les-Laumes
Alise Ste Reine
Semur-en-Auxois
Guillon
Vézelay
Avallon
Clamecy
Bierre
Précy
Cosne-Cours-s-Loire
Léré
AUTOROUTE DU SOLEIL
MICHELIN

165

Map No 4
Carte 4
km
0 10 20
166
Wellin
St Hubert
Bastogne
Clervaux
Wiltz
Vianden
Diekirch
Ettelbrück
Esch
Sûre
L U X E M B O U R G
Paliseul
Neufchâteau
Bertrix
Martelange
Redange
Larochette
Echtern
Mersch
Vresse
Regnault
Rochehaut
Renwez
Nouzonville
Bouillon
Charleville-Mézières
Sedan
Florenville
Habay
Arlon (Aarlen)
Grand Ducal de Luxembourg (L)
Kikuoka (L)
LUXEMBOURG
Flize
Poix-Terron
Carignan
Villers-devt-Orval
Raucourt-et-Flaba
Mouzon
Avioth
Virton
Aubange
Pétange
Remich
Preisch
Mondorf
Longwy
Differdange
Esch-s-A.
Villerupt
Audun-le-T.
Dudelange
Montmédy
Chiers
A R D E N N E S
08
Attigny
le Chesne
Stenay
Longuyon
Aumetz
Hettange
Cattenom
Thionville
Mazagran
Buzancy
Vouziers
Grandpré
Dun
Meuse
Damvillers
Spincourt
Audun-le-R.
Fontoy
Havange
Uckange
Fameck
Hagondange
Metz
Monthois
Aisne
Montfaucon-d'Argonne
Orne
Piennes
Briey
Rombas
Maizières
Varennes-en-A.
Charny
Etain
Conflans
Jarny
Woippy
Ville-s-Tourbe
Verdun
Mars-la-Tour
Ars
METZ
Suippes
Ste Menéhould
Clermont-en-Argonne
Fresnes-en-W.
Chambley-Bussières
Aire
AUTOROUTE DE L'EST
M E U S E
55
VOIE SACRÉE
Souilly
Triaucourt
Givry-en-A.
Vigneulles
Lac de Madine
Thiaucourt-Regniéville
Pagny
Verny
Nomeny
Pont-à-Mousson
Châlons-en-Champagne
51
Pierrefitte
St Mihiel
Blénod
Dieulouard
Rambucourt
Domèvre-en-H
Revigny
Ornain
Bar-le-Duc
Commercy
Liverdun
Frouard
Sermaize-les-Bains
M E U R T H E
54
Thiéblemont-Farémont
François
Ligny-en-Barrois
Foug
Toul
Void
Neuves-Maisons
Pont-St Vincent
Ancerville
Marne
St Dizier
Vaucouleurs
Lac de Der Chantecoq
Gondrecourt
Colombey-les-Belles
Vézelise
Wassy
Chevillon
Haroué
Montier-en-Der
Joinville
Poissons
Domrémy
Coussey
Soulaines-Dhuys
Doulevant-le-Chau
Neufchâteau
Châtenois
Mirecourt
Maison-Neuve
Doulaincourt
Liffol-le-Gd
Vignory
Andelot
St Blin
Vittel
Dompaire
Bar-s-Aube
Colombey-les-2-Eglises
Bologne
Bourmont
Bulgnéville
Contrexéville
H A U T E - M A R N E
52
Juzennecourt
Martigny-les-Bs
V O S G E S
88
Chaumont
Clefmont
Darney
Lamarche
Monthureux
Bains-les-Bains
Saône
Essoyes
Châteauvillain
Nogent
Montigny
Bourbonne
MICHELIN

Wittlich
Bitburg
Kappel
Kirchberg (Hunsrück)
Simmern
Bingen
MAINZ
Stromberg
Nierstein
Traben-Trarbach
Gemünden
Bernkastel-Kues
Bad Kreuznach
Wörrstadt
Köngernheim
P F A L Z
Schweich
Ehrang
Trittenheim
Morbach
Kirn
Nahe
Bad Münster am Stein-Ebernburg
Nahetal (D)
Westhofen
Trier
Ruwer
Thalfang
Idar-Oberstein
Meisenheim
Flörsheim-Dalsheim
Kirchheimbolanden
Konz
Grevenmacher
Hermeskeil
Birkenfeld
Lauterecken
Rockenhausen
Grünstadt
Saarburg
Zerf
Baumholder
Winnweiler
Franken
Ludwigshafen
Trassem
Primstal
Nohfelden
Kusel
Glan-Münchenweiler
Bad Dürkheim
Losheim
Mettlach
Tholey
St. Wendel
Ramstein
Frankenstein
Deidesheim
S A A R L A N D
Merzig
Lebach
Ottweiler
Kaiserslautern
Hochspeyer
Lambrecht
Landstuhl
Neustadt-a-d-W
Kalmit
Dillingen
Neunkirchen
Homburg
Edenkoben
Saarlouis
Friedrichsthal
Sulzbach
St. Ingbert
Zweibrücken
Waldfischbach-Burgalben
Annweiler
Völklingen
Dudweiler
Blieskastel
Hinterweidenthal
Landau
Creutzwald
Pte Rosselle
SAARBRÜCKEN
Pirmasens
Trifels
Boulay-Moselle
Freyming-Merlebach
Forbach
Carling
Volmunster
Dahn
Bad Bergzabern
Kandel
Sarreguemines
Bitche
Fleckenstein
Wissembourg
St. Avold
Rohrbach
Lembach
Faulquemont
Puttelange
Soultz-s/s-Forêts
Seebach
Grostenquin
Sarralbe
Niederbronn
Woerth
Hunspach
Reichshoffen
Albestroff
Sarre-Union
Soufflenheim
Delme
Morhange
Drulingen
la Pte Pierre
Ingwiller
Château-Salins
Fénétrange
Bouxwiller
Haguenau
Drusenheim
Dieuze
Phalsbourg
Hochfelden
Bischwiller
Wantzenau (La)
Arracourt
Sarrebourg
Lutzelbourg
Saverne
Truchtersheim
NCY
Marmoutier
Lorquin
Wasselonne
Achern
Début 2006
STRASBOURG
Abreschviller
Dabo
Wangenbourg
Marlenheim
Kehl
Renchen
Dombasle
Lunéville
Appenweier
Blâmont
Molsheim
Strasbourg Illkirch
Oberkirch
Cirey
Oberhaslach
Donon
Rosheim
Offenburg
Blainville
Meurthe
Col du Donon
Badonviller
Schirmeck
Obernai
Mt Ste Odile
Gerbeviller
Erstein
Bayon
Kempferhof (Le)
Baccarat
Raon-l'Etape
le Hohwald
Barr
Lahr/Schwarzwald
Benfeld
Senones
Villé
Charmes
Rambervillers
Saales
Rhinau
Provenchères
Fermeture provisoire
Haslach
Châtel-s M.
St-Dié-des-Vosges
Ste Marie-aux-Mines
Sélestat
Ettenheim
Haut-Kœnigsbourg
Herbolzheim
Thaon
Ribeauvillé
Kenzingen
Bruyères
C. du Bonhomme
Fraize
Marckolsheim
Elzach
Corcieux
Riquewihr
Kaysersberg
Emmendingen
Epinal
Granges-s-Vologne
Lapoutroie
Orbey
Riegel
Waldkirch
3 Epis
COLMAR
C. de la Schlucht
Turckheim
Eloyes
Wintzenheim
Breisach
FREIBURG
Gérardmer
Kandel
Xertigny
Grosse Pierre
Hohneck
Munster
Neuf-Brisach
St. Märgen
St Amé
la Bresse
Remiremont
MICHELIN
Rouffach
Schauinsland
Saulxures
Cornimont
Guebwiller
Titisee

167

Map No 5
Carte 5

km
0 10 20

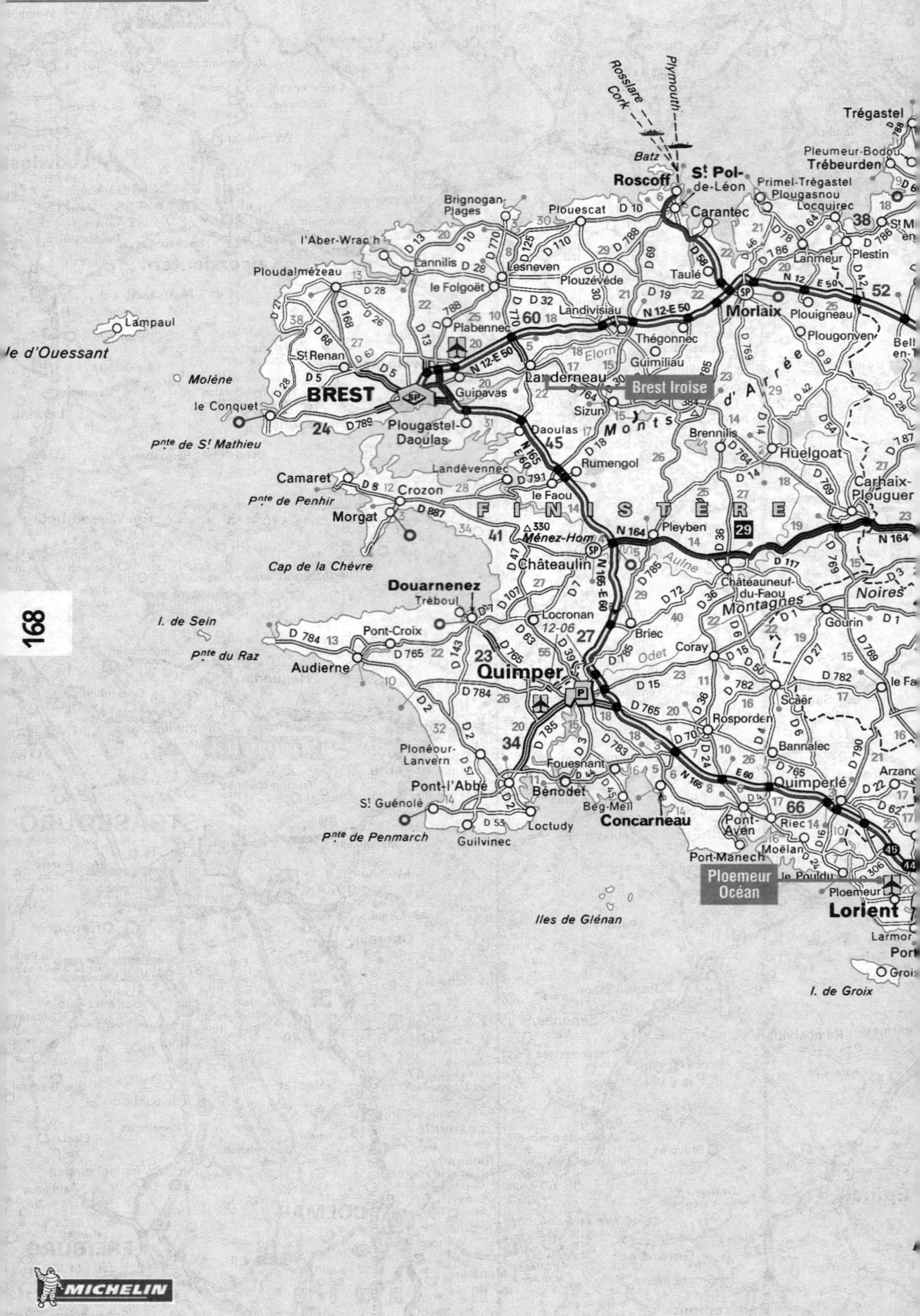

Rosslare
Cork
Plymouth
Batz
Roscoff
St Pol-de-Léon
Carantec
Tregastel
Pleumeur-Bodou
Trébeurden
Primel-Trégastel
Plougasnou
Locquirec
Plestin
Lanmeur
Brignogan-Plages
Plouescat
l'Aber-Wrac'h
Lannilis
Ploudalmézeau
Lesneven
Plouzévédé
Taulé
le Folgoët
Landivisiau
Morlaix
Plouigneau
Lampaul
Plabennec
Thégonnec
Plougonven
Ile d'Ouessant
St Renan
Guimiliau
Molène
Landerneau
Brest Iroise
BREST
Guipavas
le Conquet
Sizun
Monts d'Arrée
Plougastel-Daoulas
Daoulas
Brennilis
Pnte de St Mathieu
Huelgoat
Rumengol
Landévennec
Camaret
Crozon
le Faou
Carhaix-Plouguer
Pnte de Penhir
Morgat
FINISTÈRE
Pleyben
Ménez-Hom
Châteaulin
Aulne
Cap de la Chèvre
Châteauneuf-du-Faou
Douarnenez
Tréboul
Montagnes Noires
Locronan
Gourin
I. de Sein
Pont-Croix
Briec
Coray
Odet
Pnte du Raz
Audierne
Quimper
Scaër
Rosporden
Bannalec
Plonéour-Lanvern
Quimperlé
Arzano
Fouesnant
Pont-l'Abbé
Bénodet
Beg-Meil
St Guénolé
Concarneau
Pont-Aven
Riec
Loctudy
Pnte de Penmarch
Guilvinec
Port-Manech
Moëlan
Le Pouldu
Ploemeur Océan
Ploemeur
Lorient
Iles de Glénan
Larmor
Groix
I. de Groix

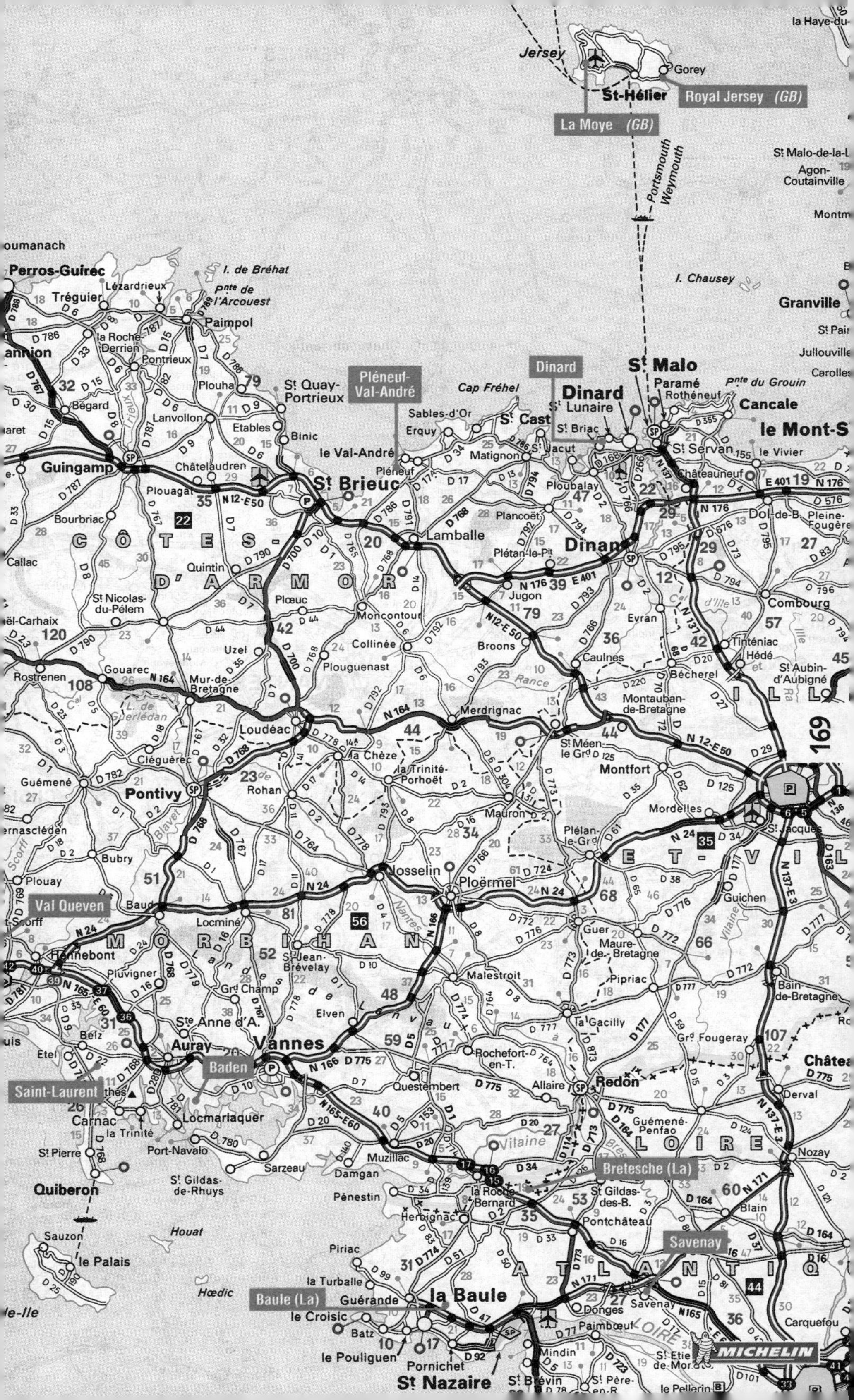

Jersey
St-Hélier
Gorey
Royal Jersey (GB)
La Moye (GB)
Portsmouth
Weymouth
St Malo-de-la-L
Agon-Coutainville
I. Chausey
Granville
I. de Bréhat
Pnte de l'Arcouest
Perros-Guirec
Lézardrieux
Tréguier
Paimpol
la Roche-Derrien
Pontrieux
Plouha
St Quay-Portrieux
Pléneuf-Val-André
Cap Fréhel
Dinard
St Malo
Paramé
Rothéneuf
Pnte du Grouin
Cancale
le Mont-S
Bégard
Lanvollon
Etables
Binic
Sables-d'Or
Erquy
St Cast
St Lunaire
St Briac
St Jacut
St Servan
le Vivier
Guingamp
Châtelaudren
Plouagat
le Val-André
Pléneuf
St Brieuc
Matignon
Ploubalay
Châteauneuf
Dol-de-B.
Pleine-Fougère
Bourbriac
CÔTES-D'ARMOR
Lamballe
Plancoët
Dinan
Callac
Quintin
Plétan-le-Pt
Jugon
Combourg
St Nicolas-du-Pélem
Plœuc
Moncontour
Evran
Tinténiac
Hédé
St Aubin-d'Aubigné
Rostrenen
Gouarec
Uzel
Collinée
Plouguenast
Broons
Caulnes
Bécherel
Mur-de-Bretagne
Loudéac
Merdrignac
Montauban-de-Bretagne
L. de Guerlédan
la Chèze
la Trinité-Porhoët
St Méen-le-Grd
Montfort
Guémené
Cléguérec
Pontivy
Rohan
Mauron
Mordelles
St Jacques
Bubry
Josselin
Ploërmel
Plélan-le-Grd
Plouay
Val Queven
Baud
Locminé
Guichen
Hennebont
MORBIHAN
St Jean-Brévelay
Guer
Maure-de-Bretagne
Pluvigner
Grd Champ
Malestroit
Pipriac
Bain-de-Bretagne
Elven
Ste Anne d'A.
Ta Gacilly
Grd Fougeray
Belz
Auray
Vannes
Rochefort-en-T.
Etel
Baden
Questembert
Allaire
Redon
Saint-Laurent
Carnac
la Trinité
Locmariaquer
Guémené-Penfao
Derval
Châtea
LOIRE
Nozay
St Pierre
Port-Navalo
Sarzeau
Muzillac
Damgan
Bretesche (La)
Quiberon
St Gildas-de-Rhuys
Pénestin
la Roche-Bernard
St Gildas-des-B.
Blain
Herbignac
Pontchâteau
Sauzon
le Palais
Houat
Piriac
Savenay
ATLANTIQUE
Hœdic
la Turballe
Baule (La)
Guérande
la Baule
Donges
le Croisic
Batz
Paimbœuf
Carquefou
le Pouliguen
Pornichet
St Nazaire
Mindin
St Brévin
St Père-en-R.
St Etie-de-Mor
le Pellerin
LOIRE
MICHELIN
169

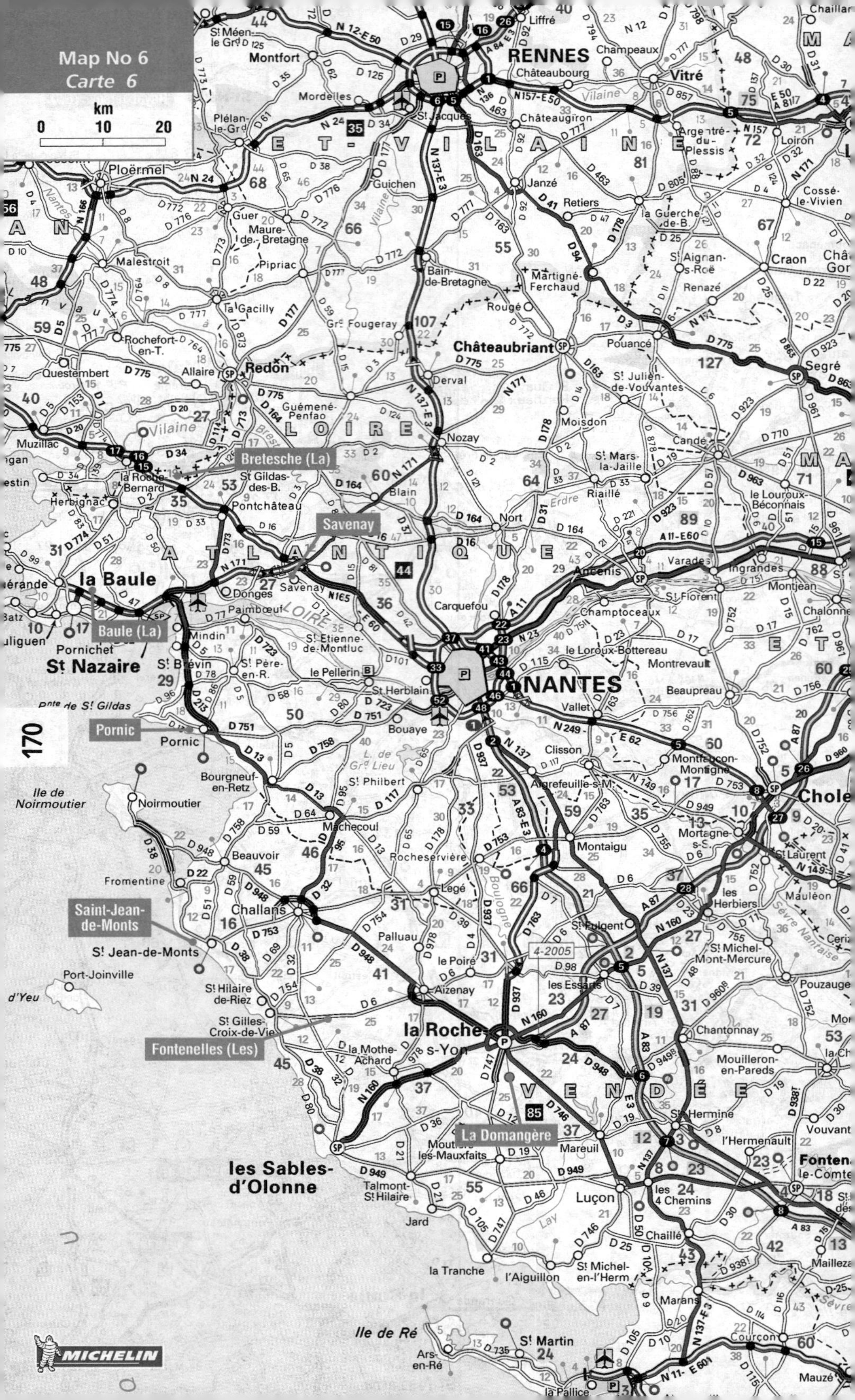

Map No 6
Carte 6
km
0 10 20
170
RENNES
Liffré
Champeaux
Vitré
Montfort
St Méen-le Gd
Mordelles
Châteaubourg
Châteaugiron
St Jacques
Plélan-le-Gd
Ploërmel
Guichen
Argentré-du-Plessis
Loiron
Janzé
Retiers
la Guerche-de-B.
Cossé-le-Vivien
Guer
Maure-de-Bretagne
Pipriac
Malestroit
Craon
St Aignan-s-Roë
Renazé
Martigné-Ferchaud
Bain-de-Bretagne
Rougé
La Gacilly
Grd Fougeray
Rochefort-en-T.
Questembert
Allaire
Redon
Châteaubriant
Pouancé
Segré
Derval
Guémené-Penfao
St Julien-de-Vouvantes
Moisdon
Candé
Nozay
Muzillac
Bretesche (La)
la Roche Bernard
Herbignac
St Gildas-des-B.
St Mars-la-Jaille
Riaillé
le Louroux-Béconnais
Blain
Pontchâteau
Savenay
Nort
Ancenis
Varades
Ingrandes
Montjean
la Baule
Baule (La)
Pornichet
St Nazaire
Donges
Paimbœuf
Mindin
St Brévin
St Père-en-R.
St Etienne-de-Montluc
Carquefou
Champtoceaux
St Florent
Chalonne
le Loroux-Bottereau
Montrevault
NANTES
le Pellerin
St Herblain
Beaupreau
Vallet
Pnte de St Gildas
Pornic
Bouaye
Clisson
Montfaucon-Montigné
Cholet
Bourgneuf-en-Retz
Ile de Noirmoutier
Noirmoutier
L. de Grd Lieu
St Philbert
Aigrefeuille-s-M.
Machecoul
Rocheservière
Montaigu
Mortagne-s-S.
St Laurent
Beauvoir
Fromentine
Challans
Legé
les Herbiers
Mauléon
St Fulgent
Saint-Jean-de-Monts
St Jean-de-Monts
Palluau
St Michel-Mont-Mercure
Port-Joinville
d'Yeu
le Poiré
les Essarts
4-2005
Pouzauges
St Hilaire de-Riez
Aizenay
St Gilles-Croix-de-Vie
Fontenelles (Les)
la Roche-s-Yon
Chantonnay
la Mothe-Achard
Mouilleron-en-Pareds
VENDÉE
Ste Hermine
La Domangère
Vouvant
Mareuil
l'Hermenault
Moutiers-les-Mauxfaits
Fontenay-le-Comte
les Sables-d'Olonne
Talmont-St Hilaire
Luçon
les 4 Chemins
Jard
Chaillé
la Tranche
l'Aiguillon
St Michel-en-l'Herm
Mailleza
Marans
Ile de Ré
St Martin
Ars-en-Ré
Courçon
Mauzé
la Pallice
LOIRE ATLANTIQUE
ILLE-ET-VILAINE
N 12-E 50
N 24
N 137-E 3
N 157-E 50
N 165
N 171
A 11-E 60
N 249-E 62
A 83-E 3
A 87
N 160
N 11-E 601
MICHELIN

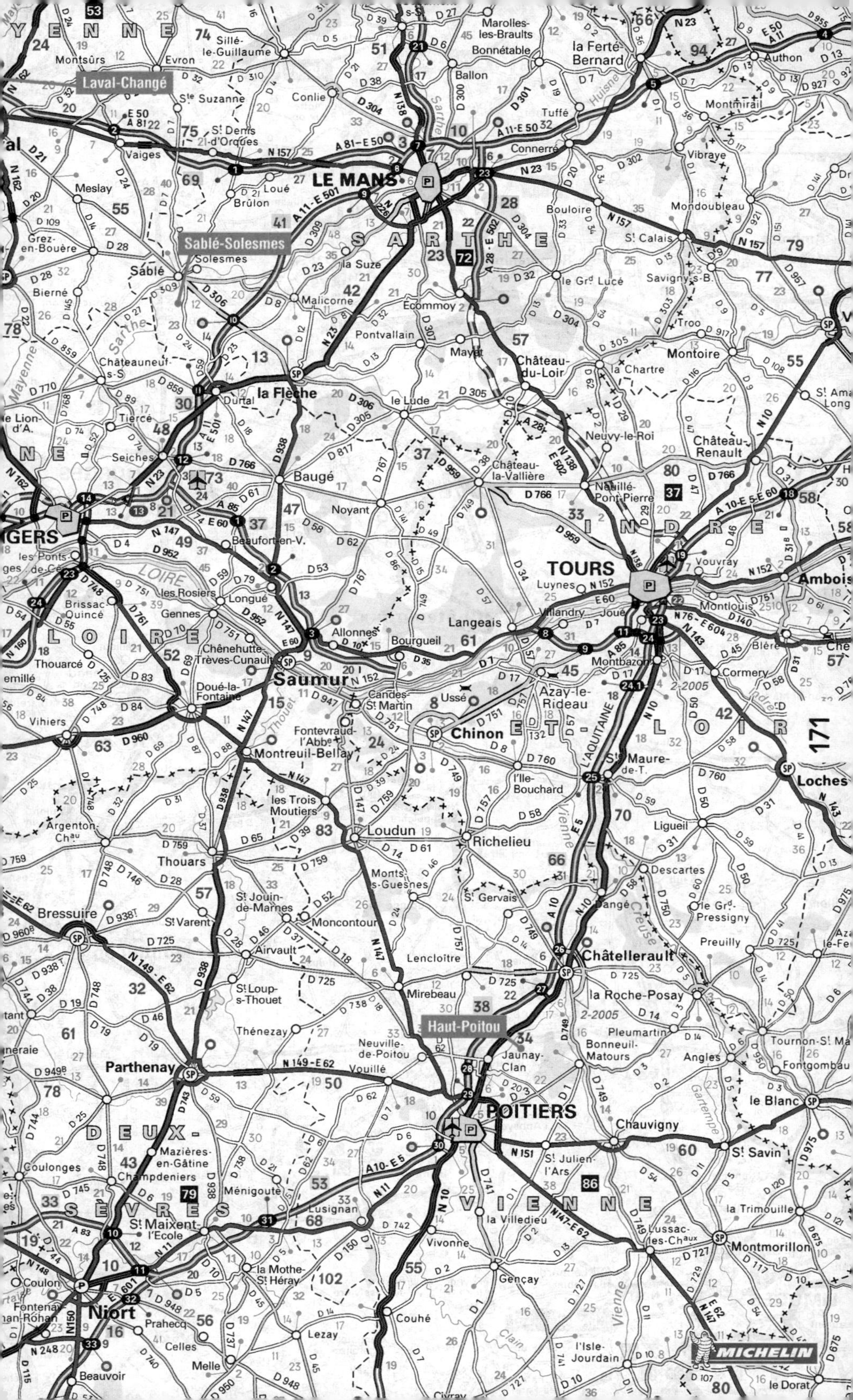

171
Laval-Changé
Sablé-Solesmes
Haut-Poitou
Montsûrs
Evron
Sillé-le-Guillaume
Marolles-les-Braults
Bonnétable
la Ferté-Bernard
Authon
Ballon
Conlie
Ste Suzanne
St Denis-d'Orques
Vaiges
Tuffé
Montmirail
Connerré
Vibraye
LE MANS
Meslay
Brûlon
Loué
Bouloire
Mondoubleau
St Calais
Grez-en-Bouère
Sablé
Solesmes
la Suze
SARTHE
le Grd Lucé
Savigny-s-B.
Bierné
Malicorne
Ecommoy
Troo
Pontvallain
Mayet
Montoire
Châteauneuf-s-S
Château-du-Loir
la Chartre
la Flèche
Durtal
le Lude
St Amand-Longpré
le Lion-d'A.
Tiercé
Seiches
Baugé
Château-la-Vallière
Neuvy-le-Roi
Château-Renault
Noyant
Neuillé-Pont-Pierre
ANGERS
Beaufort-en-V.
les Ponts-de-Cé
LOIRE
TOURS
Luynes
Vouvray
Amboise
Brissac-Quincé
les Rosiers
Longué
Gennes
Villandry
Joué
Montlouis
Langeais
Allonnes
Bourgueil
Chênehutte-Trèves-Cunault
Thouarcé
Saumur
Montbazon
Bléré
Cormery
Doué-la-Fontaine
Candes-St Martin
Ussé
Azay-le-Rideau
Vihiers
Fontevraud-l'Abbaye
Chinon
INDRE-ET-LOIRE
Montreuil-Bellay
l'Ile-Bouchard
Ste Maure-de-T.
Loches
L'AQUITAINE
les Trois Moutiers
Argenton-Château
Loudun
Richelieu
Ligueil
Thouars
Monts-s-Guesnes
St Gervais
Descartes
St Jouin-de-Marnes
Moncontour
Dangé
le Grd-Pressigny
Bressuire
St Varent
Airvault
Lencloître
Châtellerault
Preuilly
St Loup-s-Thouet
Mirebeau
la Roche-Posay
Thénezay
Neuville-de-Poitou
Pleumartin
Tournon-St Martin
Bonneuil-Matours
Angles
Fontgombault
Parthenay
Vouillé
Jaunay-Clan
le Blanc
POITIERS
Chauvigny
DEUX-SÈVRES
Mazières-en-Gâtine
St Savin
St Julien-l'Ars
Coulonges
Champdeniers
Ménigoute
Lusignan
VIENNE
la Trimouille
St Maixent-l'Ecole
la Villedieu
Lussac-les-Châteaux
Montmorillon
Vivonne
la Mothe-St Héray
Gençay
Coulon
Niort
Fontenay-Rohan-Rohan
Prahecq
Celles
Couhé
Lezay
Melle
l'Isle-Jourdain
Beauvoir
le Dorat
MICHELIN

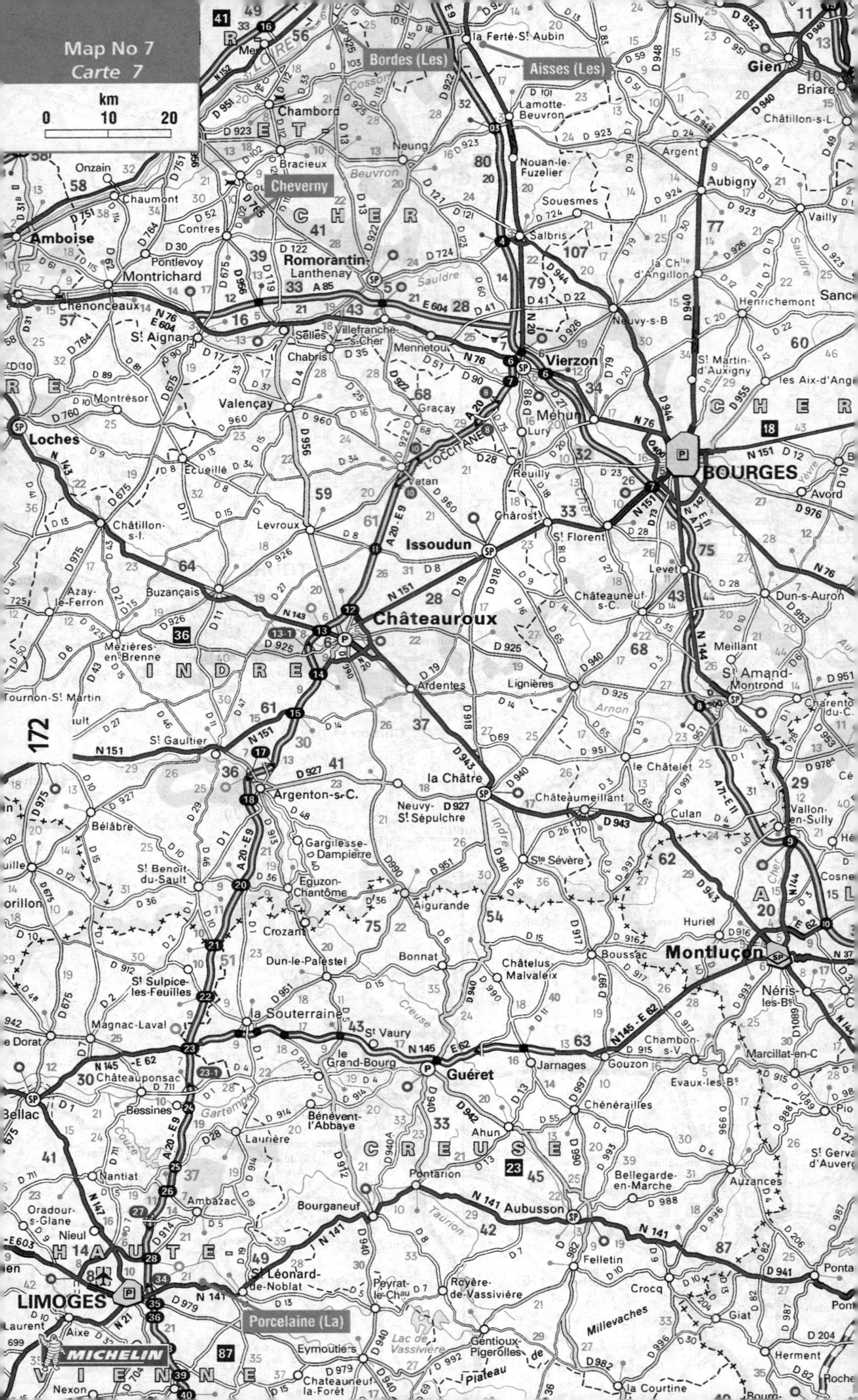
Map No 7
Carte 7
km
0 10 20
Bordes (Les)
Aisses (Les)
Cheverny
Porcelaine (La)
la Ferté-St Aubin
Sully
Gien
Briare
Chambord
Lamotte-Beuvron
Châtillon-s-L.
Neung
Bracieux
Onzain
Nouan-le-Fuzelier
Argent
Aubigny
Chaumont
Souesmes
Vailly
Amboise
Contres
Salbris
Pontlevoy
Romorantin-Lanthenay
la Chle d'Angillon
Montrichard
Henrichemont
Chenonceaux
Neuvy-s-B
St Aignan
Selles
Villefranche-s-Cher
Mennetou
Chabris
Vierzon
St Martin-d'Auxigny
les Aix-d'Angi
Montrésor
Valençay
Graçay
Mehun
Loches
Lury
Écueillé
Reuilly
BOURGES
Vatan
Avord
Châtillon-s-I.
Levroux
Issoudun
Chârost
St Florent
Levet
Azay-le-Ferron
Buzançais
Châteauroux
Châteauneuf-s-C.
Dun-s-Auron
Mézières-en-Brenne
Meillant
Ardentes
Lignières
St Amand-Montrond
Tournon-St Martin
Charenton-du-C.
St Gaultier
le Châtelet
Argenton-s-C.
la Châtre
Neuvy-St Sépulchre
Châteaumeillant
Culan
Vallon-en-Sully
Bélâbre
Gargilesse-Dampierre
St Benoît-du-Sault
Ste Sévère
Eguzon-Chantôme
Aigurande
Crozant
Huriel
Montluçon
Dun-le-Palestel
Bonnat
Châtelus-Malvaleix
Boussac
St Sulpice-les-Feuilles
Néris-les-Bs
Magnac-Laval
la Souterraine
St Vaury
le Grand-Bourg
Guéret
Jarnages
Gouzon
Chambon-s-V.
Marcillat-en-C
Châteauponsac
Evaux-les-Bs
Bellac
Bessines
Bénévent-l'Abbaye
Ahun
Chénérailles
Laurière
Nantiat
Pontarion
Bellegarde-en-Marche
Auzances
Ambazac
Bourganeuf
Aubusson
Oradour-s-Glane
Nieul
Felletin
LIMOGES
St Léonard-de-Noblat
Peyrat-le-Chau
Royère-de-Vassivière
Crocq
Giat
Lac de Vassivière
Gentioux-Pigerolles
Millevaches
Plateau de
Eymoutiers
Herment
Nexon
Châteauneuf-la-Forêt
la Courtine
CHER
INDRE
CREUSE
HAUTE-VIENNE
L'OCCITANE
MICHELIN

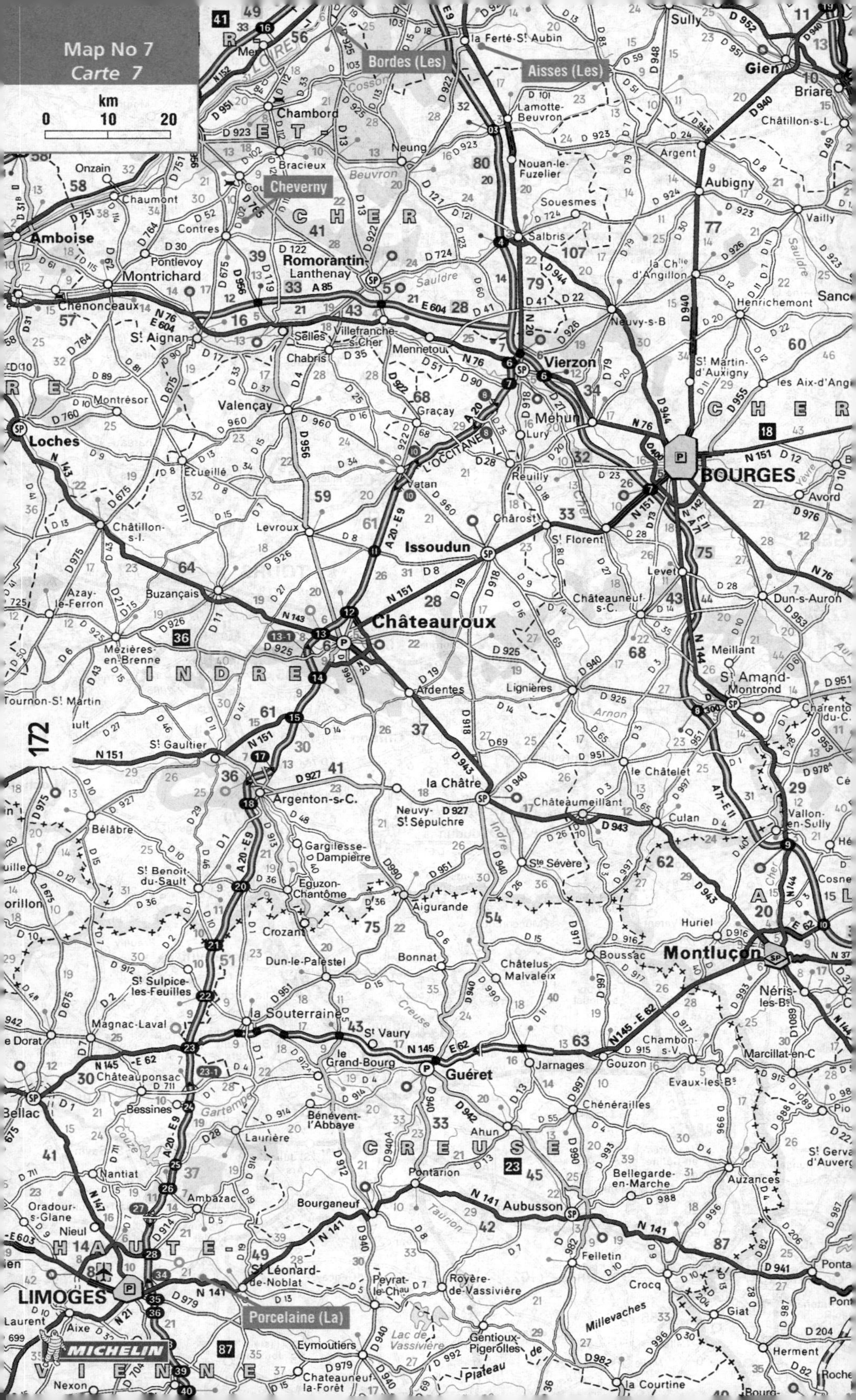

Map No 7
Carte 7
km
0 10 20
172
Bordes (Les)
Aisses (Les)
Cheverny
Porcelaine (La)
MICHELIN
la Ferté-St Aubin
Sully
Gien
Briare
Châtillon-s-L.
Chambord
Lamotte-Beuvron
Neung
Bracieux
Nouan-le-Fuzelier
Onzain
Chaumont
Contres
Amboise
Souesmes
Aubigny
Argent
Vailly
Salbris
Romorantin-Lanthenay
Pontlevoy
Montrichard
Chenonceaux
St Aignan
Selles
Villefranche-s-Cher
Mennetou
Vierzon
Neuvy-s-B
Henrichemont
Sancerre
St Martin-d'Auxigny
les Aix-d'Angillon
Chabris
Valençay
Graçay
Méhun
Lury
Montrésor
Loches
Écueillé
Vatan
Reuilly
Bourges
Avord
Châtillon-s-I.
Levroux
Issoudun
Chârost
St Florent
Levet
Azay-le-Ferron
Buzançais
Châteauroux
Châteauneuf-s-C.
Dun-s-Auron
Mézières-en-Brenne
Ardentes
Lignières
Meillant
St Amand-Montrond
Charenton-du-C.
Tournon-St Martin
St Gaultier
la Châtre
le Châtelet
Argenton-s-C.
Neuvy-St Sépulchre
Châteaumeillant
Culan
Vallon-en-Sully
Bélâbre
Gargilesse-Dampierre
St Benoît-du-Sault
Éguzon-Chantôme
Aigurande
Ste Sévère
Crozant
Huriel
Montluçon
Dun-le-Palestel
Bonnat
Boussac
Châtelus-Malvaleix
St Sulpice-les-Feuilles
Néris-les-Bs
la Souterraine
St Vaury
Magnac-Laval
le Dorat
le Grand-Bourg
Guéret
Jarnages
Gouzon
Chambon-s-V.
Marcillat-en-C
Châteauponsac
Bessines
Bellac
Bénévent-l'Abbaye
Ahun
Chénérailles
Evaux-les-Bs
Laurière
Pontarion
Bellegarde-en-Marche
Auzances
Nantiat
Ambazac
Bourganeuf
Aubusson
Oradour-s-Glane
Nieul
St Léonard-de-Noblat
Felletin
Limoges
Peyrat-le-Château
Royère-de-Vassivière
Crocq
Giat
Aixe
Eymoutiers
Gentioux-Pigerolles
Herment
Nexon
Châteauneuf-la-Forêt
la Courtine
Millevaches
Plateau de
Lac de Vassivière
LOIRE
CHER
INDRE
CREUSE
HAUTE-VIENNE
L'OCCITANE

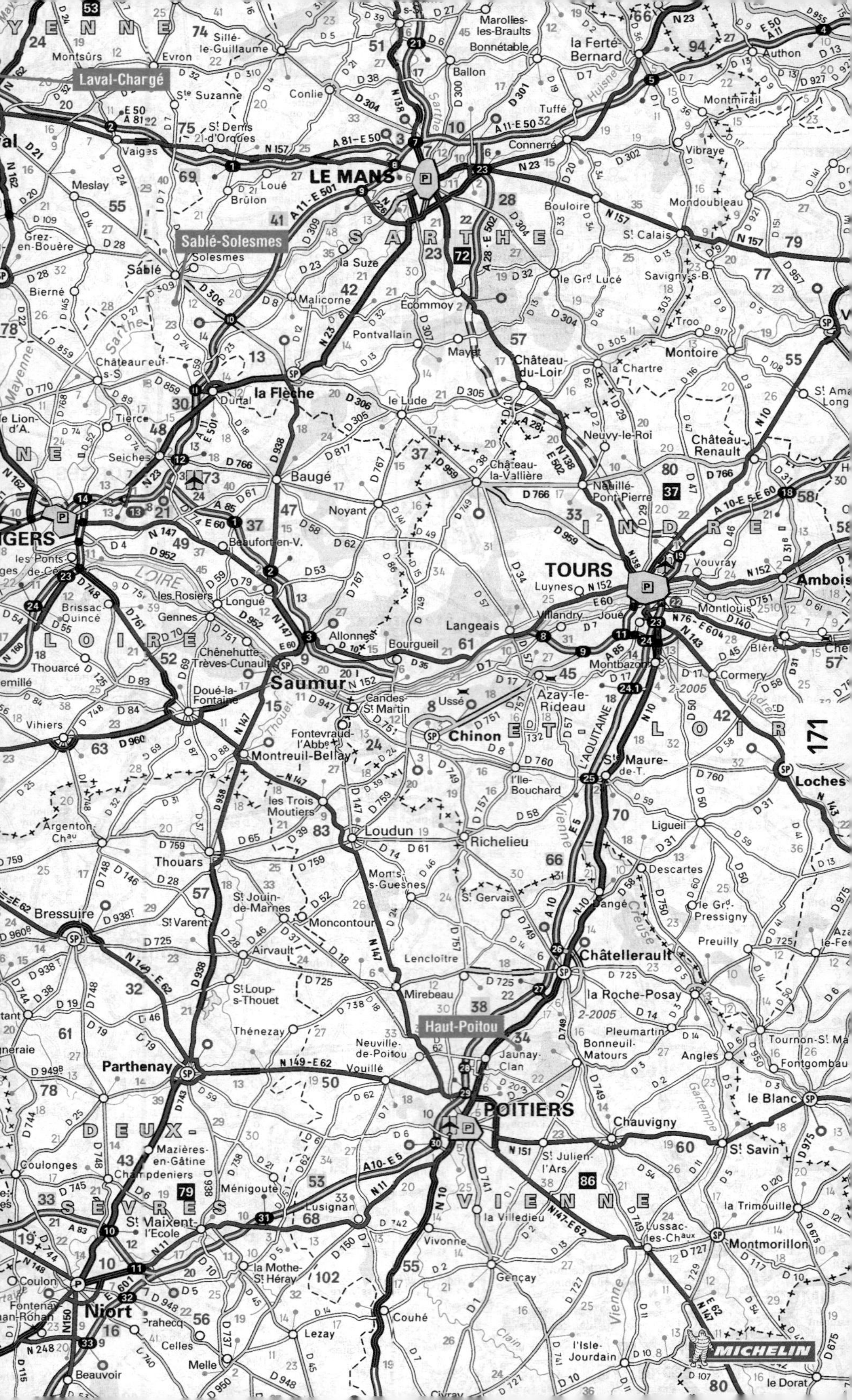

LE MANS
Laval-Chargé
Sablé-Solesmes
Haut-Poitou
SARTHE
INDRE
LOIRE
VIENNE
DEUX-SÈVRES
TOURS
POITIERS
Saumur
Chinon
Loches
Niort
Parthenay
Bressuire
Thouars
Loudun
Châtellerault
la Flèche
Sablé
Montsûrs
Evron
Sillé-le-Guillaume
Ste Suzanne
St Denis-d'Orques
Vaiges
Meslay
Brûlon
Loué
Conlie
Ballon
Bonnétable
Marolles-les-Braults
la Ferté-Bernard
Authon
Tuffé
Montmirail
Connerré
Vibraye
Bouloire
Mondoubleau
St Calais
Savigny-s-B.
le Grd Lucé
Écommoy
la Suze
Malicorne
Pontvallain
Mayet
Château-du-Loir
la Chartre
Montoire
Troo
St Amand-Long.
le Lude
Château-Renault
Neuvy-le-Roi
Château-la-Vallière
Neuillé-Pont-Pierre
Baugé
Noyant
Durtal
Châteauneuf-s-S.
Tiercé
le Lion-d'A.
Seiches
Beaufort-en-V.
Longué
les Rosiers
Gennes
Chênehutte-Trèves-Cunault
Doué-la-Fontaine
Brissac-Quincé
Thouarcé
Vihiers
Argenton-Chau
Montreuil-Bellay
les Trois Moutiers
Fontevraud-l'Abbé
Candes-St Martin
Bourgueil
Allonnes
Langeais
Azay-le-Rideau
Ussé
Villandry
Joué
Luynes
Vouvray
Montlouis
Amboise
Montbazon
Bléré
Cormery
Ste Maure-de-T.
l'Ile-Bouchard
Richelieu
Ligueil
Descartes
Dangé
le Grd-Pressigny
Preuilly
la Roche-Posay
Pleumartin
Bonneuil-Matours
Angles
Tournon-St Martin
Fontgombault
le Blanc
St Savin
Chauvigny
St Julien-l'Ars
la Trimouille
Montmorillon
Lussac-les-Chaux
la Villedieu
Vivonne
Gençay
Couhé
l'Isle-Jourdain
le Dorat
Civray
Lencloître
Mirebeau
Moncontour
Monts-s-Guesnes
St Gervais
Jaunay-Clan
Neuville-de-Poitou
Vouillé
Thénezay
St Loup-s-Thouet
Airvault
St Jouin-de-Marnes
St Varent
Lusignan
Ménigoute
Mazières-en-Gâtine
Champdeniers
Coulonges
St Maixent-l'École
la Mothe-St Héray
Prahecq
Celles
Melle
Lezay
Beauvoir
Coulon
Fontenay-Rohan-Rohan
ANGERS
171
MICHELIN

Map No 8
Carte 8
km
0 10 20
174
MICHELIN
HAUTE-MARNE
CÔTE-D'OR
SAÔNE-ET-LOIRE
JURA
Chaumont
Langres
Dijon
Beaune
Chalon-s-S.
Tournus
Mâcon
Autun
le Creusot
Montceau-les-Mines
Paray-le-Monial
Charolles
Cluny
Lons-le-Saunier
Dole
Gray
Auxonne
Louhans
Montbard
Châtillon-s-S.
Saulieu
Bar-s-Aube
Chailly (Château de)
Val de Sorne
Contrexéville
Bourbonne-les-Bains
Nuits-St Georges
Semur-en-Auxois
Arnay-le-Duc
Seurre
Oyonnax
Poligny
Arbois
Is-s-Tille
Fontaine-Française
Champlitte
Châteauvillain
Colombey-les-2-Eglises
Essoyes
Mussy
Laignes
AUTOROUTE DU SOLEIL
LA COMTOISE

YONNE
89
Roncemay
Toucy
Bléneau
St Fargeau
St Sauveur-en-Puisaye
St Amand-en-Puisaye
Coulanges-la V.
Courson-les-C.
Coulanges
Clamecy
Vermenton
Nitry
Noyers
Fontenay
Montbard
Venarey-les-Laumes
Alise Ste Reine
Semur-en-Auxois
l'Isle-s-S.
Guillon
Vézelay
Avallon
Bierre
Précy-s/s-Thil
Vitteaux
Quarré-les-Tombes
Saulieu
Pouilly-en-Auxois
Chailly (Château de)
Cosne-Cours-s-Loire
Été 2005
Donzy
Varzy
Pouilly
Brinon
Corbigny
Lormes
Montsauche
les Settons
la Charité-s-Loire
Prémery
NIÈVRE
58
Arnay-le-Duc
Lucenay-l'Evêque
Château-Chinon
Guérigny
St Saulge
Pougues-les-Eaux
Fourchambault
Nérondes
Nevers
Châtillon-en-Bazois
Moulins-Engilbert
Epinac
St Benin-d'Azy
Autun
la Guerche
Imphy
St Léger
Mont Beuvray
Etang-s-Arroux
la Machine
St Honoré
Mesvres
le Creusot
Decize
Fours
Luzy
Montcenis
Montchanin
St Pierre-le-Moûtier
Dornes
Toulon
Montceau-les-Mines
Issy-l'Evêque
SAÔNE
173
Mont-St Vincent
Bourbon-Lancy
Chevagnes
Gueugnon
Bourbon-l'Archambault
Moulins
Yzeure
Palinges
Souvigny
Dompierre
Digoin
Neuilly-le-Réal
St Bonnet-de-Joux
Paray-le-Monial
Charolles
03
le Montet
Jaligny
le Donjon
Varennes-s-A.
Anzy-le-Duc
la Clayette
Matour
Montmarault
St Pourçain
Marcigny
Lapalisse
Semur-en-B.
Chantelle
St Germain-des-Fossés
Chauffailles
la Pacaudière
Charlieu
Montaigut
St Eloy-les-M.
VICHY
Belmont
Echarmeaux
Ebreuil
Cusset
Châtel-Mgne
Ambierle
Pouilly
Cours
Gannat
Bellerive
le Mayet-de-Mgne
Roanne
Lamure
Menat
St Yorre
St Haon-le-Châtel
Perreux
Thizy
Châteauneuf-les-Bs
Aigueperse
Randan
Amplepuis
Combronde
Châteldon
Manzat
Puy-Guillaume
St Just-en-Chevalet
St Symphorien-de-Lay
Tarare
Châtelguyon
Ennezat
Maringues
St Rémy-
Volcans (Les)
Riom
Thiers
St Germain-Laval
Néronde
l'Arbresle
Pont-de-Dore
Balbigny
Noirétable
St Laurent-de-Ch.
Pont-du-Châu
Royat
CLERMONT-FERRAND
Courpière
Boën
Feurs
Monts
Ceyrat
St Georges-en-Couzan
Cournon-d'Auvergne
Billom
St Dier-d'A.
Olliergues
St Amant-Tallende
MICHELIN

Epinal
VOSGES
88
Remiremont
Plombières
Luxeuil
Gérardmer
C. de la Schlucht
C. du Bonhomme
Ribeauvillé
Riquewihr
Kaysersberg
COLMAR
Munster
Hohneck
HT-RHIN
68
Rouffach
Guebwiller
Soultz
Gd Ballon
Ensisheim
Thann
Cernay
MULHOUSE
Habsheim
Neuf-Brisach
Breisach
Bad Krozingen
Müllheim
Badenweiler
Kandern
Schopfheim
Lörrach
Altkirch
Sierentz
St Louis
BASEL
Bâle-Hagenthal
Arlesheim
Liestal
Laufen
Delémont
Balsthal
Wylihof (S)
Weissenstein
Solothurn
Grenchen
Ballon d'Alsace
Bussang
St Amarin
le Thillot
Masevaux
Giromagny
Ronchamp
Lure
Belfort
90
Héricourt
Montbéliard
Sochaux
Audincourt
Delle
Porrentruy
Largue (La)
SAÔNE
70
Vesoul
Villersexel
Rougemont
Montbozon
l'Isle-s-le-D.
Clerval
Pont-de-Roide
Baume-les-Dames
Roulans
BESANÇON
DOUBS
25
St Hippolyte
Maîche
Goumois
Saignelégier
Tavannes
Moutier
JURA
Charquemont
Pierrefontaine-les-Varans
Vercel-Villedieu
Valdahon
Ornans
le Russey
Les Bois (S)
St Imier
Biel/Bienne
Chasseral
la Chaux-de-Fonds
le Locle
Villers-le-Lac
Morteau
Col des Roches
Vue des Alpes
la Neuveville
Lyss
Aarberg
Burgdorf
BERN
Zollikofen
Worb
Münsingen
Neuchâtel (S)
Neuchâtel
Boudry
Murten
Kerzers
Ins
Mouthier
Montbenoit
Levier
Pontarlier
Cluse de Joux
Fleurier
le Chasseron
Ste Croix
Estavayer
Payerne
Fribourg
Blumisberg (S)
Schwarzenburg
Thun
Malbuisson
Jougne
Vallorbe
Dent de Vaulion
Orbe
Yverdon-les-Bains
Vuissens (S)
Romont
Moudon
Echallens
Lausanne (S)
Oron-la-Ville
Bulle
La Gruyère (S)
Schwarzsee
Jaunpass
Gruyères
Zweisimmen
Frutigen
Adelboden
Châtel-St Denis
Cossonay
VAUD
SUISSE
LAUSANNE
Ouchy
Morges
Vevey
Montreux
Château d'Oex
Saanen
Gstaad
Lenk
Wildstrubel
Domaine Impérial (S)
les Rousses
St Cergue
la Cure
la Dôle
Rolle
Nyon
Évian
LAC LÉMAN
Thonon
Yvoire
Amphion
St Gingolph
Thollon
Divonne
Maison Blanche
Evian
Montreux (S)
Crans-sur-Sierre (S)
C. du Pillon
les Diablerets
Leysin
Aigle
Villars
Bex
Montana
Crans
Sierre
Sion
Conthey
Abondance
Châtel
le Biot
Monthey
Pas de Morgins
St Maurice
Champéry
Genève (S)
GENÈVE
Annemasse
Boëge
les Gets
Morzine
Avoriaz
Gex
Ferney-Voltaire
St Laurent-en-Grandvaux
C. de la Savine
Champagnole
Mouthe
les Planches-en-Mgne
MICHELIN
175

Map No 9
Carte 9

km
0 10 20

MICHELIN

la Mothe-St Héray
Gençay
Couhé
Lezay
l'Isle-Jourdain
St Sulpice-les-Feuilles
Melle
Magnac-Laval
Civray
le Dorat
Brioux
Sauzé-Vaussais
Charroux
Availles-Limouzine
Châteauponsac
Chef-Boutonne
Mézières
Bellac
Bessines
Confolens
Villefagnan
Ruffec
Nantiat
Champagne-Mouton
Ambazac
Oradour-s-Glane
Aigre
Mansle
St Claud
Nieul
Porcelaine (La)
Chasseneuil
Chabanais
St Junien
HAUTE-VIENNE
Rochechouart
LIMOGES
Rouillac
CHARENTE
la Rochefoucauld
St Laurent
Aixe
Solignac
Oradour-s-Vayres
Ruelle
Montbron
St Mathieu
Hiersac
Angoulême
Bussière-Badil
Nexon
Pierre-Buffière
Fin 2005
Châlus
Segonzac
Châteauneuf
la Couronne
Marthon
Nontron
St Yrieix-la-Perche
St Pardoux-la-Rivière
Jumilhac-le-Grd
Blanzac
Villebois-Lavalette
Mareuil
Lubersac
Thiviers
Montmoreau
Champagnac-de-Belair
Lanouaille
Arnac-Pompadour
Brantôme
Brossac
Verteillac
Excideuil
Bourdeilles
Juillac
Aubeterre
Montagrier
Chalais
Savignac-les-Eglises
Hautefort
Montguyon
Ribérac
St Aulaye
Périgueux
la Roche-Chalais
St Astier
Terrasson-Lavilledieu
Thenon
Larche
Neuvic
St Pierre-de-Chignac
Coutras
Montpon-Ménestérol
Montignac
DORDOGNE
Mussidan
Vergt
Grotte de Lascaux
Salignac-Eyvigues
Lussac
St Emilion
Villefranche-de-Lonchat
les Eyzies de T.
Castillon-la-Bataille
le Bugue
Sarlat-la-Canéda
Souillac
Vélines
Ste-Foy-la-Grande
Bergerac
le Buisson-de-Cadouin
St Cyprien
Beynac-et-Cazenac
Branne
Pujols
Lalinde
la Roque-Gageac
Monbazillac
Cadouin
Belvès
Payrac
Domme
Beaumont-du-Périgord
Issigeac
Pellegrue
Sauveterre-de-Guyenne
Gourdon
Salviac
Duras
Eymet
Castillonnès
Monpazier
Monségur
Cazals
Lauzun
Villeréal
Villefranche-du-Périgord
Miramont-de-Guyenne
la Réole
Seyches
Cancon
Monflanquin
Chau de Bonaguil
Catus
Auros
Marmande
Tombebœuf
Fumel
Puy-l'Evêque
LOT-ET-GARONNE
le Mas-d'Agenais
Luzech
Villeneuve-s-Lot
Cahors
Castelmoron
Ste Livrade
Tournon-d'Agenais
Grignols
Tonneins
Penne-d'A.
Montaigu-de-Quercy
Casteljaloux
Montcuq
Aiguillon
MICHELIN
177

Map No 10
Carte 10
km
0 10 20
Guéret
Evaux-les-Bs
Bénévent-l'Abbaye
Laurière
Chénérailles
CREUSE
Ahun
Pontarion
Bellegarde-en-Marche
Auzances
Ambazac
Bourganeuf
Aubusson
Nieul
HAUTE-
St Léonard-de-Noblat
Felletin
Peyrat-le-Chau
Royère-de-Vassivière
Crocq
LIMOGES
Porcelaine (La)
Giat
St Laurent
Aixe
Maulde
Lac de Vassivière
Millevaches
Solignac
Eymoutiers
Gentioux-Pigerolles
Herment
VIENNE
Chateauneuf-la-Forêt
Plateau de
la Courtine
Nexon
Pierre-Buffière
Vienne
Eygurande
Bourg-Lastic
Vézère
St Germain-les-Belles
Bugeat
la Bourboule
St Yrieix-la-Perche
Treignac
Meymac
Ussel
Tauves
Jumilhac-le-Grd
La Tour-d'Auvergne
Suc-au-May
Lubersac
Isle
Uzerche
Egletons
Chau de Ventadour
Champs-s-T.-Ma.
Lanouaille
Arnac-Pompadour
Corrèze
Neuvic
Bort-les-Orgues
Vigeois
Seilhac
CORRÈZE
Excideuil
Juillac
Lapleau
Dordogne
Hautefort
Objat
Tulle
Bge de l'Aigle
Donzenac
la Roche-Canillac
Mauriac
A 89-E 70
Terrasson-Lavilledieu
Thenon
Larche
Brive-la-Gaillarde
Beynat
St Privat
Pleaux
Salers
Argentat
Maronne
Collonges-la-Rouge
St Cernin
Monts du
Puy Mary
178
Grotte de Lascaux
Salignac-Eyvigues
Mercœur
CANTAL
Les Eyzies de T.
Sarlat-la-Canéda
Martel
Vayrac
Beaulieu
Laroquebrou
Vic-s
Souillac
Bretenoux
Bge de St Etienne-Cantalès
Aurillac
St Cyprien
Beynac-et-Cazenac
Gouffre de Padirac
Sousceyrac
Alvignac
St Céré
Cère
St Mamet-la-Salvetat
Mur-de-Barrez
la Roque-Gageac
Domme
Payrac
Rocamadour
Gramat
Latronquière
Gourdon
Lacapelle-Marival
Maurs
Montsalvy
Gorges
Salviac
Livernon
Cazals
Labastide-Murat
Figeac
Lot
Entraygues
Conques
Decazeville
LOT
Chau de Bonaguil
Catus
Grte du Pech Merle
Capdenac-Gare
Puy-l'Evêque
Cabrerets
Aubin
St Géry
Cajarc
Marcillac-Vallon
Luzech
Villeneuve
Montbazens
Bozouls
Cahors
St Cirq-Lapopie
Tournon-d'Agenais
Rignac
Limogne
Villefranche-de Rouergue
Rodez
Montaigu-de-Quercy
Montcuq
Lalbenque
Aveyron
Castelnau-Montratier
Rieupeyroux
la Primaube
Pt de Sala
Bourg-de-Visa
Lauzerte
Baraqueville
Montpezat-de-Quercy
Caylus
Najac
Sauveterre-de-R.
AVEYRON
Molières
la Salvetat-Peyralès
TARN-ET-
St Antonin-Noble-Val
Naucelle
Cassagnes-Bégonhès
Caussade
Laguépie
Viaur
Salles
MICHELIN
Monestiés
N 141
N 21
N 120
N 89
N 20
N 140
N 122
N 88
A 20-E 9
A 20
A 89-E 70

Vichy
Cusset
Bellerive
Gannat
Ébreuil
Menat
Châteauneuf-les-Bs
Aigueperse
Randan
St Yorre
Châteldon
Puy-Guillaume
Combronde
Manzat
Châtelguyon
Volcans (Les)
Volvic
Riom
Ennezat
Maringues
Lezoux
Thiers
Pont-de-Dore
Pont-du-Chau
Puy de Dôme
Royat
Ceyrat
Clermont-Ferrand
Cournon-d'Auvergne
St Amant-Tallende
Veyre
Billom
Vic-le-Comte
Orcival
Randanne
Mont-Dore
Chambon-s-L.
Murol
Champeix
St Nectaire
Besse-et-St Anastaise
Super-Besse
Issoire
Sauxillanges
St Germain-Lembron
Ardes
Jumeaux
Brassac-les-Mines
Lempdes
Auzon
Condat
Blesle
Brioude
Massiac
Allanche
Murat
Le Lioran
Plomb du Cantal
St Flour
Ruynes-en-Margeride
Vduc de Garabit
Alleuze
Bge de Grandval
Chaudes-Aigues
Fournels
St Chély-d'Apcher
St Alban
le Malzieu-Ville
Saugues
Aumont-Aubrac
St Amans
Nasbinals
Laguiole
Aubrac
St Chély-d'A.
Espalion
St Geniez-d'Olt
St Germain-du-Teil
Marvejols
la Canourgue
Chanac
Mende
Bagnols-les-Bs
le Bleymard
Mt Lozère
Ste Enimie
Florac
le Massegros
Séverac-le Chau
les Vignes
le Rozier
la Malène
Aven Armand
Meyrueis
Grde de Dargilan
Chaos de Montpellier le Vx
Millau
Trèves
Mt Aigoual
St André-de-V.
St Jean-du-Gard
Barre-des-C.
St Germain-de-Calberte
Corniche des Cévennes
la Grd-Combe
Alès
Génolhac
Villefort
les Vans
Bessèges
St Ambroix
Salindres
Lussan
Barjac
Aven d'Orgnac
Vallon-Pont-d'arc
Ruoms
Joyeuse
Largentière
Aubenas
Vals-les-Bains
Thueyts
Antraigues
Montpezat-s/s-Bauzon
Valgorge
C. de Meyrand
St Laurent-les-Bains
St Etienne-de-Lugdarès
Langogne
Bge de Naussac
Pradelles
Châteauneuf-de-Randon
Grandrieu
Cayres
Solignac
Le Puy-en-Velay
Monistrol-d'A.
Loudes
St Paulien
Vorey
Allègre
Paulhaguet
Langeac
Lavoûte-Chilhac
Pinols
la Chaise-Dieu
Craponne
Arlanc
Viverols
St Germain-l'Herm
Ambert
St Amant-Roche-Savine
Cunlhat
St Dier-d'A.
Olliergues
Courpière
Noirétable
Monts du Forez
St Georges-en-Couzan
Boën
Montbrison
St Anthème
St Bonnet-le-Chau
Bas-en-Basset
Retournac
Monistrol-s-L.
Aurec-s-Loire
Yssingeaux
Montfaucon-en-Velay
Tence
le Chambon-s-Lignon
St Julien-Chapteuil
Fay-s-L.
le Monastier
Mt Mézenc
Gerbier de Jonc
St Martin-de-Valamas
Rochebonne
le Cheylard
Col des 4 Vios
Arlempdes
Firminy
le Chambon-Feugerolles
St Genest-Malifaux
St Didier-en-V.
St Etienne
St Just-St Rambert
Andrézieux-Bouthéon
St Galmier
Montrond-les-Bs
Feurs
Chazelles
St Symphorien-s
St Laurent-de-Ch.
Balbigny
Néronde
St Germain-Laval
St Just-en-Chevalet
St Symphorien-de-Lay
Tarare
Amplepuis
Roanne
Perreux
Thizy
Cours
Belmont
Lamure
Pouilly
St Haon-le-Châtel
Ambierle
Châtel-Mgne
le Mayet-de-Mgne
St Rémy
Loire
Haute-Loire
Lozère
Ardèche
Puy-de-Dôme
Allier
Tarn
Lot
Ardèche
Michelin
179

Map No 11
Carte 11
km
0 10 20
Mâcon
Bourg-en-Bresse
Bresse (La)
Gouverneur (Le)
Villette d'Anthon
Charmeil
Grenoble Bresson
Le Chambon-sur-Lignon
LYON
Roanne
Villefranche-s-Saône
Tarare
Feurs
St Etienne
Firminy
St Chamond
Rive-de-Gier
Givors
Vienne
Bourgoin-Jallieu
la Tour-du-Pin
Voiron
Belley
Nantua
Oyonnax
Bellegarde-s-V.
Ambérieu-en-Bugey
Pérouges
Meximieux
Montluel
Annonay
Tournon-s-R.
Valence
Romans
St Marcellin
Villard-de-Lans
Crest
Die
Privas
Aubenas
Montélimar
Nyons
Pierrelatte
Largentière
Vals-les-Bains
Lamastre
Dieulefit
Tain-l'Hermitage
Vinay
Tullins
Voreppe
Sassenage
Vif
la Mure
Monestier-de-C.
Luc-en-Diois
Châtillon-en-Diois
Bourg-St Andéol
St Paul-Trois-Châteaux
Valréas
Grignan
Viviers
le Teil
la Voulte
Livron
Loriol
Chabeuil
Bourg-de-Péage
RHÔNE
AIN
ISÈRE
ARDÈCHE
DRÔME
69
01
38
07
26
Mt Pilat
Mt Mézenc
Gerbier de Jonc
Col de Rousset
Col de Cabre
MICHELIN

Divonne
Gex
Genève
Maison Blanche
Annemasse
St Julien-en-G.
Reignier
Esery
Montreux (S)
Abondance
Châtel
le Biot
Pas de Morgins
Monthey
St Maurice
Aigle
Leysin
les Diablerets
Villars
Bex
Crans
Sion
Conthey
Sierre
Crans-sur-Sierre (S)
Evolène
Bge de la Grde Dixence
Verbier
Martigny
Salvan
Champéry
Morzine
Avoriaz
les Gets
St Jeoire
Taninges
Samoëns
Bonneville
Cluses
Cirque du Fer à Cheval
C. de la Forclaz
Champex
C. des Montets
Orsières
Bge de Mauvoisin
CERVINO MATTERHORN
Breuil-Cervinia
Grd Combin
P. d. Gran S. Bernardo
Col du Grd St Bernard
Traforo d. Gran S. Bernardo
Tunnel du Grd St Bernard
Bionaz
Chamonix
Chamonix-Mont-Blanc
Argentière
T. d. M. Bianco
T. du Mont Blanc
MONTE BIANCO
MONT BLANC
Plateau-d'Assy
Flaine
Sallanches
Combloux
Megève
St Gervais
les Houches
les Contamines
Praz
N.D. de Bellecombe
Thônes
Manigod
Col des Aravis
la Clusaz
le Grd Bornand
Thorens-Glières
C. de la Colombière
Cruseilles
Annecy
Veyrier
Menthon
la Tournette
Talloires
Sévrier
Duingt
Rumilly
Alby
Albens
Aix-les-Bains
Mt Revard
le Châtelard
Faverges
Ugine
Flumet
Beaufort
Cormet de Roselend
Albertville
Roignais
Bourg-St Maurice
Aime
les Arcs
Mt Pourri
la Rosière
C. d. Pic S. Bernardo
Col du Pt St Bernard
la Thuile
Entrèves
Courmayeur
Pré-St Didier
Morgex
Dora Baltea
Aosta/Aoste
Nus
Châtillon
Cogne
Valgrisenche
Valsavarenche
Rhêmes N.D.
Gran Paradiso
Colle del Nivolet
Champorcher
Valprato
Chambéry
Challes
la Féclaz
Col du Frêne
Grésy
St Pierre-d'Albigny
Montmélian
Aiguebelle
la Léchère
Moûtiers
la Plagne
Tignes
Bge de Tignes
Grde Sassière
Val d'Isère
Col de l'Iseran
Grde Casse
Parc National
Bonneval
Ceresole Reale
Locana
Groscavallo
Cantoira
Ceres
Ala di Stura
Balme
Lanzo Torinese
Viù
Usseglio
Brides
Bozel
Méribel
Courchevel
Pralognan
les Menuires
Val-Thorens
Massif de la Vanoise
C. de la Madeleine
Valmorel
St François-Longchamp
la Rochette
Pontcharra
Allevard
Goncelin
Belledonne
St Martin-de-Belleville
la Chambre
St Jean-de-Maurienne
St Michel-de-M.
Modane
Lanslebourg
Col du Mt Cenis
Susa
Bussoleno
Borgone
Almese
Torino (I)
Alpignano
Avigliana
Sacra di S. Michele
I Roveri (I)
Giaveno
Orbassano
Venaria
181
Grenoble
la Toussuire
C. du Glandon
Col de la Croix de Fer
Domène
Chamrousse
Valloire
Mt Thabor
T. d. Fréjus
Bardonècchia
Oulx
Sauze d'Oulx
Sestriere
Fenestrelle
Perosa Argentina
Perrero
Prali
Cumiana
Pinerolo
Airasca
Vigone
Torre Pellice
Bobbio Pellice
Villafranca Piemonte
Cavour
Alpe-d'Huez
le Bourg-d'Oisans
la Grave
la Meije
Col du Lautaret
Col du Galibier
Bge du Chambon
les Deux-Alpes
le Monêtier
Chantemerle
Névache
Cesana Torinese
Claviere
Montgenèvre
Col de Montgenèvre
Briançon
Serre Chevalier
Barre des Ecrins
la Bérarde
Massif des Ecrins
Parc National
Mt Pelvoux
Ailefroide
Vallouise
P. d'Olan
Valbonnais
Corps
la Chlle-en-Valgaudémar
St Firmin
Vx Chaillol
l'Argentière-la-Bessée
Col d'Izoard
Château-Queyras
Aiguilles
Abriès
Crissolio
Paesana
M. Viso
Saluzzo
Verzuolo
St Véran
Guillestre
St Etienne-en-Dévoluy
St Bonnet
Orcières
Col Bayard
Gap
la Bâtie-Neuve
Chorges
Embrun
Bge de Serre-Ponçon
Savines-le-Lac
Vars
Col de Vars
St Paul-sur-Ubaye
Casteldelfino
Sampeyre
Acceglio
Dronero
Cuneo
Veynes
Tallard
Larche
Col de Larche
Colle della Maddalena
Jausiers
Barcelonnette
le Lauzet-Ubaye
le Sauze-du-Lac
Pra-Loup
C. de la Bonette
Seyne
Turriers
la Motte
Col de Maure
Col d'Allos
Vinadio
Borgo S. Dalmazzo
Valdieri
St Etienne-
Parc
MICHELIN
HAUTE-SAVOIE
SAVOIE
HTES-ALPES
ALPES-DE-
VALAIS
VALLE D'AOSTA
PIEMONTE

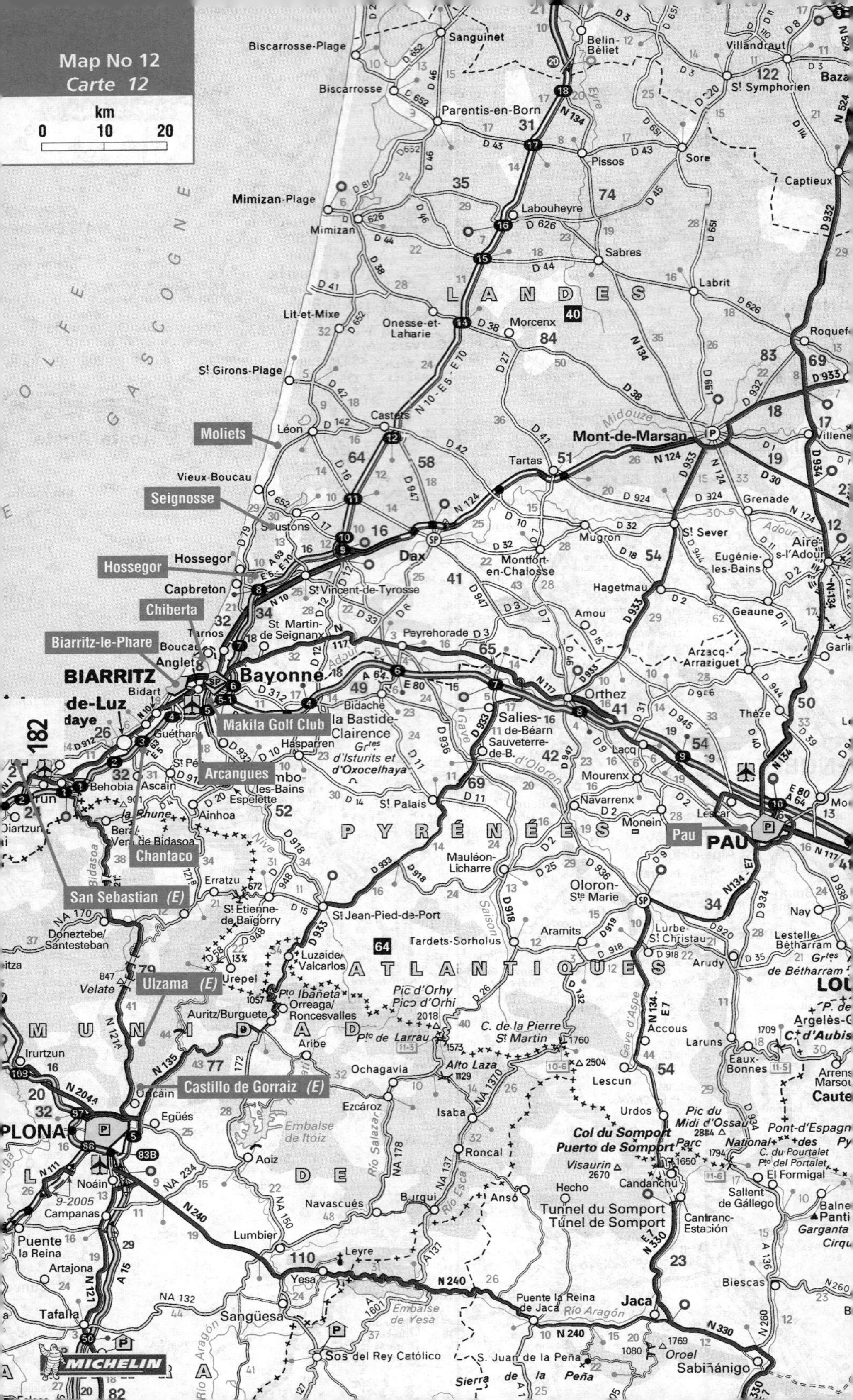

Map No 12
Carte 12
km
0 10 20
GOLFE DE GASCOGNE
LANDES
PYRÉNÉES ATLANTIQUES
MUNIDAD DE
Moliets
Seignosse
Hossegor
Chiberta
Biarritz-le-Phare
Makila Golf Club
Arcangues
Chantaco
San Sebastian (E)
Ulzama (E)
Castillo de Gorraiz (E)
Pau
Biscarrosse-Plage
Biscarrosse
Sanguinet
Belin-Béliet
Villandraut
St Symphorien
Bazas
Parentis-en-Born
Pissos
Sore
Captieux
Mimizan-Plage
Mimizan
Labouheyre
Sabres
Labrit
Lit-et-Mixe
Onesse-et-Laharie
Morcenx
Roquefort
St Girons-Plage
Léon
Castets
Mont-de-Marsan
Villeneuve
Vieux-Boucau
Tartas
Soustons
Grenade
Hossegor
Capbreton
Dax
Mugron
St Sever
Aire-s-l'Adour
Eugénie-les-Bains
Montfort-en-Chalosse
St Vincent-de-Tyrosse
Hagetmau
Geaune
Tarnos
St Martin-de-Seignanx
Peyrehorade
Amou
Boucau
Anglet
Arzacq-Arraziguet
BIARRITZ
Bayonne
Orthez
Bidart
Bidache
la Bastide-Clairence
Salies-de-Béarn
Sauveterre-de-B.
Thèze
St Jean-de-Luz
Hendaye
Guéthary
Hasparren
Grttes d'Isturits et d'Oxocelhaya
Lacq
Irun
Behobia
Ascain
St Pée
Cambo-les-Bains
Espelette
Mourenx
Navarrenx
Lescar
PAU
Ainhoa
la Rhune
Bera/Vera de Bidasoa
St Palais
Monein
Mauléon-Licharre
Oloron-Ste Marie
Nay
Erratzu
St Etienne-de-Baïgorry
St Jean-Pied-de-Port
Lurbe-St Christau
Lestelle-Bétharram
Grttes de Bétharram
Doneztebe/Santesteban
Tardets-Sorholus
Aramits
Arudy
Luzaide/Valcarlos
Urepel
Velate
Pto Ibañeta
Orreaga/Roncesvalles
Pic d'Orhy
Pico d'Orhi
Auritz/Burguete
Pto de Larrau
C. de la Pierre St Martin
Accous
Laruns
Argelès-G
C. d'Aubisque
Irurtzun
Aribe
Alto Laza
Eaux-Bonnes
Arrens-Marsous
Cauterets
Ochagavia
Lescun
Olaz-Subiza
Ezcároz
Isaba
Urdos
Pic du Midi d'Ossau
Pont-d'Espagne
PAMPLONA
Egüés
Embalse de Itoiz
Col du Somport
Puerto de Somport
Parc National des Pyrénées
C. du Pourtalet
Pto del Portalet
Roncal
Visaurin
Aoiz
Candanchú
El Formigal
Noáin
Hecho
Ansó
Tunnel du Somport
Túnel de Somport
Sallent de Gállego
Balneario de Panticosa
Garganta
Campanas
Navascués
Burgui
Canfranc-Estación
Río Salazar
Río Esca
Puente la Reina
Lumbier
Artajona
Leyre
Yesa
Biescas
Jaca
Puente la Reina de Jaca
Río Aragón
Embalse de Yesa
Tafalla
Sangüesa
Sos del Rey Católico
S. Juan de la Peña
Oroel
Sabiñánigo
Sierra de la Peña
MICHELIN

Marmande
LOT-ET-GARONNE
Tombebœuf
Monflanquin
Fumel
Chau de Bonaguil
Puy-l'Evêque
Catus
Luzech
Cahors
Auros
le Mas-d'Agenais
Castelmoron
Ste Livrade
Villeneuve-s-Lot
Tournon-d'Agenais
Grignols
Tonneins
Penne-d'A.
Montaigu-de-Quercy
Montcuq
Casteljaloux
Damazan
Aiguillon
Laroque-Timbaut
Castelnau-Montratier
Port-Ste Marie
Bourg-de-Visa
Lauzerte
Montpezat-de-Quercy
Houeillès
Agen
Molières
Lavardac
Puymirol
TARN-ET-GARONNE
Nérac
Valence-d'A
Moissac
Lafrançaise
Laplume
Astaffort
Auvillar
Castelsarrasin
St Nicolas-de-la-Grave
Mézin
Barbotan
Gabarret
Condom
Montréal
Lectoure
Lavit
Montech
Valence
St Clar
Beaumont-de-Lomagne
Verdun
Fronton
Eauze
Fleurance
Grisolles
Nogaro
Vic-Fezensac
Jegun
Mauvezin
Grenade
Montastruc-la-Conseillère
Aignan
Cologne
GERS
Auch
Toulouse-Seilh
Riscle
Blagnac
Plaisance
Gimont
l'Isle-Jourdain
Montesquiou
l'Isle-de-Noé
Léguevin
Castelnau-Rivière-Basse
Marciac
Saramon
Mirande
St Lys
Maubourguet
Seissan
Lombez
Samatan
Miélan
Masseube
Muret
Vic-en-Bigorre
Rieumes
Rabastens-de-Bigorre
l'Isle-en-Dodon
HAUTE-GARONNE
Trie
Auterive
Castelnau-Magnoac
Boulogne
le Fousseret
Carbonne
Cintegabelle
Pouyastruc
Lézat
Tarbes
HTES-PYRÉNÉES
Galan
Rieux
Ossun
Tournay
Aurignac
Boussens
Montesquieu-Volvestre
Cazères
Lannemezan
St Martory
Ste Croix-Volvestre
le Fossat
Capvern
Bagnères-de-Bigorre
la Barthe-de-Neste
St Gaudens
Salies-du-Salat
Montréjeau
St Bertrand-de-Comminges
Encausse
le Mas-d'Azil
Grte de Médous
Campan
Barbazan
Aspet
la Bastide-de-Sérou
PYRÉNÉES
Pierrefitte-Nestalas
Col d'Aspin
C. des Ares
Col de Portet d'Aspet
St Girons
P. du Midi de Bigorre
Barèges
la Mongie
Arreau
Mauléon-Barousse
St Béat
ARIÈGE
C. du Tourmalet
Bordères-Louron
Castillon-en-Couserans
Luz-St Sauveur
Vielle Aure
Fos
Oust
Massat
Col de Port
Pic de Néouvielle
St Lary-Soulan
C. de Peyresourde
Les Bossòst
Aulus-les-Bains
Grte de Niaux
Héas
Bagnères-de-Luchon
Guzet-Neige
Vicdessos
Gavarnie
Tunnel d'Aragnouet-Bielsa
Vall d'Aran
Beret
Monte Perdido
Vielha
Salardú
Baqueira
Port de la Bonaigua
Pic d'Estats
Parque Nacional de Ordesa y Monte Perdido
Pico Posets
Arties
Bielsa
Pico de Aneto
MALADETA
Benasque
Esterri d'Àneu
El Serrat
Cerler
Caldes de Boí
Parc national d'Aigüestortes
Espot
Ribera de Cardós
Ordino
Castejón de Sos
Vilaller
Llavorsí
la Vella
MICHELIN

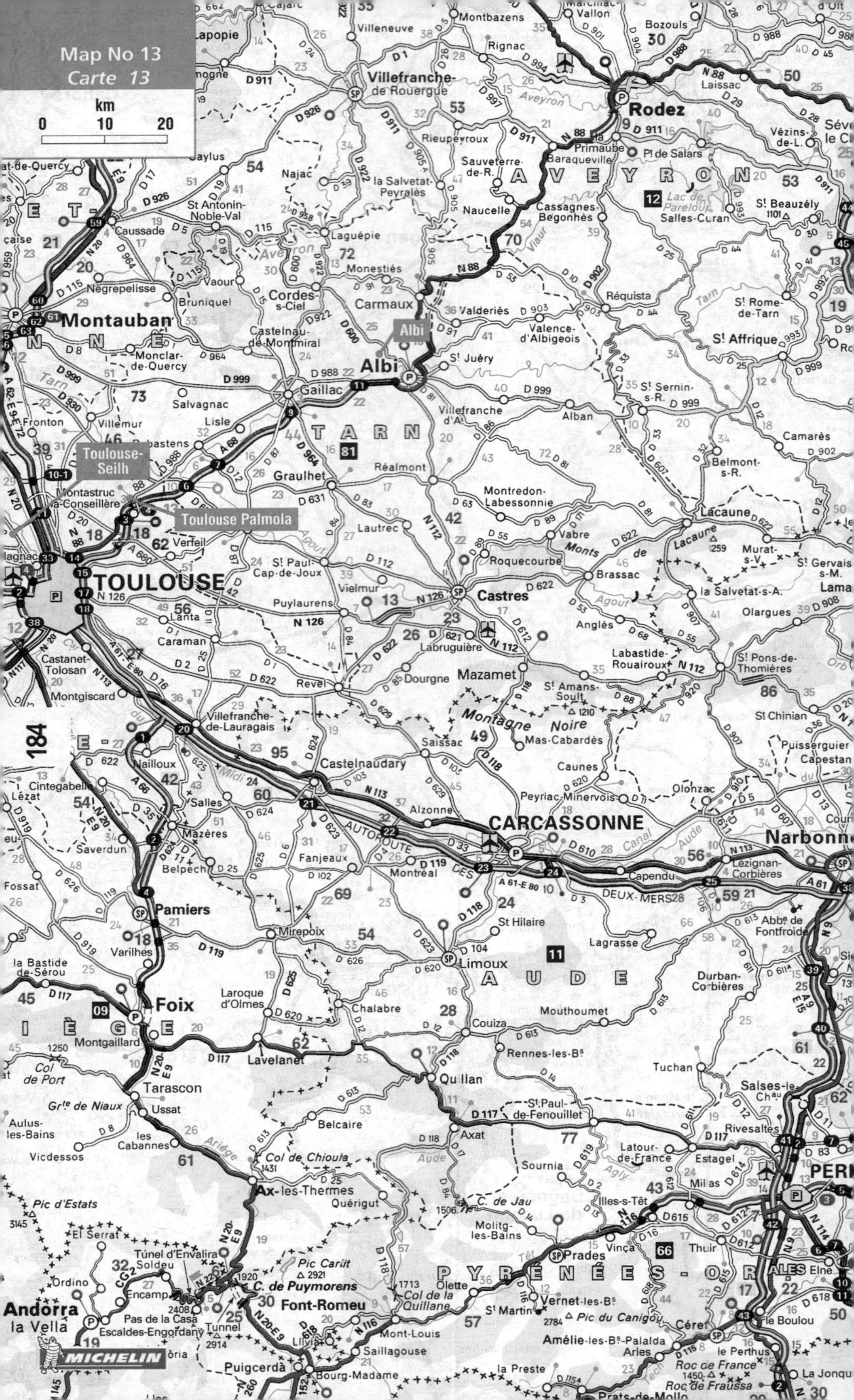

Map No 13
Carte 13
km
0 10 20
Lapopie
Villeneuve
Montbazens
Vallon
Bozouls
Rignac
Villefranche-de-Rouergue
Aveyron
Rodez
Laissac
Vézins-de-L.
Rieupeyroux
Primaube
Baraqueville
Pt de Salars
Caylus
Najac
la Salvetat-Peyralès
Sauveterre-de-R.
AVEYRON
Lac de Pareloup
Salles-Curan
St Beauzély
St Antonin-Noble-Val
Caussade
Naucelle
Cassagnes-Begonhès
Laguépie
Nègrepelisse
Vaour
Monestiés
Bruniquel
Cordes-s-Ciel
Carmaux
Valderiès
Réquista
St Rome-de-Tarn
Montauban
Castelnau-de-Montmiral
Valence-d'Albigeois
St Affrique
Monclar-de-Quercy
Albi
St Juéry
Gaillac
St Sernin-s-R.
Salvagnac
Fronton
Villemur
Lisle
Villefranche-d'A.
Alban
Camarès
Rabastens
TARN
Toulouse-Seilh
Graulhet
Réalmont
Belmont-s-R.
Montastruc-la-Conseillère
Montredon-Labessonnie
Lacaune
Toulouse Palmola
Verfeil
Lautrec
Vabre
Monts de Lacaune
Murat-s-V.
St Gervais-s-M.
St Paul-Cap-de-Joux
Roquecourbe
Brassac
TOULOUSE
Vielmur
Castres
la Salvetat-s-A.
Puylaurens
Agout
Lanta
Caraman
Anglès
Olargues
Labruguière
Labastide-Rouairoux
St Pons-de-Thomières
Castanet-Tolosan
Revel
Dourgne
Mazamet
St Amans-Soult
Montgiscard
Villefranche-de-Lauragais
Montagne Noire
Mas-Cabardès
St Chinian
184
Nailloux
Saissac
Puisserguier
Capestan
Castelnaudary
Caunes
Cintegabelle
Lézat
Salles
Peyriac-Minervois
Olonzac
Alzonne
CARCASSONNE
Narbonne
Mazères
Saverdun
Fanjeaux
Canal
Aude
Belpech
Montréal
Capendu
Lézignan-Corbières
Fossat
AUTOROUTE DES DEUX-MERS
Pamiers
St Hilaire
Abbe de Fontfroide
Mirepoix
Lagrasse
Varilhes
Limoux
la Bastide-de-Sérou
AUDE
Durban-Corbières
Foix
Laroque d'Olmes
Chalabre
Mouthoumet
Montgaillard
Couiza
Rennes-les-Bs
Col de Port
Lavelanet
Quillan
Tuchan
Tarascon
Salses-le-Chau
Grte de Niaux
Ussat
St Paul-de-Fenouillet
Aulus-les-Bains
Belcaire
Rivesaltes
Vicdessos
les Cabannes
Axat
Latour-de-France
Estagel
Col de Chioula
Sournia
Ariège
Agly
Ax-les-Thermes
Quérigut
Millas
Pic d'Estats
C. de Jau
Ille-s-Têt
El Serrat
Molitg-les-Bains
Prades
Vinça
Thuir
Túnel d'Envalira
Soldeu
Pic Carlit
Elne
Ordino
C. de Puymorens
Encamp
Olette
Col de la Quillane
Font-Romeu
Vernet-les-Bs
Andorra la Vella
Pas de la Casa
Escaldes-Engordany
Tunnel
St Martin
Pic du Canigou
Céret
le Boulou
Mont-Louis
Amélie-les-Bs-Palalda
Arles
Llivia
Saillagouse
le Perthus
Roc de France
Puigcerdà
Bourg-Madame
la Preste
Roc de Frausa
La Jonquera
PYRÉNÉES-ORIENTALES
MICHELIN

Montpellier-Massane
Fontcaude
Nîmes-Campagne
Grande Motte (La)
Cap d'Agde
MONTPELLIER
NÎMES
GARD
HÉRAULT
BOUCHES
MICHELIN
le Bleymard
Mt Lozère
Villefort
Ruoms
Donzère
la Canourgue
Chanac
Ste Enimie
le Pont-de Montvert
Parc National
Génolhac
les Vans
Vallon-Pont-d'arc
Bourg-St Andéol
Gges de l'Ardèche
Aven d'Orgnac
Barjac
le Massegros
Tarn
Florac
Bessèges
Pont-St Esprit
la Malène
Gorges du Tarn
Barre-des-C.
St Germain-de-Calberte
St Ambroix
les Vignes
Aven Armand
Corniche des Cévennes
la Grd-Combe
Salindres
Lussan
Bagnols-s-C.
le Rozier
Grte de Dargilan
Chaos de Montpellier le V.
Meyrueis
St André-de-V.
Mt Aigoual
Alès
Marcoule
Millau
Trèves
Cévennes
Valleraugue
St Jean-du-Gard
Vézénobres
Châteauneuf-du-Pape
Roquemaure
la Cavalerie
Nant
St Jean-du-Bruel
le Vigan
Lasalle
Anduze
Uzès
Villeneuve
Alzon
St Hippolyte-du-Fort
Lédignan
Remoulins
Pont du Gard
AVIGNON
la Couvertoirade
Cque de Navacelles
Ganges
Grte des Demoiselles
Sauve
Quissac
Cornus
le Caylar
Marguerittes
Beaucaire
Tarascon
St Martin-de-Londres
Bellegarde
St Guilhem-le-Désert
Lodève
les Matelles
Gallargues
Vauvert
Arles
Lunas
Grte de Clamouse
Aniane
Castries
Lunel
Aimargues
St Gilles
Gignac
Mauguio
Clermont-l'Hérault
Bédarieux
Petit-Rhône
Aigues-Mortes
Etg de Vaccarès
Carnon
la Grde Motte
le Grau-du-Roi
Palavas
Roujan
Montagnac
LA LANGUEDOCIENNE
Balaruc
Frontignan
Stes Maries-de-la-Mer
Murviel
Pézenas
Servian
Florensac
Mèze
Sète
Béziers
Bin de Thau
Marseillan
Vias
Agde
le Cap d'Agde
Valras-Plage
Narbonne-Plage
Gruissan
Port-la-Nouvelle
GOLFE DU LION
MÉDI
Port-Leucate
Port-Barcarès
St Laurent-de-la Salanque
Canet-Plage
St Cyprien-Plage
Collioure
Port-Vendres
Banyuls
Cerbère
Portbou

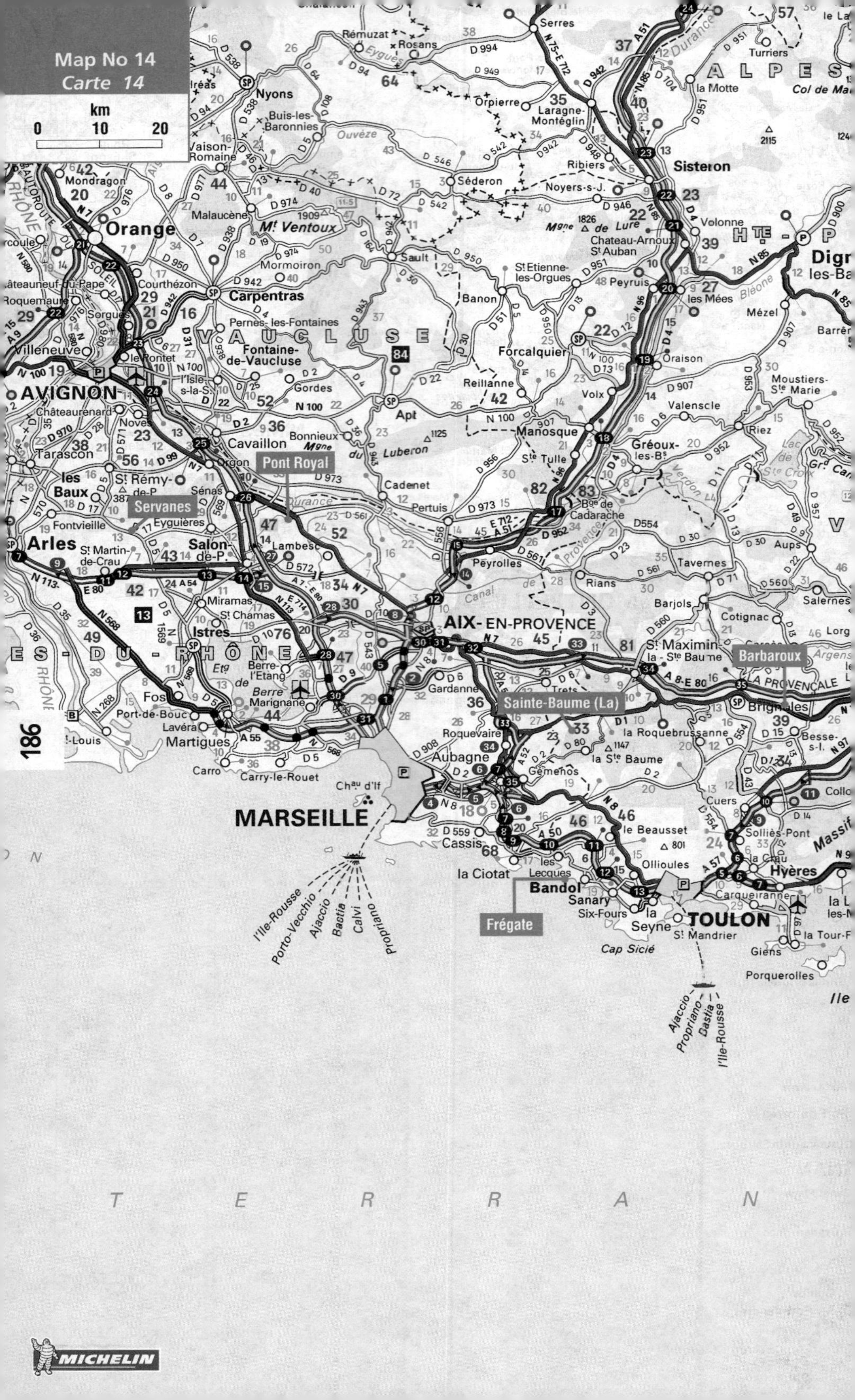

Map No 14
Carte 14
km
0 10 20
186
Orange
Avignon
Arles
Carpentras
Nyons
Vaison-la-Romaine
Cavaillon
Apt
Sault
Sisteron
Forcalquier
Manosque
Salon-de-P.
Istres
Martigues
Aix-en-Provence
Marseille
Aubagne
Cassis
la Ciotat
Bandol
Sanary
Toulon
Hyères
Digne-les-Bains
Vaucluse
Alpes
Mt Ventoux
Mgne du Luberon
Pont Royal
Servanes
Sainte-Baume (La)
Barbaroux
Frégate
la Provençale
Ch^au d'If
l'Ile-Rousse
Porto-Vecchio
Ajaccio
Bastia
Calvi
Propriano
T E R R A N
Michelin

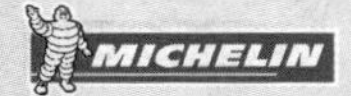

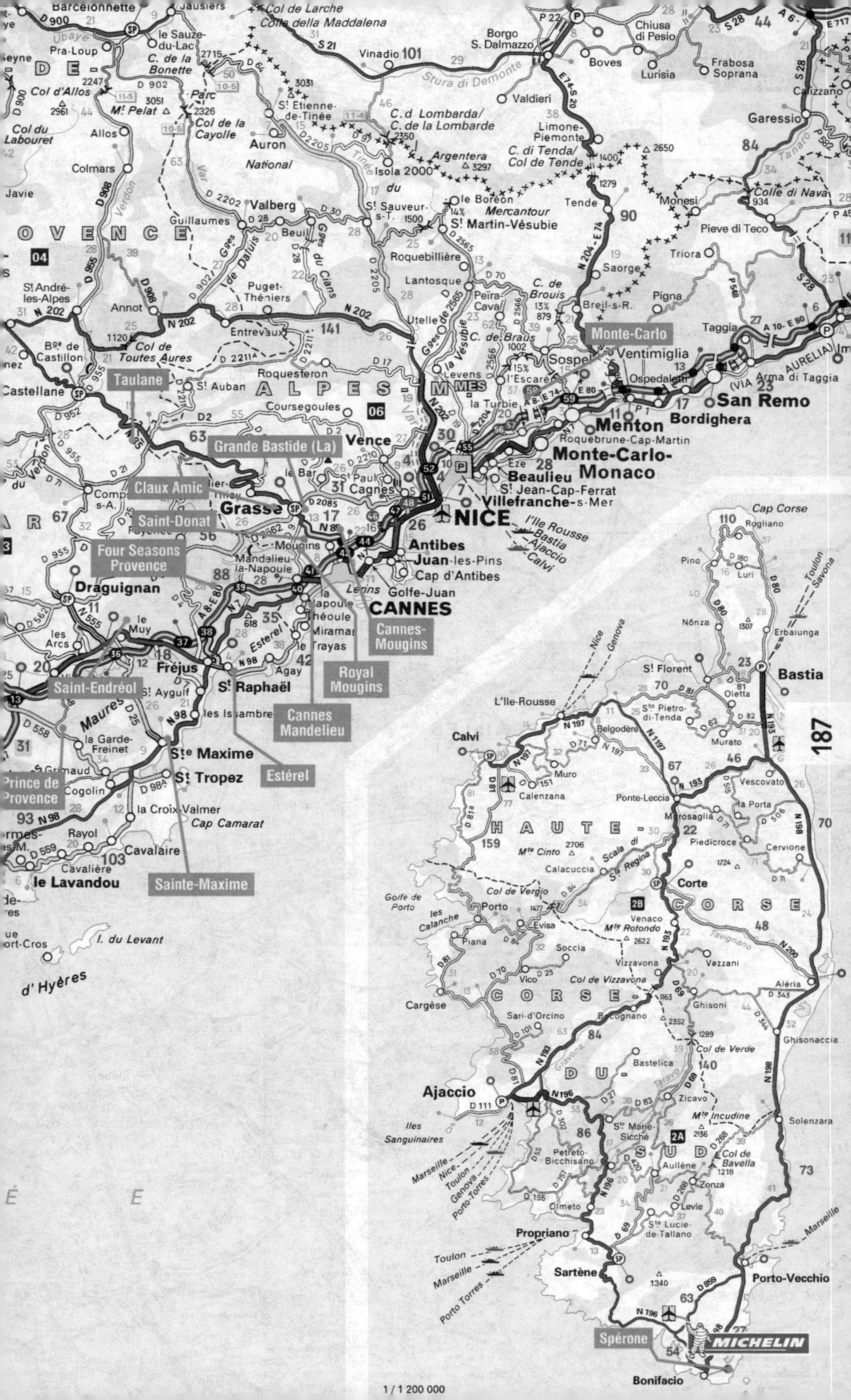

Taulane
Grande Bastide (La)
Claux Amic
Saint-Donat
Four Seasons Provence
Cannes-Mougins
Royal Mougins
Cannes Mandelieu
Estérel
Saint-Endréol
Prince de Provence
Sainte-Maxime
Monte-Carlo
Spérone
NICE
CANNES
Antibes
Juan-les-Pins
Cap d'Antibes
Golfe-Juan
Grasse
Vence
Draguignan
Fréjus
St Raphaël
Ste Maxime
St Tropez
le Lavandou
Menton
Monte-Carlo-Monaco
Beaulieu
Villefranche-s-Mer
St Jean-Cap-Ferrat
Roquebrune-Cap-Martin
San Remo
Bordighera
Ventimiglia
Sospel
Tende
Barcelonnette
Castellane
Mandelieu-la-Napoule
Théoule
ALPES-MARITIMES
HAUTE-CORSE
CORSE-DU-SUD
Cap Corse
Bastia
St Florent
L'Ile-Rousse
Calvi
Corte
Porto
Ajaccio
Propriano
Sartène
Porto-Vecchio
Bonifacio
Aléria
Ghisonaccia
Solenzara
187
MICHELIN
1 / 1 200 000

Map No 15
Carte 15
km
0 2 4
Château de la Chouette
Saint-Germain
Béthemont
Joyenval
Feucherolles
Saint-Nom-La-Bretèche
Paris International
Saint-Cloud
RCF La Boulie
Golf National
Courson
Rochefort
188
MICHELIN
PONTOISE
Cergy
Conflans Ste Honorine
Maisons-Laffitte
Argenteuil
Poissy
ST GERMAIN-EN-LAYE
Nanterre
Neuilly-s-Seine
Rueil-Malmaison
Boulogne-Billancourt
VERSAILLES
Sèvres
Meudon
Montrouge
Clamart
Sceaux
Antony
Palaiseau
Orsay
Les Ulis
Chevreuse
Rambouillet
Dampierre
Montigny-le-Bretonneux
Trappes
Maurepas
Plaisir
Meulan
Les Mureaux
Herblay
Sartrouville
Colombes
Asnières
Levallois
Clichy
Courbevoie
Puteaux
Suresnes
St Cloud
Chatou
Le Vésinet
Marly-le-Roi
Le Chesnay
Vélizy-Villacoublay
Massy
Longjumeau
Montlhéry
Limours
Forêt de Montmorency
L'Isle-Adam
Enghien-les-Bains
Epinay-s-Seine
Gennevilliers
PARC RÉGIONAL DE LA HAUTE-VALLÉE DE CHEVREUSE

Disneyland Paris
Ozoir-la-Ferrière
Etiolles
AÉROPORT DE PARIS-CHARLES-DE-GAULLE
Roissy-en-France
Goussainville
Dammartin-en-Goële
Mitry-Mory
Tremblay-en-France
Villepinte
Sevran
Aulnay-s/s-Bois
Le Bourget
Drancy
Aubervilliers
Bobigny
Pantin
Bondy
le Raincy
Montfermeil
Gagny
Chelles
Villeparisis
Claye-Souilly
Noisy-le-Sec
Romainville
Bagnolet
Montreuil
Vincennes
Rosny-s/s-Bois
Neuilly-Plaisance
Nogent-s-M
le Perreux
Noisy-le-Grand
Marne-la-Vallée
Champs-s-M.
Noisiel
Torcy
Lagny-s-M.
Bussy-St-Georges
Champigny-s-M.
Villiers-s-M.
Joinville-le-Pont
Charenton-le-Pont
Alfortville
Maisons-Alfort
CRÉTEIL
St-Maur-des-Fossés
Chennevières-s-M.
Ormesson-s-M.
Pontault-Combault
Roissy-en-Brie
Sucy-en-Brie
Boissy-St-Léger
Ivry-s-Seine
Vitry-s-Seine
Choisy-le-Roi
Thiais
Orly
Villeneuve-St-Georges
Yerres
Villecresnes
Brunoy
Montgeron
Draveil
Forêt de Sénart
Brie-Comte-Robert
Combs-la-Ville
Sénart (Ville Nle)
EVRY
Corbeil-Essonnes
St-Germain-lès-C.
Lieusaint
Moissy-Cramayel
Savigny-s-Orge
Juvisy-s-Orge
Ris-Orangis
PARIS
Sarcelles
Gonesse
Villiers-le-Bel
Écouen
Stains
Pierrefitte-s-Seine
Garges-lès-G.
DENIS
MICHELIN

CLASSIFICATION OF GOLF COURSES
CLASSEMENT DES PARCOURS

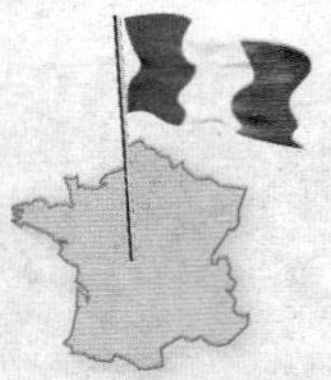

This classification gives priority consideration to the score awarded to the actual course.

Ce classement donne priorité à la note attribuée au parcours.

Within each score, the ranking is purely alphabetical

Course score / Note du parcours				Page
19	8	6	Les Bordes	221
18	7	6	Chantilly Vineuil	236
18	8	6	Le Kempferhof	283
18	7	6	Médoc Les Châteaux	291
18	6	6	Morfontaine	297
18	6	6	National L'Albatros	298
18	8	5	Prince de Provence (Vidauban)	310
18	7	5	Spérone	331
17	7	6	Barbaroux	213
17	7	3	Courson Vert/Noir	246
17	7	7	Fontainebleau	259
17	9	8	Four Seasons Provence Le Château	263
17	6	6	Limère	287
17	6	5	Moliets	293
17	7	6	Nîmes-Campagne	299
17	7	5	Pléneuf-Val-André	304
17	7	7	Saint-Germain	320
17	8	8	Saint-Nom-la-Bretèche Rouge	324
17	7	7	Seignosse	328
17	7	4	Soufflenheim	330
16	5	4	Les Aisses Rouge + Blanc	203
16	6	6	Albi	204
16	6	5	Belle-Dune	215
16	7	7	Bondues Blanc	219
16	7	6	La Bresse	223
16	6	6	Charmeil	237
16	5	6	Château de la Chouette	238
16	6	8	Chiberta	242
16	7	3	Courson Lilas + Orange	245
16	7	8	Disneyland Paris Rouge + Bleu	249
16	5	5	La Domangère	251
16	9	8	Four Seasons Provence Le Riou	264
16	7	7	Frégate	265
16	6	6	La Grande Bastide	270
16	6	4	La Grande-Motte Les Flamants Roses	271
16	7	6	Grenoble Bresson	273
16	6	6	Hardelot Les Pins	275
16	7	6	Hossegor	277
16	7	5	L'Isle Adam	279
16	8	7	Joyenval Marly	281
16	8	7	Joyenval Retz	282
16	7	5	Massane-Montpellier	290
16	7	6	Médoc Les Vignes	292
16	7	5	Paris International	302
16	7	6	Pont Royal	306
16	6	6	Rebetz	312
16	8	8	Royal Mougins	315
16	7	4	Sablé-Solesmes La Forêt + La Rivière	316
16	7	8	Saint Donat	318
16	8	8	Saint-Nom-la-Bretèche Bleu	323
16	5	7	Le Touquet La Mer	336
16	7	5	Villette d'Anthon Les Sangliers	340
16	6	6	La Wantzenau	342
15	6	5	L'Ailette	202
15	8	6	Apremont	206
15	8	8	Arcangues	208
15	7	7	Bâle-Hagenthal	212
15	7	7	Bondues Jaune	220
15	7	8	La Boulie La Vallée	222
15	7	7	La Bretesche	225
15	7	8	Cannes-Mougins	228
15	6	6	Cap d'Agde	229
15	7	6	Cély	230
15	6	7	Chamonix	233
15	7	6	Château de Preisch	239
15	7	5	Esery	252
15	6	7	Estérel	253
15	7	7	Etiolles Colonial Les Cerfs	254
15	7	9	Evian	257
15	6	5	Feucherolles	258
15	7	8	Golf Barrière Deauville Rouge + Blanc	266
15	7	8	Golf Barrière La Baule Bleu	267
15	6	6	Le Gouverneur Le Breuil	269
15	7	6	Gujan-Mestras	274
15	6	7	ICL (Le Lys-Chantilly) Les Chênes	278
15	7	5	La Largue	285
15	6	8	Makila Golf Club	289
15	6	6	Pornic	308
15	7	7	Roncemay	314
15	7	4	Saint-Endréol	319

CLASSIFICATION OF GOLF COURSES
CLASSEMENT DES PARCOURS

15	6	5	Saint-Jean-de-Monts	321
15	7	7	Strasbourg Illkirch Jaune + Rouge	332
15	7	4	Taulane	333
15	7	5	Toulouse Palmola	334
15	7	6	Toulouse-Seilh Rouge	335
14	7	8	L'Amirauté	205
14	6	6	Arras	209
14	6	5	Baden	211
14	7	7	Bélesbat	214
14	5	6	Béthemont	216
14	6	8	Biarritz-le-Phare	217
14	6	5	Bitche	218
14	7	6	Brest Iroise	224
14	7	6	Brigode	226
14	7	8	Cannes Mandelieu Old Course	227
14	8	6	Château de Chailly	231
14	5	7	Chambon-sur-Lignon	232
14	6	3	Champ de Bataille	234
14	7	7	Chantaco	235
14	6	4	Chaumont-en-Vexin	240
14	7	6	Cheverny	241
14	6	5	Dieppe-Pourville	247
14	6	7	Divonne	250
14	6	6	Fontcaude	260
14	7	5	Fontenailles Jaune + Blanc	261
14	7	5	Golf Parc Nantilly	268
14	4	4	Granville Le Links	272
14	6	5	Haut-Poitou	276
14	7	5	Laval-Changé La Chabossière	286
14	8	5	Maison Blanche	288
14	6	7	Monte Carlo (Mont Agel)	295
14	7	5	Omaha Beach La Mer + Le Bocage	300
14	7	6	Ploemeur Océan	305
14	6	4	La Porcelaine	307
14	7	5	Le Prieuré Ouest	309
14	7	5	Château de Raray La Licorne	311
14	6	4	Rochefort	313
14	8	7	Saint-Cloud Vert	317
14	7	5	Saint-Laurent	322
14	7	6	Sainte-Baume (La)	325
14	5	4	Savenay	327
14	7	5	Val de Sorne	337
14	6	5	Val Queven	338
14	7	4	La Vaucouleurs Les Vallons	339
14	6	5	Les Volcans	341
13	6	4	Ableiges Les Etangs	201
13	6	6	Arcachon	207
13	6	4	Augerville	210
13	8	6	Claux Amic	243
13	7	5	Cognac	244
13	6	7	Dinard	248
13	5	6	Etretat	255
13	6	4	Les Fontenelles	262
13	6	6	Lacanau	284
13	7	5	Ozoir-la-Ferrière Château + Monthéty	301
13	6	8	Pau	303
13	7	8	Sainte-Maxime	326
13	5	7	Servanes	329
13	4	5	Wimereux	343

HOTEL FACILITIES
ENVIRONNEMENT HOTELIER

This classification gives priority consideration to the score awarded to the hotel facilities.

Ce classement donne priorité à la note attribuée à l'environnement hôtelier.

Hotel facility score / Note de l'environnement hôtelier — Page

15	7	**9**	Evian	257
14	7	**8**	L'Amirauté	205
15	8	**8**	Arcangues	208
14	6	**8**	Biarritz-le-Phare	217
15	7	**8**	Boulie (La) La Vallée	222
14	7	**8**	Cannes Mandelieu Old Course	227
15	7	**8**	Cannes-Mougins	228
16	6	**8**	Chiberta	242
16	7	**8**	Disneyland Paris Rouge + Bleu	249
17	9	**8**	Four Seasons Provence Le Château	263
16	9	**8**	Four Seasons Provence Le Riou	264
15	7	**8**	Golf Barrière Deauville Rouge + Blanc	266
15	7	**8**	Golf Barrière La Baule Bleu	267
15	6	**8**	Makila Golf Club	289
13	6	**8**	Pau	303
16	8	**8**	Royal Mougins	315
16	7	**8**	Saint Donat	318
16	8	**8**	Saint-Nom-la-Bretèche Bleu	323
17	8	**8**	Saint-Nom-la-Bretèche Rouge	324
13	7	**8**	Sainte-Maxime	326
15	7	**7**	Bâle-Hagenthal	212
14	7	**7**	Bélesbat	214
16	7	**7**	Bondues Blanc	219
15	7	**7**	Bondues Jaune	220
15	7	**7**	La Bretesche	225

HOTEL FACILITIES
ENVIRONNEMENT HOTELIER

14	5	**7**	Chambon-sur-Lignon	232
15	6	**7**	Chamonix	233
14	7	**7**	Chantaco	235
13	6	**7**	Dinard	248
14	6	**7**	Divonne	250
15	6	**7**	Estérel	253
15	7	**7**	Etiolles Colonial Les Cerfs	254
17	7	**7**	Fontainebleau	259
16	7	**7**	Frégate	265
15	6	**7**	ICL (Le Lys-Chantilly) Les Chênes	278
16	8	**7**	Joyenval Marly	281
16	8	**7**	Joyenval Retz	282
14	6	**7**	Monte Carlo (Mont Agel)	295
15	7	**7**	Roncemay	314
14	8	**7**	Saint-Cloud Vert	317
17	7	**7**	Saint-Germain	320
17	7	**7**	Seignosse	328
13	5	**7**	Servanes	329
15	7	**7**	Strasbourg Illkirch Jaune + Rouge	332
16	5	**7**	Le Touquet La Mer	336
16	6	**6**	Albi	204
15	8	**6**	Apremont	206
13	6	**6**	Arcachon	207
14	6	**6**	Arras	209
17	7	**6**	Barbaroux	213
14	5	**6**	Béthemont	216
19	8	**6**	Les Bordes	221
16	7	**6**	La Bresse	223
14	7	**6**	Brest Iroise	224
14	7	**6**	Brigode	226
15	6	**6**	Cap d'Agde	229
15	7	**6**	Cély	230
14	8	**6**	Château de Chailly	231
18	7	**6**	Chantilly Vineuil	236
16	6	**6**	Charmeil	237
16	5	**6**	Château de la Chouette	238
15	7	**6**	Château de Preisch	239
14	7	**6**	Cheverny	241
13	8	**6**	Claux Amic	243
13	5	**6**	Etretat	255
14	6	**6**	Fontcaude	260
15	6	**6**	Le Gouverneur Le Breuil	269
16	6	**6**	La Grande Bastide	270
16	7	**6**	Grenoble Bresson	273
15	7	**6**	Gujan-Mestras	274
16	6	**6**	Hardelot Les Pins	275
16	7	**6**	Hossegor	277
18	8	**6**	Le Kempferhof	283
13	6	**6**	Lacanau	284
17	6	**6**	Limère	287
18	7	**6**	Médoc Les Châteaux	291
16	7	**6**	Médoc Les Vignes	292
18	6	**6**	Morfontaine	297
18	6	**6**	National L'Albatros	298
17	7	**6**	Nîmes-Campagne	299
14	7	**6**	Ploemeur Océan	305
16	7	**6**	Pont Royal	306
15	6	**6**	Pornic	308
16	6	**6**	Rebetz	312
14	7	**6**	La Sainte-Baume	325
15	7	**6**	Toulouse-Seilh Rouge	335
16	6	**6**	Wantzenau (La)	342
15	6	**5**	L'Ailette	202
14	6	**5**	Baden	211
16	6	**5**	Belle-Dune	215
14	6	**5**	Bitche	218
13	7	**5**	Cognac	244
14	6	**5**	Dieppe-Pourville	247
16	5	**5**	La Domangère	251
15	7	**5**	Esery	252
15	6	**5**	Feucherolles	258
14	7	**5**	Fontenailles Jaune + Blanc	261
14	7	**5**	Golf Parc Nantilly	268
14	6	**5**	Haut-Poitou	276
16	7	**5**	L'Isle Adam	279
15	7	**5**	La Largue	285
14	7	**5**	Laval-Changé La Chabossière	286
14	8	**5**	Maison Blanche	288
16	7	**5**	Massane-Montpellier	290
17	6	**5**	Moliets	293
14	7	**5**	Omaha Beach La Mer + Le Bocage	300
13	7	**5**	Ozoir-la-Ferrière Château + Monthéty	301
16	7	**5**	Paris International	302
17	7	**5**	Pléneuf-Val-André	304
14	7	**5**	Le Prieuré Ouest	309
18	8	**5**	Prince de Provence (Vidauban)	310
14	7	**5**	Château de Raray La Licorne	311
15	6	**5**	Saint-Jean-de-Monts	321
14	7	**5**	Saint-Laurent	322
18	7	**5**	Spérone	331
15	7	**5**	Toulouse Palmola	334
14	7	**5**	Val de Sorne	337
14	6	**5**	Val Queven	338
16	7	**5**	Villette d'Anthon Les Sangliers	340
14	6	**5**	Les Volcans	341
13	4	**5**	Wimereux	343
13	6	**4**	Ableiges Les Etangs	201
16	5	**4**	Les Aisses Rouge + Blanc	203
13	6	**4**	Augerville	210
14	6	**4**	Chaumont-en-Vexin	240
13	6	**4**	Les Fontenelles	262
16	6	**4**	La Grande-Motte Les Flamants Roses	271
14	4	**4**	Granville Le Links	272
14	6	**4**	La Porcelaine	307
14	6	**4**	Rochefort	313
16	7	**4**	Sablé-Solesmes La Forêt + La Rivière	316
15	7	**4**	Saint-Endréol	319
14	5	**4**	Savenay	327
17	7	**4**	Soufflenheim	330
15	7	**4**	Taulane	333
14	7	**4**	La Vaucouleurs Les Vallons	339
14	6	**3**	Champ de Bataille	234
16	7	**3**	Courson Lilas + Orange	245
17	7	**3**	Courson Vert + Noir	246

RECOMMENDED GOLFING STAY
SÉJOUR DE GOLF RECOMMANDÉ

Barbaroux	**17**	7	6	213
Bondues Blanc	**16**	7	7	219
Bondues Jaune	**15**	7	7	220
Bordes (Les)	**19**	8	6	221
Bretesche (La)	**15**	7	7	225
Courson Lilas + Orange	**16**	7	3	245
Courson Vert + Noir	**17**	7	3	246
Four Seasons Provence Le Château	**17**	9	8	263
Four Seasons Provence Le Riou	**16**	9	8	264
Golf Barrière La Baule Bleu	**15**	7	8	267
Le Gouverneur Le Breuil	**15**	6	6	269
La Grande-Motte Les Flamants Roses	**16**	6	4	271
Gujan-Mestras	**15**	7	6	274
Hardelot Les Pins	**16**	6	6	275
Massane-Montpellier	**16**	7	5	290
Médoc Les Châteaux	**18**	7	6	291
Médoc Les Vignes	**16**	7	6	292
Moliets	**17**	6	5	293
National L'Albatros	**18**	6	6	298
Pléneuf-Val-André	**17**	7	5	304
Sablé-Solesmes La Forêt + La Rivière	**16**	7	4	316
Spérone	**18**	7	5	331
Taulane	**15**	7	4	333
Toulouse-Seilh Rouge	**15**	7	6	335
Le Touquet La Mer	**16**	5	7	336

RECOMMENDED HOLIDAYS
VACANCES RECOMMANDÉES

Arcachon	**13**	6	6	207
Arcangues	**15**	8	8	208
Biarritz-le-Phare	**14**	6	8	217
Cannes Mandelieu Old Course	**14**	7	8	227
Cannes-Mougins	**15**	7	8	228
Cap d'Agde	**15**	6	6	229
Chantaco	**14**	7	7	235
Chiberta	**16**	6	8	242
Dinard	**13**	6	7	248
Disneyland Paris Rouge + Bleu	**16**	7	8	249
Estérel	**15**	6	7	253
Evian	**15**	7	9	257
Frégate	**16**	7	7	265
Golf Barrière Deauville Rouge + Blanc	**15**	7	8	266
Golf Barrière La Baule Bleu	**15**	7	8	267
La Grande Bastide	**16**	6	6	270
La Grande-Motte Les Flamants Roses	**16**	6	4	271
Gujan-Mestras	**15**	7	6	274
Hardelot Les Pins	**16**	6	6	275
Hossegor	**16**	7	6	277
Lacanau	**13**	6	6	284
Makila Golf Club	**15**	6	8	289
Moliets	**17**	6	5	293
Monte Carlo (Mont Agel)	**14**	6	7	295
Pornic	**15**	6	6	308
Royal Mougins	**16**	8	8	315
Saint Donat	**16**	7	8	318
Saint-Laurent	**14**	7	5	322
Sainte-Maxime	**13**	7	8	326
Spérone	**18**	7	5	331

Ableiges *Les Etangs*

13	6	4

L'architecture du 18 trous des "Etangs" représente différents aspects, mais sans rupture de style trop marquée dans cet agréable paysage de plaine et de vallons du Vexin. Le haut du domaine s'apparente aux links, avec de jolis mouvements de terrain, alors que la partie basse est plus "américaine". La plupart des placements de drives, tout comme les approches, exigent une bonne technique et une réflexion attentive, en raison des nombreux obstacles très en jeu, qu'il s'agisse des bunkers, du rough ou de l'eau. L'architecte Jeremy Pern a généreusement modelé et défendu les greens, et les positions de drapeau peuvent changer radicalement le jeu. Les reliefs du terrain rendent ce bon test assez physique (à jouer en voiturette). L'entretien ne rend pas vraiment justice à ce tracé, et restait un point bien faible lors de nos examens. Souhaitons que ce soit ponctuel...

The architecture of the 18 hole "Etangs" course features a number of different styles but avoids any stark contrast over the plain and the vales of Vexin. The upper plateau is links territory, with attractive sand-hills and dips, while the lower section is more American in its layout. Most tee-shots and approach-shots require good technique and careful placing of the ball owing to the numerous hazards in play, ranging from unforgiving rough to water. Architect Jeremy Pern has generously contoured and defended the greens, where the pin-positions can radically change the layout. Ableiges can be a tiring course on foot (it is worth taking a buggy). Green-keeping does not really do this layout justice and was still a weak point when we visited. Let's hope this was just one bad day.

Golf Club d'Ableiges — 1989

Chaussée Jules César
F - 95450 ABLEIGES

Office	Secrétariat	(33) 01 30 27 97 00
Pro shop	Pro-shop	(33) 01 34 27 97 00
Fax	Fax	(33) 01 30 27 97 10
Web	www.ableigesgolf.com	
Situation	Situation	Paris, 40 km

Pontoise (pop. 27 150), 9 km

Annual closure Fermeture annuelle — no
Weekly closure Fermeture hebdomadaire — no

Fees main season Tarifs haute saison — 18 holes

	Week days Semaine	We/Bank holidays We/Férié
Individual Individuel	€ 36	€ 59
Couple Couple	€ 72	€ 118

Tuesday (Mardi): GF + lunch, € 43 / Juniors: € 26/43 (We)

Caddie Caddie no — **Electric Trolley** Chariot électrique no
Buggy Voiturette yes — **Clubs** Clubs yes

Credit cards Cartes de crédit
Visa - CB - Eurocard - Mastercard - AMEX

Access Accès : A15 → Pontoise, N14. Exit (sortie) Ableiges, → Golf
Map 3 on page 164 Carte 3 Page 164

GOLF COURSE — PARCOURS — 13/20

Site	Site	
Maintenance	Entretien	
Architect	Architecte	Jeremy Pern, Jean Garaïalde
Type	Type	open country, hilly
Relief	Relief	
Water in play	Eau en jeu	
Exp. to wind	Exposé au vent	
Trees in play	Arbres en jeu	

Scorecard Carte de score	Chp. Chp.	Mens Mess.	Ladies Da.
Length Long.	6244	5640	4755
Par	72	72	72
Slope system	133	125	116

Advised golfing ability Niveau de jeu recommandé — 0 12 24 36
Hcp required Handicap exigé — 30 Men, 32 Ladies

CLUB HOUSE & AMENITIES — CLUB HOUSE ET ANNEXES — 6/10

Pro shop Pro-shop
Driving range Practice
Sheltered couvert 15 mats - On grass sur herbe yes - Putting-green putting-green yes - Pitching-green pitching green yes

HOTEL FACILITIES — ENVIRONNEMENT HOTELIER — 4/10

HOTELS HÔTELS
Astrée - 56 rooms, D € 112 - Pontoise 10 km
Tel (33) 01 34 24 94 94, Fax (33) 01 34 24 95 15

Campanile - 81 rooms, D € 61 - Pontoise 10 km
Tel (33) 01 30 38 55 44, Fax (33) 01 30 30 48 87

Mercure - 56 rooms, D € 140 - Cergy
Tel (33) 01 34 24 94 94, Fax (33) 01 34 24 95 15

RESTAURANTS RESTAURANTS
Relais Sainte-Jeanne - Cormeilles-en-Vexin 4 km
Tel (33) 01 34 66 61 56
Le Chiquito - La Bonneville 5 km - Tel (33) 01 30 36 40 23

Ailette (L')

15	6	5

Tracé sur une partie du site du Chemin des Dames, bataille meurtrière de la première Guerre Mondiale, l'Ailette est assez vallonné mais pas trop fatigant à marcher, et reste une sorte de modèle de golf public et sportif, avec un club-house sans luxe mais correct. Quelques greens très surélevés peuvent déconcerter au premier abord, accentuant le côté technique et tactique du parcours. Ses difficultés augmentent à mesure que l'on joue depuis les départs reculés, mais il reste à la portée des joueurs moyens, nombreux ici. On remarquera l'alternance de trous assez reposants et de trous plus difficiles, ce qui donne un bon rythme au jeu, et des possibilités de reprendre des forces quand il le faut. Les greens sont généralement vastes et francs, et bien défendus par des bunkers dessinés avec soin, mais avec parfois peu de positions de drapeau. Plusieurs trous sont tracés dans les bois, généralement assez éloignés du jeu, et les obstacles d'eau sont dangereux sans être trop préoccupants. Le travail de drainage a continué à améliorer le parcours les jours de pluie.

Laid out over a part of the site of the Chemin des Dames, a murderous World War I battle-field, Ailette gently undulates and so is not too tiring to play on foot. This is a sort of model public and sporting golf-course with a decent but unostentatious club-house. A number of elevated greens are a little disconcerting at first and emphasize the course's technical and tactical sides. The difficulties of playing here increase as you tee-off further back but Ailette is playable by mid-to-high handicappers. This is a nicely balanced course, with pleasant alternation between tough and easier holes allowing players breathing space and the chance to recuperate. The greens are huge, fair and well-protected by well-designed bunkers but sometimes a little short on good pin positions. Some holes run through woodland, although the trees are usually not too close, and the water hazards are dangerous but never over-bearing. Drainage work has continued to improve on wet days.

Golf de l'Ailette — 1988

F - 02860 CERNY-EN LAONNOIS

Office Secrétariat (33) 03 23 24 83 99
Pro shop Pro-shop (33) 03 23 24 81 24
Fax Fax (33) 03 23 24 84 66
E-mail golfdelailette@wanadoo.fr
Situation Situation Laon (pop. 26 490), 17 km

Annual closure Fermeture annuelle no

Weekly closure Fermeture hebdomadaire
tuesdayClub-house / mardi (01/09→31/03)

Fees main season Tarifs haute saison — 18 holes

	Week days Semaine	We/Bank holidays We/Férié
Individual Individuel	€ 40	€ 50
Couple Couple	€ 65	€ 85

Juniors € 25/30 (we)

Caddie Caddie no — **Electric Trolley** Chariot électrique no
Buggy Voiturette yes — **Clubs** Clubs yes
Credit cards Cartes de crédit
VISA - CB - Eurocard - MasterCard

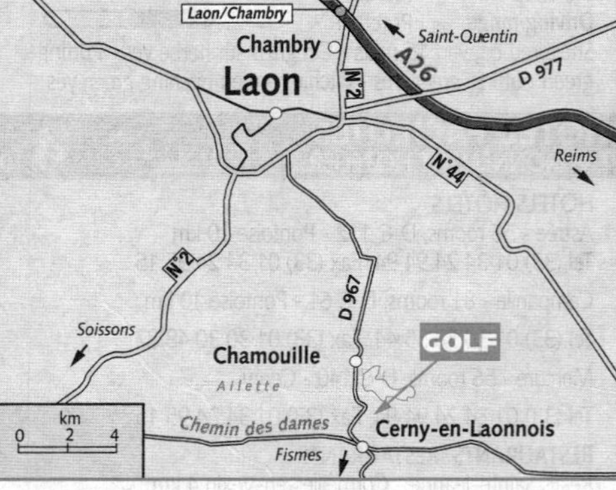

Access Accès : A 26, Exit (Sortie) Laon-Chambry.
D 967 → Fismes
Map 1 on page 161 Carte 1 Page 161

GOLF COURSE — PARCOURS 15/20

Site Site
Maintenance Entretien
Architect Architecte Michel Gayon
Type Type forest, parkland
Relief Relief
Water in play Eau en jeu
Exp. to wind Exposé au vent
Trees in play Arbres en jeu

Scorecard Carte de score	Chp. Chp.	Mens Mess.	Ladies Da.
Length Long.	6115	5727	4860
Par	72	72	72
Slope system	138	142	132

Advised golfing ability Niveau de jeu recommandé — 0 12 24 36
Hcp required Handicap exigé 35

CLUB HOUSE & AMENITIES — CLUB HOUSE ET ANNEXES 6/10

Pro shop Pro-shop
Driving range Practice
Sheltered couvert 8 mats - On grass sur herbe yes - Putting-green putting-green yes (2) - Pitching-green pitching green yes

HOTEL FACILITIES — ENVIRONNEMENT HOTELIER 5/10

HOTELS HÔTELS
Mercure Golf de l'Ailette - 58 rooms, D € 95 - Chamouille 6 km
Tel (33) 03 23 24 84 85, Fax (33) 03 23 24 81 20

Campanile - 46 rooms, D € 55 - Laon 17 km
Tel (33) 03 23 23 15 05, Fax (33) 03 23 23 04 25

RESTAURANTS RESTAURANTS
La Petite Auberge - Laon 17 km - Tel (33) 03 23 23 02 38
Bannière de France - Laon 17 km - Tel (33) 03 23 23 21 44

Aisses (Les) *Rouge/Blanc*

16	5	4

Cet ensemble est composé de trois neuf trous combinables, le Rouge, le Blanc et le Bleu, dans un domaine de 250 hectares. Sur les deux premiers parcours, d'immenses bunkers sont à la fois des obstacles (ceux de fairway sont très plats) et des éléments d'architecture pour mieux préciser les trous dans l'espace. Le paysage de Sologne est calme et séduisant, mais le relief est absent, et les architectes n'ont pas voulu modeler beaucoup le terrain. Sur le dernier 9 trous, les obstacles d'eau prennent le relais des bunkers. La végétation est assez naturelle, avec les bouleaux, hêtres, sapins et chênes de la région. Un ensemble plaisant, avec un club-house sinon luxueux, du moins digne de ce nom, dans la tradition de la région. Certes, le parcours ne mérite pas à lui seul un voyage depuis le bout du monde, mais il complète avec bonheur l'équipement golfique remarquable de la région, à côté des Bordes ou de Limère.

This is a complex of three combinable 9-hole courses - Red, White and Blue - over an estate of some 250 hectares. The first two are marked by huge bunkers (the fairway bunkers are absolutely flat) which are at once the layout's main hazards and features. The Sologne landscape is peaceful and appealing but the area is flat and the architects visibly avoided shaping the course. On the Blue layout, bunkers are largely replaced by water. Vegetation is mostly natural, with birch, beech, pine and oak trees typical of this region. A pleasant venue with at last a decent club-house, and while the course itself is hardly worth a long trip out of your way, it does complete some remarkable golfing facilities in this region alongside Les Bordes and Limère.

Golf des Aisses — 1992

Domaine des Aisses
F - 45240 LA FERTÉ-SAINT-AUBIN

Office	Secrétariat	(33) 02 38 64 80 87
Pro shop	Pro-shop	(33) 02 38 64 80 87
Fax	Fax	(33) 02 38 64 80 85
Web	www.golfdesaisses.com	
Situation	Situation	Orléans (pop. 105 111), 24 km
Annual closure	Fermeture annuelle	no
Weekly closure	Fermeture hebdomadaire	wednesday

(mercredi) : 01 & 02

Fees main season Tarifs haute saison	Full day	
	Week days Semaine	**We/Bank holidays** We/Férié
Individual Individuel	€ 37	€ 55
Couple Couple	€ 65	€ 95

Seniors: € 28 (week days) / Under 25: € 20/30 (We)

Caddie Caddie no — **Electric Trolley** Chariot électrique no
Buggy Voiturette yes — **Clubs** Clubs yes

Credit cards Cartes de crédit
VISA - CB - Eurocard - MasterCard - AMEX

Access Accès : A71 Orléans → Bourges, Exit (Sortie) Orléans La Source. N20 → La Ferté-St-Aubin, 1 km. D17 → Golf, on the left. **Map 3 on page 164** Carte 3 Page 164

GOLF COURSE — PARCOURS — 16/20

Site	Site	
Maintenance	Entretien	
Architect	Architecte	Olivier Brizon Groupe Taiyo
Type	Type	forest, parkland
Relief	Relief	
Water in play	Eau en jeu	
Exp. to wind	Exposé au vent	
Trees in play	Arbres en jeu	

Scorecard Carte de score	**Chp.** Chp.	**Mens** Mess.	**Ladies** Da.
Length Long.	6297	5844	4555
Par	72	72	72
Slope system	151	144	136

Advised golfing ability Niveau de jeu recommandé — 0 12 24 36
Hcp required Handicap exigé — no

CLUB HOUSE & AMENITIES — CLUB HOUSE ET ANNEXES — 5/10

Pro shop Pro-shop
Driving range Practice
Sheltered couvert 3 mats - On grass sur herbe yes - Putting-green putting-green yes - Pitching-green pitching green yes

HOTEL FACILITIES — ENVIRONNEMENT HOTELIER — 4/10

HOTELS HÔTELS
Château des Muids - La Ferté-Saint-Aubin 3 km - 22 rooms, D € 90 Tel (33) 02 38 64 65 14, Fax (33) 02 38 76 50 08
Tatin - 14 rooms, D € 63 - Lamotte-Beuvron 10 km
Tel (33) 02 54 88 00 03, Fax (33) 02 54 88 96 73
L'Orée des Chênes - La-Ferté-Saint-Aubin 3 km
26 rooms, D € 120
Tel (33) 02 38 64 84 00, Fax (33) 02 38 64 84 20

RESTAURANTS RESTAURANTS
Ferme de la Lande - La Ferté-Saint-Aubin 3 km
Tel (33) 02 38 76 64 37
Auberge de l'Ecu de France - La Ferté-Saint-Aubin 3 km
Tel (33) 02 38 64 69 22
Relais de Sologne - Menestreau 5 km - Tel (33) 02 38 76 97 40

Albi

16	6	6

Dans une région où l'on sait bien vivre et un très joli environnement à proximité du Tarn (avec vue imprenable sur la Cathédrale de la ville), ce parcours a été modelé dans un paysage de campagne par Jeremy Pern, auteur de nombreux bons parcours en Europe. On y retrouve sa mise en jeu classique de bunkers bien formés et d'obstacles d'eau, ici en jeu sur une demi-douzaine de trous, mais sans trop pénaliser les joueurs peu expérimentés. Une bonne alternance de trous techniques et de trous plus faciles offre un bon rythme de jeu, sans pression excessive. L'entretien reste de bonne qualité, mais la piste pour voiturettes est bienvenue en hiver. Les roughs, quand ils sont à l'état naturel, sont de dangereux mangeurs de balles, ils ont la qualité de mieux dessiner l'espace de jeu. Les fairways sont assez larges, le tracé en général très agréable et compétitif pour les meilleurs. Signalons enfin le restaurant dans une aile du Château de Lasbordes et deux practices dont un sur l'eau.

In a great region for food and wine and a very pretty setting close to the Tarn river, this course was laid out in country landscape by architect Jeremy Pern, who has designed a number of good courses in Europe. His traditional use of well-designed bunkers and water hazards is very much to the fore, coming into play on half a dozen holes but without penalizing the less experienced players. The more difficult holes alternate agreeably with the easier ones to give a good playing pattern without too much pressure. Green-keeping is still good but the cart path is a welcome addition in winter. When the rough is left untended you can lose a ball or two, but the long stuff here helps to define each hole a little more clearly. The fairways are wide enough in what is a very pleasant layout and a competitive challenge to the best golfers. A new restaurant has opened in a wing of the Château de Lasbordes and there are now two driving ranges, one of which is over water.

Golf Club d'Albi — 1989

Château de Lasbordes
F - 81000 ALBI

Office	Secrétariat	(33) 05 63 54 98 07
Pro shop	Pro-shop	(33) 05 63 54 98 07
Fax	Fax	(33) 05 63 54 98 06
Web	www.golfalbi.com	
Situation	Situation	Albi (pop. 46 580), 4 km
Annual closure	Fermeture annuelle	no
Weekly closure	Fermeture hebdomadaire	no

Fees main season Tarifs haute saison		18 holes
	Week days Semaine	We/Bank holidays We/Férié
Individual Individuel	€ 53	€ 53
Couple Couple	€ 100	€ 100

Seniors: Friday (vendredi) € 28

Caddie Caddie no — **Electric Trolley** Chariot électrique no

Buggy Voiturette yes — **Clubs** Clubs yes

Credit cards Cartes de crédit
VISA - CB - Eurocard - MasterCard

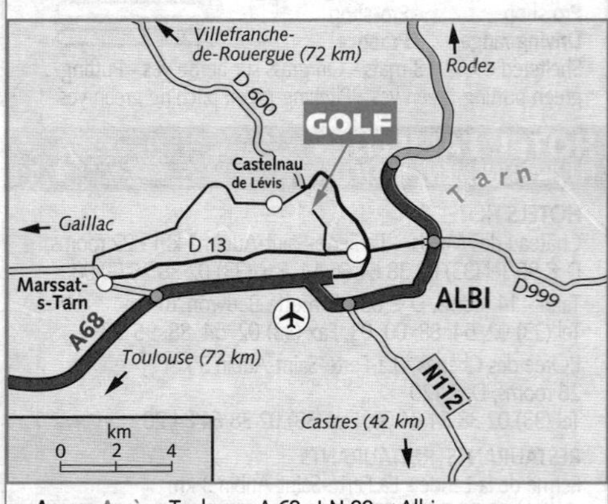

Access Accès : Toulouse, A 68 et N 88 → Albi. Albi → Villefranche-de-Rouergue, → Golf

Map 13 on page 184 Carte 13 Page 184

GOLF COURSE — PARCOURS — 16/20

Site	Site	
Maintenance	Entretien	
Architect	Architecte	Jeremy Pern Jean Garaïalde
Type	Type	parkland, links
Relief	Relief	
Water in play	Eau en jeu	
Exp. to wind	Exposé au vent	
Trees in play	Arbres en jeu	

Scorecard Carte de score	Chp. Chp.	Mens Mess.	Ladies Da.
Length Long.	6158	5755	4862
Par	72	72	72
Slope system	135	132	122

Advised golfing ability Niveau de jeu recommandé: 0 12 24 36

Hcp required Handicap exigé 35

CLUB HOUSE & AMENITIES — CLUB HOUSE ET ANNEXES — 6/10

Pro shop Pro-shop
Driving range Practice
Sheltered couvert 12 mats - On grass sur herbe yes - Putting-green putting-green yes (2) - Pitching-green pitching green yes

HOTEL FACILITIES — ENVIRONNEMENT HOTELIER — 6/10

HOTELS HÔTELS

La Réserve - 23 rooms, D € 230 - Fonvialane 3 km
Tel (33) 05 63 60 80 80, Fax (33) 05 63 47 63 60

Hostellerie Saint Antoine - 44 rooms, D € 125 - Albi 4 km
Tel (33) 05 63 54 04 04, Fax (33) 05 63 47 10 47

Mercure - 56 rooms, D € 92 - Albi 4 km
Tel (33) 05 63 47 66 66, Fax (33) 05 63 46 18 40

RESTAURANTS RESTAURANTS

Le Grand Ecuyer - Cordes 20 km - Tel (33) 05 63 53 79 50
La Taverne - Castelnau de Lévis 2 km - Tel (33) 05 63 60 90 16
L'Esprit du Vin - Albi 4 km - Tel (33) 05 63 54 60 44

Amirauté (L')

14 | 7 | 8

Dominant un paysage normand de bocage et de marais, le club house luxueux et les installations d'entraînement de bonne qualité devraient annoncer un parcours exceptionnel. Ce n'est pas tout à fait le cas, même si l'agrément est incontestable. Avec ses larges boulevards, des obstacles de fairway peu dangereux, des greens sans grande personnalité et très peu défendus, la stratégie de jeu est évidente, l'excitation de la découverte comme la motivation peuvent s'estomper si on joue souvent ici. Les obstacles d'eau constituent les seules véritables difficultés, les bunkers étant généralement peu profonds et éloignés des limites des greens, les grands roughs si utiles dans les espaces ouverts sont absents. Si les joueurs expérimentés regretteront le manque de "souffle" du parcours, généralement bien entretenu, les joueurs de tous niveaux peuvent y évoluer facilement, ce qui est bien la fonction de ce club "de vacances" et de week-end, décoré avec des sculptures contemporaines de valeur.

Overlooking a Norman landscape of farmsteads and marshland, the luxurious club-house seems to suggest an exceptional course, as do the excellent practice facilities. But this is not quite the case even though the course undeniably makes for pleasant golfing. With wide open fairways, a few benign fairway hazards and greens with little character and even fewer bunkers to guard them, playing strategy is obvious and the course loses some of its initial appeal when played often. The only real difficulties are the water hazards, as the bunkers are shallow and generally well away from the greens and the tall rough that comes in handy over wide open spaces is nowhere to be seen. While the better player may regret the course's lack of gusto, despite generally good maintenance, players of all levels will find it an easy way to improve their game, which is exactly what this "holiday" and week-end course sets out to do, enhanced with some impressive contemporary sculptures.

Golf Club de l'Amirauté — 1993

Tourgéville
F - 14800 DEAUVILLE

Office	Secrétariat	(33) 02 31 14 42 00
Pro shop	Pro-shop	(33) 02 31 14 42 09
Fax	Fax	(33) 02 31 88 32 00
Web	www.amiraute-resort.com	
Situation	Situation	Deauville, 7 km
Annual closure	Fermeture annuelle	no
Weekly closure	Fermeture hebdomadaire	no

Fees main season Tarifs haute saison — Full day

	Week days Semaine	We/Bank holidays We/Férié
Individual Individuel	€ 59	€ 74
Couple Couple	€ 118	€ 148

Juniors: – 50%

Caddie Caddie on request **Electric Trolley** Ch. électrique yes

Buggy Voiturette yes **Clubs** Clubs yes

Credit cards Cartes de crédit
VISA - CB - Eurocard - MasterCard - AMEX

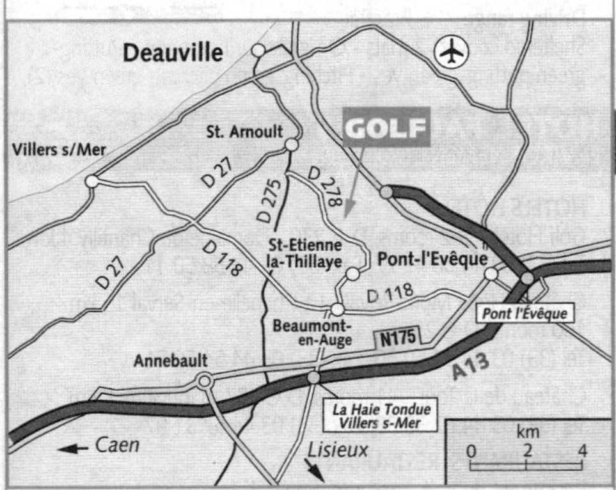

Access Accès : D27 → Saint-Arnoult, D 275 → Beaumont-en-Auge, → Golf
Map 2 on page 163 Carte 2 Page 163

GOLF COURSE — PARCOURS — 14/20

Site	Site	
Maintenance	Entretien	
Architect	Architecte	Harold (Bill) Baker
Type	Type	copse
Relief	Relief	
Water in play	Eau en jeu	
Exp. to wind	Exposé au vent	
Trees in play	Arbres en jeu	

Scorecard Carte de score	Chp. Chp.	Mens Mess.	Ladies Da.
Length Long.	6067	5806	5131
Par	73	73	73
Slope system	128	126	125

Advised golfing ability 0 12 24 36
Niveau de jeu recommandé

Hcp required Handicap exigé no

CLUB HOUSE & AMENITIES — CLUB HOUSE ET ANNEXES — 7/10

Pro shop Pro-shop
Driving range Practice
Sheltered couvert 42 mats - On grass sur herbe yes - Putting-green putting-green yes - Pitching-green pitching green yes

HOTEL FACILITIES — ENVIRONNEMENT HOTELIER — 8/10

HOTELS HÔTELS

L'Amirauté - 225 rooms, D € 133 - Touques 6 km
Tel (33) 02 31 81 82 83, Fax (33) 02 31 81 82 93

Hôtel du Golf - 178 rooms, D € 278 - Saint-Arnoult 6 km
Tel (33) 02 31 14 24 00, Fax (33) 02 31 14 39 60

Hostellerie de Tourgéville - Tourgéville 4 km
25 rooms, D € 170
Tel (33) 02 31 14 48 68, Fax (33) 02 31 14 48 69

RESTAURANTS RESTAURANTS

Le Ciro's - Deauville 7 km - Tel (33) 02 31 14 31 31
Le Central - Trouville 7 km - Tel (33) 01 31 88 80 84
Les Alizés - Deauville 7 km - Tel (33) 02 31 88 30 75

Apremont

15 | 8 | 6

Certes, le parcours aurait bénéficié d'un investissement aussi important que le luxueux mais peu chaleureux club house, mais son entretien est de bonne qualité, sinon exceptionnel. Conçu par John Jacobs, il reste très agréable à parcourir, avec 14 trous en forêt d'Halatte, (avec beaucoup de chênes et de résineux) et les quatre autres organisés autour de pièces d'eau. L'ensemble est plat, facile à marcher avec les départs très proches des greens. Certes, le dessin de John Jacobs ne propose pas de grandes émotions, visuelles ou tactiques, et la stratégie de jeu est assez évidente, mais faute d'affrontements épiques avec le parcours, on appréciera le silence des lieux et la majesté du cadre. Apremont n'a sans doute pas droit à l'appellation de chef-d'oeuvre, dans la mesure où les meilleurs golfeurs trouveront ses défis techniques un peu modestes, mais la majorité des joueurs y passeront une bonne journée, et pourront espérer évoluer à hauteur de leur handicap.

The course would certainly have benefited from the same investment that was obviously given to the luxurious but not always friendly club-house, but green-keeping is still good, although not quite perfect. Designed by John Jacobs, this is a very pleasant course to play with 14 holes in the forest of Halatte (full of oak and pines) and the four others laid out around lakes. The whole course is flat with very little distance between green and next tee. There is nothing truly exciting about this layout, whether visually or from a tactical viewpoint, and game strategy is pretty obvious too, but in the absence of epic confrontation with the course players will enjoy the silence and the majestic setting. Apremont could never really claim the label of golfing masterpiece in that the better player will find the technical challenge within easy reach, but most players spend a good day's golfing here and can hold out hopes of playing to their handicap.

Apremont Golf-Club — 1992

F - 60300 APREMONT

Office	Secrétariat	(33) 03 44 25 61 11
Pro shop	Pro-shop	(33) 03 44 25 61 11
Fax	Fax	(33) 03 44 25 11 72
Web	www.club-albatros.com	
Situation	Situation	Chantilly, 6 km
Annual closure	Fermeture annuelle	no
Weekly closure	Fermeture hebdomadaire	

monday/1/10→31/3

Fees main season Tarifs haute saison — full day

	Week days Semaine	We/Bank holidays We/Férié
Individual Individuel	€ 42	€ 74
Couple Couple	€ 84	€ 148

Special fees after 17:00: € 32 (week days) and € 42 (We)
Under 25: 50%

Caddie Caddie no — **Electric Trolley** Chariot électrique no
Buggy Voiturette yes — **Clubs** Clubs yes
Credit cards Cartes de crédit
VISA - CB - Eurocard - MasterCard - AMEX - JCB

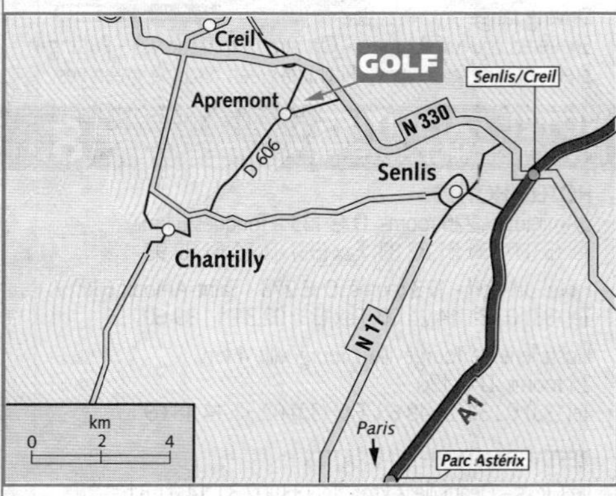

Access Accès : A1 Paris → Lille, Exit (Sortie) 8 Senlis/Creil. N 330 → Creil. 7 km. after Senlis, → Apremont on the left
Map 1 on page 160 Carte 1 Page 160

GOLF COURSE — PARCOURS — 15/20

Site	Site	
Maintenance	Entretien	
Architect	Architecte	John Jacobs
Type	Type	forest, parkland
Relief	Relief	
Water in play	Eau en jeu	
Exp. to wind	Exposé au vent	
Trees in play	Arbres en jeu	

Scorecard Carte de score	Chp. Chp.	Mens Mess.	Ladies Da.
Length Long.	6395	5804	5061
Par	72	72	72
Slope system	134	124	120

Advised golfing ability Niveau de jeu recommandé — 0 12 24 36

Hcp required Handicap exigé 54

CLUB HOUSE & AMENITIES — CLUB HOUSE ET ANNEXES — 8/10

Pro shop Pro-shop
Driving range Practice
Sheltered couvert 2 mats - On grass sur herbe yes - Putting-green putting-green yes - Pitching-green pitching green yes (2)

HOTEL FACILITIES — ENVIRONNEMENT HOTELIER — 6/10

HOTELS HÔTELS

Golf Hôtel - 202 rooms, D € 230 - Domaine de Chantilly 4 km
Tel (33) 03 44 58 47 77, Fax (33) 03 44 58 50 11

Château Hôtel Mont-Royal - La Chapelle-en-Serval 15 km
100 rooms, D € 255
Tel (33) 03 44 54 50 50, Fax (33) 03 44 54 50 21

Château de la Tour - 41 rooms, D € 157 - Gouvieux 8 km
Tel (33) 03 44 62 38 38, Fax (33) 03 44 57 31 97

RESTAURANTS RESTAURANTS

Restaurant du golf - Apremont on golf
Tel (33) 03 44 25 61 11

Verbois - Saint-Maximin 4 km - Tel (33) 03 44 24 06 22

Le Scaramouche - Senlis - Tel (33) 03 44 53 01 26

Arcachon

13 | 6 | 6

C'est depuis longtemps le golf des Bordelais en week-end, et des vacanciers du Pyla tout proche. Il n'était pas question pour eux de faire un parcours trop difficile ni audacieux. En pays de vieille tradition britannique, les architectes Blandford et Pierre Hirrigoyen ont dessiné un tracé sans grandes aspérités, épousant sans trop le bousculer un terrain accidenté à l'aller, et plus plat au retour. Avec le relief, l'approche de certains greens surélevés n'est pas toujours simple ; les fairways souvent étroits, bien défendus par les arbres, imposent de bien placer les coups de départ, quitte à laisser le driver dans le sac. Mais le parcours est assez court, et la précision plus souvent récompensée que la longueur. Avec les travaux de drainage et un entretien qui a nettement progressé, il est jouable toute l'année. Un nouveau green au 13 a rendu ce dogleg accentué plus accessible. Le club-house est placé au sommet de cet ensemble, l'ambiance y est toujours aussi familiale et amicale, même si elle est plus touristique en été.

This has long been the traditional week-end course for the good folk of Bordeaux and holiday-makers at Pylat, so don't expect an overly difficult or bold layout here. In a region of British tradition, architects laid out a subdued course which embraces but never disrupts the hilly terrain on the front nine and the flatter holes around the back. The broken relief means that the second shot to a number of elevated greens is not always easy. And a few tight fairways, well-defended by trees, require a well-placed tee-shot, even if that means leaving the driver in the bag. But the course is short and precision is more often better rewarded than length off the tee. With the lower section of the course now fitted with a new drainage system, Arcachon is playable all year. A new green on the 13th has made this over-done dogleg into a much better hole. The friendly family atmosphere in club-house overlooking the course is as warm as ever, even though tourists abound in summer.

Golf d'Arcachon — 1952

35, boulevard d'Arcachon
F - 33260 LA TESTE

Office Secrétariat (33) 05 56 54 44 00
Pro shop Pro-shop (33) 05 57 15 26 57
Fax Fax (33) 05 56 66 86 32
E-mail golfarcach@aol.com
Situation Situation Bordeaux, 68 km
Arcachon (pop. 11 770), 3 km
Annual closure Fermeture annuelle no
Weekly closure Fermeture hebdomadaire no

Fees main season Tarifs haute saison	18 holes	
	Week days Semaine	We/Bank holidays We/Férié
Individual Individuel	€ 43	€ 43
Couple Couple	€ 72	€ 72

Juniors: € 18

Caddie Caddie no **Electric Trolley** Chariot électrique no
Buggy Voiturette yes **Clubs** Clubs yes
Credit cards Cartes de crédit
VISA - CB - Eurocard - MasterCard

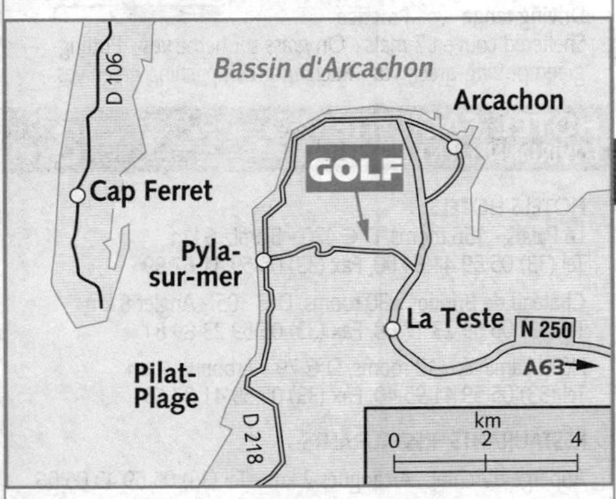

Access Accès : N250 → La Teste → Pyla-sur-Mer
Map 9 on page 176 Carte 9 Page 176

GOLF COURSE — PARCOURS — 13/20

Site Site
Maintenance Entretien
Architect Architecte Cecil R. Blandford, Pierre Hirrigoyen
Type Type seaside course, hilly
Relief Relief
Water in play Eau en jeu
Exp. to wind Exposé au vent
Trees in play Arbres en jeu

Scorecard Carte de score	Chp. Chp.	Mens Mess.	Ladies Da.
Length Long.	5820	5593	4722
Par	72	72	72
Slope system	133	131	129

Advised golfing ability Niveau de jeu recommandé 0 12 24 36
Hcp required Handicap exigé 35 (summer)

CLUB HOUSE & AMENITIES — CLUB HOUSE ET ANNEXES — 6/10

Pro shop Pro-shop
Driving range Practice
Sheltered couvert 6 mats - On grass sur herbe no, 36 mats open air - Putting-green putting-green yes - Pitching-green pitching green yes

HOTEL FACILITIES — ENVIRONNEMENT HOTELIER — 6/10

HOTELS HÔTELS
Séminaris - 20 rooms, D € 130 - Arcachon 3 km
Tel (33) 05 56 83 25 87, Fax (33) 05 57 52 22 41

Grand Hôtel Richelieu - Arcachon 3 km
43 rooms, D € 110
Tel (33) 05 56 83 16 50, Fax (33) 05 56 83 47 78

Le Parc - 30 rooms, D € 76 - Arcachon 3 km
Tel (33) 05 56 83 10 58, Fax (33) 05 56 54 05 30

RESTAURANTS RESTAURANTS
L'Ombrière - Arcachon 3 km - Tel (33) 05 56 83 86 20

Patio - Arcachon 3 km - Tel (33) 05 56 83 02 72

Arcangues

15 | 8 | 8

Le site offre de jolies vues sur la campagne basque et les Pyrénées, en particulier depuis le Club house de très bon goût, chaleureux et accueillant. Pour rendre le terrain jouable, il a fallu beaucoup en modifier les accidents, mais de nombreux dévers et pentes étaient inévitables, et peuvent entraîner des coups délicats : il faut savoir jouer des balles à effets. Pour cela, on ne le conseillera pas aux débutants, ni aux seniors, à moins de jouer en voiturette. Il n'est certes pas très long (des départs normaux), mais assez fatigant physiquement pour que l'on reste sur ses gardes jusqu'au bout. Comme souvent avec Ronald Fream, les bunkers et les greens sont très travaillés et bien en jeu : vive la précision... Et aussi la chance, car la franchise n'est pas la qualité principale de ce golf très technique : il faut le reconnaître avant d'espérer un bon score et il offre des caractéristiques bien différentes des parcours de la région. L'entretien est devenu très bon.

The setting offers beautiful views over the Basque countryside and the Pyrenees, particularly from the very tastefully designed club-house which offers the warmest of welcomes. To ensure a smooth playing pattern and to make the course more playable, some of the hillier landscape had to be leveled out but inevitably slopes and hills still remain and can lead to some tricky shots. For this reason we would not recommend Arcangues to beginners or to seniors, unless on wheels. This is by no means a long course but physically tiring enough for golfers to stayed focused until the very end. As is often the case with Ronald Fream, the bunkers and greens are carefully designed and very much in play. The watchword here is precision play... with perhaps a bit of luck thrown in, as the layout is not as fair as it might be. Arcangues is a very technical course that needs a little reconnaissance work before hoping to card a good score. And feature-wise it is very different from the other courses in the region. Green-keeping has much improved and is now very good.

Golf d'Arcangues — 1991

F - 64200 ARCANGUES

Office	Secrétariat	(33) 05 59 43 10 56
Pro shop	Pro-shop	(33) 05 59 43 10 56
Fax	Fax	(33) 05 59 43 12 60
Web	www.touradour.fr	
Situation	Situation	Biarritz, 6 km

Bayonne (pop. 40 050), 10 km

Annual closure Fermeture annuelle — no

Weekly closure Fermeture hebdomadaire — monday/lundi (30/10 → 01/03)

Fees main season Tarifs haute saison	Week days Semaine	We/Bank holidays We/Férié
	18 holes	
Individual Individuel	€ 60	€ 60
Couple Couple	€ 110	€ 110

Juniors: € 30

Caddie Caddie no — **Electric Trolley** Chariot électrique no

Buggy Voiturette yes — **Clubs** Clubs yes

Credit cards Cartes de crédit

VISA - CB - Eurocard - MasterCard

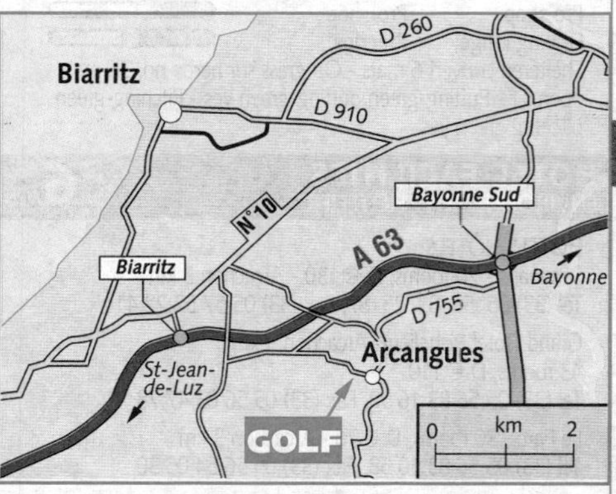

Access Accès : Biarritz, La Négresse → Arcangues

Map 12 on page 182 Carte 12 Page 182

GOLF COURSE — PARCOURS — 15/20

Site	Site	
Maintenance	Entretien	
Architect	Architecte	Ronald Fream
Type	Type	hilly
Relief	Relief	
Water in play	Eau en jeu	
Exp. to wind	Exposé au vent	
Trees in play	Arbres en jeu	

Scorecard Carte de score	Chp. Chp.	Mens Mess.	Ladies Da.
Length Long.	6105	5758	4655
Par	72	72	72
Slope system	146	139	127

Advised golfing ability Niveau de jeu recommandé — 0 12 24 36

Hcp required Handicap exigé — 35 (07/08)

CLUB HOUSE & AMENITIES — CLUB HOUSE ET ANNEXES — 8/10

Pro shop Pro-shop

Driving range Practice

Sheltered couvert 7 mats - On grass sur herbe yes - Putting-green putting-green yes - Pitching-green pitching green yes

HOTEL FACILITIES — ENVIRONNEMENT HOTELIER — 8/10

HOTELS HÔTELS

Le Palais - 156 rooms, D € 420 - Biarritz 6 km
Tel (33) 05 59 41 64 00, Fax (33) 05 59 41 67 99

Château de Brindos - 30 rooms, D € 305 - Anglet 8 km
Tel (33) 05 59 23 17 68, Fax (33) 05 59 23 89 81

Hôtel Laminak - 12 rooms, D € 79 - Arbonne 4 km
Tel (33) 05 59 41 95 40, Fax (33) 05 59 41 87 65

RESTAURANTS RESTAURANTS

Auberge d'Achtal - Arcangues 2 km - Tel (33) 05 59 43 05 56

Moulin d'Alotz - Arcangues 2 km - Tel (33) 05 59 43 04 54

Arras

14	6	6

En dehors des routes touristiques, mais bien connu grâce à son Président Gervais Martel, patron de l'équipe de football de Lens, ce parcours est le site de l'Open de France féminin. Amusant quand il est joué des départs avancés, il devient beaucoup plus technique des départs arrière (hommes ou dames). Il faut alors pas mal d'intelligence stratégique et de lucidité, un bon sens du placement de la balle. Assez vallonné, il cache parfois ses dangers, avec quelques trous aveugles et quelques greens "tordus" (dont le 17, à refaire), péchés mignons de l'architecte. Il faut bien en repérer les difficultés avant d'espérer faire un score, car il y a tout de même 12 trous avec de l'eau. Le site est agréable, avec une esthétique de parc à l'anglaise, quelques dénivellées mais pas insurmontables. Le parcours absorbe toujours lentement les pluies, en dépit d'efforts sur le drainage. 9 trous supplémentaires et l'hôtel construit à l'entrée du site complètent bien ce parcours sympathique.

Off the tourist track but well known thanks to chairman Gervais Martel, boss of First League Lens FC, this course hosts the French Ladies Open. A bag of fun when played from the front tees, the layout is much more technical when approached from the tips (men's and ladies), calling for strategic intelligence, clear-thinking and good sense for placing the ball. This rather hilly course sometimes hides its hazards with a few blind holes and a few tortuous greens (of which the 17th which needs relaying) that the architect couldn't resist. So you will need to check out these difficulties before hoping to card any sort of score, talking of which we might also add that there are 12 holes with water. The site is pleasant, a sort of English-style park with a few climbs and slopes, but nothing too insurmountable. The course still soaks up rain-water only slowly despite efforts to improve drainage. A 9-hole course and the hotel at the entrance to the site complete the picture for this pleasant course

Golf Club d'Arras — 1990

F - 62223 ANZIN-SAINT-AUBIN

Office	Secrétariat	(33) 03 21 50 24 24
Pro shop	Pro-shop	(33) 03 21 50 24 24
Fax	Fax	(33) 03 21 50 29 71
Web	www.arras-golfclub.com	
Situation	Situation	Arras (pop. 39 000), 4 km
Annual closure	Fermeture annuelle	no
Weekly closure	Fermeture hebdomadaire	no
Fees main season	Tarifs haute saison	18 holes

	Week days Semaine	We/Bank holidays We/Férié
Individual Individuel	€ 40	€ 50
Couple Couple	€ 80	€ 100

Caddie Caddie no — **Electric Trolley** Chariot électrique no

Buggy Voiturette yes — **Clubs** Clubs yes

Credit cards Cartes de crédit
VISA - CB - Eurocard - MasterCard - AMEX

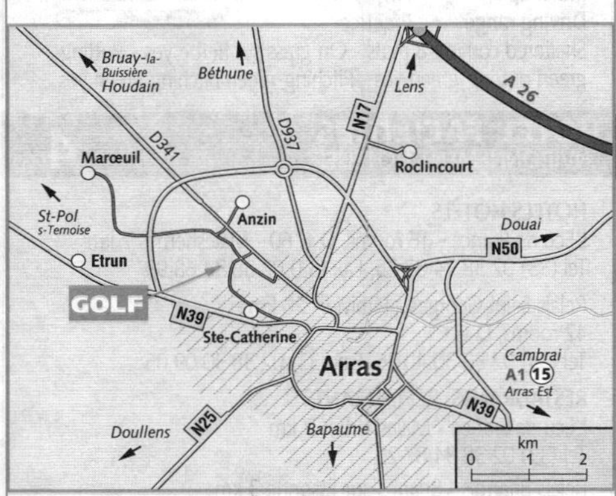

Access Accès : Paris A1. Exit (Sortie) → Arras. N39 → Le Touquet, D64 → Golf.
Map 1 on page 160 Carte 1 Page 160

GOLF COURSE — PARCOURS — 14/20

Site	Site	
Maintenance	Entretien	
Architect	Architecte	J.-Claude Cornillot
Type	Type	parkland
Relief	Relief	
Water in play	Eau en jeu	
Exp. to wind	Exposé au vent	
Trees in play	Arbres en jeu	

Scorecard Carte de score	Chp. Chp.	Mens Mess.	Ladies Da.
Length Long.	6117	5527	4830
Par	72	72	72
Slope system	137	130	129

Advised golfing ability Niveau de jeu recommandé — 0 12 24 36

Hcp required Handicap exigé — 35

CLUB HOUSE & AMENITIES — CLUB HOUSE ET ANNEXES — 6/10

Pro shop Pro-shop
Driving range Practice
Sheltered couvert 20 mats - On grass sur herbe yes - Putting-green putting-green yes (2) - Pitching-green pitching green yes

HOTEL FACILITIES — ENVIRONNEMENT HOTELIER — 6/10

HOTELS HÔTELS

Le Golf - 42 rooms, D € 97 - on site
Tel (33) 03 21 50 45 04, Fax (33) 03 21 15 07 00

L'Univers - 38 rooms, D € 115 - Arras 4 km
Tel (33) 03 21 71 34 01, Fax (33) 03 21 71 41 42

Mercure - 80 rooms, D € 99 - Arras 4 km
Tel (33) 03 21 23 88 88, Fax (33) 03 21 23 88 89

RESTAURANTS RESTAURANTS

La Faisanderie - Arras 4 km - Tel (33) 03 21 48 20 76
La Clef des Sens - Arras 4 km - Tel (33) 03 21 51 00 50
La Coupole d'Arras - Arras 4 km - Tel (33) 03 21 71 88 44

Augerville

13	6	4

Pas très long, et bien accidenté, ce parcours bénéficie d'un bel environnement forestier, et de la présence d'un château du XVIIème siècle, qui constitue un Club house très agréable. Le système d'arrosage du parcours avait notablement rehaussé l'ensemble, un peu rudimentaire à la création de ce club, et la qualité générale en a nettement bénéficié. A côté de très jolis trous, certains autres restent fort contestables, lorsque des arbres empiètent sur la ligne de jeu idéale. On doit aussi signaler la présence de quelques greens aveugles, ce que les visiteurs n'aiment généralement pas beaucoup, ils obligent non seulement à bien connaître le parcours mais aussi la position des drapeaux. Un dernier regret : la difficulté excessive du 18, qui laisse sur une impression mitigée. La beauté du cadre et les promesses du lieu incitent à conseiller une visite, mais on aimerait que le parcours soit encore plus franc, et son entretien constant pendant toute l'année, même à la saison des pluies !

Not very long and rather hilly, this course lies in a beautiful setting of forest enhanced by a 17th century castle, which forms a most pleasant club-house. A new course watering system has also worked wonders for the site, whose facilities were once pretty basic, and the whole course has improved with it. Alongside some very pretty holes, others are very questionable when trees come right into the firing line. There are also a few blind greens, which visitors generally find rather distasteful and which require prior knowledge of the course and pin-position. Our last little regret is the excessively difficult 18th hole, which leaves the golfer with a mixed impression of the course as a whole. The beauty and promise of the setting and site make this a visit we would recommend, but we would like to see the course become a fairer challenge with consistent green-keeping even when the rains come.

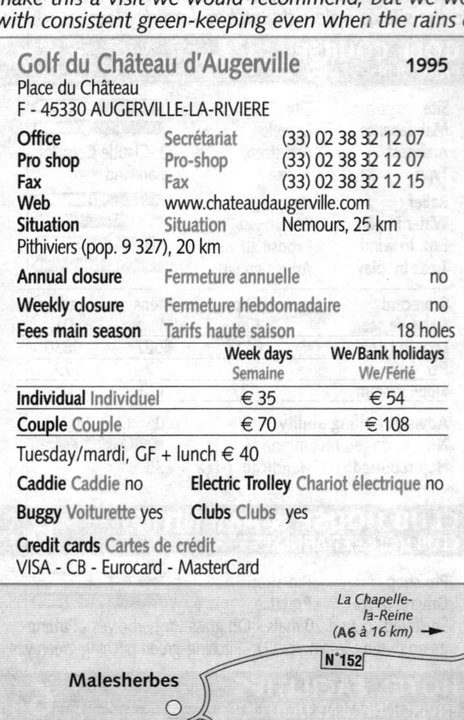

Golf du Château d'Augerville **1995**

Place du Château
F - 45330 AUGERVILLE-LA-RIVIERE

Office Secrétariat (33) 02 38 32 12 07
Pro shop Pro-shop (33) 02 38 32 12 07
Fax Fax (33) 02 38 32 12 15
Web www.chateaudaugerville.com
Situation Situation Nemours, 25 km
Pithiviers (pop. 9 327), 20 km

Annual closure Fermeture annuelle no
Weekly closure Fermeture hebdomadaire no

Fees main season Tarifs haute saison	18 holes	
	Week days Semaine	**We/Bank holidays** We/Férié
Individual Individuel	€ 35	€ 54
Couple Couple	€ 70	€ 108

Tuesday/mardi, GF + lunch € 40

Caddie Caddie no — **Electric Trolley** Chariot électrique no
Buggy Voiturette yes — **Clubs** Clubs yes

Credit cards Cartes de crédit
VISA - CB - Eurocard - MasterCard

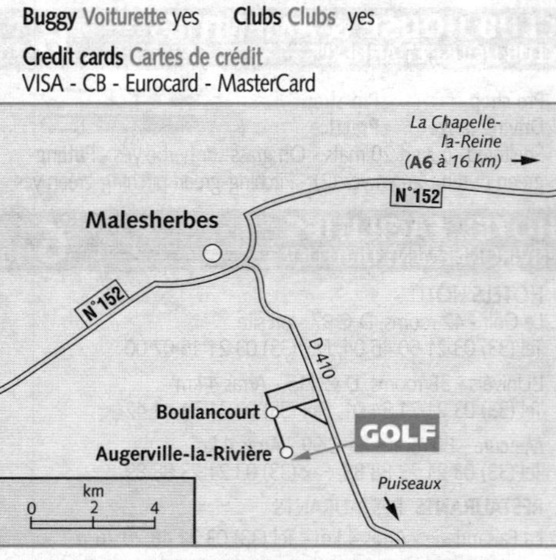

Access Accès : A6 Exit (Sortie) Ury, N152 → Malesherbes, D958 → Puiseaux, → Golf
Map 3 on page 164 Carte 3 Page 164

GOLF COURSE — PARCOURS 13/20

Site Site
Maintenance Entretien
Architect Architecte Olivier Dongradi
Type Type forest, hilly
Relief Relief
Water in play Eau en jeu
Exp. to wind Exposé au vent
Trees in play Arbres en jeu

Scorecard Carte de score	**Chp.** Chp.	**Mens** Mess.	**Ladies** Da.
Length Long.	6294	5748	4809
Par	72	72	72
Slope system	147	137	131

Advised golfing ability Niveau de jeu recommandé 0 12 24 36
Hcp required Handicap exigé 35 (We)

CLUB HOUSE & AMENITIES — CLUB HOUSE ET ANNEXES 6/10

Pro shop Pro-shop
Driving range Practice
Sheltered couvert 8 mats - On grass sur herbe yes - Putting-green putting-green yes - Pitching-green pitching green yes

HOTEL FACILITIES — ENVIRONNEMENT HOTELIER 4/10

HOTELS HÔTELS
L'Ecu de France - 16 rooms, D € 60 - Malesherbes 7 km
Tel (33) 02 38 34 87 25, Fax (33) 02 38 34 68 99

Relais Saint Georges - Pithiviers 20 km
42 rooms, D € 61
Tel (33) 02 38 30 40 25, Fax (33) 02 38 30 09 05

RESTAURANTS RESTAURANTS
L'Ecu de France - Malesherbes 7 km
Tel (33) 02 38 34 87 25

Relais Briarrois - Briarres-sur-Essonne 3 km
Tel (33) 02 38 32 11 22

Brasserie de l'Ecu de France - Malesherbes 7 km
Tel (33) 02 38 34 87 25

Baden

14	6	5

Sans être un véritable links, Baden est un bon parcours de bord de mer, dominant l'estuaire de la rivière d'Auray. Seuls quelques trous sont vraiment tracés dans les pins, mais on n'a jamais l'impression de monotonie, étant donnée la variété du tracé. Les reliefs du terrain, les arbustes, une végétation assez sauvage, quelques arbres isolés, et le dessin d'Yves Bureau en font un lieu de charme pour les yeux, et pour le jeu. Sans être un parcours de championnat, il offre aux bons joueurs un défi de bonne qualité, parfois rehaussé par le vent, tout en permettant aux joueurs moyens et même aux novices de passer une journée agréable. Un morceau de choix dans une région bien équipée en golfs. Le Club house n'est toujours pas vraiment luxueux, mais l'entretien s'est s'amélioré grâce à l'arrosage automatique des fairways, départs et greens. Certes, il crachine parfois en Bretagne, mais les périodes sèchent rendaient le sol très dur.

While not a real links, Baden is a good seaside course overlooking the estuary of the river Auray. Only a few holes are laid out really amongst the pine-trees, but given the variety the course is never tedious. The sloping terrain, bushes, wild-growing vegetation, a few isolated trees and the layout of Yves Bureau make this a charming course both to look at and play. Although hardly a championship course, it provides good players with a pretty stiff challenge, sometimes made tougher in windy weather. At the same time, high-handicappers and even beginners can enjoy a good day out. A choice venue in a region well-endowed with golf courses. The club-house is still not what you would call luxurious but green-keeping is much improved with a new automatic watering system for the fairways, tee-boxes and greens. We know it sometimes drizzles in Brittany, but long dry spells leave the fairways rock-hard.

Golf de Baden — 1989

Kernic
F - 56870 BADEN

Office Secrétariat (33) 02 97 57 18 96
Pro shop Pro-shop (33) 02 97 57 18 96
Fax Fax (33) 02 97 57 22 05
Web www.formulegolf.com
Situation Situation Vannes (pop. 45 640), 13 km
Auray (pop. 10 320), 8 km
Annual closure Fermeture annuelle no
Weekly closure Fermeture hebdomadaire no
Fees main season Tarifs haute saison 18 holes

	Week days / Semaine	We/Bank holidays / We/Férié
Individual Individuel	€ 48	€ 48
Couple Couple	€ 96	€ 96

Under 18, Students under 25: – 50%

Caddie Caddie no **Electric Trolley** Chariot électrique no
Buggy Voiturette yes **Clubs** Clubs yes
Credit cards Cartes de crédit
VISA - CB - Eurocard - MasterCard

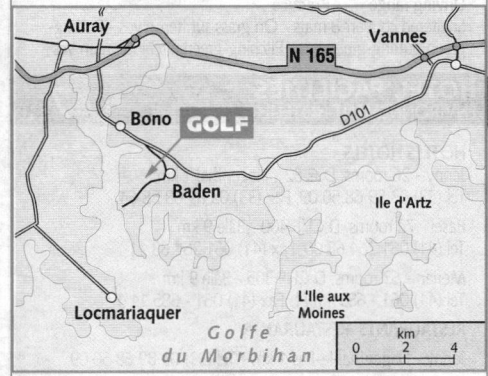

Access Accès : N165 → Le Bono, → Baden, Golf
Map 5 on page 169 Carte 5 Page 169

GOLF COURSE — PARCOURS 14/20

Site Site
Maintenance Entretien
Architect Architecte Yves Bureau
Type Type seaside course, country
Relief Relief
Water in play Eau en jeu
Exp. to wind Exposé au vent
Trees in play Arbres en jeu

Scorecard / Carte de score	Chp. / Chp.	Mens / Mess.	Ladies / Da.
Length Long.	5952	5697	5013
Par	72	72	72
Slope system	130	128	130

Advised golfing ability Niveau de jeu recommandé 0 12 24 36
Hcp required Handicap exigé 54

CLUB HOUSE & AMENITIES — CLUB HOUSE ET ANNEXES 6/10

Pro shop Pro-shop
Driving range Practice
Sheltered couvert 2 mats - On grass sur herbe yes - Putting-green putting-green yes (3) - Pitching-green pitching green yes

HOTEL FACILITIES — ENVIRONNEMENT HOTELIER 5/10

HOTELS HÔTELS
Hostellerie Abbatiale - 69 rooms, D € 110 - Le Bono 3 km
Tel (33) 02 97 57 84 00, Fax (33) 02 97 57 83 00

Le Gavrinis - 20 rooms, D € 60 - Toulbroch 2 km
Tel (33) 02 97 57 00 82, Fax (33) 02 97 57 09 47

Auberge du Forban - 18 rooms, D € 61 - Le Bono 3 km
Tel (33) 02 97 57 88 65, Fax (33) 02 97 57 92 76

RESTAURANTS RESTAURANTS
Régis Mahé - Vannes 13 km - Tel (33) 02 97 42 61 41
Le Pressoir - Vannes 13 km - Tel (33) 02 97 60 87 63
La Table des Marées - Auray 8 km
Tel (33) 02 97 56 63 60

Bâle-Hagenthal

15	7	7

Dans un très beau site de campagne et de bois, ce parcours est une sorte d'enclave suisse en France. Il a été dessiné par l'architecte allemand Bernhard von Limburger, quelques reliefs accentués obligent à réfléchir sur les choix de clubs, et sa longueur est encore accentuée par un terrain assez lourd quand il pleut. Sans présenter de caractère très original sur le plan visuel, c'est un parcours stratégique intelligent, avec des obstacles bien visibles, mais pas excessivement dangereux (sauf les arbres), seules deux petites mares constituant des obstacles d'eau. Ces difficultés raisonnables amènent à le conseiller à tous les niveaux de joueurs classés, dans la mesure où ils pourront attaquer les greens, largement ouverts, en faisant rouler la balle. Mais pour jouer son handicap, il vaut mieux savoir faire des balles à effet, et d'abord choisir les départs bien adaptés à son niveau. La deuxième partie du parcours, la plus boisée, est techniquement la plus intéressante. A connaître.

In a beautiful setting of countryside and woodland, this course is a sort of a Swiss enclave in France. Laid out by German architect Bernhard von Limburger, the course's topography calls for careful thought when choosing which club to play and yardage feels even longer when the ground gets heavy in wet weather. Although visually speaking the course is nothing to write home about, it is a strategically intelligent layout with clearly visible but not excessively dangerous hazards (except the trees). The only water hazards are two little ponds. We would therefore recommend it to high-handicappers and better, especially since the greens are wide open and reachable with easier chip shots. Being able to move the ball both ways will definitely be helpful for players looking to play to their handicap, especially if they chose the right tees for their level. The second part of the course, where the woods are thicker, is technically speaking the most interesting. Well worth a round.

Golf & Country Club de Bâle — 1968

Route de Wentzwiller
F - 68220 HAGENTHAL-LE-BAS

Office	Secrétariat	(33) 03 89 68 50 91
Pro shop	Pro-shop	(33) 03 89 68 57 36
Fax	Fax	(33) 03 89 68 55 66
E-mail		info@gccbasel.ch
Situation	Situation	Bâle (pop. 171 000), 9 km
Annual closure	Fermeture annuelle	1/1→31/1
Weekly closure	Fermeture hebdomadaire	no

Fees main season Tarifs haute saison		full day
	Week days Semaine	We/Bank holidays We/Férié
Individual Individuel	€ 70	*
Couple Couple	€ 140	*

* We: members only

Caddie Caddie no — **Electric Trolley** Chariot électrique yes

Buggy Voiturette medical reasons **Clubs** Clubs yes

Credit cards Cartes de crédit
VISA - Eurocard - MasterCard

Mulhouse
Lörrach/St-Louis
Saint-Louis
D12 bis
D105
A35
D 419
Hesingue
D 419
Altkirch
Belfort
Buschwiller
Hegenheim
BALE
D 473
Folgensbourg
GOLF
Suisse
D 12 b
D 16
Hagenthal
km
0 2 4

Access Accès : • Mulhouse A35 Exit (Sortie) Saint-Louis, → Aéroport, D473 → Hesingue, → Folgensbourg, D16 → Hagenthal. • Bâle → Hegenheim. • Belfort D419 → Bâle

Map 8 on page 175 Carte 8 Page 175

GOLF COURSE — PARCOURS — 15/20

Site	Site	
Maintenance	Entretien	
Architect	Architecte	B. von Limburger
Type	Type	forest, country
Relief	Relief	
Water in play	Eau en jeu	
Exp. to wind	Exposé au vent	
Trees in play	Arbres en jeu	

Scorecard Carte de score	Chp. Chp.	Mens Mess.	Ladies Da.
Length Long.	6255	5938	5255
Par	72	72	72
Slope system	131	127	126

Advised golfing ability — Niveau de jeu recommandé: 0 12 24 36

Hcp required Handicap exigé 28

CLUB HOUSE & AMENITIES — CLUB HOUSE ET ANNEXES — 7/10

Pro shop	Pro-shop
Driving range	Practice

Sheltered couvert 8 mats - On grass sur herbe yes - Putting-green putting-green yes - Pitching-green pitching green yes

HOTEL FACILITIES — ENVIRONNEMENT HOTELIER — 7/10

HOTELS HÔTELS

Jenny - 26 rooms, D € 82 - Hagenthal 1 km
Tel (33) 03 89 68 50 09, Fax (33) 03 89 68 58 64

Basel - 72 rooms, D CHF 400 - Bâle 9 km
Tel (41) 061 264 68 00, Fax (41) 061 264 68 11

Merian - 63 rooms, D CHF 305 - Bâle 9 km
Tel (41) 061 - 685 11 11, Fax (41) 061 - 685 11 12

RESTAURANTS RESTAURANTS

Jenny - Hagenthal-le-Bas 1 km - Tel (33) 03 89 68 50 09

Ancienne Forge - Hagenthal-le-Haut 1 km
Tel (33) 03 89 68 56 10

Bruderholz - Bâle 9 km - Tel (41) 061 361 82 22

Barbaroux

17 | 7 | 6

Un parcours controversé et passionnant, notamment par son aspect composite, un véritable exercice de styles : on a l'impression de se trouver successivement en Irlande, en Ecosse, aux Etats-Unis. Le paysage sauvage de Provence modère cependant ce manque d'unité. Barbaroux est une suite de tests techniques impossibles à détailler. Les mouvements de terrain créés par Pete et P.B. Dye, le dessin des bunkers et des greens constituent non seulement un spectacle permanent, mais aussi une série de difficultés que bien peu sauront maîtriser. Ici, il faut d'abord accepter de ne pas toujours faire un bon score avec du bon jeu, savoir accepter d'être battu par un grand parcours. L'inversion de l'aller et du retour a facilité le jeu mais diminué l'impact du final originel. Ce parcours pas trop encombré est une expérience à vivre. Depuis son rachat par des propriétaires locaux, l'arrosage et le drainage ont été restaurés, comme le confort général du site.

A course that is still as controversial as it is exciting to play, primarily because of its contrasting styles. The impression you get here is one of a catalogue for world golf-courses; one minute you could be in Ireland, the next in Scotland and the next in the United States. Yet the wild Provence landscape tempers any lack of unity, making Barbaroux a succession of technical ordeals. The contoured fairways and the design of the greens and bunkers make for not only a never-ending spectacle but also a series of difficulties that few golfers will find easy to master. Here, lesson number one is admitting that good play does not always end up as a good score, in other words accepting defeat at the hands of a great course. The reversal of the front and back nine has made things a little easier but also diminished somewhat the impact of the course's original "grand finale". This seldom busy site is an essential golfing experience especially now that the proprietors have restored the watering and draining systems and enhanced the general standard of the course.

Golf Club de Barbaroux — 1989

Route de Cabasse
F - 83170 BRIGNOLES

Office Secrétariat (33) 04 94 69 63 63
Pro shop Pro-shop (33) 04 94 69 63 63
Fax Fax (33) 04 94 59 00 93
Web www.barbaroux.com
Situation Situation Brignoles (pop. 11 240), 9 km
Annual closure Fermeture annuelle no
Weekly closure Fermeture hebdomadaire no

Fees main season Tarifs haute saison — 18 holes

	Week days Semaine	We/Bank holidays We/Férié
Individual Individuel	€ 59	€ 59
Couple Couple	€ 118	€ 118

GF full day: € 72 / Juniors: € 30

Caddie Caddie no — **Electric Trolley** Chariot électrique no
Buggy Voiturette yes — **Clubs** Clubs yes

Credit cards Cartes de crédit
VISA - CB - Eurocard - MasterCard - AMEX

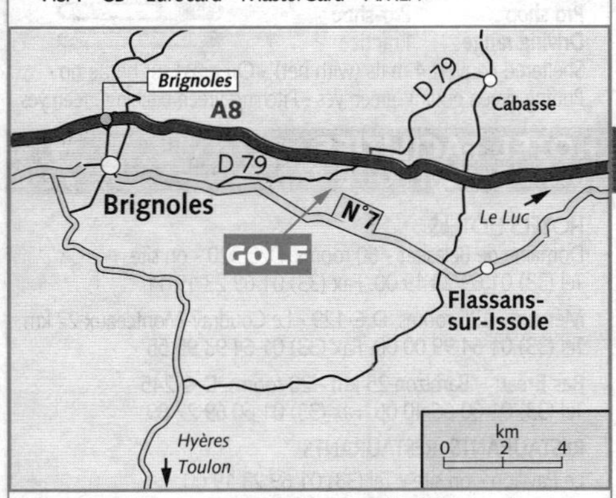

Access Accès : A8 Toulon-Cannes, Exit (Sortie) Brignoles, N7 → Flassans, Le Luc. 1,5 km, turn left on D79 → La Cabane
Map 14 on page 186 Carte 14 Page 186

GOLF COURSE — PARCOURS — 17/20

Site Site
Maintenance Entretien
Architect Architecte Pete et P.B. Dye
Type Type hilly, links
Relief Relief
Water in play Eau en jeu
Exp. to wind Exposé au vent
Trees in play Arbres en jeu

Scorecard Carte de score	Chp. Chp.	Mens Mess.	Ladies Da.
Length Long.	6069	5516	4682
Par	72	72	72
Slope system	143	138	129

Advised golfing ability Niveau de jeu recommandé 0 12 24 36
Hcp required Handicap exigé no

CLUB HOUSE & AMENITIES — CLUB HOUSE ET ANNEXES — 7/10

Pro shop Pro-shop
Driving range Practice
Sheltered couvert no - On grass sur herbe yes - Putting-green putting-green yes - Pitching-green pitching green no

HOTEL FACILITIES — ENVIRONNEMENT HOTELIER — 6/10

HOTELS HÔTELS
Golf de Barbaroux - 24 rooms, D € 108 - on site
Tel (33) 04 94 69 63 63, Fax (33) 04 94 59 00 93

La Grillade au feu de bois - Flassans-sur-Issole 8 km - 16 rooms, D € 80
Tel (33) 04 94 69 71 20, Fax (33) 04 94 59 66 11

Hostellerie de l'Abbaye - La Celle 8 km - 10 rooms, D € 310
Tel (33) 04 98 05 14 14, Fax (33) 04 98 05 14 15

RESTAURANTS RESTAURANTS
Le Lingousto - Cuers 25 km - Tel (33) 04 94 28 69 10
Le Gourmandin - Le Luc 10 km - Tel (33) 04 94 60 85 92
Hostellerie de l'Abbaye - La Celle - Tel (33) 04 98 05 14 14

Bélesbat

14	7	7

Avec dix hectares de plus et davantage d'imagination, on aurait pu avoir là un grand parcours. Mais Bélesbat reste un parcours très correct et visuellement plaisant, avec toujours une certaine faiblesse au niveau des bunkers. Bien que leurs formes soient assez torturées, la plupart des 60 et quelque bunkers sont sans grand relief et pas toujours stratégiques. De même, on peut estimer les greens parfois disproportionnés avec le coup à jouer. On peut également penser que les obstacles d'eau sont trop regroupés sur la fin, et pas toujours bien placés (les joueurs peu expérimentés auront du mal à finir), mais les architectes avaient il est vrai un cahier des charges très contraignant sur ce secteur. Reste que malgré ces observations, l'ensemble ne manque ni de beauté ou d'agrément à être joué, ni de qualités ni de grandeur, que l'hôtellerie sur place est d'excellente qualité, et que les plus charmantes des femmes ont parfois des défauts, à bien regarder.

With another 25 acres and little more imagination this could have been a masterpiece. As it stands, it is a good and visually attractive course but bunkering is still far from perfect. Although they twist and turn, most of the 60 or something bunkers are too flat and make little strategic sense. Likewise, you might find the greens sometimes a little disproportionate to the shot you need to play. You might also find that there is too much poorly positioned water hogging the back nine (inexperienced players will find the last few holes something of an ordeal) but it is true to say that the architects were given highly restrictive specifications in this respect. Despite everything, the whole course has much to be said for it in terms of beauty, golfing pleasure and standards of quality and the on-site hotel is excellent. After all, even the most beautiful face may have a few blemishes under the microscope.

Golf de Bélesbat — 1990

F - 91820 BOUTIGNY-SUR-ESSONNE

Office Secrétariat (33) 01 69 23 19 10
Pro shop Pro-shop (33) 01 69 23 19 10
Fax Fax (33) 01 69 23 19 11
Web www.belesbat.com
Situation Situation Paris, 58 km
Fontainebleau (pop. 15 714), 25 km
Annual closure Fermeture annuelle nc
Weekly closure Fermeture hebdomadaire nc

Fees main season Tarifs haute saison	18 holes	
	Week days Semaine	**We/Bank holidays** We/Férié
Individual Individuel	€ 65	€ 100
Couple Couple	€ 130	€ 200

Caddie Caddie no — **Electric Trolley** Chariot électrique no
Buggy Voiturette yes — **Clubs** Clubs yes
Credit cards Cartes de crédit
VISA - CB - Eurocard - MasterCard - AMEX - DC

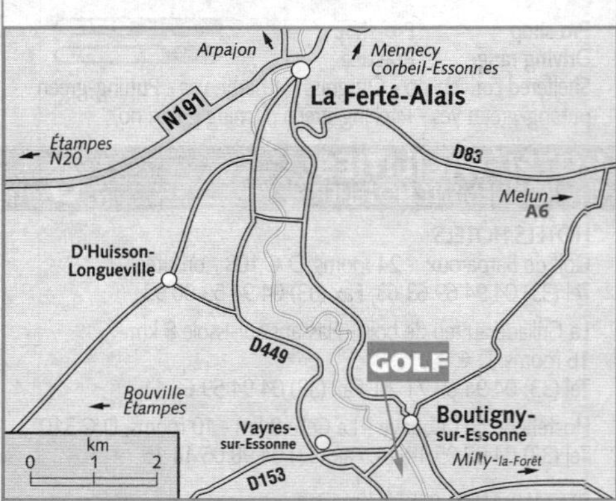

Access Accès : Paris A6 Exit (sortie) 11 → Le Coudray. D948 → Milly-la-Forêt. 9 km turn right on D83 → La Ferté-Alais. 4 km turn left on D153 to Boutigny. → Golf.
Map 3 on page 164 Carte 3 Page 164

GOLF COURSE — PARCOURS — 14/20

Site Site
Maintenance Entretien
Architect Architecte Marc Adam, Patrick Fromanger
Type Type park and
Relief Relief
Water in play Eau en jeu
Exp. to wind Exposé au vent
Trees in play Arbres en jeu

Scorecard Carte de score	**Chp.** Chp.	**Mens** Mess.	**Ladies** Da.
Length Long.	6033	5674	4750
Par	72	72	72
Slope system	138	132	129

Advised golfing ability Niveau de jeu recommandé 0 12 24 36
Hcp required Handicap exigé 54

CLUB HOUSE & AMENITIES — CLUB HOUSE ET ANNEXES — 7/10

Pro shop Pro-shop
Driving range Practice
Sheltered couvert 4 mats (with net) - On grass sur herbe no - Putting-green putting-green yes - Pitching-green pitching green yes

HOTEL FACILITIES — ENVIRONNEMENT HOTELIER — 7/10

HOTELS HÔTELS
Domaine de Belesbat - 60 rooms, D € 320 - on site
Tel (33) 01 69 23 19 00, Fax (33) 01 69 23 19 11

Mercure - 125 rooms, D € 129 - Le Coudray-Montceaux 22 km
Tel (33) 01 64 99 00 00, Fax (33) 01 64 93 95 55

Bas Bréau - Barbizon 25 km - 20 rooms, D € 245
Tel (33) 01 60 66 40 05, Fax (33) 01 60 69 22 89

RESTAURANTS RESTAURANTS
Le Pavillon - on site - Tel (33) 01 69 23 19 00
Hostellerie du Nord - Auvers 10 km - Tel (33) 01 30 36 70 74
Auberge du Grand Veneur - Barbizon 22 km
Tel (33) 01 60 66 40 44

Belle-Dune

16 | 6 | 5

Ce golf public est devenu l'un des classiques de la région. On regrette toujours que la plupart des bunkers n'aient systématiquement pas été "ensablés", car ils apporteraient des contrastes visuels dans tout ce vert, et accentueraient le caractère "dunaire" du lieu, même si l'environnement est boisé sur un grand nombre de trous : le sable dans les bunkers serait "trop difficile pour les amateurs"... Plusieurs greens sont presque aveugles, avec des contours parfois excessifs. Certes, on retrouve ces caractéristiques sur de nombreux links britanniques, mais les contraintes ne sont pas les mêmes aujourd'hui. Epousant les contours de dunes tourmentées, ce golf est assez physique pour les golfeurs rouillés mais reste jouable à pied. Alors que les arbres protègent certains trous, d'autres plus dénudés deviennent très difficiles quand le vent est violent : il faudra alors davantage "limiter les dégâts" que rechercher les exploits. Le club-house dans le style local reste très sommaire pour qui souhaite vraiment s'y détendre.

This public course has become one of the region's "must play" layouts. Sadly, though, most of the bunkers are still awaiting their sand, which would add a little visual contrast to a sea of green and emphasize the sand-dune features of the whole site, even though a number of holes are more reminiscent of a woodland course. Sand in the bunkers would apparently "be too difficult for amateurs"... Several greens are almost blind and some of the slopes are a little excessive. That is often the way it is on many British links but restrictions today are not what they were. The course hugs the sometimes excessively twisting dunes and although hilly, even the rustier golfers can play it without a buggy. While trees protect some of the holes, others are exposed and become a very tricky proposition in windy conditions. The result is often an exercise in damage limitation rather than a quest for a good card. The club-house in local style is still rather rudimentary for golfers looking to really unwind.

Golf de Belle-Dune — 1993

Promenade du Marquenterre
F - 80790 FORT-MAHON-PLAGE

Office Secrétariat (33) 03 22 23 45 50
Pro shop Pro-shop (33) 03 22 23 45 50
Fax Fax (33) 03 22 23 93 41
Web www.golfbelledune.com
Situation Situation Le Touquet, 25 km
Berck-Plage (pop. 14 160), 20 km

Annual closure Fermeture annuelle — no

Weekly closure Fermeture hebdomadaire — no
some Fridays (vendredis) from 11/11 → 31/01

Fees main season Tarifs haute saison — 18 holes

	Week days Semaine	We/Bank holidays We/Férié
Individual Individuel	€ 40	€ 49
Couple Couple	€ 71	€ 88

Juniors: € 37,50 / € 46 (We) / Under 18: € 32,50 / €39 (We)

Caddie Caddie no — **Electric Trolley** Chariot électrique yes
Buggy Voiturette yes — **Clubs** Clubs yes

Credit cards Cartes de crédit
VISA - CB - Eurocard - Mastercard

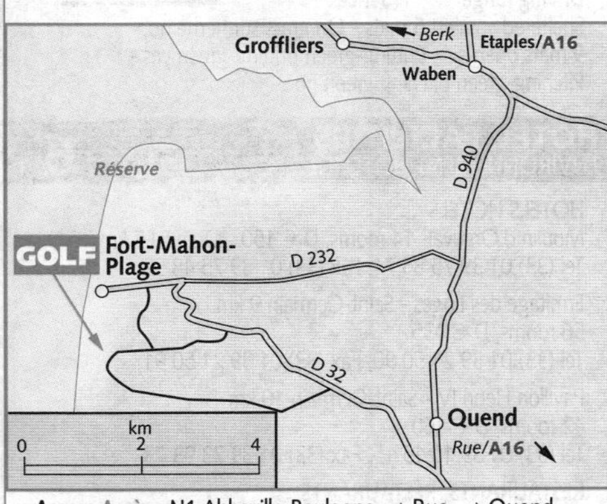

Access Accès : N1 Abbeville-Boulogne, → Rue, → Quend-Plage, D32 → Fort-Mahon-Plage, → Golf
Map 1 on page 160 Carte 1 Page 160

GOLF COURSE — PARCOURS — 16/20

Site	Site	
Maintenance	Entretien	
Architect	Architecte	Jean-Manuel Rossi
Type	Type	seaside course, forest
Relief	Relief	
Water in play	Eau en jeu	
Exp. to wind	Exposé au vent	
Trees in play	Arbres en jeu	

Scorecard Carte de score	Chp. Chp.	Mens Mess.	Ladies Da.
Length Long.	5883	5513	4617
Par	71	71	71
Slope system	146	137	130

Advised golfing ability Niveau de jeu recommandé — 0 12 24 36

Hcp required Handicap exigé — 36

CLUB HOUSE & AMENITIES — CLUB HOUSE ET ANNEXES — 6/10

Pro shop Pro-shop
Driving range Practice
Sheltered couvert 12 mats - On grass sur herbe yes - Putting-green putting-green yes (2) - Pitching-green pitching green yes (2)

HOTEL FACILITIES — ENVIRONNEMENT HOTELIER — 5/10

HOTELS HÔTELS

La Terrasse - 56 rooms, D € 65 - Fort-Mahon-Plage 1 km
Tel (33) 03 22 23 37 77, Fax (33) 03 22 23 36 74

Le Lion d'Or - 16 rooms, D € 56- Rue 12 km
Tel (33) 03 22 25 74 18, Fax (33) 03 22 25 66 63

La Chipodière - 18 rooms, D € 55 - Fort-Mahon-Plage 1 km
Tel (33) 03 22 27 70 36, Fax (33) 03 22 23 38 16

RESTAURANTS RESTAURANTS

La Grenouillère - La Madelaine sous Montreuil 18 km
Tel (33) 03 21 06 07 22

La Terrasse - Fort-Mahon-Plage 1 km - Tel (33) 03 22 23 37 77

Auberge Le Fiacre - Routhiauville 2 km
Tel (33) 03 22 23 47 30

Béthemont

14	5	6

Les premiers et derniers trous donnent l'impression d'un parcours physique, mais la plupart sont situés sur un plateau. Il est assez court, bordé d'arbres souvent bien en jeu, avec un grand nombre de bunkers, de beaux obstacles d'eau et quelques doglegs assez diaboliques. San être ici d'une puissante originalité, la signature de Bernhard Langer est évidente en ce qu'elle réclame beaucoup de précision avec les fers, de la réflexion avant de jouer plus que de la puissance. Dans ces conditions, une seule visite ne suffit pas pour prétendre le maîtriser, et les joueurs moyens risquent de le trouver trop exigeant pour eux au premier abord, d'autant que les greens sont souvent très modelés. On ne saurait placer Béthemont parmi les plus grands parcours de la région parisienne, mais on peut y passer une bonne journée. Autrefois assez humide, il a nettement bénéficié de travaux de drainage, mais l'entretien doit encore progresser avec les nouveaux propriétaires.

The first and final holes give the impression of a hilly course, but most of this layout crosses a rather flat plateau. It is quite short, lined with many very hittable trees and also throws in a large number of bunkers, pretty water hazards and some very serious dog-legs. Although hardly the most original course around, the style of Bernhard Langer is evident in that it calls for some straight and long ironwork and perhaps more brain than brawn before playing the shot. Under these conditions, it takes more than just the one round to claim any sort of ascendancy and average players may find it too demanding first time out, especially since the greens are often sharply contoured. You would not rank Béthemont amongst the greatest courses around Paris, but it certainly is a good day's golfing. What was once a rather wet course has now been much improved by drainage work, but the new owners still have a little more to do on the green-keeping.

Béthemont Golf Club — 1989

12, rue du Parc de Béthemont
F - 78300 POISSY

Office	Secrétariat	(33) 01 39 75 51 13
Pro shop	Pro-shop	(33) 01 39 75 51 13
Fax	Fax	(33) 01 39 75 49 90
Web	www.club-albatros.com	
Situation	Situation	Paris (pop. 2 175 200), 25 km
Annual closure	Fermeture annuelle	no
Weekly closure	Fermeture hebdomadaire	tuesday/mardi

Fees main season Tarifs haute saison	Week days Semaine	We/Bank holidays We/Férié
18 holes		
Individual Individuel	€ 42	€ 74
Couple Couple	€ 84	€ 148

Juniors: – 50%

Caddie Caddie no — Electric Trolley Chariot électrique no

Buggy Voiturette no — Clubs Clubs yes

Credit cards Cartes de crédit
VISA - Eurocard - MasterCard - AMEX - JCB

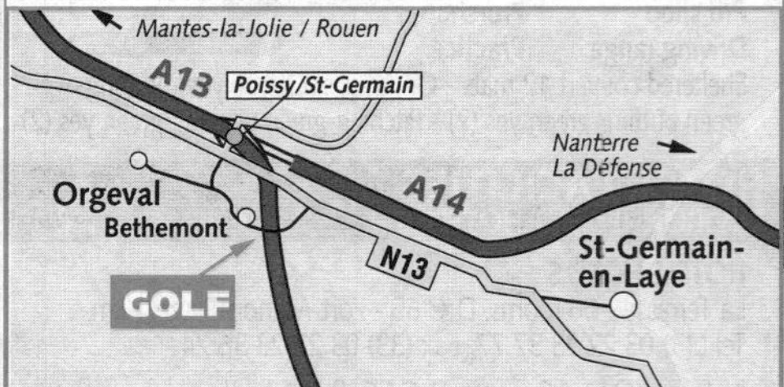

Access Accès : A13 Paris-Rouen,
Exit (Sortie) Poissy → Chambourcy,
roundabout → Saint-Germain, 1st road on the right.
Map 15 on page 188 Carte 15 Page 188

GOLF COURSE — 14/20
PARCOURS

Site	Site	
Maintenance	Entretien	
Architect	Architecte	Bernhard Langer
Type	Type	forest, hilly
Relief	Relief	
Water in play	Eau en jeu	
Exp. to wind	Exposé au vent	
Trees in play	Arbres en jeu	

Scorecard Carte de score	Chp. Chp.	Mens Mess.	Ladies Da.
Length Long.	6035	5550	4770
Par	72	72	72
Slope system	140	122	114

Advised golfing ability / Niveau de jeu recommandé: 0 12 24 36

Hcp required Handicap exigé 35

CLUB HOUSE & AMENITIES — 5/10
CLUB HOUSE ET ANNEXES

Pro shop Pro-shop
Driving range Practice
Sheltered couvert 5 mats - On grass sur herbe no,
9 mats open air - Putting-green putting-green yes -
Pitching-green pitching green no

HOTEL FACILITIES — 6/10
ENVIRONNEMENT HOTELIER

HOTELS HÔTELS

Moulin d'Orgeval- 14 rooms, D € 150 - Orgeval 5 km
Tel (33) 01 39 75 85 74, Fax (33) 01 39 75 48 52

Ermitage des Loges - Saint-Germain 9 km
56 rooms, D € 135
Tel (33) 01 39 21 50 90, Fax (33) 01 39 21 50 91

Pavillon Henri IV - Saint-Germain 10 km
42 rooms, D € 160
Tel (33) 01 39 10 15 15, Fax (33) 01 39 73 93 73

RESTAURANTS RESTAURANTS

Le Bon Vivant - Poissy 4 km - Tel (33) 01 39 65 02 14
Saint-Martin - Triel sur Seine 7 km - Tel (33) 01 39 70 32 00

Biarritz-le-Phare

14	6	8

Willie Dunn a dessiné ce parcours, mais il a été tellement modifié qu'il n'a plus rien du quasi "links" des origines. Ayant perdu ses trous de bord de mer après 1945, il a été transformé en un joli golf de parc, très court, mais pas si facile à scorer, car les greens, quand ils sont rendus fermes et rapides deviennent démoniaques, et même une attaque avec un petit fer peut alors s'avérer périlleuse. Les fairways sont séparés par de minces alignements d'arbres et arbustes, et si l'on n'est pas précis, il vaut mieux s'en écarter franchement que de rester entre deux fairways. Mais, sauf peut-être aux 1, 15 et 16, il est inutile de jouer le driver au départ, un bois 3 ou un long fer suffit largement. On peut considérer "Le Phare" comme un peu désuet par rapport aux grands monstres d'aujourd'hui, mais il résiste au temps, porte la tradition irremplaçable du golf des origines en Pays Basque, et peut être joué à tous les niveaux. Fragile en cas de fortes pluies, il a fait l'objet de travaux de drainage bienvenus et reste un incontournable que l'on a plaisir à retrouver.

We know that this course was designed by Willie Dunn but it has seen so much change that there is virtually nothing left of the original links. Having lost its sea-side holes after 1945, it has become a pretty parkland course, very short but by no means easy. The greens can be hard, fast and devilishly tricky, and even short iron approach shots can prove to be a perilous ordeal. The fairways are separated by thin rows of trees and bushes so if you are going to stray left or right, go the whole way to avoid being stuck in the middle ground. The 3-wood or a long iron will suffice here, except on the 1st, 15th and 16th holes where you can go for your driver. "Le Phare" could be considered a little antiquated compared to today's "monster" courses but it has stood the test of time and bears the irreplaceable tradition of the origins of golf in the Basque country and can be played by golfers of all levels. Although vulnerable to heavy downpours, the course has received some welcome new drainage facilities. A must that is always great fun to play.

Golf de Biarritz-Le-Phare — 1888

2, avenue Edith-Cavell
F - 64200 BIARRITZ

Office	Secrétariat	(33) 05 59 03 71 80
Pro shop	Pro-shop	(33) 05 59 03 71 80
Fax	Fax	(33) 05 59 03 26 74
Web	www.golfbiarritz.com	
Situation	Situation	Biarritz (pop. 28 740), 1 km
Annual closure	Fermeture annuelle	no
Weekly closure	Fermeture hebdomadaire	tuesday

out of main season (mardi basse saison)

Fees main season Tarifs haute saison	Full day	
	Week days Semaine	**We/Bank holidays** We/Férié
Individual Individuel	€ 65	€ 65
Couple Couple	€ 117	€ 117

Juniors: – 50%

Caddie Caddie on request **Electric Trolley** Ch. électrique yes

Buggy Voiturette yes **Clubs** Clubs yes

Credit cards Cartes de crédit
VISA - CB - Eurocard - MasterCard - AMEX

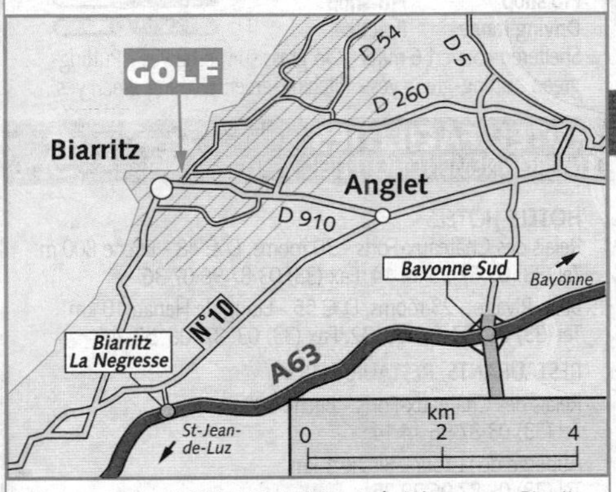

Access Accès : A63 Exit (Sortie) Biarritz la Négresse, → Biarritz, → Anglet
Map 12 on page 182 Carte 12 Page 182

GOLF COURSE — PARCOURS — 14/20

Site	Site	
Maintenance	Entretien	
Architect	Architecte	Willie Dunn
Type	Type	residential
Relief	Relief	
Water in play	Eau en jeu	
Exp. to wind	Exposé au vent	
Trees in play	Arbres en jeu	

Scorecard Carte de score	**Chp.** Chp.	**Mens** Mess.	**Ladies** Da.
Length Long.	5402	5092	4499
Par	69	69	69
Slope system	121	118	113

Advised golfing ability Niveau de jeu recommandé — 0 12 24 36

Hcp required Handicap exigé 35 (07/08)

CLUB HOUSE & AMENITIES — CLUB HOUSE ET ANNEXES — 6/10

Pro shop Pro-shop
Driving range Practice
Sheltered couvert 8 mats - On grass sur herbe no, 7 mats open air - Putting-green putting-green yes (2) - Pitching-green pitching green yes

HOTEL FACILITIES — ENVIRONNEMENT HOTELIER — 8/10

HOTELS HÔTELS
Le Palais - Biarritz 1 km - 156 rooms, D € 420
Tel (33) 05 59 41 64 00, Fax (33) 05 59 41 67 99

Mercure Regina - Biarritz 1 km - 66 rooms, D € 204
Tel (33) 05 59 41 33 00, Fax (33) 05 59 41 33 99

Florida - Biarritz 1 km - 44 rooms, D € 134
Tel (33) 05 59 24 01 76, Fax (33) 05 59 24 36 54

RESTAURANTS RESTAURANTS
Table des Frères Ibarboure - Bidart 6 km
Tel (33) 05 59 54 81 64

Clos Basque - Biarritz 2 km - Tel (33) 05 59 24 24 96

Campagne et Gourmandise - Biarritz 5 km
Tel (33) 05 59 41 10 11

Les Platanes - Biarritz 2 km - Tel (33) 05 59 23 13 68

Bitche

14 | 6 | 5

Son entretien soigné distingue toujours ce parcours, ainsi que son site pittoresque, entouré de forêt. Assez accidenté pour offrir de beaux points de vue sur la région, mais aussi demander une bonne forme physique, ses difficultés sont assez visibles pour être abordé sans complexes dès la première fois. L'architecture de Fromanger et Adam a conservé le caractère naturel du lieu, elle manque un peu de grandeur et d'inspiration, mais la franchise de leur dessin est à souligner. Il n'a pas été possible d'éviter un green aveugle (le 14), mais s'il reste le seul, les autres sont assez bien défendus pour exiger souvent de porter la balle. Quelques obstacles d'eau ponctuent le paysage, mais ils sont assez peu en jeu. Assez facile des départs avancés, le parcours progresse en difficultés à mesure que l'on recule, et sa longueur est plus effective qu'au vu de la carte, en raison des importantes dénivellations.

A course that stands out for its excellent green-keeping plus a picturesque setting surrounded by a forest. Hilly enough to provide some fine views over the region and to require a good pair of legs, the course's difficulties are visible enough for players to cope first time out. The architecture by Fromanger and Adam has preserved the site's natural character, and although sometimes lacking ambition and inspiration, the course is open and fair, a point we should like to emphasize. They were unable to avoid one blind green (the 14th) while the others are guarded enough to require lofted shots almost every time. Elsewhere, the landscape is dotted with water hazards which don't really come into play. Easy enough from the front tees, it logically gets harder as you move back and the overall yardage plays longer than you might guess from the card owing to some steep slopes.

Golf de Bitche — 1988

Rue des Prés
F - 57230 BITCHE

Office	Secrétariat	(33) 03 87 96 15 30
Pro shop	Pro-shop	no Pro Shop
Fax	Fax	(33) 03 87 96 08 04
Web	www.holigreen.com	
Situation	Situation	Haguenau, 43 km

Sarreguemines, 33 km

Annual closure	Fermeture annuelle	25/12→1/1
Weekly closure	Fermeture hebdomadaire	no

Fees main season Tarifs haute saison	Full day	
	Week days Semaine	**We/Bank holidays** We/Férié
Individual Individuel	€ 38	€ 56
Couple Couple	€ 76	€ 112

Juniors: € 17 (week days) and € 27 (w/e)

Caddie Caddie no — **Electric Trolley** Chariot électrique no
Buggy Voiturette yes — **Clubs** Clubs yes
Credit cards Cartes de crédit
VISA - CB - Eurocard - MasterCard

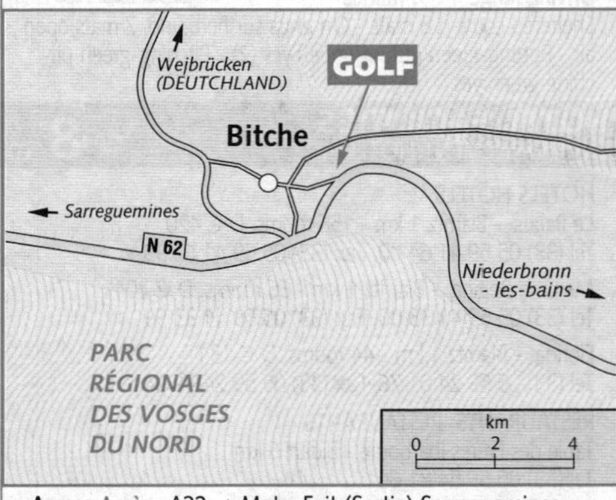

Access Accès : A32 → Metz, Exit (Sortie) Sarreguemines, N62 → Bitche
Map 4 on page 167 Carte 4 Page 167

GOLF COURSE — PARCOURS — 14/20

Site	Site	
Maintenance	Entretien	
Architect	Architecte	Marc Adam Patrick Fromanger
Type	Type	forest, hilly
Relief	Relief	
Water in play	Eau en jeu	
Exp. to wind	Exposé au vent	
Trees in play	Arbres en jeu	

Scorecard Carte de score	**Chp.** Chp.	**Mens** Mess.	**Ladies** Da.
Length Long.	6169	5941	4959
Par	73	73	73
Slope system	143	143	133

Advised golfing ability Niveau de jeu recommandé — 0 12 24 36
Hcp required Handicap exigé — 35 (We)

CLUB HOUSE & AMENITIES — CLUB HOUSE ET ANNEXES — 6/10

Pro shop	Pro-shop
Driving range	Practice

Sheltered couvert 6 mats - On grass sur herbe yes - Putting-green putting-green yes - Pitching-green pitching green yes

HOTEL FACILITIES — ENVIRONNEMENT HOTELIER — 5/10

HOTELS HÔTELS

Relais des Châteaux-Forts - 30 rooms, D € 48 - Bitche 800 m
Tel (33) 03 87 96 14 14, Fax (33) 03 87 96 07 36

Beau Rivage - 23 rooms, D € 55 - Etang de Hanau 10 km
Tel (33) 03 87 06 50 32, Fax (33) 03 87 06 57 46

RESTAURANTS RESTAURANTS

Relais des Châteaux-Forts - Bitche 800 m
Tel (33) 03 87 96 14 14

Auberge de la Tour - Bitche 1 km
Tel (33) 03 87 96 29 25

Auberge de Strasbourg - Bitche 1 km
Tel (33) 03 87 96 00 44

Bondues *Blanc*

16 | 7 | 7

Le "Blanc" offre la particularité d'offrir neuf trous de Robert Trent Jones père et neuf trous du fils, mais un style assez homogène. L'architecture est évidemment très américaine, avec de larges obstacles d'eau, en jeu sur près d'une douzaine de trous. Quand ils le peuvent, les membres se réfugient sur le "Jaune", moins pénalisant de ce point de vue. Comme les arbres sont peu menaçants, marquant simplement les limites des trous, la panoplie des obstacles est complétée par de nombreux bunkers, protégeant à la fois les arrivées de drive et les greens. Cependant, le parcours n'est pas très long, et, une fois familiarisé avec l'eau, il n'est pas impossible de jouer son handicap. Certes, les joueurs de niveau moyen auront du mal à scorer, mais ce 18 trous amène, par rapport à son voisin, une rupture des habitudes tout à fait bienvenue. Les greens sont de bonne dimension, leur profondeur peut poser des problèmes de choix de club.

The "White" course has the peculiarity of featuring nine holes designed by Robert Trent Jones Sr. and nine by his son in almost seamless style. This is evidently a very American style course with wide water hazards in play on almost a dozen holes. Whenever they can, members seek solace on the "Yellow" course, a little easier as far as water is concerned. Since the trees offer very little threat and are there simply to demarcate the holes, the panoply of hazards is completed by numerous bunkers protecting both the tee-shot landing site and the greens. Having said that, the course is not too long and once you have become acquainted with the water, playing to your handicap is not impossible. High handicappers might be hard put to card a good score but compared to its neighbour this 18-hole layout makes a welcome break. The greens are nicely sized and deep enough to pose a few problems of club selection.

Golf de Bondues — 1967

Château de la Vigne
F - 59910 BONDUES

Office	Secrétariat	(33) 03 20 23 20 62
Pro shop	Pro-shop	no Pro shop
Fax	Fax	(33) 03 20 23 24 11
Web	www.golfdebondues.com	
Situation	Situation	Lille (pop. 172 142), 6 km

Tourcoing (pop. 93 760), 4 km

Annual closure Fermeture annuelle — no

Weekly closure Fermeture hebdomadaire — tuesday/mardi

Fees main season Tarifs haute saison — 18 holes

	Week days Semaine	We/Bank holidays We/Férié
Individual Individuel	€ 40	€ 60*
Couple Couple	€ 80	€ 120*

* We: member's guests only / Under 28: € 20

Caddie Caddie no — **Electric Trolley** Chariot électrique no

Buggy Voiturette yes — **Clubs** Clubs no

Credit cards Cartes de crédit
VISA - CB

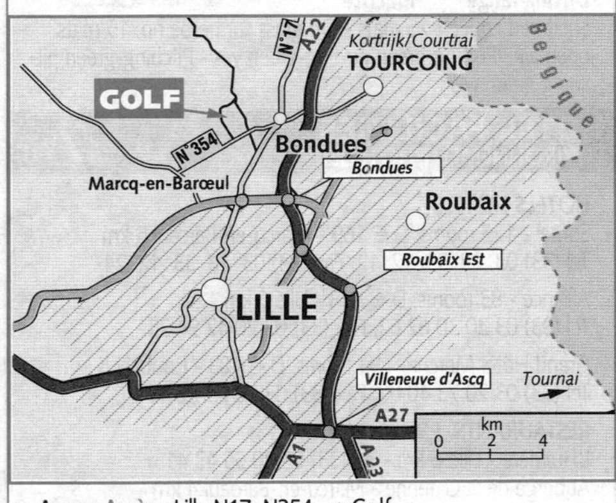

Access Accès : Lille N17, N354, → Golf
Map 1 on page 161 Carte 1 Page 161

GOLF COURSE — PARCOURS — 16/20

Site	Site	
Maintenance	Entretien	
Architect	Architecte	Robert Trent Jones, R. Trent Jones Jr
Type	Type	parkland, residential
Relief	Relief	
Water in play	Eau en jeu	
Exp. to wind	Exposé au vent	
Trees in play	Arbres en jeu	

Scorecard Carte de score	Chp. Chp.	Mens Mess.	Ladies Da.
Length Long.	6009	5470	4913
Par	72	72	72
Slope system	130	125	125

Advised golfing ability Niveau de jeu recommandé — 0 12 24 36

Hcp required Handicap exigé — 30

CLUB HOUSE & AMENITIES — CLUB HOUSE ET ANNEXES — 7/10

Pro shop Pro-shop
Driving range Practice
Sheltered couvert 25 mats - On grass sur herbe no - Putting-green putting-green yes - Pitching-green pitching green yes

HOTEL FACILITIES — ENVIRONNEMENT HOTELIER — 7/10

HOTELS HÔTELS

Sofitel - 125 rooms, D € 169 - Marcq-en-Barœul 5 km
Tel (33) 03 28 33 12 12, Fax (33) 03 28 33 12 24

Alliance - 83 rooms, D € 188 - Lille 6 km
Tel (33) 03 20 30 62 62, Fax (33) 03 20 42 94 25

Grand Hotel Mercure - 93 rooms, D € 103 - Roubaix 5 km
Tel (33) 03 20 73 40 00, Fax (33) 03 20 73 22 42

RESTAURANTS RESTAURANTS

L'Huitrière - Lille 6 km - Tel (33) 03 20 55 43 41

Auberge de la Garenne - Marcq-en-Baroeul 4 km
Tel (33) 03 20 46 20 20

Château Blanc - Verlinghem 6 km - Tel (33) 03 20 21 81 41

Le Sébastopol - Lille 6 km - Tel (33) 03 20 57 05 05

Bondues *Jaune*

15 | 7 | 7

Bondues est l'un des grands clubs traditionnels de la région lilloise, et d'un accès parfois difficile en week-end. Le parcours "Jaune" est le plus ancien, et signé Fred Hawtree, dans la pure tradition britannique, avec de multiples obstacles d'eau assez petits, mais des arbres bien en jeu et des bunkers sans originalité particulière de forme, mais toujours bien placés. En revanche, il n'est pas très facile de mémoriser le parcours, sans grande personnalité ni recherche esthétique très affirmée. Il n'en est pas plus facile pour autant d'y scorer. Bondues "Jaune" fait partie de ces parcours classiques parfaitement adaptés à leur destination : il a été essentiellement conçu pour ses membres (qui trouvent facilement leurs marques et leurs habitudes) et non pour des voyageurs de passage. Certains le préfèrent d'ailleurs à son voisin. Certes, la région n'est pas vraiment une destination de vacances, mais c'est une halte très intéressante, avec deux parcours très complémentaires.

Bondues is one of the great traditional clubs from the Lille region and is sometimes difficult to play on weekends. The "Yellow" course is the oldest and was designed by Fred Hawtree in pure British tradition with a lot of rather small water hazards but trees very much in play and bunkers that, although hardly original in shape and design, are always shrewdly placed. This is not a course that sticks in the memory: it has no clear-cut personality or elaborate style although that doesn't mean it is any easier to score on. Bondues "Yellow" is one of those classic courses that is perfectly suited to the people it was designed for, i.e. basically club members (who can easily find their landmarks and habits) and not for green-feers passing through. Some people, though, prefer this layout to its neighbour and while the region is not really a holiday destination, it makes a very interesting stop-off with two very complementary layouts.

Golf de Bondues — 1967

Château de la Vigne
F - 59910 BONDUES

Office Secrétariat (33) 03 20 23 20 62
Pro shop Pro-shop no Pro shop
Fax Fax (33) 03 20 23 24 11
Web www.golfdebondues.com
Situation Situation Lille (pop. 172 142), 6 km
Tourcoing (pop. 93 760), 4 km
Annual closure Fermeture annuelle no
Weekly closure Fermeture hebdomadaire tuesday/mardi

Fees main season Tarifs haute saison 18 holes

	Week days Semaine	We/Bank holidays We/Férié
Individual Individuel	€ 40	€ 60
Couple Couple	€ 80	€ 100

Under 28: € 20 / We: member's guests only

Caddie Caddie no — **Electric Trolley** Chariot électrique no
Buggy Voiturette yes — **Clubs** Clubs no
Credit cards Cartes de crédit
VISA - CB

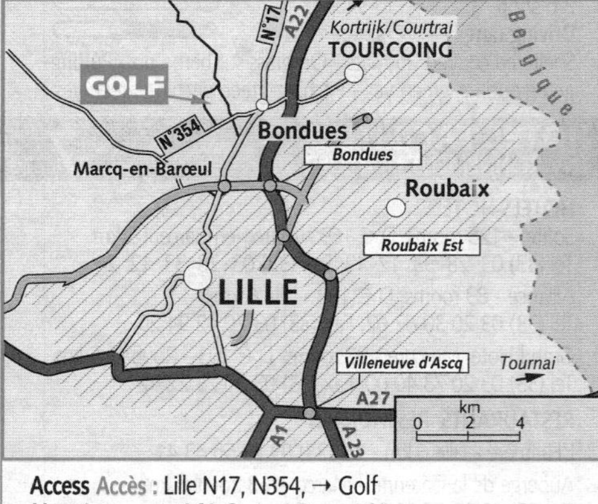

Access Accès : Lille N17, N354, → Golf
Map 1 on page 161 Carte 1 Page 161

GOLF COURSE — PARCOURS — 15/20

Site Site
Maintenance Entretien
Architect Architecte — Fred Hawtree
Type Type — parkland, residential
Relief Relief
Water in play Eau en jeu
Exp. to wind Exposé au vent
Trees in play Arbres en jeu

Scorecard Carte de score	Chp. Chp.	Mens Mess.	Ladies Da.
Length Long.	6163	5764	4193
Par	73	73	73
Slope system	130	127	125

Advised golfing ability Niveau de jeu recommandé — 0 12 24 36
Hcp required Handicap exigé 30

CLUB HOUSE & AMENITIES — CLUB HOUSE ET ANNEXES — 7/10

Pro shop Pro-shop
Driving range Practice
Sheltered couvert 25 mats - On grass sur herbe no, 15 mats open air - Putting-green putting-green yes - Pitching-green pitching green yes

HOTEL FACILITIES — ENVIRONNEMENT HOTELIER — 7/10

HOTELS HÔTELS

Sofitel - 125 rooms, D € 169 - Marcq-en-Barœul 5 km
Tel (33) 03 28 33 12 12, Fax (33) 03 28 33 12 24

Alliance - 83 rooms, D € 188 - Lille 6 km
Tel (33) 03 20 30 62 62, Fax (33) 03 20 42 94 25

Grand Hotel Mercure - 93 rooms, D € 103 - Roubaix 5 km
Tel (33) 03 20 73 40 00, Fax (33) 03 20 73 22 42

RESTAURANTS RESTAURANTS

L'Huitrière - Lille 6 km - Tel (33) 03 20 55 43 41
Auberge de la Garenne - Marcq-en-Baroeul 4 km - Tel (33) 03 20 46 20 20
Château Blanc - Verlinghem 6 km - Tel (33) 03 20 21 81 41
Le Sébastopol - Lille 6 km - Tel (33) 03 20 57 05 05

Bresse (La)

16 | 7 | 6

Dans un site calme et sur un terrain plat, Jeremy Pern a dessiné un parcours faisant appel à toutes les qualités : puissance, précision du grand jeu, subtilité du petit jeu, finesse du putting. Un peu long quand il est mouillé, il prend toute sa dimension aux beaux jours. L'entretien a été amélioré, en particulier par le drainage, mais la définition du tracé manque de raffinement. Le rythme de jeu alterne avec bonheur les trous de plaine et les trous dans les bois, permettant à tous les goûts de trouver leur plaisir. Les golfeurs expérimentés affronteront des défis intéressants, notamment pour leur choix de clubs, mais les joueurs de tous niveaux ne sont jamais vraiment intimidés. Les greens sont souvent très modelés, avec peu de positions différentes de drapeaux, et sont délicats à interpréter. Attention au score pour les négligents. Le Club-House est sympathique et accueillant, la restauration de bonne qualité est typique d'une région où l'on sait bien manger. L'un des "top" de la région Rhône-Alpes.

In a very calm site on flattish terrain, Jeremy Pern has designed a course which requires just about every golfing skill: power and precision off the tee, a sharp and clever short game and slick putting. It might be hard to play in damp conditions but when the sun shines the course comes into its own. Green-keeping has been much improved, but the way the course has been prepared lacks sophistication. The tempo of play is good here, with pleasantly alternating open-field and woodland holes. In fact, there's something for all tastes. The better golfer will enjoy the opportunity to get to grips with a number of interesting challenges, especially for club selection, but players of all levels are never really intimidated. The sometimes very undulating greens with too few different pin-positions are not always easy to read and can add a few unwelcome strokes to the card of careless putters. The club-house is pleasant and provides both a warm welcome and fine fare... typical, you might suppose, of a region where they know what good food is all about. One of the top courses in the Rhône-Alpes region.

Golf-Club de la Bresse — 1990

Domaine de Mary
F - 01400 CONDEISSIAT

Office	Secrétariat	(33) 04 74 51 42 09
Pro shop	Pro-shop	(33) 04 74 51 42 09
Fax	Fax	(33) 04 74 51 40 09
Web	www.golfdelabresse.fr	
Situation	Situation	Bourg-en-Bresse, 15 km
Annual closure	Fermeture annuelle	25/12→1/1
Weekly closure	Fermeture hebdomadaire	

Wednesday(mercredi): restaurant closed

Fees main season Tarifs haute saison	Week days Semaine	We/Bank holidays We/Férié
	18 holes	
Individual Individuel	€ 39	€ 55
Couple Couple	€ 78	€ 110

Students: € 25 (week days) and € 30 (We)

Caddie Caddie no — Electric Trolley Chariot électrique yes

Buggy Voiturette yes — Clubs Clubs yes

Credit cards Cartes de crédit
VISA - CB - Eurocard - MasterCard - AMEX - DC

Access Accès : • Lyon, N83 → Bourg-en-Bresse. Servas, → Condeissiat • Mâcon A40, Exit (Sortie) Bourg-en-Bresse Nord, D936 → Châtillon-sur-Chalaronne, on the left, Condeissiat → Servas **Map 11 on page 180** Carte 11 Page 180

GOLF COURSE — PARCOURS — 16/20

Site	Site	
Maintenance	Entretien	
Architect	Architecte	Jeremy Pern
Type	Type	open country, forest
Relief	Relief	
Water in play	Eau en jeu	
Exp. to wind	Exposé au vent	
Trees in play	Arbres en jeu	

Scorecard Carte de score	Chp. Chp.	Mens Mess.	Ladies Da.
Length Long.	6173	5645	4845
Par	72	72	72
Slope system	125	120	121

Advised golfing ability — Niveau de jeu recommandé: 0 12 24 36

Hcp required — Handicap exigé: 54

CLUB HOUSE & AMENITIES — CLUB HOUSE ET ANNEXES — 7/10

Pro shop — Pro-shop
Driving range — Practice

Sheltered couvert 7 mats - On grass sur herbe no, 20 mats open air - Putting-green putting-green yes - Pitching-green pitching green yes

HOTEL FACILITIES — ENVIRONNEMENT HOTELIER — 6/10

HOTELS HÔTELS

Georges Blanc - 38 rooms, D € 230 - Vonnas 7 km
Tel (33) 04 74 50 90 90, Fax (33) 04 74 50 08 80

La Résidence des Saules - 10 rooms, D € 140 - Vonnas 7 km
Tel (33) 04 74 50 90 51, Fax (33) 04 74 50 08 80

Hôtel de France - 44 rooms, D € 89 - Bourg-en-Bresse 12 km
Tel (33) 04 74 23 30 24, Fax (33) 04 74 23 69 90

RESTAURANTS RESTAURANTS

Georges Blanc - Vonnas 7 km - Tel (33) 04 74 50 90 90

Chez Rolande - Condeissiat 3 km - Tel (33) 04 74 51 43 08

Auberge Bressane - Bourg-en-Bresse 15 km
Tel (33) 04 74 22 22 68

Brest Iroise

14 | 7 | 6

Tracé en paysage de landes, ce golf est le plus occidental de France. Michael Fenn y a dessiné un parcours épousant un terrain qui se prêtait bien à la construction d'un golf, avec quelques dénivellations pour rompre la monotonie. Elles permettent d'offrir de beaux points de vue sur la campagne et les Monts d'Arée. Le paysage – sinon le jeu – est agrémenté d'une végétation rustique et dense, de genêts, de gros rochers et d'arbres souvent en arrière-plan des greens. De longueur raisonnable, le parcours est accessible à tous les niveaux, avec des greens généralement très fermes, et bien défendus par des bunkers au dessin cependant sans grande subtilité, en particulier sans véritables buttes, et quelques obstacles d'eau (sur trois trous). L'entretien a progressé, les importants travaux de drainage permettent de mieux jouer en hiver et les alentours ont été aménagés. Avec le Club-House intégré à un hôtel fonctionnel, Brest Iroise est une agréable destination de week-end, avec un 9 trous complémentaire.

Laid out amidst heath and moor-land, this is France's western-most course. Michael Fenn has designed a layout that hugs terrain which was almost made for golf, with a number of slopes to break the monotony. This gives some fine views over the country and the Monts d'Arée. The landscape, and the round, are enhanced with some thick country vegetation, gorse-bushes, large rocks and trees serving as a back-drop to the greens. Reasonable in length, this is a course for golfers of all standards who will enjoy greens that are generally hard and well defended by some pretty ordinary bunkers. There are no real sand-hills and only a few water hazards (on three holes). Maintenance has improved, some extensive drainage work makes it more playable in winter and much of the surrounding areas has been cleared. With the club-house now part of a comfortable hotel, Brest Iroise is a good week-end destination with an additional 9-hole course.

Golf de Brest Iroise — 1976

Parc de Lann-Rohou, Saint-Urbain
F - 29800 LANDERNEAU

Office Secrétariat (33) 02 98 85 16 17
Pro shop Pro-shop (33) 02 98 85 16 17
Fax Fax (33) 02 98 85 19 39
Web www.brest-iroise.com
Situation Situation Brest (pop. 147 950), 24 km
Landerneau (pop. 14 720), 4 km

Annual closure Fermeture annuelle no
Weekly closure Fermeture hebdomadaire no

Fees main season Tarifs haute saison 18 holes

	Week days Semaine	We/Bank holidays We/Férié
Individual Individuel	€ 40	€ 44
Couple Couple	€ 80	€ 88

Juniors & students: € 22

Caddie Caddie no — **Electric Trolley** Chariot électrique no
Buggy Voiturette yes — **Clubs** Clubs yes

Credit cards Cartes de crédit
VISA - CB - Eurocard - MasterCard - AMEX - DC - JCB

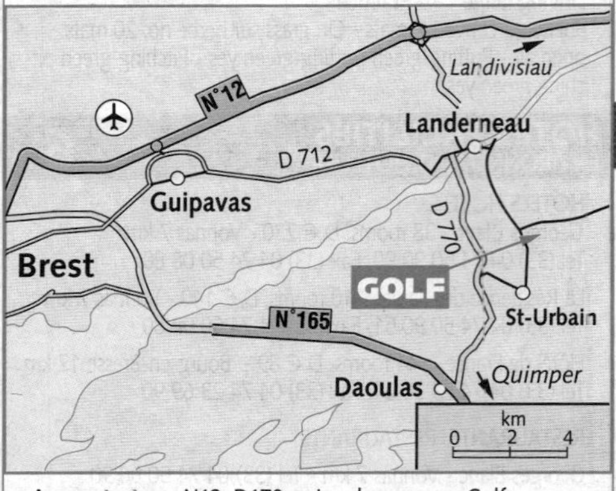

Access Accès : • N12, D170 → Landerneau, → Golf
• N165, Daoulas → Landerneau, → Golf
Map 5 on page 168 Carte 5 Page 168

GOLF COURSE — PARCOURS — 14/20

Site Site
Maintenance Entretien
Architect Architecte Michael Fenn
Type Type open country
Relief Relief
Water in play Eau en jeu
Exp. to wind Exposé au vent
Trees in play Arbres en jeu

Scorecard Carte de score	Chp. Chp.	Mens Mess.	Ladies Da.
Length Long.	5446	5188	4550
Par	71	71	71
Slope system	134	127	123

Advised golfing ability Niveau de jeu recommandé 0 12 24 36
Hcp required Handicap exigé no

CLUB HOUSE & AMENITIES — CLUB HOUSE ET ANNEXES — 7/10

Pro shop Pro-shop
Driving range Practice
Sheltered couvert 10 mats - On grass sur herbe no - Putting-green putting-green yes - Pitching-green pitching green yes

HOTEL FACILITIES — ENVIRONNEMENT HOTELIER — 6/10

HOTELS HÔTELS

Golf Hôtel de l'Iroise - 40 rooms, D € 66 - on site
Tel (33) 02 98 85 16 17, Fax (33) 02 98 85 19 39

Le Clos du Pontic - 32 rooms, D € 66 - Landerneau 3 km
Tel (33) 02 98 21 50 91, Fax (33) 02 98 21 34 33

Océania - 82 rooms, D € 91 - Brest 24 km
Tel (33) 02 98 80 66 66, Fax (33) 02 98 80 65 50

RESTAURANTS RESTAURANTS

L'Amandier - Landerneau 3 km - Tel (33) 02 98 85 10 89
Nouveau Rossini - Brest 24 km - Tel (33) 02 98 47 90 00
Ruffé - Brest 24 km - Tel (33) 02 98 46 07 70

Bretesche (La)

15 | 7 | 7

L'environnement de parc est très joli, le château séduisant : ce lieu typique d'une certaine idée de la France plaît beaucoup. Le parcours manquant un peu de longueur, on souhaiterait des greens mieux travaillés et défendus, dont l'approche soit un peu plus exigeante quand on les attaque avec des petits fers. S'il est difficile de souligner un quelconque aspect surprenant du parcours, le plaisir d'évoluer sur ce parcours bien entretenu est certain. Le dessin des trous est honorable, les greens et bunkers sans grosses difficultés, leurs défenses raisonnables. Cela fait donc un parcours sans heurts et très plaisant pour y évoluer en famille, d'autant plus que l'ensemble est très soigné (avec un autre 9 trous). Si les golfeurs moyens sont heureux de ne pas être trop secoués, les meilleurs attendent des défis plus décisifs. Dans la colonne crédits, l'aménagement de quelques obstacles d'eau et départs, le nettoyage de la forêt.

The park's surroundings are pretty and the castle appealing to both the French and foreigners, who see this as representing a typical picture of France. Since this is a shortish course, we would like to see better designed and better-guarded greens, calling for a more demanding approach shot when hitting short irons into the green. Here, it is definitely not the technical difficulty that will inspire golfers to better things. While it is difficult to underline any one surprising aspect of the course, the pleasure of playing here on a well-manicured course is obvious. The holes are pleasantly laid out and the greens and bunkers are none too difficult and reasonably well-protected. All in all, this gives a seamless course which is fun to play with all the family especially since the whole complex is a very slick affair (with another 9-hole course to boot). While the average golfer is happy when the going stays reasonably easy, the better golfer expects a tougher challenge than this. On the credit side, improvements have been made to a few water hazards and tee-boxes and the forest has been cleaned up.

Golf de la Bretesche — 1967

Domaine de la Bretesche
F - 44780 MISSILLAC

Office Secrétariat (33) 02 51 76 86 86
Pro shop Pro-shop (33) 02 51 76 86 86
Fax Fax (33) 02 40 88 36 28
Web www.golf-bretesche.com
Situation Situation La Baule (pop. 14 850), 30 km
Redon (pop. 9 260), 24 km

Annual closure Fermeture annuelle — no
Weekly closure Fermeture hebdomadaire — no

Fees main season Tarifs haute saison — 18 holes

	Week days Semaine	We/Bank holidays We/Férié
Individual Individuel	€ 73	€ 73
Couple Couple	€ 146	€ 146

Under 18: € 53

Caddie Caddie no — **Electric Trolley** Chariot électrique no
Buggy Voiturette yes — **Clubs** Clubs yes

Credit cards Cartes de crédit
VISA - CB - Eurocard - MasterCard - AMEX - DC - JCB

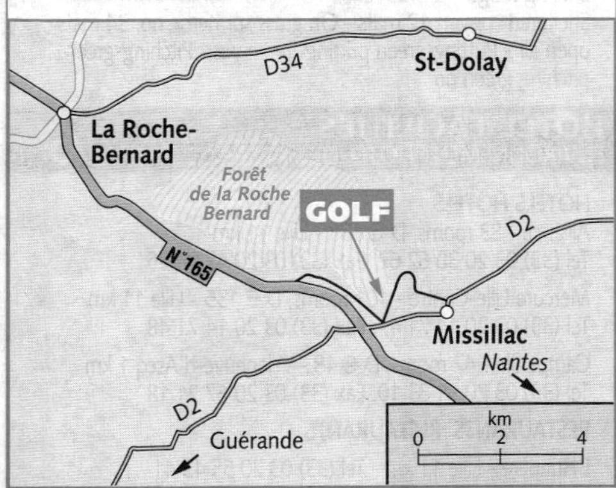

Access Accès : • Saint-Nazaire N171, D773, N165 → Golf
• La Baule D774, N165 → Golf
Map 6 on page 170 Carte 6 Page 170

GOLF COURSE — PARCOURS — 15/20

Site Site
Maintenance Entretien
Architect Architecte — Harold (Bill) Baker
Type Type — forest, parkland
Relief Relief
Water in play Eau en jeu
Exp. to wind Exposé au vent
Trees in play Arbres en jeu

Scorecard Carte de score	Chp. Chp.	Mens Mess.	Ladies Da.
Length Long.	6015	5755	4845
Par	72	72	72
Slope system	129	124	125

Advised golfing ability Niveau de jeu recommandé — 0 12 24 36
Hcp required Handicap exigé — 35

CLUB HOUSE & AMENITIES — CLUB HOUSE ET ANNEXES — 7/10

Pro shop Pro-shop
Driving range Practice
Sheltered couvert 10 mats - On grass sur herbe yes - Putting-green putting-green yes - Pitching-green pitching green yes

HOTEL FACILITIES — ENVIRONNEMENT HOTELIER — 7/10

HOTELS HÔTELS
Golf de la Bretesche - 32 rooms, D € 190 - on site
Tel (33) 02 51 76 86 96, Fax (33) 02 40 66 99 47

Manoir du Rodoir - 26 rooms, D € 95 - La Roche Bernard 11 km
Tel (33) 02 99 90 82 68, Fax (33) 02 99 90 76 22

Les Chaumières du Lac - 20 rooms, D € 72 - Saint-Lyphard 14 km
Tel (33) 02 40 91 32 32, Fax (33) 02 40 91 30 33

Auberge des Deux Magots - La Roche Bernard 11 km
15 rooms, D € 75
Tel (33) 02 99 90 60 75, Fax (33) 02 99 90 87 87

RESTAURANTS RESTAURANTS
Auberge Bretonne - La Roche-Bernard 11 km
Tel (33) 02 99 90 60 28

Brigode

14	7	6

Ce parcours signé Harold Baker est l'un des grands clubs traditionnels des Lillois, dont beaucoup y ont élu résidence, mais l'impression d'un golf immobilier n'est pas trop pesante car les maisons sont de bonne qualité. Assez plat, avec quelques obstacles d'eau, bon nombre de bunkers, et des arbres, le parcours a des allures de grand parc à la britannique, harmonieux et séduisant, avec assez de maturité pour ne plus vraiment bouger. Dans cet environnement, c'est un parcours aussi agréable pour les joueurs de bon niveau que pour les joueurs moyens. Certes, ce n'est pas un test d'une énorme difficulté, l'architecture est restée sobre, peut-être même un peu timide, mais on a visiblement recherché à favoriser le plaisir du jeu en famille. Un vrai "golf de membres" où les golfeurs de passage seront mieux accueillis en semaine, les week-ends étant souvent chargés. L'entretien a été amélioré – et surtout régularisé – par de nécessaires drainages, mais aussi par l'arrosage automatique.

This Harold Baker course is one of the great traditional clubs of Lille and many people have bought homes here, although the quality standard of houses fortunately rules out any great impression of this being a property development course. Being rather flat, with a few water hazards and a good number of bunkers and trees, Brigode looks like a British park, at once rather harmonious and attractive, and mature enough to stay the way it is for ever. In this setting, the course is pleasant for skilled and less skilful golfers alike. It is certainly not too tough a test for the better golfer as the architecture is unobtrusive and even a little on the shy side, but the designers visibly were looking to promote the pleasure of family golfing. This is a real "members' club" where green-fees get a warmer welcome during the week. Week-ends are often heavily booked. Maintenance has been improved by some necessary drainage work and the installation of automatic irrigation systems.

Golf de Brigode — 1967

36, avenue du Golf
F - 59650 VILLENEUVE-D'ASCQ

Office	Secrétariat	(33) 03 20 91 17 86
Pro shop	Pro-shop	no Pro shop
Fax	Fax	(33) 03 20 91 17 13
E-mail		golfdebrigode@wanadoo.fr
Situation	Situation	Lille (pop. 172 142), 11 km
Annual closure	Fermeture annuelle	no
Weekly closure	Fermeture hebdomadaire	tuesday/mardi

Fees main season / Tarifs haute saison	Week days / Semaine	We/Bank holidays / We/Férié
18 holes		
Individual Individuel	€ 40	€ 35*
Couple Couple	€ 80	€ 70*

* Only with a member at week ends / Students: –50%

Caddie Caddie no — Electric Trolley Chariot électrique no

Buggy Voiturette yes — Clubs Clubs no

Credit cards Cartes de crédit
VISA - CB - Eurocard - MasterCard

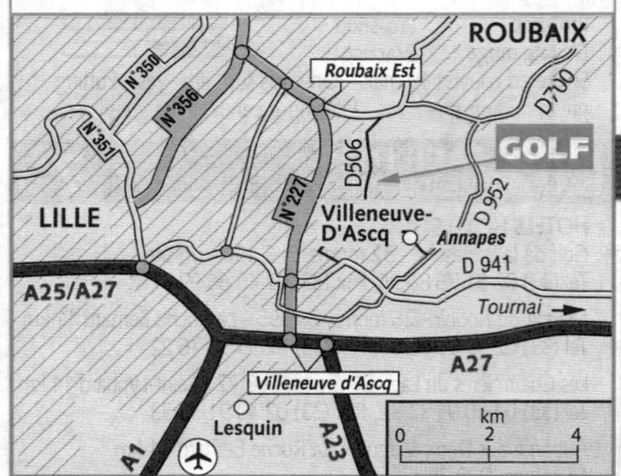

Access Accès : "Rocade" Paris-Gand • Paris/Lille, Exit (Sortie) Pont de Bois → Annappes-cousinerie • Gand-Tourcoing, Exit (Sortie) Roubaix-Est, 1 km on the right → Annappes. 2 km, in front of Stadium → Golf

Map 1 on page 161 Carte 1 Page 161

GOLF COURSE — PARCOURS — 14/20

Site	Site	
Maintenance	Entretien	
Architect	Architecte	Harold (Bill) Baker
Type	Type	parkland
Relief	Relief	
Water in play	Eau en jeu	
Exp. to wind	Exposé au vent	
Trees in play	Arbres en jeu	

Scorecard / Carte de score	Chp. / Chp.	Mens / Mess.	Ladies / Da.
Length Long.	6010	5628	4780
Par	72	72	72
Slope system	134	132	124

Advised golfing ability / Niveau de jeu recommandé: 0 12 24 36

Hcp required / Handicap exigé: 30

CLUB HOUSE & AMENITIES — CLUB HOUSE ET ANNEXES — 7/10

Pro shop / Pro-shop

Driving range / Practice

Sheltered couvert 12 mats - On grass sur herbe no, 34 mats open air - Putting-green putting-green yes - Pitching-green pitching green no

HOTEL FACILITIES — ENVIRONNEMENT HOTELIER — 6/10

HOTELS HÔTELS

Alliance - 83 rooms, D € 188 - Lille 11 km
Tel (33) 03 20 30 62 62, Fax (33) 03 20 42 94 25

Mercure Lille-Centre - 101 rooms, D € 135 - Lille 11 km
Tel (33) 03 20 14 71 47, Fax (33) 03 20 14 71 48

Campanile - 47 rooms, D € 48 - Villeneuve-d'Ascq 1 km
Tel (33) 03 20 91 83 10, Fax (33) 03 20 67 21 18

RESTAURANTS RESTAURANTS

L'Huitrière - Lille 11 km - Tel (33) 03 20 55 43 41

L'Assiette du Marché - Lille 11 km - Tel (33) 03 20 06 83 61

Champlain - Lille 11 km - Tel (33) 03 20 54 01 38

Boulie (La) *La Vallée*

15 | 7 | 8

Le seul véritable reproche que l'on puisse faire à ce parcours, c'est que les arbres ont pris une telle densité depuis les origines que l'on peut éprouver sinon une sensation de claustrophobie, du moins s'y trouver à l'étroit. Les tempêtes de 1999 ont un peu éclairci le paysage, mais ceux qui aiment les grands espaces – comme ce parcours en présentait au moment de sa construction – ne seront pas à l'aise. Parcours original du Golf de Paris, devenu Golf du Racing-Club de France (le plus grand club omnisports français), "La Vallée" réclame un jeu très complet, des drives puissants et droits, des fers très précis pour des greens souvent assez animés, et une grande maîtrise des coups de rattrapage (balles basses sous les arbres !). Sans oublier les sorties de bunker car ils protègent solidement les greens. Quelques rares coups aveugles sont inévitables en raison du relief général assez prononcé mais sans difficulté excessive (sauf au 9). Un classique de la région, dont l'entretien y est généralement très satisfaisant.

The only real reproach you can level at this course is that the trees have grown so thick since its inception that they often create a feeling of having very little space to play in. The storms back in 1999 cleared the landscape somewhat but golfers who prefer wide open spaces – a feature of this course when it first opened – will not feel too easy about playing here. "La Vallée", the Golf du Racing-Club de France (France's biggest all sports club), requires a good all-round game, powerful and straight driving, accurate ironwork for greens that are often bouncy and skills in the art of recovery (particularly knock-down shots from under the trees). Not to mention sand shots from bunkers that offer a solid line of defence around the greens. A few blind shots were unavoidable here owing to the sloping terrain which is hilly but not too tiring (except the 9th). One of the classic courses in the region where green-keeping is generally very satisfactory.

Golf de La Boulie - Racing Club de France 1901

F - 78000 VERSAILLES

Office	Secrétariat	(33) 01 39 50 59 41
Pro shop	Pro-shop	(33) 01 39 49 92 77
Fax	Fax	(33) 01 39 49 04 16
Web	www.racingclubdefrance.org	
Situation	Situation	Paris, 22 km
Annual closure	Fermeture annuelle	25/12→1/1
Weekly closure	Fermeture hebdomadaire	tuesday/mardi

Fees main season Tarifs haute saison	18 holes	
	Week days Semaine	**We/Bank holidays** We/Férié
Individual Individuel	€ 55	€ 70
Couple Couple	€ 110	€ 140

Members' guests: € 40/50 (We)
– 25: € 35 (Week days only)

Caddie Caddie no — **Electric Trolley** Chariot électrique yes

Buggy Voiturette no — **Clubs** Clubs yes

Credit cards Cartes de crédit VISA - CB

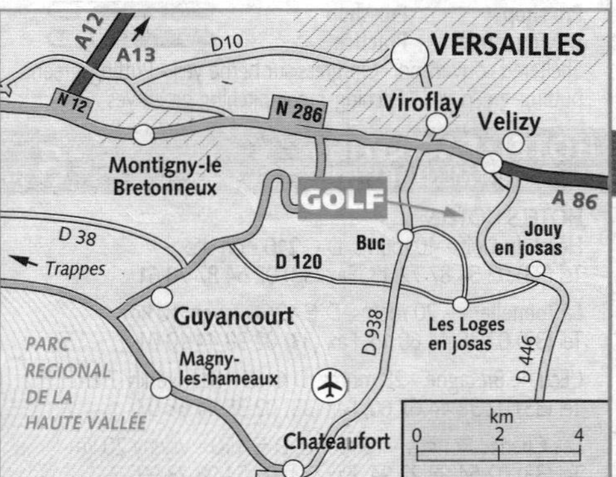

Access Accès : Paris A13 → Rouen, Exit (Sortie) Versailles-Vaucresson. D182 → Versailles, D185 → Château, → Versailles-Chantiers. N186 → Golf.

Map 15 on page 188 Carte 15 Page 188

GOLF COURSE — PARCOURS 15/20

Site	Site	
Maintenance	Entretien	
Architect	Architecte	unknown
Type	Type	forest
Relief	Relief	
Water in play	Eau en jeu	
Exp. to wind	Exposé au vent	
Trees in play	Arbres en jeu	

Scorecard Carte de score	**Chp.** Chp.	**Mens** Mess.	**Ladies** Da.
Length Long.	5995	5698	5062
Par	72	72	72
Slope system	138	135	138

Advised golfing ability Niveau de jeu recommandé — 0 12 24 36

Hcp required Handicap exigé — 24 Men, 28 Ladies

CLUB HOUSE & AMENITIES — CLUB HOUSE ET ANNEXES 7/10

Pro shop Pro-shop
Driving range Practice
Sheltered couvert 20 mats - On grass sur herbe no, 5 mats open air - Putting-green putting-green yes
Pitching-green pitching green yes

HOTEL FACILITIES — ENVIRONNEMENT HOTELIER 8/10

HOTELS HÔTELS

Trianon Palace - 192 rooms, D € 500 - Versailles 3 km
Tel (33) 01 30 84 50 00, Fax (33) 01 30 84 51 21

Pavillon Trianon - 99 rooms, D € 320 - Versailles 3 km
Tel (33) 01 30 84 50 00, Fax (33) 01 30 89 50 01

Résidence du Berry - 38 rooms, D € 125 - Versailles 3 km
Tel (33) 01 39 49 07 07, Fax (33) 01 39 50 59 40

RESTAURANTS RESTAURANTS

Les Trois Marches - Versailles 3 km - Tel (33) 01 39 50 25 08

La Marée de Versailles - Versailles 3 km
Tel (33) 01 30 21 73 73

Le Potager du Roy - Versailles 3 km - Tel (33) 01 39 50 35 34

Bordes (Les)

19 | 8 | 6

Ce parcours créé par Marcel Bich reste incontestablement au premier rang français, l'un de ceux auxquels il faut absolument se confronter, pour son tracé d'une grande variété de jeu et de stratégie, et pour son environnement : Les Bordes est une initiation à la Sologne, le parcours un lieu de méditation sur la vérité de son propre jeu, où il est impossible de maquiller ses faiblesses. Si vous abordez ce parcours avec simplicité, intelligence et surtout humilité, il pourra se montrer généreux, car il ne cache rien de ses difficultés et sait parfois se montrer aussi indulgent qu'il peut être cruel. Le practice, le Club-House, les chambres d'hôtes (il y en a 40) sont exemplaires mais austères. Ici, l'argent investi ne s'étale pas, comme si cet ensemble récent avait des siècles d'existence. Cet "incontournable" du golf est comme une grande adresse gastronomique où le prix du plaisir n'a pas d'importance. Après avoir un moment été un club exclusif et privé, Les Bordes est de nouveau ouvert aux joueurs extérieurs. Une vraie bonne nouvelle…

This course is still unquestionably one of France's top-rate golf courses and one of those you simply have to play for its variety in layout, its ever-changing game strategy and setting. Les Bordes is an introduction to the Sologne and the course an arena of meditation for the truth about your golfing ability. Any chinks in your game are ruthlessly exposed. If you approach the course with simplicity, intelligence and especially humility, it can be rewarding because all of its difficulties are there to see and sometimes can be as forgiving as they can be cruel. The driving range, club-house and guestrooms are first-rate but a little austere. And there are no flashy signs of new money and investment, rather as if this recently-designed course had been around for ages. This golfing "must" is like a top gourmet address where the price of pleasure matters little. After having been for a while an exclusive and private club, Les Bordes is now open to visitors again. A real privilege.

Golf International des Bordes — 1987

F - 41220 SAINT-LAURENT-NOUAN

Office Secrétariat (33) 02 54 87 72 13
Pro shop Pro-shop (33) 02 54 87 72 13
Fax Fax (33) 02 54 87 78 61
Web www.lesbordes.com
Situation Situation Orléans (pop. 105 110), 30 Km
Beaugency (pop. 6 917), 11 km

Annual closure Fermeture annuelle no
Golf closed one month in winter (ask for details)

Weekly closure Fermeture hebdomadaire no

Fees main season Tarifs haute saison 18 holes

	Week days Semaine	We/Bank holidays We/Férié
Individual Individuel	€ 120	€ 150
Couple Couple	€ 240	€ 300

Hotels guests: € 75/90 (We)

Caddie Caddie no — **Electric Trolley** Chariot électrique no
Buggy Voiturette yes — **Clubs** Clubs yes
Credit cards Cartes de crédit
VISA - CB - Eurocard - MasterCard - AMEX

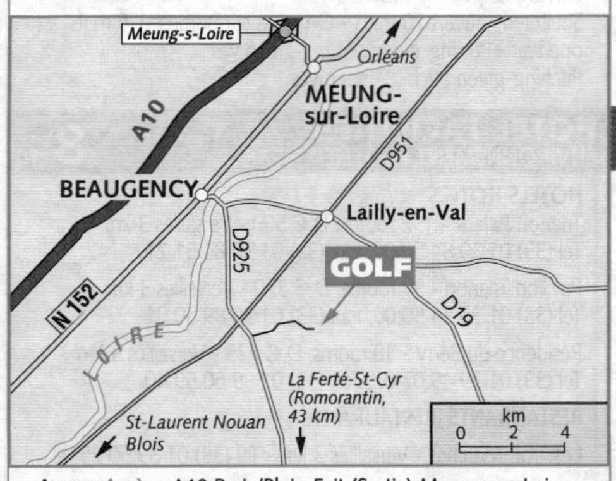

Access Accès : A10 Paris/Blois, Exit (Sortie) Meung-sur-Loire, N152 → Beaugency. In Beaugency → Lailly-en-Val. Cross over the Loire, → La Ferté Saint- Cyr (D925)
Map 3 on page 164 Carte 3 Page 164

GOLF COURSE — PARCOURS — 19/20

Site Site
Maintenance Entretien
Architect Architecte Robert von Hagge
Type Type forest, open country
Relief Relief
Water in play Eau en jeu
Exp. to wind Exposé au vent
Trees in play Arbres en jeu

Scorecard / Carte de score	Chp. / Chp.	Mens / Mess.	Ladies / Da.
Length Long.	6409	6023	4586
Par	72	72	72
Slope system	154	147	132

Advised golfing ability Niveau de jeu recommandé 0 12 24 36
Hcp required Handicap exigé 35

CLUB HOUSE & AMENITIES — CLUB HOUSE ET ANNEXES — 8/10

Pro shop Pro-shop
Driving range Practice
Sheltered couvert no - On grass sur herbe yes - Putting-green putting-green yes - Pitching-green pitching green yes

HOTEL FACILITIES — ENVIRONNEMENT HOTELIER — 6/10

HOTELS HÔTELS
Hôtel du Golf - 40 rooms, D € 210 - on site
Tel (33) 02 54 87 72 13, Fax (33) 02 54 87 78 61

La Tonnellerie - 20 rooms, D € 126 - Tavers 10 km
Tel (33) 02 38 44 68 15, Fax (33) 02 38 44 10 01

L'Ecu de Bretagne - 28 rooms, D € 65 - Beaugency 7 km
Tel (33) 02 38 44 67 60, Fax (33) 02 38 44 68 07

Les Chênes Rouges - 10 rooms, D € 110 - Villeny 20 km
Tel (33) 02 54 98 23 94, Fax (33) 02 54 98 23 99

RESTAURANTS RESTAURANTS
Le Petit Bateau - Beaugency 11 km - Tel (33) 02 38 44 56 38
Auberge Gourmande - Baule 16 km - Tel (33) 02 38 45 01 02

Cannes Mandelieu *Old Course* 14 | 7 | 8

Si personne ne connaît l'auteur du 18 trous original de Mandelieu, on sait que le grand architecte Harry Colt a participé à son remaniement, comme en témoigne la forme des bunkers, parfois assez profonds pour poser problème aux joueurs moyens. Pourtant, ce sont les pins parasols qui constituent les principaux obstacles, leur envergure impressionnante rendant bien étroits les fairways. Les techniciens adorent ce parcours, car la plupart des coups de départ demandent des effets de fade ou de draw, un contrôle précis des trajectoires, un choix de club très subtil pour se retrouver en bonne position et signer les birdies que l'on peut espérer. Si sa longueur ne répond plus tout à fait aux exigences du jeu moderne, Cannes-Mandelieu est un parcours de charme, où les par 3 (il y en a cinq) sont d'une remarquable diversité. Des travaux d'irrigation importants ont été effectués, mais l'entretien reste inégal. Son voisin Cannes-Mandelieu Riviera est une agréable alternative à ce classique.

While no-one knows exactly who laid out the original 18 holes at Mandelieu, we do know that the great Harry Colt had a hand in re-designing the course, as seen in the shape of the bunkers that are sometimes deep enough to cause high-handicappers real problems. Yet the main hazards here are the huge parasol pines, which stretch majestically upward and outward and make a number of fairways a little on the tight side. The more technically-minded golfers love this course because the majority of tee-shots require draws or fades, precise flight control and very careful club selection to get into the right position to line up the birdies we all hope and pray for. While not as long as the modern game might require, Cannes-Mandelieu remains a charming course where the five par 3s are all remarkably different. Significant irrigation work has been carried out but green-keeping is still inconsistent. The neighbouring course of Cannes-Mandelieu Riviera is a pleasant alternative.

Golf de Cannes Mandelieu Old Course 1891

Route du Golf
F - 06210 MANDELIEU

Office	Secrétariat	(33) 04 92 97 32 00
Pro shop	Pro-shop	(33) 04 92 97 32 00
Fax	Fax	(33) 04 93 49 92 90
Web	www.golfoldcourse.com	
Situation	Situation	Cannes (pop. 68 670), 5 km
Annual closure	Fermeture annuelle	no
Weekly closure	Fermeture hebdomadaire	no
Fees main season	Tarifs haute saison	full day

	Week days Semaine	We/Bank holidays We/Férié
Individual Individuel	€ 70	€ 70
Couple Couple	€ 140	€ 140

Under 18 and Students: € 45

Caddie Caddie no — **Electric Trolley** Chariot électrique no

Buggy Voiturette yes — **Clubs** Clubs yes

Credit cards Cartes de crédit
VISA - CB - Eurocard - MasterCard - AMEX

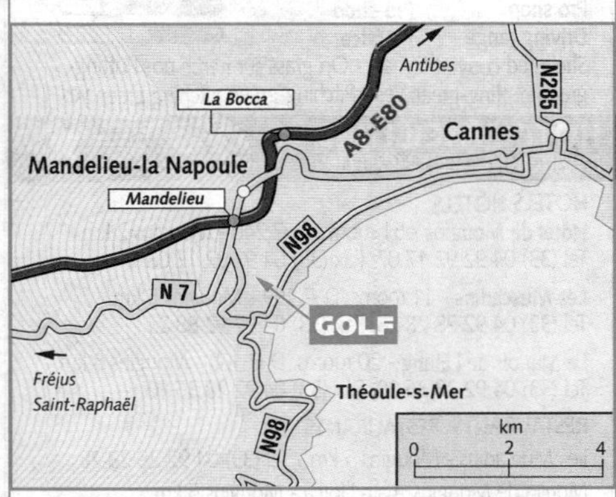

Access Accès : A8 Exit (Sortie) Mandelieu-La Napoule, → Mandelieu, → "Old Course"
Map 14 on page 187 Carte 14 Page 187

GOLF COURSE — PARCOURS 14/20

Site	Site	
Maintenance	Entretien	
Architect	Architecte	Harry S. Colt
Type	Type	seaside course, forest
Relief	Relief	
Water in play	Eau en jeu	
Exp. to wind	Exposé au vent	
Trees in play	Arbres en jeu	

Scorecard Carte de score	Chp. Chp.	Mens Mess.	Ladies Da.
Length Long.	5745	5520	4999
Par	71	71	71
Slope system	121	122	122

Advised golfing ability Niveau de jeu recommandé: 0 12 24 36

Hcp required Handicap exigé 28

CLUB HOUSE & AMENITIES — CLUB HOUSE ET ANNEXES 7/10

Pro shop Pro-shop
Driving range Practice
Sheltered couvert 17 mats - **On grass** sur herbe yes - **Putting-green** putting-green yes - **Pitching-green** pitching green yes

HOTEL FACILITIES — ENVIRONNEMENT HOTELIER 8/10

HOTELS HÔTELS

Hostellerie du Golf - 55 rooms, D € 127 - Mandelieu 1 km
Tel (33) 04 93 49 11 66, Fax (33) 04 92 97 04 01

Majestic - 305 rooms, D € 600 - Cannes 5 km
Tel (33) 04 92 98 77 00, Fax (33) 04 93 38 97 90

Paris - 50 rooms, D € 150 - Cannes 5 km
Tel (33) 04 93 38 30 89, Fax (33) 04 93 39 04 61

RESTAURANTS RESTAURANTS

La Palme d'Or - Cannes 5 km - Tel (33) 04 92 98 74 14

Arcimboldo - Cannes 5 km - Tel (33) 04 93 94 14 15

Villa des Lys (Majestic) - Cannes 5 km - Tel (33) 04 92 98 77 41

Cannes-Mougins

15	7	8

Longtemps le club le plus prestigieux de la région, il s'est un peu endormi face à la concurrence, mais veut retrouver tout son prestige. La séduction apparente du lieu dissimule les réelles difficultés du parcours. Les obstacles d'eau ne sont pas nombreux, mais ils sont placés de manière très stratégique. Si on peut avoir l'impression de pouvoir signer un bon score, le parcours résiste bien, notamment parce qu'il est difficile de récupérer le par quand on a manqué un green. Très divers dans son tracé, très bien paysagé, il ne récompense que les meilleurs, et surtout les techniciens du golf, les manieurs de balles. Pendant plus de dix ans, Cannes-Mougins a servi de cadre à un Open européen, ce qui a contribué à améliorer la qualité du terrain et à imposer des transformations. La grandeur passée de Cannes-Mougins revit parfois ici mais l'accueil est souvent distant, et les travaux effectués sur le parcours par des responsables locaux depuis quelques années restent d'un intérêt discutable.

For many a year the region's most prestigious golf course, Cannes-Mougins has of late been caught napping by its rivals but is striving to recover its prestige. The course's visible appeal tends to hide the real difficulties. There are not many water hazards, but they are strategically placed. And while signing for a good score might look a possibility, the course always fights back, especially since saving par can be so hard when you miss a green. Full of variety and nicely landscaped, this course rewards only the best, and especially skilled flighters of the ball. Cannes-Mougins has hosted a European Open event for more than 10 years, which has helped to improve the quality of the course and led to necessary changes. You sometimes get glimpses of the past greatness of Cannes-Mougins but the welcome is often rather cool and some of the work carried out by the locals on the course in recent years seems highly questionable.

Golf Country Club de Cannes Mougins 1978

175, Avenue du Golf
F - 06250 MOUGINS

Office Secrétariat (33) 04 93 75 79 13
Pro shop Pro-shop (33) 04 93 75 53 32
Fax Fax (33) 04 93 75 27 60
Web www.golf-cannes-mougins.com
Situation Situation Cannes (pop. 68 670), 9 km
Annual closure Fermeture annuelle no
Weekly closure Fermeture hebdomadaire no

Fees main season Tarifs haute saison		18 holes
	Week days Semaine	**We/Bank holidays** We/Férié
Individual Individuel	€ 100	€ 100
Couple Couple	€ 200	€ 200

Under 21: – 50%

Caddie Caddie on request **Electric Trolley** Char. électrique no

Buggy Voiturette yes **Clubs** Clubs yes

Credit cards Cartes de crédit
VISA - CB - Eurocard - MasterCard - AMEX

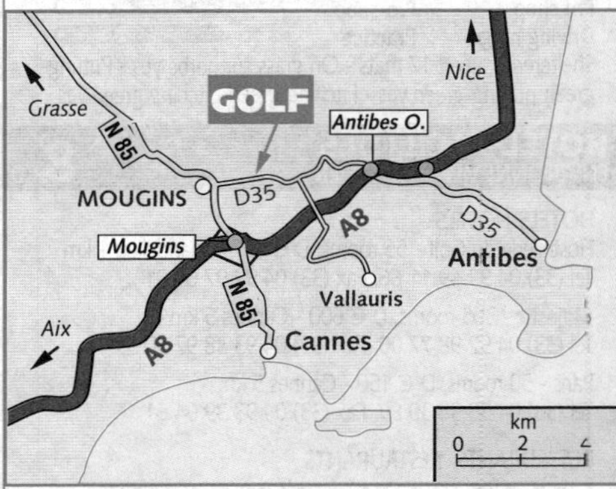

Access Accès : A8. Exit (Sortie) Mougins, → Grasse, Exit (Sortie) Antibes, → Golf
Map 14 on page 187 Carte 14 Page 187

GOLF COURSE 15/20
PARCOURS

Site Site
Maintenance Entretien
Architect Architecte Peter Alliss, Dave Thomas
Type Type forest, parkland
Relief Relief
Water in play Eau en jeu
Exp. to wind Exposé au vent
Trees in play Arbres en jeu

Scorecard Carte de score	**Chp.** Chp.	**Mens** Mess.	**Ladies** Da.
Length Long.	6312	5876	5049
Par	72	72	72
Slope system	136	129	125

Advised golfing ability Niveau de jeu recommandé 0 12 24 36
Hcp required Handicap exigé 28

CLUB HOUSE & AMENITIES 7/10
CLUB HOUSE ET ANNEXES

Pro shop Pro-shop
Driving range Practice
Sheltered couvert 5 mats - On grass sur herbe no- Putting-green putting-green yes - Pitching-green pitching green yes

HOTEL FACILITIES 8/10
ENVIRONNEMENT HOTELIER

HOTELS HÔTELS

Hôtel de Mougins - 51 rooms, D € 240 - Mougins 2 km
Tel (33) 04 92 92 17 07, Fax (33) 04 92 92 17 08

Les Muscadins - 11 rooms, D € 199 - Mougins 5 km
Tel (33) 04 92 28 28 28, Fax (33) 04 92 92 88 23

Le Manoir de l'Etang - 20 rooms, D € 160 - Mougins 5 km
Tel (33) 04 92 28 36 00, Fax (33) 04 92 28 36 10

RESTAURANTS RESTAURANTS

Les Muscadins - Mougins 5 km - Tel (33) 04 92 28 28 28

Moulin de Mougins-Alain Llorca - Mougins 5 km
Tel (33) 04 93 75 78 24

L'Amandier de Mougins - Mougins 5 km
Tel (33) 04 93 90 00 91

Cap d'Agde

15 | 6 | 6

La station balnéaire de Cap d'Agde est très proche et pas bien belle, mais sa présence n'est pas trop envahissante, grâce aux modelages du parcours, et à une certaine végétation. Le dessin de Ronald Fream reste de grande qualité, les abords immédiats des fairways restent parfois un peu rocailleux, mais les efforts entrepris pour y remédier méritent d'être salués. C'est tant mieux car on doit prendre quelques risques pour espérer un bon score sur des trous qui demandent une bonne dose de réflexion, mais récompensent l'audace. Les obstacles sont bien visibles, mais leur nombre et leur placement stratégique poseront des problèmes aux débutants. Les joueurs moyens s'en sortiront mieux, et les frappeurs devront être d'une grande précision, surtout quand le vent souffle, ce qui arrive assez souvent ici. Une belle réussite d'architecture de golf, dont le style exige un entretien parfait. La politique de qualité générale doit se poursuivre, mais on est sur la bonne voie.

The seaside resort of Cap d'Agde is close by and hardly the most beautiful sight on earth, but the way the course is contoured and the vegetation keep most of it out of view. This Ronald Fream layout is excellent but the areas immediately skirting the fairways are still a little rocky. However, the efforts made to remedy the situation should be saluted and so much the better, because here you have to take a few risks if you are hoping to score well on holes that call for careful thought and tend to reward the brave. Even though most hazards are there to be seen, their number and strategic placement might be a little too much for beginners. Mid-handicappers should get by a little easier although big-hitters should aim for precision, especially when the wind blows as it does fairly often. In architectural terms this is an impressive site, but one which requires perfect green-keeping. Ongoing improvement work is definitely a step in the right direction and should be pursued.

Golf du Cap d'Agde — 1989

4, avenue des Alizés
F - 34300 CAP D'AGDE

Office Secrétariat (33) 04 67 26 54 40
Pro shop Pro-shop (33) 04 67 26 54 40
Fax Fax (33) 04 67 26 97 00
Web www.ville-agde.fr
Situation Situation Béziers (pop. 71 000), 22 km
Annual closure Fermeture annuelle no
Weekly closure Fermeture hebdomadaire no

Fees main season Tarifs haute saison	Week days Semaine	We/Bank holidays We/Férié
	18 holes	
Individual Individuel	€ 54	€ 54
Couple Couple	€ 108	€ 108

Under 20: € 28 / Students: € 33

Caddie Caddie no **Electric Trolley** Chariot électrique no

Buggy Voiturette yes **Clubs** Clubs yes

Credit cards Cartes de crédit
VISA - CB - Eurocard - MasterCard

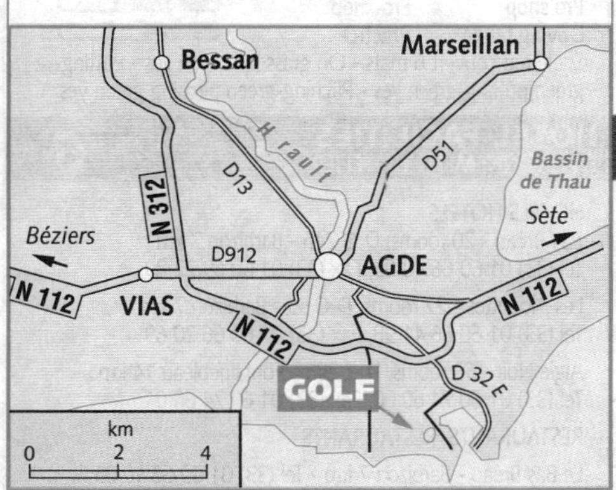

Access Accès : A9 Exit (Sortie) 34 → Agde, → "Ile des Loisirs", golf in front of "Aqualand"
Map 13 on page 184 Carte 13 Page 184

GOLF COURSE
PARCOURS — 15/20

Site Site
Maintenance Entretien
Architect Architecte Ronald Fream
Type Type seaside course, open country
Relief Relief
Water in play Eau en jeu
Exp. to wind Exposé au vent
Trees in play Arbres en jeu

Scorecard Carte de score	Chp. Chp.	Mens Mess.	Ladies Da.
Length Long.	6279	5875	5039
Par	72	72	72
Slope system	137	130	128

Advised golfing ability Niveau de jeu recommandé 0 12 24 36
Hcp required Handicap exigé no

CLUB HOUSE & AMENITIES
CLUB HOUSE ET ANNEXES — 6/10

Pro shop Pro-shop
Driving range Practice
Sheltered couvert 18 mats - On grass sur herbe yes - Putting-green putting-green yes - Pitching-green pitching green yes

HOTEL FACILITIES
ENVIRONNEMENT HOTELIER — 6/10

HOTELS HÔTELS
Palmyra Golf Hôtel - 34 rooms, D € 150 - on site
Tel (33) 04 67 01 50 15, Fax (33) 04 67 01 50 14

Hôtel du Golf - 50 rooms, D € 157 - Cap d'Agde 2 km
Tel (33) 04 67 26 87 03, Fax (33) 04 67 26 26 89

Capaô - 55 rooms, D € 102 - Cap d'Agde 2 km
Tel (33) 04 67 26 99 44, Fax (33) 04 67 26 55 41

Azur - 34 rooms, D € 89 - Cap d'Agde 2 km
Tel (33) 04 67 26 98 22, Fax (33) 04 67 26 48 14

RESTAURANTS RESTAURANTS
Calamar - La Tamarissière 2 km - Tel (33) 04 67 94 05 06
La Table d'Emilie - Marseillan 6 km - Tel (33) 04 67 77 63 59

Cély

15 | 7 | 6

Dessiné par Fromanger et Adam, ce parcours remodelé à la suite de son achat par un groupe japonais est alors devenu un véritable jardin, très paysagé, où le moindre détail était autrefois très soigné, un peu moins aujourd'hui et l'on remarque d'autant plus le bruit de l'autoroute toute proche. Longtemps célèbre par un Club house luxueux et un entretien éblouissant, il a subi quelques revers financiers et ces avantages se sont aujourd'hui estompés, révélant les insuffisances du tracé. C'est un très agréable parcours, mais il manque de longueur et de difficultés stratégiques pour passionner les joueurs de bon niveau. Son tracé est plaisant, les attaques de green sont très intéressantes, les trous sont de profils variés, mais il manque sans doute un zeste de génie et de "souffle" pour en faire un "grand" parcours. Jouer Cély est à recommander, le jouer souvent est une autre question. On attend beaucoup du changement de propriétaire...

Originally designed by Fromanger and Adam, Cély was restyled further to a buy-out by a Japanese group and turned into a landscaped garden once perfectly manicured, now a little less so. The noise from the nearby motorway seems all the louder for it. Famous for its luxurious club-house and beautifully maintained fairways and greens, the club met with a few financial difficulties and these features have lost some of their shine, revealing in the process some of the layout's shortcomings. This is a very pleasant course but it lacks the length and strategic complexity to excite the best players. The layout is pleasing with some interesting approach shots to the greens, and the holes offer variety enough, but it almost certainly lacks that touch of genius and the staying power to be a truly great course. A round of golf at Cély is to be recommended, but playing it often is another matter. Expectations are high following a change of proprietor.

Cély Golf Club — 1990

Château de Cély, route de Saint-Germain
F - 77930 CELY-EN-BIERE

Office Secrétariat (33) 01 64 38 03 07
Pro shop Pro-shop no pro shop
Fax Fax (33) 01 64 38 08 78
Web www.club-albatros.com
Situation Situation Fontainebleau, 14 km
Melun (pop. 35 320), 12 km

Annual closure Fermeture annuelle no
Weekly closure Fermeture hebdomadaire no

Fees main season Tarifs haute saison	18 holes	
	Week days Semaine	We/Bank holidays We/Férié
Individual Individuel	€ 42	€ 74
Couple Couple	€ 84	€ 148

Under 25: – 50 %

Caddie Caddie no — **Electric Trolley** Chariot électrique yes
Buggy Voiturette no — **Clubs** Clubs yes
Credit cards Cartes de crédit
VISA - CB - Eurocard - MasterCard - AMEX

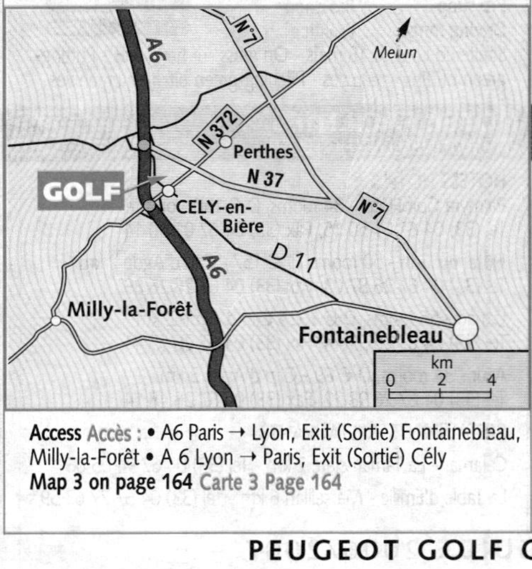

Access Accès : • A6 Paris → Lyon, Exit (Sortie) Fontainebleau, Milly-la-Forêt • A 6 Lyon → Paris, Exit (Sortie) Cély
Map 3 on page 164 Carte 3 Page 164

GOLF COURSE — PARCOURS 15/20

Site Site
Maintenance Entretien
Architect Architecte Marc Adam, Patrick Fromanger
Type Type parkland
Relief Relief
Water in play Eau en jeu
Exp. to wind Exposé au vent
Trees in play Arbres en jeu

Scorecard / Carte de score	Chp. / Chp.	Mens / Mess.	Ladies / Da.
Length Long.	5874	5424	4686
Par	72	72	72
Slope system	133	131	123

Advised golfing ability Niveau de jeu recommandé 0 12 24 36
Hcp required Handicap exigé 30

CLUB HOUSE & AMENITIES — CLUB HOUSE ET ANNEXES 7/10

Pro shop Pro-shop
Driving range Practice
Sheltered couvert 6 mats - On grass sur herbe yes - Putting-green putting-green yes - Pitching-green pitching green yes

HOTEL FACILITIES — ENVIRONNEMENT HOTELIER 6/10

HOTELS HÔTELS
Bas Bréau - 20 rooms, D € 245 - Barbizon 7 km
Tel (33) 01 60 66 40 05, Fax (33) 01 60 69 22 89

Les Alouettes - 22 rooms, D € 55 - Barbizon 7 km
Tel (33) 01 60 66 41 98, Fax (33) 01 60 66 20 69

Aigle Noir - 53 rooms, D € 205 - Fontainebleau 14 km
Tel (33) 01 60 74 60 00, Fax (33) 01 60 74 60 01

RESTAURANTS RESTAURANTS
Le Bas Bréau - Barbizon 7 km - Tel (33) 01 60 66 40 05
L'Angelus - Barbizon 7 km - Tel (33) 01 60 66 40 30
Le Relais de Barbizon - Barbizon 7 km - Tel (33) 01 60 66 40 28

Chailly (Château de)

14	8	6

Avec ce golf à proximité de Dijon et de l'autoroute A6 (sans bruits), le propriétaire souhaitait faire un "links" à l'intérieur des terres. On peut regretter pour l'animation du paysage qu'il n'ait pas voulu faire beaucoup de plantations dans cet espace d'origine agricole de 75 hectares parcouru par un ruisseau, et parsemé de quelques grandes pièces d'eau. L'architecture de Thierry Sprecher et Géry Watine est de bonne qualité et de bon goût, mais reste un peu timide et sans personnalité frappante. Alors que les intentions de départ auraient dû imposer quelques modelages et davantage de violence visuelle, ils sont peu importants. On en garde une certaine impression de platitude, avec en contrepartie l'avantage de permettre aux joueurs de tous niveaux de ne pas connaître trop de problèmes. Le château du domaine a été aménagé avec des chambres d'hôtel et un restaurant gastronomique, qui ont beaucoup contribué à la réputation du lieu.

The owner of this course close to Dijon and the A6 motorway (no noise) set out to create an inland links. He had no intention of planting more trees or bushes on a site which was originally 75 hectares of farming land crossed by a stream and dotted with a few stretches of water, and seeing the landscape today, we wonder whether this was the right option. The design by Thierry Sprecher and Géry Watine is high class and tasteful but lacks boldness or any striking personality. While original designs would have required a little shaping of ground and greater visual impact, neither one nor the other is very much in evidence. This leaves an impression of flatness and a round of golf where players of all levels should stay out of trouble. The estate's castle has been refurbished with hotel rooms and a gourmet restaurant, which have done much to enhance the course's reputation.

Golf Club du Château de Chailly — 1990

F - 21320 CHAILLY-SUR-ARMENCON

Office Secrétariat (33) 03 80 90 30 40
Pro shop Pro-shop (33) 03 80 90 30 40
Fax Fax (33) 03 80 90 30 05
Web www.chailly.com
Situation Situation Dijon (pop. 146 700), 55 km
Pouilly-en-Auxois (pop. 1 370), 5 km
Annual closure Fermeture annuelle 1/1→31/1
Weekly closure Fermeture hebdomadaire no

Fees main season Tarifs haute saison		Full day
	Week days Semaine	We/Bank holidays We/Férié
Individual Individuel	€ 35	€ 55
Couple Couple	€ 70	€ 110

Week end = Friday, Saturday, Sunday

Caddie Caddie no — **Electric Trolley** Chariot électrique yes
Buggy Voiturette yes — **Clubs** Clubs yes
Credit cards Cartes de crédit
VISA - CB - Eurocard - MasterCard - AMEX - DC - JCB

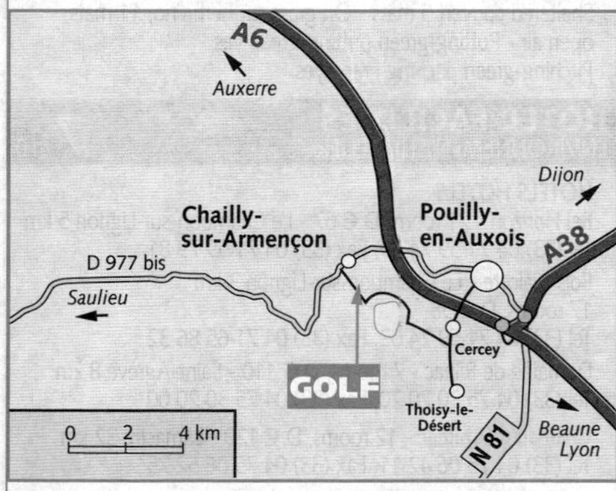

Access Accès : A6 Exit (Sortie) Pouilly-en-Auxois, D977 bis → Saulieu
Map 7 on page 173 Carte 7 Page 173

GOLF COURSE — PARCOURS — 14/20

Site Site
Maintenance Entretien
Architect Architecte Thierry Sprecher, Géry Watine
Type Type open country
Relief Relief
Water in play Eau en jeu
Exp. to wind Exposé au vent
Trees in play Arbres en jeu

Scorecard Carte de score	Chp. Chp.	Mens Mess.	Ladies Da.
Length Long.	6087	5835	4887
Par	72	72	72
Slope system	130	124	126

Advised golfing ability Niveau de jeu recommandé 0 12 24 36
Hcp required Handicap exigé no

CLUB HOUSE & AMENITIES — CLUB HOUSE ET ANNEXES — 8/10

Pro shop Pro-shop
Driving range Practice
Sheltered couvert 12 mats - On grass sur herbe no - Putting-green putting-green yes - Pitching-green pitching green yes

HOTEL FACILITIES — ENVIRONNEMENT HOTELIER — 6/10

HOTELS HÔTELS
Château de Chailly - 45 rooms, D € 295 - on site
Tel (33) 03 80 90 30 30, Fax (33) 03 80 90 30 00

Château de Sainte-Sabine - Sainte-Sabine 14 km
30 rooms, D € 54
Tel (33) 03 80 49 22 01, Fax (33) 03 80 49 20 01

Hostellerie du Château - 17 rooms, D € 61 - Châteauneuf 15 km
Tel (33) 03 80 49 22 00, Fax (33) 03 80 49 21 27

RESTAURANTS RESTAURANTS
Le Relais Bernard Loiseau - Saulieu 20 km
Tel (33) 03 80 90 53 53
L'Armançon - on site - Tel (33) 03 80 90 30 30
L'Auxois - Vandenesse-en-Auxois 8 km - Tel (33) 03 80 49 22 36

Chambon-sur-Lignon (Le)

14 | 5 | 7

Dans les montagnes au sud de Saint-Etienne, tout près de la vieille cité épiscopale du Puy-en-Velay, la petite ville de Chambon sur Lignon est au départ de randonnées superbes du printemps à l'automne car les hivers sont parfois rigoureux à mille mètres d'altitude. Il fallait pas mal de foi pour y construire un golf. Visuellement, et par le caractère de son architecture insinuée dans le relief, il rappelle parfois les parcours des Highlands écossais, avec en prime quelques panoramas somptueux, depuis les départs du 6 et du 13 en particulier. Nul ici ne prétend au luxe d'un entretien à l'américaine, mais l'atmosphère est sympathique, l'entretien très correct, avec généralement de bons greens, bien dessinés. Quelques coups aveugles réservent des émotions inévitables avec les dénivellées, comme au 14. On conseillera la voiturette à ceux qui veulent faire les 18 trous sans arrêt. Le charme et la variété de ce parcours méconnu, la beauté de son décor surprennent toujours.

In the mountains to the south of Saint Etienne, close to the old Episcopal city of Puy-en-Velay, the small town of Chambon sur Lignon is the starting point for some wonderful hikes. From spring to autumn that is, because at an altitude of 1,000 metres the winters are sometimes harsh. It took a lot of faith to build a golf course here but this unpretentious layout is well worth a visit. Visually, and through architecture which winds it way through some marked topography, it is sometimes reminiscent of the Scottish highland courses with a few splendid vistas to boot, particularly from the 6th and 13th tees. Nobody should expect US-style standards of green-keeping here but the atmosphere is cheerful and maintenance pretty fair, with good and well-designed greens by and large. A few blind shots will set the pulse racing (on the 14th hole) but this was hardly to be avoided on a rather hilly course where a buggy is recommended if you want to play 18 holes without stopping off for lunch. The charm, the variety and the beautiful setting of this little known course surprise the visitor every time.

Golf du Chambon-sur-Lignon — 1994

Riondet, La Pierre de la Lune, BP 12
F - 43400 LE CHAMBON-SUR-LIGNON

Office	Secrétariat	(33) 04 71 59 28 10
Pro shop	Pro-shop	(33) 04 71 59 28 10
Fax	Fax	(33) 04 71 65 87 14
Web	www.golf-chambon.com	
Situation	Situation	St-Etienne, 68 km
Annual closure	Fermeture annuelle	11/11→1/4
Weekly closure	Fermeture hebdomadaire	no

Fees main season / Tarifs haute saison	18 holes	
	Week days / Semaine	We/Bank holidays / We/Férié
Individual Individuel	€ 42	€ 42
Couple Couple	€ 74	€ 74

Under 14: € 15 / Under 18 & Students: € 25

Caddie Caddie no — Electric Trolley Chariot électrique yes

Buggy Voiturette yes — Clubs Clubs yes

Credit cards Cartes de crédit
VISA - Eurocard - MasterCard

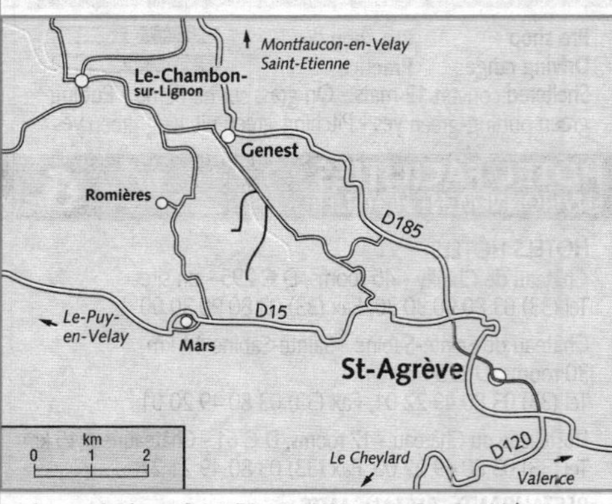

Access Accès : • Saint-Etienne, N88 → Le-Puy-en-Velay. Yssingeaux, D103 → Tence, D151 → Le Chambon-sur-Lignon. SE, D103, D155 → Golf. • Valence, D533 → Lamastre, St Agrève. D185, D151 → Chambon-sur-Lignon.

Map 11 on page 180 Carte 11 Page 180

GOLF COURSE — PARCOURS — 14/20

Site	Site	
Maintenance	Entretien	
Architect	Architecte	Michel Gayon
Type	Type	hilly, forest
Relief	Relief	
Water in play	Eau en jeu	
Exp. to wind	Exposé au vent	
Trees in play	Arbres en jeu	

Scorecard / Carte de score	Chp. / Chp.	Mens / Mess.	Ladies / Da.
Length Long.	5882	5521	4639
Par	72	72	72
Slope system	146	137	137

Advised golfing ability / Niveau de jeu recommandé: 0 12 24 36

Hcp required / Handicap exigé: 54

CLUB HOUSE & AMENITIES — CLUB HOUSE ET ANNEXES — 5/10

Pro shop — Pro-shop
Driving range — Practice
Sheltered couvert 5 mats - On grass sur herbe no, 11 mats open air - Putting-green putting-green yes
Pitching-green pitching green yes

HOTEL FACILITIES — ENVIRONNEMENT HOTELIER — 7/10

HOTELS HÔTELS

Bel Horizon - 21 rooms D € 67 - Le Chambon-sur-Lignon 5 km
Tel (33) 04 71 59 74 39, Fax (33) 04 71 59 79 81

Bois Vialotte - Le Chambon-sur-Lignon 3 km
17 rooms, D € 58
Tel (33) 04 71 59 74 03, Fax (33) 04 71 65 86 32

Domaine de Rilhac - 7 rooms, D € 110 - Saint-Agrève 8 km
Tel (33) 04 75 30 20 20, Fax (33) 04 75 30 20 00

Château d'Urbilhac - 12 rooms, D € 120 - Lamastre 32 km
Tel (33) 04 75 06 42 11, Fax (33) 04 75 06 52 75

RESTAURANTS RESTAURANTS

Domaine de Rilhac - Saint-Agrève 8 km Tel (33) 04 75 30 20 20
Vidal - Saint-Julien-Chapteuil 25 km - Tel (33) 04 71 08 70 50

Chamonix

15 | 6 | 7

C'est l'un des meilleurs parcours de montagne, et le point de départ de balades magnifiques au pied du Mont Blanc. Ce 18 trous dessiné par Robert Trent Jones était autrefois difficile à entretenir, mais les travaux de drainage ont été efficaces et l'état du parcours peut être remarquable quand la saison est favorable : les greens demandent une attention permanente à cette altitude. Dans ce site exceptionnel, orné de sapins et de bouleaux, il n'a de golf de montagne que son paysage, car son relief est raisonnable. Parcouru par de petits ruisseaux et par l'Arve, ses difficultés ne sont pas insurmontables pour un joueur de bon niveau capable de réfléchir sur la stratégie mais il peut être délicat pour un débutant, en raison de l'étroitesse de ses fairways. Conçu comme un golf de vacances, il peut être joué plusieurs fois sans ennui, mais ses difficultés assez subtiles apparaissent vite quand on chasse un bon score. Une bonne idée, les conseils sur l'étiquette sur le parcours. Une mauvaise, un service parfois problématique au restaurant.

This is one of the best mountain courses around and a great base-camp for some magnificent hikes at the foot of Mont Blanc. On this course designed by Robert Trent Jones, recent drainage work has had effective results and the condition of the course can be very good in season. At this altitude, the greens require constant maintenance. Laid out over an exceptional site lined with fir and birch trees, the only thing mountainous about this course is the landscape because topography is reasonable. Crossed by a number of streams and the gushing Arve river, the difficulties here are not impossible for a player with good ability and a strategic brain, but the course can pose a problem or two for beginners owing to a number of tight fairways. You can play it several times with the same fun and enthusiasm, although the subtle difficulties tend to emerge pretty quickly when you are looking for a good score. One good idea: advice for on-course etiquette. One bad idea: sometimes poor service in the restaurant.

Golf Club de Chamonix — 1934

35, route du Golf
F - 74400 CHAMONIX

Office Secrétariat (33) 04 50 53 06 28
Pro shop Pro-shop (33) 04 50 53 45 23
Fax Fax (33) 04 50 53 38 69
Web www.golfdechamonix.com
Situation Situation Chamonix, 3 km
Genève, 85 km
Annual closure Fermeture annuelle 1/11→15/3
Weekly closure Fermeture hebdomadaire no
Fees main season Tarifs haute saison 18 holes

	Week days / Semaine	We/Bank holidays / We/Férié
Individual Individuel	€ 6870	€ 70
Couple Couple	€ 140	€ 140

Caddie Caddie on request
Electric Trolley Chariot électrique yes
Buggy Voiturette yes (ask before) **Clubs** Clubs yes
Credit cards Cartes de crédit
VISA - CB - Eurocard - MasterCard

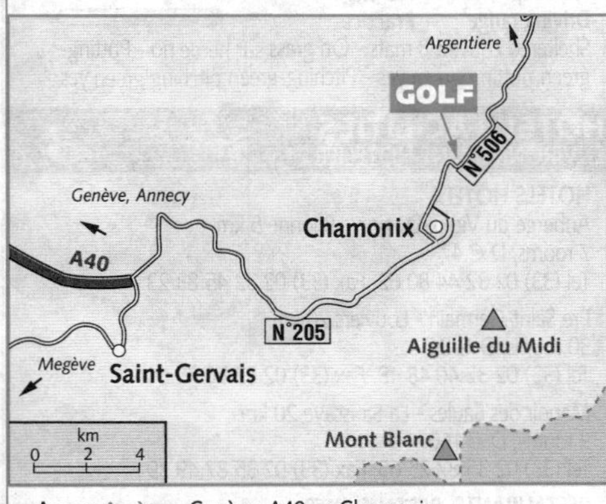

Access Accès : • Genève, A40 → Chamonix
• Megève, N212, D909, N205
Map 11 on page 181 Carte 11 Page 181

GOLF COURSE — PARCOURS 15/20

Site Site
Maintenance Entretien
Architect Architecte Robert Trent Jones
Type Type parkland, mountain
Relief Relief
Water in play Eau en jeu
Exp. to wind Exposé au vent
Trees in play Arbres en jeu

Scorecard / Carte de score	Chp. / Chp.	Mens / Mess.	Ladies / Da.
Length Long.	6076	5855	4786
Par	72	72	72
Slope system	125	117	119

Advised golfing ability 0 12 24 36
Niveau de jeu recommandé
Hcp required Handicap exigé 36 in 07/08

CLUB HOUSE & AMENITIES — CLUB HOUSE ET ANNEXES 6/10

Pro shop Pro-shop
Driving range Practice
Sheltered couvert 14 mats - On grass sur herbe no, 18 mats open air - Putting-green putting-green yes - Pitching-green pitching green yes (2)

HOTEL FACILITIES — ENVIRONNEMENT HOTELIER 7/10

HOTELS HÔTELS
Le Labrador - 32 rooms, D € 156 - on site
Tel (33) 04 50 55 90 09, Fax (33) 04 50 53 15 85

Albert 1er - Chamonix 2 km
42 rooms, D € 270
Tel (33) 04 50 53 05 09, Fax (33) 04 50 53 95 48

Beausoleil - 17 rooms, D € 88 - Le Lavancher 2 km
Tel (33) 04 50 54 00 78, Fax (33) 04 50 54 17 34

RESTAURANTS RESTAURANTS
Albert 1er - Chamonix 2 km - Tel (33) 04 50 53 05 09
Atmosphère - Chamonix 2 km - Tel (33) 04 50 55 97 97
Maison Carrier - Chamonix 2 km - Tel (33) 04 50 53 00 03

Champ de Bataille

14 | 6 | 3

Ce parcours accidenté, dessiné par Nelson et Huau, est une jolie promenade dans les bois, avec quelques spécimens d'arbres magnifiques, mais des fairways généralement de bonne taille. De nombreux sapins font parfois imaginer être en montagne, alors que nous sommes au coeur de la Normandie. Chez les architectes, on sent les paysagistes sans doute plus que les golfeurs, mais si l'on peut regretter un certain manque de souffle épique, il n'y a pas de fautes graves, ce qui incite à le recommander davantage aux amoureux de belles balades en famille (ou avec des amis) qu'aux joueurs de haut niveau à la recherche de grands défis. Autrefois dépendant du château, ce club s'en est détaché pour avoir son propre Club House. Si l'on y a un peu perdu en prestige aristocratique, les insipides premier et dernier trou, "à la française" ont été remplacés par deux trous dûs à un autre architecte, Jean-Manuel Rossi. C'est un peu dommage pour le style, mais le tracé général est meilleur.

This hilly course designed by Nelson and Huau is a beautiful stroll through the woods, where some magnificent trees leave enough room for some decently sized fairways. With some of the pine-trees you'd think you were in the Alps rather than in the heart of Normandy. Architecturally speaking, the course is the work of landscapers rather than golfers, but if we overlook a little lack of punch there is nothing at all wrong with this course, which is to be recommended more for family outings (or rounds with friends) rather than for skilful players looking for a tough challenge. Once very dependent on the castle, the club has broken away with its own club-house. While the course has a little of its aristocratic prestige, the bland first and last holes, originally inspired by French style gardens, have been replaced by holes designed by Jean-Manuel Rossi. Too bad for the style, all the better for the overall layout.

Golf du Champ de Bataille — 1988

Château du Champ-de-Bataille
F - 27110 LE NEUBOURG

Office	Secrétariat	(33) 02 32 35 03 72
Pro shop	Pro-shop	(33) 02 32 35 03 72
Fax	Fax	(33) 02 32 35 83 10
Web	www.champdebataille.com	
Situation	Situation	Evreux (pop. 49 100), 27 km
Annual closure	Fermeture annuelle	no
Weekly closure	Fermeture hebdomadaire	no

Fees main season Tarifs haute saison	18 holes	
	Week days Semaine	We/Bank holidays We/Férié
Individual Individuel	€ 40	€ 60
Couple Couple	€ 80	€ 120

Under 25: € 25 (week days) and € 35 (We) / Wednesday (mercredi): € 25

Caddie Caddie no **Electric Trolley** Chariot électrique no

Buggy Voiturette yes **Clubs** Clubs yes

Credit cards Cartes de crédit
VISA - CB - Eurocard - MasterCard - AMEX

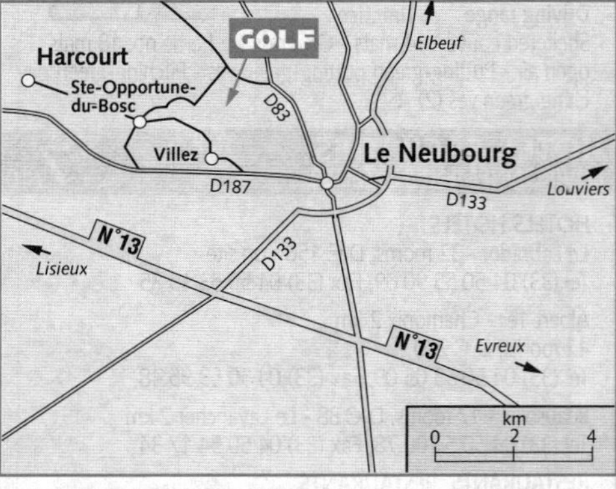

Access Accès : • Evreux, N13 → Lisieux → Le Neubourg
• Caen or Lisieux, N13 → Evreux → Le Neubourg
Map 2 on page 163 Carte 2 Page 163

GOLF COURSE — PARCOURS — 14/20

Site	Site	
Maintenance	Entretien	
Architect	Architecte	Robin Nelson, Thierry Huau
Type	Type	forest
Relief	Relief	
Water in play	Eau en jeu	
Exp. to wind	Exposé au vent	
Trees in play	Arbres en jeu	

Scorecard Carte de score	Chp. Chp.	Mens Mess.	Ladies Da.
Length Long.	5987	5615	4465
Par	72	72	72
Slope system	137	135	131

Advised golfing ability Niveau de jeu recommandé: 0 12 24 36

Hcp required Handicap exigé: no

CLUB HOUSE & AMENITIES — CLUB HOUSE ET ANNEXES — 6/10

Pro shop Pro-shop
Driving range Practice
Sheltered couvert 8 mats - On grass sur herbe no - Putting-green putting-green yes - Pitching-green pitching green yes

HOTEL FACILITIES — ENVIRONNEMENT HOTELIER — 3/10

HOTELS HÔTELS

Auberge du Vieux-Donjon - Brionne 5 km
7 rooms, D € 47
Tel (33) 02 32 44 80 62, Fax (33) 02 32 45 83 23

Pré Saint-Germain - Louviers 20 km
30 rooms, D € 86
Tel (33) 02 32 40 48 48, Fax (33) 02 32 50 75 60

Manoir des Saules - La Saussaye 20 km
9 rooms, D € 160
Tel (33) 02 35 87 25 65, Fax (33) 02 35 87 49 39

RESTAURANTS RESTAURANTS

Les Saisons - Vironvay 25 km - Tel (33) 02 32 40 02 56
Le Logis de Brionne - Brionne 5 km - Tel (33) 02 32 44 81 73

Chantaco

14	7	7

Un incontournable pour le charme, l'ambiance et la tradition sportive, cultivée par la famille Lacoste. Relativement accidenté, il est cependant peu fatigant. Il promet une journée tranquille, mais résiste bien aux ambitieux : souvent étroit, avec quelques dévers redoutables et de petits greens, il demande plus de précision que de longueur. Si l'on ne cherche pas à défier un monstre pendant ses vacances, Chantaco reste par beau temps un parcours plaisant. L'architecte originel était Harry Colt, mais la diversité des styles montre que son travail a été modifié, moins sans doute à l'aller, d'un niveau supérieur au reste du parcours. Son final alambiqué a longtemps été critiqué. Mais la refonte de plusieurs trous du retour a constitué un réel progrès. Le 14, par 3, demande de la précision car les alentours sont sévères. Bordé d'un hors limites avec le practice, le 17 aurait bénéficié de quelques mouvements de terrain. Le club house et le restaurant participent fortement au charme du lieu, et l'entretien est devenu de très bonne qualité.

Chantaco is a must for its charm, atmosphere and sporting tradition, nurtured by the Lacoste family. Although rather hilly, it is not really tiring and promises a quiet day's golfing, although even the most ambitious golfer will find it more than a handful. Often tight with a few formidably sloping fairways and small greens, the course demands precision more than length off the tee. Avoid trying to defy this monster and you will find Chantaco a very pleasant course when the weather is fine. The original architect was Harry Colt but the variety of styles shows that his design has been altered here and there, perhaps less so on the front 9, which are of a higher standard than the rest of the course. The 14th hole, a par 3, calls for precision in very tight surroundings. Edged by OB and the driving range, the 17th might have been better with some grading work. The clubhouse and restaurant add a great deal to the charm of this venue, and green-keeping has become very good.

Golf de Chantaco — 1928

Route d'Ascain
F - 64500 SAINT-JEAN-DE-LUZ

Office Secrétariat (33) 05 59 26 14 22
Pro shop Pro-shop (33) 05 59 26 21 45
Fax Fax (33) 05 59 26 48 37
Web www.golfdechantaco.com
Situation Situation Saint-Jean-de-Luz, 2 km
Biarritz (pop. 28 740), 15 km

Annual closure Fermeture annuelle — no

Weekly closure Fermeture hebdomadaire
tuesday except during holidays (mardi sauf vacances)

Fees main season Tarifs haute saison	18 holes	
	Week days Semaine	**We/Bank holidays** We/Férié
Individual Individuel	€ 66	€ 66
Couple Couple	€ 110	€ 110

Under 21: € 38

Caddie Caddie on request **Electric Trolley** Char. électrique yes
Buggy Voiturette yes **Clubs** Clubs yes
Credit cards Cartes de crédit
VISA - CB - Eurocard - MasterCard - AMEX

Access Accès : A63 Biarritz → Saint-Jean-de-Luz, Exit (Sortie) Saint-Jean-de-Luz Nord, D918 → Chantaco, Ascain
Map 12 on page 182 Carte 12 Page 182

GOLF COURSE — PARCOURS — 14/20

Site Site
Maintenance Entretien
Architect Architecte — Harry S. Colt
Type Type — forest, parkland
Relief Relief
Water in play Eau en jeu
Exp. to wind Exposé au vent
Trees in play Arbres en jeu

Scorecard Carte de score	**Chp.** Chp.	**Mens** Mess.	**Ladies** Da.
Length Long.	5833	5395	4651
Par	70	70	70
Slope system	133	128	119

Advised golfing ability 0 12 24 36
Niveau de jeu recommandé
Hcp required Handicap exigé 35

CLUB HOUSE & AMENITIES — CLUB HOUSE ET ANNEXES — 7/10

Pro shop Pro-shop
Driving range Practice
Sheltered couvert 4 mats - On grass sur herbe yes - Putting-green putting-green yes - Pitching-green pitching green yes

HOTEL FACILITIES — ENVIRONNEMENT HOTELIER — 7/10

HOTELS HÔTELS
Chantaco - 23 rooms, D € 190 - on site
Tel (33) 05 59 26 14 76, Fax (33) 05 59 26 35 97

La Devinière - 10 rooms, D € 135 - Saint-Jean-de-Luz 2 km
Tel (33) 05 59 26 05 51, Fax (33) 05 59 51 26 38

Parc Victoria - 20 rooms, D € 152 - Saint-Jean-de-Luz 2 km
Tel (33) 05 59 26 78 78, Fax (33) 05 59 26 78 08

RESTAURANTS RESTAURANTS
Taverne Basque - Saint-Jean-de-Luz 2 km
Tel (33) 05 59 26 01 26
Chez Dominique - Ciboure 3 km - Tel (33) 05 59 47 29 16
Panxua - Ciboure (port de Socoa) 3 km
Tel (33) 05 59 47 13 73

Chantilly *Vineuil*

18	7	6

C'est le grand classique britannique en France, et si le passage du golf à 36 trous en a modifié le déroulement, notamment le finale, aucune blessure n'a été infligée aux trous "Simpson", une marque de respect dont bien des golfs auraient dû s'inspirer. Bien des architectes aussi, qui devraient faire des stages prolongés ici, tant s'y exprime la grandeur dans la sobriété et la franchise, la subtilité technique dans la beauté esthétique. Hautement et diaboliquement intelligent, Vineuil exige une stratégie exactement adaptée à ses limites du moment, et se révèle un sérieux examen de passage des capacités à jouer au golf. Très difficile des départs les plus reculés, plus aimable des départs normaux, c'est tout simplement un très grand parcours. Les progrès de l'entretien, notamment au niveau de la vitesse des greens, ont rendu à Chantilly sa noblesse, son prestige et l'exigence d'un grand challenge. A jouer en semaine dans la configuration "Vineuil", qui comprend les trois magnifiques derniers trous annexés par le parcours "Longères".

This is the great British classic course in France, and while the upgrading to 36 holes has changed the way the course unwinds, particularly the finish of the former 18 holes, no harm has been done to Simpson's original layout, a mark of respect that many golf clubs might do well to ponder. And many designers, as well, who should come here for extended training to see just how well greatness can spring from discretion and honesty, and technical subtlety from sheer beauty. Highly and devilishly intelligent, Vineuil requires strategy tailored to your limitations and can prove to be a very serious examination of your golfing ability. Very tough indeed from the back tees, this is simply a great course. Seriously improved maintenance, particularly concerning the speed of the greens, has restored the nobility, prestige and status of Chantilly as a most exacting challenge. Play the Vineuil layout on a week-day, it includes the wonderful three closing holes taken by the Longères course.

Golf de Chantilly — 1906

F - 60500 CHANTILLY

Office	Secrétariat	(33) 03 44 57 04 43
Pro shop	Pro-shop	(33) 03 44 57 04 43
Fax	Fax	(33) 03 44 57 26 54
Web	www.golfdechantilly.com	
Situation	Situation	Paris, 41 km
Annual closure	Fermeture annuelle	no
Weekly closure	Fermeture hebdomadaire	thursday/jeudi

Fees main season Tarifs haute saison — 18 holes

	Week days / Semaine	We/Bank holidays / We/Férié
Individual Individuel	€ 90**	*
Couple Couple	€ 180**	*

* Members and guests only (membres et invités)
** Only Monday → Wednesday (lundi → mercredi)
Friday morning (vendredi matin): € 100

Caddie Caddie no — **Electric Trolley** Chariot électrique no
Buggy Voiturette no — **Clubs** Clubs yes
Credit cards Cartes de crédit
VISA - CB - Eurocard - MasterCard

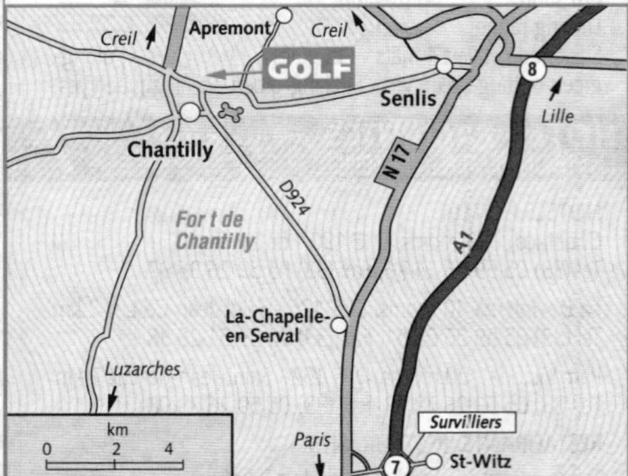

Access Accès : A1 Exit (Sortie) Survilliers, D922 → Fosses. N17 → La Chapelle en Serval. In La Chapelle, go left D924 → Chantilly. Après le Château, à droite → Vineuil, Golf.
Map 3 on page 164 Carte 3 Page 164

GOLF COURSE — PARCOURS — 18/20

Site	Site	
Maintenance	Entretien	
Architect	Architecte	Tom Simpson
Type	Type	forest, inland
Relief	Relief	
Water in play	Eau en jeu	
Exp. to wind	Exposé au vent	
Trees in play	Arbres en jeu	

Scorecard / Carte de score	**Chp.** / Chp.	**Mens** / Mess.	**Ladies** / Da.
Length Long.	6396	5935	4888
Par	71	71	73
Slope system	134	130	132

Advised golfing ability — 0 12 24 36
Niveau de jeu recommandé
Hcp required Handicap exigé — 28 Men, 30 Ladies

CLUB HOUSE & AMENITIES — CLUB HOUSE ET ANNEXES — 7/10

Pro shop Pro-shop
Driving range Practice
Sheltered couvert 4 mats - On grass sur herbe yes - Putting-green putting-green yes - Pitching-green pitching green yes

HOTEL FACILITIES — ENVIRONNEMENT HOTELIER — 6/10

HOTELS HÔTELS

Le Parc - 57 rooms, D € 120 - Chantilly 3 km
Tel (33) 03 44 58 20 00, Fax (33) 03 44 57 31 10

Château de la Tour - 41 rooms, D € 157 - Gouvieux 6 km
Tel (33) 03 44 62 38 38, Fax (33) 03 44 57 31 97

Relais d'Aumale - 24 rooms, D € 140 - Montgrésin 8 km
Tel (33) 03 44 54 61 31, Fax (33) 03 44 54 69 15

RESTAURANTS RESTAURANTS

La Renardière - Gouvieux 6 km - Tel (33) 03 44 57 08 23

Auberge de la Grange aux Loups - Apremont 4 km
Tel (33) 03 44 25 33 79

Le Vertugadin - Chantilly 3 km - Tel (33) 03 44 57 03 19

Charmeil

16	6	6

Avec une moitié de trous dans une forêt de chênes et l'autre en plaine, ce parcours assez plat n'est jamais monotone. Jeremy Pern aime l'architecture de links, et le montre par son modelage de buttes par petites touches, et une utilisation raisonnée de bunkers de toutes tailles, y compris des "pot-bunkers". Les obstacles d'eau sont pratiquement tous naturels, alimentés par un un étang de trois hectares, ce qui apporte de jolis éléments paysagers. Un joueur réfléchi peut toujours jouer la sécurité, ce qui rend le parcours amusant pour tous les niveaux, les difficultés étant visibles, mais les frappeurs peuvent aussi s'exprimer, s'ils ont le goût du risque. Franc et plaisant, il peut cependant être un peu long pour les joueurs de plus de 24 de handicap. Les greens sont assez faciles à lire, mais certaines attaques sont délicates à apprécier. Ce beau tracé bénéficie d'un entretien correct (beaucoup de départs ont été rénovés), mais il vaut mieux jouer hors des périodes d'humidité. L'hôtel sur place est pratique et fonctionnel.

With half the holes in an oak forest and the other half in open country, this is a fairly flat but never tedious course. Architect Jeremy Pern is fond of links layouts and shows it here, with carefully shaped mounds and the widespread use of bunkers in all shapes and sizes, including a number of pot-bunkers. Nearly all the water is natural, fed by a lake of some 7 acres or more, which adds to the pretty landscape. A thoughtful player, as always, can play safe, thus making this an amusing course for all golfers of all abilities, as the difficulties are there to be seen, but big-hitters can show their mettle too if they like taking a few risks. Open and pleasant to play, it can however be a little long for high-handicappers. The greens are easy to read but some approach shots tend to be a little tricky to assess. The standard of green-keeping for this fine layout is good (many of the tee-boxes have been re-laid) but this is a course for the drier days. The on-site hotel is convenient and functional.

Golf de Grenoble Charmeil — 1987

Saint-Quentin-sur-Isère
F - 38210 SAINT-QUENTIN-SUR-ISERE

Office	Secrétariat	(33) 04 76 93 35 65
Pro shop	Pro-shop	(33) 04 76 93 35 65
Fax	Fax	(33) 04 76 93 62 04
Web	www.golfhotelcharmeil.com	
Situation	Situation	Grenoble, 24 km
Annual closure	Fermeture annuelle	25/12→1/1
Weekly closure	Fermeture hebdomadaire	no
Fees main season	Tarifs haute saison	18 holes

	Week days Semaine	We/Bank holidays We/Férié
Individual Individuel	€ 38	€ 50
Couple Couple	€ 76	€ 100

Juniors under 21 & Students under 25: € 22 / 38 (We)

Caddie Caddie no — **Electric Trolley** Chariot électrique no

Buggy Voiturette yes — **Clubs** Clubs yes

Credit cards Cartes de crédit
VISA - CB - Eurocard - MasterCard - AMEX - DC

Access Accès : • Grenoble A49 → Valence
• Lyon A48 → Grenoble → A49 Valence,
Exit (Sortie) Tullins → Saint-Quentin-sur-Isère
Map 11 on page 180 Carte 11 Page 180

GOLF COURSE — PARCOURS — 16/20

Site	Site	
Maintenance	Entretien	
Architect	Architecte	Jeremy Pern Jean Garaïalde
Type	Type	open country, forest
Relief	Relief	
Water in play	Eau en jeu	
Exp. to wind	Exposé au vent	
Trees in play	Arbres en jeu	

Scorecard Carte de score	Chp. Chp.	Mens Mess.	Ladies Da.
Length Long.	6114	5735	4941
Par	73	73	73
Slope system	127	125	124

Advised golfing ability 0 12 24 36
Niveau de jeu recommandé
Hcp required Handicap exigé no

CLUB HOUSE & AMENITIES — CLUB HOUSE ET ANNEXES — 6/10

Pro shop Pro-shop
Driving range Practice
Sheltered couvert 8 mats - On grass sur herbe yes - Putting-green putting-green yes (2) - Pitching-green pitching green yes

HOTEL FACILITIES — ENVIRONNEMENT HOTELIER — 6/10

HOTELS HÔTELS
Golf Hôtel du Charmeil - 49 rooms, D € 90 - on site
Tel (33) 04 76 93 67 28, Fax (33) 04 76 93 67 28

Auberge de Malatras - 17 rooms, D € 41 - Tullins 6 km
Tel (33) 04 76 07 02 30, Fax (33) 04 76 07 76 48

Campanile - 39 rooms, D € 80 - Saint-Egrène 10 km
Tel (33) 04 76 75 57 88, Fax (33) 04 76 75 06 49

RESTAURANTS RESTAURANTS
Philippe Serratrice - Voiron 16 km - Tel (33) 04 76 05 29 88

La Queue de Cochon - Fontanil-Cornillon 24 km
Tel (33) 04 76 75 65 54

Auberge de Malatras - Tullins 6 km - Tel (33) 04 76 07 02 30

Château de la Chouette

16	5	6

Construit en deux étapes, ce tracé de Robert Trent Jones Jr a pris une juste place parmi les golfs de l'ouest parisien, en dépit de l'absence d'un vrai et vaste club house, ainsi que d'un practice digne de ce nom. Le site est très beau et très vallonné, il s'agit d'un grand parc avec des arbres aussi anciens que magnifiques. Le parcours n'est pas si facile avec ses nombreuses pièces d'eau (qui animent aussi l'esthétique du lieu), mais si les néophytes seront intimidés, les meilleurs joueurs prendront vite la mesure de ces difficultés plus apparentes que dramatiques, d'autant qu'on leur demandera pas davantage de taper la balle que de la travailler. De plus, les bunkers ne sont généralement pas trop en jeu. Après de seconds coups bien portés, comme l'exige le style plutôt américain du dessin, le travail n'est pas fini car les greens ont de beaux mouvements et peuvent devenir difficiles s'ils sont rapides. Le manque de voiturettes restreint sérieusement la clientèle du lieu, mais ce parcours bien pensé entre eau et forêt mérite le déplacement, d'autant que le rapport qualité/prix est excellent.

This Robert Trent Jones Jr. layout has assumed its rightful place amongst the best courses to the west of Paris despite the absence of any real sizeable club-house and practice facilities. The site is magnificent with rolling valleys in a large park with old and impressive trees. The actual layout is not that easy with any number of water hazards but while beginners might be frightened off, the better players will quickly come to terms with difficulties that look much worse than they actually are. Flighting the ball is perhaps more important than hitting it for miles. After pitched rather than rolled approach shots, as demanded by the course's rather more American style, you are still not home and dry because the greens are impressively contoured and can pose a number of problems when playing really fast. The shortage of buggies places a serious limit on the numbers of people playing here, but this course is well worth a round or two : excellent value for money.

Golf du château de la Chouette 2001

1, place de la Mairie
F - 78250 GAILLON

Office	Secrétariat	(33) 01 30 91 23 91
Pro shop	Pro-shop	(33) 01 30 91 23 91
Fax	Fax	(33) 01 30 91 23 92
E-mail	golfdelachouette@wanadoo.fr	
Situation	Situation	Paris, 40 km
Annual closure	Fermeture annuelle	no
Weekly closure	Fermeture hebdomadaire	Monday

lundi: restaurant closed

Fees main season Tarifs haute saison	Week days Semaine	We/Bank holidays We/Férié
		18 holes
Individual Individuel	€ 33	€ 58
Couple Couple	€ 66	€ 116

Under 25 & students : € 20 / 30 (We) / Seniors Thursday (jeudi), Ladies Friday (vendredi) : € 28

Caddie Caddie no — **Electric Trolley** Chariot électrique yes
Buggy Voiturette no — **Clubs** Clubs yes
Credit cards Cartes de crédit
VISA - CB - Eurocard - MasterCard

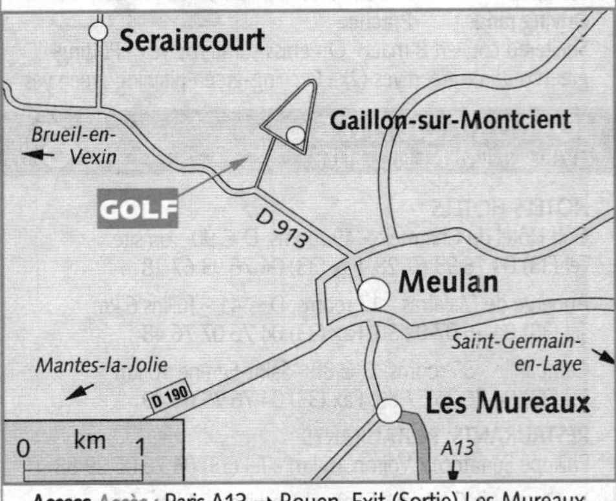

Access Accès : Paris A13 → Rouen. Exit (Sortie) Les Mureaux. After the Seine river, go left on D 913. After 2 km, in Gaillon, turn right → Gaillon. Golf entrance in the village (Place de la Mairie). **Map 15 on page 188** Carte 15 Page 188

GOLF COURSE
PARCOURS — 16/20

Site	Site	
Maintenance	Entretien	
Architect	Architecte	R. Trent Jones Jr
Type	Type	inland, hilly
Relief	Relief	
Water in play	Eau en jeu	
Exp. to wind	Exposé au vent	
Trees in play	Arbres en jeu	

Scorecard Carte de score	Chp. Chp.	Mens Mess.	Ladies Da.
Length Long.	5960	5551	4659
Par	72	72	72
Slope system	141	134	125

Advised golfing ability Niveau de jeu recommandé — 0 12 24 36
Hcp required Handicap exigé 54

CLUB HOUSE & AMENITIES
CLUB HOUSE ET ANNEXES — 5/10

Pro shop Pro-shop
Driving range Practice
Sheltered couvert no - On grass sur herbe no - Putting-green putting-green yes - Pitching-green pitching green yes

HOTEL FACILITIES
ENVIRONNEMENT HOTELIER — 6/10

HOTELS HÔTELS
Mercure - 69 rooms, D € 96 - Meulan 4 km
Tel (33) 01 34 74 63 63, Fax (33) 01 34 74 00 98

Moulin d'Orgeval - 14 rooms, D € 150 - Orgeval 14 km
Tel (33) 01 39 75 85 74, Fax (33) 01 39 75 48 52

RESTAURANTS RESTAURANTS
Relais Ste Jeanne - Cormeilles-en-Vexin 15 km
Tel (33) 01 34 66 61 56

Les Charmilles - Vernouillet 8 km
Tel (33) 01 39 71 64 02

Saint-Martin - Triel-sur-Seine 9 km
Tel (33) 01 39 70 32 00

Le Bon Vivant - Poissy 15 km - Tel (33) 01 39 65 02 14

Château de Preisch

15	7	6

Sur cet espace frontalier de 107 ha, dont la moitié de forêts, trois 9 trous combinables ont été dessinés, mais le parcours de référence réunit France et Luxembourg (Allemagne vient d'être homologué). Trois trous sont en forêt, une demi-douzaine d'autres mettent pas mal d'eau en jeu (on ne la voit pas toujours), les autres sont assez classiques, avec des buttes pour paysager l'espace, et peu d'arbres. Le vent peut y jouer un rôle d'autant plus important que l'ensemble est assez long, et plus encore quand le temps est hostile. L'attaque des greens n'en sera pas facilitée, car leur pente générale est souvent très marquée. Il est difficile d'espérer maîtriser ce parcours sans l'avoir joué plusieurs fois, car il ne faut pas se fier à l'apparente franchise qu'offrent des fairways un peu "boulevards", qui mériteraient un tracé plus imaginatif. Au moins, les frappeurs pourront s'y déchaîner. En résumé, un ensemble très honorable, bien construit, et sans doute un peu difficile pour les débutants.

In this frontier region of some 107 hectares, one half of which is forest, there are three 9-hole courses, but the main course seems to be the France and Luxembourg (Germany has recently been given a seal of approval). Three holes run through a forest, half a dozen others bring water into play (not always visibly so) and the rest is classical in style, with sand-hills and few trees. The wind can be an important factor, especially since the whole course is long and plays even longer in rough weather. Attacking the pins is never easy because of the very marked slopes on the greens. It would be hard to imagine getting the better of this course without at least a few practice rounds, and you should be wary of the apparent openness of the wide fairways, which might have deserved a more imaginative layout. At least the big-hitters can enjoy themselves. A very respectful, well-designed course but perhaps a little difficult for beginners.

Château de Preisch — 1997

1, rue du Vieux Moulin
F - 57570 BASSE RENTGEN

Office	Secrétariat	(33) 03 82 83 00 00
Pro shop	Pro-shop	no pro shop
Fax	Fax	(33) 03 82 83 00 09
Web		www.golf-de-preisch.com
Situation	Situation	Luxembourg, 13 km
Annual closure	Fermeture annuelle	24/12→2/1
Weekly closure	Fermeture hebdomadaire	

Monday(lundi) from 01/11 to 31/03

Fees main season / Tarifs haute saison	18 holes	
	Week days / Semaine	We/Bank holidays / We/Férié
Individual Individuel	€ 63	€ 85
Couple Couple	€ 126	€ 170

Juniors & students under 25: € 44 / 49 (We)

Caddie Caddie no — Electric Trolley Chariot électrique yes
Buggy Voiturette yes — Clubs Clubs yes

Credit cards Cartes de crédit
VISA - Eurocard - MasterCard - AMEX - DC

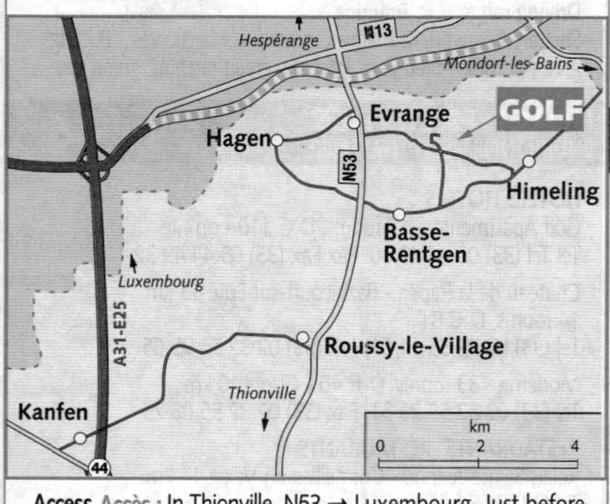

Access Accès : In Thionville, N53 → Luxembourg. Just before Evrange, turn right → Himeling. Golf on left hand side.
Map 4 on page 166 Carte 4 Page 166

GOLF COURSE — PARCOURS — 15/20

Site	Site	
Maintenance	Entretien	
Architect	Architecte	William Amick
Type	Type	inland, forest
Relief	Relief	
Water in play	Eau en jeu	
Exp. to wind	Exposé au vent	
Trees in play	Arbres en jeu	

Scorecard / Carte de score	Chp. / Chp.	Mens / Mess.	Ladies / Da.
Length Long.	6448	6081	5101
Par	72	72	72
Slope system	133	133	123

Advised golfing ability / Niveau de jeu recommandé: 0 12 24 36
Hcp required — Handicap exigé: 50 / 36 (We)

CLUB HOUSE & AMENITIES — CLUB HOUSE ET ANNEXES — 7/10

Pro shop — Pro-shop
Driving range — Practice
Sheltered couvert 25 mats - On grass sur herbe no - Putting-green putting-green yes - Pitching-green pitching green yes

HOTEL FACILITIES — ENVIRONNEMENT HOTELIER — 6/10

HOTELS HÔTELS
Le Parc - 124 rooms, D € 158 - Mondorf-les-Bains (Lux.) 7 km
Tel (352) 23 66 60, Fax (352) 23 66 10 93

Hôtel de la Frontière - Frisange (Luxembourg) 3 km
18 rooms, D € 70
Tel (352) 23 61 51, Fax (352) 23 66 17 53

RESTAURANTS RESTAURANTS
Léa Linster - Frisange (Luxembourg) 3 km
Tel (352) 23 66 84 11

L'Agath - Hesperange (Luxembourg) 14 km
Tel (352) 48 86 87

La Rameaudière - Ellange Gare (Mondorf) 9 km
Tel (352) 23 66 10 63

Chaumont-en-Vexin

14	6	4

C'est à la fois l'aîné et le voisin de Rebetz, dans un site constitué de deux plateaux de niveaux très différents (un peu physique pour les seniors !). L'entrée comme le château en font un lieu assez prestigieux, mais pas trop luxueux. En fait, c'est une belle "maison de campagne". Dessiné par Donald Harradine, le parcours est plutôt franc, même si certains dénivellés, quelques greens élevés, ou à plateaux obligent à réfléchir et à prendre des risques. Très varié de décor comme de tracé, les 18 trous constituent pourtant un ensemble cohérent. Si les difficultés dépendent pour beaucoup de la vitesse des greens, il faut être constamment attentif, car quelques ruisseaux et de puissants arbres menacent constamment. Pour la beauté du cadre et l'intérêt d'un parcours amusant à tous niveaux, Chaumont-en-Vexin (ou Bertichère comme on le nomme aussi) mérite une visite, même si ce n'est pas tout à fait un "grand" parcours. Le drainage a amélioré les parties basses du lieu, et l'arrosage automatique es parties hautes !

The driveway and the castle make this a very prestigious location but not that luxurious. In fact it is more like a beautiful "country house". The course, designed by Donald Harradine, is candid enough, although a few slopes, elevated greens and plateaux call for some serious thought and risk calculation. Although very varied in setting and layout, the 18 holes form a rather consistent whole, and while the difficulty here depends for a large part on the speed of the greens, you have to be constantly on your toes owing to the threat of streams and some sturdy trees. Chaumont-en-Vexin (or Bertichère as it is often called) is fun for golfers of all abilities owing to the beauty of the setting and appeal of the course. Even though nobody would call this a "great" course, it is well worth a visit. Drainage has much improved the lower part of the layout and automatic irrigation the upper section.

Golf de Chaumont-en-Vexin — 1968

Château de Bertichère
F - 60240 CHAUMONT-EN-VEXIN

Office	Secrétariat	(33) 03 44 49 00 81
Pro shop	Pro-shop	(33) 03 44 49 00 81
Fax	Fax	(33) 03 44 49 32 71
Web	www.golf-paris.net	
Situation	Situation	Pontoise (pop. 27 150), 25 km
Annual closure	Fermeture annuelle	no
Weekly closure	Fermeture hebdomadaire	no

Fees main season Tarifs haute saison	Week days Semaine	We/Bank holidays We/Férié
		18 holes
Individual Individuel	€ 33	€ 55
Couple Couple	€ 66	€ 110

Under 18: € 29 (W/e) - Seniors (Wednesday/mercredi) & Ladies (Thursday/jeudi):

Caddie Caddie no **Electric Trolley** Chariot électrique yes

Buggy Voiturette yes **Clubs** Clubs yes

Credit cards Cartes de crédit
VISA - CB - Eurocard - MasterCard

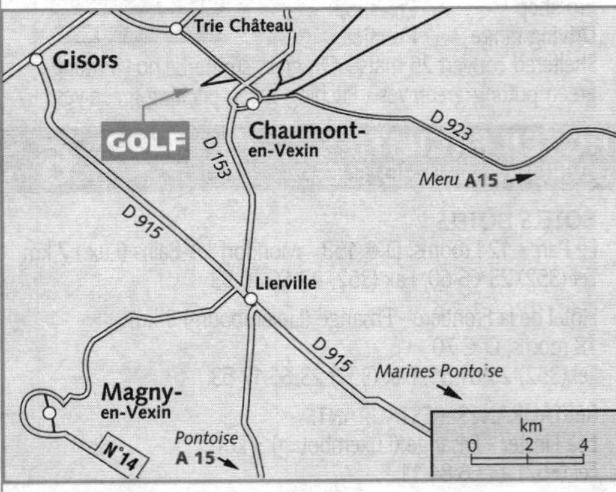

Access Accès : Paris A15 → Pontoise, N14 → Magny-en-Vexin, D153 → Chaumont-en-Vexin. Chaumont → Golf Bertichère.

Map 1 on page 160 Carte 1 Page 160

GOLF COURSE — PARCOURS — 14/20

Site	Site	
Maintenance	Entretien	
Architect	Architecte	Donald Harradine
Type	Type	parkland, hilly
Relief	Relief	
Water in play	Eau en jeu	
Exp. to wind	Exposé au vent	
Trees in play	Arbres en jeu	

Scorecard Carte de score	Chp. Chp.	Mens Mess.	Ladies Da.
Length Long.	6137	5720	5089
Par	72	72	72
Slope system	144	138	135

Advised golfing ability Niveau de jeu recommandé — 0 12 24 36

Hcp required Handicap exigé — no

CLUB HOUSE & AMENITIES — CLUB HOUSE ET ANNEXES — 6/10

Pro shop Pro-shop
Driving range Practice
Sheltered couvert 12 mats - On grass sur herbe yes - Putting-green putting-green yes - Pitching-green pitching green yes

HOTEL FACILITIES — ENVIRONNEMENT HOTELIER — 4/10

HOTELS HÔTELS

Golf Apartments - 17 rooms, D € 110 - on site
Tel Tel (33) 03 44 49 00, Fax Fax (33) 03 44 49 32

Château de la Rapée - Bazincourt-sur-Epte 13 km
14 rooms, D € 81
Tel (33) 02 32 55 11 61, Fax (33) 02 32 55 95 65

Moderne - 33 rooms, D € 40 - Gisors 10 km
Tel (33) 02 32 55 23 51, Fax (33) 02 32 55 08 75

RESTAURANTS RESTAURANTS

Relais Sainte-Jeanne - Cormeilles-en-Vexin 14 km
Tel (33) 01 34 66 61 56

Le Cappeville - Gisors 10 km - Tel (33) 02 32 55 11 08

Chiquito - Méry-sur-Oise 27 km - Tel (33) 03 30 36 40 23

Cheverny

14 | 7 | 6

A proximité immédiate du château historique de Cheverny, ce parcours contribue favorablement au "parcours golfique" des Châteaux de la Loire. Il se déroule en partie en forêt, mais aussi autour de l'étang de la Rousselière. De nombreux petits obstacles d'eau apportent des éléments de jeu bienvenus dans un espace très plat. L'architecte Olivier van der Vynckt a très peu bougé le terrain, recherché la subtilité des formes, notamment au niveau des alentours de green, mais on aurait souhaité que le terrain soit davantage modelé pour lui donner "de la hauteur", ou les différentes tontes plus contrastées pour mieux définir les trous dans cet espace, et donner de meilleurs points de repère : on se trompe facilement de club quand on ne connaît pas bien le parcours. Le rythme de jeu est plaisant, les différents départs permettent de l'adapter à tous les niveaux, d'autant qu'il n'est pas nécessaire d'être un très fin technicien. Une réalisation de bonne facture, avec un club-house sympathique et une bonne table.

In the immediate vicinity of the historic Château de Cheverny, the course of the same name is one of a trail of golfing venues amidst the castles of the Loire valley. It is laid out partly through a forest but also around a lake. Numerous minor water hazards add welcome spice to a very flat setting. Architect Olivier van der Vynckt moved very little earth and preferred a more subtle touch particularly around the greens. However, a little more shaping of terrain to give it more height and greater contrast between lengths of grass would have been welcome, if only to create greater definition for individual holes and clearer points of reference. You can easily choose the wrong club when you don't know the course well enough. Overall, the balance is pleasing and the difference in tee-boxes makes this a course for all abilities, especially since you don't really need to be a single-figure handicapper. A good quality course with a friendly club-house and good food.

Golf de Cheverny — 1988

La Rousselière
F - 41700 CHEVERNY

Office	Secrétariat	(33) 02 54 79 24 70
Pro shop	Pro-shop	(33) 02 54 79 24 70
Fax	Fax	(33) 02 54 79 25 52
Web	www.golf-cheverny.com	
Situation	Situation	Blois (pop. 49 310), 15 km
Annual closure	Fermeture annuelle	no
Weekly closure	Fermeture hebdomadaire	no
Fees main season	Tarifs haute saison	full day

	Week days Semaine	We/Bank holidays We/Férié
Individual Individuel	€ 50	€ 50
Couple Couple	€ 100	€ 100

Under 25: – 50%

Caddie Caddie no **Electric Trolley** Chariot électrique no

Buggy Voiturette yes **Clubs** Clubs yes

Credit cards Cartes de crédit
VISA - CB - Eurocard - MasterCard - AMEX - DC

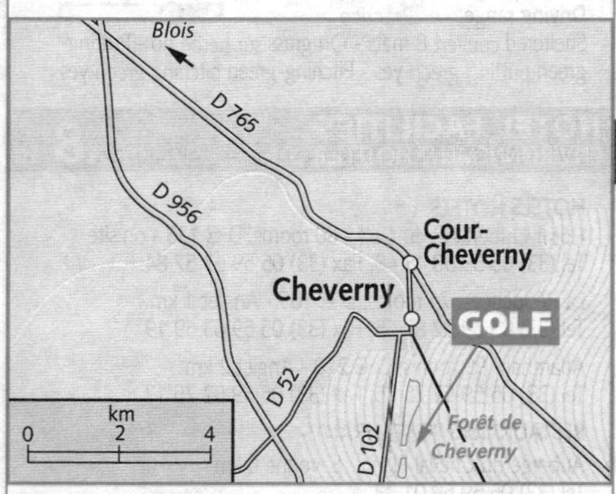

Access Accès : A10 Paris-Bordeaux, Exit (Sortie) Blois → D765 → Romorantin → Cour-Cheverny, → Golf
Map 3 on page 164 Carte 3 Page 164

GOLF COURSE — PARCOURS — 14/20

Site	Site	
Maintenance	Entretien	
Architect	Architecte	O. van der Vynckt
Type	Type	forest, open country
Relief	Relief	
Water in play	Eau en jeu	
Exp. to wind	Exposé au vent	
Trees in play	Arbres en jeu	

Scorecard Carte de score	Chp. Chp.	Mens Mess.	Ladies Da.
Length Long.	5832	5682	4780
Par	71	71	71
Slope system	120	120	107

Advised golfing ability Niveau de jeu recommandé — 0 12 24 36

Hcp required Handicap exigé — no

CLUB HOUSE & AMENITIES — CLUB HOUSE ET ANNEXES — 7/10

Pro shop Pro-shop
Driving range Practice

Sheltered couvert 4 mats - On grass sur herbe no, 16 mats open air - Putting-green putting-green yes - Pitching-green pitching green yes

HOTEL FACILITIES — ENVIRONNEMENT HOTELIER — 6/10

HOTELS HÔTELS

Château du Breuil - 18 rooms, D € 120 - Cour-Cheverny 2 km
Tel (33) 02 54 44 20 20, Fax (33) 02 54 44 30 40

Les Trois Marchands - Cour-Cheverny 2 km
24 rooms, D € 42
Tel (33) 02 54 79 96 44, Fax (33) 02 54 79 25 60

Saint Hubert - 20 rooms, D € 46 - Cour-Cheverny 2 km
Tel (33) 02 54 79 96 60, Fax (33) 02 54 79 21 17

RESTAURANTS RESTAURANTS

Les Trois Marchands - Cour-Cheverny 2 km
Tel (33) 02 54 79 96 44

Restaurant du Golf - Tel (33) 02 54 79 23 02

Chiberta

16 | 6 | 8

Un des superbes exemples français de links, signé par le légendaire Tom Simpson. L'essentiel de son dessin a été préservé, même si les aspects les plus sauvages ont été gommés par l'arrosage automatique et certaines "améliorations" pas toujours inspirées. La disparition de quelques difficultés et de quelques arbres a rendu le parcours accessible à tous les niveaux, surtout par beau temps bien entendu. Les greens sont de bonne qualité, les obstacles bien visibles, la stratégie assez évidente, l'absence de relief et le confort d'un sol sablonneux rendent la marche plaisante. Mais, quand le vent souffle, Chiberta devient un test où la maîtrise des trajectoires de balles et du petit jeu sont essentiels. A jouer sans réserve, y compris par mauvais temps. On pourrait presque dire surtout par grand vent ! Les bâtiments d'accueil sont refaits à neuf, ce qui était indispensable dans un club aussi fréquenté. On parle d'une réhabilitation de ce tracé selon les volontés de Simpson. Quelle bonne idée !

One of the great French examples of a links course, designed by the legendary Tom Simpson. The original basic design has been preserved, although the wilder features have been smoothed away by automatic sprinklers and a number of "improvements" which are not quite as inspired as we might have hoped. With the disappearance of a number of difficulties and a few trees, Chiberta is more amenable for all golfers especially in fine weather, as is always the case on a seaside course. The greens are good, the hazards clearly visible, strategy is pretty obvious, and the absence of any real relief with the comfort of sandy soil make for a pleasant walk. But once the wind starts to blow, Chiberta becomes a test where ball-control and tight short game are essential. Reception facilities have been upgraded, a necessary step for such a busy club, and there is talk of restyling the course the way Simpson would have wanted. A great idea.

Golf de Chiberta — 1927

104, bd des Plages
F - 64600 ANGLET

Office	Secrétariat	(33) 05 59 52 51 10
Pro shop	Pro-shop	(33) 05 59 63 17 87
Fax	Fax	(33) 05 59 52 51 11
E-mail		golf.chiberta@wanadoo.fr
Situation	Situation	Biarritz, 3 km
Annual closure	Fermeture annuelle	no
Weekly closure	Fermeture hebdomadaire	thursday/jeudi

(except school holidays)

Fees main season Tarifs haute saison — 18 holes

	Week days / Semaine	We/Bank holidays / We/Férié
Individual Individuel	€ 70	€ 70
Couple Couple	€ 120	€ 120

Under 21: € 28 / under 25: € 37

Caddie Caddie on request **Electric Trolley** Char. électrique yes

Buggy Voiturette no **Clubs** Clubs yes

Credit cards Cartes de crédit
VISA - CB - Eurocard - MasterCard - AMEX

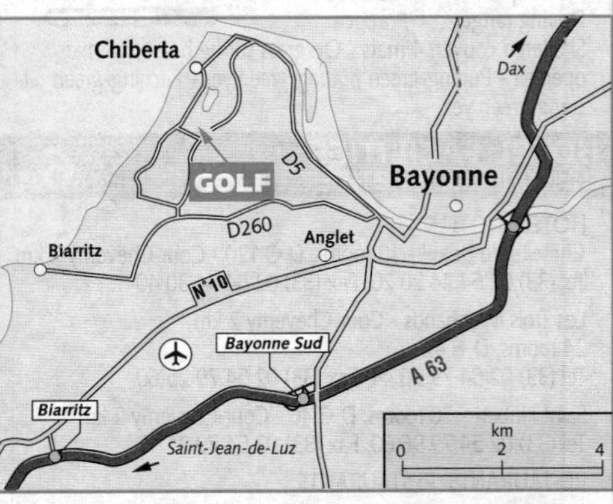

Access Accès : A63, Exit (Sortie) Biarritz. Biarritz → Anglet
Map 12 on page 182 Carte 12 Page 182

GOLF COURSE — PARCOURS — 16/20

Site	Site	
Maintenance	Entretien	
Architect	Architecte	Tom Simpson
Type	Type	links, forest
Relief	Relief	
Water in play	Eau en jeu	
Exp. to wind	Exposé au vent	
Trees in play	Arbres en jeu	

Scorecard Carte de score	**Chp.** Chp.	**Mens** Mess.	**Ladies** Da.
Length Long.	5647	5261	4727
Par	70	70	70
Slope system	125	124	124

Advised golfing ability Niveau de jeu recommandé — 0 12 24 36

Hcp required Handicap exigé — 35 (30 high season)

CLUB HOUSE & AMENITIES — CLUB HOUSE ET ANNEXES — 6/10

Pro shop Pro-shop
Driving range Practice
Sheltered couvert 8 mats - On grass sur herbe no - Putting-green putting-green yes - Pitching-green pitching green yes

HOTEL FACILITIES — ENVIRONNEMENT HOTELIER — 8/10

HOTELS HÔTELS

Hôtel Chiberta et du Golf - 80 rooms, D € 133 - on site
Tel (33) 05 59 58 48 48, Fax (33) 05 59 63 57 84

La Résidence - 71 rooms, D € 105 - Anglet 1 km
Tel (33) 05 59 52 87 65, Fax (33) 05 59 63 59 19

Atlanthal - 99 rooms, D € 210 - Anglet 2 km
Tel (33) 05 59 52 75 75, Fax (33) 05 59 52 75 13

RESTAURANTS RESTAURANTS

Auberge du Cheval Blanc - Bayonne 6 km
Tel (33) 05 59 59 01 33

François Miura - Bayonne 6 km - Tel (33) 05 59 59 49 89

Le Bayonnais - Bayonne 6 km - Tel (33) 05 59 25 61 19

Claux Amic

13	8	6

A côté de très jolis trous (le 2 ou le 7), d'autres paraissent d'une étonnante banalité, certains greens dépourvus de défenses, et on sent que ce parcours dessiné par Jean-Pascal Fourès n'a pas été achevé par le même architecte, tant le style est inégal. La forêt de chênes est belle, les fairways étroits sont bordés de roughs très améliorés. Ils obligent néanmoins à la prudence, ou à la précision si l'on veut bien scorer. A 600 mètres d'altitude, les points de vue sur la région de Cannes et la mer sont magnifiques, et le climat contraste en été avec les chaleurs du littoral. Les joueurs assez droits prendront cependant du plaisir à faire une belle balade en moyenne montagne, plutôt que de vouloir batailler contre un parcours toujours vainqueur. Comme il est plutôt accidenté, on leur conseille la voiturette. Après la réfection du lac du 1, la création de nouveaux départs, et la rénovation du club-house, le nettoyage des sous-bois continue à faire progresser le parcours.

This layout, designed by Jean-Pascal Fourès, is so inconsistent in style as to leave the impression of a course that was not completed by the same architect. Next to some very pretty holes (N° 2 or N° 7), others seem amazingly ordinary while some of the greens are devoid of any protection whatsoever. The oak-forest is a real beauty, the tight fairways are edged with rough that has been much improved. For a good card, they call for great care or extreme precision (or both). But at 600 m above-sea level, the views over the Mediterranean and the region of Cannes are magnificent and the climate in summer is a pleasant contrast to the heat on the Riviera. Straight-hitters will have more fun roaming through this upland terrain than they will trying to take on the course which always ends up the winner. Being rather hilly, we recommend a buggy every time. This course continues to get better with the creation of new tee-boxes, a refurbished club-house and the clearing of undergrowth.

Golf du Claux Amic — 1992

Lieu-dit "Claux Amic"
F - 06130 GRASSE

Office	Secrétariat	(33) 04 93 60 55 44
Pro shop	Pro-shop	(33) 04 93 60 55 44
Fax	Fax	(33) 04 93 60 55 19
Web	www.claux-amic.com	
Situation	Situation	Grasse (pop. 41 380), 5 km
Annual closure	Fermeture annuelle	no
Weekly closure	Fermeture hebdomadaire	no

Fees main season Tarifs haute saison	18 holes	
	Week days Semaine	**We/Bank holidays** We/Férié
Individual Individuel	€ 60	€ 60
Couple Couple	€ 120	€ 120

Juniors: € 30 / Students: € 45

Caddie Caddie no **Electric Trolley** Chariot électrique yes

Buggy Voiturette yes **Clubs** Clubs yes

Credit cards Cartes de crédit
VISA - CB - Eurocard - MasterCard

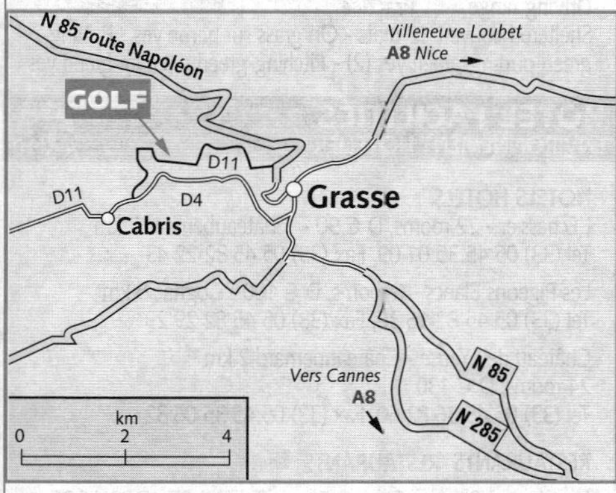

Access Accès : Cannes → Grasse (Motorway).
In Grasse, → Golf Claux-Amic
Map 14 on page 187 Carte 14 Page 187

GOLF COURSE — PARCOURS 13/20

Site	Site	
Maintenance	Entretien	
Architect	Architecte	Jean-Pascal Fourès
Type	Type	forest, hilly
Relief	Relief	
Water in play	Eau en jeu	
Exp. to wind	Exposé au vent	
Trees in play	Arbres en jeu	

Scorecard Carte de score	**Chp.** Chp.	**Mens** Mess.	**Ladies** Da.
Length Long.	5896	5334	4332
Par	72	72	72
Slope system	133	122	114

Advised golfing ability Niveau de jeu recommandé — 0 12 24 36

Hcp required Handicap exigé 36

CLUB HOUSE & AMENITIES — CLUB HOUSE ET ANNEXES 8/10

Pro shop Pro-shop
Driving range Practice
Sheltered couvert 5 mats - On grass sur herbe yes - Putting-green putting-green yes - Pitching-green pitching green yes

HOTEL FACILITIES — ENVIRONNEMENT HOTELIER 6/10

HOTELS HÔTELS

Bastide Saint Antoine - Grasse 6 km
11 rooms, D € 275
Tel (33) 04 93 70 94 94, Fax (33) 04 93 70 94 95

L'Horizon - 22 rooms, D € 80- Cabris 3 km
Tel (33) 04 93 60 51 69, Fax (33) 04 93 60 56 29

Hôtel du Patti - Grasse 5 km
61 rooms, D € 89
Tel (33) 04 93 36 01 00, Fax (33) 04 93 36 36 40

RESTAURANTS RESTAURANTS

Bastide Saint Antoine - Grasse 6 km - Tel (33) 04 93 70 94 94
Vieux Château - Cabris 3 km - Tel (33) 04 93 60 50 12
Arnaud - Grasse 5 km - Tel (33) 04 93 36 44 88

Cognac

13 | 7 | 5

Dans une région aussi touristique en raison de ses vignobles, la création de ce golf était bienvenue, et on notera dès l'arrivée un club-house sympathique, aménagé dans une ancienne ferme. Le paysage est un mélange plaisant de campagne et de bocages, au relief modéré. L'architecture du parcours est agréable visuellement et très honnête sur le plan du jeu, sans recherche excessive d'originalité. Les coups imprécis sont rarement pénalisés, car les fairways sont assez larges, les greens sont peu complexes et les bunkers rarement très dangereux. Seuls deux trous comportent des obstacles d'eau. Visiblement, alors que l'on dessinait à l'époque des parcours "de championnat" qui n'en ont jamais reçu, ce parcours a été destiné en priorité aux joueurs moyens, c'est un "produit" utile et de qualité pour la majorité des golfeurs, de la région ou de passage. Les meilleurs joueurs ne s'y ennuieront pas. Une ombre au tableau, la fragilité du parcours quand il pleut, que les drainages n'ont pas totalement résolu.

The opening of this course was most welcome in a region where vineyards attract tourists in their droves. The landscape is a pleasing "blend" (this is cognac country, after all) of open country and green pastures. The design is visually attractive and very fair in golfing terms, albeit not excessively original. Wayward shots are only rarely heavily penalized as the fairways are wide, the greens comparatively straightforward and the bunkers seldom too dangerous. There are water hazards on two holes only. At a time when people were laying out courses for championships that were never actually held, this course was designed for the average golfer, thus making it a useful "product" of considerable class for the majority of golfers, whether local or passing through, but even the best players will enjoy their golf here. The one flaw is the state of the course after heavy rain, a problem that new drainage systems have not completely cleared up.

Golf du Cognac — 1988
Saint-Brice
F - 16100 COGNAC

Office Secrétariat (33) 05 45 32 18 17
Pro shop Pro-shop (33) 05 45 32 37 60
Fax Fax (33) 05 45 35 10 76
Web www.golfducognac.asso.fr
Situation Situation Cognac (pop. 19 520), 5 km
Angoulême (pop. 42 880), 32 km

Annual closure Fermeture annuelle — no
Weekly closure Fermeture hebdomadaire — Tuesday
(mardi) 30/9→30/4

Fees main season Tarifs haute saison — full day

	Week days Semaine	We/Bank holidays We/Férié
Individual Individuel	€ 49	€ 49
Couple Couple	€ 84	€ 84

Students: € 20

Caddie Caddie no **Electric Trolley** Chariot électrique yes
Buggy Voiturette yes **Clubs** Clubs yes
Credit cards Cartes de crédit
VISA - CB - Eurocard - MasterCard

Saintes
Royan
A10
D 731
E 603
Cognac
GOLF
Saint-Brice
D 15
Julienne
Charente
N°141
D 731
km
0 2 4
Jarnac
Angoulême

Access Accès : Cognac N141 → Angoulême, D15 → Saint-Brice, → Golf
Map 9 on page 176 Carte 9 Page 176

GOLF COURSE
PARCOURS — **13**/20

Site Site
Maintenance Entretien
Architect Architecte — Jean Garaïalde
Type Type — copse, country
Relief Relief
Water in play Eau en jeu
Exp. to wind Exposé au vent
Trees in play Arbres en jeu

Scorecard Carte de score	Chp. Chp.	Mens Mess.	Ladies Da.
Length Long.	6125	5701	4929
Par	72	72	72
Slope system	135	130	129

Advised golfing ability Niveau de jeu recommandé — 0 12 24 36
Hcp required Handicap exigé — no

CLUB HOUSE & AMENITIES
CLUB HOUSE ET ANNEXES — **7**/10

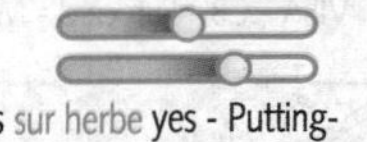

Pro shop Pro-shop
Driving range Practice
Sheltered couvert 12 mats - On grass sur herbe yes - Putting-green putting-green yes (2) - Pitching-green pitching green yes

HOTEL FACILITIES
ENVIRONNEMENT HOTELIER — **5**/10

HOTELS HÔTELS
L'Echassier - 22 rooms, D € 90 - Châteaubernard 2 km
Tel (33) 05 45 35 01 09, Fax (33) 05 45 32 22 43

Les Pigeons Blancs - 6 rooms, D € 100 - Cognac 5 km
Tel (33) 05 45 82 16 36, Fax (33) 05 45 82 29 29

Château de l'Yeuse - Châteaubernard 2 km
24 rooms, D € 130
Tel (33) 05 45 36 82 60, Fax (33) 05 45 35 06 32

RESTAURANTS RESTAURANTS
Les Pigeons Blancs - Cognac 5 km - Tel (33) 05 45 82 16 36
L'Echassier - Châteaubernard 2 km - Tel (33) 05 45 35 01 09

Courson *Lilas/Orange*

16 | 7 | 3

Grand club omnisports, le Stade Français a créé sur ce terrain de 110 hectares un complexe golfique composé de quatre neuf trous, dont la configuration idéale est Vert-Noir et Lilas-Orange. Ce dernier 18 trous est le plus court, mais pas moins exigeant techniquement. Dans cet immense espace vierge, Bob von Hagge a beaucoup modelé le terrain pour isoler les fairways, ce qui lui donne un aspect un peu lunaire. L'esthétique est assez américaine, avec une définition très précise des fairways, sans refuser pour autant certaines références aux links. Le "Orange" est assez accidenté, sans être vraiment fatigant : après quatre trous assez tranquilles, il en offre cinq de toute beauté, où les scores peuvent s'alourdir. Plus classique, le "Lilas" met en jeu quelques redoutables obstacles d'eau, généralement plus intimidants visuellement que dangereux. Ici, l'important est d'être précis, et de bien maîtriser le petit jeu quand on manque les greens. Un parcours méticuleusement dessiné.

Le Stade Français, one of the country's leading multi-sports clubs, has created a golf complex over some 110 hectares formed from four 9-hole courses. The ideal combinations are Vert/Noir and Lilas/Orange. The latter is the shortest but technically just as demanding. Over a huge area of untouched land, Bob van Hagge shifted a lot of earth to isolate the fairways and form a sort of lunar landscape. Although rather American in style with now very clearly defined fairways, there is something of the links about all four courses. The "Orange" course is hilly but not too tiring. After four average holes, the next five are simply beautiful... The "Lilas" course involves some formidable water hazards, which are generally more intimidating to the eye than dangerous to the score. What matters here is straight-hitting and a sharp short game when you miss the greens. A meticulously designed course.

Golf Courson-Monteloup — 1991

Stade Français
F - 91680 COURSON-MONTELOUP

Office Secrétariat (33) 01 64 58 80 80
Pro shop Pro-shop (33) 01 64 58 80 80
Fax Fax (33) 01 64 58 83 06
Web www.golf-stadefrancais.com
Situation Situation Paris, 34 km
Annual closure Fermeture annuelle 25/12→1/1
Weekly closure Fermeture hebdomadaire
Wednesday/mercredi

Fees main season Tarifs haute saison — full day

	Week days Semaine	We/Bank holidays We/Férié
Individual Individuel	€ 47	€ 70
Couple Couple	€ 94	€ 140

Tuesday (mardi): € 30 / Under 24: € 34 / 37 (We)

Caddie Caddie no **Electric Trolley** Chariot électrique yes
Buggy Voiturette yes **Clubs** Clubs yes
Credit cards Cartes de crédit
VISA - CB - Eurocard - MasterCard

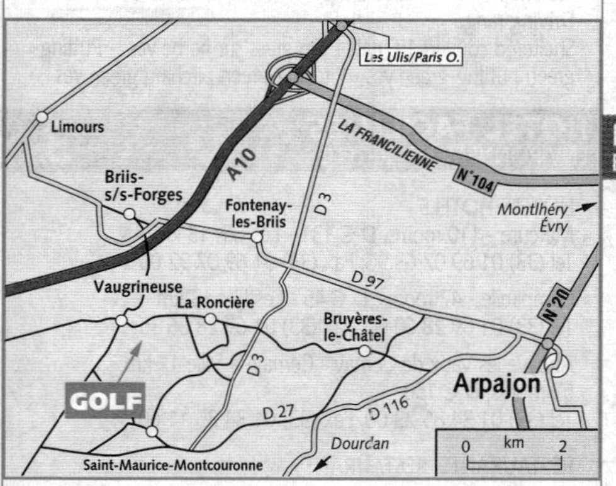

Access Accès : A10, Exit (Sortie) les Ulis, D3 → Dourdan, Château de Courson, La Roncière, → Golf
Map 15 on page 188 Carte 15 Page 188

GOLF COURSE — PARCOURS — 16/20

Site Site
Maintenance Entretien
Architect Architecte — Robert von Hagge
Type Type — open country
Relief Relief
Water in play Eau en jeu
Exp. to wind Exposé au vent
Trees in play Arbres en jeu

Scorecard Carte de score	Chp. Chp.	Mens Mess.	Ladies Da.
Length Long.	6184	5753	4555
Par	72	72	72
Slope system	135	126	120

Advised golfing ability 0 12 24 36
Niveau de jeu recommandé
Hcp required Handicap exigé 35 / 24 (We)

CLUB HOUSE & AMENITIES — CLUB HOUSE ET ANNEXES — 7/10

Pro shop Pro-shop
Driving range Practice
Sheltered couvert 15 mats - On grass sur herbe yes - Putting-green putting-green yes - Pitching-green pitching green yes

HOTEL FACILITIES — ENVIRONNEMENT HOTELIER — 3/10

HOTELS HÔTELS
Mercure - 110 rooms, D € 131 - Les Ulis 13 km
Tel (33) 01 69 07 63 96, Fax (33) 01 69 07 92 00

Campanile - 47 rooms, D € 45 - Les Ulis 13 km
Tel (33) 01 69 28 60 60, Fax (33) 01 69 28 06 35

Abbaye les Vaux de Cernay - Cernay-la-Ville 11 km
57 rooms, D € 150
Tel (33) 01 34 85 23 00, Fax (33) 01 34 85 11 60

RESTAURANTS RESTAURANTS
Le Saint-Clément - Arpajon 10 km - Tel (33) 01 64 90 21 01

Auberge de la Cressonière - Saint-Chéron 9 km
Tel (33) 01 64 56 60 55

Courson *Vert/Noir*

17 | 7 | 3

Les quatre 9 trous de Courson constituent une véritable création en trois dimensions à partir d'un terrain sans grand relief. Sur le "Vert", il vaut mieux partir des départs avancés, car sa longueur peut décourager les joueurs moyens (les pars 4 sont redoutables). Le "Noir" est moins brutal, parfois accidenté, mais les derniers trous mettent beaucoup d'eau en jeu. Le paysage ne manque pas de majesté, et les trous ont été bien isolés par la création de buttes spectaculaires, dont l'aspect visuel peut surprendre ! Très protégés par de beaux bunkers, les greens sont très vastes et souvent à multiples plateaux : il faut choisir celui où est le drapeau pour ne pas craindre les "trois-putts". Comme les par 5 sont difficilement prenables en deux coups, il est difficile d'y scorer très bien. Un vrai parcours de championnat, qui vous apprend à jouer au golf, où il faut utiliser la tête autant que les clubs, pas très "naturel" peut-être, mais quel parti von Hagge a tiré d'un terrain au départ très banal !

The four 9-hole courses at Courson form a genuine 3-dimensional creation built out of terrain with no great natural relief. On the "Vert" course, swallow your pride and play from the forward tees; it's long enough to discourage any mid-handicapper. The "Noir" course is a little kinder and sometimes hilly, and the last few holes involve a lot of water. There is something very majestic about the landscape here, and the holes are clearly separated by spectacular sand-hills which from a visual point of view can come as a surprise. The greens are huge, often multi-tiered and defended by magnificent bunkers, so wayward approach shots are often greeted with 3 putts. And as the par 5s are tough to reach in two, a good score is not always easy. A real championship course which teaches you a thing or two about golf and where brains are almost as important as your clubs. Not very "natural", but von Hagge has squeezed an excellent course out of what was originally ordinary terrain.

Golf Courson-Monteloup — 1991

Stade Français
F - 91680 COURSON-MONTELOUP

Office	Secrétariat	(33) 01 64 58 80 80
Pro shop	Pro-shop	(33) 01 64 58 80 80
Fax	Fax	(33) 01 64 58 83 06
Web	www.golf-stadefrancais.com	
Situation	Situation	Paris, 34 km
Annual closure	Fermeture annuelle	25/12→1/1
Weekly closure	Fermeture hebdomadaire	

Wednesday/mercredi

Fees main season Tarifs haute saison — full day

	Week days / Semaine	We/Bank holidays / We/Férié
Individual Individuel	€ 47	€ 70
Couple Couple	€ 94	€ 140

Tuesday (mardi): € 30 / Under 24: € 34 / 37 (We)

Caddie Caddie no **Electric Trolley** Chariot électrique yes

Buggy Voiturette yes **Clubs** Clubs yes

Credit cards Cartes de crédit
VISA - CB - Eurocard - MasterCard

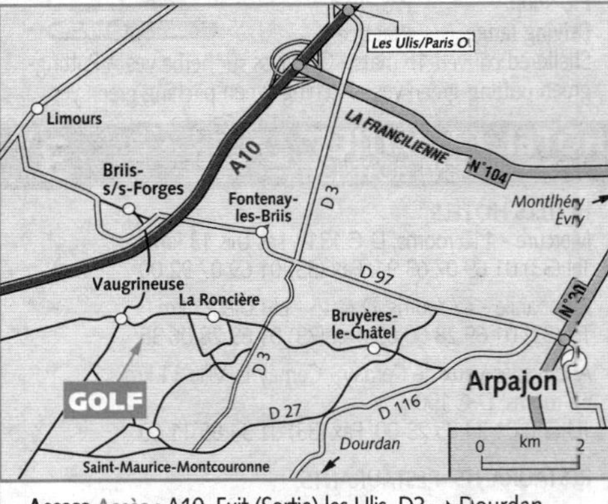

Access Accès : A10, Exit (Sortie) les Ulis, D3 → Dourdan, Château de Courson, La Roncière, → Golf
Map 15 on page 188 Carte 15 Page 188

GOLF COURSE — PARCOURS — 17/20

Site	Site	
Maintenance	Entretien	
Architect	Architecte	Robert von Hagge
Type	Type	open country
Relief	Relief	
Water in play	Eau en jeu	
Exp. to wind	Exposé au vent	
Trees in play	Arbres en jeu	

Scorecard / Carte de score	Chp. / Chp.	Mens / Mess.	Ladies / Da.
Length Long.	6557	6035	4803
Par	72	72	72
Slope system	134	129	125

Advised golfing ability / Niveau de jeu recommandé: 0 12 24 36
Hcp required Handicap exigé: 35 / 24 (We)

CLUB HOUSE & AMENITIES — CLUB HOUSE ET ANNEXES — 7/10

Pro shop Pro-shop
Driving range Practice
Sheltered couvert 15 mats - On grass sur herbe yes - Putting-green putting-green yes - Pitching-green pitching green yes

HOTEL FACILITIES — ENVIRONNEMENT HOTELIER — 3/10

HOTELS HÔTELS

Mercure - 110 rooms, D € 131 - Les Ulis 13 km
Tel (33) 01 69 07 63 96, Fax (33) 01 69 07 92 00

Campanile - 47 rooms, D € 45 - Les Ulis 13 km
Tel (33) 01 69 28 60 60, Fax (33) 01 69 28 06 35

Abbaye les Vaux de Cernay - Cernay-la-Ville 11 km
57 rooms, D € 150
Tel (33) 01 34 85 23 00, Fax (33) 01 34 85 11 60

RESTAURANTS RESTAURANTS

Le Saint-Clément - Arpajon 10 km - Tel (33) 01 64 90 21 01

Auberge de la Cressonière - Saint-Chéron 9 km
Tel (33) 01 64 56 60 55

Dieppe-Pourville

14	6	5

Un golf familial, dont le parcours tracé par le grand Willie Park en 1897 a été notablement modifié depuis, notamment après la dernière guerre et l'occupation. 9 des 27 trous d'avant-guerre n'ont pas été réouverts. L'ambiance, sans prétention, est très plaisante, comme la simplicité des équipements. On ne perd certes pas sa journée à jouer ici, entre amis et en famille, un golf décontracté et sportif. Situé en bord de mer, ce n'est pas exactement un links, étant donné la nature du terrain mais les conditions de jeu en sont souvent proches (attention au vent !). Pour accentuer cet aspect "maritime", quatre nouveaux trous ont été tracés sur la falaise, avec une vue imprenable. Le style du parcours reste très britannique, avec des greens bien protégés, mais souvent accessibles avec des "pitch and run". Sa longueur est raisonnable, mais les scores ne sont pas toujours tels qu'on pourrait les espérer en regardant la carte, plutôt aimable. Le relief est modéré, ce qui convient bien aux joueurs de tous âges comme de tous niveaux.

A family club whose course designed by the great Willie Park in 1897 has been considerably restyled over the years, particularly since the end of last war and the occupation and in fact 9 of the 27 pre-war holes were closed for good. The atmosphere is unpretentious and pleasant. You certainly will not waste your time spending a day's golfing here, with friends or the family, in a relaxed and very sporting atmosphere. Laid out along the sea-shore, this is not exactly a links course, given the nature of the terrain, but conditions of play are often very similar. To emphasize this "seaside" impression, four new holes have been laid out along the cliff-top and provide a breath-taking view. Dieppe is still a very British style course with well protected greens. It is a reasonable length, but scores are not always as low as you might have hoped for when looking at a card that looks friendly enough when starting out. Rather hilly but suitable for players of all abilities.

Dieppe-Pourville Golf Club — 1897

Route de Pourville
F - 76200 DIEPPE

Office	Secrétariat	(33) 02 35 84 25 05
Pro shop	Pro-shop	(33) 02 32 84 25 05
Fax	Fax	(33) 02 35 84 97 11
Web	www.golf-dieppe.com	
Situation	Situation	Dieppe (pop. 5 890), 2 km
Annual closure	Fermeture annuelle	no
Weekly closure	Fermeture hebdomadaire	no
Fees main season	Tarifs haute saison	18 holes

	Week days Semaine	We/Bank holidays We/Férié
Individual Individuel	€ 47	€ 52
Couple Couple	€ 94	€ 104

Juniors: – 50% / After 18:00, € 25

Caddie Caddie on request Electric Trolley Chariot électrique yes

Buggy Voiturette yes Clubs Clubs yes

Credit cards Cartes de crédit
VISA - CB - Eurocard - MasterCard

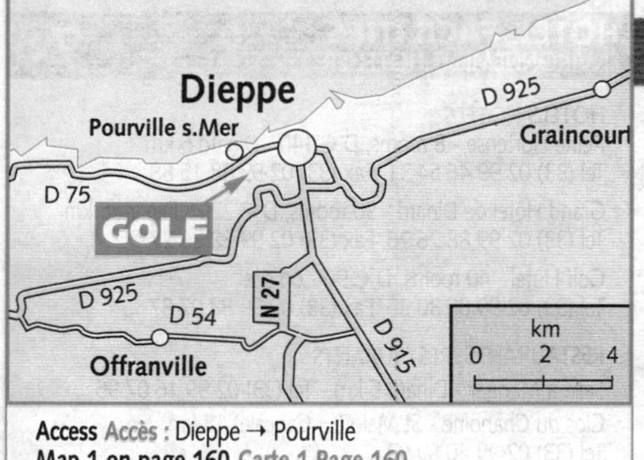

Access Accès : Dieppe → Pourville
Map 1 on page 160 Carte 1 Page 160

GOLF COURSE — PARCOURS — 14/20

Site	Site	
Maintenance	Entretien	
Architect	Architecte	Willie Park Jr
Type	Type	seaside course, links
Relief	Relief	
Water in play	Eau en jeu	
Exp. to wind	Exposé au vent	
Trees in play	Arbres en jeu	

Scorecard Carte de score	Chp. Chp.	Mens Mess.	Ladies Da.
Length Long.	5780	5534	4816
Par	70	70	70
Slope system	131	125	124

Advised golfing ability — 0 12 24 36
Niveau de jeu recommandé

Hcp required — Handicap exigé — no

CLUB HOUSE & AMENITIES — CLUB HOUSE ET ANNEXES — 6/10

Pro shop — Pro-shop
Driving range — Practice

Sheltered couvert 6 mats - On grass sur herbe yes - Putting-green putting-green yes - Pitching-green pitching green yes

HOTEL FACILITIES — ENVIRONNEMENT HOTELIER — 5/10

HOTELS HÔTELS

La Présidence - 89 rooms, D € 100 - Dieppe 2 km
Tel (33) 02 35 84 31 31, Fax (33) 02 35 84 86 70

Aguado - 54 rooms, D € 98 - Dieppe 2 km
Tel (33) 02 35 84 27 00, Fax (33) 02 35 06 17 61

La Terrasse - 22 rooms, D € 52 - Vastérival 9 km
Tel (33) 02 35 85 12 54, Fax (33) 02 35 85 11 70

RESTAURANTS RESTAURANTS

La Mélie - Dieppe 2 km - Tel (33) 02 35 84 21 19

Auberge du Trou Normand - Pourville, close
Tel (33) 02 35 84 59 84

Marmite Dieppoise - Dieppe 2 km - Tel (33) 02 35 84 24 26

Dinard

13	6	7

Ouvert en 1890, ce parcours a été, comme Biarritz, originellement dessiné par Willie Dunn, mais remanié depuis à tel point qu'il ne reste qu'une dizaine de trous d'une esthétique spécifiquement écossaise. Ils suffisent à faire de Dinard un golf à connaître. Sa longueur peut paraître dérisoire, même avec un par 68, mais attendez que le vent souffle un peu... il faut être alors spécialiste en balistique pour calculer les dérives ! Et un seul par 5 offre une franche occasion de birdie. Ici, le choix de club est difficile, et l'on se retrouve sans cesse "entre deux clubs" pour attaquer les drapeaux. Les greens sont bien défendus, et souvent de petite taille, ce qui oblige à une extrême précision. Un golf très amusant, à jouer avec les golfeurs de tous niveaux dans une ambiance sportive : c'est le rendez-vous de vacances de familles de grands golfeurs parisiens. L'arrosage des fairways a nettement amélioré l'entretien en été, et la vue sur la mer reste splendide par tous les temps, et exceptionnelle au petit matin ou au crépuscule.

Opened in 1890, this course was originally designed, like Biarritz, by Willie Dunn, but it has been restyled so many times over the years that only about ten holes have preserved their special Scottish flavour. And they alone are enough to make Dinard a course worth knowing. The length may appear derisory by today's standards, but when the wind howls, it feels and plays much longer. Specializing in ballistics can be a handy asset here to calculate flight and deviation. Only one par 5 provides a real birdie chance. Elsewhere, difficulties arise from club selection and players are often stuck "between two clubs" for their approach shots. The greens are frequently small and well defended, thus calling for extreme precision. An entertaining course with a great sporting atmosphere and a holiday rendez-vous for the families of top Parisian golfers. The watering of fairways has significantly improved green-keeping during summer months and the view over the Channel is splendid.

Golf de Dinard — 1890

Boulevard de la Houle
F - 35 800 SAINT-BRIAC-SUR-MER

Office	Secrétariat	(33) 02 99 88 32 07
Pro shop	Pro-shop	(33) 02 99 88 30 55
Fax	Fax	(33) 02 99 88 04 53
Web	www.dinardgolf.com	
Situation	Situation	Dinard (pop. 9 920), 5 km
Annual closure	Fermeture annuelle	no
Weekly closure	Fermeture hebdomadaire	no

Fees main season / Tarifs haute saison	18 holes	
	Week days / Semaine	We/Bank holidays / We/Férié
Individual Individuel	€ 59	€ 59
Couple Couple	€ 118	€ 118

Under 18: – 50%

Caddie Caddie no **Electric Trolley** Chariot électrique no

Buggy Voiturette yes **Clubs** Clubs yes

Credit cards Cartes de crédit
VISA - CB - Eurocard - MasterCard

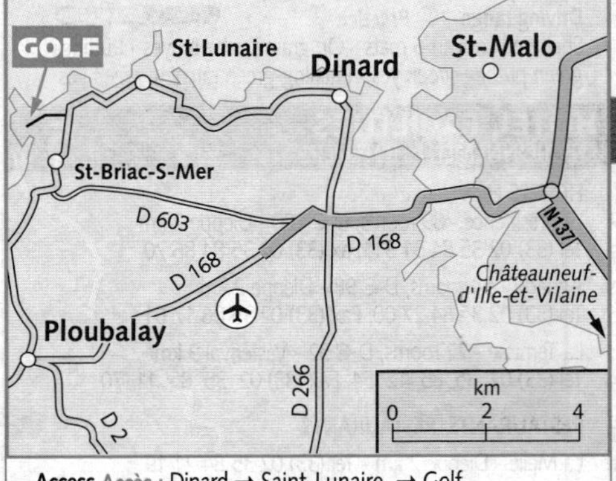

Access Accès : Dinard → Saint-Lunaire, → Golf
Map 5 on page 169 Carte 5 Page 169

GOLF COURSE — PARCOURS — 13/20

Site	Site	
Maintenance	Entretien	
Architect	Architecte	Willie Dunn
Type	Type	seaside course, links
Relief	Relief	
Water in play	Eau en jeu	
Exp. to wind	Exposé au vent	
Trees in play	Arbres en jeu	

Scorecard / Carte de score	Chp. / Chp.	Mens / Mess.	Ladies / Da.
Length Long.	5316	5043	4499
Par	68	68	68
Slope system	125	122	117

Advised golfing ability / Niveau de jeu recommandé: 0 12 24 36

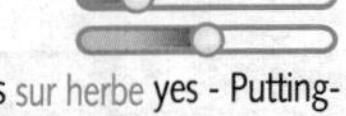

Hcp required Handicap exigé 35

CLUB HOUSE & AMENITIES — CLUB HOUSE ET ANNEXES — 6/10

Pro shop — Pro-shop
Driving range — Practice
Sheltered couvert 4 mats - On grass sur herbe yes - Putting-green putting-green yes - Pitching-green pitching green yes

HOTEL FACILITIES — ENVIRONNEMENT HOTELIER — 7/10

HOTELS HÔTELS
Reine Hortense - 8 rooms, D € 140 - Dinard 5 km
Tel (33) 02 99 46 54 31, Fax (33) 02 99 88 15 88

Grand Hôtel de Dinard - 90 rooms, D € 220 - Dinard 5 km
Tel (33) 02 99 88 26 26, Fax (33) 02 99 88 26 27

Golf Hôtel - 40 rooms, D € 90 - on site
Tel (33) 02 99 88 30 30, Fax (33) 02 99 88 07 87

RESTAURANTS RESTAURANTS
Salle à Manger - Dinard 5 km - Tel (33) 02 99 16 07 95
Clos du Chanoine - St Malo (→ Cancale) 18 km
Tel (33) 02 99 40 89 93
Le Chalut - Saint-Malo 12 km - Tel (33) 02 99 56 71 58

Disneyland Paris *Rouge + Bleu*

16	7	8

Ce n'est pas un énorme complexe golfique comme Disneyworld à Orlando, mais Disneyland Paris offre néanmoins un 18 trous et un 9 trous de bonne valeur, construits par Ronald Fream sur un terrain plat, mais fortement modelé. Cet ensemble paraît plus complexe techniquement qu'il ne l'est vraiment, les pièges sont immédiatement visibles et les grands espaces favorisent les longs frappeurs. Cependant, les contours assez tourmentés des greens et quelques difficultés stratégiques permettent aux techniciens d'exprimer leur virtuosité. L'ensemble présente un visage très américain, il ne faudra pas s'en étonner, avec bon nombre d'obstacles d'eau qui ont paysagé l'espace. Si les trois parcours de 9 trous possèdent leur propre personnalité, le club-house et les équipements sont fonctionnels, mais manquent toujours de chaleur. C'est un complexe évidemment commercial, sans véritable vie de Club... même si certains joueurs de la région y ont pris leurs habitudes, il est avant tout destiné aux joueurs de passage.

This is not yet your actual outsized golfing resort as in Disneyworld Orlando, but Disneyland Paris presently provides an 18-hole and a good 9-hole course built by Ronald Fream over flat terrain bulldozed into shape. Technically speaking, the course is not too complex, as traps are immediately visible and wide open space is a give-away for long-hitters. However, the twisting greens and a number of strategic difficulties also give the finer artistes a chance to practice their skills. Not surprisingly, the whole layout has a very American look to it with a good number of water hazards that have landscaped the open space. While the three 9-hole courses gradually forge a personality, the club-house and facilities are functional but still lack soul. This is obviously a business venture without any real club life and even though certain local players are now regulars, it is intended first and foremost for people passing through.

Golf Disneyland Paris — 1992

Allée de la Mare-Houleuse
F - 77450 MAGNY-LE-HONGRE

Office Secrétariat (33) 01 60 45 68 90
Pro shop Pro-shop (33) 01 60 45 68 90
Fax Fax (33) 01 60 45 68 33
Web www.disneylandparis.com
Situation Situation Paris, 38 km
Annual closure Fermeture annuelle no
Weekly closure Fermeture hebdomadaire no

Fees main season Tarifs haute saison	27 holes	
	Week days Semaine	**We/Bank holidays** We/Férié
Individual Individuel	€ 34	€ 56
Couple Couple	€ 68	€ 112

Under 18: € 29 / 44 (We) / Seniors: € 26 (Week days) and 23 (tuesday/mardi)

Caddie Caddie no **Electric Trolley** Chariot électrique no
Buggy Voiturette yes **Clubs** Clubs yes
Credit cards Cartes de crédit
VISA - CB - Eurocard - MasterCard - AMEX - DC - JCB

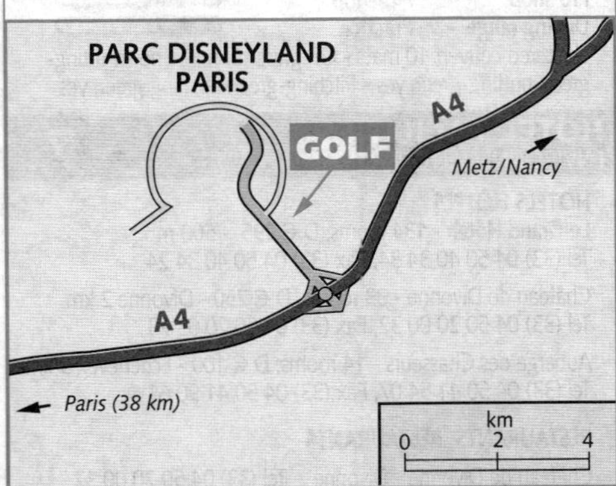

Access Accès : A4 Paris-Metz/Nancy, → "Parc Disneyland Paris"
Map 15 on page 189 Carte 15 Page 189

GOLF COURSE — PARCOURS 16/20

Site Site
Maintenance Entretien
Architect Architecte Ronald Fream
Type Type open country
Relief Relief
Water in play Eau en jeu
Exp. to wind Exposé au vent
Trees in play Arbres en jeu

Scorecard Carte de score	**Chp.** Chp.	**Mens** Mess.	**Ladies** Da.
Length Long.	6032	5593	4773
Par	72	72	72
Slope system	132	129	120

Advised golfing ability Niveau de jeu recommandé 0 12 24 36
Hcp required Handicap exigé no

CLUB HOUSE & AMENITIES — CLUB HOUSE ET ANNEXES 7/10

Pro shop Pro-shop
Driving range Practice
Sheltered couvert 10 mats - On grass sur herbe no - Putting-green putting-green yes - Pitching-green pitching green yes

HOTEL FACILITIES — ENVIRONNEMENT HOTELIER 8/10

HOTELS HÔTELS
Booking/reservations - Tel (33) 0825 30 60 30 - on site
Disneyland - 496 rooms, D € 527
Tel (33) 01 60 45 65 00, Fax (33) 01 60 45 65 33
Séquoia Lodge - 1001 rooms, D € 248 - on site, close
Tel (33) 01 60 45 51 00, Fax (33) 01 60 45 51 33
Cheyenne - 1000 rooms, D € 200 - on site, close
Tel (33) 01 60 45 62 00, Fax (33) 01 60 45 62 33

RESTAURANTS RESTAURANTS
Auberge de la Brie - Couilly-Pont-aux-Dames 10 km
Tel (33) 01 64 63 51 80
Invention - Hôtel Disneyland - Tel (33) 01 60 45 65 00
Cape Cod, Yacht Club - Hôtel New-Port - on site, close
Tel (33) 01 60 45 55 00

Divonne

14 | 6 | 7

Avec six par 4, six par 5 et six par 3, le parcours de Divonne est original, mais le fait de commencer et de terminer par des par 3 n'est pas son point fort. Dominant le Lac Léman, ce parcours de moyenne montagne est assez bien rythmé pour ne pas être épuisant, quand il n'est pas trop humide. L'environnement boisé est très plaisant, et permet au minimum de transformer une mauvaise partie en jolie promenade. Peut-être un peu difficile pour les joueurs non classés, Divonne permet cependant aux golfeurs de tous niveaux de jouer ensemble, et c'est un challenge appréciable pour les meilleurs frappeurs, qui auront de multiples occasions de prendre des risques, même si l'absence de subtilités stratégiques empêche de renouveler constamment le plaisir. C'est une halte de qualité à la belle saison, très fréquentée par les Suisses, mais comme on ne manque pas trop de moyens ici, on peut imaginer un remodelage par un grand architecte…

With six par 4s, six par 5s and six par 3s, Divonne is an original course, but starting and finishing with par 3s is hardly its strong point. Overlooking lake Geneva, Divonne is a mid-mountain course which is not too tiring when the weather is not too damp. The woody surroundings are very pleasant (especially in autumn) and at the very least can help change a rotten round into a pleasant walk. Divonne might be a little too tough for very high handicappers but it does allow golfers of all abilities to play together. It is certainly quite some challenge for the longer-hitters, who have countless opportunities to take risks, even though the course lacks any strategic subtlety. At all events, this is a great stop-off over the summer months and one that is very popular with the Swiss. As the course certainly has the resources, we can only imagine what a top architect would produce if asked to do a little restyling work.

Golf de Divonne — 1931

F - 01220 DIVONNE-LES-BAINS

Office	Secrétariat	(33) 04 50 40 34 11
Pro shop	Pro-shop	(33) 04 50 40 34 11
Fax	Fax	(33) 04 50 40 34 25
Web	www.domaine-de-divonne.com	
Situation	Situation	Genève, 17 km
Annual closure	Fermeture annuelle	no
Weekly closure	Fermeture hebdomadaire	no

Fees main season Tarifs haute saison	Week days Semaine	We/Bank holidays We/Férié
	18 holes	
Individual Individuel	€ 50	€ 80
Couple Couple	€ 100	€ 160

Under 15: – 50%

Caddie Caddie on request **Electric Trolley** Chariot électrique yes

Buggy Voiturette yes **Clubs** Clubs yes

Credit cards Cartes de crédit
VISA - CB - Eurocard - MasterCard - AMEX - DC - JCB

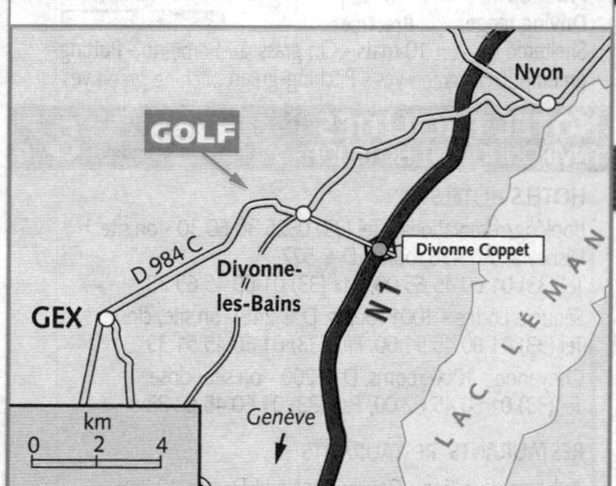

Access Accès : • Genève → Nyon/Lausanne, Exit (Sortie) Divonne, → Golf
• Gex (France) D 984 → Divonne

Map 8 on page 175 Carte 8 Page 175

GOLF COURSE — PARCOURS — 14/20

Site	Site	
Maintenance	Entretien	
Architect	Architecte	M. Nakowsky Donald Harradine
Type	Type	parkland, hilly
Relief	Relief	
Water in play	Eau en jeu	
Exp. to wind	Exposé au vent	
Trees in play	Arbres en jeu	

Scorecard Carte de score	Chp. Chp.	Mens Mess.	Ladies Da.
Length Long.	5858	5433	4614
Par	72	72	72
Slope system	122	117	124

Advised golfing ability Niveau de jeu recommandé — 0 12 24 36

Hcp required Handicap exigé 36

CLUB HOUSE & AMENITIES — CLUB HOUSE ET ANNEXES — 6/10

Pro shop Pro-shop
Driving range Practice
Sheltered couvert 10 mats - On grass sur herbe no - Putting-green putting-green yes - Pitching-green pitching green yes

HOTEL FACILITIES — ENVIRONNEMENT HOTELIER — 7/10

HOTELS HÔTELS

Le Grand Hôtel - 134 rooms, D € 295 - 500 m
Tel (33) 04 50 40 34 34, Fax (33) 04 50 40 34 24

Château de Divonne - 33 rooms, D € 250 - Divonne 2 km
Tel (33) 04 50 20 00 32, Fax (33) 04 50 20 03 73

Auberge des Chasseurs - 14 rooms, D € 100 - Echenevex 9 km
Tel (33) 04 50 41 54 07, Fax (33) 04 50 41 90 61

RESTAURANTS RESTAURANTS

Château de Divonne - Divonne - Tel (33) 04 50 20 00 32

La Terrasse - Divonne - Tel (33) 04 50 40 35 39

Auberge du Vieux Bois - Divonne 1 km
Tel (33) 04 50 20 01 43

Domangère (La)

16 | 5 | 5

Ce parcours reste par son tracé l'un des meilleurs dans l'ouest de la France, et les progrès de son entretien justifient un retour dans ce guide. Michel Gayon a produit là un de ses meilleurs dessins, dans une esthétique plus "américaine" que britannique, mais le paysage la justifie – modérément boisé et pourvu d'eau en abondance. Tout l'aller se situe dans la partie basse du site, ce qui oblige certes à remonter ensuite, mais permet de tester pleinement les joueurs avec cinq grands obstacles d'eau. Cependant, en dépit d'incontestables difficultés et d'exigences techniques, les joueurs prudents et intelligents trouveront bien le moyen de sauver à peu près leur carte. On regrette l'inversion de l'aller et du retour, même si l'on trouve sur celui-ci le plus long par 5 de France, avec 600 mètres, que seuls les gros frappeurs d'aujourd'hui voudront le tester du fond. Un vrai challenge à connaître, hors des sentiers battus.

The layout of this course makes it one of the very best in western France and the vastly improved green-keeping warrants its return to our Guide. Michel Gayon has produced here one of his best layouts, more in the American style than British, but the landscape was almost made for it – not too many trees and water everywhere. The outward nine cross the lower part of the site, which of course means having to climb back up for the homeward stretch, but it is also a meaningful test with five large water hazards. Yet despite the course's unquestionable difficulties and technical demands, cautious and smart players should come up with a means to save their card, more or less. It is a pity they reversed the out and in holes, even though the home stretch does include the longest par 5 in France, a full 660 yards that today only the longest hitters might attempt from the tips. A real challenge to play, and off the beaten track.

Golf de la Domangère — 1988

Route de la Rochelle
F - 85310 NESMY

Office	Secrétariat	(33) 02 51 07 65 90
Pro shop	Pro-shop	(33) 02 51 07 65 90
Fax	Fax	(33) 02 51 07 65 95
Web	www.formule-golf.com	
Situation	Situation	La Roche-sur-Yon, 9 km
Annual closure	Fermeture annuelle	no
Weekly closure	Fermeture hebdomadaire	tuesday

(mardi) 1/11→31/3

Fees main season / Tarifs haute saison	Week days / Semaine	We/Bank holidays / We/Férié
18 holes		
Individual Individuel	€ 46	€ 46
Couple Couple	€ 92	€ 92

01/10 → 31/3: GF € 34 / Under 21 & Students under 25: – 50%

Caddie Caddie no — Electric Trolley Chariot électrique no

Buggy Voiturette yes — Clubs Clubs yes

Credit cards Cartes de crédit
VISA - CB - Eurocard - MasterCard

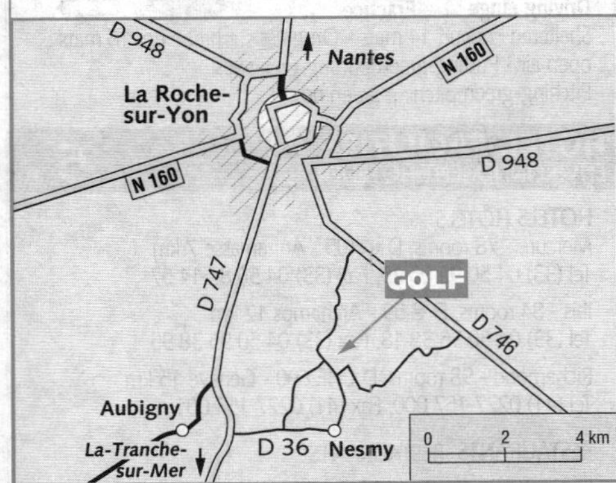

Access Accès : A11 Paris-Nantes, Nantes → La Roche-sur-Yon. D746 → La Rochelle, D36 → Nesmy
Map 6 on page 170 Carte 6 Page 170

GOLF COURSE — PARCOURS — 16/20

Site	Site	
Maintenance	Entretien	
Architect	Architecte	Michel Gayon
Type	Type	parkland, open country
Relief	Relief	
Water in play	Eau en jeu	
Exp. to wind	Exposé au vent	
Trees in play	Arbres en jeu	

Scorecard / Carte de score	Chp. / Chp.	Mens / Mess.	Ladies / Da.
Length Long.	6479	6015	5046
Par	72	72	72
Slope system	150	143	137

Advised golfing ability / Niveau de jeu recommandé: 0 12 24 36

Hcp required / Handicap exigé: no

CLUB HOUSE & AMENITIES — CLUB HOUSE ET ANNEXES — 5/10

Pro shop — Pro-shop
Driving range — Practice
Sheltered couvert 7 mats - On grass sur herbe yes - Putting-green putting-green yes - Pitching-green pitching green yes

HOTEL FACILITIES — ENVIRONNEMENT HOTELIER — 5/10

HOTELS HÔTELS

Napoléon - 29 rooms, D € 70 - La Roche sur Yon 8 km
Tel (33) 02 51 05 33 56, Fax (33) 02 51 62 01 69

Mercure - 67 rooms, D € 90 - La Roche sur Yon 8 km
Tel (33) 02 51 46 28 00, Fax (33) 02 51 46 28 98

RESTAURANTS RESTAURANTS

Le Pavillon Gourmand - La Roche sur Yon 8 km
Tel (33) 02 51 07 08 09

Rivoli - La Roche sur Yon 8 km - Tel (33) 02 51 37 43 41

Le Clémenceau - La Roche sur Yon 8 km
Tel (33) 02 51 37 10 20

Le Bistro Yonnais - La Roche sur Yon 8 km
Tel (33) 02 51 46 28 00

Esery

15	7	5

Pratiquement annexé par les Suisses, ce parcours a été dessiné par Michel Gayon sur un terrain accidenté, avec très peu d'arbres, dans un site classé offrant des vues magnifiques, et bien préservé des pressions immobilières. Ses difficultés viennent essentiellement des dévers, du relief, des rivières traversant les fairways et de quelques mares. Il serait sans doute plus délicat à négocier avec des roughs plus épais. Les greens sont vastes, dessinés avec beaucoup de soin, protégés par le relief naturel du terrain et par un grand nombre de bunkers, tout comme les arrivées de drive. Pour les joueurs à partir de 15 de handicap, il peut être très long, mais de nombreux départs différents permettent de se faire un parcours "à sa main", si l'on ne veut pas trop forcer son talent. Le rythme général est assez heurté, avec des trous difficiles en succession, puis des moments de relâchement, mais la fin de parcours est technique, montant en puissance à partir du 13. L'entretien reste de très bonne qualité.

Virtually taken over by Swiss golfers, Esery was designed by Michel Gayon over a hilly terrain with very few trees on a listed site which provides some wonderful views and has avoided the pressure of real estate promoters. The major difficulty comes from the sloping fairways, the rivers crossing the fairways and a few ponds, but it would certainly be a tougher test with thicker rough. The greens are huge, have been very carefully designed and are very well defended, not only by the naturally hilly terrain but also by well-placed bunkers. The same goes for the fairways at driving distance. For players with handicaps in the upper teens, this could prove to be a very long course, but the large number of tees lets you tailor the course to your own ability if you don't feel up to the test. The overall balance is a little disjointed with a series of difficult holes followed by a number of easier ones. The run-in is more technical, getting harder from the 13th hole onwards. Green-keeping is very good.

Golf Club d'Esery — 1990

Esery
F - 74930 REIGNIER

Office Secrétariat (33) 04 50 36 58 70
Pro shop Pro-shop (33) 04 50 31 20 15
Fax Fax (33) 04 50 36 57 62
Web www.golf-club-esery.com
Situation Situation Genève, 12 km
Annual closure Fermeture annuelle 24/12→1/1
Weekly closure Fermeture hebdomadaire Monday
(lundi): club-house closed

Fees main season Tarifs haute saison	18 holes	
	Week days Semaine	**We/Bank holidays** We/Férié
Individual Individuel	€ 65	*
Couple Couple	€ 130	*

*Week-end: members only

Caddie Caddie on request **Electric Trolley** Chariot électrique yes
Buggy Voiturette yes **Clubs** Clubs yes
Credit cards Cartes de crédit
VISA - CB - Eurocard - MasterCard

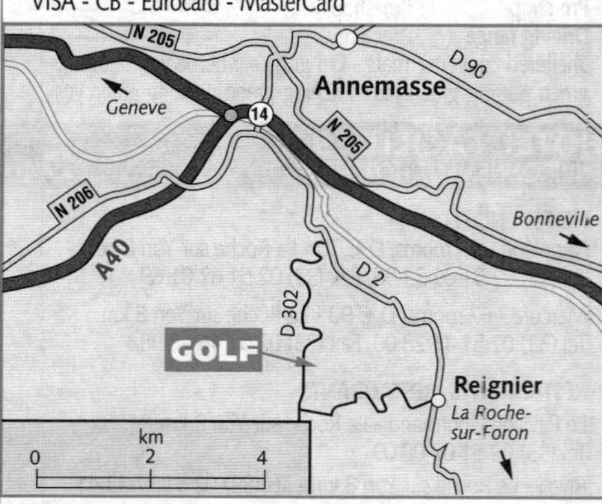

Access Accès : • Genève, A40 Exit (Sortie) Annemasse → Reignier
• Annecy, A41 Exit (Sortie) 14, → Reignier
Map 11 on page 181 Carte 11 Page 181

GOLF COURSE — PARCOURS — 15/20

Site	Site	
Maintenance	Entretien	
Architect	Architecte	Michel Gayon
Type	Type	mountain, hilly
Relief	Relief	
Water in play	Eau en jeu	
Exp. to wind	Exposé au vent	
Trees in play	Arbres en jeu	

Scorecard Carte de score	**Chp.** Chp.	**Mens** Mess	**Ladies** Da.
Length Long.	6019	5507	4646
Par	72	72	72
Slope system	132	133	116

Advised golfing ability Niveau de jeu recommandé 0 12 24 36
Hcp required Handicap exigé 30

CLUB HOUSE & AMENITIES — CLUB HOUSE ET ANNEXES — 7/10

Pro shop Pro-shop
Driving range Practice
Sheltered couvert 14 mats - On grass sur herbe no, 16 mats open air - Putting-green putting-green yes
Pitching-green pitching green no

HOTEL FACILITIES — ENVIRONNEMENT HOTELIER — 5/10

HOTELS HÔTELS

Mercure - 78 rooms, D € 105 - Annemasse 7 km
Tel (33) 04 50 92 05 25, Fax (33) 04 50 87 14 57

Ibis - 84 rooms, D € 59 - Archamps 12 km
Tel (33) 04 50 95 38 18, Fax (33) 04 50 95 38 95

Richemond - 98 rooms, D CHF 600 - Genève 15 km
Tel (41) 0227 157 000, Fax (41) 0227 157 001

RESTAURANTS RESTAURANTS

Le Neptune - Genève 12 km - Tel (41) 022 - 909 00 06
La Perle du Lac - Genève 12 km - Tel (41) 0229 091 020

Estérel

15 | 6 | 7

A proximité immédiate du "vieux" Valescure, un peu surranné mais toujours sympathique, l'Estérel constitue un ensemble touristique bâti dans une pinède sur un terrain modérément accidenté. Robert Trent Jones y a tracé un parcours techniquement très intéressant, d'une grande diversité de difficultés et souvent spectaculaire : notamment le 15, petit par 3 où il faut franchir un véritable gouffre. Il faut savoir bien étudier chaque coup, travailler la balle pour y scorer convenablement, et choisir soigneusement son club, le driver n'étant surtout pas obligatoire sur chaque départ. Des dizaines de bunkers et quelques obstacles d'eau très en jeu imposent de définir soigneusement sa stratégie. Les greens sont le point faible de ce parcours tactique par des ondulations excessives qui laissent trop de place à la chance, et leur état n'est pas toujours parfait... Un parcours à connaître, dont le déroulement initial a été repris... mais les maisons enserrent de très près ce golf de style "resort".

Close to the "old" Valescure course, a little dated but as agreeable as ever, Estérel is a tourist resort in a setting of pine forest and pretty hilly countryside. Robert Trent Jones has laid out what is technically a very interesting course with a number of varied and often spectacular hazards. This is particularly so on the 15th, a short 3-par, where a sort of chasm separates tee from green. Astute club selection, careful thought for each shot and ball-control are the key to a goodish score at Estérel, where the driver can certainly be banished on several holes. Dozens of bunkers and a few water hazards call for deliberate strategy. The weak point on this tactical course comes from the greens, excessively contoured and so leaving too much to chance, and not always in top condition. A course worth knowing despite the infringing presence of condos lining this resort style complex.

Golf Estérel — 1989

Avenue du Golf
F - 83700 SAINT-RAPHAEL

Office	Secrétariat	(33) 04 94 52 68 30
Pro shop	Pro-shop	(33) 04 94 52 68 30
Fax	Fax	(33) 04 94 52 68 31
Web	www.formule-golf.com	
Situation	Situation	Saint-Raphaël, 3 km
Annual closure	Fermeture annuelle	no
Weekly closure	Fermeture hebdomadaire	no
Fees main season	Tarifs haute saison	full day

	Week days / Semaine	We/Bank holidays / We/Férié
Individual Individuel	€ 59	€ 59
Couple Couple	€ 118	€ 118

Under 18: – 50% / Under 21: – 30%
After 15:30, GF € 35

Caddie Caddie on request **Electric Trolley** Chariot électrique yes

Buggy Voiturette yes **Clubs** Clubs yes

Credit cards Cartes de crédit
VISA - CB - Eurocard - MasterCard - AMEX

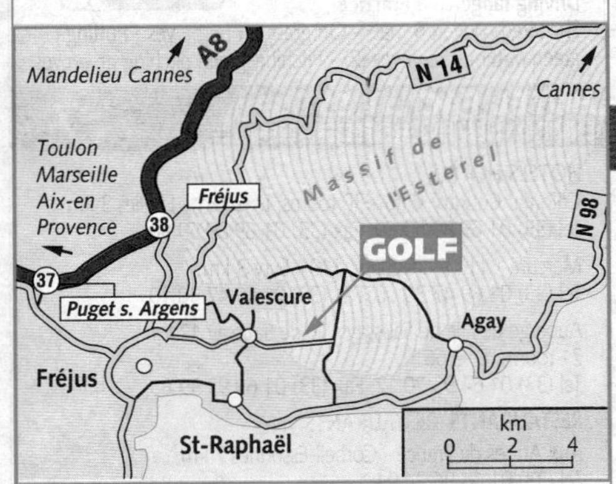

Access Accès : A 8, Exit (Sortie) Fréjus Saint-Raphaël, → Saint-Raphaël, then Agay and Valescure
Map 14 on page 186 Carte 14 Page 186

GOLF COURSE — PARCOURS — 15/20

Site	Site	
Maintenance	Entretien	
Architect	Architecte	Robert Trent Jones
Type	Type	forest, residential
Relief	Relief	
Water in play	Eau en jeu	
Exp. to wind	Exposé au vent	
Trees in play	Arbres en jeu	

Scorecard Carte de score	Chp. Chp.	Mens Mess.	Ladies Da.
Length Long.	5852	5417	4527
Par	71	71	71
Slope system	139	129	123

Advised golfing ability Niveau de jeu recommandé: 0 12 24 36
Hcp required Handicap exigé: no

CLUB HOUSE & AMENITIES — CLUB HOUSE ET ANNEXES — 6/10

Pro shop Pro-shop
Driving range Practice
Sheltered couvert 15 mats - On grass sur herbe yes - Putting-green putting-green yes - Pitching-green pitching green yes

HOTEL FACILITIES — ENVIRONNEMENT HOTELIER — 7/10

HOTELS HÔTELS

Latitudes Valescure - 95 rooms, D € 165 - on site
Tel (33) 04 94 52 68 00, Fax (33) 04 94 52 68 01

San Pedro - 28 rooms, D € 160 - Saint-Raphaël 1 km
Tel (33) 04 94 19 90 20, Fax (33) 04 94 19 90 21

Hôtel du Golf de Valescure - Valescure 3 km
40 rooms, D € 165
Tel (33) 04 94 52 85 00, Fax (33) 04 94 82 41 88

RESTAURANTS RESTAURANTS

L'Arbousier - Saint-Raphaël 4 km - Tel (33) 04 94 95 25 00
San Pedro - Saint-Raphaël 1 km - Tel (33) 04 94 19 90 20
Jardin de Sébastien - Valescure 1 km - Tel (33) 04 94 44 66 56

Etiolles Colonial *Les Cerfs*

15	7	7

Construit dans une très vaste clairière, avec quelques maisons assez séduisantes, Etiolles est un exemple de bon parcours commercial, indulgent aux coups décentrés, et donc accessible à tous. Dessiné par Michel Gayon, il permet à chacun de trouver son bonheur. Les fairways sont de bonne dimension et bien isolés par des buttes importantes, qui non seulement ajoutent du relief à un terrain assez plat, mais ramènent souvent les balles en jeu. Quelques départs surélevés donnent une meilleure appréciation de la façon d'aborder certains trous, ainsi que des mouvements de terrain derrière certains greens. Généralement, les greens sont vastes, mais pas très difficiles à lire. Logiquement, ils ne sont pas trop défendus sur une approche avec un long fer ou un bois. Parmi les trous remarquables, on distinguera le 18, très américain dans son dessin, ramenant vers le club-house de style colonial (d'où le nom du club), un peu étrange dans cette région. On notera l'entretien très correct, et un neuf trous de bonne qualité.

Laid out over a huge clearing with some attractive houses, Etiolles is a good example of a successful business golfing venture. Designed by Michel Gayon, there is something for everyone here on a course that is often forgiving to mis-hit shots. The wide fairways are neatly isolated by mounds, which not only add a little relief to a flat terrain but also obligingly often bring the ball back into play. Some elevated tee-boxes give a clearer appreciation of how to tackle certain holes, as do the sand-hills behind some greens. The greens are generally large but not too difficult to read and so logically they are not over-protected when hitting into them with a long iron or fairway wood. One of the most remarkable holes is the American style 18th, leading the player back to the colonial style club-house, which looks a little odd in this part of the world. Green-keeping is very good.

Etiolles Colonial Country Club 1990

Vieux Chemin de Paris
F - 91450 ETIOLLES

Office	Secrétariat	(33) 01 69 89 59 59
Pro shop	Pro-shop	(33) 01 60 75 59 59
Fax	Fax	(33) 01 69 89 59 90
Web	www.golf-paris.com	
Situation	Situation	Paris, 37 km
Annual closure	Fermeture annuelle	no
Weekly closure	Fermeture hebdomadaire	no
Fees main season	Tarifs haute saison	full day

	Week days Semaine	We/Bank holidays We/Férié
Individual Individuel	€ 47,5	€ 70
Couple Couple	€ 72	€ 108

Under 21: € 24 / Students: € 24 (wednesday/thursday - mercredi/jeudi)

Caddie Caddie no **Electric Trolley** Chariot électrique yes

Buggy Voiturette yes **Clubs** Clubs yes

Credit cards Cartes de crédit
VISA - CB - Eurocard - MasterCard - Amex

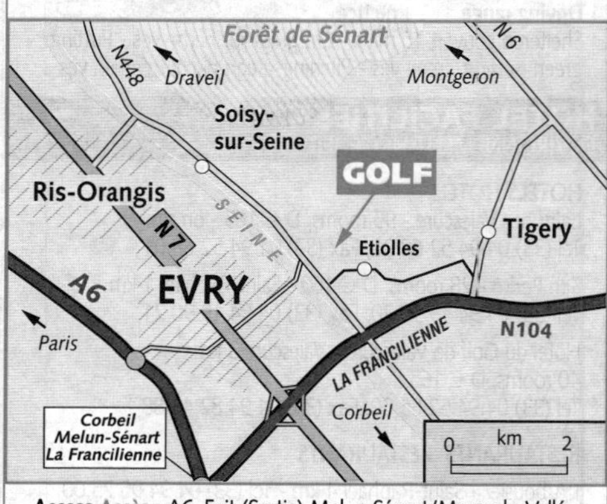

Access Accès : A6, Exit (Sortie) Melun Sénart/Marne-la-Vallée, Francilienne (N104) 3 km, Exit (Sortie) Etiolles

Map 15 on page 189 Carte 15 Page 189

GOLF COURSE PARCOURS 15/20

Site	Site	
Maintenance	Entretien	
Architect	Architecte	Michel Gayon
Type	Type	open country
Relief	Relief	
Water in play	Eau en jeu	
Exp. to wind	Exposé au vent	
Trees in play	Arbres en jeu	

Scorecard Carte de score	Chp. Chp.	Mens Mess.	Ladies Da.
Length Long.	6232	5777	4877
Par	73	73	73
Slope system	120	115	115

Advised golfing ability Niveau de jeu recommandé 0 12 24 36

Hcp required Handicap exigé no

CLUB HOUSE & AMENITIES CLUB HOUSE ET ANNEXES 7/10

Pro shop Pro-shop
Driving range Practice
Sheltered couvert 9 mats - On grass sur herbe yes - Putting-green putting-green yes (2) - Pitching-green pitching green yes

HOTEL FACILITIES ENVIRONNEMENT HOTELIER 7/10

HOTELS HÔTELS

Colonial Country Club - 30 rooms, D € 181 - Etiolles 3 km
Tel (33) 01 69 89 59 69, Fax (33) 01 69 89 59 90

Mercure - 114 rooms, D € 110 - Evry 3 km
Tel (33) 01 69 47 30 00, Fax (33) 01 69 47 30 10

Auberge de l'Ile de Saussay - Ile de Saussay 17 km
21 rooms, D € 66
Tel (33) 01 64 93 20 12, Fax (33) 01 69 93 39 88

RESTAURANTS RESTAURANTS

Aux Armes de France - Corbeil-Essonnes 7 km
Tel (33) 01 64 96 24 04

Le Canal - Evry-Courcouronnes 7 km - Tel (33) 01 60 78 34 72

Auberge du Barrage - Le Coudray-Montceaux 8 km
Tel (33) 01 64 93 81 16

Etretat

13 | 5 | 6

La vue sur la mer, les falaises et la ville est splendide. On ne se lassera pas du 10, plongeant au drive en bord de mer, pour remonter ensuite vers le green sur un plateau, remodelé dernièrement. Ouvert à tous les vents, ce parcours a fait l'objet de modifications sympathiques depuis sa création en 1908. Mais pour le classer parmi les grands parcours de bord de mer, il faudrait reprendre pas mal de bunkers, animer quelques greens aux surfaces souvent sans intérêt, et déplacer plusieurs départs. C'est un vœu pieux, car ce golf familial ne dispose pas des moyens des clubs prestigieux et les améliorations ne peuvent être que progressives. Cela dit, on peut jouer ici plusieurs jours avec beaucoup de plaisir, par beau temps au moins. Quand le vent souffle, c'est une bataille contre le parcours, et il vaut mieux jouer en match-play ! Le profil général du parcours en fait un "challenge" attachant, ne serait ce que pour apprendre à travailler les balles basses. L'atmosphère du club est agréable mais le confort du club-house est limité.

The view over the sea, cliffs and the town is magnificent, and the 10th hole, with a drive plunging seaward from the cliffs before sweeping back up to an elevated and recently restyled green, is a moment to cherish. Exposed to all winds, the course has been altered several times since its creation, but to be ranked among the truly great seaside courses a number of bunkers require attention, some of the bland putting surfaces could do with a little contouring and several tees need moving. This is all wishful thinking, as Etretat is a family club that lacks the resources of the more prestigious courses and improvements can only come gradually. Having said that, you can play here and enjoy every minute, at least if the weather holds. When the wind blows, it is a tough battle with the course. The general layout makes this a pleasing challenge, if only for the opportunity to practice those knock-down shots. The club has a friendly atmosphere, but only limited amenities.

Golf d'Etretat — 1908

Route du Havre
F - 76790 ETRETAT

Office Secrétariat (33) 02 35 27 04 89
Pro shop Pro-shop (33) 02 35 27 04 89
Fax Fax (33) 02 35 29 49 02
Web www.golfetretat.com
Situation Situation Le Havre, 30 km
Fécamp (pop. 20 800), 16 km
Annual closure Fermeture annuelle no
Weekly closure Fermeture hebdomadaire Tuesday (mardi): 09 → 03

Fees main season Tarifs haute saison	18 holes	
	Week days Semaine	We/Bank holidays We/Férié
Individual Individuel	€ 50	€ 60
Couple Couple	€ 85	€ 108

Students under 25: € 21 / 32 (We)

Caddie Caddie no — **Electric Trolley** Chariot électrique yes
Buggy Voiturette yes — **Clubs** Clubs yes
Credit cards Cartes de crédit
VISA - CB - Eurocard - MasterCard

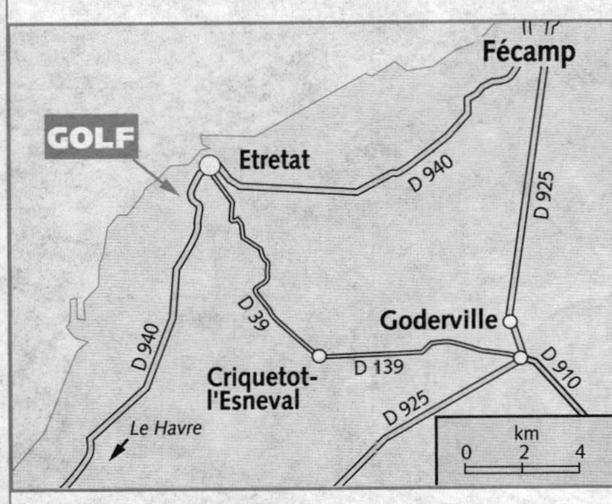

Access Accès : D940 Etretat-Le Havre
Map 2 on page 163 Carte 2 Page 163

GOLF COURSE — PARCOURS — 13/20

Site Site
Maintenance Entretien
Architect Architecte M. Chantepie, D. Fruchet (4 holes)
Type Type seaside course, open country
Relief Relief
Water in play Eau en jeu
Exp. to wind Exposé au vent
Trees in play Arbres en jeu

Scorecard Carte de score	Chp. Chp.	Mens Mess.	Ladies Da.
Length Long.	6073	5679	4786
Par	72	72	72
Slope system	129	122	122

Advised golfing ability Niveau de jeu recommandé 0 12 24 36
Hcp required Handicap exigé 35 (We)

CLUB HOUSE & AMENITIES — CLUB HOUSE ET ANNEXES — 5/10

Pro shop Pro-shop
Driving range Practice
Sheltered couvert 2 mats - On grass sur herbe yes (in Summer) - Putting-green putting-green yes - Pitching-green pitching green yes

HOTEL FACILITIES — ENVIRONNEMENT HOTELIER — 6/10

HOTELS HÔTELS

Dormy House Golf Hôtel - 61 rooms, D € 167 - 500 m
Tel (33) 02 35 27 07 88, Fax (33) 02 35 29 86 19

Le Donjon - 21 rooms, D € 160 - Etretat 2 km
Tel (33) 02 35 27 08 23, Fax (33) 02 35 29 92 24

Les Falaises - 24 rooms, D € 62 - Etretat 2 km
Tel (33) 02 35 27 02 77, Fax (33) 02 35 28 87 59

RESTAURANTS RESTAURANTS

Le Belvédère - Etretat 2 km - Tel (33) 02 35 20 13 76
Le Galion - Etretat 2 km - Tel (33) 02 35 29 48 74
Auberge de la Rouge - Fécamp 17 km
Tel (33) 02 35 28 07 59

Evian

15 | 7 | 9

Le remodelage effectué par Cabell Robinson en 1990 a fait oublier ce qu'était autrefois ce parcours. L'approche des greens constitue la difficulté majeure car ils sont très protégés par des buttes et de nombreux bunkers, mettant l'accent sur les aspects techniques du jeu. Certains joueurs ont pu regretter ces nouvelles difficultés, mais le parcours a pris son rang parmi les meilleurs de la région lémanique. Assez accidenté (voiturette conseillée pour les seniors), quasiment comme un golf de montagne, Evian n'est pas très long, mais les dénivellations peuvent être trompeuses, notamment au 15, petit par 3 très spectaculaire dominant le lac Léman. C'est le plus joli point de vue du parcours, couronnant l'impression très agréable d'évoluer dans un beau parc. L'entretien est généralement excellent, dans la continuité de l'Evian Masters qui s'y joue chaque année et laisse en souvenir de redoutables roughs. Les puristes trouveront qu'il y a un abus de petites fleurs, mais cet amour du jardinage va bien dans l'univers d'Evian.

The restyling carried out by Cabell Robinson in 1990 has erased the memory of how this course used to be. Approach shots are the major concern as the greens are now particularly well guarded with a series of sandhills and numerous bunkers, thus placing more emphasis on technical skills. High-handicappers might regret these difficulties, but the course is one of the region's very best. Hilly enough to be virtually a mountain course (buggy recommended for seniors), Evian is not very long but changes in altitude can be deceiving, especially on the 15th, a highly spectacular short par 3 overlooking Lake Geneva. This is the prettiest spot on the course and crowns the pleasant impression of playing golf in a nice park. Green-keeping is by and large excellent, as befits a course which hosts the Evian Masters each year, and the formidable rough preys on the mind. The purists also find that there are too many flowerbeds but gardening fits in so well with the world of Evian.

Evian Masters Golf Club — 1904/1990

B.P. No 8
F - 74502 EVIAN

Office Secrétariat (33) 04 50 75 46 66
Pro shop Pro-shop (33) 04 50 75 51 96
Fax Fax (33) 04 50 75 65 54
Web www.evianmasters.com
Situation Situation Genève, 46 km
Evian (pop. 8 900), 2.5 km

Annual closure Fermeture annuelle 7/12→31/1
Weekly closure Fermeture hebdomadaire no
Fees main season Tarifs haute saison 18 holes

	Week days Semaine	We/Bank holidays We/Férié
Individual Individuel	€ 57	€ 67
Couple Couple	€ 114	€ 134

Juniors under 18: – 50%

Caddie Caddie on request **Electric Trolley** Chariot électrique yes

Buggy Voiturette yes **Clubs** Clubs yes

Credit cards Cartes de crédit
VISA - CB - Eurocard - MasterCard - AMEX - DC - JCB

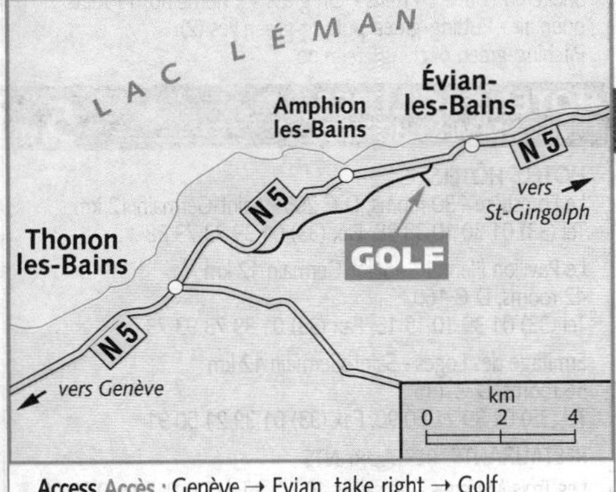

Access Accès : Genève → Evian, take right → Golf
Map 8 on page 175 Carte 8 Page 175

GOLF COURSE — PARCOURS 15/20

Site Site
Maintenance Entretien
Architect Architecte Cabell B. Robinson
Type Type parkland, hilly
Relief Relief
Water in play Eau en jeu
Exp. to wind Exposé au vent
Trees in play Arbres en jeu

Scorecard Carte de score	Chp. Chp.	Mens Mess.	Ladies Da.
Length Long.	6006	5651	4780
Par	72	72	72
Slope system	131	126	131

Advised golfing ability Niveau de jeu recommandé 0 12 24 36
Hcp required Handicap exigé 35

CLUB HOUSE & AMENITIES — CLUB HOUSE ET ANNEXES 7/10

Pro shop Pro-shop
Driving range Practice
Sheltered couvert 20 mats - On grass sur herbe yes - Putting-green putting-green yes (2) - Pitching-green pitching green yes

HOTEL FACILITIES — ENVIRONNEMENT HOTELIER 9/10

HOTELS HÔTELS
Le Royal - 153 rooms, D from € 400 - Evian 3 km
Tel (33) 04 50 26 85 00, Fax (33) 04 50 75 61 00

L'Ermitage - 96 rooms, D from € 300 - Evian 2 km
Tel (33) 04 50 26 85 00, Fax (33) 04 50 75 61 00

La Verniaz - 33 rooms, D € 125 - Evian 2 km
Tel (33) 04 50 75 04 90, Fax (33) 04 50 70 78 92

Bourgogne et Ducs de Savoie - 32 rooms, D € 71 - Evian 2 km
Tel (33) 04 50 75 01 05, Fax (33) 04 50 75 04 05

RESTAURANTS RESTAURANTS
Café Royal - Evian 3 km - Tel (33) 04 50 26 85 00
Prieuré - Thonon-les-Bains 10 km - Tel (33) 04 50 71 31 89

Feucherolles

15 | 6 | 5

Sur ce parcours assez vallonné, la mise en oeuvre des reliefs a été faite avec intelligence, et avec le souci d'éviter les coups aveugles. Cette franchise a beaucoup contribué à sa réputation. Très varié, le dessin de Jean-Marie Poellot met en jeu tous les types d'obstacles (il y a cinq lacs) et exige tous les coups de golf; il propose fréquemment des choix stratégiques intéressants, et des situations de petit jeu excitantes. Les trous sont de bonne longueur, à l'exception du 13, un par 3 démesuré, mais on ne recommandera les départs arrière qu'aux handicaps très bas. Très travaillés, les greens demandent beaucoup de finesse et d'attention pour ne pas y abandonner trop de points. Déjà grands à leur plantation, les arbres délimitent maintenant beaucoup mieux les trous. Le fonctionnement du club est résolument commercial, mais l'ensemble est, sinon chaleureux, du moins accueillant. Cependant, le club-house mériterait pour le moins un rafraîchissement, bien qu'il ne soit pas si ancien.

A comparatively hilly course where relief has been employed intelligently to carefully avoid blind shots. This honest side to the layout has done much to help the course's reputation. The very varied design of the architect Jean-Marie Poellot brings all types of hazard into play (there are 5 lakes) and demands every shot in the book. Interestingly, the layout often gives a choice of strategy and some exciting short-game situations around the greens. All the holes are of a good length except the outsized 13th hole, a par-3 of over 220 yards, but generally the back-tees are to be recommended for single-figure handicappers only. A lot of work has gone into the greens, which require more than a touch of finesse if you want to avoid too many 3-putts. Already tall when planted, trees now outline holes much more clearly. The club is a totally commercial affair but the whole place, although lacking warmth, does at least extend a welcome. The club-house has lost some of its polish.

Golf de Feucherolles — 1993

Sainte-Gemme
F -78810 FEUCHEROLLES

Office	Secrétariat	(33) 01 30 54 94 94
Pro shop	Pro-shop	(33) 01 30 54 94 94
Fax	Fax	(33) 01 30 54 92 37
Web	www.golf-de-feucherolles.com	
Situation	Situation	Paris, 39 km
Annual closure	Fermeture annuelle	no
Weekly closure	Fermeture hebdomadaire	Wednesday

(mercredi) 1/11→28/2

Fees main season Tarifs haute saison — 18 holes

	Week days Semaine	We/Bank holidays We/Férié
Individual Individuel	€ 49	€ 65
Couple Couple	€ 98	€ 130

Under 26: € 30 (week days)
Special GF for Seniors and Ladies: monday (lundi)

Caddie Caddie on request **Electric Trolley** Chariot électrique yes
Buggy Voiturette yes **Clubs** Clubs yes
Credit cards Cartes de crédit
VISA - CB - Eurocard - MasterCard - AMEX - DC - JCB

Access Accès : Paris A13 → Versailles, Exit (Sortie) Saint-Germain-en-Laye → Saint-Nom-la- Bretèche, → Feucherolles
Map 15 on page 188 Carte 15 Page 188

GOLF COURSE — PARCOURS — 15/20

Site	Site	
Maintenance	Entretien	
Architect	Architecte	Jean-Marie Poellot
Type	Type	parkland, open country
Relief	Relief	
Water in play	Eau en jeu	
Exp. to wind	Exposé au vent	
Trees in play	Arbres en jeu	

Scorecard Carte de score	Chp. Chp.	Mens Mess.	Ladies Da.
Length Long.	6348	5877	4960
Par	72	72	72
Slope system	141	138	137

Advised golfing ability Niveau de jeu recommandé — 0 12 24 36
Hcp required Handicap exigé — 36 (w/e)

CLUB HOUSE & AMENITIES — CLUB HOUSE ET ANNEXES — 6/10

Pro shop Pro-shop
Driving range Practice
Sheltered couvert 4 mats - On grass sur herbe no, 11 mats open air - Putting-green putting-green yes (2)
Pitching-green pitching green no

HOTEL FACILITIES — ENVIRONNEMENT HOTELIER — 5/10

HOTELS HÔTELS

La Forestière - 30 rooms, D € 205 - Saint-Germain 12 km
Tel (33) 01 30 10 38 38, Fax (33) 01 39 73 73 88

Le Pavillon Henri IV - Saint-Germain 12 km
42 rooms, D € 160
Tel (33) 01 39 10 15 15, Fax (33) 01 39 73 93 73

Ermitage des Loges - Saint-Germain 12 km
56 rooms, D € 135
Tel (33) 01 39 21 50 90, Fax (33) 01 39 21 50 91

RESTAURANTS RESTAURANTS

Les Trois Marches - Versailles 10 km - Tel (33) 01 39 50 25 08
Le Potager du Roy - Versailles 10 km - Tel (33) 01 39 50 35 34
La Feuillantine - Saint-Germain 12 km - Tel (33) 01 34 51 04 24

Fontainebleau

17 | 7 | 7

Situé à l'orée de la superbe forêt de Fontainebleau, ce parcours est l'un des plus tranquilles de la région parisienne, et fait partie de ces grands refuges d'une certaine tradition britannique. Au cours des années, certaines retouches – pas toujours heureuses – ont été apportées au dessin original, notamment sur quelques greens, comme celui du 15 aveugle et plat. De même, le profil des buttes de bunkers devrait être restauré dans le style de Simpson (voir les exemples à Chantilly). C'est un regret mineur en regard des satisfactions visuelles et golfiques que l'on peut éprouver ici, au milieu des chênes, des pins et des hêtres, où l'on devine parfois les ombres des biches, où l'on dérange souvent lièvres et lapins. Grâce au terrain très sablonneux et au gazon très souple, on peut découvrir ici toute l'année un parcours plus que plaisant mais pas si facile, car les greens sont souvent petits et parfois très torturés, bien protégés et un bon score n'est jamais le fait du hasard. Un parcours complet, où l'aspect visuel ne cesse d'être travaillé.

This course, lying on the edge of the magnificent forest of Fontainebleau, is one of the great bastions of British tradition around Paris. Over the years, a number of alterations have been made to the original layout, particularly on a number of greens, one example being the 15th green which is now flat and blind. Likewise, the shapes of bunker sand-hills should be restored to the original Simpson style (cf. Chantilly). This is only a minor gripe given the visual and golfing pleasure to be had here amidst the oak, pine and beech trees, where you can sometimes catch sight of deer or disturb hares and rabbits. With very sandy terrain and plush grass, you can play this more than pleasant and none too difficult course all year, although the greens are often small, very torturous and well protected. Here, a good score is never down to chance on a course that has everything and where visual appeal has been further improved by removing the unsightly paths from tee to green.

Golf de Fontainebleau — 1909

Route d'Orléans
F - 77300 FONTAINEBLEAU

Office	Secrétariat	(33) 01 64 22 22 95
Pro shop	Pro-shop	(33) 01 64 22 74 19
Fax	Fax	(33) 01 64 22 63 76
E-mail		golf.fontainebleau@wanadoo.fr
Situation	Situation	Fontainebleau, 1 km
Annual closure	Fermeture annuelle	no
Weekly closure	Fermeture hebdomadaire	tuesday/mardi
Fees main season	Tarifs haute saison	full day

	Week days Semaine	We/Bank holidays We/Férié
Individual Individuel	€ 75	€ 100*
Couple Couple	€ 150	€ 200*

* We : members & guests (membres et invités)
07/08: open at We (ouvert en We)

Caddie Caddie on request **Electric Trolley** Chariot électrique yes

Buggy Voiturette no **Clubs** Clubs yes

Credit cards Cartes de crédit
VISA - CB - MasterCard - Eurocard

Access Accès : A6 Exit (Sortie) Fontainebleau.
N7 → Fontainebleau. "Carrefour de l'Obélisque",
N152 → Malesherbes. Golf 500 m on right hand side.
Map 3 on page 164 Carte 3 Page 164

GOLF COURSE — PARCOURS — 17/20

Site	Site	
Maintenance	Entretien	
Architect	Architecte	Tom Simpson
Type	Type	forest
Relief	Relief	
Water in play	Eau en jeu	
Exp. to wind	Exposé au vent	
Trees in play	Arbres en jeu	

Scorecard Carte de score	Chp. Chp.	Mens Mess.	Ladies Da.
Length Long.	6074	5711	4833
Par	72	72	72
Slope system	130	124	115

Advised golfing ability Niveau de jeu recommandé — 0 12 24 36

Hcp required Handicap exigé — no

CLUB HOUSE & AMENITIES — CLUB HOUSE ET ANNEXES — 7/10

Pro shop Pro-shop
Driving range Practice
Sheltered couvert 6 mats - On grass sur herbe yes - Putting-green putting-green yes - Pitching-green pitching green yes

HOTEL FACILITIES — ENVIRONNEMENT HOTELIER — 7/10

HOTELS HÔTELS
Aigle Noir - 53 rooms, D € 205 - Fontainebleau 2 km
Tel (33) 01 60 74 60 00, Fax (33) 01 60 74 60 01

Napoléon - 57 rooms, D € 125 - Fontainebleau 2 km
Tel (33) 01 60 39 50 50, Fax (33) 01 64 22 20 87

Hôtel de Londres - 12 rooms, D € 138 - Fontainebleau 2 km
Tel (33) 01 64 22 20 21, Fax (33) 01 60 72 39 16

RESTAURANTS RESTAURANTS
L'Angélus - Barbizon 10 km - Tel (33) 01 60 66 40 30

Table des Maréchaux - Fontainebleau 2 km
Tel (33) 01 60 39 50 50

Croquembouche - Fontainebleau 2 km
Tel (33) 01 64 22 01 57

Fontcaude

14 | 6 | 6

L'environnement immobilier est assez massif et pas très beau, mais ce parcours est un bon complément dans une région de bonne qualité golfique, notamment avec La Grande Motte, Massane, Cap d'Agde et Nîmes-Campagne. Il a été dessiné par Chris Pittman sur un terrain relativement mouvementé, où quelques accidents de terrain, des arbustes, la garrigue et quelques grands arbres interviennent pour compliquer le jeu, ainsi que des dénivellations et dévers parfois préoccupants. Si l'on ajoute quelques trous en bordure de rivière, des greens bien modelés à l'américaine et des bunkers assez profonds pour inciter à s'entraîner avant de les affronter, les joueurs trouveront là un parcours intelligent, varié et amusant, mais les meilleurs estimeront toujours qu'il manque "un petit quelque chose" pour en faire un grand parcours. On imagine une préparation de parcours plus exigeante, mais elle ne convient pas toujours aux joueurs moyens…

Laid out in an environment of property development singularly lacking in appeal, this course is a good addition to a great region for golf, with in particular La Grande Motte, Massane, Cap d'Agde and Nîmes-Campagne in the neighbourhood. It was designed by Chris Pittman over comparatively hilly terrain where a few drastic features, small bushes, the "garrigue" and a few hefty trees actively complicate the course. The same applies to some of the steep slopes and inclines, which may cause considerable concern. Add to this a few holes alongside a river, well-contoured US-style greens and bunkers that are deep enough to prompt some sand practice before the round, and you have here a varied and amusing course but one where the best players will doubtless feel that there is something missing for it to become great. We feel that Fontcaude could benefit from a more demanding set-up, but mid- to high-handicappers might not agree.

Golf de Fontcaude 1991
Domaine de Fontcaude
F - 34990 JUVIGNAC

Office	Secrétariat	(33) 04 67 45 90 10
Pro shop	Pro-shop	(33) 04 67 45 90 10
Fax	Fax	(33) 04 67 45 90 20
Web	www.golfhotelmontpellier.com	
Situation	Situation	Montpellier, 2 km
Annual closure	Fermeture annuelle	no
Weekly closure	Fermeture hebdomadaire	no

Fees main season Tarifs haute saison 18 holes

	Week days / Semaine	We/Bank holidays / We/Férié
Individual Individuel	€ 53	€ 53
Couple Couple	€ 106	€ 106

Under 18 and Students (–25): € 40

Caddie Caddie no — **Electric Trolley** Chariot électrique no
Buggy Voiturette yes — **Clubs** Clubs yes
Credit cards Cartes de crédit
VISA - CB - Eurocard - MasterCard - AMEX - DC - JCB

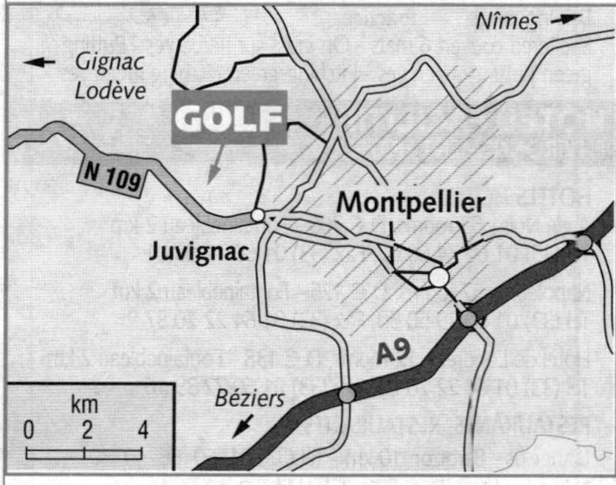

Access Accès : Montpellier, N109 → Lodève
Map 13 on page 185 Carte 13 Page 185

GOLF COURSE — PARCOURS 14/20

Site	Site	
Maintenance	Entretien	
Architect	Architecte	Chris Pittman
Type	Type	residential, hilly
Relief	Relief	
Water in play	Eau en jeu	
Exp. to wind	Exposé au vent	
Trees in play	Arbres en jeu	

Scorecard / Carte de score	Chp. / Chp.	Mens / Mess.	Ladies / Da.
Length Long.	5917	5465	4666
Par	72	72	72
Slope system	134	123	124

Advised golfing ability / Niveau de jeu recommandé: 0 12 24 36

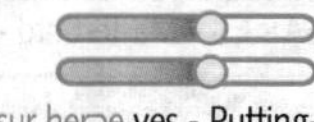

Hcp required Handicap exigé 35

CLUB HOUSE & AMENITIES — CLUB HOUSE ET ANNEXES 6/10

Pro shop Pro-shop
Driving range Practice
Sheltered couvert 5 mats - On grass sur herbe yes - Putting-green putting-green yes - Pitching-green pitching green yes

HOTEL FACILITIES — ENVIRONNEMENT HOTELIER 6/10

HOTELS HÔTELS
Golf de Fontcaude - 46 rooms, D € 126 - on site
Tel (33) 04 67 45 90 00, Fax (33) 04 67 45 90 20

Holiday Inn Métropole - Montpellier 2 km
80 rooms, D € 175
Tel (33) 04 67 12 32 32, Fax (33) 04 67 92 13 02

Hôtel Guilhem - 35 rooms, D € 130 - Montpellier 2 km
Tel (33) 04 67 52 90 90, Fax (33) 04 67 60 57 67

RESTAURANTS RESTAURANTS
Jardin des Sens - Montpellier 2 km - Tel (33) 04 99 58 38 38
L'Olivier - Montpellier 2 km - Tel (33) 04 67 92 86 28
Cellier Morel - Montpellier 2 km - Tel (33) 04 67 66 46 36

Fontenailles *Jaune + Blanc*

14 | 7 | 5

Confortable et plaisant, le complexe club-house-Hôtel mérite que l'on s'y attarde après avoir joué. Dans cet ensemble ambitieux de 27 trous, le 18 trous "Blanc" est considéré comme le parcours principal, même si le "Rouge" propose aussi quelques bons trous. L'architecte Michel Gayon a travaillé avec dextérité et imagination ce vaste espace plat et joliment boisé. Quelques trous assez courts permettent de ne pas trop gâter une carte de score forcément mise à mal sur d'autres trous, qui exigent beaucoup de puissance au drive et des seconds coups longs et précis. C'est en général un parcours mieux adapté aux frappeurs qu'aux purs techniciens, comme souvent avec son auteur. En tout cas, certains obstacles peu visibles impliquent de le jouer plusieurs fois pour bien le connaître avant d'espérer bien y scorer. L'entretien du parcours est généralement de bonne qualité, mais il reste toujours un peu humide en hiver, notamment dans les zones les plus ombragées.

The club-house and hotel resort is comfortable and pleasant enough to spend some time there after a round. In this ambitious 27-hole complex, the 18-hole "White" course is considered to be the main layout, even though the 9-hole "Red" alternative also features a few interesting holes. Architect Michel Gayon has employed a lot of skill and imagination in developing this enormous flat space, which has more than its fair share of woodland. Here, you take advantage of a few short holes in order to protect a card that will definitely be hard pushed to survive some of the others, which require power-play off the tee followed by long, straight second shots. Generally speaking, this is a course for long-hitters rather than for the artiste, as is often the case with Gayon. In any case, a number of hard-to-see hazards call for several outings before hoping to card a good score. Green-keeping is generally good but the course is bit damp in winter, especially in the shadier areas.

Golf de Fontenailles — 1991

Domaine de Bois-Boudran
F - 77370 FONTENAILLES

Office	Secrétariat	(33) 01 64 60 51 52
Pro shop	Pro-shop	(33) 01 64 60 51 52
Fax	Fax	(33) 01 60 67 52 12
Web	www.hotel.fontenailles.com	
Situation	Situation	Melun (pop. 35 320), 25 km
Annual closure	Fermeture annuelle	24/12→6/1
Weekly closure	Fermeture hebdomadaire	no

Fees main season Tarifs haute saison — full day

	Week days Semaine	We/Bank holidays We/Férié
Individual Individuel	€ 35	€ 60
Couple Couple	€ 60	€ 100

Under 21: € 10 / 35 (We)

Caddie Caddie no — **Electric Trolley** Chariot électrique yes

Buggy Voiturette yes — **Clubs** Clubs yes

Credit cards Cartes de crédit
VISA - CB - Eurocard - MasterCard - AMEX - DC - JCB

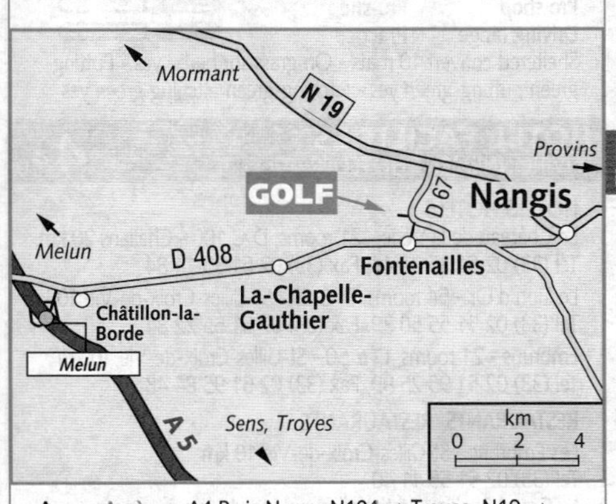

Access Accès : • A4 Paris-Nancy, N104 → Troyes, N19 → Provins • A5 → Melun, Exit (Sortie) 16 Châtillon-la-Borde, D408 → Nangis
Map 3 on page 165 Carte 3 Page 165

GOLF COURSE — PARCOURS 14/20

Site	Site	
Maintenance	Entretien	
Architect	Architecte	Michel Gayon
Type	Type	parkland
Relief	Relief	
Water in play	Eau en jeu	
Exp. to wind	Exposé au vent	
Trees in play	Arbres en jeu	

Scorecard Carte de score	Chp. Chp.	Mens Mess.	Ladies Da.
Length Long.	6229	5875	4947
Par	72	72	72
Slope system	138	137	129

Advised golfing ability Niveau de jeu recommandé — 0 12 24 36

Hcp required Handicap exigé — no

CLUB HOUSE & AMENITIES — CLUB HOUSE ET ANNEXES 7/10

Pro shop Pro-shop
Driving range Practice
Sheltered couvert 5 mats - On grass sur herbe yes (Summer) - Putting-green putting-green yes - Pitching-green pitching green yes

HOTEL FACILITIES — ENVIRONNEMENT HOTELIER 5/10

HOTELS HÔTELS

Domaine de Bois-Boudran - 51 rooms, D € 145 - on site
Tel (33) 01 64 60 51 00, Fax (33) 01 60 67 52 12

La Forge - 16 rooms, D € 39 - Fontenailles 1 km
Tel (33) 01 64 08 44 11, Fax (33) 01 60 67 56 26

RESTAURANTS RESTAURANTS

Domaine de Bois-Boudran - on site
Tel (33) 01 64 60 51 00

La Forge - Fontenailles 1 km
Tel (33) 01 64 08 44 11

Fontenelles (Les)

13 | 6 | 4

Non loin de Saint-Jean-de-Monts, ce golf complète un bel itinéraire dans la province historique de Vendée. A proximité de la station balnéaire de Saint-Gilles-Croix-de-Vie, l'architecte Yves Bureau a conçu (comme à son habitude) un parcours très honnête et pour tous niveaux, dans un site de campagne aux reliefs très doux, dans un paysage de chênes verts et de pins maritimes. Des plans d'eau pas trop en jeu agrémentent sur une demi-douzaine de trous un dessin sans pièges, en harmonie visuelle avec les marais de la région adapté à tous les types de joueurs. Ce parcours est de longueur respectable des départs arrière, ce qui permettra aux meilleurs de s'exprimer avec plaisir mais sans trop de soucis. Pour eux, certains des plans d'eau compliquent un peu les choses. Notons quelques modifications, le 3 devenant un par 3 et le 6 un par 5. Un bon et joli golf de vacances, où le vent peut apporter un piment.

Close to Saint-Jean-de-Monts, this course is a fine addition to a great golfing itinerary through the historical province of La Vendée. Not far from the seaside resort of Saint-Gilles-Croix-de-Vie, architect Yves Bureau has, as usual, designed a very fair golf course for all golfers in gently undulating countryside, lined with oak trees and maritime pines. On half a dozen holes, stretches of water enhance a layout that is free of hidden traps and tailored to all types of golfer. Visually, the course also blends in well with the region's marshlands. This is a good length course from the back tees, thus giving the better players the chance to show their mettle without too much to worry about, although for them certain new stretches of water can make life a little more complicated. Make a note of a few alterations: hole N°3 is now a par 3 and N°6 a par 5. A good and pretty holiday course where the wind can add a little spice.

Golf des Fontenelles — 1990

F - 85220 L'AIGUILLON-SUR-VIE

Office	Secrétariat	(33) 02 51 54 13 94
Pro shop	Pro-shop	(33) 02 51 54 13 94
Fax	Fax	(33) 02 51 55 45 77
Web	www.formule-golf.com	
Situation	Situation	Nantes, 65 km

St-Gilles-Croix-de-Vie (pop. 6 290), 10 km

Annual closure — Fermeture annuelle — no

Weekly closure — Fermeture hebdomadaire — monday/lundi (01/11 → 01/03)

Fees main season / Tarifs haute saison — 18 holes	Week days / Semaine	We/Bank holidays / We/Férié
Individual Individuel	€ 46	€ 46
Couple Couple	€ 92	€ 92

Juniors: – 50%

Caddie Caddie no — Electric Trolley Chariot électrique no

Buggy Voiturette yes — Clubs Clubs yes

Credit cards Cartes de crédit
VISA - CB - Eurocard - MasterCard

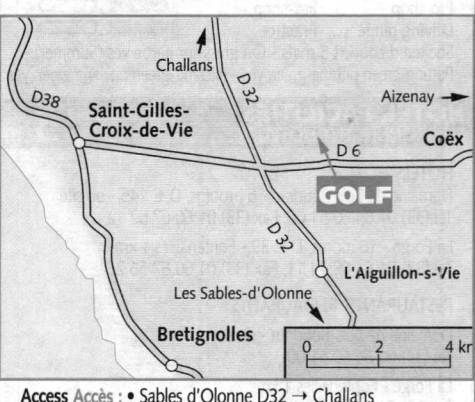

Access Accès : • Sables d'Olonne D32 → Challans
• La Roche-sur-Yon → Aizenay/St-Gilles-Croix-de-Vie D6.
Go through Coëx, Golf 2 km.

Map 6 on page 170 Carte 6 Page 170

GOLF COURSE — PARCOURS — 13/20

Site	Site	
Maintenance	Entretien	
Architect	Architecte	Yves Bureau
Type	Type	copse
Relief	Relief	
Water in play	Eau en jeu	
Exp. to wind	Exposé au vent	
Trees in play	Arbres en jeu	

Scorecard / Carte de score	Chp. / Chp.	Mens / Mess.	Ladies / Da.
Length Long.	6042	5597	4640
Par	72	72	72
Slope system	132	125	119

Advised golfing ability / Niveau de jeu recommandé — 0 12 24 36

Hcp required — Handicap exigé — no

CLUB HOUSE & AMENITIES — CLUB HOUSE ET ANNEXES — 6/10

Pro shop — Pro-shop
Driving range — Practice
Sheltered couvert 10 mats - On grass sur herbe yes - Putting-green putting-green yes - Pitching-green pitching green yes

HOTEL FACILITIES — ENVIRONNEMENT HOTELIER — 4/10

HOTELS HÔTELS

Le Château de la Vérie - 21 rooms, D € 100 - Challans 20 km
Tel (33) 02 51 35 33 44, Fax (33) 02 51 35 14 84

Le Lion d'Or - 54 rooms, D € 60 - St-Gilles-Croix-de-Vie 10 km
Tel (33) 02 51 55 50 39, Fax (33) 02 51 55 22 84

Embruns - 21 rooms, D € 50 - St-Gilles-Croix-de-Vie 10 km
Tel (33) 02 51 95 25 99, Fax (33) 02 51 95 84 48

RESTAURANTS RESTAURANTS

Les Embruns - St-Gilles-Croix-de-Vie 10 km
Tel (33) 02 51 55 11 40

La Grand Roche - Bretignolles-sur-Mer 10 km
Tel (33) 02 51 90 15 21

Gîte du Tourne-Pierre - Challans (D 69) 20 km
Tel (33) 02 51 68 14 78

Four Seasons Provence *Château* 17 | 9 | 8

L'alliance du géant de l'informatique Dietmar Hopp et du groupe Four Seasons a permis la création de ce vaste resort dont on ne trouve guère l'équivalent qu'aux Etats-Unis. Deux parcours de 18 trous y ont vu le jour dans l'arrière-pays provençal, tous deux dûs au crayon de Dave Thomas. "Le Château" est l'une de ses meilleures créations, par l'exigence qu'il impose, tant du point de vue de la précision que de la longueur. De ce côté d'ailleurs, on pourrait souhaiter quelques départs avancés supplémentaires pour rendre le parcours plus "humain" au commun des mortels, bien que la beauté des paysages atténue leurs possibles frustrations. En dépit d'un relief certain et de nombreux obstacles stratégiquement placés, ce "Château" est très hospitalier dans la mesure où il ne dissimule pas ses pièges. L'architecte a particulièrement soigné les aspects paysagers, et joué avec bonheur avec les éléments naturels, rochers, arbres et cours d'eau. Visuellement et techniquement, une réussite... peut-être pas pour tous les swings !

IT giant Dietmar Hopp and the Four Seasons group joined forces to produce this huge resort that only has any real equivalent in the USA. Two 18-hole courses have been built in the Provence hinterland, both designed by Dave Thomas. "Le Château" is one of his best achievements through the demands its places on golfers in terms of both accuracy and length. Talking of length, it might have been good to build some extra tee-boxes further forward to make the course more of a feasible proposition for the common mortal, even though the beautiful landscape all around may soothe the frustration. Despite some definite slopes and the many strategically placed bunkers, this course does show some mercy in that the traps are never sneakily concealed. The architect has taken special care over his landscaping and has successfully played around with the natural elements such as rocks, trees and streams. Visually and technically this is great golfing, but maybe not for every kind of golfer.

Four Seasons Golf Club Provence at Terre Blanche — 2000

Domaine de Terre Blanche
F - 83440 TOURRETTES

Office	Secrétariat	(33) 04 94 39 36 93
Pro shop	Pro-shop	(33) 04 94 39 36 93
Fax	Fax	(33) 04 94 39 36 98
Web	www.fourseasons.com/provence	
Situation	Situation	Cannes, 45 km
Annual closure	Fermeture annuelle	no
Weekly closure	Fermeture hebdomadaire	no

Fees main season Tarifs haute saison	18 holes	
	Week days Semaine	We/Bank holidays We/Férié
Individual Individuel	€ 95	€ 95
Couple Couple	€ 190	€ 190

Juniors: € 71

Caddie Caddie no — **Electric Trolley** Chariot électrique yes

Buggy Voiturette yes — **Clubs** Clubs yes

Credit cards Cartes de crédit
VISA - CB - Eurocard - MasterCard - AMEX - DC - JCB

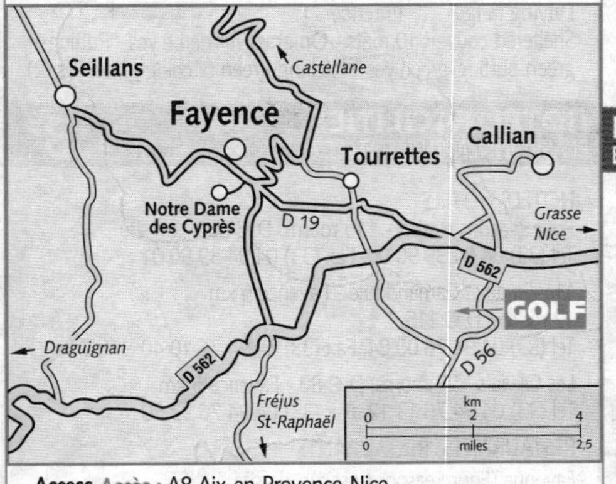

Access Accès : A8 Aix-en-Provence-Nice,
Exit Fayence (39) → Fayence, → Bagnols-en-Forêt
Map 14 on page 187 Carte 14 Page 187

GOLF COURSE — PARCOURS 17/20

Site	Site	
Maintenance	Entretien	
Architect	Architecte	Dave Thomas
Type	Type	country, forest
Relief	Relief	
Water in play	Eau en jeu	
Exp. to wind	Exposé au vent	
Trees in play	Arbres en jeu	

Scorecard Carte de score	Chp. Chp.	Mens Mess.	Ladies Da.
Length Long.	6616	6044	5178
Par	72	72	72
Slope system	149	146	138

Advised golfing ability Niveau de jeu recommandé: 0 12 24 36

Hcp required Handicap exigé: 35

CLUB HOUSE & AMENITIES — CLUB HOUSE ET ANNEXES 9/10

Pro shop Pro-shop
Driving range Practice
Sheltered couvert 10 mats - On grass sur herbe yes - Putting-green putting-green yes - Pitching-green pitching green yes (2)

HOTEL FACILITIES — ENVIRONNEMENT HOTELIER 8/10

HOTELS HÔTELS
Four Seasons Resort - 115 rooms, D € 600 - on site
Tel (33) 04 94 39 90 00, Fax (33) 04 94 39 90 01

Moulin de la Camandoule - Fayence 5 km
12 rooms, D € 115
Tel (33) 04 94 76 00 84, Fax (33) 04 94 76 10 40

Les Oliviers - 22 rooms, D € 80 - Fayence 5 km
Tel (33) 04 94 76 13 12, Fax (33) 04 94 76 92 50

RESTAURANTS RESTAURANTS
Faventia (Four Seasons Resort) - on site
Tel (33) 04 94 39 90 00
Le Castellaras - Fayence 7 km - Tel (33) 04 94 76 13 80
Le Temps des Cerises - Fayence 5 km - Tel (33) 04 94 76 01 19

Four Seasons Provence *Le Riou*

16	9	8

Si "Le Château" se défend beaucoup par sa longueur, "Le Riou" le fait par sa technicité. L'architecte Dave Thomas a voulu préserver au maximum la forêt de pins et de chênes, il faudra souvent s'en remettre à la sagesse pour bien le négocier. L'utilisation d'une voiturette permet d'en mieux absorber les reliefs, ainsi que de préserver sa lucidité pour en négocier les difficultés, celles-ci tenant d'ailleurs plus souvent d'un judicieux choix de club que de nécessité d'être un virtuose. Soyez sûr que vos 14 clubs seront nécessaires. On remarquera aussi l'attention apportée au dessin des greens sur les deux parcours, dont les modulations peuvent surprendre. Deux parcours complémentaires, un ensemble hôtelier raffiné, une restauration déjà étoilée, des services impeccables, tout cela se paie, c'est évident. Mais le sourire largement dispensé ici n'a pas de prix. On aimerait le trouver plus souvent ailleurs...

While "Le Château" keeps golfers at bay with its length, "Le Riou" is perhaps more for the arty technician. Architect Dave Thomas sets out to preserve as much as possible the forest of pine and oak and you will need your thinking cap firmly in place if you hope to get around safely. A buggy will help with the sloping terrain and also let you keep a clear head to weather the difficulties which, more often than not, come down to the right choice of club rather than virtuoso golfing prowess. Make sure your 14 clubs are what you really need. Equally impressive is the care taken over the contouring of the greens on both courses; the breaks and slopes have surprised more than one golfer. So, two complementary courses, a sophisticated hotel resort, a gourmet restaurant (already star-rated) and immaculate service... and it all comes at a price, of course. But the cheerful welcome that abounds here is simply priceless. How we would like to see it more often elsewhere.

Four Seasons Golf Club Provence at Terre Blanche — 2001

Domaine de Terre Blanche
F - 83440 TOURRETTES

Office	Secrétariat	(33) 04 94 39 36 93
Pro shop	Pro-shop	(33) 04 94 39 36 93
Fax	Fax	(33) 04 94 39 36 98
Web	www.fourseasons.com/provence	
Situation	Situation	Cannes, 45 km
Annual closure	Fermeture annuelle	no
Weekly closure	Fermeture hebdomadaire	no

Fees main season Tarifs haute saison — 18 holes

	Week days Semaine	We/Bank holidays We/Férié
Individual Individuel	€ 95	€ 95
Couple Couple	€ 190	€ 190

Juniors: € 71

Caddie Caddie no — **Electric Trolley** Chariot électrique yes

Buggy Voiturette yes **Clubs** Clubs yes

Credit cards Cartes de crédit

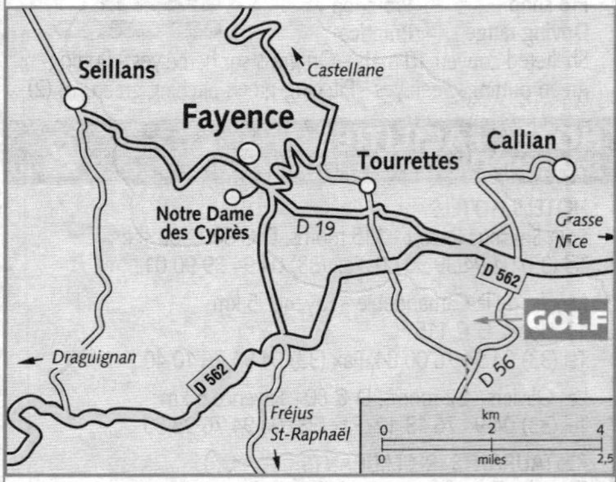

VISA - CB - Eurocard - MasterCard - AMEX - DC - JCB

Access Accès : A8 Aix-en-Provence-Nice, Exit Fayence (39) → Fayence, → Bagnols-en-Forêt

Map 14 on page 187 Carte 14 Page 187

GOLF COURSE — PARCOURS 16/20

Site	Site	
Maintenance	Entretien	
Architect	Architecte	Dave Thomas
Type	Type	forest, hilly
Relief	Relief	
Water in play	Eau en jeu	
Exp. to wind	Exposé au vent	
Trees in play	Arbres en jeu	

Scorecard / Carte de score	Chp. / Chp.	Mens / Mess.	Ladies / Da.
Length Long.	6005	5591	4926
Par	72	72	72
Slope system	146	139	132

Advised golfing ability Niveau de jeu recommandé — 0 12 24 36

Hcp required Handicap exigé 35

CLUB HOUSE & AMENITIES — CLUB HOUSE ET ANNEXES 9/10

Pro shop Pro-shop

Driving range Practice

Sheltered couvert 10 mats - On grass sur herbe yes - Putting-green putting-green yes - Pitching-green pitching green yes (2)

HOTEL FACILITIES — ENVIRONNEMENT HOTELIER 8/10

HOTELS HÔTELS

Four Seasons Resort - 115 rooms, D € 600 - on site
Tel (33) 04 94 39 90 00, Fax (33) 04 94 39 90 01

Moulin de la Camandoule - Fayence 5 km
12 rooms, D € 115
Tel (33) 04 94 76 00 84, Fax (33) 04 94 76 10 40

Les Oliviers - 22 rooms, D € 80 - Fayence 5 km
Tel (33) 04 94 76 13 12, Fax (33) 04 94 76 92 50

RESTAURANTS RESTAURANTS

Faventia (Four Seasons Resort) - on site
Tel (33) 04 94 39 90 00

Le Castellaras - Fayence 7 km - Tel (33) 04 94 76 13 80

Le Temps des Cerises - Fayence 5 km - Tel (33) 04 94 76 01 19

Frégate

16	7	7

Ronald Fream a tiré le meilleur parti d'un site très accidenté, raisonnablement urbanisé, avec un hôtel confortable. Les vues sur la mer sont splendides et les trous souvent spectaculaires. Il faut payer le prix de ce décor tourmenté, dans une région où les reliefs sont très accentués : de nombreux dévers peuvent rendre les mises en jeu problématiques, quelques coups sont aveugles, le rough est souvent très pénalisant, les fairways parfois étroits, et quelques rochers viennent dangereusement en jeu. Les départs dominent en général les trous, ce qui permet de mesurer les risques. Fort heureusement, beaucoup de bordures de fairway ont été très bien aménagées, et les dangers sont fréquemment plus visuels que réels. Très bien paysagé, très technique, c'est un parcours qu'il vaut mieux jouer en voiturette, pour conserver des forces physiques et mentales, non seulement pour choisir les bons clubs, mais aussi pour les utiliser. Si l'on connaît mal le parcours, ou avec le vent, il faut d'abord penser à s'amuser.

Ronald Fream has made good use of a very hilly and now reasonably urbanized site with a good hotel. The views over the Mediterranean are splendid and some holes often quite spectacular. But this twisted and winding scenery comes at a cost in a region of rolling hills and dales. A lot of slanting fairways make life a little difficult at times, a few shots are blind, the rough gives no quarter, the fairways are sometimes very tight indeed and a few rocks come dangerously into play. Tee-boxes are mostly elevated so you can clearly see the risks awaiting you below and fortunately many of the fairway edges have been cleaned up. The dangers are in fact often more visual than real. Beautifully landscaped and a technically demanding course, Frégate is better played with a buggy in order to preserve mental and physical strength, not only for choosing the right club but also for using it in the right way. If you don't know the course or if it's too windy, just have fun.

Golf de Frégate — 1992

Route de Bandol RD 559
F - 83270 SAINT-CYR-SUR-MER

Office Secrétariat (33) 04 94 29 38 00
Pro shop Pro-shop (33) 04 94 29 38 00
Fax Fax (33) 04 94 29 96 94
Web www.fregate.dolce.com
Situation Situation Toulon, 25 km
Bandol (pop. 7 430), 3 km
Annual closure Fermeture annuelle no
Weekly closure Fermeture hebdomadaire no

Fees main season Tarifs haute saison 18 holes

	Week days Semaine	We/Bank holidays We/Férié
Individual Individuel	€ 65	€ 65
Couple Couple	€ 130	€ 130

Juniors: – 50% / Students: – 30%

Caddie Caddie on request **Electric Trolley** Chariot électrique yes

Buggy Voiturette yes **Clubs** Clubs yes

Credit cards Cartes de crédit
VISA - CB - Eurocard - MasterCard - AMEX

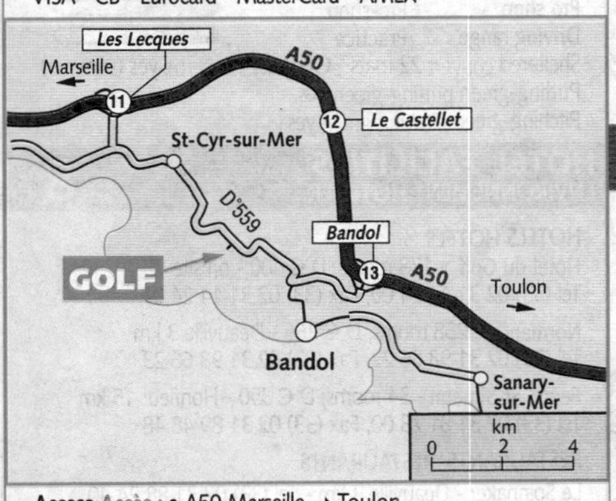

Access Accès : • A50 Marseille → Toulon, Exit (Sortie) Saint-Cyr-sur-Mer
• A50 Toulon → Marseille, Exit Bandol, D559
Map 14 on page 186 Carte 14 Page 186

GOLF COURSE PARCOURS 16/20

Site Site
Maintenance Entretien
Architect Architecte Ronald Fream
Type Type seaside course, hilly
Relief Relief
Water in play Eau en jeu
Exp. to wind Exposé au vent
Trees in play Arbres en jeu

Scorecard Carte de score	Chp. Chp.	Mens Mess.	Ladies Da.
Length Long.	6398	5847	4567
Par	72	72	72
Slope system	134	127	128

Advised golfing ability Niveau de jeu recommandé 0 12 24 36
Hcp required Handicap exigé no

CLUB HOUSE & AMENITIES CLUB HOUSE ET ANNEXES 7/10

Pro shop Pro-shop
Driving range Practice
Sheltered couvert 20 mats - On grass sur herbe no, 32 mats open air - Putting-green putting-green yes (2) - Pitching-green pitching green yes

HOTEL FACILITIES ENVIRONNEMENT HOTELIER 7/10

HOTELS HÔTELS
Frégate - 133 rooms, D € 200 - on site
Tel (33) 04 94 29 39 39, Fax (33) 04 94 29 39 40

L'Ile Rousse - 55 rooms, D € 212 - Bandol 4 km
Tel (33) 04 94 29 33 00, Fax (33) 04 94 29 49 49

Bérard - La Cadière-d'Azur 7 km
34 rooms, D € 180
Tel (33) 04 94 90 11 43, Fax (33) 04 94 90 01 94

RESTAURANTS RESTAURANTS
L'Ile Rousse - Bandol 4 km - Tel (33) 04 94 29 33 00
Le Mas des Vignes - on site - Tel (33) 04 94 29 39 39
Le Clocher - Bandol 4 km - Tel (33) 04 94 32 47 65

Golf Barrière Deauville

15	7	8

Un ensemble de 27 trous avec un bon 9 trous et un 18 trous de bon niveau, de style très britannique, assez vallonné sans être trop fatigant. Dessiné en 1929 par Tom Simpson, il a été agrandi et beaucoup remanié par Henry Cotton en 1964. Dans un agréable paysage normand, ce parcours avait tendance à se banaliser mais un dessin plus précis des limites de fairways et des roughs, la modification de certains bunkers, la végétation même lui ont donné une nouvelle jeunesse, et imposent de réfléchir davantage sur la stratégie : c'est pourquoi les joueurs de bon niveau y prennent bien plus de plaisir. Il s'agit certes d'un golf commercial, pour les golfeurs en week-end et en vacances, et il convient d'assurer leur satisfaction, mais les progrès réalisés le placent désormais plus haut dans la hiérarchie. C'est bien le meilleur parcours de la région, avec une qualité d'entretien plus constante, facilitée par les travaux de drainage. Il reste court, mais il y a peu de terrain disponible pour l'allonger.

A 27-hole complex with a good 9-hole course and an excellent British style 18-hole layout over rolling countryside. Designed in 1929 by Tom Simpson, it was enlarged and very much restyled by Henry Cotton in 1964. Set in pleasant Normandy countryside, the course was beginning to look a bit ordinary, but clearer demarcation of the fairways and rough, plus changes to certain bunkers and to the general decor have given Deauville a new lease of life and call for more thoughtful strategy. This is why the better players have more fun here than the rest. This is a business venture, of course, for week-enders and holiday-makers, and their enjoyment is naturally important, but with what has been achieved here the course has soared in the rankings. It is the best course in the region with more consistent standards of green-keeping made easier by drainage work. It is still short but there is little land available to make it any longer.

New Golf de Deauville — 1929

Saint-Arnoult
F - 14800 DEAUVILLE

Office	Secrétariat	(33) 02 31 14 24 24
Pro shop	Pro-shop	(33) 02 31 14 24 24
Fax	Fax	(33) 02 31 14 24 25
Web	www.lucienbarriere.com	
Situation	Situation	Deauville, 3 km
Annual closure	Fermeture annuelle	no
Weekly closure (except holidays)	Fermeture hebdomadaire	tuesday/mardi

Fees main season Tarifs haute saison	18 holes	
	Week days Semaine	We/Bank holidays We/Férié
Individual Individuel	€ 50	€ 80
Couple Couple	€ 100	€ 160

After 16:00, GF € 32 (week days) and € 45 (We) / Under 18: € 16 and € 24 (We)

Caddie Caddie on request **Electric Trolley** Chariot électrique yes

Buggy Voiturette yes **Clubs** Clubs yes

Credit cards Cartes de crédit
VISA - CB - Eurocard - MasterCard - AMEX - DC

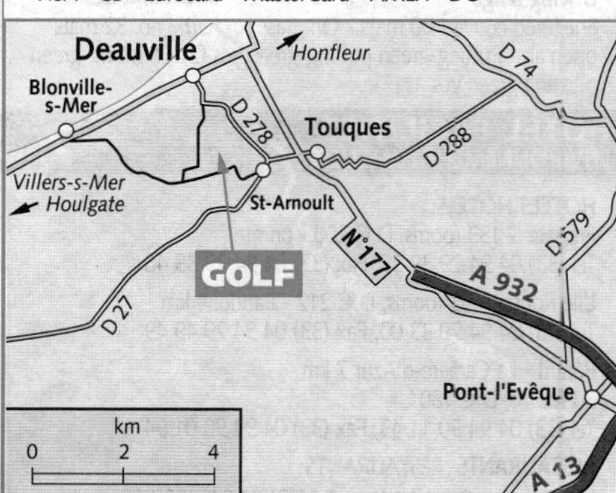

Access Accès : Paris A13, Exit (Sortie) Deauville, N177 → Deauville. Touques, D27 → New Golf
Map 2 on page 163 Carte 2 Page 163

GOLF COURSE — PARCOURS — 15/20

Site	Site	
Maintenance	Entretien	
Architect	Architecte	Tom Simpson, Henry Cotton
Type	Type	parkland, copse
Relief	Relief	
Water in play	Eau en jeu	
Exp. to wind	Exposé au vent	
Trees in play	Arbres en jeu	

Scorecard Carte de score	Chp. Chp.	Mens Mess.	Ladies Da.
Length Long.	5951	5742	4722
Par	71	71	71
Slope system	130	127	124

Advised golfing ability Niveau de jeu recommandé: 0 12 24 36

Hcp required Handicap exigé: 24 Men, 28 Ladies

CLUB HOUSE & AMENITIES — CLUB HOUSE ET ANNEXES — 7/10

Pro shop Pro-shop
Driving range Practice
Sheltered couvert 22 mats - On grass sur herbe yes (summer)
Putting-green putting-green yes
Pitching-green pitching green yes

HOTEL FACILITIES — ENVIRONNEMENT HOTELIER — 8/10

HOTELS HÔTELS

Hôtel du Golf - 178 rooms, D € 400 - on site
Tel (33) 02 31 14 24 00, Fax (33) 02 31 14 24 01

Normandy - 258 rooms, D € 366 - Deauville 3 km
Tel (33) 02 31 98 66 22, Fax (33) 02 31 98 66 23

Ferme St-Siméon - 34 rooms, D € 350 - Honfleur 15 km
Tel (33) 02 31 81 78 00, Fax (33) 02 31 89 48 48

RESTAURANTS RESTAURANTS

Le Spinnaker - Deauville 3 km - Tel (33) 02 31 88 24 40
Le Ciro's - Deauville 3 km - Tel (33) 02 31 14 31 31
La Terrasse et l'Assiette - Honfleur 15 km
Tel (33) 02 31 89 31 33

Golf Barrière La Baule *Bleu*

15 | **7** | **8**

Dans ce resort de 45 trous, l'un des 18 trous (le Rouge) est constitué de 9 trous tracés par Michel Gayon, 9 des 18 trous originaux dessinés par Alliss et Thomas en 1978, les autres constituant un par 35. Le manque d'unité de style a été gommé avec le temps, mais le plaisir d'évoluer dans les espaces ouverts de la campagne de La Baule reste intact, à quelques kilomètres des plages. Un autre 18 trous (Le Bleu) a été dessiné par Michel Gayon et Jacques Lebreton. Il est plus long, plus homogène, dans le même esprit de mise en valeur du paysage, mais avec des aspects stratégiques et sportifs plus marqués. Ceux qui connaissent les dessins de Gayon y retrouveront son style de greens et de bunkers, réalisés avec beaucoup d'attention et de relief, mais on aurait peut-être pu attendre plus encore d'exigence. Dans un ensemble aussi touristique, on attend un entretien de première qualité, ce n'est pas toujours le cas. Le "Rouge" est aussi appelé le "Lucien Barrière", le "Bleu" le "Diane Barrière Dessaigne"…

Over this resort, one of the 18-hole courses (Red) comprises 9 holes laid out by Michel Gayon and 9 of the original 18 holes designed by Aliss and Thomas in 1978. The other 9 form a par 35 layout. The lack of unity of style has been erased with time and it is still as pleasing as ever to walk the open spaces of the countryside, a few kilometres from the sea. Another 18-hole course (Blue) has been designed by Michel Gayon and Jacques Lebreton. It is longer, more consistent and has been landscaped in the same spirit of adventure but the strategic and playing sides to the course are more marked. Golfers who know other Gayon layouts will recognize his style of greens and bunkers, created with great care and relief, but we might have expected a little more technical sophistication. In this sort of resort, you also expect top-notch green-keeping but this is not always the case. The "Red" course is also called the "Lucien Barrière" and its "Blue" counterpart the "Diane Barrière Dessaigne".

Golf Barrière La Baule — 1994

Domaine de Saint-Denac
F - 44117 SAINT-ANDRE-DES-EAUX

Office Secrétariat (33) 02 40 60 46 18
Pro shop Pro-shop (33) 02 40 60 46 18
Fax Fax (33) 02 40 60 41 41
Web www.lucienbarriere.com
Situation Situation St-Nazaire, 12 km
La Baule (pop. 14 850), 7 km
Annual closure Fermeture annuelle no
Weekly closure Fermeture hebdomadaire tuesday
(mardi) 1/11→31/3

Fees main season Tarifs haute saison	18 holes	
	Week days Semaine	**We/Bank holidays** We/Férié
Individual Individuel	€ 68	€ 68
Couple Couple	€ 136	€ 136

Students: – 50%

Caddie Caddie no **Electric Trolley** Chariot électrique no
Buggy Voiturette yes **Clubs** Clubs yes
Credit cards Cartes de crédit
VISA - CB - Eurocard - MasterCard - AMEX

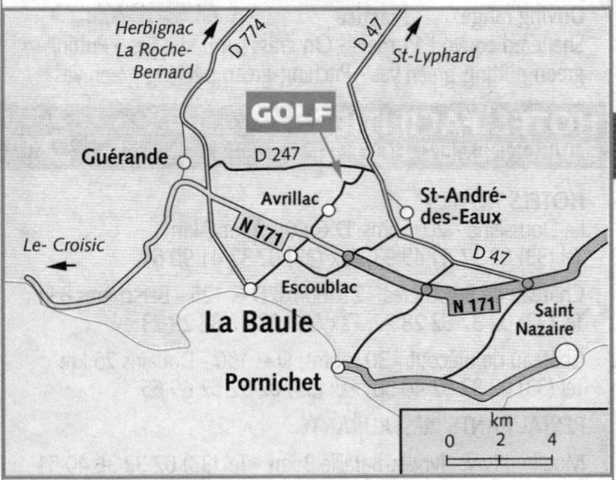

Access Accès : La Baule → La Baule-Escoublac, cross the road N171. → Golf
Map 5 on page 169 Carte 5 Page 169

GOLF COURSE — PARCOURS — 15/20

Site Site
Maintenance Entretien
Architect Architecte Michel Gayon, Jacques Lebreton
Type Type open country
Relief Relief
Water in play Eau en jeu
Exp. to wind Exposé au vent
Trees in play Arbres en jeu

Scorecard Carte de score	**Chp.** Chp.	**Mens** Mess.	**Ladies** Da.
Length Long.	6301	5861	4840
Par	72	72	72
Slope system	140	136	131

Advised golfing ability Niveau de jeu recommandé 0 12 24 36
Hcp required Handicap exigé 30 (main season)

CLUB HOUSE & AMENITIES — CLUB HOUSE ET ANNEXES — 7/10

Pro shop Pro-shop
Driving range Practice
Sheltered couvert 10 mats - On grass sur herbe yes - Putting-green putting-green yes - Pitching-green pitching green yes

HOTEL FACILITIES — ENVIRONNEMENT HOTELIER — 8/10

HOTELS HÔTELS

Castel Marie-Louise - 31 rooms, D from € 280 - La Baule 7 km
Tel (33) 02 40 11 48 38, Fax (33) 02 40 11 48 35

Hermitage - 207 rooms, D from € 300 - La Baule 7 km
Tel (33) 02 40 11 46 46, Fax (33) 02 40 11 48 87

Saint-Christophe - 32 rooms, D € 99 - La Baule 7 km
Tel (33) 02 40 62 40 00, Fax (33) 02 40 62 40 40

Hotel du Golf - 145 rooms, € 239 - St André des Eaux
Tel (33) 02 40 17 57 57, Fax (33) 02 40 17 57 58

RESTAURANTS RESTAURANTS

Le Loft - La Baule 7 km - Tel (33) 02 40 24 51 14

L'Hermitage - La Baule 7 km - Tel (33) 02 40 11 46 46

Golf Parc Nantilly

14	7	5

Ce parcours était la "folie" du magnat de la presse Robert Hersant, aujourd'hui disparu. Amoureux des arbres, il a en a planté ici 15.000 specimens, dont de nombreux adultes : sequoias, douglas ou gingkos viennent ainsi se mêler aux espèces natives. Le tracé original dû à Ronald Fream a été notablement bouleversé par le maître des lieux, d'où certains greens très torturés et pentus, des angles d'attaque assez compliqués, mais heureusement, ces aspects discutables sont peu à peu gommés et rectifiés, de même que certains fairways commencent à être mieux définis dans l'espace. Tout cela fait un parcours que beaucoup aiment et que certains détestent, mais dont la personnalité ne peut guère être ignorée. Ses aspects baroques ne doivent pas faire croire qu'il est inaccessible. De fait, les obstacles ne sont pas insurmontables et les joueurs de tous niveaux pourront tirer leur épingle du jeu. évoluer au milieu d'un spectacle somptueux, à déguster sans modération au printemps et en automne.

This course is the madcap scheme of the late press magnate Robert Hersant. The man was a lover of trees and here planted 15,000 specimens including a number of fully grown Sequoias, Douglas firs or Gingkoes which blend in prettily with indigenous varieties. The original layout by Ronald Fream was disrupted somewhat by the master schemer, whence a number of tortuous greens and complicated angles of approach, but fortunately these debatable points are slowly being erased and put right. Likewise some of the fairways are now more clearly outlined. All this boils down to a course that many love and some hate but whose personality refuses to go away. The baroque side to the course should not lead to anyone considering this an unplayable layout. In fact hazards are not insurmountable and players of all levels can make something of it going round the course, enjoying the sumptuous surroundings. Most definitely worth playing as often as you can, preferably in the spring and autumn.

Le Golf Parc Nantilly — 1998

F - 28260 LA CHAUSSEE D'IVRY

Office Secrétariat (33) 02 37 63 06 30
Pro shop Pro-shop (33) 02 37 63 06 30
Fax Fax (33) 02 37 64 59 40
Web www.legolfparc.com
Situation Situation Paris, 70 km

Annual closure Fermeture annuelle 24/12→2/1

Weekly closure Fermeture hebdomadaire
Wednesday(mercredi), in low season

Fees main season Tarifs haute saison — Full day

	Week days Semaine	We/Bank holidays We/Férié
Individual Individuel	€ 59	€ 77
Couple Couple	€ 118	€ 154

Seniors & Juniors: € 48 (week-days/semaine)

Caddie Caddie no — **Electric Trolley** Chariot électrique no
Buggy Voiturette yes — **Clubs** Clubs no

Credit cards Cartes de crédit
VISA - CB - Eurocard - MasterCard

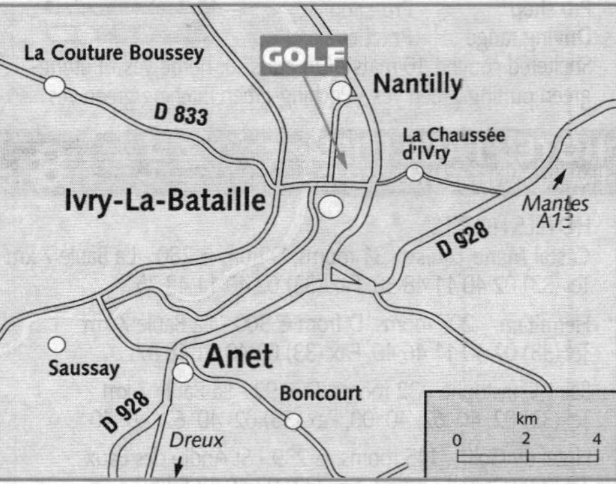

Access Accès : A 13, then A12 → St Quentin. Exit Dreux and N12. Exit → Maulette, Houdan, → Houdan, Anet. In La Chaussée d'Ivry, traffic lights turn left → Ivry la Bataille.
Map 3 on page 164 Carte 3 Page 164

GOLF COURSE — PARCOURS 14/20

Site Site
Maintenance Entretien
Architect Architecte Ronald Fream, Robert Hersant
Type Type forest, parkland
Relief Relief
Water in play Eau en jeu
Exp. to wind Exposé au vent
Trees in play Arbres en jeu

Scorecard Carte de score	Chp. Chp.	Mens Mess.	Ladies Da.
Length Long.	6379	5996	4960
Par	72	72	72
Slope system	138	135	129

Advised golfing ability Niveau de jeu recommandé — 0 12 24 36
Hcp required Handicap exigé 54

CLUB HOUSE & AMENITIES — CLUB HOUSE ET ANNEXES 7/10

Pro shop Pro-shop
Driving range Practice
Sheltered couvert 11 mats - On grass sur herbe yes - Putting-green putting-green yes - Pitching-green pitching green yes

HOTEL FACILITIES — ENVIRONNEMENT HOTELIER 5/10

HOTELS HÔTELS

La Dousseine - 20 rooms, D € 60 - Anet 6 km
Tel (33) 02 37 41 49 93, Fax (33) 02 37 41 90 54

Château de Berschères - 21 rooms, D € 125 - Berschères 8 km
Tel (33) 02 37 82 28 22, Fax (33) 02 37 82 28 23

Château de Brécout - 30 rooms, D € 150 - Douains 25 km
Tel (33) 02 32 52 40 50, Fax (33) 02 32 52 69 65

RESTAURANTS RESTAURANTS

Moulin d'Ivry - Ivry-la-Bataille 3 km - Tel (33) 02 32 36 40 51
Auberge de la Rose - Anet 6 km - Tel (33) 02 37 41 90 64
Manoir d'Anet - Anet 6 km - Tel (33) 02 37 41 91 05

Gouverneur (Le) *Le Breuil*

15 | 6 | 6

Des deux 18 trous de ce complexe, Le Breuil est le plus "héroïque" dans son déroulement, notamment avec neuf trous insinués entre les superbes étangs de la Dombes, dont l'aspect sauvage a été préservé. Plat et très long, bien drainé, c'est l'un des parcours les plus exigeants de la région lyonnaise, il affiche avec franchise ses difficultés stratégiques, mais les redoutables hauts roughs ont perdu un peu de leur importance. On pourra lui reprocher la longueur uniforme de ses par 3, des bunkers peu dangereux et un manque certain d'animation des alentours de green et des greens, peu complexes à lire. Ce parcours doit être joué des départs normaux par les golfeurs moyens, en particulier le superbe passage du 12 au 15, la fin étant moins excitante. L'autre 18 trous, "Montaplan" est amusant, plus court et technique, mais laisse une curieuse impression d'inachevé. Un site où un grand architecte aurait pu faire des merveilles.

"Le Breuil" is the boldest of the two 18-hole courses in this golfing resort, with nine holes winding their way across the superb lakes of La Dombes, which have lost nothing of their wild natural character. Flat, very long and well-drained, Le Breuil is one of the most demanding courses in the Lyons region, but the strategic difficulties are openly visible and the once formidably tall rough has lost some of its significance. The only criticisms that might be levelled are the similar yardage for all the par 3s, rather meek bunkers, a lack of relief around the greens and putting surfaces that are none too difficult to read. This is a course that must be played from the front (yellow) tees by mid-handicappers, particularly for the brilliant stretch between the 12th and 15th holes. The closing holes are a little less exciting. The other 18-hole course ("Montaplan") is fun, shorter and technical but leaves the odd impression of being unfinished. A site where a top architect could work wonders.

Golf du Gouverneur — 1992

Château du Breuil
F - 01390 MONTHIEUX

Office	Secrétariat	(33) 04 72 26 40 34
Pro shop	Pro-shop	(33) 04 72 26 40 34
Fax	Fax	(33) 04 72 26 41 61
Web	www.golfgouverneur.fr	
Situation	Situation	Lyon, 28 km
Annual closure	Fermeture annuelle	no
Weekly closure	Fermeture hebdomadaire	no

Fees main season Tarifs haute saison — 18 holes

	Week days Semaine	We/Bank holidays We/Férié
Individual Individuel	€ 39	€ 55
Couple Couple	€ 70	€ 100

Students: € 25 / 30 (We)

Caddie Caddie no — Electric Trolley Chariot électrique yes

Buggy Voiturette yes — Clubs Clubs yes

Credit cards Cartes de crédit
VISA - CB - Eurocard - MasterCard - AMEX

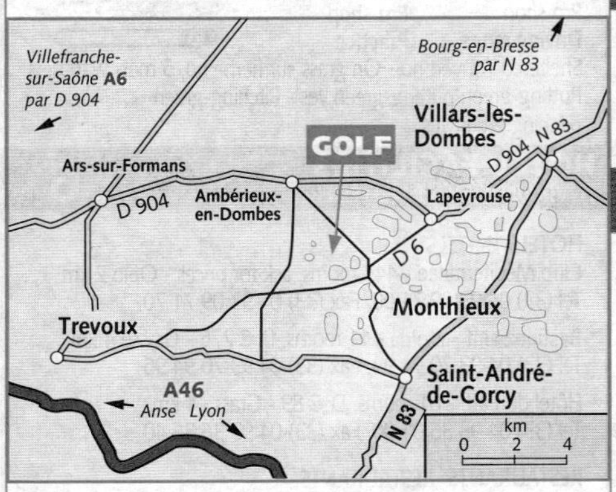

Access Accès : • A46, Exit (Sortie) Bourg-en-Bresse, N83 → Bourg-en-Bresse. In St-André de Corcy → Monthieux • A6, Exit Villefranche, → Bourg, Ars, Ambérieux-en-Dombes → Monthieux

Map 11 on page 180 Carte 11 Page 180

GOLF COURSE PARCOURS — 15/20

Site	Site	
Maintenance	Entretien	
Architect	Architecte	Didier Fruchet George Will
Type	Type	open country
Relief	Relief	
Water in play	Eau en jeu	
Exp. to wind	Exposé au vent	
Trees in play	Arbres en jeu	

Scorecard Carte de score	Chp. Chp.	Mens Mess.	Ladies Da.
Length Long.	6162	5657	4914
Par	72	72	72
Slope system	130	123	120

Advised golfing ability Niveau de jeu recommandé — 0 12 24 36

Hcp required Handicap exigé — 36 (We)

CLUB HOUSE & AMENITIES CLUB HOUSE ET ANNEXES — 6/10

Pro shop — Pro-shop
Driving range — Practice

Sheltered couvert 12 mats - On grass sur herbe yes - Putting-green putting-green yes - Pitching-green pitching green yes (+ 2 holes)

HOTEL FACILITIES ENVIRONNEMENT HOTELIER — 6/10

HOTELS HÔTELS

Hôtel Le Gouverneur - 53 rooms, D € 105 - on site
Tel (33) 04 72 26 42 00, Fax (33) 04 72 26 42 20

Auberge Les Bichonnières - Ambérieux-en-Dombes 4 km
9 rooms, D € 50
Tel (33) 04 74 00 82 07, Fax (33) 04 74 00 89 61

RESTAURANTS RESTAURANTS

Alain Chapel - Mionnay 8 km - Tel (33) 04 78 91 82 02

Auberge des Chasseurs - Bouligneux 8 km
Tel (33) 04 74 98 10 02

Le Gouverneur - on site - Tel (33) 04 72 26 42 00

Auberge de Rancé - Rancé 5 km - Tel (33) 04 74 00 81 83

Grande Bastide (La)

16	6	6

Repris par la chaîne Open Golf, ce 18 trous occupe une place de choix parmi les bons parcours de la région. L'architecte Cabell Robinson a voulu faire un parcours "tous usages", jouable par tous, et si quelques obstacles d'eau peuvent effrayer les débutants, ils peuvent être contournés. Les arrivées de drive sont assez larges, mais la densité des roughs incite à taper droit. Les obstacles tiennent essentiellement des mouvements de terrain et des vastes bunkers, souvent très en jeu, qui délimitent bien les fairways. Le programme de plantations a atténué une certaine imprécision des trous dans un si vaste espace, mais il doit être poursuivi. Les greens très modelés imposent une grande maîtrise du petit jeu et du putting, mais leurs reliefs restent assez faciles à déchiffrer. Amusant à jouer et très divers dans son tracé, ce parcours se joue facilement à pied, ce qui n'est pas si fréquent sur la Côte d'Azur. Certes, les joueurs sont nombreux ici, et pas toujours très rapides, mais en jouant tôt le matin, il n'y a pas de problèmes.

Taken over by the Open Golf chain, this 18-hole course enjoys deserved status as one of the region's very best. Cabell Robinson set out to build an "all-purpose" course for all golfers, and while a number of water hazards might well scare off the real beginner, you can get around them easily enough. At driving distance, the fairways are wide enough but the thick rough is a good reason for hitting it in the fairway. The basic hazards here are the graded fairways and huge bunkers, which are often fully in play and clearly demarcate the playing area. The new plantation programme is beginning to give greater definition to some holes laid out over such a wide area but we would like to see it completed. The well-contoured greens require a sharp short game and good putting, although putting surfaces here are easy enough to read. Fun to play with variety all round, this is an easily walkable course. The players can be slow, but if you play early in the morning there is no problem.

Golf de la Grande Bastide — 1990

Chemin des Picholines
F - 06740 CHATEAUNEUF-DE-GRASSE

Office Secrétariat (33) 04 93 77 70 08
Pro shop Pro-shop (33) 04 93 77 70 08
Fax Fax (33) 04 93 77 72 36
Web www.opengolfclub.com
Situation Situation Nice (pop. 345 670), 27 km
Cannes (pop. 68 670), 17 km

Annual closure Fermeture annuelle — no
Weekly closure Fermeture hebdomadaire — no

Fees main season Tarifs haute saison	18 holes	
	Week days Semaine	We/Bank holidays We/Férié
Individual Individuel	€ 62	€ 62
Couple Couple	€ 122	€ 122

GF evening (soir) € 47 / Under 21 and students: € 31

Caddie Caddie no — **Electric Trolley** Chariot électrique yes
Buggy Voiturette yes — **Clubs** Clubs yes

Credit cards Cartes de crédit
VISA - CB - Eurocard - MasterCard - AMEX

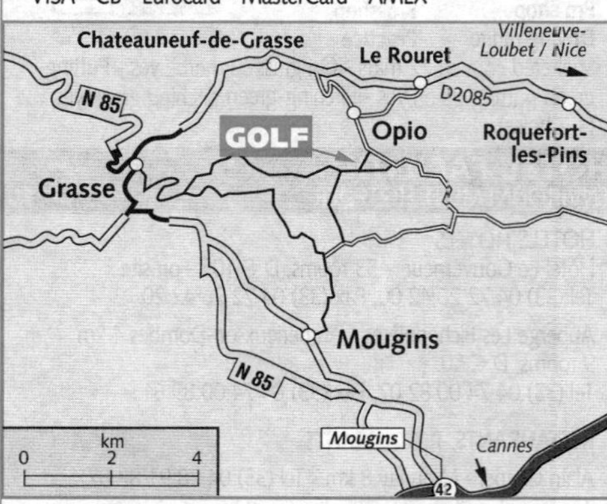

Access Accès : • Cannes, N85 → Valbonne
• Nice, A8 Exit (Sortie) Villeneuve-Loubet → Grasse, Roquefort-les-Pins, → Opio

Map 14 on page 187 Carte 14 Page 187

GOLF COURSE — PARCOURS — 16/20

Site Site
Maintenance Entretien
Architect Architecte — Cabell B. Robinson
Type Type — open country
Relief Relief
Water in play Eau en jeu
Exp. to wind Exposé au vent
Trees in play Arbres en jeu

Scorecard Carte de score	Chp. Chp.	Mens Mess.	Ladies Da.
Length Long.	6105	5610	4760
Par	72	72	72
Slope system	128	116	118

Advised golfing ability 0 12 24 36
Niveau de jeu recommandé
Hcp required Handicap exigé — no

CLUB HOUSE & AMENITIES — CLUB HOUSE ET ANNEXES — 6/10

Pro shop Pro-shop
Driving range Practice
Sheltered couvert no - On grass sur herbe no, 5 mats with nets
Putting-green putting-green yes - Pitching-green pitching green yes

HOTEL FACILITIES — ENVIRONNEMENT HOTELIER — 6/10

HOTELS HÔTELS
Club Méditerranée - 443 rooms, ask for prices - Opio 2 km
Tel (33) 04 93 09 71 00, Fax (33) 04 93 09 71 70

Bastide Saint Antoine - 11 rooms, D € 275 - Grasse 4 km
Tel (33) 04 93 70 94 94, Fax (33) 04 93 70 94 95

Hôtel du Patti - 61 rooms, D € 89 - Grasse 4 km
Tel (33) 04 93 36 01 00, Fax (33) 04 93 36 36 40

RESTAURANTS RESTAURANTS
Bastide Saint Antoine - Grasse 5 km - Tel (33) 04 93 70 94 94
L'Auberge Fleurie - Valbonne 5 km - Tel (33) 04 93 12 02 80
Lou Cigalou - Valbonne 5 km - Tel (33) 04 93 12 27 07

Grande-Motte (La) *Les Flamants Roses* | 16 | 6 | 4

En paysage d'étangs, à partir d'un terrain sans reliefs naturels, et très peu boisé, Robert Trent Jones a signé un parcours de grande qualité technique, modelé avec une grande intelligence, sans jamais donner l'impression de monotonie. Certes, les longs frappeurs peuvent s'y déchaîner, mais les seconds coups, le petit jeu et le putting demandent beaucoup d'inspiration, et les joueurs précis pourront eux aussi réussir. L'eau joue un rôle important, mais sans sévérité excessive. Avec une bonne connaissance de ce parcours bien défini dans l'espace, aux obstacles très visibles, et un peu de réflexion, tous les joueurs peuvent y prendre plaisir, à l'exception des débutants, qui trouveront avec un joli parcours de 6 trous et un 18 trous de par 58 de quoi largement s'occuper et s'aguerrir. La Grande-Motte est un golf commercial, son club-house manque de chaleur et de distinction, et les constructions adjacentes ne sont guère séduisantes, mais il suffit de garder les yeux sur ce parcours superbe.

Set in a landscape of lakes with no natural relief and very few trees, Robert Trent Jones has cleverly shaped a high class technical course which never seems monotonous. Long-hitters can definitely open their shoulders, but approach shots, short play and putting call for a lot of inspiration which should suit the more accurate players. Water is a significant part of the course but is never too severe a test. When you get to know this neatly laid-out course with hazards clear to see and with a little careful thought, every golfer will enjoy playing here, except beginners, who can learn the ropes and get to grips with the compact 6-holer and the par-58 18 hole course. La Grande-Motte is a business venture course and the club-house lacks both warmth and distinction. Likewise the adjoining buildings are not the most attractive ever built, but just keep your eyes on this superb course.

Golf de La Grande-Motte — 1987

BP 16
F - 34280 LA GRANDE-MOTTE

Office	Secrétariat	(33) 04 67 56 05 00
Pro shop	Pro-shop	(33) 04 67 56 35 27
Fax	Fax	(33) 04 67 29 18 84
E-mail	golf@lagrandemotte.fr	
Situation	Situation	Montpellier, 22 km
Annual closure	Fermeture annuelle	no
Weekly closure	Fermeture hebdomadaire	no

Fees main season Tarifs haute saison		full day
	Week days Semaine	**We/Bank holidays** We/Férié
Individual Individuel	€ 44	€ 52
Couple Couple	€ 88	€ 104

Under 18: – 50% - Under 25: – 30%

Caddie Caddie no — **Electric Trolley** Chariot électrique no
Buggy Voiturette yes **Clubs** Clubs yes
Credit cards Cartes de crédit
VISA - Eurocard - MasterCard

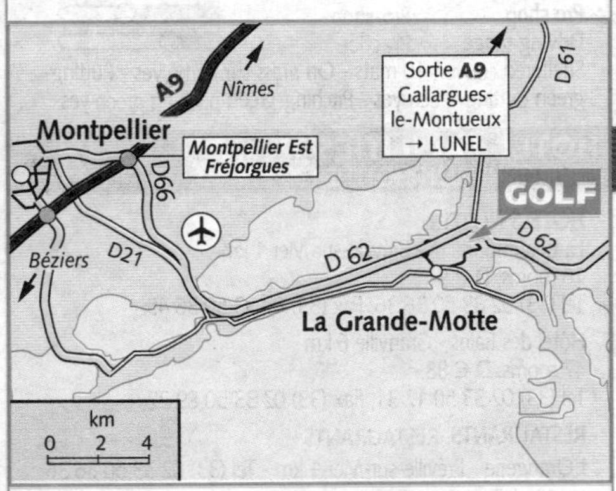

Access Accès : • Nîmes, A9, Exit (Sortie) 26 Gallargues, N113 → Lunel, D61 → La Grande-Motte • Montpellier A9 Exit Fréjorgues, D21 et D62 → La Grande-Motte
Map 13 on page 185 Carte 13 Page 185

GOLF COURSE — PARCOURS — 16/20

Site	Site	
Maintenance	Entretien	
Architect	Architecte	Robert Trent Jones
Type	Type	seaside course, residential
Relief	Relief	
Water in play	Eau en jeu	
Exp. to wind	Exposé au vent	
Trees in play	Arbres en jeu	

Scorecard Carte de score	**Chp.** Chp.	**Mens** Mess.	**Ladies** Da.
Length Long.	6161	5768	4874
Par	72	72	72
Slope system	133	126	126

Advised golfing ability Niveau de jeu recommandé — 0 12 24 36
Hcp required Handicap exigé — 35

CLUB HOUSE & AMENITIES — CLUB HOUSE ET ANNEXES — 6/10

Pro shop Pro-shop
Driving range Practice
Sheltered couvert 7 mats - On grass sur herbe yes - Putting-green putting-green yes - Pitching-green pitching green yes

HOTEL FACILITIES — ENVIRONNEMENT HOTELIER — 4/10

HOTELS HÔTELS
Golf Hôtel Best Western - 45 rooms, D € 113 - 300 m
Tel (33) 04 67 29 72 00, Fax (33) 04 67 56 12 44

Hôtel des Corallines - La Grande Motte 1 km
42 rooms, D € 176
Tel (33) 04 67 29 13 13, Fax (33) 04 67 29 14 74

Les Templiers - 11 rooms, D € 100 - Aigues-Mortes 11 km
Tel (33) 04 66 53 66 56, Fax (33) 04 66 53 69 61

RESTAURANTS RESTAURANTS
Alexandre - La Grande Motte 1 km - Tel (33) 04 67 56 63 63
Arcades - Aigues-Mortes 11 km - Tel (33) 04 66 53 81 13

Granville *Le Links*

14 | 4 | 4

Originellement dessiné par Colt et Alison, Granville était un chef-d'oeuvre à l'écart des sentiers battus. Ce grand links était traversé par une petite route, qui a obligé à modifier beaucoup de trous, alors qu'elle aurait sans doute pu être déviée. Hélas, ces trous n'ont pas été les seuls altérés, et une bonne partie du caractère originel a été perdue, notamment dans le dessin des bunkers. Autrefois au niveau du Touquet et de Chiberta, Granville a souffert de quelques décisions iconoclastes. Il reste néammoins une bonne douzaine de bons trous, qui justifient une visite, mais les autres, qui seraient très honnêtes dans un autre environnement, laissent une impression étrange aux amoureux de l'architecture classique. Granville est par l'absurde, une leçon d'architecture, et une bonne leçon de prudence et de respect pour les golfs qui veulent s'engager dans un remodelage. La réfection du club-house n'est qu'une bien faible consolation. Il est plus facile de défaire que de refaire...

Designed by Colt and Alison, Granville used to be a masterpiece. Unfortunately, this great links course was crossed by a small road, which could have been re-routed, and a number of holes had to be altered. Worse, other features of the course were also tampered with and a lot of its original character was lost, most notably the style of bunkering. Once on a par with Le Touquet or Chiberta, Granville has suffered from a number of sacrilegious decisions. There are still a dozen excellent holes remaining, and they are worth the visit in themselves, but the others, which would be decent enough anywhere else, leave a weird impression on admirers of classic golf architecture. Through an absurd course of events, Granville has proven to be a lesson in architecture, underlining the caution and respect that should be shown by any golf course that might be considering a change in style. The re-designed club-house is scant consolation.

Golf de Granville — 1912

Pavillon du Golf
F - 50290 BREVILLE

Office	Secrétariat	(33) 02 33 50 23 06
Pro shop	Pro-shop	(33) 02 33 50 23 06
Fax	Fax	(33) 02 33 61 91 87
Web	www.golfdegranville.com	
Situation	Situation	Granville, 6 km
Annual closure	Fermeture annuelle	no
Weekly closure	Fermeture hebdomadaire	no
Fees main season	Tarifs haute saison	full day

	Week days Semaine	We/Bank holidays We/Férié
Individual Individuel	€ 47	€ 47
Couple Couple	€ 85	€ 85

Under 21: € 34

Caddie Caddie no — **Electric Trolley** Chariot électrique no

Buggy Voiturette yes — **Clubs** Clubs yes

Credit cards Cartes de crédit
VISA - CB - Eurocard - MasterCard

Coutances
GOLF
La Belle-Croix
Coudeville-Sur-Mer
Breville-Sur-Mer
Granville
D 971
Vire
D 924
D 973
Baie du Mont-Saint-Michel
km
0 2 4
Vers Avranches et Le Mont-Saint-Michel (44 km)

Access Accès : Avranches D973 → Granville, Bréville s/Mer

Map 2 on page 162 Carte 2 Page 162

GOLF COURSE — PARCOURS — 14/20

Site	Site	
Maintenance	Entretien	
Architect	Architecte	Colt, Alison M. Hawtree (1992)
Type	Type	links
Relief	Relief	
Water in play	Eau en jeu	
Exp. to wind	Exposé au vent	
Trees in play	Arbres en jeu	

Scorecard Carte de score	Chp. Chp.	Mens Mess.	Ladies Da.
Length Long.	5834	5513	4696
Par	71	71	71
Slope system	125	124	124

Advised golfing ability Niveau de jeu recommandé: 0 12 24 36

Hcp required Handicap exigé 35

CLUB HOUSE & AMENITIES — CLUB HOUSE ET ANNEXES — 4/10

Pro shop Pro-shop
Driving range Practice
Sheltered couvert 10 mats - On grass sur herbe yes - Putting-green putting-green yes - Pitching-green pitching green yes

HOTEL FACILITIES — ENVIRONNEMENT HOTELIER — 4/10

HOTELS HÔTELS

La Beaumonderie - Bréville-sur-Mer 1 km
16 rooms, D € 90
Tel (33) 02 33 50 36 36, Fax (33) 02 33 50 36 45

Hôtel des Bains - Granville 6 km
47 rooms, D € 88
Tel (33) 02 33 50 17 31, Fax (33) 02 33 50 89 22

RESTAURANTS RESTAURANTS

L'Orangerie - Bréville-sur-Mer 1 km - Tel 33) 02 33 50 36 36
La Citadelle - Granville 6 km - Tel (33) 02 33 50 34 10
La Gentilhommière - Granville 6 km - Tel (33) 02 33 50 17 99

Grenoble Bresson

16	7	6

Ce terrain très accidenté est parfois même épuisant (voiturette conseillée), mais Robert Trent Jones Jr a réussi l'exploit de ne pas imposer de coups aveugles. Cependant, le site ne lui a pas permis d'éviter trois ou quatre trous assez indifférents dans un ensemble autrement de belle qualité, et même excitant à parcourir. Souvent spectaculaire, ce parcours ne livre pas facilement ses secrets, et mérite d'être joué plusieurs fois, ne serait-ce que pour négocier les greens. Dans un paysage quasiment montagnard, des hêtres, des chênes et des genêts apportent des touches de végétation au modelage des fairways, à la sculpture des nombreux bunkers. Quelle que soit la beauté de la balade, la maîtrise du jeu que réclame Bresson incite à ne pas le recommander aux joueurs à haut handicap. Ce parcours exige un dessin précis des fairways et un entretien méticuleux, ce qui n'est pas le cas en permanence, il faut bien le dire.

This is a very hilly and sometimes exhausting course (buggy recommended) but Robert Trent Jones Jr. has achieved the virtually impossible by avoiding blind shots. Nonetheless, the site made it impossible for him to avoid three or four rather ordinary holes in an otherwise excellent setting, which makes for exciting golf. This sometimes spectacular course does not give up its secrets easily and deserves a number of rounds, if only to get to grips with the greens. In virtually mountainous landscape, oak-trees, beech and gorse add a touch of vegetation to the contoured fairways and numerous bunkers. But however beautiful the scenery, the skill required to play Bresson is perhaps beyond the average high-handicapper. The course also calls for tightly-mown fairways and meticulous green-keeping, which is not always the case here, it should be said.

Golf International de Grenoble — 1990

Route de Montavie
F - 38320 BRESSON

Office	Secrétariat	(33) 04 76 73 65 00
Pro shop	Pro-shop	(33) 04 76 73 65 00
Fax	Fax	(33) 04 76 73 65 51
Web	www.golfinternationalgrenoble.com	
Situation	Situation	Grenoble, 5 km
Annual closure	Fermeture annuelle	20/12→20/1
Weekly closure	Fermeture hebdomadaire	no

Fees main season / Tarifs haute saison	Week days / Semaine	We/Bank holidays / We/Férié
		Full day
Individual Individuel	€ 50	€ 50
Couple Couple	€ 100	€ 100

Juniors & Students (- 25): – 50%

Caddie Caddie no Electric Trolley Chariot électrique on request

Buggy Voiturette yes (on request) Clubs Clubs yes

Credit cards Cartes de crédit
VISA - CB - Eurocard - MasterCard

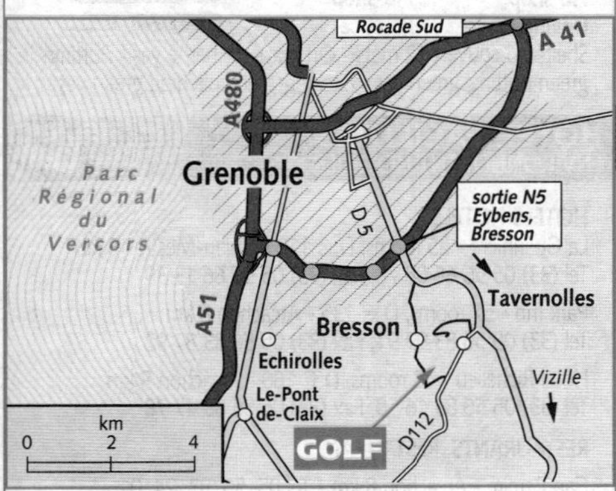

Access Accès : Lyon A48 → Chambéry.
At toll (Péage) go to the "Rocade",
Exit 5, Eybens, Bresson → Tavernolles, → Golf
Map 11 on page 180 Carte 11 Page 180

GOLF COURSE — PARCOURS — 16/20

Site	Site	
Maintenance	Entretien	
Architect	Architecte	R. Trent Jones Jr
Type	Type	montagne
Relief	Relief	
Water in play	Eau en jeu	
Exp. to wind	Exposé au vent	
Trees in play	Arbres en jeu	

Scorecard / Carte de score	Chp. / Chp.	Mens / Mess.	Ladies / Da.
Length Long.	6201	5876	4750
Par	73	73	73
Slope system	145	139	136

Advised golfing ability / Niveau de jeu recommandé: 0 12 24 36

Hcp required / Handicap exigé: no

CLUB HOUSE & AMENITIES — CLUB HOUSE ET ANNEXES — 7/10

Pro shop — Pro-shop
Driving range — Practice
Sheltered couvert 8 mats - On grass sur herbe yes - Putting-green putting-green yes - Pitching-green pitching green yes

HOTEL FACILITIES — ENVIRONNEMENT HOTELIER — 6/10

HOTELS HÔTELS

Chavant - 7 rooms, D € 120 - Bresson 2 km
Tel (33) 04 76 25 25 38, Fax (33) 04 76 62 06 55

Château de la Commanderie - Eybens 2 km
25 rooms, D € 96
Tel (33) 04 76 25 34 58, Fax (33) 04 76 24 07 31

Park Hôtel - 50 rooms, D € 225 - Grenoble 5 km
Tel (33) 04 76 85 81 23, Fax (33) 04 76 46 49 88

Grand Hôtel - 42 rooms, D € 105 - Uriage 7 km
Tel (33) 04 76 89 10 80, Fax (33) 04 76 89 04 62

RESTAURANTS RESTAURANTS

Chavant - Bresson 2 km - Tel (33) 04 76 25 25 38
Auberge Napoléon - Grenoble 5 km - Tel (33) 04 76 87 53 64

Gujan-Mestras

15 | 7 | 6

Entre Arcachon et Bordeaux, ce 18 trous (complété par un petit 9 trous) a été dessiné par Alain Prat avec beaucoup de bon sens : il n'a pas voulu exagérer les difficultés et son tracé ne pénalise que ceux qui prennent des risques excessifs. Le terrain plat a été légèrement modelé pour les besoins de la cause, et le sol sablonneux est idéal pour le golf. Ainsi, on remarquera à peine que le 9 ne revient pas au club-house. Le déroulement dans la bruyère et les pins (beaucoup ont été victimes de la tempête de 1999) est agréable, avec des difficultés mesurées pour ne rebuter personne, les principaux dangers (en dehors de quelques obstacles d'eau) étant constitués par les bunkers et les arbres, qui laissent souvent libres les accès aux vastes greens. Mais les débutants auront sans doute du mal quand ils sont très défendus. On peut jouer facilement ici toute l'année : les hivers sont plutôt doux, le parcours est assez large, il supporte bien les intempéries et son entretien est généralement très correct.

Located between Arcachon and Bordeaux, this 18-hole course was designed by Alain Prat. Using a lot of good sense, he has avoided any excessive difficulties and the layout only penalizes the players who take one risk too many. The flat terrain has been slightly graded for greater relief and the sandy sub-soil is ideal for a golf course. You hardly even notice that the 9th hole does not quite make it back to the club-house as the course winds its way pleasantly through the heather and pine-trees, with playing difficulties carefully gauged to avoid scaring the lesser player. Aside from the few water hazards, the main problems are the bunkers and trees, which generally speaking afford easy access to the greens. Beginners will probably find the going a little harder when dealing with some of the better-protected holes. You can easily play here all year as the winters are mild, the course expansive and the ground withstands all weathers. Green-keeping is generally speaking good.

Golf de Gujan-Mestras — 1990

Route de Sanguinet
F - 33470 GUJAN-MESTRAS

Office	Secrétariat	(33) 05 57 52 73 73
Pro shop	Pro-shop	(33) 05 57 52 73 73
Fax	Fax	(33) 05 56 66 10 93
Web	www.bluegreen.com	
Situation	Situation	Arcachon, 12 km

Bordeaux, 56 km

Annual closure	Fermeture annuelle	no
Weekly closure	Fermeture hebdomadaire	no
Fees main season	Tarifs haute saison	full day

	Week days Semaine	We/Bank holidays We/Férié
Individual Individuel	€ 45	€ 45
Couple Couple	€ 82	€ 82

Under 18: € 26,50 / Students (– 25): € 33

Caddie Caddie no — **Electric Trolley** Chariot électrique no

Buggy Voiturette yes — **Clubs** Clubs yes

Credit cards Cartes de crédit
VISA - CB - Eurocard - MasterCard - AMEX - DC

Access Accès : Bordeaux, A63, Exit (Sortie) Arcachon, at Aqua City, → Golf
Map 9 on page 176 Carte 9 Page 176

GOLF COURSE — PARCOURS — 15/20

Site	Site	
Maintenance	Entretien	
Architect	Architecte	Alain Prat
Type	Type	forest
Relief	Relief	
Water in play	Eau en jeu	
Exp. to wind	Exposé au vent	
Trees in play	Arbres en jeu	

Scorecard Carte de score	Chp. Chp.	Mens Mess.	Ladies Da.
Length Long.	6000	5650	4800
Par	72	72	72
Slope system	129	127	125

Advised golfing ability Niveau de jeu recommandé — 0 12 24 36

Hcp required Handicap exigé — 54

CLUB HOUSE & AMENITIES — CLUB HOUSE ET ANNEXES — 7/10

Pro shop Pro-shop
Driving range Practice
Sheltered couvert 12 mats - On grass sur herbe yes - Putting-green putting-green yes - Pitching-green pitching green yes

HOTEL FACILITIES — ENVIRONNEMENT HOTELIER — 6/10

HOTELS HÔTELS

La Guérinière - 25 rooms, D € 110 - Gujan-Mestras 6 km
Tel (33) 05 56 66 08 78, Fax (33) 05 56 66 13 39

Park Inn - 57 rooms, D € 135 - Arcachon 8 km
Tel (33) 05 56 83 99 91, Fax (33) 05 56 83 87 92

Hôtel Richelieu - 43 rooms, D € 160 - Arcachon 8 km
Tel (33) 05 56 83 16 50, Fax (33) 05 56 83 47 78

RESTAURANTS RESTAURANTS

Cap Pereire - Arcachon 8 km - Tel 05 56 83 24 01

Le Patio - Arcachon 8 km - Tel (33) 05 56 83 02 72

Hardelot *Les Pins* 16 6 6

Depuis sa création, "Les Pins" est un des excellents exemples du style de Tom Simpson, un témoignage de l'architecture classique britannique. Quelques coups sont aveugles, mais faussement trompeurs et sans véritable gêne pour le jeu. Avec des greens subtils, des reliefs bien utilisés, des bunkers diaboliquement placés, le parcours impose d'être précis, et de savoir quand attaquer. On doit simplement suivre les pas de l'architecte pour le négocier correctement, tant le dessin est empreint de bon sens et de culture golfique. "Les Pins" est de ces parcours polis par le temps que l'on doit absolument connaître si l'on ne connaît que des golfs "modernes". Tout ici est empreint de tradition et les Anglais ne s'y trompent pas, qui y viennent nombreux. Les bémols, un environnement immobilier de plus en plus envahissant, un club-house un peu spartiate. Les investissements consentis sur l'arrosage automatique ont commencé à lui donner plus de régularité d'entretien en toutes saisons.

"Les Pins" is one of the great examples of the Tom Simpson style, a testimony to classic British architecture. Some shots are blind but never really deceive the player or affect play. With subtle greens and devilishly well-placed bunkers, this course cries out for precision stroke-making and the ability to exploit opportunities for attacking play. The impression is one of simply following in the footsteps of the architect in order to play the course correctly. That is how sensible the layout is, steeped in golfing culture. "Les Pins" is one of those courses that becomes more polished with time and is an absolute must for anyone raised exclusively on "modern" courses. The British know a good golf course when they see one, and a lot of Brits come and play here. On the downside, the real estate programme is increasingly obtrusive and the club-house rather Spartan. The investment made in automatic watering systems has started to produce more consistent standards of green-keeping whatever the season.

Golf d'Hardelot-les-Pins **1931**
3, avenue du Golf
F - 62152 HARDELOT

Office	Secrétariat	(33) 03 21 83 73 10
Pro shop	Pro-shop	(33) 03 21 83 73 10
Fax	Fax	(33) 03 21 83 24 33
Web	www.opengolf.com	
Situation	Situation	Boulogne s/Mer, 15 km
Annual closure	Fermeture annuelle	no
Weekly closure	Fermeture hebdomadaire	no

Fees main season Tarifs haute saison	**Week days** Semaine	**We/Bank holidays** We/Férié
		18 holes
Individual Individuel	€ 59	€ 69
Couple Couple	€ 118	€ 138

We: Fri/Sat/Sun.(Vend/Sam/Dim) / Students: € 35

Caddie Caddie on request **Electric Trolley** Chariot électrique no

Buggy Voiturette yes **Clubs** Clubs yes

Credit cards Cartes de crédit
VISA - Eurocard - MasterCard - AMEX - DC - JCB

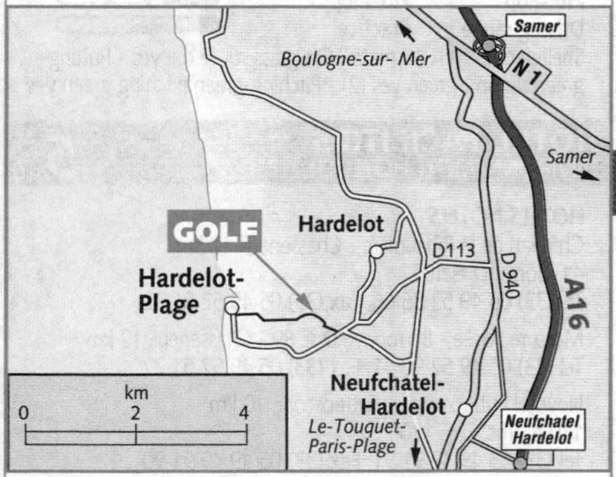

Access Accès : • Boulogne, A16 → Calais,
N1 → Montreuil, through Pont-de-Briques, turn right on D940 → Hardelot • Montreuil,
N1 → Boulogne-sur-Mer, or D940 coming from Le Touquet
Map 1 on page 160 Carte 1 Page 160

GOLF COURSE 16/20
PARCOURS

Site	Site	
Maintenance	Entretien	
Architect	Architecte	Tom Simpson
Type	Type	forest, parkland
Relief	Relief	
Water in play	Eau en jeu	
Exp. to wind	Exposé au vent	
Trees in play	Arbres en jeu	

Scorecard Carte de score	**Chp.** Chp.	**Mens** Mess.	**Ladies** Da.
Length Long.	5926	5605	4985
Par	73	73	73
Slope system	138	133	131

Advised golfing ability Niveau de jeu recommandé 0 12 24 36

Hcp required Handicap exigé 28 Men, 32 Ladies

CLUB HOUSE & AMENITIES 6/10
CLUB HOUSE ET ANNEXES

Pro shop Pro-shop
Driving range Practice
Sheltered couvert 6 mats - On grass sur herbe no, 6 mats open air - Putting-green putting-green yes - Pitching-green pitching green yes

HOTEL FACILITIES 6/10
ENVIRONNEMENT HOTELIER

HOTELS HÔTELS
Hôtel du Parc - 106 rooms, D € 129 - Hardelot 1 km
Tel (33) 03 21 33 22 11, Fax (33) 03 21 83 29 71

Cléry - 28 rooms, D € 115 - Hesdin-l'Abbé 7 km
Tel (33) 03 21 83 19 83, Fax (33) 03 21 87 52 59

Régina - 40 rooms, D € 64 - Hardelot 1 km
Tel (33) 03 21 83 81 88, Fax (33) 03 21 87 44 01

RESTAURANTS RESTAURANTS
La Matelote - Boulogne-sur-Mer 15 km
Tel (33) 03 21 30 17 97

Host. de la Rivière - Pont-de-Briques 7 km
Tel (33) 03 21 32 22 81

Haut-Poitou

14 | 6 | 5

Un parcours paradoxalement difficile pour une région où les néophytes sont nombreux, avec un relief qui rend assez fatigants les neuf derniers trous, tracés dans une zone agréable de pins et de bouleaux. A cause de sa longueur (même avec un par 73), on conseillera à tous de ne pas partir des départs les plus reculés, s'ils espèrent jouer leur handicap. Les neuf premiers trous sont plus plats, avec des obstacles d'eau pas trop pénalisants. L'architecture du parcours manque certes d'originalité (le 13 est joli), mais les greens sont en majorité bien dessinés, et quelques bunkers ont été drainés et refaits pour la qualité du jeu, ainsi que plusieurs départs. Si l'on ajoute des travaux de drainage de fairways, c'est en résumé un golf à jouer quand on se trouve dans la région. Pour agrémenter un séjour en famille, un petit parcours de 9 trous permet d'aguerrir les débutants. Une base de loisirs est toute proche pour les non-golfeurs, ainsi que le Futuroscope de Poitiers.

A paradoxically tough course in region where beginners abound. The sloping terrain makes the back 9 a tiring but pleasant walk through pines and birch trees. Haut-Poitou is a long course, and even at a par 73 we would not recommend the back tees to anyone wishing to play to his handicap. The front 9 are flatter with water hazards that could be rated as avoidable and so not too heavy on the score. The overall architecture probably lacks originality and charm (although the 13th is a pretty hole), but the majority of greens are well-designed and a few bunkers have been drained and reshaped for the better, as have several tee-boxes. In short, and if we add the draining work now completed, this is a course worth playing if you are in the region. To make things more pleasant for all the family, a neighbouring 9 hole pitch 'n putt is ideal for beginners while non-golfers will enjoy the nearby leisure centre and Futuroscope theme park.

Golf Club du Haut-Poitou — 1987

F - 86130 SAINT-CYR

Office Secrétariat (33) 05 49 62 53 62
Pro shop Pro-shop (33) 05 49 62 53 62
Fax Fax (33) 05 49 88 77 14
Web www.golfduhautpoitou.com
Situation Situation Poitiers (pop. 78 890), 20 km
Châtellerault, 15 km
Annual closure Fermeture annuelle no
Weekly closure Fermeture hebdomadaire no
Fees main season Tarifs haute saison full day

	Week days Semaine	We/Bank holidays We/Férié
Individual Individuel	€ 50	€ 50
Couple Couple	€ 82	€ 82

Under 25: € 35
Caddie Caddie no — **Electric Trolley** Chariot électrique no
Buggy Voiturette yes — **Clubs** Clubs yes
Credit cards Cartes de crédit
VISA - CB - Eurocard - MasterCard

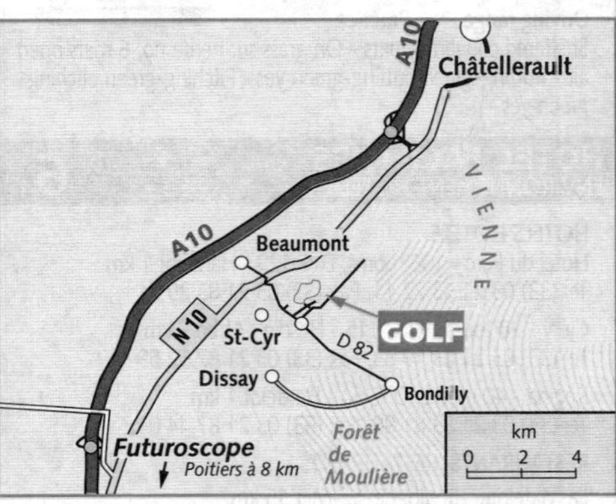

Access Accès : From Poitiers or Châtellerault, N10, Exit (Sortie) Beaumont, → Golf
Map 6 on page 171 Carte 6 Page 171

GOLF COURSE — PARCOURS 14/20

Site Site
Maintenance Entretien
Architect Architecte Harold (Bill) Baker
Type Type open country, forest
Relief Relief
Water in play Eau en jeu
Exp. to wind Exposé au vent
Trees in play Arbres en jeu

Scorecard Carte de score	Chp. Chp.	Mens Mess.	Ladies Da.
Length Long.	6612	6207	4940
Par	73	73	73
Slope system	143	141	130

Advised golfing ability Niveau de jeu recommandé 0 12 24 36
Hcp required Handicap exigé 54

CLUB HOUSE & AMENITIES — CLUB HOUSE ET ANNEXES 6/10

Pro shop Pro-shop
Driving range Practice
Sheltered couvert 18 mats - On grass sur herbe yes - Putting-green putting-green yes (2) - Pitching-green pitching green yes

HOTEL FACILITIES — ENVIRONNEMENT HOTELIER 5/10

HOTELS HÔTELS
Château de la Ribaudière - Chasseneuil 12 km
41 rooms, D € 105
Tel (33) 05 49 52 86 66, Fax (33) 05 49 52 86 32

Mercure Alisée - 80 rooms, D € 89 - Chasseneuil 12 km
Tel (33) 05 49 52 90 41, Fax (33) 05 49 52 51 72

Novotel Futuroscope - Futuroscope 10 km
110 rooms, D € 120
Tel (33) 05 49 49 91 91, Fax (33) 05 49 49 91 90

RESTAURANTS RESTAURANTS
Maxime - Poitiers 20 km - Tel (33) 05 49 41 09 55
Benjamin - Dissay 2 km - Tel (33) 05 49 52 42 37
Vingelique - Poitiers 20 km - Tel (33) 05 49 55 07 03

Hossegor

16 | 7 | 6

L'architecture d'Hossegor rappelle les "inland" de Grande-Bretagne, où les obstacles sont surtout les arbres et les bunkers et qui a heureusement été préservée. Dans un espace aussi propice au golf, il n'était pas utile de beaucoup modeler le terrain (pas de bulldozers à l'époque). Le parcours est plat, et de bonne qualité toute l'année, grâce au sol sablonneux. Les obstacles bien visibles, la variété des trous et le profil des greens en font un test de stratégie et de jeu, qui masque ses réelles difficultés sous un visage souriant. Depuis les années 30, le dessin n'a gère été changé, ce respect est à saluer mais il était souhaitable de l'adapter davantage au jeu actuel, car certains bunkers de fairway ne mettent plus en danger les bons joueurs. Un "restyling" par Cabell Robinson devrait moderniser ce tracé. Un excellent parcours, qu'il s'agisse de jouer en compétition, ou en famille, où l'on a toujours plaisir à retrouver des détails que l'on avait négligés. Un des grands classiques de la "Côte Basque", où l'immobilier est malheureusement trop visible.

The architecture of Hossegor is reminiscent of traditional British inland courses, where the hazards are primarily trees and bunkers. On a site so obviously made for golf, there was hardly any need to shape the terrain (anyway there were no bulldozers around at the time). The course is flat and plays beautifully all year thanks to the sandy sub-soil. Clearly visible hazards, variety and the neat greens make this a fine test of golfing ability and strategy and one that conceals its real difficulties beneath a cheerful exterior. Although built in the 1930s, the course belies its age, but we still feel that Hossegor should be adapted a little to suit today's playing standards. A little restyling by Cabell Robinson will do the trick. An excellent course for tournaments or for all the family, where it is always fun to get back to the long-neglected details of golf. One of the great classics on the Basque coast but unfortunately the houses lining the course are too prominent.

Golf Club d'Hossegor — 1930

Avenue du Golf
F - 40150 HOSSEGOR

Office Secrétariat (33) 05 58 43 56 99
Pro shop Pro-shop (33) 05 58 43 56 99
Fax Fax (33) 05 58 43 98 52
Web www.golfhossegor.com
Situation Situation Dax (pop. 19 310), 32 km
Bayonne (pop. 40 050), 20 km
Annual closure Fermeture annuelle no
Weekly closure Fermeture hebdomadaire tuesday
mardi (except holidays)

Fees main season Tarifs haute saison	18 holes	
	Week days Semaine	**We/Bank holidays** We/Férié
Individual Individuel	€ 60	€ 60
Couple Couple	€ 120	€ 120

Under 25: – 50%
Caddie Caddie on request **Electric Trolley** Chariot électrique yes
Buggy Voiturette no **Clubs** Clubs yes
Credit cards Cartes de crédit
VISA - CB - Eurocard - MasterCard

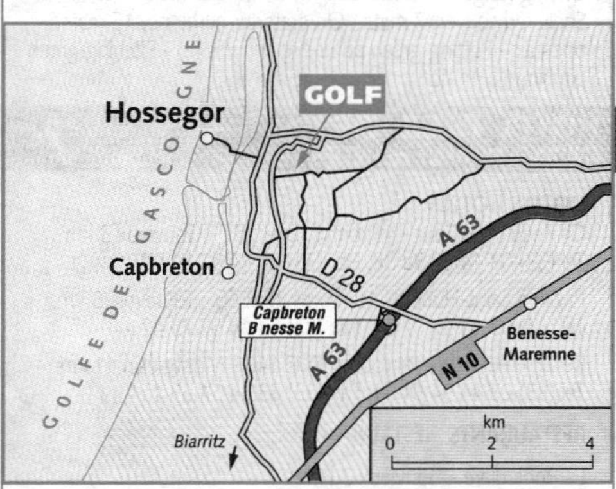

Access Accès : A63 Exit (Sortie) Capbreton/Benesse-Maremne → "Hossegor Centre Ville"
Map 12 on page 182 Carte 12 Page 182

GOLF COURSE — PARCOURS — 16/20

Site Site
Maintenance Entretien
Architect Architecte T. Morrison
Type Type forest, residential
Relief Relief
Water in play Eau en jeu
Exp. to wind Exposé au vent
Trees in play Arbres en jeu

Scorecard Carte de score	**Chp.** Chp.	**Mens** Mess.	**Ladies** Da.
Length Long.	6006	5704	4881
Par	71	71	71
Slope system	134	130	124

Advised golfing ability Niveau de jeu recommandé 0 12 24 36
Hcp required Handicap exigé 36

CLUB HOUSE & AMENITIES — CLUB HOUSE ET ANNEXES — 7/10

Pro shop Pro-shop
Driving range Practice
Sheltered couvert 20 mats - On grass sur herbe no - Putting-green putting-green yes - Pitching-green pitching green yes

HOTEL FACILITIES — ENVIRONNEMENT HOTELIER — 6/10

HOTELS HÔTELS
Pavillon Bleu - 20 rooms, D € 99 - Hossegor 2 km
Tel (33) 05 58 41 99 50, Fax (33) 05 58 41 99 59

Les Hortensias du Lac - Hossegor 2 km
24 rooms, D € 150
Tel (33) 05 58 43 99 00, Fax (33) 05 58 43 42 81

RESTAURANTS RESTAURANTS
Café Bellevue - Capbreton 3 km
Tel (33) 05 58 72 10 30
Regalty - Capbreton 3 km - Tel (33) 05 58 72 22 80
Cottage - Hossegor - Tel (33) 05 58 43 31 39

ICL (Le Lys-Chantilly) *Les Chênes* | 15 | 6 | 7

Le Lys est magnifiquement logé au milieu des bois à côté de Chantilly, au royaume du pur-sang. Deux parcours font partie de cet ensemble prestigieux, dont "Les Chênes" est le fleuron. Dans un site à la fois plat et très boisé, ce n'est pas un parcours difficile ni très pénalisant quand on sait rester droit, l'essentiel des obstacles étant constitué par les arbres et certains bunkers de fairway. On pourrait d'ailleurs imaginer de durcir un peu plus le terrain, avec des fairways plus étroits et des zones de haut rough pour pimenter le jeu. Mais cela permet aussi, dans un club très "famille" de faire jouer tout le monde assez rapidement, tous les obstacles étant visibles, et les greens peu protégés. Le parcours est signé Tom Simpson, mais on peut supposer que des modifications ont été apportées à son dessin, car il avait l'habitude d'être encore plus exigeant avec les golfeurs, en particulier au niveau des "cross-bunkers". Un peu frustrant pour les meilleurs, mais très agréable néanmoins avec son sol sablonneux.

Le Lys is magnificently sited amidst a forest next to Chantilly in the land of yearlings and thoroughbreds. This complex comprises two courses, of which "Les Chênes" holds pride of place. Laid out over a flat site strewn with trees, this course is neither too difficult nor too penalising as long as you keep the ball in the fairway, as the hazards are trees and a number of fairway bunkers. We might easily imagine this layout a little trickier with tighter fairways and tall rough to add a little spice to your round, but in what is a very "family" type club this keeps everyone playing a little faster. All hazards are clearly visible and there is little protection around the greens. The course was originally designed by Simpson, but we suspect that a number of changes have been made over the years, as the Simpson style is usually more challenging than this and he liked to add a few cross-bunkers. A wee bit frustrating for the better players but very enjoyable nonetheless.

Club du Lys-Chantilly — 1929

Rond-Point du Grand Cerf
F - 60260 LAMORLAYE

Office Secrétariat (33) 03 44 21 26 00
Pro shop Pro-shop (33) 03 44 21 36 73
Fax Fax (33) 03 44 21 35 52
Web www.golf-lys-chantilly.com
Situation Situation Paris, 40 km

Annual closure Fermeture annuelle no
Weekly closure Fermeture hebdomadaire Tuesday(mardi)

Fees main season Tarifs haute saison	18 holes	
	Week days / Semaine	We/Bank holidays / We/Férié
Individual Individuel	€ 50	€ 80*
Couple Couple	€ 100	€ 160*

* Restrictions for visitors at weekends (call before coming)

Caddie Caddie no — **Electric Trolley** Chariot électrique yes
Buggy Voiturette yes — **Clubs** Clubs yes
Credit cards Cartes de crédit
VISA - CB - Eurocard - Mastercard - AMEX

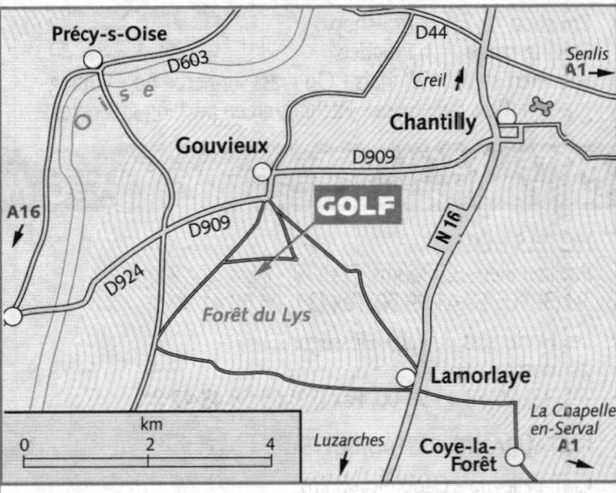

Access Accès : Paris A1 → Lille. Exit Survilliers. D922 → Fosses. N17 → La-Chapelle-en-Serval, then D924 to Chantilly. In Chantilly N16 → Paris, International Club du Lys on right hand side.
Map 3 on page 164 Carte 3 Page 164

GOLF COURSE — PARCOURS 15/20

Site Site
Maintenance Entretien
Architect Architecte Tom Simpson
Type Type Inland, parkland
Relief Relief
Water in play Eau en jeu
Exp. to wind Exposé au vent
Trees in play Arbres en jeu

Scorecard Carte de score	Chp. / Chp.	Mens / Mess.	Ladies / Da.
Length Long.	5863	5517	4818
Par	70	70	70
Slope system	112	110	111

Advised golfing ability Niveau de jeu recommandé 0 12 24 36
Hcp required Handicap exigé 35

CLUB HOUSE & AMENITIES — CLUB HOUSE ET ANNEXES 6/10

Pro shop Pro-shop
Driving range Practice
Sheltered couvert 7 mats - On grass sur herbe no, 15 mats open air - Putting-green putting-green yes (2) - Pitching-green pitching green no

HOTEL FACILITIES — ENVIRONNEMENT HOTELIER 7/10

HOTELS HÔTELS

Château de la Tour - 41 rooms, D € 157 - Gouvieux 3 km
Tel (33) 03 44 62 38 38, Fax (33) 03 44 57 31 97

Pavillon Saint-Hubert - 18 rooms, D € 60 - Toutevoie 5 km
Tel (33) 03 44 57 07 04, Fax (33) 03 44 57 75 42

Relais d'Aumale - 24 rooms, D € 140 - Montgrésin 11 km
Tel (33) 03 44 54 61 31, Fax (33) 03 44 54 69 15

RESTAURANTS RESTAURANTS

La Renardière - Gouvieux 3 km
Tel (33) 03 44 57 08 23

Verbois - St Maximin (RN 16) 12 km
Tel (33) 03 44 24 06 22

Isle Adam (L')

16 | 7 | 5

Ce parcours a vite conquis une belle réputation. Par la franchise et la grande variété de dessin et d'environnement des trous, tracés en partie dans une forêt, en partie sur un beau plateau. Le seul inconvénient, c'est de passer de l'une à l'autre et la montée est épuisante, un transport pour l'éviter serait le bienvenu. La stratégie de jeu est évidente dès la première visite, les fairways sont larges, mais le placement de la balle est crucial pour pouvoir ensuite approcher les greens en bonne position, car leurs modelages et leurs dimensions exigent beaucoup d'attention. L'architecte Ronald Fream a beaucoup travaillé le terrain, dans une synthèse heureuse des tendances britannique et américaine, permettant à tous les niveaux et tous les styles de jeu de s'exprimer. Les arbres et bunkers sont bien en jeu, et l'eau présente sur trois trous seulement. Une bonne réussite, d'autant plus que les importants travaux de drainage ont permis d'atténuer les conséquences des pluies.

This course has rapidly gained a fine reputation for its fairness and for the great variety in the design and setting of holes, some of which are laid out through a forest, others on a pretty plateau. The only drawback is walking from one part of the course to the other and some form of conveyance would be most welcome. Game strategy is clear from the very first visit; the fairways are wide, but it is essential to position the tee-shot accurately in order to get a good look at greens whose slopes and size require great care. Architect Ronald Fream has shaped the terrain a great deal and created a happy combination of British and American trends. The course is fun for golfers of all abilities and styles. The trees and bunkers are clearly in play and water threatens on just three holes. A good course, especially now that significant drainage work helps to lessen the effects of heavy rain.

Golf de l'Isle-Adam — 1995
1, chemin des Vanneaux
F - 95290 L'ISLE-ADAM

Office	Secrétariat	(33) 01 34 08 11 11
Pro shop	Pro-shop	(33) 01 34 08 11 11
Fax	Fax	(33) 01 34 08 11 19
Web	www.golfisleadam.com	
Situation	Situation	Paris, 35 km
Annual closure	Fermeture annuelle	24/12→1/1
Weekly closure	Fermeture hebdomadaire	tuesday/mardi

Fees main season Tarifs haute saison	18 holes	
	Week days Semaine	We/Bank holidays We/Férié
Individual Individuel	€ 43	€ 63
Couple Couple	€ 86	€ 126

Under 18: € 21 / 31 (We)
Seniors & Ladies: special offer on thursdays (jeudi)

Caddie Caddie no — **Electric Trolley** Chariot électrique yes
Buggy Voiturette yes — **Clubs** Clubs yes
Credit cards Cartes de crédit
VISA - CB - Eurocard - MasterCard - AMEX - DC

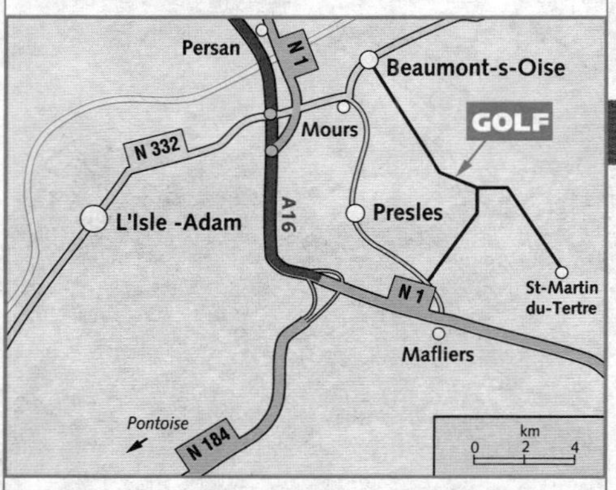

Access Accès : • A1 Paris (Porte de la Chapelle), Exit (Sortie) Beauvais, N1, Exit Beaumont-sur-Oise • A15 Paris (Porte de Clignancourt), → Pontoise, → N184, Exit Beaumont-sur-Oise
Map 3 on page 164 Carte 3 Page 164

GOLF COURSE — PARCOURS 16/20

Site	Site	
Maintenance	Entretien	
Architect	Architecte	Ronald Fream
Type	Type	forest, open country
Relief	Relief	
Water in play	Eau en jeu	
Exp. to wind	Exposé au vent	
Trees in play	Arbres en jeu	

Scorecard Carte de score	Chp. Chp.	Mens Mess.	Ladies Da.
Length Long.	6188	5696	4612
Par	72	72	72
Slope system	131	128	121

Advised golfing ability Niveau de jeu recommandé — 0 12 24 36
Hcp required Handicap exigé — 54

CLUB HOUSE & AMENITIES — CLUB HOUSE ET ANNEXES 7/10

Pro shop Pro-shop
Driving range Practice
Sheltered couvert 12 mats - On grass sur herbe yes (summer) - Putting-green putting-green yes - Pitching-green pitching green yes

HOTEL FACILITIES — ENVIRONNEMENT HOTELIER 5/10

HOTELS HÔTELS
Novotel Château de Mafflers
99 rooms, D € 125 - Mafflers 7 km
Tel (33) 01 34 08 35 35, Fax (33) 01 34 08 35 00

Etap Hôtel - 68 rooms, D € 37 - L'Isle-Adam 1 km
Tel (33) 01 90 68 32 03, Fax (33) 01 34 69 11 85

Grand Hôtel - 43 rooms, D € 150 - Enghien 12 km
Tel (33) 01 39 34 10 04, Fax (33) 01 39 34 10 01

RESTAURANTS RESTAURANTS
Relais Fleuri - L'Isle-Adam 2 km -
Tel (33) 01 34 69 01 85

Gai Rivage - L'Isle-Adam 2 km
Tel (33) 01 34 69 01 09

Joyenval *Marly*

16 | 8 | 7

Le Golf de Joyenval a trouvé sa vitesse de croisière, mais il n'entr'ouvre ses portes qu'aux invités des membres. L'avantage d'une fréquentation réduite, c'est que son entretien, notamment au niveau des greens, était généralement bon. Après une période de rodage, les choses vont bien mieux de ce côté sous la direction d'un greenkeeper américain. Des deux parcours, Marly est celui qui a le moins souffert des contraintes administratives, souvent abusives, liées à la proximité du Désert de Retz (monument historique), mais on aimerait voir les trous (en particulier les zones de driving) souvent mieux définis par des plantations ou – à défaut – par des différences de hauteur de tonte. Actuellement, on ne distingue parfois plus que les bunkers, aussi impressionnants à voir qu'à visiter, et dont l'entretien a été soigné. Très varié de paysage et de style, ce parcours est d'autant plus technique que les greens sont très difficiles à lire.

The Joyenval club now looks to be up and running but half-opens its gates only to members' guests. The upside of being under-played is that green-keeping and the greens in particular are generally good. After a period of "running-in", things have much improved in this respect under the management of an American greenkeeper. Of the two courses, Marly is the one that suffered the least from often excessive administrative requirements related to the closeness of the Désert de Retz (an historical landmark), although we would like to see the holes (and particularly the drive landing-areas) better defined with a tree planting programme or different cuts. Right now, the only distinction is sometimes the actual bunkers, which are as impressive to see as they are to be in and which have been very carefully maintained. Very varied in style and landscape, the course is made all the more technical by greens that are very difficult to read.

Golf de Joyenval — 1992

Chemin de la Tuilerie
F - 78240 CHAMBOURCY

Office Secrétariat (33) 01 39 22 27 61
Pro shop Pro-shop (33) 01 39 22 27 50
Fax Fax (33) 01 30 65 94 26
E-mail joyenval@wanadoo.fr
Situation Situation Paris, 28 km
Annual closure Fermeture annuelle no
Weekly closure Fermeture hebdomadaire monday/lundi
Fees main season Tarifs haute saison 18 holes

	Week days Semaine	We/Bank holidays We/Férié
Individual Individuel	*	*
Couple Couple	*	*

* members & their guests only (membres et invités)

Caddie Caddie on request **Electric Trolley** Chariot électrique yes
Buggy Voiturette yes **Clubs** Clubs yes
Credit cards Cartes de crédit
VISA - CB - Eurocard - MasterCard

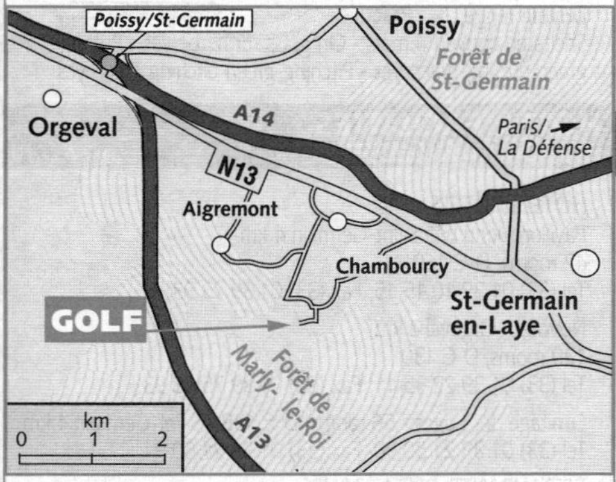

Access Accès : A13 Exit (Sortie) → Saint-Germain. N13 → Poissy, → Orgeval. After Chambourcy, take left → Désert de Retz, Golf de Joyenval.
Map 15 on page 188 Carte 15 Page 188

GOLF COURSE PARCOURS 16/20

Site Site
Maintenance Entretien
Architect Architecte Robert Trent Jones
Type Type parkland, forest
Relief Relief
Water in play Eau en jeu
Exp. to wind Exposé au vent
Trees in play Arbres en jeu

Scorecard Carte de score	Chp. Chp.	Mens Mess.	Ladies Da.
Length Long.	6249	5776	4532
Par	72	72	72
Slope system	148	141	129

Advised golfing ability Niveau de jeu recommandé 0 12 24 36
Hcp required Handicap exigé no

CLUB HOUSE & AMENITIES CLUB HOUSE ET ANNEXES 8/10

Pro shop Pro-shop
Driving range Practice
Sheltered couvert 4 mats - On grass sur herbe yes - Putting-green putting-green yes - Pitching-green pitching green yes

HOTEL FACILITIES ENVIRONNEMENT HOTELIER 7/10

HOTELS HÔTELS
Pavillon Henri IV - Saint-Germain 4 km
42 rooms, D € 160
Tel (33) 01 39 10 15 15, Fax (33) 01 39 73 93 73

Novotel - Orgeval 4 km
120 rooms, D € 130
Tel (33) 01 39 22 35 11, Fax (33) 01 39 75 48 93

Ermitage des Loges - 56 rooms, D € 138 - Saint-Germain 4 km
Tel (33) 01 39 21 50 90, Fax (33) 01 39 21 50 91

RESTAURANTS RESTAURANTS
L'Esturgeon - Poissy 5 km - Tel (33) 01 39 65 00 04
Cazaudehore - Saint-Germain 5 km
Tel (33) 01 30 61 64 64

Joyenval *Retz*

16	8	7

Le site est exceptionnel, entre la forêt de Marly et une vallée que les poètes n'aurait pas reniée, à proximité immédiate du Désert de Retz, folie architecturale dûe à l'imagination d'un gentilhomme du XVIII ème siècle. On aurait d'ailleurs aimé que le parcours soit vraiment une réponse moderne à cet esprit baroque, mais le crayon parfois austère de Trent Jones a permis de limiter au minimum les contraintes. Il reste quelques trous de haute volée, entre forêt et plaine, entre parc et jardin, avec des aspects évidemment américains dans leur franchise et leur brutal té, mais aussi britanniques quand les contours deviennent plus flous, plus subtils. Très scénique, moins stratégique que "Marly", ce parcours est peut-être aussi moins exigeant pour les joueurs moyens, d'autant que les sous-bois ont été sérieusement nettoyés.

The site is outstanding, between the forest of Marly and a valley to make any poet wax lyrical, within the immediate vicinity of the Désert de Retz, a piece of architectural folly born from the imagination of an 18th century gentleman. We would have liked this course really to be a modern response to this baroque spirit, but the often austere design of Trent Jones helped keep restrictions to a minimum. There are a few top-notch holes between forest and plain, park-land and garden, obviously looking very American in their openness and toughness, but also British when contours grow a little less sharp and more subtle. Very scenic and less strategic than Marly, Retz is perhaps also less demanding for the average golfer, especially now that the undergrowth has been seriously cut back.

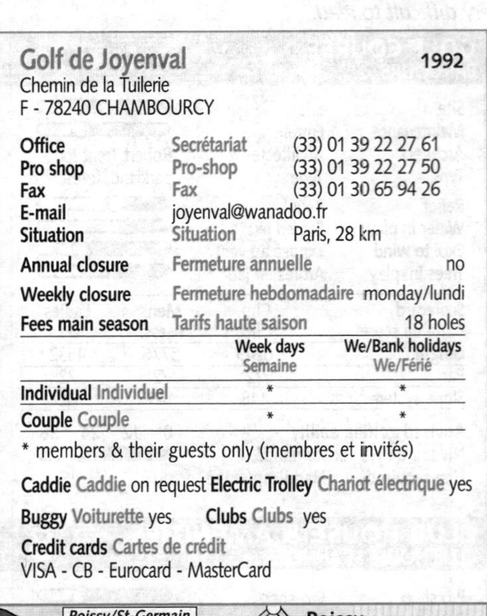

Golf de Joyenval **1992**
Chemin de la Tuilerie
F - 78240 CHAMBOURCY

Office	Secrétariat	(33) 01 39 22 27 61
Pro shop	Pro-shop	(33) 01 39 22 27 50
Fax	Fax	(33) 01 30 65 94 26
E-mail	joyenval@wanadoo.fr	
Situation	Situation	Paris, 28 km
Annual closure	Fermeture annuelle	no
Weekly closure	Fermeture hebdomadaire	monday/lundi

Fees main season Tarifs haute saison	18 holes	
	Week days Semaine	We/Bank holidays We/Férié
Individual Individuel	*	*
Couple Couple	*	*

* members & their guests only (membres et invités)

Caddie Caddie on request **Electric Trolley** Chariot électrique yes

Buggy Voiturette yes **Clubs** Clubs yes

Credit cards Cartes de crédit
VISA - CB - Eurocard - MasterCard

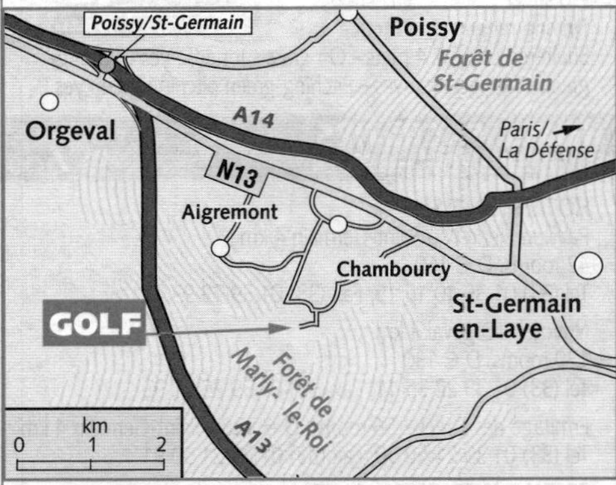

Access Accès : A13 Exit (Sortie) → Saint-Germain. N13 → Poissy, → Orgeval. After Chambourcy, take left → Désert de Retz, Golf de Joyenval.
Map 15 on page 188 Carte 15 Page 188

GOLF COURSE — PARCOURS 16/20

Site	Site	
Maintenance	Entretien	
Architect	Architecte	Robert Trent Jones
Type	Type	forest, parkland
Relief	Relief	
Water in play	Eau en jeu	
Exp. to wind	Exposé au vent	
Trees in play	Arbres en jeu	

Scorecard Carte de score	Chp. Chp.	Mens Mess.	Ladies Da.
Length Long.	6211	5728	4674
Par	72	72	72
Slope system	144	134	125

Advised golfing ability 0 12 24 36
Niveau de jeu recommandé

Hcp required Handicap exigé no

CLUB HOUSE & AMENITIES — CLUB HOUSE ET ANNEXES 8/10

Pro shop — Pro-shop
Driving range — Practice
Sheltered couvert 4 mats - On grass sur herbe yes - Putting-green putting-green yes - Pitching-green pitching green yes

HOTEL FACILITIES — ENVIRONNEMENT HOTELIER 7/10

HOTELS HÔTELS

Pavillon Henri IV - Saint-Germain 4 km
42 rooms, D € 160
Tel (33) 01 39 10 15 15, Fax (33) 01 39 73 93 73

Novotel - Orgeval 4 km
120 rooms, D € 130
Tel (33) 01 39 22 35 11, Fax (33) 01 39 75 48 93

Ermitage des Loges - 56 rooms, D € 138 - Saint-Germain 4 km
Tel (33) 01 39 21 50 90, Fax (33) 01 39 21 50 91

RESTAURANTS RESTAURANTS

L'Esturgeon - Poissy 5 km - Tel (33) 01 39 65 00 04

Cazaudehore - Saint-Germain 5 km
Tel (33) 01 30 61 64 64

Kempferhof (Le)

18 | 8 | 6

La séduction est immédiate : l'impression de finition et de soin du détail se confirme sur le parcours, situé dans un environnement de campagne, avec des sapins, des hêtres et des bouleaux pour décor. Il est certes difficile de jouer son handicap mais ce parcours facile à marcher est accessible à tous les niveaux, sauf aux néophytes. Ils seront intimidés par quelques obstacles d'eau dangereux, et ce genre de parcours ne les met pas en confiance. Très sélectif, il demande de travailler la balle et de démontrer sa maîtrise de tous les clubs, avec un accent aigu sur la précision, notamment pour approcher les vastes greens, très travaillés. Tous les obstacles étant visibles, ce parcours ne cache rien de ses exigences. Le terrain a été beaucoup modelé dans la tradition de son architecte von Hagge, mais sans bouleverser la nature, donnant au lieu une belle impression de calme. Une réussite de grand standing, et la personnalité des chambres du joli hôtel est un argument de plus pour visiter cette région magnifique.

The appeal of the place hits you as soon as you arrive, and the first impression of a carefully groomed course with attention to detail is confirmed when out on the fairways in a country setting of pine-trees, beech and birch. Playing to your handicap might be too much to ask, but this easily walkable course can be played by all except by beginners, who might be unsettled by a few dangerous water hazards and for whom this type of course hardly instills confidence. It is very selective, calling for skill in ball-control and stroke-making, especially when approaching the carefully designed greens. As all the hazards are there to be seen, the course hides nothing of what it demands from golfers. The terrain has been contoured in the tradition of architect von Hagge, but mother nature keeps the upper hand. This unquestionably great course stays right up there with the best and the style and personality of the pretty hotel is a further good reason to visit this magnificent part of the country.

Kempferhof Golf Club — 1990

351, rue du Moulin
F - 67115 PLOBSHEIM

Office	Secrétariat	(33) 03 88 98 72 72
Pro shop	Pro-shop	(33) 03 88 98 72 72
Fax	Fax	(33) 03 88 98 74 76
Web	www.golf-kempferhof.com	
Situation	Situation	Strasbourg, 15 km
Annual closure	Fermeture annuelle	21/12→12/1
Weekly closure	Fermeture hebdomadaire	tuesday

mardi (01/11 → 01/04)

Fees main season Tarifs haute saison	18 holes	
	Week days Semaine	**We/Bank holidays** We/Férié
Individual Individuel	€ 75	€ 95
Couple Couple	€ 150	€ 190

Under 18: – 50%

Caddie Caddie on request **Electric Trolley** Chariot électrique no

Buggy Voiturette yes **Clubs** Clubs yes

Credit cards Cartes de crédit
VISA - CB - Eurocard - MasterCard - AMEX

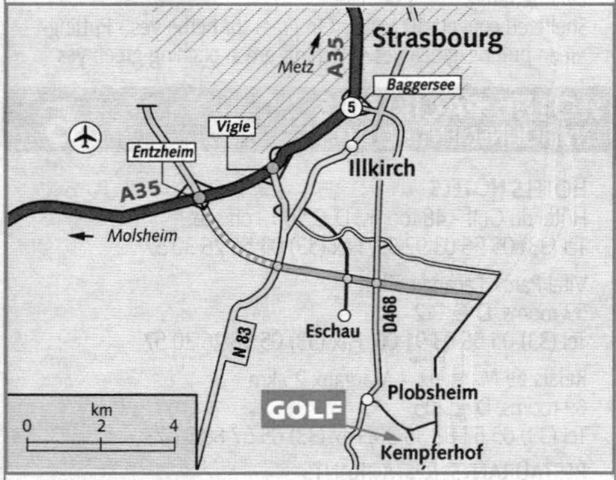

Access Accès : Strasbourg A35, Exit (Sortie) N°5 Baggersee → Eschau, → Plobsheim, → Golf

Map 4 on page 167 Carte 4 Page 167

GOLF COURSE — PARCOURS 18/20

Site	Site	
Maintenance	Entretien	
Architect	Architecte	Robert von Hagge
Type	Type	parkland, country
Relief	Relief	
Water in play	Eau en jeu	
Exp. to wind	Exposé au vent	
Trees in play	Arbres en jeu	

Scorecard Carte de score	Chp. Chp.	Mens Mess.	Ladies Da.
Length Long.	6024	5613	4493
Par	72	72	72
Slope system	145	137	127

Advised golfing ability 0 12 24 36
Niveau de jeu recommandé

Hcp required Handicap exigé 35, We

CLUB HOUSE & AMENITIES — CLUB HOUSE ET ANNEXES 8/10

Pro shop Pro-shop
Driving range Practice
Sheltered couvert 10 mats - On grass sur herbe yes - Putting-green putting-green yes - Pitching-green pitching green no

HOTEL FACILITIES — ENVIRONNEMENT HOTELIER 6/10

HOTELS HÔTELS

Kempferhof Hotel - 29 rooms, D € 180 - on site
Tel (33) 03 88 98 72 72, Fax (33) 03 88 98 74 76

Holiday Inn Garden Court - Illkirch 5 km
68 rooms, D € 109
Tel (33) 03 88 40 84 84, Fax (33) 03 88 66 22 83

Alizés - Lipsheim 3 km - 50 rooms, D € 64
Tel (33) 03 88 59 02 00, Fax (33) 03 88 64 21 61

RESTAURANTS RESTAURANTS

Buerehiesel - Strasbourg 13 km - Tel (33) 03 88 45 56 65
Le Crocodile - Strasbourg 13 km - Tel (33) 03 88 32 13 02
L'Arsenal - Strasbourg 15 km - Tel (33) 03 88 35 03 69

Lacanau

13 | 6 | 6

Le site est beau et tranquille, modérément vallonné au milieu des pins, et le parcours aurait pu être un chef d'œuvre, avec un architecte plus audacieux. Dans son dessin très honorable, une demi-douzaine de trous restent vraiment en mémoire. Des obstacles d'eau apportent un élément paysager intéressant, et quelques interrogations, sans être trop intimidants. Certes, il faut jouer plusieurs fois pour bien comprendre la stratégie en fonction des différents départs, ou de quelques dénivellés, mais seuls les mauvais coups sont vraiment pénalisés. Les débutants ne seront pas partout à l'aise, mais tous les niveaux peuvent s'exprimer sans ennui et passer un séjour vivifiant à proximité de l'Atlantique, pratiquement toute l'année : le sol sablonneux du parcours absorbe bien la pluie. On ne peut ignorer l'immobilier environnant, mais il ne gêne pas le jeu. L'entretien est en amélioration, l'accueil peu au niveau d'un golf qui se veut "international".

The site is a magnificent and peaceful setting with gently rolling terrain through a pine forest, and the course itself could have been a true masterpiece with a more daring architect. Of this very pleasant design, only about half a dozen holes leave a lasting impression. Water hazards are an attractive addition to the general landscape and call for a little forethought but they are less than awesome. Naturally, you need to play the course several times to grasp the ideal strategy depending on the tees you choose, but here only the really bad shots are penalized. Beginners will find a number of holes tight but all golfers can have fun and never grow tired of Lacanau while spending an invigorating holiday close to the Atlantic Ocean. They can play virtually all year, too, as the sandy terrain soaks up the rain. The ever-expanding real estate programme is an eye-sore without actually catching the eye, green-keeping is now improving after a purple-patch, but the facilities here are not what one might expect from a club that calls itself "international".

Golf de Lacanau — 1980

Domaine de l'Ardilouse
F - 33680 LACANAU

Office	Secrétariat	(33) 05 56 03 92 98
Pro shop	Pro-shop	(33) 05 56 03 92 98
Fax	Fax	(33) 05 56 03 15 19
Web	www.golf-lacanau.com	
Situation	Situation	Bordeaux, 50 km
Annual closure	Fermeture annuelle	no
Weekly closure	Fermeture hebdomadaire	no

Fees main season Tarifs haute saison	full day	
	Week days Semaine	**We/Bank holidays** We/Férié
Individual Individuel	€ 49	€ 49
Couple Couple	€ 98	€ 98

Under 18 and Students (under 26): – 50%

Caddie Caddie no — **Electric Trolley** Chariot électrique no

Buggy Voiturette yes — **Clubs** Clubs yes

Credit cards Cartes de crédit
VISA - CB - Eurocard - MasterCard

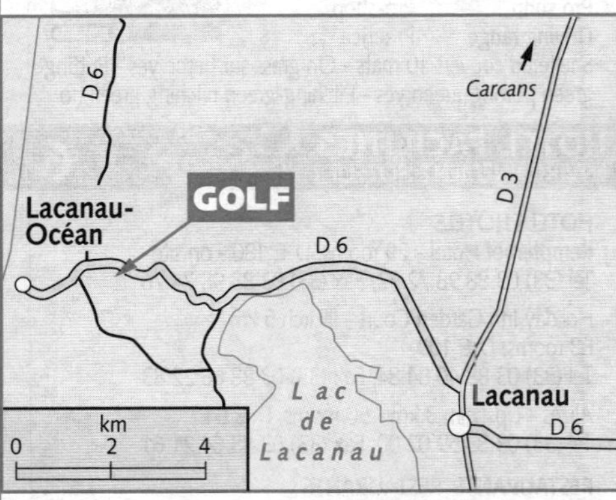

Access Accès : Ring Road ("Rocade Ouest") of Bordeaux, Exit (Sortie) No 7, N 215, D6 → Lacanau Océan
Map 9 on page 176 Carte 9 Page 176

GOLF COURSE — PARCOURS — 13/20

Site	Site	
Maintenance	Entretien	
Architect	Architecte	John Harris
Type	Type	forest, hilly
Relief	Relief	
Water in play	Eau en jeu	
Exp. to wind	Exposé au vent	
Trees in play	Arbres en jeu	

Scorecard Carte de score	**Chp.** Chp.	**Mens** Mess.	**Ladies** Da.
Length Long.	5934	5406	4502
Par	72	72	72
Slope system	137	134	133

Advised golfing ability Niveau de jeu recommandé: 0 12 24 36

Hcp required Handicap exigé 54

CLUB HOUSE & AMENITIES — CLUB HOUSE ET ANNEXES — 6/10

Pro shop Pro-shop
Driving range Practice
Sheltered couvert 10 mats - On grass sur herbe yes - Putting-green putting-green yes - Pitching-green pitching green yes

HOTEL FACILITIES — ENVIRONNEMENT HOTELIER — 6/10

HOTELS HÔTELS

Hôtel du Golf - 48 rooms, D € 100 - on site
Tel (33) 05 56 03 92 92, Fax (33) 05 56 26 30 57

Vital Parc - Lacanau 5 km
59 rooms, D € 112
Tel (33) 05 56 03 91 00, Fax (33) 05 56 26 30 57

Relais de Margaux - Margaux 25 km
69 rooms, D € 205
Tel (33) 05 57 88 38 30, Fax (33) 05 57 88 31 73

RESTAURANTS RESTAURANTS

Savoie - Margaux 25 km - Tel (33) 05 57 88 31 76
La Vieille Auberge - Le Porge 10 km - Tel (33) 05 56 26 50 40

Largue (La)

15	7	5

Dans une jolie propriété, traversée par la ligne Maginot, offrant alternativement un environnement de forêt et des trous de style links, ce parcours est accidenté mais plaisant, avec quelques pièces d'eau, en jeu sur cinq trous. Plus impressionnants visuellement que réellement, ses obstacles principaux sont les arbres et les nombreux bunkers. Les bunkers de green, bien travaillés, mais parfois peu visibles constituent les principales difficultés (avec les arbres), mais le choix de clubs est surtout délicat, avec la topographie très vallonnée (voiturette recommandée pour les seniors). L'entretien est soigné, les greens de bonne qualité, bien conçus et assez rapides : certains sont surélevés et demandent de porter la balle. Un parcours d'entraînement de 9 trous permet de faire tranquillement progresser les néophytes. Mais on a l'impression d'être ici en Suisse, le site web est certes aussi en français… avec des fautes !

This is a hilly but pleasant course with a few stretches of water coming into play on five holes, located on a pretty estate crossed by the Maginot line. Part woodland and part links, this is a visually impressive layout where the main hazards are the trees and numerous bunkers. The green-side bunkers, well-designed but sometimes hard to spot, pose the biggest problems (with the trees) but the trickiest point is perhaps club selection owing to the hilly terrain (a buggy is recommended for senior players). Green-keeping is generally good and the greens are good standard, well laid-out and pretty fast. A number of elevated greens call for long high approaches. A 9-hole practice course is good news for beginners still learning the game. But here you get the impression of being in Switzerland although the website now also features a French version (well, sort of).

Golf de La Largue — 1989

Chemin du Largweg
F - 68580 MOOSLARGUE

Office	Secrétariat	(33) 03 89 07 67 67
Pro shop	Pro-shop	(33) 03 89 07 67 67
Fax	Fax	(33) 03 89 25 62 83
Web	www.golf-lalargue.com	
Situation	Situation	Bâle /Basel, 30 km

Altkirch (pop. 5 090), 24 km

Annual closure	Fermeture annuelle	15/12→10/2
Weekly closure	Fermeture hebdomadaire	no
Fees main season	Tarifs haute saison	18 holes

	Week days Semaine	We/Bank holidays We/Férié
Individual Individuel	€ 60	€ 70
Couple Couple	€ 120	€ 140

Juniors: € 25 / 31 (We)

Caddie Caddie no — **Electric Trolley** Chariot électrique no

Buggy Voiturette yes — **Clubs** Clubs yes

Credit cards Cartes de crédit
VISA - CB - Eurocard - MasterCard

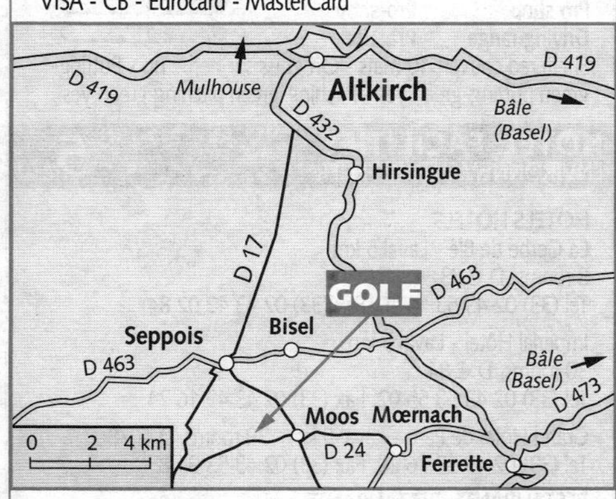

Access Accès : • Mulhouse → Altkirch → Hirsingue → Seppois • Bâle, Motorway → Delémont, Exit Reinach sud → Therwil → Leymen → Linsdorf → Ferrette → Moos

Map 8 on page 175 Carte 8 Page 175

GOLF COURSE — PARCOURS — 15/20

Site	Site	
Maintenance	Entretien	
Architect	Architecte	Jeremy Pern Jean Garaïalde
Type	Type	forest, parkland
Relief	Relief	
Water in play	Eau en jeu	
Exp. to wind	Exposé au vent	
Trees in play	Arbres en jeu	

Scorecard Carte de score	Chp. Chp.	Mens Mess.	Ladies Da.
Length Long.	6142	5662	4965
Par	72	72	72
Slope system	138	133	130

Advised golfing ability Niveau de jeu recommandé — 0 12 24 36

Hcp required Handicap exigé — 36

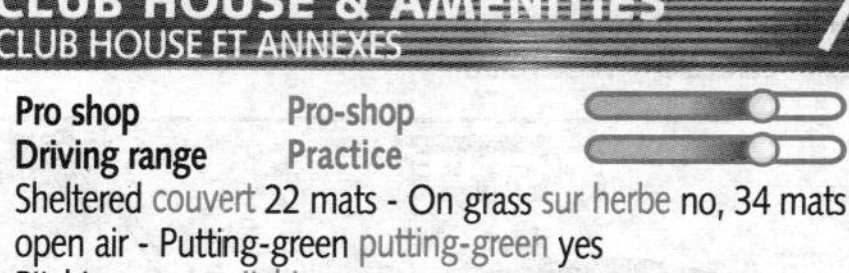

CLUB HOUSE & AMENITIES — CLUB HOUSE ET ANNEXES — 7/10

Pro shop	Pro-shop
Driving range	Practice

Sheltered couvert 22 mats - On grass sur herbe no, 34 mats open air - Putting-green putting-green yes
Pitching-green pitching green yes

HOTEL FACILITIES — ENVIRONNEMENT HOTELIER — 5/10

HOTELS HÔTELS

Le Petit Kohlberg - 35 rooms, D € 78 - Lucelle 12 km
Tel (33) 03 89 40 85 30, Fax (33) 03 89 40 89 40

Aux Deux Clefs - 7 rooms, D € 45 - Ferrette 9 km
Tel (33) 03 89 40 80 56, Fax (33) 03 89 08 10 47

Le Moulin Bas - 7 rooms, D € 75 - Ligsdorf 13 km
Tel (33) 03 89 40 31 25, Fax (33) 03 89 08 24 01

RESTAURANTS RESTAURANTS

Hostellerie de l'Illberg - Hirtzbach 15 km
Tel (33) 03 89 40 93 22

Aux Deux Clefs - Moernach 5 km - Tel (33) 03 89 40 80 56

Moulin Bas - Ligsdorf 13 km - Tel (33) 03 89 40 31 25

Laval-Changé *La Chabossière*

14	7	5

Malheureusement proche de l'autoroute, ce parcours a été dessiné par Jean-Pascal Fourès dans un site dégagé et au relief assez prononcé. Le manque d'arbres ne permet toujours pas de bien délimiter les trous quand on vient pour la première fois, mais le tracé des fairways et des roughs est déjà meilleur, le drainage semble efficace. De longueur raisonnable, le tracé général est de bonne qualité, avec quelques coups aveugles, mais inévitables en raison du terrain. De même, certains trous sont un peu "tricky" comme le 6 et le 7. Les greens sont raisonnablement modelés, de bonnes dimensions et de très bonne qualité. Ce golf a visiblement été pensé pour des membres permanents, et pour tous les niveaux de jeu, car ce n'est pas vraiment une région traditionnelle de vacances, ou sur un itinéraire golfique particulier. Mais ses jolis points de vue sur la Mayenne et son ambiance amicale plairont aux visiteurs de passage dans la région, ils seront récompensés de leur curiosité et bien accueillis...

Unhappily located within the immediate vicinity of a motorway, this course was designed by Jean-Pascal Fourès in an open and rather hilly site. The shortage of trees still makes it difficult to clearly distinguish a number of holes when playing for the first time but fairways and rough are now more distinctly outlined and drainage looks to be effective. The general layout is of reasonable length and good standard, although there are the few unavoidable blind holes on such sloping terrain. Likewise a few holes like the 6th or 7th are a little tricky, too. The greens are reasonably well contoured, nicely sized and excellent to play. This course is not really in traditional holiday country or on any special golfing trail, but it has visibly been designed for permanent members and golfers of all playing skills. Pretty panoramas over the Mayenne river and the club's friendly atmosphere will appeal to visitors passing through, who will always find a warm welcome here.

Golf de Laval-Changé — 1992

«La Chabossière»
F - 53810 CHANGE

Office	Secrétariat	(33) 02 43 53 16 03
Pro shop	Pro-shop	(33) 02 43 53 16 03
Fax	Fax	(33) 02 43 49 35 15
E-mail	golf53.laval@wanadoo.fr	
Situation	Situation	Laval (pop. 50 470), 5 km
Annual closure	Fermeture annuelle	24/12→3/1
Weekly closure	Fermeture hebdomadaire	no
Fees main season	Tarifs haute saison	Full day

	Week days Semaine	We/Bank holidays We/Férié
Individual Individuel	€ 28	€ 35
Couple Couple	€ 46	€ 55

Students: € 9 (week days/semaine) and – 50% (We)

Caddie Caddie no — **Electric Trolley** Chariot électrique yes

Buggy Voiturette yes — **Clubs** Clubs yes

Credit cards Cartes de crédit
VISA - Eurocard - MasterCard

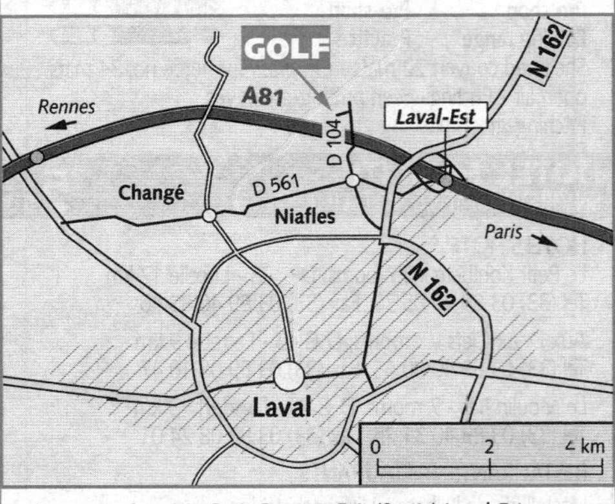

Access Accès : A81 Paris-Rennes, Exit (Sortie) Laval-Est
Map 2 on page 162 Carte 2 Page 162

GOLF COURSE — PARCOURS 14/20

Site	Site	
Maintenance	Entretien	
Architect	Architecte	Jean-Pascal Fourès
Type	Type	country, hilly
Relief	Relief	
Water in play	Eau en jeu	
Exp. to wind	Exposé au vent	
Trees in play	Arbres en jeu	

Scorecard Carte de score	Chp. Chp.	Mens Mess.	Ladies Da.
Length Long.	6111	5706	4776
Par	72	72	72
Slope system	138	130	125

Advised golfing ability — Niveau de jeu recommandé: 0 12 24 36

Hcp required — Handicap exigé: no

CLUB HOUSE & AMENITIES — CLUB HOUSE ET ANNEXES 7/10

Pro shop Pro-shop
Driving range Practice
Sheltered couvert 10 mats - On grass sur herbe no - Putting-green putting-green yes - Pitching-green pitching green yes

HOTEL FACILITIES — ENVIRONNEMENT HOTELIER 5/10

HOTELS HÔTELS

La Gerbe de Blé - Laval 5 km
8 rooms, D € 83
Tel (33) 02 43 53 14 10, Fax (33) 02 43 49 02 84

Impérial Hôtel - Laval 5 km
30 rooms, D € 84
Tel (33) 02 43 53 55 02, Fax (33) 02 43 49 16 74

Grand Hôtel de Paris - Laval 5 km - 39 rooms, D € 78
Tel (33) 02 43 53 76 20, Fax (33) 02 43 53 91 83

RESTAURANTS RESTAURANTS

Bistro de Paris - Laval 5 km - Tel (33) 02 43 56 98 29
Table Ronde - Changé 2 km - Tel (33) 02 43 53 43 33
Le Capucin Gourmand - Laval 5 km - Tel (33) 02 43 66 02 02

Limère

17 | 6 | 6

Limère reste l'un des meilleurs parcours français de la "période moderne", et un exemple d'architecture. Quand beaucoup affichent vouloir faire des parcours réellement accessibles à tous les niveaux, Cabell Robinson a réussi à faire un parcours passionnant pour tous les joueurs, dont la difficulté peut beaucoup changer selon les départs. Plat et peu fatigant, il est modérément modelé, toujours dans l'intérêt du jeu. Beaucoup d'arbres, de bunkers et quelques obstacles d'eau viennent menacer ceux qui manquent les fairways pourtant larges. Les approches de green peuvent être délicates, et les placements de drapeau rendent plus intéressants encore les greens subtils et intelligemment construits. Sans excès esthétiques, le parcours se déroule avec un excellent rythme de difficultés, auquel tous les coups devront répondre ici ou là. Limère mérite le détour, et un séjour, même si le club-house est plus fonctionnel qu'élégant. Limère reste un des rares parcours de haut niveau à faire l'unanimité.

This is one of the finest French courses built in the last fifteen years and is quite exemplary. At a time when many designers claim to build courses really accessible to all, Cabell Robinson succeeded in producing an exciting layout that can be played by all golfers, and one where the difficulty varies a lot from one tee-box to the next. Flat and relaxing, the terrain has been given quite a bit of shape but always in the right way. A lot of trees, bunkers and a few water hazards threaten balls that miss the wide fairways, approach-shots to the greens can be tricky and pin-positions make the subtle and cleverly built greens even more enticing. Without any needless visual effects, the course unwinds with a nice balance of hazards and difficulties, which sooner or later call for every shot in the book. Limère is well worth the trip and a few days stay, even though the club-house is only functional. This is one of those rare first-rate courses that wins everyone's vote.

Golf de Limère — 1992

Allée de la Pomme-de-Pin
F - 45160 ARDON

Office	Secrétariat	(33) 02 38 63 89 40
Pro shop	Pro-shop	(33) 02 38 63 89 40
Fax	Fax	(33) 02 38 63 05 20
Web	www.bluegreen.com	
Situation	Situation	Orléans (pop. 105 110), 13 km
Annual closure	Fermeture annuelle	no
Weekly closure	Fermeture hebdomadaire	no

Fees main season Tarifs haute saison	**Week days** Semaine	**We/Bank holidays** We/Férié
		18 holes
Individual Individuel	€ 40	€ 58
Couple Couple	€ 80	€ 116

€ 30 on Wednesday (mercredi) / Under 25: € 18 / 34 (We)

Caddie Caddie no **Electric Trolley** Chariot électrique no

Buggy Voiturette yes **Clubs** Clubs yes

Credit cards Cartes de crédit
VISA - CB - Eurocard - MasterCard - AMEX - DC

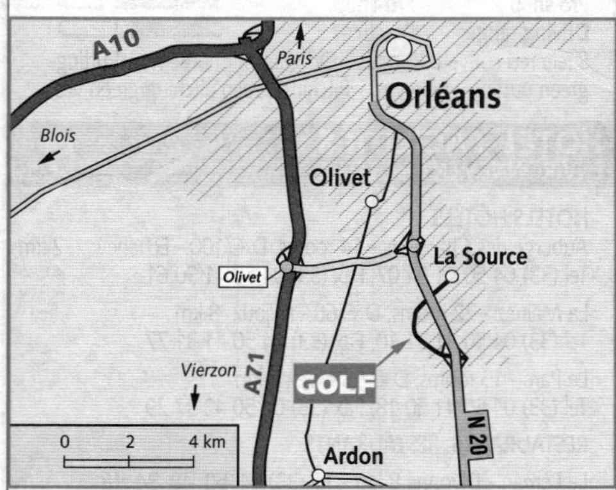

Access Accès : → Orléans La Source, sortie Olivet, RN20 → La Source, → Golf
Map 3 on page 164 Carte 3 Page 164

GOLF COURSE — PARCOURS — 17/20

Site	Site	
Maintenance	Entretien	
Architect	Architecte	Cabell B. Robinson
Type	Type	forest, parkland
Relief	Relief	
Water in play	Eau en jeu	
Exp. to wind	Exposé au vent	
Trees in play	Arbres en jeu	

Scorecard Carte de score	**Chp.** Chp.	**Mens** Mess.	**Ladies** Da.
Length Long.	6191	5720	4825
Par	72	72	72
Slope system	139	131	129

Advised golfing ability Niveau de jeu recommandé: 0 12 24 36

Hcp required Handicap exigé: no

CLUB HOUSE & AMENITIES — CLUB HOUSE ET ANNEXES — 6/10

Pro shop Pro-shop
Driving range Practice
Sheltered couvert 15 mats - On grass sur herbe yes - Putting-green putting-green yes - Pitching-green pitching green yes

HOTEL FACILITIES — ENVIRONNEMENT HOTELIER — 6/10

HOTELS HÔTELS

Domaine des Portes de Sologne - on site
240 rooms, D € 106
Tel (33) 02 38 49 99 99, Fax (33) 02 38 49 99 00

Rivage - 17 rooms, D € 75 - Olivet 6 km
Tel (33) 02 38 66 02 93, Fax (33) 02 38 56 31 11

Novotel Orléans - 119 rooms, D € 105 - La Source 3 km
Tel (33) 02 38 63 04 28, Fax (33) 02 38 69 24 04

RESTAURANTS RESTAURANTS

Rivage - Olivet 6 km - Tel (33) 02 38 66 02 93
Les Antiquaires - Orléans 13 km - Tel (33) 02 38 53 63 48
Laurendière - Olivet 6 km - Tel (33) 02 38 51 06 78

Maison Blanche

14	8	5

Avec d'aussi splendides vues sur les Alpes et un club-house luxueux, on attend un parcours constamment impeccable, car la concurrence est rude avec les autres golfs de la région lémanique, "colonisés" par les exigeants joueurs helvétiques. Malheureusement, le terrain reste sensible à l'humidité et en dépit des efforts, du standing et des ambitions de Maison Blanche, on sort parfois d'ici avec une légère impression que l'on "pouvait encore mieux faire". Ce parcours comprend de nombreux obstacles d'eau, des arbres très en jeu et des reliefs assez prononcés. Ils peuvent poser des problèmes aux débutants, mais les autres joueurs prendront plaisir à un tracé intéressant, sinon inoubliable, et garderont au minimum l'impression d'avoir effectué une belle balade en montagne, avec quelques pentes et dénivellés à négocier avec attention. On regrettera un dessin et une position des bunkers simplement moyens, ils auraient pu gêner davantage les joueurs expérimentés et ajouter un peu de panache esthétique à ce tracé.

With so magnificent views over the Alps and a luxurious club-house, you expect a consistently immaculate course, as these days competition is tough from other courses in the region of Geneva, "colonized" by demanding Swiss golfers. Unfortunately the terrain still does not take too kindly to wet weather and despite the status and ambitions of Maison Blanche, you go away with a slight impression that this course could be even better. The layout features any number of water hazards and trees, plus some undulating fairways. These may pose a few problems for beginners, but other players will have fun on this interesting if not unforgettable strip, and at the very least will feel like having enjoyed a beautiful mountain stroll with a few slopes and differences in altitude that need to be negotiated with care. The bunkering is average only in design and positioning and sand should have been located to cause more problems to experienced players and add a little panache to the beauty of the site.

Golf de Maison Blanche — 1992

Naz-Dessous
F - 01170 ECHENEVEX

Office Secrétariat (33) 04 50 42 44 42
Pro shop Pro-shop (33) 04 50 42 47 27
Fax Fax (33) 04 50 42 44 43
Web www.golfmaisonblanche.fr
Situation Situation Genève, 15 km
Annual closure Fermeture annuelle 1/12→1/3
Weekly closure Fermeture hebdomadaire no

Fees main season Tarifs haute saison	18 holes	
	Week days Semaine	**We/Bank holidays** We/Férié
Individual Individuel	€ 80	€ 60
Couple Couple	€ 160	€ 120

* We: members' guests only (invités des membres seulement)

Caddie Caddie on request **Electric Trolley** Chariot électrique yes

Buggy Voiturette medical, + 65 y-o **Clubs** Clubs yes

Credit cards Cartes de crédit
VISA - CB - Eurocard - MasterCard

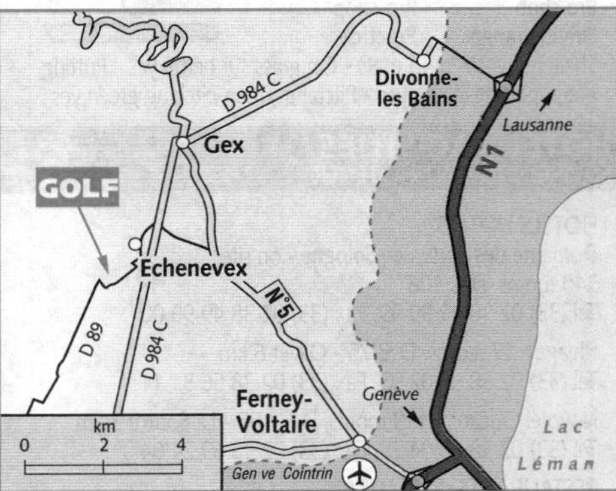

Access Accès : → Airport Genève-Cointrin → Ferney-Voltaire, → Gex, → Golf, on left hand side
Map 8 on page 175 Carte 8 Page 175

GOLF COURSE — PARCOURS — 14/20

Site Site
Maintenance Entretien
Architect Architecte Peter Harradine, Olivier Dongradi
Type Type country, hilly
Relief Relief
Water in play Eau en jeu
Exp. to wind Exposé au vent
Trees in play Arbres en jeu

Scorecard Carte de score	**Chp.** Chp.	**Mens** Mess.	**Ladies** Da.
Length Long.	6163	5782	4824
Par	72	72	72
Slope system	129	124	120

Advised golfing ability Niveau de jeu recommandé 0 12 24 36
Hcp required Handicap exigé 30

CLUB HOUSE & AMENITIES — CLUB HOUSE ET ANNEXES — 8/10

Pro shop Pro-shop
Driving range Practice
Sheltered couvert 10 mats - On grass sur herbe no - Putting-green putting-green yes - Pitching-green pitching green yes

HOTEL FACILITIES — ENVIRONNEMENT HOTELIER — 5/10

HOTELS HÔTELS

Auberge des Chasseurs - 14 rooms, D € 100 - Echenevex 2 km
Tel (33) 04 50 41 54 07, Fax (33) 04 50 41 90 61

La Mainaz - 22 rooms, D € 60 - Mijoux 8 km
Tel (33) 04 50 41 31 10, Fax (33) 04 50 41 31 77

Le Parc - 15 rooms, D € 56 - Gex 2 km
Tel (33) 04 50 41 50 18, Fax (33) 04 50 42 37 29

RESTAURANTS RESTAURANTS

Le Léman - Divonne 8 km - Tel (33) 04 50 40 34 18

La Cravache - Gex 2 km - Tel (33) 04 50 41 69 61

Auberge des Chasseurs - Echenevex 2 km
Tel (33) 04 50 41 54 07

Makila Golf Club

15	6	8

Parmi de très beaux chênes sur fond de Pyrénées, l'ampleur de cet espace a permis de créer de larges fairways (parfois trop) tout en préservant l'isolement d'un trou à l'autre. Rocky Roquemore a dessiné un parcours de style américain, avec des trous très variés, où l'on passe de la montagne aux plaines bordées d'obstacles d'eau. Les reliefs sont assez prononcés (sur trois trous), mais il était difficile de faire autrement dans cette superbe région et seuls les golfeurs en bonne condition physique pourront y évoluer sans voiturette. Avec près de 6200 mètres du fond, c'est un parcours solide pour les bons joueurs, mais les départs normaux permettent aux golfeurs de niveau moyen de savoir quoi faire : les obstacles sont bien visibles, la stratégie assez évidente, les difficultés bien réparties, quelques dévers et coups en pente pimentent le jeu. L'entretien est bon, le terrain fragile par temps humide, mais le programme de drainage (un trou par an) y remédie progressivement.

Lined with beautiful age-old oaks, this huge site gave the architect the possibility to lay out wide fairways and keep holes well apart. Rocky Roquemore has produced an American style layout set beneath the Pyrenees. Variety is the key word, ranging from mountain-side holes to lower-level holes edged with water hazards. It is pretty hilly (3 holes in particular) but it would have been difficult to do otherwise in this superb region. If you are not in top shape, take a buggy. This course plays 6,800 yards from the back tees and so is a good test for the better player, but the middle tees help the mid-handicapper to better see what needs to be done. The hazards are visible, strategy obvious, difficulties evenly spread around the course and a few inclines and sloping lies add a little spice to the round. Green-keeping is good but the terrain often suffers in wet weather, although the drainage programme (one hole a year) is gradually putting things right.

Makila Golf Club 1992
Route de Cambo-Biarritz
F - 64200 BASSUSSARRY

Office	Secrétariat	(33) 05 59 58 42 42
Pro shop	Pro-shop	(33) 05 59 58 42 42
Fax	Fax	(33) 05 59 58 42 48
Web	www.makilagolfclub.com	
Situation	Situation	Biarritz (pop. 28 740), 5 km

Bayonne (pop. 40 050), 6 km

Annual closure	Fermeture annuelle	no
Weekly closure	Fermeture hebdomadaire	no
Fees main season	Tarifs haute saison	18 holes

	Week days Semaine	We/Bank holidays We/Férié
Individual Individuel	€ 59	€ 59
Couple Couple	€ 108	€ 108

Under 21: – 50%

Caddie Caddie no — **Electric Trolley** Chariot électrique no

Buggy Voiturette yes — **Clubs** Clubs yes

Credit cards Cartes de crédit
VISA - CB - Eurocard - MasterCard - AMEX

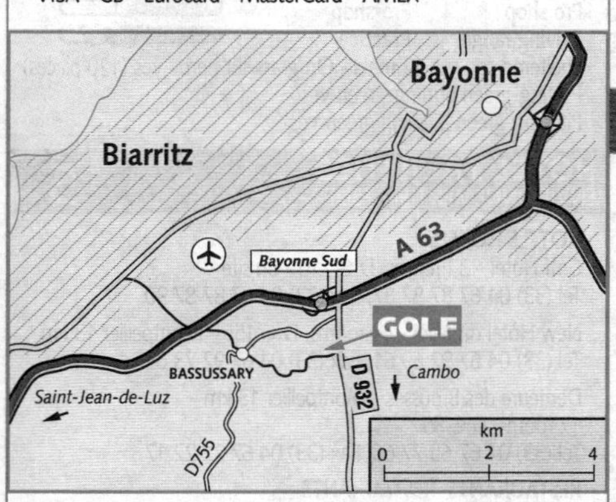

Access Accès : A63, Exit (Sortie) N° 5 Bayonne Sud → Cambo D932. Golf 800 m. after roundabout
Map 12 on page 182 Carte 12 Page 182

GOLF COURSE — PARCOURS 15/20

Site	Site	
Maintenance	Entretien	
Architect	Architecte	Rocky Roquemore
Type	Type	parkland, hilly
Relief	Relief	
Water in play	Eau en jeu	
Exp. to wind	Exposé au vent	
Trees in play	Arbres en jeu	

Scorecard Carte de score	Chp. Chp.	Mens Mess.	Ladies Da.
Length Long.	6134	5692	4988
Par	72	72	72
Slope system	135	127	121

Advised golfing ability Niveau de jeu recommandé: 0 12 24 36

Hcp required Handicap exigé no

CLUB HOUSE & AMENITIES — CLUB HOUSE ET ANNEXES 6/10

Pro shop Pro-shop
Driving range Practice
Sheltered couvert 12 mats - On grass sur herbe yes - Putting-green putting-green yes - Pitching-green pitching green no

HOTEL FACILITIES — ENVIRONNEMENT HOTELIER 8/10

HOTELS HÔTELS
Le Palais - 156 rooms, D € 420 - Biarritz 5 km
Tel (33) 05 59 41 64 00, Fax (33) 05 59 41 67 99

Table des Frères Ibarboure - Bidart 5 km
8 rooms, D € 168
Tel (33) 05 59 54 81 64, Fax (33) 05 59 54 75 65

Château du Clair de Lune - Biarritz 4 km
17 rooms, D € 120
Tel (33) 05 59 25 70 00, Fax (33) 05 59 23 39 13

RESTAURANTS RESTAURANTS
Moulin d'Alotz - Arcangues 3 km - Tel (33) 05 59 43 04 54
Auberge d'Achtal - Arcangues 2 km - Tel (33) 05 59 43 05 56
Table des Frères Ibarboure - Bidart 5 km
Tel (33) 05 59 54 81 64

Massane-Montpellier

16	7	5

Dessiné par Ronald Fream, le golf de Massane n'est certes pas à conseiller aux débutants. Et, pour vraiment s'amuser, les joueurs simplement moyens devront absolument choisir les départs avancés. En revanche, les golfeurs confirmés y trouveront largement de quoi se perfectionner et tester l'ensemble de leur jeu. De nombreux obstacles d'eau, des bunkers frontaux, différentes alternatives d'attaque des trous obligent à bien se connaître pour décider de rester court ou de passer les obstacles, quelle tactique choisir : il faut parfois se résigner à la prudence pour ramener un bon score. Ce parcours se joue avec tous ses clubs, et vraiment avec sa tête. Les bunkers et les greens sont remarquablement dessinés, avec les formes voluptueuses caractéristiques de Ronald Fream, et nécessite la panoplie complète d'un petit jeu. Un parcours parfois controversé, surprenant parfois, qui mérite un entretien impeccable, mais que l'on est heureux de connaître et de retrouver, en oubliant l'immobilier environnant...

The Massane course is not for beginners, but if the average hacker wants to enjoy a good round of golf he should make straight for the front tees. By contrast, skilled golfers will definitely find this a great way to hone their skills and an excellent test for every aspect of their game. Numerous water hazards, front bunkers and different lines of approach to the green call for introspection and force players into tactical decisions and into choosing exactly when to lay up short or when to carry the hazard. A good score sometimes comes more from caution than from daring. This is another course where you really do play with all your clubs. The bunkers and greens are very well designed with the typically smooth shapes of a Ronald Fream design and call for an all-round, well-honed short game. A sometimes controversial and surprising course, which deserves immaculate green-keeping, but also one you are glad to play while turning a blind eye to the surrounding condos...

Golf de Massane-Montpellier 1988

Mas de Massane
F - 34670 BAILLARGUES

Office Secrétariat (33) 04 67 87 87 89
Pro shop Pro-shop (33) 04 67 87 87 89
Fax Fax (33) 04 67 87 87 90
Web www.massane.com
Situation Situation Nîmes, 34 km
Montpellier (pop. 210 860), 13 km
Annual closure Fermeture annuelle no
Weekly closure Fermeture hebdomadaire

Fees main season Tarifs haute saison 18 holes

	Week days Semaine	We/Bank holidays We/Férié
Individual Individuel	€ 53	€ 53
Couple Couple	€ 106	€ 106

Juniors: € 23 / 40 (We)

Caddie Caddie no
Electric Trolley Chariot électrique no
Buggy Voiturette yes
Clubs Clubs yes
Credit cards Cartes de crédit
VISA - CB - Eurocard - MasterCard - AMEX - DC

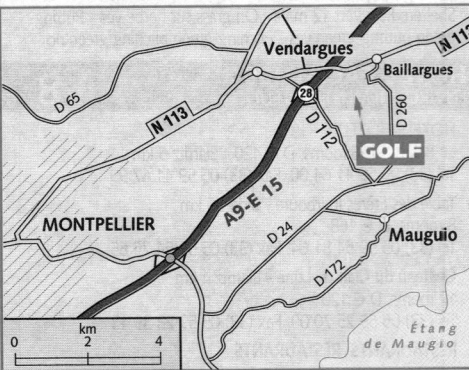

Vendargues
N 113
Baillargues
D 65
28
N 113
D 112
D 260
GOLF
A9-E 15
MONTPELLIER
D 24
Mauguio
D 172
km
0 2 4
Étang de Maugio

Access Accès : A9, Exit (Sortie) Vendargues- Baillargues, N113 → Baillargues
Map 13 on page 185 Carte 13 Page 185m

GOLF COURSE — PARCOURS 16/20

Site Site
Maintenance Entretien
Architect Architecte Ronald Fream
Type Type open country, residential
Relief Relief
Water in play Eau en jeu
Exp. to wind Exposé au vent
Trees in play Arbres en jeu

Scorecard Carte de score	Chp. Chp.	Mens Mess.	Ladies Da.
Length Long.	6064	5694	4972
Par	72	72	72
Slope system	141	135	130

Advised golfing ability Niveau de jeu recommandé 0 12 24 36
Hcp required Handicap exigé no

CLUB HOUSE & AMENITIES — CLUB HOUSE ET ANNEXES 7/10

Pro shop Pro-shop
Driving range Practice
Sheltered couvert 12 mats - On grass sur herbe yes (120 places)
Putting-green putting-green yes
Pitching-green pitching green yes

HOTEL FACILITIES — ENVIRONNEMENT HOTELIER 5/10

HOTELS HÔTELS
Golf Hôtel - 32 rooms, D € 110 - on site
Tel (33) 04 67 87 87 87, Fax (33) 04 67 87 87 90

New Hôtel du Midi - 44 rooms, D € 155 - Montpellier 13 km
Tel (33) 04 67 92 69 61, Fax (33) 04 67 92 73 63

Demeure des Brousses - Montpellier 13 km
17 rooms, D € 85
Tel (33) 04 67 65 77 66, Fax (33) 04 67 22 22 17

RESTAURANTS RESTAURANTS
Jardin des Sens - Montpellier 13 km
Tel (33) 04 99 58 38 38

Anis et Canisses - Montpellier 13 km - Tel (33) 04 67 42 54 48

Médoc *Les Châteaux*

18	7	6

Le parcours des "Châteaux" est de meilleur cru encore que son voisin des "Vignes", et se bonifie en vieillissant comme un bon Médoc. Sa réputation est largement méritée : dû au crayon expert de l'Américain Bill Coore, il se déroule dans un paysage de plaine modelé comme un links, avec des buissons de genêts, de bruyères et d'ajoncs mais sans les dunes. Des obstacles d'eau et des "ditchs" viennent perturber le golfeur, mais la variété tactique des trous, les ondulations du fairway, le dessin des bunkers, la bonne densité des roughs et le profil des vastes greens en font un parcours remarquable. Les amateurs de forêts peuvent sans doute lui reprocher une légère monotonie visuelle mais, à mesure qu'on le joue, il s'avère de plus en plus passionnant, notamment par le placement très précis des bunkers sur les dog-legs. Ce parcours est le plus technique de la région, très facile à jouer à pied, avec un entretien de très bon niveau. La maturité n'a fait que renforcer sa place parmi les grands parcours français.

The "Châteaux" course is an even finer vintage than it neighbour, "Les Vignes", and gets better and better as the years roll by, rather like a good bottle of Médoc wine. It is well worth its reputation. Designed by the American Bill Coore, the course unfolds over flat open country designed to play like a links course with gorse, heather and bramble but no dunes. Some water hazards and ditches can be a little trying but tactical variety, rolling fairways, well-designed bunkers, thick rough and the profile of the huge greens make this a remarkable course. People who prefer woodland courses will probably knock "Les Châteaux" as being visually boring, but it gets more and more exciting the more you play it, particularly with some very astute bunkering on the dog-legs. It is the most technical course in the region, very easy to play on foot, with top-notch green-keeping. The more it matures, the more Le Médoc has to be ranked amongst the great French courses.

Golf du Médoc — 1989

Chemin de Courmateau
F - 33290 LE PIAN-MEDOC

Office	Secrétariat	(33) 05 56 70 11 90
Pro shop	Pro-shop	(33) 05 56 70 11 90
Fax	Fax	(33) 05 56 70 11 99
Web	www.golf-du-medoc.com	
Situation	Situation	Bordeaux, 15 km
Annual closure	Fermeture annuelle	no
Weekly closure	Fermeture hebdomadaire	no

Fees main season Tarifs haute saison — 18 holes

	Week days Semaine	We/Bank holidays We/Férié
Individual Individuel	€ 60	€ 60
Couple Couple	€ 108	€ 108

Under 25: € 30

Caddie Caddie on request **Electric Trolley** Chariot électrique no

Buggy Voiturette yes **Clubs** Clubs yes

Credit cards Cartes de crédit
VISA - CB - Eurocard - MasterCard - AMEX - DC

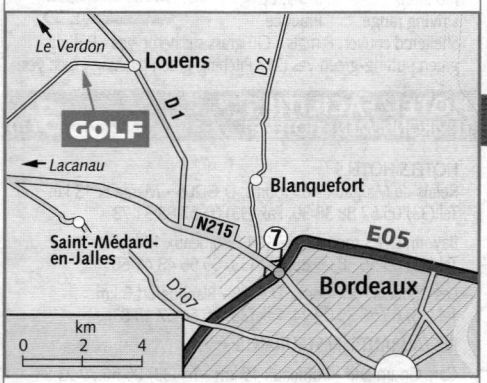

Access Accès : Bordeaux, Ring road (Rocade), Exit (Sortie) N° 7 → Lacanau, go right on D1 → Le Verdon
Map 9 on page 176 Carte 9 Page 176

GOLF COURSE — PARCOURS — 18/20

Site	Site	
Maintenance	Entretien	
Architect	Architecte	Bill Coore
Type	Type	open country, links
Relief	Relief	
Water in play	Eau en jeu	
Exp. to wind	Exposé au vent	
Trees in play	Arbres en jeu	

Scorecard / Carte de score	Chp. / Chp.	Mens / Mess.	Ladies / Da.
Length Long.	6325	5720	4779
Par	71	71	71
Slope system	130	120	118

Advised golfing ability Niveau de jeu recommandé — 0 12 24 36

Hcp required Handicap exigé — no

CLUB HOUSE & AMENITIES — CLUB HOUSE ET ANNEXES — 7/10

Pro shop Pro-shop
Driving range Practice
Sheltered couvert 8 mats - On grass sur herbe yes - Putting-green putting-green yes (2) - Pitching-green pitching green yes

HOTEL FACILITIES — ENVIRONNEMENT HOTELIER — 6/10

HOTELS HÔTELS

Relais de Margaux - 69 rooms, D € 205 - Margaux 13 km
Tel (33) 05 57 88 38 30, Fax (33) 05 57 88 31 73

Bayonne - 63 rooms, D € 114 - Bordeaux 15 km
Tel (33) 05 56 48 00 88, Fax (33) 05 56 48 41 60

Les Criquets - 21 rooms, D € 78 - Blanquefort 8 km
Tel (33) 05 56 35 09 24, Fax (33) 05 56 57 13 83

RESTAURANTS RESTAURANTS

Le Chapon Fin - Bordeaux 15 km - Tel (33) 05 56 79 10 10
Le Vieux Bordeaux - Bordeaux 15 km - Tel (33) 05 56 52 94 36
Jean Ramet - Bordeaux 15 km - Tel (33) 05 56 44 12 51
Savoie - Margaux 13 km - Tel (33) 05 57 88 31 76

Médoc *Les Vignes*

16 | 7 | 6

Le terrain plat permet de jouer facilement l'ensemble des 36 trous du golf du Médoc. Après le paysage très peu arboré du parcours des "Châteaux", le parcours des "Vignes" offrait un contraste, mais les tempêtes de 1999 ont singulièrement éclairci la petite pinède qui enserrait un certain nombre de trous. Les amoureux des parcours dans les arbres en seront frustrés mais le jeu n'en est pas facilité pour autant et le parcours a prouvé que sa qualité avait résisté, et il a paradoxalement trouvé une sorte de pureté. La végétation est plus légère, mais beaucoup de buissons et d'arbustes sont nettement en jeu. Tout comme sur l'autre parcours, les greens sont de bonne qualité, sans reliefs excessifs, mais assez subtils à déchiffrer. Certes, "Les Châteaux" représente un défi plus relevé et une attention de tous les instants, mais cet ensemble s'est incontestablement imposé comme l'un des tout meilleurs des régions touristiques, et comme le plus intéressant à proximité immédiate de Bordeaux.

Laid out over what is generally flat terrain, the 36 holes at Le Pian Médoc can easily be played in one day. After the tree-less landscape of "Les Châteaux", "Les Vignes" provided a welcome contrast until the 1999 storms wreaked havoc with the pine forest which enclosed a number of holes. This has not made golfing here any easier and the course has proved that sheer quality can withstand anything. Paradoxically the course has a sort of new-found purity about it. Vegetation is now a little lighter but many of the bushes and shrubs are very much in play. The greens are excellent, not too undulating and never easy to read. "Les Châteaux" is certainly a stiffer challenge calling for unwavering concentration, but the whole complex still constitutes one of the best golfing venues in French tourist regions and definitely the number one choice within the immediate vicinity of Bordeaux. You will also find a warm welcome, a friendly club-house and great food.

Golf du Médoc — 1991

Chemin de Courmateau
F - 33290 LE PIAN-MEDOC

Office Secrétariat (33) 05 56 70 11 90
Pro shop Pro-shop (33) 05 56 70 11 90
Fax Fax (33) 05 56 70 11 99
Web www.golf-du-medoc.com
Situation Situation Bordeaux, 15 km
Annual closure Fermeture annuelle no
Weekly closure Fermeture hebdomadaire no

Fees main season Tarifs haute saison	full day	
	Week days / Semaine	We/Bank holidays / We/Férié
Individual Individuel	€ 60	€ 60
Couple Couple	€ 108	€ 108

Under 25: € 30

Caddie Caddie on request **Electric Trolley** Chariot électrique no
Buggy Voiturette yes **Clubs** Clubs yes
Credit cards Cartes de crédit
VISA - CB - Eurocard - MasterCard - AMEX - DC

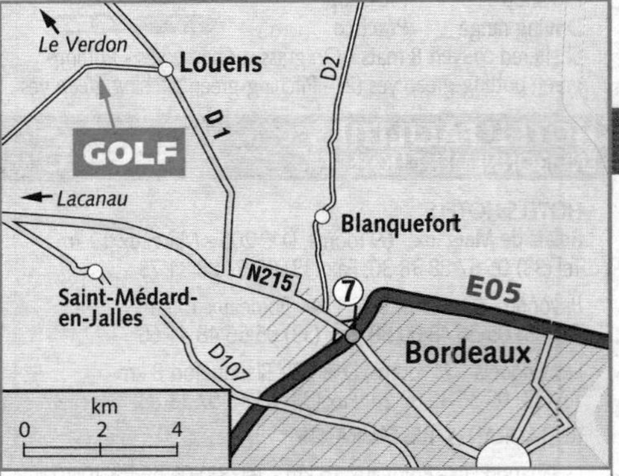

Access Accès : Bordeaux, Ring road (Rocade), Exit (Sortie) N° 7 → Lacanau, go right on D1 → Le Verdon
Map 9 on page 176 Carte 9 Page 176

GOLF COURSE — PARCOURS — 16/20

Site Site
Maintenance Entretien
Architect Architecte Rod Whitman
Type Type forest, open country
Relief Relief
Water in play Eau en jeu
Exp. to wind Exposé au vent
Trees in play Arbres en jeu

Scorecard / Carte de score	Chp. / Chp.	Mens / Mess.	Ladies / Da.
Length Long.	6237	5704	4672
Par	71	71	71
Slope system	127	125	116

Advised golfing ability 0 12 24 36
Niveau de jeu recommandé
Hcp required Handicap exigé no

CLUB HOUSE & AMENITIES — CLUB HOUSE ET ANNEXES — 7/10

Pro shop Pro-shop
Driving range Practice

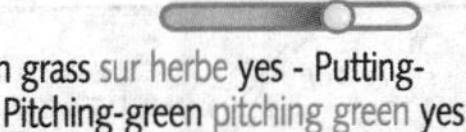

Sheltered couvert 8 mats - On grass sur herbe yes - Putting-green putting-green yes (2) - Pitching-green pitching green yes

HOTEL FACILITIES — ENVIRONNEMENT HOTELIER — 6/10

HOTELS HÔTELS

Relais de Margaux - 69 rooms, D € 205 - Margaux 13 km
Tel (33) 05 57 88 38 30, Fax (33) 05 57 88 31 73

Bayonne - 63 rooms, D € 114 - Bordeaux 15 km
Tel (33) 05 56 48 00 88, Fax (33) 05 56 48 41 60

Les Criquets - 21 rooms, D € 78 - Blanquefort 8 km
Tel (33) 05 56 35 09 24, Fax (33) 05 56 57 13 83

RESTAURANTS RESTAURANTS

Café Gourmand - Bordeaux 15 km - Tel (33) 05 56 79 23 85
Le Vieux Bordeaux - Bordeaux 15 km - Tel (33) 05 56 52 94 36
Jean Ramet - Bordeaux 15 km - Tel (33) 05 56 44 12 51
Savoie - Margaux 13 km - Tel (33) 05 57 88 31 76

Moliets

17 | 6 | 5

Ce parcours remarquable et généralement bien entretenu a été réalisé dans la forêt de pins des Landes (treize trous), et en bord de mer (cinq trous). L'architecte Robert Trent Jones l'a signé par son esthétique, mais aussi par des enjeux techniques et stratégiques très variés dénotant une connaissance profonde du golf : si les joueurs de haut niveau y trouveront un "challenge" difficile, partir des départs avancés permet davantage d'erreurs. Visuellement, ses fameux bunkers dentelés défendent remarquablement les greens aux surfaces modelées sans excès, dont trois sont pratiquement aveugles. Les larges fairways favorisent le rythme de jeu, et le sol sablonneux permet de jouer facilement toute l'année : quelques drainages nécessaires ont ainsi été effectués (notamment au 4). Il n'est pas trop fatigant, mais les distances entre les trous sont très importantes... Un bon 9 trous occupe les débutants de la famille, et un centre d'entraînement très complet permet de se perfectionner. Un regret, l'immobilier trop proche des trous.

This remarkable and well-maintained course was laid out in the pine forests of Les Landes and along the coast (five holes). Welcome to a typical Robert Trent Jones design, where detail to style and the very varied technical and strategic challenges reflect an in-depth knowledge of golf. While the more proficient golfer will find this a tough challenge, playing from the forward tees is, funnily enough, often more conducive to error. The famous jagged bunkers are a remarkable form of defence for the green, and the putting surfaces are neatly but never excessively contoured. The wide fairways help speed up the game and the sandy sub-soil keeps the course easily playable all year. This is not a tiring course but distances between holes are very long, so be warned. A good adjoining 9 hole course is ideal for beginners in the family and a very comprehensive training centre is just the job for getting that handicap down. The one regret is the property scheme, sometimes too close for comfort.

Golf de Moliets — 1989

Rue Mathieu Desbieys
F - 40660 MOLIETS

Office Secrétariat (33) 05 58 48 54 65
Pro shop Pro-shop (33) 05 58 48 54 65
Fax Fax (33) 05 58 48 54 88
Web www.golfmoliets.com
Situation Situation Dax 35 km - Bayonne 40 km

Annual closure Fermeture annuelle no
1 week at end of 03 and of 09 (1 semaine fin 03 et fin 09)

Weekly closure Fermeture hebdomadaire no

Fees main season Tarifs haute saison	18 holes	
	Week days Semaine	**We/Bank holidays** We/Férié
Individual Individuel	€ 57,20	€ 57,20
Couple Couple	€ 114,20	€ 114,20

Juniors and students (under 24): € 28,6

Caddie Caddie no — **Electric Trolley** Chariot électrique no
Buggy Voiturette yes — **Clubs** Clubs yes

Credit cards Cartes de crédit
VISA - CB - Eurocard - MasterCard

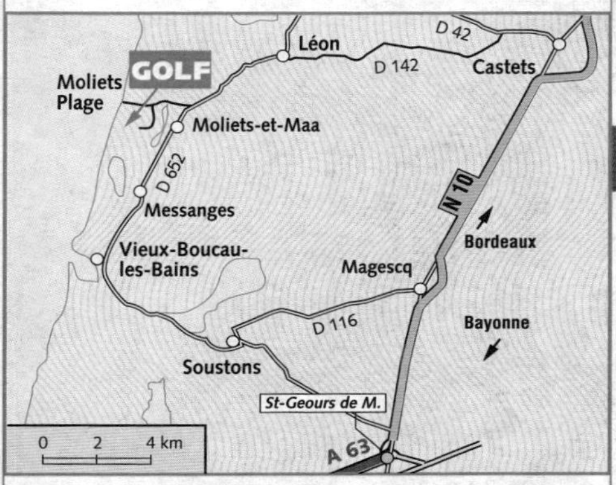

Access Accès : • Bordeaux, N10 → Castets. D142 → Léon, Moliets • Bayonne, N10 → Magescq, D116 → Soustons, D652 → Vieux-Boucau-les-Bains, Moliets
Map 12 on page 182 Carte 12 Page 182

GOLF COURSE — PARCOURS 17/20

Site Site
Maintenance Entretien
Architect Architecte Robert Trent Jones
Type Type forest, links
Relief Relief
Water in play Eau en jeu
Exp. to wind Exposé au vent
Trees in play Arbres en jeu

Scorecard Carte de score	**Chp.** Chp.	**Mens** Mess.	**Ladies** Da.
Length Long.	6173	5504	4653
Par	72	72	72
Slope system	133	128	126

Advised golfing ability Niveau de jeu recommandé 0 12 24 36
Hcp required Handicap exigé 36

CLUB HOUSE & AMENITIES — CLUB HOUSE ET ANNEXES 6/10

Pro shop Pro-shop
Driving range Practice

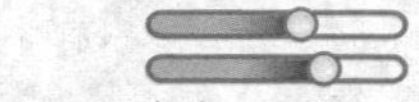

Sheltered couvert 10 mats - On grass sur herbe no - 20 mats open air - Putting-green putting-green yes
Pitching-green pitching green yes

HOTEL FACILITIES — ENVIRONNEMENT HOTELIER 5/10

HOTELS HÔTELS
Hôtel du Golf - 40 rooms, D € 1069 (7 days) - on site
Tel (33) 05 58 49 16 00, Fax (33) 05 58 49 16 29

Relais de la Poste - 17 rooms, D € 175 - Magescq 20 km
Tel (33) 05 58 47 70 25, Fax (33) 05 58 47 76 17

Côte d'Argent - 36 rooms, D € 50 - Vieux-Boucau 10 km
Tel (33) 05 58 48 13 17, Fax (33) 05 58 48 01 15

RESTAURANTS RESTAURANTS
Cabanon et Grange aux Canards - Magescq 21 km
Tel (33) 05 58 47 71 51

Relais de la Poste - Magescq 20 km - Tel (33) 05 58 47 70 25

Marinero - Vieux-Boucau 10 km - Tel (33) 05 58 48 14 15

Monte Carlo (Mont Agel)

14	6	7

En évoquant Monte Carlo, on pouvait imaginer une sorte de somptueux club à l'américaine, très "people". En fait, le plus "Monte Carlo", c'est le panorama. A plus de 800 mètres, Monaco apparaît en contrebas comme un village de poupée, et la vue s'étend à l'infini sur la Méditerranée et la Riviera, parfois même la Corse. Quant au golf, sa sobriété est la marque du vrai luxe. On joue dans une atmosphère tranquille et presque familiale, pas pour se faire voir. Le parcours a récemment fait l'objet de travaux en tous genres, du plus minuscule au plus impressionnant pour lui donner un peu de longueur et de largeur, mais le tracé est resté à peu près celui de Willie Park il y a presque un siècle. Très britannique de style, il n'est pas d'une grande difficulté, a priori, mais les greens sont assez petits, le relief parfois prononcé, les pieds pas toujours à plat, et comme les amateurs ne pensent pas toujours clairement à leur golf, les scores sont parfois surprenants. Ce n'est pas la force qui l'emporte ici, c'est la précision, la finesse et une élégance... princière bien sûr.

You might expect a sort of sumptuous golf club full of celebrities. In fact the most sumptuous thing here is the view. Monaco lies 800 metres below you like a doll's village and the vista stretches over the Mediterranean right across the French and Italian Rivieras. Sometimes you can even see Corsica. The actual course is a picture of sobriety, but isn't that the sign of real luxury? You play here in a family atmosphere, not just to be seen. The course has undergone all sorts of refurbishing work to make it longer but the layout remains very much the same as that built almost a century ago. Very British in style, it is certainly not the hardest course around but the greens are smallish, topography sometimes severe and flat lies in short supply. And as clear-thinking is not always the forte of amateur golfers, scores can sometimes come as a surprise. Accuracy and finesse are more valuable assets than brute strength on a course where you are asked for a little golfing elegance, in princely style, of course.

Monte Carlo Golf Club — 1911

Route du Mont Agel
06320 LA TURBIE

Office	Secrétariat	(33) 04 92 41 50 70
Pro shop	Pro-shop	(33) 04 93 41 04 46
Fax	Fax	(33) 04 93 41 09 55
E-mail	monte_carlo_golf_club@wanadoo.fr	
Situation	Situation	Monaco, 15 km

Nice (pop. 342 439), 16 km

Annual closure	Fermeture annuelle	no
Weekly closure	Fermeture hebdomadaire	no

Fees main season Tarifs haute saison	Full day	
	Week days Semaine	**We/Bank holidays** We/Férié
Individual Individuel	€ 90	€ 110
Couple Couple	€ 180	€ 220

Juniors and Students: – 50%

Caddie Caddie on request **Electric Trolley** Chariot électrique yes

Buggy Voiturette no **Clubs** Clubs yes

Credit cards Cartes de crédit
VISA - Eurocard - MasterCard

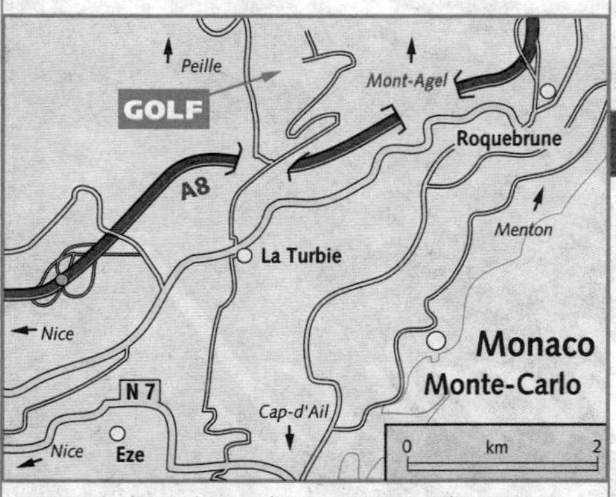

Access Accès : 10 km N. of Monaco. → La Turbie, → Mont Agel, Monte Carlo Golf Club.
Map 14 on page 187 Carte 14 Page 187

GOLF COURSE — PARCOURS — 14/20

Site	Site	
Maintenance	Entretien	
Architect	Architecte	Willie Park
Type	Type	hilly, parkland
Relief	Relief	
Water in play	Eau en jeu	
Exp. to wind	Exposé au vent	
Trees in play	Arbres en jeu	

Scorecard Carte de score	**Chp.** Chp.	**Mens** Mess.	**Ladies** Da.
Length Long.	5688	5688	4938
Par	71	71	71
Slope system	129	129	129

Advised golfing ability Niveau de jeu recommandé: 0 12 24 36

Hcp required Handicap exigé: 35 (week), 32 (We)

CLUB HOUSE & AMENITIES — CLUB HOUSE ET ANNEXES — 6/10

Pro shop Pro-shop
Driving range Practice
Sheltered couvert 4 mats - On grass sur herbe no, 10 mats open air - Putting-green putting-green yes (2)
Pitching-green pitching green yes

HOTEL FACILITIES — ENVIRONNEMENT HOTELIER — 7/10

HOTELS HÔTELS

Hotel de Paris - Monaco 15 km
191 rooms, D € 580
Tel (377) 92 16 30 00, Fax (377) 92 16 38 50

Hotel Hermitage - 280 rooms, D € 490 - Monaco 15 km
Tel (377) 92 16 40 00, Fax (377) 92 16 38 52

Balmoral - 65 rooms, D € 140 - Monaco 15 km
Tel (377) 93 50 62 37, Fax (377) 93 15 08 69

RESTAURANTS RESTAURANTS

Café de Paris - Monaco 15 km - Tel (377) 92 16 20 20

Louis XV - Monaco 15 km - Tel (377) 92 16 30 01

Chez Gianni - Monaco 15 km - Tel (377) 93 30 46 33

HAPPY SPIRIT
Chopard

Morfontaine

18	6	6

Il est des lieux où le monde paraît s'être arrêté au bon moment. Celui-ci est un paradis pour ses membres, qui n'y acceptent que leurs invités. Beaucoup aimeraient en être, tant Morfontaine s'est construit une réputation de Belle au bois dormant que l'on se doit de séduire un jour. Ici, on aime assez le golf et ses traditions pour défendre le dessin du parcours par Tom Simpson. Et les retouches apportées récemment par Kyle Phillips (surtout au 12, redevenu un vrai par 5) portent la marque de ce respect. Certes, les frappeurs iconoclastes le jugeront toujours un peu court, mais n'est-il pas mal élevé de taper ici très fort, tout comme d'élever la voix ? La difficulté consiste plutôt à négocier avec les arbres splendides, la bruyère, des bunkers diablement bien placés. A Morfontaine, on ne cherche pas à épater la galerie, on joue au golf, dans une atmosphère familiale, loin des foules. Le 18 trous est harmonieux, technique, noble. Et le 9 trous de Vallières constitue un dessert savoureux. Un modèle de club de golf !

There are places where the world seems to have stood still just at the right moment. Morfontaine is a paradise for members who admit only their own guests. A lot of people would like to be amongst their ranks, such is the reputation forged by this sleeping beauty of a course waiting to be awoken. The traditions of golf are respected here in staunch defence of Tom Simpson's original layout. The touch-ups recently made by Kyle Philips (especially hole N°12, now a real par 5) bear the hallmarks of such respect. Today's iconoclastic long hitters will certainly find it short but hitting the ball too hard here would be tantamount to raising your voice in a hallowed sanctuary. The difficulty is to steer clear of the splendid trees, heather and reasonable number of wickedly located bunkers. At Morfontaine you just play golf in a family atmosphere far from the madding crowd. The 18-hole course is a technical picture of nobility and harmony. A model golf club.

Golf de Morfontaine — 1913

F - 60128 MORTEFONTAINE

Office Secrétariat (33) 03 44 54 68 27
Pro shop Pro-shop no pro shop
Fax Fax (33) 03 44 54 60 57
Web —
Situation Situation Paris, 45 km
Senlis (pop. 14 439), 15 km

Annual closure Fermeture annuelle no
Weekly closure Fermeture hebdomadaire no

Fees main season Tarifs haute saison	18 holes	
	Week days Semaine	**We/Bank holidays** We/Férié
Individual Individuel	*	*
Couple Couple	*	*

* Members and their guests only

Caddie Caddie on request **Electric Trolley** Chariot électrique no
Buggy Voiturette no **Clubs** Clubs no
Credit cards Cartes de crédit no

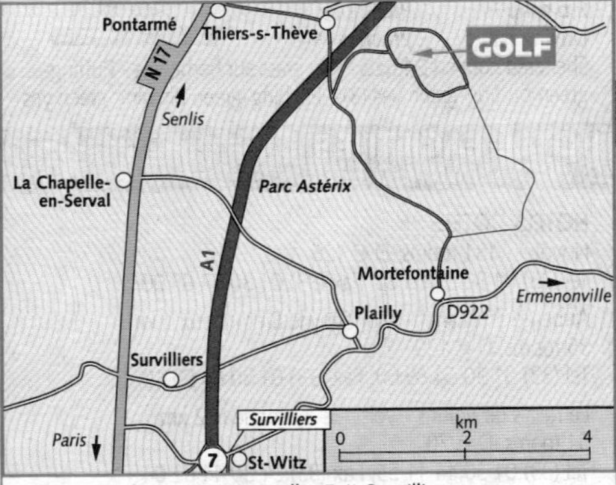

Access Accès : A1 Paris → Lille, Exit Survilliers, turn right on D126 → Plailly. In the middle of Mortefontaine village, turn left on D607 → Golf.
Map 3 on page 164 Carte 3 Page 164

GOLF COURSE — PARCOURS 18/20

Site Site
Maintenance Entretien
Architect Architecte Tom Simpson
Type Type inland, forest
Relief Relief
Water in play Eau en jeu
Exp. to wind Exposé au vent
Trees in play Arbres en jeu

Scorecard Carte de score	Chp. Chp.	Mens Mess.	Ladies Da.
Length Long.	6070	5700	5300
Par	70	70	72
Slope system	131	130	132

Advised golfing ability 0 12 24 36
Niveau de jeu recommandé
Hcp required Handicap exigé 28

CLUB HOUSE & AMENITIES — CLUB HOUSE ET ANNEXES 6/10

Pro shop Pro-shop
Driving range Practice
Sheltered couvert 4 mats - On grass sur herbe yes - Putting-green putting-green yes - Pitching-green pitching green yes

HOTEL FACILITIES — ENVIRONNEMENT HOTELIER 6/10

HOTELS HÔTELS
Relais d'Aumale - 24 rooms, D € 140 - Montgrésin 7 km
Tel (33) 03 44 54 61 31, Fax (33) 03 44 54 69 15

Mont-Royal - La-Chapelle-en-Serval 7 km
99 rooms, D € 255
Tel (33) 03 44 54 50 50, Fax (33) 03 44 54 50 21

Château d'Ermenonville - Ermenonville 10 km
50 rooms, D € 150
Tel (33) 03 44 54 00 26, Fax (33) 03 44 54 01 00

RESTAURANTS RESTAURANTS

Relais d'Aumale - Montgrésin 6 km - Tel (33) 03 44 54 61 31
La Table des Lions - Chantilly 2 km - Tel (33) 03 44 58 54 40
Le Goutillon - Chantilly 2 km - Tel (33) 03 44 58 01 00

National *L'Albatros*

18 | 6 | 6

L'Albatros (site de l'Open de France) a été dessiné par R. von Hagge et H. Chesneau à partir d'un terrain plat métamorphosé par d'énormes dunes artificielles prévues pour accueillir les spectateurs. En contrebas, le joueur oublie vite l'environnement industriel du lieu. Le parcours alterne des trous à l'américaine et des trous inspirés des links, où la moindre erreur stratégique ou technique peut s'avérer catastrophique. Il vaut mieux choisir des départs à son niveau... Chacun des 18 trous est défendu par toutes sortes d'obstacles, mais les difficultés sont bien réparties, et les quatre derniers trous sont toujours décisifs. Pour atténuer cette exigence, le parcours est d'une grande franchise, mais quelques greens auraient mérité plus de modelage. Les longs frappeurs trouveront aussi qu'ils ont peu d'occasions de marquer un avantage en prenant des risques calculés. C'est d'abord un parcours "de seconds coups", à connaître absolument... même si l'environnement n'est pas à la hauteur du tracé.

The "Albatros" (the venue for the French Open) was designed by R. von Hagge and H. Chesneau over a flat terrain transformed by huge artificial dunes designed to cater to spectators. Down in the playing arena, you forget the site's industrial background. The layout alternates between US-style holes and holes inspired by links courses; the slightest strategic or technical slip anywhere can lead to disaster: make sure you choose the right tee-box for your game. Each hole is defended by all sorts of hazard and difficulties are finely balanced over the whole course, even though the last 4 holes are decisive. To soften the blow, as it were, the course openly shows its hand, even though some greens might have been shaped a little better. Long-hitters will also find that they have few opportunities to make headway, given the size of each calculated risk. This is primarily a "second-shot" course, and a must... even if the course's surroundings are not always on a par with the actual layout.

Le Golf National — 1990

2, avenue du Golf
F - 78280 GUYANCOURT

Office Secrétariat (33) 01 30 43 36 00
Pro shop Pro-shop (33) 01 30 43 36 00
Fax Fax (33) 01 30 43 85 58
Web www.golf-national.com
Situation Situation Paris, 30 km - Versailles, 14 km
Annual closure Fermeture annuelle — no
Weekly closure Fermeture hebdomadaire — wednesday
mercredi (01/11 → 30/06)

Fees main season Tarifs haute saison	Full day	
	Week days Semaine	We/Bank holidays We/Férié
Individual Individuel	€ 50	€ 70
Couple Couple	€ 100	€ 140

Under 21: € 36 /€ 44 (We) / Seniors (tuesday/mardi) & Ladies (Thursday/jeudi): € 40

Caddie Caddie on request **Electric Trolley** Chariot électrique no
Buggy Voiturette no **Clubs** Clubs yes
Credit cards Cartes de crédit
VISA - CB - Eurocard - MasterCard - AMEX

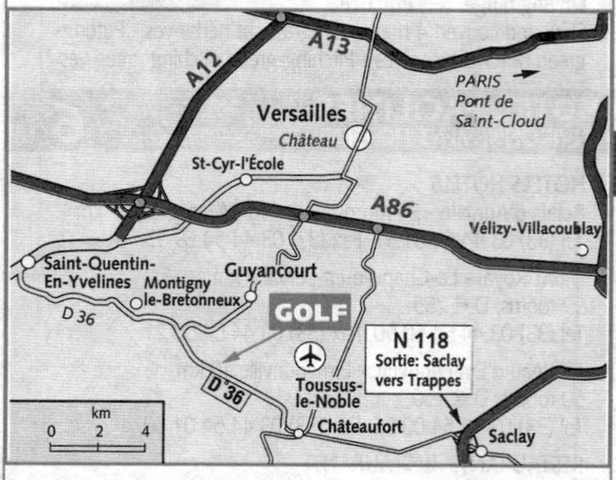

Access Accès : • Paris A13, A12 → St-Quentin en Y., Exit (Sortie) Montigny-le-Bretonneux • Paris N118 → Chartres (A10), Exit Saclay, D36 → Châteaufort, Trappes
Map 15 on page 188 Carte 15 Page 188

GOLF COURSE — PARCOURS — 18/20

Site Site
Maintenance Entretien
Architect Architecte — Hubert Chesneau, R.v.Hagge (consult.)
Type Type — links, open country
Relief Relief
Water in play Eau en jeu
Exp. to wind Exposé au vent
Trees in play Arbres en jeu

Scorecard Carte de score	Chp. Chp.	Mens Mess.	Ladies Da.
Length Long.	6270	5815	4895
Par	72	72	72
Slope system	143	137	135

Advised golfing ability Niveau de jeu recommandé — 0 12 24 36
Hcp required Handicap exigé — 24 Men, 28 Ladies (We) - 35 (weekdays)

CLUB HOUSE & AMENITIES — CLUB HOUSE ET ANNEXES — 6/10

Pro shop Pro-shop
Driving range Practice
Sheltered couvert 24mats - On grass sur herbe yes - Putting-green putting-green yes (3) - Pitching-green pitching green yes

HOTEL FACILITIES — ENVIRONNEMENT HOTELIER — 6/10

HOTELS HÔTELS

Novotel - 131 rooms, D € 126
Tel (33) 01 30 57 65 65, Fax (33) 01 30 57 65 00

Auberge du Manet - Montigny le Bretonneux 4 km
35 rooms, D € 130
Tel (33) 01 30 64 89 00, Fax (33) 01 30 64 55 10

Le Relais de Voisins - Voisin-le-Bretonneux 2 km
54 rooms, D € 70
Tel (33) 01 30 44 11 55, Fax (33) 01 30 44 02 04

RESTAURANTS RESTAURANTS

Les Trois Marches - Versailles 14 km - Tel (33) 01 39 50 25 08
La Belle Epoque - Châteaufort 4 km - Tel (33) 01 39 56 95 48

Nîmes-Campagne

17	7	6

Comme un ami de longue date, Nîmes Campagne paraît ne jamais changer, mais on a toujours plaisir à retrouver ce "classique" de la région, dont la tradition sportive se perpétue... Dessiné par Morandi et Donald Harradine, il s'impose toujours comme un vrai parcours de championnat, surtout quand souffle le vent. Alors, les chênes et cyprès bleus deviennent redoutables, et la maîtrise des balles basses obligatoire, d'autant que quelques obstacles d'eau stratégiques viennent perturber le jugement comme la confiance. Les greens sont généralement bien dessinés, pas toujours très vastes, et souvent rapides. Pour les bons joueurs, la précision devra s'allier alors à la puissance, car les trous sont rarement courts des départs arrière : les moins expérimentés ne devront pas hésiter à choisir les départs normaux. Les abords ont été bien paysagés aux 13 et 14, ou à la remontée du trou 18. Ce golf bien entretenu est très fréquenté par ses nombreux membres, il est conseillé de réserver en toute saison.

Like a life-long friend, Nîmes Campagne never seems to change but it's always magic to return to play this "classic" course which continues to enjoy a well established sporting tradition... Designed by Morandi and Donald Harradine, this is a real championship course, especially when the wind blows. Then the oaks and the blue cypress trees are formidable foes and make knock-down shots a must, especially since a few strategic water hazards can affect both judgment and confidence. The greens are generally well-designed, not always that large and often fast. For the better player, the course demands both power and precision, as holes are seldom short from the back tees. The less experienced players should use the normal tees. The approaches to holes 13 and 14 have been landscaped, as has the climb up to the 18th hole. The course is well maintained and played by a large number of members, so whatever the season, always book a tee-off time.

Golf de Nîmes-Campagne — 1968

Route de Saint-Gilles
F - 30900 NIMES

Office	Secrétariat	(33) 04 66 70 17 37
Pro shop	Pro-shop	(33) 04 66 70 17 37
Fax	Fax	(33) 04 66 70 03 14
Web	www.golfnimescampagne.fr.st	
Situation	Situation	Nîmes (pop. 128 470), 10 km
Annual closure	Fermeture annuelle	no
Weekly closure	Fermeture hebdomadaire	no

Fees main season Tarifs haute saison	Week days Semaine	We/Bank holidays We/Férié
		Full day
Individual Individuel	€ 65	€ 65
Couple Couple	€ 130	€ 130

Juniors and Students: € 25

Caddie Caddie no — **Electric Trolley** Chariot électrique yes

Buggy Voiturette yes — **Clubs** Clubs yes

Credit cards Cartes de crédit
VISA - CB - Eurocard - MasterCard

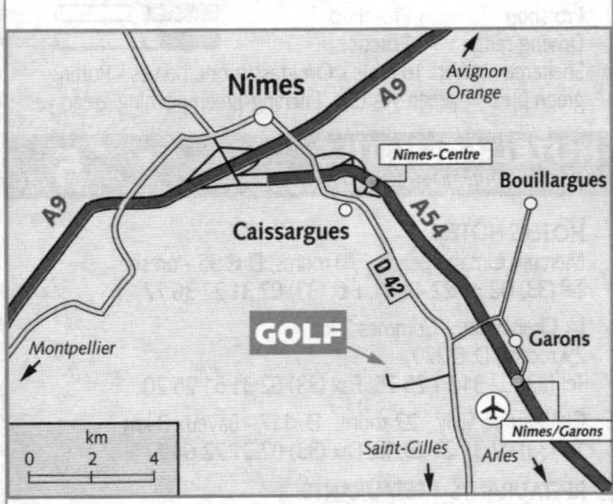

Access Accès : Montpellier or Avignon, A9, Exit (Sortie) Nîmes Centre, D42 → Saint-Gilles, take on the right of the airport, → Golf
Map 13 on page 185 Carte 13 Page 185

GOLF COURSE — PARCOURS — 17/20

Site	Site	
Maintenance	Entretien	
Architect	Architecte	Léonard Morandi, Donald Harradine
Type	Type	country, parkland
Relief	Relief	
Water in play	Eau en jeu	
Exp. to wind	Exposé au vent	
Trees in play	Arbres en jeu	

Scorecard Carte de score	Chp. Chp.	Mens Mess.	Ladies Da.
Length Long.	6135	5599	5045
Par	72	72	72
Slope system	139	135	129

Advised golfing ability Niveau de jeu recommandé: 0 12 24 36

Hcp required Handicap exigé 36

CLUB HOUSE & AMENITIES — CLUB HOUSE ET ANNEXES — 7/10

Pro shop Pro-shop
Driving range Practice
Sheltered couvert 4 mats - On grass sur herbe no - Putting-green putting-green yes Pitching-green pitching green yes

HOTEL FACILITIES — ENVIRONNEMENT HOTELIER — 6/10

HOTELS HÔTELS

Imperator Concorde - 59 rooms, D € 144 - Nîmes 10 km
Tel (33) 04 66 21 90 30, Fax (33) 04 66 67 70 25

Les Aubuns - 25 rooms, D € 92 - Caissargues 6 km
Tel (33) 04 66 70 10 44, Fax (33) 04 66 70 14 97

New Hôtel La Baume - 34 rooms, D € 120 - Nîmes 10 km
Tel (33) 04 66 76 28 42, Fax (33) 04 66 76 28 45

RESTAURANTS RESTAURANTS

Alexandre - Garons 4 km - Tel (33) 04 66 70 08 99
Aux Plaisirs des Halles - Nîmes 10 km - Tel (33) 04 66 36 01 02
Lisita - Nîmes 10 km - Tel (33) 04 66 67 29 15
Le Bouchon et l'Assiette - Nîmes - Tel (33) 04 66 62 02 93

Omaha Beach *La Mer/Le Bocage* | 14 | 7 | 5

Les trois 9 trous sont combinables, mais "L'Etang", assez dénudé et accidenté, n'est pas aussi caractéristique que "Le Bocage" (dans un paysage typiquement normand) et "La Mer". Ces deux derniers parcours forment la combinaison la plus cohérente au plan du jeu et de l'unité esthétique, où l'architecte Yves Bureau a utilisé les reliefs naturels sans trop bouleverser le terrain, ponctuant la route des greens de quelques grands bunkers. "La Mer", assez vallonné, propose quelques trous sur un plateau dominant l'une des plages du Débarquement, avec de magnifiques points de vue sur la côte et la mer. Ces trous sur la mer n'ont pas vraiment le caractère de links, étant donné la nature du sol et l'absence de dunes (ils se rapprochent du style d'Etretat), mais le vent peut les rendre redoutables pour le jeu et surtout pour les scores. Une réalisation sympathique et de qualité, où le souci des améliorations est permanent, et la situation à proximité immédiate des plages du Débarquement de 1944, source d'émotions.

The three 9 hole courses can be played in any combination, but "L'Etang", a barren and hilly layout, does not have the character of "Le Bocage" (in typically Norman countryside) or "La Mer". The latter two form the most consistent combination in terms of golfing and visual unity, where architect Yves Bureau has employed the natural relief without too much excavation work, dotting the fairways with a few large bunkers. "La Mer", which unwinds over rolling landscape, includes a few holes on a plateau overlooking one of the D-Day beaches and providing magnificent views over the coastline and English channel. The seaboard holes are hardly your typical links holes, given the nature of the soil and the absence of dunes, but the wind can play havoc with your game and your card. A very pleasant golf course of excellent standard, where concern for improvements is a constant factor and the nearby Normandy Landing beaches a rather moving reminder.

Omaha Beach Golf Club — 1987

La Ferme Saint-Sauveur
F - 14520 PORT-EN-BESSIN

Office Secrétariat (33) 02 31 22 12 12
Pro shop Pro-shop (33) 02 31 22 76 45
Fax Fax (33) 02 31 22 12 13
Web www.omahabeachgolfclub.com
Situation Situation Bayeux (pop. 14 700), 10 km
Annual closure Fermeture annuelle no
Weekly closure Fermeture hebdomadaire no

Fees main season Tarifs haute saison	18 holes	
	Week days / Semaine	We/Bank holidays / We/Férié
Individual Individuel	€ 55	€ 55
Couple Couple	€ 100	€ 100

Juniors and Students: € 37

Caddie Caddie on request **Electric Trolley** Chariot électrique no
Buggy Voiturette yes **Clubs** Clubs yes
Credit cards Cartes de crédit
VISA - CB - Eurocard - MasterCard

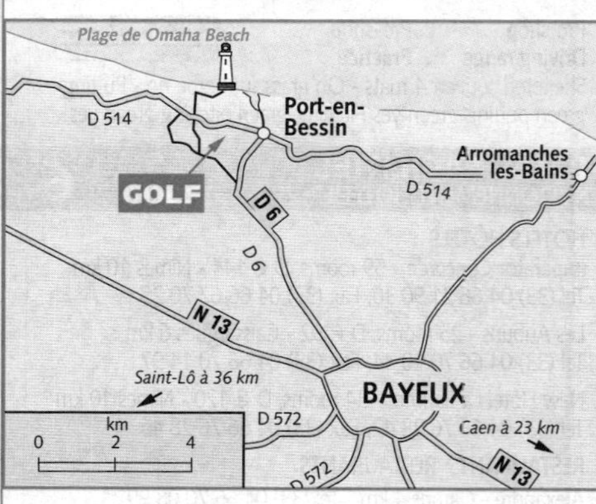

Access Accès : Bayeux, D6 → Port-en-Bessin
Map 2 on page 162 Carte 2 Page 162

GOLF COURSE — PARCOURS 14/20

Site Site
Maintenance Entretien
Architect Architecte Yves Bureau
Type Type seaside course, copse
Relief Relief
Water in play Eau en jeu
Exp. to wind Exposé au vent
Trees in play Arbres en jeu

Scorecard / Carte de score	Chp. / Chp.	Mens / Mess.	Ladies / Da.
Length Long.	5974	5647	4810
Par	72	72	72
Slope system	127	123	126

Advised golfing ability Niveau de jeu recommandé 0 12 24 36
Hcp required Handicap exigé no

CLUB HOUSE & AMENITIES — CLUB HOUSE ET ANNEXES 7/10

Pro shop Pro-shop
Driving range Practice
Sheltered couvert 16 mats - On grass sur herbe yes - Putting-green putting-green yes (3) - Pitching-green pitching green yes

HOTEL FACILITIES — ENVIRONNEMENT HOTELIER 5/10

HOTELS HÔTELS
Mercure Omaha Beach - 70 rooms, D € 95 - on site
Tel (33) 02 31 22 44 44, Fax (33) 02 31 22 36 77

La Chenevière - Commes 2 km
29 rooms, D € 270
Tel (33) 02 31 51 25 25, Fax (33) 02 31 51 25 20

Château de Sully - 22 rooms, D 117 - Bayeux 8 km
Tel (33) 02 31 22 29 48, Fax (33) 02 31 22 64 77

RESTAURANTS RESTAURANTS
Marine - Port-en-Bessin 2 km - Tel (33) 02 31 21 70 08
Château de Sully - Bayeux 6 km - Tel (33) 02 31 22 29 48
Bistrot de Paris - Bayeux 8 km - Tel (33) 02 31 92 00 82

Ozoir-la-Ferrière *Château/Monthéty*

13	7	5

Dans un superbe parc plat, mais avec un sol parfois humide, de larges avenues bordées de grands arbres offrent le sentiment d'espace que l'on attend d'un golf. Même si certains trous restent assez étroits pour exiger de la précision, les longs frappeurs trouveront aussi de quoi s'exprimer. On peut regretter que les fairways n'aient guère été modelés le jeu en est facilité, il est vrai, mais les meilleurs joueurs n'y trouveront pas tout à fait un test complet. Les bunkers sont, avec les arbres, les principaux obstacles, l'eau ne venant en jeu que sur deux trous. Les greens sont de qualité, assez classiques. Certains ont été refaits, ce que beaucoup de clubs devraient faire périodiquement. Un très décent parcours de 9 trous, avec beaucoup d'obstacles d'eau, complète cet équipement de bon niveau, sinon exceptionnel, où les membres paraissent vivre heureux et sans histoires. Ils sont chez eux, avec le parcours le plus "parisien" à l'est de Paris, comme en témoigne le très bourgeois club-house, une vénérable maison de maître.

In a beautiful, flat park, wide fairways lined by tall trees give the feeling of space you expect from a golf course. Although some holes are rather tight and demand precision play, long-hitters can let fly at Ozoir. We thought it a shame that no contouring has been done to the fairways. True, they are easier to play as they are, but they could be made more challenging for the better players. Bunkers and trees are the main hazards, as water enters the fray on only two holes. The greens are generally good and classically styled, some of which have been re-laid, something many other clubs should do from time to time. A very decent 9-holer with a lot of water hazards completes this excellent, if not to say exceptional, golfing complex where members seem to live a happy and untroubled golfing existence. They are very much at home here in what is the most "Parisian" course to the east of Paris, as seen with the classy club-house, a true mansion.

Ozoir-la-Ferrière — 1928

Château des Agneaux
F - 77330 OZOIR-LA-FERRIERE

Office	Secrétariat	(33) 01 60 02 60 79
Pro shop	Pro-shop	(33) 01 64 40 23 49
Fax	Fax	(33) 01 64 40 28 20
Web	www.golfozoir.org	
Situation	Situation	Paris, 36 km

Pontault-Combault (pop. 26 800), 5 km

Annual closure Fermeture annuelle — no

Weekly closure Fermeture hebdomadaire — Tuesday
(mardi): 12 → 02

Fees main season Tarifs haute saison — 18 holes

	Week days Semaine	We/Bank holidays We/Férié
Individual Individuel	€ 44	€ 70
Couple Couple	€ 88	€ 140

Under 20: € 26 / 35 (We)

Caddie Caddie no — **Electric Trolley** Chariot électrique yes

Buggy Voiturette yes — **Clubs** Clubs yes

Credit cards Cartes de crédit
VISA - CB - Eurocard - MasterCard

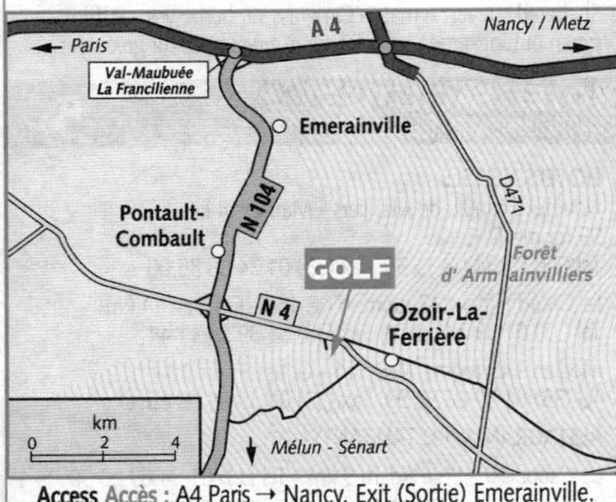

Access Accès : A4 Paris → Nancy, Exit (Sortie) Emerainville. N104 ("la Francilienne") → Pontault-Combault, N4 → Ozoir-la-Ferrière

Map 15 on page 189 Carte 15 Page 189

GOLF COURSE — PARCOURS 13/20

Site	Site	
Maintenance	Entretien	
Architect	Architecte	unknown
Type	Type	parkland
Relief	Relief	
Water in play	Eau en jeu	
Exp. to wind	Exposé au vent	
Trees in play	Arbres en jeu	

Scorecard Carte de score	Chp. Chp.	Mens Mess.	Ladies Da.
Length Long.	5859	5591	4672
Par	71	71	71
Slope system	134	130	122

Advised golfing ability Niveau de jeu recommandé — 0 12 24 36

Hcp required Handicap exigé — 24 Men, 28 Ladies (We)

CLUB HOUSE & AMENITIES — CLUB HOUSE ET ANNEXES 7/10

Pro shop Pro-shop
Driving range Practice
Sheltered couvert 8 mats - On grass sur herbe no, 10 mats open air - Putting-green putting-green yes
Pitching-green pitching green yes

HOTEL FACILITIES — ENVIRONNEMENT HOTELIER 5/10

HOTELS HÔTELS

Saphir Hôtel - 179 rooms, D € 115 - Pontault-Combault 4 km
Tel (33) 01 64 43 45 47, Fax (33) 01 64 40 52 43

Le Pavillon Bleu - 37 rooms, D € 51 - Ozoir-la-Ferrière 2 km
Tel (33) 01 64 40 05 56, Fax (33) 01 64 40 29 74

Relais de Pincevent - La-Queue-en-Brie 7 km
54 rooms, D € 65
Tel (33) 01 45 94 61 61, Fax (33) 01 45 93 32 69

RESTAURANTS RESTAURANTS

Auberge du Petit Caporal - La-Queue-en-Brie 7 km
Tel (33) 01 45 76 30 06

La Gueulardière - Ozoir-la-Ferrière 2 km
Tel (33) 01 60 02 94 56

Paris International

16	7	5

Avec sa situation très favorable au nord de Paris et à proximité de l'aéroport Charles-de-Gaulle, ce parcours était d'autant plus espéré que son dessin était confié à Jack Nicklaus. Mais autant on peut reconnaître sa patte sur une douzaine de trous, où un espace très ouvert lui permettait de donner sa pleine mesure, autant on a l'impression qu'il s'est trouvé à l'étroit dans les trous en forêt, où l'on a du mal à identifier la réalité de sa signature, et où les très bons joueurs auront plus de mal à s'exprimer. Ces réserves viennent surtout de la hauteur des espérances, et pour garder le meilleur souvenir du parcours, on conseillera de commencer par le retour et de finir par ce superbe aller. A connaître néanmoins, car le terrain a été très amélioré avec d'importants travaux de drainage. On attend maintenant un peu de stabilité du club et une consolidation de l'entretien, car Michael Smurfit (promoteur du K-Club à Dublin) a déjà revendu le club à la chaîne Blue Green.

Neatly located to the north of Paris, this course was long awaited in that the designer was a one Jack Nicklaus. But as easily as you will recognize his style on a dozen or so holes, where wide open space gave him full scope for expression, as easily you will feel that the great man was not quite comfortable and even a little cramped on the holes through the forest. Here, his style is not nearly as clear-cut and even good players will have problems coming to terms with the homeward nine. These reservations are of course matched to our high expectations. To get the best impression of this course, we would advise you to start from the 10th and leave the superb outward 9 for the end. Worth playing nonetheless, as the terrain has been much improved by some extensive drainage work. We now await a little stability and consolidation of standards of green-keeping, as Michael Smurfit (promoter of the Dublin K-Club) has already sold the club to the Blue Green chain.

Paris International Golf Club — 1990

18, route du Golf
F - 95560 BAILLET-en-FRANCE

Office	Secrétariat	(33) 01 34 69 90 00
Pro shop	Pro-shop	(33) 01 34 69 90 00
Fax	Fax	(33) 01 34 69 97 15
Web	www.paris-golf.com	
Situation	Situation	Paris, 30 km
Annual closure	Fermeture annuelle	25/12→1/1
Weekly closure	Fermeture hebdomadaire	monday/lundi

Fees main season Tarifs haute saison	Week days Semaine	We/Bank holidays We/Férié
18 holes		
Individual Individuel	€ 75	€ 100
Couple Couple	€ 150	€ 200

Members' guests only

Caddie Caddie on request **Electric Trolley** Chariot électrique yes

Buggy Voiturette yes **Clubs** Clubs yes

Credit cards Cartes de crédit
VISA - Eurocard - MasterCard - AMEX

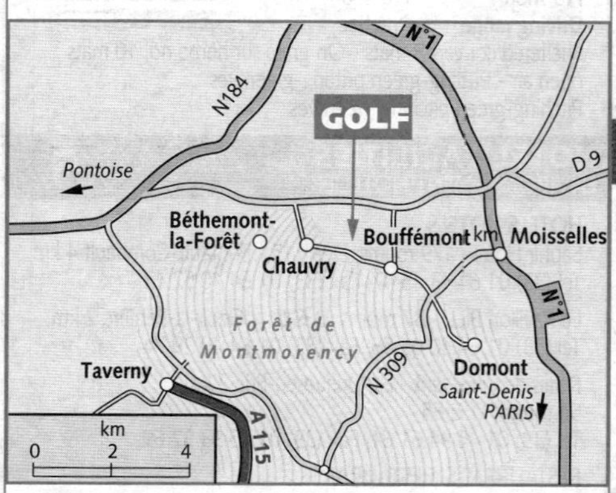

Access Accès : Paris, A1, N1. Turn left on D3 → Baillet-en-France
Map 15 on page 188 Carte 15 Page 188

GOLF COURSE — PARCOURS — 16/20

Site	Site	
Maintenance	Entretien	
Architect	Architecte	Jack Nicklaus
Type	Type	parkland, hilly
Relief	Relief	
Water in play	Eau en jeu	
Exp. to wind	Exposé au vent	
Trees in play	Arbres en jeu	

Scorecard Carte de score	Chp. Chp.	Mens Mess.	Ladies Da.
Length Long.	6119	5740	4885
Par	72	72	72
Slope system	140	138	138

Advised golfing ability Niveau de jeu recommandé — 0 12 24 36

Hcp required Handicap exigé 36

CLUB HOUSE & AMENITIES — CLUB HOUSE ET ANNEXES — 7/10

Pro shop Pro-shop
Driving range Practice

Sheltered couvert 6 mats - On grass sur herbe yes - Putting-green putting-green yes - Pitching-green pitching green yes

HOTEL FACILITIES — ENVIRONNEMENT HOTELIER — 5/10

HOTELS HÔTELS

Novotel Château de Maffliers - Maffliers 4 km
99 rooms, D € 125
Tel (33) 01 34 08 35 35, Fax (33) 01 34 08 35 00

Le Grand Hôtel - 43 rooms, D € 150 - Enghien 14 km
Tel (33) 01 39 34 10 04, Fax (33) 01 39 34 11 44

Median - 49 rooms, D € 115 - Goussainville 10 km
Tel (33) 01 39 88 93 93, Fax (33) 01 39 88 75 65

RESTAURANTS RESTAURANTS

Le Cabouillet - L'Isle Adam 9 km - Tel (33) 01 34 69 00 90
Le Troubadour - L'Isle Adam 11 km - Tel (33) 01 34 08 10 34
La Ferme de Bouffémont - Bouffémont 2 km
Tel (33) 01 39 35 14 35

Pau

13 | 6 | 8

Le plus ancien parcours d'Europe continentale n'est peut-être pas un chef-d'oeuvre, il est amusant et relaxant à jouer même s'il n'a plus grand chose des origines. Il a au moins gardé le goût de la décoration florale et les arbres ont grandi, tout en laissant des vues séduisantes sur les Pyrénées. La présence du Gave de Pau apporte un intérêt au jeu, dont les seules difficultés consistent à apprécier les distances: le parcours est plat et étroit (avec pas mal de hors-limites). Sa longueur réduite peut décevoir les vedettes du driver, mais c'est parfait pour affûter ses petits fers. Le putting et le petit jeu jouant un rôle essentiel, le green du 4 a été entièrement refait, de très gros efforts ont été réalisés sur les bunkers et la qualité des fairways, en particulier autour des greens ce qui permet un chipping de qualité. La chaleur de l'accueil dans le Sud-Ouest, le charme des lieux, la situation en ville et le culte de la tradition en font un joli lieu de promenade. Un gros travail d'aération des greens semble avoir été bénéfique pour fêter dignement en 2006 le 150e anniversaire.

This oldest course on the continent of Europe may not be a masterpiece, but it is great fun and relaxing to play even though little remains of its original features. It has retained the tasteful floral decoration and the trees have grown, leaving some eye-catching sights over the Pyrenees. The "Gave de Pau" (a mountain stream) adds a little spice to your round, the only real difficulty of which is appreciating the distances: the course is flat and tight (with a lot of out-of-bounds to cope with). Putting and a good short game obviously play a key role, green N°4 has been re-laid and a lot of work has been done on bunkering and the quality of fairways, especially around the greens where chipping is now almost a pleasure. The warm welcome of this region of France, the charming site and the course's long-standing origins make this a lovely walk. Some extensive aeration work on the greens seems to have produced the goods and the course is ready to celebrate in style its 150th anniversary.

Pau Golf-Club — 1856

Rue du Golf
F - 64140 BILLERE

Office	Secrétariat	(33) 05 59 13 18 56
Pro shop	Pro-shop	(33) 05 59 13 18 56
Fax	Fax	(33) 05 59 13 18 57
Web	www.paugolfclub.com	
Situation	Situation	Pau (pop. 82 150), 2 km
Annual closure	Fermeture annuelle	no
Weekly closure	Fermeture hebdomadaire	monday

(lundi): restaurant

Fees main season Tarifs haute saison	18 holes	
	Week days Semaine	**We/Bank holidays** We/Férié
Individual Individuel	€ 45	€ 50
Couple Couple	€ 70	€ 80

Under 25: € 30

Caddie Caddie no — **Electric Trolley** Chariot électrique no

Buggy Voiturette no — **Clubs** Clubs yes

Credit cards Cartes de crédit
VISA - CB - Eurocard - MasterCard

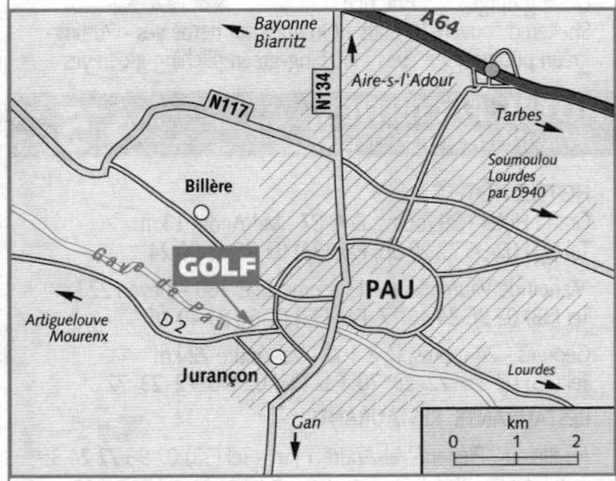

Access Accès : next to the Gave de Pau and "Parc National"

Map 12 on page 182 Carte 12 Page 182

GOLF COURSE — PARCOURS — 13/20

Site	Site	
Maintenance	Entretien	
Architect	Architecte	B. Ducwing
Type	Type	parkland
Relief	Relief	
Water in play	Eau en jeu	
Exp. to wind	Exposé au vent	
Trees in play	Arbres en jeu	

Scorecard Carte de score	**Chp.** Chp.	**Mens** Mess.	**Ladies** Da.
Length Long.	5314	5314	4623
Par	69	69	69
Slope system	124	124	116

Advised golfing ability — Niveau de jeu recommandé: 0 12 24 36

Hcp required — Handicap exigé: no

CLUB HOUSE & AMENITIES — CLUB HOUSE ET ANNEXES — 6/10

Pro shop Pro-shop
Driving range Practice

Sheltered couvert 6 mats - On grass sur herbe yes - Putting-green putting-green yes (2) - Pitching-green pitching green yes (3)

HOTEL FACILITIES — ENVIRONNEMENT HOTELIER — 8/10

HOTELS HÔTELS

Hôtel de Gramont - Pau 2 km
34 rooms, D € 60
Tel (33) 05 59 27 84 04, Fax (33) 05 59 27 62 23

Commerce - Pau 2 km - 51 rooms, D € 48
Tel (33) 05 59 27 24 40, Fax (33) 05 59 83 81 74

Novotel - Lescar 6 km - 89 rooms, D € 100
Tel (33) 05 59 13 04 04, Fax (33) 05 59 13 04 13

RESTAURANTS RESTAURANTS

Chez Ruffet - Jurançon 2 km - Tel (33) 05 59 06 25 13
Chez Pierre - Pau 2 km - Tel (33) 05 59 27 76 86
La Michodière - Pau 2 km - Tel (33) 05 59 27 53 85

Pléneuf-Val-André

17	7	5

Pléneuf Val André a conquis une enviable réputation, et dans cette jolie réussite signée par Alain Prat, entre les landes et la mer, on appréciera d'abord une bonne montée en puissance des difficultés du parcours en général sans pour autant le rattacher tout à fait au style de links traditionnels. Les fairways sont généralement assez larges, ce qui facilite la plupart des mises en jeu, mais les greens sont ensuite particulièrement défendus par de nombreux bunkers de sable et d'herbe, stratégiquement placés. Le trou le plus spectaculaire est le 11, un par 5 au départ arrière situé sur un éperon rocheux, et qui a apporté une sorte de prime à la réputation du lieu. Il se situe dans la partie la plus accidentée du parcours, mais ce n'est pas un golf trop fatigant, sauf pour le swing quand il faut s'arranger des dévers ou lutter avec le vent. On notera la qualité particulière des installations d'entraînement, et de jolis points de vue, mais le club-house est simplement moyen. L'entretien reste un peu inégal, mais les greens et départs ont encore été améliorés.

Pléneuf Val André has gained an enviable reputation with this pretty layout by Alain Prat, lying between moorland and sea-shore. The way difficulties gradually pile on the pressure as the round wears on is a great feature, but without the traditional links feel. The fairways are, by and large, rather wide for easier tee-shots but the greens are well defended by numerous bunkers and dips, all of which are strategically located. The signature hole is the 11th, a par 5 whose back-tee is placed on a rocky spur and which adds a distinct bonus to the course's reputation. Here, you are on the hilliest part of the course, but there is nothing too tiring about Pléneuf except when getting to grips with sloping lies or swinging in a stiff breeze. Practice facilities are very good and there are also some pretty viewpoints, but the club-house is average only. Green-keeping is still inconsistent but the greens and tee-boxes continue to improve.

Golf de Pléneuf-Val-André — 1992

Rue de la Plage des Vallées
F - 22370 PLENEUF-VAL-ANDRE

Office	Secrétariat	(33) 02 96 63 01 12
Pro shop	Pro-shop	(33) 02 96 63 01 12
Fax	Fax	(33) 02 96 63 01 06
Web	www.bluegreen.com	
Situation	Situation	Saint-Brieuc, 25 km
Annual closure	Fermeture annuelle	no
Weekly closure	Fermeture hebdomadaire	

Tuesday &Wednesday in winter (mardi et mercredi d'hiver): restaurant closed

Fees main season Tarifs haute saison — 18 holes

	Week days / Semaine	We/Bank holidays / We/Férié
Individual Individuel	€ 47	€ 47
Couple Couple	€ 94	€ 94

Under 25: € 16 / 23 (We)

Caddie Caddie no **Electric Trolley** Chariot électrique no

Buggy Voiturette yes **Clubs** Clubs yes

Credit cards Cartes de crédit
VISA - CB - Eurocard - MasterCard - AMEX - DC

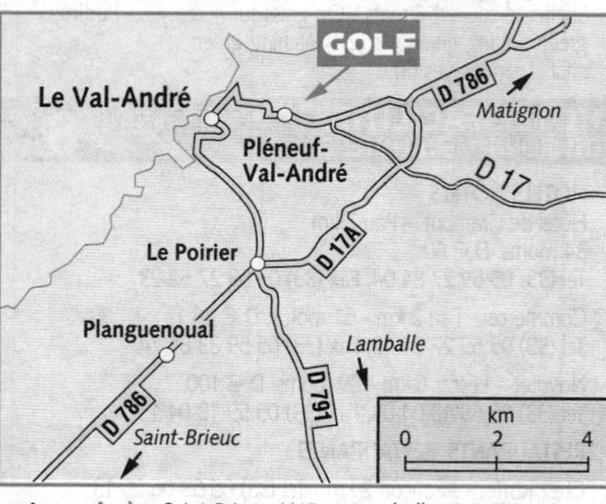

Access Accès : Saint-Brieuc, N12 → Lamballe, Exit (Sortie) Saint-René. D786 → Pléneuf- Val-André

Map 5 on page 169 Carte 5 Page 169

GOLF COURSE — PARCOURS — 17/20

Site	Site	
Maintenance	Entretien	
Architect	Architecte	Alain Prat
Type	Type	seaside course
Relief	Relief	
Water in play	Eau en jeu	
Exp. to wind	Exposé au vent	
Trees in play	Arbres en jeu	

Scorecard Carte de score	Chp. Chp.	Mens Mess.	Ladies Da.
Length Long.	5797	5564	4664
Par	72	72	72
Slope system	135	131	124

Advised golfing ability / Niveau de jeu recommandé — 0 12 24 36

Hcp required Handicap exigé — 54 main season

CLUB HOUSE & AMENITIES — CLUB HOUSE ET ANNEXES — 7/10

Pro shop	Pro-shop	
Driving range	Practice	

Sheltered couvert 10 mats - On grass sur herbe yes - Putting-green putting-green yes - Pitching-green pitching green yes

HOTEL FACILITIES — ENVIRONNEMENT HOTELIER — 5/10

HOTELS HÔTELS

Grand Hôtel - 39 rooms, D € 87 - Val-André 1 km
Tel (33) 02 96 72 20 56, Fax (33) 02 96 63 00 24

Manoir de Vaumadeuc - 13 rooms, D € 160 - Pleven 22 km
Tel (33) 02 96 84 46 17, Fax (33) 02 96 84 40 16

Georges - 24 rooms, D € 100 - Val-André 22 km
Tel (33) 02 96 72 23 70, Fax (33) 02 96 72 23 72

RESTAURANTS RESTAURANTS

Au Biniou - Pléneuf-Val-André 1 km - Tel (33) 02 96 72 24 35
Antre Amis - Pléneuf-Val-André - Tel (33) 02 96 72 25 07
La Mer - Val-André 1 km - Tel (33) 02 96 72 20 44

Ploemeur Océan

14	7	6

A proximité de Lorient, Ploëmeur Océan a pris place dans un vaste espace de bord de mer et de campagne, avec une végétation austère constituée principalement de lichens, de buissons et de genêts. Ce parcours signé Quenouille et MacAuley est très agréable, avec de jolis trous, des fairways bien fournis, des greens très corrects et de bons bunkers. Certains coups et approches sont assez techniques, mais les difficultés ne sont pas très accentuées, ce qui permet à tous les niveaux d'y évoluer simultanément. L'aller se déroule dans une sorte de vallon avec de petits étangs. Le retour est plus "marin", mais sans qu'il s'agisse vraiment d'un links. Les quatre derniers trous ramènent à la terre ferme. Dans une région aujourd'hui bien fournie en golfs, c'est un plaisant parcours, mais sans doute pas un grand test de golf pour les meilleurs. Il n'y prétend pas, d'ailleurs. L'entretien est correct, les tarifs très modérés !

Not far from Lorient, Ploëmeur Océan stretches over a huge chunk of seaside and country land lined with the stark vegetation of a few low-cut lichen bushes, scrub and broom. Designed by Quenouille and MacAuley back in 1990, Ploemeur is a pleasant course with a few pretty holes, well-grassed fairways, very decent greens and some good bunkers to boot. Some shots require a lot of technique but the difficulties are never excessive, so that players of all aspirations can enjoy a round together. The outward nine run through a sort of vale with small lakes while the homeward nine have more of a seaside flavour without ever playing like a true links course. The 4 closing holes bring you back to dry land. A pleasant course in a region that today has more than its fair share of golfing facilities, but probably not a major test of golf for the best players. And it does not claim to be, either. Green-keeping is good and green-fees very reasonable.

Golf de Ploemeur Océan — 1990

Saint-Jude - Kerham
F - 56270 PLOEMEUR

Office Secrétariat (33) 02 97 32 81 82
Pro shop Pro-shop (33) 02 97 32 81 82
Fax Fax (33) 02 97 32 80 90
Web www.formule-golf.com
Situation Situation Lorient (pop. 59 270), 10 km
Annual closure Fermeture annuelle no
Weekly closure Fermeture hebdomadaire tuesday
(mardi): 01/12 → 28/02

Fees main season Tarifs haute saison 18 holes

	Week days Semaine	We/Bank holidays We/Férié
Individual Individuel	€ 48	€ 48
Couple Couple	€ 96	€ 96

Under 21 and students under 25: - 50%

Caddie Caddie no — **Electric Trolley** Chariot électrique no
Buggy Voiturette yes — **Clubs** Clubs yes
Credit cards Cartes de crédit
VISA - CB - Eurocard - MasterCard

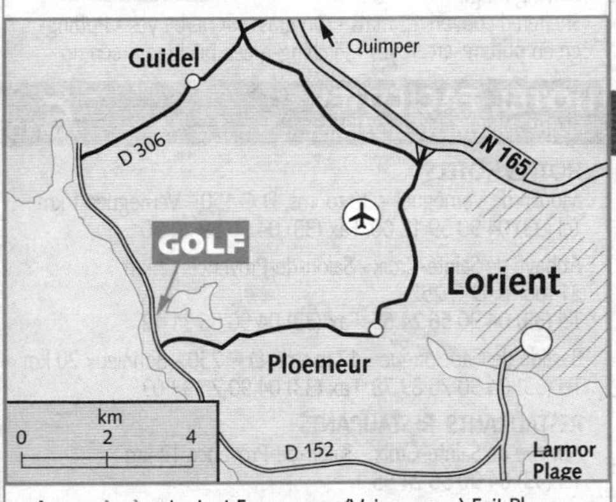

Access Accès : Lorient Expressway (Voie express) Exit Ploemeur → Airport Lann-Bihoué → Fort Bloqué
Map 5 on page 168 Carte 5 Page 168

GOLF COURSE — PARCOURS 14/20

Site Site
Maintenance Entretien
Architect Architecte Quenouille, MacAuley
Type Type seaside course
Relief Relief
Water in play Eau en jeu
Exp. to wind Exposé au vent
Trees in play Arbres en jeu

Scorecard Carte de score	Chp. Chp.	Mens Mess.	Ladies Da.
Length Long.	5819	5606	4820
Par	72	72	72
Slope system	128	126	126

Advised golfing ability Niveau de jeu recommandé 0 12 24 36
Hcp required Handicap exigé no

CLUB HOUSE & AMENITIES — CLUB HOUSE ET ANNEXES 7/10

Pro shop Pro-shop
Driving range Practice
Sheltered couvert 16 mats - On grass sur herbe yes - Putting-green putting-green yes - Pitching-green pitching green yes

HOTEL FACILITIES — ENVIRONNEMENT HOTELIER 6/10

HOTELS HÔTELS

Les Astéries - 36 rooms, D € 60 - Ploemeur 4 km
Tel (33) 02 97 86 21 97, Fax (33) 02 97 86 34 33

Le Vivier - 14 rooms, D € 72 - Lomener 6 km
Tel (33) 02 97 82 99 60, Fax (33) 02 97 82 88 89

Château de Locguénolé - Hennebont 20 km
22 rooms, D € 185
Tel (33) 02 97 76 76 76, Fax (33) 02 97 76 82 35

RESTAURANTS RESTAURANTS

L'Amphitryon - Lorient 10 km - Tel (33) 02 97 83 34 04
Vents d'Ouest - Lorient 10 km - Tel (33) 02 97 21 57 06
Château de Locguénolé - Hennebont 20 km
Tel (33) 02 97 76 76 76

Pont Royal

16 | 7 | 6

Premier parcours français signé par Ballesteros, avec un immobilier très présent, Pont Royal a toujours bénéficié d'un bon entretien. La dimension généreuse des bunkers frappe d'abord, mais c'est une spécialité du champion espagnol, qui peut réserver aux joueurs de longues sorties, cauchemar des amateurs comme des professionnels. Avec divers obstacles d'eau (rivière, étangs), quelques dangereux ravins, un relief assez accidenté (voiturette conseillée), Pont Royal réclame pas mal de technique, de sens tactique et une grande habileté dans le choix des clubs. Les frappeurs auront de belles occasions de prendre des risques, avec émotions garanties. Beaucoup d'arbres aussi sont en jeu, mais un travail d'élagage et de dégagement a bien arrangé plusieurs trous. Quelques autres trous au dessin quelque peu torturé exigent d'être reconnus avant d'être négociés correctement, surtout quand souffle le mistral ! En ce cas, il vaut mieux oublier la carte de scores, comme on conseillera aux néophytes de le faire.

Pont Royal, the first French course designed by Ballesteros and where real estate is very now much in view, has always been kept in good condition. The very large bunkers, one of the Spaniard's hallmarks, are stunning and lead to some very long escape shots from sand, often a nightmare for amateurs and pros alike. With a number of different water hazards (a river and ponds), a few dangerous ravines and hilly landscape (buggy recommended), Pont Royal requires a lot of technique, a good tactical mind and skill in choosing the right club. Long-hitters have exciting opportunities to take risks and set their pulses racing. A lot of trees are also in play but pruning and clearing work has been pretty effective on several holes. Several others, with a sometimes twisted layout, need a little reconnaissance before hoping to make any impression, especially when the Mistral is blowing. In this case, take the advice we would give to any beginner here and forget the scorecard.

Pont Royal Golf Club — 1992

F - 13370 MALLEMORT

Office Secrétariat (33) 04 90 57 40 79
Pro shop Pro-shop (33) 04 90 57 40 79
Fax Fax (33) 04 90 57 50 19
Web www.golf-pontroyal.com
Situation Situation Salon-de-Provence, 20 km
Annual closure Fermeture annuelle no
Weekly closure Fermeture hebdomadaire
Wednesdayin low season (mercredi basse saison)

Fees main season Tarifs haute saison	Week days Semaine	We/Bank holidays We/Férié
	18 holes	
Individual Individuel	€ 65	€ 65
Couple Couple	€ 130	€ 130

Under 25: € 39
Caddie Caddie no — **Electric Trolley** Chariot électrique no
Buggy Voiturette yes — **Clubs** Clubs yes
Credit cards Cartes de crédit
VISA - CB - Eurocard - MasterCard

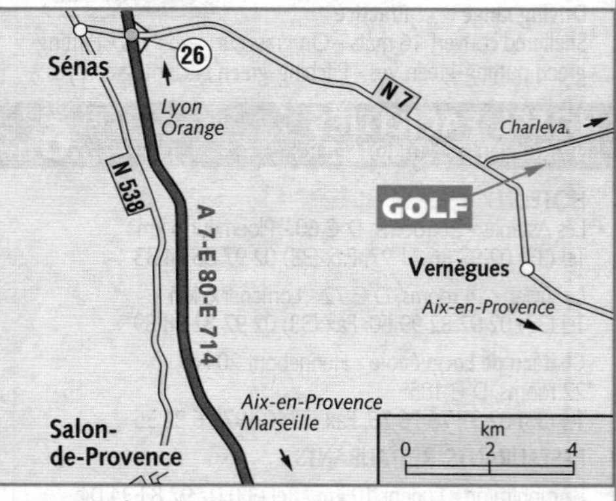

Access Accès : A7, Exit (Sortie) Sénas, N7 → Aix-en-Provence, Golf 10 km
Map 14 on page 186 Carte 14 Page 186

GOLF COURSE — PARCOURS — 16/20

Site Site
Maintenance Entretien
Architect Architecte — Seve Ballesteros
Type Type — country, hilly
Relief Relief
Water in play Eau en jeu
Exp. to wind Exposé au vent
Trees in play Arbres en jeu

Scorecard Carte de score	Chp. Chp.	Mens Mess.	Ladies Da.
Length Long.	6123	5778	4847
Par	72	72	72
Slope system	151	149	139

Advised golfing ability Niveau de jeu recommandé — 0 12 24 36
Hcp required Handicap exigé — no

CLUB HOUSE & AMENITIES — CLUB HOUSE ET ANNEXES — 7/10

Pro shop Pro-shop
Driving range Practice
Sheltered couvert 12 mats - On grass sur herbe yes - Putting-green putting-green yes - Pitching-green pitching green no

HOTEL FACILITIES — ENVIRONNEMENT HOTELIER — 6/10

HOTELS HÔTELS
Moulin de Vernègues - 38 rooms, D € 150 - Vernègues 1 km
Tel (33) 04 90 59 12 00, Fax (33) 04 90 59 15 90

Abbaye de Sainte-Croix - Salon-de-Provence 12 km
21 rooms, D € 252
Tel (33) 04 90 56 24 55, Fax (33) 04 90 56 31 12

Bastide de Capelongue - 17 rooms, D € 250 - Bonnieux 20 km
Tel (33) 04 90 75 89 78, Fax (33) 04 90 75 93 03

RESTAURANTS RESTAURANTS
Abbaye de Sainte-Croix - Salon-de-Provence 12 km
Tel (33) 04 90 56 24 55

Le Mas du Soleil - Salon-de-Provence - Tel (33) 04 90 56 06 53
Bastide de Capelongue - Bonnieux 20 km
Tel (33) 04 90 75 89 78

Porcelaine (La)

14 | 6 | 4

Avec son relief accidenté et la nature de son terrain, La Porcelaine reste agréable à jouer aux beaux jours, du printemps à l'automne, quand la végétation prend ses couleurs séduisantes. Ce parcours a été conçu comme une alternative privée au golf de Limoges, premier golf public en France. Des obstacles d'eau entrent en jeu sur la moitié des trous, et constituent, avec des arbres stratégiquement utilisés, les principales entraves à de bons scores. Ce parcours, bien au large sur 75 hectares, a été destiné essentiellement à ses membres, résidents de la région, et pas à des touristes de passage. A noter qu'il commence assez en douceur par un par 5 puis un court par 4, pour se mettre bien en jambes. On remarquera aussi la grande variété des formes de greens, certains étant étroits, souvent à plateaux et leur accès bien défendu. Les grands voyageurs de golf trouveront sans doute l'architecture de ce parcours sans grandes surprises, mais l'ambiance est ici sans prétention, avec un club-house aussi plaisamment "campagnard" que le parcours.

With its steep slopes and characteristic soil, La Porcelaine is pleasant to play when the weather is at its best from spring to autumn and when the vegetation blooms into colour. This course was designed as a private alternative to Limoges, France's first public course. Water hazards are in play on one half of the course and, along with some strategically located trees, are the main stumbling blocks to a good score. This sprawling course of some 75 hectares was designed essentially to satisfy local members and less for tourists in transit. It starts out sweetly enough with a par 5 and short par 4 to get you into the swing of things and from then on you can appreciate the variety in the way greens are shaped, some of which are narrow, multi-tiered and well-defended up-front. Hardened golf-trotters will probably find that the architecture lacks any real surprise, but the atmosphere is anything but pretentious and the club-house as pleasantly "rural" as the course itself.

Golf de la Porcelaine — 1988

Célicroux
F - 87350 PANAZOL

Office	Secrétariat	(33) 05 55 31 10 69
Pro shop	Pro-shop	(33) 05 55 31 10 69
Fax	Fax	(33) 05 55 31 10 69
Web		www.golf-porcelaine.com
Situation	Situation	Limoges (pop. 133 460), 6 km
Annual closure	Fermeture annuelle	no
Weekly closure	Fermeture hebdomadaire	tuesday

(Mardi): 01/10 → 31/03

Fees main season Tarifs haute saison	Week days Semaine	We/Bank holidays We/Férié
		Full day
Individual Individuel	€ 40	€ 45
Couple Couple	€ 80	€ 90

Caddie Caddie no — **Electric Trolley** Chariot électrique no
Buggy Voiturette yes — **Clubs** Clubs yes
Credit cards Cartes de crédit
VISA - CB - Eurocard - MasterCard

Access Accès : Limoges, D941 → Clermont-Ferrand, → Golf
Map 7 on page 172 Carte 7 Page 172

GOLF COURSE — PARCOURS — 14/20

Site	Site	
Maintenance	Entretien	
Architect	Architecte	Jean Garaïalde
Type	Type	country
Relief	Relief	
Water in play	Eau en jeu	
Exp. to wind	Exposé au vent	
Trees in play	Arbres en jeu	

Scorecard Carte de score	Chp. Chp.	Mens Mess.	Ladies Da.
Length Long.	6035	5562	4882
Par	72	72	72
Slope system	135	127	131

Advised golfing ability Niveau de jeu recommandé — 0 12 24 36
Hcp required Handicap exigé — no

CLUB HOUSE & AMENITIES — CLUB HOUSE ET ANNEXES — 6/10

Pro shop Pro-shop
Driving range Practice
Sheltered couvert 6 mats - On grass sur herbe yes - Putting-green putting-green yes - Pitching-green pitching green no

HOTEL FACILITIES — ENVIRONNEMENT HOTELIER — 4/10

HOTELS HÔTELS
Chapelle Saint-Martin - Saint-Martin-du-Fault 18 km
13 rooms, D € 165
Tel (33) 05 55 75 80 17, Fax (33) 05 55 75 89 50

Royal Limousin - 77 rooms, D € 85 - Limoges 6 km
Tel (33) 05 55 34 65 30, Fax (33) 05 55 34 55 21

Gd-Saint-Léonard - Saint-Léonard-de-Noblat 13 km
14 rooms, D € 54
Tel (33) 05 55 56 18 18, Fax (33) 05 55 56 98 32

RESTAURANTS RESTAURANTS
Philippe Redon - Limoges 6 km - Tel (33) 05 55 34 66 22
Amphytrion - Limoges 6 km - Tel (33) 05 55 33 36 39
Chapelle Saint-Martin - Saint-Martin-du Fault 18 km
Tel (33) 05 55 75 80 17

Pornic

15 | 6 | 6

A partir du neuf trous ouvert en 1929, un 18 trous très intéressant a été reconstruit en 1991, dans un espace assez accidenté et pratiquement en ville. C'est une région traditionnelle de vacances, au sud de Nantes, mais il n'est jamais vraiment difficile d'y trouver un départ. De plus, le sol sablonneux permet de le recommander toute l'année. Cinq trous sont agrémentés de pins, les treize autres se trouvent dans une zone de bord de mer, où les fairways sont séparés par des buttes, créant ainsi un peu d'intimité. On regrettera qu'ils soient à peu près tous parallèles, mais cela permet aux frappeurs sauvages de s'écarter du droit chemin sans être trop pénalisés, et sans trop menacer les joueurs de tous niveaux pouvant évoluer ici. L'espace était certes limité (35 hectares !), mais il a été bien occupé, le parcours est assez long des départs arrière, la disposition des départs permettant de se faire un parcours "à sa main". On soulignera les bienfaits du drainage sur la partie originale du parcours.

Starting out with a 9-holer opened in 1929, an interesting 18-hole course was rebuilt in 1991 over very hilly terrain and virtually in town. This is traditional holiday territory, but getting a tee-off time poses no real problem. In addition, the sandy sub-soil makes it playable all year. Five holes are enhanced with pine-trees, the thirteen others run along the sea-shore, where the fairways are separated by sand-hills and are sometimes a little too close together. It is a shame they all run more or less parallel, up and down, although this allows wild-hitters to wander off the straight and narrow without too much penalty and encourages players of all abilities to play here together. Space was certainly at a premium (86 acres!) but it has been used well. And although Pornic is rather long from the back tees, the number of different boxes allows golfers to choose a course to suit their game. Lastly, we can report on the improvements obtained with extensive new drainage.

Golf de Pornic — 1912

Avenue Scalby-Newby
F - 44210 SAINTE-MARIE-SUR-MER

Office	Secrétariat	(33) 02 40 82 06 69
Pro shop	Pro-shop	(33) 02 40 82 06 69
Fax	Fax	(33) 02 40 82 80 65
Web	www.formule-golf.com	
Situation	Situation	Nantes, 52 km

Pornic (pop. 13 000), 2 km

Annual closure Fermeture annuelle — no
Weekly closure Fermeture hebdomadaire — no

Fees main season Tarifs haute saison — 18 holes

	Week days Semaine	We/Bank holidays We/Férié
Individual Individuel	€ 46	€ 46
Couple Couple	€ 92	€ 92

Under 21 & Students: – 50%

Caddie Caddie no — **Electric Trolley** Chariot électrique yes
Buggy Voiturette yes — **Clubs** Clubs yes

Credit cards Cartes de crédit
VISA - CB - Eurocard - MasterCard

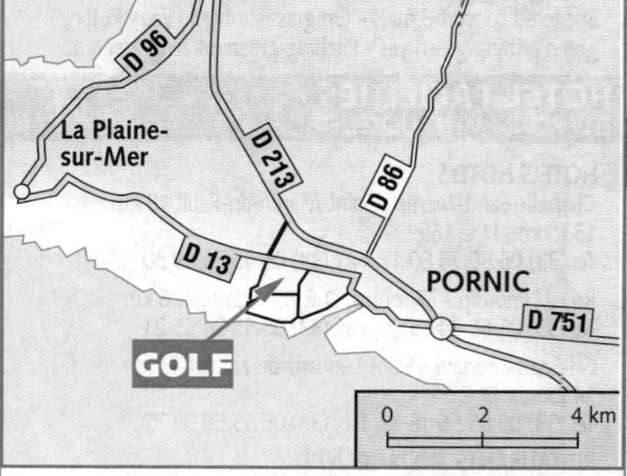

Access Accès : Nantes D751, Exit (Sortie) Pornic Ouest → Sainte-Marie-sur-Mer
Map 6 on page 170 Carte 6 Page 170

GOLF COURSE — PARCOURS — 15/20

Site	Site	
Maintenance	Entretien	
Architect	Architecte	Michel Gayon, Jacques Lebreton
Type	Type	links, forest
Relief	Relief	
Water in play	Eau en jeu	
Exp. to wind	Exposé au vent	
Trees in play	Arbres en jeu	

Scorecard Carte de score	Chp. Chp.	Mens Mess.	Ladies Da.
Length Long.	6082	5515	4470
Par	72	72	72
Slope system	144	133	128

Advised golfing ability Niveau de jeu recommandé — 0 12 24 36
Hcp required Handicap exigé — no

CLUB HOUSE & AMENITIES — CLUB HOUSE ET ANNEXES — 6/10

Pro shop Pro-shop
Driving range Practice
Sheltered couvert 5 mats - On grass sur herbe yes - Putting-green putting-green yes - Pitching-green pitching green yes

HOTEL FACILITIES — ENVIRONNEMENT HOTELIER — 6/10

HOTELS HÔTELS

Alliance - 120 rooms, D € 140 - Pornic 2 km
Tel (33) 02 40 82 21 21, Fax (33) 02 40 82 80 89

Relais Saint Gilles - 25 rooms, D € 67 - Pornic 2 km
Tel (33) 02 40 82 02 25

Les Sablons - 28 rooms, D € 73 - Sainte-Marie 1 km
Tel (33) 02 40 82 09 14, Fax (33) 02 40 82 04 26

RESTAURANTS RESTAURANTS

Le Beau Rivage - Pornic 2 km - Tel (33) 02 40 82 03 08

Anne de Bretagne - La Plaine-sur-Mer 10 km
Tel (33) 02 40 21 54 72

Prieuré (Le) *Ouest*

14	7	5

Ceux qui connaissent le style Hawtree ne seront guère surpris par ce tracé très honnête mais sans grandes surprises. Le parcours "Est" est sans doute plus varié et amusant, mais moins harmonieux dans son déroulement : le parcours "Ouest" constitue à l'évidence la référence de ce golf. Dans un grand parc orné de quelques très beaux spécimens d'arbres, le parcours se déroule de manière assez conventionnelle avec des défenses de green le plus souvent latérales, quelques mouvements sur les surfaces de putting, un bon équilibre des difficultés, une longueur très respectable, mais peu de chocs visuels ou de très grands défis techniques. Il n'est guère d'autres options que de taper loin et droit, de bien frapper ses fers et de putter correctement ! On est certes heureux d'avoir joué ce classique, à tous les sens du terme, mais l'émotion est rarement au rendez-vous car l'architecte Hawtree n'a guère pris de risques. Ce parcours reste humide en hiver, mais l'arrosage automatique a bien arrangé cet ensemble en été.

Golfers acquainted with the Hawtree style will not be surprised by this more than fair layout where there is little to raise any golfer's eyebrows. The "East" course is certainly the most varied and fun to play even though its layout lacks balance. The "West" course is evidently the club's "flagship". On a site of expansive parkland and a few fine trees, the course unwinds in a very classical style with greens often guarded by lateral bunkers, a few contours on the greens, well-balanced difficulties, very respectable yardage but few visual thrills or tough technical challenges. There is nothing else for it but to hit the ball long and straight, strike some clean iron shots and putt decently. Golf should be so simple. In other words, you are glad to have played this classic layout, in every sense of the term, but it's difficult to get too excited about it because architect Hawtree hardly took any risk at all. The course stays wet in winter but automatic sprinklers keep the course in fine fettle over the summer.

Golf du Prieuré — 1965

F - 78440 SAILLY

Office	Secrétariat	(44) 01 34 76 65 65
Pro shop	Pro-shop	(44) 01 34 76 65 65
Fax	Fax	(44) 01 34 76 65 50
Web	www.golfduprieure.com	
Situation	Situation	Paris, 55 km
Annual closure	Fermeture annuelle	no
Weekly closure	Fermeture hebdomadaire	tuesday

(mardi) / one week, end of 12 (une semaine fin 12)

Fees main season Tarifs haute saison — 18 holes

	Week days / Semaine	We/Bank holidays / We/Férié
Individual Individuel	€ 60	€ 75
Couple Couple	€ 120	€ 150

We: members' guests only (invités)
Under 18: € 30 / 44 (We) / Students: € 34

Caddie Caddie on request **Electric Trolley** Chariot électrique yes

Buggy Voiturette yes **Clubs** Clubs yes

Credit cards Cartes de crédit
VISA - CB - Eurocard - MasterCard

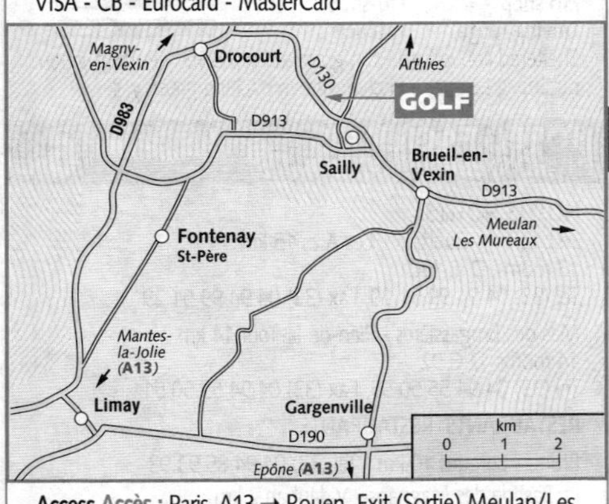

Access Accès : Paris, A13 → Rouen. Exit (Sortie) Meulan/Les Mureaux. After bridge over river Seine, take D913 to Oinville, Brueil-en-Vexin. 1 km after, turn right into Sailly, Golf 2 km

Map 3 on page 164 Carte 3 Page 164

GOLF COURSE / PARCOURS — 14/20

Site	Site	
Maintenance	Entretien	
Architect	Architecte	Fred Hawtree
Type	Type	parkland
Relief	Relief	
Water in play	Eau en jeu	
Exp. to wind	Exposé au vent	
Trees in play	Arbres en jeu	

Scorecard / Carte de score	Chp. / Chp.	Mens / Mess.	Ladies / Da.
Length Long.	6185	5716	4872
Par	72	72	72
Slope system	123	119	117

Advised golfing ability / Niveau de jeu recommandé — 0 12 24 36

Hcp required Handicap exigé 35

CLUB HOUSE & AMENITIES / CLUB HOUSE ET ANNEXES — 7/10

Pro shop	Pro-shop
Driving range	Practice

Sheltered couvert 7 mats - On grass sur herbe yes - Putting-green putting-green yes - Pitching-green pitching green yes

HOTEL FACILITIES / ENVIRONNEMENT HOTELIER — 5/10

HOTELS HÔTELS

Mercure - 69 rooms, D € 96 - Meulan 12 km
Tel (33) 01 34 74 63 63, Fax (33) 01 34 74 00 98

Moulin d'Orgeval - Orgeval 27 km
14 rooms, D € 150
Tel (33) 01 39 75 85 74, Fax (33) 01 39 75 48 52

RESTAURANTS RESTAURANTS

Moulin de la Reillère - Mantes la Ville 12 km
Tel (33) 01 30 92 22 00

Auberge de la Truite - Rosay 22 km
Tel (33) 01 34 76 30 52

Le Bon Vivant - Poissy 30 km
Tel (33) 01 39 65 02 14

Prince de Provence (Vidauban) 18 | 8 | 6

Ce golf est très privé, mais nous ne pouvions l'ignorer tant sont flagrantes sa qualité et sa beauté. Le terrain est aimablement animé, bien boisé sans être oppressant. En une sorte de synthèse de l'architecture, l'emplacement du drapeau détermine ce qu'il faut jouer, la stratégie est aussi importante que le jeu: aucun drive n'y est impossible, mais chacun doit être réfléchi en vue du coup suivant. L'esthétique du lieu comme du tracé sont d'une exemplaire sobriété. Quelques pins solitaires empiètent comme des sentinelles menaçantes sur les fairways. Tout aussi rares, les obstacles d'eau sont aussi nécessaires que suffisants. Il faut ici contrôler ses trajectoires et ses effets, maîtriser tous les clubs et tous les coups en fonction de son choix de départs. Et comme les alentours des greens exigent un petit jeu d'une rare finesse, on aura compris la sensation de privilège que l'on éprouve ici. Unique, splendide, princier, c'est un chef-d'œuvre en péril face à des procédures administratives. La qualité de l'entretien n'est plus toujours au niveau du tracé (d'où la baisse de note).

This golf is totally private but its excellence meant we could not ignore it. On this pleasantly sloping terrain, architecture and golf combine in such a way that pin positions decide which club you use off the tee, as strategy is just as important as power or precision. No drive is impossible but the tee-shot does have to be carefully considered with a view to what you do next. The beauty of the site and the course are wonderfully discreet. A few solitary pine-trees jut onto the fairways like threatening sentinels. And equally rare water hazards are as necessary as they are sufficient in number. Control is the key-word here, of flight, spin, clubs and every shot you make. And as the cleverly designed areas around the greens call for a very sharp short game, you can understand the privilege to play here. A princely course, but now a masterpiece under threat from administrative rulings. The standard of green-keeping is a bit down (as is the mark).

Le Prince de Provence 1999

Route Départementale 72
F - 83550 VIDAUBAN

Office	Secrétariat	(33) 04 94 73 55 87
Pro shop	Pro-shop	(33) 04 94 73 55 87
Fax	Fax	(33) 04 94 73 57 24
Web	—	
Situation	Situation	Cannes (pop. 68 676), 68 km

St Tropez (pop. 5 754), 25 km

Annual closure Fermeture annuelle no

Weekly closure Fermeture hebdomadaire no

Fees main season Tarifs haute saison 18 holes

	Week days Semaine	We/Bank holidays We/Férié
Individual Individuel	*	*
Couple Couple	*	*

Members' guests only

Caddie Cadie no **Electric Trolley** Chariot électrique no

Buggy Voiturette yes **Clubs** Clubs yes

Credit cards Cartes de crédit
VISA - Eurocard - MasterCard - AMEX

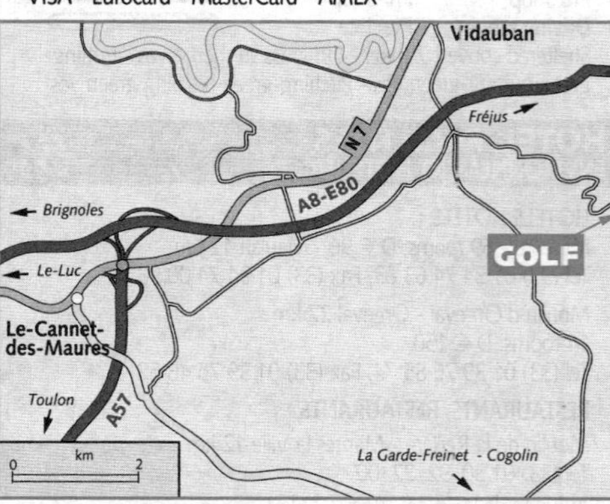

Access Accès : A 8 Nice/Aix-en-Provence. Exit Vidauban, then N7 → Vidauban/Le Luc. In Vidauban, D 48 on left hand side → La Garde-Freinet, D 72 → Plan-de-la-Tour
Map 14 on page 187 Carte 14 Page 187

GOLF COURSE 18/20
PARCOURS

Site Site
Maintenance Entretien
Architect Architecte Robert Trent Jones, R. Trent Jones Jr
Type Type inland, open country
Relief Relief
Water in play Eau en jeu
Exp. to wind Exposé au vent
Trees in play Arbres en jeu

Scorecard Carte de score	Chp. Chp.	Mens Mess.	Ladies Da.
Length Long.	6190	5686	4801
Par	72	72	72
Slope system	0	0	0

Advised golfing ability 0 12 24 36
Niveau de jeu recommandé
Hcp required Handicap exigé no

CLUB HOUSE & AMENITIES 8/10
CLUB HOUSE ET ANNEXES

Pro shop Pro-shop
Driving range Practice
Sheltered couvert no - On grass sur herbe yes - Putting-green putting-green yes - Pitching-green pitching green yes

HOTEL FACILITIES 6/10
ENVIRONNEMENT HOTELIER

HOTELS HÔTELS

Le Logis du Guetteur - Les Arcs 15 km
13 rooms, D € 130
Tel (33) 04 94 99 51 10, Fax (33) 04 94 99 51 29

Mas des Brugassières - Plan-de-la-Tour 14 km
14 rooms, D € 92
Tel (33) 04 94 55 50 55, Fax (33) 04 94 55 50 51

RESTAURANTS RESTAURANTS

Bruno - Lorgues 10 km - Tel (33) 04 94 85 93 93

La Bastide des Magnans - Vidauban 2 km
Tel (33) 04 94 99 43 91

Concorde - Vidauban 4 km - Tel (33) 04 94 73 01 19

Raray (Château de) *La Licorne* 14 7 5

Ce parcours d'inspiration britannique a été tracé par Patrice Léglise, head pro à Chantilly. Plusieurs trous inspirés à la fois du style de Tom Simpson et des links ont été tracés en plaine, et les autres insinués dans une belle forêt. L'ensemble est d'une grande franchise, les difficultés techniques sont réelles mais raisonnables, avec quelques fossés d'apparence naturelle venant en jeu. Le dessin des bunkers est aussi sobre qu'esthétiquement réussi, de même que leur placement très stratégique. Le 18, dans une allée bordée de grands arbres, est d'une esthétique "à la française" très adéquate pour un retour vers le château, autrefois utilisé comme décor du film "La Belle et la Bête" de Jean Cocteau, et qui a été restauré en hôtel avec restaurant, salles de séminaire et club-house. Le parcours plat permet aux joueurs de tous âges d'y évoluer. Autrefois fragile par temps de pluie, le jeu a été nettement amélioré par des drainages, mais aussi par un nettoyage attentif des sous-bois et des roughs, ceux-ci ayant parfois laissés au naturel, dans l'esprit du tracé.

This very British style course was laid out by the professional Patrice Léglise. There are several holes inspired by both Tom Simpson and links courses that run across open countryside, while the others run through a beautiful forest. The whole course is an honest test of golf with real but reasonable technical difficulties and a few natural-looking ditches which come into play. The bunkers are discreet in design, pleasant to look at and strategically located. The 18th hole, laid out along a wide alley edged by large trees is very French in style and a suitable way to return to the castle. It has now been restored and transformed into a hotel with a restaurant, seminar rooms and club-house. A flat course for golfers of all ages but preferably in dry weather. Although once very prone to wet weather, it is more fun playing here now that drainage has been installed and the undergrowth carefully trimmed back. Some rough has though been left to grow wild in the spirit of the layout.

Château de Raray 1988

4, rue Nicolas Lancy
F - 60810 RARAY

Office	Secrétariat	(33) 03 44 54 70 61
Pro shop	Pro-shop	(33) 03 44 54 70 61
Fax	Fax	(33) 03 44 54 72 57
Web	www.chateau_raray.com	
Situation	Situation	Paris, 54 km
Annual closure	Fermeture annuelle	no
Weekly closure	Fermeture hebdomadaire	tuesday

(mardi): 01/11 → 31/03

Fees main season Tarifs haute saison	18 holes	
	Week days Semaine	**We/Bank holidays** We/Férié
Individual Individuel	€ 43	€ 70
Couple Couple	€ 86	€ 135

Under 18 & students: € 20 / 30 (We) /
Special offers for Ladies & Seniors

Caddie Caddie no — **Electric Trolley** Chariot électrique no

Buggy Voiturette yes — **Clubs** Clubs yes

Credit cards Cartes de crédit
VISA - CB - Eurocard - MasterCard - AMEX

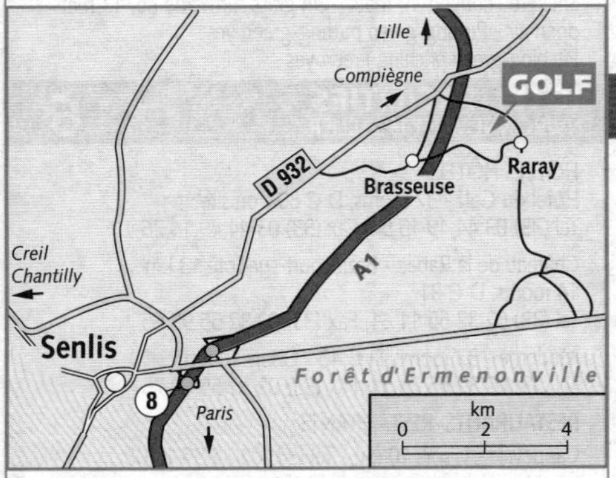

Access Accès : A1 Paris Lille, Exit (Sortie) No 8 Senlis → Creil/Chantilly, D932 → Compiègne, → Château de Raray
Map 3 on page 164 Carte 3 Page 164

GOLF COURSE 14/20
PARCOURS

Site	Site	
Maintenance	Entretien	
Architect	Architecte	Patrice Léglise
Type	Type	forest, open country
Relief	Relief	
Water in play	Eau en jeu	
Exp. to wind	Exposé au vent	
Trees in play	Arbres en jeu	

Scorecard Carte de score	**Chp.** Chp.	**Mens** Mess.	**Ladies** Da.
Length Long.	6145	5758	4906
Par	72	72	72
Slope system	133	129	124

Advised golfing ability Niveau de jeu recommandé — 0 12 24 36

Hcp required Handicap exigé 54

CLUB HOUSE & AMENITIES 7/10
CLUB HOUSE ET ANNEXES

Pro shop Pro-shop
Driving range Practice
Sheltered couvert 8 mats - On grass sur herbe yes - Putting-green putting-green yes - Pitching-green pitching green yes

HOTEL FACILITIES 5/10
ENVIRONNEMENT HOTELIER

HOTELS HÔTELS
Château de Raray - on site
10 rooms, D € 135
Tel (33) 03 44 54 59 30, Fax (33) 03 44 54 74 97

Auberge de Fontaine - Fontaine-Chaalis 11 km
7 rooms, D € 55
Tel (33) 03 44 54 20 22, Fax (33) 03 44 60 25 38

RESTAURANTS RESTAURANTS
Scaramouche - Senlis 6 km - Tel (33) 03 44 53 01 26

La Maison du Gourmet - Le Meux 12 km
Tel (33) 03 44 91 10 10

Bourgeois Gentilhomme - Senlis
Tel (33) 03 44 53 13 22

Rebetz

16 | 6 | 6

Ce parcours reconnu pour la qualité de son architecture évolue avec la croissance des plantations. Les zones de plaine constituant la majorité du parcours sont ainsi bien paysagées, et les trous mieux délimités, notamment avec les roughs. Relativement aisé par beau temps, il devient plus complexe avec le vent, souvent fréquent ici, comme sur un links, auxquels certains trous font référence. L'eau vient en jeu sur huit trous, complétant la diversité des obstacles. Les greens sont souvent très modelés, et les placements de drapeau peuvent en modifier considérablement l'attaque, mais leur qualité reste très élevée (notamment en hiver). Le budget était réduit mais l'architecte Jean-Pascal Fourès l'a magnifiquement utilisé : on s'étonne de ne pas trouver plus souvent sa signature en France. Le club-house est une véritable maison de campagne à l'ambiance chaleureuse. Les autres bâtiments autour d'une vaste cour intérieure ont été aménagés de manière très plaisante en chambres d'hôtel et appartements. Un ensemble achevé et accueillant.

This course, acknowledged for the excellence of its architecture, is improving in pace with the growth of plantation programmes. The areas of open countryside are slickly landscaped and holes have gained in individuality. Relatively easy in fine weather, the frequent wind makes playing golf a trickier business. Water is in play on eight holes and completes the diversity of the course's hazards. The greens are often well-contoured and pin-positions can considerably change the configuration of approach shots, but they remain consistently excellent putting surfaces (even in winter). Resources were limited, but architect Jean-Pascal Fourès has put all he had to magnificent use. It is surprising we do not see more of his work in France. The club-house is a genuine country-style manor. The other buildings around a huge inner courtyard have been developed very tastefully into hotel rooms and apartments. A complex now in its prime and extending a warm welcome to all.

Golf Club de Rebetz — 1988

Route de Noailles
F - 60240 CHAUMONT-EN-VEXIN

Office Secrétariat (33) 03 44 49 15 54
Pro shop Pro-shop (33) 03 44 49 15 54
Fax Fax (33) 03 44 49 14 26
Web www.rebetz.com
Situation Situation Paris, 67 km

Annual closure Fermeture annuelle no
Weekly closure Fermeture hebdomadaire no

Fees main season Tarifs haute saison — 18 holes

	Week days Semaine	We/Bank holidays We/Férié
Individual Individuel	€ 36	€ 62
Couple Couple	€ 72	€ 124

Friday (vendredi): € 22 / Under 18: € 21 / 38 (We)
Seniors: € 24

Caddie Caddie no **Electric Trolley** Chariot électrique yes

Buggy Voiturette yes **Clubs** Clubs yes

Credit cards Cartes de crédit
VISA - CB - Eurocard - MasterCard - AMEX

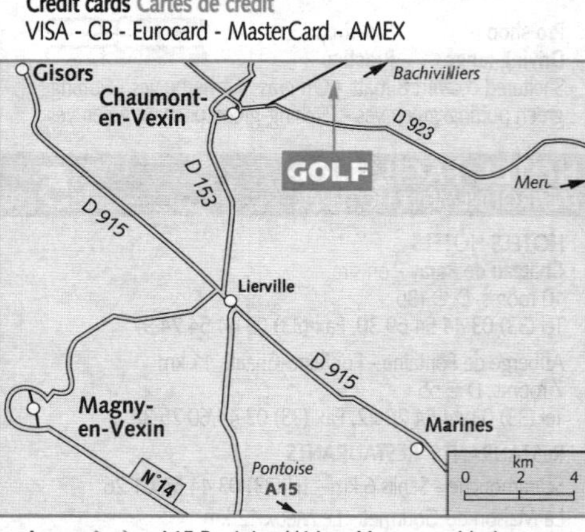

Access Accès : A15 Pontoise, N14 → Magny-en-Vexin, turn right on D153 → Chaumont-en-Vexin, turn right in Chaumont-en-Vexin → Golf

Map 3 on page 164 Carte 3 Page 164

GOLF COURSE — PARCOURS — 16/20

Site Site
Maintenance Entretien
Architect Architecte Jean-Pascal Fourès
Type Type parkland, open country
Relief Relief
Water in play Eau en jeu
Exp. to wind Exposé au vent
Trees in play Arbres en jeu

Scorecard Carte de score	Chp. Chp.	Mens Mess.	Ladies Da.
Length Long.	6409	5885	4999
Par	73	73	73
Slope system	127	120	122

Advised golfing ability 0 12 24 36
Niveau de jeu recommandé
Hcp required Handicap exigé no

CLUB HOUSE & AMENITIES — CLUB HOUSE ET ANNEXES — 6/10

Pro shop Pro-shop
Driving range Practice
Sheltered couvert 10 mats - On grass sur herbe no, 13 mats open air - Putting-green putting-green yes
Pitching-green pitching green yes

HOTEL FACILITIES — ENVIRONNEMENT HOTELIER — 6/10

HOTELS HÔTELS
Hôtel du Golf - 37 rooms, D € 80 - on site
Tel (33) 03 44 49 15 54, Fax (33) 03 44 49 14 26

Château de la Rapée - Bazincourt-sur-Epte 13 km
14 rooms, D € 81
Tel (33) 02 32 55 11 61, Fax (33) 02 32 55 95 65

Moderne - 33 rooms, D € 40 - Gisors 10 km
Tel (33) 02 32 55 23 51, Fax (33) 02 32 55 08 75

RESTAURANTS RESTAURANTS
Cappeville - Gisors 10 km - Tel (33) 02 35 55 11 08
La Pommeraie - Gisors 13 km - Tel (33) 02 32 55 11 61
Auberge de l'Atelier - Saint-Denis-le-Ferment
Tel (33) 02 32 55 24 00

Rochefort

14 | 6 | 4

C'est toujours un plaisir de retrouver ce type de parcours en forêt, car on ne peut plus guère en construire aujourd'hui. Il offre de magnifiques lumières au printemps et en automne, ajoutant à l'agrément du jeu sur un sol de sable et de terre de bruyère. Ce n'est sans doute pas un chef-d'œuvre absolu (il n'est pas exempt de monotonie), on peut l'apparenter à des "inland" tel que The Berkshire, mais il reste très plaisant à jouer malgré son manque de longueur, offrant une grande variété de coups, et nécessitant un bon travail des trajectoires de balle. Les obstacles sont essentiellement les arbres – souvent très dangereux car le parcours est assez étroit – mais aussi les bunkers de fairway et de green, et le relief parfois assez prononcé pour troubler dans le choix des clubs. Ce classique de Fred Hawtree a changé de propriétaire, on espère voir cette belle endormie se réveiller. Un modelage des greens généralement sans relief serait bienvenu, un practice et un club-house mieux adaptés aux golfeurs également.

It is always a pleasure to play this type of woodland course, which nowadays is virtually impossible to build. The light and reflections in spring and autumn are still a joy to behold, adding to the pleasure of playing on sandy sub-soil and moor-land. Rochefort is probably not an absolute masterpiece, but it does bear comparison with inland courses such as The Berkshire, and despite its lack of yards it is a very pleasant course to play, requiring a whole variety of shots and ball-control. The hazards are basically the trees, often dangerous as they lean over some pretty tight fairways. But don't forget the fairway and green-side bunkers, either, or the sharp relief which makes club selection harder than usual. This classic layout designed by Fred Hawtree has seen a change of proprietor and we look forward to a revival in its fortunes. Reshaping of the flat greens would be most welcome, as would a driving range and club-house better suited to golfers.

Rochefort Country Club — 1964

Route de la Bâte
F - 78730 ROCHEFORT-EN-YVELINES

Office	Secrétariat	(33) 01 30 41 31 81
Pro shop	Pro-shop	(33) 01 30 41 31 81
Fax	Fax	(33) 01 30 41 94 01
Web	www.club-albatros.com	
Situation	Situation	Paris, 45 km

Rambouillet (pop. 24 340), 15 km

Annual closure	Fermeture annuelle	no
Weekly closure	Fermeture hebdomadaire	no

Fees main season Tarifs haute saison	Week days Semaine	We/Bank holidays We/Férié
	Full day	
Individual Individuel	€ 42	€ 74
Couple Couple	€ 84	€ 148

Juniors: – 50%

Caddie Caddie no — **Electric Trolley** Chariot électrique yes

Buggy Voiturette yes — **Clubs** Clubs no

Credit cards Cartes de crédit
VISA - Eurocard - MasterCard - AMEX

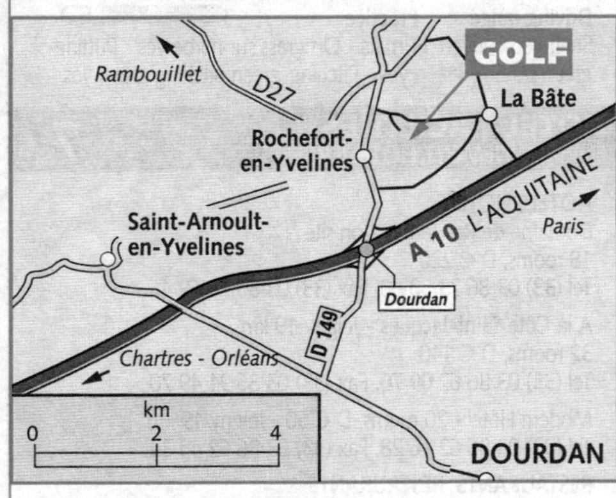

Access Accès : A10 Paris Chartres/Orléans, Exit (Sortie) Dourdan

Map 3 on page 164 Carte 3 Page 164

GOLF COURSE — PARCOURS — 14/20

Site	Site	
Maintenance	Entretien	
Architect	Architecte	Fred Hawtree
Type	Type	forest
Relief	Relief	
Water in play	Eau en jeu	
Exp. to wind	Exposé au vent	
Trees in play	Arbres en jeu	

Scorecard Carte de score	Chp. Chp.	Mens Mess.	Ladies Da.
Length Long.	5709	5442	4821
Par	71	71	71
Slope system	125	122	116

Advised golfing ability — Niveau de jeu recommandé: 0 12 24 36

Hcp required — Handicap exigé: 35

CLUB HOUSE & AMENITIES — CLUB HOUSE ET ANNEXES — 6/10

Pro shop — Pro-shop
Driving range — Practice

Sheltered couvert 6 mats - On grass sur herbe no, 10 mats open air - Putting-green putting-green yes
Pitching-green pitching green yes

HOTEL FACILITIES — ENVIRONNEMENT HOTELIER — 4/10

HOTELS HÔTELS

Abbaye les Vaux de Cernay - Cernay-la-Ville 11 km
57 rooms, D € 150
Tel (33) 01 34 85 23 00, Fax (33) 01 34 85 11 60

Blanche de Castille - 21 rooms, D € 80 - Dourdan 9 km
Tel (33) 01 60 81 19 10, Fax (33) 01 64 59 48 90

RESTAURANTS RESTAURANTS

Le Cheval Rouge - Rambouillet 15 km
Tel (33) 01 30 88 80 61

L'Escu de Rohan - Rochefort-en-Yvelines 2 km
Tel (33) 01 30 41 31 33

Auberge de l'Angélus - Dourdan 9 km
Tel (33) 01 64 59 83 72

Roncemay

15 | 7 | 7

Tracé principalement en forêt de chênes, hêtres et bouleaux (avec une demi-douzaine de trous de style links), et sur un terrain peu accidenté, ce parcours porte bien la signature de Jeremy Pern, pour le nombre et le dessin des bunkers, de fairways comme de défense des greens. Assez varié, le dessin exige tous les types de coups, offrant souvent un choix entre les approches roulées à la britannique et le "jeu de cible" à l'américaine. Les obstacles d'eau sont peu nombreux et pas trop dangereux, tous les niveaux de jeu peuvent donc cohabiter sur ce golf plaisant, dans un décor très agréable, que l'on jouera plus volontiers du printemps à l'automne. Les greens sont de bonne dimension, et très modelés : attention aux trois putts... Avec un hôtel de charme sur place, confortable, pourvu d'une bonne table dirigée par Marc Meneau (avec une étoile au Michelin), ce golf constitue un ensemble plein de charme, et une plaisante destination de week-end. Les non-golfeurs ne s'y ennuieront pas non plus.

This course is basically laid out through a forest of oak, beech and birch trees (plus half a dozen links holes) over flattish terrain. Looking at the number and design of bunkers, the fairways and greens, there is no doubt that this is a Jeremy Pern creation. The layout is varied enough to demand every shot in the book or even offer a choice between British "bump and run" shots and American-style target golf. Water hazards are few and far between and not too dangerous, so players of all abilities can play this pleasant course in a very attractive setting, with a preference from Spring to Autumn. The greens are large and sharply contoured, so watch out for the 3 putts. With a very charming and comfortable hotel on site serving excellent food now run by Marc Meneau (and boasting its first star in the Michelin Guide), this delightful set-up is a pleasant destination for a quiet weekend. Non-golfers will enjoy the site as well.

Domaine de Roncemay — 1991

F - 89110 CHASSY

Office	Secrétariat	(33) 03 86 73 50 50
Pro shop	Pro-shop	(33) 03 86 73 50 52
Fax	Fax	(33) 03 86 73 69 46
Web	www.roncemay.com	
Situation	Situation	Joigny (pop. 9 690), 19 km

Auxerre (pop. 38 810), 20 km

Annual closure	Fermeture annuelle	no
Weekly closure	Fermeture hebdomadaire	no

Fees main season Tarifs haute saison	Week days Semaine	We/Bank holidays We/Férié
		Full day
Individual Individuel	€ 48	€ 60
Couple Couple	€ 80	€ 100

Under 21 and students: € 30 / 40 (We)

Caddie Caddie no — **Electric Trolley** Chariot électrique yes

Buggy Voiturette yes — **Clubs** Clubs yes

Credit cards Cartes de crédit

VISA - CB - Eurocard - MasterCard - AMEX - DC

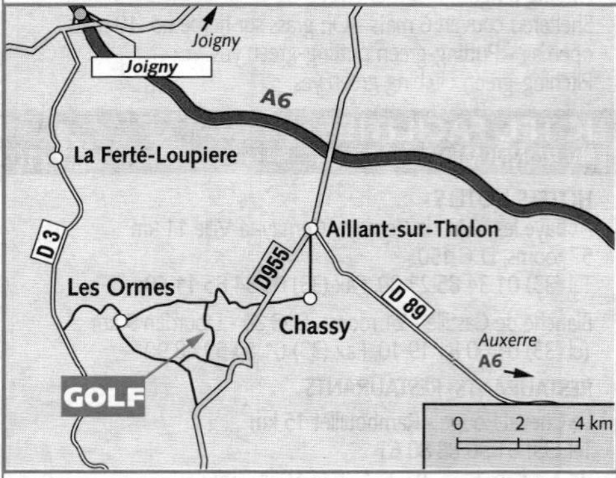

Access Accès : • Paris A6, Exit (Sortie) Joigny, → Golf
• Lyon A6, Exit (Sortie) Auxerre Nord → Aillant-sur-Tholon par D 89, → Golf

Map 3 on page 165 Carte 3 Page 165

GOLF COURSE — PARCOURS — 15/20

Site	Site	
Maintenance	Entretien	
Architect	Architecte	Jeremy Pern
Type	Type	forest, open country
Relief	Relief	
Water in play	Eau en jeu	
Exp. to wind	Exposé au vent	
Trees in play	Arbres en jeu	

Scorecard Carte de score	Chp. Chp.	Mens Mess.	Ladies Da.
Length Long.	6270	5702	4864
Par	72	72	72
Slope system	140	128	128

Advised golfing ability Niveau de jeu recommandé — 0 12 24 36

Hcp required Handicap exigé — 35

CLUB HOUSE & AMENITIES — CLUB HOUSE ET ANNEXES — 7/10

Pro shop	Pro-shop
Driving range	Practice

Sheltered couvert 11 mats - On grass sur herbe yes - Putting-green putting-green yes - Pitching-green pitching green yes

HOTEL FACILITIES — ENVIRONNEMENT HOTELIER — 7/10

HOTELS HÔTELS

Domaine de Roncemay - on site
18 rooms, D € 220
Tel (33) 03 86 73 50 50, Fax (33) 03 86 73 69 46

A la Côte Saint-Jacques - Joigny 19 km
32 rooms, D € 140
Tel (33) 03 86 62 09 70, Fax (33) 03 86 91 49 70

Modern'Hôtel - 20 rooms, D € 50 - Joigny 19 km
Tel (33) 03 86 62 16 28, Fax (33) 03 86 62 43 33

RESTAURANTS RESTAURANTS

Domaine de Roncemay - on site - Tel (33) 03 86 73 50 50
La Côte Saint-Jacques - Joigny 20 km - Tel (33) 03 86 62 09 70
Jean-Luc Barnabet - Auxerre 20 km - Tel (33) 03 86 51 68 88

Royal Mougins

16 | 8 | 8

Bob von Hagge a bien utilisé un espace limité et dessiné un parcours excitant et spectaculaire, qui ne laisse personne indifférent. Certains joueurs discutent le "modernisme" du parcours comme son étroitesse, mais celle-ci est plus visuelle que réelle: certes, de nombreux mouvements de terrain animent de manière spectaculaire les limites de fairway, mais ils ramènent la balle en jeu. Ici, il faut faire des choix de clubs réfléchis, et jouer avec précision,au moins pour éviter les obstacles d'eau qui ponctuent ce parcours de longueur raisonnable. A défaut de s'exprimer avec le driver, les frappeurs peuvent jouer leurs coups de départ avec un bois 3 ou un long fer, mais les manieurs de balle s'amusent davantage : la plupart du temps, les seconds coups sont joués avec des petits et moyens fers. Le club-house est très confortable. Avec un nouveau propriétaire, des changements sont apportés au parcours, nous attendrons pour en juger. Le prix du green-fee impose un entretien immaculé...

Bob von Hagge has made very intelligent use of limited space and created an exciting and spectacular course, with no room for indifference. Royal Mougins is well worth a close visit if only to judge for yourself. Some players question the course's modernism and tightness. We agree that the slanting terrain can sometimes result in the ball doing weird things at the edges of the fairway, but it also helps bring the thing back into play. This is a course where you have to think before choosing your club and hit it straight, if only to avoid the water hazards dotted around the 18 holes. Rather than pull out their driver, big-hitters can easily tee off with a 3-wood or long iron to stay in the fairway but benders of the ball will have more fun: approach shots are played mostly with short or mid-irons. With a new proprietor, changes are being made to the course so we will withhold judgment. The price of playing here certainly calls for immaculate green-keeping.

Royal Mougins Golf Club — 1993

424, avenue du Roi
F - 06250 MOUGINS

Office Secrétariat (33) 04 92 92 49 69
Pro shop Pro-shop (33) 04 92 92 49 79
Fax Fax (33) 04 92 92 49 72
Web www.royalmougins.fr
Situation Situation Cannes, 10 km
Grasse (pop. 41 390), 20 km
Annual closure Fermeture annuelle no
Weekly closure Fermeture hebdomadaire no
Fees main season Tarifs haute saison 18 holes

	Week days Semaine	We/Bank holidays We/Férié
Individual Individuel	€ 160*	€ 200*
Couple Couple	€ 320*	€ 400*

* GF + practice + buggy

Caddie Caddie no — **Electric Trolley** Chariot électrique yes
Buggy Voiturette yes — **Clubs** Clubs yes
Credit cards Cartes de crédit
VISA - Eurocard - MasterCard - AMEX - DC

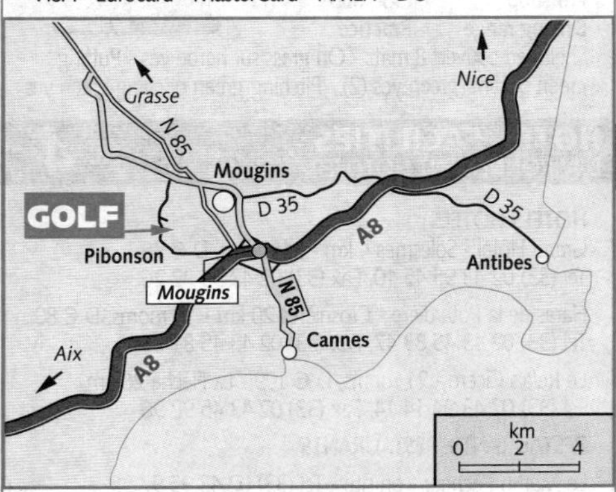

Access Accès : A8 sortie Cannes-Grasse → Grasse, 3e sortie Mougins Pibonson, Saint-Martin
Map 14 on page 187 Carte 14 Page 187

GOLF COURSE — PARCOURS 16/20

Site Site
Maintenance Entretien
Architect Architecte Robert von Hagge
Type Type forest, hilly
Relief Relief
Water in play Eau en jeu
Exp. to wind Exposé au vent
Trees in play Arbres en jeu

Scorecard Carte de score	Chp. Chp.	Mens Mess.	Ladies Da.
Length Long.	6004	5697	4482
Par	71	71	71
Slope system	141	144	129

Advised golfing ability Niveau de jeu recommandé 0 12 24 36
Hcp required Handicap exigé 30

CLUB HOUSE & AMENITIES — CLUB HOUSE ET ANNEXES 8/10

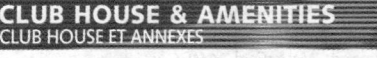

Pro shop Pro-shop
Driving range Practice
Sheltered couvert 5 mats - On grass sur herbe yes - Putting-green putting-green yes - Pitching-green pitching green yes

HOTEL FACILITIES — ENVIRONNEMENT HOTELIER 8/10

HOTELS HÔTELS
Mas Candille - 40 rooms, D € 365 - Mougins 3 km
Tel (33) 04 92 28 43 43, Fax (33) 04 92 28 43 40
Hôtel de Mougins - 51 rooms, D € 240 - Mougins 3 km
Tel (33) 04 92 92 17 07, Fax (33) 04 92 92 17 08
Le Manoir de l'Etang - 20 rooms, D € 160 - Mougins 3 km
Tel (33) 04 92 28 36 00, Fax (33) 04 92 28 36 10

RESTAURANTS RESTAURANTS
Les Muscadins - Mougins 3 km - Tel (33) 04 92 28 28 28
Le Feu Follet - Mougins 3 km - Tel (33) 04 93 90 15 78
La Ferme de Mougins - Mougins 3 km
Tel (33) 04 93 90 03 74

Sablé-Solesmes *La Forêt/La Rivière* 16 | 7 | 4

Entre Angers et Le Mans, cet ensemble ambitieux de 27 trous s'est imposé dans le groupe de tête des parcours français, alors que l'on ne s'attendait pas à trouver des tracés d'une telle qualité en pleine campagne de la vallée de la Sarthe, à l'écart des routes traditionnelles du golf. En limite de la Forêt de Pincé, Michel Gayon a dessiné trois 9 trous combinables de longueur raisonnable et le terrain moyennement accidenté permet de les jouer tous en une seule journée. Sur la combinaison classique "La Forêt-La Rivière", l'eau intervient sur une dizaine de trous, sans être trop effrayante pour autant. "La Cascade" revendique un caractère plus écossais, avec beaucoup de bosses, de bunkers d'herbe et de sable, mais aussi un peu d'eau, comme au 8. On éprouve ici une très agréable impression d'espace et de calme, propice à la concentration que réclame ce golf à connaître. Cet ensemble de grande qualité, désormais bien élaboré, soigne sa finition, avec des plantations et une floraison splendide au printemps.

Between Angers and Le Mans, this ambitious 27-hole resort has edged its way into the group of leading French courses at a time when no-one was expecting such a great layout out in Sarthe Valley country so far off the traditional golfing path. On the edge of the Pincé forest, Michel Gayon designed three combinable 9-hole courses of reasonable length and on flattish terrain all three can be played in one day. On the classic "Forêt-Rivière" combination, water is present on ten holes but never too intimidating. "La Cascade" is more Scottish in nature, with an array of sand-hills, grass- and sand-bunkers and also a little water, like on the 8th. Here you get a very pleasant feeling of space and of tranquillity conducive to the concentration required when playing a course like this. A club that is well worth discovering and now an elaborate complex which is looking smarter than ever with plantations and splendid flowers in the Spring.

Golf de Sablé-Solesmes — 1991

Domaine de l'Outinière, route de Pincé
F - 72300 SABLE-SUR-SARTHE

Office	Secrétariat	(33) 02 43 95 28 78
Pro shop	Pro-shop	(33) 02 43 95 28 78
Fax	Fax	(33) 02 43 92 39 05
Web	www.golf-sable-solesmes.com	
Situation	Situation	La Flèche, 26 km

Le Mans (pop. 145 500), 59 km

Annual closure	Fermeture annuelle	no
Weekly closure	Fermeture hebdomadaire	no
Fees main season	Tarifs haute saison	18 holes

	Week days / Semaine	We/Bank holidays / We/Férié
Individual Individuel	€ 46	€ 60
Couple Couple	€ 84	€ 108

Under 18: € 24 / 31 (We) / Students: € 33 / 43 (We)

Caddie Caddie on request **Electric Trolley** Chariot électrique yes

Buggy Voiturette yes **Clubs** Clubs yes

Credit cards Cartes de crédit
VISA - Eurocard - MasterCard - AMEX

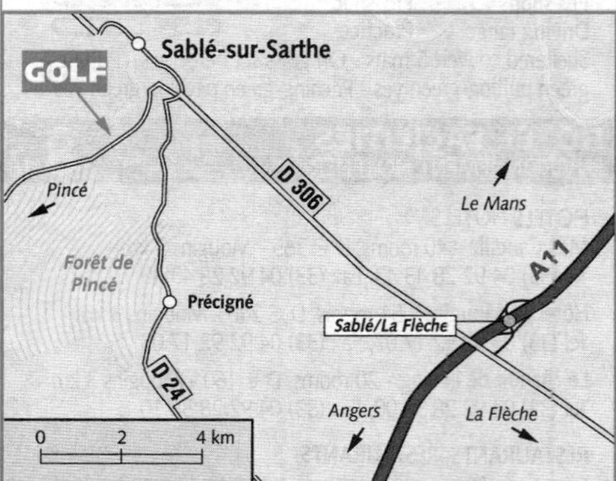

Access Accès : Le Mans-Angers, A11 Exit (Sortie) La Flèche, turn right on D306 → Sablé-sur-Sarthe
Map 6 on page 171 Carte 6 Page 171

GOLF COURSE — PARCOURS 16/20

Site	Site	
Maintenance	Entretien	
Architect	Architecte	Michel Gayon
Type	Type	open country
Relief	Relief	
Water in play	Eau en jeu	
Exp. to wind	Exposé au vent	
Trees in play	Arbres en jeu	

Scorecard Carte de score	Chp. Chp.	Mens Mess.	Ladies Da.
Length Long.	6189	5737	4782
Par	72	72	72
Slope system	137	133	125

Advised golfing ability 0 12 24 36
Niveau de jeu recommandé
Hcp required Handicap exigé 35

CLUB HOUSE & AMENITIES — CLUB HOUSE ET ANNEXES 7/10

Pro shop	Pro-shop
Driving range	Practice

Sheltered couvert 8 mats - On grass sur herbe yes - Putting-green putting-green yes (2) - Pitching-green pitching green yes

HOTEL FACILITIES — ENVIRONNEMENT HOTELIER 4/10

HOTELS HÔTELS

Grand Hôtel - Solesmes 4 km - 34 rooms, D € 96
Tel (33) 02 43 95 45 10, Fax (33) 02 43 95 22 26

Haras de la Potardière - Crosnières 20 km - 18 rooms, D € 80
Tel (33) 02 43 45 83 47, Fax (33) 02 43 45 81 06

Le Relais Cicero - 21 rooms, D € 109 - La Flèche 26 km
Tel (33) 02 43 94 14 14, Fax (33) 02 43 45 98 96

RESTAURANTS RESTAURANTS

Le Martin Pêcheur - on site - Tel (33) 02 43 95 97 55

Hostellerie Saint-Martin - Sablé 6 km - Tel (33) 02 43 95 00 03

Le Moulin des 4 Saisons - La Flèche 26 km
Tel (33) 02 43 45 12 12

Saint-Cloud *Vert*

14	8	7

La proximité immédiate de Paris a beaucoup contribué à la réputation de Saint-Cloud, mais aussi à la difficulté d'y jouer. A côté du petit parcours "Jaune," dont une moitié des trous au moins ne manque pas d'intérêt, le "Vert" a reçu de nombreuses compétitions internationales, mais sa longueur peut paraître aujourd'hui insuffisante. Sa technicité en fait la relative difficulté. Il a été dessiné par Harry S. Colt, mais a fait l'objet d'aménagements qui ont souvent fait perdre de vue l'original et donnent parfois l'impression d'un style hybride, en particulier pour le dessin des bunkers, avec même quelques pot-bunkers peu à leur place ici. Très agréable dans son déroulement, avec des vues superbes sur Paris, pas trop accidenté, ornementé d'une végétation somptueuse (surtout en automne !), Saint-Cloud reste l'une des jolies oasis de la région, à déguster quand les membres sont en vacances. Il fait l'objet actuellement de drainages importants qui devraient porter rapidement leurs fruits.

Being the closest club to Paris has done much for its reputation. Alongside the smaller "Jaune" layout, of which at least one half of the holes are good golfing, the "Vert" course has hosted any number of international tournaments, but its length may appear a little on the short side. The difficulty here has always been the technical side to the layout. It was designed by Harry Colt but has been restyled in a variety of ways which often mask the original layout and sometimes give the impression of a hybrid style. There are even a number of pot-bunkers that seem rather out of place here. Unfolding very pleasantly with some superb views over Paris, not too hilly and adorned with some sumptuous flowers and plants, Saint Cloud remains one of the region's golfing oases. A great place to enjoy on summer evenings when members are away on holiday. Extensive drainage work is ongoing and should quickly prove a welcome addition.

Golf de Saint-Cloud — 1912

60, rue du 19 Janvier
F - 92380 GARCHES

Office	Secrétariat	(33) 01 47 01 01 85
Pro shop	Pro-shop	(33) 01 47 41 01 45
Fax	Fax	(33) 01 47 01 19 57
Web	www.golfsaintcloud.com	
Situation	Situation	Paris, 15 km
Annual closure	Fermeture annuelle	no
Weekly closure	Fermeture hebdomadaire	monday/lundi

Fees main season Tarifs haute saison	18 holes	
	Week days Semaine	We/Bank holidays We/Férié
Individual Individuel	€ 90*	€ 120*
Couple Couple	€ 180*	€ 240*

* with a member (avec un membre)

Caddie Caddie on request **Electric Trolley** Chariot électrique yes

Buggy Voiturette no **Clubs** Clubs yes

Credit cards Cartes de crédit
VISA - CB - Eurocard - MasterCard

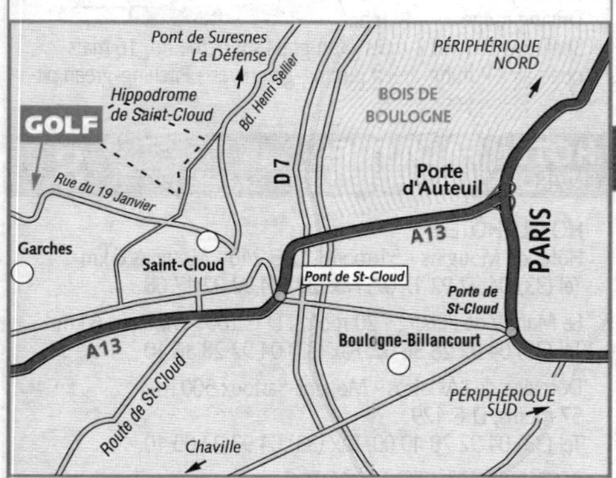

Access Accès : Paris Porte Maillot, Bois de Boulogne → Suresnes. Pont de Suresnes, Bld H. Sellier, → Hippodrome St Cloud. Turn right into Rue du 19 janvier. → Golf St Cucufa.
Map 15 on page 188 Carte 15 Page 188

GOLF COURSE — PARCOURS — 14/20

Site	Site	
Maintenance	Entretien	
Architect	Architecte	Harry S. Colt
Type	Type	parkland
Relief	Relief	
Water in play	Eau en jeu	
Exp. to wind	Exposé au vent	
Trees in play	Arbres en jeu	

Scorecard Carte de score	Chp. Chp.	Mens Mess.	Ladies Da.
Length Long.	5939	5708	4967
Par	72	72	72
Slope system	138	131	123

Advised golfing ability Niveau de jeu recommandé — 0 12 24 36

Hcp required Handicap exigé — 24 Men, 28 Ladies

CLUB HOUSE & AMENITIES — CLUB HOUSE ET ANNEXES — 8/10

Pro shop Pro-shop
Driving range Practice
Sheltered couvert 46 mats - On grass sur herbe no - Putting-green putting-green yes (2) - Pitching-green pitching green yes (2)

HOTEL FACILITIES — ENVIRONNEMENT HOTELIER — 7/10

HOTELS HÔTELS

Villa Henri IV - 36 rooms, D € 86 - Saint-Cloud 4 km
Tel (33) 01 46 02 59 30, Fax (33) 01 49 11 11 02

Quorum - Saint-Cloud 4 km
58 rooms, D € 89
Tel (33) 01 47 71 22 33, Fax (33) 01 46 02 75 64

Concorde La Fayette - Paris Porte Maillot 10 km
950 rooms, D € 338
Tel (33) 01 40 68 50 68, Fax (33) 01 40 68 50 43

RESTAURANTS RESTAURANTS

Guy Savoy - Paris 17è 12 km - Tel (33) 01 43 80 40 61
La Poularde - Vaucresson 5 km - Tel (33) 01 47 41 13 47
Michel Rostang - Paris 17è 12 km - Tel (33) 01 47 63 40 77

Saint Donat

16 | 7 | 8

L'un des premiers parcours de l'époque "moderne" sur la Côte d'Azur, longtemps marquée par les britanniques. Robert Trent Jones Jr lui a donné des contours très variés, utilisant avec intelligence la végétation existante, les reliefs et modelant sans excès les espaces plus plats. Ce qui donne un dessin très précis, où les méandres d'une petite rivière viennent en jeu sur une bonne demi-douzaine de trous. De nombreux bunkers et des bouquets d'arbres (notamment de très beaux vieux chênes) constituent des obstacles parfois préoccupants, souvent à proximité de greens bien modelés et variés. Ici, il faut s'appuyer sur la technique, la sagesse dans le choix de club et pas sur la longueur, mais les joueurs de tous niveaux peuvent y évoluer, s'ils ne sont pas trop ambitieux. Les dix premiers trous sont assez plats, le retour est accidenté, avec quelques trous très spectaculaires, mais assez "tricky". Un parcours assez facile à marcher en condition physique normale, mais les chemins de voiturettes sont bienvenus. L'entretien n'est pas très régulier.

One of the first "modern-age" courses on the French Riviera, a region long marked by British-style architecture. Robert Trent Jones Jr. moulded Saint Donat into a variety of shapes, making intelligent use of existing vegetation and topography and contouring the flatter areas without ever going over the top. The result is a very precise layout, where the meanders of a small river come into play on half a dozen or so holes. A good number of bunkers and groups of trees form some distinctly worrying hazards often placed close to some well-designed and varied greens. Emphasis should be on technique and caution in the choice of club not on length, although players of all levels can enjoy a round of golf here as long as they are not over-ambitious. The first ten holes are rather flat and the back eight hilly encounters with a few spectacular but rather tricky holes. A course that is easy enough to walk for the average able-bodied golfer but the cart-paths are most welcome.

Golf de Saint Donat — 1993

270, route de Cannes
F - 06130 PLAN-DE-GRASSE

Office Secrétariat (33) 04 93 09 76 60
Pro shop Pro-shop (33) 04 93 09 76 60
Fax Fax (33) 04 93 09 76 63
Web www.golfsaintdonat.com
Situation Situation Cannes (pop. 68 670), 18 km
Grasse (pop. 41 390), 2 km

Annual closure Fermeture annuelle — no
Weekly closure Fermeture hebdomadaire — no

Fees main season Tarifs haute saison — 18 holes

	Week days Semaine	We/Bank holidays We/Férié
Individual Individuel	€ 67	€ 67
Couple Couple	€ 134	€ 134

Juniors: € 36 / Students: € 47

Caddie Caddie on request **Electric Trolley** Chariot électrique yes
Buggy Voiturette yes **Clubs** Clubs yes
Credit cards Cartes de crédit
VISA - CB - Eurocard - MasterCard - AMEX - DC

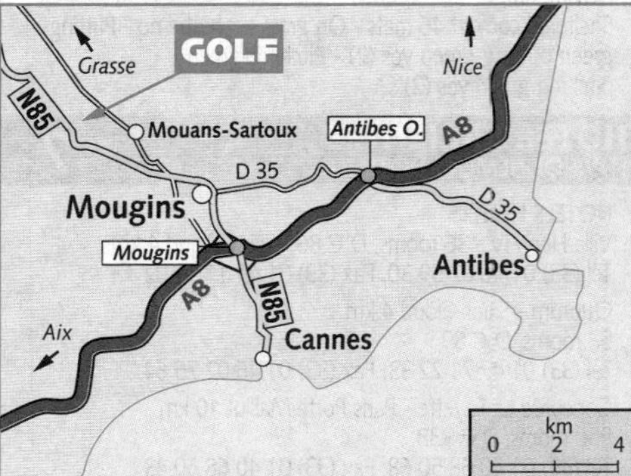

Access Accès : • Grasse N85 → Plan-de-Grasse
• Cannes, Motorway → N85 Grasse,
Mouans-Sartoux, → Golf de Saint Donat
Map 14 on page 187 Carte 14 Page 187

GOLF COURSE — PARCOURS — 16/20

Site Site
Maintenance Entretien
Architect Architecte — R. Trent Jones Jr
Type Type — hilly, parkland
Relief Relief
Water in play Eau en jeu
Exp. to wind Exposé au vent
Trees in play Arbres en jeu

Scorecard Carte de score	Chp. Chp.	Mens Mess.	Ladies Da.
Length Long.	6031	5558	4535
Par	71	71	71
Slope system	129	124	121

Advised golfing ability Niveau de jeu recommandé — 0 12 24 36
Hcp required Handicap exigé — 36

CLUB HOUSE & AMENITIES — CLUB HOUSE ET ANNEXES — 7/10

Pro shop Pro-shop
Driving range Practice
Sheltered couvert 8 mats - On grass sur herbe no, 16 mats open air - Putting-green putting-green yes - Pitching-green pitching green yes

HOTEL FACILITIES — ENVIRONNEMENT HOTELIER — 8/10

HOTELS HÔTELS
Hôtel de Mougins - 51 rooms, D € 240 - Mougins 6 km
Tel (33) 04 92 92 17 07, Fax (33) 04 92 92 17 08

Le Manoir de l'Etang - 20 rooms, D € 160 - Mougins 6 km
Tel (33) 04 92 28 36 00, Fax (33) 04 92 28 36 10

Domaine de l'Albatros - Mouans-Sartoux 500 m
57 rooms, D € 129
Tel (33) 04 92 28 40 00, Fax (33) 04 92 92 05 10

RESTAURANTS RESTAURANTS
Bastide Saint Antoine - Grasse 2 km - Tel (33) 04 93 70 94 94
Les Muscadins - Mougins 6 km - Tel (33) 04 92 28 28 28
La Toque Blanche - Magagnosc 8 km - Tel (33) 04 93 36 20 64

Saint-Endréol

15	7	4

Ce parcours épouse les reliefs d'un paysage typique de Provence, d'où quelques greens aveugles, qui auraient pu être en partie évités. Certains coups forcément hasardeux (vers le green du 6 !) atténuent un peu le plaisir que l'on éprouve sur ce golf en pleine nature, dont le relief accentué incite à jouer en voiturette. Parce que la tactique de jeu n'est pas évidente à assimiler, parce qu'il faut connaître le parcours pour bien évaluer les distances, parce que la chance joue ici un rôle important, on s'amusera beaucoup plus en match-play qu'en stroke play. Avec plusieurs trous spectaculaires et pour la beauté de son environnement, Saint-Endréol vaut incontestablement le détour. On jouera le 17 en par 5, comme il a été dessiné, et tant pis pour la carte officielle ! L'hôtel sur place, le spa et un immobilier de standing représentent d'importants investissements, et témoignent d'une politique très active. On souhaite aussi que l'entretien du parcours reste constamment impeccable, surtout en hiver.

This course hugs the contours of typical Provence style countryside, whence a number of blind holes which in part could have been avoided. Certain necessarily hazardous shots (to the 6th green for example) tend to dampen the enjoyment of this course right out in the country where hilly terrain makes a buggy a wise decision. This is a match-play course rather than a course for stroke-play, simply because the tactics needed here are not always obvious, because you need to know the course to evaluate distances, and because luck plays a bigger role than usual. With several spectacular holes and a beautiful setting, Saint-Endréol is most certainly well worth the visit. The 17th should be played as a par 5, the way it was designed to. The development of an on-site hotel and high-standing real estate programme are significant investments and testify to a very active policy from the club. We would also like to see green-keeping consistently immaculate, especially in Winter.

Golf de Saint-Endréol — 1992

Route de Bagnols-en-Forêt
F - 83920 LA MOTTE-EN-PROVENCE

Office Secrétariat (33) 04 94 51 89 89
Pro shop Pro-shop (33) 04 94 51 89 89
Fax Fax (33) 04 94 51 89 90
Web www.st-endreol.com
Situation Situation Draguignan, 10 km
Saint-Raphaël (pop. 26 620), 18 km

Annual closure Fermeture annuelle — no
Weekly closure Fermeture hebdomadaire — no

Fees main season Tarifs haute saison	18 holes	
	Week days Semaine	**We/Bank holidays** We/Férié
Individual Individuel	€ 68	€ 68
Couple Couple	€ 136	€ 136

Under 21: – 50% / GF after 17:30, € 55

Caddie Caddie no — **Electric Trolley** Chariot électrique no
Buggy Voiturette yes — **Clubs** Clubs yes
Credit cards Cartes de crédit
VISA - CB - Eurocard - MasterCard - AMEX

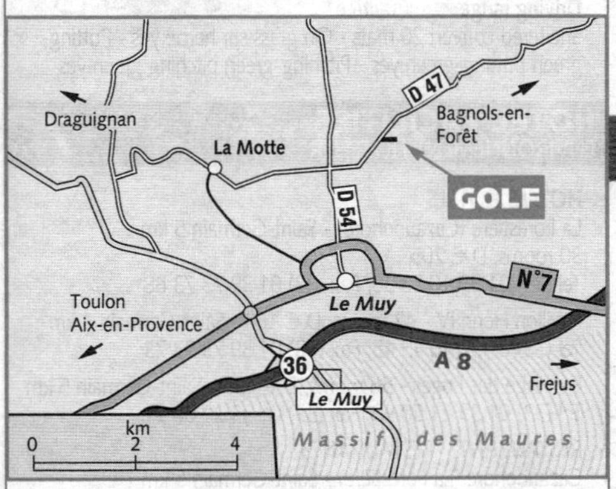

Access Accès : Saint-Raphaël, N7, Exit (Sortie) Le Muy, D54 → La Motte-en- Provence, → Golf
Map 14 on page 187 Carte 14 Page 187

GOLF COURSE — PARCOURS 15/20

Site	Site	
Maintenance	Entretien	
Architect	Architecte	Michel Gayon
Type	Type	hilly, forest
Relief	Relief	
Water in play	Eau en jeu	
Exp. to wind	Exposé au vent	
Trees in play	Arbres en jeu	

Scorecard Carte de score	**Chp.** Chp.	**Mens** Mess.	**Ladies** Da.
Length Long.	6219	5945	4624
Par	72	72	72
Slope system	142	145	128

Advised golfing ability Niveau de jeu recommandé — 0 12 24 36
Hcp required Handicap exigé — 30 (morning)

CLUB HOUSE & AMENITIES — CLUB HOUSE ET ANNEXES 7/10

Pro shop Pro-shop
Driving range Practice
Sheltered couvert 7 mats - On grass sur herbe no, 8 mats open air - Putting-green putting-green yes - Pitching-green pitching green yes

HOTEL FACILITIES — ENVIRONNEMENT HOTELIER 4/10

HOTELS HÔTELS
Domaine de Saint-Endréol - 35 rooms, D € 205 - on site
Tel (33) 04 94 51 89 80, Fax (33) 04 94 51 89 81
Le Logis du Guetteur - 13 rooms, D € 130 - Les Arcs 6 km
Tel (33) 04 94 99 51 10, Fax (33) 04 94 99 51 29
Les Gorges de Pennafort - 16 rooms, D € 185 - Callas 11 km
Tel (33) 04 94 76 66 51, Fax (33) 04 94 76 67 23

RESTAURANTS RESTAURANTS
Les Pignatelles - La Motte 5 km - Tel (33) 04 94 70 25 70
Le Logis du Guetteur - Les Arcs 6 km - Tel (33) 04 94 99 51 10
Les Gorges de Pennafort - Callas 11 km
Tel (33) 04 94 76 66 51

Saint-Germain

17 | 7 | 7

6122 mètres, c'est bien suffisant pour 99,99 % des golfeurs, qui ont souvent du mal à y jouer leur handicap ! Il faut un jeu complet, et d'abord ne pas se laisser endormir par la séduction du lieu. C'est ici la quintessence de l'architecture britannique, sur un terrain plat et très ramassé, avec un très bon rythme d'enchaînement des trous et des difficultés, quelques reliefs subtils, notamment en approche des greens et sur ceux-ci, généralement très vastes. Les trous sont variés, et les manieurs de balle prendront vite l'ascendant sur les frappeurs à l'aveugle. Les obstacles essentiels sont les arbres, majestueux mais pas oppressants, et les bunkers, souvent de formes très belles et typiques des idées stratégiques de l'architecte. Pour modifier quelques détails des trous dans l'esprit de Colt, le club envoie régulièrement à Edimbourg un adjoint au green-keeper, pour qu'il approfondisse ses connaissances. Et si l'on ajoute un bon petit 9 trous et une excellente zone d'entraînement, Saint-Germain reste l'un des golfs les plus attachants de la région parisienne.

The course's 6,734 yards are more than enough for 99.9% of golfers. You need an all-round game to score well here and don't let the balmy appeal of the site distract you from the task at hand. We see it rather as the quintessence of British-style design over flat and very squat landscape. There is a remarkable continuity between holes and difficulties plus some subtly-shaped terrain, particularly when approaching or actually on the generally very large greens. Holes are very varied and shapers of the ball will quickly get the better of the "smash-it-as-far-as-you-can" boys. The basic hazards are trees, majestic enough but not too obtrusive, and bunkers, often beautifully shaped and typical of the architect's strategic thinking. To alter some of the course's finer details in his spirit, the club regularly sends an assistant green-keeper to Edinburgh to carry on learning what it is all about. With a 9-holer and excellent practice area, it is one of the most likeable courses around Paris.

Golf de Saint-Germain — 1922

Route de Poissy
F - 78100 SAINT-GERMAIN-EN-LAYE

Office Secrétariat (33) 01 39 10 30 30
Pro shop Pro-shop (33) 01 39 73 87 48
Fax Fax (33) 01 39 10 30 31
Web www.golfstgermain.org
Situation Situation Paris, 26 km
Saint-Germain (pop. 39 320), 4 km

Annual closure Fermeture annuelle 25/12→1/1
Weekly closure Fermeture hebdomadaire monday/lundi

Fees main season Tarifs haute saison 18 holes

	Week days / Semaine	We/Bank holidays / We/Férié
Individual Individuel	€ 80	*
Couple Couple	€ 160	*

* We : only members and guests (membres et leurs invités)
Under 21 and tudents: € 40

Caddie Caddie on request **Electric Trolley** Chariot électrique yes
Buggy Voiturette no **Clubs** Clubs yes
Credit cards Cartes de crédit
VISA - CB - Eurocard - MasterCard - AMEX

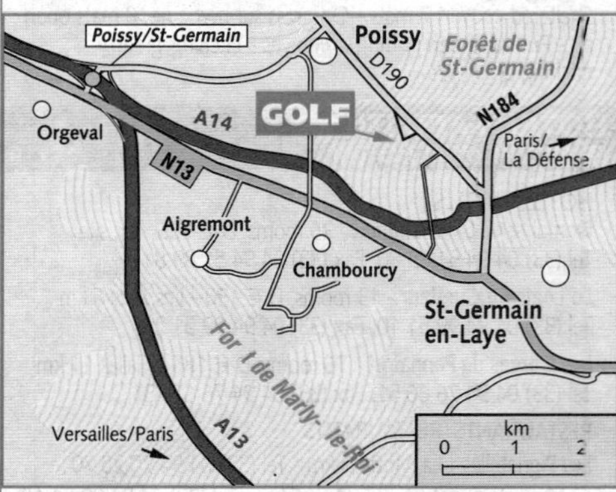

Access Accès : Paris A13, Exit (Sortie) → Saint-Germain. N13 → Poissy, N184 then D190 → Poissy. Golf on left hand side.
Map 15 on page 188 Carte 15 Page 188

GOLF COURSE — PARCOURS — 17/20

Site	Site	
Maintenance	Entretien	
Architect	Architecte	Harry S. Colt
Type	Type	forest
Relief	Relief	
Water in play	Eau en jeu	
Exp. to wind	Exposé au vent	
Trees in play	Arbres en jeu	

Scorecard Carte de score	Chp. / Chp.	Mens / Mess.	Ladies / Da.
Length Long.	6122	5810	5224
Par	72	72	72
Slope system	136	128	131

Advised golfing ability 0 12 24 36
Niveau de jeu recommandé
Hcp required Handicap exigé 24 Men, 28 Ladies

CLUB HOUSE & AMENITIES — CLUB HOUSE ET ANNEXES — 7/10

Pro shop Pro-shop
Driving range Practice
Sheltered couvert 20 mats - On grass sur herbe yes - Putting-green putting-green yes - Pitching-green pitching green yes

HOTEL FACILITIES — ENVIRONNEMENT HOTELIER — 7/10

HOTELS HÔTELS
La Forestière (Cazaudehore) - Saint-Germain 5 km
30 rooms, D € 205
Tel (33) 01 39 10 38 38, Fax (33) 01 39 73 73 88

Pavillon Henri IV - 42 rooms, D € 160 - Saint-Germain 4 km
Tel (33) 01 39 10 15 15, Fax (33) 01 39 73 93 73

Ermitage des Loges - 56 rooms, D € 135 - Saint-Germain 5 km
Tel (33) 01 39 21 50 90, Fax (33) 01 39 21 50 91

RESTAURANTS RESTAURANTS
Cazaudehore (La Forestière) - Saint-Germain 5 km
Tel (33) 01 30 61 64 64

La Feuillantine - Saint-Germain 4 km - Tel (33) 01 34 51 04 24

Top Model - St-Germain 5 km - Tel (33) 01 34 51 77 78

Saint-Jean-de-Monts

15	6	5

Ce parcours avait démontré que l'on peut faire de bons parcours avec de petits budgets, une bonne intelligence du jeu et du terrain... Situé en bord de mer, son dessin est un hommage à l'architecture de links, mais la dizaine de trous situés dans une forêt de pins maritimes et de chênes verts restent trop étroits pour que l'on s'y exprime librement. Les fairways très modelés, les greens souvent à double ou même triple plateau suivent les reliefs des dunes, dans un souci évident de préserver la nature. Contraint par une superficie réduite, l'architecte Yves Bureau insiste davantage sur la précision que sur la longueur, mais une solide frappe n'est pourtant pas inutile quand le vent rend ce parcours très difficile : alors, les passages boisés constituent un abri illusoire, car il y tourbillonne volontiers. L'entretien n'est pas tout à fait manucuré, mais le parcours est jouable sans problème toute l'année, et ses tarifs raisonnables en font toujours l'un des meilleurs rapports qualité/prix de France.

This course proved that with a low budget, smart golfing brain and intelligent use of terrain good courses are possible. Laid out along the sea, this is a homage to links golf, even though the ten or so holes which wind their way through a forest of maritime pines and oak trees are too tight to really swing freely. The highly contoured fairways and two- or even three-tiered greens hug the relief of the dunes with an obvious preference for preserving the natural landscape. Restricted by lack of space, architect Yves Bureau has emphasized more the need for precision rather than length, although a solid hit comes in handy when the wind makes this a very tough course even in the woods, where it seems to swirl in all directions. The British certainly feel at home here. Green-keeping is not quite top-notch but Saint-Jean-de-Monts is easily playable all year and green fees are very reasonable and continue to make this one of the best values for money in France.

Golf de Saint-Jean-de-Monts — 1988

Avenue des Pays-de-la-Loire
F - 85160 SAINT-JEAN-DE-MONTS

Office Secrétariat (33) 02 51 58 82 73
Pro shop Pro-shop (33) 02 51 58 82 73
Fax Fax (33) 02 51 59 18 32
Web www.golfy.fr
Situation Situation Nantes, 70 km
Challans (pop. 14 200), 17 km

Annual closure Fermeture annuelle — no

Weekly closure Fermeture hebdomadaire — no
Tuesday & wednesday (mardi/mercredi): restaurant closed from 01/11 to 15/04

Fees main season Tarifs haute saison	18 holes	
	Week days Semaine	**We/Bank holidays** We/Férié
Individual Individuel	€ 58	€ 58
Couple Couple	€ 116	€ 116

Students (under 25): – 50%

Caddie Caddie no — **Electric Trolley** Chariot électrique yes
Buggy Voiturette yes — **Clubs** Clubs yes
Credit cards Cartes de crédit
VISA - CB - Eurocard - MasterCard

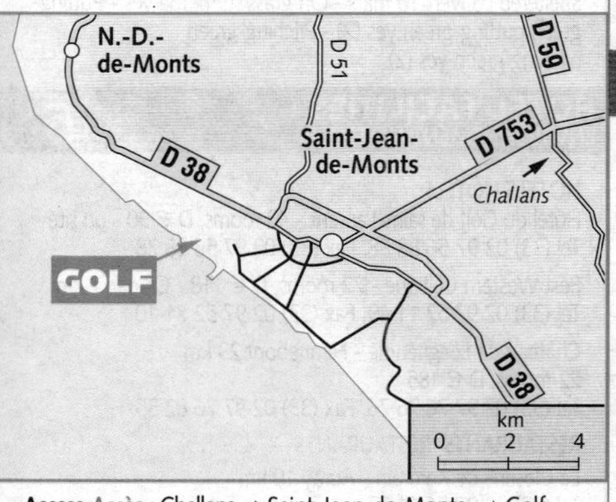

Access Accès : Challans → Saint-Jean-de-Monts, → Golf
Map 6 on page 170 Carte 6 Page 170

GOLF COURSE — PARCOURS — 15/20

Site Site
Maintenance Entretien
Architect Architecte — Yves Bureau
Type Type — forest, links
Relief Relief
Water in play Eau en jeu
Exp. to wind Exposé au vent
Trees in play Arbres en jeu

Scorecard Carte de score	**Chp.** Chp.	**Mens** Mess.	**Ladies** Da.
Length Long.	5937	5623	4754
Par	72	72	72
Slope system	145	140	132

Advised golfing ability Niveau de jeu recommandé — 0 12 24 36
Hcp required Handicap exigé — no

CLUB HOUSE & AMENITIES — CLUB HOUSE ET ANNEXES — 6/10

Pro shop Pro-shop
Driving range Practice
Sheltered couvert 10 mats - On grass sur herbe yes - Putting-green putting-green yes - Pitching-green pitching green yes

HOTEL FACILITIES — ENVIRONNEMENT HOTELIER — 5/10

HOTELS HÔTELS
Mercure - 44 rooms, D € 128 - 100 m
Tel (33) 02 51 59 15 15, Fax (33) 02 51 59 91 03

L'Espadon - 27 rooms, D € 63 - St-Jean-de-Monts 5 km
Tel (33) 02 51 58 03 18, Fax (33) 02 51 59 16 11

Château de la Vérie - 21 rooms, D € 96 - Challans 15 km
Tel (33) 02 51 35 33 44, Fax (33) 02 51 35 14 84

RESTAURANTS RESTAURANTS
Auberge de la Chaumière - St-Jean-de-Monts 5 km
Tel (33) 02 51 58 67 44

Petit St-Jean - St-Jean-de-Monts 1 km
Tel (33) 02 51 59 78 50

Quich'Notte - St-Jean-de-Monts 1 km
Tel (33) 02 51 58 62 64

Saint-Laurent

14 | 7 | 5

Beaucoup de golfs prétendent convenir à tout le monde, mais ce n'est pas toujours vrai. Le 9 trous signé Yves Bureau est idéal pour initier les aspirants golfeurs. Et le 18 trous est un parcours réellement praticable par les joueurs de tous niveaux, même les joueurs de handicap élevé, qui y perdront moins de balles que de points. Situé dans un bel espace vallonné et planté de pins ou de chênes, le 18 trous signé par Michael Fenn se déroule sans imagination particulière, mais il a été conçu et réalisé très sérieusement. Beaucoup de trous sont parallèles, c'est plus facile en cas de vent, mais un peu moins intéressant. Les 600 arbres plantés ont accentué l'exigence comme l'agrément visuel du tracé. Un entretien de bonne qualité incite à recommander la visite, d'autant que cette belle région est une destination traditionnelle de vacances. Sachant que la mer et les activités balnéaires sont à proximité, un golfeur pourra sans trop de scrupules abandonner sa famille quelques heures.

A lot of courses claim to be suitable for all golfers but are not. The 9-hole course designed by Yves Bureau is the ideal venue for beginners and new-comers to the game. And the 18-hole layout is a course that really is playable by golfers of all abilities, even high-handicappers, who will probably lose fewer balls than they drop strokes. Located in rolling landscape planted with pines and oak-trees, Michael Fenn's 18-hole course unfolds with no great imagination but was designed and built with the most serious of intentions. The 600 newly planted trees have made it both more challenging and more aesthetically pleasing. Good maintenance makes it well worth a visit, especially in this traditional holiday region. With the sea and holiday resorts nearby, golfers can abandon the family for a few hours without remorse.

Golf de Saint-Laurent — 1976

Ploemel
F - 56400 AURAY

Office	Secrétariat	(33) 02 97 56 85 18
Pro shop	Pro-shop	(33) 02 97 56 85 18
Fax	Fax	(33) 02 97 56 89 99
Web	www.formule-golf.com	
Situation	Situation	Vannes (pop. 45 640), 44 km
Annual closure	Fermeture annuelle	no
Weekly closure	Fermeture hebdomadaire	no

Restaurant closed tuesday (mardi), from 11 → 02

Fees main season Tarifs haute saison — 18 holes

	Week days Semaine	We/Bank holidays We/Férié
Individual Individuel	€ 48	€ 48
Couple Couple	€ 96	€ 96

Under 21 & Students: – 50%

Caddie Caddie no — **Electric Trolley** Chariot électrique yes
Buggy Voiturette yes — **Clubs** Clubs yes

Credit cards Cartes de crédit
VISA - CB - Eurocard - MasterCard - AMEX

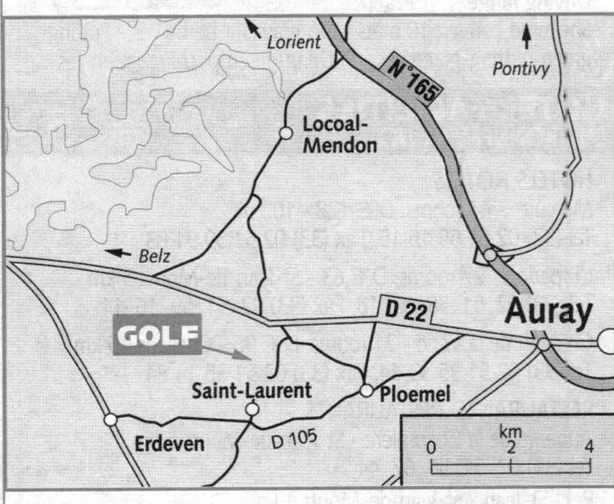

Access Accès : N165 ("Voie Express"), Exit (Sortie) Carnac-Quiberon, D22 → Belz-Etel. 6 km → Golf
Map 5 on page 169 Carte 5 Page 169

GOLF COURSE — PARCOURS — 14/20

Site	Site	
Maintenance	Entretien	
Architect	Architecte	Michael Fenn
Type	Type	forest
Relief	Relief	
Water in play	Eau en jeu	
Exp. to wind	Exposé au vent	
Trees in play	Arbres en jeu	

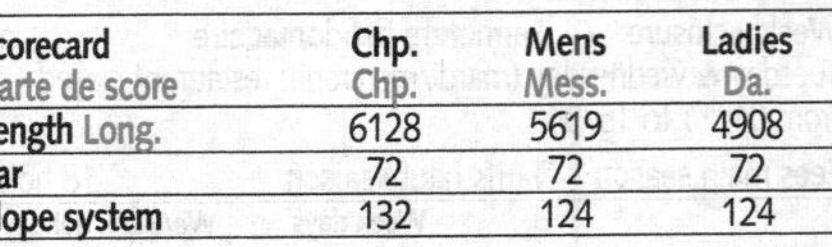

Scorecard Carte de score	**Chp.** Chp.	**Mens** Mess.	**Ladies** Da.
Length Long.	6128	5619	4908
Par	72	72	72
Slope system	132	124	124

Advised golfing ability Niveau de jeu recommandé — 0 12 24 36
Hcp required Handicap exigé — 36

CLUB HOUSE & AMENITIES — CLUB HOUSE ET ANNEXES — 7/10

Pro shop Pro-shop
Driving range Practice
Sheltered couvert 10 mats - On grass sur herbe yes - Putting-green putting-green yes (2) - Pitching-green pitching green yes (2)

HOTEL FACILITIES — ENVIRONNEMENT HOTELIER — 5/10

HOTELS HÔTELS
Hôtel du Golf de saint-Laurent - 42 rooms, D € 90 - on site
Tel (33) 02 97 56 88 88, Fax (33) 02 97 56 88 28

Best Western Celtique - 72 rooms, D € 118 - Carnac 7 km
Tel (33) 02 97 52 11 49, Fax (33) 02 97 52 71 10

Château de Locguénolé - Hennebont 23 km
22 rooms, D € 185
Tel (33) 02 97 76 76 76, Fax (33) 02 97 76 82 35

RESTAURANTS RESTAURANTS
La Closerie de Kerdrain - Auray 10 km
Tel (33) 02 97 56 61 27

Chebaudière - Auray 10 km - Tel (33) 02 97 24 09 84

Saint-Nom-la-Bretèche *Bleu*

16	8	8

Saint-Nom fut à son ouverture un exemple de golf résidentiel prestigieux, qui, après des efforts patients, a acquis sa maturité, en même temps que les arbres en prenaient. Comme le "Rouge", celui-ci a été dessiné par Fred Hawtree, mais beaucoup de changements ont été effectués, souvent avec bonheur, et de nombreux arbres plantés, ce qui constitue un bienfait visuel et technique. Un léger vallonnement le rend agréable à jouer, et ajoute de l'intérêt au choix de clubs. Mieux qu'un parent pauvre d'un parent prestigieux, ce parcours offre quelques pars 4 très musclés, et peu de vraies occasions de birdies. L'utilisation de sept de ses trous pour le parcours composite du Trophée Lancôme a été l'occasion d'y apporter autrefois des modifications importantes, rehaussant l'ensemble. Au pied d'un club-house toujours superbe, avec un entretien de très bon niveau, le "Bleu" a bénéficié du remodelage très réussi de 9 greens, aux normes USGA, et dans un style respectueux de l'esthétique du parcours.

When first opened, Saint-Nom was an example of a prestigious residential golf club which after much patient work has grown to maturity in pace with the trees. Like the "Rouge" course, the "Bleu" layout was designed by Hawtree, although a lot of changes have been made to it, often to the better, with many new trees planted to add visual appeal. The slightly rolling landscape makes it a pleasant course to play and underlines the importance of choosing the right club. Better than a poor relation to a prestigious neighbour, this layout contains a number of very demanding par 4s and few real birdie chances. The use of seven holes to form the composite course for the "Lancôme" was the opportunity to introduce some significant changes and enhance the layout as a whole. Beneath a club-house that looks as magnificent as ever, the "Blue" course has very successfully re-laid 9 of its greens to USGA standards in a style that respects the beauty of the whole course.

Golf de Saint-Nom-la-Bretèche 1959

Hameau de la Tuilerie Bignon
F - 78860 SAINT-NOM-LA-BRETECHE

Office	Secrétariat	(33) 01 30 80 04 40
Pro shop	Pro-shop	(33) 01 30 80 04 40
Fax	Fax	(33) 01 34 62 60 44
E-mail		direction@golfsaintnom.com
Situation	Situation	Paris, 22 km - Versailles, 9 km
Annual closure	Fermeture annuelle	27/12→3/1
Weekly closure	Fermeture hebdomadaire	tuesday(mardi)

Fees main season Tarifs haute saison 18 holes

	Week days / Semaine	We/Bank holidays / We/Férié
Individual Individuel	€ 65*	€ 100*
Couple Couple	€ 130*	€ 200*

* with a member (accompagné d'un membre)
Under 20: € 30 and € 40 (We)

Caddie Caddie on request **Electric Trolley** Chariot électrique yes
Buggy Voiturette medical reasons **Clubs** Clubs yes
Credit cards Cartes de crédit
VISA - CB - Eurocard - Mastercard

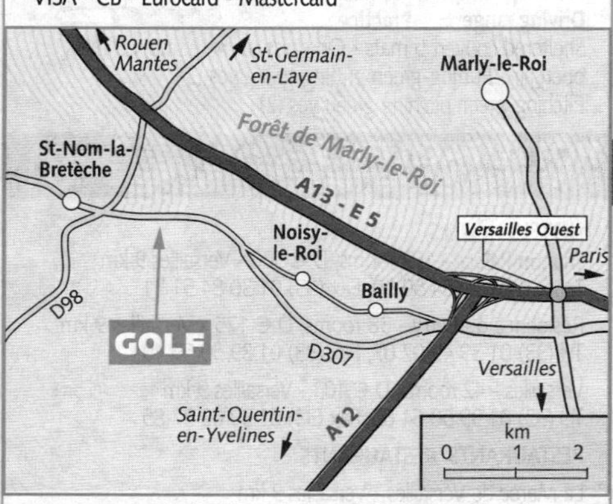

Access Accès : Paris A13 → Rouen. Exit (Sortie) Versailles-Ouest. → Versailles. 500 m turn right on D307 → Noisy-le-Roy, Saint-Nom-la-Bretèche
Map 15 on page 188 Carte 15 Page 188

GOLF COURSE 16/20
PARCOURS

Site	Site	
Maintenance	Entretien	
Architect	Architecte	Fred Hawtree
Type	Type	parkland, residential
Relief	Relief	
Water in play	Eau en jeu	
Exp. to wind	Exposé au vent	
Trees in play	Arbres en jeu	

Scorecard / Carte de score	Chp. / Chp.	Mens / Mess.	Ladies / Da.
Length Long.	6167	5807	4971
Par	72	72	72
Slope system	142	138	130

Advised golfing ability 0 12 24 36
Niveau de jeu recommandé
Hcp required Handicap exigé 24 Men, 28 Ladies

CLUB HOUSE & AMENITIES 8/10
CLUB HOUSE ET ANNEXES

Pro shop Pro-shop
Driving range Practice
Sheltered couvert 5 mats - On grass sur herbe no, 25 mats open air - Putting-green putting-green yes (3) - Pitching-green pitching green yes (2)

HOTEL FACILITIES 8/10
ENVIRONNEMENT HOTELIER

HOTELS HÔTELS
Trianon Palace - 192 rooms, D € 500 - Versailles 9 km
Tel (33) 01 30 84 50 00, Fax (33) 01 30 84 51 21

Résidence du Berry - 38 rooms, D € 125 - Versailles 9 km
Tel (33) 01 39 49 07 07, Fax (33) 01 39 50 59 40

Versailles - 42 rooms, D € 103 - Versailles 9 km
Tel (33) 01 39 50 64 65, Fax (33) 01 39 02 37 85

RESTAURANTS RESTAURANTS
La Marée de Versailles - Versailles 9 km
Tel (33) 01 30 21 73 73
Les Trois Marches - Versailles 9 km - Tel (33) 01 39 50 25 08
La Poularde - Vaucresson 10 km - Tel (33) 01 47 41 13 47

Saint-Nom-la-Bretèche *Rouge*

17 | 8 | 8

Ce club a été rendu célèbre par le Trophée Lancôme, qui était disputé sur un composite des deux parcours. Le "Rouge" nécessite un driving très précis si l'on veut espérer scorer, et attaquer les greens en bonne posture. La stratégie de jeu est assez claire, la seule chose que l'on ne maîtrise pas immédiatement, c'est le putting, car les contours des greens sont peu visibles. Assez vallonné, mais sans être trop fatigant à marcher, ce parcours réclame de savoir faire (et bien faire) tous les coups de golf. La variété du dessin, la progression des difficultés permet de renouveler l'intérêt : jouer ici pour le plaisir ou en compétition n'est pas du tout la même chose ! L'entretien y est d'excellente qualité tout au long de l'année, et cela ne devrait guère changer, l'équipe du greenkeeper ayant effectué – comme sur le "Bleu" – un remodelage de 8 greens selon les normes très strictes de l'USGA (seul le 2 n'est pas très heureux).

This course owes its fame to the Trophée Lancôme, which was played on a combination of the two courses. The "Rouge" course requires very straight driving if you want to card a good score and attack the greens from the ideal position. Game strategy is clear enough and the only thing you will immediately find anything but easy is putting. The contours of these greens are not all that visible. Rather hilly but not too tiring on the legs, this course demands every shot in the book (and as the book tells you). The variety of the layout and the way difficulties slowly pile up make this an interesting course every time. But here, playing for fun and playing in a tournament are two very different propositions. Green-keeping is excellent all year and is destined to stay that way. As on the Bleu course, green-keeping staff have recently relaid 8 greens to the stringent standards laid down by the USGA (only the green on hole N° 2 leaves a little to be desired)..

Golf de Saint-Nom-la-Bretèche 1959

Hameau de la Tuilerie Bignon
F - 78860 SAINT-NOM-LA-BRETECHE

Office	Secrétariat	(33) 01 30 80 04 40
Pro shop	Pro-shop	(33) 01 30 80 04 40
Fax	Fax	(33) 01 34 62 60 44
E-mail	direction@golfsaintnom.com	
Situation	Situation	Paris, 22 km - Versailles, 9 km
Annual closure	Fermeture annuelle	27/12→3/1
Weekly closure	Fermeture hebdomadaire	tuesday(mardi)

Fees main season Tarifs haute saison	18 holes	
	Week days Semaine	We/Bank holidays We/Férié
Individual Individuel	€ 65*	€ 100*
Couple Couple	€ 130*	€ 200*

* with a member (accompagné d'un membre)
Under 20: € 30 and € 40 (We)

Caddie Caddie on request **Electric Trolley** Chariot électrique yes
Buggy Voiturette medical reasons **Clubs** Clubs yes
Credit cards Cartes de crédit
VISA - CB - Eurocard - Mastercard

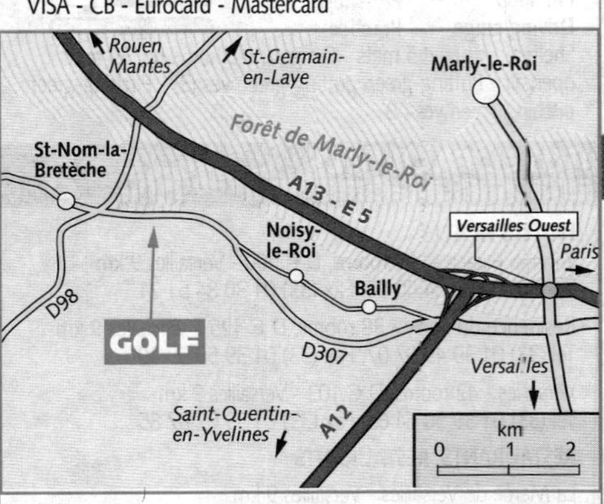

Access Accès : Paris A13 → Rouen. Exit (Sortie) Versailles-Ouest. → Versailles. 500 m turn right on D307 → Noisy-le-Roy, Saint-Nom-la-Bretèche
Map 15 on page 188 Carte 15 Page 188

GOLF COURSE PARCOURS 17/20

Site	Site	
Maintenance	Entretien	
Architect	Architecte	Fred Hawtree
Type	Type	parkland, residential
Relief	Relief	
Water in play	Eau en jeu	
Exp. to wind	Exposé au vent	
Trees in play	Arbres en jeu	

Scorecard Carte de score	Chp. Chp.	Mens Mess.	Ladies Da.
Length Long.	6252	5877	4920
Par	72	72	72
Slope system	145	136	126

Advised golfing ability Niveau de jeu recommandé: 0 12 24 36
Hcp required Handicap exigé: 24 Men, 28 Ladies

CLUB HOUSE & AMENITIES CLUB HOUSE ET ANNEXES 8/10

Pro shop Pro-shop
Driving range Practice
Sheltered couvert 5 mats - On grass sur herbe no, 25 mats open air - Putting-green putting-green yes (3)
Pitching-green pitching green yes (2)

HOTEL FACILITIES ENVIRONNEMENT HOTELIER 8/10

HOTELS HÔTELS

Trianon Palace - 192 rooms, D € 500 - Versailles 9 km
Tel (33) 01 30 84 50 00, Fax (33) 01 30 84 51 21

Résidence du Berry - 38 rooms, D € 125 - Versailles 9 km
Tel (33) 01 39 49 07 07, Fax (33) 01 39 50 59 40

Versailles - 42 rooms, D € 103 - Versailles 9 km
Tel (33) 01 39 50 64 65, Fax (33) 01 39 02 37 85

RESTAURANTS RESTAURANTS

La Marée de Versailles - Versailles 9 km
Tel (33) 01 30 21 73 73

Les Trois Marches - Versailles 9 km - Tel (33) 01 39 50 25 08

La Poularde - Vaucresson 10 km - Tel (33) 01 47 41 13 47

Sainte-Baume (La)

14 | 7 | 6

Ce 18 trous aurait pu être une complète réussite sans quelques "idées d'architecte" un peu plus paysagères que golfiques. Etant un parcours commercial, il devrait pouvoir être joué dès la première fois sans cacher ses obstacles, alors que certains trous manquent de franchise, par rapport à d'autres presque trop faciles. La stratégie n'est alors pas évidente. De fait, on a l'impression d'un ensemble de bonnes idées graphiques, mais parfois aussi d'un manque d'unité. Les joueurs moyens ou débutants seront sans doute moins sensibles à ces quelques défauts que les joueurs qui attachent une grande importance à la logique des obstacles, à la cohérence et au rythme d'un parcours. En dépit de ces appréciations, pour l'utilité de ses installations dans cette région, pour la beauté de l'environnement et la bonne qualité de son entretien, ce parcours mérite largement une visite. Et un séjour au Domaine de Châteauneuf qui jouxte le parcours n'est pas à négliger, c'est un Relais et Châteaux…

This 18-hole course could have been a total success if it weren't for a few architectural ideas that have more to do with landscaping than with golf. Being a commercial course, it should be playable first time out without concealing its hazards, but some holes here are distinctly sneaky while others are almost too easy. This makes strategy a little more difficult. The overall impression is that of a whole series of good graphic ideas but sometimes the feeling of a disjointed layout. Mid-handicappers and beginners will probably be less sensitive to these few flaws than players who attach considerable importance to the logic of hazards and to the consistency and overall balance of a course. Despite these views, the course is well worth a visit for the utility of facilities in this region, the beauty of the setting and excellent standards of green-keeping. In addition, a stay at the Domaine de Châteauneuf – a Relais & Châteaux hotel - alongside the course is not to be sniffed at.

Golf de la Sainte-Baume — 1988

F - 83860 NANS-LES-PINS

Office	Secrétariat	(33) 04 94 78 60 12
Pro shop	Pro-shop	(33) 04 94 78 92 74
Fax	Fax	(33) 04 94 78 63 52
Web	www.opengolfclub.com/gsb/	
Situation	Situation	Marseille, 44 km
Annual closure	Fermeture annuelle	no
Weekly closure	Fermeture hebdomadaire	no

Fees main season Tarifs haute saison		18 holes
	Week days Semaine	**We/Bank holidays** We/Férié
Individual Individuel	€ 56	€ 56
Couple Couple	€ 112	€ 112

Under 25: – 50% / Seniors: € 44

Caddie Caddie no **Electric Trolley** Chariot électrique no

Buggy Voiturette yes **Clubs** Clubs yes

Credit cards Cartes de crédit
VISA - CB - Eurocard - MasterCard - AMEX - DC

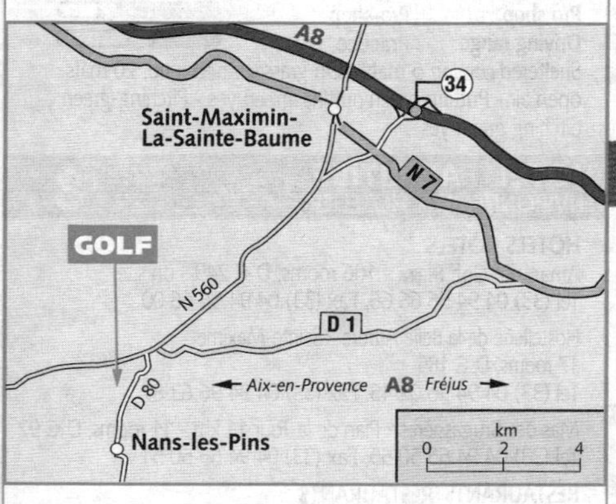

Access Accès : A8 Aix-en-Provence → Nice, Exit (Sortie) Saint-Maximin → La Sainte-Baume, Nans-les-Pins
Map 14 on page 186 Carte 14 Page 186

GOLF COURSE — PARCOURS — 14/20

Site	Site	
Maintenance	Entretien	
Architect	Architecte	Robert Berthet
Type	Type	country
Relief	Relief	
Water in play	Eau en jeu	
Exp. to wind	Exposé au vent	
Trees in play	Arbres en jeu	

Scorecard Carte de score	**Chp.** Chp.	**Mens** Mess.	**Ladies** Da.
Length Long.	6062	5842	5013
Par	72	72	72
Slope system	124	123	122

Advised golfing ability Niveau de jeu recommandé: 0 12 24 36

Hcp required Handicap exigé: 35

CLUB HOUSE & AMENITIES — CLUB HOUSE ET ANNEXES — 7/10

Pro shop Pro-shop
Driving range Practice
Sheltered couvert 10 mats - On grass sur herbe no, 20 mats open air - Putting-green putting-green yes - Pitching-green pitching green yes

HOTEL FACILITIES — ENVIRONNEMENT HOTELIER — 6/10

HOTELS HÔTELS

Domaine de Châteauneuf - 34 rooms, D € 244 - 400 m
Tel (33) 04 94 78 90 06, Fax (33) 04 94 78 63 30

Plaisance - 13 rooms, D € 63 - Saint-Maximin 7 km
Tel (33) 04 94 78 16 74, Fax (33) 04 94 78 18 39

Hôtel de France - 26 rooms, D € 70 - Saint-Maximin 7 km
Tel (33) 04 94 78 00 14, Fax (33) 04 94 59 83 80

RESTAURANTS RESTAURANTS

Domaine de Châteauneuf - 400 m
Tel (33) 04 94 78 90 06

Château de Nans - Nans-les-Pins 2 km
Tel (33) 04 94 78 92 06

Sainte-Maxime

13	7	8

Il faut parfois grimper haut (il y a un téléphérique entre le 10 et le 11), et ce parcours est épuisant à pied, mais les vues sur la baie de Saint-Tropez récompensent des efforts. Taillé pour une bonne part dans la colline, les travaux ont atténué les rebonds indésirables sur des rochers qui n'étaient pas toujours très honnêtes. On comprend que l'architecte Donald Harradine ait adapté son dessin au terrain, mais certains greens aveugles auraient pu être évités. Les fairways sont rarement larges, de nombreux arbres menacent les trajectoires de balle mais la longueur assez réduite du parcours permet de laisser souvent le driver de côté. Il faut soigneusement éviter de jouer en stroke-play, mais on peut beaucoup s'amuser en match-play. Pour les joueurs peu expérimentés, si ce parcours s'avère difficile, ils pourront profiter pleinement du spectacle splendide sur la mer. Après les incendies de l'été 2003, la fin du parcours a été modifiée, avec un grand souci de qualité, et le 18 est passé en par 5.

You sometimes have to scale considerable heights (a cable-car links the 10th and 11th holes) and the course is generally speaking exhausting to walk, but the views over the bay of Saint-Tropez are more than worth the effort. Mostly cut out of a hill, recent improvement work has reduced the number of bad bounces on rocks that were a touch unfair. Architect Donald Harradine understandably adapted his layout to the terrain, but certain blind greens could have been avoided. The fairways are seldom wide and numerous pine-trees encroach upon the ball's flight-path, but you can always leave the driver in the bag. Make a point of not playing stroke-play, you will have much more fun with the match-play format. A sometimes dispiriting course for inexperienced golfers but they'll love the wonderful view over the sea. After the forest fires of summer 2003, the end of the course has been altered without impairing the general standard of excellence. Hole N° 18 is now a par 5.

Golf de Sainte-Maxime — 1991

Route du Débarquement
F - 83120 SAINTE-MAXIME

Office	Secrétariat	(33) 04 94 55 02 02
Pro shop	Pro-shop	(33) 04 94 55 02 02
Fax	Fax	(33) 04 93 55 02 03
Web		www.bluegreen.com
Situation	Situation	Sainte-Maxime, 2 km
Annual closure	Fermeture annuelle	no
Weekly closure	Fermeture hebdomadaire	no

Fees main season Tarifs haute saison	18 holes	
	Week days Semaine	**We/Bank holidays** We/Férié
Individual Individuel	€ 60	€ 60
Couple Couple	€ 120	€ 120

Students under 26: – 40% / Sunday: 2 GF + buggy, € 120 (not in 07/08)

Caddie Caddie no — **Electric Trolley** Chariot électrique no
Buggy Voiturette yes — **Clubs** Clubs yes
Credit cards Cartes de crédit
VISA - CB - Eurocard - MasterCard - AMEX - DC

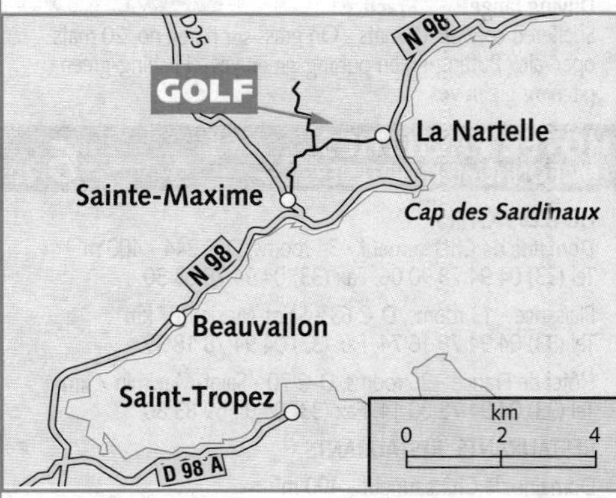

Access Accès : A8 Exit (Sortie) 36, D25 → Sainte-Maxime, → Golf
Map 14 on page 187 Carte 14 Page 187

GOLF COURSE — PARCOURS — 13/20

Site	Site	
Maintenance	Entretien	
Architect	Architecte	Donald Harradine Peter Harradine
Type	Type	hilly, residential
Relief	Relief	
Water in play	Eau en jeu	
Exp. to wind	Exposé au vent	
Trees in play	Arbres en jeu	

Scorecard Carte de score	**Chp.** Chp.	**Mens** Mess.	**Ladies** Da.
Length Long.	6130	5955	4591
Par	72	72	72
Slope system	137	129	128

Advised golfing ability Niveau de jeu recommandé: 0 12 24 36
Hcp required Handicap exigé: 35

CLUB HOUSE & AMENITIES — CLUB HOUSE ET ANNEXES — 7/10

Pro shop Pro-shop
Driving range Practice
Sheltered couvert 5 mats - On grass sur herbe no, 20 mats open air - Putting-green putting-green yes - Pitching-green pitching green yes

HOTEL FACILITIES — ENVIRONNEMENT HOTELIER — 8/10

HOTELS HÔTELS

Amarante Golf Plaza - 106 rooms, D € 249 - on site
Tel (33) 04 94 56 66 66, Fax (33) 04 94 56 66 00

Hostellerie de la Belle Aurore - Sainte-Maxime
17 rooms, D € 185
Tel (33) 04 94 96 02 45, Fax (33) 04 94 96 63 87

Mas des Brugassières - Plan de la Tour 11 km - 11 rooms, D € 92
Tel (33) 04 94 55 50 55, Fax (33) 04 94 55 50 51

RESTAURANTS RESTAURANTS

La Belle Aurore - Sainte-Maxime 2 km - Tel (33) 04 94 96 02 45
L'Amiral - Sainte-Maxime 2 km - Tel (33) 04 94 43 99 36
Le Cap Sud - Sainte-Maxime 2 km - Tel (33) 04 94 43 96 45

Savenay

14	5	4

Entre Nantes et Saint-Nazaire, et dominant la Loire, Savenay est situé au cœur d'une région aujourd'hui riche en golfs de qualité. Un voyage de golf est ainsi agréable pour tous les types de joueurs, de la Vendée à la côte sud de Bretagne, dans les paysages très caractéristiques de ces régions. Ce parcours (complété par un 9 trous d'entraînement) a été dessiné par Michel Gayon dans un site alternant les trous larges volontiers inspirés des "links" (par leur dessin et l'abondance des bunkers stratégiques), et des trous plus intimes, notamment les 7 et 8, le long d'une pièce d'eau. Les arbres (beaucoup de châtaigniers) sont assez nombreux, mais sans que l'on éprouve une impression d'étouffement. Un petit regret : le grand nombre de trous parallèles, mais avec des variations par rapport au sens du vent, une certaine monotonie aussi. Soulignons la longueur du parcours, mais il y a cinq par 5, trous à birdie comme chacun sait... Un bon équipement pour la majorité des joueurs.

Between Nantes and Saint-Nazaire overlooking the Loire river, Savenay stands at the heart of a region which today boasts any number of excellent courses. This makes a golfing holiday to Brittany a pleasant proposition for all, from the Vendée to the southern Breton coastline all in typical settings. This is a rather long course (there is also a 9 hole pitch 'n putt) designed by Michel Gayon, on a site where deliberately wide holes, designed and strategically bunkered in true links style, alternate with more intimate holes, notably the 7th and 8th along a stretch of water. Trees abound (a lot of chestnut trees) but are never too imposing a presence. The one little regret is the number of holes running parallel, only with wind varying in different directions, plus a slight feeling of monotony. The length of the course is worth mentioning, but there are five par 5s, which as everyone knows are birdie holes... A good facility for most golfers.

Golf de Savenay 1990
Le Chambeau
F - 44260 SAVENAY

Office	Secrétariat	(33) 02 40 56 88 05
Pro shop	Pro-shop	(33) 02 40 56 88 05
Fax	Fax	(33) 02 40 56 89 04
Web	www.formule-golf.com	
Situation	Situation	Saint-Nazaire, 26 km
Annual closure	Fermeture annuelle	no
Weekly closure	Fermeture hebdomadaire	Tuesday

(mardi): 1/11→31/3

Fees main season Tarifs haute saison	18 holes	
	Week days Semaine	**We/Bank holidays** We/Férié
Individual Individuel	€ 46	€ 46
Couple Couple	€ 92	€ 92

Under 21 & Students: – 50%

Caddie Caddie no — **Electric Trolley** Chariot électrique no

Buggy Voiturette yes — **Clubs** Clubs yes

Credit cards Cartes de crédit
VISA - CB - Eurocard - MasterCard

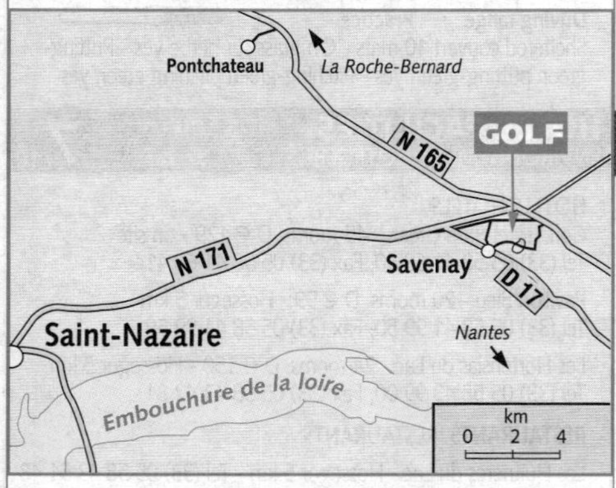

Access Accès : • Saint-Nazaire N171, Exit (Sortie) Châteaubriand • Nantes N165, Exit Blain-Bouvron

Map 6 on page 170 Carte 6 Page 170

GOLF COURSE
PARCOURS — 14/20

Site	Site	
Maintenance	Entretien	
Architect	Architecte	Michel Gayon
Type	Type	open country, parkland
Relief	Relief	
Water in play	Eau en jeu	
Exp. to wind	Exposé au vent	
Trees in play	Arbres en jeu	

Scorecard Carte de score	**Chp.** Chp.	**Mens** Mess.	**Ladies** Da.
Length Long.	6250	5741	4831
Par	73	73	73
Slope system	141	128	127

Advised golfing ability Niveau de jeu recommandé — 0 12 24 36

Hcp required Handicap exigé — no

CLUB HOUSE & AMENITIES
CLUB HOUSE ET ANNEXES — 5/10

Pro shop Pro-shop

Driving range Practice

Sheltered couvert 9 mats - On grass sur herbe no, 34 mats open air - Putting-green putting-green yes - Pitching-green pitching green yes (3)

HOTEL FACILITIES
ENVIRONNEMENT HOTELIER — 4/10

HOTELS HÔTELS

Auberge du Chêne Vert - 20 rooms, D € 40 - Savenay 1 km
Tel (33) 02 40 56 90 16, Fax (33) 02 40 56 99 60

Manoir du Rodoir - La Roche-Bernard 30 km
24 rooms, D € 95
Tel (33) 02 99 90 82 68, Fax (33) 02 99 90 76 22

Berry - 29 rooms, D € 82 - Saint-Nazaire 23 km
Tel (33) 02 40 22 42 61, Fax (33) 02 40 22 45 34

RESTAURANTS RESTAURANTS

Moderne - Saint-Nazaire 23 km - Tel (33) 02 40 22 55 88

Au Bon Accueil - Saint-Nazaire 23 km - Tel (33) 02 40 22 07 05

Table d'Harmonie - Saint-Nazaire 23 km
Tel (33) 02 51 76 04 10

Seignosse

17	7	7

Ce parcours ne laisse personne indifférent. A proximité d'Hossegor, il se déroule dans un paysage bien plus accidenté, planté de pins et de chênes-liège. Les différences de dénivellation et l'étroitesse des fairways incitent à le conseiller aux joueurs en forme et bons stratèges. En revanche (si l'on fait abstraction de quelques longues promenades des greens aux départs) il n'est pas très long (notamment les par 3, sauf le 16). Il demande un bon jeu de fers, en particulier pour attaquer les drapeaux, car les greens sont très modelés, de dimensions variées, souvent à plateaux et le manque de précision peut gonfler démesurément le score. Les contours de fairway très travaillés et les abords des greens sont typiques de von Hagge, de même que l'alternance de bunkers de sable et d'herbe et le dessin des pièces d'eau (sur cinq trous). Souvent spectaculaire, intimidant, il ne se maîtrise pas d'emblée. C'est un parcours follement amusant en match-play. Si on joue bien ici, on peut aller partout, car il est très formateur et ne laisse pas place à l'improvisation.

A course that leaves no-one indifferent. Not far from Hossegor, Seignosse is laid out over very different terrain which is hilly and planted with pine-trees and cork oaks. The differences in altitude and narrow fairways mean this is a layout for seasoned players on top of their game, who know the meaning of the word strategy. By contrast, if you disregard a few long walks from green to next tee, the course is not long but does require precision ironwork, especially when attacking the pins. The greens are heavily contoured, come in all shapes and sizes and are often multi-tiered. The rolling fairways and edges of the greens are typical of von Hagge, as are the alternating grass-bunkers and sand-traps and the design of the water hazards. Often spectacular and intimidating, most golfers will and do have trouble first time out. A good course and great fun in match-play. If you play well here you will play well anywhere, as Seignosse teaches you a great deal and leaves no room for improvisation.

Golf de Seignosse — 1989

Avenue du Belvédère
F - 40510 SEIGNOSSE

Office Secrétariat (33) 05 58 41 68 30
Pro shop Pro-shop (33) 05 58 41 68 30
Fax Fax (33) 05 58 41 68 31
Web www.golfseignosse.com
Situation Situation Bayonne (pop. 40 050), 28 km
Annual closure Fermeture annuelle no
Weekly closure Fermeture hebdomadaire thursday in winter (jeudi en hiver)

Fees main season Tarifs haute saison	18 holes	
	Week days Semaine	**We/Bank holidays** We/Férié
Individual Individuel	€ 65	€ 65
Couple Couple	€ 130	€ 130

Under 21 & Students: € 45

Caddie Caddie no — **Electric Trolley** Chariot électrique no
Buggy Voiturette yes — **Clubs** Clubs yes
Credit cards Cartes de crédit
VISA - CB - Eurocard - MasterCard - AMEX - DC

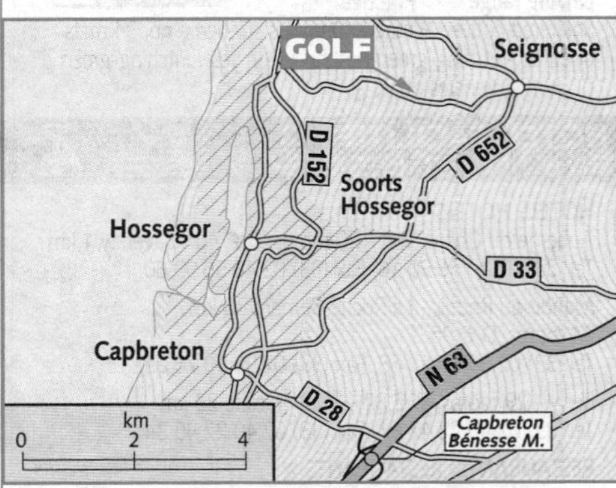

Access Accès : • Bayonne A63 → Bordeaux, Exit (Sortie) Capbreton → Capbreton/Hossegor • Bordeaux A63 → Bayonne, Exit Saint-Geours-de-Marenne → Seignosse

Map 12 on page 182 Carte 12 Page 182

GOLF COURSE — PARCOURS — 17/20

Site Site
Maintenance Entretien
Architect Architecte Robert von Hagge
Type Type forest, hilly
Relief Relief
Water in play Eau en jeu
Exp. to wind Exposé au vent
Trees in play Arbres en jeu

Scorecard Carte de score	**Chp.** Chp.	**Mens** Mess.	**Ladies** Da.
Length Long.	6129	5774	4381
Par	72	72	72
Slope system	144	142	123

Advised golfing ability Niveau de jeu recommandé 0 12 24 36
Hcp required Handicap exigé no

CLUB HOUSE & AMENITIES — CLUB HOUSE ET ANNEXES — 7/10

Pro shop Pro-shop
Driving range Practice
Sheltered couvert 10 mats - On grass sur herbe yes - Putting-green putting-green yes - Pitching-green pitching green yes

HOTEL FACILITIES — ENVIRONNEMENT HOTELIER — 7/10

HOTELS HÔTELS

Golf Hôtel Blue Green - 45 rooms, D € 129 - on site
Tel (33) 05 58 41 68 40, Fax (33) 05 58 41 68 41

Pavillon Bleu - 20 rooms, D € 99 - Hossegor 5 km
Tel (33) 05 58 41 99 50, Fax (33) 05 58 41 99 59

Les Hortensias du Lac - 24 rooms, D € 150 - Hossegor 5 km
Tel (33) 05 58 43 99 00, Fax (33) 05 58 43 42 81

RESTAURANTS RESTAURANTS

Les Huîtrières du Lac - Hossegor 5 km - Tel (33) 05 58 43 51 48

Auberge du Cheval Blanc - Bayonne 28 km
Tel (33) 05 59 59 01 33

François Miura - Bayonne 28 km - Tel (33) 05 59 59 49 89

Servanes

13 | 5 | 7

Servanes est en Provence, nul n'en ignore face aux reliefs blancs et rocailleux des Alpilles, aux oliviers, cyprès et platanes, avec parfois un méchant coup de mistral. Il devrait empoisonner les golfeurs, mais ils en sont relativement protégés ici. Dans un site de campagne à peu près préservé d'immobilier, Sprecher et Watine ont dessiné un parcours bien paysagé, techniquement honnête, mais sans imagination excessive. Les contours de fairway auraient sans doute pu être mieux travaillés : en Provence, on préfère les sentiers aux boulevards. Autrement, il n'y a pas de grands commentaires à faire, sinon que, tout comme les joueurs de niveau moyen, les joueurs peu expérimentés trouveront ici le calme et de quoi assouvir leur passion naissante dans un cadre magnifique, à proximité du splendide village des Baux-de-Provence. Certes, le charme de la région joue sur l'appréciation, mais pourquoi bouder son plaisir ? Le système d'arrosage a bien arrangé ce parcours, ce n'était pas un luxe dans cette région souvent très ensoleillée.

Servanes is Provence through and through, with the white rocky terrain of the Alpilles, cypress and plane trees, and sometimes a gust of mistral which can play havoc, although golfers are relatively sheltered on this course. On a country site more or less protected from property development, Sprecher and Watine have designed a nicely landscaped course which is technically fair but none too rich in imagination. The fairways could certainly have been better contoured, and in Provence they prefer pathways to boulevards. Otherwise, there is little else to say, except that high-handicappers and beginners alike will find the calm and the course they are looking for to satisfy their nascent enthusiasm for the game. All this in a magnificent setting close to the splendid village of Baux-de-Provence. The charm of the surrounding region certainly has an influence on anyone's opinion of this course, but why deny the pleasure? The watering system has much improved the layout.

Golf Country-Club de Servanes — 1989

Domaine de Servanes
F - 13890 MOURIES

Office Secrétariat (33) 04 90 47 59 95
Pro shop Pro-shop (33) 04 90 47 65 70
Fax Fax (33) 04 90 47 52 58
Web www.opengolf.com
Situation Situation Arles (pop. 52 050), 25 km
Annual closure Fermeture annuelle no
Weekly closure Fermeture hebdomadaire no
Fees main season Tarifs haute saison full day

	Week days Semaine	We/Bank holidays We/Férié
Individual Individuel	€ 55	€ 55
Couple Couple	€ 110	€ 110

Under 18 and Students: € 33

Caddie Caddie on request **Electric Trolley** Chariot électrique no
Buggy Voiturette yes **Clubs** Clubs no
Credit cards Cartes de crédit
VISA - CB - Eurocard - MasterCard - AMEX

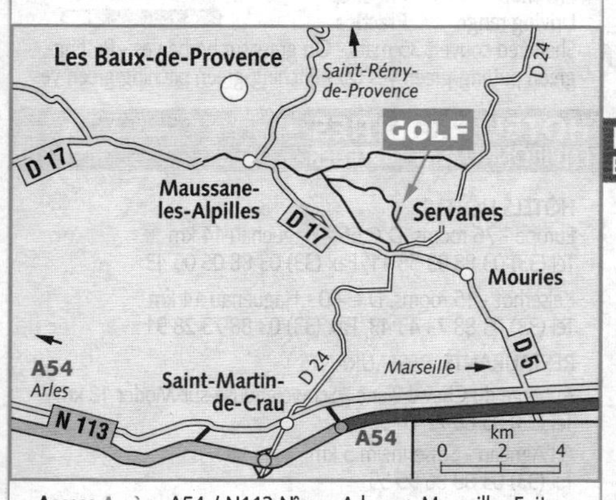

Access Accès : A54 / N113 Nîmes-Arles, → Marseille, Exit (Sortie) Saint-Martin-de-Crau → Mouriès
Map 14 on page 186 Carte 14 Page 186

GOLF COURSE — PARCOURS 13/20

Site Site
Maintenance Entretien
Architect Architecte Thierry Sprecher, Géry Watine
Type Type country
Relief Relief
Water in play Eau en jeu
Exp. to wind Exposé au vent
Trees in play Arbres en jeu

Scorecard Carte de score	Chp. Chp.	Mens Mess.	Ladies Da.
Length Long.	6181	5721	4811
Par	72	72	72
Slope system	138	129	130

Advised golfing ability Niveau de jeu recommandé 0 12 24 36
Hcp required Handicap exigé ???

CLUB HOUSE & AMENITIES — CLUB HOUSE ET ANNEXES 5/10

Pro shop Pro-shop
Driving range Practice
Sheltered couvert 5 mats - On grass sur herbe no - Putting-green putting-green yes - Pitching-green pitching green yes

HOTEL FACILITIES — ENVIRONNEMENT HOTELIER 7/10

HOTELS HÔTELS
Oustau de Baumanière - Les Baux-de-Provence 8 km
19 rooms, D € 260
Tel (33) 04 90 54 33 07, Fax (33) 04 90 54 40 46

Cabro d'Or - 31 rooms, D € 170 - Les Baux-de-Provence 8 km
Tel (33) 04 90 54 33 21, Fax (33) 04 90 54 45 98

Val Baussenc - 22 rooms, D € 108 - Maussane 7 km
Tel (33) 04 90 54 38 90, Fax (33) 04 90 54 33 36

RESTAURANTS RESTAURANTS
Oustau de Baumanière - Les Baux-de-Provence 8 km
La Petite France - Maussane 9 km - Tel (33) 04 90 54 41 91
La Riboto de Taven - Les Baux-de-Provence 8 km
Tel (33) 04 90 54 34 23

Soufflenheim

17	7	4

Avec ce golf, l'Alsace a enrichi sa panoplie de bons parcours, même si les voisins allemands l'attachent à Baden-Baden. Bernhard Langer (avec Kurt Rossknecht) a produit un dessin très technique, où les obstacles sont visuellement et réellement menaçants. La présence de nombreux bunkers de greens et de fairways, comme des obstacles d'eau (sur 14 trous) exige une attention et un rythme constants, mais les joueurs peu expérimentés pourront généralement les contourner. De nombreuses buttes séparent les fairways et entourent la plupart des greens, ajoutant du relief à cet espace plat et entouré de forêts. Les greens sont de bonne dimension, souvent bien modelés, ajoutant à l'intérêt du jeu. De nombreuses plantations (arbustes, bosquets, buissons), ainsi que le retour de la végétation naturelle en bordure des 18 plans d'eau ont encore augmenté le plaisir, pour les joueurs comme pour le gibier d'eau qui y trouve refuge et bonheur. Une belle réalisation parvenue à maturité, avec 15 trous d'entraînement.

With this course, Alsace has enhanced its panoply of good courses, even though its German neighbours consider it to be a part of Baden-Baden. Bernhard Langer (with Kurt Rossknecht) has created a very technical layout where hazards are visually and truly threatening. The numerous green-side and fairway bunkers and the water hazards (on 14 holes) demand constant care and good tempo but inexperienced golfers will generally get around them easily. The fairways are separated by numerous sand-hills, which also surround most of the greens, thus adding relief to a flat terrain encircled by a forest. The large greens are often well contoured, thus adding extra spice to the course. A large number of plantation programmes (shrubs, small trees and bushes) and the return of natural vegetation edging the 18 stretches of water are a further improvement for both golfers and the wildlife that take refuge there. A fine course now maturing nicely, with 15 practice holes.

Soufflenheim Baden Baden **1995**
Allée du Golf
F - 67620 SOUFFLENHEIM

Office	Secrétariat	(33) 03 88 05 77 00
Pro shop	Pro-shop	(33) 03 88 05 77 00
Fax	Fax	(33) 03 88 05 77 01
Web	www.golfclub-soufflenheim.com	
Situation	Situation	Strasbourg, 40 km
Annual closure	Fermeture annuelle	no
Weekly closure	Fermeture hebdomadaire	no

monday (lundi), restaurant closed

Fees main season Tarifs haute saison		Full day
	Week days Semaine	**We/Bank holidays** We/Férié
Individual Individuel	€ 60	€ 80
Couple Couple	€ 120	€ 160

Under 18: – 50% / Before 9:00 and after 16:00 or 17:00: – 50%

Caddie Caddie on request **Electric Trolley** Chariot électrique no
Buggy Voiturette yes **Clubs** Clubs yes
Credit cards Cartes de crédit
VISA - CB - Eurocard - MasterCard - DC

Access Accès : Strasbourg, A4, Exit (Sortie) Karlsruhe-Lauterburg to D300. 15 km, Exit Soufflenheim → Golf
Map 4 on page 167 Carte 4 Page 167

GOLF COURSE
PARCOURS **17/20**

Site	Site	
Maintenance	Entretien	
Architect	Architecte	Bernhard Langer
Type	Type	forest, open country
Relief	Relief	
Water in play	Eau en jeu	
Exp. to wind	Exposé au vent	
Trees in play	Arbres en jeu	

Scorecard Carte de score	**Chp.** Chp.	**Mens** Mess.	**Ladies** Da.
Length Long.	6357	6053	5217
Par	72	72	72
Slope system	144	140	134

Advised golfing ability Niveau de jeu recommandé: 0 12 24 36
Hcp required Handicap exigé 36

CLUB HOUSE & AMENITIES
CLUB HOUSE ET ANNEXES **7/10**

Pro shop Pro-shop
Driving range Practice
Sheltered couvert 35 mats - On grass sur herbe yes - Putting-green putting-green yes (2) - Pitching-green pitching green yes

HOTEL FACILITIES
ENVIRONNEMENT HOTELIER **4/10**

HOTELS HÔTELS
Europe - 76 rooms, D € 55 - Haguenau 14 km
Tel (33) 03 88 93 58 11, Fax (33) 03 88 06 05 43

Kaiserhof - 15 rooms, D € 60 - Haguenau 14 km
Tel (33) 03 88 73 43 43, Fax (33) 03 88 73 28 91

RESTAURANTS RESTAURANTS
Auberge du Cheval Blanc - Schweighouse-sur-Moder 18 km - Tel (33) 03 88 72 76 96

A l'Agneau - Sessenheim 5 km
Tel (33) 03 88 86 95 55

Au Boeuf - Sessenheim 5 km - Tel (33) 03 88 86 97 14

Barberousse - Haguenau 14 km - Tel (33) 03 88 73 31 09

Spérone

18 | 7 | 5

Dans un des plus magnifiques sites d'Europe, Robert Trent Jones a tracé un parcours en plein maquis, avec en couronnement six trous inoubliables en bord de falaise, d'où l'on découvre la Méditerranée et la Sardaigne en arrière-plan. Pas très long, mais très technique et assez accidenté (voiturette conseillée), ce parcours spectaculaire ne laisse personne indifférent. Si les joueurs peu expérimentés souffriront, tous les autres adoreront tenter de maîtriser un tracé parfois déconcertant, ses provocations, ses greens très modelés. Avec ses couleurs, ses lumières, les odeurs de la flore, ce parcours est magique, mais parfois injuste quand le vent vient lui donner un air d'Ecosse en plein soleil. Alors, gare à ceux qui maîtrisent mal les balles basses! Une cinquantaine de maisons de remarquable architecture moderne sont dissimulées dans ce vaste domaine. Spérone mérite sa gloire pour ses grands mérites golfiques... et son adhésion au programme européen de protection de l'environnement. A connaître sans faute.

On one of Europe's most fabulous sites, Trent Jones designed this course amidst gorse and heather, with on top of everything else six unforgettable holes along the cliffs from where you can see Sardinia in the distance over the shimmering Mediterranean. Not particularly long but very much a course for the artist and hilly to boot (buggy recommended), this spectacular course leaves no-one indifferent. And while it may be considered tough for inexperienced golfers, the rest will love trying to come to terms with a sometimes disconcerting layout, its provocative nature and the switchback greens. With its colours, light and fragrances, this is sheer magic but sometimes a little unjust when the wind blows and brings along a breath of Scottish air under the Corsican sun. In this case, low shots are an absolute must to keep a decent score. Spérone deserves full glory as a wonderful golf course and for its support for the European Environmental Programme. A definite must.

Golf de Spérone — 1990

Domaine de Spérone
F - 20169 SPERONE

Office — Secrétariat — (33) 04 95 73 17 13
Pro shop — Pro-shop — (33) 04 95 73 17 13
Fax — Fax — (33) 04 95 73 17 85
Web — www.sperone.net
Situation — Situation — Bonifacio (pop. 2 680), 6 km
Annual closure — Fermeture annuelle — 1/1→31/1
Weekly closure — Fermeture hebdomadaire — thursday afternoon except holidays (jeudi après-midi sauf jours fériés)

Fees main season Tarifs haute saison	Week days Semaine	We/Bank holidays We/Férié
		18 holes
Individual Individuel	€ 80	€ 80
Couple Couple	€ 160	€ 160

Under 18: € 47
Caddie Caddie no — Electric Trolley Chariot électrique yes
Buggy Voiturette yes — Clubs Clubs yes
Credit cards Cartes de crédit
VISA - CB - Eurocard - MasterCard - AMEX - DC

Access Accès : Bonifacio → Phare de Pertusato, → Golf
Map 14 on page 187 Carte 14 Page 187

GOLF COURSE — PARCOURS — 18/20

Site — Site
Maintenance — Entretien
Architect — Architecte — Robert Trent Jones
Type — Type — seaside course, hilly
Relief — Relief
Water in play — Eau en jeu
Exp. to wind — Exposé au vent
Trees in play — Arbres en jeu

Scorecard Carte de score	Chp. Chp.	Mens Mess.	Ladies Da.
Length Long.	6106	5416	4318
Par	72	72	72
Slope system	158	148	137

Advised golfing ability — Niveau de jeu recommandé — 0 12 24 36
Hcp required — Handicap exigé — 54

CLUB HOUSE & AMENITIES — CLUB HOUSE ET ANNEXES — 7/10

Pro shop — Pro-shop
Driving range — Practice
Sheltered couvert 4 mats - On grass sur herbe no, 25 mats open air - Putting-green putting-green yes (2) - Pitching-green pitching green yes

HOTEL FACILITIES — ENVIRONNEMENT HOTELIER — 5/10

HOTELS HÔTELS

A Trama - 25 rooms, D € 140 - Bonifacio 4 km
Tel (33) 04 95 73 17 17, Fax (33) 04 95 73 17 79

Genovese - 15 rooms, D € 230 - Bonifacio 6 km
Tel (33) 04 95 73 12 34, Fax (33) 04 95 73 09 03

Roy d'Aragon - 31 rooms, D € 90 - Bonifacio 6 km
Tel (33) 04 95 73 03 99, Fax (33) 04 95 73 07 94

RESTAURANTS RESTAURANTS

Stella d'Oro - Bonifacio 6 km - Tel (33) 04 95 73 03 63
Marina di Cavu - Bonifacio 3 km - Tel (33) 04 95 73 14 13
Domaine de Licetto - Bonifacio 6 km
Tel (33) 04 95 73 19 48

Strasbourg Illkirch *Jaune + Rouge* | 16 | 7 | 7

C'était autrefois le seul golf des Strasbourgeois, avant la création de la Wantzenau et du Kempferhof. L'architecture en est plus traditionnelle, avec des obstacles d'eau sur la moitié des 18 trous du Rouge/Jaune. Les trous les plus durs sont groupés au début du Jaune, mais cet ensemble n'est pas intimidant, et si son classicisme ne suscite pas les grandes émotions visuelles ou techniques des parcours modernes, les meilleurs joueurs imprécis peuvent connaître des problèmes. Les nombreux membres y évoluent avec plaisir en famille, d'autant que les fairways et les greens sont excellents en toutes saisons. Les greens sont bien défendus, mais il est souvent possible d'y accéder en faisant rouler la balle car ils sont peu surélevés. Il s'agit là avant tout d'un club pour les membres locaux, avec une belle vie sportive, et cependant ouvert aux joueurs extérieurs (accès limité en week-end). De passage à Strasbourg, ils seront bien accueillis et passeront une journée plaisante sur un parcours de qualité, avec une halte au confortable club-house.

By comparison with Wantzenau and Kempferhof, the architecture looks more traditional with a few water hazards on half of the Rouge/Jaune course. The hardest holes are grouped at the start of the Jaune course but the full layout is anything but intimidating, and while this classic set-up hardly has the same visual or technical excitement of modern courses, even the best players will find themselves in trouble if they don't keep it straight. The many members enjoy playing here with the family, especially since the fairways and greens are in excellent condition all year round. The greens are well defended and only a few are elevated so they can often be reached by rolling the ball on from the front. This is first and foremost a club for the locals with lots of sporting activities going on, although the course is open to green-fees. When passing through Strasbourg, they will be warmly welcomed and will spend a pleasant day on a quality course, including a stop-off at the cosy club-house.

Golf de Strasbourg-Illkirch — 1934

Route du Rhin
F - 67400 ILLKIRCH

Office	Secrétariat	(33) 03 88 66 17 22
Pro shop	Pro-shop	(33) 03 88 66 93 34
Fax	Fax	(33) 03 88 65 05 67
Web	www.golf-strasbourg.com	
Situation	Situation	Strasbourg , 12 km
Annual closure	Fermeture annuelle	22/12→3/1
Weekly closure	Fermeture hebdomadaire	no

wednesday (mercredi): restaurant closed

Fees main season Tarifs haute saison — 18 holes

	Week days Semaine	We/Bank holidays We/Férié
Individual Individuel	€ 50	€ 60*
Couple Couple	€ 100	€ 120*

* We, with members only (avec membres seulement)
Students: € 10 and € 16 (We)

Caddie Caddie no — **Electric Trolley** Chariot électrique no
Buggy Voiturette no — **Clubs** Clubs no

Credit cards Cartes de crédit
VISA - CB - Eurocard - MasterCard

Access Accès : • Strasbourg A35, Exit (Sortie) Baggersee, 1st roundabout → Markolsheim, 2nd roundabout, Expressway, → Golf • Colmar N83, go through Fegersheim → Illkirch
Map 4 on page 167 Carte 4 Page 167

GOLF COURSE — PARCOURS — 16/20

Site	Site	
Maintenance	Entretien	
Architect	Architecte	Donald Harradine
Type	Type	country
Relief	Relief	
Water in play	Eau en jeu	
Exp. to wind	Exposé au vent	
Trees in play	Arbres en jeu	

Scorecard Carte de score	Chp. Chp.	Mens Mess.	Ladies Da.
Length Long.	6131	5741	4877
Par	73	73	73
Slope system	130	125	128

Advised golfing ability / Niveau de jeu recommandé — 0 12 24 36
Hcp required Handicap exigé — 35

CLUB HOUSE & AMENITIES — CLUB HOUSE ET ANNEXES — 7/10

Pro shop Pro-shop
Driving range Practice
Sheltered couvert 15 mats - On grass sur herbe yes (not in winter) - Putting-green putting-green yes - Pitching-green pitching green yes

HOTEL FACILITIES — ENVIRONNEMENT HOTELIER — 7/10

HOTELS HÔTELS

Beaucour - 49 rooms, D € 129 - Strasbourg 12 km
Tel (33) 03 88 76 72 00, Fax (33) 03 88 76 72 60

Château de l'Ile - 62 rooms, D € 180 - Ostwald 5 km
Tel (33) 03 88 66 85 00, Fax (33) 03 88 66 85 49

Hôtel des Rohan - 36 rooms, D € 99 - Strasbourg 12 km
Tel (33) 03 88 32 85 11, Fax (33) 03 88 75 65 37

RESTAURANTS RESTAURANTS

La Vieille Enseigne - Strasbourg 12 km - Tel (33) 03 88 32 58 50
Maison des Tanneurs - Strasbourg 12 km
Tel (33) 03 88 32 79 70
Maison Kammerzell et Baumann - Strasbourg 12 km
Tel (33) 03 88 32 42 14

Taulane

15 | 7 | 4

Gary Player a remodelé et complètement restructuré un tracé ancien. On reconnaît son souci de faire des parcours accessibles à la majorité des joueurs, de ne pas trop bouleverser un site, et il a visiblement voulu préserver la beauté du lieu (l'automne y est splendide). Le tracé est très intéressant, sa difficulté globale raisonnable,mais il peut être exigeant des départs arrière (avec quelques départs provocants), et réclame de toute façon un bon bagage technique pour faire un bon score. Il reste cependant à la portée des joueurs de tous niveaux, de préférence en voiturette car les reliefs sont parfois prononcés. Le dessin vous impose le jeu, mais le plaisir demeure. Les amoureux de la nature vont adorer, d'autant que l'hôtel sur place est très agréable et la restauration de qualité. Situé à moyenne altitude, ce parcours n'est ouvert que huit mois par an, dans un site isolé, très naturel, d'un calme extrême. En été, échapper ainsi à la foule et aux chaleurs de la Côte constitue un plaisir raffiné.

An old layout completely restyled by Gary Player. You can recognize his concern for designing courses that are playable by nearly everyone and for not disrupting natural sites, and here he visibly set out to protect the area's natural beauty (wonderful in autumn). The layout is very interesting and overall difficulty quite reasonable but it can be a handful when playing from the back tees (a number of provocative tee-shots) and a good round here requires a sound technique. But it is still a course for golfers of all levels to enjoy, preferably on 4-wheels since some of the slopes are on the steep side. The architecture imposes a certain style of golf with very few options, but the course is good fun. Nature-enthusiasts will love the site, which also boasts a very pleasant hotel and good food. Located at mid-altitude, Taulane is open just eight months a year in an isolated site which gives a feeling of immense calm. In summer, getting away from the crowds and the heat on the coast is a real treat.

Golf de Taulane — 1992

RN 85
F - 83840 LA MARTRE

Office	Secrétariat	(33) 04 93 60 31 30
Pro shop	Pro-shop	(33) 04 93 60 31 30
Fax	Fax	(33) 04 93 60 33 23
Web	www.chateau-taulane.com	
Situation	Situation	

Grasse (pop. 41 380), 50 km

Annual closure	Fermeture annuelle	1/11→1/4
Weekly closure	Fermeture hebdomadaire	no

Fees main season Tarifs haute saison	18 holes	
	Week days Semaine	**We/Bank holidays** We/Férié
Individual Individuel	€ 90	€ 90
Couple Couple	€ 180	€ 180

Caddie Caddie no — **Electric Trolley** Chariot électrique yes

Buggy Voiturette yes — **Clubs** Clubs yes

Credit cards Cartes de crédit
VISA - CB - Eurocard - MasterCard - AMEX - DC

Access Accès : From Nice or Cannes → Grasse/Digne → Le Logis du Pin, "Route Napoléon"
Map 14 on page 187 Carte 14 Page 187

GOLF COURSE — PARCOURS — 15/20

Site	Site	
Maintenance	Entretien	
Architect	Architecte	Gary Player
Type	Type	forest
Relief	Relief	
Water in play	Eau en jeu	
Exp. to wind	Exposé au vent	
Trees in play	Arbres en jeu	

Scorecard Carte de score	**Chp.** Chp.	**Mens** Mess.	**Ladies** Da.
Length Long.	6240	5775	4866
Par	72	72	72
Slope system	134	131	124

Advised golfing ability / Niveau de jeu recommandé: 0 12 24 36

Hcp required Handicap exigé 30

CLUB HOUSE & AMENITIES — CLUB HOUSE ET ANNEXES — 7/10

Pro shop Pro-shop
Driving range Practice

Sheltered couvert 8 mats - On grass sur herbe yes - Putting-green putting-green yes - Pitching-green pitching green yes

HOTEL FACILITIES — ENVIRONNEMENT HOTELIER — 4/10

HOTELS HÔTELS

Château de Taulane - 45 rooms, D € 215 - on site
Tel (33) 04 93 40 60 80, Fax (33) 04 93 60 37 48

Château de Trigance - Trigance 20 km
10 rooms, D € 120
Tel (33) 04 94 76 91 18, Fax (33) 04 94 85 68 99

Auberge du Teillon - La Garde 9 km
8 rooms, D € 49
Tel (33) 04 92 83 60 88, Fax (33) 04 92 83 74 08

RESTAURANTS RESTAURANTS

Nouvel Hôtel du Commerce - Castellane 15 km
Tel (33) 04 92 83 61 00

Auberge du Teillon - La Garde 9 km - Tel (33) 04 92 83 60 88

Toulouse Palmola

15	7	5

Un club vivant et professionnel, où il fait bon s'arrêter. Bien à l'abri du vent, avec de beaux chênes, quelques trouées offrant de jolies vues sur la vallée du Tarn, ce parcours a bien respecté l'environnement. Cette réussite générale rend certainement exigeant. Pour en faire un grand parcours, on souhaiterait bien sûr une modernisation, avec des bunkers un peu plus profonds par exemple. Mais ce n'est pas forcément réclamé par les membres très attachés à leur club. En l'état, il faut déjà savoir jouer tous les coups, et utiliser tous les clubs du sac : les joueurs de bon handicap apprécieront particulièrement sa technicité. Assez varié pour ne jamais être ennuyeux, le tracé de Michael Fenn a évité les trous parallèles, et offre un rythme de jeu bien équilibré, alternant les trous difficiles et les trous plus reposants. Un golf très familial, avec une bonne politique sportive, qui mérite largement la visite, et garde le sens de la mesure : les modifications se font par petites touches. Ainsi, le nouveau départ du 11, 25 m plus loin...

A very lively club where it is always a pleasure to stop-off. Nicely sheltered from the wind, this is a course that has embraced its environment and is laid out amidst some beautiful oaks. A few holes provide splendid views over the Tarn river. This initial positive impression makes the visitor slightly more demanding when it comes to the rest. A little modernization is in order with slightly deeper bunkers, for example, but such changes are not necessarily on the agenda for members who are very attached to their club. As it is, it demands every shot in the book and probably every club in your bag. Low handicappers in particular will enjoy the course's technical aspect. With enough variety never to be boring, Michael Fenn's layout has avoided parallel holes and provides a nicely balanced course. A family-style course which is well organized sports-wise and has retained a sense of proportion. Changes are being made slowly, for instance a new tee-box on hole N°11, pushed back some 27 yards.

Golf de Toulouse Palmola — 1974

F - 31660 BUZET-SUR-TARN

Office	Secrétariat	(33) 05 61 84 20 50
Pro shop	Pro-shop	(33) 05 61 84 20 50
Fax	Fax	(33) 05 61 84 48 92
Web	www.golf.palmola.fr	
Situation	Situation	Toulouse, 20 km
Annual closure	Fermeture annuelle	no
Weekly closure	Fermeture hebdomadaire	tuesday/mardi

Fees main season Tarifs haute saison — 18 holes

	Week days / Semaine	We/Bank holidays / We/Férié
Individual Individuel	€ 50	€ 60
Couple Couple	€ 100	€ 120

Caddie Caddie on request **Electric Trolley** Chariot électrique no

Buggy Voiturette yes **Clubs** Clubs no

Credit cards Cartes de crédit
VISA - CB - Eurocard - MasterCard - AMEX

Access Accès : • A 68 Toulouse → Albi, Exit (Sortie) No 4 Gémil-Buzet sur Tarn • Albi → Toulouse, Exit Montastruc la Conseillière, → Albi (N88), → Golf

Map 13 on page 184 Carte 13 Page 184

GOLF COURSE — PARCOURS — 15/20

Site	Site	
Maintenance	Entretien	
Architect	Architecte	Michael Fenn
Type	Type	forest, residential
Relief	Relief	
Water in play	Eau en jeu	
Exp. to wind	Exposé au vent	
Trees in play	Arbres en jeu	

Scorecard Carte de score	Chp. Chp.	Mens Mess.	Ladies Da.
Length Long.	6181	5949	5292
Par	72	72	72
Slope system	132	131	126

Advised golfing ability Niveau de jeu recommandé: 0 12 24 36

Hcp required Handicap exigé no

CLUB HOUSE & AMENITIES — CLUB HOUSE ET ANNEXES — 7/10

Pro shop Pro-shop

Driving range Practice

Sheltered couvert 4 mats - On grass sur herbe yes - Putting-green putting-green yes - Pitching-green pitching green yes

HOTEL FACILITIES — ENVIRONNEMENT HOTELIER — 5/10

HOTELS HÔTELS

Grand Hôtel de l'Opéra - 57 rooms, D € 161 - Toulouse 20 km
Tel (33) 05 61 21 82 66, Fax (33) 05 61 23 41 04

Beaux Arts - 19 rooms, D € 125 - Toulouse 20 km
Tel (33) 05 34 45 42 42, Fax (33) 05 34 45 42 43

Courtois - 14 rooms, D € 150 - Toulouse 20 km
Tel (33) 05 34 31 94 80, Fax (33) 05 34 31 94 81

RESTAURANTS RESTAURANTS

Les Jardins de l'Opéra - Toulouse 20 km
Tel (33) 05 61 23 07 76

Michel Sarran - Toulouse 20 km - Tel (33) 05 61 12 32 32

Auberge de la Pointe - Saint-Sulpice 10 km
Tel (33) 05 63 41 80 14

Toulouse-Seilh *Rouge*

15	7	6

Un Jeremy Pern typique. Partant d'un terrain plat, il a bien modelé ses mouvements de terrain comme ses bunkers, de toutes formes et de toutes dimensions. Les greens sont vastes, avec des reliefs subtils, permettant de multiples positions de drapeaux. Les obstacles d'eau jouent évidemment un grand rôle dans la stratégie, mais ils ne présentent pas forcément les mêmes dangers selon le vent et les joueurs prudents ont toujours la solution de jouer à l'écart. Peu boisé à l'origine, il a bénéficié d'un programme de plantations, et fait l'objet de programmes immobiliers, mais pas trop agressifs visuellement. Ce parcours de style américain réclame un jeu très complet, et notamment un petit jeu bien affûté, il joue donc bien son rôle de "formation de golfeurs". Ici, la chance ne peut jouer aucun rôle dans un bon score. Les installations sont fonctionnelles, mais elles manquent un peu de charme : un golf commercial a rarement l'aspect familial d'un club privé...

This is a typical Jeremy Pern layout, starting out with flat terrain and carefully designing-in sloping terrain and bunkers of all shapes and sizes. The greens are huge with subtle breaks and afford numerous different pin positions. Water hazards play a major role in game strategy here but are more or less dangerous depending on the wind. The cautious player will of course lay up or play around them. Although there were originally few trees, the plantation programme is beginning to mature as is the number of property developments, which fortunately are not too hard on the eye. Toulouse-Seilh is an American style course requiring an all-round game and some slick short irons, thereby fulfilling its role as a course for "schooling golfers". A good score here owes nothing to luck. The facilities are functional but lack a little charm. Having said that, a business venture like this seldom has the family atmosphere of a private club.

Golf de Toulouse-Seilh Latitudes — 1988

Route de Grenade
F - 31860 SEILH

Office	Secrétariat	(33) 05 62 13 14 14
Pro shop	Pro-shop	(33) 05 62 13 14 14
Fax	Fax	(33) 05 61 42 34 17
Web	www.maeva-latitudes-toulouse.com	
Situation	Situation	Toulouse, 10 km
Annual closure	Fermeture annuelle	no
Weekly closure	Fermeture hebdomadaire	no

Fees main season Tarifs haute saison — full day

	Week days Semaine	We/Bank holidays We/Férié
Individual Individuel	€ 33	€ 49
Couple Couple	€ 66	€ 98

Under 21: € 8 / 23 (We) / Students, € 23 (week only/semaine) / Ladies & Seniors:

Caddie Caddie no — **Electric Trolley** Chariot électrique no

Buggy Voiturette yes — **Clubs** Clubs yes

Credit cards Cartes de crédit
VISA - CB - Eurocard - MasterCard - AMEX - DC

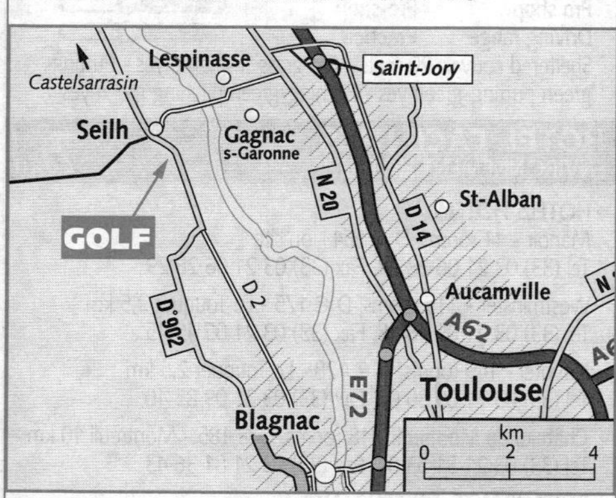

Access Accès : A62 or A61 → Toulouse,
Exit (Sortie) Saint-Jory → Lespinasse → Blagnac, → Golf
Map 12 on page 183 Carte 12 Page 183

GOLF COURSE — PARCOURS — 15/20

Site	Site	
Maintenance	Entretien	
Architect	Architecte	Jeremy Pern, Jean Garaïalde
Type	Type	open country, residential
Relief	Relief	
Water in play	Eau en jeu	
Exp. to wind	Exposé au vent	
Trees in play	Arbres en jeu	

Scorecard Carte de score	Chp. Chp.	Mens Mess.	Ladies Da.
Length Long.	6331	5862	4737
Par	72	72	72
Slope system	136	134	128

Advised golfing ability — 0 12 24 36
Niveau de jeu recommandé
Hcp required Handicap exigé 24

CLUB HOUSE & AMENITIES — CLUB HOUSE ET ANNEXES — 7/10

Pro shop Pro-shop
Driving range Practice
Sheltered couvert 30 mats - On grass sur herbe yes - Putting-green putting-green yes - Pitching-green pitching green yes

HOTEL FACILITIES — ENVIRONNEMENT HOTELIER — 6/10

HOTELS HÔTELS

Maeva Latitudes - 172 rooms, D € 104 - on site
Tel (33) 05 62 13 14 15, Fax (33) 05 61 59 77 97

Jean Jaurès "Les Capitouls" - Toulouse 10 km
51 rooms, D € 110
Tel (33) 05 34 41 31 21, Fax (33) 05 61 63 15 17

Holiday Inn Toulouse Centre - Toulouse 10 km
160 rooms, D € 135
Tel (33) 05 61 10 70 70, Fax (33) 05 61 21 96 70

RESTAURANTS RESTAURANTS

Frégate - Toulouse 10 km - Tel (33) 05 61 21 62 45
Le Pastel - Toulouse-Mirail 18 km - Tel (33) 05 62 87 84 30
7 Place Saint Sernin - Toulouse 10 km - Tel (33) 05 62 30 05 30

Touquet (Le) *La Mer*

16 | 5 | 7

Avec des reliefs modérés, des fairways travaillés, des bunkers redoutables et des greens parfois déconcertants, ce 18 trous est un links classique. Une bonne partie des trous se déroulent dans des dunes spectaculaires : ici, il faut être humble avec son golf, les erreurs sont immédiatement punies et plus encore quand le vent s'en mêle. Alors, les "manieurs de balles" et les tacticiens prennent le dessus sur les purs frappeurs. Difficile pour les débutants, ce parcours reste passionnant pour les joueurs aguerris, mais ceux qui le connaissaient "avant" peuvent avoir des regrets sur sa restauration. Le rétablissement d'un tracé proche de celui d'avant-guerre, n'a pas vraiment été fait avec la rigueur architecturale nécessaire et la fidélité au style des architectes originaux Taylor et Harry Colt. "La Mer" n'est plus tout à fait ce qu'elle était, mais reste à connaître. L'autre 18 trous (La Forêt) est un bon complément, le club-house pas à la hauteur de cet ensemble...

With moderately undulating and carefully designed fairways, some formidable bunkers and sometimes disconcerting greens, this 18-hole layout is your classic links course. A good number of holes are laid out amongst some spectacular dunes and call for a little humility: mis-hit shots are punished immediately, especially when the wind lends a hand. Flighters of the ball and the shrewd tactician will find the going easier than the long-hitter. A tough course for beginners but one that is exciting for the seasoned golfer, although players who knew it "before" may still rue the way it has been restored. The return to a layout close to the original pre-war design has not really been carried out with the architectural thoroughness or fidelity to the style preferred by the original architects Taylor and Harry Colt. These days, "La Mer" is not quite what it used to be but is worth getting to know. The other 18-hole layout (La Forêt) is a good complementary course but the club-house does not measure up.

Golf du Touquet — 1904

Avenue du Golf
F - 62520 LE TOUQUET

Office Secrétariat (33) 03 21 06 28 00
Pro shop Pro-shop (33) 03 21 06 28 00
Fax Fax (33) 03 21 06 28 01
Web www.opengolfclub.com
Situation Situation Le Touquet, 2,5 km

Annual closure Fermeture annuelle — no
Weekly closure Fermeture hebdomadaire — no

Fees main season Tarifs haute saison	Week days Semaine	We/Bank holidays We/Férié
	18 holes	
Individual Individuel	€ 59	€ 69
Couple Couple	€ 118	€ 138

Under 25: – 30%

Caddie Caddie on request **Electric Trolley** Chariot électrique no
Buggy Voiturette yes **Clubs** Clubs yes
Credit cards Cartes de crédit
VISA - CB - Eurocard - MasterCard - AMEX

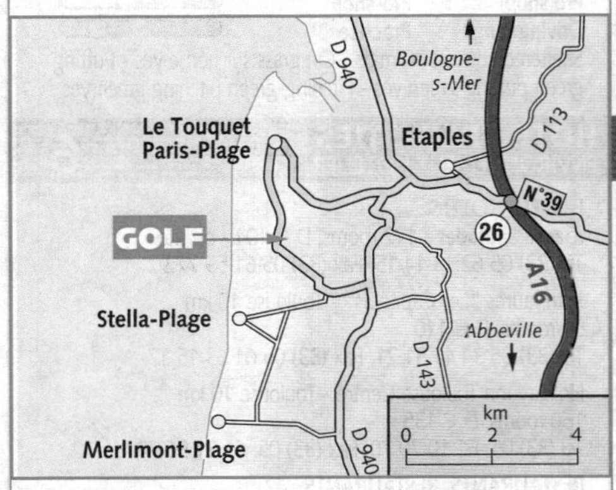

Access Accès : Le Touquet, → Golf
Map 1 on page 160 Carte 1 Page 160

GOLF COURSE — PARCOURS 16/20

Site Site
Maintenance Entretien
Architect Architecte — J.H. Taylor, Harry S. Colt
Type Type — links
Relief Relief
Water in play Eau en jeu
Exp. to wind Exposé au vent
Trees in play Arbres en jeu

Scorecard Carte de score	Chp. Chp.	Mens Mess.	Ladies Da.
Length Long.	6275	5890	5005
Par	72	72	72
Slope system	131	129	120

Advised golfing ability Niveau de jeu recommandé — 0 12 24 36
Hcp required Handicap exigé — 24 Men, 28 Ladies

CLUB HOUSE & AMENITIES — CLUB HOUSE ET ANNEXES 5/10

Pro shop Pro-shop
Driving range Practice
Sheltered couvert 20 mats - On grass sur herbe yes - Putting-green putting-green yes - Pitching-green pitching green yes

HOTEL FACILITIES — ENVIRONNEMENT HOTELIER 7/10

HOTELS HÔTELS
Manoir - 41 rooms, D € 164 - on site
Tel (33) 03 21 06 28 28, Fax (33) 03 21 06 28 29

Westminster - 115 rooms, D € 175 - Le Touquet 2,5 km
Tel (33) 03 21 05 48 48, Fax (33) 03 21 05 45 45

Novotel - 149 rooms, D € 128 - Le Touquet 2,5 km
Tel (33) 03 21 09 85 00, Fax (33) 03 21 09 85 40

Château de Montreuil - 18 rooms, D € 185 - Montreuil 10 km
Tel (33) 03 21 81 53 04, Fax (33) 03 21 81 36 43

RESTAURANTS RESTAURANTS
Le Village Suisse - Le Touquet 2,5 km - Tel (33) 03 21 05 69 93
Château de Montreuil - Montreuil 10 km
Tel (33) 03 21 81 53 04

Val de Sorne

14	7	5

Dans une région pas très riche en golfs, la création de ce golf était bienvenue. Dessiné sur un terrain modérément accidenté par Hugues Lambert dans un style plus américain que britannique, il comporte des obstacles d'eau sur une demi-douzaine de trous. En jouant des départs avancés et même si certains dévers obligent à des coups délicats dans les pentes, il est accessible à tous les niveaux, à l'exception du 16, par 4 difficile dont le green est très défendu par l'eau. Le déroulement du parcours est assez agréable, sans être d'un tracé vraiment exceptionnel, les arbres sont souvent bien en jeu (comme au 13), mais il vaut mieux le visiter entre mai et octobre, même si des drainages efficaces ont été effectués. Les greens sont de dimensions et de difficultés moyennes : leur modelage un peu timide conviendra à tous les handicaps, et leurs défenses ne sont pas trop hermétiques. L'entretien est très correct, les vues sur le Jura très jolies. Un ensemble plaisant et sympathique avec hôtel sur place.

This course was most welcome in a region where golf playing facilities are few and far between. Laid out over a moderately hilly terrain by Hugues Lambert in a rather more American style than British, it features water hazards on half a dozen or so holes. From the front-tees, and despite sloping fairways which call for some tricky shot-making, the course can be played by golfers of all abilities, with the possible exception of the 16th, a difficult par 4 where the green is tightly protected by water. The course unfolds in a pleasant manner without ever being outstanding and trees are often very much in play (on the 13th, for example). And even though drainage work looks to be effective, the best time to play here is between May and October. The greens are averagely large and difficult but sufficiently flat and bunker-free to appeal to all handicaps. Green-keeping is very decent and the views of the Jura mountains a pretty sight indeed. A pleasant and friendly club with an on-site hotel.

Golf du Val de Sorne — 1993

Vernantois
F - 39570 LONS-LE-SAUNIER

Office	Secrétariat	(33) 03 84 43 04 80
Pro shop	Pro-shop	(33) 03 84 43 04 80
Fax	Fax	(33) 03 84 47 31 21
Web	www.valdesorne.com	
Situation	Situation	Lons-le-Saunier, 6 km
Annual closure	Fermeture annuelle	18/12→2/1
Weekly closure	Fermeture hebdomadaire	no

Fees main season Tarifs haute saison — 18 holes

	Week days Semaine	We/Bank holidays We/Férié
Individual Individuel	€ 42	€ 53
Couple Couple	€ 76	€ 94

Under 18 and Students: – 50%(week days) and –30% (We)

Caddie Caddie no — **Electric Trolley** Chariot électrique no
Buggy Voiturette yes — **Clubs** Clubs yes
Credit cards Cartes de crédit
VISA - CB - Eurocard - MasterCard - AMEX

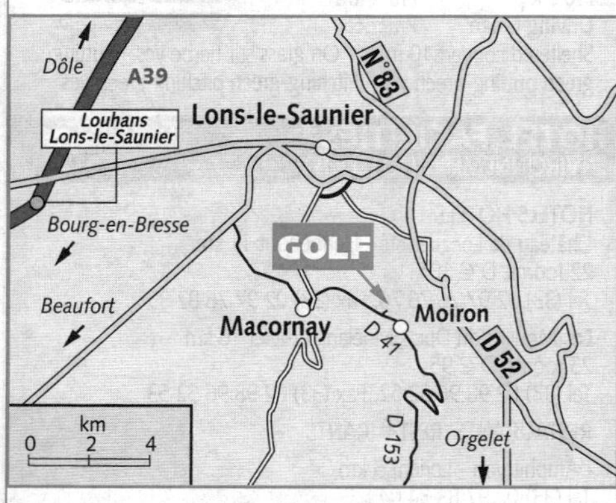

Access Accès : Lons-le-Saunier → Macornay, then → Vernantois, → Golf
Map 8 on page 174 Carte 8 Page 174

GOLF COURSE — PARCOURS — 14/20

Site	Site	
Maintenance	Entretien	
Architect	Architecte	Hugues Lambert
Type	Type	parkland
Relief	Relief	
Water in play	Eau en jeu	
Exp. to wind	Exposé au vent	
Trees in play	Arbres en jeu	

Scorecard Carte de score	Chp. Chp.	Mens Mess.	Ladies Da.
Length Long.	6000	5809	4927
Par	72	72	72
Slope system	131	131	128

Advised golfing ability Niveau de jeu recommandé — 0 12 24 36
Hcp required Handicap exigé — no

CLUB HOUSE & AMENITIES — CLUB HOUSE ET ANNEXES — 7/10

Pro shop Pro-shop
Driving range Practice
Sheltered couvert 5 mats - On grass sur herbe no - Putting-green putting-green yes - Pitching-green pitching green yes

HOTEL FACILITIES — ENVIRONNEMENT HOTELIER — 5/10

HOTELS HÔTELS
Hôtel du Golf - 36 rooms, D € 110 - on site
Tel (33) 03 84 43 04 80, Fax (33) 03 84 47 31 21

Hostellerie des Monts-de-Vaux - Poligny 29 km
10 rooms, D € 150
Tel (33) 03 84 37 12 50, Fax (33) 03 84 37 09 07

Moulin de Bourgchâteau - 19 rooms, D € 60 - Louhans 26 km
Tel (33) 03 85 75 37 12, Fax (33) 03 85 75 45 11

RESTAURANTS RESTAURANTS
La Comédie - Lons-le-Saunier 6 km - Tel (33) 03 84 24 20 66
Auberge de Chavannes - Courlans 8 km
Tel (33) 03 84 47 05 52
Relais d'Alsace - Lons-le-Saunier 6 km - Tel (33) 03 84 47 24 70

Val Queven

14 | 6 | 5

Cet espace vallonné dans la vallée du Scorff, en pleine campagne bretonne, est ponctué de beaux arbres, notamment des chênes et châtaigniers, qui protègent bien du vent assez fréquent dans la région sans être oppressants. Comme à son habitude, l'architecte Yves Bureau a dessiné un parcours très honorable, bien paysagé et assez large pour être rassurant, assez technique pour renouveler l'intérêt. Les bons scores ne sont pourtant pas si faciles car il faut tenir compte des dénivellations et de la présence de nombreux bunkers bien découpés. Les greens sont de bonne dimension, et bien construits, les obstacles d'eau peu nombreux. Tous les niveaux de jeu peuvent cohabiter ici, les joueurs moyens comme les meilleurs handicaps. Comme souvent en Bretagne, on peut y croiser de nombreux Britanniques, ils y sont à l'aise car le style du parcours ne les dépayse pas trop. La présence d'un tumulus antique fera rêver les amateurs d'histoire.

This is a site of rolling landscape in the Scorff valley at the heart of Breton countryside. It is dotted with some fine trees, particularly oak and horse-chestnut, which afford good protection from the frequent wind but are never too intrusive. As usual, architect Yves Bureau has laid out a very respectable course, full of variety, well-landscaped and wide enough to reassure most of us, yet technically difficult enough to keep it interesting. Having said that, good scores here are not always easy to come by, courtesy of some steep slopes and numerous neatly outlined bunkers. The greens are of a good size and well designed, and water hazards are rare. Golfers of all handicaps can play together here. And as is often the case in Brittany, you will encounter a large number of Brits for whom this style of course is almost like home from home. One little curiosity is the presence on the course of a "tumulus" or sepulchral mound.

Golf de Val Queven — 1990

Kerruisseau
F - 56530 QUEVEN

Office Secrétariat (33) 02 97 05 17 96
Pro shop Pro-shop (33) 02 97 05 17 96
Fax Fax (33) 02 97 05 19 18
Web www.formulegolf.com
Situation Situation Lorient (pop. 59 270), 8 km
Annual closure Fermeture annuelle no
Weekly closure Fermeture hebdomadaire tuesday
(mardi): 12 → 02

Fees main season Tarifs haute saison	18 holes	
	Week days Semaine	**We/Bank holidays** We/Férié
Individual Individuel	€ 48	€ 48
Couple Couple	€ 96	€ 96

Under 21 & Students (under 25): – 50%

Caddie Caddie no — **Electric Trolley** Chariot électrique no
Buggy Voiturette yes — **Clubs** Clubs yes
Credit cards Cartes de crédit
VISA - CB - Eurocard - MasterCard

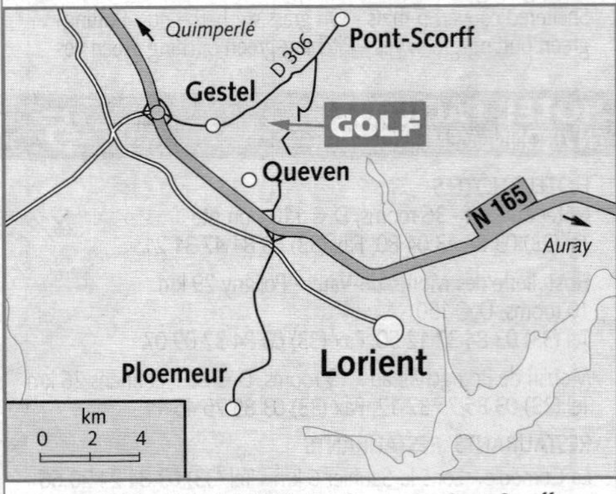

Access Accès : N165, Exit (Sortie) Queven → Pont-Scorff. Queven, 1 km → Golf
Map 5 on page 169 Carte 5 Page 169

GOLF COURSE — PARCOURS — 14/20

Site Site
Maintenance Entretien
Architect Architecte Yves Bureau
Type Type country, forest
Relief Relief
Water in play Eau en jeu
Exp. to wind Exposé au vent
Trees in play Arbres en jeu

Scorecard Carte de score	**Chp.** Chp.	**Mens** Mess.	**Ladies** Da.
Length Long.	6017	5657	4968
Par	72	72	72
Slope system	123	118	121

Advised golfing ability 0 12 24 36
Niveau de jeu recommandé
Hcp required Handicap exigé no

CLUB HOUSE & AMENITIES — CLUB HOUSE ET ANNEXES — 6/10

Pro shop Pro-shop
Driving range Practice
Sheltered couvert 10 mats - On grass sur herbe yes - Putting-green putting-green yes - Pitching-green pitching green yes

HOTEL FACILITIES — ENVIRONNEMENT HOTELIER — 5/10

HOTELS HÔTELS
Château de Locguénolé - Hennebont 11 km
22 rooms, D € 185
Tel (33) 02 97 76 76 76, Fax (33) 02 97 76 82 35

Les Moulins du Duc - Moëlan-sur-Mer 16 km
25 rooms, D € 95
Tel (33) 02 98 96 52 52, Fax (33) 02 98 96 52 53

RESTAURANTS RESTAURANTS
L'Amphitryon - Lorient 5 km
Tel (33) 02 97 83 34 04

Le Jardin Gourmand - Lorient 8 km
Tel (33) 02 97 64 17 24

Vents d'Ouest - Lorient 8 km - Tel (33) 02 97 21 57 06

Vaucouleurs (La) *Les Vallons* | 14 | 7 | 4

Beaucoup moins boisé que le parcours de "La Rivière", "Les Vallons" est d'un style radicalement différent, où l'architecte Michel Gayon a rendu hommage aux links britanniques. Il s'agit d'une sorte de parcours de bord de mer sans la mer, avec de nombreuses buttes délimitant bien les fairways, et donnant du relief à un terrain originellement assez plat. Il n'est pas très long, et les frappeurs pourront se livrer, mais c'est un parcours plus dangereux et difficile à scorer qu'il n'y paraît et les greens peuvent être parfois complexes à lire. Quelques nouveaux bunkers (avec les traditionnels renforts de bois) vont renforcer leurs défenses et on souhaite que les roughs (élément essentiel ici) soient maintenus à leur niveau, même si le slope est ridiculement bas pour un parcours aussi exposé au vent. Un regret : le seul obstacle d'eau (au 18) ne pénalise que les "moins bons" joueurs. Le complexe de La Vaucouleurs est un ensemble à connaître pour sa variété, et ce parcours est moins sensible que son voisin à l'humidité.

With little or no woodland, "Les Vallons" is radically different from "La Rivière" and is something of a tribute by architect Michel Gayon to British style links golfing. It is certainly a sort of seaside course, without the sea of course, with a number of sand-hills and rough clearly defining the fairways and giving considerable relief to terrain that was originally flat. It is not very long and big-hitters can let fly, but the course is more dangerous and harder to master than it looks, and some of the greens are tricky to read. A few new bunkers (with the traditional wooden rail-sleepers) have strengthened the course's defences and we would like to always see the rough kept at its "high" level, even though the slope index is ridiculously low for a course that is so exposed to the wind. Our one regret is that the single water hazard (on the 18th) penalizes only the "not-so-good" golfer. This estate of La Vaucouleurs is a complex worth getting to know for its variety.

Golf-Club de la Vaucouleurs — 1989

F - 78910 CIVRY-LA-FORET

Office	Secrétariat	(33) 01 34 87 62 29
Pro shop	Pro-shop	(33) 01 34 87 62 29
Fax	Fax	(33) 01 34 87 70 09
Web	www.vaucouleurs.fr	
Situation	Situation	Paris, 61 km
Annual closure	Fermeture annuelle	23/12→2/1
Weekly closure	Fermeture hebdomadaire	

wednesday/mercredi, from 01/10 to 31/03

Fees main season Tarifs haute saison	full day	
	Week days Semaine	**We/Bank holidays** We/Férié
Individual Individuel	€ 44	€ 65
Couple Couple	€ 77	€ 120

Students and under 25: € 30 / 45 (We)
Tuesday (mardi): GF € 35

Caddie Caddie no — **Electric Trolley** Chariot électrique yes
Buggy Voiturette yes — **Clubs** Clubs yes
Credit cards Cartes de crédit
VISA - CB - Eurocard - MasterCard - AMEX

Access Accès : A13 Paris/Rouen, Exit (Sortie) Mantes-la-Jolie, D983 → Houdan. In Orvilliers, turn right → Golf
Map 3 on page 164 Carte 3 Page 164

GOLF COURSE — PARCOURS 14/20

Site	Site	
Maintenance	Entretien	
Architect	Architecte	Michel Gayon
Type	Type	links, country
Relief	Relief	
Water in play	Eau en jeu	
Exp. to wind	Exposé au vent	
Trees in play	Arbres en jeu	

Scorecard Carte de score	**Chp.** Chp.	**Mens** Mess.	**Ladies** Da.
Length Long.	5533	5145	4284
Par	70	70	70
Slope system	121	114	117

Advised golfing ability Niveau de jeu recommandé — 0 12 24 36
Hcp required Handicap exigé — no

CLUB HOUSE & AMENITIES — CLUB HOUSE ET ANNEXES 7/10

Pro shop Pro-shop
Driving range Practice
Sheltered couvert 6 mats - On grass sur herbe yes (summer)
Putting-green putting-green yes - Pitching-green pitching green yes

HOTEL FACILITIES — ENVIRONNEMENT HOTELIER 4/10

HOTELS HÔTELS
Dousseine - 20 rooms, D € 60 - Anet 16 km
Tel (33) 02 37 41 49 93, Fax (33) 02 37 41 90 54
Château de Berchères - Berchères-sur-Vesgre 7 km
21 rooms, D € 130
Tel (33) 02 37 82 28 22, Fax (33) 02 37 82 28 23

RESTAURANTS RESTAURANTS
Moulin de la Reillère - Mantes-la-Ville 18 km
Tel (33) 01 30 92 22 00
Auberge de la Truite - Rosay 10 km
Tel (33) 01 34 76 30 52
Manoir d'Anet - Anet 16 km - Tel (33) 02 37 41 91 05

Villette d'Anthon *Les Sangliers*

16	7	5

A côté du très honnête 18 trous des "Brocards", qui permet à tous les niveaux d'évoluer sans grande pression, le plus récent 18 trous (Les Sangliers), signé par Hugues Lambert, mérite largement le détour, mais ce sont les joueurs de moins de 24 de handicap qui l'apprécieront le plus. Très long (parfois à l'excès), avec de l'eau en jeu sur la moitié des trous, quelques buttes, des arbres menaçants et pas mal de bunkers, il exige un jeu très complet, et beaucoup de puissance si l'on veut tenir son handicap, même des départs avancés. Ses nombreux obstacles impliquent de le jouer plusieurs fois avant d'en comprendre les aspects stratégiques. Si l'on manque les greens, bien travaillés, il faut bien savoir manier la balle. Malgré certains trous un peu uniformes, et quelques dessins de bunkers à revoir, c'est incontestablement l'un des meilleurs parcours de la région. Une récente redéfinition des fairways et roughs par une tonte attentive en a beaucoup amélioré l'aspect. Ce genre d'effort est trop rare pour ne pas être salué.

Besides "Les Brocards", a fair 18-hole course and a pleasant round of golf for players of all levels, the more recent "Les Sangliers" is a much more enticing proposition, although a 24 handicap would seem to be the minimum requirement for enjoying the course. Very long (sometimes excessively so) with water on half the holes, a few sand-hills, some threatening trees and a lot of bunkers, the course demands an all-round game and power, even from the front tees. The countless hazards imply several exploratory rounds before fully understanding the strategic side to the course. If you miss the carefully designed greens, you will need some excellent ball-control to recover. Despite a certain number of slightly monotonous holes and bunkering that could do with some redesigning in places, this is unquestionably one of the region's very best courses. Recent redefinition of the fairways and rough has done much to improve appearances. This kind of effort is all too rare for us not to mention it.

Golf Club de Lyon — 1992

F - 38280 VILLETTE-D'ANTHON

Office	Secrétariat	(33) 04 78 31 11 33
Pro shop	Pro-shop	(33) 04 78 31 11 33
Fax	Fax	(33) 04 72 02 48 27
Web	www.golfclubdelyon.com	
Situation	Situation	Lyon, 20 km
Annual closure	Fermeture annuelle	no
Weekly closure	Fermeture hebdomadaire	no

Fees main season Tarifs haute saison		18 holes
	Week days Semaine	**We/Bank holidays** We/Férié
Individual Individuel	€ 50	€ 70
Couple Couple	€ 100	€ 140

Under 18 wednesday (mercredi): € 30 / 18/07 → 31/08: GF € 30

Caddy Caddy on request **Electric Trolley** Chariot électrique no

Buggy Voiturette yes **Clubs** Clubs yes

Credit cards Cartes de crédit
VISA - CB - Eurocard - MasterCard - AMEX - DC

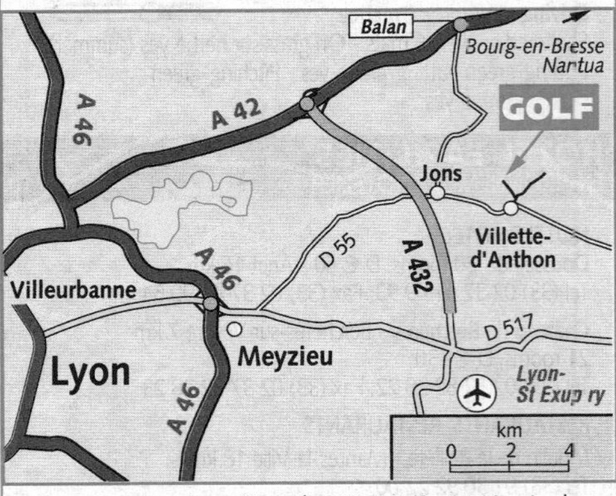

Access Accès : • Lyon, "Rocade Est", Exit (Sortie) Meyzieu le Carreau → Villette d'Anthon • A42 Bourg-en-Bresse Lyon, Exit (Sortie) Balan, → Jons, Villette d'Anthon

Map 11 on page 180 Carte 11 Page 180

GOLF COURSE — PARCOURS 16/20

Site	Site	
Maintenance	Entretien	
Architect	Architecte	Hugues Lambert
Type	Type	forest, country
Relief	Relief	
Water in play	Eau en jeu	
Exp. to wind	Exposé au vent	
Trees in play	Arbres en jeu	

Scorecard Carte de score	**Chp.** Chp.	**Mens** Mess.	**Ladies** Da.
Length Long.	6228	5911	5058
Par	72	72	72
Slope system	131	125	129

Advised golfing ability Niveau de jeu recommandé: 0 12 24 36

Hcp required Handicap exigé 35

CLUB HOUSE & AMENITIES — CLUB HOUSE ET ANNEXES 7/10

Pro shop Pro-shop

Driving range Practice

Sheltered couvert 12 mats - On grass sur herbe yes - Putting-green putting-green yes - Pitching-green pitching green yes (3)

HOTEL FACILITIES — ENVIRONNEMENT HOTELIER 5/10

HOTELS HÔTELS

Mont-Joyeux - 20 rooms, D € 112 - Meyzieu 12 km
Tel (33) 04 78 04 21 32, Fax (33) 04 72 02 85 72

Auberge de Jons - 25 rooms, D € 92 - Jons 5 km
Tel (33) 04 78 31 29 85, Fax (33) 04 72 02 48 24

Villa Florentine - 20 km - Lyon (Vieux-Lyon)
28 rooms, D € 250
Tel (33) 04 72 56 56 56, Fax (33) 04 72 40 90 56

RESTAURANTS RESTAURANTS

Paul Bocuse - Collonges-au-Mont-d'Or 25 km
Tel (33) 04 72 42 90 90

Léon de Lyon - Lyon 20 km - Tel (33) 04 72 10 11 12

Le Jura (Bouchon) - Lyon 20 km - Tel (33) 04 78 42 20 57

Volcans (Les)

14	6	5

Situé à près de 900 mètres d'altitude au pied du Puy de Dôme, ce parcours peut parfois être gelé le matin, sauf en été, il faut s'en informer avant de prendre la route. Environné de bouleaux, de pins, de buissons sauvages et de bruyère, il présente une forte montée du 9 au 10, mais pas assez épuisante pour obliger à prendre une voiturette. Le dessin du professionnel local, Lucien Roux, ne prétend certes pas aux plus hautes distinctions, mais il reste plaisant et varié, avec une bonne utilisation des arbres et des bunkers, quelques greens délicats à double plateau, et un bon rythme de distribution des difficultés. Le parcours peut paraître un peu long du fond, mais les balles portent plus loin en altitude, et les départs avancés (notamment sur les longs par 3) permettent de prendre beaucoup de plaisir dans ce golf sympathique et très familial, situé dans un environnement magnifique et calme, avec neuf trous supplémentaires. Les professionnels du "Challenge Tour" jouent tous les ans ici avec plaisir, on les comprend.

Lying 900 metres above sea level at the foot of the Puy de Dôme, this course is often frost-bound in the morning outside the summer months, so call the secretary before setting out. Surrounded by birch trees, pines, wild bushes and heather, there is a steep climb between the 9th and 10th, although not tiring enough to warrant a buggy. Designed by local pro Lucien Roux, the layout cannot and would not claim any of the higher accolades, but it is a pleasant and varied course with excellent use of trees and bunkers, a few tricky, two-tiered greens and nicely balanced hazards and trouble. The course looks a little long from the back-tees, but the thin air at altitude adds length to the drive. Playing from the front tees (especially the long par 3s) is great fun in this very friendly and family-style club, located in a magnificently calm setting and now boasting an additional 9-hole course. Pros on the Challenge Tour play here every year and thoroughly enjoy it. Play it and you will understand why.

Golf des Volcans — 1985

La Bruyère des Moines
F - 63870 ORCINES

Office	Secrétariat	(33) 04 73 62 15 51
Pro shop	Pro-shop	(33) 04 73 62 15 51
Fax	Fax	(33) 04 73 62 26 52
Web	www.golfdesvolcans.com	
Situation	Situation	Clermont-Ferrand, 8 km
Annual closure	Fermeture annuelle	no
Weekly closure	Fermeture hebdomadaire	no

Restaurant closed Tuesday (mardi) (15/01 → 31/03)

Fees main season Tarifs haute saison 18 holes

	Week days Semaine	We/Bank holidays We/Férié
Individual Individuel	€ 43	€ 49
Couple Couple	€ 75	€ 85

Under 25 & Students: € 23 / 28 (We)

Caddy Caddy no — **Electric Trolley** Chariot électrique no

Buggy Voiturette yes — **Clubs** Clubs yes

Credit cards Cartes de crédit
VISA - CB - Eurocard - MasterCard

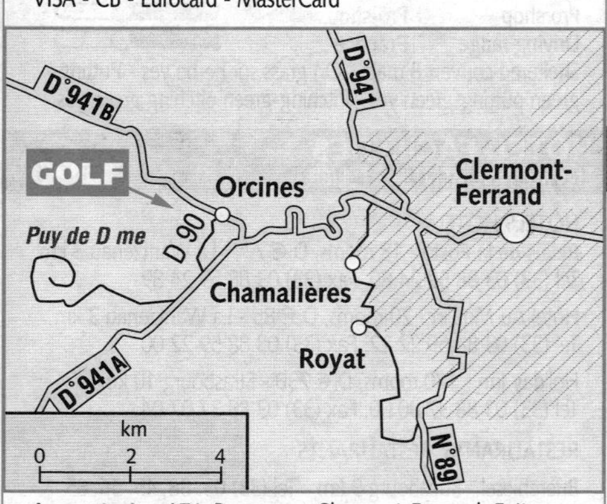

Access Accès : A71, Bourges → Clermont-Ferrand, Exit (Sortie) Clermont-Ferrand Centre → Le Puy-de-Dôme → Orcines

Map 10 on page 179 Carte 10 Page 179

GOLF COURSE
PARCOURS — 14/20

Site	Site	
Maintenance	Entretien	
Architect	Architecte	Lucien Roux
Type	Type	country, mountain
Relief	Relief	
Water in play	Eau en jeu	
Exp. to wind	Exposé au vent	
Trees in play	Arbres en jeu	

Scorecard Carte de score	Chp. Chp.	Mens Mess.	Ladies Da.
Length Long.	6136	5892	4962
Par	72	72	72
Slope system	126	123	122

Advised golfing ability Niveau de jeu recommandé — 0 12 24 36

Hcp required Handicap exigé 35

CLUB HOUSE & AMENITIES
CLUB HOUSE ET ANNEXES — 6/10

Pro shop Pro-shop
Driving range Practice
Sheltered couvert 20 mats - On grass sur herbe no, 20 mats open air - Putting-green putting-green yes (3) - Pitching-green pitching green yes

HOTEL FACILITIES
ENVIRONNEMENT HOTELIER — 5/10

HOTELS HÔTELS

Hôtel Radio - 26 rooms, D € 86 - Chamalières 3 km
Tel (33) 04 73 30 87 83, Fax (33) 04 73 36 42 44

Holiday Inn Garden Court - Clermont-Ferrand 8 km
94 rooms, D € 120
Tel (33) 04 73 17 48 48, Fax (33) 04 73 35 58 47

Europe Hôtel - 33 rooms, D € 59 - Chamalières 3 km
Tel (33) 04 73 37 61 35, Fax (33) 04 73 31 16 59

RESTAURANTS RESTAURANTS

Hôtel Radio - Chamalières 3 km - Tel (33) 04 73 30 87 33
Bernard Andrieux - Durtol 5 km - Tel (33) 04 73 19 25 00
Emmanuel Hodencq - Clermont-Ferrand 8 km
Tel (33) 04 73 31 23 23

Wantzenau (La)

16	6	6

C'est la Floride à l'alsacienne, avec un club-house de couleur locale et plutôt réussi. Le paysage est parsemé d'étangs venant en jeu sur une grande partie des 18 trous, essentiellement au retour, ce qui crée une forte pression sur les joueurs peu expérimentés. On signalera la grande qualité de dessin des par 5, très risqués à attaquer au deuxième coup, et l'habileté de Jeremy Pern à tirer parti d'un espace très plat : les amateurs de Toulouse-Seilh ou de La Bresse n'en seront pas surpris. Les mouvements de terrain sont subtils et utiles, les greens assez vastes, mais leur entrée est généralement ouverte, ce qui permet de jouer la sécurité dans la plupart des cas, quitte à faire confiance à son petit jeu pour sauver le par. Même si l'on est bien loin de tout océan, le vent peut intervenir de manière importante sur ce parcours de très bonne facture, aux obstacles bien visibles, et technique quel que soit le départ choisi. Une belle réalisation dans une région riche en parcours de qualité.

Welcome to Florida in Alsace, where US style golf combines with a rather attractive local-style club-house. The landscape is dotted with lakes in play on the large majority of the 18 holes, basically on the back nine, and this puts a lot of pressure on inexperienced players. The par 5s are particularly well-laid out and going for the green in two is a risky business. Architect Jeremy Pern has intelligently made the best use of very flat terrain. Golfers who like Toulouse-Seilh or La Bresse will not be surprised here. There has been some subtle and useful grading work and the greens are huge and generally undefended up-front, thus allowing players to play safe, even if it means counting on their short game to save par. Although the course is far from any sea, it can get windy and this makes a big difference on what is an excellent course with clearly visible hazards, whichever tees you play from. A fine layout in a region where excellent golf courses abound.

Golf de la Wantzenau — 1991

CD 302
F - 67610 LA WANTZENAU

Office Secrétariat (33) 03 88 96 37 73
Pro shop Pro-shop (33) 03 88 96 33 71
Fax Fax (33) 03 88 96 34 71
Web www.golf-wantzenau.fr
Situation Situation Strasbourg, 12 km
Annual closure Fermeture annuelle 23/12→2/1
Weekly closure Fermeture hebdomadaire no

Fees main season Tarifs haute saison — 18 holes

	Week days / Semaine	We/Bank holidays / We/Férié
Individual Individuel	€ 61	€ 61
Couple Couple	€ 122	€ 122

Under 18: – 50%

Caddy Caddy no **Electric Trolley** Chariot électrique no
Buggy Voiturette yes **Clubs** Clubs yes
Credit cards Cartes de crédit
VISA - CB - Eurocard - MasterCard

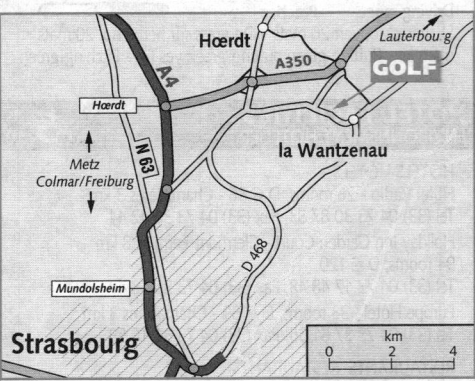

Access Accès : Strasbourg, D468 → La Wantzenau, → Golf
Map 4 on page 167 Carte 4 Page 167

GOLF COURSE — PARCOURS — 16/20

Site Site
Maintenance Entretien
Architect Architecte Jeremy Pern, Jean Garaïalde
Type Type open country, residential
Relief Relief
Water in play Eau en jeu
Exp. to wind Exposé au vent
Trees in play Arbres en jeu

Scorecard / Carte de score	Chp. / Chp.	Mens / Mess.	Ladies / Da.
Length Long.	6162	5641	4827
Par	72	72	72
Slope system	138	129	127

Advised golfing ability Niveau de jeu recommandé 0 12 24 36
Hcp required Handicap exigé no

CLUB HOUSE & AMENITIES — CLUB HOUSE ET ANNEXES — 6/10

Pro shop Pro-shop
Driving range Practice
Sheltered couvert 8 mats - On grass sur herbe yes - Putting-green putting-green yes - Pitching-green pitching green yes

HOTEL FACILITIES — ENVIRONNEMENT HOTELIER — 6/10

HOTELS HÔTELS
Relais de la Poste - 18 rooms, D € 77 - La Wantzenau 3 km
Tel (33) 03 88 59 24 80, Fax (33) 03 88 59 24 89

Hôtel Au Moulin - 20 rooms, D € 85 - La Wantzenau 3 km
Tel (33) 03 88 59 22 22, Fax (33) 03 88 59 22 00

Holiday Inn - 170 rooms, D € 230 - Strasbourg 10 km
Tel (33) 03 88 37 80 00, Fax (33) 03 88 37 07 04

RESTAURANTS RESTAURANTS
Buerehiesel - Strasbourg 9 km - Tel (33) 03 88 45 56 65
Au Moulin - La Wantzenau 3 km - Tel (33) 03 88 96 20 01
Au Crocodile - Strasbourg 10 km
Tel (33) 03 88 32 13 02

Wimereux

13 | 4 | 5

Si l'on recherche le confort et luxe, il faut passer son chemin, les installations étant spartiates. En revanche, cette simplicité contribue à en faire probablement le parcours français le plus proche des premiers links d'Ecosse, jusqu'aux trous de lapins dans le sol sablonneux, qui occupent fermement les lieux. Généralement plat, avec une multitude de profonds bunkers, Wimereux peut présenter un visage aussi souriant et indulgent par beau temps (quand les balles roulent bien) qu'il peut se montrer brutal dès que souffle le vent. Créé en 1907, il a été remanié en 1958 sans trop perdre de son caractère ni de son charme un peu désuet. Ce refus de tout aspect sophistiqué, l'absence d'obstacles d'eau (la mer est à 200 mètres) et d'arbres en jeu peuvent rassurer les amateurs de tous niveaux, qui devront néanmoins éviter les écarts, le grand rough étant redoutable. On souhaiterait cependant une modernisation respectueuse des lieux, face à la concurrence, et l'arrosage automatique était un minimum.

If you are looking for comfort and luxury, drive on, as the facilities here are Spartan. This simplicity probably helps make this the closest French course to the original Scottish links, even as far as the many rabbit-holes in the sandy soil (all part of the scenery). Generally flat with any number of deep bunkers, Wimereux can be as leisurely and forgiving in fine weather as it can be mean and unloving when the wind blows. Created in 1907, it was restyled in 1958 without sacrificing too much of the original character or yesteryear charm. This refusal of anything over-sophisticated, the absence of water hazards (the sea is 200 metres away) and trees in play are enough to reassure golfers of all playing abilities, as long as they keep on the straight and narrow. Be warned, the rough is wicked. We would however like to see some modernization work done here, given the competition from other courses, and an automatic watering was a basic minimum.

Golf de Wimereux — 1907

Route d'Ambleteuse
F - 62930 WIMEREUX

Office Secrétariat (33) 03 21 32 43 20
Pro shop Pro-shop (33) 03 21 32 43 20
Fax Fax (33) 03 21 33 62 21
Web www.golf-wimereux.com
Situation Situation Boulogne-sur-Mer, 6 km
Annual closure Fermeture annuelle no
Weekly closure Fermeture hebdomadaire Monday
(lundi): closed from 01/11 to 01/03

Fees main season Tarifs haute saison	18 holes	
	Week days Semaine	**We/Bank holidays** We/Férié
Individual Individuel	€ 48	€ 56
Couple Couple	€ 96	€ 112

Under 20 and Students: – 30%

Caddy Caddy no — **Electric Trolley** Chariot électrique no
Buggy Voiturette yes — **Clubs** Clubs no

Credit cards Cartes de crédit
VISA - CB - Eurocard - MasterCard

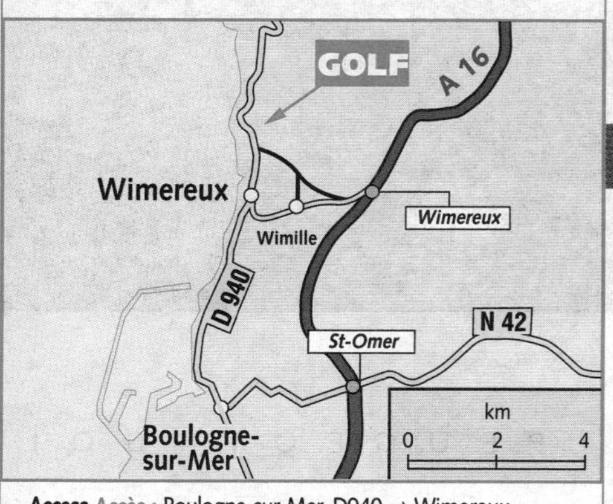

Access Accès : Boulogne-sur-Mer, D940 → Wimereux
Map 1 on page 160 Carte 1 Page 160

GOLF COURSE — PARCOURS — 13/20

Site Site
Maintenance Entretien
Architect Architecte Sir Guy Campbell, C.K. Hutchinson
Type Type links
Relief Relief
Water in play Eau en jeu
Exp. to wind Exposé au vent
Trees in play Arbres en jeu

Scorecard Carte de score	**Chp.** Chp.	**Mens** Mess.	**Ladies** Da.
Length Long.	6150	5887	4961
Par	72	72	72
Slope system	132	129	124

Advised golfing ability Niveau de jeu recommandé 0 12 24 36
Hcp required Handicap exigé 35

CLUB HOUSE & AMENITIES — CLUB HOUSE ET ANNEXES — 4/10

Pro shop Pro-shop
Driving range Practice
Sheltered couvert 10 mats - On grass sur herbe yes - Putting-green putting-green yes - Pitching-green pitching green yes

HOTEL FACILITIES — ENVIRONNEMENT HOTELIER — 5/10

HOTELS HÔTELS
Centre - 23 rooms, D € 55 - Wimereux 2 km
Tel (33) 03 21 32 41 08, Fax (33) 03 21 33 82 48

Hôtel Matelote - 29 rooms, D € 110 - Boulogne-sur-Mer 6 km
Tel (33) 03 21 30 33 33, Fax (33) 03 21 30 87 40

Métropole - 25 rooms, D € 80 - Boulogne-sur-Mer 2 km
Tel (33) 03 21 31 54 30, Fax (33) 03 21 30 45 72

RESTAURANTS RESTAURANTS
Epicure - Wimereux 3 km - Tel (33) 03 21 83 21 83
Matelote - Boulogne-sur-Mer 6 km - Tel (33) 03 21 30 17 97
Liégeoise (Atlantic Hôtel) - Wimereux 2 km
Tel (33) 03 21 32 41 01

DEUTSCHLAND

GERMANY

Sporting Club Berlin

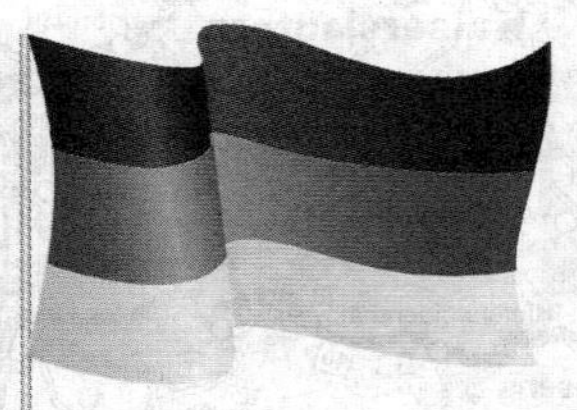

GERMANY

Germany today counts around 490,000 registered golfers and numbers are growing as fast as probably anywhere else in Europe. There are now more than 650 golf-courses to meet the demand, most of which are located around major cities such as Düsseldorf, Hamburg, Stuttgart, Munich or Berlin, or again in favourite tourist locations like Bavaria or even way out in the country. The new states in eastern Germany have some catching up to do, except for Brandenburg, where you will find a lot of courses around Berlin. The majority of clubs are private but they all admit visitors – who have to be bona fide members of a golf club and have an official handicap – at least during the week, but may sometimes impose restrictions on week-ends. These are mentioned in the Guide. This makes it difficult for groups to book tee-off times on a Saturday or Sunday, but visitors playing alone can often team up with members. Phone early and try your luck.

DEUTSCHLAND

In Deutschland, welches den stärksten Zuwachs ganz Europas aufweist, gibt es heute rund 490 000 Golfer und ca. 650 Plätze. Viele befinden sie sich in der Nähe größerer Städte wie Düsseldorf, Hamburg, Stuttgart, München oder Berlin oder in stark touristisch erschlossenen Regionen wie Bayern, doch auch auf dem Land sind in den letzten Jahren viele Plätze entstand, so dass man in Deutschland fast überall spielen kann. Lediglich die neuen Bundesländer mit Ausnahme von Berlin/Brandenburg haben noch einen Nachholbedarf. Fast alle sind Privatsclubs, die jedoch für alle Besucher (Mitgliedsausweis und Handicap-Nachweis erforderlich) offen sind, zumindest unter der Woche. An den Wochenenden ist der Zutritt oft beschränkt, was wir denn auch beim jeweiligen Beschreibung vermerkt haben. Für Gruppen sind Reservierungen für das Wochenende daher schwierig, aber einzelne Spieler haben oft die Möglichkeit, mit Clubmitgliedern zu spielen. Rufen Sie deshalb unbedingt vorher an.

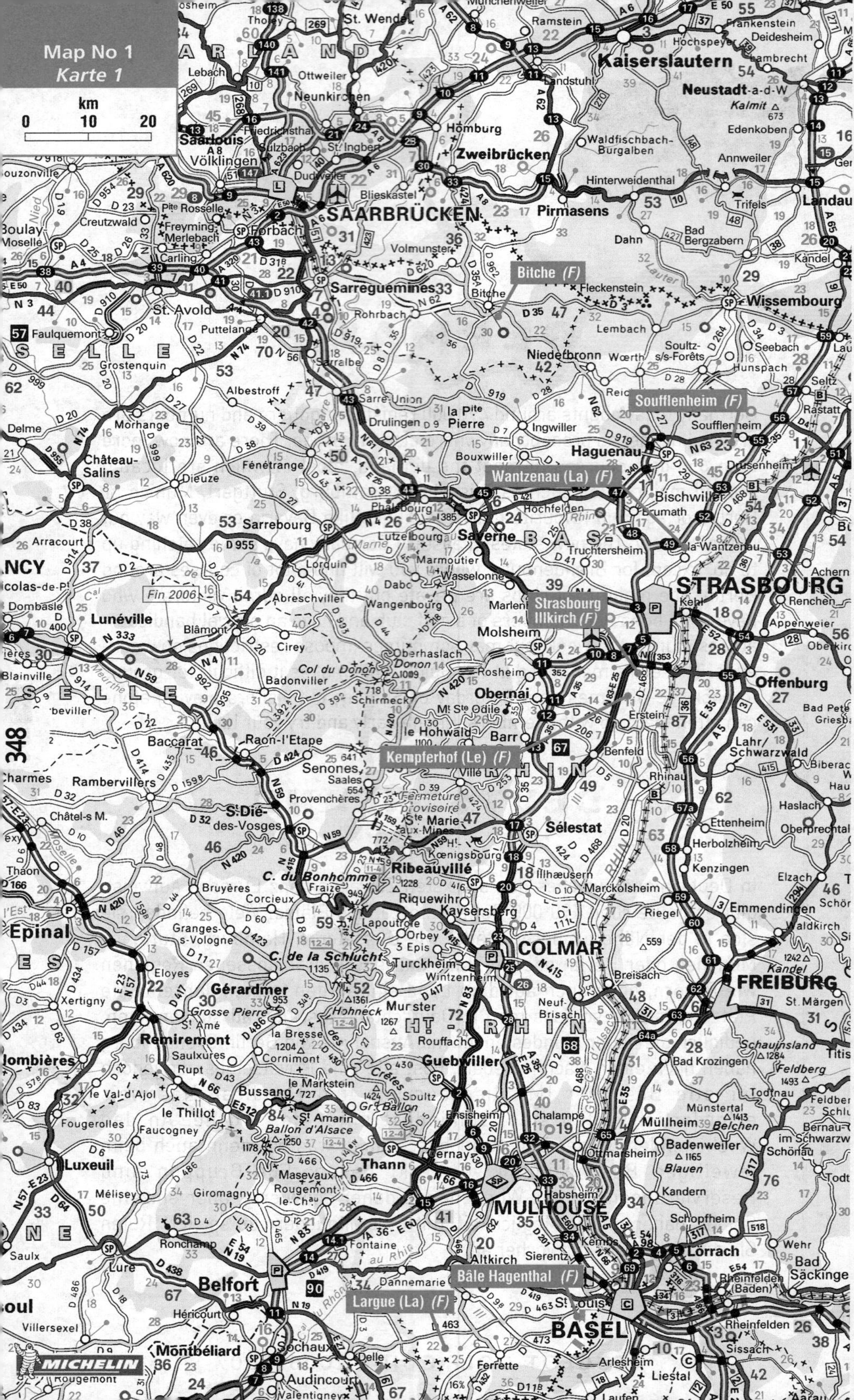
Map No 1
Karte 1
km
0 10 20
Bitche (F)
Soufflenheim (F)
Wantzenau (La) (F)
Strasbourg Illkirch (F)
Kempferhof (Le) (F)
Bâle Hagenthal (F)
Largue (La) (F)
Fin 2006
Kaiserslautern
Neustadt-a-d-W
Saarlouis
Völklingen
Saarbrücken
Zweibrücken
Pirmasens
Homburg
Landau
Wissembourg
Sarreguemines
Forbach
St. Avold
Haguenau
Saverne
Sarrebourg
Lunéville
Strasbourg
Kehl
Offenburg
Molsheim
Obernai
Sélestat
Colmar
Freiburg
Épinal
Gérardmer
Remiremont
Luxeuil
Mulhouse
Belfort
Montbéliard
Basel
Lörrach
Michelin

348

St. Leon-Rot
Schloss Nippenburg
Stuttgarter Solitude
Hechingen-Hohenzollern
Oberschwaben Bad Waldsee
Fürstlicher Bad Waldsee
Öschberghof
Schloss Langenstein
Lindau-Bad Schachen
Breitenloo (S)
Speyer
Heilbronn
Mosbach
Schwäbisch Hall
Künzelsau
Bad Wimpfen
Bruchsal
KARLSRUHE
Pforzheim
Ludwigsburg
STUTTGART
Esslingen
Göppingen
Schwäbisch Gmünd
Backnang
Sindelfingen
Böblingen
Tübingen
Reutlingen
Nürtingen
Kirchheim u. Teck
Geislingen
Baden-Baden
Calw
Freudenstadt
Hechingen
Balingen
Rottweil
Schramberg
Sigmaringen
Biberach a.d. Riß
Ehingen
Villingen-Schwenningen
Donaueschingen
Tuttlingen
Ravensburg
Friedrichshafen
Konstanz
Lindau
Singen
Schaffhausen
Winterthur
Frauenfeld
Baden
WÜRTTEMBERG
BADEN-
MICHELIN
d'après base de données au 1/1 000 000 - édition 2005.
Autorisation n°0501023.

Map No 2
Karte 2
km
0 10 20
DEUTSCHLAND
BAY
350
Bad Abbach
Wittelsbacher
Gut Häusern
Schloss Klingenburg
Gut Ludwigsberg
Münchner-Strasslach
Feldafing
München-Riedhof
Hohenpähl
Tutzing
Beuerberg
Memmingen-Gut Westerhart
St. Eurach
Iffeldorf
Tegernseer Bad Wiessee
Garmisch-Partenkirchen
Windsbach
Abenberg
Merkendorf
Hilpoltstein
Parsberg
Berching
Greding
Dietfurt
Hemau
Nittendorf
Gunzenhausen
Pleinfeld
Thalmässing
Ellingen
Weißenburg
Beilngries
Wassertrüdingen
Riedenburg
Kelheim
Weltenburg
Saal
Treuchtlingen
Pappenheim
Denkendorf
Oettingen
Eichstätt
Neustadt
Abensberg
Wallerstein
Wemding
Lenting
Bopfingen
Nördlingen
Monheim
Ingolstadt
Manching
Aalen
Harburg
Kaisheim
Donau
Karlshuld
Geisenfeld
Elsendorf
Neresheim
Donauwörth
Neuburg
Reichertshofen
Mainburg
Langenbruck
Wolnzach
Rain
Heidenheim
Pörnbach
Au
Pöttmes
Höchstädt
Giengen
Dillingen
Lauingen
Schrobenhausen
Pfaffenhofen
Moosburg
Wertingen
Meitingen
Gundelfingen
Niederstotzingen
Allershausen
Freising
Langenau
Aichach
Gersthofen
Leipheim
Günzburg
Burgau
Markt Indersdorf
Dasing
Friedberg
Odelzhausen
Zusmarshausen
Göggingen
Sulzemoos
Unterschleissheim
Haunstetten
AUGSBURG
Dachau
Ismaning
Weißenhorn
Bobingen
Mering
Maisach
Karlsfeld
Thannhausen
Königsbrunn
Krumbach
Fürstenfeldbruck
Schwabmünchen
Germering
Gilching
Grafelfing
Haar
Babenhausen
Unterhaching
Ottobrunn
Gauting
Türkheim
Buchloe
Landsberg
Inning
Grünwald
Hofolding
Mindelheim
Utting
Starnberg
Herrsching
Heimertingen
Steinheim
Bad Wörishofen
Dießen
Wolfratshausen
Memmingen
Holzkirchen
Ottobeuren
Rott
Weilheim
Wessobrunn
Schongau
Peißenberg
Penzberg
Gronenbach
Obergünzburg
Hohenpeißenberg
Gmund
Dietmannsried
Peiting
Bad Tölz
Leutkirch
Marktoberdorf
Bichl
Bad Wiessee
Benediktbeuern
Großweil
Kempten
Steingaden
Wies
Murnau
Kochel
Ohlstadt
Urfeld
Isny
Roßhaupten
Vorderriß
Achenkirch
Oy-Mittelberg
Nesselwang
Oberammergau
Linderhof
Walchensee
Wertach
Pfronten
Füssen
Königsschlösser
Oberau
Ammer-Sattel
Garmisch
Krün
Achensee
Pertisau
Oberstaufen
Immenstadt
Oberjoch-P.
Partenkirchen
Mittenwald
Sonthofen
Hindelang
Reutte
Plansee
Grainau
Zugspitze
Steibis
Tannheim
Eng
Balderschwang
Fischen
Weißenbach
Ehrwald
Scharnitz
Karwendelgebirge
Nebelhorn
Berwang
Lermoos
Fernpaß
Seefeld
INNSBRUCK
Hall in Tirol
Oberstdorf
Telfs
Holzleitner Sattel
Obsteig
Wattens
Volders
Riezlern
Hirschegg
Kleinwalsertal
Nassereith
Zirl
Mittelberg
Elbigenalp
Stams
Silz
Igls
Baad
Axams
Europabrücke
Imst
Warth
Holzgau
Oetz
Gries-im Sellrain
Schönberg
Lanersbach
Alpenstraße
Romantische Straße
Deutsche Alpenstraße
Staffelsee
Ammersee
Starnberger See
Isar
Lech
Iller
MICHELIN

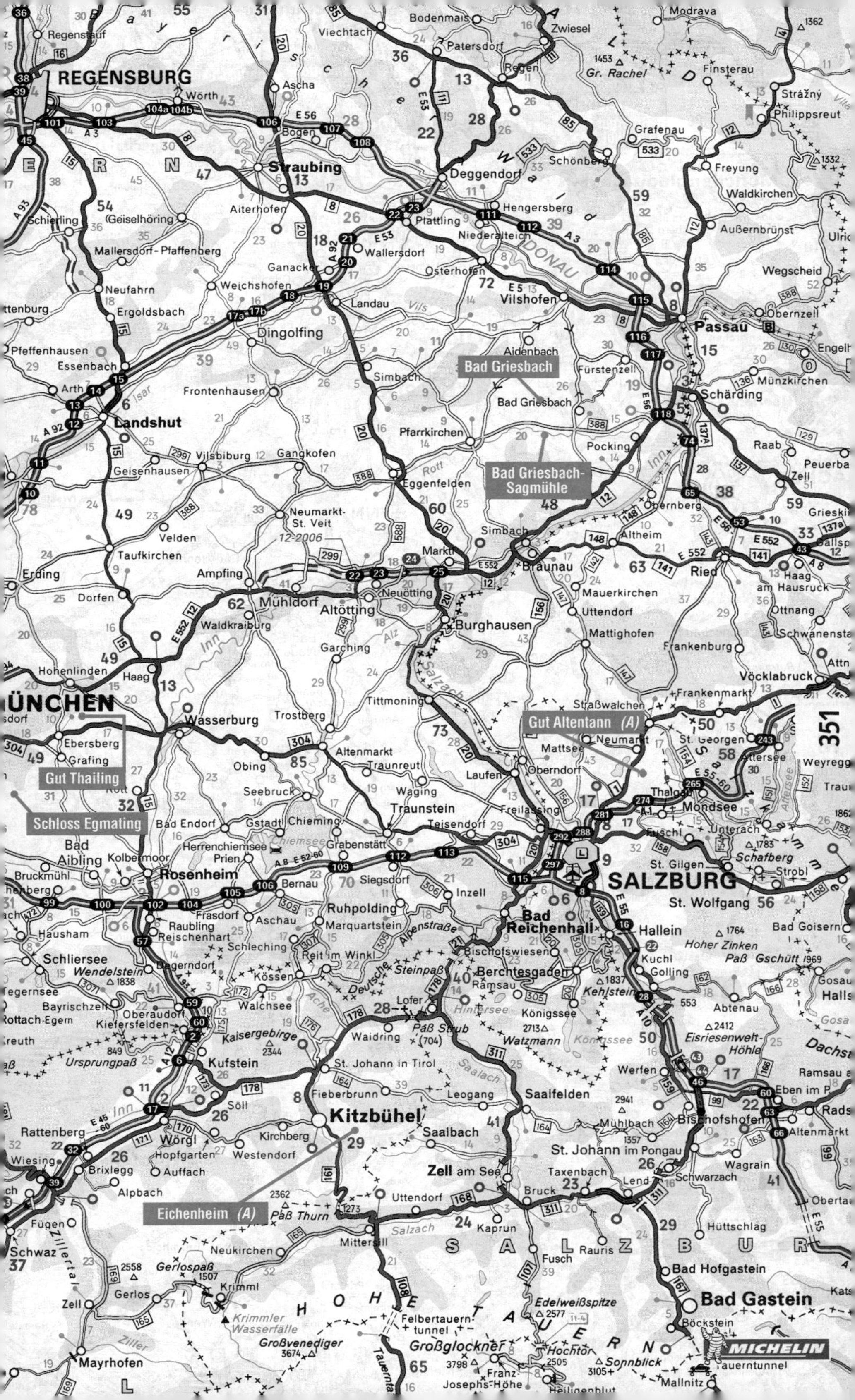

351
REGENSBURG
Regenstauf
Wörth
Straubing
Deggendorf
Plattling
Bodenmais
Viechtach
Patersdorf
Zwiesel
Regen
Gr. Rachel
Modrava
Finsterau
Strážný
Philippsreut
Grafenau
Schönberg
Freyung
Waldkirchen
Außernbrünst
Wegscheid
Obernzell
Passau
Engelh
Münzkirchen
Schärding
Fürstenzell
Aidenbach
Bad Griesbach
Bad Griesbach-Sagmühle
Pocking
Vilshofen
Hengersberg
Niederalteich
Osterhofen
DONAU
Wallersdorf
Ganacker
Landau
Vils
Aiterhofen
Ascha
Bogen
Schierling
Geiselhöring
Mallersdorf-Pfaffenberg
Neufahrn
Ergoldsbach
Weichshofen
Dingolfing
Pfeffenhausen
Essenbach
Arth
Landshut
Isar
Frontenhausen
Simbach
Pfarrkirchen
Rott
Eggenfelden
Vilsbiburg
Gangkofen
Geisenhausen
Neumarkt-St. Veit
12-2006
Velden
Taufkirchen
Erding
Dorfen
Ampfing
Mühldorf
Altötting
Neuötting
Marktl
Simbach
Braunau
Altheim
Obernberg
Ried
Raab
Zell
Peuerba
Grieskir
Haag am Hausruck
Ottnang
Schwanensta
Mauerkirchen
Uttendorf
Mattighofen
Burghausen
Frankenburg
Vöcklabruck
Waldkraiburg
Inn
Garching
Alz
Salzach
Hohenlinden
Haag
MÜNCHEN
Ebersberg
Grafing
Gut Thailing
Schloss Egmating
Wasserburg
Trostberg
Tittmoning
Obing
Altenmarkt
Traunreut
Seebruck
Waging
Traunstein
Laufen
Oberndorf
Mattsee
Neumarkt
Straßwalchen
Frankenmarkt
Gut Altentann (A)
St. Georgen
Attersee
Weyregg
Thalgau
Mondsee
Freilassing
Teisendorf
Fuschl
Unterach
Schafberg
Strobl
St. Gilgen
SALZBURG
St. Wolfgang
Bad Endorf
Gstadt
Chieming
Chiemsee
Herrenchiemsee
Grabenstätt
Prien
Bad Aibling
Kolbermoor
Bruckmühl
Rosenheim
Bernau
Siegsdorf
Inzell
Ruhpolding
Bad Reichenhall
Hallein
Hoher Zinken
Paß Gschütt
Bad Goisern
Frasdorf
Aschau
Raubling
Reischenhart
Marquartstein
Alpenstraße
Hausham
Schliersee
Schleching
Reit im Winkl
Bischofswiesen
Berchtesgaden
Ramsau
Kuchl
Golling
Wendelstein
Degerndorf
Kössen
Deutsche
Steinpaß
Kehlstein
Tegernsee
Bayrischzell
Walchsee
Lofer
Hintersee
Königssee
Abtenau
Rottach-Egern
Oberaudorf
Kiefersfelden
Kaisergebirge
Paß Strub
Watzmann
Eisriesenwelt-Höhle
Kreuth
Ursprungpaß
Kufstein
Waidring
Saalach
Werfen
Dachst
Ramsau a
St. Johann in Tirol
Eben im P
Fieberbrunn
Leogang
Saalfelden
Rattenberg
Söll
Kitzbühel
Saalbach
Mühlbach
Bischofshofen
Altenmarkt
Wörgl
Kirchberg
Wiesing
Brixlegg
Hopfgarten
Westendorf
St. Johann im Pongau
Wagrain
Auffach
Zell am See
Taxenbach
Schwarzach
Alpbach
Eichenheim (A)
Uttendorf
Bruck
Lend
Obertau
Paß Thurn
Kaprun
Fügen
Zillertal
Salzach
Hüttschlag
Schwaz
Mittersill
S A L Z B U R
Neukirchen
Fusch
Rauris
Gerlospaß
Krimml
Bad Hofgastein
Gerlos
Edelweißspitze
Bad Gastein
Zell
Krimmler Wasserfälle
H O H E T A U E R N
Felbertauern-tunnel
Böckstein
Großvenediger
Großglockner
Hochtor
Sonnblick
MICHELIN
Tauerntunnel
Mayrhofen
Ziller
Franz-Josephs-Höhe
Heiligenblut
Mallnitz
Tauernta

Map No 3
Karte 3
km
0 10 20
Elfrather Mühle
Krefelder
Rittergut Birkhof
Essener Oefte
Bergisch Land Wuppertal
Düsseldorfer
Hubbelrath
Schloss Myllendonk
Gut Lärchenhof
Köln (Refrath)
Am Alten Fliess
Spa (Les Fagnes) (B)
Mittelrheinischer
Jakobsberg
Bitburger Land
Grand Ducal de Luxembourg (L)
Kikuoka (L)
DUISBURG
ESSEN
WUPPERTAL
DÜSSELDORF
KÖLN
BONN
AACHEN
LUXEMBOURG
Mönchengladbach
Krefeld
Trier
Koblenz
RHEINLAND-PFALZ
SAARLAND
MICHELIN

KASSEL
Brilon
Bad Arolsen
Niederelsungen
Burghasungen
Wolfhagen
Istha
Witzenhausen
Helsa
Hessisch-Lichtenau
Arnsberg
Sundern
Meschede
Nuttlar
Olsberg
Willingen
Usseln
Korbach
Westernbödefeld
Eslohe
Waldeck
Altastenberg
Nordenau
Winterberg
Medebach
Plettenberg
Oberkirchen
Neuastenberg
Sauerland
Schmallenberg
Hallenberg
Eder-Stausee
Bad Wildungen
Fritzlar
Wabern
Melsungen
Spangenberg
Grevenbrück
Lennestadt
Altenhundem
Kirchhundem
Bad Berleburg
Frankenberg
Homberg
Rotenburg
Battenberg
Gemünden
Olpe
Hilchenbach
Erndtebrück
Münchhausen
Schwalmstadt
Ziegenhain
Treysa
Neuenstein
Bad Hersfeld
Kreuztal
Bad Laasphe
Biedenkopf
Neustadt
Kirchheim
Siegen
Wilnsdorf
Marburg
Kirchhain
Kirtorf
Alsfeld
Niederjossa
Niederaula
Gladenbach
Homberg
Schlitz
Betzdorf
Burbach
Dillenburg
Herborn
Lauterbach
Bad Salzschlirf
Hachenburg
Rennerod
Gießen
Grünberg
Golf Park Winnerod
Herbstein
Fulda
Langenhahn
Westerburg
Schloss Braunfels
Wetzlar
Lich
Schotten
Vogelsberg
Braunfels
Weilburg
Münzenberg
Gedern
Hadamar
Butzbach
HESSEN
Limburg
Diez
Bad Nauheim
Schlüchtern
Holzappel
Bad Ems
Altweilnau
Usingen
Friedberg
Lindenhof Bad Vilbel
Bad Soden-Salmünster
Steinau
Wächtersbach
Bad Camberg
Nassau
Esch
Bad Homburg
Gr. Feldberg
Nidderau
Bad Orb
Burgjoß
Hanau-Wilhelmsbad
Gelnhausen
Idstein
Oberursel
Bad Vilbel
Taunusstein-Neuhof
Main-Taunus
FRANKFURT
Bad Soden
Hanau
Hof Trages
Bad Schwalbach
Goarshausen
Espenschied
Frankfurter GC
WIESBADEN
Offenbach
Alzenau
Frammersbach
Loreley
Kaub
Schlangenbad
Selingenstadt
Hösbach
Lorch
Aßmannshausen
Rüdesheim
Rüsselsheim
Neu-Isenburg
Aschaffenburg
Weibersbrunn
Bingen
MAINZ
Langen
Dietzenbach
Babenhausen
Mespelbrunn
Rheinhessen
Gr. Gerau
Darmstadt
Dieburg
Rohrbrunn
Nierstein
Oppenheim
Gr.-Umstadt
Roßdorf
Obernburg
Bad Kreuznach
Wörrstadt
Köngernheim
Reinheim
Wörth
Domtal-Mommenheim
Pfungstadt
Höchst
Seeheim-Jugenheim
Bad König
Großheubach
Wertheim
Freudenberg
Bad Münster am Stein-Ebernburg
Nahetal
Alzey
Westhofen
Gernsheim
Fürstenlager
Miltenberg
Külsheim
Bensheim
Michelstadt
Amorbach
Flörsheim-Dalsheim
Kirchheimbolanden
Worms
Bürstadt
Heppenheim
Erbach
Walldürn
Grünstadt
Lampertheim
Viernheim
Beerfelden
Wald-Michelbach
Mudau
Buchen
Winnweiler
Frankenthal
Weinheim
Kailbach
Ludwigshafen
MANNHEIM
Eberbach
Osterburken
Bad Dürkheim
HEIDELBERG
Neckarsteinach
Frankenstein
Deidesheim
Adelsheim
Kaiserslautern
Hochspeyer
Lambrecht
Mutterstadt
Schwetzingen
Schifferstadt
Neckargemünd
Neckar
Neckarelz
Mosbach
Gundelsheim
Main
Lahn
Fulda
Nidda
Eder
Ruhr
Lenne
MICHELIN

353

Map No 4
Karte 4
km
0 10 20
THÜRINGEN
Thüringer Wald
Mühlhausen
Bad Tennstedt
Sömmerda
Kölleda
Eckartsberga
Straußfurt
Buttstädt
Bad Sulza
Diedorf
Treffurt
Gebesee
Bad Langensalza
Unstrut
Apolda
Weimar
Dornburg
Buchenwald
ERFURT
11-2006
Gotha
Herleshausen
Eisenach
Richelsdorf
Bebra
Mellingen
Jena
Hönebach
Berka
Waltershausen
Bad Berka
Kranichfeld
Blankenhain
Stadroda
Kahla
Ruhla
Gr. Inselsberg
982
Friedrichroda
Ohrdruf
Arnstadt
Dorndorf
Vacha
Bad Liebenstein
Barchfeld
Bad Salzungen
Breitungen
Crawinkel
Stadtilm
Rudolstadt
Pößneck
Schwarza
Bad Blankenburg
Schmalkalden
Oberhof
Zella-Mehlis
Steinbach-Hallenberg
Ilmenau
Königsee
Saalfeld
Rasdorf
Geisa
Dermbach
Wasungen
Gr. Beerberg
Gehren
Suhl
Hünfeld
Tann
Kaltennordheim
Großbreitenbach
Leutenberg
Probstzella
Meiningen
Rohr
Schleusingen
Neuhaus
Ludwigsstadt
Lobenstein
Hilders
Melpers
Fladungen
Henneberg
Themar
Rodacherbrunn
Wasser-Kuppe
950
Ehrenberg
Eußenhausen
Hildburghausen
Eisfeld
Steinach
Ostheim
Nordhalben
Mellrichstadt
Römhild
Sonneberg
Gersfeld
Rottenbach
Neustadt
Neuhaus-Schierschnitz
Burggrub
Bischofsheim
Lirden
Bad Rodach
Wallenfels
Bad Königshofen
Trappstadt
Kronach
Bad Neustadt
Heldburg
Coburg
Obereßfeld
Stadtsteinach
Fränk. Saale
Münnerstadt
Burgkunstadt
Bad Kissingen
Lichtenfels
Vierzehnheiligen
Kulmbach
Hofheim
Staffelstein
Weismain
Ebern
Oberfranken
Poppenhausen
Schweinfurt
Haßfurt
Bamberg
Bayreuth
Breitengüßbach
Scheßlitz
Hollfeld
Arnstein
Werneck
Eltmann
Hallstadt
Fränkische Schweiz
Waischenfeld
Wiesenttal
Streitberg
Behringersmühle
Gerolzhofen
Volkach
Ebrach
Ebermannstadt
Gössweinstein
Dettelbach
Wiesentheid
Pommersfelden
Egloffstein
Würzburg
Höchberg
Schlüsselfeld
Forchheim
Kitzingen
Biebelried
Iphofen
Höchstadt
Gräfenberg
Reichswald-Nürnberg
Scheinfeld
Erlangen
Forth
Marktbreit
Ochsenfurt
Neustadt an der Aisch
Herzogenaurach
Heroldsberg
Lauf
Hersbruck
Tauberbischofsheim
Reichsstadt Bad Windsheim
Emskirchen
Aub
Uffenheim
Markt Erlbach
Fürth
Rothenbach
Bad Windsheim
Langenzenn
Zirndorf
NÜRNBERG
Fischbach
Bad Mergentheim
Creglingen
Burgbernheim
Großhabersdorf
Stein
Altdorf
Weikersheim
Feucht
Oberölsbach
Niederstetten
Lichtenau-Weickershof
Heilsbronn
Rothenburg ob der Tauber
Lehrberg
Schwabach
Neumarkt
Dörzbach
Schrozberg
Ansbach
Roth
Allersberg
Leutershausen
Windsbach
Blaufelden
Abenberg
Künzelsau
Herrieden
Merkendorf
Hilpoltstein
Gerabronn
Bechhofen
DEUTSCHLAND
MICHELIN

Teuchern
Zeitz
Meuselwitz
Rochlitz
Siebenlehn
Freiberg
Mittweida
Hainichen
Dippoldiswalde
Frohburg
Altenburg
Penig
Burgstädt
12-2006
Eisenberg
Hartmannsdorf
Waldenburg
Limbach
Frankenberg
Flöha
Oederan
Brand-Erbisdorf
Langenberg
Schmölln
Gößnitz
Meerane
CHEMNITZ
Frauenstein
Hermsdorf
Gera
Ronneburg
Crimmitschau
Glauchau
Hohenstein
Augustusburg
Zschopau
Lengefeld
Lichtenstein
Lugau
Stollberg
Weida
Werdau
Zwickau
Oelsnitz
Thalheim
Thum
Zöblitz
Olbernhau
Loučná
Litvínov
Triptis
Auma
Wilkau-Haßlau
Kirchberg
Zwönitz
Marienberg
Greiz
Reichenbach
Lößnitz
Annaberg-Buchholz
Reitzenhain
Most
Elsterberg
Zeulenroda
Schneeberg
Aue
Schwarzenberg
Hora Svatého Šebestiána
Jirkov
Lengenfeld
Rodewisch
Chomutov
Schleiz
Mühltroff
Treuen
Auerbach
Eibenstock
Vod. n. Nechranice
Plauen
Falkenstein
Oberwiesenthal
Boží Dar
Johanngeorgenstadt
Klášterec
Kadaň
Gefell
Klínovec
Jáchymov
Oelsnitz
Hirschberg
Schöneck
Klingenthal
Nejdek
Ostrov
Töpen
Blosenberg
Ebmath
Adorf
Kraslice
Jindřichovice
Nová Role
Podbořany
Karlovy Vary (CZ)
Kyselka
Hof
Hranice
Markneukirchen
Bad Elster
Chodov
Karlovy Vary
Rehau
Aš
Bad Brambach
Schönberg
Sokolov
Loket
Bochov
Lubenec
Selb
Schwarzenbach
Vojtanov
Horn Slavkov
Žlutice
Münchberg
Kirchenlamitz
Františkovy Lázně
Bečov
Toužim
Manětín
Kralovice
Gefrees
Weissenstadt
Schirnding
Cheb
Pomezí
Lázně Kynžvart
Fichtel-
Schneeberg
Wunsiedel
Arzberg
Mariánské Lázně (CZ)
Teplá
Bischofsgrün
Waldsassen
Mariánské Lázne
Bad Berneck
Marktredwitz
Luisenburg
Mitterteich
Konstantinovy Lázně
Warmensteinach
Mähring
Úněšov
Plana
Lestkov
g e b i r g e
Wiesau
Tirschenreuth
Pernarec
PLZ
Kemnath
Erbendorf
Vod. n. Hrachólusky
Mže
Bärnau
Creußen
Tachov
Stříbro
Nýřany
Windischeschenbach
Bor
Eschenbach
Pressath
Kirchenthumbach
Neustadt a.d.Waldnaab
Stod
Grafenwöhr
Waidhaus
Rozvadov
Přeštice
Weiden
Bělá
Radbuza
Auerbach
Vohenstrauß
Schwanhof
Staňkov
Freihung
Eslarn
Horšovský Týn
Švihov
Schnaittenbach
Wernberg
Koloveč
Hannbach
Hirschau
Schönsee
Pfreimd
Draženov
Domažlice
Klatov
Sulzbach-Rosenberg
Nabburg
Oberviechtach
Kdyně
Amberg
Waldmünchen
Čerchov
Folmava
Schwarzenfeld
Schönthal
Nýrsko
Furth
Rötz
Neunburg
Jura Golf
Am Habsberg
Kastl
Schwandorf
Bodenwöhr
Schmidmühlen
Cham
Kötzting
Lam
Lohberg
Bruck
Maxhütte-Haidhof
Velburg
Burglengenfeld
Nittenau
Roding
Miltach
Železná
Bayerisch Eisenstein
Regen
Großer Arber
Bodenmais
Viechtach
Kallmünz
Parsberg
Regenstauf
Zwiesel
Patersdorf
B a y e r i s c h e
L A N D
REGENSBURG
Hemau
Wörth
Ascha
MICHELIN

Map No 5
Karte 5
km
0 10 20
Gelpenberg (NL)
Sybrook (NL)
Twente (NL)
Rheine/ Mesum
Graafschap (NL)
Wasserburg-Anholt
Elfrather Mühle
Essener Oefte
MICHELIN
Emden
Delfzijl
Appingedam
Leer
Hesel
Westerstede
Wiefelstede
Bad Zwischenahn
Nieuweschans
Winschoten
Hoogezand
Haren
Veendam
Papenburg
Assen
Stadskanaa
Emmen
Hoogeveen
Coevorden
Meppen
Lingen
Cloppenburg
Löningen
Quakenbrück
Nordhorn
Almelo
Hengelo
Enschede
Rheine
Ibbenbüren
Münster
Coesfeld
Bocholt
Dülmen
Recklinghsn
Gelsenkchn
Bochum
ESSEN
DORTMUND
Hagen
Iserlohn
Hamm
DUISBURG
Mülheim
Moers
Wesel
Zwolle
Deventer
Zutphen
Doetinchem
Emmerich
Kleve
Goch
Xanten
Winterswijk

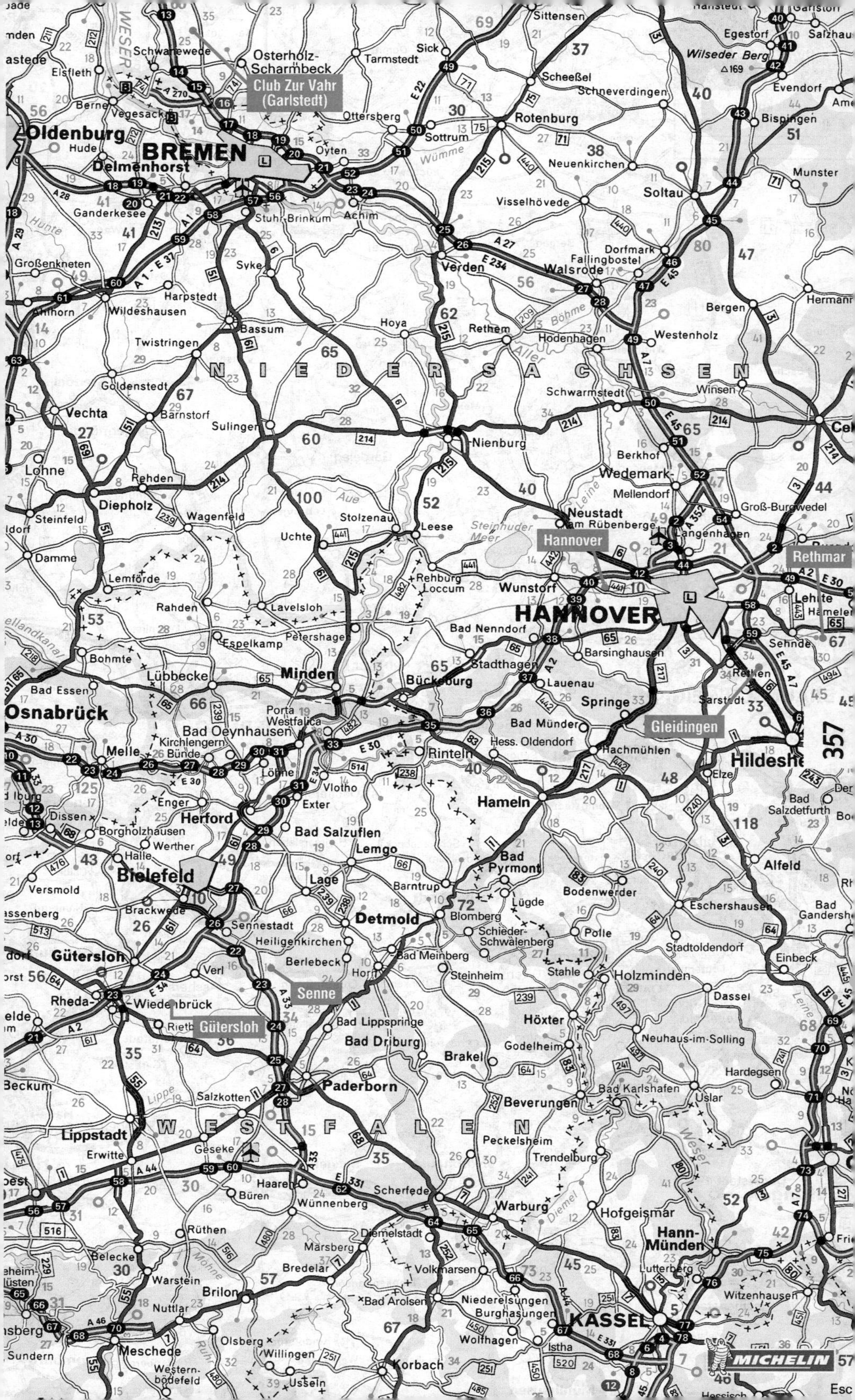

Club Zur Vahr
(Garlstedt)
Hannover
Rethmar
Gleidingen
Senne
Gütersloh
BREMEN
HANNOVER
KASSEL
Oldenburg
Delmenhorst
Osterholz-Scharmbeck
Schwanewede
Elsfleth
Berne
Vegesack
Hude
Ganderkesee
Stuhr-Brinkum
Achim
Oyten
Ottersberg
Sottrum
Tarmstedt
Sick
Sittensen
Scheeßel
Schneverdingen
Rotenburg
Neuenkirchen
Soltau
Visselhövede
Verden
Walsrode
Dorfmark
Fallingbostel
Bergen
Westenholz
Hodenhagen
Rethem
Hoya
Syke
Harpstedt
Wildeshausen
Ahlhorn
Großenkneten
Bassum
Twistringen
Goldenstedt
Vechta
Barnstorf
Sulingen
Lohne
Rehden
Diepholz
Steinfeld
Damme
Wagenfeld
Lemförde
Rahden
Lavelsloh
Uchte
Stolzenau
Leese
Nienburg
Schwarmstedt
Winsen
Berkhof
Wedemark-Mellendorf
Neustadt am Rübenberge
Langenhagen
Groß-Burgwedel
Wunstorf
Rehburg Loccum
Steinhuder Meer
Bad Nenndorf
Barsinghausen
Stadthagen
Bückeburg
Minden
Petershagen
Espelkamp
Bohmte
Lübbecke
Bad Essen
Osnabrück
Melle
Bünde
Kirchlengern
Bad Oeynhausen
Porta Westfalica
Löhne
Vlotho
Exter
Rinteln
Hess. Oldendorf
Hameln
Bad Münder
Springe
Lauenau
Hachmühlen
Elze
Sarstedt
Rethen
Sehnde
Lehrte
Hämelerwald
Hildesheim
Bad Salzdetfurth
Alfeld
Bad Gandersheim
Einbeck
Dassel
Stadtoldendorf
Eschershausen
Bodenwerder
Polle
Holzminden
Höxter
Godelheim
Neuhaus-im-Solling
Uslar
Hardegsen
Bad Karlshafen
Beverungen
Trendelburg
Hofgeismar
Hann.-Münden
Lutterberg
Witzenhausen
Warburg
Scherfede
Diemelstadt
Marsberg
Volkmarsen
Bad Arolsen
Niederelsungen
Burghasungen
Wolfhagen
Istha
Korbach
Willingen
Usseln
Brilon
Olsberg
Meschede
Bestwig
Nuttlar
Warstein
Belecke
Rüthen
Büren
Haaren
Wünnenberg
Geseke
Erwitte
Lippstadt
Salzkotten
Paderborn
Bad Driburg
Brakel
Steinheim
Bad Lippspringe
Horn
Bad Meinberg
Berlebeck
Heiligenkirchen
Detmold
Blomberg
Schieder-Schwalenberg
Lügde
Bad Pyrmont
Barntrup
Lemgo
Lage
Bad Salzuflen
Herford
Enger
Dissen
Borgholzhausen
Werther
Halle
Bielefeld
Brackwede
Sennestadt
Verl
Gütersloh
Rheda-Wiedenbrück
Rietberg
Versmold
Beckum
Sundern
Westernbödefeld
Peckelsheim
Stahle
WESER
Wümme
Aller
Böhme
Leine
Hunte
Lippe
Möhne
Ruhr
Diemel
Weser
Aue
Wilseder Berg
Egestorf
Salzhausen
Evendorf
Bispingen
Munster
Hermannsburg
NIEDERSACHSEN
WESTFALEN
MICHELIN

Map No 6
Karte 6
km
0 10 20
Bad Bevensen
Hardenberg
MICHELIN
BUNDESREPUBLIK
SACHSEN-ANHALT
Darchau
Hitzacker
Dömitz
Karstädt
Perleberg
Lenzen
Dannenberg
Schnackenburg
Gartow
Wittenberge
Bömenzien
Bad Wilsnack
Ebstorf
Uelzen
Lüchow
Lemgow
Seehausen
Lübbow
Arendsee
Werben
Havel
Sandau
Seebenau
Bergen
Salzwedel
Osterburg
Bodenteich
Diesdorf
Meßdorf
Wittingen
Hankensbüttel
Beetzendorf
Kalbe
Bismark
Eschede
Stendal
Klötze
Mellin
Tangermünde
Brome
Ehra-Lessien
Gardelegen
Jävenitz
Jerichow
Celle
Wesendorf
Tangerhütte
Letzlingen
Gifhorn
Dolle
Uetze
Vorsfelde
Oebisfelde
Velpke
Calvörde
Wolfsburg
Fallersleben
Rogätz
Haldensleben
Weferlingen
Burg
Wenden
Lehre
Grasleben
Wolmirstedt
Peine
Königslutter
Uhrsleben
Morsleben
BRAUNSCHWEIG
Helmstedt
Möckern
Schöningen
MAGDEBURG
Eilsleben
Seehausen
Leitzkau
Wolfenbüttel
Schöppenstedt
Wanzleben
Gommern
Jerxheim
Oschersleben
Schönebeck
Winnigstedt
Barby
Hornburg
Hadmersleben
Salzgitter-Bad
Osterwieck
Schwanebeck
Dardesheim
Egeln
Vienenburg
Gröningen
Kroppenstedt
Calbe
Förderstedt
Langelsheim
Halberstadt
Wegeleben
Staßfurt
Nienburg
Goslar
Derenburg
Hecklingen
Seesen
Oker
Ilsenburg
Güsten
Bad Harzburg
Bernburg
Lautenthal
Brocken
Wernigerode
Hoym
Blankenburg
Quedlinburg
Aschersleben
Elbingerode
Altenau
Clausthal-Zellerfeld
Nationalpark Harz
Thale
Gernrode
Ballenstedt
Ermsleben
Aisleben
Könnern
Echte
St. Andreasberg
Braunlage
Hasselfelde
Hettstedt
Osterode
Gerbstedt
Northeim
Katlenburg
Benneckenstein
Harzgerode
Mansfeld
Wettin
Herzberg
Bad Lauterberg
Bad Sachsa
Ellrich
Stolberg
Halle-Neustadt
Eisleben
Gieboldehausen
Mackenrode
Nordhausen
Sangerhausen
Riestedt
Duderstadt
Göttingen
Bad Lauchstädt
Berga
Kelbra
Allstedt
Schafstädt
Bleicherode
Artern
Querfurt
Merseburg
Worbis
Mücheln
Friedland
Sondershausen
Leinefelde
Heiligenstadt
Bad Frankenhausen
Heldrungen
Nebra
Wiehe
Dingelstädt
Ebeleben
Bad Bibra
Schlotheim
Kindelbrück
Rastenberg
Naumburg
Greußen
Weißensee
Kölleda
Geismar
Mühlhausen
Sömmerda
Eckartsberga
A 2 - E 30
A 14 - E 49
A 38
A 39
A 7
12-2006
7-2006
Elbe
Saale
Bode
Aland
Biese
Ohre
Jeetze
Oker
Aller
Unstrut
Helme
Wipper
Elbe-Seitenkanal
Weser-Elbe Kanal

359
Herzsprung
Kyritz
Wusterhausen
Neuruppin
Ruppiner See
Alt Ruppin
Lindow
Gransee
Zehdenick
Joachimsthal
Parsteiner See
Werbellinsee
Groß-Schönebeck
Oderberg
Löwenberg
Liebenwalde
Finowfurt
Finow
Eberswalde
Bad Freienwalde
Havel
Dosse
BRANDENBURG
Neustadt
Bückwitz
Fehrbellin
Kremmen
Stolper Heide
Wandlitz
Oranienburg
Biesenthal
Lanke
Bernau
Schloss Wilkendorf
Tiefensee
Werneuchen
Prötzel
Rhinow
Friesack
Semlin am See
Börnicke
Velten
Birkenwerder
Hennigsdorf
Strausberg
Blumberg
Altlandsberg
Vogelsdorf
Müncheberg
BERLIN
Pankow
Tegel
Spandau
Falkensee
Nauen
Rathenow
Premnitz
Wachow
Märkischer Potsdam
Ketzin
Pritzerbe
Köpenick
Erkner
Rüdersdorf
Fürstenwalde
Spree
Tempelhof
POTSDAM
Babelsberg
Teltow
Werder
Plaue
Brandenburg
Wusterwitz
Plauer See
Michendorf
Lehnin
Königs-Wusterhausen
Rangsdorf
Friedersdorf
Storkow
Mittenwalde
Ludwigsfelde
Berlin-Wannsee
Sporting Club Berlin
Ziesar
Golzow
Wollin
Beelitz
Trebbin
Zossen
Wünsdorf
Seddiner See
Motzener See
Teupitz
Halbe
Märkisch Buchholz
Neu Lübbenau
Brück
Görzke
Belzig
Luckenwalde
Baruth
Treuenbrietzen
Wiesenburg
Loburg
Niemegk
Jüterbog
Golßen
Duben
Dahme
Luckau
Zahna
Seyda
Zerbst
Coswig
Wittenberg
Roßlau
Dessau
Wörlitz
Oranienbaum
ELBE
Jessen
Schweinitz
Schönewalde
Schlieben
Sonnewalde
Finsterwalde
Kemberg
Annaburg
Schwarze Elster
Herzberg
Pretzsch
Prettin
Gräfenhainichen
Bad Schmiedeberg
Dommitzsch
Köthen
Raguhn
Jeßnitz
Wolfen
Doberlug-Kirchhain
Uebigau
Falkenberg
Elster
Schwarzheide
Zörbig
Bitterfeld
Bad Düben
Torgau
Bad Liebenwerda
Lauchhammer
Brehna
Elsterwerda
Landsberg
Delitzsch
Eilenburg
Schildau
Belgern
Mühlberg
Gröditz
Ortrand
Taucha
Wurzen
Dahlen
Strehla
Großenhain
Gr. Röder
Thiendorf
Schkeuditz
Brandis
Oschatz
Riesa
Leuna
Markranstädt
LEIPZIG
Trebsen
Wermsdorf
Radeburg
Bad Dürrenberg
Markkleeberg
Naunhof
Mutzschen
Mügeln
Lommatzsch
Moritzburg
Lützen
Grimma
Meißen
Coswig
Radebeul
Freibg. Mulde
Leisnig
Zwenkau
Pegau
Rötha
Böhlen
Bad Lausick
Colditz
Hartha
Döbeln
Roßwein
Hohenmölsen
Groitzsch
Borna
Geringswalde
Waldheim
Nossen
Lucka
Geithain
Rochlitz
Siebenlehn
Freital
Teuchern
MICHELIN

Map No 7
Karte 7
km
0
10
20
Haderslev
Åbenrå
Løgumkloster
Rødekro
Tinglev
Kruså
Padborg
Flensburg
Nordborg
Als
Hardeshøj
Augustenborg
Sønderborg
Gråsten
Broager
Sønderby
Fynshav
Mommark
Søby
Ærøskøbing
Ærø
Marstal
Rudkøbing
Spodsbjerg
Bagenkop
Svendborg
Tåsinge
Fåborg
Bøjden
Kværndrup
Egeskov
Hårby
Glücksburg
Flensborg Fjord
Gelting
Sterup
Kappeln
Kopperby
Satrup
Süderbrarup
Leck
Klixbüll
Risum-Lindholm
Bylderup-Bov
Wanderup
Tarp
Bredstedt
Schleswig
Eckernförde
Treia
Nordstrand
Husum
Dörpstedt
Kropp
Friedrichstadt
Gettorf
Altenholz
Friedrichsort
Laboe
Schönberg
Heikendorf
Hohwacht Bucht
Selenter See
KIEL
Kieler Bucht
Oslo-Göteborg
Rauma
St. Peterburg
Tallinn
Klaipėda
Kaliningrad
Lütjenburg
Preetz
Malente-Gremsmühlen
Plön
Eutin
Ascheberg
Bordesholm
Neumünster
Bornhöved
Büdelsdorf
Fockbek
Rendsburg
Jevenstedt
Hamdorf
Nortorf
Legan
Ostsee-Kanal
Hanerau-Hademarschen
Hohenwestedt
Schenefeld
Tönning
Lunden
Erfde
Tellingstedt
Heide
Albersdorf
Meldorf
Büsum
Trischen
Friedrichskoog
St-Michaelisdonn
Marne
Wilster
Itzehoe
Brunsbüttel
St. Margarethen
Cuxhaven
Otterndorf
Neuhaus
Cadenberge
Wischhafen
Glückstadt
Elmshorn
Hohenlockstedt
Kellinghusen
Bad Bramstedt
Lentföhrden
Brande-Hörnerkirchen
Barmstedt
Kaltenkirchen
Henstedt-Ulzburg
Bargteheide
Ahrensburg
Norderstedt
Quickborn
Uetersen
Pinneberg
Schenefeld
Wedel
Stade
Drochtersen
Hemmoor
Wanna
Bederkesa
Lamstedt
Bremerhaven
Bremervörde
Beverstedt
Stotel
Rhade
Zeven
Sittensen
Tostedt
Hollenstedt
Harsefeld
Horneburg
Buxtehude
HAMBURG
Harburg
Buchholz
Hanstedt
Egestorf
Garlstorf
Salzhausen
Lüneburg
Melbeck
Winsen
Seevetal-Maschen
Bergedorf
Geesthacht
Lauenburg
Reinbek
Schwarzenbek
Trittau
Rahlstedt
Bad Oldesloe
Reinfeld
Moisling
Kastdorf
Stockelsdorf
Bad Schwartau
Ratekau
Ahrensbök
Bad Segeberg
Wahlstedt
Rickling
Freiburg
SCHLESWIG
HOLSTEIN
ELBE
Gut Kaden
Pinnau
Wendlohe
Walddörfer
Hamburg-Ahrensburg
Falkenstein
Deinster Mühle
Buxtehude
St. Dionys
Schloss Lüdersburg
Green Eagle
MICHELIN
360

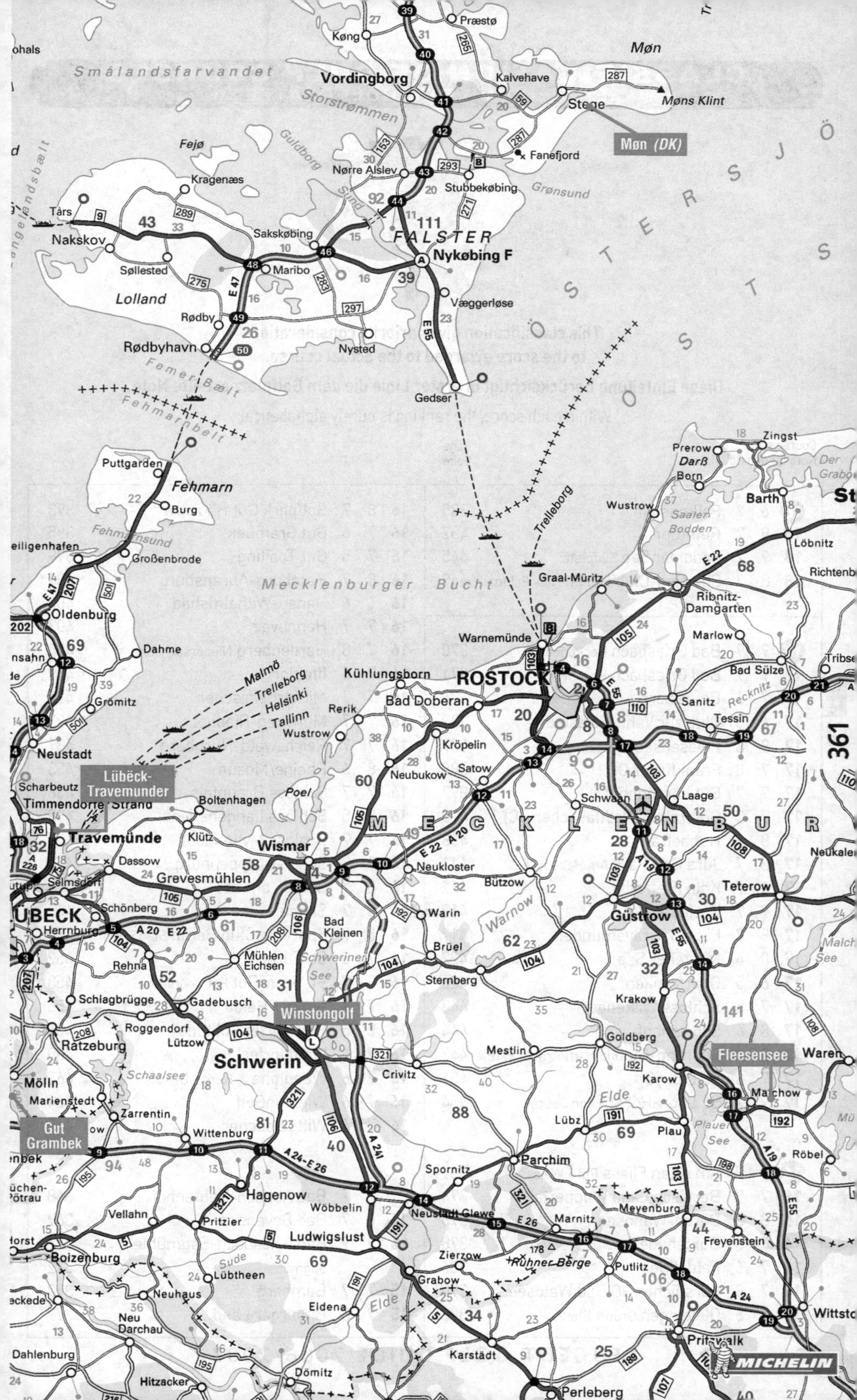
Smålandsfarvandet
Vordingborg
Præstø
Køng
Møn
Kalvehave
Stege
Møns Klint
Møn (DK)
Storstrømmen
Fanefjord
Grønsund
Fejø
Guldborg Sund
Nørre Alslev
Stubbekøbing
Kragenæs
Tårs
Nakskov
Sakskøbing
FALSTER
Nykøbing F
Maribo
Søllested
Lolland
Væggerløse
Rødby
Rødbyhavn
Nysted
Gedser
Femer Bælt
Fehmarnbelt
ÖSTERSJÖN
Puttgarden
Fehmarn
Burg
Fehmarnsund
Großenbrode
Heiligenhafen
Oldenburg
Dahme
Grömitz
Neustadt
Scharbeutz
Timmendorfer Strand
Lübeck-Travemunder
Travemünde
Dassow
Selmsdorf
LÜBECK
Herrnburg
Schönberg
Mecklenburger Bucht
Malmö
Trelleborg
Helsinki
Tallinn
Kühlungsborn
Rerik
Wustrow
Bad Doberan
Kröpelin
Neubukow
Satow
Poel
Boltenhagen
Klütz
Wismar
Grevesmühlen
Neukloster
Bützow
Warin
Bad Kleinen
Brüel
Mühlen Eichsen
Rehna
Schlagbrügge
Gadebusch
Roggendorf
Lützow
Ratzeburg
Schaalsee
Mölln
Marienstedt
Zarrentin
Gut Grambek
Wittenburg
Schwerin
Schweriner See
Winstongolf
Sternberg
Crivitz
Warnow
Graal-Müritz
Warnemünde
ROSTOCK
Schwaan
Laage
Güstrow
Krakow
Goldberg
Mestlin
Lübz
Elde
Karow
Plau
Plauer See
Parchim
Spornitz
Hagenow
Wöbbelin
Neustadt Glewe
Ludwigslust
Marnitz
Meyenburg
Freyenstein
Ruhner Berge
Putlitz
Zierzow
Grabow
Eldena
Karstädt
Perleberg
Pritzwalk
Wittstock
Dömitz
Hitzacker
Dahlenburg
Neu Darchau
Neuhaus
Lübtheen
Boizenburg
Vellahn
Pritzier
Sude
Zingst
Prerow
Darß
Born
Wustrow
Saaler Bodden
Barth
Löbnitz
Richtenberg
Ribnitz-Damgarten
Marlow
Bad Sülze
Tribsees
Sanitz
Recknitz
Tessin
MECKLENBURG
Teterow
Neukalen
Malchiner See
Fleesensee
Malchow
Waren
Röbel
Trelleborg
MICHELIN
361

CLASSIFICATION OF GOLF COURSES

EINTEILUNG DER GOLFPLÄTZE

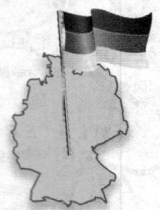

This classification gives priority consideration to the score awarded to the actual course.

Diese Einteilung berücksichtigt in erster Linie die dem Golfplatz erteilte Note.

Within each score, the ranking is purely alphabetical

Course score / Note für den Golfplatz				Page / Seite
18	6	7	Falkenstein	385
18	8	7	Rethmar	432
18	9	7	Seddiner See Südplatz	445
18	8	7	Sporting-Club Berlin Nick Faldo	449
17	9	9	Bad Griesbach Beckenbauer	370
17	9	9	Bad Griesbach Brunnwies	371
17	7	6	Beuerberg	376
17	6	5	Club zur Vahr (Garlstedt)	379
17	8	8	Fleesensee Schloss	387
17	7	8	Frankfurter GC	388
17	9	7	Gut Lärchenhof	397
17	7	7	Gütersloh (Westfälischer GC)	400
17	8	6	Hubbelrath	408
17	8	7	Jura Golf Park Am Habsberg	411
17	6	7	Köln (Refrath)	412
17	7	7	Krefelder	413
17	8	8	Lübeck-Travemünder	417
17	8	6	Motzener See	422
17	6	5	Oberfranken	426
17	7	5	Schloss Wilkendorf	443
17	8	6	Schwanhof	444
17	8	7	Sporting-Club Berlin Arnold Palmer	448
17	7	6	St. Dionys	451
17	9	7	St. Leon-Rot St. Leon Course	454
16	9	8	Am Alten Fliess Rot + Weiss	367
16	7	7	Bergisch Land Wuppertal	374
16	8	8	Berlin-Wannsee	375
16	7	6	Buxtehude	378
16	7	6	Feldafing	386
16	7	8	Fürstlicher GC Bad Waldsee	390
16	7	8	Gleidingen Grün + Blau	392
16	8	7	Golfpark Gut Häusern	393
16	7	6	Gut Grambek	395
16	7	5	Gut Thailing	399
16	8	7	Hamburg-Ahrensburg	401
16	6	6	Hanau-Wilhelmsbad	402
16	7	7	Hannover	403
16	7	8	Hardenberg Niedersachsen	404
16	7	6	Iffeldorf	409
16	7	7	Mittelrheinischer	421
16	7	7	München-Riedhof	423
16	7	7	Reichswald-Nürnberg	431
16	8	6	Rheine/Mesum	433
16	7	7	Schloss Braunfels	436
16	8	5	Schloss Langenstein	439
16	7	7	Schloss Myllendonk	441
16	8	7	Schloss Nippenburg	442
16	8	7	Semlin am See	446
16	8	7	Senne	447
16	8	7	Sporting-Club Berlin Stan Eby	450
16	7	6	St. Eurach	452
16	9	7	St. Leon-Rot Rot Course	453
16	7	7	Stolper Heide	455
16	5	5	Stuttgarter Solitude	456
16	7	6	Walddörfer	460
16	7	6	Wendlohe A-Kurs + B-Kurs	462
16	7	6	WinstonGolf	464
16	7	6	Wittelsbacher	465
15	7	7	Bad Abbach-Deutenhof	368
15	5	7	Bad Bevensen	369
15	9	9	Bad Griesbach-Sagmühle Sagmühle	372
15	7	7	Bamberg	373
15	7	8	Bitburger Land	377

CLASSIFICATION OF GOLF COURSES
EINTEILUNG DER GOLFPLÄTZE

15	7	7	Deinster Mühle	380
15	7	7	Düsseldorfer	382
15	8	7	Essener Oefte	384
15	2	6	Green Eagle Süd	394
15	7	6	Gut Kaden	396
15	6	7	Gut Ludwigsberg	398
15	7	5	Hof Trages	406
15	7	6	Hohenpähl	407
15	7	6	Lichtenau-Weickershof	414
15	7	8	Lindau-Bad Schachen	415
15	6	7	Münchner-Strasslach	424
15	6	6	Oberschwaben Bad Waldsee	427
15	7	7	Öschberghof	428
15	8	7	Rittergut Birkhof	435
15	7	7	Schloss Egmating	437
15	6	6	Schloss Klingenburg	438
15	7	6	Schloss Lüdersburg Old Course	440
15	6	8	Sylt	457
15	7	6	Tutzing	459
15	7	7	Wasserburg Anholt	461
15	8	7	Winnerod	463
14	7	6	Abenberg	366
14	7	7	Domtal-Mommenheim	381
14	7	7	Elfrather Mühle	383
14	7	5	Fränkische Schweiz	389
14	6	7	Garmisch-Partenkirchen	391
14	6	6	Hechingen-Hohenzollern	405
14	7	6	Jakobsberg	410
14	8	8	Lindenhof	416
14	7	7	Main-Taunus	418
14	7	6	Märkischer Potsdam	419
14	6	6	Memmingen Gut Westerhart	420
14	8	6	Nahetal	425
14	6	6	Pinnau	429
14	6	7	Reichsstadt Bad Windsheim	430
14	8	7	Rheinhessen	434
14	7	8	Tegernseer Bad Wiessee	458

HOTEL FACILITIES
EINTEILUNG DES HOTELANGEBOTS DER UMGEBUNG

This classification gives priority consideration to the score awarded to the hotel facilities.

Diese Klassifikation berücksichtigt in erster Linie die Bewertung für das Hotelangebot.

Hotel facility score / Note für das Hotelangebot der Umgebung — Page / Seite

17	9	**9**	Bad Griesbach Beckenbauer	370
17	9	**9**	Bad Griesbach Brunnwies	371
15	9	**9**	Bad Griesbach-Sagmühle Sagmühle	372
16	9	**8**	Am Alten Fliess Rot + Weiss	367
16	8	**8**	Berlin-Wannsee	375
15	7	**8**	Bitburger Land	377
17	8	**8**	Fleesensee Schloss	387
17	7	**8**	Frankfurter GC	388
16	7	**8**	Fürstlicher GC Bad Waldsee	390
16	2	**8**	Gleidingen Grün + Blau	392
16	7	**8**	Hardenberg Niedersachsen	404
15	7	**8**	Lindau-Bad Schachen	415
14	8	**8**	Lindenhof	416

HOTEL FACILITIES

EINTEILUNG DES HOTELANGEBOTS DER UMGEBUNG

17	8	**8**	Lübeck-Travemünder	417
15	6	**8**	Sylt	457
14	7	**8**	Tegernseer Bad Wiessee	458
15	7	**7**	Bad Abbach-Deutenhof	368
15	5	**7**	Bad Bevensen	369
15	7	**7**	Bamberg	373
16	7	**7**	Bergisch Land Wuppertal	374
15	7	**7**	Deinster Mühle	380
14	7	**7**	Domtal-Mommenheim	381
15	7	**7**	Düsseldorfer	382
14	7	**7**	Elfrather Mühle	383
15	8	**7**	Essener Oefte	384
18	6	**7**	Falkenstein	385
14	6	**7**	Garmisch-Partenkirchen	391
16	8	**7**	Golfpark Gut Häusern	393
17	9	**7**	Gut Lärchenhof	397
15	6	**7**	Gut Ludwigsberg	398
17	7	**7**	Gütersloh (Westfälischer GC)	400
16	8	**7**	Hamburg-Ahrensburg	401
16	7	**7**	Hannover	403
17	8	**7**	Jura Golf Park Am Habsberg	411
17	6	**7**	Köln (Refrath)	412
17	7	**7**	Krefelder	413
14	7	**7**	Main-Taunus	418
16	7	**7**	Mittelrheinischer	421
16	7	**7**	München-Riedhof	423
15	6	**7**	Münchner-Strasslach	424
15	7	**7**	Öschberghof	428
14	6	**7**	Reichsstadt Bad Windsheim	430
16	7	**7**	Reichswald-Nürnberg	431
18	8	**7**	Rethmar	432
14	8	**7**	Rheinhessen	434
15	8	**7**	Rittergut Birkhof	435
16	7	**7**	Schloss Braunfels	436
15	7	**7**	Schloss Egmating	437
16	7	**7**	Schloss Myllendonk	441
16	8	**7**	Schloss Nippenburg	442
18	9	**7**	Seddiner See Südplatz	445
16	8	**7**	Semlin am See	446
16	8	**7**	Senne	447
17	8	**7**	Sporting-Club Berlin Arnold Palmer	448
18	8	**7**	Sporting-Club Berlin Nick Faldo	449
16	8	**7**	Sporting-Club Berlin Stan Eby	450
16	9	**7**	St. Leon-Rot Rot Course	453
17	9	**7**	St. Leon-Rot St Leon Course	454
16	7	**7**	Stolper Heide	455
15	7	**7**	Wasserburg Anholt	461
15	8	**7**	Winnerod	463
14	7	**6**	Abenberg	366
17	7	**6**	Beuerberg	376
16	7	**6**	Buxtehude	378
16	7	**6**	Feldafing	386
15	2	**6**	Green Eagle Süd	394
16	7	**6**	Gut Grambek	395
15	7	**6**	Gut Kaden	396
16	6	**6**	Hanau-Wilhelmsbad	402
14	6	**6**	Hechingen-Hohenzollern	405
15	7	**6**	Hohenpähl	407
17	8	**6**	Hubbelrath	408
16	7	**6**	Iffeldorf	409
14	7	**6**	Jakobsberg	410
15	7	**6**	Lichtenau-Weickershof	414
14	7	**6**	Märkischer Potsdam	419
14	6	**6**	Memmingen Gut Westerhart	420
17	8	**6**	Motzener See	422
14	8	**6**	Nahetal	425
15	6	**6**	Oberschwaben Bad Waldsee	427
14	6	**6**	Pinnau	429
16	8	**6**	Rheine/Mesum	433
15	6	**6**	Schloss Klingenburg	438
15	7	**6**	Schloss Lüdersburg Old Course	440
17	8	**6**	Schwanhof	444
17	7	**6**	St. Dionys	451
16	7	**6**	St. Eurach	452
15	7	**6**	Tutzing	459
16	7	**6**	Walddörfer	460
16	7	**6**	Wendlohe A-Kurs + B-Kurs	462
16	7	**6**	WinstonGolf	464
16	7	**6**	Wittelsbacher	465
17	6	**5**	Club zur Vahr (Garlstedt)	379
14	7	**5**	Fränkische Schweiz	389
16	7	**5**	Gut Thailing	399
15	7	**5**	Hof Trages	406
17	6	**5**	Oberfranken	426
16	8	**5**	Schloss Langenstein	439
17	7	**5**	Schloss Wilkendorf	443
16	5	**5**	Stuttgarter Solitude	456

RECOMMENDED GOLFING STAY
EMPFOHLENER GOLF AUFENTHALT

Bad Griesbach Beckenbauer	**17**	9	9	370	Semlin am See	**16**	8	7	446
Bad Griesbach Brunnwies	**17**	9	9	371	Sporting-Club Berlin				
Bad Griesbach-Sagmühle					Arnold Palmer	**17**	8	7	448
Sagmühle	**15**	9	9	372	Sporting-Club Berlin Nick Faldo	**18**	8	7	449
Fleesensee Schloss	**17**	8	8	387	Sporting-Club Berlin Stan Eby	**16**	8	7	450
Hardenberg Niedersachsen	**16**	7	8	404	St. Leon-Rot Rot Course	**16**	9	7	453
Sedditer See Südplatz	**18**	9	7	445	St. Leon-Rot St Leon Course	**17**	9	7	454

RECOMMENDED HOLIDAYS
EMPFOHLENER FERIENORT

Garmisch-Partenkirchen	14	6	7	391	Öschberghof	15	7	7	428
Lindau-Bad Schachen	15	7	8	415	Sylt	15	6	8	457
Lübeck-Travemünder	17	8	8	417					

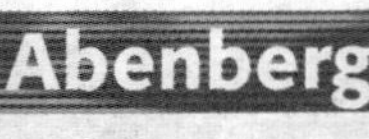

Abenberg

14	7	6

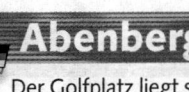

Der Golfplatz liegt so nahe bei Nürnberg, dass man sich in dieser deutschen Hochburg des Mittelalters, in der Albrecht Dürer wohnte, gut einquartieren kann. Die Altstadt und das Germanische Nationalmuseum lohnen einen erholsamen Tag zwischen zwei Partien Golf! Die Spielbahn liegt in einem flachen Gelände mit vielen Bäumen. Die riesigen Bäume stellen einen wichtigen Teil der Schwierigkeiten dar, unter anderem verlangen auch die Fairways und die Länge von manchen Par-4-Löchern bei bestimmten Abschlägen eine sehr sorgfältige Auswahl des Schlägers: Wenn man den Ball nicht lange und gerade schlagen kann, muss man einige Bogeys in Kauf nehmen. Die Bunker sind recht zahlreich, aber meist nur um die mittelgrossen, wenig welligen Greens angeordnet. Zwei Greens sind erhöht und zwei auf doppelten Stufen angelegt. Eine ehrliche, offene Anlage, auch wenn die Gestaltung und die Ausprägung der Erhebungen zu wünschen übrig lässt.

The Abenberg course is close enough to Nürnberg for you to establish base-camp in this high spot of Middle-Age Germany, where Albrecht Dürer once lived. The old town and the Germanisches Nationalmuseum are well worth a day's rest between two rounds of golf ! This course is laid out on generally flat terrain in very woody countryside, so big trees are not surprisingly a major factor in the difficulties awaiting you on either side of the fairways. On top of that, the length of some par 4s calls for very careful club selection from a number of tees. If you are not too sure of hitting it long and straight, there'll be a few bogeys in store. Bunkers abound but are basically placed around averagely-sized greens with few contours. Two greens are elevated, two are two-tiered. A very decent course, but perhaps lacking a little contouring work to give the layout greater shape.

Golf Club Abenberg e.V. — 1988

Am Golfplatz 19
D - 91183 ABENBERG

Office	Sekretariat	(49) 09178 - 98 960
Pro shop	Pro shop	(49) 09178 - 98 960
Fax	Fax	(49) 09178 - 989 696
Web		www.golfclub-abenberg.de
Situation	Lage	Nürnberg, 25 km
Annual closure	Jährliche Schliessung	1/12→28/2
Weekly closure	Wöchentliche Schliessung	no

Monday (Montag): Restaurant closed

Fees main season / Preisliste hochsaison	Week days / Woche	We/Bank holidays / We/Feiertag
18 holes		
Individual Individuell	€ 40	€ 50*
Couple Ehepaar	€ 80	€ 100*

*We: Members only (nur Mitglieder)/ –22 & Students: –50%

Caddie Caddie no — Electric Trolley Elektrokarren no

Buggy Elektrischer Wagen yes — Clubs Leihschläger yes

Credit cards Kreditkarten
VISA - Eurocard - MasterCard - AMEX

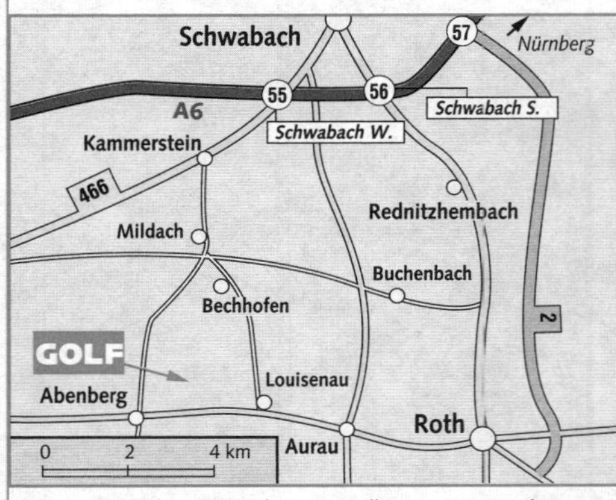

Access Zufahrt : A6 Nürnberg → Heilbronn. Exit (Ausf.) Schwabach West/ Abenberg. B466 → Abenberg

Map 4 on page 354 Karte 4 Seite 354

GOLF COURSE — PLATZ — 14/20

Site	Lage	
Maintenance	Instandhaltung	
Architect	Architekt	unknown
Type	Typ	forest, open country
Relief	Begehbarkeit	
Water in play	Platz mit Wasser	
Exp. to wind	Wind ausgesetzt	
Trees in play	Platz mit Bäumen	

Scorecard Scorekarte	Chp. Chp.	Mens Herren	Ladies Damen
Length Länge	6148	5969	5288
Par	72	72	72
Slope system	131	129	130

Advised golfing ability / Empfohlene Spielstärke: 0 12 24 36

Hcp required — Min. Handicap — 36

CLUB HOUSE & AMENITIES — KLUBHAUS UND NEBENGEBÄUDE — 7/10

Pro shop — Pro shop
Driving range — Übungsplatz

Sheltered überdacht 6 mats - On grass auf Rasen yes - Putting-green Putting-grün yes - Pitching-green Pitching-grün yes

HOTEL FACILITIES — HOTEL BESCHREIBUNG — 6/10

HOTELS HOTELS

Burghotel Abenberg - 17 rooms, D € 65 - Abenberg 5 km
Tel (49) 09178 - 982 990, Fax (49) 09178 -982 9996

Agneshof - 74 rooms, D € 130 - Nürnberg 25 km
Tel (49) 0911 - 214 440, Fax (49) 0911- 214 44144

Zum Heidenberg - Büchenbach-Kühendorf 4 km
32 rooms, D € 73
Tel (49) 09171 - 84 40, Fax (49) 09171 - 84 480

RESTAURANTS RESTAURANTS

Goldener Stern - Schwabach 10 km - Tel (49) 09122 - 2335

Zirbelstube - Nürnberg-Worzeldorf 25 km
Tel (49) 0911 - 998 820

Am Alten Fliess *Rot + Weiss*

16	9	8

Die 27 Löcher des Platzes mit dem luxuriösen Clubhaus sind auf leicht hügeligen, aber weit offenem Gelände angelegt, das den Talenten des Architekten Kurt Rossknecht viel Spielraum liess. Von den möglichen Neun-Loch-Kombinationen bevorzugen wir die Variante "Rot-Weiss" mit zwei vorzüglichen Schlusslöchern um einen See herum. Neben dem gelungenen Layout ist die vorzügliche Drainage des Platzes ein weiteres Argument für den Nachbarn des Nicklaus-Designs Gut Lärchenhof. Obwohl der Platz sich an amerikanischen Vorbildern orientiert, liess der Architekt verschiedene Optionen offen, um das Grün zu erreichen. Man kann den Ball rollend oder auch hoch als Pitch-Schlag auf die Puttingoberfläche befördern - und bis auf die beiden erwähnten Löcher 9 und 18 muss man dabei nie gefährliche Hindernisse überwinden. Der Platz weist leider auch ein paar schwächere Löcher auf, aber dafür sieht man alle Schwierigkeiten und es gibt keine Entschuldigung für eine schlechte Runde.

Just behind a village dominated by a luxurious club-house and, in the background on a clear day, the familiar outline of Cologne cathedral, Am Alten Fliess assumes its status as one of the city's great courses laid out over friendly rolling terrain and wide open space which provided a window for the talent of architect Rossknecht. Of the three 9-hole combinations, we preferred the more demanding "Rot + Weiss" pairing which, with holes 9 and 18 around a lake, provides two excellent closing holes. The seriousness of the layout is a solid argument in favour of this course, especially the excellent drainage system. Although the style owes much to the American school, the architect has kept all options open for reaching the green – you can roll it as well as pitch it – and has not gone over the top with insurmountable hazards. A few very ordinary holes are the only blips on what is a very satisfactory course. On the upside, the layout is very open and fair: what you see is what you get. So no excuses for a poor round.

Golf Club Am Alten Fliess — 1995

Am Alten Fliess 66
D - 50129 BERGHEIM-FLIESTEDEN

Office	Sekretariat	(49) 02238 - 944 10
Pro shop	Pro shop	(49) 02238 - 944 10
Fax	Fax	(49) 02238 - 944 119
Web	www.golfplatz-koeln.de	
Situation	Lage	Köln, 25 km
Annual closure	Jährliche Schliessung	no
Weekly closure	Wöchentliche Schliessung	Monday

(Montag): restaurant closed

Fees main season Preisliste hochsaison	18 holes	
	Week days Woche	**We/Bank holidays** We/Feiertag
Individual Individuell	€ 60	€ 80
Couple Ehepaar	€ 120	€ 160

Under 18: € 30 / 40 (We)

Caddie Caddie no — **Electric Trolley** Elektrokarren no
Buggy Elektrischer Wagen yes — **Clubs** Leihschläger yes
Credit cards Kreditkarten Eurocard

Access Zufahrt : Köln, A1 Exit (Ausfahrt) K-Böcklemund, then B59 → Pulheim. In Pulheim, L187 → Mandstedten and Fliesteden. Before Fliesteden, turn left on L91 → Giessen, golf on the right hand side (Not easy to find out from all directions).
Map 3 on page 352 Karte 3 Seite 352

GOLF COURSE — PLATZ 16/20

Site	Lage	
Maintenance	Instandhaltung	
Architect	Architekt	Kurt Rossknecht
Type	Typ	open country
Relief	Begehbarkeit	
Water in play	Platz mit Wasser	
Exp. to wind	Wind ausgesetzt	
Trees in play	Platz mit Bäumen	

Scorecard Scorekarte	**Chp.** Chp.	**Mens** Herren	**Ladies** Damen
Length Länge	6210	6057	5394
Par	72	72	72
Slope system	127	127	124

Advised golfing ability Empfohlene Spielstärke — 0 12 24 36
Hcp required Min. Handicap 36

CLUB HOUSE & AMENITIES — KLUBHAUS UND NEBENGEBÄUDE 9/10

Pro shop Pro shop
Driving range Übungsplatz
Sheltered überdacht 17 mats - On grass auf Rasen yes
Putting-green Putting-grün yes - Pitching-green Pitching-grün yes

HOTEL FACILITIES — HOTEL BESCHREIBUNG 8/10

HOTELS HOTELS

Brenner'scher Hof- Junkersdorf 15 km
49 rooms, D € 135
Tel (49) 0221 - 948 6000, Fax (49) 0221 - 94860010

Ascari Hotel - Pulheim 5 km
70 rooms, D € 120
Tel (49) 02238 - 8040, Fax (49) 02238 - 804 140

Dom Hotel - Köln 8 km
130 rooms, D € 340
Tel (49) 0221 - 202 40, Fax (49) 0221 - 202 4444

RESTAURANTS RESTAURANTS

Zur Traube - Grevenbroich 18 km - Tel (49) 02281 - 687 67
Landhaus Ville - Danswieler 2 km - Tel (49) 02234 - 833 45

Bad Abbach-Deutenhof

15 | 7 | 7

Dieser Platz liegt südlich der Stadt Regensburg, die in ihrem Stadtbild die Geschichte des Deutschen Kaiserreichs widerspiegelt. Viele Gebäude stammen noch aus dem Mittelalter und der Renaissance. Diese Verbundenheit mit der deutschen Geschichte wird in der Walhalla symbolisiert, einem Denkmal hoch über der Donau, das Ludwig I. von Bayern errrichten liess. Der neue Platz in der Kurstadt Bad Abbach, der auf weit offenem Gelände erbaut wurde, gilt schon heute als einer der besten neuen Plätze in Bayern. Der Platz weist keine Heimtücken auf, hier kann man auf Birdies hoffen, statt ständig Bogeys oder Schlimmeres zu befürchten. Bad Abbach hat sich damit in der Kürze der Zeit einen vorzüglichen Ruf erworben, obwohl es ein wenig abseits der grossen Touristenrouten liegt. Die Schwierigkeiten sind gut über den Platz verteilt. Der Platz ist für Golfer aller Spielstärken zu bewältigen. Sein einziger Nachteil ist das bergige Gelände, so dass Golfer, die körperlich nicht fit sind, schnell ermüden.

This course is located to the south of the city of Regensburg, one of the high-spots of the history of the German Empire where much of the architecture recalls the Middle Ages and the Renaissance. Such union with German history is equally symbolized by the Walhalla, a sort of memorial overlooking the Danube. This course, laid out in a spa city over rather wide open space, has become established as one of the better new courses in Bavaria. Rather forthright and indulgent to golfers who tend to stumble across birdies rather than actively go looking for them, this Rainer Preismann design tends to bare its teeth more to the reckless golfer. Nicely balanced and with a rather likeable personality, Bad Abbach is making a name for itself on account of its excellent attributes, despite being a little off the busier tourist routes. With difficulties fairly spread around the course and playable by golfers of all levels, its only failing is perhaps the hilly terrain which make this a tiring round of golf for physically unfit players.

Golfclub Bad Abbach-Deutenhof — 1996

Gut Deutenhof
D - 93077 BAD ABBACH

Office	Sekretariat	(49) 09405 - 953 20
Pro shop	Pro shop	(49) 09405 - 953 20
Fax	Fax	(49) 09405 - 953 219
Web	www.golf-badabbach.de	
Situation	Lage	Regensburg, 10 km
Annual closure	Jährliche Schliessung	no
Weekly closure	Wöchentliche Schliessung	no
Fees main season	Preisliste hochsaison	18 holes

	Week days Woche	We/Bank holidays We/Feiertag
Individual Individuell	€ 38	€ 50
Couple Ehepaar	€ 76	€ 100

– 21 & Students: – 50%

Caddie Caddie no — **Electric Trolley** Elektrokarren yes
Buggy Elektrischer Wagen yes — **Clubs** Leihschläger yes
Credit cards Kreditkarten no

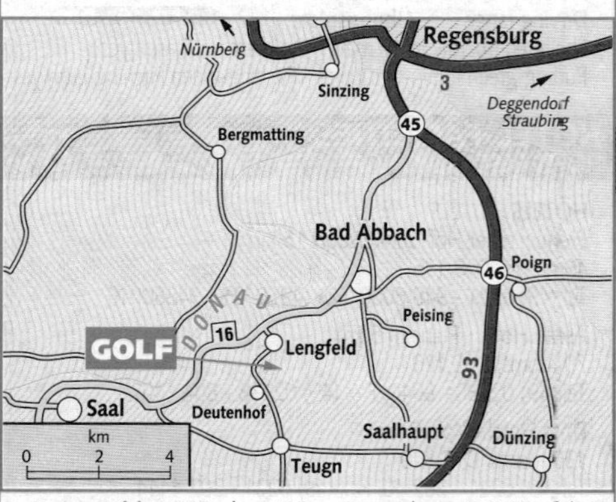

Access Zufahrt : München A93 → Regensburg. Exit (Ausfahrt) Hausen, → Teugn, → Lengfeld. Golf on right side.
Map 2 on page 350 Karte 2 Seite 350

GOLF COURSE — PLATZ — 15/20

Site	Lage	
Maintenance	Instandhaltung	
Architect	Architekt	Rainer Preismann DeutscheGolfConsult
Type	Typ	open country
Relief	Begehbarkeit	
Water in play	Platz mit Wasser	
Exp. to wind	Wind ausgesetzt	
Trees in play	Platz mit Bäumen	

Scorecard Scorekarte	Chp. Chp.	Mens Herren	Ladies Damen
Length Länge	6150	5817	5159
Par	72	72	72
Slope system	127	123	124

Advised golfing ability Empfohlene Spielstärke: 0 12 24 36
Hcp required Min. Handicap: 35

CLUB HOUSE & AMENITIES — KLUBHAUS UND NEBENGEBÄUDE — 7/10

Pro shop Pro shop
Driving range Übungsplatz
Sheltered überdacht 6 mats - On grass auf Rasen yes - Putting-green Putting-grün yes - Pitching-green Pitching-grün yes

HOTEL FACILITIES — HOTEL BESCHREIBUNG — 7/10

HOTELS HOTELS

Landgasthof Gut Deutenhof - 13 rooms, D € 95 - on site
Tel (49) 09405 - 953 230, Fax (49) 09405 - 953 239

Parkhotel Maximilian - Regensburg 10 km
52 rooms, D € 150
Tel (49) 0941 - 568 50, Fax (49) 0941 - 529 42

Altstadthotel Arch - Regensburg 10 km
65 rooms, D € 100
Tel (49) 0941 - 586 60, Fax (49) 0941 -5866 168

RESTAURANTS RESTAURANTS

Rosenpalais - Regensburg 10 km - Tel (49) 09415 - 997 579
Hagens Auberge - Regensburg 10 km - Tel (49) 09418 - 44 13

Bad Bevensen

15 | 5 | 7

Dieser Platz im ländlichen Norddeutschland wirkt auf den ersten Blick wie ein grosser Bauernhof, eine Atmosphäre wie man sie selten auf modernen Plätzen findet. Hier ist man weit weg von der Hektik der Grossstadt. Die freundliche Umgebung führt leicht dazu, dass man den Platz unterschätzt - ein Fehler. Das Gelände ist ziemlich hügelig, aber gut begehbar. Einige blinde Löchern wollen mit Überlegung attackiert werden. Die Schwierigkeiten sind gut über den Platz verteilt und meist vom Abschlag deutlich zu erkennen. Einziger Schwachpunkt ist das erste Loch, bei dem gute Spieler und Longhitter über eine Pferdekoppel abschlagen müssen. Der Platz ist originell, gut in die Landschaft eingepasst, allerdings werden hohe Handicaps auf diesem Platz Mühe haben, vor allem, wenn sie mit einstelligen Golfern unterwegs. Obwohl der Platz nicht sonderlich lang, ist es keineswegs einfach mit einem guten Ergebnis ins Clubhaus zurückzukehren.

Here were are in the middle of the North German countryside on a course that looks like a huge farm in a rural setting. Bad Bevensen gives new meaning to the expression "getting away from it all". This sort of scenery from another age is something of a rarity on modern golf courses. In such a friendly setting, you might be tempted to underestimate the course, but watch out. The terrain is relatively hilly but definitely walkable, and some virtually blind holes call for extreme caution. Elsewhere, difficulties of all sorts are mostly visible from the tees and cleverly spread around. We did have our reservations about the first hole, where long-hitters have to drive over a horse corral. Original and finely-landscaped, the course as a whole can prove to be awkward when playing amongst players of different abilities, as higher-handicappers will have problems overcoming all the difficulties and keeping up with the others. Despite being on the short side, this is a difficult course to score on..

Golf Club Bad Bevensen e.V. — 1991

Dorfstrasse 22
D - 29575 ALTENMEDINGEN, ORSTEIL SECKLENDORF

Office	Sekretariat	(49) 05821 - 98 250
Pro shop	Pro shop	(49) 05821 - 98 250
Fax	Fax	(49) 05821 - 42 595
Web	www.gc-badbevensen.de	
Situation	Lage	Lüneburg, 24 km
Annual closure	Jährliche Schliessung	no
Weekly closure	Wöchentliche Schliessung	no

Fees main season Preisliste hochsaison		18 holes
	Week days Woche	**We/Bank holidays** We/Feiertag
Individual Individuell	€ 35	€ 45
Couple Ehepaar	€ 70	€ 90

– 21 & Students: – 50%

Caddie Caddie no — **Electric Trolley** Elektrokarren no
Buggy Elektrischer Wagen yes — **Clubs** Leihschläger yes
Credit cards Kreditkarten no

Access Zufahrt : Hamburg, A250 → Lüneburg. B4 → Uelzen. Exit (Ausf.) Bad Bevensen → Secklendorf Altenmedingen. Secklendorf → Golf.
Map 6 on page 358 Karte 6 Seite 358

GOLF COURSE — PLATZ — 15/20

Site	Lage	
Maintenance	Instandhaltung	
Architect	Architekt	Ulrich Schmidt
Type	Typ	country
Relief	Begehbarkeit	
Water in play	Platz mit Wasser	
Exp. to wind	Wind ausgesetzt	
Trees in play	Platz mit Bäumen	

Scorecard Scorekarte	**Chp.** Chp.	**Mens** Herren	**Ladies** Damen
Length Länge	5808	5808	5463
Par	71	71	71
Slope system	120	120	123

Advised golfing ability Empfohlene Spielstärke — 0 12 24 36
Hcp required Min. Handicap no

CLUB HOUSE & AMENITIES — KLUBHAUS UND NEBENGEBÄUDE — 5/10

Pro shop Pro shop
Driving range Übungsplatz
Sheltered überdacht 2 mats - On grass auf Rasen yes - Putting-green Putting-grün yes - Pitching-green Pitching-grün yes

HOTEL FACILITIES — HOTEL BESCHREIBUNG — 7/10

HOTELS HOTELS

Zur Amtsheide - Bad Bevensen 3 km
101 rooms, D € 110
Tel (49) 05821 - 8 51, Fax (49) 05821 - 853 38

Grünings Landhaus - Bad Bevensen 5 km
24 rooms, D € 122
Tel (49) 05821 - 984 00, Fax (49) 05821 - 984 041

Fährhaus - 60 rooms, D € 100 - Bad Bevensen 5 km
Tel (49) 05821 - 50 00, Fax (49) 05821 - 50 089

RESTAURANTS RESTAURANTS

Zur Linde - Secklendorf 1 - Tel (49) 05821 - 7589
Zur Amstheide - Bad Bevensen 3 km - Tel (49) 05821 - 1249
Grünings Restaurant - Bad Bevensen 5 km
Tel (49) 05821 - 984 00

Bad Griesbach *Beckenbauer*

17	9	9

"Beckenbauer ist Deutschlands berühmtester Golfer, Bernhard Langer ist der beste." So begründete Alois Hartl, der Eigentümer des Plus Resort Europe in Bad Griesbach, warum er wieder auf den deutschen Meisterschwinger und Kurt Rossknecht zurückgriff, als es darum ging, einen 18-Loch-Platz zu bauen, der den Namen des „Kaisers" tragen sollte. Der Beckenbauer-Platz gilt als der schwierigste des niederbayrischen Resorts, einmal durch seine Länge, aber auch die vielen Wasserhindernisse und ein Links Design, bei dem die Bunker nicht immer vom Abschlag sichtbar sind. Der Platz wird einer Familie auf einer gemeinsamen Golfrunde wenig Freude bereiten, es sei denn, alle sind vorzüglich Golfer. Dieser Platz ist sicherlich nicht jedermanns Liebling, aber dafür ist er auch niemals so überlaufen wie die anderen Plätze des Resorts. Turnierspieler und Longhitter werden diesen qualitativ hochwertigen Platz ob seines anspruchsvollen Designs, seinem originellen und wenig Fehler verzeihenden Layouts schätzen.

"Beckenbauer is Germany's most famous golfer, Bernhard Langer is the best." This is why Alois Hartl, the proprietor of the Plus Resort Europe once again called upon Herr "Meisterswinger" and Kurt Rossknecht to build an 18-hole course named after the Kaiser Beckenbauer, a regular visitor to this venue. This particular course is also the toughest on the site through its length, the number of water hazards and a links style layout where the traps are not always visible. It would be hard to imagine a family on holiday having fun on it if they are not all pretty good golfers. In other words this course is not everyone's favourite, but the upside is that it is never overcrowded like the resort's other courses. Tournament freaks and big-hitters will appreciate much more what is a high quality, demanding, original and unforgiving layout.

Golf Resort Bad Griesbach — 2002

Holzhäuser 8
D - 94 086 BAD GRIESBACH

Office	Sekretariat	(49) 08535 - 92 440
Pro shop	Pro shop	(49) 08535 - 90 440
Fax	Fax	(49) 08535 - 924 429
Web	www.hartl.de	
Situation	Lage	Passau, 40 km

Griesbach (pop. 8 200), 3 km

Annual closure	Jährliche Schliessung	15/11→15/3
Weekly closure	Wöchentliche Schliessung	no
Fees main season	Preisliste hochsaison	18 holes

	Week days Woche	We/Bank holidays We/Feiertag
Individual Individuell	€ 53	€ 63
Couple Ehepaar	€ 106	€ 126

Under 27: – 50%

Caddie Caddie on request — **Electric Trolley** Elektrokarren yes
Buggy Elektrischer Wagen yes — **Clubs** Leihschläger yes
Credit cards Kreditkarten VISA - Eurocard - MasterCard

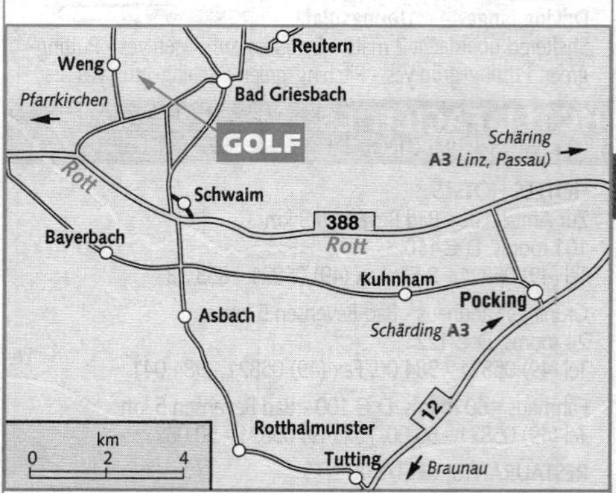

Access Zufahrt : A3 Nürnberg-Regensburg-Passau. Exit (Ausf.) Pocking. B12 and B388 → Bad Griesbach. → Golf
Map 2 on page 351 Karte 2 Seite 351

GOLF COURSE — PLATZ — 17/20

Site	Lage	
Maintenance	Instandhaltung	
Architect	Architekt	Bernhard Langer, Kurt Rossknecht
Type	Typ	parkland
Relief	Begehbarkeit	
Water in play	Platz mit Wasser	
Exp. to wind	Wind ausgesetzt	
Trees in play	Platz mit Bäumen	

Scorecard Scorekarte	Chp. Chp.	Mens Herren	Ladies Damen
Length Länge	6500	6078	5174
Par	72	72	72
Slope system	129	127	125

Advised golfing ability Empfohlene Spielstärke — 0 12 24 36
Hcp required Min. Handicap — no

CLUB HOUSE & AMENITIES — KLUBHAUS UND NEBENGEBÄUDE — 9/10

Pro shop Pro shop
Driving range Übungsplatz
Sheltered überdacht 8 mats - On grass auf Rasen no, 20 mats open air - Putting-green Putting-grün yes - Pitching-green Pitching-grün yes

HOTEL FACILITIES — HOTEL BESCHREIBUNG — 9/10

HOTELS HOTELS

Golfhotel Maximilian - 229 rooms, D € 130 - Golf Resort
Tel (49) 08532 - 79 50, Fax (49) 08532 - 795 151

Fürstenhof - 148 rooms, D € 190 - Golf Resort
Tel (49) 08532 - 98 10, Fax (49) 08532 - 981 135

Parkhotel - 159 rooms, D € 220 (with dinner) - Golf Resort
Tel (49) 08532 - 2 80, Fax (49) 08532 - 28 204

König Ludwig - 184 rooms, D € 250 (with diner) - Golf Resort
Tel (49) 08532 - 79 90, Fax (49) 08532 - 799 799

RESTAURANTS RESTAURANTS

Fürstenstube - Golf Resort - Tel (49) 08532 - 98 10
Gutshof Uttlau - Golf Resort - Tel (49) 08535 - 1890

Bad Griesbach *Brunnwies*

17	9	9

Das Golf Resort Bad Griesbach umfasst seit 2003 sechs 18-Loch Anlagen. Brunnwies sowie Sagmühle sind die beiden Top-Plätze des Resorts; Uttlau und Lederbach haben ebenfalls ihre Qualitäten, sind aber sehr hügelig (Golfwagen wird empfohlen)und stehen mittlerweile im Schatten der beiden neuen Plätze Beckenbauer und Jaguar. Brunnwies ist zwar auch auf unebenem Terrain angelegt, dieser Eindruck wird aber durch die hervorragende Platzgestaltung des Architekten Bernhard Langer weitgehend entschärft. Auffallend ist die sorgfältige Gestaltung des Geländes vom Abschlag zum Grün, wodurch die einzelnen Löchern eine deutliche Form und Definition erhalten. Grosse Beachtung wurde auch der Anlage breiter Fairways, sowie der Fairway- und Grünbunker geschenkt, die noch stärker ins Spiel kommen als die Bäume und das Wasser. Gute Spieler tun sich auf Brunnwies schwerer als Durchschnittsgolfer, genau so soll es sein. Eine faszinierende Anlage mit einem sehr schönen Clubhaus im Stil der lokalen Bauernhöfe.

Since 2003 this enormous resort comprises six 18-hole courses. This and Sagmühle are two gems, while Uttlau and Lederbach, despite their qualities, are very hilly (buggy recommended) and are overshadowed by the two new courses (Beckenbauer, named after the football great, and Jaguar). Brunnwies is steep, too, but the excellence of architect Bernhard Langer tends to keep your mind off geographical considerations. The first thing you notice is the care taken over contouring the terrain, from tee to green, giving clear shape, form and physical definition to holes. There was also concern for wide fairways and fairway and green-side bunkers that are even more in play than the trees or water. It's tough for the good player but an easier proposition for the average golfer, so who could ask for more? A spectacular layout with a very pretty clubhouse in the style of the region's farmhouses.

Golf Resort Bad Griesbach — 1996

Holzhäuser 8
D - 94 086 BAD GRIESBACH

Office	Sekretariat	(49) 08535 - 92 440
Pro shop	Pro shop	(49) 08535 - 90 440
Fax	Fax	(49) 08535 - 924 429
Web	www.hartl.de	
Situation	Lage	Passau, 40 km

Griesbach (pop. 8 200), 3 km

Annual closure	Jährliche Schliessung	15/11→15/3
Weekly closure	Wöchentliche Schliessung	no
Fees main season	Preisliste hochsaison	18 holes

	Week days Woche	We/Bank holidays We/Feiertag
Individual Individuell	€ 60	€ 70
Couple Ehepaar	€ 120	€ 140

Under 27: – 50%

Caddie Caddie on request	Electric Trolley Elektrokarren yes
Buggy Elektrischer Wagen yes	Clubs Leihschläger yes
Credit cards Kreditkarten	VISA - Eurocard - MasterCard

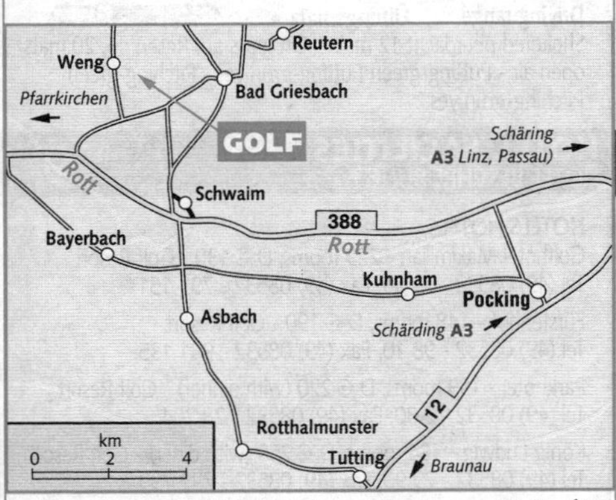

Access Zufahrt : A3 Nürnberg-Regensburg-Passau. Exit (Ausf.) Pocking. B12 and B388 → Bad Griesbach. → Golf

Map 2 on page 351 Karte 2 Seite 351

GOLF COURSE — PLATZ — 17/20

Site	Lage	
Maintenance	Instandhaltung	
Architect	Architekt	Bernhard Langer
Type	Typ	open country, hilly
Relief	Begehbarkeit	
Water in play	Platz mit Wasser	
Exp. to wind	Wind ausgesetzt	
Trees in play	Platz mit Bäumen	

Scorecard Scorekarte	Chp. Chp.	Mens Herren	Ladies Damen
Length Länge	6117	5689	4976
Par	70	70	71
Slope system	121	120	118

Advised golfing ability — Empfohlene Spielstärke: 0 12 24 36

Hcp required — Min. Handicap: no

CLUB HOUSE & AMENITIES — KLUBHAUS UND NEBENGEBÄUDE — 9/10

Pro shop — Pro shop

Driving range — Übungsplatz

Sheltered überdacht 8 mats - On grass auf Rasen no, 20 mats open air - Putting-green Putting-grün yes - Pitching-green Pitching-grün yes

HOTEL FACILITIES — HOTEL BESCHREIBUNG — 9/10

HOTELS HOTELS

Golfhotel Maximilian - 229 rooms, D € 130 - Golf Resort
Tel (49) 08532 - 79 50, Fax (49) 08532 - 795 151

Fürstenhof - 148 rooms, D € 190 - Golf Resort
Tel (49) 08532 - 98 10, Fax (49) 08532 - 981 135

Parkhotel - 159 rooms, D € 220 (with dinner) - Golf Resort
Tel (49) 08532 - 2 80, Fax (49) 08532 - 28 204

König Ludwig - 184 rooms, D € 250 (with diner) - Golf Resort
Tel (49) 08532 - 79 90, Fax (49) 08532 - 799 799

RESTAURANTS RESTAURANTS

Fürstenstube - Golf Resort - Tel (49) 08532 - 98 10
Gutshof Uttlau - Golf Resort - Tel (49) 08535 - 1890

Bad Griesbach-Sagmühle *Sagmühle* 15 | 9 | 9

Dies ist der älteste der sechs Plätze in Deutschlands grösstem Golf-Resort. In etwas Enfernung zu den drei anderen Plätzen gelegen verläuft Sagmühle auf wesentlich flacherem Gelände im Flusstal der Rott, deren Nebenarm immer wieder die Spielbahnen kreuzt. Wasser, ob als seitliches oder frontales Hindernis, ist die Hauptschwierigkeit auf diesem intelligent konzipierten Golfplatz, der leider häufig recht feucht ist. Um nicht allzuviele Bälle zu verlieren, sollte man daher seine eigenen Schlaglängen gut einschätzen können. Der Platz spielt sich insgesamt nicht allzu lang, sofern man nicht die hinteren Abschläge wählt. Bäume und Bunker sind so in das Platzdesign integriert, dass der Spieler auf der Runde mit allen möglichen Situationen und Hindernissen konfrontiert wird. Die gesamte Anlage, an der Grenze zwischen Bayern und Oberösterreich gelegen, umfasst ausserdem eine riesige Driving Range, eine Golfschule, zwei Kurz-Plätze und bietet zahlreiche weitere Aktivitäten für jeden Geschmack - egal ob Anfänger oder Könner.

This is the "oldest" of the six courses which grace Germany's largest golfing resort. A little out of the way from the three others, it is also much flatter and lies in the valley of the river Rott, a branch of which continually flows in and out of the course. As a frontal or lateral hazard, water is the main difficulty on this intelligently-designed (but often damp) layout, so it helps to know exactly what distance you can cover with each club to avoid losing too many balls. The overall yardage, though, is not excessive providing you steer clear of the back tees. With trees and bunkers, the course appears to be designed to put players in every imaginable situation with every possible hazard. The whole resort, located on the frontier between Bavaria and upper Austria, also features a huge driving range, a golfing school, two small courses and many other activities to keep everyone happy - the good, the not so good and the beginners.

Golf-Club Sagmühle 1984

Schwaim 52
D - 94 086 BAD GRIESBACH

Office Sekretariat (49) 08532 - 2038
Pro shop Pro shop (49) 08532 - 7173
Fax Fax (49) 08532 - 3165
Web www.hartl.de
Situation Lage Passau, 40 km
Griesbach (pop. 8 200), 3 km
Annual closure Jährliche Schliessung 15/11→15/3
Weekly closure Wöchentliche Schliessung no
Fees main season Preisliste hochsaison 18 holes

	Week days Woche	We/Bank holidays We/Feiertag
Individual Individuell	€ 53	€ 58
Couple Ehepaar	€ 106	€ 116

Under 27: – 50%

Caddie Caddie on request — **Electric Trolley** Elektrokarren yes
Buggy Elektrischer Wagen yes — **Clubs** Leihschläger yes
Credit cards Kreditkarten VISA - Eurocard - MasterCard

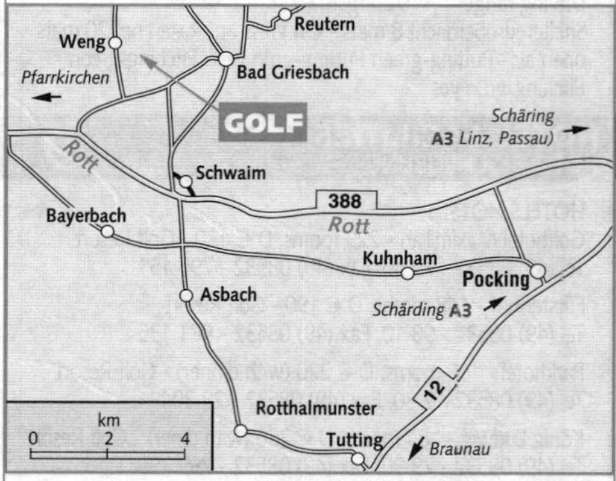

Access Zufahrt : A3 Nürnberg-Regensburg-Passau. Exit (Ausf.) Pocking. B12 and B388 → Bad Griesbach. → Golf
Map 2 on page 351 Karte 2 Seite 351

GOLF COURSE PLATZ 15/20

Site Lage
Maintenance Instandhaltung
Architect Architekt Kurt Rossknecht
Type Typ parkland
Relief Begehbarkeit
Water in play Platz mit Wasser
Exp. to wind Wind ausgesetzt
Trees in play Platz mit Bäumen

Scorecard Scorekarte	Chp. Chp.	Mens Herren	Ladies Damen
Length Länge	6150	5895	5180
Par	72	72	72
Slope system	125	123	127

Advised golfing ability Empfohlene Spielstärke 0 12 24 36
Hcp required Min. Handicap no

CLUB HOUSE & AMENITIES KLUBHAUS UND NEBENGEBÄUDE 9/10

Pro shop Pro shop
Driving range Übungsplatz
Sheltered überdacht 12 mats - On grass auf Rasen no, 20 mats open air - Putting-green Putting-grün yes - Pitching-green Pitching-grün yes

HOTEL FACILITIES HOTEL BESCHREIBUNG 9/10

HOTELS HOTELS

Golfhotel Maximilian - 229 rooms, D € 130 - Golf Resort
Tel (49) 08532 - 79 50, Fax (49) 08532 - 795 151

Fürstenhof - 148 rooms, D € 190 - Golf Resort
Tel (49) 08532 - 98 10, Fax (49) 08532 - 981 135

Parkhotel - 159 rooms, D € 220 (with dinner) - Golf Resort
Tel (49) 08532 - 2 80, Fax (49) 08532 - 28 204

König Ludwig - 184 rooms, D € 250 (with diner) - Golf Resort
Tel (49) 08532 - 79 90, Fax (49) 08532 - 799 799

RESTAURANTS RESTAURANTS

Fürstenstube - Golf Resort - Tel (49) 08532 - 98 10
Gutshof Uttlau - Golf Resort - Tel (49) 08535 - 1890

Bamberg

15	7	7

Schöne Aussicht auf ein Schloss und das Dorf Altenhof, aber die erhöhte Lage hat auch Nachteile. Das Gelände ist extrem hügelig, so dass wir Senioren und konditionsschwachen Spielern diesen Platz nicht empfehlen können, es sei denn sie lassen sich von jemandem die Golftasche tragen. Darüberhinaus müssen vielfach Bälle aus ganz unterschiedlichen Schräglagen gespielt werden, was hohe Anforderungen an die Beherrschung solcher Schläge stellt. Am besten spielt man hier mitten in der Saison, wenn der Schwung gut funktioniert und man konditionell auf der Höhe ist, da einem der Platz wirklich alles abverlangt. Bamberg hat einen hohen technischen Standard, mit vielen Bäumen und einigen gefährlichen Wasserhindernissen. Hier sein Handicap zu spielen, ist eine gute Leistung. Es lohnt sich, diesen Platz kennenzulernen, wenn man in der Gegend ist.

You are greeted here by some pretty vistas over a castle and the village of Altenhof, but the elevated location does have its drawbacks. The terrain is very hilly so we would definitely not advise seniors and players short on physical fitness to come and play here, unless accompanied by someone to carry their bag. Besides, this configuration results in a good number of shots being played from all sorts of slopes, a good test for skill in this department of your game. The best time to play here is in mid-season, when there is less chance of your swing and legs throwing in the towel. You will need all the strength you can muster. With this said, Bamberg is a course of excellent technical standard with lots of trees and a few dangerous water hazards. Playing to your handicap is already a good performance. Well worth getting to know if you are in the region.

Golfclub Bamberg e.V. auf Gut Leimershof — 1973

Gut Leimershof 5
D - 96149 BREITENGÜSSBACH / OT LEIMERSHOF

Office	Sekretariat	(49) 09547 - 7109
Pro shop	Pro shop	(49) 09547 - 921 414
Fax	Fax	(49) 09547 - 7817
Web	www.golfclubbamberg.de	
Situation	Lage	Bamberg 15 km
Annual closure	Jährliche Schliessung	1/12→28/2
Weekly closure	Wöchentliche Schliessung	no

Monday (Montag): Restaurant closed

Fees main season Preisliste hochsaison — 18 holes

	Week days Woche	We/Bank holidays We/Feiertag
Individual Individuell	€ 35	€ 45
Couple Ehepaar	€ 70	€ 90

– 21 & Students: special fees

Caddie Caddie on request — **Electric Trolley** Elektrokarren no
Buggy Elektrischer Wagen yes — **Clubs** Leihschläger yes
Credit cards Kreditkarten VISA Eurocard - MasterCard - AMEX

Access Zufahrt : BAB Nürnberg-Bamberg. B173 → Breitengüssbach. → Zückshut → Hohengüssbach
Map 4 on page 354 Karte 4 Seite 354

GOLF COURSE — PLATZ — 15/20

Site	Lage	
Maintenance	Instandhaltung	
Architect	Architekt	unknown
Type	Typ	open country, hilly
Relief	Begehbarkeit	
Water in play	Platz mit Wasser	
Exp. to wind	Wind ausgesetzt	
Trees in play	Platz mit Bäumen	

Scorecard Scorekarte	Chp. Chp.	Mens Herren	Ladies Damen
Length Länge	6070	6070	5372
Par	72	72	72
Slope system	133	133	132

Advised golfing ability Empfohlene Spielstärke — 0 12 24 36
Hcp required Min. Handicap — 35

CLUB HOUSE & AMENITIES — KLUBHAUS UND NEBENGEBÄUDE — 7/10

Pro shop Pro shop
Driving range Übungsplatz
Sheltered überdacht 5 mats - On grass auf Rasen yes - Putting-green Putting-grün yes - Pitching-green Pitching-grün yes

HOTEL FACILITIES — HOTEL BESCHREIBUNG — 7/10

HOTELS HOTELS

Residenzschloss Bamberg - Bamberg 15 km
184 rooms, D € 162
Tel (49) 0951 - 60 910, Fax (49) 0951 - 609 1701

Hotel Sankt Nepomuk - 51 rooms, D € 115 - Bamberg 15 km
Tel (49) 0951 - 984 20, Fax (49) 0951 - 984 2100

Vier Jahreszeiten - 35 rooms, D € 80 - Breitengüssbach 6 km
Tel (49) 09544 - 92 90, Fax (49) 09544 - 929 292

RESTAURANTS RESTAURANTS

Schlencherla - Bamberg 15 km - Tel (49) 0951 - 56 060

Romantik-Restaurant-Weinhaus - Bamberg 15 km
Tel (49) 0951 - 27 866

Bergisch Land Wuppertal

16 | 7 | 7

Im Grossraum Düsseldorf findet man in Wuppertal einen der besten klassischen Golfplätze des Landes. Der Platz hat sich seit seiner Eröffnung im Jahre 1928 kaum verändert, aber die Länge des Platzes ist auch für den heutigen Standard ausreichend, auch wenn es keine Meisterschaftsabschläge (Tiger Tees) gibt. Der Platz wirkt auf den ersten Blick nicht allzu einschüchternd. Golfer werden nicht mit übergrossen Schwierigkeiten konfrontiert, es werden keine "Carries" über für Durchschnittsgolfer kaum überwindbare Distanzen verlangt. Trotz des hügeligen Geländes sind die meisten Hindernisse, darunter herrliche alte Bäume, immer gut auszumachen. Die Fairways sind relativ breit und werden nur gelegentlich von Wasser gesäumt. Trotzdem erfordert der Platz alle Konzentration, da die Bunker gut platziert und die Grüns nicht einfach zu lesen sind. Obwohl hier Golfer aller Spielstärken spielen können, ist ein gutes Bruttoergebnis nicht einfach zu erzielen. Dies ist ein klassischer Club-Platz, den man Dutzende Male spielen kann, ohne ihn als langweilig zu empfinden.

It is one of the country's great classic golf courses. The course has changed little since it was opened back in 1928, but yardage still meets today's standards and there are no "tiger" tees to talk of. This apparent friendly face is, what's more, an excellent argument, as golfers can come and enjoy playing here without encountering any impossible difficulties or superhuman angles and distances. Despite the hilly terrain, most of the hazards, including some superb trees, are clearly visible at first glance and the fairways are wide with only a few stretches of water to clutter the wide open spaces. But be careful though, as the bunkering is first rate and the greens tricky to read. While golfers of all abilities can play here, carding a good gross score is certainly no foregone conclusion. A real club course that you can play dozens of times and never grow tired of.

Golf Club Bergisch Land Wuppertal — 1928

Siebeneickerstrasse 386
D - 42111 WUPPERTAL

Office	Sekretariat	(49) 02053 - 70 77
Pro shop	Pro shop	(49) 02053 - 48 168
Fax	Fax	(49) 02053 - 73 03
E-mail	gc.bergisch.land@t-online.de	
Situation	Lage	Wuppertal, 5 km
Annual closure	Jährliche Schliessung	no
Weekly closure	Wöchentliche Schliessung	no

Fees main season Preisliste hochsaison	18 holes	
	Week days Woche	We/Bank holidays We/Feiertag
Individual Individuell	€ 40	€ 50*
Couple Ehepaar	€ 80	€ 100*

* We: only with members (nur in Mitgliederbegleitung)

Caddie Caddie no — Electric Trolley Elektrokarren no

Buggy Elektrischer Wagen no — Clubs Leihschläger no

Credit cards Kreditkarten
VISA - Eurocard - MasterCard - AMEX - DC - JCB

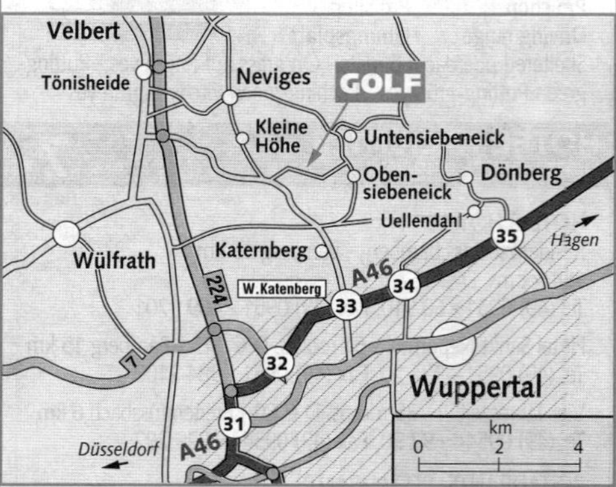

Access Zufahrt : A46. Exit (Ausf.) Wuppertal-Katernberg. → Neviges/Velbert. 2.5 km turn right → Golf.

Map 3 on page 352 Karte 3 Seite 352

GOLF COURSE PLATZ — 16/20

Site	Lage	
Maintenance	Instandhaltung	
Architect	Architekt	unknown
Type	Typ	forest, hilly
Relief	Begehbarkeit	
Water in play	Platz mit Wasser	
Exp. to wind	Wind ausgesetzt	
Trees in play	Platz mit Bäumen	

Scorecard Scorekarte	Chp. Chp.	Mens Herren	Ladies Damen
Length Länge	5937	5937	5224
Par	72	72	72
Slope system	134	134	132

Advised golfing ability Empfohlene Spielstärke: 0 12 24 36

Hcp required Min. Handicap 36

CLUB HOUSE & AMENITIES KLUBHAUS UND NEBENGEBÄUDE — 7/10

Pro shop Pro shop
Driving range Übungsplatz
Sheltered überdacht 5 mats - On grass auf Rasen yes - Putting-green Putting-grün yes - Pitching-green Pitching-grün yes

HOTEL FACILITIES HOTEL BESCHREIBUNG — 7/10

HOTELS HOTELS

Lindner Golfhotel Juliana - Wuppertal-Barmen 7 km
135 rooms, D € 130
Tel (49) 0202 - 647 50, Fax (49) 0202 - 647 5777

Intercityhotel Kaiserhof - Wuppertal-Elberfeld 5 km
160 rooms, D € 155
Tel (49) 0202 - 43 060, Fax (49) 0202 - 456 959

Villa Christina - 7 rooms, D € 102 - Wuppertal-Barmen 6 km
Tel (49) 0202 - 621 736, Fax (49) 0202 - 620 499

RESTAURANTS RESTAURANTS

Schmitz Jägerhaus - Wuppertal 12 km - Tel (49) 0202 - 464 602
Jagdhaus Mollenkotten - Wuppertal-Barmen 6 km
Tel (49) 0202 - 522 643
Scarpati - Wuppertal-Vohwinkel 10 km - Tel (49) 0202 - 784 074

Berlin-Wannsee

16	8	8

Der Mauerfall und die Wiedervereinigung Deutschlands haben dem Golfsport in der neuen Hauptstadt Auftrieb verliehen, wobei dieser Golfplatz der älteste Berlins ist. 1895 angelegt, wurde der Platz in den zwanziger Jahren von Grund auf umgestaltet und weist für moderne Ansprüche eine ansenhliche Länge auf. Nach der Wiedervereinigung wurden 1994 die neun Löcher des deutschen Clubs und die 18 Löcher des amerikanischen Clubs wieder zusammengelegt, so dass der Club heute über 18 Löcher des Meisterschaftsplatzes und noch einmal 9 Löcher des Schäferbergplatzes verfügt. Die grösste Schwierigkeit ist es, auf den Spielbahnen zu bleiben und die Bäume entlang den Fairways zu vermeiden, allerdings sind die Fairways bis auf wenige Ausnahmen relativ breit. Die Grüns sind teilweise einfach zu lesen und nicht übermässig geschützt. Wasser kommt nur am 17. Loch, einem Par 3, ins Spiel und auch nur für schwächere Spieler. Diese schöne und für alle Spielstärke gut zu spielende Anlage ist eine reizvolle Abwechslung zu den modernen, neuen Anlagen, die um Berlin herum entstanden sind.

It is the oldest course of Berlin, and the ideal base-camp for people looking to combine sport and culture. Designed back in 1895, the course was radically overhauled in the mid-1920s and now features a very decent length to today's standards. In 1994 the 9 holes of the German club and the 18 holes of the American club were reunited, so the club now boasts an 18 hole championship course and the 9-hole Schäferberg Platz (the old back nine of the American club). The basic problem is that of staying on the fairway and avoiding the trees on both sides, but with few exceptions most fairways are of generous width. There is only one water harzard, on hole 17 (Par 3), but it should only come into play for lesser players. The greens are none too difficult to read. A very pleasant course to see and play and an excellent companion for the other modern and more demanding courses in the region.

Golf-Club Berlin-Wannsee e.V. — 1895

Golfweg 22
D - 14109 BERLIN

Office	Sekretariat	(49) 030 - 806 7060
Pro shop	Pro shop	(49) 030 - 806 70619
Fax	Fax	(49) 030 - 806 70610
Web	www.glcbw.de	
Situation	Lage	Berlin, 12 km
Annual closure	Jährliche Schliessung	1/1→31/1
Weekly closure	Wöchentliche Schliessung	Monday

(Montag): Restaurant closed

Fees main season Preisliste hochsaison	18 holes	
	Week days Woche	**We/Bank holidays** We/Feiertag
Individual Individuell	€ 70	€ 65*
Couple Ehepaar	€ 140	€ 130*

* We & holidays: with members (nur in Mitgliederbegleitung)

Caddie Caddie no — **Electric Trolley** Elektrokarren yes
Buggy Elektrischer Wagen no — **Clubs** Leihschläger yes
Credit cards Kreditkarten VISA - Eurocard - Mastercard

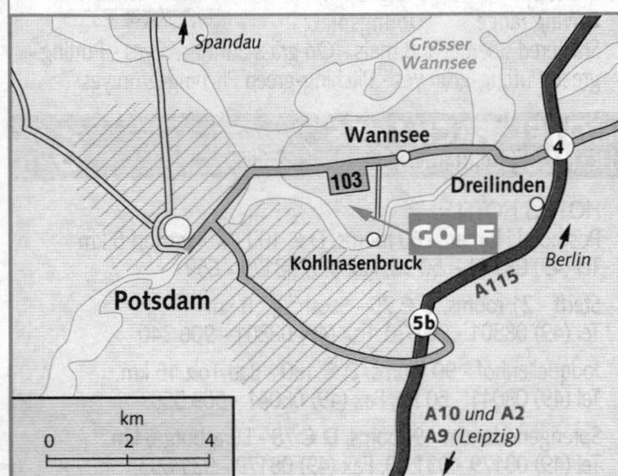

Access Zufahrt : Berlin-Zentrum → Wannsee. Königstrasse, left in Friedenstrasse, 20 m, 'Golfweg' on right hand side.
Map 6 on page 359 Karte 6 Seite 359

GOLF COURSE — PLATZ — 16/20

Site	Lage	
Maintenance	Instandhaltung	
Architect	Architekt	F.A. Harris
Type	Typ	forest
Relief	Begehbarkeit	
Water in play	Platz mit Wasser	
Exp. to wind	Wind ausgesetzt	
Trees in play	Platz mit Bäumen	

Scorecard Scorekarte	**Chp.** Chp.	**Mens** Herren	**Ladies** Damen
Length Länge	5873	5612	4847
Par	72	72	72
Slope system	127	126	124

Advised golfing ability Empfohlene Spielstärke: 0 12 24 36
Hcp required Min. Handicap 34

CLUB HOUSE & AMENITIES — KLUBHAUS UND NEBENGEBÄUDE — 8/10

Pro shop Pro shop
Driving range Übungsplatz
Sheltered überdacht 11 mats - On grass auf Rasen no, mats open air - Putting-green Putting-grün yes
Pitching-green Pitching-grün yes (2)

HOTEL FACILITIES — HOTEL BESCHREIBUNG — 8/10

HOTELS HOTELS

Hotel Petit - 11 rooms, D € 88 - Berlin-Wannsee 2 km
Tel (49) 030 - 80691 80, Fax (49) 030 - 80691 840

Am Jäger Tor - 62 rooms, D € 161 - Potsdam 6 km
Tel (49) 0331 - 201 1100, Fax (49) 0331 - 201 1333

Hotel Griebnitzsee - Potsdam-Badelsberg 6 km
88 rooms, D € 120
Tel (49) 0331 - 70 910, Fax (49) 0331 - 70 9111

RESTAURANTS RESTAURANTS

Schloss Glienicke Remise - Wannsee 3 km
Tel (49) 030 - 805 4000

Friedrich Wilhelm - Potsdam 6 km - Tel (49) 0331 - 55 050

Beuerberg

17	7	6

Der nationale und internationale Ruf dieses Golfplatzes ist hauptsächlich auf sein aussergewöhnliches Panorama der bayerischen Alpen zurückzuführen. Ihr Anblick tröstet über einen schlechten Score hinweg. Wem es gelingt, seine Aufmerksamkeit nicht nur der Lage und den herrlichen Ausblicken zu widmen, der wird auch vom Platz selbst - einem der besten Entwürfe Donald Harradines - nicht enttäuscht sein. Obwohl recht hoch gelegen, gibt es keine extremen Geländeerhebungen und trotz der vielen Bäume hat man nie den Eindruck, dass diese das Spiel einengen würden. Während die Wasserhindernisse ziemlich bedrohlich wirken, sind die Grüns nur mittelmässig durch Bunker verteidigt. Nach modernen Designkriterien wäre sicherlich eine grössere Anzahl von Bunkern angelegt worden, um die besseren Spieler stärker zu fordern. In seinem jetzigen Zustand begünstigt der Platz Spieler mit mittleren und hohen Handicaps. Ein Besuch in Beuerberg lohnt sich in jedem Fall, vor allem auch wegen der hervorragenden Küche.

This course's national and international reputation stems widely from the exceptional view here over the Bavarian Alps. The sights can easily make up for a poor score. If you can put the sight and setting to the back of your mind, you won't be disappointed by the course, either, one of the best ever designed by Donald Harradine. Although high up, relief is never excessive, and while trees abound, they never give the impression of narrowness. Rather strangely, there are only three par 3s and five par 5s, but enough short par 4s to hope to bag a few birdies. The water hazards are rather threatening but the greens are only averagely guarded by bunkers: if modern-day criteria were followed, if they had wanted to upset the better players, they might have designed a few more. As it is, the game is made easier for mid- to high-handicappers. Beuerberg is well worth the journey, even more so because the cuisine in the club-house is excellent.

Golfclub Beuerberg e.V. — 1983

Gut Sterz
D - 82547 BEUERBERG

Office Sekretariat (49) 08179 - 617
Pro shop Pro shop (49) 08179 - 1229
Fax Fax (49) 08179 - 5234
Web www.gc-beuerberg.de
Situation Lage München 45 km
Wolfratshausen (pop. 16 000), 15 km

Annual closure Jährliche Schliessung 15/11→15/3
Weekly closure Wöchentliche Schliessung no

Fees main season Preisliste hochsaison	18 holes	
	Week days Woche	**We/Bank holidays** We/Feiertag
Individual Individuell	€ 60	€ 70
Couple Ehepaar	€ 120	€ 140

Caddie Caddie on request — **Electric Trolley** Elektrokarren yes
Buggy Elektrischer Wagen yes — **Clubs** Leihschläger yes
Credit cards Kreditkarten no

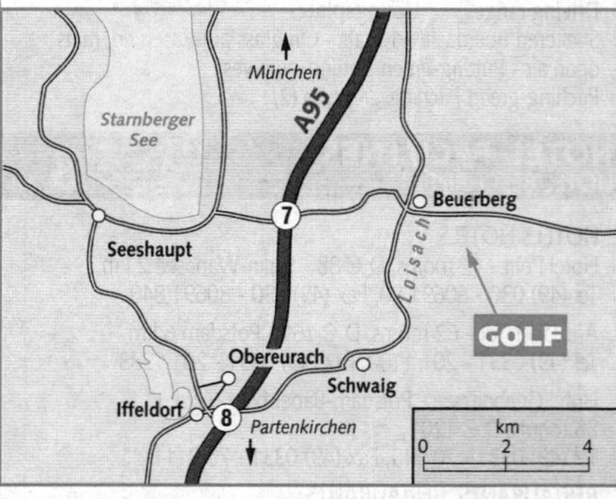

Access Zufahrt : A95 München → Garmisch-Partenkirchen. Exit (Ausf.) Seeshaupt, → Beuerberg
Map 2 on page 350 Karte 2 Seite 350

GOLF COURSE 17/20
PLATZ

Site Lage
Maintenance Instandhaltung
Architect Architekt Donald Harradine
Type Typ parkland
Relief Begehbarkeit
Water in play Platz mit Wasser
Exp. to wind Wind ausgesetzt
Trees in play Platz mit Bäumen

Scorecard Scorekarte	**Chp.** Chp.	**Mens** Herren	**Ladies** Damen
Length Länge	6250	5820	5204
Par	74	74	74
Slope system	132	123	125

Advised golfing ability Empfohlene Spielstärke 0 12 24 36
Hcp required Min. Handicap 36

CLUB HOUSE & AMENITIES 7/10
KLUBHAUS UND NEBENGEBÄUDE

Pro shop Pro shop
Driving range Übungsplatz
Sheltered überdacht 8 mats - On grass auf Rasen yes - Putting-green Putting-grün yes - Pitching-green Pitching-grün yes

HOTEL FACILITIES 6/10
HOTEL BESCHREIBUNG

HOTELS HOTELS
Posthotel Hofherr - 60 rooms, D € 100 - Königsdorf 5 km
Tel (49) 08179 - 50 90, Fax (49) 08179 - 659

Sterff - 21 rooms, D € 75 - Seeshaupt 8 km
Tel (49) 08801 - 90 630, Fax (49) 08801 - 906 340

Jodquellenhof - 90 rooms, D € 180 - Bad Tölz 15 km
Tel (49) 08041 - 50 90, Fax (49) 08041 - 509 555

Sprengenöderalm - 9 rooms, D € 78 - Eurasburg 6 km
Tel (49) 08179 - 931 00, Fax (49) 08179 - 931 093

RESTAURANTS RESTAURANTS
Altes Fährhaus - Bad Tölz 15 km - Tel (49) 08041 - 60 30
Jägerwirt - Bad Tölz/Kirchbichl 15 km - Tel (49) 08041 - 95 48

Bitburger Land

15 | 7 | 8

Die Mittelgebirgslandschaft der südlichen Eifel mit den malerischen Tälern ist ein sehr populäres Feriengebiet unweit von Luxemburg. Der Platz ist wie zu erwarten bergig, ein Golfwagen ist zumindest an heiss-schwülen Tagen empfehlenswert, da das Gelände sehr offen ist und kaum Sonnenschutz bietet. Durch die grossen Höhenunterschiede sind drei blinde Löcher entstanden, die die Schlägerwahl sehr schwierig machen, insbesondere am 2. Loch. Abgesehen davon sind Spielstrategie und die Wasserhindernisse klar zu erkennen, dennoch wird man sich auf der zweiten Runde leichter tun, da man dann auch weiss, wo die zum Teil vom Abschlag nicht einzusehenden Bunker lauern. Die Grüns sind ziemlich gross und nicht mir allzu viel Konturen, dafür aber gut verteidigt und dennoch oftmals mit flachen Chips anzuspielen. Karl Grohs entwarf diesen natürlich wirkenden Platz, ohne der Versuchung zu erliegen, einen extrem langen Platz zu entwerfen, der schwächere Spieler einschüchtert. Golfer aller Spielstärken werden diesen Platz geniessen.

This is a very popular region with tourists and lovers of mountain landscapes and nature, with the typical scenery of the small picturesque valleys in the south of Eifel, not far from Luxembourg. The course is hilly, no surprise there, and a buggy is recommended in hot weather as the terrain is very open and exposed. A few sharp changes in altitude have produced three blind greens, which make club selection a tricky business (particularly on the 2nd hole). Apart from that, game strategy is not what you could call complex (the water hazards are clearly in view) but it will be easier second time around, when the half-obscured bunkers will have lost their element of surprise. The greens are rather large, not too sharply contoured and well guarded, but you can often hit them with low running shots. Karl Grohs designed this course with a good deal of imagination, retaining its natural look and refusing to design in the length that puts so many players off. So golfers of all abilities can have fun.

Golf Resort Bitburger Land — 1994

Zur Weilersheck
D - 54636 WISSMANNSDORF

Office	Sekretariat	(49) 06527 - 927 20
Pro shop	Pro shop	(49) 06527 - 927 216
Fax	Fax	(49) 06527 - 927 230
Web	www.bitgolf.de	
Situation	Lage	Trier, 30 km
Annual closure	Jährliche Schliessung	no
Weekly closure	Wöchentliche Schliessung	no

Fees main season Preisliste hochsaison	Week days Woche	We/Bank holidays We/Feiertag
		18 holes
Individual Individuell	€ 40	€ 50
Couple Ehepaar	€ 80	€ 100

Students under 25: – 50%

Caddie Caddie on request — **Electric Trolley** Elektrokarren yes

Buggy Elektrischer Wagen yes — **Clubs** Leihschläger yes

Credit cards Kreditkarten
VISA - Eurocard - MasterCard - AMEX

Access Zufahrt : • Köln, A1 → Trier. B51 → Bitburg/Prüm. • Koblenz, A48 → Trier → Dreieck Vulkaneifel-Daun, B257 → Bitburg. • Bitburg → Vlanden → "Golf Resort"

Map 3 on page 352 Karte 3 Seite 352

GOLF COURSE — PLATZ — 15/20

Site	Lage	
Maintenance	Instandhaltung	
Architect	Architekt	Karl F. Grohs
Type	Typ	open country, hilly
Relief	Begehbarkeit	
Water in play	Platz mit Wasser	
Exp. to wind	Wind ausgesetzt	
Trees in play	Platz mit Bäumen	

Scorecard Scorekarte	**Chp.** Chp.	**Mens** Herren	**Ladies** Damen
Length Länge	6056	6056	5316
Par	72	72	72
Slope system	128	128	128

Advised golfing ability Empfohlene Spielstärke — 0 12 24 36

Hcp required Min. Handicap 36

CLUB HOUSE & AMENITIES — KLUBHAUS UND NEBENGEBÄUDE — 7/10

Pro shop Pro shop
Driving range Übungsplatz
Sheltered überdacht 12 mats - On grass auf Rasen yes
Putting-green Putting-grün yes - Pitching-green Pitching-grün yes

HOTEL FACILITIES — HOTEL BESCHREIBUNG — 8/10

HOTELS HOTELS

Dorint Resort & Spa - 104 rooms, D € 150 - Biersdorf 3.5 km
Tel (49) 06569 - 9 90, Fax (49) 06569 - 79 09

Leander - 17 rooms, D € 65 - Bitburg 2 km
Tel (49) 06561 - 34 22, Fax (49) 06561 - 940 118

Am Wisselbach - 23 rooms, D € 90 - Rittersdorf 3 km
Tel (49) 06561 - 959 70, Fax (49) 06561 -959 7150

Eifelbräu - 32 rooms, D € 80 - Bitburg 2 km
Tel (49) 06561 - 91 00, Fax (49) 06561 - 910 100

RESTAURANTS RESTAURANTS

Burg Rittersdorf - Rittersdorf 3 km - Tel (49) 06561 - 965 70
Simonbräu - Bitburg 6 km - Tel (49) 06561 - 3333

Buxtehude

16 | 7 | 6

Ein originelles Beispiel der sehr strengen Architektur Siegmanns, bei dem drei verschiedene Stile vorzufinden sind: Wald, offene Fläche und beinahe alpine Landschaft, wobei letztere körperlich die anstrengendste ist (bei drei Löchern). Der Architekt hat sich dem Gelände gefügt, ohne es stark umzugestalten, daher auch der etwas uneinheitliche Stil. Doch der Platz ist dadurch sehr abwechslungsreich und interessant und die Hindernisse sind von den Abschlägen aus gut sichtbar. Man muss jedoch sein Spiel schnell an die Gegebenheiten anpassen können. Spieler mit weniger guten Reflexen werden etwas Mühe haben. Buxtehude ist sehr lang, daher ergeben seine sechs Par 5 Löcher ein ansprechendes Par 74. Die Greens sind teils erhöht, teils auf Doppelstufen und recht klein, was äusserste Genauigkeit erfordert. Dafür sind ihre Verteidigungen durchaus zu durchbrechen. Geeignet für die ganze Familie, ohne sich allzusehr um den Score zu kümmern.

An original example of Siegmann's very serious style of architecture, where you find three different styles: one in the woods, another in more open countryside and the last virtually up in the hills and physically the most trying (over three holes). The designer has bowed to the landscape more than he has modelled it, hence the impression of a rather unassertive style. In contrast, the course is great fun to play with a lot of variety and clearly visible hazards from the tees. You have to adjust your game quickly, and players with slow reflexes will find it hard work. Buxtehude is very long, but the six par 5s make this a more reasonable par 74. The greens are sometimes elevated and two-tiered, and they are rather small, so extreme accuracy is essential. In contrast, their defences are not unbreachable. Play with all the family and don't worry too much about the score.

Golf-Club Buxtehude — 1986

Zum Lehmfeld 1
D - 21614 BUXTEHUDE-DAENSEN

Office Sekretariat (49) 04161 - 81 333
Pro shop Pro shop (49) 04161 - 558 705
Fax Fax (49) 04161 - 87 268
Web www.golfclubbuxtehude.de
Situation Lage Hamburg, 50 km
Buxtehude (pop. 34 000), 5 km
Annual closure Jährliche Schliessung no
Weekly closure Wöchentliche Schliessung Monday
(Montag): Restaurant closed

Fees main season Preisliste hochsaison	18 holes	
	Week days Woche	We/Bank holidays We/Feiertag
Individual Individuell	€ 35	€ 45
Couple Ehepaar	€ 70	€ 90

– 21 & Students: – 50%

Caddie Caddie on request — **Electric Trolley** Elektrokarren no
Buggy Elektrischer Wagen yes — **Clubs** Leihschläger no
Credit cards Kreditkarten no

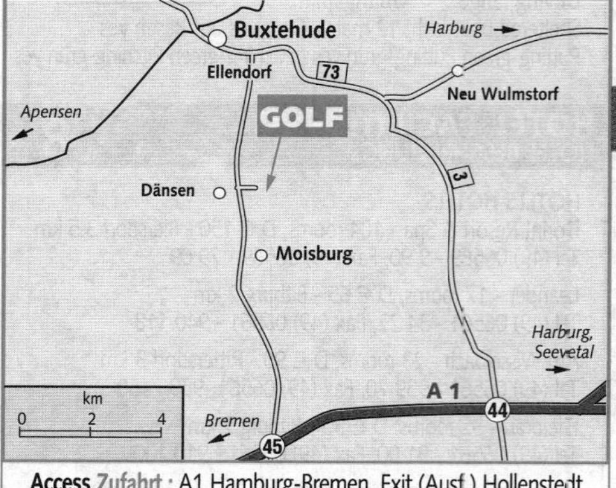

Access Zufahrt : A1 Hamburg-Bremen. Exit (Ausf.) Hollenstedt → Moisburg, Buxtehude. Daensen → Golf
Map 7 on page 360 Karte 7 Seite 360

GOLF COURSE PLATZ — 16/20

Site Lage
Maintenance Instandhaltung
Architect Architekt W. Siegmann
Type Typ forest, open country
Relief Begehbarkeit
Water in play Platz mit Wasser
Exp. to wind Wind ausgesetzt
Trees in play Platz mit Bäumen

Scorecard Scorekarte	Chp. Chp.	Mens Herren	Ladies Damen
Length Länge	6318	6318	5554
Par	74	74	74
Slope system	133	133	130

Advised golfing ability Empfohlene Spielstärke 0 12 24 36
Hcp required Min. Handicap 36

CLUB HOUSE & AMENITIES KLUBHAUS UND NEBENGEBÄUDE — 7/10

Pro shop Pro shop
Driving range Übungsplatz
Sheltered überdacht 9 mats - On grass auf Rasen yes - Putting-green Putting-grün yes - Pitching-green Pitching-grün yes

HOTEL FACILITIES HOTEL BESCHREIBUNG — 6/10

HOTELS HOTELS
Seeburg - 14 rooms, D € 85 - Buxtehude-Neukloster 5 km
Tel (49) 04161 - 74 100, Fax (49) 04161 - 741 074

An der Linah - 30 rooms, D € 80 - Buxtehude 7 km
Tel (49) 04161 - 600 90, Fax (49) 04161 - 600 910

Zur Mühle - 41 rooms, D € 92 - Buxtehude 7 km
Tel (49) 04161 - 50 650, Fax (49) 04161 - 506 530

Am Stadtpark - 20 rooms, D € 85 - Buxtehude 7 km
Tel (49) 04161 - 506 810, Fax (49) 04161 - 506 815

RESTAURANTS RESTAURANTS
Seeburg - Buxtehude-Neukloster 5 km
Tel (49) 04161 - 82 071
Herbstprinz - Jork 8 km - Tel (49) 04162- 7403

Club zur Vahr (Garlstedt)

17 | 6 | 5

An vier Löchern kommt Wasser ins Spiel; grosse Pinien dominieren den Platzcharakter. Die Grüns sind bemerkenswert gut verteidigt, obschon die sie umgebenden Bunker weder besonders zahlreich noch allzu bedrohlich sind. Angesichts der Tatsache, dass die meisten Schwierigkeiten gut auszumachen sind und das Gelände nur wenige Unebenheiten aufweist, erkennt man, dass die Probleme, die einem dieser Platz bereitet, sehr subtiler Art sein müssen. Dazu gehören Länge, die Beherrschung einer Vielzahl von Schlagvarianten, die Fähigkeit den Ball vom Abschlag aus so zu platzieren, dass man das Grün mit dem zweiten Schlag gut anspielen kann, sowie die Allgegenwärtigkeit von Bäumen und Heidekraut, die alle verunglückten Schläge bestrafen. Nur die sehr guten Spieler werden sich für die hinteren Abschläge entscheiden, wenngleich die sechs Par 5 Löcher gute Gelegenheiten zu einem Birdie bieten. Es ist ein absolutes Vergnügen hier zu spielen.

This is one of Germany's oldest and most celebrated golf courses. Designed in 1905, it was re-modelled in the early 1960s with water on four holes, tall pine-trees virtually everywhere. The greens are remarkably well guarded, even though the protective bunkers are neither too numerous nor too dangerous. If we add to this the fact that most difficulties are clearly visible and relief never more than a gentle roll, you will understand how subtle the problems are here. Length has a lot to do with this, as does the variety of shots to be played, the positioning of each shot to approach the greens from the best angle and the presence of trees and heather, which punish all wayward shots. Only the very good players will choose the back tees, even though the six par 5s are good opportunities for birdies. A real treat to play.

Club zur Vahr e.V., Bremen, Platz Garlstedter Heide — 1905

Am Golfplatz 10
D - 27711 GARLSTEDT/OHZ

Office Sekretariat (49) 04795 - 954 258
Pro shop Pro shop (49) 0421 - 231 467
Fax Fax (49) 04795 - 70 46
Web www.club-zur-vahr-bremen.de
Situation Lage Bremerhaven, 39 km
Bremen (pop. 552 000), 26 km

Annual closure Jährliche Schliessung 1/1→1/3
Weekly closure Wöchentliche Schliessung Monday
(Montag): Restaurant closed

Fees main season Preisliste hochsaison 18 holes

	Week days / Woche	We/Bank holidays / We/Feiertag
Individual Individuell	€ 45	€ 55
Couple Ehepaar	€ 90	€ 110

We: with members (nur in Mitgliederbegleitung)

Caddie Caddie no — **Electric Trolley** Elektrokarren no
Buggy Elektrischer Wagen no — **Clubs** Leihschläger no
Credit cards Kreditkarten no

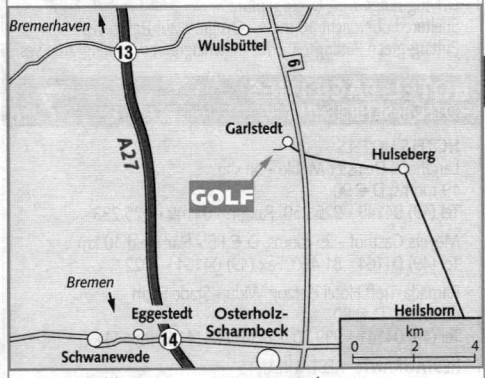

Access Zufahrt : Bremen, A27 → Bremerhaven. Exit (Ausf.) Ihlpol, B6 → Bremerhaven. 10 km until Garlstedt. → Golf on the left.
Map 5 on page 357 Karte 5 Seite 357

GOLF COURSE — PLATZ — 17/20

Site Lage
Maintenance Instandhaltung
Architect Architekt — B. von Limburger
Type Typ — forest, parkland
Relief Begehbarkeit
Water in play Platz mit Wasser
Exp. to wind Wind ausgesetzt
Trees in play Platz mit Bäumen

Scorecard / Scorekarte	Chp. / Chp.	Mens / Herren	Ladies / Damen
Length Länge	6435	6283	5369
Par	73	74	74
Slope system	132	135	130

Advised golfing ability Empfohlene Spielstärke — 0 12 24 36
Hcp required Min. Handicap 36

CLUB HOUSE & AMENITIES — KLUBHAUS UND NEBENGEBÄUDE — 6/10

Pro shop Pro shop
Driving range Übungsplatz
Sheltered überdacht no - On grass auf Rasen yes - Putting-green Putting-grün yes - Pitching-green Pitching-grün yes

HOTEL FACILITIES — HOTEL BESCHREIBUNG — 5/10

HOTELS HOTELS

Zum alten Torfkahn - Osterholz-Scharmbeck 6 km
11 rooms, D € 75
Tel (49) 04791 - 76 08, Fax (49) 04791 - 59 606

Eichenhof - 20 rooms, D € 143 - Worpswede 18 km
Tel (49) 04792 - 26 76, Fax (49) 04792 - 44 27

Strandlust Vegesack - Bremen (Vegesack) 16 km
45 rooms, D € 120
Tel (49) 0421 - 66 090, Fax (49) 0421 - 6609111

RESTAURANTS RESTAURANTS

Tietjen's Hütte - Osterholz-Scharmbeck - Tel (49) 04791 - 922 00
Zum alten Torfkahn - Osterholz-Scharmbeck 6 km
Tel (49) 04791 - 76 08
L'Orchidée - Bremen 25 km - Tel (49) 0421 - 334 7927

Deinster Mühle

15 | 7 | 7

Die Anlage insgesamt ist wahrscheinlich beeindruckender als der Platz. Ein Hotel, ein Restaurant, ein Forellenteich und eine Fisch-Räucherei wurde um eine 800 Jahre alte Mühle erbaut. Die Familie Steffen, die die gesamte Anlage führt, lebt seit 350 Jahren auf dem Gut. Der Platz selbst ist kurz, so kurz, dass selbst mittlere Handicaps von den hinteren Abschlägen spielen sollten. Bessere Spieler sollten den Driver in der Tasche lassen, um etwas mehrgefordert zu werden. Das Gelände ist ziemlich offen, mit wenigen Bäumen, eben eine typische norddeutsche Landschaft. Der von dem Kanadier David Krause, einem Schüler von Robert Trent Jones, entworfene Platz weist einige exzellente, aber auch etliche schwache Löcher auf. Die Hindernisse wirken nicht zu bedrohlich, obwohl einige Bunker vor den Grüns akkurate Pitch-Schläge verlangen. Alles in allem, ein gutes Golfresort, das einen Aufenthalt lohnt.

An impressive resort, probably more so than the actual course. A hotel, a real restaurant and a trout-fishing farm with a fish-smoking house have been built around an ancient mill that is some 800 years old. The Steffen family, which promoted the resort, has lived on the estate for 350 years. The course itself is none too long to the extent where even mid-handicappers can play from the back and where the better players will keep the driver in the bag to make it all a little more challenging. The site is wide open with few trees in the style of the countryside found in Northern Germany. Although given serious thought, laid out under the supervision of David Krause (ex-Trent Jones) and intelligently designed into the site, we found the course a little inconsistent. Some of the holes are excellent, others fail to measure up. Hazards are in play but none too frightening, although some bunkers in front of the greens call for accurate pitching. All in all, one of the region's very good golfing resorts.

Golf Club Deinster Mühle — 1994

Im Mühlenfeld
D - 21717 DEINSTE

Office	Sekretariat	(49) 04149 - 925 112
Pro shop	Pro shop	(49) 04149 - 925 112
Fax	Fax	(49) 04149 - 925 111
Web	www.gut-deinster-muehle.de	
Situation	Lage	Hamburg, 57 km
Annual closure	Jährliche Schliessung	no
Weekly closure	Wöchentliche Schliessung	

Fees main season Preisliste hochsaison — 18 holes

	Week days Woche	We/Bank holidays We/Feiertag
Individual Individuell	€ 35	€ 45
Couple Ehepaar	€ 70	€ 90

Students: – 50 %

Caddie Caddie no **Electric Trolley** Elektrokarren yes

Buggy Elektrischer Wagen no **Clubs** Leihschläger yes

Credit cards Kreditkarten
VISA - Eurocard - MasterCard - AMEX - DC

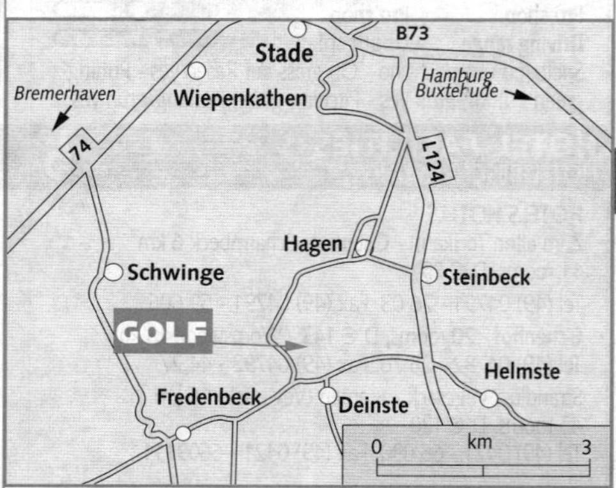

Access Zufahrt : Hamburg: A 7 Exit (Ausfahrt) Heimfeld, B 73 → Cuxhaven, Exit Horneburg, at last traffic lights in Horneburg (Höhe Baumarkt Heinssen) turn left → Bremervörde, → Fredenbeck-Deinste, in Deinste → "Golf Park".

Map 7 on page 360 Karte 7 Seite 360

GOLF COURSE — PLATZ — 15/20

Site	Lage	
Maintenance	Instandhaltung	
Architect	Architekt	David Krause
Type	Typ	open country
Relief	Begehbarkeit	
Water in play	Platz mit Wasser	
Exp. to wind	Wind ausgesetzt	
Trees in play	Platz mit Bäumen	

Scorecard Scorekarte	Chp. Chp.	Mens Herren	Ladies Damen
Length Länge	5986	5569	4823
Par	72	72	72
Slope system	129	123	122

Advised golfing ability Empfohlene Spielstärke — 0 12 24 36

Hcp required Min. Handicap — no

CLUB HOUSE & AMENITIES — KLUBHAUS UND NEBENGEBÄUDE — 7/10

Pro shop Pro shop
Driving range Übungsplatz
Sheltered überdacht 10 mats - On grass auf Rasen yes - Putting-green Putting-grün yes - Pitching-green Pitching-grün yes

HOTEL FACILITIES — HOTEL BESCHREIBUNG — 7/10

HOTELS HOTELS

Landhotel Deinster Mühle - on site
19 rooms, D € 90
Tel (49) 04149 - 925 250, Fax (49) 04149 - 925 233

Meyers Gasthof - 25 rooms, D € 85 - Härsefeld 10 km
Tel (49) 04164 - 81 460, Fax (49) 04164 - 3022

Ramada-Treff Hotel Herzog Widu - Stade 8 km
45 rooms, D € 80
Tel (49) 04141 - 999 80, Fax (49) 04141 999 8444

RESTAURANTS RESTAURANTS

Alte Lohmühle - on site - Tel (49) 04149 - 925 218
Insel Restaurant - Stade 8 km - Tel (49) 04141 - 20 31
Meyers Gasthof - Härsefeld 10 km - Tel (49) 04164 - 81 460

Domtal-Mommenheim

14	7	7

Domtal-Mommenheim ist ein gutes Beispiel für einen Platz, der mit begrenzten Mitteln erbaut wurde. Für das Design zeichnet Siegfried Heinz verantwortlich, der sein Handwerk bei Altmeister Bernhard von Limburger erlernte. Er hatte beim Entwurf vor allem die Mehrzahl der Golfer, also mittlere bis hohe Handicaps, im Auge. Der Platz hat sein Ziel erreicht, Mitglieder und Gastspieler kommen nicht nur aus dem nahegelegenen Mainz. Der Platz wirkt scheinbar leicht, und dennoch finden auch gute Spieler hier genügend Herausforderung. Dies ist ein Platz, auf dem Longhitter richtig draufhauen können, obwohl es genügend Hindernisse gibt, die aber für gute Spieler selten bedrohlich sind, mit Ausnahme des kurzen 16. Loch (einem Par 3) und dem 18. Loch, bei dem man über Wasser so weit abkürzen kann wie man es sich zutraut. Dennoch muss man den Ball gut treffen, um ein gutes Ergebnis zu erzielen. Alles in allem ist dies ein Platz, auf dem das Spielen in der schönen Umgebung der Weinberge von Rheinhessen richtig Spass macht.

Domtal-Mommenheim is a fine example of a course which was built with a restricted budget, which was designed by owner Siegfried Heinz (who learned his trade as shaper for Bernhard von Limburger) essentially for the vast majority of golfers, i.e. mid-and high-handicappers, and which has successfully reached its target. And by target we don't mean only the inhabitants of Mainz. Yet the apparent facility of this course can be deceiving and good players also have fun playing here. Firstly, long-hitters can open their shoulders because although there is no shortage of hazards they are seldom dangerous, except on the short 16th and on the 18th, where you can cut off as much as you dare over the water hazard. Next, you have to strike the ball well to score well, as shots off-target rarely find any sort of reward. All in all, this is great fun amidst the very pleasant landscape of the Rheinhessen vineyards.

Golf Club Domtal-Mommenheim — 1997

Am Golfplatz 1
D - 55278 MOMMENHEIM

Office	Sekretariat	(49) 06138 - 920 20
Pro shop	Pro shop	(49) 06138 - 940 170
Fax	Fax	(49) 06138 - 920 231
Web		www.golfanlage-domtal-mommenheim.de
Situation	Lage	Mainz, 10 km
Annual closure	Jährliche Schliessung	no
Weekly closure	Wöchentliche Schliessung	no
Fees main season	Preisliste hochsaison	18 holes

	Week days / Woche	We/Bank holidays / We/Feiertag
Individual Individuell	€ 30	€ 42
Couple Ehepaar	€ 60	€ 84

– 21 & Students: – 50%

Caddie Caddie no — **Electric Trolley** Elektrokarren yes
Buggy Elektrischer Wagen yes — **Clubs** Leihschläger yes
Credit cards Kreditkarten — Eurocard - MasterCard

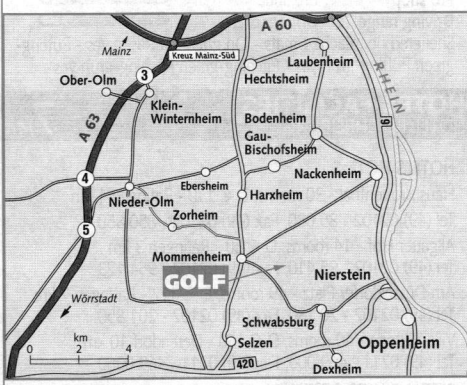

Access Zufahrt : Mainz A63. Exit (Ausf.) Nieder-Olm. → Zornheim, → Mommenheim. 1 km → Schwasburg-Nierstein. → Golf.
Map 3 on page 353 Karte 3 Seite 353

GOLF COURSE — PLATZ — 14/20

Site	Lage	
Maintenance	Instandhaltung	
Architect	Architekt	Siegfried Heinz
Type	Typ	open country
Relief	Begehbarkeit	
Water in play	Platz mit Wasser	
Exp. to wind	Wind ausgesetzt	
Trees in play	Platz mit Bäumen	

Scorecard Scorekarte	Chp. Chp.	Mens Herren	Ladies Damen
Length Länge	6153	5880	5283
Par	72	72	72
Slope system	129	122	120

Advised golfing ability Empfohlene Spielstärke: 0 12 24 36
Hcp required Min. Handicap 45

CLUB HOUSE & AMENITIES — KLUBHAUS UND NEBENGEBÄUDE — 7/10

Pro shop Pro shop
Driving range Übungsplatz
Sheltered überdacht 6 mats - On grass auf Rasen yes - Putting-green Putting-grün yes - Pitching-green Pitching-grün yes

HOTEL FACILITIES — HOTEL BESCHREIBUNG — 7/10

HOTELS HOTELS

Wein- und Park Hotel - 55 rooms, D € 157 - Nierstein 5 km
Tel (49) 06133 - 50 80, Fax (49) 06133 - 508 333

Zum Storchennest - 22 rooms, D € 60 - Mommenheim 1 km
Tel (49) 06138 - 12 33, Fax (49) 06138 - 12 40

Hilton International - 433 rooms, D € 160 - Mainz 15 km
Tel (49) 06131 - 24 50, Fax (49) 06131 - 245 589

RESTAURANTS RESTAURANTS

Weingut Nack - Gau-Bischofsheim 4 km
Tel (49) 06135 - 30 43

Stein's Traube - Mainz-Finthen 10 km - Tel (49) 06131 - 402 49

Gänsthaler's Kuchlmasterei - Mainz-Finthen 10 km
Tel (49) 06131 - 474 275

Düsseldorfer

15	7	7

Der Düsseldorfer Golf Club liegt in Ratingen, wenige Kilometer von der Stadtgrenze der Nordrhein-Westfälischen Landeshauptstadt. Aber trotz der guten Verkehrsanbindung ist der Platz weit von der Hektik der Grossstadt entfernt. Auf einem dicht bewaldeten, hügeligen Gelände entwarf der englische Architekt Donald Harradine 1961 einen Platz, der nicht nur idyllisch gelegen ist, sondern auch mit seinem abwechslungsreichen Design begeistert. Die Hauptschwierigkeit sind die teilweise engen Spielbahnen, der Wald am Rand der Fairways und die drei Teiche sowie einige seitliche Wasserhindernisse. Alle Schwierigkeiten auf diesem Parklandplatz sind vom Abschlag aus zu erkennen, etwas, was vor allem bessere Spieler schätzen. Lediglich beim 15. Loch, einem Par 3 von 148 Länge und 80 Metern Höhenunterschied wird man sich beim erstenmal schwertun. Im Juli 1999 wurden neue Grüns eingeweiht, die wesentlich mehr Ondulationen als die alten aufweisen. Jetzt ist auch das Putten auf diesem Platz interessant und abwechslungsreich. Diesen Platz sollte man sich nicht entgehen lassen.

This golf club is located in Ratingen, a few kilometers from the city limits of the capital of Northrine-Westfalia. The course is easily reached from Düsseldorf but miles away from the hustle and bustle of the big city. English architect Donald Harradine designed a course in a densely wooded area which is not only idyllic but also a pleasure to play, provided your ball stays out of the forest bordering the sometimes narrow fairways. All difficulties on the parkland style course are visible from the tee boxes, a fact better players appreciate. The 15th, a par 3 of 149 metres and an elevation drop of 80 metres, is perhaps the only hole where first-timers will have a hard time picking the right club. In July 1999, the club opened 18 new greens which have far more contours than the old ones and make putting more of a challenge. This is one course not to be missed.

Düsseldorfer Golf Club e.V. — 1961

Rittergut Rommeljansweg
D - 40882 RATINGEN

Office Sekretariat (49) 02102 - 81 092
Pro shop Pro shop (49) 02102 - 83 683
Fax Fax (49) 02102 - 81 782
Web www.duesseldorfer-golf-club.de
Situation Lage Düsseldorf , 10 km
Ratingen (pop. 91 000), 1 km
Annual closure Jährliche Schliessung 20/12→10/2
Weekly closure Wöchentliche Schliessung Monday
(Montag): Restaurant closed

Fees main season Preisliste hochsaison 18 holes

	Week days Woche	We/Bank holidays We/Feiertag
Individual Individuell	€ 52	€ 36*
Couple Ehepaar	€ 104	€ 72*

* We: with members (nur in Mitgliederbegleitung)
– 21 & Students: – 50 %

Caddie Caddie on request — **Electric Trolley** Elektrokarren yes
Buggy Elektrischer Wagen no — **Clubs** Leihschläger yes
Credit cards Kreditkarten no

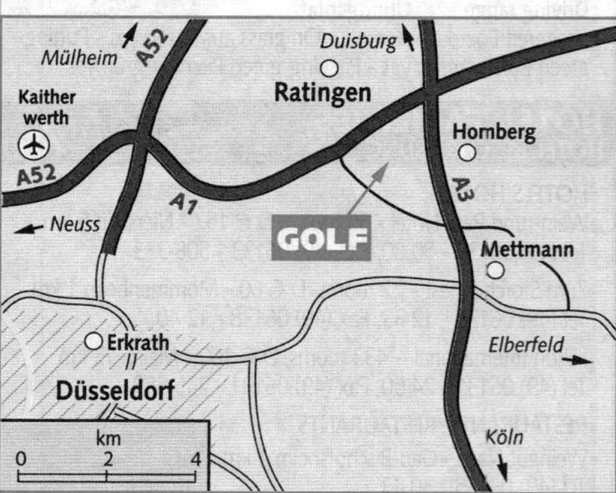

Access Zufahrt : A3, Exit (Ausf.) Ratingen-Wülfrath, → Ratingen. 400 m turn right → Golf
Map 3 on page 352 Karte 3 Seite 352

GOLF COURSE — PLATZ 15/20

Site Lage
Maintenance Instandhaltung
Architect Architekt Donald Harradine
Type Typ forest
Relief Begehbarkeit
Water in play Platz mit Wasser
Exp. to wind Wind ausgesetzt
Trees in play Platz mit Bäumen

Scorecard Scorekarte	Chp. Chp.	Mens Herren	Ladies Damen
Length Länge	5781	5781	5105
Par	71	71	71
Slope system	124	124	123

Advised golfing ability Empfohlene Spielstärke 0 12 24 36
Hcp required Min. Handicap 36

CLUB HOUSE & AMENITIES — KLUBHAUS UND NEBENGEBÄUDE 7/10

Pro shop Pro shop
Driving range Übungsplatz
Sheltered überdacht 4 mats - On grass auf Rasen yes - Putting-green Putting-grün yes - Pitching-green Pitching-grün yes

HOTEL FACILITIES — HOTEL BESCHREIBUNG 7/10

HOTELS HOTELS
Haus Kronenthal - 30 rooms, D € 130 - Ratingen 1 km
Tel (49) 02102 - 85 080, Fax (49) 02102 - 850 850
Allgäuer Hof - 14 rooms, D € 80 - Ratingen 3 km
Tel (49) 02102 - 95 410, Fax (49) 02102 - 954 123
Am Düsseldorfer Platz - 49 rooms, D € 112 - Ratingen 2 km
Tel (49) 02102 - 20 180, Fax (49) 02102 - 201 850
Villa Viktoria - 40 rooms, D € 160 - Derendorf 10 km
Tel (49) 0211 - 469 000, Fax (49) 0211 - 469 0060

RESTAURANTS RESTAURANTS
Haus zum Haus - Ratingen 2 km - Tel (49) 02102 - 22 586
Victorian - Düsseldorf 10 km - Tel (49) 0211 - 865 5022
Hummerstübchen - Düsseldorf-Lörick 15 km - Tel 0211 - 594 402

Elfrather Mühle

14	7	7

Eine alte, sorgfältig restaurierte Windmühle beeindruckt den Besucher gleich auf Anhieb. Der Eindruck von dem noch ziemlich jungen Platz ist dagegen weniger überwältigend. Trotzdem rechtfertigt sein allgemeiner Zustand, ihn mal zu spielen. Der Stil ist eher amerikanisch, mit einigen Wasserhindernissen, aber nur wenigen Bäumen, was den Platz sehr windanfällig macht. Es ist hier von Vorteil, den Ball flach schlagen zu können. Gleichzeitig wird es schwierig, die gut verteidigten Grüns anzuspielen, wenn man dem Ball nicht genügend Spin mitgibt. Durch den sandigen Untergrund ist der Platz auch bei nassem Wetter gut bespielbar. Das gesamte Layout wurde mit viel Sorgfalt angelegt, insbesondere die zum Teil in mehreren Stufen aufgebauten Grüns, die sehr interessant zu Lesen sind. Einige recht spektakuläre Löcher heben diesen Platz über das allgemeine Niveau hinaus, allerdings fehlt ihm zu einem wirklich grossartigen Kurs das gewisse Etwas. Dennoch eine gute Anlage, deren hügelige ersten neun Löcher zweifellos anspruchsvoller als die zweiten Neun sind.

An old but very carefully restored windmill gives an excellent first impression. The actual course is not quite as exceptional, but the overall standard makes it worth a round or two. The style is a little on the American side, with a few water hazards in play but very few trees. This adds to the difficulties when the wind gets up. Hitting low balls is an asset here, and it is difficult to reach and stay on certain well-protected greens without enough spin on the ball. The sandy soil also makes this a playable course in wet weather. The whole layout has been carefully designed, especially the greens, which are sometimes multi-tiered and always interesting to read. A number of rather spectacular holes lift the overall standard a little above average, but that little spark of genius, which makes a good course a great course, is missing. A competent course all the same with a hilly and doubtless more demanding front nine.

Golf Club Elfrather Mühle GmbH — 1992

An der Elfrather Mühle 145
D - 47802 KREFELD-TRAAR

Office Sekretariat (49) 02151 - 46 690
Pro shop Pro shop (49) 02151 - 496 922
Fax Fax (49) 02151 - 477 459
Web www.gc-elfrathermuehle.de
Situation Lage Düsseldorf, 30 km
Krefeld (pop. 242 000), 5 km

Annual closure Jährliche Schliessung no
Weekly closure Wöchentliche Schliessung no
Monday (Montag): Restaurant closed

Fees main season Preisliste hochsaison 18 holes

	Week days Woche	We/Bank holidays We/Feiertag
Individual Individuell	€ 50	€ 70
Couple Ehepaar	€ 100	€ 140

Caddie Caddie on request — **Electric Trolley** Elektrokarren no
Buggy Elektrischer Wagen yes — **Clubs** Leihschläger yes
Credit cards Kreditkarten
VISA - Eurocard - MasterCard - AMEX - DC

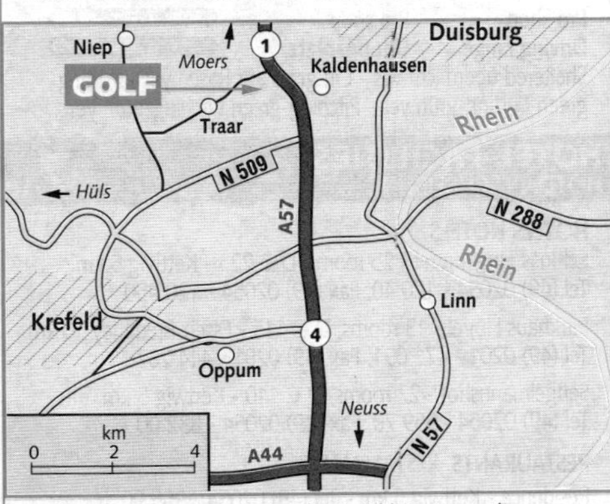

Access Zufahrt : A57 Exit (Ausf.) Krefeld/Gartenstadt.
→ Krefeld/Gartenstadt. Right in Werner-Voss-Strasse
→ Traar/Elfrath. Left in An der Elfrather Mühle.
Map 3 on page 352 Karte 3 Seite 352

GOLF COURSE — PLATZ — 14/20

Site Lage
Maintenance Instandhaltung
Architect Architekt — Ron Kirby, Fritz Beindorf
Type Typ — open country
Relief Begehbarkeit
Water in play Platz mit Wasser
Exp. to wind Wind ausgesetzt
Trees in play Platz mit Bäumen

Scorecard Scorekarte	Chp. Chp.	Mens Herren	Ladies Damen
Length Länge	6251	6125	5323
Par	72	72	72
Slope system	123	123	122

Advised golfing ability Empfohlene Spielstärke — 0 12 24 36
Hcp required Min. Handicap — 36/We 28

CLUB HOUSE & AMENITIES — KLUBHAUS UND NEBENGEBÄUDE — 7/10

Pro shop Pro shop
Driving range Übungsplatz
Sheltered überdacht 8 mats - On grass auf Rasen yes - Putting-green Putting-grün yes - Pitching-green Pitching-grün yes

HOTEL FACILITIES — HOTEL BESCHREIBUNG — 7/10

HOTELS HOTELS

Dorint Hotel - 159 rooms, D € 178 - Krefeld-Traar 5 km
Tel (49) 02151 - 95 60, Fax (49) 02151 - 956 100

Parkhotel Krefelder Hof - 150 rooms, D € 150 - Krefeld 5 km
Tel (49) 02151 - 58 40, Fax (49) 02151 - 58 435

Garden Hotel - 51 rooms, D € 112 - Krefeld 5 km
Tel (49) 02151 - 535 230, Fax (49) 02151-5352 3999

Zentral Hotel Poststuben - 31 rooms, D € 85 - Krefeld 5 km
Tel (49) 02151 - 24 656, Fax (49) 02151 - 802 888

RESTAURANTS RESTAURANTS

Kaffeehaus Schmitz - Krefeld 5 km - Tel (49) 02151 - 311 840
Et Bröckske - Krefeld 5 km - Tel (49) 02151 - 29 740

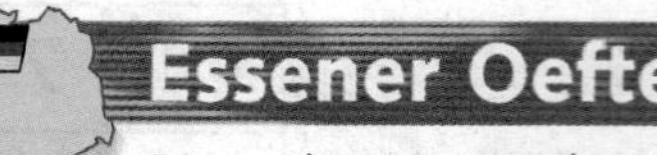

Essener Oefte

15 | 8 | 7

Dieser Platz inmitten des Tals der Ruhr, ist ein Hort der Ruhe, ein Golfpark mit einigen tropischen Bäumen und einem Klubhaus in einem alten Schloss, das mehr als tausend Jahre alt ist. Die ersten neun Löcher sind hügelig undziemlich eng mit einigen blinden Löchern, die zweiten Neun sind flachener und offener und geben Longhittern die Möglichkeit, den Frust der ersten Neun loszuwerden, aber sie sollten dabei Vorsicht walten lassen, den auch die Back Nine haben Tücken. Kenner der Kunst des Architekten Bernharc von Limburger erkennen sein unverkennbaren Stil. Die Schwierigkeiten sind gut über den Platz verteilt. Der Platz wirkt etwas altmodisch, aber selbst wenn dies nicht der beste Platz im Land ist, ist er immer noch einer der besten der Gegend.

Right in the Ruhr valley, this course is a heaven of tranquillity, a golf park where you will be surprised by some of the tropical trees, and even more so by the club-house set in a former castle which dates back more than a thousand years. Intelligently, the front nine are steep and not very wide (with several blind greens), the back nine are much flatter and open. Big-hitters can give vent to their frustration that mounts over the front nine, but they should be careful: the difficulties are not only on the first nine holes. Connoisseurs of the skills of Bernhard von Limburger will recognize his golfing insight in the way hazards are spread around the course. Others might find this a little dated, but while this is not the most impressive course in the whole country, it is still one of the very best in this region.

Essener Golf-Club Haus Oefte e.V. — 1959

Laupendahler Landstrasse
D - 45219 ESSEN

Office	Sekretariat	(49) 02054 - 839 11
Pro shop	Pro shop	(49) 02054 - 847 22
Fax	Fax	(49) 02054 - 838 50
Web	—	
Situation	Lage	Essen, 12 km
Annual closure	Jährliche Schliessung	1/11→1/3
Weekly closure	Wöchentliche Schliessung	no

Fees main season Preisliste hochsaison — 18 holes

	Week days Woche	We/Bank holidays We/Feiertag
Individual Individuell	€ 50	€ 60*
Couple Ehepaar	€ 100	€ 120*

* We: with members (nur in Mitgliederbegleitung)
– 21 & Students: - 50 %

Caddie Caddie no **Electric Trolley** Elektrokarren yes

Buggy Elektrischer Wagen no **Clubs** Leihschläger yes

Credit cards Kreditkarten
VISA - Eurocard - MasterCard

Access Zufahrt : A52 Essen-Düsseldorf. Exit (Ausf.) Essen-Haarzopf → Werden. Go on E-Werden (Ruhrbrücke), Laupendahler Strasse → E-Kettwig.

Map 3 on page 352 Karte 3 Seite 352

GOLF COURSE — PLATZ 15/20

Site	Lage	
Maintenance	Instandhaltung	
Architect	Architekt	B. von Limburger
Type	Typ	forest
Relief	Begehbarkeit	
Water in play	Platz mit Wasser	
Exp. to wind	Wind ausgesetzt	
Trees in play	Platz mit Bäumen	

Scorecard Scorekarte	Chp. Chp.	Mens Herren	Ladies Damen
Length Länge	6011	6011	5262
Par	72	72	72
Slope system	126	126	126

Advised golfing ability Empfohlene Spielstärke — 0 12 24 36

Hcp required Min. Handicap — 29/27 (We)

CLUB HOUSE & AMENITIES — KLUBHAUS UND NEBENGEBÄUDE 8/10

Pro shop Pro shop
Driving range Übungsplatz
Sheltered überdacht yes - On grass auf Rasen yes - Putting-green Putting-grün yes - Pitching-green Pitching-grün yes

HOTEL FACILITIES — HOTEL BESCHREIBUNG 7/10

HOTELS HOTELS

Schloss Hugenpoet - 25 rooms, D € 225 - Kettwig 5 km
Tel (49) 02054 - 120 40, Fax (49) 02054 - 120 450

Parkhaus Hügel - 13 rooms, D € 115 - Essen-Bredeney 10 km
Tel (49) 0201 - 471 091, Fax (49) 0201 - 444 207

Sengelmannshof - 27 rooms, D € 110 - Kettwig 5 km
Tel (49) 02054 - 959 70, Fax (49) 02054 - 832 00

RESTAURANTS RESTAURANTS

Residence - Kettwig 5 km - Tel (49) 02054 - 955 90
Hugenpöttchen - Kettwig 5 km - Tel (49) 02054 - 120 436
Parkhaus Hügel - Essen-Bredeney 10 km
Tel (49) 0201 - 471 091

Falkenstein

18 | 6 | 7

Ein Klassiker traditioneller, englischer Landschaftsarchitektur, umgeben von Wald (Pinien und weisse Birken) und Heidekraut. Auf den ersten Blick fallen die gestalterischen Feinheiten nicht auf, doch wird der Golfplatz durch sie zunehmend interessanter. Die variantenreichen Löcher und die nüchterne Weite des Platzes auf diesem leicht hügeligen Terrain stellen eine echte Herausforderung dar. Die Hindernisse sind einfach und zugleich raffiniert angelegt. Jeder Schlag muss wohlüberlegt sein und alle spielerischen Aspekte müssen in die Überlegungen miteinbezogen werden. Die Greens, teils auf mehreren Stufen, teils erhöht, sind immer gut verteidigt und können die Scores ebenso zunichte machen wie unpräzise Schläge. Gerade Löcher wechseln mit spektakulären Doglegs ab. Falkenstein ist wohl einer der schönsten Golfplätze Europas, ein grossartiges Beispiel guter Golfarchitektur. Unglücklicherweise ist der Platz für heutige Profiturnier zu kurz, aber für normale Golfer ist dieser Platz lang genug.

One of the great classics and a traditional British design, set in a forest of pine and silver birch, with heather thrown in for good measure. It is not easy to appreciate the subtlety of the course at first sight, but this serves to make the course more exciting every time. The variety of holes and the forbidding size of the layout on moderately hilly terrain produce a thoroughly good test of golf. Hazards are spread with an equal measure of simplicity and strategic intelligence, and each shot demands a lot of thought in every compartment of the game. Sometimes multi-tiered, often elevated but always well-protected, the greens can ruin your card as easily as fluffed shots. With alternating straight holes and spectacular dog-legs, Falkenstein remains one of Europe's greatest courses and a perfect showpiece for golf design. Unfortunately the course is too short for modern tournament pros, but still long enough for all other golfers.

Hamburger Golf Club 1930

In De Bargen 59
D - 22587 HAMBURG

Office	Sekretariat	(49) 040 - 812 177
Pro shop	Pro shop	(49) 040 - 866 3612
Fax	Fax	(49) 040 - 817 315
Web	www.hamburgergolf-club.de	
Situation	Lage	Hamburg, 10 km
Annual closure	Jährliche Schliessung	no
Weekly closure	Wöchentliche Schliessung	Monday

(Montag): Restaurant closed

Fees main season Preisliste hochsaison	Week days Woche	We/Bank holidays We/Feiertag
18 holes		
Individual Individuell	€ 50	€ 60*
Couple Ehepaar	€ 90	€ 110*

* We: only with members (nur in Mitgliederbegleitung)
– 25 & Students: – 50%

Caddie Caddie	on request	**Electric Trolley** Elektrokarren	yes
Buggy Elektrischer Wagen	no	**Clubs** Leihschläger	yes
Credit cards Kreditkarten	no		

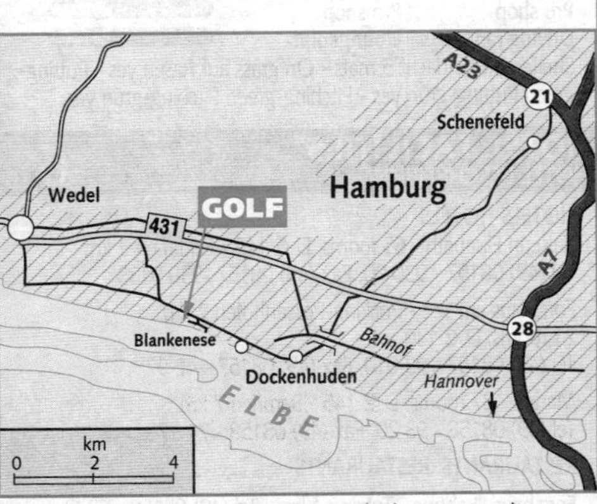

Access Zufahrt : A7. → Blankenese. Blankeneser Landtrasse. Risener Landstrasse. Turn left in De Bargen.
Map 7 on page 360 Karte 7 Seite 360

GOLF COURSE PLATZ 18/20

Site	Lage	
Maintenance	Instandhaltung	
Architect	Architekt	Harry S. Colt Alison, Morrison
Type	Typ	forest, Park
Relief	Begehbarkeit	
Water in play	Platz mit Wasser	
Exp. to wind	Wind ausgesetzt	
Trees in play	Platz mit Bäumen	

Scorecard Scorekarte	Chp. Chp.	Mens Herren	Ladies Damen
Length Länge	5838	5763	5092
Par	72	72	72
Slope system	131	126	130

Advised golfing ability Empfohlene Spielstärke: 0 12 24 36
Hcp required Min. Handicap: 36

CLUB HOUSE & AMENITIES KLUBHAUS UND NEBENGEBÄUDE 6/10

Pro shop Pro shop
Driving range Übungsplatz
Sheltered überdacht 4 mats - On grass auf Rasen yes - Putting-green Putting-grün yes - Pitching-green Pitching-grün yes

HOTEL FACILITIES HOTEL BESCHREIBUNG 7/10

HOTELS HOTELS
Strandhotel Blankenese - 16 rooms, D € 130 - Hamburg 4 km
Tel (49) 040 - 861 344, Fax (49) 040 - 846 936

Hotel Senator - 46 rooms, D € 96 - Wedel 5 km
Tel (49) 04103 - 807 70, Fax (49) 04103 -807 7250

Hotel Diamant - 39 rooms, D € 95 - Wedel 5 km
Tel (49) 04103 - 702 600, Fax (49) 04103 - 702 700

RESTAURANTS RESTAURANTS
Fischerei Hafen Restaurant - Hamburg Altona 10 km
Tel (49) 040 - 381 816
Sülberg-Seven Seas - Blankenese 3 km
Tel (49) 040 - 866 25 20

Feldafing

16 | 7 | 6

Feldafing wurde nach Umbau- und Verjüngungsmassnahmen von Heinz Fehring im Jahre 1997 wieder eröffnet, aber es immer noch ein kurzer und enger Platz, allerdings sind die Grüns jetzt stark onduliert. Die Anlage liegt etwas erhöht direkt am Starnberger See, auf einem Gelände, das früher Maximilian II gehörte, dessen Schloss unmittelbar an die Anlage angrenzt. Trotz dieser Lage bietet sich nur selten ein freier Blick auf den See, da der Platz von einer Vielzahl grosser alter Bäume umrahmt wird, die gleichzeitig einen Grossteil der Schwierigkeiten auf diesem Platz darstellen. Bernhard von Limburger hat das ziemlich hügelige Gelände hervorragend zu nutzen verstanden, so dass ein für ihn typisches Design entstanden ist das sich durch eine nüchtern-eleganten und dabei immer seriösen Stil ausgezeichnet. Feldafing ist ein reizvoller Golfplatz, der sich zudem wunderbar in die ihn umgebende Landschaft einfügt und den man allein schon aus diesem Grund unbedingt kennen lernen sollte.

Feldafing underwent a welcome and successful rejuvenation scheme by Heinz Fehring, but it is still a narrow and short course. Located on an estate formerly belonging to Maximilian II - his castle stands on the edge of the course - Feldafing overlooks the Starnberger See, although the view is not completely clear owing to the very many old trees which form the major share of hazards. Bernhard von Limburger made excellent use of rather hilly terrain (rather tiring when walking) and it is always a pleasure to see his elegant, sober and serious style again. An often spectacular course which blends wonderfully with its natural surroundings. Well worth getting to know.

Golf Club Feldafing e.V. — 1926

Tutzinger Strasse 15
D - 82340 TUTZING

Office	Sekretariat	(49) 08157 - 93 340
Pro shop	Pro shop	(49) 08157 - 933 490
Fax	Fax	(49) 08157 - 933 499
Web	www.golfclub-feldafing.de	
Situation	Lage	München, 40 km
Annual closure	Jährliche Schliessung	no
Weekly closure	Wöchentliche Schliessung	Monday

(Montag): Restaurant closed

Fees main season Preisliste hochsaison	Week days Woche	We/Bank holidays We/Feiertag
18 holes		
Individual Individuell	€ 60	€ 70*
Couple Ehepaar	€ 120	€ 140*

* We: with members (nur in Mitgliederbegleitung)

Caddie Caddie on request — **Electric Trolley** Elektrokarren no
Buggy Elektrischer Wagen no — **Clubs** Leihschläger yes
Credit cards Kreditkarten no

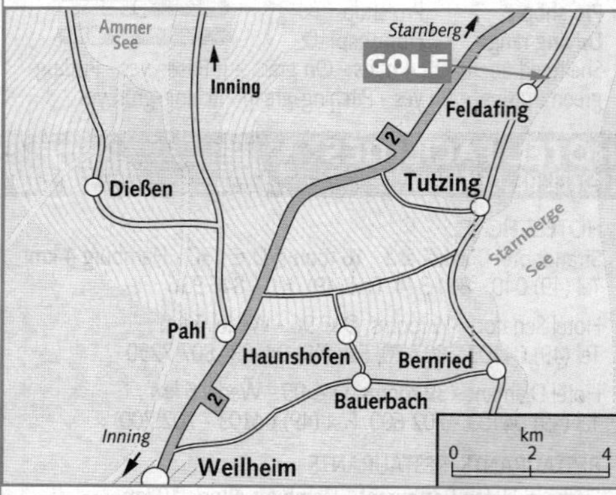

Access Zufahrt : A95 München-Starnberg. Exit (Ausf.) Starnberg. Durch Starnberg. B2 → Pöcking. → Tutzing/ Deldafing, right on Tutzinger Strasse. 1 km left, Golf.

Map 2 on page 350 Karte 2 Seite 350

GOLF COURSE — PLATZ 16/20

Site	Lage	
Maintenance	Instandhaltung	
Architect	Architekt	B. von Limburger
Type	Typ	mountain
Relief	Begehbarkeit	
Water in play	Platz mit Wasser	
Exp. to wind	Wind ausgesetzt	
Trees in play	Platz mit Bäumen	

Scorecard Scorekarte	Chp. Chp.	Mens Herren	Ladies Damen
Length Länge	5738	5482	4794
Par	71	70	70
Slope system	132	129	127

Advised golfing ability Empfohlene Spielstärke — 0 12 24 36
Hcp required Min. Handicap 34

CLUB HOUSE & AMENITIES — KLUBHAUS UND NEBENGEBÄUDE 7/10

Pro shop Pro shop
Driving range Übungsplatz
Sheltered überdacht 5 mats - On grass auf Rasen yes - Putting-green Putting-grün yes - Pitching-green Pitching-grün yes

HOTEL FACILITIES — HOTEL BESCHREIBUNG 6/10

HOTELS HOTELS

Kaiserin Elisabeth - 65 rooms, D € 145 - Feldafing 3 km
Tel (49) 08157 - 930 90, Fax (49) 08157 -930 9133

Forsthaus am See - Pöcking-Possenhofen 2 km
21 rooms, D € 140
Tel (49) 08157 - 93 010, Fax (49) 08157 - 42 92

Marina - 87 rooms, D € 145 - Bernried 7 km
Tel (49) 08158 - 93 20, Fax (49) 08158 - 71 17

RESTAURANTS RESTAURANTS

Forsthaus Ilkahöhe - Tutzing 4 km - Tel (49) 08158 - 8242
Starnberger Alm - Starnberg 6 km - Tel (49) 08151 - 155 77
La Dolce Vita - Starnberg 6 km - Tel (49) 08151 - 167 80

Fleesensee *Schloss*

17	8	8

Die Eröffnung des Platzes im Mai 2000 in der mecklenburgischen Seenplatte war ein Ereignis, das in ganz Deutschland viel Beachtung fand, besonders da dieses Resort die bisher aufwendigste Tourismus-Projekt in Ostdeutschland darstellt. Zum Resort gehören drei 18-Loch-Plätze, der Par-67-Tschibo-Platz, der vorwiegend für jüngere und neue Golfer geeignet ist, der Scandinavian Course im Stil eines Links Courses, der ideal für Durchschnittsgolfer ist und neben der Schlossplatz, der Golfern alles abverlangt. Wasserhindernisse kommen an zehn Löchern ins Spiel, dazu lauern viele Bunker, etliche davon tiefe Topfbunker auf Bälle. Der Amerikaner Stan Eby hat ein intelligentes Design umgesetzt, das leichte, mittelschwere und extrem schwere Löcher zu einem vorzüglichen Golfplatz kombiniert, ein Platz, der britische und amerikanische Stilelemente kombiniert und trotzdem wie aus einem Guss wirkt. Um allerdings ein gutes Ergebnis zu erzielen, muss man die Grüns genau anspielen. Fleesensee ist eines der besten deutschen Golfresort, eines das mit zunehmendem Alter nur noch besser werden kann.

The opening of this course in a region of lakes and one of the most picturesque in eastern Germany was quite an event, even more so considering the scope of the project. There are three 18-hole courses: a par 67 (Tschibo Course) much appreciated by younger and new golfers, a par 72 (Scandinavian Course) rather similar in style to a links course and ideal for average golfers to hone their skills, and this one, the most challenging layout where you will need to be on top of your game. Water comes into play on about ten holes and the very many sand-traps, including some deep pot-bunkers, also tend to complicate matters. Stan Eby has done another good job, smoothly combining easy, not so easy and downright difficult holes throughout a very forthright layout which cleverly blends American style golf with a definite British influence. Having said that, you will need some good old "target golf" shots to hit most of the greens. One of Germany's best golfing resorts which can only get better.

Golf & Country Club Fleesensee - Schlossplatz — 2000

Tanneweg 1
D - 17213 GÖHREN-LEBBIN

Office	Sekretariat	(49) 039932 - 80 400
Pro shop	Pro shop	(49) 039932 -204 033
Fax	Fax	(49) 039932 -804 020
Web	www.golfclub-fleesensee.de	
Situation	Lage	Malchow, 5 km
Annual closure	Jährliche Schliessung	no
Weekly closure	Wöchentliche Schliessung	no

Fees main season Preisliste hochsaison	18 holes	
	Week days Woche	We/Bank holidays We/Feiertag
Individual Individuell	€ 70	€ 70
Couple Ehepaar	€ 140	€ 140

– 18 and Students: – 50%

Caddie Caddie no — **Electric Trolley** Elektrokarren yes
Buggy Elektrischer Wagen yes — **Clubs** Leihschläger yes
Credit cards Kreditkarten VISA - Eurocard - AMEX

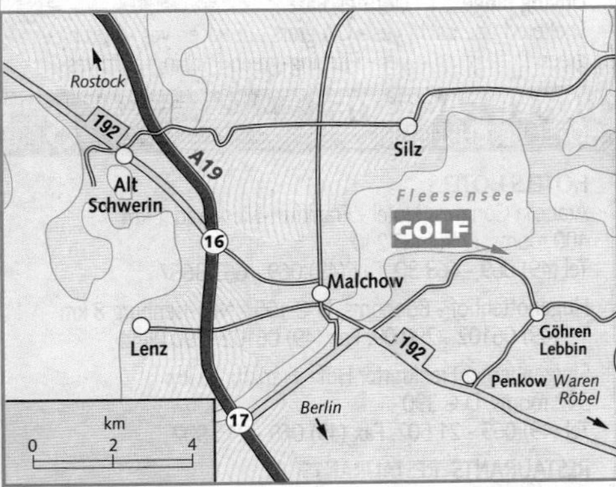

Access Zufahrt : Berlin, A24 → Hamburg. Exit 20, then A19 → Rostock. Exit 17 (Waren-Petersdorf) to Malchow. B192 → Sietow. Golf on left hand side close to Göhren-Lebbin.
Map 7 on page 361 Karte 7 Seite 361

GOLF COURSE — PLATZ — 17/20

Site	Lage	
Maintenance	Instandhaltung	
Architect	Architekt	Stan Eby European Golf Design
Type	Typ	parkland, links
Relief	Begehbarkeit	
Water in play	Platz mit Wasser	
Exp. to wind	Wind ausgesetzt	
Trees in play	Platz mit Bäumen	

Scorecard Scorekarte	Chp. Chp.	Mens Herren	Ladies Damen
Length Länge	6335	5919	4877
Par	72	72	72
Slope system	138	133	133

Advised golfing ability Empfohlene Spielstärke — 0 12 24 36
Hcp required Min. Handicap — 36 (Summer)

CLUB HOUSE & AMENITIES — KLUBHAUS UND NEBENGEBÄUDE — 8/10

Pro shop Pro shop
Driving range Übungsplatz
Sheltered überdacht 80 mats - On grass auf Rasen yes - Putting-green Putting-grün yes - Pitching-green Pitching-grün yes

HOTEL FACILITIES — HOTEL BESCHREIBUNG — 8/10

HOTELS HOTELS

SAS Radisson Schl. Fleesensee - on site
184 rooms, D € 165
Tel (49) 039932 - 80 100, Fax (49) 039932-80108010

Sporthotel - 40 rooms, D € 80 - Malchow 8 km
Tel (49) 039932 - 890, Fax (49) 039932 - 89 222

Müritz Strandhotel - 52 rooms, D € 75 - Röbel 15 km
Tel (49) 039931 - 530050, Fax (49) 039931 - 530520

RESTAURANTS RESTAURANTS

Müritz-Terrasse - Röbel 15 km - Tel (49) 039931 - 8910
Seestern - Röbel 15 km - Tel (49) 039931 - 58 030
Reusenhaus - Waren 15 km - Tel (49) 039931 -666 897

Frankfurter GC

17	7	8

Viele Jahre zählte der Frankfurter Club zu den Plätzen, die bis 1989 gut genug waren, die German Open neunmal auszutragen. Doch fehlte dem Platz die Länge, um die Tourspielern zu testen. Bis Juni 2002 passte Kurt Rossknecht den Platz an die modernen Schlaglängen an und verlegte etliche Bunker und Abschläge, so dass sie jetzt auch für Longhitter wieder ins Spiel kommen.. Das Layout der leicht hügeligen Anlage ist typisch britisch. Kein Wunder, trägt der Platz doch die Handschrift von Colt und Morrison, was auch in der im Spielverlauf allmählich spürbaren Steigerung der an den Golfer gestellten Anforderungen zum Ausdruck kommt. Durchschnittliche Spieler werden ihren Spass haben, während die besseren Spieler in guter Form sein müssen, um ein gutes Ergebnis zu erzielen. Der Platz erfordert gerade Schläge ebenso wie die Beherrschung unterschiedlicher Ball-Flugkurven, um die vielen Bäumen vermeiden bzw. um diese herumspielen zu können. Die Grüns sind gut geformt, von mittlerer Grösse und gut verteidigt ohne unzugänglich zu sein.

For many a year this was one of the courses used for the German Open, but after intensive relocating of some bunkers and tees by German golf course architect Kurt Rossknecht the course tests the modern day long hitters. Playing on this track within the city limits is a real joy for the beauty of its setting, despite the airport being a shade too close for comfort. The layout is sometimes hilly, but never excessively so. It is plainly very British in style, and the Colt and Morrison label is a guarantee of quality and technical skill, with the course gradually getting harder geared to the golfer's ability. Average players will have fun, the better players will need to be on their toes to card a good score. Here, of course, you have to play straight and sometimes flight the ball to avoid, or escape from, the many trees. The greens are well-contoured, medium-sized and reasonably well-protected, although never inaccessible. Since the top soil is sand, the course drains very well and can be played even after heavy rainfall.

Frankfurter Golf Club e.V. **1913**
Golfstrasse 41
D - 60528 FRANKFURT

Office	Sekretariat	(49) 069 - 666 2318
Pro shop	Pro shop	(49) 069 - 666 2441
Fax	Fax	(49) 069 - 666 7018
Web	www.fgc.de	
Situation	Lage	Frankfurt, 3 km
Annual closure	Jährliche Schliessung	no
Weekly closure	Wöchentliche Schliessung	Monday

(Montag): Restaurant closed

Fees main season Preisliste hochsaison — 18 holes

	Week days Woche	We/Bank holidays We/Feiertag
Individual Individuell	€ 60	€ 70
Couple Ehepaar	€ 120	€ 140

– 21& Students: – 50%

Caddie Caddie on request — **Electric Trolley** Elektrokarren no
Buggy Elektrischer Wagen no — **Clubs** Leihschläger yes
Credit cards Kreditkarten no

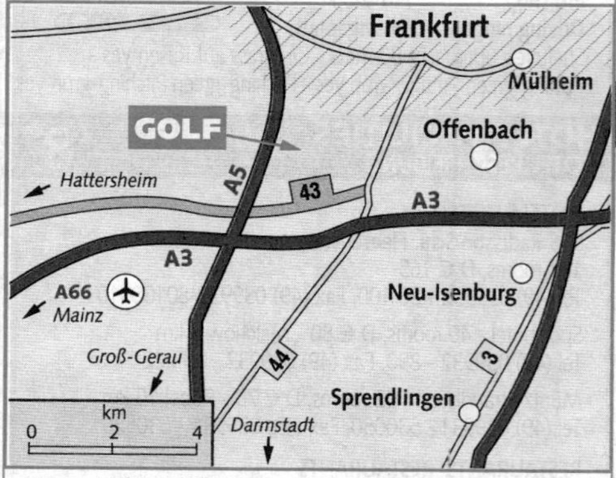

Access Zufahrt : A3, Exit (Ausf.) Frankfurt Süd → Niederrad, Flughafenstrasse, Golfstrasse.
Map 3 on page 353 Karte 3 Seite 353

GOLF COURSE — PLATZ 17/20

Site	Lage	
Maintenance	Instandhaltung	
Architect	Architekt	Harry S. Colt
Type	Typ	forest
Relief	Begehbarkeit	
Water in play	Platz mit Wasser	
Exp. to wind	Wind ausgesetzt	
Trees in play	Platz mit Bäumen	

Scorecard Scorekarte	Chp. Chp.	Mens Herren	Ladies Damen
Length Länge	6209	6087	4949
Par	71	71	71
Slope system	129	123	118

Advised golfing ability Empfohlene Spielstärke 0 12 24 36
Hcp required Min. Handicap 32

CLUB HOUSE & AMENITIES — KLUBHAUS UND NEBENGEBÄUDE 7/10

Pro shop Pro shop
Driving range Übungsplatz
Sheltered überdacht yes - On grass auf Rasen yes - Putting-green Putting-grün yes - Pitching-green Pitching-grün yes

HOTEL FACILITIES — HOTEL BESCHREIBUNG 8/10

HOTELS HOTELS

Arabella Congress Hotel - Frankfurt-Niederrad 1 km
400 rooms, D from € 240
Tel (49) 069 - 663 30, Fax (49) 069 - 663 3667

Hugenottenhof - 86 rooms, D € 105 - Neu-Isenburg 8 km
Tel (49) 06102 - 290 09, Fax (49) 06102 -290 0444

Steigenberger Frankfurter Hof - Frankfurt 6 km
342 rooms, D € 390
Tel (49) 069 - 21 502, Fax (49) 069 - 215 902

RESTAURANTS RESTAURANTS

Weinhaus Brückenkeller - Frankfurt 6 km
Tel (49) 069 - 298 00 70
Weidemann - Frankfurt-Niederrad 2 km - Tel (49) 069 - 675 996
Tiger Restaurant - Frankfurt 6 km - Tel (49) 069 -920 022 25

Fränkische Schweiz

14	7	5

Die beste Zeit diesen Platz zu spielen ist Ende Frühling, wenn die Apfel- und Kirschbäume in voller Blüte stehen. Seit seiner Erweiterung zur 18-Loch-Anlage ist der GC Fränkische Schweiz, zwischen Nürnberg und Bamberg gelegen, zum beliebten Ziel für Golfer geworden. Die eine Hälfte der Löcher liegt im Wald, die andere in offenerem Gelände, wo auch die längsten Löcher zu finden sind und die Spieler mit langem Drive voll zum Zug kommen. Der Platz ist sehr natürlich angelegt. Wenngleich die Bunker besser modelliert sein könnten, bereiten sie doch auch so den meisten Spielern genug Kopfzerbrechen. Dasselbe gilt auch für die Grüns. Während Gestaltung und Formgebung der Grüns bei älteren Anlagen häufig nicht sehr ausgeprägt ist, hat man sich bei neueren Plätzen in dieser Hinsicht an ein aufwendigeres Design gewöhnt. Zusammenfassend können wir sagen, dass dieser Platz einen recht ausgewogenen Eindruck macht, angenehm zu spielen ist und Golfern aller Spielstärken entgegenkommt. Die Fränkische Schweiz ist zudem eine sehr reizvolle Gegend.

The best season to play here is in late spring, when the apple- and cherry-trees are in blossom. Between Nürnberg and Bamberg, this has been a traditional stop-off for golfers since it was enhanced to 18-hole status in 1989. Half the holes run through the woods, the other half in more open country, where the holes are longer and big-hitters can open their shoulders. The layout is very natural, and while we might have hoped for better contoured bunkers, there is no denying that they do pose a considerable problem for most players. The same observation applies to the greens; while older greens were often a little less elaborate, recent courses have accustomed us to a little more research. With that said, this is a very pleasant and friendly course for players of all levels, and it is well-balanced throughout. Fränkische Schweiz is also a very pretty region.

Golf-Club Fränkische Schweiz e.V. — 1974

Kanndorf 8
D - 91320 EBERMANNSTADT

Office Sekretariat (49) 09194 - 4827
Pro shop Pro shop (49) 09194 - 4827
Fax Fax (49) 09194 - 5410
E-mail gcfraenkischeschweiz@t-online.de
Situation Lage Nürnberg, 45 km
Bamberg, 35 km
Annual closure Jährliche Schliessung 30/11→31/3
Weekly closure Wöchentliche Schliessung Monday
(Montag): restaurant closed

Fees main season Preisliste hochsaison	18 holes	
	Week days Woche	**We/Bank holidays** We/Feiertag
Individual Individuell	€ 35	€ 45
Couple Ehepaar	€ 70	€ 90

– 21 / Students: – 50%

Caddie Caddie no — **Electric Trolley** Elektrokarren no
Buggy Elektrischer Wagen no — **Clubs** Leihschläger yes
Credit cards Kreditkarten no

Access Zufahrt : BAB-A73 Nürnberg-Bamberg. Exit (Ausf.) Forchheim. B470 → Ebermannstadt. → Kanndorf, Golf
Map 4 on page 354 Karte 4 Seite 354

GOLF COURSE — PLATZ 14/20

Site Lage
Maintenance Instandhaltung
Architect Architekt unknown
Type Typ country, forest
Relief Begehbarkeit
Water in play Platz mit Wasser
Exp. to wind Wind ausgesetzt
Trees in play Platz mit Bäumen

Scorecard Scorekarte	**Chp.** Chp.	**Mens** Herren	**Ladies** Damen
Length Länge	6050	6050	5388
Par	72	72	72
Slope system	125	125	127

Advised golfing ability Empfohlene Spielstärke 0 12 24 36
Hcp required Min. Handicap 35

CLUB HOUSE & AMENITIES — KLUBHAUS UND NEBENGEBÄUDE 7/10

Pro shop Pro shop
Driving range Übungsplatz
Sheltered überdacht 3 mats - On grass auf Rasen no, 10 mats open air - Putting-green Putting-grün yes - Pitching-green Pitching-grün yes

HOTEL FACILITIES — HOTEL BESCHREIBUNG 5/10

HOTELS HOTELS
Schwanenbrau - Ebermannstadt 2 km
13 rooms, D € 56
Tel (49) 09194 - 209, Fax (49) 09194 - 5836

Resengörg - Ebermannstadt 2 km
39 rooms, D € 65
Tel (49) 09194 - 73 930, Fax (49) 09194 - 739 373

Residenzschloss - 184 rooms, D € 162 - Bamberg 35 km
Tel (49) 0951 - 609 10, Fax (49) 0951 - 609 1701

RESTAURANTS RESTAURANTS
Feiler - Muggendorf 4 km - Tel (49) 09196 - 92 950
Resengörg - Ebermannstadt 5 km - Tel (49) 09194 - 739 30

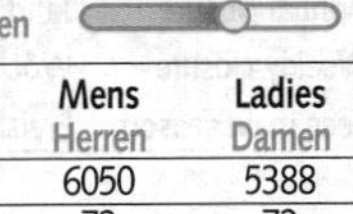

Fürstlicher GC Bad Waldsee

16	7	8

Dieser 1998 eröffnete Platz liegt nur 50 m vom wesentlich älteren Golf Club Oberschwaben Bad Waldsee entfernt, den man mit einem Lobwedge über die Bäume leicht erreichen könnte. Der neue Platz ist anders, aber ebenso reizvoll wie der alte Nachbarplatz. Der Platz liegt herrlich eingebettet in einer Waldlandschaft. Die dreimalige deutsche Amateurmeister Thomas Himmel und der Pro Carlo Knauss entwarfen den 18-Loch-Platz. Es ist das erste gemeinsame Werk dieser beiden, und es ist ihnen gut gelungen. Sie haben dem modernen Trend zu immer mehr Länge widerstanden und betonen statt dessen die Werte von intelligentem und strategischem Golf : easy bogey, tough par. Höhepunkt der Runde sind die Löcher 12 bis 16, die sich um einen riesigen ehemaligen Baggersee schlängeln. Da auch noch ein Hotel direkt am Platz liegt, ist Waldsee ideal für einen Kurzurlaub.

You only need a lob-wedge shot over the trees to reach the neighbouring course of the older Golf Club Oberschwaben Bad Waldsee, located only 50 metres from this course opened in 1998. The old course is beautifully integrated within a wonderful forest, the new course is a modern lay-out. Three-time German Amateur champion Thomas Himmel and Pro Carlo Knauss collaborated on this course for the first time and they really got it right first time out. Himmel and Knauss resisted the modern trend of extreme length and put more stress on intelligent and strategic golf: easy bogey, tough par. The highlights of the round are holes 12 through 16 which meander around a flooded gravel pit. With a wonderful on-site hotel, Waldsee is an ideal setting for a short break from the daily grind.

Fürstlicher Golfclub Bad Waldsee e.V. 1998

Hopfenweiler 14
D - 88339 BAD WALDSEE

Office	Sekretariat	(49) 07524 -401 7200
Pro shop	Pro shop	(49) 07524 -401 7200
Fax	Fax	(49) 07524 -401 7100
Web	www.waldsee-golf.de	
Situation	Lage	Ravensburg, 24 km
Annual closure	Jährliche Schliessung	no
Weekly closure	Wöchentliche Schliessung	no

Fees main season Preisliste hochsaison		18 holes
	Week days Woche	We/Bank holidays We/Feiertag
Individual Individuell	€ 55	€ 70
Couple Ehepaar	€ 110	€ 140

Caddie Caddie no — **Electric Trolley** Elektrokarren yes
Buggy Elektrischer Wagen yes — **Clubs** Leihschläger yes
Credit cards Kreditkarten
VISA - Eurocard - MasterCard - AMEX - DC

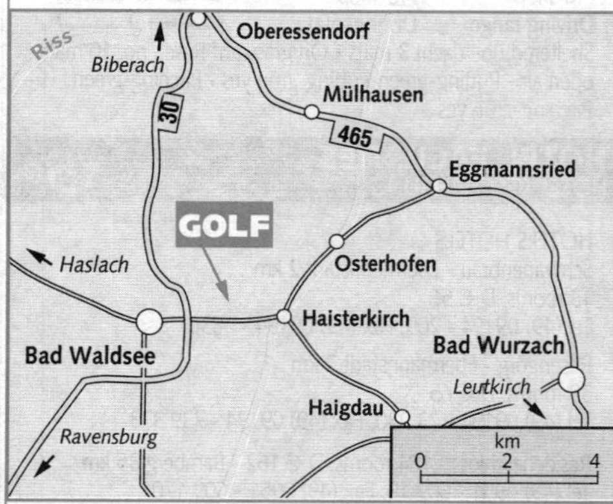

Access Zufahrt : A8 München-Stuttgart. Exit (Ausf.) Ulm-West. B30 → Bodensee. Bad Waldsee → Golf
Map 1 on page 349 Karte 1 Seite 349

GOLF COURSE — PLATZ 16/20

Site	Lage	
Maintenance	Instandhaltung	
Architect	Architekt	Thomas Himmel, Carlo Knauss
Type	Typ	forest, open country
Relief	Begehbarkeit	
Water in play	Platz mit Wasser	
Exp. to wind	Wind ausgesetzt	
Trees in play	Platz mit Bäumen	

Scorecard Scorekarte	Chp. Chp.	Mens Herren	Ladies Damen
Length Länge	6415	5982	5315
Par	72	72	72
Slope system	130	130	128

Advised golfing ability Empfohlene Spielstärke — 0 12 24 36
Hcp required Min. Handicap — 32 (We)

CLUB HOUSE & AMENITIES — KLUBHAUS UND NEBENGEBÄUDE 7/10

Pro shop	Pro shop
Driving range	Übungsplatz

Sheltered überdacht 15 mats - On grass auf Rasen yes - Putting-green Putting-grün yes - Pitching-green Pitching-grün yes

HOTEL FACILITIES — HOTEL BESCHREIBUNG 8/10

HOTELS HOTELS

Golf & Vitalpark Bad Waldsee - 40 rooms, D € 150 - on site
Tel (49) 07524 - 401 70, Fax (49) 07524 -401 7100

Kur-Parkhotel - Bad Waldsee 2 km
54 rooms, D from € 80
Tel (49) 07524 - 97 070, Fax (49) 07524 - 970 775

Altes Tor - 27 rooms, D € 90 - Bad Waldsee 2 km
Tel (49) 07524 - 971 90, Fax (49) 07524 - 971 997

RESTAURANTS RESTAURANTS

Waldhorn - Ravensburg 20 km - Tel (49) 0751 - 36 120
Krone - Schlier 25 km - Tel (49) 07529 - 1292
Scala - Bad Waldsee 2 km - Tel (49) 07524 - 913 200

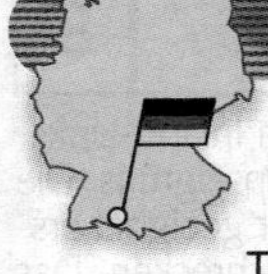

Garmisch-Partenkirchen

14 | 6 | 7

In unmittelbarer Nähe zu einem der bekanntesten Winter- und Sommersportorte Europas gelegen, verläuft dieser Platz auf so ebenem Terrain, dass man ihn als Flachland-Platz inmitten einer Alpin-Region bezeichnen kann. Der Platz ist daher auch mühelos zu bewältigen. Trotz der schwierigen Witterungsbedingungen - lange kalte Winter, heisse Sommer - macht der Platz einen sehr gepflegten Eindruck. Um auf diesem Platz gut zu spielen, sollte man nicht allzu sehr streuen, da die Fairways, eingegrenzt durch Bäume, Büsche und Felsen, recht schmal sind. Die Tücken dieses Platzes, der deutlich zu erkennende Hindernisse hat, sind eher psychologischer denn realer Natur. Spieler, die den Ball gerade schlagen, werden die Runde geniessen. Dasselbe gilt für Spieler mit mittlerem Handicap sowie jene, denen es an Länge fehlt. Das 'persönliche Par' ist immer möglich. Einen zusätzlichen Anreiz dieses Ortes bietet das ausgezeichnete Restaurant im Clubhaus mit seiner typisch bayerischen Atmosphäre, in dem man einen schönen Golftag ausklingen lassen sollte.

Very close to one of Europe's most celebrated winter and summer resorts, this course is flat enough to be considered a lowland course transposed to the mountains. You can play it tirelessly. Green-keeping is very decent, given the length of the winters and the hot summers, but this is not a course we would recommend to wild hitters: the fairways are tight and guarded by trees, bushes and rocks. The dangers here are perhaps more psychological than real (hazards are clearly visible) and straight players will enjoy their round. The same might apply to mid-handicappers and players lacking length. On most holes you can play your "personal par" (with handicap strokes). To enjoy your day to the full, pop inside the very country-style club-house and enjoy the excellent restaurant and typically Bavarian atmosphere. It is a great bonus for an excellent site.

Golf-Club Garmisch-Partenkirchen e.V. 1928

Gut Buchwies
D - 82496 OBERAU

Office	Sekretariat	(49) 08824 - 8344
Pro shop	Pro shop	(49) 08824 - 1679
Fax	Fax	(49) 08824 - 944 198
Web	www.golfclub-garmisch-partenkirchen.de	
Situation	Lage	München, 81 km

Garmisch-Partenkirchen, 8 km -

Annual closure Jährliche Schliessung 1/12→31/3

Weekly closure Wöchentliche Schliessung Monday (Montag): Restaurant closed

Fees main season Preisliste hochsaison 18 holes

	Week days Woche	We/Bank holidays We/Feiertag
Individual Individuell	€ 50	€ 60
Couple Ehepaar	€ 100	€ 120

– 21 / Students: – 50%

Caddie Caddie on request — **Electric Trolley** Elektrokarren no
Buggy Elektrischer Wagen yes — **Clubs** Leihschläger yes
Credit cards Kreditkarten AMEX

Access Zufahrt : A95 and B2 München → Garmisch-Partenkirchen. Exit (Ausf.) Oberau. Left over the Loisach → Gut Buchwies, Golf
Map 2 on page 350 Karte 2 Seite 350

GOLF COURSE PLATZ 14/20

Site	Lage	
Maintenance	Instandhaltung	
Architect	Architekt	unknown
Type	Typ	parkland
Relief	Begehbarkeit	
Water in play	Platz mit Wasser	
Exp. to wind	Wind ausgesetzt	
Trees in play	Platz mit Bäumen	

Scorecard Scorekarte	Chp. Chp.	Mens Herren	Ladies Damen
Length Länge	6093	6093	5338
Par	72	72	72
Slope system	125	125	128

Advised golfing ability Empfohlene Spielstärke 0 12 24 36
Hcp required Min. Handicap no

CLUB HOUSE & AMENITIES KLUBHAUS UND NEBENGEBÄUDE 6/10

Pro shop Pro shop
Driving range Übungsplatz
Sheltered überdacht 4 mats - On grass auf Rasen yes - Putting-green Putting-grün yes - Pitching-green Pitching-grün yes

HOTEL FACILITIES HOTEL BESCHREIBUNG 7/10

HOTELS HOTELS

Grand Hotel Sonnenbichl - Garmisch-Partenkirchen 7 km
96 rooms, D € 140
Tel (49) 08821 - 70 20, Fax (49) 08821 - 702 131

Reindl's Partenkirchner Hof - Garmisch-Partenkirchen 8 km
72 rooms, D € 115
Tel (49) 08821 - 58 025, Fax (49) 08821 - 9438725

Tonihof - Eschenlohe 5 km - 25 rooms, D € 100
Tel (49) 08824 - 929 30, Fax (49) 08824 - 929 399

RESTAURANTS RESTAURANTS

Husar - Garmisch-Partenkirchen 8 km - Tel (49) 08821 - 1713
Alpenhof - Garmisch-Partenkirchen - Tel (49) 08821 - 59 055
Cafe Riessersee - Garmisch-Partenkirchen
Tel (49) 08821 - 95 440

Gleidingen *Blau / Grün*

16 | 7 | 8

Dieser von David Krause entworfene Platz ist ein Kompromiss zwischen einem Inland-Links-Course und einem typischen amerikanischen Design mit Inselgrüns und Halbinselgrüns. Die sehr menschliche Länge des Platzes lassen den Platz auch für schwächere Spieler geeignet erscheinen, wären da nicht die vielen Wasserhindernisse, die hohe Handicaps abschrecken. Das gesamte Design wirkt gefällig, angemessen schwierig, die Grüns sind immer klar zu sehen und viele Löcher bieten interessante Optionen. Dies trifft besonders zu wenn der Wind, ein regelmässiger Besucher dieser Gegend, kräftig weht und den Ball ins hohe Rough blasen kann. Die Anlage verfügt über drei 9-Loch-Schleifen, von denen Blau-Grün die beste Kombination darstellt. Der erste Teil ist ziemlich "wässrig", der zweite hügelig. Gleidingen hat das Angebot an Golfplätzen im Grossraum Hannover deutlich verbessert. Ein Platz mit einem moderne Clubhaus, den man unbedingt spielen muss.

This course is a compromise between the inland links style, suggested by some very open spaces, and a number of very distinctly American features like the layout of greens beside water hazards and even some full- or half-island greens. The relatively humane yardage makes this a course for everyone but the "water, water everywhere" option often tends to scare off the lesser player. The whole layout exudes thoroughness of design that is smooth and pleasing to the eye, reasonable difficulties, clearly visible greens and interesting options for the player. This is especially so with the wind, a frequent visitor to these parts which can easily send high balls veering into thick rough. The resort boasts three combinable 9-hole courses, the best mix being the "Blau-Grün" combination. The first part is a little "watery", the second a little hillier. Gleidingen has considerably enhanced the panoply of courses in the region of Hanover and the club-house is well-equipped.

Golf Gleidingen — 1998

Am Golfplatz 1
D - 30880 LAATZEN-GLEIDINGEN

Office	Sekretariat	(49) 0512 - 3011
Pro shop	Pro shop	(49) 0512 - 3011
Fax	Fax	(49) 0512 - 3099
Web	www.golf-gleidingen.de	
Situation	Lage	Hannover, 20 km
Annual closure	Jährliche Schliessung	no
Weekly closure	Wöchentliche Schliessung	no
Fees main season	Preisliste hochsaison	18 holes

	Week days Woche	We/Bank holidays We/Feiertag
Individual Individuell	€ 35	€ 45
Couple Ehepaar	€ 70	€ 90

Caddie Caddie no — **Electric Trolley** Elektrokarren yes
Buggy Elektrischer Wagen no — **Clubs** Leihschläger yes
Credit cards Kreditkarten
VISA - Eurocard - MasterCard - AMEX

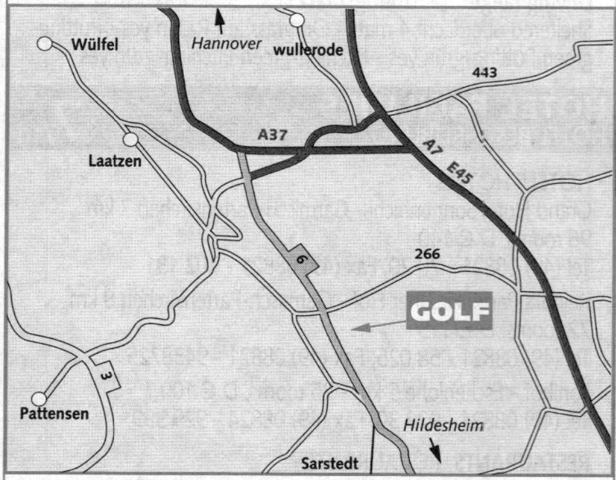

Wülfel
Hannover
wullerode
443
A37
A7 E45
Laatzen
266
6
GOLF
3
Pattensen
Hildesheim
Sarstedt

Access Zufahrt : A 7 Hannover → Hildesheim, Exit (Ausfahrt) Laatzen. B 6 (Messeschnellweg) → Sarstedt-Hildesheim, Exit 1. Traffic lights turn left → Algermissen-Oesselse, 400 m golf on right hand side. **Map 5 on page 357** Karte 5 Seite 357

GOLF COURSE
PLATZ — 16/20

Site	Lage	
Maintenance	Instandhaltung	
Architect	Architekt	David Krause
Type	Typ	inland, links
Relief	Begehbarkeit	
Water in play	Platz mit Wasser	
Exp. to wind	Wind ausgesetzt	
Trees in play	Platz mit Bäumen	

Scorecard Scorekarte	**Chp.** Chp.	**Mens** Herren	**Ladies** Damen
Length Länge	6087	5740	4673
Par	72	72	72
Slope system	125	125	121

Advised golfing ability Empfohlene Spielstärke — 0 12 24 36
Hcp required Min. Handicap 54

CLUB HOUSE & AMENITIES
KLUBHAUS UND NEBENGEBÄUDE — 7/10

Pro shop Pro shop
Driving range Übungsplatz
Sheltered überdacht 15 mats - On grass auf Rasen yes
Putting-green Putting-grün yes - Pitching-green Pitching-grün yes

HOTEL FACILITIES
HOTEL BESCHREIBUNG — 8/10

HOTELS HOTELS

Radisson Sas - Hannover-Messe 10 km
250 rooms, D € 119
Tel (49) 0511 - 383 830, Fax (49) 0511-38383 8000

Copthorne - Laatzen 10 km
222 rooms, D € 190
Tel (49) 0511 - 983 60, Fax (49) 0511 - 983 6667

Maritim Stadthotel - Hannover 20 km - 291 rooms, D € 140
Tel (49) 0511 - 989 40, Fax (49) 0511 - 989 4900

RESTAURANTS RESTAURANTS

Clichy Restaurant - Hannover 20 km - Tel (49) 0511 - 312 447
Georgenhof Stern - Hannover 20 km - Tel (49) 0511 - 702 244

Golfpark Gut Häusern

16	8	7

Er gehört zu den zur Arabella-Gruppe zählenden Plätzen von Eschenried, die allerdings rund 20 Auto-Minuten entfernt sind. Ohne Zweifel ist dies das bisher beste Design von Peter Harradine, der mit zahlreichen Erdbewegungen, Wasser und Sand den Platz ausgesprochen interessant gestaltete. Der Platz mutet manchmal etwas schottisch an, aber der Gesamteindruck erinnert eher an amerikanische Plätze. Besonders zu erwähnen sind drei Löcher auf den zweiten Neun, die wirken als wären sie in ein Meer von Sand gelegt. Wasser-Hindernisse kommen an fünf Löchern ins Spiel, insbesondere am 9. und 18. Loch. Besonders am 9. Loch, einem langen Par 4 und am 18. Loch, einem Par 5, an dem gleich zwei Teiche überwunden werden müssen, kann man sich die Scorekarte ruinieren. Auf diesem leicht zu begehende Platz ist die Strategie für jedes Loch vom Abschlag oder genauer von den Abschlägen erkennbar. Denn insgesamt sechs Tee-Boxes sorgen dafür, dass auf diesem insgesamt 6740 Meter langen Platz jeder seinen Spass hat – vom Profi bis zum Anfänger.

This course laid out in a beautiful rural region of Bavaria complements the Eschenried course, both under the wing of Arabella Golf. It is Peter Harradine's best design, where fine earth-grading has enhanced landscape lined with water, woods and sand. This means the occasional Scottish feel here and there, but appearances are generally more American. Of special note are three holes on the homeward nine laid out in a sea of sand dotted only by the fairways and greens. The water is in play on five holes, especially on the 9th and 18th, the former a tough par 4 and the final hole one where water has to be carried twice. Many a promising card can literally go under at the end of your round. This easy-to-walk course gives obvious clues to strategy from the tee of each hole. Or should we say tees, as there are six boxes on each hole, enough to stretch Gut Häusern to 7,300 yards albeit with a par 74. Whether a tough competitor or new to the game, you will find a length of course to match your abilities.

Golfpark Gut Häusern — 2003

Gut Häusern 2
D - 85229 MARKT INDERSDORF

Office	Sekretariat	(49) 08139 - 93280
Pro shop	Pro shop	(49) 08139 - 93280
Fax	Fax	(49) 08139 - 932 828
Web	www.golf-gh.de	
Situation	Lage	München 25 km
Annual closure	Jährliche Schliessung	no
Weekly closure	Wöchentliche Schliessung	no
Fees main season	Preisliste hochsaison	18 holes

	Week days Woche	We/Bank holidays We/Feiertag
Individual Individuell	€ 55	€ 70
Couple Ehepaar	€ 110	€ 140

Juniors: – 50%

Caddie Caddie on request — **Electric Trolley** Elektrokarren no

Buggy Elektrischer Wagen yes — **Clubs** Leihschläger yes

Credit cards Kreditkarten VISA - Eurocard

Access Zufahrt : A92 Exit (Ausfahrt) Lohhof. B13 → Ingolstadt. In Farenzhausen, turn left → Petershausen/Dachau. After 50 m, right → Lotzbach. → Röhrmoos, then follow signs to Gut Häusern

Map 2 on page 350 Karte 2 Seite 350

GOLF COURSE — PLATZ 16/20

Site	Lage	
Maintenance	Instandhaltung	
Architect	Architekt	Peter Harradine
Type	Typ	open country
Relief	Begehbarkeit	
Water in play	Platz mit Wasser	
Exp. to wind	Wind ausgesetzt	
Trees in play	Platz mit Bäumen	

Scorecard Scorekarte	Chp. Chp.	Mens Herren	Ladies Damen
Length Länge	6705	6104	5105
Par	74	72	72
Slope system	132	125	124

Advised golfing ability Empfohlene Spielstärke — 0 12 24 36

Hcp required Min. Handicap 45

CLUB HOUSE & AMENITIES — KLUBHAUS UND NEBENGEBÄUDE 8/10

Pro shop Pro shop

Driving range Übungsplatz

Sheltered überdacht 8 mats - On grass auf Rasen yes - Putting-green Putting-grün yes - Pitching-green Pitching-grün yes

HOTEL FACILITIES — HOTEL BESCHREIBUNG 7/10

HOTELS HOTELS

Golf Landhaus Eschenried - Eschenried 10 km
16 rooms, D € 75
Tel (49) 08131 - 850 91, Fax (49) 08131 - 567 418

Lansgasthof Brummer - Röhrmoos 3 km
13 rooms, D € 65
Tel (49) 08139 - 72 20, Fax (49) 08139 - 87 90

Kriemhild - München-Nymphenburg 10 km
17 rooms, D € 90
Tel (49) 089 - 171 1170, Fax (49) 089 -171 11755

RESTAURANTS RESTAURANTS

Landgasthof Brummer - Röhrmoos 3 km - Tel (49) 08139 - 72 20
Schuhbeck's - München 25 km - Tel (49) 089 - 216 69 00

Green Eagle *Süd*

15 | 2 | 6

Mit einer Länger von etwas über 6000 Meter scheint der Süd Course auf den ersten Blick nicht so schwierig wie das im Bau befindliche 7010 Meter lange Monster des Nord Course auf der gegenüberliegenden Strassenseite. Doch weit gefehlt: Auf dem Süd Course lauern überall Wasserhindernisse, die schwächere Spieler entmutigen und selbst besser Golfer einschüchtern können. Das Gelände ist flach, und mit Hilfe eines Birdie-Buchs und einer realistischen Einschätzung des eigenen Könnens, kann man die Schwierigkeiten gut umschiffen. Die bestens verteidigten Grüns verlangen hohe Schläge in die Grüns.Anfänger sind besser beraten auf diesem Platz nur spazieren zu gehen. Der Eigentümer, Michael Blesch, ein ehemaliger Golfpro, hat einen Platz für Männer entworfen. Da der Platz jeden Fehlschlag unbarmherzig bestraft, ist allen, die angenehme Erinnerungen mit nach Hause nehmen wollen, zum Lochspiel zu raten. Das Fehlen eines Clubhauses unterstreicht das Gefühl, sich hier einem Golfabenteuer zu unterziehen.

With a length of barely more than 6,600 yards, as opposed to a monster 7,700 yards for the Nord Course still under construction, you might think this an easy course. But not a bit of it. Water hazards are everywhere and are certainly numerous enough to worry the more wayward players and intimidate the others. On land this flat, strategy comes with the help of the course guide and good insight into one's own game. As the well-defended greens impose high approach shots, beginners will understandably settle for walking and watching. Architect Michael Blesch has delivered here a "course for men", and its unquestionable penal qualities make this first and foremost a course for match-play when looking for any idea of "winning" or exciting memories. The temporary absence of any club-house accentuates the feeling of adventure golf.

Green Eagle Golfanlage — 2000

Radbrucher Str. 200
D - 21423 WINSEN (LUHE)

Office	Sekretariat	(49) 07178 - 2241
Pro shop	Pro shop	(49) 07178 - 2241
Fax	Fax	(49) 07178 - 2242
Web	www.greeneagle.de	
Situation	Lage	Hamburg, 35 km

Lüneburg, 20 km

Annual closure	Jährliche Schliessung	no
Weekly closure	Wöchentliche Schliessung	no
Fees main season	Preisliste hochsaison	18 holes

	Week days Woche	We/Bank holidays We/Feiertag
Individual Individuell	€ 40	€ 55
Couple Ehepaar	€ 80	€ 110

Juniors/Students: € 30

Caddie Caddie no — **Electric Trolley** Elektrokarren no
Buggy Elektrischer Wagen yes — **Clubs** Leihschläger yes
Credit cards Kreditkarten no

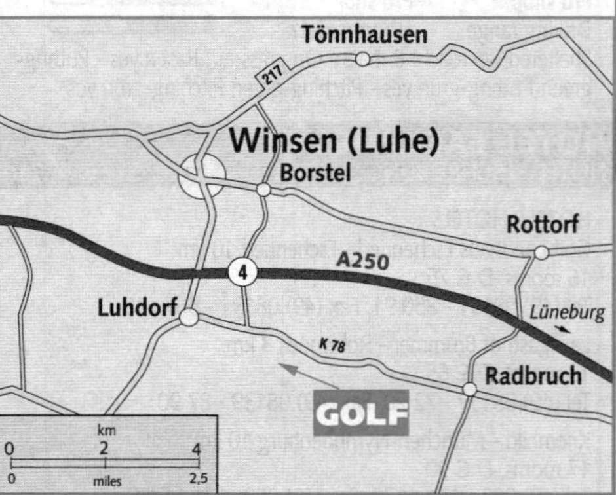

Access Zufahrt : Hamburg, A250 → Lüneburg. Exit (Ausfahrt) Winsen-Ost. Turn left, then left again → Golf
Map 7 on page 360 Karte 7 Seite 360

GOLF COURSE — PLATZ — 15/20

Site	Lage	
Maintenance	Instandhaltung	
Architect	Architekt	Michael Blesch
Type	Typ	inland
Relief	Begehbarkeit	
Water in play	Platz mit Wasser	
Exp. to wind	Wind ausgesetzt	
Trees in play	Platz mit Bäumen	

Scorecard Scorekarte	Chp. Chp.	Mens Herren	Ladies Damen
Length Länge	6033	6033	5183
Par	72	72	72
Slope system	—	130	128

Advised golfing ability Empfohlene Spielstärke — 0 12 24 36
Hcp required Min. Handicap — no

CLUB HOUSE & AMENITIES — KLUBHAUS UND NEBENGEBÄUDE — 2/10

Pro shop Pro shop
Driving range Übungsplatz
Sheltered überdacht 19 mats - On grass auf Rasen yes
Putting-green Putting-grün yes - Pitching-green Pitching-grün yes

HOTEL FACILITIES — HOTEL BESCHREIBUNG — 6/10

HOTELS HOTELS

Hotel Zum Weissen Ross - 10 rooms, D € 80 - Winsen 4 km
Tel (49) 04171 - 658 50, Fax (49) 04171 - 6585

Romantik Hotel Josthof - Salzhausen 25 km
16 rooms, D € 100
Tel (49) 04172 - 90 980, Fax (49) 04172 - 6225

Residenz - 30 rooms, D € 125 - Lüneburg 20 km
Tel (49) 04131 -759 910, Fax (49) 04131 -759 9175

Sellhorn - 59 rooms, D € 105 - Haustedt/Nordheide 10 km
Tel (49) 04184 - 8010, Fax (49) 04184 - 801 333

RESTAURANTS RESTAURANTS

Zum Heidkrug - Lüneburg 20 km - Tel (49) 04131 - 241 60
Kronen-Bauhaus - Lüneburg 20 km - Tel (49) 04133 - 713 200

Gut Grambek

16 | 7 | 6

Gut Grambek liegt östlich von Hamburg im Naturpark Lauenburgische See inmitten einer für Holstein typischen Landschaft. Das alte Bauernhaus wurde in das heimelige Clubhaus umfunktioniert. Der Parkland-Platz ist relativ flach mit Sandboden, der sich für Golfplätze besser eignet als für Landwirtschaft. Der 1981 eröffnete Platz ist über die Jahre gereift. Durch ständige Verbesserungen gehört er nun zu den besten Plätzen der Region. Der Platz ist kurz, aber dadurch selbst für niedrige Handicaps nicht leicht, da man den Weg durch Wälder, Bunkder, Büschen und Rough finden muss, die jeden Ball, der vom geraden Weg abkommt, verschlucken. Dies gilt selbstverständlich auch für die vielen Wasserhindernisse. Auf diesem Platz ist Präzision gefragt. Wer den Ball mit Draw spielen kann, hat deutliche Vorteile. Ein Platz, den es lohnt, zu spielen.

To the east of Hamburg, Gut Grambek golf club lies in the nature park of Lauenburgische See amidst landscapes that are typical of the Holstein countryside. The club-house actually uses the buildings of an old farmhouse. The large park's landscape is rather flat with sandy soil, which makes it better for golfing than for growing crops. Opened in 1981, the course has gradually matured by dint of constant improvement schemes and now deserves to rate amongst the region's best. It could be criticised for its lack of yardage, but this does not make it any easier to play, especially for low-handicappers, who have to pick their way through woods, bunkers, bushes and rough, that are all waiting to snap up the slightly wayward shot, not to mention the rather substantial number of water hazards. Here, accuracy is at a premium, with the ability to draw the ball an added bonus. Well worth playing.

Golf-Club Gut Grambek e.V. — 1981

Schlossstrasse 21
D - 23883 GRAMBEK

Office	Sekretariat	(49) 04542 - 841 474
Pro shop	Pro shop	(49) 04542 - 841 475
Fax	Fax	(49) 04542 - 841 476
Web	www.gcgrambek.de	
Situation	Lage	Mölln, 5 km
Annual closure	Jährliche Schliessung	no
Weekly closure	Wöchentliche Schliessung	no

Fees main season Preisliste hochsaison — 18 holes

	Week days Woche	We/Bank holidays We/Feiertag
Individual Individuell	€ 30	€ 45
Couple Ehepaar	€ 60	€ 90

Juniors, Students: – 50%

Caddie Caddie no — **Electric Trolley** Elektrokarren no

Buggy Elektrischer Wagen yes — **Clubs** Leihschläger yes

Credit cards Kreditkarten — VISA - Eurocard - MasterCard

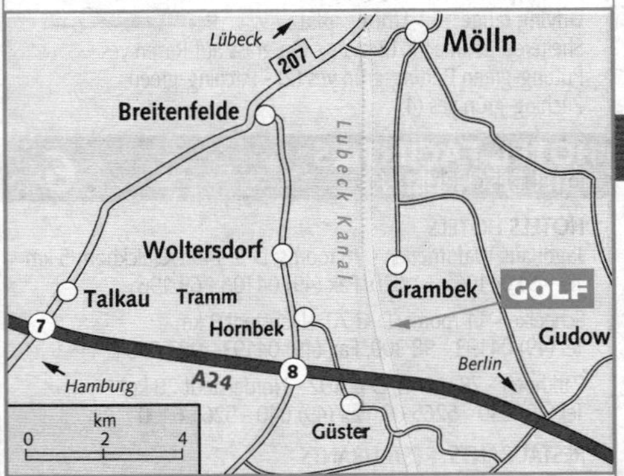

Access Zufahrt : Hamburg, E24 → Berlin. Exit 7 (Ausfahrt 7) Talkau, then B207 → Mölln. Exit Alt Mölln → Mölln. After the bridge over Elbe channel, turn right ↔ Grambek, → Golf.

Map 7 on page 361 Karte 7 Seite 361

GOLF COURSE — PLATZ — 16/20

Site	Lage	
Maintenance	Instandhaltung	
Architect	Architekt	unknown
Type	Typ	pakland
Relief	Begehbarkeit	
Water in play	Platz mit Wasser	
Exp. to wind	Wind ausgesetzt	
Trees in play	Platz mit Bäumen	

Scorecard Scorekarte	Chp. Chp.	Mens Herren	Ladies Damen
Length Länge	5877	5877	5174
Par	71	71	71
Slope system	129	129	126

Advised golfing ability Empfohlene Spielstärke — 0 12 24 36

Hcp required Min. Handicap — 36

CLUB HOUSE & AMENITIES — KLUBHAUS UND NEBENGEBÄUDE — 7/10

Pro shop Pro shop

Driving range Übungsplatz

Sheltered überdacht 3 mats - On grass auf Rasen yes - Putting-green Putting-grün yes - Pitching-green Pitching-grün yes

HOTEL FACILITIES — HOTEL BESCHREIBUNG — 6/10

HOTELS HOTELS

Schwanenhof - Mölln 7 km
30 rooms, D € 100
Tel (49) 04542 - 848 30, Fax (49) 04542 - 848 383

Quellenhof - Mölln 7 km
18 rooms, D € 85
Tel (49) 04542 - 85 420, Fax (49) 04542 - 72 26

Beim Wasserkrüger - 30 rooms, D € 68 - Mölln 7 km
Tel (49) 04542 - 70 91, Fax (49) 04542 - 18 11

RESTAURANTS RESTAURANTS

Historischer Ratskeller - Mölln 7 km - Tel (49) 04542 - 853 888

Zum Weissen Ross - Mölln - Tel (49) 04542 - 27 72

Gut Kaden *B + C*

15	7	6

Der Turnierplatz (B + C) besteht aus 9 der 18 ursprünglichen Bahnen, sowie weiteren 9 Löchern, die 1993 fertiggestellt wurden. Der schöne A-Platz eignet sich für Spieler mit höherem Handicap. Dank der vorhandenen Übungseinrichtungen (dazu gehören Indoor Driving Range und Putting Grün) zählt Gut Kaden zu den Anlagen gehobener Klasse. Der Fluss Pinnau durchquert das bei Nässe sehr gut abtrocknende Golfgelände, auf dem es sich zudem sehr angenehm läuft. Der Platz liegt ziemlich offen und ist gespickt mit vielen Wasserhindernissen (6 Löcher mit frontalem Wasser) sowie einer beträchtlichen Anzahl geschickt positionierter Bunker. Diese vielfältigen Gefahren sind jedoch gut erkennbar, so dass ein einziger Besuch genügt, den klug angelegten Spielbahnverlauf schätzen zu lernen, was allerdings nicht als Garantie für einen guten Score misszuverstehen ist. Die richtige Schlägerwahl ist hier ausschlaggebend, besonders beim Anspiel der großflächigen Grüns, die teilweise auf mehreren Stufen angelegt und sehr gut verteidigt sind. Gutes Putten ist gefragt auf diesem Platz, den man spielen sollte, wenn man in der Nähe ist.

The championship course is formed from 9 of the original 18 holes and from a further 9 holes completed in 1993. The pretty A course is more suitable for higher-handicappers. Gut Kaden as a whole is a class set-up, thanks in particular to the practice facilities (which include an indoor driving range and putting-green). Crossed by the river Pinnau, this is an estate that drains well and is pleasant to walk. The course is rather open and brings a large number of water hazards into play (6 holes feature frontal water) plus a considerable number of very well-sited bunkers. But these manifold hazards are clearly visible and a single visit is enough for a player to appreciate the intelligent design, if not to guarantee a good score. Here, the choice of club is of key importance, especially when approaching the large greens that are sometimes multi-tiered and very well-guarded.

Gut Kaden Golf und Land Club — 1986

Kadener Strasse 9
D - 25486 ALVESLOHE

Office Sekretariat (49) 04193 - 99 290
Pro shop Pro shop (49) 04193 - 91 541
Fax Fax (49) 04193 - 992 919
Web www.gutkaden.de
Situation Lage Norderstedt, 10 km
Quickborn (pop. 18 500), 5 km

Annual closure Jährliche Schliessung no
Weekly closure Wöchentliche Schliessung no

Fees main season Preisliste hochsaison 18 holes

	Week days Woche	We/Bank holidays We/Feiertag
Individual Individuell	€ 50	€ 70
Couple Ehepaar	€ 100	€ 140

– 21: – 50%

Caddie Caddie no — **Electric Trolley** Elektrokarren no
Buggy Elektrischer Wagen no — **Clubs** Leihschläger yes
Credit cards Kreditkarten no

Access Zufahrt : A7 Hamburg-Kiel. Exit (Ausfahrt) Quickborn. Left → Ellerau, Kaltenkirchen. Right → Alveslohe.
Map 7 on page 360 Karte 7 Seite 360

GOLF COURSE — PLATZ 15/20

Site Lage
Maintenance Instandhaltung
Architect Architekt Frank Pennink (A+B), Karl F. Grohs (C)
Type Typ open country
Relief Begehbarkeit
Water in play Platz mit Wasser
Exp. to wind Wind ausgesetzt
Trees in play Platz mit Bäumen

Scorecard Scorekarte	Chp. Chp.	Mens Herren	Ladies Damen
Length Länge	6543	5989	5185
Par	72	72	72
Slope system	136	128	128

Advised golfing ability Empfohlene Spielstärke 0 12 24 36
Hcp required Min. Handicap 36

CLUB HOUSE & AMENITIES — KLUBHAUS UND NEBENGEBÄUDE 7/10

Pro shop Pro shop
Driving range Übungsplatz
Sheltered überdacht 12 mats - On grass auf Rasen yes - Putting-green Putting-grün yes (2) - Pitching-green Pitching-grün yes (4)

HOTEL FACILITIES — HOTEL BESCHREIBUNG 6/10

HOTELS HOTELS

Jagdhaus Waldfrieden - 26 rooms, D € 145 - Quickborn 5 km
Tel (49) 04106 - 61 020, Fax (49) 04106 - 69 196

Scheelke - 11 rooms, D € 70 - Henstedt 3 km
Tel (49) 04193 - 98 300, Fax (49) 04193 - 983 040

Parkhotel - 78 rooms, D € 102 - Norderstedt 20 km
Tel (49) 040 - 5265 60, Fax (49) 040 - 5265 6400

RESTAURANTS RESTAURANTS

Jagdhaus Waldfrieden - Quickborn 5 km
Tel (49) 04106 - 610 020

Restaurant Scheelke - Henstedt-Ulzburg 4 km
Tel (49) 04193 - 98 300

Gut Lärchenhof

17	9	7

Man muss am riesigen Tor klingeln, damit man eingelassen werden, man muss sich auf eine saftige Rechnung im Restaurant, das einen Stern im Michelin Guide hat, einstellen und ein hohes Greenfee zahlen. Aber das Geld ist gut angelegt: Gut Lärchenhof ist einer der eindrucksvollen neuen Plätze in Deutschland. Der Platz ist ein typisches Beispiel für die Arbeit des Architekten. Wie immer bei Nicklaus findert man ein klares Layout mit sorgfältig angelegten Fairways, strategisch gut platzierten Bunkern, aber auch eine Tendenz alles zu auf kreative Art und Weise zu formen, auch wenn der Platz dann nicht mehr allzu natürlich wirkt oder sich harmonisch in die Landschaft fügt. Nicklaus macht Golf zu einem Spektakel, er entwirft Plätze auf den man den Ball mit unterschiedlichen Flugkurven ins Ziel steuern muss, wo man ein vorzügliches kurzes Spiel und ein guten Touch auf den Grüns haben muss, um einen guten Score zu erzielen. Gut Lärchenhof ist ein moderner Platz im wahrsten Sinne des Wortes, der aber trotzdem selbst für durchschnittliche Golfer gut spielbar ist.

You have to ring a bell to get in here, meet a sizeable bill in the restaurant (1 star rating in the Michelin Guide) and pay some of the most expensive green-fees in Germany. But the money is well spend in one of the most prestigious recent courses. It is a typical example of the work of Jack Nicklaus. Obviously you will discover the very strategic use of water and sandtraps, a crisp and clear design, very carefully laid-out fairways and a lot of emphasis on shaping everything on the course in an imaginative and also sometimes artificial style. Nothing is really very natural here or subtly blended into the natural surroundings. Nicklaus likes to turn golf into a spectacle, making each course a setting where you have to bend balls, possess an immaculately honed short game and a perfect putting stroke to card a score. Gut Lärchenhof is a modern course in every sense of the word, but is playable even by very average golfers.

Golf Club Gut Lärchenhof — 1997

Hahnenstrasse - Gut Lärchenhof
D - 50259 PULHEIM

Office	Sekretariat	(49) 02238 - 923 900
Pro shop	Pro shop	(49) 02238 - 923 170
Fax	Fax	(49) 02238 - 923 9010
Web	www.gutlaerchenhof.de	
Situation	Lage	Köln, 20 km
Annual closure	Jährliche Schliessung	no
Weekly closure	Wöchentliche Schliessung	no

Fees main season Preisliste hochsaison — 18 holes

	Week days Woche	We/Bank holidays We/Feiertag
Individual Individuell	€ 90	€ 130*
Couple Ehepaar	€ 180	€ 260*

* We & holidays: with members (nur in Mitgliederbegleitung)

Caddie Caddie no — **Electric Trolley** Elektrokarren yes
Buggy Elektrischer Wagen yes — **Clubs** Leihschläger yes
Credit cards Kreditkarten — VIS - Eurocard - MasterCard

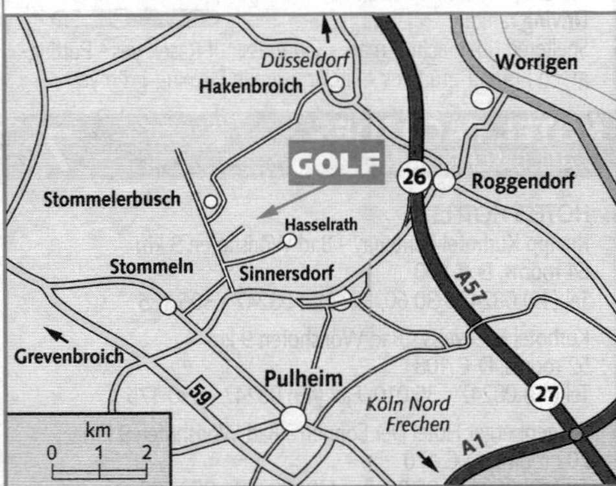

Access Zufahrt : A57, Exit (Ausf.)26 Köln-Worringen, → Simmersdorf, → Stommeln, right → Stommelerbusch. → Gut Lärchenhof
Map 3 on page 352 Karte 3 Seite 352

GOLF COURSE — PLATZ — 17/20

Site	Lage	
Maintenance	Instandhaltung	
Architect	Architekt	Jack Nicklaus
Type	Typ	open country
Relief	Begehbarkeit	
Water in play	Platz mit Wasser	
Exp. to wind	Wind ausgesetzt	
Trees in play	Platz mit Bäumen	

Scorecard Scorekarte	Chp. Chp.	Mens Herren	Ladies Damen
Length Länge	6356	6015	5052
Par	72	72	72
Slope system	138	136	135

Advised golfing ability Empfohlene Spielstärke — 0 12 24 36
Hcp required Min. Handicap — 24/28

CLUB HOUSE & AMENITIES — KLUBHAUS UND NEBENGEBÄUDE — 9/10

Pro shop Pro shop
Driving range Übungsplatz
Sheltered überdacht 9 mats - On grass auf Rasen yes - Putting-green Putting-grün yes - Pitching-green Pitching-grün yes

HOTEL FACILITIES — HOTEL BESCHREIBUNG — 7/10

HOTELS HOTELS

Ascari - 70 rooms, D € 129 - Pulheim 3 km
Tel (49) 02238 - 80 40, Fax (49) 02238 - 804 140

Halm Schützenhaus - 39 rooms, D from € 100 - Frechen 6 km
Tel (49) 02234 - 957 000, Fax (49) 02234 - 522 32

Brauhaus Gäffel - 18 rooms, D € 66 - Stommeln 3 km
Tel (49) 02238 - 2015, Fax (49) 02238 - 3844

RESTAURANTS RESTAURANTS

Restaurant Gut Lärchenhof - Tel (49) 02238 - 923 100
Ristorante Ermanno - Frechen 6 km - Tel (49) 02234 - 141 63
Früh am Dom - Köln 20 km - Tel (49) 0221 - 50 667
Börsen-Restaurant & Stube - Köln 20 km
Tel (49) 0221 - 133 021

Gut Ludwigsberg

15 | 6 | 7

Ein Golfplatz für Sportliche, dessen Clubhaus und Einrichtungen bedauerlicherweise nicht den andernorts üblichen höheren Standards entsprechen. Da die Anlage noch relativ jung ist, bleibt zu hoffen, dass sich dies mit der Zeit ändern wird. Die Lage des Platzes ist eindrucksvoll: An klaren Tagen kann man bis zu 150 km weit sehen, insbesondere Richtung Deutsche Alpenstrasse im Süden, an deren Streckenverlauf von Lindau über Garmisch-Partenkirchen nach Salzburg die verückten Schlösser Ludwigs II von Bayern einen Besuch lohnen. Architekt Rossknecht hat den weitgehend flachen Parcours mit einer enormen Vielfalt an Hindernissen versehen, wobei alle Arbeiten mit der für ihn üblichen Sorgfalt ausgeführt wurden. Die Grüns sind ausgezeichnet gestaltet, besonders hervorzuheben ist in diesem Zusammenhang das Inselgrün am 18. Loch. Obschon eine harte Nuss von den hinteren Abschlägen, ist der Platz von weiter vorne durchaus für alle Spielstärken geeignet. Zwischen dem 5. und 17. Loch ändert sich der Charakter des Platzes von Parkland hin zu einem eher amerikanischen Stil, wo "Target Golf" vom Spieler gefordert wird.

A sporting man's golf course where you might wonder why the club-house does not have higher standard facilities. Perhaps they will come in time, as the course is still young. The location is rather remarkable: on a clear day you can see for 150 km, especially toward the Deutsche Alpenstrasse to the south, the road running from Lindau to Garmisch-Partenkirchen and Salzburg, where the crazy castles of Louis II of Bavaria are well worth a visit. The course has been designed on easily walkable terrain, with the usual care associated with a designer such as Rossknecht. The greens are particularly well shaped, especially the island green on the 18th. A tough number from the back tees, the course gets a little more human the further forward you go. From the 5th to the 17th holes, you leave a park style landscape to encounter a more American style of course, where target golf is the order of the day.

Golfclub zu Gut Ludwigsberg — 1988

Augsburgerstrasse 51
D - 86842 TÜRKHEIM

Office Sekretariat (49) 08245 - 3322
Pro shop Pro shop (49) 08245 - 3934
Fax Fax (49) 08245 - 3789
Web www.golfclub-tuerkheim.de
Situation Lage München, 50 km
Augsburg (pop. 265 000), 35 km
Annual closure Jährliche Schliessung 1/12→31/3
Weekly closure Wöchentliche Schliessung no
Fees main season Preisliste hochsaison 18 holes

	Week days Woche	We/Bank holidays We/Feiertag
Individual Individuell	€ 40	€ 50
Couple Ehepaar	€ 80	€ 100

Caddie Caddie no — **Electric Trolley** Elektrokarren yes
Buggy Elektrischer Wagen yes — **Clubs** Leihschläger yes
Credit cards Kreditkarten no

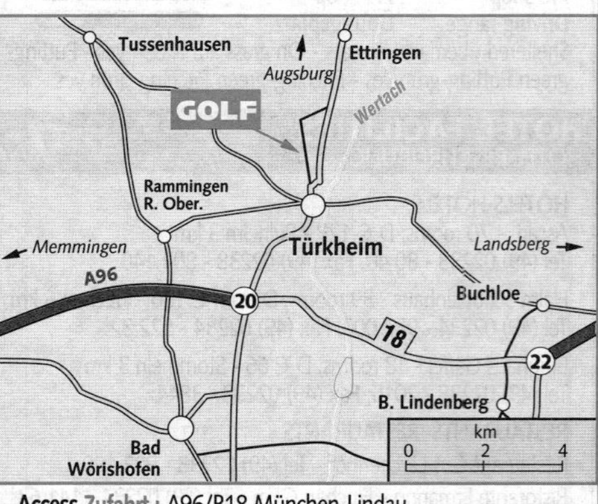

Access Zufahrt : A96/B18 München-Lindau. B18 Exit (Ausf.) Türkheim-Bad Wörishofen. → Ettringen/Schwabmünchen. → Golf
Map 2 on page 350 Karte 2 Seite 350

GOLF COURSE — PLATZ — 15/20

Site Lage
Maintenance Instandhaltung
Architect Architekt — Kurt Rossknecht
Type Typ — open country, parkland
Relief Begehbarkeit
Water in play Platz mit Wasser
Exp. to wind Wind ausgesetzt
Trees in play Platz mit Bäumen

Scorecard Scorekarte	Chp. Chp.	Mens Herren	Ladies Damen
Length Länge	6078	5820	5253
Par	72	72	72
Slope system	123	123	125

Advised golfing ability Empfohlene Spielstärke — 0 12 24 36
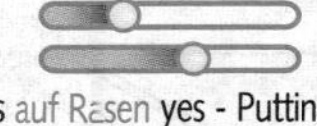
Hcp required Min. Handicap no

CLUB HOUSE & AMENITIES — KLUBHAUS UND NEBENGEBÄUDE — 6/10

Pro shop Pro shop
Driving range Übungsplatz
Sheltered überdacht 5 mats - On grass auf Rasen yes - Putting-green Putting-grün yes - Pitching-green Pitching-grün yes

HOTEL FACILITIES — HOTEL BESCHREIBUNG — 7/10

HOTELS HOTELS
Kneipp Kurhotel Fontenay - Bad Wörishofen 9 km
64 rooms, D € 190
Tel (49) 08247 - 30 60, Fax (49) 08247 - 306 185

Kurhotel Edelweiss - Bad Wörishofen 9 km
52 rooms, D € 108
Tel (49) 08247 - 35 010, Fax (49) 08247 - 350 175

Steigenberger Hotel Der Sonnen - Bad Wörishofen 9 km
202 rooms, D € 170
Tel (49) 08247 - 95 90, Fax (49) 08247 - 959 599

Gut Thailing

16	7	5

Thailing wirkt aufgrund seiner Nähe, demselben Architekten sowie dem Geländecharakter wie der zweieige Zwilling von Schloss Egmating. Nur das hier, insbesondere auf den zweiten 9 Löchern, weitaus öfter Wasser ins Spiel kommt, was diesem Platz einen ganz eigenständigen Charakter verleiht. Die Fairwaybunker sind aus genehmigungs-rechtlichen Gründen nicht mit Sand gefüllt sondern nur mit Gras, während die hervorragend geformten Grünbunker die sehr sorgfältig gestalteten Grüns (viele davon sind in mehreren Stufen angelegt) sehr wirkungsvoll verteidigen. Dies ist ein weitgehend offener Golfplatz, dessen umfangreiche Neuanpflanzungen noch einige Jahre brauchen werden, bevor sie eine wirkliche Gefahr darstellen. Man benötigt einige Runden, um mit dem leicht hügeligen Gelände vertraut zu werden. Charakter und Schwierigkeit der Löcher, von denen einige auf Spieler mit hohem Handicap ziemlich einschüchternd wirken können, lassen sich durch mehrere zur Auswahl stehende Abschlag-Boxen verändern. Dies ist eine der vielversprechendsten neuen Anlagen, die zudem bislang noch nicht überlaufen ist.

This is the false twin to Schloss Egmating through closeness, name of designer and character of terrain. Only here, there is much more water in play, emphatically so on one half of the course, thus giving it its own personality. For administrative reasons, the fairway bunkers do not contain sand but grass, but their green-side counterparts are well shaped and jealously guard the very carefully crafted putting surfaces (beware the multi-tiered greens). This is by and large an open space course with a lot of newly-planted saplings, which will need a number of years to grow into a real threat. While you need to play here several times to get to grips with a slightly hilly terrain (but never excessively so), the variety of tee-off areas also changes the character of holes, some of which are pretty intimidating for high-handicappers.

Golfclub Gut Thailing e.V. — 1994

Thailing 4
D - 85643 STEINHÖRIG

Office	Sekretariat	(49) 08094 - 9210
Pro shop	Pro shop	(49) 08094 - 9210
Fax	Fax	(49) 08094 - 9220
Web	www.thailing.de	
Situation	Lage	München, 35 km

Ebersberg, 5 km

Annual closure	Jährliche Schliessung	no
Weekly closure	Wöchentliche Schliessung	no
Fees main season	Preisliste hochsaison	18 holes

	Week days / Woche	We/Bank holidays / We/Feiertag
Individual Individuell	€ 50	€ 65
Couple Ehepaar	€ 100	€ 130

Caddie Caddie no — **Electric Trolley** Elektrokarren no
Buggy Elektrischer Wagen yes — **Clubs** Leihschläger yes
Credit cards Kreditkarten
Eurocard - Mastercard - AMEX

Access Zufahrt : München, A94 → Passau. Forstinning, B12 → Passau. Hohenlinden → Ebersberg. 5,5 km, left → Golf
Map 2 on page 351 Karte 2 Seite 351

GOLF COURSE — PLATZ — 16/20

Site	Lage	
Maintenance	Instandhaltung	
Architect	Architekt	Kurt Rossknecht
Type	Typ	open country
Relief	Begehbarkeit	
Water in play	Platz mit Wasser	
Exp. to wind	Wind ausgesetzt	
Trees in play	Platz mit Bäumen	

Scorecard / Scorekarte	Chp. / Chp.	Mens / Herren	Ladies / Damen
Length Länge	6101	5930	5086
Par	72	72	72
Slope system	131	126	123

Advised golfing ability Empfohlene Spielstärke: 0 12 24 36
Hcp required Min. Handicap 36

CLUB HOUSE & AMENITIES — KLUBHAUS UND NEBENGEBÄUDE — 7/10

Pro shop Pro shop
Driving range Übungsplatz
Sheltered überdacht 12 mats - On grass auf Rasen yes - Putting-green Putting-grün yes - Pitching-green Pitching-grün yes

HOTEL FACILITIES — HOTEL BESCHREIBUNG — 5/10

HOTELS HOTELS

Hölzerbräu - Ebersberg 5 km
48 rooms, D € 85
Tel (49) 08092 - 24 020, Fax (49) 08092-8525 8944

Klostersee - Ebersberg 5 km
24 rooms, D from € 75
Tel (49) 08092 - 82 850, Fax (49) 08092 - 828 550

Huber - Ebersberg 8 km
50 rooms, D € 80
Tel (49) 08092 - 21 026, Fax (49) 08092 - 21 442

RESTAURANTS RESTAURANTS

Hölzerbrau - Ebersberg 5 km - Tel (49) 08092 - 24 020
Klostersee - Ebersberg 5 km - Tel (49) 08092 - 82 850

Gütersloh (Westfälischer GC) 17 7 7

Der zwischen Birken und Eichen liegende Platz des Westfälische Golf Clubs in Gütersloh genießt zu recht einen beneidenswerten Ruf. Die Länge des Platzes flößt Respekt ein, ohne die Gesamtlänge eines der modernen Monster aufzuweisen. Doch die von herrlichen alten Bäumen gesäumten Fairways verlangen Präzision, dazu erschweren Wasserhindernisse (Teiche und Gräben) dem ehrgeizigen Golfer das Leben. Wer seine Schläge den vielen Doglegs anpassen kann, wer sicher einen Draw vom Abschlag spielen kann, ist im Vorteil, während der Fade beim Anspielen der grossen und gut verteidigten Grüns zu bevorzugen ist. Dieser Platz ist einer der besten Arbeiten von Bernhard von Limburger, der in Gütersloh ein abwechslungsreiches Layout entwarf, das alle Bereiche des Spiels testet, ohne übermäßig spektakulär zu wirken. Der gesamte Platz strahlt eine nüchterne Eleganz und viel Einfallsreichtum des Architekten aus. Dazu kommt noch die wunderschöne Umgebung, die Ruhe und Stille auf den Spielbahnen, die gut von einander getrennt sind.

Laid out amidst birch and oak trees, this course has gained an enviable reputation. The yardage commands respect without ever making this a modern-day monster course but the ever-present trees form a line of defence which calls for great accuracy, a feat that is not always compatible with big-hitting. What's more, water hazards tend to make life more complicated for the more ambitious golfer. There's no doubt that good benders of the ball will be in their element here; the few dog-legs provide the opportunity to show-off that well-honed draw from the tee before changing to fading the ball to pitch the huge and well-guarded greens. This is one of the great designs from Bernhard von Limburger, an excellent connoisseur of golf but no lover of the more decorative style of course. Everything here is very sober in a sort of austere elegance. Add to this the beautiful surroundings, peace and quiet and the isolation of each hole and you will understand why this is a great classic course you can't miss.

Westfälischer Golf Club Gütersloh 1969

Gütersloher Strasse 127
D - 33397 RIETBERG

Office	Sekretariat	(49) 05244 - 23 40
Pro shop	Pro shop	(49) 05244 - 18 45
Fax	Fax	(49) 05244 - 13 88
Web	www.golf-gt.de	
Situation	Lage	Gütersloh, 8 km
Annual closure	Jährliche Schliessung	no
Weekly closure	Wöchentliche Schliessung	no
Fees main season	Preisliste hochsaison	18 holes

	Week days Woche	We/Bank holidays We/Feiertag
Individual Individuell	€ 40	€ 50
Couple Ehepaar	€ 80	€ 100

– 21 & Students: – 50%

Caddie Caddie no — **Electric Trolley** Elektrokarren no
Buggy Elektrischer Wagen yes — **Clubs** Leihschläger yes
Credit cards Kreditkarten VISA - Eurocard - MasterCard

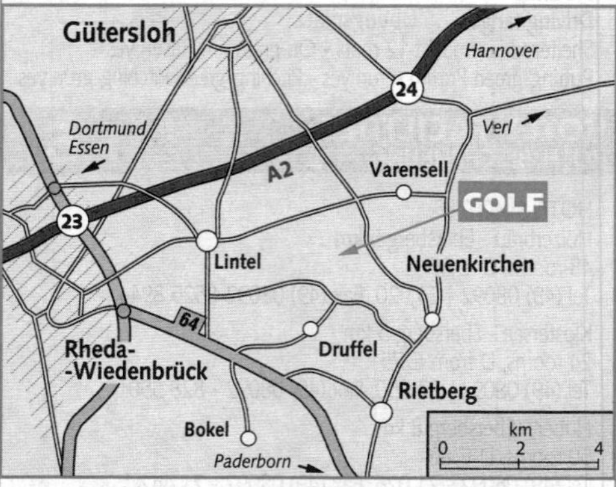

Access Zufahrt : Hannover A2 → Ruhr. Exit (Ausf.) → Gütersloh. 3rd light, take left on Bruder-Konrad-Strasse, then right → Rietberg. 3.5 km, right → Golf.
Map 5 on page 357 Karte 5 Seite 357

GOLF COURSE PLATZ 17/20

Site	Lage	
Maintenance	Instandhaltung	
Architect	Architekt	B. von Limburger
Type	Typ	parkland
Relief	Begehbarkeit	
Water in play	Platz mit Wasser	
Exp. to wind	Wind ausgesetzt	
Trees in play	Platz mit Bäumen	

Scorecard Scorekarte	Chp. Chp.	Mens Herren	Ladies Damen
Length Länge	6135	6044	5303
Par	72	72	72
Slope system	127	127	130

Advised golfing ability Empfohlene Spielstärke — 0 12 24 36
Hcp required Min. Handicap — 35

CLUB HOUSE & AMENITIES KLUBHAUS UND NEBENGEBÄUDE 7/10

Pro shop Pro shop
Driving range Übungsplatz
Sheltered überdacht 6 mats - On grass auf Rasen yes - Putting-green Putting-grün yes - Pitching-green Pitching-grün yes

HOTEL FACILITIES HOTEL BESCHREIBUNG 7/10

HOTELS HOTELS

Parkhotel Gütersloh - Gütersloh 8 km
106 rooms, D € 170 / 135 We
Tel (49) 05241 - 8770, Fax (49) 05241 - 877 400

Hotel Stadt Gütersloh - 56 rooms, D € 130 - Gütersloh 10 km
Tel (49) 05241 - 10 50, Fax (49) 05241 - 105 100

Landhotel Altdeutsche - Verl 15 km
45 rooms, D € 108
Tel (49) 05246 - 96 60, Fax (49) 05246 - 966 299

RESTAURANTS RESTAURANTS

Sinfonie - Gütersloh 8 km - Tel (49) 05241 - 864 269
Schiffchen (Hotel Stadt Güt.) - Gütersloh 8 km
Tel (49) 05241 - 10 50

Hamburg-Ahrensburg

16	8	7

Das Original-Platzdesign von Bernhard von Limburger wurde 1977 von Robert Trent Jones leicht verändert. Diese Änderungen haben den Platz für den Durchschnittsgolfer nicht schwerer gemacht, wenngleich jetzt gelegentlich Wasser zu überwinden ist. Kein Par 4 erreicht 400 Meter, einige sind sogar recht kurz, so dass praktisch alle Eisen zum Einsatz kommen. Trotz des eher flachen Geländes gibt es zwei praktisch blinde Grüns, deren Anspiel "Target Golf" erfordert. Diese Anforderung gilt im Grunde generell, da die Grüns durchgehend gut verteidigt sind. Dieser Platz, bei dem alle Schwierigkeiten deutlich sichtbar sind, ist eingebettet in eine parkartige Landschaft, in der sich eine Anzahl exotischer Bäume findet. Auffallend ist auch der Abwechslungsreichtum der Löcher, von denen praktisch jedes auf unterschiedliche Art verteidigt wird, sei es in Form von Büschen, Bäumen, Bunkern und/oder Wasserhindernissen. Man braucht einen kühlen Kopf und gute Ballkontrolle, wenn man hier sein Handicap spielen will.

The original design by Bernhard von Limburger was slightly altered in 1977 by Robert Trent Jones. This has not made it any tougher for average players, even though there is now some water to cross. No one par 4 reaches 400 metres, and some are even short, thus allowing a wide choice of irons. Despite rather flat terrain, two greens are virtually blind and call for some target play, but this is a general feature here owing to the well-guarded greens. In a parkland landscape (with a number of exotic varieties of tree), this is a course with difficulties for all to see. Also noteworthy is the variety of holes, with each having practically its own style of defence: bushes, trees, bunkers and/or water hazards. With a cool head and good ball control, you can hope to play to your handicap.

Golf Club Hamburg-Ahrensburg — 1964

Am Haidschlag 39-45
D - 22926 AHRENSBURG

Office Sekretariat (49) 04102 - 51 309
Pro shop Pro shop (49) 04102 - 57 626
Fax Fax (49) 04102 - 81 410
Web www.golfclub-ahrensburg.de
Situation Lage Hamburg, 20 km
Ahrensburg (pop. 27 000), 500 m

Annual closure Jährliche Schliessung no

Weekly closure Wöchentliche Schliessung Monday
(Montag): Restaurant closed

Fees main season Preisliste hochsaison 18 holes

	Week days Woche	We/Bank holidays We/Feiertag
Individual Individuell	€ 45	€ 50
Couple Ehepaar	€ 90	€ 100

Caddie Caddie on request — **Electric Trolley** Elektrokarren no
Buggy Elektrischer Wagen yes — **Clubs** Leihschläger on request
Credit cards Kreditkarten no

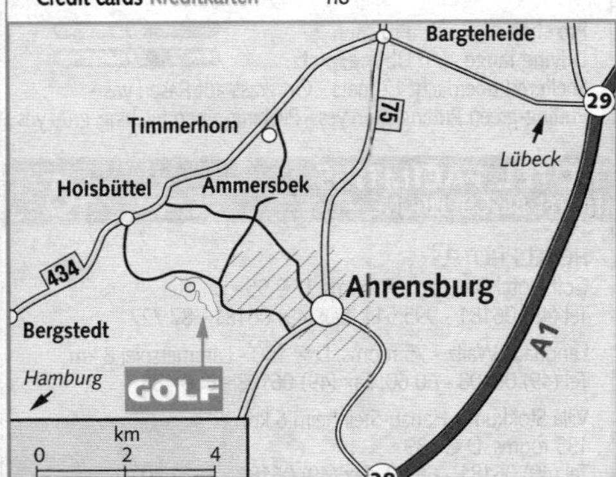

Access Zufahrt : A1 Hamburg-Lübeck, Exit (Ausfahrt) Ahrensburg. B434 → Bargteheide. → Ammersbeck. In Bunningstedt, Franz-Kruse-Strasse → Siedlung Daheim. Am Haidschlag → Golf

Map 7 on page 360 Karte 7 Seite 360

GOLF COURSE — PLATZ — 16/20

Site Lage
Maintenance Instandhaltung
Architect Architekt B. von Limburger
Type Typ parkland
Relief Begehbarkeit
Water in play Platz mit Wasser
Exp. to wind Wind ausgesetzt
Trees in play Platz mit Bäumen

Scorecard Scorekarte	Chp. Chp.	Mens Herren	Ladies Damen
Length Länge	5728	5613	5007
Par	71	71	71
Slope system	128	127	127

Advised golfing ability Empfohlene Spielstärke 0 12 24 36
Hcp required Min. Handicap 36

CLUB HOUSE & AMENITIES — KLUBHAUS UND NEBENGEBÄUDE — 8/10

Pro shop Pro shop
Driving range Übungsplatz
Sheltered überdacht 6 mats - On grass auf Rasen no, 10 mats open air - Putting-green Putting-grün yes - Pitching-green Pitching-grün yes

HOTEL FACILITIES — HOTEL BESCHREIBUNG — 7/10

HOTELS HOTELS

Park Hotel Ahrensburg - Ahrensburg 1 km
117 rooms, D € 129
Tel (49) 04102 - 23 00, Fax (49) 04102 - 230 100

Ring Hotel Ahrensburg - Ahrensburg 2 km
24 rooms, D € 100
Tel (49) 04102 - 51 560, Fax (49) 04102 - 515 656

Hafen Hamburg - 355 rooms, D € 140 - Hamburg 20 km
Tel (49) 040 - 311 130, Fax (49) 040 - 3111 3755

RESTAURANTS RESTAURANTS

Golf Club Restaurant - Tel (49) 04102 - 57 522

Le Marron (Park Hotel) - Ahrensburg 1 km
Tel (49) 04102 - 23 00

Hanau-Wilhelmsbad

16	6	6

Der Golfplatz wurde 1959 auf der ehemaligen Fasanenzuchtfarm der Familie Hesse errichtet, ganz in der Nähe von Schloss Wilhelmsbad, einem der zahlreichen Mineral- und Thermalkurorte dieser Gegend. Dieser alte Besitz verfügt über einen großzügigen alten Baumbestand. Daher rührt auch der Eindruck eines gemütlichen Spaziergangs inmitten eines großen Parks, den man während der Runde auf dem völlig ebenen Platz gewinnt, dessen 18 Loch ganz mühelos zu Gehen sind. Dank ihres anspruchsvollen Layouts war die Anlage in der Vergangenheit mehrmals Austragungsort der Nationalen Offenen Deutschen Golf-Meisterschaften. Die guten Spieler werden versuchen den Amateur-Rekord von 70 Schlägen zu brechen, während die weniger Ehrgeizigen unter uns, von den vorderen Abschlägen aus, einen großartigen Golftag verbringen können. Da die Runde von Bäumen und einer kleinen Anzahl gefährlicher Wasserhindernisse gewürzt wird, sollten sie nicht zögern, von den vorderen Abschlägen zu spielen. Dies gilt speziell an Loch 7, einem Par 5 von 558 Metern Länge.

This course was designed on the former pheasant farm of the Hesse family, close to the castle of Wilhelmsbad, one of the many spas and hydrotherapy centres found in this part of the world. The estate is lavishly lined with old trees, whence the very pleasant impression of a lovely walk in a huge park without any relief to speak of to stop you from walking the 18 holes. The layout is demanding enough for the National German Championships to have been held here several times, and while skilled players will relish the chance to attack the amateur record of 70, the less ambitious amongst us will play from the forward tees and spend a great day's golfing. The trees and a few dangerous water hazards tend to add a little spice to life, so don't shy away from playing the front tees, especially on the 7th hole, a par 5 of some 558 metres (610 yds). The course has no unfair difficulties.

Golf-Club Hanau-Wilhelmsbad e.V. 1959

Wilhelmsbader Allee 32
D - 63454 HANAU-WILHELMSBAD

Office Sekretariat (49) 06181 - 180 190
Pro shop Pro shop (49) 06181 - 81 775
Fax Fax (49) 06181 -180 1910
Web www.golfclub-hanau.de
Situation Lage Frankfurt, 20 km
Hanau (pop. 90 000), 3 km
Annual closure Jährliche Schliessung no
Weekly closure Wöchentliche Schliessung Monday
(Montag): Restaurant closed

Fees main season Preisliste hochsaison 18 holes

	Week days Woche	We/Bank holidays We/Feiertag
Individual Individuell	€ 50	€ 60
Couple Ehepaar	€ 100	€ 120

– 21 & Students: - 50%
We/holidays: with members only (nur in Mitgliederbegleitung)

Caddie Caddie no — **Electric Trolley** Elektrokarren no
Buggy Elektrischer Wagen no — **Clubs** Leihschläger yes
Credit cards Kreditkarten no

Bruchköbel
Rückingen
A66
45
Frankfurt
A66
34
36
Hanau
37
GOLF
43
Mülheim
8
A45
Lämmerspiel
Offenbach
A42
Obertshausen
km 0 2 4

Access Zufahrt : Frankfurt, A66. Exit (Ausf.) Hanau Nord. Right on B8/40 until → Wilhelmsbad. 20 m, right (Wilhelmsbader Allee)

Map 3 on page 353 Karte 3 Seite 353

GOLF COURSE — PLATZ 16/20

Site Lage
Maintenance Instandhaltung
Architect Architekt M. Kothe
Type Typ park
Relief Begehbarkeit
Water in play Platz mit Wasser
Exp. to wind Wind ausgesetzt
Trees in play Platz mit Bäumen

Scorecard Scorekarte	Chp. Chp.	Mens Herren	Ladies Damen
Length Länge	6110	5914	5175
Par	73	73	73
Slope system	133	130	132

Advised golfing ability Empfohlene Spielstärke 0 12 24 36
Hcp required Min. Handicap 32/28 (We)

CLUB HOUSE & AMENITIES — KLUBHAUS UND NEBENGEBÄUDE 6/10

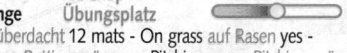

Pro shop Pro shop
Driving range Übungsplatz
Sheltered überdacht 12 mats - On grass auf Rasen yes - Putting-green Putting-grün yes - Pitching-green Pitching-grün yes

HOTEL FACILITIES — HOTEL BESCHREIBUNG 6/10

HOTELS HOTELS
Golf Hotel Da Enzo - 7 rooms, D € 95 - on site
Tel (49) 06181 - 995 511, Fax (49) 06181 - 87 722

Landhaus Waitz - 75 rooms, D € 150 - Lämmerspiel 8 km
Tel (49) 06108 - 60 60, Fax (49) 06108 - 60€ 488

Villa Stokkum - Hanau-Steinheim 6 km
135 rooms, D € 139
Tel (49) 06181 - 66 40, Fax (49) 06181 - 661 580

RESTAURANTS RESTAURANTS
Villa Stokkum - Hanau-Steinheim 6 km - Tel (49) 06181 - 66 40
Hesslers - Mülheim Dörningheim 8 km
Tel (49) 06181 - 43 030

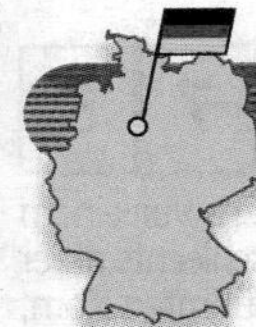

Hannover

16	7	7

Der 1923 gebaute Platz wurde später von Bernhard von Limburger umgestaltet, der seine klassische Handschrift hinterließ. Diese zeigt sich in einem klugen Platzdesign, das sich auszeichnet durch die ebenso angemessene wie geschickte Verwendung von Hindernissen, deren Platzierung gute Schläge nicht betraft. Die Lärmbelästigung durch die nahegelegene Autobahn wird von den vielen Bäumen etwas gedämpft, davon abgesehen lohnt sich der Besuch der insgesamt ausgezeichneten Anlage unbedingt. Die bereits erwähnten Bäume verlangen nach geraden Schlägen, um die engen Fairways zu treffen; vielfach ist man sogar gezwungen, einen Fade oder Draw zu spielen, um in die beste Position zu gelangen. Die ziemlich flachen, gut gestalteten Grüns werden von einer Reihe, teilweise sehr tiefer Bunker verteidigt. Die erforderliche Spielstrategie ist offensichtlich, so dass man schon auf der ersten Runde hoffen kann, einen guten Score zu erzielen. Hannover ist einer der besten Plätze der Region und abwechslungsreich genug, um auch bei mehrmaligem Spielen interessant zu bleiben.

Designed in 1923, the course was reshaped by Bernhard von Limburger, who has left his own, very classical stamp with a sensible layout and reasonable use of hazards, always well placed but not too penalising for good shots. The one regret is the closeness of the motorway, but the general excellence of the course makes it well worth visiting, and the very many trees do tend to dampen the noise somewhat. On the downside, these same trees leave the fairways rather narrow, hence the need to play straight or even flight the ball with fade and draw shots to get into the best position. The greens are well designed and relatively flat, but are protected by a host of bunkers, some of which are often very deep. Game strategy is pretty obvious to try and return a goodish card first time out, and the course is varied enough to keep it interesting. This is one of the region's best courses.

Golf-Club Hannover e.V. — 1923

Am Blauen See 120
D - 30823 GARBSEN

Office	Sekretariat	(49) 05137 - 73 068
Pro shop	Pro shop	(49) 05137 - 71 004
Fax	Fax	(49) 05137 - 75 851
Web	www.golfclub-hannover.de	
Situation	Lage	Hannover, 15 km
Annual closure	Jährliche Schliessung	1/1→31/1
Weekly closure	Wöchentliche Schliessung	Monday

(Montag): Restaurant closed

Fees main season Preisliste hochsaison	Week days Woche	We/Bank holidays We/Feiertag
18 holes		
Individual Individuell	€ 35	€ 45
Couple Ehepaar	€ 70	€ 90

– 21 & Students: – 50%

Caddie Caddie no — **Electric Trolley** Elektrokarren no
Buggy Elektrischer Wagen yes — **Clubs** Leihschläger yes
Credit cards Kreditkarten no

Access Zufahrt : Hannover, Westschnellweg. Exit (Ausf.) Herrenhausen. A2 until Rasthaus "Blauer See". 1,5 km, Golf South of A2

Map 5 on page 357 Karte 5 Seite 357

GOLF COURSE — PLATZ 16/20

Site	Lage	
Maintenance	Instandhaltung	
Architect	Architekt	B. von Limburger
Type	Typ	country, forest
Relief	Begehbarkeit	
Water in play	Platz mit Wasser	
Exp. to wind	Wind ausgesetzt	
Trees in play	Platz mit Bäumen	

Scorecard Scorekarte	Chp. Chp.	Mens Herren	Ladies Damen
Length Länge	5685	5685	5102
Par	71	71	71
Slope system	133	133	131

Advised golfing ability Empfohlene Spielstärke — 0 12 24 36
Hcp required Min. Handicap — 36

CLUB HOUSE & AMENITIES — KLUBHAUS UND NEBENGEBÄUDE 7/10

Pro shop Pro shop
Driving range Übungsplatz
Sheltered überdacht 3 mats - On grass auf Rasen June → Sept.
Putting-green Putting-grün yes - Pitching-green Pitching-grün yes

HOTEL FACILITIES — HOTEL BESCHREIBUNG 7/10

HOTELS HOTELS

Maritim Grand Hotel Hannover - Hannover 15 km
300 rooms, D € 174
Tel (49) 0511 - 36 770, Fax (49) 0511 - 325 195

Landhaus am See - Garbsen-Berenbostel 3 km
37 rooms, D € 102
Tel (49) 05131 - 468 60, Fax (49) 05131 - 468 666

Bullerdieck - 56 rooms, D € 90 - Garbsen-Frielingen 6 km
Tel (49) 05131 - 45 80, Fax (49) 05131 - 458 222

RESTAURANTS RESTAURANTS

Landhaus Ammann - Hannover 15 km
Tel (49) 0511 - 830 818
Gattopardo - Hannover 15 km - Tel (49) 0511 - 14 375

Hardenberg *Niedersachsen*

16 | 7 | 8

Im Jahre 1330 warnte das laute Grunzen eines Keilers den Grafen von Hardenberg vor einem Angriff auf seine Burg. Der Keilerkopf wurde daraufhin zum Wappen des Adelsgeschlechts derer von Hardenberg und ziert seit mehr als 300 Jahren die Schnäpse, vor allem den berühmten Korn, aus der Brennerei der Familie. Da lag es nahe dem Grün des 11. Loch, einem langen Par 3 mit einem Inselgrün, die Form eines Keilerkopfes zu geben. Der von dem Kanadier David Krause entworfene Platz ist ziemlich hügelig und die Strategie für einige Löcher wird einem erst nach einigen Runden klar, zumal blinde Abschläge und erhöhte Grüns so manche Überraschung in sich bergen. Der Platz in der ländlichen Umgebung ist mit seinen vielen Abschlägen und der ausgewogenen Verteilung aller Schwierigkeiten für alle Spielstärken ausgesprochen reizvoll. Zu dem Resort gehört ein zweiter Platz, sowie ein sehr gutes Relais & Chateaux Hotel. Zudem kann man die Brennerei-Führungen buchen und sich im Keilerkaden mit den örtlichen, hochprozentigen Produkten eindecken.

In 1330 it was the powerful roar of a wild boar that warned the Count of Hardenberg of an attack on his castle. Its head then formed the arms of the dynasty and for 300 years has featured on the liqueurs from the local distillery. More recently it inspired the shape of hole N° 11 here, a par 3 with an island green. This course, designed by Canadian David Krause, is rather hilly and the strategy for certain holes should be more obvious after several rounds, as several blind shots or approaches into elevated greens can come as a surprise. Laying this course out in a country landscape has been a marked success with considerable care taken over the balancing of difficulties and great versatility courtesy of the numerable tee-boxes. There is also a second course here plus a very good Relais & Châteaux hotel, plus products from the distillery to take home with a (good) score card after a short visit to the very lively student city of Göttingen.

Golf Resort Hardenberg — 2003

Gut Levershausern
D - 37154 NORTHEIM

Office Sekretariat (49) 05551 - 908 380
Pro shop Pro shop (49) 05551 -908 3817
Fax Fax (49) 05551 -908 3820
Web www.gchardenberg.de
Situation Lage Göttingen, 12 km
Annual closure Jährliche Schliessung no
Weekly closure Wöchentliche Schliessung Monday
(Montag), restaurant

Fees main season Preisliste hochsaison 18 holes

	Week days Woche	We/Bank holidays We/Feiertag
Individual Individuell	€ 49	€ 59
Couple Ehepaar	€ 98	€ 118

Monday (Montag): € 25 / under 27: – 50%

Caddie Caddie no — **Electric Trolley** Elektrokarren yes
Buggy Elektrischer Wagen yes — **Clubs** Leihschläger yes
Credit cards Kreditkarten VISA - Eurocard - MasterCard

Access Zufahrt : • A7 Hannover → Göttingen, Exit (Ausfahrt) Northeim-West → Northeim, B3 → Göttingen, 500 m after Südheim, turn left → Katlenburg. Golf 3 km • A7 Göttingen → Hannover, Exit (Ausfahrt) Nörten-Hardenberg. B3 → Northeim. Before Südheim, turn right → Katlenburg. Golf 3 km **Map 6 on page 358** Karte 6 Seite 358

GOLF COURSE — PLATZ — 16/20

Site Lage
Maintenance Instandhaltung
Architect Architekt — David Krause
Type Typ — inland, hilly
Relief Begehbarkeit
Water in play Platz mit Wasser
Exp. to wind Wind ausgesetzt
Trees in play Platz mit Bäumen

Scorecard Scorekarte	Chp. Chp.	Mens Herren	Ladies Damen
Length Länge	6337	6069	4994
Par	72	72	72
Slope system	132	131	126

Advised golfing ability Empfohlene Spielstärke — 0 12 24 36
Hcp required Min. Handicap 54

CLUB HOUSE & AMENITIES — KLUBHAUS UND NEBENGEBÄUDE — 7/10

Pro shop Pro shop
Driving range Übungsplatz
Sheltered überdacht 6 mats - On grass auf Rasen yes - Putting-green Putting-grün yes - Pitching-green Pitching-grün yes

HOTEL FACILITIES — HOTEL BESCHREIBUNG — 8/10

HOTELS HOTELS

Hardenberg Burghotel - Nörten Hardenberg 5 km
42 rooms, D from € 175
Tel (49) 05503 - 9810, Fax (49) 05503 - 981 666

Hardenberg Ratskeller - 7 rooms, D € 70 - Nörten H. 6 km
Tel (49) 05503 - 805 332, Fax (49) 05503 - 805 333

Hotel Gebhardts - 61 rooms, D from € 135 - Göttingen 15 km
Tel (49) 0551 - 496 80, Fax (49) 0551 - 496 8110

RESTAURANTS RESTAURANTS

Novalis (Burghotel) - Nörten H. 6 km - Tel (49) 05503 - 9810
Hardenberg KeilerSchänke - Nörten Hardenberg 6 km
Tel (49) 05503 - 9810
Gauss am Theater - Göttingen 15 km - Tel (49) 0551 - 566 16

Hechingen-Hohenzollern

14 | 6 | 6

Die Nähe zum Schloss der Hohenzollern - dessen Lage weitaus beeindruckender ist als die nicht so alten Gebäude - haben viel zum Ruf und Bekannheitsgrad dieses Golfplatzes beigetragen. Seine idyllische Lage ist für viele, in dieser Hinsicht empfängliche Golfer, ein stichhaltiger Grund, hier zu spielen. Wer seine Aufmerksamkeit von der Umgebung dem Kurs zuwendet, entdeckt einen hübschen Platz mit engen, häufig baumbestandenen Fairways und einer Anzahl gefährlicher Büsche, welche die Hauptschwierigkeit dieser Anlage darstellen. Zwar gibt es auch Fairway- und Grünbunker, jedoch sind diese nicht wirklich gefährlich genug, um gute Spieler ernsthaft daran hindern zu können, die wohlproportionierten, leicht modellierten Grüns anzuspielen. Geeignet für alle Spielklassen, fehlt es diesem Platz ein wenig an Charakter, um den besseren Spielern auch langfristig Vergnügen zu bereiten. Beim Bau der Anlage stand sicherlich im Vordergrund, dass golfende Familien hier Spass haben sollen.

Being so close to the castle of Hohenzollern (even though the site is more impressive than the not-so-old buildings) has done much for the reputation and recognition of this course. Its idyllic setting is also a sound argument for players who are sensitive to this particular aspect of golf. If you can tear your eyes away from the surroundings, you are left facing a pretty course with narrow fairways often protected by trees and, above all, some dangerous bushes, which form the main hazard. The fairway and green-side bunkers are there all right, but are not really dangerous enough to worry good players unduly and prevent them from homing in on nicely-sized and discreetly contoured greens. Accessible to players of all abilities, this course is a little too short of personality to keep the better players happy for too long. Working for the enjoyment of family golf was certainly a major consideration when designing the course.

Golf Club Hechingen-Hohenzollern — 1955

Auf dem Hagelwasen, Postfach 1124
D - 72379 HECHINGEN

Office	Sekretariat	(49) 07471 - 26 00
Pro shop	Pro shop	(49) 07471 - 62 272
Fax	Fax	(49) 07471 - 147 76
Web	www.golfclub-hechingen.de	
Situation	Lage	Tübingen, 25 km

Hechingen (pop. 16 600), 2 km

Annual closure Jährliche Schliessung 1/11→31/3

Weekly closure Wöchentliche Schliessung Monday (Montag): Restaurant closed

Fees main season Preisliste hochsaison	18 holes	
	Week days Woche	We/Bank holidays We/Feiertag
Individual Individuell	€ 35	€ 45
Couple Ehepaar	€ 70	€ 90

– 21 & Students: – 50%

Caddie Caddie no — **Electric Trolley** Elektrokarren yes
Buggy Elektrischer Wagen yes — **Clubs** Leihschläger yes
Credit cards Kreditkarten no

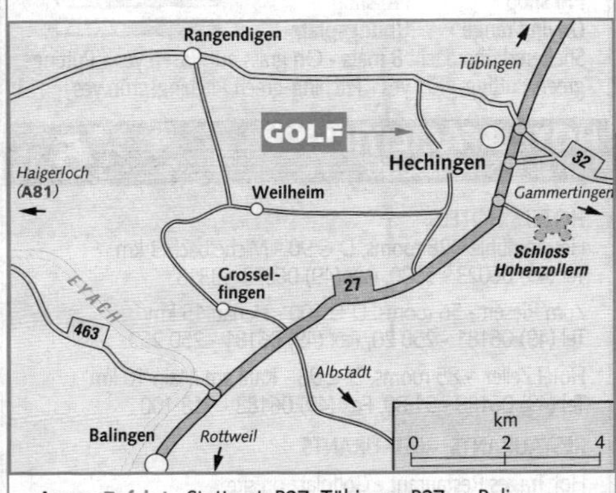

Access Zufahrt : Stuttgart, B27. Tübingen B27 → Balingen. Hechingen → Burg Hohenzollern, → Hechingen-Weilheim, → Golf

Map 1 on page 349 Karte 1 Seite 349

GOLF COURSE — PLATZ — 14/20

Site	Lage	
Maintenance	Instandhaltung	
Architect	Architekt	unknown
Type	Typ	open country, hilly
Relief	Begehbarkeit	
Water in play	Platz mit Wasser	
Exp. to wind	Wind ausgesetzt	
Trees in play	Platz mit Bäumen	

Scorecard Scorekarte	Chp. Chp.	Mens Herren	Ladies Damen
Length Länge	6164	5920	5261
Par	72	72	72
Slope system	126	124	122

Advised golfing ability Empfohlene Spielstärke — 0 12 24 36
Hcp required Min. Handicap 36

CLUB HOUSE & AMENITIES — KLUBHAUS UND NEBENGEBÄUDE — 6/10

Pro shop Pro shop
Driving range Übungsplatz
Sheltered überdacht 6 mats - On grass auf Rasen yes (April→Oct.) - Putting-green Putting-grün yes - Pitching-green Pitching-grün yes

HOTEL FACILITIES — HOTEL BESCHREIBUNG — 6/10

HOTELS HOTELS

Hotel Brielhof - 25 rooms, D € 95 - Hechingen 5 km
Tel (49) 07471 - 988 60, Fax (49) 07471 - 16 908

Café Klaiber - 28 rooms, D € 80 - Hechingen 3 km
Tel (49) 07471 - 22 57, Fax (49) 07471 - 13 918

Domizil - 79 rooms, D € 115 - Tübingen 25 km
Tel (49) 07071 - 13 90, Fax (49) 07071 - 13 9250

RESTAURANTS RESTAURANTS

Waldhorn - Tübingen-Bebenhausen 30 km
Tel (49) 07071 - 61 270

Kupferfanne - Hechingen 3 km - Tel (49) 07471 - 54 00

Rosenau - Tübingen 25 km - Tel (49) 07071 - 68 866

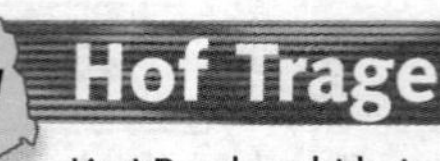

Hof Trages

15 | 7 | 5

Kurt Rossknecht hat seinen Ruf als einer der kreativsten Golf-Architekten Europas mit dieser ausgezeichneten Anlage untermauert, die sich als perfekte Ergänzung zu einem der beeindruckendsten Clubhäuser Deutschlands erweist. Der leicht hügelige Platz leugnet nicht die amerikanischen Einflüsse, welche besonders an einer Vielzahl von Wasserhindernissen deutlich werden, die den Spielern, neben einigen durch den Wald verlaufenden Spielbahnen, die grössten Probleme bereiten. Obschon die Schwierigkeiten klar erkennbar sind, muss man doch einige Runden hier spielen, um die vorhandenen strategischen Fallen genau auszumachen. Der Platz ist nicht übermässig lang, so dass Spieler aller Kategorien hier einen schönen Golftag verleben können, sofern sie sich darauf konzentrieren ihr Handicap zu spielen, und keine Schläge unnötig verschenken. Die Grüns sind von guter Qualität, wie auch die gesamte Anlage bereits gut eingewachsen ist. Am 18 Loch, einem schwierigen Par 3, muss man acht geben in Hessen zu bleiben. Wer hier sliced, findet seinen Ball wahrhaft "out of bounds" - nämlich im benachbarten Bayern.

Kurt Rossknecht has asserted his status as one of the most creative course architects in Europe, and this good layout is the perfect complement to one of Germany's most impressive club-houses. Over averagely hilly terrain, the course doesn't try to hide its American influence, and water hazards abound as an obvious danger alongside the stretches through the forest. Even though the difficulties are clearly seen, you need to play the course several times to get a clear picture of the strategic traps. It is not excessively long and players of all levels can spend a good day's golfing if they don't throw strokes away and concentrate on keeping to their handicap. The greens are good and the course has already matured nicely. At the 18th, a tough par 3, be careful to stay in Hesse – if you slice, you will find your ball out of bounds in neighbouring Bavaria!

Golfclub Hof Trages — 1994

Hofgut Trages
D - 65379 FREIGERICHT

Office	Sekretariat	(49) 06055 - 913 80
Pro shop	Pro shop	(49) 06055 - 993 818
Fax	Fax	(49) 06055 - 913 838
Web	www.hoftrages.de	
Situation	Lage	Frankfurt, 35 km
Annual closure	Jährliche Schliessung	no
Weekly closure	Wöchentliche Schliessung	no

Fees main season Preisliste hochsaison — 18 holes

	Week days Woche	We/Bank holidays We/Feiertag
Individual Individuell	€ 45	€ 55
Couple Ehepaar	€ 90	€ 110

We: with members (nur in Mitgliederbegleitung)
–21 & Students: – 50%

Caddie Caddie on request — **Electric Trolley** Elektrokarren no
Buggy Elektrischer Wagen yes — **Clubs** Leihschläger yes
Credit cards Kreditkarten
VISA - Eurocard - MasterCard - AMEX

Access Zufahrt : A66 Frankfurt → Gelnhausen. Exit (Ausf.) Erlensee → Rodenbach → Niederrodenbach, Oberrodenbach. Golf 3 km

Map 3 on page 353 Karte 3 Seite 353

GOLF COURSE — PLATZ — 15/20

Site	Lage	
Maintenance	Instandhaltung	
Architect	Architekt	Kurt Rossknecht
Type	Typ	parkland, open country
Relief	Begehbarkeit	
Water in play	Platz mit Wasser	
Exp. to wind	Wind ausgesetzt	
Trees in play	Platz mit Bäumen	

Scorecard Scorekarte	**Chp.** Chp.	**Mens** Herren	**Ladies** Damen
Length Länge	5940	5583	4868
Par	71	71	71
Slope system	121	129	127

Advised golfing ability Empfohlene Spielstärke — 0 12 24 36
Hcp required Min. Handicap — 36 (28 We)

CLUB HOUSE & AMENITIES — KLUBHAUS UND NEBENGEBÄUDE — 7/10

Pro shop Pro shop
Driving range Übungsplatz
Sheltered überdacht 8 mats - On grass auf Rasen yes - Putting-green Putting-grün yes - Pitching-green Pitching-grün yes

HOTEL FACILITIES — HOTEL BESCHREIBUNG — 5/10

HOTELS HOTELS

Herrenmühle - 28 rooms, D € 90 - Michelbach 3 km
Tel (49) 06023 - 5080, Fax (49) 06023 - 3313

Zum Riesen - 56 rooms, D € 100 - Hanau 15 km
Tel (49) 06181 - 250 20, Fax (49) 06181 - 250 259

Hotel Zeller - 85 rooms, D € 98 - Kahl am Main 10 km
Tel (49) 06188 - 91 80, Fax (49) 06188 - 918 100

RESTAURANTS RESTAURANTS

Hof Trages Restaurant - Golfplatz on site
Tel (49) 06055 - 91 380

Dörfler - Kahl am Main 15 km
Tel (49) 06188 - 910 10

Hohenpähl

15 | 7 | 6

Hohenpähl liegt in einer Parklandschaft zwischen Ammersee und Starnberger See. Trotz der hügeligen Landschaft hat sich Architekt Kurt Rosskneckt bemüht, blinde Löcher möglichst zu vermeiden, was ihm aufgrund der Topographie aber nicht immer gelang. Die gesamte Anlage strahlt viel Ruhe aus, ab und an überquert Wild die Fairways. An Löchern, an denen Bäume und Wasser bereits genug Gefahr darstellen, erschweren nicht noch zusätzlich Bunker das Spiele. Ungeübten Spielern werden im Verlauf der Runde, die eine Vielzahl von Problemen für sie bereithält, deutlich ihre Schwächen aufgezeigt. Dieser meist recht enge Platz verlangt vom Spieler sehr kontrolliertes Golf. Erwähnenswert ist auch die "Ehrlichkeit" des Layouts, abgesehen vom 4. Loch, wo ein vom Abschlag aus nicht sichtbarer Graben das Fairway in Höhe der Drive-Landezone kreuzt. Hohenpähl ist zwar anspruchsvoll, jedoch kein "Monsterplatz". Daher ist Loch 8, die schwerste Bahn des Platzes, an der Bogey ein gutes Ergebnis ist, eher die Ausnahme.

Hohenpähl is located in a parkland setting between Ammersee and Starnberger See, two of the most beautiful lakes in Bavaria. In spite of the hilly terrain architect Kurt Rossknecht tried everything to avoid blind holes, but the topography decided otherwise. The site is haven of tranquillity, as the rabbits and deer seem to sense as they bound across the fairways. There are no needless traps here: when the trees and water present an obvious danger, this is never compounded by the addition of bunkers. Inexperienced players will certainly encounter a few problems on the way, but they will also get an insight into their weaknesses. This often narrow course demands good control over your game and its honesty deserves a definite mention, except on the 4th hole where a concealed ditch crosses exactly where the drive should land. Hohenpähl is no monster and only the 8th is really tough going. It's a par 4 but the bogey will do nicely.

Golf Club Hohenpähl — 1988

D - 82396 PÄHL

Office Sekretariat (49) 08808 - 920 20
Pro shop Pro shop (49) 08808 - 1308
Fax Fax (49) 08808 - 920 222
Web www.golfclub-hohenpaehl.de
Situation Lage München, 44 km
Weilheim (pop. 18 500), 9 km

Annual closure Jährliche Schliessung 1/11→31/3
Weekly closure Wöchentliche Schliessung no

Fees main season Preisliste hochsaison 18 holes

	Week days / Woche	We/Bank holidays / We/Feiertag
Individual Individuell	€ 50	€ 65
Couple Ehepaar	€ 100	€ 130

We: with members (nur in Mitgliederbegleitung)
–21 & Students : –50%

Caddie Caddie on request
Electric Trolley Elektrokarren yes
Buggy Elektrischer Wagen no
Clubs Leihschläger yes
Credit cards Kreditkarten no

Access Zufahrt : München, A99 → Garmisch-Partenkirchen. Exit (Ausf.) Starnberg. In Starnberg, B2 → Weilheim. Km 41, turn right → Pähl → Golf
Map 2 on page 350 Karte 2 Seite 350

GOLF COURSE — PLATZ 15/20

Site Lage
Maintenance Instandhaltung
Architect Architekt Kurt Rossknecht
Type Typ forest, parkland
Relief Begehbarkeit
Water in play Platz mit Wasser
Exp. to wind Wind ausgesetzt
Trees in play Platz mit Bäumen

Scorecard / Scorekarte	Chp. / Chp.	Mens / Herren	Ladies / Damen
Length Länge	5964	5692	5055
Par	71	71	71
Slope system	130	126	125

Advised golfing ability Empfohlene Spielstärke 0 12 24 36
Hcp required Min. Handicap 36

CLUB HOUSE & AMENITIES — KLUBHAUS UND NEBENGEBÄUDE 7/10

Pro shop Pro shop
Driving range Übungsplatz
Sheltered überdacht yes - On grass auf Rasen yes - Putting-green Putting-grün yes - Pitching-green Pitching-grün yes

HOTEL FACILITIES — HOTEL BESCHREIBUNG 6/10

HOTELS HOTELS
Kaiserin Elisabeth - Feldafing 15 km
65 rooms, D € 145
Tel (49) 08157 - 930 90, Fax (49) 08157 -930 9133

Engelhof - Tutzing 4 km
12 rooms, D € 80
Tel (49) 08158 - 30 61, Fax (49) 08158 - 67 85

Ammersee Hotel - Herrsching 20 km - 40 rooms, D € 125
Tel (49) 08152 - 968 70, Fax (49) 08152 - 53 74

RESTAURANTS RESTAURANTS
Seehaus - Diessen-Riederau 12 km - Tel (49) 08807 - 7300
Forsthaus Ilkahöhe - Tutzing 12 km - Tel (49) 08158 - 8242

Hubbelrath

17 | 8 | 6

Er ist gleichzeitig eines der besten Beispiele für das Können Bernhard von Limburgers, dessen Kunst, sich das hier ziemlich hügelige Gelände zunutze zu machen, von wirklich grosser Inspiration zeugt. Aufgrund teilweise nicht immer erkennbarer Schwierigkeiten ist dies ein Platz für erfahrene Spieler. Eine gute Ballkontrolle vorausgesetzt, werden diese mit den Hindernissen besser zurechtkommen als der schwächere Golfer, auch deswegen, weil sie sich von den vielen blinden Schlägen und Grüns weniger einschüchtern lassen. Die Hindernisse sind ebenso zahlreich wie gefährlich und können den Eindruck eines tückischen Platzes vermitteln. Man braucht schon einige Runden, um den Kurs einigermassen in den Griff zu bekommen, was aber angesichts des Vergnügens hier zu spielen, leicht zu verschmerzen ist. Abgeschirmt von der Hektik des Ruhrgebiets, befindet sich der Platz in erhöhter Lage auf einem bewaldeten Hügel, von wo sich schöne Blicke auf Düsseldorf und Ratingen eröffnen. Hubbelrath offeriert in schöner Umgebung eine sportliche Herausforderung ersten Ranges.

This is one of the finest testimonies to the skill of Bernhard von Limburger, whose use of a rather hilly terrain can only be described as truly inspired. The sometimes concealed difficulties make this a layout reserved for experienced players; if they know how to control the ball, they will cope with the hazards better than the rest and, importantly, will be somewhat less intimidated by a number of blind shots and greens. The hazards are as numerous as they are truly dangerous and can give you the impression of playing a treacherous course. You certainly need to play several rounds to get to grips with it, but it is always a pleasure to come back here. Sheltered from the rumbling Ruhr region, its elevated location on a wood-covered hill provides some fine views over Düsseldorf and Ratingen. Hubbelrath is a lovely walk and an exciting challenge of the highest order.

Golf Club Hubbelrath e.V. — 1964

Bergische Landtrasse 700
D - 40629 DÜSSELDORF

Office Sekretariat (49) 02104 - 72 178
Pro shop Pro shop (49) 02104 - 72 178
Fax Fax (49) 02104 - 75 685
Web www.gc-hubbelrath.de
Situation Lage Düsseldorf, 15 km
Mettmann (pop. 40 000), 2 km
Annual closure Jährliche Schliessung no
Weekly closure Wöchentliche Schliessung no
Monday (Montag): Restaurant closed

Fees main season Preisliste hochsaison 18 holes

	Week days Woche	We/Bank holidays We/Feiertag
Individual Individuell	€ 60	€ 80*
Couple Ehepaar	€ 120	€ 160*

*We: with members (nur in Mitgliederbegleitung)

Caddie Caddie yes — **Electric Trolley** Elektrokarren yes
Buggy Elektrischer Wagen no — **Clubs** Leihschläger yes
Credit cards Kreditkarten no

Access Zufahrt : Düsseldorf, A3 → Oberhausen. Exit (Ausf.) Düsseldorf-Mettmann. B7 → Mettmann. 800 m, → Golf on the left
Map 3 on page 352 Karte 3 Seite 352

GOLF COURSE — PLATZ 17/20

Site Lage
Maintenance Instandhaltung
Architect Architekt B. von Limburger, Howard Swan
Type Typ forest, hilly
Relief Begehbarkeit
Water in play Platz mit Wasser
Exp. to wind Wind ausgesetzt
Trees in play Platz mit Bäumen

Scorecard Scorekarte	Chp. Chp.	Mens Herren	Ladies Damen
Length Länge	6260	5975	5269
Par	72	72	72
Slope system	132	135	130

Advised golfing ability Empfohlene Spielstärke 0 12 24 36
Hcp required Min. Handicap 26

CLUB HOUSE & AMENITIES — KLUBHAUS UND NEBENGEBÄUDE 8/10

Pro shop Pro shop
Driving range Übungsplatz
Sheltered überdacht 11 mats - On grass auf Rasen no, 35 mats open air - Putting-green Putting-grün yes - Pitching-green Pitching-grün yes

HOTEL FACILITIES — HOTEL BESCHREIBUNG 6/10

HOTELS HOTELS
Hansa Hotel - Mettmann 2 km
178 rooms, D from € 146
Tel (49) 02104 - 98 60, Fax (49) 02104 - 986 150

Gut Höhne - Mettmann 4 km
137 rooms, D € 150
Tel (49) 02104 - 7780, Fax (49) 02104 - 778 778

RESTAURANTS RESTAURANTS
Im Schiffchen - Düsseldorf 10 km - Tel (49) 0211 - 401 050
Zum Schlüssel - Düsseldorf 10 km - Tel (49) 0211 - 828 9550
Weinhaus Tante Anna - Düsseldorf 15 km
Tel (49) 0211 - 131 163

Iffeldorf

16	7	6

Der zwischen Garmisch-Partenkirchen und München befindliche Teil Bayerns ist gesegnet mit zahlreichen Golfplätzen, von denen viele in die wunderschöne Voralpenlandschaft zwischen offenem Hügelland und Gebirgsszenerie eingebettet sind. Die meisten dieser Plätze sind naturgemäss ziemlich hügelig und damit ein echter Fitness-Test für die meist stadtverwöhnten Golfer. Iffeldorf ist in dieser Hinsicht ganz anders. Die Anlage ist ein ausgezeichnetes Beispiel für einen Golfplatz mit einem guten, wenn auch nicht herausragendem Design, das einerseits der ganzen Familie ungetrübtes Spielvergnügen bereitet, andererseits aber auch den guten Spielern genügend interessante Herausforderungen stellt. Das Layout ist sehr "ehrlich" und man findet die unterschiedlichsten Hindernisse vor, so dass der Platz auch bei oftmaligem Spielen nicht langweilig wird. Das Sahnestück dieser qualitativ hochwertigen Anlage sind zweifellos die Grüns, die hervorragend gestaltet, von ausreichender Grösse und sorgfältig verteidigt sind.

From Garmisch-Partenkirchen to Munich, Bavaria is full of courses often set in wonderful landscapes between the open countryside and mountain scenery, doubtless a little hilly for town folk a great way to get fit again. The actual course is something else. It is a good example of an excellent golf course, well if not exceptionnally designed where all the family can play without any problem and where good players come face to face with interesting challenges. It is a very honest layout where difficulties are evenly spread around the course and varied enough to always enjoy coming back for more. The greens are of the same quality, well designed, reasonably sized and carefully protected.

Golfplatz Iffeldorf e.V. — 1990

Gut Rettenberg 3
D - 82393 IFFELDORF

Office Sekretariat (49) 08856 - 9255 55
Pro shop Pro shop (49) 08856 - 9255 20
Fax Fax (49) 08856 - 9255 59
Web www.golf-iffeldorf.de
Situation Lage München, 50 km
Garmisch-Partenkirchen (pop. 26 500), 35 km
Annual closure Jährliche Schliessung no
Weekly closure Wöchentliche Schliessung no

Fees main season Preisliste hochsaison — 18 holes

	Week days / Woche	We/Bank holidays / We/Feiertag
Individual Individuell	€ 50	€ 70
Couple Ehepaar	€ 100	€ 140

Caddie Caddie yes — **Electric Trolley** Elektrokarren yes
Buggy Elektrischer Wagen yes — **Clubs** Leihschläger yes
Credit cards Kreditkarten
VISA - Eurocard - JCB

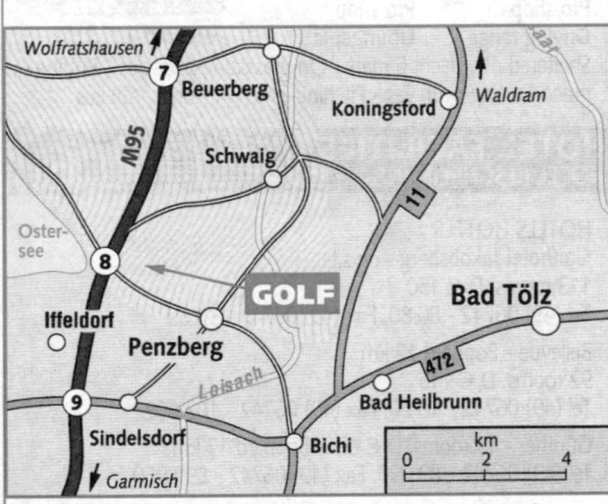

Access Zufahrt : A95 München → Garmisch. Exit (Ausf.) Iffeldorf-Penzberg. → Penzberg, Golf 200 m left towards Gut Rettenberg.
Map 2 on page 350 Karte 2 Seite 350

GOLF COURSE — PLATZ — 16/20

Site Lage
Maintenance Instandhaltung
Architect Architekt — P. Postel
Type Typ — forest, mountain
Relief Begehbarkeit
Water in play Platz mit Wasser
Exp. to wind Wind ausgesetzt
Trees in play Platz mit Bäumen

Scorecard / Scorekarte	Chp. / Chp.	Mens / Herren	Ladies / Damen
Length Länge	5803	5803	5154
Par	72	72	72
Slope system	123	123	121

Advised golfing ability Empfohlene Spielstärke — 0 12 24 36
Hcp required Min. Handicap — no

CLUB HOUSE & AMENITIES — KLUBHAUS UND NEBENGEBÄUDE — 7/10

Pro shop Pro shop
Driving range Übungsplatz
Sheltered überdacht 3 mats - On grass auf Rasen yes - Putting-green Putting-grün yes - Pitching-green Pitching-grün yes

HOTEL FACILITIES — HOTEL BESCHREIBUNG — 6/10

HOTELS HOTELS

Berggeist - Penzberg 4 km
45 rooms, D € 90
Tel (49) 08856 - 80 10, Fax (49) 08856 - 81 913

Sterff - Seeshaupt 8 km
21 rooms, D € 75
Tel (49) 08801 - 906 30, Fax (49) 08801 - 906 340

Jodquellenhof - Bad Tölz 10 km - 90 rooms, D € 180
Tel (49) 08041 - 50 90, Fax (49) 08041 - 509 555

RESTAURANTS RESTAURANTS

La Traviata - on site - Tel (49) 08856 - 9255 30
Troadstadl - Penzberg 3 km - Tel (49) 08856 - 9482

Jakobsberg

14	7	6

Ganz in der Nähe befinden sich auch die Schlösser und der Fels der Lorelei. Der Platz selbst zählt zu den sehr guten Anlagen neueren Datums. Seine grossen Vorzüge liegen in der abwechslungsreichen Gestaltung der Löcher, sowie der klaren Erkennbarkeit der anzuwendenden Spieltaktik. Lediglich der Abschlag an den Löchern 5 und 7 und das Grünanspiel an Loch 17, wo man jeweils sehr auf der Hut sein muss, bilden in dieser Hinsicht eine Ausnahme. Loch 7 ist der einzige Schwachpunkt eines ansonsten sehr ausgewogenen Layouts, bei dem die Hindernisse (Bunker und Wasser) zwar immer im Spiel sind, aber niemals allzu bedrängend wirken. Dies wiederum ermöglicht ein reibungsloses Vorankommen bei Flights, die sich aus Spielern unterschiedlichen Niveaus zusammensetzen, sofern von den entsprechenden Abschlägen gespielt wird. Diesen Golfplatz sollten Sie auf keinen Fall verpassen, zumal die umliegende Region mit ihrer landschaftlichen Schönheit, der Kultur und den Weinbergen ein enormes touristisches Potential bietet.

Located in one of the cradles of German romanticism, overlooking the most boxed-in section of the Rhine valley (the views are superb) and close to the castles and the rock of Loreley, Jakobsberg is one of the very good recent courses. The variety of holes is an asset, as is the clarity of the tactics needed to play here, with the exception of the tee-shot on the 5th and the green on the 17th, which call for particular attention. The 7th is the only weak link on a course that is well-balanced overall, and where difficulties (bunkers and water) are in play but are never too oppressive. This means that players of all levels can get along well together, as long as they are wise enough to choose the right tees. In a region which has such fascinating potential for tourists (landscapes, culture and vineyards), this course is a stop-off of considerable merit.

Golf-Club Jakobsberg — 1992

Im Tal der Loreley
D - 56154 BOPPARD

Office	Sekretariat	(49) 06742 - 808 491
Pro shop	Pro shop	(49) 06742 - 899 273
Fax	Fax	(49) 06742 - 808 493
Web	www.jakobsberg.de	
Situation	Lage	Koblenz, 10 km
Annual closure	Jährliche Schliessung	no
Weekly closure	Wöchentliche Schliessung	no

Fees main season Preisliste hochsaison — 18 holes

	Week days / Woche	We/Bank holidays / We/Feiertag
Individual Individuell	€ 45	€ 60
Couple Ehepaar	€ 90	€ 120

– 21 & Students: – 50%

Caddie Caddie no — **Electric Trolley** Elektrokarren yes
Buggy Elektrischer Wagen yes — **Clubs** Leihschläger yes
Credit cards Kreditkarten
VISA - Eurocard - MasterCard - AMEX - DC

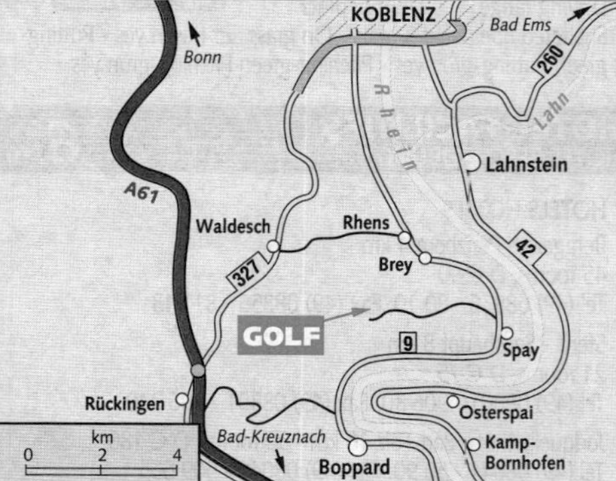

Access Zufahrt : A61 Mainz-Köln/Bonn. Exit (Ausf.) Koblenz-Waldesch, → Rhens, B9 Brey. Turn right → Golf
Map 3 on page 352 Karte 3 Seite 352

GOLF COURSE — PLATZ — 14/20

Site	Lage	
Maintenance	Instandhaltung	
Architect	Architekt	Wolfgang Jersombek
Type	Typ	open country, hilly
Relief	Begehbarkeit	
Water in play	Platz mit Wasser	
Exp. to wind	Wind ausgesetzt	
Trees in play	Platz mit Bäumen	

Scorecard Scorekarte	Chp. / Chp.	Mens / Herren	Ladies / Damen
Length Länge	6200	5950	5195
Par	72	72	72
Slope system	126	126	123

Advised golfing ability Empfohlene Spielstärke — 0 12 24 36
Hcp required Min. Handicap — no

CLUB HOUSE & AMENITIES — KLUBHAUS UND NEBENGEBÄUDE — 7/10

Pro shop Pro shop
Driving range Übungsplatz
Sheltered überdacht 5 mats - On grass auf Rasen yes - Putting-green Putting-grün yes - Pitching-green Pitching-grün yes

HOTEL FACILITIES — HOTEL BESCHREIBUNG — 6/10

HOTELS HOTELS

Golfhotel Jakobsberg - on site
113 rooms, D € 150
Tel (49) 06742 - 80 80, Fax (49) 06742 - 30 69

Bellevue - Boppard 12 km
92 rooms, D € 115
Tel (49) 06742 - 10 20, Fax (49) 06742 - 102 602

Günther - 19 rooms, D € 65 - Boppard 12 km
Tel (49) 06742 - 89 090, Fax (49) 06742 - 890 950

RESTAURANTS RESTAURANTS

Königstuhl - Rhens 3 km - Tel (49) 02628 - 2244
Stresemann - Koblenz 15 km - Tel (49) 0261 - 15 464

Jura Golf Park *Am Habsberg*

17	8	7

Unter dem Gipfel des Habsbergs mit seiner Pilgerkapelle liegt in den sanften Hügeln der Oberpfalz der Platz "Am Habsberg" des Jura Golf Clubs. Das Gelände ist nicht extrem bergig, allerdings sind einige blinde Abschläge nicht zu vermeiden. Der australische Pro Graham Marsch entwarf hier seinen ersten Platz in Europa (er arbeitet ausserdem an einem Projekt in Tschechien). Schon bei der Eröffnung im Jahre 2003 wurde der Platz viel gelobt. In der idyllischen Umgebung scheint man weit weg von der Alltagshektik. Allerdings gilt es hier, sich voll auf sein Spiel zu konzentrieren. Es gilt 98 perfekt platzierte Bunker (viele in Form eines Kleeblatts) zu vermeiden. Wasserhindernisse (Bäche und Teiche) kommen bei einem Drittel der Löcher ins Spiel. Der Platz ist von den hinteren Abschlägen sehr ausgewogen und anspruchsvoll, ohne den Golfer zu zwingen beim Abschlag einen Fade oder Draw zu spielen. Zum Club gehört ein weiterer etwas einfachere Platz "Hilzhofen", der drei Kilometer entfernt liegt. Alles in allem ein vorzüglicher Platz nahe Nürnberg.

Beneath the summit of Habsberg and the church of the pilgrims in the region of the upper Palatinate, the "Am Habsberg" course is laid out in rather rolling but never excessively hilly terrain (a number of blind shots notwithstanding). Australian golfer Graham Marsh was assigned with this, his first design in Europe (he has also a project in the Czech Republic), which was much acclaimed the moment it opened in 2003. An idyllic environment takes you far away from the fray of modern-day life but it is time here for you to concentrate on your game, as you have to contend with some very fine bunkers (in the shape of clover-leaves) and water hazards (small lakes and streams) in play on a good one-third of the course. Although well-balanced and very demanding from the tips, it does not call for a great deal of shaping of the ball. The Hilzhofen course belonging to the same club three kilometres down the road is an easier alternative. A very well-designed course, close to Nuremberg.

Jura Golf Park GmbH — 2003

Im Golfplatz 1, Unterwiesenacker
D - 92355 VELBURG

Office	Sekretariat	(49) 09182 - 931 910
Pro shop	Pro shop	(49) 09182 - 931 910
Fax	Fax	(49) 09182 -931 9111
Web	www.juragolf.de	
Situation	Lage	Nürnberg, 50 km
Annual closure	Jährliche Schliessung	1/12→28/2
Weekly closure	Wöchentliche Schliessung	
Fees main season	Preisliste hochsaison	18 holes

	Week days Woche	We/Bank holidays We/Feiertag
Individual Individuell	€ 49	€ 59
Couple Ehepaar	€ 98	€ 118

Juniors € 25-30 (We) / Students under 27: € 15-20 (We)

Caddie Caddie no — **Electric Trolley** Elektrokarren yes
Buggy Elektrischer Wagen yes — **Clubs** Leihschläger no
Credit cards Kreditkarten VISA - Eurocard

Access Zufahrt : • Nürnberg, A3 → Regensburg. Exit (Ausfahrt) Neumarkt. U45/B299 → Amberg. After Pfefferhofen, turn right → Laaber, Golf • Regensburg, A3 → Nürnberg. Exit (Ausfahrt) Velburg. → Lengenfeld. Turn right → Deusmauer. Follow signs to golf **Map 4 on page 355** Karte 4 Seite 355

GOLF COURSE — PLATZ — 17/20

Site	Lage	
Maintenance	Instandhaltung	
Architect	Architekt	Graham Marsh
Type	Typ	inland
Relief	Begehbarkeit	
Water in play	Platz mit Wasser	
Exp. to wind	Wind ausgesetzt	
Trees in play	Platz mit Bäumen	

Scorecard Scorekarte	Chp. Chp.	Mens Herren	Ladies Damen
Length Länge	6482	6090	5220
Par	72	72	72
Slope system	0	129	129

Advised golfing ability Empfohlene Spielstärke — 0 12 24 36
Hcp required Min. Handicap — 45 Men, 54 Ladies

CLUB HOUSE & AMENITIES — KLUBHAUS UND NEBENGEBÄUDE — 8/10

Pro shop Pro shop
Driving range Übungsplatz
Sheltered überdacht no - On grass auf Rasen yes - Putting-green Putting-grün yes - Pitching-green Pitching-grün yes

HOTEL FACILITIES — HOTEL BESCHREIBUNG — 7/10

HOTELS HOTELS

Hotel Gasthof Lehmeier - 20 rooms, D € 85 - Neumarkt 6 km
Tel (49) 09181 - 257 30, Fax (49) 09181 - 257 337

Winkler Bräustüberl - Lengenfeld 12 km
55 rooms, D € 95
Tel (49) 09182 - 170, Fax (49) 09182 - 171 10

Hotel Mehl - 23 rooms, D € 100 - Neumarkt 15 km
Tel (49) 09181 - 2920, Fax (49) 09181 - 292 110

RESTAURANTS RESTAURANTS

Jura Golf Restaurant - on site - Tel (49) 09182 - 939 531
Hotel Mehl Restaurant - Neumarkt 15 km
Tel (49) 09181 - 2920
Winkler Bräustüberl - Lengenfeld 12 km - Tel (49) 09182 - 170

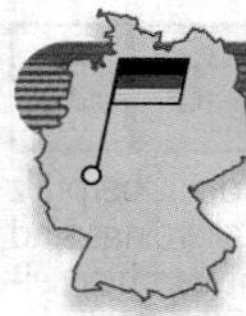

Köln (Refrath)

17 | 6 | 7

Abgeschieden von der Aussenwelt, ist "Refrath" ein typischer Vertreter eines im traditionellen Stil erbauten Golfplatzes, bei dem der Waldcharakter dominiert, ohne dass dabei der Eindruck von Weitläufigkeit verloren geht. Longhittern, die sich hier etwas beengt fühlen können, mag er ein wenig kurz erscheinen. Für Normalsterbliche hingegen ist er lang genug, nicht zuletzt weil der Weg zum Grün oft blockiert ist, wenn man die zahlreichen Doglegs nicht von der richtigen Seite anspielt. An Hindernissen gibt es neben einem kleinen Bach, der an einigen Löchern ins Spiel kommt, eine grosse Anzahl geschickt platzierter, teilweise tiefer Bunker, die bei ungenauen Schlägen eine Menge Probleme bereiten können. Spieler, die den Ball gerade schlagen, können zahlreiche Grüns auch mit der Variante "bump and run" anspielen, wenngleich grosses Können erforderlich ist, den Ball auf diese Weise nahe der Fahne zu platzieren. Immer makellos gepflegt, zeichnet sich das klare und ehrliche Layout von Köln besonders durch die abwechslungsreiche Gestaltung seiner Löcher - egal ob Par 5, Par 4 oder Par 3 - aus.

Withdrawn from the outside world, "Refrath" stands for the pure tradition of forest golf courses, without forasmuch being too narrow. It may certainly look a little short for the long-hitters (but some works are in progress), but it is long enough for the common mortal, who will see his or her path to the green irritatingly blocked if they take the dog-legs on the wrong side. Hazard-wise, there is just a little stream that comes into play on a few holes, but the very many bunkers, well located and sometimes very deep, will cause a lot of problems to wayward hitters. The straighter hitters can often bump and run their ball onto the greens, but getting close to the pin needs a lot of skill. Clear, honest and well upkept, Köln stands out for the diversity of its holes, whether playing the par 5s, the par 4s or the three par 3s, all within a remarkable unity of style.

Golf- und Land Club Köln — 1906

Golfplatz 2, Bensberg-Refrath
D - 51429 BERGISCH-GLADBACH

Office	Sekretariat	(49) 02204 - 927 60
Pro shop	Pro shop	(49) 02204 - 23 471
Fax	Fax	(49) 02204 - 927 615
Web	www.glckoeln.de	
Situation	Lage	Köln, 20 km
Annual closure	Jährliche Schliessung	no
Weekly closure	Wöchentliche Schliessung	Monday

(Montag): Restaurant closed

Fees main season Preisliste hochsaison	18 holes	
	Week days Woche	**We/Bank holidays** We/Feiertag
Individual Individuell	€ 65	€ 65*
Couple Ehepaar	€ 130	€ 130*

*We: with members only (nur in Mitgliederbegleitung)
– 18 & Students € 35

Caddie Caddie no — **Electric Trolley** Elektrokarren yes
Buggy Elektrischer Wagen no — **Clubs** Leihschläger yes
Credit cards Kreditkarten no

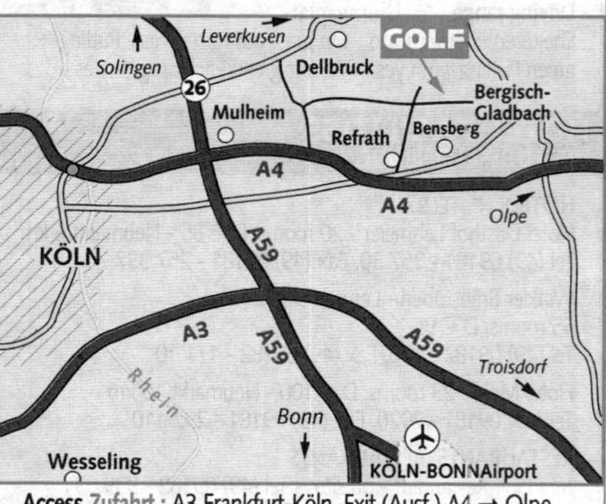

Access Zufahrt : A3 Frankfurt-Köln. Exit (Ausf.) A4 → Olpe. Exit Bergisch-Gladbach-Refrath. B55, 1.5 km. → Bensberg. Dolmanstrasse. Turn right in Altrefratherstr.
Map 3 on page 352 Karte 3 Seite 352

GOLF COURSE — PLATZ — 17/20

Site	Lage	
Maintenance	Instandhaltung	
Architect	Architekt	B. von Limburger
Type	Typ	forest
Relief	Begehbarkeit	
Water in play	Platz mit Wasser	
Exp. to wind	Wind ausgesetzt	
Trees in play	Platz mit Bäumen	

Scorecard Scorekarte	**Chp.** Chp.	**Mens** Herren	**Ladies** Damen
Length Länge	6199	5980	5286
Par	72	72	72
Slope system	137	134	136

Advised golfing ability Empfohlene Spielstärke — 0 12 24 36
Hcp required Min. Handicap — 35

CLUB HOUSE & AMENITIES — KLUBHAUS UND NEBENGEBÄUDE — 6/10

Pro shop Pro shop
Driving range Übungsplatz
Sheltered überdacht 6 mats - On grass auf Rasen yes - Putting-green Putting-grün yes - Pitching-green Pitching-grün yes

HOTEL FACILITIES — HOTEL BESCHREIBUNG — 7/10

HOTELS HOTELS

Waldhotel Mangold - 22 rooms, D € 155 - Bensberg 3 km
Tel (49) 02204 - 95 550, Fax (49) 02204 - 955 560

Gronauer Tannenhof - 32 rooms, D € 120 - Gronau 3 km
Tel (49) 02202 - 941 40, Fax (49) 02202 - 941 444

Schlosshotel Lerbach - 58 rooms, D € 227 - Bergisch-Gladbach
Tel (49) 02202 - 20 40, Fax (49) 02202 - 204 940

RESTAURANTS RESTAURANTS

Restaurant Dieter Müller - Bergisch-Gladbach 3 km
Tel (49) 02202 - 2040

Das Kleine Stapelhäuschen - Köln 20 km
Tel (49) 0221 - 257 7862

Hanse Stube - Köln 20 km - Tel (49) 0221 - 27 01

Krefelder

17 | 7 | 7

Der Platz ist somit typisch für eine Zeit, in der den Architekten weder die technischen noch die finanziellen Mittel zur Verfügung standen, das Gelände grundlegend zu verändern. So folgen die Spielbahnen den kleinen, natürlichen Unebenheiten des Geländes und führen durch teilweise sehr enge, baumgesäumte Fairwayschluchten, was den Spielern präzise Schläge abverlangt. Bei den zehn als Dogleg verlaufenden Bahnen erweist sich eine Draw vom Abschlag als sehr hilfreich. Strategische Überlegungen erfordert in erster Linie das Anspiel der Grüns, die mittelgross, leicht gewellt und halbwegs gut verteidigt sind. "Bump and run" Schläge empfehlen sich nur während der Sommermonate, wenn der Boden hart und trocken ist, ansonsten muss man versuchen die Grüns mit hohen Pitch- und Lobschlägen anzugreifen. Putten ist in den seltensten Fällen eine Formsache, doch wird einem dieser Platz in der Hinsicht wenig Ungemach bereiten. Wasser ist kaum im Spiel, so erkennt man schnell, dass dies die Art von Platz ist, an dem Schläge vorwiegend durch unpräzises Spiel eingebüsst werden.

Built more than 60 years ago, this is a "senior" course that is typical of an age when designers did not have the financial resources to change the lie of the land. The course hugs the lightly rolling natural contours and winds its way (sometimes very tightly) through trees, which call for some straight hitting. A draw off the tee will come in handy as well to cope with the ten dog-legs. The basic strategy lies before you reach the greens, since these are mid-sized, moderately contoured and averagely well-guarded but no more. Bump and run shots are recommended only in summer, when the ground is dry enough, otherwise this is a place for pitchers and lobbers. Actual putting is hardly a formality, but there are few nasty surprises in store. As water is only rarely in play, you will soon realize that this is the kind of course where you insidiously drop strokes through lack of accuracy.

Krefelder Golf Club e.V. — 1930

Eltweg 2
D - 47748 KREFELD-LINN

Office	Sekretariat	(49) 02151 - 570 073
Pro shop	Pro shop	(49) 02151 - 520 128
Fax	Fax	(49) 02151 -579 9011
Web	www.krefelder-gc.de	
Situation	Lage	Krefeld, 6 km
Annual closure	Jährliche Schliessung	no
Weekly closure	Wöchentliche Schliessung	Monday

(Montag): Restaurant closed

Fees main season Preisliste hochsaison	18 holes	
	Week days Woche	**We/Bank holidays** We/Feiertag
Individual Individuell	€ 45	€ 55*
Couple Ehepaar	€ 90	€ 110*

*We: with members (nur in Mitgliederbegleitung)
– 21 & Students: – 50%

Caddie Caddie no — **Electric Trolley** Elektrokarren no
Buggy Elektrischer Wagen yes — **Clubs** Leihschläger yes
Credit cards Kreditkarten no

Access Zufahrt : A57 Köln-Moers. Exit (Ausf.) Krefeld-Oppum. First traffic lights turn right, next ones, right again → Autobahnbrücke. → Golf
Map 3 on page 352 Karte 3 Seite 352

GOLF COURSE — PLATZ — 17/20

Site	Lage	
Maintenance	Instandhaltung	
Architect	Architekt	B. von Limburger
Type	Typ	forest
Relief	Begehbarkeit	
Water in play	Platz mit Wasser	
Exp. to wind	Wind ausgesetzt	
Trees in play	Platz mit Bäumen	

Scorecard Scorekarte	**Chp.** Chp.	**Mens** Herren	**Ladies** Damen
Length Länge	6082	5811	5321
Par	72	72	72
Slope system	126	122	126

Advised golfing ability Empfohlene Spielstärke — 0 12 24 36
Hcp required Min. Handicap 28

CLUB HOUSE & AMENITIES — KLUBHAUS UND NEBENGEBÄUDE — 7/10

Pro shop Pro shop
Driving range Übungsplatz
Sheltered überdacht 6 mats - On grass auf Rasen yes - Putting-green Putting-grün yes - Pitching-green Pitching-grün yes

HOTEL FACILITIES — HOTEL BESCHREIBUNG — 7/10

HOTELS HOTELS

Parkhotel Krefelder Hof - Krefeld 6 km
157 rooms, D € 145
Tel (49) 02151 - 58 40, Fax (49) 02151 - 584 900

Garden Hotel - 51 rooms, D € 112 - Krefeld 6 km
Tel (49) 02151 - 535 230, Fax (49) 02151-5352 3999

Alte Post - 33 rooms, D € 90 - Krefeld-Bockum 3 km
Tel (49) 02151 - 588 40, Fax (49) 02151 - 500 888

Dorint Novotel - 159 rooms, D € 178 - Krefeld-Traar 15 km
Tel (49) 02151 - 95 60, Fax (49) 02151 - 956 100

RESTAURANTS RESTAURANTS

Winkmannshof - Krefeld-Linn 1 km - Tel (49) 02151 - 571 466

Villa Medici - Krefeld 8 km - Tel (49) 02151 - 506 60

Lichtenau-Weickershof

15	7	6

Der Golfplatz befindet sich in unmittelbarer Nachbarschaft der Kleinstadt Ansbach, deren Ortsbild mit seiner Mischung aus mittelalterlichen und barocken Elementen noch heute an die Familie der Hohenzollern erinnert, denen die Stadt einst Ruhm und höfisches Leben verdankte. Der Platz selbst ist eingebettet in eine typisch fränkische Landschaft. Die ersten neun Löcher führen durch hügeliges Gelände, während die zweiten neun auf flachem, offenem Terrain liegen. Die Bemühungen um die Erhaltung des natürlichen Ökosystems der zum Golfgelände gehörenden Wälder und Wasserläufe haben dem Platz 1994 einen Sonderpreis für Umweltschutz-Massnahmen eingebracht. Eine respektable Länge sowie zahlreiche Hindernisse lassen den Platz eher für gute Golfer geeignet erscheinen, doch selbst denen wird es nicht leicht fallen, hier ihr Handicap zu spielen. Dies liegt zum einen an den recht eigenwilligen, aber gut erkennbaren Hindernissen, wie auch an den enorm grossen, hervorragend gestalteten und gut verteidigten Grüns.

Here, we are next door to Ansbach, a small town mingling memories of the Middle Ages and the baroque era, which owed its fame and court life to a Hohenzollern lineage. The course is located in a typical Franconia landscape, with alternating rolling hills (the front 9) and flat open land (on the way in). It cares enough for its appearance and for the balance of an ecosystem of woods and streams to have won a special award in 1994 for environmental protection. Very respectable yardage and the number of hazards make this a course more for the good golfer, who will be hard pushed to play to his or her handicap owing to the course's peculiar difficulties (well visible first time around) and the greens, which are huge, well-contoured and well-guarded. It doesn't have quite the personality to be rated amongst the best, but it does deserve a serious visit.

Golf- und Landclub Lichtenau-Weickershof e.V. — 1980

Weickershof 1
D - 91586 LICHTENAU

Office	Sekretariat	(49) 09827 - 920 40
Pro shop	Pro shop	(49) 09827 - 920 440
Fax	Fax	(49) 09827 - 920 444
Web	www.gclichtenau.de	
Situation	Lage	Nürnberg, 40 km
Annual closure	Jährliche Schliessung	30/11→28/2
Weekly closure	Wöchentliche Schliessung	Monday

(Montag): Restaurant closed

Fees main season Preisliste hochsaison	18 holes	
	Week days Woche	**We/Bank holidays** We/Feiertag
Individual Individuell	€ 35	€ 45
Couple Ehepaar	€ 70	€ 90

– 18 & Students: – 50%

Caddie Caddie on request — **Electric Trolley** Elektrokarren yes
Buggy Elektrischer Wagen yes — **Clubs** Leihschläger yes
Credit cards Kreditkarten
VISA - Eurocard - MasterCard - AMEX

Access Zufahrt : BAB A6 Nürnberg-Heilbronn. Exit (Ausf.) Lichtenau. → Golf
Map 4 on page 354 Karte 4 Seite 354

GOLF COURSE — PLATZ — 15/20

Site	Lage	
Maintenance	Instandhaltung	
Architect	Architekt	unknown
Type	Typ	parkland, country
Relief	Begehbarkeit	
Water in play	Platz mit Wasser	
Exp. to wind	Wind ausgesetzt	
Trees in play	Platz mit Bäumen	

Scorecard Scorekarte	**Chp.** Chp.	**Mens** Herren	**Ladies** Damen
Length Länge	6116	6115	5153
Par	72	72	72
Slope system	126	126	124

Advised golfing ability Empfohlene Spielstärke — 0 12 24 36
Hcp required Min. Handicap — 35

CLUB HOUSE & AMENITIES — KLUBHAUS UND NEBENGEBÄUDE — 7/10

Pro shop Pro shop
Driving range Übungsplatz
Sheltered überdacht 6 mats - On grass auf Rasen yes - Putting-green Putting-grün yes - Pitching-green Pitching-grün yes

HOTEL FACILITIES — HOTEL BESCHREIBUNG — 6/10

HOTELS HOTELS
Golfhotel - 7 rooms, D € 52 - on site
Tel (49) 09827 - 920 424

Am Drechselgarten - 51 rooms, D € 128 - Ansbach 15 km
Tel (49) 0981 - 89 020, Fax (49) 0981 - 8902 605

Gasthof Sonne - 37 rooms, D € 68 - Neuendettelsau 10 km
Tel (49) 09874 - 50 80, Fax (49) 09874 - 508 18

RESTAURANTS RESTAURANTS
Landgasthof Kaesser - Brodswinden 7 km
Tel (49) 0981 - 970 180
Gasthaus Kronacher - Ansbach 15 km
Tel (49) 0981 - 970 180

Lindau-Bad Schachen

15	7	8

Der Golfplatz wurde rund um das Schloss Schönbühl angelegt, und verfügt über ein modernes, sehr komfortables Clubhaus mit einem hervorragenden Restaurant. Die Lage selbst ist beeindruckend, bietet sie doch schöne Ausblicke über den tiefer gelegenen Bodensee (mit der Insel Mainau) und auf die nahen Alpengipfel. In dieser Region grenzen drei Länder aneinander - Deutschland, Österreich und die Schweiz. Daher rührt die Vielfalt der touristischen Attraktionen, über die man beinahe den Golfsport vergessen könnte. Dies wäre jedoch schade, denn obwohl der Platz weder in spieltechnischer noch ästhetischer Hinsicht Herausragendes bietet, zählt er doch zum besseren Durchschnitt. Mittelklasse-Spielern, deren Streben einem gemütlichen Golftag gilt, bereitet der Platz keine grossen Schwierigkeiten. Aus demselben Grund werden ihn bessere Spieler nicht sonderlich aufregend finden. Letzteren sei empfohlen, sich auf der Runde um die schwächeren Golfer in der Familie zu kümmern, ohne Gefahr zu laufen, sich dadurch den eigenen Score zu ruinieren.

This course is laid out around the castle of Schönbühl, with a modern and comfortable club-house which includes a very good restaurant. The site itself is quite remarkable, with some superb views over the Bodensee (with the Mainau Island down below) and the peaks of the Alps. This region lies at the cross-roads between three countries – Germany, Austria and Switzerland – so there is much for tourists to see and do, perhaps almost enough to coax you off the golf-course. That would be a shame, because although not an exceptional layout in terms of golfing or style, this course rates well above average. It should hardly pose too many problems for average players whose first desire is to spend a relaxing day, but by the same token it will hardly excite the more proficient golfers. They can make up for it by helping the lesser golfers in the family without too much risk of spoiling their own card.

Golf-Club Lindau-Bad Schachen e.V. 1954

Am Schönbühl 5
D - 88131 LINDAU

Office	Sekretariat	(49) 08382 - 961 70
Pro shop	Pro shop	(49) 08382 - 947 152
Fax	Fax	(49) 08382 - 961 750
Web		www.gc-lindau-bad-schachen.de
Situation	Lage	Lindau, 1.5 km
Annual closure	Jährliche Schliessung	no
Weekly closure	Wöchentliche Schliessung	Monday

(Montag): Restaurant closed

Fees main season Preisliste hochsaison	18 holes	
	Week days Woche	**We/Bank holidays** We/Feiertag
Individual Individuell	€ 45	€ 55
Couple Ehepaar	€ 90	€ 110

– 21 / Students: – 50%

Caddie Caddie no — **Electric Trolley** Elektrokarren yes
Buggy Elektrischer Wagen no — **Clubs** Leihschläger yes
Credit cards Kreditkarten no

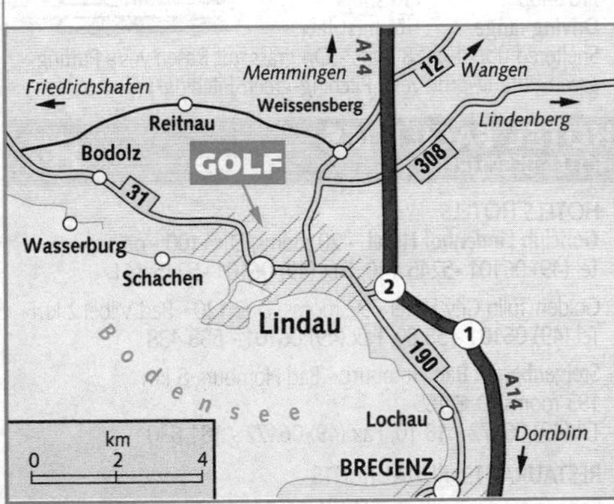

Access Zufahrt : A96 München-Lindau. Exit (Ausf.) Sigmarszell. 3 km → Golf
Map 1 on page 349 Karte 1 Seite 349

GOLF COURSE — PLATZ 15/20

Site	Lage	
Maintenance	Instandhaltung	
Architect	Architekt	unknown
Type	Typ	parkland
Relief	Begehbarkeit	
Water in play	Platz mit Wasser	
Exp. to wind	Wind ausgesetzt	
Trees in play	Platz mit Bäumen	

Scorecard Scorekarte	Chp. Chp.	Mens Herren	Ladies Damen
Length Länge	5776	5591	4803
Par	71	71	71
Slope system	122	116	118

Advised golfing ability Empfohlene Spielstärke — 0 12 24 36
Hcp required Min. Handicap 36

CLUB HOUSE & AMENITIES — KLUBHAUS UND NEBENGEBÄUDE 7/10

Pro shop Pro shop
Driving range Übungsplatz
Sheltered überdacht 4 mats - On grass auf Rasen no - Putting-green Putting-grün yes - Pitching-green Pitching-grün yes

HOTEL FACILITIES — HOTEL BESCHREIBUNG 8/10

HOTELS HOTELS

Villino - 17 rooms, D € 160 - Lindau-Hoyren 1 km
Tel (49) 08382 - 934 50, Fax (49) 08382 - 934 512

Bad Schachen - 129 rooms, D € 180 - Lindau-Bad Schachen 1 km
Tel (49) 08382 - 29 80, Fax (49) 08382 - 25 390

Bayerischer Hof - 97 rooms, D € 180 - Lindau-Insel 2 km
Tel (49) 08382 - 91 50, Fax (49) 08382 - 915 591

RESTAURANTS RESTAURANTS

Hoyerberg Schlössle - Lindau 1 km - Tel (49) 08382 - 25 295
Villino - Lindau-Hoyren 1 km - Tel (49) 08382 - 934 50
Schachener Hof - Lindau-Bad Schachen 1 km
Tel (49) 08382 - 31 16

Lindenhof

14 | 8 | 8

Dieser 1994 eröffnete Platz nahe Frankfurt und des Taunus Mittelgebirges mit herrlichen Wäldern und Mineralwasser-Quellen. Der berühmte Kurort Bad Homburg, die Sommerresidence der preußischen Könige, liegt nur wenige Kilometer entfernt. Bad Vilbel, ebenfalls ein Kurort, ist vor allem durch seine Mineralwasserquellen berühmt. Der Platz liegt im Tal des Nidda und ist flach. Exzellente Drainage macht diesen Platz das ganze Jahr gut bespielbar, zumal das Greenkeeper-Team zahlreicher ist als der deutsche Durchschnitt. Dies ist kein herausragender Platz, aber ein guter, auf dem Golfer aller Spielstärken Spaß haben, obwohl etliche Wasserhindernisse an den Nerven weniger erfahrener Golfer zehren können. Die Schwierigkeiten sind gut über den Platz verteilt. Die ersten Löcher sind relativ leicht, ideal um Selbstvertrauen für den Rest der Runde aufzubauen. Die einzelnen Spielbahnen liegen relativ nah beieinander, trotzdem ist dies ein Platz, den man spielen sollte, wenn man in der Nähe ist.

This course was opened in 1994 close to Frankfurt and the Taunus, a region of low mountains, superb forests and famous spa town of Bad Homburg, the summer residence of the kings of Prussia, and Bad Vilbel, a dainty little spa town with mineral water springs. The site lies prettily in the Nidda valley and is perfectly flat. Excellent drainage makes this a playable course all year round and maintenance is much aided by a larger team of green-keepers than is usual in Germany. At least here they have understood that this is the price to pay for a quality course. This is certainly not a great course, but a good one all the same where all golfers can have fun together, even though some of the water hazards may unnerve the less experienced player. Trouble is well spread around the course, which starts off easily enough to instil early confidence. A little more space to give golfers more elbow room would probably not go amiss, but Lindenhof is still well worth a visit when in the region.

Bad Vilbeler Golfclub Lindenhof e.V. 1994

Lindenhof
D - 61118 BAD VILBEL-DORTELWEIL

Office	Sekretariat	(49) 06101 -5245 200
Pro shop	Pro shop	(49) 06101 -5245 220
Fax	Fax	(49) 06101 -5245 202
Web	www.bvgc.de	
Situation	Lage	Frankfurt, 12 km
Annual closure	Jährliche Schliessung	no
Weekly closure	Wöchentliche Schliessung	Monday

(Montag)

416

Fees main season Preisliste hochsaison 18 holes

	Week days Woche	We/Bank holidays We/Feiertag
Individual Individuell	€ 65	€ 75
Couple Ehepaar	€ 130	€ 150

Caddie Caddie no **Electric Trolley** Elektrokarren no

Buggy Elektrischer Wagen no **Clubs** Leihschläger yes

Credit cards Kreditkarten
VISA - Eurocard - MasterCard - AMEX

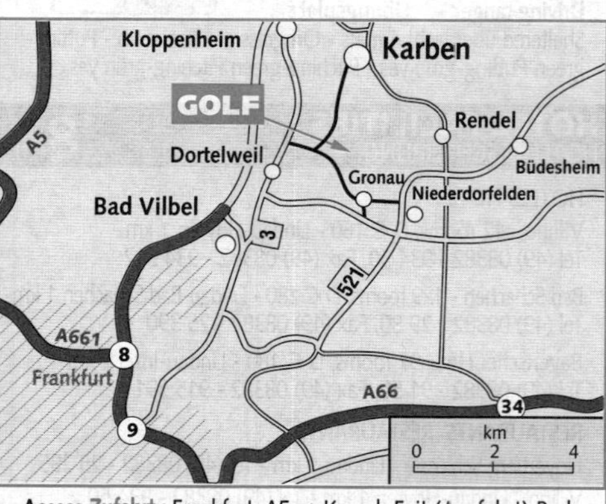

Access Zufahrt : Frankfurt, A5 → Kassel. Exit (Ausfahrt) Bad Homburg/Bad Vilbel, then A661/B3A → Bad Vilbel . Exit Bad Vilbel, then B3 → Friedberg. In Dortelweil, → Golf.
Map 3 on page 353 Karte 3 Seite 353

GOLF COURSE PLATZ 14/20

Site	Lage	
Maintenance	Instandhaltung	
Architect	Architekt	W. Siegmann
Type	Typ	open country
Relief	Begehbarkeit	
Water in play	Platz mit Wasser	
Exp. to wind	Wind ausgesetzt	
Trees in play	Platz mit Bäumen	

Scorecard Scorekarte	Chp. Chp.	Mens Herren	Ladies Damen
Length Länge	5974	5762	5036
Par	72	72	72
Slope system	126	120	117

Advised golfing ability Empfohlene Spielstärke 0 12 24 36

Hcp required Min. Handicap 36 (Week ends)

CLUB HOUSE & AMENITIES KLUBHAUS UND NEBENGEBÄUDE 8/10

Pro shop Pro shop
Driving range Übungsplatz
Sheltered überdacht 8 mats - On grass auf Rasen yes - Putting-green Putting-grün yes - Pitching-green Pitching-grün no

HOTEL FACILITIES HOTEL BESCHREIBUNG 8/10

HOTELS HOTELS

Golfclub Lindenhof Hotel - 20 rooms, D € 100 - on site
Tel (49) 06101 -5245 140, Fax (49) 06101 -5245 141

Golden Tulip City Hotel - 92 rooms, D € 120 - Bad Vilbel 2 km
Tel (49) 06101 - 58 80, Fax (49) 06101 - 588 488

Steigenberger Bad Homburg - Bad Homburg 8 km
183 rooms, D € 185
Tel (49) 06172 - 18 10, Fax (49) 06172 - 181 630

RESTAURANTS RESTAURANTS

Sängers Restaurant - Bad Homburg 8 km
Tel (49) 06101 - 928 839

Toscana (City Hotel) - Bad Vilbel 2 km - Tel (49) 06101 - 58 80

Casa Rosa - Bad Homburg 8 km - Tel (49) 06172) 917 399

Lübeck-Travemünder

17	8	8

Der Strand von Lübeck liegt in Travemünde, einem Seebad mit einem Kasino und einem Golfplatz. Da viele Löcher nahe an der Ostsee entlang führen, genießt man während der Runde herrliche Ausblicke. Trotzdem wirkt der Platz mit den vielen alten, prächtigen Bäumen eher wie ein Park. Das vollständig renovierte Clubhaus steht unter Denkmalsschutz. Seit der Eröffnung der ersten neun Löcher im Jahre 1921 sind die 18 Löcher immer wieder überarbeitet und verändert worden. Am 23. Juni 2001 eröffnete der Club weitere neun Löcher, die von Karl Grohs entworfen wurden. Die 3x9 Löcher (weiss, blau, rot) können beliebig kombiniert werden. Die 18 Löcher der weiß-blauen Kombination gelten als einer der schwierigsten Plätze in Deutschland. Der Club nahm außerdem eine neue Driving Range in Betrieb. Beim Bälle schlagen genießt man den Blick auf die Ostsee, eine schönere Aussicht bietet wohl keine andere Übungswiese in Deutschland. Da das Gelände sehr flach ist, ist die Spielstrategie offensichtlich. Dennoch wird man erst nach mehreren Runde die Feinheiten des Platzes kennen.

The beach of Lübeck is Travemünde, a seaside resort with casino and golf course. With many of the holes close to the Baltic sea, the course offers some great views, but the magnificent trees make this look more like a park, with a club-house listed as an historical monument. The club has opened a third nine hole loop designed by Karl Grohs. The three nines (white, blue and red) can be combined as you please, the white-blue combination is rated one of the most difficult layouts in Germany. On top of the extension the club opened a new driving range where you hit balls towards the Baltic Sea - probably the range with the best view in Germany. Since the terrain is virtually flat, game strategy is pretty clear, although playing several rounds will help you to discover some of the more subtle touches. The imagination and technical thinking that went into this course make it a very pleasant golf and holidays destination for players of all abilities.

Lübeck-Travemünder Golf-Klub e.V. 1928

Kowitzberg 41
D - 23570 LÜBECK-TRAVEMÜNDE

Office	Sekretariat	(49) 04502 - 74 018
Pro shop	Pro shop	(49) 04502 - 73 975
Fax	Fax	(49) 04502 - 72 184
Web	www.ltgk.de	
Situation	Lage	Lübeck, 19 km
Annual closure	Jährliche Schliessung	no
Weekly closure	Wöchentliche Schliessung	no

Fees main season Preisliste hochsaison 18 holes

	Week days Woche	We/Bank holidays We/Feiertag
Individual Individuell	€ 40	€ 50
Couple Ehepaar	€ 80	€ 100

– 21 / Students: – 50%

Caddie Caddie no **Electric Trolley** Elektrokarren no

Buggy Elektrischer Wagen yes (Seniors) **Clubs** Leihschläger yes

Credit cards Kreditkarten
VISA - Eurocard - MasterCard - AMEX - DC

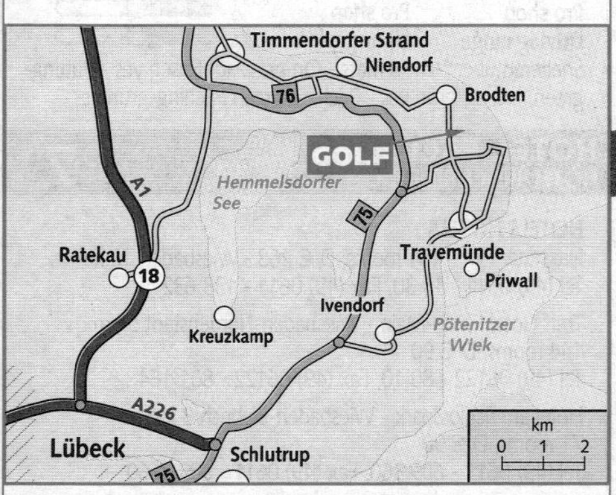

Access Zufahrt : Hamburg A1 → Travemünde. B75 → Travemünde, → Strand/Brodner Ufte, 100 m Kowizberg Str.

Map 7 on page 361 Karte 7 Seite 361

GOLF COURSE
PLATZ **17**/20

Site	Lage	
Maintenance	Instandhaltung	
Architect	Architekt	Unknown, Karl Grohs
Type	Typ	seaside course, parkland
Relief	Begehbarkeit	
Water in play	Platz mit Wasser	
Exp. to wind	Wind ausgesetzt	
Trees in play	Platz mit Bäumen	

Scorecard Scorekarte	Chp. Chp.	Mens Herren	Ladies Damen
Length Länge	6088	6088	5293
Par	72	72	72
Slope system	130	130	133

Advised golfing ability Empfohlene Spielstärke 0 12 24 36

Hcp required Min. Handicap 36

CLUB HOUSE & AMENITIES
KLUBHAUS UND NEBENGEBÄUDE **8**/10

Pro shop Pro shop
Driving range Übungsplatz
Sheltered überdacht 2 bays - On grass auf Rasen yes - Putting-green Putting-grün yes - Pitching-green Pitching-grün yes

HOTEL FACILITIES
HOTEL BESCHREIBUNG **8**/10

HOTELS HOTELS

Vier Jahreszeiten Casino - Travemünde 2 km
78 rooms, D € 180
Tel (49) 04502 - 30 80, Fax (49) 04502 - 308 333

Landhaus Carstens - Timmendorfer Strand 10 km
33 rooms, D € 160
Tel (49) 04503 - 60 80, Fax (49) 04503 -60 860

Maritim - 250 rooms, D € 150 - Travemünde 1 km
Tel (49) 04502 - 890, Fax (49) 04502 - 892 020

RESTAURANTS RESTAURANTS

Orangerie - Timmendorfer Strand 10 km
Tel (49) 04503 - 898 850

Hermannshöhe - Travemünde 0.5 km - Tel (49) 04502 - 730 21

Main-Taunus

14	7	7

Die Lage von Main-Taunus zwischen Wiesbaden und Frankfurt ist ein beachtlicher Vorzug, der zum Teil für die nahe Luftwaffenbasis und den häufigen Blick auf eine Zementfabrik entschädigt. Eine weitere Stärke liegt in der Handschrift Bernhard von Limburgers, auch wenn dieser Platz sicherlich nicht zu dessen besten Arbeiten zählt. Die Junganpflanzungen auf diesem offenen Gelände werden in absehbarer Zeit die intime Atmosphäre dieser Anlage noch verstärken. Als Hindernisse sind die Bäume jedoch keineswegs unüberwindlich. Im Gegensatz dazu kann das Wasser durchaus zum Problem werden. Es kommt bei etwa 10 Löchern ins Spiel und ist der Preis, der für einen Golfplatz mitten in einem Vogelschutzgebiet zu zahlen ist. Die nicht übermäßig stark bebunkerten Grüns sind von guter Qualität, allerdings mangelt es ihnen nach heutigem Standard etwas an Form und Gestaltung. Dieser klassische Platz hat ein höchst interessantes und schwieriges Finish, bei dem einem - zumindest auf der ersten Runde - eine Lochbeschreibung sehr gelegen kommt, um die lauernden Hindernisse auszumachen.

The position of Main-Taunus between Wiesbaden and Frankfurt is a considerable advantage, which in part makes up for the closeness of a neighbouring air-base and frequent views of a cement factory. Another strong point is the Bernhard von Limburger label, even though this is not one of his most inspired works. Over this open land, the saplings should eventually add to the intimate atmosphere, but the trees in general are not insurmountable hazards. By contrast, the water can be a problem, coming into play on ten or so holes, a fair price to pay for designing a course in a natural bird reserve. The greens are good but not over-guarded by bunkers, and to modern standards lack a little surface relief. This rather classic design has an intriguing and tough finish, where a map of the course will come in handy to spot the hazards, at least for the first time out.

Golf-Club Main-Taunus e.V. 1980

Lange Seegewann 2
D - 65205 WIESBADEN-DELKENHEIM

Office	Sekretariat	(49) 06122 - 52 550
Pro shop	Pro shop	(49) 06122 - 935 078
Fax	Fax	(49) 06122 - 936 099
Web	www.golfclub-maintaunus.de	
Situation	Lage	Frankfurt, 19 km

Wiesbaden, 12 km

Annual closure	Jährliche Schliessung	no
Weekly closure	Wöchentliche Schliessung	Monday

(Montag): Restaurant closed

Fees main season Preisliste hochsaison	**Week days** Woche	**We/Bank holidays** We/Feiertag
		18 holes
Individual Individuell	€ 45	€ 55
Couple Ehepaar	€ 90	€ 110

– 21 / Students: – 50%

Caddie Caddie no — **Electric Trolley** Elektrokarren yes

Buggy Elektrischer Wagen yes — **Clubs** Leihschläger yes

Credit cards Kreditkarten VISA - Eurocard - MasterCard

Nordenstadt
Wiesbaden
Frankfurt
Delkenheim
GOLF
A3
Hanau
RHEIN
40
Wicker
Offenbach
48
Hochheim
Flörsheim
A67
A60
A63
Mainz
Groß-Gerau
km
0 2 4

Access Zufahrt : A66 Frankfurt-Wiesbaden. Exit (Ausf.) Wiesbaden Nordenstadt. → Delkenheim, Hochheim.

Map 3 on page 353 Karte 3 Seite 353

GOLF COURSE PLATZ 14/20

Site	Lage	
Maintenance	Instandhaltung	
Architect	Architekt	B. von Limburger
Type	Typ	open country
Relief	Begehbarkeit	
Water in play	Platz mit Wasser	
Exp. to wind	Wind ausgesetzt	
Trees in play	Platz mit Bäumen	

Scorecard Scorekarte	**Chp.** Chp.	**Mens** Herren	**Ladies** Damen
Length Länge	6083	5840	5137
Par	72	72	72
Slope system	126	126	122

Advised golfing ability Empfohlene Spielstärke — 0 12 24 36

Hcp required Min. Handicap 36 (26 We)

CLUB HOUSE & AMENITIES KLUBHAUS UND NEBENGEBÄUDE 7/10

Pro shop Pro shop
Driving range Übungsplatz
Sheltered überdacht 6 mats - On grass auf Rasen yes - Putting-green Putting-grün yes - Pitching-green Pitching-grün yes

HOTEL FACILITIES HOTEL BESCHREIBUNG 7/10

HOTELS HOTELS

Nassauer Hof - 181 rooms, D € 268 - Wiesbaden 10 km
Tel (49) 0611 - 13 30, Fax (49) 0611 - 133 632

Treff Hotel Rhein-Main - Wiesbaden-Nordenstadt 5 km
144 rooms, D € 90
Tel (49) 06122 - 80 10, Fax (49) 06122 - 801 164

Hotel am Schlosspark - Wiesbaden-Biebrich 8 km
71 rooms, D € 90
Tel (49) 0611 - 609 360, Fax (49) 0611 - 609 3660

RESTAURANTS RESTAURANTS

Ente - Wiesbaden 10 km - Tel (49) 0611 - 133 666
Käfer's Bistro - Wiesbaden 10 km - Tel (49) 0611 - 536 200

Märkischer Potsdam

14	7	6

Der Westen Berlins ist durchzogen von Kanälen und Seen und Potsdam gilt als historisches Zentrum mit dem wunderschönen Schloss Sanssouci und dem beeindruckenden Neuen Palais, die von Friedrich II von Preußen, einem aufgeklärten und kultivierten Herrscher sowie einem Freund Voltaires, erstellt wurden. Eine Besichtigung der Räumlichkeiten und des 300 Hektaren großen Parks sollte man nicht verpassen. Etwa eine Viertelstunde von Potsdam ist der Golfplatz Märkischer Potsdam, der 1995 von Christoph Städler realisiert wurde. Ein welliges Gelände mit wenig Bäumen, die nie wirklich in die Spielbahn kommen, im Gegensatz zu den Fairway- und Greenbunkern sowie den Wasserhindernissen. Allerdings ist dies kein allzu schwieriger Platz, und die (zahlreichen) Mittelklasse-Spieler werden begeistert sein. Da die Schwierigkeiten gut sichtbar sind, ist es möglich (aber nicht sicher), sein Handicap zu spielen. Ein Platz von durchschnittlich-guter Qualität.

The west of Berlin is a region of canals and lakes, whose historical centre is Potsdam, a city with the extraordinary Schloss Sanssouci and Neues Palais. Both were creations of Frederick II of Prussia, an enlightened and cultured monarch, and friend of Voltaire. Visit both, and the 300 hectares of grounds that go with it. Twenty or so minutes away lies the Märkischer Potsdam course, created in 1995 by Christoph Städler over relatively hilly terrain. The land is rather woody but trees never really come into play, as opposed to the fairway and green-side bunkers and the water hazards. However, this is not the world's toughest course and golfers of only average ability (and there are quite a few of those !) will love it. And as the difficulties are clearly visible, it is possible (but it is no give-away) to play to your handicap. A generally excellent course.

Märkischer Golfclub Potsdam e.V. — 1995

Kemnitzer Schmiedeweg 1
D - 14542 WERDER / OT KEMNITZ

Office	Sekretariat	(49) 03327 - 663 70
Pro shop	Pro shop	(49) 03327 - 663 723
Fax	Fax	(49) 03327 - 663 737
Web	www.mgc-potsdam.de	
Situation	Lage	Berlin, 45 km

Potsdam (pop. 140 000), 20 km

Annual closure	Jährliche Schliessung	no
Weekly closure	Wöchentliche Schliessung	no
Fees main season	Preisliste hochsaison	18 holes

	Week days Woche	We/Bank holidays We/Feiertag
Individual Individuell	€ 45	€ 55
Couple Ehepaar	€ 90	€ 110

Caddie Caddie no — **Electric Trolley** Elektrokarren no
Buggy Elektrischer Wagen yes — **Clubs** Leihschläger yes
Credit cards Kreditkarten no

Access Zufahrt : Berlin A115 → Magdeburg. Drewitz A10 → Hamburg (Berliner Ring). Exit (Ausf.) Phöben → Golf.
Map 6 on page 359 Karte 6 Seite 359

GOLF COURSE — PLATZ 14/20

Site	Lage	
Maintenance	Instandhaltung	
Architect	Architekt	Christoph Städler
Type	Typ	parkland
Relief	Begehbarkeit	
Water in play	Platz mit Wasser	
Exp. to wind	Wind ausgesetzt	
Trees in play	Platz mit Bäumen	

Scorecard Scorekarte	Chp. Chp.	Mens Herren	Ladies Damen
Length Länge	6341	6114	5424
Par	72	72	73
Slope system	123	120	121

Advised golfing ability Empfohlene Spielstärke — 0 12 24 36
Hcp required Min. Handicap 32

CLUB HOUSE & AMENITIES — KLUBHAUS UND NEBENGEBÄUDE 7/10

Pro shop Pro shop
Driving range Übungsplatz
Sheltered überdacht 12 mats - On grass auf Rasen yes - Putting-green Putting-grün yes - Pitching-green Pitching-grün yes

HOTEL FACILITIES — HOTEL BESCHREIBUNG 6/10

HOTELS HOTELS

Steigenberger Hotel Sanssouci - Potsdam 20 km
137 rooms, D € 130
Tel (49) 0331 - 909 10, Fax (49) 0331 - 909 1909

Schlosshotel Cecilienhof - 41 rooms, D € 150 - Potsdam 20 km
Tel (49) 0331 - 370 50, Fax (49) 0331 - 292 498

Wirtshaus zum Rittermeister - Kemnitz 3 km
28 rooms, D from € 70
Tel (49) 03327 - 46 46, Fax (49) 03327 - 464 747

RESTAURANTS RESTAURANTS

Friedrich Wilhelm - Potsdam 20 km - Tel (49) 0331 - 550 50
Speckers Gaststätte - Potsdam 20 km
Tel (49) 0331 - 280 4311

Memmingen Gut Westerhart

14	6	6

Dieser Platz wurde in einer Region eröffnet, der es an Golfanlagen nicht mangelt. Man findet ihn unweit von München, Augsburg und Ulm gelegen, in der Umgebung der alten Reichsstadt Memmingen, deren Stadtbild noch gut erhaltene Spuren des Mittelalters und der Renaissance trägt. Trotz seines jungen Alters präsentiert sich der Platz bereits in ausgezeichnetem Zustand, der sich mit der Zeit weiter verbessern sollte. Lediglich der Boden ist noch etwas hart. Die gut gearbeiteten Grüns, die schon dicht mit Gras bewachsen sind, spielen sich etwas weich. Zudem hätte es nicht geschadet, die Grünkörper stärker zu kontourieren, um das Putten, diesen für den Score so ausschlaggebenden Teil des Spiels etwas interessanter zu machen. Während freistehende Bäume nur vereinzelt eine Rolle spielen, kommt dem Wind als Gefahrenelement eine weitaus grössere Bedeutung zu, insbesondere da man auch noch mit dichtem Rough, Büschen, Fairway- und Grünbunkern, sowie einigen Wasserhindernissen fertigwerden muss. Von mittlerem Schwierigkeitsgrad, ohne nenneswerte Erhebungen, eignet sich der Platz für alle Spielstärken.

This course was opened in a region where golfing facilities abound, and close to the former imperial city of Memmingen, which has preserved its vestiges of the past (Middle Ages and Renaissance). Despite this being early days, the course is already in excellent condition and should age well (the ground is still a little hard). The well-built greens are already well covered and soft on top, but a little more contouring would not have gone amiss to add a little spice to this department of the game which is so important for scoring. Only a few isolated trees come into play and the wind can be a significant element to be considered, especially with thick rough, bushes, fairway and green-side bunkers and a few water hazards to contend with. Averagely difficult with no significant geographical relief, this is a course for all levels.

Golfclub Memmingen Gut Westerhart e.V. — 1994

Westerhart 1b
D - 87740 BUXHEIM

Office Sekretariat (49) 08331 - 71 016
Pro shop Pro shop (49) 08331 - 71 016
Fax Fax (49) 08331 - 71 018
Web www.golf.de/memmingen
Situation Lage Ulm (Donau), 55 km
Annual closure Jährliche Schliessung 1/11→1/4
Weekly closure Wöchentliche Schliessung Monday
(Montag): Restaurant closed

Fees main season Preisliste hochsaison	18 holes	
	Week days Woche	We/Bank holidays We/Feiertag
Individual Individuell	€ 40	€ 50
Couple Ehepaar	€ 80	€ 100

Students: – 50%
Caddie Caddie no — **Electric Trolley** Elektrokarren yes
Buggy Elektrischer Wagen yes (medical reason)
Clubs Leihschläger yes
Credit cards Kreditkarten no

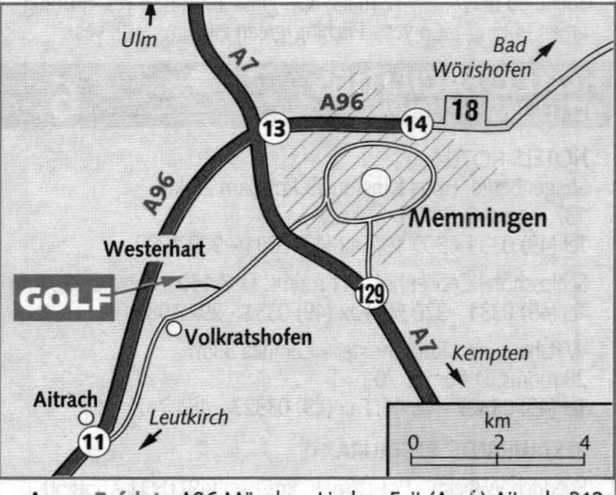

Access Zufahrt : A96 München-Lindau, Exit (Ausf.) Aitrach, B12 → Memmingen, → Westerhart
Map 2 on page 350 Karte 2 Seite 350

GOLF COURSE PLATZ — 14/20

Site Lage
Maintenance Instandhaltung
Architect Architekt unknown
Type Typ parkland, open country
Relief Begehbarkeit
Water in play Platz mit Wasser
Exp. to wind Wind ausgesetzt
Trees in play Platz mit Bäumen

Scorecard Scorekarte	Chp. Chp.	Mens Herren	Ladies Damen
Length Länge	6199	6095	5507
Par	72	72	72
Slope system	124	122	122

Advised golfing ability Empfohlene Spielstärke 0 12 24 36
Hcp required Min. Handicap 54

CLUB HOUSE & AMENITIES KLUBHAUS UND NEBENGEBÄUDE — 6/10

Pro shop Pro shop
Driving range Übungsplatz
Sheltered überdacht 10 mats - On grass auf Rasen no - Putting-green Putting-grün yes - Pitching-green Pitching-grün yes

HOTEL FACILITIES HOTEL BESCHREIBUNG — 6/10

HOTELS HOTELS

Falken - 39 rooms, D € 100 - Memmingen 6 km
Tel (49) 08331 - 945 10, Fax (49) 08331 -9451 500

Park-Hotel an der Stadthalle - Memmingen 6 km
93 rooms, D € 99
Tel (49) 08331 - 9320, Fax (49) 08331 - 484 39

Weisses Ross - 52 rooms, D € 80 - Memmingen 6 km
Tel (49) 08331 - 93 60, Fax (49) 08331 - 936 150

RESTAURANTS RESTAURANTS

Weinstube Weber am Bach - Memmingen 6 km
Tel (49) 08331 - 2414

Weinhaus Knöringer - Memmingen 6 km
Tel (49) 08331 - 2715

Weiherhaus - Memmingen 6 km - Tel (49) 08331 - 721 23

Mittelrheinischer

16 | 7 | 7

Der Mittelrheinische Golfclub liegt gleich neben dem Kurort Bad Ems, wo man sich auf die Behandlung von Hals- und Nasenkrankheiten spezialisiert hat. Der 1928 gebaute Platz ist eingebettet in dichte Vegetation und eröffnet immer wieder schöne Ausblicke auf die Höhenzüge von Eiffel und Taunus. Aufgrund des hügeligen Geländes wird man im Verlauf der Runde mit etwa einem halben Dutzend blinder Abschläge konfrontiert. Die Grüns jedoch sind alle gut einsehbar. Leicht gewellt und von mittlerer Grösse bieten sie kaum Anlass für Desaster beim Putten. Golfer, die einen Fade spielen können, haben angesichts der engen Spielbahnen einen kleinen, wenn auch nicht entscheidenden Vorteil. Den Longhittern bieten sich an den fünf Par 5 Löchern gute Birdie-Chancen. Mit fünf Par-3-Löchern hat der Platz eine eher ungewöhnliche Konfiguration. Die nicht übermäßige Länge des Kurses (nur 9 Löcher verfügen über hintere Abschläge) erleichtert das Miteinander guter und weniger guter Golfer auf einer gemeinsamen Runde. Der Platz lohnt einen Besuch.

The Mittelrheinischer course is located next to the spa of Bad Ems, which specialises in nasal and throat affections. Designed in 1928, the course winds its way through thick vegetation while offering pretty vistas over the Eifel and Taunus uplands. Slightly hilly, the layout entails half a dozen blind shots but all the greens are clearly visible, moderately contoured and of average size (putting disasters are rare). Faders of the ball will enjoy a slight advantage in coping with the narrow fairways, but this is hardly a decisive factor. Long-hitters can look for birdies on the five par 5s; and with five par 3s as well, the course has a rather unusual feel to it. The overall length is very reasonable (there are back tees on 9 holes only) thus making it easier for experienced and inexperienced players to enjoy a round together. Worth knowing.

Mittelrheinischer Golf Club Bad Ems e.V. 1928

Denzerheide
D - 56130 BAD EMS

Office	Sekretariat	(49) 02603 - 6541
Pro shop	Pro shop	(49) 02603 - 14 510
Fax	Fax	(49) 02603 - 13 995
Web	www.mgcbadems.de	
Situation	Lage	Koblenz, 10 km
Annual closure	Jährliche Schliessung	no
Weekly closure	Wöchentliche Schliessung	Monday

(Montag): Restaurant closed

Fees main season Preisliste hochsaison	18 holes	
	Week days Woche	**We/Bank holidays** We/Feiertag
Individual Individuell	€ 40	€ 50
Couple Ehepaar	€ 80	€ 100

– 21: – 50%

Caddie Caddie on request — **Electric Trolley** Elektrokarren yes
Buggy Elektrischer Wagen no — **Clubs** Leihschläger yes
Credit cards Kreditkarten no

Access Zufahrt : A3 Frankfurt-Köln. Exit (Ausf.) Montabaur. B49 → Koblenz. → Bad Ems/Denzerheide.
Map 3 on page 352 Karte 3 Seite 352

GOLF COURSE — PLATZ 16/20

Site	Lage	
Maintenance	Instandhaltung	
Architect	Architekt	Karl-Heinz Hoffmann
Type	Typ	parkland
Relief	Begehbarkeit	
Water in play	Platz mit Wasser	
Exp. to wind	Wind ausgesetzt	
Trees in play	Platz mit Bäumen	

Scorecard Scorekarte	**Chp.** Chp.	**Mens** Herren	**Ladies** Damen
Length Länge	5925	5925	5243
Par	72	72	72
Slope system	134	134	129

Advised golfing ability Empfohlene Spielstärke — 0 12 24 36
Hcp required Min. Handicap — 36

CLUB HOUSE & AMENITIES — KLUBHAUS UND NEBENGEBÄUDE 7/10

Pro shop Pro shop
Driving range Übungsplatz
Sheltered überdacht 8 mats - On grass auf Rasen yes - Putting-green Putting-grün yes - Pitching-green Pitching-grün yes

HOTEL FACILITIES — HOTEL BESCHREIBUNG 7/10

HOTELS HOTELS

Golf Hotel Denzerheide - 7 rooms, D € 95 - on site
Tel (49) 02603 - 6159, Fax (49) 02603 - 13995

Häcker's Kurhotel - 110 rooms, D € 135 - Bad Ems 3 km
Tel (49) 02603 - 79 90, Fax (49) 02603 - 799 252

Kleiner Riesen - 28 rooms, D € 90 - Koblenz 10 km
Tel (49) 0261 - 303 460, Fax (49) 0261 - 160 725

Mercure - 168 rooms, D € 120 - Koblenz 10 km
Tel (49) 0261 - 13 60, Fax (49) 0261 - 136 199

RESTAURANTS RESTAURANTS

Schweizer Haus - Bad Ems 3 km - Tel (49) 02603 - 936 30
Weinhaus Hubertus - Koblenz 15 km - Tel (49) 0261 - 311 77

Motzener See

17	8	6

Dies ist einer der neuen, guten Plätze, die in jüngerer Zeit in Deutschland entstanden sind. Seine hohen technischen Qualitäten werden vor allem den besseren Golfern auffallen. Kurt Rossknecht ließ sich beim Bau der Anlage sowohl von amerikanischen wie auch schottischen Stilelementen inspirieren. Entstanden ist dabei ein Platz, der mittels wellenförmiger Fairways und tiefer Bunkerprofile wie die moderne Version eines Linksplatzeses wirkt. Die gut erkennbaren Hindernisse geben die ideale Spiellinie vor. Zudem sind sie so klug positioniert, dass gute Golfschläge nicht bestraft werden. Diese Feststellung gilt im übrigen für das gesamte Layout des Platzes. Allrounder werden diesen Platz ob seines abwechslungsreichen Lochdesigns - an 7 Löchern kommt Wasser ins Spiel - lieben. Je nach Charakter des Loches sind sowohl flache lang ausrollende, als auch hohe Schläge zum Grün gefordert, für deren Ausführung der komplette Schlägersatz herhalten muss. Die große Anzahl verschiedener Abschläge erlaubt jedem Golfer eine seiner Spielstärke entsprechende Wahl, aber auch die Möglichkeit je nach Tagesform und Lust zu variieren.

This is one of the best recent courses in Germany, with technical virtues that are more obvious to top level golfers. Kurt Rossknecht was inspired by both American and Scottish styles and has come up with a sort of modernized links (rolling fairways and shaped bunkers). The very clear view of hazards points to the ideal line of play, while their clever positioning and the honest layout never penalizes good golf shots. Good all-round players will love this course, where they can chop and change between low rolled shots and high approaches required by the variety of holes (water is in play on seven holes). Here, you will play every club in the bag. The large number of tees makes this a course that caters to each level of proficiency, and to each player's form and mood... not forgetting that the latter may grow darker with the pin positions on the huge, well-contoured greens.

Berliner Golf- & Country Club am Motzener See e.V. — 1991

Am Golfplatz 5
D - 15749 MITTENWALDE / OT MOTZEN

Office	Sekretariat	(49) 033769 - 50 130
Pro shop	Pro shop	(49) 033769 -208 906
Fax	Fax	(49) 033769 - 50 134
Web	www.golfclubmotzen.de	
Situation	Lage	Berlin, 40 km
Annual closure	Jährliche Schliessung	1/1→1/2
Weekly closure	Wöchentliche Schliessung	no

Monday (Montag): Restaurant closed

Fees main season Preisliste hochsaison	18 holes	
	Week days Woche	**We/Bank holidays** We/Feiertag
Individual Individuell	€ 50	€ 70
Couple Ehepaar	€ 100	€ 140

– 21 & Students: – 50%

Caddie Caddie yes — **Electric Trolley** Elektrokarren no
Buggy Elektrischer Wagen yes — **Clubs** Leihschläger yes
Credit cards Kreditkarten no

Access Zufahrt : Berlin, A13 → Dresden. Exit (Ausf.) Mittenwalde → Gallun-Bestensee → Golf
Map 6 on page 359 Karte 6 Seite 359

GOLF COURSE — PLATZ — 17/20

Site	Lage	
Maintenance	Instandhaltung	
Architect	Architekt	Kurt Rossknecht
Type	Typ	open country
Relief	Begehbarkeit	
Water in play	Platz mit Wasser	
Exp. to wind	Wind ausgesetzt	
Trees in play	Platz mit Bäumen	

Scorecard Scorekarte	**Chp.** Chp.	**Mens** Herren	**Ladies** Damen
Length Länge	6287	5884	5147
Par	73	72	72
Slope system	132	132	127

Advised golfing ability Empfohlene Spielstärke — 0 12 24 36
Hcp required Min. Handicap 36

CLUB HOUSE & AMENITIES — KLUBHAUS UND NEBENGEBÄUDE — 8/10

Pro shop Pro shop
Driving range Übungsplatz
Sheltered überdacht 9 mats - On grass auf Rasen yes - Putting-green Putting-grün yes - Pitching-green Pitching-grün yes

HOTEL FACILITIES — HOTEL BESCHREIBUNG — 6/10

HOTELS HOTELS

Residenz am Motzener See - Motzen 1 km
60 rooms, D from € 125
Tel (49) 033769 - 850, Fax (49) 033769 - 85 100

Schlosshotel Teupitz - Teupitz 8 km - 38 rooms, D € 95
Tel (49) 033766 - 216 00, Fax (49) 033766 - 216 02

RESTAURANTS RESTAURANTS

Residenz am Motzener See - Motzen 1 km
Tel (49) 033769 - 850

Schlosshotel Teupitz - Teupitz 8 km
Tel (49) 033766 - 600

München-Riedhof

16 | 7 | 7

Riedhof liegt in unmittelbarer Nähe zum Starnberger See, einem der größten bayrischen Seen, auf halbem Weg zwischen München und den Alpen. Der von Heinz Fehring entworfene Platz ist vom Layout, dem Pflegezustand und vor allem dem Service her sehr amerikanisch. Greenfeespieler erhalten neben den Pin-Positions auch die Informationen über die "Schnelligkeit" der Grüns (Stimpmeter). Das US-Flair wird durch die vielen Wasserhindernisse (Teiche) verstärkt. Dazu gibt einige Erhebungen im Gelände, die die Schlägerwahl erheblich erschweren. Die Schwierigkeiten sind gut erkennbar. Das gilt auch für die Wasserhindernisse, die für missratene Schläge allerdings weniger Gefahr darstellen, als dies Bäume und Bunker tun. Der größtenteils spektakuläre, manchmal etwas trügerische Platz bleibt einem gut im Gedächtnis haften, was ein gutes Zeichen ist. Da die Grüns sehr gut verteidigt sind, ist eine gute Ballkontrolle unerlässlich; dennoch werden durchschnittliche Spieler hier ebenso auf ihre Kosten kommmen wie Fortgeschrittene.

The south of Munich is a very privileged region for the number of courses which offer a wide variety of styles. München-Riedhof is within immediate reach of the Starnberger See, one of Bavaria's largest lakes half-way between Munich and the Bavarian Alps. The course, designed by Heinz Fehring, is not the easiest in the world owing to yardage, water hazards and some steeply contoured terrain, which complicates appreciation of distance. The course is, though, very pleasant to walk around. The difficulties are there to be seen; water is, too, but is not so dangerous for mis-hit shots as the trees and bunkers. Often spectacular and sometimes a wee treacherous, the course sticks in your memory, which is a good sign. As the greens are very well guarded, good ball control is, as always, important, but average players will have as much fun as the experts.

Golfclub München-Riedhof e.V. — 1989

Riedhof 16
D - 85244 EGLING-RIEDHOF

Office	Sekretariat	(49) 08171 - 219 50
Pro shop	Pro shop	(49) 08171 - 219 530
Fax	Fax	(49) 08171 - 219 511
Web	www.riedhof.de	
Situation	Lage	München, 25 km

Wolfratshausen, 3 km

Annual closure Jährliche Schliessung — no

Weekly closure Wöchentliche Schliessung — Monday
(Montag): Restaurant closed

Fees main season Preisliste hochsaison		18 holes
	Week days Woche	**We/Bank holidays** We/Feiertag
Individual Individuell	€ 90	€ 60*
Couple Ehepaar	€ 180	€ 120*

* We: with members only (nur in Mitgliederbegleitung)

Caddie Caddie no — **Electric Trolley** Elektrokarren no
Buggy Elektrischer Wagen no — **Clubs** Leihschläger no
Credit cards Kreditkarten no

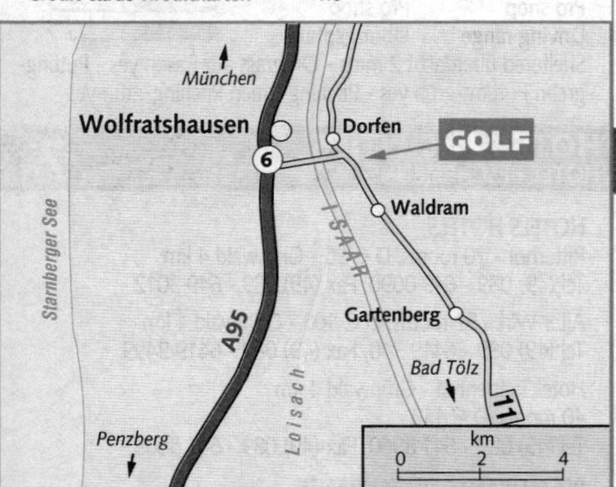

Access Zufahrt : A95 München-Garmisch-Partenkirchen. Exit (Ausf.) Wolfratshausen, → Autobahn Salzburg-Wolfratshausen. → Egling
Map 2 on page 350 Karte 2 Seite 350

GOLF COURSE — PLATZ — 16/20

Site	Lage	
Maintenance	Instandhaltung	
Architect	Architekt	Heinz Fehring
Type	Typ	open country, hilly
Relief	Begehbarkeit	
Water in play	Platz mit Wasser	
Exp. to wind	Wind ausgesetzt	
Trees in play	Platz mit Bäumen	

Scorecard Scorekarte	**Chp.** Chp.	**Mens** Herren	**Ladies** Damen
Length Länge	6150	6024	5307
Par	72	72	72
Slope system	128	126	126

Advised golfing ability Empfohlene Spielstärke — 0 12 24 36
Hcp required Min. Handicap — 34

CLUB HOUSE & AMENITIES — KLUBHAUS UND NEBENGEBÄUDE — 7/10

Pro shop Pro shop
Driving range Übungsplatz
Sheltered überdacht 10 mats - On grass auf Rasen yes - Putting-green Putting-grün yes - Pitching-green Pitching-grün yes

HOTEL FACILITIES — HOTEL BESCHREIBUNG — 7/10

HOTELS HOTELS

Thalhammer - 24 rooms, D € 85 - Wolfratshausen 5 km
Tel (49) 08171 - 42 190, Fax (49) 08171 - 421 950

Märchenwald - 14 rooms, D € 70 - Wolfratshausen 5 km
Tel (49) 08171 - 414 790, Fax (49) 08171 - 22 236

Ritterhof - 20 rooms, D € 95 - Grünwald 10 km
Tel (49) 089 - 649 0090, Fax (49) 089 - 649 3012

Hotel Tannenhof - 40 rooms, D € 110 - Grünwald 10 km
Tel (49) 089 - 641 8960, Fax (49) 089 - 641 5608

RESTAURANTS RESTAURANTS

Patrizier Hof - Wolfratshausen 5 km - Tel (49) 08171 - 225 33
Vogelbauer - Neufahrn 5 km - Tel (49) 08171 - 290 63

Münchner-Strasslach

15	6	7

In der Umgebung der Metropole München ist dies wohl einer der meist bespielten Golfplätze. Gastspieler sind am Wochenende nur in Begleitung eines Mitglieds willkommen.Der Platz wurde 1910 inmitten einer typisch bayrischen Landschaft auf leicht hügeligem Terrain angelegt. Auf dem Platz findet sich eine Anzahl wunderschöner großer Bäume, die an den Doglegs gefährlich ins Spiel kommen. Einige Seen und Wasserläufe sowie knapp 50 sehr sorgfältig platzierte Bunker komplettieren das Repertoire an Hindernissen. Auf den ersten Blick mag der Platz nicht sonderlich schwierig erscheinen, dieser Eindruck wird sich allerdings im Verlauf der Runde revidieren, nicht zuletzt aufgrund einer Reihe schlecht erkennbarer Hindernisse. Auf der zweiten Runde fühlt man sich schon weitaus wohler, da man dann weiß, wie der Platz taktisch zu spielen ist. Der ausgezeichnete Hauptplatz wird ergänzt durch einen nicht minder guten 9-Loch-Kurzplatz, der allerdings noch einwachsen muss.

Münchner-Strasslach is one of the busiest courses around the magnificent greater metropolitan area of Munich, and playing here on week-ends can be very difficult for green-feers. Created in 1910 over averagely-hilly terrain, the course runs over typically Bavarian landscape, with some beautiful big trees (very dangerous on the dog-legs), a few lakes and streams and a little under 50 carefully-located bunkers. At first sight it doesn't look too difficult, but out on the course it can be quite a handful with a number of hazards hidden from view. Second time out, you feel more comfortable and playing tactics are clearer. A class course supplemented by a very good and shortish 9-holer.

Münchner Golf Club e.V., Strasslach — 1910

Tölzerstrasse 95
D - 82064 STRASSLACH

Office Sekretariat (49) 08170 -929 1811
Pro shop Pro shop (49) 08170 - 7254
Fax Fax (49) 08170 -929 1820
Web www.golf.de/mgc
Situation Lage München, 25 km
Strasslach (pop. 2 700), 3 km
Annual closure Jährliche Schliessung 1/12→1/3
Weekly closure Wöchentliche Schliessung Monday
(Montag): Restaurant closed

Fees main season Preisliste hochsaison	18 holes	
	Week days Woche	**We/Bank holidays** We/Feiertag
Individual Individuell	€ 65	€ 80*
Couple Ehepaar	€ 130	€ 160*

* We: with members only (nur in Mitgliederbegleitung)

Caddie Caddie no — **Electric Trolley** Elektrokarren yes
Buggy Elektrischer Wagen yes — **Clubs** Leihschläger yes
Credit cards Kreditkarten no

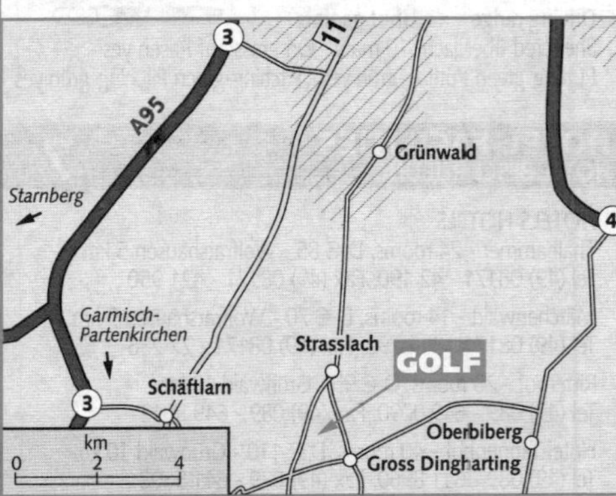

Access Zufahrt : München Süd → Grünwald.
In Grünwald → Bad Tölz. Golf on the left.
Map 2 on page 350 Karte 2 Seite 350

GOLF COURSE — PLATZ — 15/20

Site Lage
Maintenance Instandhaltung
Architect Architekt unknown
Type Typ open country
Relief Begehbarkeit
Water in play Platz mit Wasser
Exp. to wind Wind ausgesetzt
Trees in play Platz mit Bäumen

Scorecard Scorekarte	**Chp.** Chp.	**Mens** Herren	**Ladies** Damen
Length Länge	6126	6126	5432
Par	72	72	72
Slope system	129	129	125

Advised golfing ability Empfohlene Spielstärke 0 12 24 36
Hcp required Min. Handicap 34

CLUB HOUSE & AMENITIES — KLUBHAUS UND NEBENGEBÄUDE — 6/10

Pro shop Pro shop
Driving range Übungsplatz
Sheltered überdacht 2 mats - On grass auf Rasen yes - Putting-green Putting-grün yes - Pitching-green Pitching-grün yes

HOTEL FACILITIES — HOTEL BESCHREIBUNG — 7/10

HOTELS HOTELS
Ritterhof - 20 rooms, D € 95 - Grünwald 4 km
Tel (49) 089 - 649 0090, Fax (49) 089 - 649 3012

Alter Wirt - 52 rooms, D € 100 - Grünwald 4 km
Tel (49) 089 - 6419 340, Fax (49) 089 - 6419 3499

Hotel Tannenhof - Grünwald 4 km
40 rooms, D € 110
Tel (49) 089 - 641 8960, Fax (49) 089 - 641 5608

RESTAURANTS RESTAURANTS
Gasthof zum Wildpark - Strasslach 1 km
Tel (49) 08170 - 996 20

Foresta Verde - Grünwald 5 km - Tel (49) 089 - 641 1857

Nahetal

14 | 8 | 6

Der Golfclub Nahetal wurde 1998 modernisiert, wobei aber die alten Schwierigkeiten erhalten blieben. Erste Notwendigkeit hier ist Präzision, da die Fairways meist nicht sehr breit und zudem von dichtem Wald umgeben sind, was dem Platz den angenehmen Nebeneffekt von Ruhe und Abgeschiedenheit vermittelt. Im Zug des Umbaus wurden fast alle Löcher modifiziert und Wasserteiche am 3. Und am 14. Loch gebaut. Der Platz ist sehr ungewöhnlich, da alle zehn Par-4-Löcher und alle vier Par-5-Löcher "blind" sind, d.h. man sieht am Abschlag nur von den Par 3-Löchern die Fahne. Die Spiellinie ist deshalb für bessere Spieler nicht erkennbar. Man benötigt etliche Runden oder die Begleitung eines Platzkenners, um sie herauszufinden. Das ungewöhnlichste Loch ist wohl das 7. Loch, ein Par 4 von 340 m, wo gute Spieler mit einem Eisen 7 über die hohen Bäume am Knick des Doglegs schlagen und dann ein Eisen 8 zum Grün spielen. Schwächere Spieler müssen gerade schlagen und haben dann noch ein langes Eisen oder ein Fairway-Holz zum Grün. Dafür entschädigt der Ausblick auf den spektakulären Rotenfels für diese architektonische Sünde.

You need to play straight, as the fairways are not always wide and are lined with some pretty dense trees, a feature that adds to a pleasant impression of peace and quiet. During the modernization in 1998, most holes have been modified and ponds added on holes 3 and 14. The design is rather unusual since all ten par 4 holes and all four par 5 holes are blind so you can see the flagstick only on the par 3 holes. The line of play is for better players hardly visible, you need several rounds or the advice of a local player. The most unusual hole is No. 7, a par 4 of 340 m, where good players hit a 7 iron over the high trees over the turn of the dogleg and a 8 iron into the green. However lesser players have to go the straight route which means hitting a long iron or a fairway wood into the green. The spectacular view of the Rotenfels makes up for this sin in golf course design.

Golfclub Nahetal e.V. — 1976

Drei Buchen
D - 55583 BAD MÜNSTER AM STEIN-EBERNBURG

Office	Sekretariat	(49) 06708 - 2145
Pro shop	Pro shop	(49) 06708 - 641 444
Fax	Fax	(49) 06708 - 1731
Web	www.golfclub-nahetal.de	
Situation	Lage	Bad Kreuznach, 12 km
Annual closure	Jährliche Schliessung	no
Weekly closure	Wöchentliche Schliessung	Monday

(Montag): Restaurant closed

Fees main season Preisliste hochsaison — 18 holes

	Week days Woche	We/Bank holidays We/Feiertag
Individual Individuell	€ 40	€ 50
Couple Ehepaar	€ 80	€ 100

– 21 / Students: – 50%

Caddie Caddie on request — **Electric Trolley** Elektrokarren yes
Buggy Elektrischer Wagen medical reasons
Clubs Leihschläger yes
Credit cards Kreditkarten only Pro Shop

Access Zufahrt : Mainz A60 W, Kreuz Bingen A61 Süd. Exit (Ausf.) Bad Kreuznach. Bad Kreuznach B48 → Bad Münster → Ebernburg. Right in Schlossgartenstr. Right, Wanderweg Dreibuchen. **Map 3 on page 353** Karte 3 Seite 353

GOLF COURSE — PLATZ — 14/20

Site	Lage	
Maintenance	Instandhaltung	
Architect	Architekt	Armin Keller
Type	Typ	forest
Relief	Begehbarkeit	
Water in play	Platz mit Wasser	
Exp. to wind	Wind ausgesetzt	
Trees in play	Platz mit Bäumen	

Scorecard Scorekarte	Chp. Chp.	Mens Herren	Ladies Damen
Length Länge	6090	5629	4922
Par	72	72	72
Slope system	134	129	123

Advised golfing ability Empfohlene Spielstärke — 0 12 24 36
Hcp required Min. Handicap — We: 36

CLUB HOUSE & AMENITIES — KLUBHAUS UND NEBENGEBÄUDE — 8/10

Pro shop Pro shop
Driving range Übungsplatz
Sheltered überdacht 10 mats - On grass auf Rasen yes - Putting-green Putting-grün yes - Pitching-green Pitching-grün yes

HOTEL FACILITIES — HOTEL BESCHREIBUNG — 6/10

HOTELS HOTELS

Parkhotel Kurhaus - Bad Kreuznach 12 km
124 rooms, D € 120
Tel (49) 0671 - 80 20, Fax (49) 0671 - 354 77

Landhotel Kauzenberg - Bad Kreuznach 4 km
45 rooms, D € 90
Tel (49) 0671 - 38 000, Fax (49) 0671 - 3800 124

Hotel am Kurpark - Bad Münster am Stein 2 km
28 rooms, D € 95
Tel (49) 06708 - 629 000, Fax (49) 06708 -629 0029

RESTAURANTS RESTAURANTS

Metzlers Gasthof - Bad Kreuznach-Hackenheim 14 km - Tel (49) 0671 - 65 312

Die Kauzenburg - Bad Kreuznach 12 km - Tel (49) 0671 - 38 000

Oberfranken

17	6	5

Diese ruhige Gegend Frankens wird in erster Linie von Liebhabern barocker Architektur, und mehr noch, von den Besuchern der Bayreuther Festspiele frequentiert. Von wagnerischem Pomp ist auf dem Golfplatz nichts zu spüren. Oberfranken ist eine klassisch konzipierte Anlage, die sich gut in das unebene Gelände einfügt, und daher vor allem Spielern mit guter Kondition zu empfehlen ist. Schöner, alter Baumbestand schmückt die Landschaft und stellt auf den ersten Blick die Hauptschwierigkeit dar, obschon auch Wasser und Bunker manchmal recht gefährlich werden können. Golfer mittlerer Spielstärke werden sich sicher schwer tun, hier ihr Handicap zu schaffen, obwohl das technische Niveau des Platzes eigentlich von allen Spielern zu meistern ist. Der diskret-elegante Kurs, der sich in der Zeit zwischen spätem Frühling und Frühherbst von seiner schönsten Seite zeigt, zählt zweifellos zu den besten Anlagen der Region.

This peaceful region of Franconia comes alive with visits from lovers of baroque architecture and, more particularly, from "pilgrims" to the Bayreuth Festival. But there's nothing grandiose or Wagnerian about this course, which is very classical in style and naturally hugs a terrain that is hilly enough to recommend it basically for golfers in good physical shape. Beautiful old trees enhance the landscape and at first sight form the main hazards, although water and sand are also sometimes a dangerous proposition. Mid-handicappers will certainly find it hard here to achieve a good score, even though the course is technically speaking within the grasp of most golfers. A discreet and elegant course, Oberfranken is at its best from late spring to early autumn and is one of the region's best golfing stop-offs.

Golf Club Oberfranken e.V., Thurnau — 1965

Petershof 1
D - 95349 THURNAU

Office	Sekretariat	(49) 09228 - 319
Pro shop	Pro shop	(49) 09228 - 1022
Fax	Fax	(49) 09228 - 7219
Web	www.golf.de/gcoberfranken	
Situation	Lage	Nürnberg, 80 km

Bayreuth (pop. 72 000), 25 km

Annual closure Jährliche Schliessung 30/11→28/2

Weekly closure Wöchentliche Schliessung Monday
(Montag): Restaurant closed

Fees main season Preisliste hochsaison 18 holes

	Week days Woche	We/Bank holidays We/Feiertag
Individual Individuell	€ 40	€ 50
Couple Ehepaar	€ 80	€ 100

– 21 / Students: – 50%

Caddie Caddie no — **Electric Trolley** Elektrokarren yes
Buggy Elektrischer Wagen yes — **Clubs** Leihschläger yes
Credit cards Kreditkarten no

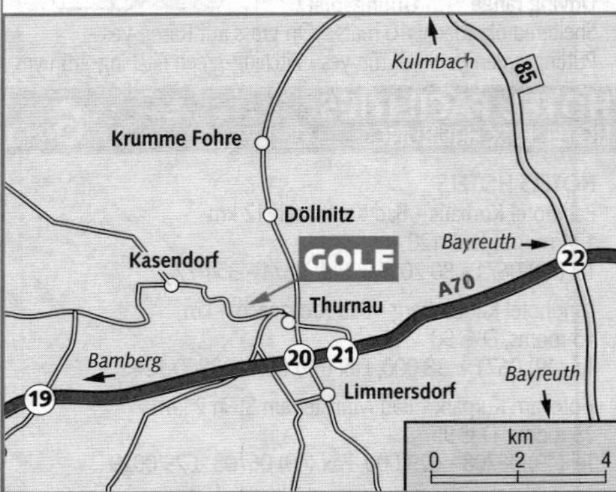

Access Zufahrt : Nürnberg, A9 → Berlin. Exit (Ausf.) Kulmbach-Bayreuth. B505 Exit Thurnau.
Map 4 on page 354 Karte 4 Seite 354

GOLF COURSE — PLATZ — 17/20

Site	Lage	
Maintenance	Instandhaltung	
Architect	Architekt	B. von Limburger, Donald Harradine
Type	Typ	forest, parkland
Relief	Begehbarkeit	
Water in play	Platz mit Wasser	
Exp. to wind	Wind ausgesetzt	
Trees in play	Platz mit Bäumen	

Scorecard Scorekarte	Chp. Chp.	Mens Herren	Ladies Damen
Length Länge	5932	5932	5213
Par	72	72	72
Slope system	123	123	121

Advised golfing ability Empfohlene Spielstärke 0 12 24 36
Hcp required Min. Handicap 36

CLUB HOUSE & AMENITIES — KLUBHAUS UND NEBENGEBÄUDE — 6/10

Pro shop Pro shop
Driving range Übungsplatz
Sheltered überdacht 12 mats - On grass auf Rasen yes - Putting-green Putting-grün yes - Pitching-green Pitching-grün yes

HOTEL FACILITIES — HOTEL BESCHREIBUNG — 5/10

HOTELS HOTELS

Brauerei-Gasthof Schnupp - Neudrossenfeld 11 km
27 rooms, D € 95
Tel (49) 09203 - 99 20, Fax (49) 09203 - 99 250

Bayerischer Hof - 50 rooms, D € 100 - Bayreuth 20 km
Tel (49) 0921 - 786 00, Fax (49) 0921 - 786 0560

Goldener Hirsch - 40 rooms, D € 95 - Bayreuth 20 km
Tel (49) 0921 - 230 46, Fax (49) 0921 - 224 83

RESTAURANTS RESTAURANTS

Schloss-Restaurant - Neudrossenfeld 10 km
Tel (49) 09203 - 68 368

Schlosshotel Thiergarten - Bayreuth 28 km
Tel (49) 09209 - 98 40

Oberschwaben Bad Waldsee

15	6	6

Der Platz liegt in einer traditionell bayerischen Umgebung, die einer dicht-bewaldeten Parkanlage ähnelt. Am Platz wurden einige Änderungen vorgenommen, die das Spielvergnügen noch weiter steigerten. Es gibt hier jeweils fünf Par 3 und Par 5 Löcher, an denen kürzere Spieler genügend gute Chancen aufs Par haben, der Tatsache Rechnung tragend, dass sich der Durchschnitts-Golfer in dieser Hinsicht an Par 4 Löchern häufig am schwersten tut. Aus dem gleichen Grund sollte man die hinteren Abschläge meiden. Der schön gelegene Platz weist eine respektable Länge auf. Senioren empfehlen wir wegen des etwas hügeligen Geländes die Benutzung eines Golfwagens. Die heikelste Passage lauert zwischen Loch 10 und 12. Da der Boden oft feucht ist und ein halbes Dutzend Grüns erhöht liegen, sollte man einen hohen Pitch beherrschen. Insgesamt sind die einen erwartenden Schwierigkeiten keineswegs so bedrohlich, dass Mittelklasse-Spieler sich davon entmutigen lassen. Angenehm zu spielen und abwechslungsreich gestaltet, lohnt die Anlage einen Besuch sowohl der Lage als auch des Layouts wegen.

In a traditional Bavarian setting of densely wooded park-land, we can firstly only hope that the planned alterations will enhance the pleasure of playing here. With five par 5s and five par 3s, the course gives short-hitters the chance to sign for a few pars, knowing full well that the average hacker has the biggest problems with par 4s. In this case, don't opt for the back-tees. Set in a pretty region, the course is a little hilly for senior players (buggy recommended) and respectable in length; the trickiest section awaits you between the 10th and 12th. Since it is often wet and half a dozen greens are elevated, the high pitch shot is a must, but the hardships here are not threatening enough to discourage the average golfer. Pleasant and nicely varied, this course is worth the trip for both the layout and the site.

Golf-Club Oberschwaben Bad Waldsee 1968

Hofgut Hopfenweiler
D - 88339 BAD WALDSEE

Office	Sekretariat	(49) 07524 - 5900
Pro shop	Pro shop	(49) 07524 - 48 778
Fax	Fax	(49) 07524 - 6106
Web	www.golfcluboberschwaben.com	
Situation	Lage	Ravensburg, 20 km
Annual closure	Jährliche Schliessung	1/11→31/3
Weekly closure	Wöchentliche Schliessung	Monday

(Montag): Restaurant closed

Fees main season Preisliste hochsaison	18 holes	
	Week days Woche	**We/Bank holidays** We/Feiertag
Individual Individuell	€ 50	€ 60
Couple Ehepaar	€ 100	€ 120

– 21 & Students: – 50%

Caddie Caddie no — **Electric Trolley** Elektrokarren yes
Buggy Elektrischer Wagen yes — **Clubs** Leihschläger yes
Credit cards Kreditkarten no

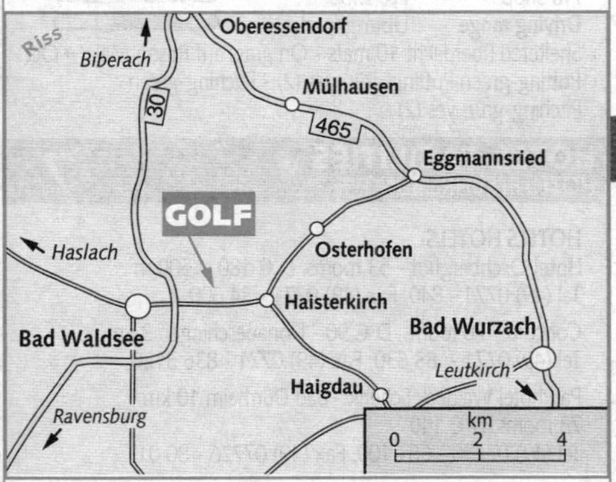

Access Zufahrt : A8 München-Stuttgart. Exit (Ausf.) Ulm-West. B30 → Bodensee. Bad Waldsee → Golf
Map 1 on page 349 Karte 1 Seite 349

GOLF COURSE
PLATZ — **15**/20

Site	Lage	
Maintenance	Instandhaltung	
Architect	Architekt	unknown
Type	Typ	forest, parkland
Relief	Begehbarkeit	
Water in play	Platz mit Wasser	
Exp. to wind	Wind ausgesetzt	
Trees in play	Platz mit Bäumen	

Scorecard Scorekarte	**Chp.** Chp.	**Mens** Herren	**Ladies** Damen
Length Länge	5986	5986	5307
Par	72	72	72
Slope system	133	133	131

Advised golfing ability Empfohlene Spielstärke — 0 12 24 36
Hcp required Min. Handicap — 34

CLUB HOUSE & AMENITIES
KLUBHAUS UND NEBENGEBÄUDE — **6**/10

Pro shop Pro shop
Driving range Übungsplatz
Sheltered überdacht yes - On grass auf Rasen yes - Putting-green Putting-grün yes - Pitching-green Pitching-grün yes

HOTEL FACILITIES
HOTEL BESCHREIBUNG — **6**/10

HOTELS HOTELS
Kur-Parkhotel - Bad Waldsee 2 km
54 rooms, D from € 80
Tel (49) 07524 - 97 070, Fax (49) 07524 - 970 775

Altes Tor - Bad Waldsee 2 km
27 rooms, D € 90
Tel (49) 07524 - 971 90, Fax (49) 07524 - 971 997

RESTAURANTS RESTAURANTS
Restaurants in Bad Waldsee
Waldhorn - Ravensburg 20 km - Tel (49) 0751 - 36 120
Krone - Schlier 25 km - Tel (49) 07529 - 1292

Öschberghof

15	7	7

Der ideale Ort um ein paar Golftage zu verbringen und die herrlichen Umgebung von Schwarzwald und Donauquelle zu erkunden. Übernachten können Sie im gut ausgestatteten, komfortablen Hotel der Anlage. Er verläuft auf relativ ebenem Gelände und kann so leicht zu Fuß bewältigt werden. Obwohl die Hindernisse alle gut erkennbar sind, muss man mehrere Runden spielen um die strategischen Nuancen des Layouts zu begreifen. Ein Wasserlauf kreuzt acht Spielbahnen und bildet eine der Hauptschwierigkeiten, zu denen ebenfalls zahlreiche Bäume und Bunker zählen. Zum Glück sind die Grüns nicht ausgesprochen gut verteidigt, so dass auch der Durchschnitts-Golfer sie einigermaßen gut anspielen kann. Der Platz ist in der Tat so angelegt, dass er nervenschonendes Vergnügen bereitet und schmeichlerische Ergebnisse ermöglicht – ein typischer Urlaubsplatz eben.

An ideal site for a few days golfing, staying in a well-equipped, comfortable hotel (with pool, sauna and jacuzzi) or for exploring this superb region of the Black Forest and sources of the Danube. The course is flat enough for easy walking. It is very reasonable in terms of yardage (from the "medal tees"!), but although the hazards are generally visible on each hole, you need several rounds to appreciate the course's strategic "nuances". A stream winds its way across eight holes and forms a major, but not the only, difficulty, as trees and bunkers abound. Fortunately, the greens are not over-protected and approach shots are not too complicated for the average golfer. This is indeed a course designed for enjoyment, where you can card sometimes flattering scores without suffering from nervous exhaustion, so it's just the job for the holidays.

Land- und Golf-Club Öschberghof — 1980

Golflatz 1
D - 78166 DONAUESCHINGEN

Office	Sekretariat	(49) 0771 - 84 525
Pro shop	Pro shop	(49) 0771 - 84 530
Fax	Fax	(49) 0771 - 84 540
Web	www.oeschberghof.com	
Situation	Lage	Donaueschingen, 5 km
Annual closure	Jährliche Schliessung	1/11→31/3
Weekly closure	Wöchentliche Schliessung	Monday

(Montag): Restaurant closed

Fees main season Preisliste hochsaison	Week days Woche	We/Bank holidays We/Feiertag
	18 holes	
Individual Individuell	€ 55	€ 70
Couple Ehepaar	€ 110	€ 140

– 25: – 50%

Caddie Caddie no — **Electric Trolley** Elektrokarren yes

Buggy Elektrischer Wagen yes — **Clubs** Leihschläger yes

Credit cards Kreditkarten
VISA - Eurocard - MasterCard - AMEX - DC

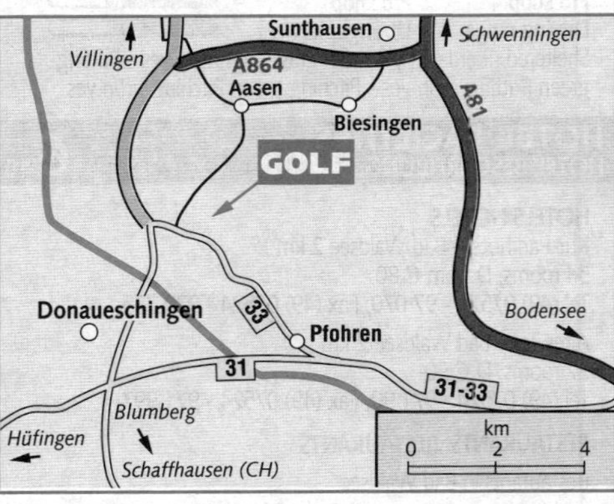

Access Zufahrt : A81 Stuttgart-Singen. Exit (Ausf.) Bad Dürenheimer Kreuz, E70 → Donaueschingen. Exit Donaueschingen-Mitte. → Golf

Map 1 on page 349 Karte 1 Seite 349

GOLF COURSE — PLATZ — 15/20

Site	Lage	
Maintenance	Instandhaltung	
Architect	Architekt	DeutscheGolfConsult
Type	Typ	open country, parkland
Relief	Begehbarkeit	
Water in play	Platz mit Wasser	
Exp. to wind	Wind ausgesetzt	
Trees in play	Platz mit Bäumen	

Scorecard Scorekarte	Chp. Chp.	Mens Herren	Ladies Damen
Length Länge	6448	5970	5223
Par	74	72	74
Slope system	130	128	124

Advised golfing ability Empfohlene Spielstärke — 0 12 24 36

Hcp required Min. Handicap — 35

CLUB HOUSE & AMENITIES — KLUBHAUS UND NEBENGEBÄUDE — 7/10

Pro shop Pro shop
Driving range Übungsplatz
Sheltered überdacht 10 mats - On grass auf Rasen May → Oct.
Putting-green Putting-grün yes (2) - Pitching-green Pitching-grün yes (2)

HOTEL FACILITIES — HOTEL BESCHREIBUNG — 7/10

HOTELS HOTELS

Hotel Öschberghof - 53 rooms, D € 180 - 500 m
Tel (49) 0771 - 840, Fax (49) 0771 - 84 600

Concord - 76 rooms, D € 90 - Donaueschingen 3 km
Tel (49) 0771 - 83 630, Fax (49) 0771 - 836 3120

Parkhotel Waldeck Schenk - Bad Dürrheim 10 km
73 rooms, D € 140
Tel (49) 07726 - 663 100, Fax (49) 07726 - 80 01

RESTAURANTS RESTAURANTS

Hotel Öschberghof - 500 m - Tel (49) 0771 - 84 610

Ochsen - Donaueschingen 3 km - Tel (49) 0771 - 809 90

Pinnau

14	6	6

Der Platz verdankt seinen Namen dem Fluss Pinnau, der teilweise entlang des Golfgeländes verläuft. Obwohl der Fluss selbst nie ins Spiel kommt, gibt es andere Wasserhindernisse in bedrohlicher Lage vor den Grüns, um unerfahrene Spieler einzuschüchtern, die hier schnell einige Schläge verlieren können. Spielern mit hohen Handicaps machen auch die Grüns zu schaffen, die teilweise stark onduliert sind, aber in gestalterischer Hinsicht zu wünschen übrig lassen. Dieser Platz favorisiert technisch versierte Spieler, die es verstehen, mit den einzeln stehenden Bäumen fertigzuwerden, die vom Architekten geschickt mit ins strategische Kalkül einbezogen wurden. Der flache Platz ist einfach zu Gehen und trocknet gut ab. Golfer aller Spielstärken können sich hier entfalten, wenngleich methodische Spieler gegenüber Longhittern im Vorteil sind. Wenn möglich sollten Sie an der 10 beginnen, da die zweiten Neun etwas weniger interessant sind als der Rest.

Pinnau takes its name from the river that partly skirts the course. And although this running water never really comes into play, other water hazards in front of the greens are threatening enough to intimidate the more inexperienced players, who can quickly suffer here. High-handicappers will also find the putting surfaces a handful, too, which are sometimes excessively contoured and lacking in inspiration designwise. With that said, this is a course for the technicians, who will have to cope with strategically located isolated trees, the finest of which have been smartly used by the designer. Flattish and well-drained, the course is a pleasant one to walk, where golfers of all abilities can unfold their game, even though the thoughtful technician will have the upper hand over the long-hitter. If you can, tee off at the 10th, as the back nine are a little less exciting than the rest.

Golf Club An der Pinnau — 1982

Pinneberger Strasse 81a
D - 25451 QUICKBORN-RENZEL

Office	Sekretariat	(49) 04106 - 81 800
Pro shop	Pro shop	(49) 04106 - 60 876
Fax	Fax	(49) 04106 - 82 003
Web	www.pinnau.de	
Situation	Lage	Hamburg, 25 km
Annual closure	Jährliche Schliessung	no
Weekly closure	Wöchentliche Schliessung	no

Fees main season Preisliste hochsaison	Week days Woche	We/Bank holidays We/Feiertag
18 holes		
Individual Individuell	€ 40	€ 45
Couple Ehepaar	€ 80	€ 90

– 21: – 50%

Caddie Caddie on request — Electric Trolley Elektrokarren no
Buggy Elektrischer Wagen no — Clubs Leihschläger no
Credit cards Kreditkarten no

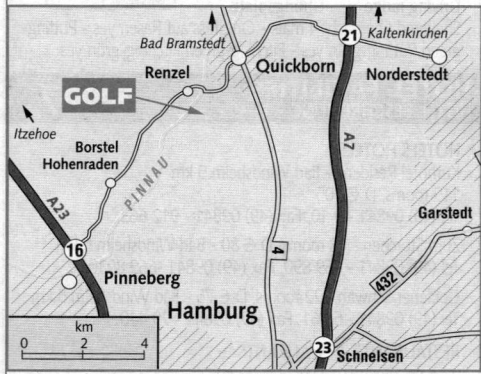

Access Zufahrt : A7 Hamburg → Flensburg. Exit (Ausf.) Quickborn. → Quickborn, Renzel → Pinneberg.
Map 7 on page 360 Karte 7 Seite 360

GOLF COURSE — PLATZ — 14/20

Site	Lage	
Maintenance	Instandhaltung	
Architect	Architekt	unknown
Type	Typ	parkland, open country
Relief	Begehbarkeit	
Water in play	Platz mit Wasser	
Exp. to wind	Wind ausgesetzt	
Trees in play	Platz mit Bäumen	

Scorecard Scorekarte	Chp. Chp.	Mens Herren	Ladies Damen
Length Länge	6023	6023	5231
Par	72	72	72
Slope system	127	127	127

Advised golfing ability / Empfohlene Spielstärke: 0 12 24 36
Hcp required — Min. Handicap: 36

CLUB HOUSE & AMENITIES — KLUBHAUS UND NEBENGEBÄUDE — 6/10

Pro shop — Pro shop
Driving range — Übungsplatz
Sheltered überdacht 4 mats - On grass auf Rasen yes - Putting-green Putting-grün yes - Pitching-green Pitching-grün yes

HOTEL FACILITIES — HOTEL BESCHREIBUNG — 6/10

HOTELS HOTELS

Jagdhaus Waldfrieden - Quickborn 3 km
26 rooms, D € 145
Tel (49) 04106 - 61 020, Fax (49) 04106 - 69 196

Aussen Alster - Hamburg 25 km
28 rooms, D € 130
Tel (49) 040 - 241 557, Fax (49) 040 - 280 3231

Wiking Hotel - Henstedt-Ulzburg 10 km
68 rooms, D € 80
Tel (49) 04193 - 9080, Fax (49) 04193 - 92 323

RESTAURANTS RESTAURANTS

Jagdhaus Waldfrieden - Quickborn 3 km
Tel (49) 04106 - 610 020

Reichsstadt Bad Windsheim

14 | 6 | 7

Nahe Würzburg und Nürnberg liegt der Golfplatz an der "Romantischen Straße", die von Würzburg über Augsburg, durch die Schweiz nach Italien führt, und an deren Weg sich immer wieder Städte und Schlösser aus den Epochen des Mittelalters, der Renaissance und des Barock finden. Gleichermaßen erwähnenswert sind die Weinberge (Frankenwein) des Maintals. Falls Sie sich von den kulturellen Attraktionen losreissen können, verpassen Sie auf keinen Fall die Golfplätze dieser Gegend, insbesondere nicht diesen, der ebenso handfest und bodenständig ist wie die regionale Küche. Ebene Flächen wechseln sich ab mit hügeligerem Terrain auf einem Platz, der insgesamt einen sehr ausgewogenen Eindruck macht. Die Grüns sind enorm groß und sehr gut verteidigt. Es gibt praktisch keine Bäume, was den Platz sehr windanfällig macht. Einige Wasserhindernisse, gefährliche Bunker, Dickicht und Rough tragen dazu bei, dass der Score voraussichtlich ein paar Schläge über dem Handicap liegen wird. Daher sollten unerfahrene Golfer einfach die Runde geniessen ohne allzu sehr auf ihr Ergebnis zu achten.

This course is on the "Romantic Road", which started out from Würzburg and ran down to Augsburg then on to Switzerland and Italy, crossing towns and castles testifying to the Middle Ages, the Renaissance and the Baroque period. Equally important are the vineyards in the Main valley (Franconia wine). If you can tear yourself away from the cultural fascinations, don't miss the golf courses in this province, especially this one, as serious a layout as the regional cooking. With flat spaces alternating with hillier terrain and well-balanced overall, the course has huge, well-guarded greens, is virtually tree-less and can get very tough when the wind blows. A few water hazards and dangerous bunkers, the thickets and rough are all there to nudge your score a few strokes above your handicap. Inexperienced golfers will enjoy their round even more if they prefer not to count their score.

Golf Club Reichsstadt Bad Windsheim e.V. 1991

Am Weinturm 2
D - 91438 BAD WINDSHEIM

Office	Sekretariat	(49) 09841 - 5027
Pro shop	Pro shop	(49) 09841 - 2497
Fax	Fax	(49) 09841 - 3448
Web	www.golf-bw.de	
Situation	Lage	Würzburg, 40 km
Annual closure	Jährliche Schliessung	no
Weekly closure	Wöchentliche Schliessung	Monday

(Montag): Restaurant closed

430

Fees main season Preisliste hochsaison	18 holes	
	Week days Woche	**We/Bank holidays** We/Feiertag
Individual Individuell	€ 30	€ 45
Couple Ehepaar	€ 60	€ 90

– 18 & Students: – 50%

Caddie Caddie on request — **Electric Trolley** Elektrokarren no

Buggy Elektrischer Wagen no — **Clubs** Leihschläger yes

Credit cards Kreditkarten no

Uffenheim
Berolzheim
Oberntief
Erkenbrechtshofen
GOLF
Külsheim
Neuherberg
Ergersheim
Bad Windsheim
13
Illesheim
Neustadt a. d. Aisch
470
A7
107
Ansbach
km 0 2 4

Access Zufahrt **:** • A7 Ulm-Würzburg. Exit (Ausf.) Bad Windsheim. B470 → Neustadt/Bad Windsheim. In Bad Windsheim → Oberntief. • Nürnberg → Fürth. B8 to Neustadt. B470 → Bad Windsheim **Map 4 on page 354** Karte 4 Seite 354

GOLF COURSE
PLATZ — **14**/20

Site	Lage	
Maintenance	Instandhaltung	
Architect	Architekt	unknown
Type	Typ	open country
Relief	Begehbarkeit	
Water in play	Platz mit Wasser	
Exp. to wind	Wind ausgesetzt	
Trees in play	Platz mit Bäumen	

Scorecard Scorekarte	**Chp.** Chp.	**Mens** Herren	**Ladies** Damen
Length Länge	6198	6198	5494
Par	73	73	73
Slope system	125	123	124

Advised golfing ability Empfohlene Spielstärke — 0 12 24 36

Hcp required Min. Handicap 36

CLUB HOUSE & AMENITIES
KLUBHAUS UND NEBENGEBÄUDE — **6**/10

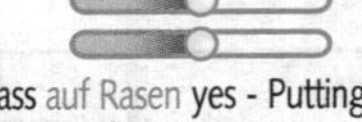

Pro shop Pro shop
Driving range Übungsplatz

Sheltered überdacht 4 mats - On grass auf Rasen yes - Putting-green Putting-grün yes - Pitching-green Pitching-grün yes

HOTEL FACILITIES
HOTEL BESCHREIBUNG — **7**/10

HOTELS HOTELS

Kurhotel Residenz - Bad Windsheim 5 km
119 rooms, D € 105
Tel (49) 09841 - 9 10, Fax (49) 09841 - 912 663

Zum Storchen - 18 rooms, D € 80 - Bad Windsheim 5 km
Tel (49) 09841 - 669 890, Fax (49) 09841 -669 8930

Goldener Schwan - 22 rooms, D € 75 - Bad Windsheim 5 km
Tel (49) 09841 - 50 61, Fax (49) 09841 - 79 440

RESTAURANTS RESTAURANTS

Zum Storchen - Bad Windsheim 5 km
Tel (49) 09841 - 669 890

Kurhotel Residenz - Bad Windsheim 5 km
Tel (49) 09841 - 910

Reichswald-Nürnberg

16 | 7 | 7

Der Wald spiegelt wohl am besten den Geist der deutschen Romantik wider. Seine Erhaltung und sein Schutz sind zu einem wichtigen gesellschaftlichen Anliegen, insbesondere der Umweltschützer, geworden. Eine ganze Runde in einem solch mächtigen Wald zu spielen, vermittelt einem das Gefühl von Ruhe und Zufriedenheit - es ist, als wäre man ganz alleine auf der Welt. Hier muss man in Topform sein und den Ball kontrolliert schlagen, um den allgegenwärtigen Pinienbäumen aus dem Weg zu gehen und mit dem Drive in eine Position zu gelangen, die einem das Anspiel der gut durch Bunker verteidigten Grüns ermöglicht. Wenn man gut spielt, werden einen die Wasserläufe und Hindernisse, die ein - wenn auch nicht übermäßiges - Gefahrenelement darstellen, weniger einschüchtern. Spieler, denen es an Übung und Genauigkeit fehlt, werden vermutlich einen Einbruch erleben, aber schließlich zwingt sie ja niemand dazu, all ihre Schläge auch zu zählen. Reichswald ist ohne Zweifel einer der besten Plätze der Region, der auch nach oftmaligem Spielen immer wieder Spass macht.

Forests are one of the key constituents of the German romantic soul; their conservation and protection are one of society's major concerns. Playing a whole course in a forest such as this procures a feeling of incomparable tranquillity and contentment; on the course, you feel as if you are the only soul in the world. Here, you will need to be on top of your game to keep out of the pine-trees and flight your ball to land the drive in the best position to approach the greens (which are well guarded by bunkers). If you're playing well, you won't be too scared of the streams and hazards that add an element of difficulty but never excessively so. Players with little experience and problems of direction will probably suffer, but they don't have to count every stroke, do they? One of the region's top layouts, this is a spectacular course which is fun to play again and again.

Golf Club Am Reichswald e.V., Nürnberg — 1960

Schiestlstrasse 100
D - 90427 NÜRNBERG

Office	Sekretariat	(49) 0911 - 305 730
Pro shop	Pro shop	(49) 0911 - 305 959
Fax	Fax	(49) 0911 - 301 200
Web		www.golfclub-nuernberg.de
Situation	Lage	Nürnberg, 5 km
Annual closure	Jährliche Schliessung	15/12→1/3
Weekly closure	Wöchentliche Schliessung	Monday

(Montag): Restaurant closed

Fees main season Preisliste hochsaison	18 holes	
	Week days Woche	We/Bank holidays We/Feiertag
Individual Individuell	€ 50	€ 65
Couple Ehepaar	€ 100	€ 130

Students: – 50%

Caddie Caddie on request — Electric Trolley Elektrokarren no
Buggy Elektrischer Wagen no — Clubs Leihschläger yes
Credit cards Kreditkarten no

Access Zufahrt: BAB A3 Nürnberg → Würzburg. Exit (Ausf.) Tennenlohe. B4 → Nürnberg. Kraftshof, turn right → Golf
Map 4 on page 354 Karte 4 Seite 354

GOLF COURSE — PLATZ 16/20

Site	Lage	
Maintenance	Instandhaltung	
Architect	Architekt	unknown
Type	Typ	forest
Relief	Begehbarkeit	
Water in play	Platz mit Wasser	
Exp. to wind	Wind ausgesetzt	
Trees in play	Platz mit Bäumen	

Scorecard Scorekarte	Chp. Chp.	Mens Herren	Ladies Damen
Length Länge	6220	6041	5306
Par	72	72	72
Slope system	133	129	130

Advised golfing ability — Empfohlene Spielstärke: 0 12 24 36
Hcp required — Min. Handicap: 36

CLUB HOUSE & AMENITIES — KLUBHAUS UND NEBENGEBÄUDE 7/10

Pro shop — Pro shop
Driving range — Übungsplatz

Sheltered überdacht 5 mats - On grass auf Rasen no, 12 mats open air - Putting-green Putting-grün yes - Pitching-green Pitching-grün yes

HOTEL FACILITIES — HOTEL BESCHREIBUNG 7/10

HOTELS HOTELS

Maritim - 319 rooms, D € 190 - Nürnberg 7 km
Tel (49) 0911 - 23 630, Fax (49) 0911 - 236 3823

Intercity Hotel - 158 rooms, D € 150 - Nürnberg 7 km
Tel (49) 0911 - 24 780, Fax (49) 0911 - 247 8999

Tassilo - 79 rooms, D € 118 - Nürnberg 5 km
Tel (49) 0911 - 326 66, Fax (49) 0911 - 326 6799

Am Jakobsmarkt - 77 rooms, D € 105 - Nürnberg 5 km
Tel (49) 0911 - 200 70, Fax (49) 0911 - 200 7200

RESTAURANTS RESTAURANTS

Schwarzer Adler - Kraftshof 2 km - Tel (49) 0911 - 305 858
Alte Post - Kraftshof 2 km - Tel (49) 0911 - 396 215
Essigbrätlein - Nürnberg 5 km - Tel (49) 0911 - 225 131

Rethmar

18 | 8 | 7

Zweimal neun Löcher wurden bereits für die Expo 2000 fertiggestellt. Die dritten neun Löcher sind in Planung und werden diesen hervorragenden Golfplatz noch reizvoller gestalten, als er ohnehin schon ist. Der bereits erwähnte Wort Dünen kommt nicht von ungefähr: Der Platz hat die Anmutung eines klassischen Linksplatzes, allerdings erinnern die Dünen mehr an County Louth oder Cruden Bay als an Ballybunion. Der Platz ist mit insgesamt 25 Hektar von Seen und Teichen gespickt, die durch das intelligente Design von Arnold Palmer und Ed Seay ins Spiel gebracht werden. Dieser Platz spiegelt den modernen "Zürück zur Natur-Trend" wider, obwohl man bei vielen Löchern die Wahl hat zwischen der britischen Variante, den Ball rollend zum Grün zu befördern oder die amerikanische Art des hohen Anspiels. Rethmar ist flach und verbirgt kein Hindernis. Der Platz ist geschickt und auffällig gestylt und variiert in seiner Schwierigkeit mit dem Wind. Die Grüns gelten als die besten in Deutschland. Aber nicht nur deshalb gehört Rethmar mittlerweile zu den Plätzen, die selbst die weiteste Anreise rechtfertigen.

Two 9-hole courses have been built for the Hanover World Expo 2000, while a third 9-hole layout is still in the planning. With dunes on the site, they give the site the links appeal claimed by the designers, although in terms of size the dunes here are more in the style of County Louth than Ballybunion. The estate is dotted with 25 hectares of lakes and ponds, deliberately brought into play by Palmer and Seay. This is an example of the ongoing "back to nature" trend in course design, although you often have the choice in the way you approach the greens, rolling the ball in British style or opting for the more American target golf. Rethmar, flat and with nothing to hide, sensibly landscaped and more or less challenging depending on the wind, is fast becoming one of those excellent courses with the kind of greens sought after by people who are really looking to test their game.

Rethmar Golf Links e.V. 1999
Seufzerallee 10
D - 313 319 SEHNDE-RETHMAR

Office	Sekretariat	(49) 05138 - 700 530
Pro shop	Pro shop	(49) 05138 - 70 053
Fax	Fax	(49) 05138 - 613 840
Web	www.rethmar-golf-links.de	
Situation	Lage	Hannover, 20 km
Annual closure	Jährliche Schliessung	no
Weekly closure	Wöchentliche Schliessung	Monday

(Montag): Restaurant closed in Winter

Fees main season Preisliste hochsaison	18 holes	
	Week days Woche	**We/Bank holidays** We/Feiertag
Individual Individuell	€ 40	€ 50
Couple Ehepaar	€ 80	€ 100

– 25: € 28 / 35 (We)

Caddie Caddie yes — **Electric Trolley** Elektrokarren no
Buggy Elektrischer Wagen yes — **Clubs** Leihschläger yes
Credit cards Kreditkarten
VISA - Eurocard - MasterCard - AMEX

Access Zufahrt : Hannover, B65 South (Südschnellweg) → Sehnde. In Sehnde → Peine. In Rethmar, third on the right, Osterkamp, follow → Golf.
Map 5 on page 357 Karte 5 Seite 357

GOLF COURSE
PLATZ — **18**/20

Site	Lage	
Maintenance	Instandhaltung	
Architect	Architekt	Arnold Palmer, Ed Seay
Type	Typ	open country, links
Relief	Begehbarkeit	
Water in play	Platz mit Wasser	
Exp. to wind	Wind ausgesetzt	
Trees in play	Platz mit Bäumen	

Scorecard Scorekarte	**Chp.** Chp.	**Mens** Herren	**Ladies** Damen
Length Länge	6440	5864	5163
Par	72	72	72
Slope system	137	133	130

Advised golfing ability Empfohlene Spielstärke — 0 12 24 36
Hcp required Min. Handicap 36

CLUB HOUSE & AMENITIES
KLUBHAUS UND NEBENGEBÄUDE — **8**/10

Pro shop Pro shop
Driving range Übungsplatz
Sheltered überdacht 8 mats - On grass auf Rasen yes - Putting-green Putting-grün yes - Pitching-green Pitching-grün yes

HOTEL FACILITIES
HOTEL BESCHREIBUNG — **7**/10

HOTELS HOTELS
Parkhotel Bilm - Sehnde-Bilm 5 km
50 rooms, D € 106 (with buffet)
Tel (49) 05138 - 60 90, Fax (49) 05138 - 609 100
Landhaus Bolzum - 20 rooms, D € 60 - Bolzum 5 km
Tel (49) 05138 - 608 290, Fax (49) 05138 - 6082920
Karstens Hotel Luisenhof - Hannover 20 km
154 rooms, D € 190
Tel (49) 0511 - 304 40, Fax (49) 0511 - 304 807

RESTAURANTS RESTAURANTS
Vitax - Sehnde 5 km - Tel (49) 05138 - 16 60
Anno - Hohenhameln-Clauen 8 km - Tel (49) 05128 - 409 714
Clichy - Hannover 20 km - Tel (49) 0511 - 312 447

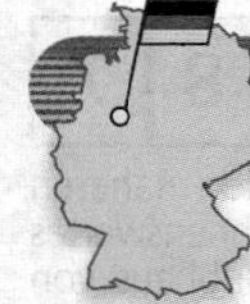

Rheine/Mesum

16 | 8 | 6

Rheine-Mesum ist einer der Plätze, auf denen man das ganze Jahr auf Grund des sandigen Bodens und der effektiven Drainage vorzüglich spielen kann. Der mittlerweile für seine guten Layouts bekannte Architekt Christoph Städler hat auch hier eine attraktiven Anlage entworfen, bei dem die Schwierigkeiten sehr gut über den gesamten Platz verteilt sind. Städler legte durch geschickte Erdbewegungen und Einbeziehung von Bäumen, Bunkern und Wasserhindernissen einen ausgewogenen, reizvollen Platz in die flache, leicht zu begehende und weitgehend offene Landschaft. Der Wind spielt hier gelegentlich ebenfalls eine Rolle. Alle Schwierigkeiten sind in der Regel vom Abschlag gut zu erkennen, aber eine Birdie-Karte ist sehr hilfreich. Das Eröffnungsloch fordert den meisten Spielern schon alles ab, dennoch fühlen sich auch schwächere Spieler auf dem Platz wohl, vorausgesetzt sie wählen die richtigen Abschläge. Ein hübsches Hotel auf dem Platz ergänzt das Angebot dieser überaus gastfreundlichen und service-orientierten Anlage.

This is first and foremost one of the most easily playable courses all year round on account of very sandy sub-soil and a particularly efficient drainage system. Course architect Christoph Städler needs no introduction and is known for his polished style producing attractive courses where difficulties are always very carefully designed into the layout. Here, on open and easily walkable terrain, he has very effectively moved a lot of earth and played with trees, bunkers and water to give the course great balance. The wind also has its say but that's something players have to cope with by themselves. Trouble is generally clearly in view, but the yardage book will be a great help. The first hole is a tough starter, but the average player should not be too worried about the rest, as this is a friendly course as long as you play from the tees that suit your game. A pretty on-site hotel completes the picture and makes this a course well worth the visit.

Golfsport Club Rheine/Mesum — 1998

Gut Winterbrock
D - 48432 RHEINE

Office Sekretariat (49) 05975 - 94 90
Pro shop Pro shop (49) 05975 - 919 200
Fax Fax (49) 05975 - 94 91
Web www.golfclub-rheine.de
Situation Lage Rheine, 7 km
Münster, 35 km
Annual closure Jährliche Schliessung no
Weekly closure Wöchentliche Schliessung Monday
(Montag),: Restaurant closed 10 → 03

Fees main season Preisliste hochsaison	18 holes	
	Week days Woche	**We/Bank holidays** We/Feiertag
Individual Individuell	€ 40	€ 50
Couple Ehepaar	€ 80	€ 100

Juniors – 18: – 50%

Caddie Caddie no — **Electric Trolley** Elektrokarren no
Buggy Elektrischer Wagen yes — **Clubs** Leihschläger yes
Credit cards Kreditkarten VISA - Eurocard

Access Zufahrt : Münster A1 → Osnabrück. Exit 76 (Ausfahrt 76), then Road 481 to Greven and → Rheine. After Emsdetten, turn → Mesum and Steinfurt. 500 m, turn left → Golf. **Map 5 on page 356** Karte 5 Seite 356

GOLF COURSE — PLATZ — 16/20

Site Lage
Maintenance Instandhaltung
Architect Architekt — Christoph Städler, Euro Golf Projekt
Type Typ — inland
Relief Begehbarkeit
Water in play Platz mit Wasser
Exp. to wind Wind ausgesetzt
Trees in play Platz mit Bäumen

Scorecard Scorekarte	**Chp.** Chp.	**Mens** Herren	**Ladies** Damen
Length Länge	6345	6036	4998
Par	72	72	72
Slope system	122	122	119

Advised golfing ability Empfohlene Spielstärke — 0 12 24 36
Hcp required Min. Handicap — 36

CLUB HOUSE & AMENITIES — KLUBHAUS UND NEBENGEBÄUDE — 8/10

Pro shop Pro shop
Driving range Übungsplatz
Sheltered überdacht 12 mats - On grass auf Rasen yes - Putting-green Putting-grün yes - Pitching-green Pitching-grün yes

HOTEL FACILITIES — HOTEL BESCHREIBUNG — 6/10

HOTELS HOTELS
Golf Hotel Gut Winterbrock - 8 rooms, D € 90 - on site
Tel (49) 05975 - 919 560, Fax (49) 05975 -917 5715
Altes Gasthaus Borcharding - Rheine-Mesum 2 km
9 rooms, D € 80
Tel (49) 05975 - 12 70, Fax (49) 05975 - 35 07
Zum Alten Brunnen - 18 rooms, D € 110 - Rheine 8 km
Tel (49) 05971 - 961 715, Fax (49) 05971 -961 7166

RESTAURANTS RESTAURANTS
Altes Gasthaus Borcharding - Rheine-Mesum 2 km
Tel (49) 05975 - 12 70
Zum Splenterkotten - Rheine-Elte 4 km - Tel (49) 05975 - 285
Zum Alten Brunnen - Rheine 8 km - Tel (49) 05971 - 961 715

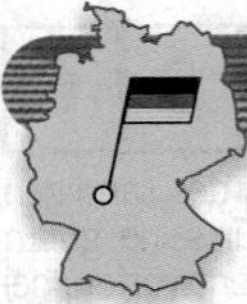

Rheinhessen

14 | 8 | 7

Mit den Nachbarplätzen von Domtal-Mommenhein und Nahetal in der näheren Umgebung, sind die Weinberg zwischen der Mosel und dem Rhein sind ein lohnenswertes Ausflugsziel. Für Golfer bietet sich ein Aufenthalt im exzellenten Hotel im Klubhaus von Rheinhessen an. Hier, ein wenig abseits der ausgetretenen Pfade, kann man sich entspannen, von der Klubhaus-Terasse das phantastische Panorama der Weinberge geniessen. Der Platz ist keineswegs perfekt, weil zu viele Löcher "blind" sind, ein Fehler, der wie schon in Nahetal leicht hätte vermieden werden können. Ein anderer Negativpunkt ist der Graben und der Teich am 14. Loch, einem Par 5, nach 245 m, genau dort, wo der Drive von guten Spielern landet. Dies zwingt dazu, entweder den Ball kurz abzulegen oder ein unkalkulierbares Risiko einzugehen. Wer hier zum erstenmal spielt, wird die Spielstrategie nicht immer erkennen und viele Überraschungen erleben. Dennoch ist das Layout reizvoll, obwohl die vielen Schräglagen viele Golfer überfordern können.

With the vineyards of Nahe between the Moselle and the Rhine this is an attractive region to visit. For golfers, a stay at the excellent hotel in the Rheinhessen club-house is most relaxing, a little off the beaten track. The club-house overlooks the vineyards and provides a superb panorama. The course itself is by no means perfect, as too many holes are blind, a mistake that could have been avoided. Another rather negative feature is the ditch and pond 245 metres from the 14th tee, just where a good drive should be landing. This forces the golfer to take unreasonable risks or to lay up ridiculously short. People playing here for the first time may well encounter problems of strategy and a number of surprises. Otherwise the layout is pleasant enough, the difficulties are often visible and only the contoured relief might handicap players who are not on top of their swing.

Golf Club Rheinhessen Hofgut Wissberg-St.Johann e.V. — 1993

Hofgut Wissberg
D - 55578 ST. JOHANN

Office	Sekretariat	(49) 06701 - 200 80
Pro shop	Pro shop	(49) 06701 - 8326
Fax	Fax	(49) 06701 - 200 825
Web	www.gc-rheinhessen.de	
Situation	Lage	Mainz, 25 km
Annual closure	Jährliche Schliessung	no
Weekly closure	Wöchentliche Schliessung	no
Fees main season	Preisliste hochsaison	18 holes

	Week days Woche	We/Bank holidays We/Feiertag
Individual Individuell	€ 50	€ 70
Couple Ehepaar	€ 100	€ 140

– 21 & Students: – 50%

Caddie Caddie no — **Electric Trolley** Elektrokarren no
Buggy Elektrischer Wagen no — **Clubs** Leihschläger yes
Credit cards Kreditkarten no

Access Zufahrt : Mainz, A60, A60 until AK Nahetal
Map 3 on page 353 Karte 3 Seite 353

GOLF COURSE — PLATZ — 14/20

Site	Lage	
Maintenance	Instandhaltung	
Architect	Architekt	Armin Keller
Type	Typ	open country, hilly
Relief	Begehbarkeit	
Water in play	Platz mit Wasser	
Exp. to wind	Wind ausgesetzt	
Trees in play	Platz mit Bäumen	

Scorecard Scorekarte	Chp. Chp.	Mens Herren	Ladies Damen
Length Länge	6225	6067	5321
Par	72	72	72
Slope system	129	129	129

Advised golfing ability Empfohlene Spielstärke — 0 12 24 36
Hcp required Min. Handicap — We: 28/32

CLUB HOUSE & AMENITIES — KLUBHAUS UND NEBENGEBÄUDE — 8/10

Pro shop Pro shop
Driving range Übungsplatz
Sheltered überdacht 4 mats - On grass auf Rasen yes - Putting-green Putting-grün yes - Pitching-green Pitching-grün yes

HOTEL FACILITIES — HOTEL BESCHREIBUNG — 7/10

HOTELS HOTELS

Golf Hotel Rheinessen - 21 rooms, D € 110 - on site
Tel (49) 06701 - 916 450, Fax (49) 06701 - 916 455

Landhotel Kauzenberg - Bad Kreuznach 15 km
45 rooms, D € 90
Tel (49) 0671 - 38 000, Fax (49) 0671 - 3800 124

Insel-Stuben - 22 rooms, D € 92 - Bad Kreuznach 15 km
Tel (49) 0671 - 837 990, Fax (49) 0671 - 837 9955

RESTAURANTS RESTAURANTS

Metzlers Gasthof - Hackenheim 17 km - Tel (49) 0671 - 653 12
Im Gütchen - Bad Kreuznach 15 km - Tel (49) 0671 - 426 26
Weinwelt im Dienheimer Hof - Bad Kreuznach 15 km
Tel (49) 0671 - 920 0811

Rittergut Birkhof

15	8	7

Nach der Anfahrt durch eine Lindenallee erreicht man einen weiteren Platz des viel beschäftigten Golfplatz-Architekten Kurt Rossknecht. Das Gelände strahlt viel Geschichte aus, denn die Besitzerfamilie lebt seit dem 14. Jahrhundert auf dem alten Rittergut. 84 Hektar einer ehemaligen Baumschule und von Tulpenfeldern wurden für den Bau des Golfplatzes genutzt. Der Platz ist in jeder Beziehung hervorragend, ein landschaftlich gut gestalteter Platz, auf dem man gerne jeden Tag spielt. Die Qualität des Layouts, die abwechslungsreichen Löcher, das Gefühl der Offenheit und die Abwesenheit von Schwierigkeiten, die für Durchschnittsgolfer nicht zu bewältigen sind, sprechen für den Platz. Man muss lediglich den Ball aus dem dichten, hohen Rough heraushalten, das den Spielbahnen Kontur verleiht. Das Rittergut Birkhof ist ein guter Familienplatz, weil ihn auch Golfer unterschiedlicher Spielstärke genießen können. Abgerundet wird das Angebot durch vorzügliche Einrichtungen, darunter zwei Restaurants und ein Café.

After a driveway lined with old lime-trees, you reach a fine course designed by the most prolific course architect in Germany today, Kurt Rossknecht. There is an historical flavour to the site, as the same family has lived here since the 14th century and has now dedicated 84 hectares of former nurseries and tulip fields to the building of a golf course. An excellent course in every respect, this imaginative and well-landscaped layout is one where you would willingly play as a member because it is nonstop pleasure every time. The quality of layout, the variety of holes, the feeling of wide open space and the friendliness for the family to play, as everyone will have fun at their own level. Completing the picture for this fine course are the club's excellent facilities, including two restaurants and a café.

Golf Club Rittergut Birkhof e.V. — 1995

Rittergut Birkhof
D - 41352 KORSCHENBROICH

Office	Sekretariat	(49) 02131 - 510 660
Pro shop	Pro shop	(49) 02131 - 510 614
Fax	Fax	(49) 02131 - 153 225
Web	www.gc-rittergutbirkhof.de	
Situation	Lage	Düsseldorf, 20 km
Annual closure	Jährliche Schliessung	no
Weekly closure	Wöchentliche Schliessung	no

Fees main season Preisliste hochsaison — 18 holes

	Week days Woche	We/Bank holidays We/Feiertag
Individual Individuell	€ 43	€ 53
Couple Ehepaar	€ 86	€ 106

Sudents (under 25): – 50 %

Caddie Caddie no — **Electric Trolley** Elektrokarren yes

Buggy Elektrischer Wagen no — **Clubs** Leihschläger yes

Credit cards Kreditkarten
VISA - Eurocard - MasterCard - AMEX - DC

Access Zufahrt : A57 Köln-Neuss-Krefeld. Exit (Ausf.) 19 Neuss-Büttgen. L381 → Büttgen, after 5 km turn left on L32 (Büttger Weg) → Korschenbroich-Glehn, then first road on the left → Rittergut Birkhof.

Map 3 on page 352 Karte 3 Seite 352

GOLF COURSE — PLATZ — 15/20

Site	Lage	
Maintenance	Instandhaltung	
Architect	Architekt	Kurt Rossknecht
Type	Typ	parkland
Relief	Begehbarkeit	
Water in play	Platz mit Wasser	
Exp. to wind	Wind ausgesetzt	
Trees in play	Platz mit Bäumen	

Scorecard Scorekarte	Chp. Chp.	Mens Herren	Ladies Damen
Length Länge	6247	5832	5114
Par	73	73	73
Slope system	136	132	132

Advised golfing ability Empfohlene Spielstärke — 0 12 24 36

Hcp required Min. Handicap — 36

CLUB HOUSE & AMENITIES — KLUBHAUS UND NEBENGEBÄUDE — 8/10

Pro shop Pro shop
Driving range Übungsplatz
Sheltered überdacht 18 mats - On grass auf Rasen yes - Putting-green Putting-grün yes - Pitching-green Pitching-grün yes

HOTEL FACILITIES — HOTEL BESCHREIBUNG — 7/10

HOTELS HOTELS

Elisenhof - Rheydt (Mönchengladbach) 15 km
67 rooms, D € 110
Tel (49) 02166 - 93 30, Fax (49) 02166 - 933 400

Gästehaus Bienefeld - 14 rooms, D € 105 - Kleinenbroich 4 km
Tel (49) 02161 - 998 300, Fax (49) 02161 998 3099

Coenen - 50 rooms, D € 120 - Rheydt 12 km
Tel (49) 02166 - 160 06, Fax (49) 02166 - 186 795

RESTAURANTS RESTAURANTS

Gasthaus Stappen - Steinhausen 5 km
Tel (49) 02166 - 882 26
Zur Traube - Kleinenbroich 5 km - Tel (49) 02161 - 670 404

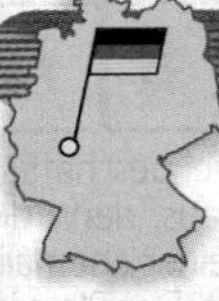

Schloss Braunfels

16	7	7

Die alten Bauernhäuser, die einen willkommen heissen, sind gleichermassen beeindruckend wie die Aussicht auf Schloss Braunfels. Der Architekt hat das für einen Golfplatz gut geeignete Gelände absichtlich nur wenig verändert. Die Höhenunterschiede, die einen nicht davon abhalten sollten zu Fuss zu Gehen, spielen eine erheblich Rolle bei der Schlägerwahl, der wiederum eine Schlüsselrolle zukommt beim Anspiel einiger der zahlreichen, erhöht angelegten Grüns. Priorität hat auch die Vermeidung der Bäume und der Wasserhindernisse, letztere kommen an vier Löchern ins Spiel. Schloss Braunfels verlangt von den Spielern sicherlich kein überdurchschnittliches Können, dennoch kann die Fähigkeit den Ball sowohl mit Draw als auch Fade spielen zu können, bei der Endabrechnung von entscheidendem Vorteil sein. Sein Lage, die Umgebung, Vielseitigkeit und dazu ein komfortables Clubhaus – alles Faktoren, die für diesen Platz sprechen. Zudem liegt Wetzlar ganz in der Nähe, die Heimatstadt von Charlotte, der Heldin in Goethes "Werther".

The old farm buildings that welcome you are impressive, as are the views of Braunfels castle. The designer visibly did not want to upset terrain that is easily adaptable to golf. Although easy enough to play on foot, the slopes need to be reckoned with, at least when it comes to choosing the right club, a key factor here for attacking some of the many elevated greens. The first job is to avoid the trees and the water hazards in play on four holes. Schloss Braunfels certainly does not require above-average virtuosity, but being able to flight the ball both ways can be important in the final count. The location, the comfortable club-house, the setting and variety are major assets, as is the closeness to Wetzlar, the town of Charlotte, Goethe's heroine in "Werther".

Golf Club Schloss Braunfels — 1970

Homburger Hof
D - 35619 BRAUNFELS-LAHN

Office Sekretariat (49) 06442 - 4530
Pro shop Pro shop (49) 06442 - 5752
Fax Fax (49) 06442 - 6683
Web www.golfclub-braunfels.de
Situation Lage Frankfurt, 80 km
Wetzlar (pop. 53 000), 15 km
Annual closure Jährliche Schliessung no
Weekly closure Wöchentliche Schliessung Monday
(Montag): Restaurant closed

Fees main season Preisliste hochsaison	18 holes	
	Week days Woche	**We/Bank holidays** We/Feiertag
Individual Individuell	€ 35	€ 50
Couple Ehepaar	€ 70	€ 100

– 21 / Students: € 20 / 30 (We)

Caddie Caddie on request — **Electric Trolley** Elektrokarren no
Buggy Elektrischer Wagen no — **Clubs** Leihschläger yes
Credit cards Kreditkarten no

Access Zufahrt : Frankfurt A5 Nord, A45 → Wetzlar. Exit (Ausf.) Wetzlar Ost, B49 → Limburg. Leun, → Braunfels. Restaurant Obermühle, → Golf
Map 3 on page 353 Karte 3 Seite 353

GOLF COURSE — PLATZ 16/20

Site Lage
Maintenance Instandhaltung
Architect Architekt B. von Limburger
Type Typ parkland
Relief Begehbarkeit
Water in play Platz mit Wasser
Exp. to wind Wind ausgesetzt
Trees in play Platz mit Bäumen

Scorecard Scorekarte	**Chp.** Chp.	**Mens** Herren	**Ladies** Damen
Length Länge	6104	5940	5216
Par	73	73	73
Slope system	125	122	126

Advised golfing ability Empfohlene Spielstärke 0 12 24 36
Hcp required Min. Handicap 36

CLUB HOUSE & AMENITIES — KLUBHAUS UND NEBENGEBÄUDE 7/10

Pro shop Pro shop
Driving range Übungsplatz
Sheltered überdacht 6 mats - On grass auf Rasen yes - Putting-green Putting-grün yes - Pitching-green Pitching-grün yes

HOTEL FACILITIES — HOTEL BESCHREIBUNG 7/10

HOTELS HOTELS

Schloss-Hotel Braunfels - Braunfels 4 km
30 rooms, D € 90
Tel (49) 06442 - 30 50, Fax (49) 06442 - 305 222

Zum Alten Amtsgericht - Braunfels 3 km
22 rooms, D € 115
Tel (49) 06442 - 93 480, Fax (49) 06442 - 934 811

Schloss-Hotel Weilburg - 50 rooms, D € 110 - Weilburg 8 km
Tel (49) 06471 - 509 00, Fax (49) 06471 -509 0111

RESTAURANTS RESTAURANTS

La Lucia - Weilburg 8 km - Tel (49) 06471 - 2130
Zum Alten Amtsgericht - Braunfels 3 km
Tel (49) 06442 - 93 480

Schloss Egmating

15	7	7

Der Architekt Kurt Rossknecht versteht es, den von ihm entworfenen Anlagen seinen ganz persönlichen Stempel aufzudrücken, was in erster Linie in der sorgfältigen Gestaltung und Positionierung von Bunkern und Grüns zum Ausdruck kommt. Da auf Schloss Egmating wenig Wasser und so gut wie keine Bäume ins Spiel kommen, bilden hier vor allem das hügelige Terrain sowie die Fairway-Bunker den Schwerpunkt der Verteidigung zwischen Abschlag und Grün. Wer glaubt, dass Longhitter hier im Vorteil sind, sollte nicht die Vorzüge eines guten kurzen Spiels sowie die Fähigkeit guter Techniker, den Ball in unterschiedlichen Flugkurven zu spielen, unterschätzen. Letzteres gilt umso mehr, als eine Mischung aus hohen Lob und "bump and run" Schlägen erforderlich ist, um die Grüns anzuspielen. Wenn der Wind weht, ist es recht hilfreich die Flugbahn des Balles richtig einschätzen zu können. Die grosse Anzahl von Abschlägen an jedem Loch macht den Platz für alle Spielstärken zugänglich, solange bei Spielern mit hohem Handicap der Score nicht zu sehr im Vordergund steht. Den Platz sollte man auch in den nächsten Jahren im Auge behalten.

Kurt Rossknecht likes to give courses his own personal stamp, if only through the careful attention he pays to the design of bunkers, to their positioning and to putting surfaces. At Schloss Egmating, water is not a major feature and trees hardly feature at all, so sloping terrain and fairway bunkers form the core of the difficulties en route to the green. You might think that long-hitters would have the upper hand here, but greater rewards often go to the technicians, the flighters of the ball, and even to the short game experts, who have to alternate between high lob and bump and run shots to get home and dry. If the wind blows, a sound knowledge of the science of trajectories will come in handy. The large number of tee-areas makes this a course for all skills, as long as high-handicappers don't worry unduly about a three-figure score. A course well worth watching in the years ahead.

Schloss Egmating 1990
Schlosstrasse 15
D - 85658 EGMATING

Office	Sekretariat	(49) 08095 - 90 860
Pro shop	Pro shop	(49) 08095 - 908 610
Fax	Fax	(49) 08095 - 9086-66
Web	www.golf.de/egmating	
Situation	Lage	München, 25 km

Aying (pop. 3 000), 3 km

Annual closure	Jährliche Schliessung	1/12→31/3
Weekly closure	Wöchentliche Schliessung	no

Fees main season Preisliste hochsaison	Week days Woche	We/Bank holidays We/Feiertag
		18 holes
Individual Individuell	€ 65	€ 80
Couple Ehepaar	€ 130	€ 160

Caddie Caddie on request — **Electric Trolley** Elektrokarren yes
Buggy Elektrischer Wagen yes — **Clubs** Leihschläger yes
Credit cards Kreditkarten no

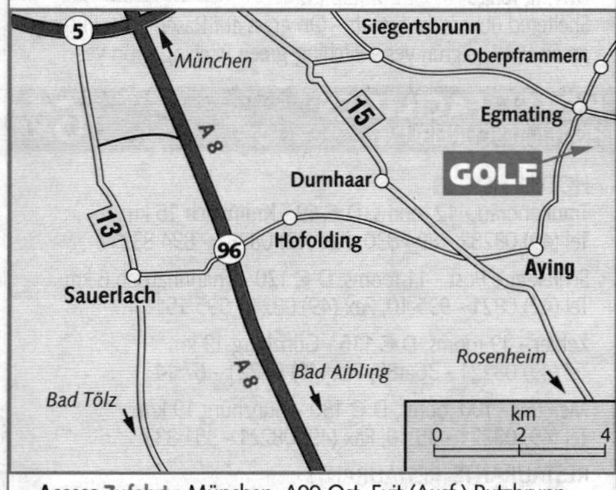

Access Zufahrt : München, A99 Ost. Exit (Ausf.) Putzbrunn → Oberpframmen → Golf
Map 2 on page 351 Karte 2 Seite 351

GOLF COURSE
PLATZ — 15/20

Site	Lage	
Maintenance	Instandhaltung	
Architect	Architekt	Kurt Rossknecht
Type	Typ	open country
Relief	Begehbarkeit	
Water in play	Platz mit Wasser	
Exp. to wind	Wind ausgesetzt	
Trees in play	Platz mit Bäumen	

Scorecard Scorekarte	Chp. Chp.	Mens Herren	Ladies Damen
Length Länge	6364	6014	5272
Par	72	72	72
Slope system	130	128	126

Advised golfing ability Empfohlene Spielstärke: 0 12 24 36
Hcp required Min. Handicap 36

CLUB HOUSE & AMENITIES
KLUBHAUS UND NEBENGEBÄUDE — 7/10

Pro shop Pro shop
Driving range Übungsplatz
Sheltered überdacht yes - On grass auf Rasen yes - Putting-green Putting-grün yes - Pitching-green Pitching-grün yes

HOTEL FACILITIES
HOTEL BESCHREIBUNG — 7/10

HOTELS HOTELS
Brauereigasthof Aying - 34 rooms, D from € 135 - Aying 3 km
Tel (49) 08095 - 906 50, Fax (49) 08095 - 906 566

Aigner - 73 rooms, D € 100 - Ottobrunn 13 km
Tel (49) 089 - 608 170, Fax (49) 089 -6083 213

Arabella - München-Bogenhausen 25 km
657 rooms, D from € 200
Tel (49) 089 - 92 640, Fax (49) 089 - 9264 8009

RESTAURANTS RESTAURANTS
Tantris - München-Schwabing 25 km - Tel (49) 089 - 362 061
Haflhof - Münster b. Egmating 1 km - Tel (49) 08093 - 5336
Wirtshaus zum Schweinsbrau - Glonn 6 km
Tel (49) 08093 - 909 445

Schloss Klingenburg

15	6	6

In einem alten Schlosspark gelegen ist der Platz mit einer Vielzahl herrlicher Bäume unterschiedlicher Art bestanden. Der Ort strahlt, verstärkt durch den umliegenden Wald, eine Aura von Ruhe und Abgeschiedenheit aus. Obwohl der Platz angenehm zu spielen ist, bleibt er angesichts der idealen Voraussetzungen, die den Architekten zu einem Meisterwerk hätten beflügeln sollen, etwas hinter den Erwartungen zurück. Dieser schien jedoch mehr darum besorgt einen spielbaren Platz zu entwerfen als den Platz zu einer echten Herausforderung zu machen. Die wenigen Fairwaybunker haben ein sehr flaches Profil. Bäume, Grünbunker und Wasserhindernisse dagegen stellen eine angemessene Gefahr dar. Abgesehen von den Eröffnungs- und Schlusslöchern verläuft der Platz über relativ ebenes Terrain, auf dem alle Hindernisse gut erkennbar sind. Klingenburgs gut verteidigte Grüns (fünf davon sind blind) verlangen nach "Target Golf", so dass Spieler, die den Ball faden können, einen gewissen Vorteil haben.

Laid out in old castle grounds, this course has retained some superb varieties of trees, and the impression of peace and tranquillity that exudes from the overall setting is enhanced by the surrounding forest. But while the course is pleasant to play, it doesn't quite come up to expectations. A site as fine as this should have galvanised the architect into creating greater things. He was probably more concerned with designing a pleasant course rather than looking for stiff challenges, so the rare fairway bunkers are virtually flat, and trees, green-side bunkers and water hazards were most likely thought to be too penalising. A somewhat flattish course without any hidden traps, Schloss Klingenburg is more of a target golf course with well-protected greens (some are blind) and will give greater help to people who fade the ball. In theory within the grasp of anyone, you need to be on top of your game to get a good score.

Golf-Club Schloss Klingenburg 1980

Schloss Klingenburg
D - 89343 JETTINGEN-SCHEPPACH

Office	Sekretariat	(49) 08225 - 30 30
Pro shop	Pro shop	(49) 08225 - 30 320
Fax	Fax	(49) 08225 - 30 350
Web	www.golf-klingenburg.de	
Situation	Lage	Augsburg 50 km

Ulm (pop. 110 000), 45 km

Annual closure Jährliche Schliessung — no

Weekly closure Wöchentliche Schliessung — Monday
(Montag): Restaurant closed

Fees main season Preisliste hochsaison	18 holes	
	Week days Woche	**We/Bank holidays** We/Feiertag
Individual Individuell	€ 45	€ 60
Couple Ehepaar	€ 90	€ 120

– 21 / Students: – 50%

Caddie Caddie	no	**Electric Trolley** Elektrokarren	no
Buggy Elektrischer Wagen	no	**Clubs** Leihschläger	yes
Credit cards Kreditkarten	no		

Access Zufahrt : A8 Stuttgart-München. Exit (Ausf.) Burgau. → Jettingen. Schöneberg. 8 km → Golf

Map 2 on page 350 Karte 2 Seite 350

GOLF COURSE
PLATZ — 15/20

Site	Lage	
Maintenance	Instandhaltung	
Architect	Architekt	Donald Harradine
Type	Typ	parkland
Relief	Begehbarkeit	
Water in play	Platz mit Wasser	
Exp. to wind	Wind ausgesetzt	
Trees in play	Platz mit Bäumen	

Scorecard Scorekarte	**Chp.** Chp.	**Mens** Herren	**Ladies** Damen
Length Länge	6178	6007	5354
Par	72	72	72
Slope system	130	128	128

Advised golfing ability Empfohlene Spielstärke — 0 12 24 36

Hcp required Min. Handicap — 35

CLUB HOUSE & AMENITIES
KLUBHAUS UND NEBENGEBÄUDE — 6/10

Pro shop	Pro shop
Driving range	Übungsplatz

Sheltered überdacht 5 mats - On grass auf Rasen yes - Putting-green Putting-grün yes - Pitching-green Pitching-grün yes

HOTEL FACILITIES
HOTEL BESCHREIBUNG — 6/10

HOTELS HOTELS

Traubenbräu - 12 rooms, D € 69 - Krumbach 15 km
Tel (49) 08282 - 894 830, Fax (49) 08282 - 894 833

Schreiegg's Post - 11 rooms, D € 120 - Thannhausen 6 km
Tel (49) 0821 - 995 10, Fax (49) 0821 - 995 151

Zettler - 49 rooms, D € 115 - Günzburg 19 km
Tel (49) 08221 - 36 480, Fax (49) 08221 - 67 14

Mercure - 100 rooms, D € 130 - Günzburg 19 km
Tel (49) 08221 - 35 10, Fax (49) 08221 - 351 333

RESTAURANTS RESTAURANTS

Gasthof Traubenbräu - Krumbach - Tel (49) 08282 - 32093
Sonnenhof - Thannhausen 6 km - Tel (49) 08281 - 2014
Schreiegg's Post - Thannhausen 6 km - Tel (49) 0821 - 995 10

Schloss Langenstein

16 | 8 | 5

Die Nähe zur Schweiz und der schönen Stadt Konstanz, sowie prächtige Ausblicke auf den Bodensee verleihen diesem noch recht neuen Golfplatz eine unbestreitbare Anziehungskraft. Der Föhn kann die Ankunft des Frühlings hier etwas beschleunigen, während der Rest von Deutschland noch vor Kälte bibbert. Das ziemlich hügelige Terrain verlangt vom Spieler eine gute Kondition. Trotz der Geländeunebenheiten sind die Hindernisse gut erkennbar und gibt es keine blinden Grüns. Das Schlüsselwort Kontrolle gilt sowohl für den Ball als auch das eigene Spiel, da die "wilderen" Golfer hier häufig ernsthaft in Schwierigkeiten geraten können. Ehrlich gesagt sollten Anfänger und "Hacker" ihre Schläger hier besser im Auto lassen und stattdessen den guten Spielern zuschauen, es sein denn, sie sind bereit die Runde als Teil des Lernprozesses zu betrachten. Gut ausgewogen und kompetent konzipiert ist Schloss Langenstein ein Muss für den der diese schöne Gegend erkundet.

Being very close to Switzerland and to the pretty town of Konstanz, and offering some fabulous views of the Bodensee, this course has unquestionable appeal. The foehn wind can bring spring a little early here, while the rest of Germany is still shivering, but you need to be in good shape, even early in the year, because the terrain is rather hilly. Despite the relief, difficulties are rarely hidden from view and no greens are blind. The key word here is control - of your ball and your game - as the wilder players can often end up in serious trouble. To be honest, even though the course makes for a superb walk, beginners and hackers are better off leaving their clubs in the car and watching the good players ply their trade... unless they consider a round here to be part of the learning process. Well-balanced and tastefully designed, Schloss Langenstein is a must if you are exploring this pretty region.

Country Club Schloss Langenstein — 1991

Schloss Langenstein
D - 78359 ORSINGEN-NENZINGEN

Office Sekretariat (49) 07774 - 50 651
Pro shop Pro shop (49) 07774 - 50 672
Fax Fax (49) 07774 - 50 699
Web www.schloss-langenstein.de
Situation Lage Singen, 8 km
Stockach (pop. 15 200), 6 km
Annual closure Jährliche Schliessung 1/12→28/2
Weekly closure Wöchentliche Schliessung Monday
(Montag): Restaurant closed

Fees main season Preisliste hochsaison	18 holes	
	Week days Woche	**We/Bank holidays** We/Feiertag
Individual Individuell	€ 50	€ 70
Couple Ehepaar	€ 100	€ 140

– 21 / Students: – 50%

Caddie Caddie no — **Electric Trolley** Elektrokarren yes
Buggy Elektrischer Wagen yes — **Clubs** Leihschläger yes
Credit cards Kreditkarten no

Access Zufahrt : A81 Stuttgart-Singen. Exit (Ausf.) Engen. B31 → Stockach. In Eigeltingen, turn right → Schloss Langenstein.
Map 1 on page 349 Karte 1 Seite 349

GOLF COURSE — PLATZ — 16/20

Site Lage
Maintenance Instandhaltung
Architect Architekt — unknown
Type Typ — open country, hilly
Relief Begehbarkeit
Water in play Platz mit Wasser
Exp. to wind Wind ausgesetzt
Trees in play Platz mit Bäumen

Scorecard Scorekarte	**Chp.** Chp.	**Mens** Herren	**Ladies** Damen
Length Länge	6389	5961	5268
Par	73	72	72
Slope system	128	127	128

Advised golfing ability Empfohlene Spielstärke — 0 12 24 36
Hcp required Min. Handicap — 36 (30 We)

CLUB HOUSE & AMENITIES — KLUBHAUS UND NEBENGEBÄUDE — 8/10

Pro shop Pro shop
Driving range Übungsplatz
Sheltered überdacht 15 mats - On grass auf Rasen yes (April → Oct) - Putting-green Putting-grün yes - Pitching-green Pitching-grün yes

HOTEL FACILITIES — HOTEL BESCHREIBUNG — 5/10

HOTELS HOTELS
Haus Sättele - 15 rooms, D € 85 - Steisslingen 5 km
Tel (49) 07738 - 929 050, Fax (49) 07738 - 929 059

Flohr's - 9 rooms, D € 115 - Überlingen 10 km
Tel (49) 07731 - 93 230, Fax (49) 07731 - 932 323

Art Villa Am See - 10 rooms, D from € 150 - Radolfzell 3 km
Tel (49) 07732 - 944 40, Fax (49) 07732 - 944 410

RESTAURANTS RESTAURANTS
Flohr's - Überlingen 10 km - Tel (49) 07731 - 93 230
Salzburger Stub'n - Rielasingen-Worblingen 12 km
Tel (49) 07731 - 27 349

Schloss Lüdersburg *Old Course*

15	7	6

Die 18 von Dr. Wolfgang Siegmann entworfenen Löcher des Old Courses wurden um die 18 Spielbahnen des von Nicklaus Design gestalteten Lakes Courses erweitert. Sämtliche Löcher können als technisch anspruchsvoll und optisch gelungen bezeichnet werden. Wenn man nur einen Platz spielt, sollte man die alten 18 Löcher wählen. Dieser Platz mit seinen engen, von grossen Bäume gesäumten Spielbahnen wird von einem Wasserlauf durchschnitten, der an sechs Fairways als nur eines von vielen Wasserhindernissen ins Spiel kommt. Von diesen kleinen Boshaftigkeiten sollten sich auch durchschnittliche Spieler nicht abschrecken lassen. Zwar werden diese hier womöglich keinen guten Score erzielen, aber schliesslich hängt der Spass am Golf nicht allein vom Ergebnis ab. Wer den alten Löcher erfolgreich bewältigen will, darf in seiner Aufmerksamkeit und Konzentration nie nachlassen. Dieser Platz passt gut in eine Region, der es an anspruchsvollen Golfplätzen nicht mangelt. Er wird einem selbst nach häufigem Spielen nie langweilig.

The original 18 holes designed by Dr. Wolfgang Siegmann (Old Course) have been supplemented by the 18 holer Lakes Course laid out by Nicklaus Design. They are all as technical as they are agreeable to the eye, but if you cannot play all 36, and without wishing to offend the Golden Bear and his team, you are best advised going for the unity of style offered by the original layout. It is rather narrow, lined with large trees and cut by a stream that crosses the fairways six times as one of the many water hazards. However, Lüdersburg is not spiteful enough to put off the average player. They may not return a fabulous card, but the fun of golf does not depend solely on performance. The holes call for some hard work if they are to be successfully negotiated, enough to keep the player constantly on his toes. In a region where there is no shortage of challenging golf courses, this one is well placed. What's more, you can play it again and again without a minute's boredom.

Golf- und Landclub Schloss Lüdersburg 1986

Lüdersburger Strasse 21
D - 21379 LÜDERSBURG/LÜNEBURG

Office	Sekretariat	(49) 04139 - 697 00
Pro shop	Pro shop	(49) 04139 - 699 250
Fax	Fax	(49) 04139 - 697 070
Web	www.luedersburg.de	
Situation	Lage	Hamburg 50 km

Lüneburg, 15 km

Annual closure	Jährliche Schliessung	no
Weekly closure	Wöchentliche Schliessung	no
Fees main season	Preisliste hochsaison	18 holes

	Week days Woche	We/Bank holidays We/Feiertag
Individual Individuell	€ 35	€ 55
Couple Ehepaar	€ 70	€ 110

Students – 27: – 50%

Caddie Caddie no — **Electric Trolley** Elektrokarren no

Buggy Elektrischer Wagen yes — **Clubs** Leihschläger yes

Credit cards Kreditkarten Eurocard - MasterCard

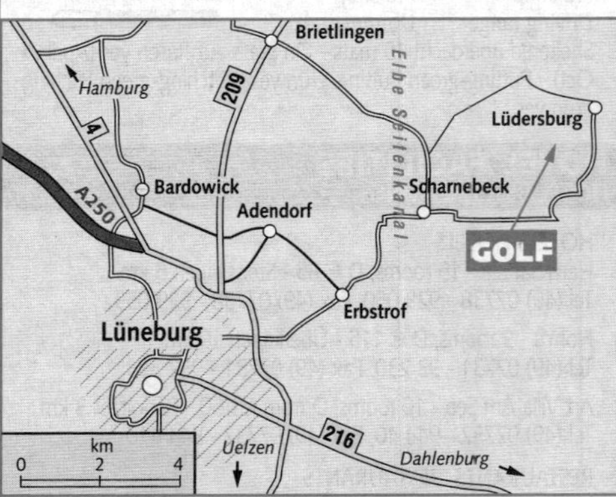

Access Zufahrt : A250 Hamburg-Lüneburg.
Exit (Ausf.) Lüneburg/Ebersberg. Scranebeck, Lüdersburg.
Map 7 on page 360 Karte 7 Seite 360

GOLF COURSE — PLATZ 15/20

Site	Lage	
Maintenance	Instandhaltung	
Architect	Architekt	W. Siegmann Jack Nicklaus
Type	Typ	parkland
Relief	Begehbarkeit	
Water in play	Platz mit Wasser	
Exp. to wind	Wind ausgesetzt	
Trees in play	Platz mit Bäumen	

Scorecard Scorekarte	Chp. Chp.	Mens Herren	Ladies Damen
Length Länge	6568	5912	5229
Par	73	73	73
Slope system	128	128	126

Advised golfing ability Empfohlene Spielstärke: 0 12 24 36

Hcp required Min. Handicap 36

CLUB HOUSE & AMENITIES — KLUBHAUS UND NEBENGEBÄUDE 7/10

Pro shop Pro shop
Driving range Übungsplatz
Sheltered überdacht yes - On grass auf Rasen yes - Putting-green Putting-grün yes - Pitching-green Pitching-grün yes

HOTEL FACILITIES — HOTEL BESCHREIBUNG 6/10

HOTELS HOTELS

Golf Schloss Lüdersburg - 45 rooms, D from € 120 - on site
Tel (49) 04139 - 697 00, Fax (49) 04139 -697 0700

Seminaris - 191 rooms, D € 120 - Lüneburg 16 km
Tel (49) 04131 - 71 30, Fax (49) 04131 - 713 128

Hof Reinstorf - 87 rooms, D € 120 - Reinstorf 15 km
Tel (49) 04137 - 80 90, Fax (49) 04137 - 80 9100

Lauenburger Mühle - 34 rooms, D € 94 - Lauenburg 9 km
Tel (49) 04153 - 58 90, Fax (49) 04153 - 55 555

RESTAURANTS RESTAURANTS

Hof Reinstorf - Reinstorf 15 km - Tel (49) 04137 - 8090
Zum Heidkrug - Lüneburg 16 km - Tel (49) 04131 - 241 60

Schloss Myllendonk

16	7	7

Das im Mittelalter erbaute Schloss Myllendonk dient nicht nur als Clubhaus, sondern gibt dem Golfplatz, der im übrigen einen ausgezeichneten Ruf hat, auch seinen Namen. Die schöne Lage täuscht in vielen Fällen über schwerwiegende Schwächen beim Platzdesign hinweg. So enttäuscht uns eine Anzahl sehr nahe beieinander liegender Spielbahnen, trotz der sie begrenzenden schönen Bäume, die das Spiel erschweren. Genaue Drives und kontrolliert geschlagene Bälle sind Voraussetzung, um die Grüns von der besten Position aus angreifen zu können. Aufgrund des sehr ebenen Geländes sind die meisten Hindernisse gut erkennbar. Dies verleiht denen, die hier zum ersten mal spielen, eine gewisse Zuversicht, wenngleich einen das berechtigte Gefühl beschleicht, dass die Wasserläufe und Seen nur darauf lauern, einem das Leben schwer zu machen. Ungeübte Golfer, denen der Platz möglicherweise etwas schwierig erscheint, seien daran erinnert, dass der Score nicht alles ist, worum es beim Golf geht.

The castle of Myllendonk, which dates from the Middle Ages, gives this course of excellent repute both its name and its club-house. The beauty of the setting can often conceal some glaring errors in design, and while we might regret a number of fairways which are too close to each other, the trees between them are magnificent and really add to the playing difficulty. Accurate driving and flighted shots are vital if you want to have any hope of hitting the greens from the easiest position. As the terrain is very flat, most hazards are clearly visible. This gives the new-comer a certain degree of confidence first time out, even though you can feel that streams and lakes are lying in wait to make life more difficult (a feeling that proves to be true!). Inexperienced golfers might find the layout a little tough, but just tell them that the score is not the only thing in golf...

Golf Club Schloss Myllendonk e.V. Korschenbroich — 1965

Myllendonker Strasse 113
D - 41352 KORSCHENBROICH

Office	Sekretariat	(49) 02161 - 641 049
Pro shop	Pro shop	(49) 02161 - 644 955
Fax	Fax	(49) 02161 - 648 806
Web	www.gcsm.de	
Situation	Lage	Düsseldorf, 25 km

Mönchengladbach, 5 km

Annual closure	Jährliche Schliessung	no
Weekly closure	Wöchentliche Schliessung	no

Monday (Montag): Restaurant closed

Fees main season Preisliste hochsaison	Week days Woche	We/Bank holidays We/Feiertag
	18 holes	
Individual Individuell	€ 45	€ 50
Couple Ehepaar	€ 90	€ 100

Caddie Caddie no — **Electric Trolley** Elektrokarren no
Buggy Elektrischer Wagen no — **Clubs** Leihschläger yes
Credit cards Kreditkarten no

Access Zufahrt : A44 Exit (Ausf.) Mönchengladbach-Ost → "Gewerbegebiet Üdding". 1 km left in Jakobshöhe Strasse. 600 m, left in Myllendonker Strasse. → Schlosshof-Parkplatz. **Map 3 on page 352** Karte 3 Seite 352

GOLF COURSE — PLATZ 16/20

Site	Lage	
Maintenance	Instandhaltung	
Architect	Architekt	Donald Harradine
Type	Typ	parkland, forest
Relief	Begehbarkeit	
Water in play	Platz mit Wasser	
Exp. to wind	Wind ausgesetzt	
Trees in play	Platz mit Bäumen	

Scorecard Scorekarte	Chp. Chp.	Mens Herren	Ladies Damen
Length Länge	5971	5539	5255
Par	72	72	72
Slope system	128	131	127

Advised golfing ability Empfohlene Spielstärke — 0 12 24 36
Hcp required Min. Handicap 36

CLUB HOUSE & AMENITIES — KLUBHAUS UND NEBENGEBÄUDE 7/10

Pro shop Pro shop
Driving range Übungsplatz
Sheltered überdacht 2 mats - On grass auf Rasen yes (Summer)
Putting-green Putting-grün yes - Pitching-green Pitching-grün yes

HOTEL FACILITIES — HOTEL BESCHREIBUNG 7/10

HOTELS HOTELS

Queens Hotel - Mönchengladbach-Rheydt 5 km
127 rooms, D € 115
Tel (49) 02161 - 93 80, Fax (49) 02161 - 938 807

Dorint Mercure - Mönchengladbach 5 km
167 rooms, D € 145
Tel (49) 02161 - 89 30, Fax (49) 02161 - 893 617

Gästehaus Bienenfeld - Korschenbroich 5 km
15 rooms, D € 95
Tel (49) 02161 - 998 300, Fax (49) 02161 -998 3099

RESTAURANTS RESTAURANTS

Michelangelo - Mönchengladbach 5 km
Tel (49) 02161 - 208 583

Zur Traube - Korschenbroich 3 km - Tel (49) 02161 - 670 404

Schloss Nippenburg

16	8	7

Die Bäume am Rande der Spielbahnen sind schon etwas seit der Eröffnung im Jahre 1993 gewachsen, aber es wird noch Jahre dauern ehe sie wirklich zur Gefahr werden. Im Augenblick sind die Bunker, Wasser und das Auf und Ab der Spielbahnen mit vielen Schräglagen die Hauptschwierigkeiten. Es gibt drei erhöhte Grüns und ein halbes Dutzend, die tiefer liegen als die Spielbahn. Wenn der Wind hier bläst, ist der Platz um vieles schwieriger. Bernhard Langer hatte beim Entwurf schottische Küstenplätze im Sinn, aber er hat nicht vergessen, dass Golf kein Spiel nur für Professionals und gute Amateure ist. Wenn der Wind nicht weht, ist der Platz für die Mehrzahl der Golfer gut spielbar, vorausgesetzt sie kommen mit hängenden Balllagen zurecht. Der einzige Nachteil sind die extrem langen Wege vom Grün zum nächsten Abschlag und der ermüdende, bergauf führende Weg vom Parkplatz zum ultramodernen Clubhaus.

The trees alongside this rather open course have grown since it was first opened in 1993, but it will take a few more years before they really become dangerous. For the moment, the main difficulties are the bunkers, water and contoured landscape which leads to sloping lies, three elevated greens and half a dozen downhill greens. If the wind decides to blow, the course assumes a whole new dimension and requires good ball control if you want to card any sort of score, even though the yardage is reasonable. When designing Schloss Nippenburg, Bernhard Langer obviously had the Scottish links style in mind, but according to the proper tradition he never forgot that golf is not a game reserved only for professionals and good amateur players. If the wind is not blowing the course is not too difficult for the majority of players if they can play sloping lies. The only drawback of the course are the long walks from green to the next tee and the long tiring uphill walk from the parking lot to the ultramodern club-house.

Schloss Nippenburg Golfclub — 1993

Nippenburg 21
D - 71701 SCHWIEBERDINGEN

Office	Sekretariat	(49) 07150 - 395 30
Pro shop	Pro shop	(49) 07150 - 302 840
Fax	Fax	(49) 07150 - 353 518
Web	www.schlossnippenburg.de	
Situation	Lage	Stuttgart, 10 km
Annual closure	Jährliche Schliessung	no
Weekly closure	Wöchentliche Schliessung	no
Fees main season	Preisliste hochsaison	18 holes

	Week days Woche	We/Bank holidays We/Feiertag
Individual Individuell	€ 45	€ 65*
Couple Ehepaar	€ 90	€ 130*

* Sunday (Sonntag) € 75 / – 21 & Students: – 50%

Caddie Caddie no — **Electric Trolley** Elektrokarren no

Buggy Elektrischer Wagen yes — **Clubs** Leihschläger yes

Credit cards Kreditkarten
VISA - Eurocard - Mastercard - AMEX

Access Zufahrt : A81 Stuttgart-Heilbronn. Exit (Ausf.) Stuttgart-Zuffenhausen. B10 → Vaihingen. Münchingen → Hemmingen. → Golf

Map 1 on page 349 Karte 1 Seite 349

GOLF COURSE — PLATZ — 16/20

Site	Lage	
Maintenance	Instandhaltung	
Architect	Architekt	Bernhard Langer
Type	Typ	country, open country
Relief	Begehbarkeit	
Water in play	Platz mit Wasser	
Exp. to wind	Wind ausgesetzt	
Trees in play	Platz mit Bäumen	

Scorecard Scorekarte	Chp. Chp.	Mens Herren	Ladies Damen
Length Länge	6045	5866	5152
Par	71	71	71
Slope system	137	134	132

Advised golfing ability Empfohlene Spielstärke — 0 12 24 36

Hcp required Min. Handicap — 54 (36 We)

CLUB HOUSE & AMENITIES — KLUBHAUS UND NEBENGEBÄUDE — 8/10

Pro shop Pro shop
Driving range Übungsplatz

Sheltered überdacht 6 mats - On grass auf Rasen yes - Putting-green Putting-grün yes - Pitching-green Pitching-grün yes

HOTEL FACILITIES — HOTEL BESCHREIBUNG — 7/10

HOTELS HOTELS

Hotel Mercure - Korntal-Münchingen 3 km
206 rooms, D from € 80
Tel (49) 07150 - 130, Fax (49) 07150 - 132 66

Wörtz zur Weinsteige - 33 rooms, D € 140 - Stuttgart 10 km
Tel (49) 0711 - 236 7000, Fax (49) 0711 - 236 7007

Am Schlossgarten - 120 rooms, D € 258 - Stuttgart 10 km
Tel (49) 0711 - 202 60, Fax (49) 0711 - 202 6888

RESTAURANTS RESTAURANTS

Zirbelstube - Stuttgart 10 km - Tel (49) 0711 - 202 6828
Di Gennaro - Stuttgart 10 km - Tel (49) 0711 - 222 9603
Clubhaus Restaurant - Tel (49) 07150 - 324 72

Schloss Wilkendorf

17	7	5

Dies ist Lyles erstes Projekt in Kontinental-Europa, und er hat erstklassige Arbeit auf sanft gewellten ehemaligen Ackerland abgeliefert. Der Platz ist perfekt in die Umgebung eingebettet, er wirkt als gäbe es ihn schon seit Ewigkeiten. Alle Spielbahn sind weit von einander getrennt, so dass man sich nie ins Gehege kommt. Neben Bäumen, hohem Rough, wenigen Wasserhindernisse kommen selbstverständlich auch zahlreiche Fairwaybunker ins Spiel, die aber eher unauffällig ins Design integriert sind. Man muss vom Abschlag schon genau hinschauen, um die gut plazierten Sandhindernisse zu erkannen. Die Grüns sind auch relativ flach, dafür aber gut verteidigt. In einer Umfrage unter Berliner Golfern wurde dieser Platz zum besten der Region gewählt, sicherlich auch,weil er nicht ganz so schwierig wie der Faldo- oder der Robert-Trent-Jones-Jr.-Platz am Seddiner See ist. Der Westside Platz ist der einzig öffentliche Platz in Berlin und Brandenburg, man kann also ohne Handicap und Clubmitgliedschaft hier spielen.

This course is laid out across rolling countryside which used to be farm land. The course is new but looks as if it has been around here for years, as it blends beautifully with the environment. Even though the bunkers are threatening they are not as conspicuous as at the nearby courses of Seddiner See South Course or the Faldo course at the Sporting Club Berlin Scharmützelsee. The course boasts wonderful variety, with no two holes alike. One fine example is the short 15th, where the tee shot has to be neatly slotted through a small gap of trees. The only drawback here is the course's relatively remote location to the north east of Berlin. But in spite of the long drive - almost 90 minutes from the centre of Berlin - this is one course not to be missed when in the German capital. The former British Open and US Masters Champion Sandy Lyle has proved that he is as good a golf course designer as he was a player.

Golfpark Schloss Wilkendorf e.V. — 1995

Am Weiher 1
D - 15345 WILKENDORF

Office	Sekretariat	(49) 03341 - 330 960
Pro shop	Pro shop	(49) 03341 -330 6967
Fax	Fax	(49) 03341 - 330 961
Web	www.golfpark-schloss-wilkendorf.com	
Situation	Lage	Berlin 70 km

Strausberg, 7 km

Annual closure Jährliche Schliessung 15/11→15/3

Weekly closure Wöchentliche Schliessung Monday (Montag): Restaurant closed

Fees main season Preisliste hochsaison	18 holes	
	Week days Woche	**We/Bank holidays** We/Feiertag
Individual Individuell	€ 38	€ 55
Couple Ehepaar	€ 76	€ 110

Caddie Caddie no — **Electric Trolley** Elektrokarren yes

Buggy Elektrischer Wagen no — **Clubs** Leihschläger yes

Credit cards Kreditkarten no

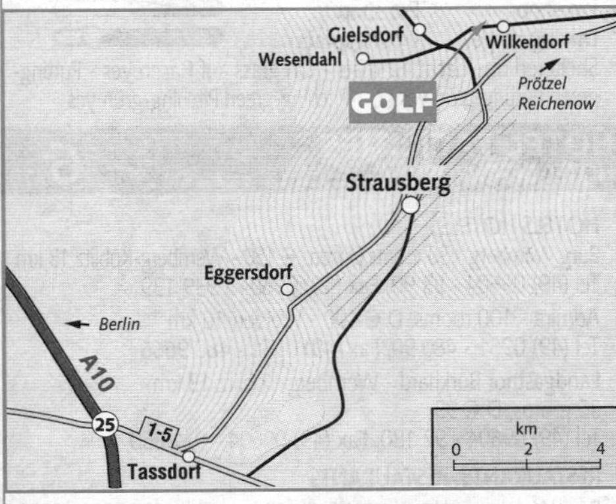

Access Zufahrt : B1-5 Berlin → Frankfurt/Oder to Berliner Ring (A10). 1 km left → Strausberg. → Golf.

Map 6 on page 359 Karte 6 Seite 359

GOLF COURSE — PLATZ — 17/20

Site	Lage	
Maintenance	Instandhaltung	
Architect	Architekt	Sandy Lyle
Type	Typ	inland
Relief	Begehbarkeit	
Water in play	Platz mit Wasser	
Exp. to wind	Wind ausgesetzt	
Trees in play	Platz mit Bäumen	

Scorecard Scorekarte	**Chp.** Chp.	**Mens** Herren	**Ladies** Damen
Length Länge	6517	6096	5302
Par	74	72	72
Slope system	131	128	124

Advised golfing ability Empfohlene Spielstärke — 0 12 24 36

Hcp required Min. Handicap 36

CLUB HOUSE & AMENITIES — KLUBHAUS UND NEBENGEBÄUDE — 7/10

Pro shop Pro shop
Driving range Übungsplatz
Sheltered überdacht 16 mats - On grass auf Rasen yes - Putting-green Putting-grün yes - Pitching-green Pitching-grün yes

HOTEL FACILITIES — HOTEL BESCHREIBUNG — 5/10

HOTELS HOTELS

Lakeside Hotel - Strausberg 2 km
51 rooms, D € 110
Tel (49) 03341 - 346 90, Fax (49) 03341 - 346 915

Schloss Reichenow - Reichenow 15 km
20 rooms, D from € 120
Tel (49) 033437 - 30 80, Fax (49) 033437 - 30 888

Landgasthof zum Mühlenteich - Eggersdorf 15 km
19 rooms, D € 100
Tel (49) 03341 - 426 60, Fax (49) 03341 - 426 666

RESTAURANTS RESTAURANTS

Stobber Mühle - Bucklow 15 km - Tel (49) 033433 - 668 33
Goldene Kartoffel - Prötzel 7 km - Tel (49) 0334 - 364 92

Schwanhof

17	8	6

Die ruhige ländliches Atmosphäre der bayrischen Oberpfalz nahe Weiden mit seiner Landschaft machen Golf zu einem Vergnügen, besonders, da der Platz für Golfer aller Spielstärken geeignet ist. Auf über 90 Hektar offenen Land haben Jerry Pate und Reinhold Weishaupt einen Topplatz entworfen. Auf den ersten Blick wirken nur das 5. Loch und das 18. Loch mit dem Inselgrün als überaus schwierig, doch testet der Platz mit seinen subtilen Schwierigkeiten selbst Professionals, die ständig hier Turniere der German PGA Tour austragen. Die Fairways sind weit und fehlerverzeihend, ab und an geht es steil bergauf und bergab. Trotz der hügeligen Topografie, die einen Golfwagen bei Hitze empfehlenswert macht, sind alle Hindernisse, meist in der Form gut platzierter Bunker, gut zu erkennen. Der Platz schüchtert nicht ein und wirkt wie die ganze Gegend gastfreundlich. Zusammen mit dem luxuriösen Clubhaus ist dies einer der besten deutschen Plätze.

Come here to play golf and enjoy the romantic and chivalrous side of historic Germany with a stay at the nearby Burg Wernberg hotel. The calm, country atmosphere near Weiden along with the landscape add to the pleasure of playing golf, especially as here there is something for everyone. Over 80 hectares of very open land, Jerry Pate and Reinhold Weishaupt have designed a top-class 18-hole course with the emphasis on adapting the layout to golfers of all different abilities. Only the 5th and 18th (island green) holes are perhaps slightly tougher propositions. The fairways are wide and forgiving, sometimes climbing steeply up and down, sufficiently so to warrant a buggy in hot weather. Despite the topography, trouble in store is clearly there to be seen basically in the form of well-located bunkers. Rarely intimidating, hospitable, intelligently designed and well drained, Schwanhof boasts excellent facilities and is one of the finest courses around.

Golfclub Schwanhof e.V. 1990

Klaus-Conrad-Allee 1
D - 92706 LUHE-WILDENAU

Office	Sekretariat	(49) 09607 - 92 020
Pro shop	Pro shop	(49) 09607 - 92 020
Fax	Fax	(49) 09607 - 920 248
Web	www.golfclub-schwanhof.de	
Situation	Lage	Weiden, 10 km
Annual closure	Jährliche Schliessung	1/1→31/1
Weekly closure	Wöchentliche Schliessung	no

Fees main season Preisliste hochsaison	Week days Woche	We/Bank holidays We/Feiertag
	18 holes	
Individual Individuell	€ 50	€ 65
Couple Ehepaar	€ 100	€ 130

Caddie Caddie yes — Electric Trolley Elektrokarren yes
Buggy Elektrischer Wagen yes — Clubs Leihschläger yes
Credit cards Kreditkarten
VISA - Eurocard - MasterCard - AMEX - DC

Ober-Wildenau
Weiden i.d.OPF
GOLF
26
Gelpertsricht
Luhe
Neudorf
A93
Holzhammer
14
27
km 0 2 4
Regensburg

Access Zufahrt : • München, A93 → Regensburg, then Weiden i.d. Oberpfalz. Exit 26 (Ausfahrt 26) Luhe-Wildenau → Golf Schloss Schwanhof. • Nürnberg, A6 → Amberg. Exit 65 Amberg West. B299/B14 → Hirschau. Left → Luhe-Wildenau. → Golf Schloss Schwanhof. **Map 4 on page 355** Karte 4 Seite 355

GOLF COURSE — PLATZ 17/20

Site	Lage	
Maintenance	Instandhaltung	
Architect	Architekt	Jerry Pate, Reinhold Weishaupt
Type	Typ	open country, hilly
Relief	Begehbarkeit	
Water in play	Platz mit Wasser	
Exp. to wind	Wind ausgesetzt	
Trees in play	Platz mit Bäumen	

Scorecard Scorekarte	Chp. Chp.	Mens Herren	Ladies Damen
Length Länge	6034	5696	4916
Par	72	72	72
Slope system	124	122	121

Advised golfing ability Empfohlene Spielstärke: 0 12 24 36
Hcp required Min. Handicap: no

CLUB HOUSE & AMENITIES — KLUBHAUS UND NEBENGEBÄUDE 8/10

Pro shop Pro shop
Driving range Übungsplatz
Sheltered überdacht 12 mats - On grass auf Rasen yes - Putting-green Putting-grün yes (2) - Pitching-green Pitching-grün yes

HOTEL FACILITIES — HOTEL BESCHREIBUNG 6/10

HOTELS HOTELS

Burg Wernberg - 30 rooms D from € 150 - Wernberg-Köblitz 13 km
Tel (49) 09604 - 93 90, Fax (49) 09604 - 939 139

Admira - 100 rooms, D € 100 - Weiden 10 km
Tel (49) 0961 - 480 90, Fax (49) 0961 - 480 9666

Landgasthof Burkhard - Wernberg-Köblitz 13 km
35 rooms, D € 95
Tel (49) 09604 - 92 180, Fax (49) 09604 - 921 850

RESTAURANTS RESTAURANTS

Burg Wernberg - Wernberg-Köblitz 13 km - Tel (49) 09604 - 9390
Kaminstube (Landg. Burkhard) - Wernberg 13 km
Tel (49) 09604 - 921 80
Schwanhof - on site - Tel (49) 09607 - 920 20

Seddiner See *Südplatz*

18	9	7

Zusammen mit dem Faldo-Platz am SC Berlin ist dies der beste neue Platz in Deutschland. Er besticht vor allem mit seinem Abwechslungsreichtum und vor allem den geschickt platzierten Bunkern, die optisch attraktiv sind und vor allem jedem Loch eine klare Kontur verleihen. Hinzu kommen einige attraktive Wasserhindernisse. Insgesamt ist dies ein Platz, der jeden Golfer begeistern wird. Durch geschickte Erdbe- wegungen wirken manchen Hindernisse und Grüns näher oder weiter entfernt als sie tatsächlich sind, deshalb gilt es der Birdie-Karte zu vetrauen. Dies ist ein Platz der intelligentes Spiel erfordert, aber für alle Spielstärke schwer ist. Wählen Sie deshalb die richtigen Abschläge, die hinteren "Tiger-Tees" sind ausschliesslich für Profis und Longhitter. Den Südplatz kann man am Wochenende nur in Begleitung eines Mitglieds spielen. Der andere Platz des Clubs, der von Rainer Preismann entworfene Nordplatz, ist dagegen ohne Einschränkung für Gastspieler offen. Das luxuriöse Clubhaus und die Übungsreinrichtungen entsprechen dem hohen Standard des Platz, der nur 25 Auto-Minuten vom Ku-Damm entfernt ist.

This is one of the best recently built layouts for its variety and remarkable bunkering which, although sometimes deceiving to the eye, perfectly outlines the shape of holes over often very open space. If we add the presence of a few attractive water hazards, you get a course of sheer pleasure. Some clever earthwork here and there might give the illusion of hazards and greens being closer or further away than they actually are, so trust the yardage book. This is a very intelligent course that is tough for everyone, so choose your tees wisely: the "tiger" tees are reserved for very long-hitters. This "South" course can only be played with a member on weekends, the other "North" course has no such restrictions but is much more ordinary. Facilities here are on a par with prices: the club-house is luxurious and the driving range excellent. A 25 minute drive from Berlin Ku-Damm, this course is a must.

Golf Club Seddiner See — 1997

Zum Weiher 44
D - 1455 WILDENBRUCH

Office	Sekretariat	(49) 033205 - 7320
Pro shop	Pro shop	(49) 033205 - 73 251
Fax	Fax	(49) 033205 - 73 229
Web	www.gccseddinersee.de	
Situation	Lage	Berlin, 30 km
Annual closure	Jährliche Schliessung	no
Weekly closure	Wöchentliche Schliessung	Monday

(Montag): Restaurant closed

Fees main season Preisliste hochsaison	18 holes	
	Week days Woche	**We/Bank holidays** We/Feiertag
Individual Individuell	€ 60	€ 70*
Couple Ehepaar	€ 120	€ 140*

* On request, with members (nur in Mitgliederbegleitung)
– 21 & Students: - 50%

Caddie Caddie no — **Electric Trolley** Elektrokarren no
Buggy Elektrischer Wagen no — **Clubs** Leihschläger yes
Credit cards Kreditkarten VISA - Eurocard - AMEX

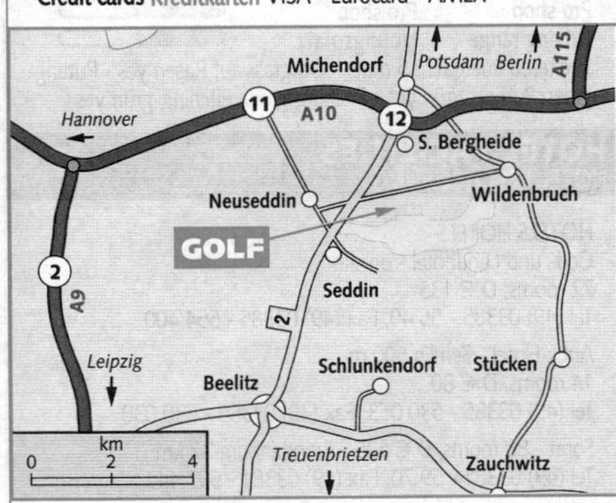

Access Zufahrt : Berlin, A115 Süd, A10 West.
Exit (Ausf.) 12 → Beelitz
Map 6 on page 359 Karte 6 Seite 359

GOLF COURSE — 18/20
PLATZ

Site	Lage	
Maintenance	Instandhaltung	
Architect	Architekt	R. Trent Jones Jr.
Type	Typ	country
Relief	Begehbarkeit	
Water in play	Platz mit Wasser	
Exp. to wind	Wind ausgesetzt	
Trees in play	Platz mit Bäumen	

Scorecard Scorekarte	**Chp.** Chp.	**Mens** Herren	**Ladies** Damen
Length Länge	6486	6046	5514
Par	72	72	72
Slope system	132	132	134

Advised golfing ability Empfohlene Spielstärke — 0 12 24 36
Hcp required Min. Handicap 28

CLUB HOUSE & AMENITIES — 9/10
KLUBHAUS UND NEBENGEBÄUDE

Pro shop Pro shop
Driving range Übungsplatz
Sheltered überdacht 20 mats - On grass auf Rasen yes -
Putting-green Putting-grün yes - Pitching-green Pitching-grün yes

HOTEL FACILITIES — 7/10
HOTEL BESCHREIBUNG

HOTELS HOTELS
Am Jäger Tor - 62 rooms, D € 161 - Potsdam 15 km
Tel (49) 0331 - 201 1100, Fax (49) 0331 - 201 1333

Landhaus Haveltreff - Schwielowsee-Caputh 10 km
27 rooms, D € 90
Tel (49) 03329 - 780, Fax (49) 03329 - 78 100

Haus am See - 21 rooms, D € 90 - Ferch 12 km
Tel (49) 033209 - 709 55, Fax (49) 033209 - 704 96

Brandenburger Hof - 86 rooms, D € 245 - Berlin 30 km
Tel (49) 030 - 214 050, Fax (49) 030 - 2140 5100

RESTAURANTS RESTAURANTS
Borchardt - Berlin 30 km - Tel (49) 030 - 229 3144
Juliette - Potsdam 30 km - Tel (49) 0331 - 270 1791

Semlin am See

16 | 8 | 7

Semlin wurde wie auch der Märkische Golfclub Potsdam von Christoph Städler entworfen. Mit ihrem dazugehörigen Hotel entspricht die Anlage einem Resort, und eignet sich somit ausgezeichnet als Wochenend-Ziel für Golfgruppen - auch solche deren Handicaps weit auseinanderklaffen, wenngleich "Hacker" den Platz als etwas zu schwer empfinden mögen. Die Schwierigkeiten sind recht gut erkennbar, so dass man durchaus gleich die erste Runde in Zählspiel absolvieren kann, obschon Matchplay sicherlich genauso viel Spass macht. Das Fehlen gefahrbringender Bäume, die Gestaltung der Grüns und Bunker, sowie das fast völlig ebene Gelände erinnern stark an Florida, damit ist aber nicht eine simple Kopie der dortigen Plätze gemeint. Die Schwierigkeiten sind gut verteilt, so wechseln sich im Verlauf der Runde schwierige und leichtere Löcher miteinander ab. Als sehr hilfreich erweist sich die Fähigkeit den Ball sowohl mit Draw als auch Fade spielen zu können. Die Grüns sind ausgezeichnet und der sandige Boden gewährleistet eine gute Drainage.

Like Märkischer Potsdam, Semlin am See chose Christoph Städler as course architect. This is a sort of resort, with a hotel on site, another 9-hole course and can be a very decent week-end destination for a group of golfers, even playing to very different handicaps, although the hackers might find it a little too tough for their liking. The difficulties are visible enough to consider stroke-play first time out, although match-play will be at least just as much fun. The absence of dangerous trees, the design of the greens and bunkers and the very slight physical relief are reminiscent of Florida, but this is no carbon copy. The difficulties are well spread around, with tough holes alternating nicely with easier numbers. Moving the ball (deliberately) both ways will be a great help. The greens are excellent and the sandy soil gives good drainage.

Golf- und Landclub Semlin am See — 1993

Ferchesarer Strasse 8b
D - 14712 SEMLIN

Office	Sekretariat	(49) 03385 - 55 40
Pro shop	Pro shop	(49) 03385 - 554 474
Fax	Fax	(49) 03385 - 554 400
Web	www.golfhotelsemlin.de	
Situation	Lage	Berlin, 70 km

Rathenow (pop. 28 000), 5 km

Annual closure	Jährliche Schliessung	no
Weekly closure	Wöchentliche Schliessung	no
Fees main season	Preisliste hochsaison	18 holes

	Week days Woche	We/Bank holidays We/Feiertag
Individual Individuell	€ 30	€ 50
Couple Ehepaar	€ 60	€ 100

– 21 & Students: € 20/35 (We)

Caddie Caddie on request — **Electric Trolley** Elektrokarren no
Buggy Elektrischer Wagen yes — **Clubs** Leihschläger yes
Credit cards Kreditkarten
VISA - Eurocard - MasterCard - AMEX - DC

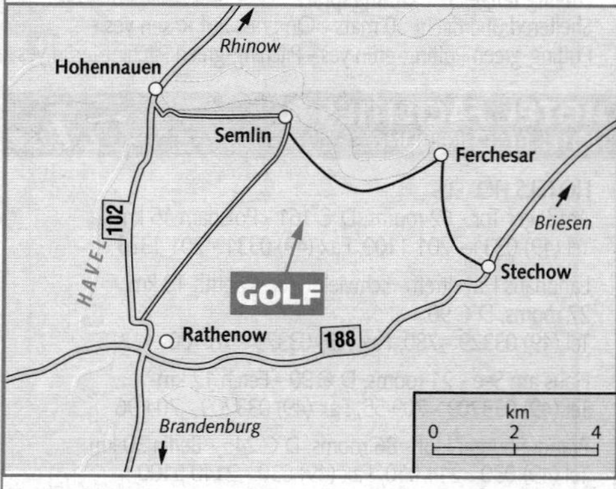

Access Zufahrt : Berlin, B5. Brisen, B188 → Rathenow. Stechow → Ferchesar. → Golf
Map 6 on page 359 Karte 6 Seite 359

GOLF COURSE — PLATZ — 16/20

Site	Lage	
Maintenance	Instandhaltung	
Architect	Architekt	Christoph Städler
Type	Typ	forest, parkland
Relief	Begehbarkeit	
Water in play	Platz mit Wasser	
Exp. to wind	Wind ausgesetzt	
Trees in play	Platz mit Bäumen	

Scorecard Scorekarte	Chp. Chp.	Mens Herren	Ladies Damen
Length Länge	6290	5928	5272
Par	72	72	72
Slope system	133	130	127

Advised golfing ability Empfohlene Spielstärke — 0 12 24 36
Hcp required Min. Handicap 36

CLUB HOUSE & AMENITIES — KLUBHAUS UND NEBENGEBÄUDE — 8/10

Pro shop Pro shop
Driving range Übungsplatz
Sheltered überdacht 5 mats - On grass auf Rasen yes - Putting-green Putting-grün yes - Pitching-green Pitching-grün yes

HOTEL FACILITIES — HOTEL BESCHREIBUNG — 7/10

HOTELS HOTELS
Golf- und Landhotel - on site
72 rooms, D € 135
Tel (49) 03385 - 55 40, Fax (49) 03385 - 554 400

Antik Hotel - Semlin 500 m
14 rooms, D € 80
Tel (49) 03385 - 530 053, Fax (49) 03385 - 530 030

Sorat - 88 rooms, D € 125 - Brandenburg 37 km
Tel (49) 03381 - 59 70, Fax (49) 03381 - 597 444

RESTAURANTS RESTAURANTS
Golf- und Landhotel - on site
Tel (49) 03385 - 554 412

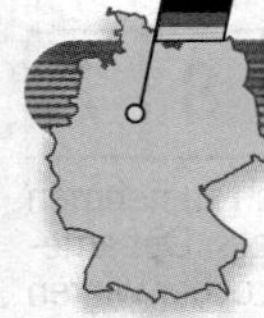

Senne

16	8	7

Dieser Platz liegt in der typischen Senne-Landschaft, die sich mit ihrem Heideboden ideal für Golfplätze eignet. Der Sandboden sorgt dafür, dass der Platz viel Regen aufnehmen kann und ganzjährige auf Sommergrüns bespielbar ist. Der Platz vermittelt den manchmal täuschenden Eindruck von weiten, offenen Fairways, was besonders schwächere Spieler schätzen. Aber auch Longhitter werden sich hier wohlfühlen, doch die vielen Bunker, hohes Rough, einige Bäume und Wasserhindernisse verlangen Präzision. Das gilt besonders für das 13. Loch ein trickreiches Par 3 oder für das 18. Loch, ein kurzes Par 4 mit einem gut verteidigten Grün. Christoph Städler entwarf ein exzellentes Layout, bei dem sich alle Löcher deutlich voneinander unterscheiden und im Zusammenspiel einen überaus reizvollen Platz ergeben. Das ist allerdings keine Überraschung: Als ehemaliger deutscher Amateur-Nationalspieler versteht Städler viel von Golf. Diese Platz werden Golfer geniessen, selbst wenn der Wind bläst, was in dieser Gegend häufig vorkommt.

This course was laid out in countryside that is typical of the region of Senne on heather-strewn sandy soil, which is so well suited to golf courses, especially when it comes to successfully soaking up the rain. There is a lot of open space, so golfers of all levels can enjoy their round and big hitters really let it rip, even though they could be asking for trouble: watch out for the bunkers, tall rough, a few trees in play and water hazards lining one half of the course. At the 13th for example, a very tricky par 3, or the 18th, a rather short par 4 with a very well guarded green. Christoph Städler has produced an excellent layout where no two holes are alike and where everything seems to neatly fit together. This is hardly surprising, as this former German amateur champion knows a thing or two about golf and golfers. You will enjoy this course, even when the wind starts to blow, a frequent occurrence in these parts.

Senne Golfclub Gut Welschof e.V. 1992

Augustdorfer Strasse 72
D - 33758 SCHLOSS HOLTE-STUKENBROCK

Office Sekretariat (49) 05207 - 920 936
Pro shop Pro shop (49) 05207 - 920 936
Fax Fax (49) 05207 - 887 88
Web www.sennegolfclub.de
Situation Lage Bielefeld, 22 km
Annual closure Jährliche Schliessung 23/12→6/1
Weekly closure Wöchentliche Schliessung Monday
(Montag): Restaurant closed

Fees main season Preisliste hochsaison 18 holes

	Week days Woche	We/Bank holidays We/Feiertag
Individual Individuell	€ 36	€ 48
Couple Ehepaar	€ 72	€ 96

Caddie Caddie no **Electric Trolley** Elektrokarren yes
Buggy Elektrischer Wagen yes **Clubs** Leihschläger yes
Credit cards Kreditkarten
VISA - Eurocard - MasterCard - AMEX

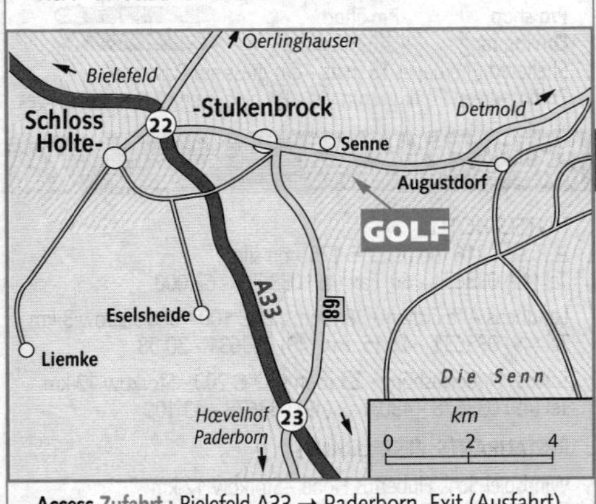

Access Zufahrt : Bielefeld A33 → Paderborn. Exit (Ausfahrt) Schloss Holte-Stukenbrock, then B68. In Stukenbrock → Augustdorf/Detmold. 2.5 km, → Golf.
Map 5 on page 357 Karte 5 Seite 357

GOLF COURSE PLATZ 16/20

Site Lage
Maintenance Instandhaltung
Architect Architekt Christoph Städler
Type Typ heathland, open country
Relief Begehbarkeit
Water in play Platz mit Wasser
Exp. to wind Wind ausgesetzt
Trees in play Platz mit Bäumen

Scorecard Scorekarte	Chp. Chp.	Mens Herren	Ladies Damen
Length Länge	6122	5924	5254
Par	72	72	72
Slope system	127	123	125

Advised golfing ability Empfohlene Spielstärke 0 12 24 36
Hcp required Min. Handicap 36

CLUB HOUSE & AMENITIES KLUBHAUS UND NEBENGEBÄUDE 8/10

Pro shop Pro shop
Driving range Übungsplatz
Sheltered überdacht 6 mats - On grass auf Rasen yes - Putting-green Putting-grün yes (2) - Pitching-green Pitching-grün yes

HOTEL FACILITIES HOTEL BESCHREIBUNG 7/10

HOTELS HOTELS
Westhoff - 32 rooms, D € 90 - Schloss-Holte-Stukenbrock 5 km
Tel (49) 05207 - 911 00, Fax (49) 05207 - 911 051

Ravensberger Hof - 51 rooms, D € 135 - Bielefeld 20 km
Tel (49) 0521 - 962 11, Fax (49) 0521 - 962 1300

Parkhotel Gütersloh - Gütersloh 23 km
106 rooms, D € 170 / 135 We
Tel (49) 05241 - 8770, Fax (49) 05241 - 877 400

RESTAURANTS RESTAURANTS
Altdeutsche Bierstube - Oerlinghausen 5 km
Tel (49) 05202 - 35 60

Gasthaus Bockskrug - Gütersloh 23 km
Tel (49) 05241 - 543 70

Sporting-Club Berlin *Arnold Palmer* 17 8 7

Die Investoren zögerten nicht, für ihr Projekt die Mitarbeit der Besten in Anspruch zu nehmen und beauftragten Arnold Palmer mit dem Bau seines in Deutschland ersten Platzes. Der amerikanische Stil ist nur auf den ersten 9 Löchern offensichtlich, die zweiten neun Löcher wirken dagegen wie ein alter klassischer Waldplatz und sind der schönste Teil des Platzes. Das Layout ist gut durchdacht und so machen es die vorhandenen Schwierigkeiten nötig, mehrere Runden hier zu spielen, bis man sich mit der Anlage vertraut fühlt. Natürlich ist der Platz, besonders von den hinteren Abschlägen, auch sehr anspruchsvoll. Mehrere Abschlag-Boxen pro Loch ermöglichen es aber jedem Spieler, eine seinem Niveau entsprechende Wahl zu treffen. Besondere Aufmerksamkeit wurde der Gestaltung der Grüns gewidmet, der erst kürzlich erstellte Golfplatz ist Teil eines 54-Loch Resorts, zu dem auch ein von Nick Faldo entworfener 18-Loch Platz sowie der weniger anspruchsvolle Stan Eby Platz gehört. Aber auch der Pflegezustand der gesamten Anlage hebt diesen Platz aus der Masse der deutschen Plätze heraus.

The reunification of Germany has opened up new development in this region, particularly close to the huge Scharmützelsee. The present recent course is part of a 54-hole resort which also includes a Nick Faldo and a Stan Eby offering. The investors didn't hesitate to call on the best, and this is Germany's first course designed by Arnold Palmer. The American style is only obvious on the front nine, the back nine being more like a traditional German forest course. The design is very intelligent, but the difficulties call for several rounds before getting fully acclimatized. Obviously, it is also very demanding, especially from the back tees, but there are enough tee-boxes for everyone to play the course that suits them best. The greens are especially well-designed and the standard of maintenance of the whole resort makes for three excellent courses.

Sporting Club Berlin (Scharmützelsee) 1995

Parkallee 3
D - 15526 BAD SAAROW

Office	Sekretariat	(49) 033631 - 63 300
Pro shop	Pro shop	(49) 033631 - 61 070
Fax	Fax	(49) 033631 - 63 310
Web	www.a-rosa.de	
Situation	Lage	Berlin, 75 km

Frankfurt/Oder, 35 km

Annual closure	Jährliche Schliessung	30/11→1/3
Weekly closure	Wöchentliche Schliessung	no

Fees main season Preisliste hochsaison 18 holes

	Week days Woche	We/Bank holidays We/Feiertag
Individual Individuell	€ 70	€ 70
Couple Ehepaar	€ 140	€ 140

Special fees for Hotel guests

Caddie Caddie no — **Electric Trolley** Elektrokarren yes

Buggy Elektrischer Wagen yes — **Clubs** Leihschläger yes

Credit cards Kreditkarten
VISA - Eurocard - MasterCard - AMEX - DC - JCB

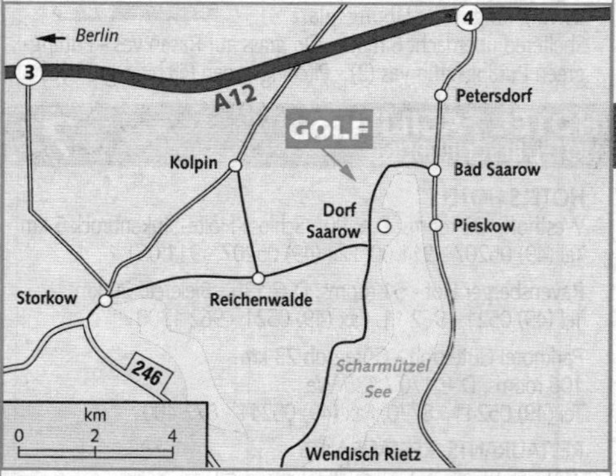

Access Zufahrt : Berlin A12 → Frankfurt/Oder. Exit (Ausf.) Fürstenwalde, → Bad Saarow → Golf.

Map 6 on page 359 Karte 6 Seite 359

GOLF COURSE
PLATZ 17/20

Site	Lage	
Maintenance	Instandhaltung	
Architect	Architekt	Arnold Palmer
Type	Typ	forest, parkland
Relief	Begehbarkeit	
Water in play	Platz mit Wasser	
Exp. to wind	Wind ausgesetzt	
Trees in play	Platz mit Bäumen	

Scorecard Scorekarte	Chp. Chp.	Mens Herren	Ladies Damen
Length Länge	6566	6078	5361
Par	72	72	72
Slope system	135	130	128

Advised golfing ability Empfohlene Spielstärke 0 12 24 36

Hcp required Min. Handicap 36

CLUB HOUSE & AMENITIES
KLUBHAUS UND NEBENGEBÄUDE 8/10

Pro shop Pro shop
Driving range Übungsplatz
Sheltered überdacht 16 mats - On grass auf Rasen yes - Putting-green Putting-grün yes - Pitching-green Pitching-grün yes

HOTEL FACILITIES
HOTEL BESCHREIBUNG 7/10

HOTELS HOTELS

A-Rosa - 216 rooms, D € 175 - on site
Tel (49) 033631 - 60, Fax (49) 033631 - 62 000

Landhaus Alte Eichen - 38 rooms, D € 100 - Bad Saarow 3 km
Tel (49) 033631 - 41 15, Fax (49) 033631 - 20 58

Schloss Hubertushöhe - 23 rooms, D € 200 - Storkow 12 km
Tel (49) 033678 - 430, Fax (49) 033678 - 43 100

RESTAURANTS RESTAURANTS

Windspiel-Schl. Hubertus Höhe - Storkow 12 km
Tel (49) 033678 - 43 0

Landhaus Alte Eichen - Bad Saarow 3 km
Tel (49) 033678 - 41 15

Sporting-Club Berlin *Nick Faldo*

18	8	7

Grosse Champions müssen sich oft den Vorwurf gefallen lassen, Plätze zu gestalten, ohne die dafür erforderliche Zeit und Mühe aufzuwenden. Auf Nick Faldo trifft dies nicht zu, da bei den leider nur wenigen von ihm bislang entworfenen Platzen seine ganz persönliche Handschrift deutlich erkennbar ist. Angesichts des herausragenden Designs dieses auf flachem, offenen Gelände erbauten Golfplatzes wünscht er sich, dass man bald eimal Gelegenheit bekommt, sein Können an einem Streifen "echten" Links-Terrains auszuprobieren. Die natürlichen und künstlichen Unebenheiten des häufig spektakulär und respekteinflössend anmutenden Geländes nutzt er geschickt für sein Spiel mit Links-typischen Elementen. Deshalb eignet sich der Platz nur für Golfer, die mindestens sicheres Bogey-Golf spielen können (die hinteren Abschläge sind für Pros reserviert). Obwohl alle Schwierigkeiten gut erkennbar sind, benötigt man sicherlich einige Runden der Gewöhnung, bevor man hoffen darf, diesen Platz mit einem guten Ergebnis zu absolvieren. Unglücklicherweise wird auf dem Platz mit 120 Euro das höchste Greenfee in Deutschland verlangt.

Great champions are often accused of signing courses without designing them too much. Not so for Nick Faldo, who visibly leaves his mark on the courses he designs. When you see the excellence of this course over a flat, open site, you can hardly wait to see him get to grips with a grand links site. He has toyed with the links idea here, using the natural and artificial undulations of often very spectacular and intimidating terrain. This course is only recommended for anyone who can at least play bogey golf (the back-tees are for the pros). Although the difficulties are clearly there to be seen, you will need to play this course several times (and in match-play) before even thinking about returning a good card at the end of the day. Unfortunately, the green-fee is one of the most expensive in Germany.

Sporting Club Berlin (Scharmützelsee) 1997

Parkallee 3
D - 15526 BAD SAAROW

Office	Sekretariat	(49) 033631 - 63 300
Pro shop	Pro shop	(49) 033631 - 61 070
Fax	Fax	(49) 033631 - 63 310
Web	www.a-rosa.de	
Situation	Lage	Berlin, 75 km

Frankfurt/Oder, 35 km

Annual closure	Jährliche Schliessung	30/11→1/3
Weekly closure	Wöchentliche Schliessung	no

Fees main season Preisliste hochsaison		18 holes
	Week days Woche	**We/Bank holidays** We/Feiertag
Individual Individuell	€ 120	€ 120
Couple Ehepaar	€ 240	€ 240

Special fees for hotel guests

Caddie Caddie no — **Electric Trolley** Elektrokarren yes

Buggy Elektrischer Wagen yes — **Clubs** Leihschläger yes

Credit cards Kreditkarten
VISA - Eurocard - MasterCard - AMEX - DC - JCB

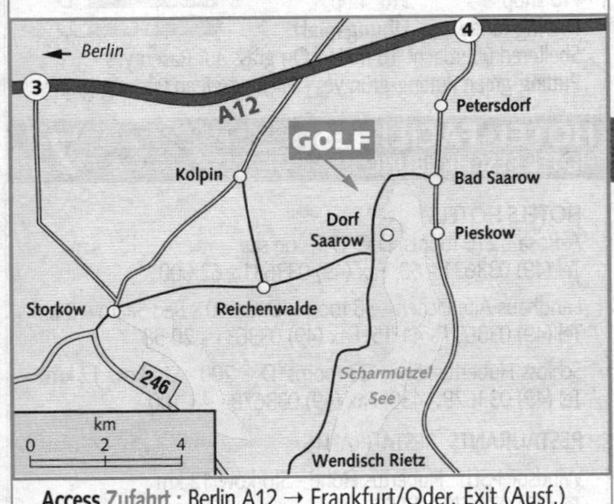

Access Zufahrt : Berlin A12 → Frankfurt/Oder. Exit (Ausf.) Fürstenwalde, → Bad Saarow → Golf.

Map 6 on page 359 Karte 6 Seite 359

GOLF COURSE PLATZ 18/20

Site	Lage	
Maintenance	Instandhaltung	
Architect	Architekt	Nick Faldo
Type	Typ	links
Relief	Begehbarkeit	
Water in play	Platz mit Wasser	
Exp. to wind	Wind ausgesetzt	
Trees in play	Platz mit Bäumen	

Scorecard Scorekarte	**Chp.** Chp.	**Mens** Herren	**Ladies** Damen
Length Länge	6477	6095	5722
Par	72	72	72
Slope system	145	141	138

Advised golfing ability Empfohlene Spielstärke — 0 12 24 36

Hcp required Min. Handicap 36

CLUB HOUSE & AMENITIES KLUBHAUS UND NEBENGEBÄUDE 8/10

Pro shop Pro shop
Driving range Übungsplatz
Sheltered überdacht 16 mats - On grass auf Rasen yes - Putting-green Putting-grün yes - Pitching-green Pitching-grün yes

HOTEL FACILITIES HOTEL BESCHREIBUNG 7/10

HOTELS HOTELS

A-Rosa - 216 rooms, D € 175 - on site
Tel (49) 033631 - 60, Fax (49) 033631 - 62 000

Landhaus Alte Eichen - 38 rooms, D € 100 - Bad Saarow 3 km
Tel (49) 033631 - 41 15, Fax (49) 033631 - 20 58

Schloss Hubertushöhe - 23 rooms, D € 200 - Storkow 12 km
Tel (49) 033678 - 430, Fax (49) 033678 - 43 100

RESTAURANTS RESTAURANTS

Windspiel-Schl. Hubertus Höhe - Storkow 12 km
Tel (49) 033678 - 43 0

Landhaus Alte Eichen - Bad Saarow 3 km
Tel (49) 033678 - 41 15

Sporting-Club Berlin *Stan Eby*

16	8	7

Die Schwierigkeiten beginnen nämlich mit dem Schlag aufs Grün. Die Grüns sind riesig, sehr gut verteidigt, und vor einigen lauern die selben tiefen Topfbunker wie auf dem Faldo Course (bei dem Stan Eby als Co-Designer fungierte). Das Anspielen der Grüns wird noch zusätzlich dadurch erschwert, dass viele Grüns quer zur Spielrichtung liegen. Aber selbst, wenn man das Grün „in regulation" erreicht hat, ist Par oder Birdie längst nicht sicher. Da die Grüns extrem onduliert sind, muss man den Ball auf der selben Ebene wie die Fahne platzieren. Ansonsten drohen mindestens drei Putts. Der Pflegezustand des Platzes ist wie der seiner beiden Nachbarn ausgezeichnet. Uns gefiel ganz besonders das 8. Loch, ein Par 5, bei dem einen herrlichen Blick über das gesamte Resort geniesst und das 9. Loch, eine wundervolles Par 3. Das 18. Loch, ein Par mit einem kleinen Bach vor dem Grün, bildet den gelungenen Abschluss der Runde.

The Stan Eby course is a lot shorter than its two neighbours. However it is no push-over for the better player, who here should tee off from the back tees. The real difficulties start with the shot into the green. The greens are huge, very well defended and some have the same deep pot bunkers as the Faldo course (where Stan Eby was much involved too). To compound the difficulty of the second shot is the fact that a lot of greens run diagonally to the fairway. But the fun often starts when you are actually on the putting surface, where par or birdie are a tough call: the greens are sharply contoured. This makes it so important to hit your approach to the right place on the green if you want to avoid three-putt-territory. We especially liked the 8th hole, a par 5 where you have a great view over the whole resort and the 9th, a wonderful par 3. The 18th, a par 5 with a creek in front of the green is a great finishing hole.

Sporting Club Berlin (Scharmützelsee) 2001

Parkallee 3
D - 15526 BAD SAAROW

Office	Sekretariat	(49) 033631 - 63 300
Pro shop	Pro shop	(49) 033631 - 61 070
Fax	Fax	(49) 033631 - 63 310
Web	www.a-rosa.de	
Situation	Lage	Berlin, 75 km

Frankfurt/Oder, 35 km

Annual closure	Jährliche Schliessung	30/11→1/3
Weekly closure	Wöchentliche Schliessung	no
Fees main season	Preisliste hochsaison	18 holes

	Week days Woche	We/Bank holidays We/Feiertag
Individual Individuell	€ 60	€ 60
Couple Ehepaar	€ 120	€ 120

Special fees for Hotel guests

Caddie Caddie no — **Electric Trolley** Elektrokarren yes
Buggy Elektrischer Wagen yes — **Clubs** Leihschläger yes
Credit cards Kreditkarten
VISA - Eurocard - MasterCard - AMEX - DC - JCB

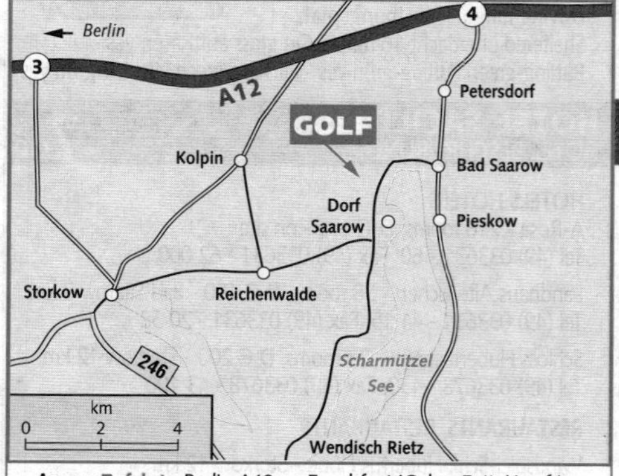

Access Zufahrt : Berlin A12 → Frankfurt/Oder. Exit (Ausf.) Fürstenwalde, → Bad Saarow → Golf.
Map 6 on page 359 Karte 6 Seite 359

GOLF COURSE
PLATZ — **16**/20

Site	Lage	
Maintenance	Instandhaltung	
Architect	Architekt	Stan Eby
Type	Typ	parkland
Relief	Begehbarkeit	
Water in play	Platz mit Wasser	
Exp. to wind	Wind ausgesetzt	
Trees in play	Platz mit Bäumen	

Scorecard Scorekarte	Chp. Chp.	Mens Herren	Ladies Damen
Length Länge	5950	5593	4558
Par	71	71	71
Slope system	124	122	122

Advised golfing ability Empfohlene Spielstärke: 0 12 24 36
Hcp required Min. Handicap: no

CLUB HOUSE & AMENITIES
KLUBHAUS UND NEBENGEBÄUDE — **8**/10

Pro shop Pro shop
Driving range Übungsplatz
Sheltered überdacht 16 mats - On grass auf Rasen yes - Putting-green Putting-grün yes - Pitching-green Pitching-grün yes

HOTEL FACILITIES
HOTEL BESCHREIBUNG — **7**/10

HOTELS HOTELS

A-Rosa - 216 rooms, D € 175 - on site
Tel (49) 033631 - 60, Fax (49) 033631 - 62 000

Landhaus Alte Eichen - 38 rooms, D € 100 - Bad Saarow 3 km
Tel (49) 033631 - 41 15, Fax (49) 033631 - 20 58

Schloss Hubertushöhe - 23 rooms, D € 200 - Storkow 12 km
Tel (49) 033678 - 430, Fax (49) 033678 - 43 100

RESTAURANTS RESTAURANTS

Windspiel-Schl. Hubertus Höhe - Storkow 12 km
Tel (49) 033678 - 43 0

Landhaus Alte Eichen - Bad Saarow 3 km
Tel (49) 033678 - 41 15

St. Dionys

17 | 7 | 6

St. Dionys, in einiger Entfernung zu Hamburg gelegen, bietet einen guten Vorwand zur Erkundung der Lüneburger Heide, einer Moorlandschaft, deren Bild geprägt wird von Pinien, Birken und Heidekraut. Gerade Letzteres taucht diese ansonsten karge Gegend im August und September in üppige Farben. Der Platz selbst weist nur leichte Unebenheiten auf und kann so jedermann empfohlen werden. Die Vegetation ist teilweise sehr dominant, dennoch gibt es auch für Longhitter genügend offene Flächen. Obwohl die gut gestalteten Grüns meist ausgezeichnet verteidigt sind, ist es doch in vielen Fällen möglich, sie flach anzuspielen. Ärgerlich ist die Position einiger Fairwaybunker, durch die gute Schläge bestraft werden können. Es ist nichts Neues, dass für ein gutes Ergebnis lange und gerade Schläge von Bedeutung sind. Diese Feststellung ist hier jedoch - vor allem von den hinteren Abschlägen - ganz besonders zutreffend. Das Vergnügen St. Dionys zu spielen geht weit über den landschaftlichen Reiz der Umgebung hinaus.

St. Dionys is some distance from Hamburg but is a good excuse for discovering the "Lüneburger Heide", moorland dotted with pine-trees and birch and covered with heather. Both add sumptuous colour to rather austere landscape in August and September. The course itself is only moderately hilly and so can be recommended for everyone. The vegetation is sometimes very much to the fore but there is no lack of open space to attract the big-hitters. While the greens are generally well-designed and frequently well-guarded, you can often run the ball in. One regret is the layout of some fairway bunkers, which can penalise good shots. Saying you have to play long and straight for a good round is stating the obvious, but here it really is very true, especially from the back tees. The fun of playing St. Dionys is more than simply admiring the surroundings.

Golf Club St. Dionys — 1972

Widukindweg
D - 21357 ST. DIONYS

Office	Sekretariat	(49) 04133 - 213 311
Pro shop	Pro shop	(49) 04133 - 213 315
Fax	Fax	(49) 04133 - 213 313
Web	www.golfclub-st-dionys.de	
Situation	Lage	Winsen, 8 km

Lüneburg (pop. 65 000), 10 km

Annual closure Jährliche Schliessung — no

Weekly closure Wöchentliche Schliessung — Monday
(Montag): restaurant closed

Fees main season Preisliste hochsaison — 18 holes

	Week days Woche	We/Bank holidays We/Feiertag
Individual Individuell	€ 45	€ 55
Couple Ehepaar	€ 90	€ 110

Students: – 50%

Caddie Caddie no — **Electric Trolley** Elektrokarren yes
Buggy Elektrischer Wagen yes — **Clubs** Leihschläger no
Credit cards Kreditkarten no

Access Zufahrt : A7 Hamburg → Hannover. Exit (Ausf.) Maschen. A250 → Lüneburg. Exit Winsen Ost. B4 → Lüneburg. Wittorf, left to Barum. → St. Dionys.
Map 7 on page 360 Karte 7 Seite 360

GOLF COURSE — PLATZ — 17/20

Site	Lage	
Maintenance	Instandhaltung	
Architect	Architekt	Harald Gratenau
Type	Typ	moorland
Relief	Begehbarkeit	
Water in play	Platz mit Wasser	
Exp. to wind	Wind ausgesetzt	
Trees in play	Platz mit Bäumen	

Scorecard Scorekarte	Chp. Chp.	Mens Herren	Ladies Damen
Length Länge	6255	6058	5083
Par	72	72	72
Slope system	127	124	122

Advised golfing ability Empfohlene Spielstärke — 0 12 24 36
Hcp required Min. Handicap — 36

CLUB HOUSE & AMENITIES — KLUBHAUS UND NEBENGEBÄUDE — 7/10

Pro shop Pro shop
Driving range Übungsplatz
Sheltered überdacht 5 mats - On grass auf Rasen yes - Putting-green Putting-grün yes - Pitching-green Pitching-grün yes

HOTEL FACILITIES — HOTEL BESCHREIBUNG — 6/10

HOTELS HOTELS

Hotel Bergström - 123 rooms, D € 135 - Lüneburg 11 km
Tel (49) 04131 - 30 80, Fax (49) 04131 - 308 499

Landhotel Frank - Lüneburg 2 km
32 rooms, D from € 80
Tel (49) 04133 - 400 90, Fax (49) 04133 - 400 933

Castanea Resort - 125 rooms, D € 150 - Adendorf 6 km
Tel (49) 04131 - 223 30, Fax (49) 04131-2233 2233

RESTAURANTS RESTAURANTS

Restaurant Hotel Zum Heidkrug - Lüneburg 11 km
Tel (49) 04131 - 241 60
Ratskeller - Lüneburg 11 km - Tel (49) 04131 - 317 57
Kronen-Bauhaus - Lüneburg 11 km - Tel (49) 04133 - 713 200

St. Eurach

16 | 7 | 6

Mit seinem dominierenden Clubhaus, dem Platz, dessen Spielbahnen sich durch Bäume und Wälder winden, und dem Blick auf die Alpen im Hintergrund vermittelt St. Eurach den Eindruck von Exklusivität, der durch das Greenfee bestätigt wird. Der Reiz der umgebenden Natur hinterlässt einen ebenso starken Eindruck wie die sehr traditionelle Platz. Der lange und enge Platz wurde durch die von Bernhard Langer vorgenommenen Veränderungen an den Bunkern zusätzlich erschwert. Dennoch ist der Platz kein Monster und im grossen und ganz fair, d.h. gute Schläge werden belohnt, schlechte bestraft. Die BMW International Open, ein Turnier der europäischen PGA Tour, wurde hier von 1994 bis 1996 ausgetragen und der Platz dadurch zu seinem Vorteil verändert.

With the estate dominated by the club-house, a course winding its way through trees and the Alps visible in the background on a clear day, St. Eurach gives the impression of an exclusive site, an impression confirmed by the green fee (so avoid week-ends). When thinking about it, the natural environment leaves a greater impression than the actual course, and it certainly has the glamour to offset a rather bland personality. When it comes to playing, and we hate to put visitors off, high-handicappers will be hard pushed to enjoy their golf here. The layout is long and narrow, and the alterations made to bunkers by Bernhard Langer have added a little spice, but all this implies complete control of your game if you want to excel. You have to feel easy with all your clubs, including those you need for recovery shots. A demanding course to play when on top of your game. Keep to match-play, there are a lot of surprises in store.

St. Eurach Land- und Golf Club e.V. 1973

Eurach 8
D - 82393 IFFELDORF

Office	Sekretariat	(49) 08801 - 1332
Pro shop	Pro shop	(49) 08801 - 1532
Fax	Fax	(49) 08801 - 2523
Web	www.eurach.de	
Situation	Lage	München, 35 km

Penzberg, 5 km

Annual closure	Jährliche Schliessung	15/11→15/4
Weekly closure	Wöchentliche Schliessung	no

452

Fees main season Preisliste hochsaison	18 holes	
	Week days Woche	**We/Bank holidays** We/Feiertag
Individual Individuell	€ 65	€ 80*
Couple Ehepaar	€ 130	€ 160*

* We & holidays: with members only
(nur in Mitgliederbegleitung)

Caddie Caddie on request — **Electric Trolley** Elektrokarren yes
Buggy Elektrischer Wagen yes — **Clubs** Leihschläger yes
Credit cards Kreditkarten no

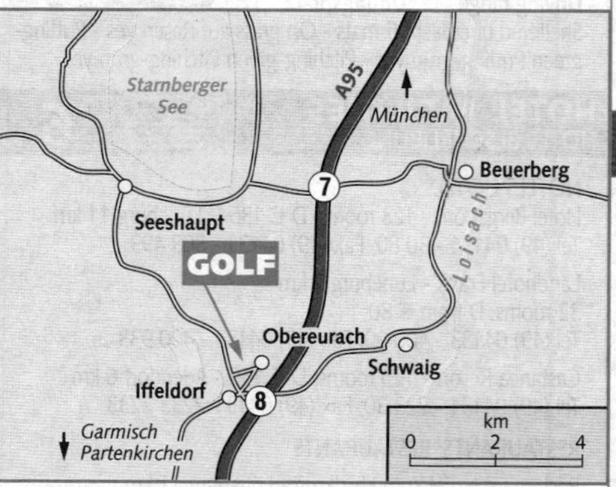

Access Zufahrt : München, A95 → Garmisch-Partenkirchen. Exit (Ausf.) Penzberg → Iffeldorf-Seeshaupt. 1,5 km → Golf on the right.
Map 2 on page 350 Karte 2 Seite 350

GOLF COURSE — PLATZ 16/20

Site	Lage	
Maintenance	Instandhaltung	
Architect	Architekt	Donald Harradine
Type	Typ	forest
Relief	Begehbarkeit	
Water in play	Platz mit Wasser	
Exp. to wind	Wind ausgesetzt	
Trees in play	Platz mit Bäumen	

Scorecard Scorekarte	**Chp.** Chp.	**Mens** Herren	**Ladies** Damen
Length Länge	6430	5907	5267
Par	71	71	74
Slope system	135	131	126

Advised golfing ability Empfohlene Spielstärke — 0 12 24 36
Hcp required Min. Handicap — 35

CLUB HOUSE & AMENITIES — KLUBHAUS UND NEBENGEBÄUDE 7/10

Pro shop Pro shop
Driving range Übungsplatz
Sheltered überdacht no - On grass auf Rasen yes - Putting-green Putting-grün yes - Pitching-green Pitching-grün yes

HOTEL FACILITIES — HOTEL BESCHREIBUNG 6/10

HOTELS HOTELS

Landgasthof Osterseen - 24 rooms, D € 95 - Iffeldorf 2 km
Tel (49) 08856 - 928 60, Fax (49) 08856 - 928 645

Stadthotel Berggeist - 45 rooms, D € 90 - Penzberg 6 km
Tel (49) 08856 - 80 10, Fax (49) 08856 - 81 913

Sterff - 21 rooms, D € 75 - Seeshaupt 5 km
Tel (49) 08801 - 906 30, Fax (49) 08801 - 906 340

RESTAURANTS RESTAURANTS

Landgasthof Osterseen - Iffeldorf 2 km
Tel (49) 08856 - 1011

Stadthotel Berggeist - Penzberg 6 km
Tel (49) 08856 - 78 99

St. Leon-Rot *"Rot" Course*

16 | 9 | 7

Der Platz gehört Dietmar Hopp, einem der Gründer und ehemaligen Vorstandsvorsitzender von SAP, dem drittgrössten Software-Haus der Welt. Seltsamer weise wurde dieser ältere Platz des luxuriöse und ultra-moderne Projekt nicht von einem der bekannten Golfplatz-Architekten, sondern von einem Landschaftsarchitekten entworfen, der nie zuvor in Leben für das Design eines Golfplatzes verantworlich gezeichnet hatte. Deshalb musste der Platz für die TPC of Europe gründlich überarbeitet werden. Tiger Woods, der die "Deutsche Bank - SAP Open TPC of Europe" auf diesem Platz 1999 und 2001 gewann, gefiel der Platz. Nach den vielen Umbauten ist ein Platz entstanden, der zu den besten in Deutschland gehört. Die Hauptschwierigkeit des Platzes sind Wasserhindernisse an neun Löchern (das 7. Loch hat ein Inselgrün) und die viele Biotope, die als seitliches Wasserhinderniss gepflockt sind. Deshalb sind eigentlich nur das erste und das letzte Loch einfach. Diesen Platz wird man eben so wenig vergessen.

This is the brain child of Dietmar Hopp, the founder and former chairman of SAP, the third biggest software company of the world. But strangely enough, this luxurious and ultra-modern project was laid out not by a high-tech golf course architect but by a skilled landscape gardener, who had never designed a golf course in his life before. As a result, a good part of the course had to be re-shaped and holes re-routed in order to host the Deutsche Bank-SAP Open. The result satisfied Tiger Woods, who won the tournament here in 1999 and 2001. After all the alterations, the course has joined the ranks of the best in Germany. An important feature here is not only the presence of water hazards on nine holes (the 7th has an island green), but also the huge areas protected owing to environmental considerations, which are considered as lateral water hazards. If only because the first and last holes are easy, you will not forget this course in a hurry.

Golf Club St. Leon-Rot — 1997

Opelstrasse 30
D - 68789 ST. LEON-ROT

Office	Sekretariat	(49) 06227 - 860 80
Pro shop	Pro shop	(49) 06227 - 860 392
Fax	Fax	(49) 06227 - 860 888
Web	www.golfclub-stleon-rot.de	
Situation	Lage	Heidelberg, 15 km
Annual closure	Jährliche Schliessung	no
Weekly closure	Wöchentliche Schliessung	no

Fees main season Preisliste hochsaison — 18 holes

	Week days / Woche	We/Bank holidays / We/Feiertag
Individual Individuell	€ 80	€ 90
Couple Ehepaar	€ 160	€ 180

Students: € 40 / 55 (We)

Caddie Caddie no — **Electric Trolley** Elektrokarren yes
Buggy Elektrischer Wagen yes — **Clubs** Leihschläger yes
Credit cards Kreditkarten — VISA - Eurocard

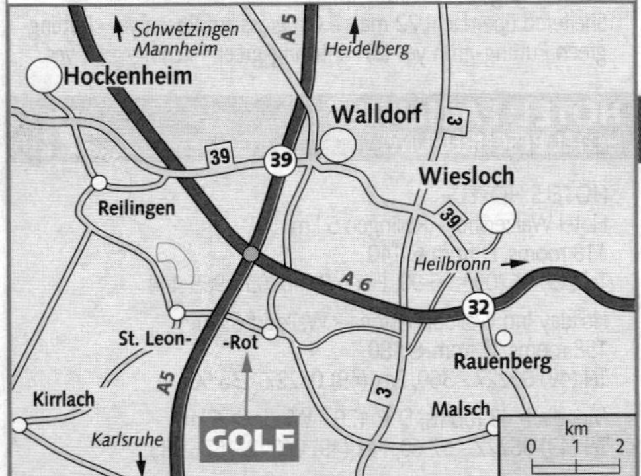

Access Zufahrt : A6 → Heilbronn. Exit (Ausf.) Wiesloch/Rauenberg. → Walldorf. 2nd traffic lights → St. Leon-Rot. 3rd street, turn left in Opelstrasse.
Map 1 on page 349 Karte 1 Seite 349

GOLF COURSE — PLATZ — 16/20

Site	Lage	
Maintenance	Instandhaltung	
Architect	Architekt	Hannes Schreiner
Type	Typ	parkland, open country
Relief	Begehbarkeit	
Water in play	Platz mit Wasser	
Exp. to wind	Wind ausgesetzt	
Trees in play	Platz mit Bäumen	

Scorecard Scorekarte	Chp. / Chp.	Mens / Herren	Ladies / Damen
Length Länge	6587	6047	5329
Par	72	72	72
Slope system	137	133	133

Advised golfing ability Empfohlene Spielstärke — 0 12 24 36
Hcp required Min. Handicap — 36

CLUB HOUSE & AMENITIES — KLUBHAUS UND NEBENGEBÄUDE — 9/10

Pro shop Pro shop
Driving range Übungsplatz
Sheltered überdacht 22 mats - On grass auf Rasen yes - Putting-green Putting-grün yes (3) - Pitching-green Pitching-grün yes

HOTEL FACILITIES — HOTEL BESCHREIBUNG — 7/10

HOTELS HOTELS

Hotel Walkershof - Reilingen 5 km
118 rooms, D from € 140
Tel (49) 06205 - 95 90, Fax (49) 06205 - 959 444

Holiday Inn Walldorf Astoria - Walldorf 6 km
158 rooms, D from € 180
Tel (49) 06227 - 360, Fax (49) 06227 - 36 504

Mondial - 43 rooms, D € 120 - Wiesloch 6 km
Tel (49) 06222 - 57 60, Fax (49) 06222 - 576 333

RESTAURANTS RESTAURANTS

Mondial - Wiesloch 6 km - Tel (49) 06222 - 57 60
Freihof - Wiesloch 6 km - Tel (49) 06227 - 25 17
Langen's Turmstuben - Wiesloch 6 km - Tel (49) 06222 - 10 00

St. Leon-Rot *"St. Leon" Course*

17	9	7

Wie bei dem Terre Blanche Projekt in der französischen Provence vertraute er auch beim zweiten 18 Löcher, dem St. Leon-Platz auf die Design-Arbeit von Dave Thomas. Der englische Architekt ist bekannt dafür, dass er grosse Erdbewegungen vornimmt, was allerdings dazu führt, dass sich viele seiner Plätze und Löcher ähneln. Dadurch ist es schwierig, sich nach ein paar Tagen an einzelne Löcher zu erinnern. Hier bleiben nur das 2. Loch, das entlang des renaturierten Kraichbachs verläuft und das 5. Loch nachhaltig im Gedächtnis. Der über ein Kilometer lange Kraichbach, die vielen Wasserhindernisse, die zahlreichen Bunker und die grossen, stark ondulierten Grüns machen die Hauptschwierigkeit dieses Platzes aus, zumindest so lange wie die angepflanzten Bäume noch relativ klein sind. Auf diesem Platz sollte man den Ball lang und hoch spielen können, Fähigkeiten die eher niedrige Handicaps beherrschen. Alles in allem ein Platz von hoher Qualität und exzellentem Pflegezustand, auf dem Tiger Woods 2002 die Deutsche Bank-SAP Open gewann.

As with his Terre Blanche courses in the French Provence, he called in course architect Dave Thomas, one of the great earth-shapers of our day and age, despite there sometimes being a little sameness about his work. This can make it difficult to remember individual holes, and here only the 2nd and 5th holes really stick in the mind. Starting with a patch of flat open land, he has introduced any number of water hazards and brought the little Kraichbach stream back from the dead and into play over more than a kilometre. Add to this very many well designed bunkers and huge greens that are rather well contoured and very well protected, then you get some idea of the difficulties already in play while waiting for the trees to grow. Dave Thomas has clearly chosen sides here, opting for a strategic, penalising and even somewhat athletic style of architecture, because you need to hit it long and hit it high. In other words, skills generally reserved for low-handicappers. All in all, the quality and finish of the whole layout are really excellent.

Golf Club St. Leon-Rot — 2000

Opelstrasse 30
D - 68789 ST. LEON-ROT

Office	Sekretariat	(49) 06227 - 860 80
Pro shop	Pro shop	(49) 06227 - 860 392
Fax	Fax	(49) 06227 - 860 888
Web	www.golfclub-stleon-rot.de	
Situation	Lage	Heidelberg, 15 km
Annual closure	Jährliche Schliessung	no
Weekly closure	Wöchentliche Schliessung	no

Fees main season Preisliste hochsaison	18 holes	
	Week days Woche	**We/Bank holidays** We/Feiertag
Individual Individuell	€ 80	€ 90
Couple Ehepaar	€ 160	€ 180

Students: € 40 / 55 (We)

Caddie Caddie no — **Electric Trolley** Elektrokarren yes
Buggy Elektrischer Wagen yes — **Clubs** Leihschläger yes
Credit cards Kreditkarten VISA - Eurocard
Access Zufahrt : A6 → Heilbronn. Exit (Ausf.)

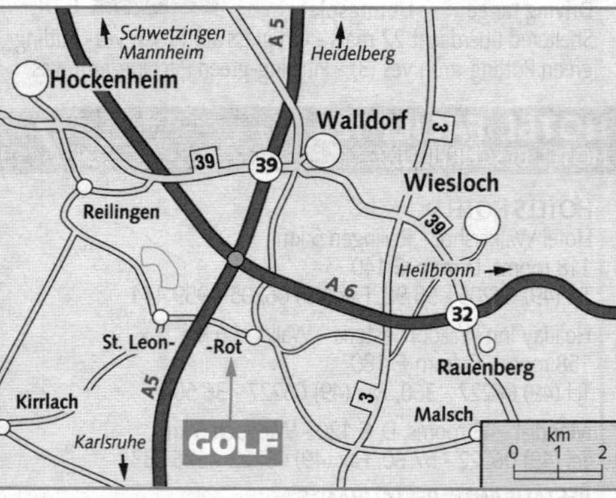

Wiesloch/Rauenberg. → Walldorf. 2nd traffic lights → St. Leon-Rot. 3rd street, turn left in Opelstrasse.
Map 1 on page 349 Karte 1 Seite 349

GOLF COURSE — PLATZ — 17/20

Site	Lage	
Maintenance	Instandhaltung	
Architect	Architekt	Dave Thomas
Type	Typ	open country
Relief	Begehbarkeit	
Water in play	Platz mit Wasser	
Exp. to wind	Wind ausgesetzt	
Trees in play	Platz mit Bäumen	

Scorecard Scorekarte	**Chp.** Chp.	**Mens** Herren	**Ladies** Damen
Length Länge	6518	6142	5020
Par	72	72	72
Slope system	133	130	130

Advised golfing ability Empfohlene Spielstärke — 0 12 24 36
Hcp required Min. Handicap 36

CLUB HOUSE & AMENITIES — KLUBHAUS UND NEBENGEBÄUDE — 9/10

Pro shop Pro shop
Driving range Übungsplatz
Sheltered überdacht 22 mats - On grass auf Rasen yes - Putting-green Putting-grün yes (3) - Pitching-green Pitching-grün yes

HOTEL FACILITIES — HOTEL BESCHREIBUNG — 7/10

HOTELS HOTELS

Hotel Walkershof - Reilingen 5 km
118 rooms, D from € 140
Tel (49) 06205 - 95 90, Fax (49) 06205 - 959 444

Holiday Inn Walldorf Astoria - Walldorf 6 km
158 rooms, D from € 180
Tel (49) 06227 - 360, Fax (49) 06227 - 36 504

Mondial- 43 rooms, D € 120 - Wiesloch 6 km
Tel (49) 06222 - 57 60, Fax (49) 06222 - 576 333

RESTAURANTS RESTAURANTS

Mondial - Wiesloch 6 km - Tel (49) 06222 - 57 60
Freihof - Wiesloch 6 km - Tel (49) 06227 - 25 17
Langen's Turmstuben - Wiesloch 6 km - Tel (49) 06222 - 10 00

Stolper Heide

16 | 7 | 7

Stolper Heide ist Bestandteil einer schnell-wachsenden Wohnanlage und ist zweifellos einer der vielversprechendsten Golfplätze in ganz Deutschland. Die Namen Bernhard Langer und Kurt Rossknecht bürgen für ehrlichen Charakter und den Abwechslungsreichtum des Designs, das sich hervorragend an die unterschiedlichen Spielstärken der Golfer anpasst, wenngleich insbesondere die besseren Spieler ihren Spass daran haben werden, die strategischen Herausforderungen des Platzes zu meistern. Auf dem ausgezeichnet und intelligent gestalteten Gelände brauchen die Baüme sicherlich noch Zeit ihr Wachstum zu entfalten, aber bereits jetzt weisen die sorgfältig gearbeiteten Abgrenzungen zwischen Fairway und Rough dem Golfer deutlich die Spiellinie für den nächsten Schlag. Die Schlusslöcher stellen die Spieler vor allem im Match-Play vor eine interessante Aufgabe. Die Pflegezustand des Platzes, besonders im Bereich der sorgfältig gestalteten Grüns, ist ausgezeichnet.

In a fast-growing residential area, Stolper Heide is one of Germany's most promising courses. The names of Bernhard Langer and Rossknecht were sure-fire guarantees for the honesty and variety of this layout and for the way it adapts to different levels of proficiency, although the better players will have the most fun here solving questions of strategy. Well-landscaped and intelligent, the course needs the trees to grow but the careful way in which the fairways and roughs are demarcated means you are never in any doubt as to where the next shot should go. The finishing holes are particularly interesting here if competing in match-play. The green-keeping is already very good, particularly the carefully designed greens.

Stolper Heide Golf Club — 1997

Frihnauer Weg 3
D - 16540 STOLPE

Office	Sekretariat	(49) 03303 -5490 214
Pro shop	Pro shop	(49) 03303 - 549 214
Fax	Fax	(49) 03303 - 549 222
Web	www.golfclub-stolperheide.de	
Situation	Lage	Berlin, 20 km
Annual closure	Jährliche Schliessung	1/1→31/1
Weekly closure	Wöchentliche Schliessung	no

Fees main season Preisliste hochsaison	18 holes	
	Week days Woche	We/Bank holidays We/Feiertag
Individual Individuell	€ 33	€ 50
Couple Ehepaar	€ 66	€ 100

Students: – 50%

Caddie Caddie no — **Electric Trolley** Elektrokarren no

Buggy Elektrischer Wagen yes — **Clubs** Leihschläger yes

Credit cards Kreditkarten
VISA - Eurocard - Mastercard - AMEX

Access Zufahrt : Berlin A111 → Hamburg. Exit (Ausf.) Henningsdorf-Stolpe. Left → Stolpe.

Map 6 on page 359 Karte 6 Seite 359

GOLF COURSE — PLATZ — 16/20

Site	Lage	
Maintenance	Instandhaltung	
Architect	Architekt	Bernhard Langer, Kurt Rossknecht
Type	Typ	parkland
Relief	Begehbarkeit	
Water in play	Platz mit Wasser	
Exp. to wind	Wind ausgesetzt	
Trees in play	Platz mit Bäumen	

Scorecard Scorekarte	Chp. Chp.	Mens Herren	Ladies Damen
Length Länge	6255	5974	5222
Par	72	72	72
Slope system	128	126	124

Advised golfing ability Empfohlene Spielstärke — 0 12 24 36

Hcp required Min. Handicap — 36 (weekends)

CLUB HOUSE & AMENITIES — KLUBHAUS UND NEBENGEBÄUDE — 7/10

Pro shop Pro shop
Driving range Übungsplatz
Sheltered überdacht 15 mats - On grass auf Rasen yes - Putting-green Putting-grün yes - Pitching-green Pitching-grün yes

HOTEL FACILITIES — HOTEL BESCHREIBUNG — 7/10

HOTELS HOTELS

Hotel Palace - 301 rooms, D € 250 - Berlin 15 km
Tel (49) 030 - 25 020, Fax (49) 030 - 250 21119

Sorat Hotel - 120 rooms, D € 150 - Berlin-Tegel 8 km
Tel (49) 030 - 439 040, Fax (49) 030 -439 04 444

Landgasthof zur Krummen Linde - Stolpe 1 km
14 rooms, D € 100
Tel (49) 03303 - 533 60, Fax (49) 03303 - 533 630

RESTAURANTS RESTAURANTS

Landgasthof zur Krummen Linde - Stolpe 1 km
Tel (49) 03303 - 533 60

Stuttgarter Solitude

16	5	5

Solitude erweist sich als echter Gütetest für das Können eines Golfers, insbesondere dessen Fähigkeit gerade Drives zu schlagen. Kraftvollen Spielern werden die Fairways – Genauigkeit vorausgesetzt – vergleichsweise breit erscheinen, aber auch das Anspiel der mittelgroßen, erst kürzlich umgebauten Grüns erfordert in vielen Fällen nochmals höchste Präzision. Kürzere Spieler müssen sich vor allem auf gute lange Eisen oder Fairway-Hölzer oder/und und ihr kurzes Spiel verlassen können. Dies gilt im besonderen an den langen Par-4-Löchern, die regulär nur schwer zu erreichen sind, sowie den ausgezeichneten Par-3-Löchern. Wasser kommt nur selten ins Spiel, so ist es primär der Wald der nicht nur den optischen sondern auch den spieltechnischen Charakter dieses Platzes prägt. Dank eines sehr durchdachten Layouts macht der bis auf das 6. Loch (Via Mala) leicht begehbare Platz einen ausgewogenen Eindruck. Solitude ist eine Anlage, die man kaum ignorieren kann, eignet sich aber eher für die etwas besseren Golfer.

A good example of a von Limburger concern for the demands of golf. While golf is the examination of a player's abilities, Solitude is a test of value with emphasis on straight driving. If they play straight, powerful hitters will find the fairways comparatively wide, but they will need extreme accuracy to reach a number of mid-sized elevated greens that have been reshaped. The shorter-hitters will have to sharpen up their long irons or fairway woods and even their short game on some of the long par 4s, that are tough to hit in regulation, and the very good par 3s. As there is little water to speak of, the course's visual appeal is primarily the forest. The forest is, in fact, the whole point of the course, which is well-balanced, easy on the legs except the very strenuous climb to the 6th tee-box, and a thoroughly well designed affair. It is difficult to overlook Solitude, but it is a course reserved for golfers who can play a bit.

Stuttgarter Golf-Club Solitude — 1968

Schlossfeld
D - 71297 MÖNSHEIM

Office	Sekretariat	(49) 07044 -911 0410
Pro shop	Pro shop	(49) 07044 -911 0413
Fax	Fax	(49) 07044 -911 0420
Web	www.golfclub-stuttgart.com	
Situation	Lage	Stuttgart, 20 km
Annual closure	Jährliche Schliessung	25/12→7/1
Weekly closure	Wöchentliche Schliessung	Monday

(Montag): restaurant closed

Fees main season Preisliste hochsaison		18 holes
	Week days Woche	**We/Bank holidays** We/Feiertag
Individual Individuell	€ 45	€ 55*
Couple Ehepaar	€ 90	€ 110*

* We: only with members (nur in Mitgliederbegleitung)

Caddie Caddie on request — **Electric Trolley** Elektrokarren yes
Buggy Elektrischer Wagen yes — **Clubs** Leihschläger yes
Credit cards Kreditkarten no

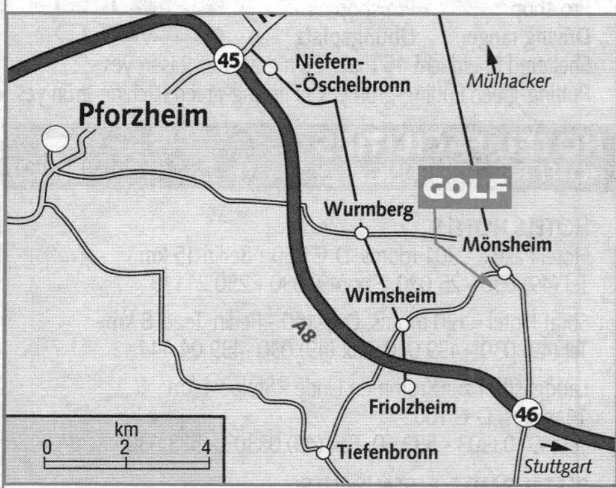

Access Zufahrt : A8 Stuttgart-Karlsruhe. Exit (Ausf.) Heimsheim-Mönsheim. Golf → Mönsheim
Map 1 on page 349 Karte 1 Seite 349

GOLF COURSE — PLATZ — 16/20

Site	Lage	
Maintenance	Instandhaltung	
Architect	Architekt	B. von Limburger
Type	Typ	open country, forest
Relief	Begehbarkeit	
Water in play	Platz mit Wasser	
Exp. to wind	Wind ausgesetzt	
Trees in play	Platz mit Bäumen	

Scorecard Scorekarte	Chp. Chp.	Mens Herren	Ladies Damen
Length Länge	6188	5949	5335
Par	72	72	72
Slope system	131	128	125

Advised golfing ability Empfohlene Spielstärke — 0 12 24 36
Hcp required Min. Handicap — 36

CLUB HOUSE & AMENITIES — KLUBHAUS UND NEBENGEBÄUDE — 5/10

Pro shop Pro shop
Driving range Übungsplatz
Sheltered überdacht 6 mats - On grass auf Rasen yes - Putting-green Putting-grün yes - Pitching-green Pitching-grün yes

HOTEL FACILITIES — HOTEL BESCHREIBUNG — 5/10

HOTELS HOTELS
Parkhotel - Pforzheim 12 km
208 rooms, D € 120
Tel (49) 07231 - 16 10, Fax (49) 07231 - 1616 90

Ochsen Post - Tiefenbronn 6 km
19 rooms, D € 80
Tel (49) 07234 - 954 50, Fax (49) 07234 -954 5145

RESTAURANTS RESTAURANTS
Häckermühle - Tiefenbronn 10 km - Tel (49) 07234 - 6111
Ochsenpost - Tiefenbronn 6 km - Tel (49) 07234 - 920 578
Widmann - Wimsheim 2 km - Tel (49) 07044 - 413 23

Sylt

15 | 6 | 8

Westerland ist das grösste Seebad Deutschlands, Kampen das exklusivste. Auf dieser seltsam geformten Insel von 40 km Länge, die von Klippen, Stränden und Dünen gesäumt ist, erwartet man natürlich einen Links Course. Donald Harradine hat hier eine seiner besten Designs abgeliefert, obwohl der Platz nicht mit den Meisterwerken der Links Courses der Britischen Inseln mithalten kann. Auch auf diesem Küstenplatz ist der Wind ein bestimmender Faktor. Der sandige Boden sorgt für hervorragende Drainage, aber diese trockene Bodenbeschaffenheit erschwert die Schläge zum Grün. Um die Bälle auf den Grüns zum Halten zubringen, muss man einkalkulieren wie weit der Ball rollt, wobei bei starkem Wind das Beherrschen von "knock-down-shots" hilfreich ist. Es gibt keine blinden Löcher und Fallen, man sieht immer, wohin man den Ball zu spielen hat. Dieser Platz ist auch ein Naturerlebnis in klarer Seeuft, die prickelnd wie Champagner schmeckt.

This is the northernmost of the North Friesian Islands, next to Denmark, where the largest town, Westerland, is Germany's biggest seaside resort. Over this strangely shaped isle (40 km in length) with alternating cliffs, beaches and dunes, a virtual links course was only to be expected. Donald Harradine has produced here a fine design, even though it doesn't really measure up to the British masterpieces. The wind is a key factor, naturally, as is the joy of breathing air as sharp as chilled champagne. The sand gives ideal turf and perfect draining, but the dryness of the soil and the wind make for difficult approach shots to the green. For the ball to stay on the green, you need to know how to roll it on, taking a chance on the likely trajectory. There are no blind shots here and no traps in what is very varied and well-utilised landscape; you can clearly see what needs to be done and you alone are responsible for any high-scoring.

Golf Club Sylt e.V. — 1982

D - 25996 WENNINGSTEDT

Office	Sekretariat	(49) 04651 -915 9811
Pro shop	Pro shop	(49) 04651 -995 9832
Fax	Fax	(49) 04651 -915 9819
Web	www.golfclubsylt.de	
Situation	Lage	Sylt Island, close to Denmark
Annual closure	Jährliche Schliessung	no
Weekly closure	Wöchentliche Schliessung	no

Fees main season Preisliste hochsaison — 18 holes

	Week days / Woche	We/Bank holidays / We/Feiertag
Individual Individuell	€ 55	€ 55
Couple Ehepaar	€ 110	€ 110

– 21: – 50%

Caddie Caddie no — **Electric Trolley** Elektrokarren yes

Buggy Elektrischer Wagen no — **Clubs** Leihschläger yes

Credit cards Kreditkarten no

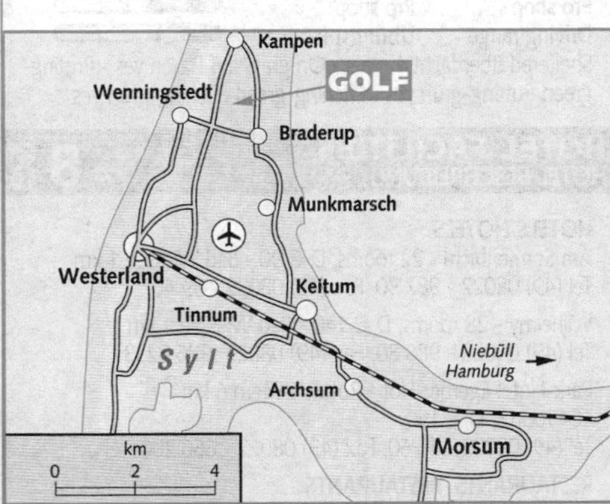

Access Zufahrt : Hamburg E45 to Flensburg, then 199 to Niebüll → Westerland/Sylt, Wennigstedt → List

Map 1 on page 122 Karte 1 Seite 122

GOLF COURSE — PLATZ — 15/20

Site	Lage	
Maintenance	Instandhaltung	
Architect	Architekt	Donald Harradine
Type	Typ	links, open country
Relief	Begehbarkeit	
Water in play	Platz mit Wasser	
Exp. to wind	Wind ausgesetzt	
Trees in play	Platz mit Bäumen	

Scorecard / Scorekarte	Chp. / Chp.	Mens / Herren	Ladies / Damen
Length Länge	6129	5650	4845
Par	72	72	72
Slope system	127	123	121

Advised golfing ability Empfohlene Spielstärke — 0 12 24 36

Hcp required Min. Handicap 36

CLUB HOUSE & AMENITIES — KLUBHAUS UND NEBENGEBÄUDE — 6/10

Pro shop Pro shop

Driving range Übungsplatz

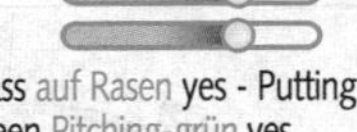

Sheltered überdacht 6 mats - On grass auf Rasen yes - Putting-green Putting-grün yes - Pitching-green Pitching-grün yes

HOTEL FACILITIES — HOTEL BESCHREIBUNG — 8/10

HOTELS HOTELS

Rungholt - 83 rooms, D € 215 - Kampen 3 km
Tel (49) 04651 - 44 80, Fax (49) 04651 - 44 848

Benen-Diken-Hof - Keitum 6 km
45 rooms, D € 175
Tel (49) 04651 - 938 30, Fax (49) 04651 -9383 183

Strandhörn - 45 rooms, D € 190 - Wenningsten 2 km
Tel (49) 04651 - 945 00, Fax (49) 04651 - 457 77

RESTAURANTS RESTAURANTS

Bodendorf's - Tinnum 6 km - Tel (49) 04651 - 889 90
Gogärtchen - Kampen 3 km - Tel (49) 04651 - 412 42
Manne Pahl - Kampen 3 km - Tel (49) 04651 - 425 10

Tegernseer Bad Wiessee

14	7	8

Der Platz liegt in einer der schönsten Gegenden Deutschland. Der Platz liegt oberhalb des Tegernsees. Leider ist der Platz nicht so schön wie die Gegend, der Platz ist eher wegen seiner illustren Mitgliedschaft als wegen seines Designs berühmt. Neun Löcher sind ordentlich, die anderen neun eher schrecklich. Die Platz ist kurz, aber das Anspielen der relativ kleinen Grüns ist extrem schwierig. Das Clubhaus strahlt viel Gemütlichkeit aus. Mit etwas Glück trifft man hier die Reichen und Schönen Deutschlands, von Boris Becker über Gunter Sachs bis hin zu Willy Bogner. Ein Gang durch die Umkleide mit den Namen auf den Spinden erinnert an das deutsche "Who is Who". Der vielbeschäftigte Donald Harradine entwarf den Platz 1960, aber komplett fertiggestellt wurde er erst im Jahr 1984. Der Platz ist recht hügelig, dennoch benötigen nur ältere oder untrainierte Spieler einen Golfwagen.

It is hardly more than an hour's drive to the Austrian border and not much more to visit Innsbrück once you have discovered all the charms of the lake lying at the foot of the course here. While this layout is hardly a world-beater, it does, like its neighbours, have the advantage of an exceptional natural setting. In this sense, Bavaria is a real golfing destination. Designed in 1960 by Donald Harradine, a decidedly prolific architect, it was only really completed in 1984. It shows all the typical features of its designer, who was undoubtedly less concerned with marking his period than many of his colleagues, but it is very British in style as far as understanding the game at all levels is concerned. We sometimes felt he might have contoured the fairways and bunkers a little more, but this sobriety has the advantage of preserving the terrain's natural aspect. The course is rather hilly but only the more elderly or very unfit golfers will need a buggy.

Tegernseer Golf-Club Bad Wiessee e.V. 1960

Robognerhof
D - 83707 BAD WIESSEE

Office	Sekretariat	(49) 08022 - 8769
Pro shop	Pro shop	(49) 08022 - 82 350
Fax	Fax	(49) 08022 - 82 747
Web	www.tegernseer-golf-club.de	
Situation	Lage	Bad Tölz, 18 km
Annual closure	Jährliche Schliessung	1/12→31/3
Weekly closure	Wöchentliche Schliessung	Monday

(Montag): restaurant closed

Fees main season Preisliste hochsaison	18 holes	
	Week days Woche	**We/Bank holidays** We/Feiertag
Individual Individuell	€ 60	€ 70*
Couple Ehepaar	€ 120	€ 140*

* We: ask before coming (begrenzte Spielmöglichkeit)
– 21: – 50%

Caddie Caddie no — **Electric Trolley** Elektrokarren yes
Buggy Elektrischer Wagen no — **Clubs** Leihschläger yes
Credit cards Kreditkarten no

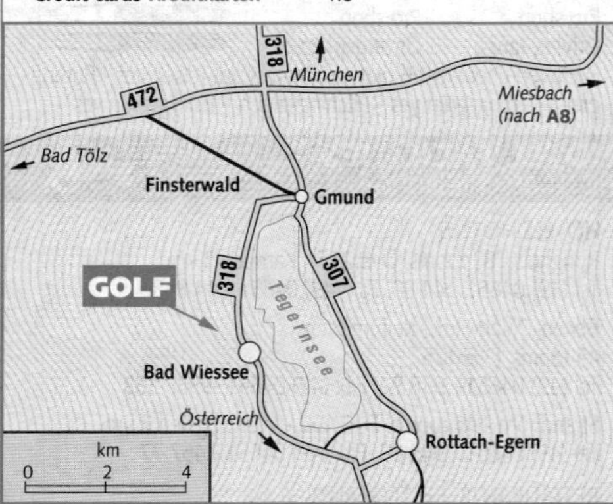

Access Zufahrt : A8 München → Salzburg. Exit (Ausf.) Holzkirchen. 318 → Gmund. In Gmund 318 → Bad Wiessee.
Map 2 on page 350 Karte 2 Seite 350

GOLF COURSE — PLATZ 14/20

Site	Lage	
Maintenance	Instandhaltung	
Architect	Architekt	Donald Harradine
Type	Typ	mountain, parkland
Relief	Begehbarkeit	
Water in play	Platz mit Wasser	
Exp. to wind	Wind ausgesetzt	
Trees in play	Platz mit Bäumen	

Scorecard Scorekarte	**Chp.** Chp.	**Mens** Herren	**Ladies** Damen
Length Länge	5459	5459	4818
Par	70	70	70
Slope system	130	130	125

Advised golfing ability Empfohlene Spielstärke — 0 12 24 36
Hcp required Min. Handicap 36

CLUB HOUSE & AMENITIES — KLUBHAUS UND NEBENGEBÄUDE 7/10

Pro shop Pro shop
Driving range Übungsplatz
Sheltered überdacht 4 mats - On grass auf Rasen yes - Putting-green Putting-grün yes - Pitching-green Pitching-grün yes

HOTEL FACILITIES — HOTEL BESCHREIBUNG 8/10

HOTELS HOTELS

Am Sonnenbichl - 22 rooms, D € 90 - Bad Wiessee 1 km
Tel (49) 08022 - 987 30, Fax (49) 08022 - 89 40

Wilhelmy - 28 rooms, D € 140 - Bad Wiessee 1 km
Tel (49) 08022 - 986 80, Fax (49) 08022 -986 8233

Park-Hotel Egerner-Hof - Rottach-Egern 6 km
104 rooms, D € 190
Tel (49) 08022 - 66 60, Fax (49) 08022 - 666 200

RESTAURANTS RESTAURANTS

Freihaus Brenner - Bad Wiessee 1 km - Tel (49) 08022 - 82 004

Patrizierhof - Bad Wiessee 1 km - Tel (49) 08022 - 987 30

Altes Fährhaus - Bad Tölz 18 km - Tel (49) 08041 - 60 30

Tutzing

15 | 7 | 6

Der auf 700 Meter Höhe gelegene Golfplatz ist wie viele andere Plätze dieser Region besonders bei Touristen sehr beliebt. Am schönsten spielt sich Tutzing entweder im Herbst oder aber im Frühling, wenn die Vegetation nach dem Winter wieder voll erblüht ist. Die bayrischen Alpen bilden einen malerischen Hintergrund und verstärken so das Spielvergnügen auf dieser ausgezeichneten Anlage mit zahlreichen Bäumen und einigen hübschen Wasserläufen, welche die Spielbahnen - nicht selten zum Verdruss der Golfer - kreuzen. Der Kurs verfügt über keinerlei aussergewöhnliche aufregende Designelemente, sondern spiegelt vielmehr die Absicht des Architekten wider, in erster Linie einen Platz zu bauen, bei dem das Golfvergnügen im Vordergrund steht. Wenn Sie sich in dieser herrlichen Gegend aufhalten, sollten Sie diesen schön gelegenen Golfplatz und das dazugehörige Clubhaus im Stil eines Chalets keinesfalls links liegen lassen.

At an altitude of 700 metres and like most courses in this region very popular with tourists, Tutzing is particularly pleasant to play from the middle of Spring - when the vegetation is filling out after Winter - to the middle of Autumn. The backdrop of the Bavarian Alps adds to the pleasure of this excellent course with its numerous trees and pretty streams which cross the course, sometimes to the distress of the golfer. Don't look for anything outstandingly exciting design-wise here; this is the work of a serious artist who was thinking first and foremost of golfing pleasure. When you are in this superb region, Tutzing is a course not to be missed and a charming site enhanced by the chalet-style club-house.

Golf-Club Tutzing e.V. — 1983

Deixlfurt 7
D - 82327 TUTZING

Office	Sekretariat	(49) 08158 - 3600
Pro shop	Pro shop	(49) 08158 - 259 930
Fax	Fax	(49) 08158 - 7234
Web	www.golfclub-tutzing.de	
Situation	Lage	München, 40 km
Annual closure	Jährliche Schliessung	15/11→15/2
Weekly closure	Wöchentliche Schliessung	no

Fees main season Preisliste hochsaison	18 holes	
	Week days Woche	We/Bank holidays We/Feiertag
Individual Individuell	€ 50	€ 65
Couple Ehepaar	€ 100	€ 130

– 19: – 50%

Caddie Caddie no — **Electric Trolley** Elektrokarren no
Buggy Elektrischer Wagen yes — **Clubs** Leihschläger yes
Credit cards Kreditkarten no

Access Zufahrt : A95 München → Starnberg. Von Starnberg, B2 (Olympiastr.) → Weilheim. After Traubing, 1km left → Deixlfurt.
Map 2 on page 350 Karte 2 Seite 350

GOLF COURSE — PLATZ 15/20

Site	Lage	
Maintenance	Instandhaltung	
Architect	Architekt	C. Kramer
Type	Typ	mountain
Relief	Begehbarkeit	
Water in play	Platz mit Wasser	
Exp. to wind	Wind ausgesetzt	
Trees in play	Platz mit Bäumen	

Scorecard Scorekarte	Chp. Chp.	Mens Herren	Ladies Damen
Length Länge	6041	6041	5427
Par	72	72	72
Slope system	125	125	128

Advised golfing ability Empfohlene Spielstärke — 0 12 24 36
Hcp required Min. Handicap — 35

CLUB HOUSE & AMENITIES — KLUBHAUS UND NEBENGEBÄUDE 7/10

Pro shop Pro shop
Driving range Übungsplatz
Sheltered überdacht 3 mats - On grass auf Rasen yes - Putting-green Putting-grün yes - Pitching-green Pitching-grün yes

HOTEL FACILITIES — HOTEL BESCHREIBUNG 6/10

HOTELS HOTELS
Kaiserin Elisabeth - 65 rooms, D € 145 - Feldafing 3 km
Tel (49) 08157 - 930 90, Fax (49) 08157 -930 9133

Forsthaus am See - Pöcking-Possenhofen 10 km
21 rooms, D € 140
Tel (49) 08157 - 93 010, Fax (49) 08157 - 42 92

Marina - Bernried 12 km - 87 rooms, D € 145
Tel (49) 08158 - 93 20, Fax (49) 08158 - 71 17

RESTAURANTS RESTAURANTS
Forsthaus Ilkahöhe - Tutzing 4 km - Tel (49) 08158 - 8242
Starnberger Alm - Starnberg 10 km - Tel (49) 08151 - 155 77
La Dolce Vita - Starnberg 10 km - Tel (49) 08151 - 167 80

Walddörfer

16 | 7 | 6

Wie Ahrensburg ist auch Walddörfer am Ufer des Bredenbeker Sees gelegen, inmitten einer Parklandschaft mit für diese Region typischen Hecken und Bäumen. Dutzende unterschiedlicher Baumarten verleihen vielen Spielbahnen ihren ganz eigenen Charakter. Die hügeligen ersten neun Löcher mit ihren durchgehend engen Fairways zwingen speziell beim Abschlag zur Vorsicht. Die Spielbahnen sind zudem noch recht lang; es gibt vier Par 5, drei Par 3 und zwei Par 4 Löcher. Auf den zweiten Neun wird das Gelände flacher und offener. Besonders bei aufkommendem Wind werden sich selbst Longhitter schwer tun, ihr Schläge gutzumachen, wenn sie auf den ersten Neun zu sehr gestreut haben. Bemerkenswert am Layout von Walddörfer ist, dass es nur sieben Par-4-Löcher gibt. Die gut erkennbaren Schwierigkeiten kommen stark ins Spiel. Das letzte Wort gebührt der ausgezeichneten 18. Bahn, die den würdigen Abschluss einer grossartigen Golfrunde bildet.

Like Ahrensburg, Walddörfer is located on the banks of lake Bredenbeker, in a setting of parkland, hedgerows and trees that are typical of the region. The trees are magnificent, with dozens of varieties giving a distinctive flavour to different holes. The front nine are hilly, with generally narrow fairways calling for care, especially off the tee. The holes are pretty long, too, and there are four par 5s, two par 3s and two par 4s. The landscape then becomes flatter and wider, although big-hitters will still be hard-pushed to repair their card if they were too wayward over the front 9, especially if the unstoppable wind gets up. In all, there are only seven par 4s here, a feature that adds to the originality of Walddörfer. Difficulties are very much in play and generally very visible. One last word should go to the 18th, an excellent hole with which to complete a great round of golf.

Golfclub Hamburg-Walddörfer — 1960

Schevenbarg
D - 22949 AMMERSBEK

Office	Sekretariat	(49) 040 - 605 1337
Pro shop	Pro shop	(49) 040 - 605 1337
Fax	Fax	(49) 040 - 605 4879
Web	www.gchw.de	
Situation	Lage	Hamburg, 20 km
Annual closure	Jährliche Schliessung	no
Weekly closure	Wöchentliche Schliessung	Monday

(Montag): restaurant closed

Fees main season Preisliste hochsaison		18 holes
	Week days Woche	**We/Bank holidays** We/Feiertag
Individual Individuell	€ 45	€ 55*
Couple Ehepaar	€ 90	€ 110*

*We: only with members (nur in Mitgliederbegleitung)
– 21 & Students: – 50%

Caddie Caddie no — **Electric Trolley** Elektrokarren no
Buggy Elektrischer Wagen no — **Clubs** Leihschläger yes
Credit cards Kreditkarten no

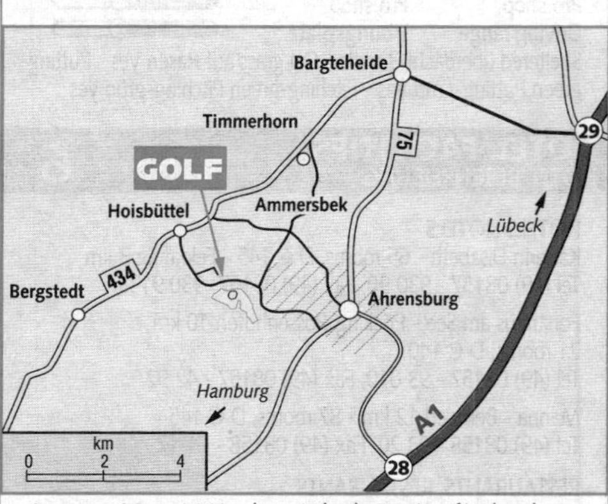

Access Zufahrt : A1 Hamburg-Lübeck. Exit (Ausf.) Ahrenburg. B434 → Ammersbek. In Ortsteil Hoisbüttel, turn right: Wulfsdorfer Weg → Golf

Map 7 on page 360 Karte 7 Seite 360

GOLF COURSE — PLATZ — 16/20

Site	Lage	
Maintenance	Instandhaltung	
Architect	Architekt	B. von Limburger
Type	Typ	forest, parkland
Relief	Begehbarkeit	
Water in play	Platz mit Wasser	
Exp. to wind	Wind ausgesetzt	
Trees in play	Platz mit Bäumen	

Scorecard Scorekarte	**Chp.** Chp.	**Mens** Herren	**Ladies** Damen
Length Länge	6093	5909	5272
Par	73	73	73
Slope system	131	130	129

Advised golfing ability Empfohlene Spielstärke — 0 12 24 36
Hcp required Min. Handicap — 36

CLUB HOUSE & AMENITIES — KLUBHAUS UND NEBENGEBÄUDE — 7/10

Pro shop Pro shop
Driving range Übungsplatz
Sheltered überdacht 8 mats - On grass auf Rasen yes - Putting-green Putting-grün yes - Pitching-green Pitching-grün no

HOTEL FACILITIES — HOTEL BESCHREIBUNG — 6/10

HOTELS HOTELS

Park Hotel Ahrensburg - Ahrensburg 6 km
117 rooms, D € 129
Tel (49) 04102 - 23 00, Fax (49) 04102 - 230 100

Ring Hotel Ahrensburg - Ahrensburg 6 km
24 rooms, D € 100
Tel (49) 04102 - 51 560, Fax (49) 04102 - 515 656

Am Schloss - 79 rooms, D € 95 Ahrensburg 6 km
Tel (49) 04102 - 80 55, Fax (49) 04102 - 18 01

RESTAURANTS RESTAURANTS

Golf restaurant - Tel (49) 040 - 605 4211

Le Marron (Park Hotel) - Ahrensburg 6 km
Tel (49) 04102 - 23 00

Wasserburg Anholt

15	7	7

Ein sehr gepflegter, klassischer Parkland Course mit altem Baumbestand in einem Teil des Schlossparks der Anholter Wasserburg. Der Meisterschaftsplatz wurde von Bernhard von Limburger gekonnt in das Landschaftsschutzgebiet Anholter Schweiz mit seinen beiden Flussläufen Issel und Wasserstrang gelegt. Das Platz ist abwechslungsreich und einprägsam, weil jedes der 18 Löcher seinen eigenenen Charakter hat und spezifische Herausforderung bietet. Besonders reizvoll sind die vier Par-3-Löcher, obwohl sie nach modernen Gesichtspunkten nicht sonderlich lang sind (zwischen 119 und 170 m). Dafür sind sie durch Wasser- und Sandhindernisse sehr gut verteidigt. Die anderen Löchern erfordern eine Kombination aus präzisem, langen Spiel und strategischem Geschick.

A very well groomed classical parkland course lined by mature trees located in a part of the old park of the water castle (Wasserschloss) Anholt. This championship course was designed by Bernhard von Limburger who laid out the course masterfully in the environmentally protected area of the Anholter Schweiz with the two streams of Issel and Wolfstrang. The course stays in your mind because each and every hole has its own character and challenge. The four par 3 holes on this course really stand out, even though they are not long by modern standards (between 119 and 170 m), but they are well defended by water hazards and sand traps. All other holes require a combination of long, precise shots and strategic skill.

Golf Club Wasserburg-Anholt e.V. — 1974

Am Schloss 3
D - 46419 ISSELBURG-ANHOLT

Office	Sekretariat	(49) 02874 - 915 120
Pro shop	Pro shop	(49) 02874 - 915 130
Fax	Fax	(49) 02874 - 915 128
Web	www.golfclub-anholt.de	
Situation	Lage	Bocholt, 16 km
Annual closure	Jährliche Schliessung	no
Weekly closure	Wöchentliche Schliessung	Monday

(Montag): restaurant closed

Fees main season Preisliste hochsaison	18 holes	
	Week days Woche	**We/Bank holidays** We/Feiertag
Individual Individuell	€ 45	€ 60
Couple Ehepaar	€ 90	€ 120

– 21 / Students: € 20 / 25 (We)

Caddie Caddie on request — **Electric Trolley** Elektrokarren no

Buggy Elektrischer Wagen yes — **Clubs** Leihschläger yes

Credit cards Kreditkarten
Visa - Eurocard - Mastercard - AMEX - DC

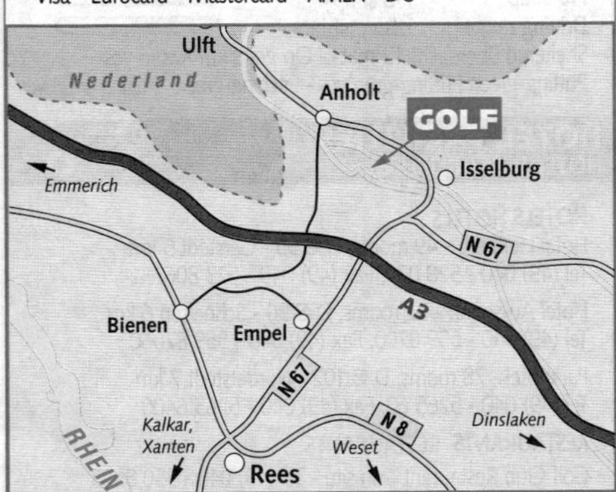

Access Zufahrt : A3 Oberhausen → Arnhem, Exit (Ausf.) Rees. B67 → Rees. Right on 458 → Millingen. Right → Anholt. 3 km right on 459 → Wasserburg-Anholt.
Map 5 on page 356 Karte 5 Seite 356

GOLF COURSE — PLATZ — 15/20

Site	Lage	
Maintenance	Instandhaltung	
Architect	Architekt	B. von Limburger
Type	Typ	forest, parkland
Relief	Begehbarkeit	
Water in play	Platz mit Wasser	
Exp. to wind	Wind ausgesetzt	
Trees in play	Platz mit Bäumen	

Scorecard Scorekarte	**Chp.** Chp.	**Mens** Herren	**Ladies** Damen
Length Länge	6063	6063	5319
Par	72	72	72
Slope system	126	126	123

Advised golfing ability Empfohlene Spielstärke — 0 12 24 36

Hcp required Min. Handicap — 45 (36 We)

CLUB HOUSE & AMENITIES — KLUBHAUS UND NEBENGEBÄUDE — 7/10

Pro shop Pro shop
Driving range Übungsplatz
Sheltered überdacht 9 mats - On grass auf Rasen yes - Putting-green Putting-grün yes - Pitching-green Pitching-grün yes

HOTEL FACILITIES — HOTEL BESCHREIBUNG — 7/10

HOTELS HOTELS
Parkhotel Wasserburg Anholt - on site
30 rooms, D from € 135
Tel (49) 02874 - 45 90, Fax (49) 02874 - 40 35

Nienhaus - Isselburg 4 km
12 rooms, D € 75
Tel (49) 02874 - 770, Fax (49) 02874 - 45 673

Legeland - 7 rooms, D € 65 - Anholt 1 km
Tel (49) 02874 - 837, Fax (49) 02874 - 45 417

RESTAURANTS RESTAURANTS
Parkhotel Wasserburg Anholt - on site - Tel (49) 02874 - 45 90
Legeland - Anholt 1 km - Tel (49) 02874 - 837

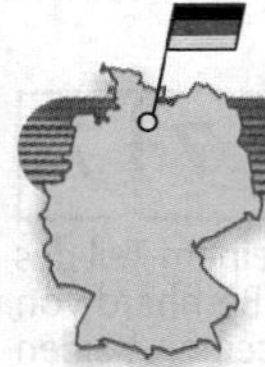

Wendlohe *A-Kurs + B-Kurs*

16	7	6

Die grosszügige Weite Schleswig-Holsteins bildet die ruhige und beschauliche Umgebung für Wendlohe, wo die zahlreichen Bäume kaum beunruhigen, da man seinen Ball auch unter den Bäumen immer in einer guten Lage vorfindet. Wenig Wasser und nur vereinzelte Fairway-Bunker weisen darauf hin, dass die Hauptschwierigkeit im Anspiel der Grüns liegt. Unterschiedlich gross, mit starken Kontouren versehen und teilweise auf mehreren Stufen angelegt, sind diese ohne Frage die interessantesten Grüns weit und breit. Sie sind durchgängig gut verteidigt, sehr schnell aber nie unspielbar. Um sie von der richtigen Position aus anzuspielen, bedarf es sehr präziser Eisenschläge. Deswegen wird es einem auch zumindest auf der ersten Runde schwerfallen, ein seinem Handicap entsprechendes Ergebnis zu spielen. Im Winter ist der Platz etwas feucht. Das Clubhaus erfreut sich einer schönen Terrasse, von der aus man das 18. Loch einsehen kann.

The wide open spaces of Schleswig-Holstein provide a calm and pastoral setting at "Auf der Wendlohe", where trees are hardly a worry. There are enough of them, but you always find your ball well-placed when you meet them. With only a little water and few fairway bunkers, you will guess that the main problem is the approach to the greens. These are unquestionably some of the most interesting putting surfaces to contend with in this part of the world, with different sizes, serious contours and multi-tiering. They are generally fast, well-protected but never unplayable. To approach them from the right position, you need a sharp and accurate iron game. This is why returning a card to reflect your handicap is hardly likely, at least not the first time out. A wee damp in winter, the course boasts a pretty terrace overlooking the 18th hole.

Golf Club auf der Wendlohe — 1964

Oldesloer Strasse 251
D - 22457 HAMBURG

Office	Sekretariat	(49) 040 - 550 5014
Pro shop	Pro shop	(49) 040 - 550 6151
Fax	Fax	(49) 040 - 550 3668
Web	www.wendlohe.de	
Situation	Lage	Hamburg, 15 km
Annual closure	Jährliche Schliessung	no
Weekly closure	Wöchentliche Schliessung	no

Fees main season Preisliste hochsaison	18 holes	
	Week days Woche	**We/Bank holidays** We/Feiertag
Individual Individuell	€ 36	€ 47*
Couple Ehepaar	€ 72	€ 94*

* We: only with members (nur in Mitgliederbegleitung)

Caddie Caddie on request — **Electric Trolley** Elektrokarren yes
Buggy Elektrischer Wagen yes — **Clubs** Leihschläger yes
Credit cards Kreditkarten no

Access Zufahrt : A7 Hamburg-Kiel. Exit (Ausf.) Hamburg-Schnelsen-Nord. 432 → Norderstedt (Oldesloher-Strasse). Left on Wendloher Weg → Golf
Map 7 on page 360 Karte 7 Seite 360

GOLF COURSE — PLATZ — 16/20

Site	Lage	
Maintenance	Instandhaltung	
Architect	Architekt	E.D. Hess
Type	Typ	country, open country
Relief	Begehbarkeit	
Water in play	Platz mit Wasser	
Exp. to wind	Wind ausgesetzt	
Trees in play	Platz mit Bäumen	

Scorecard Scorekarte	**Chp.** Chp.	**Mens** Herren	**Ladies** Damen
Length Länge	5964	5885	5079
Par	72	72	72
Slope system	131	130	126

Advised golfing ability Empfohlene Spielstärke — 0 12 24 36
Hcp required Min. Handicap 36

CLUB HOUSE & AMENITIES — KLUBHAUS UND NEBENGEBÄUDE — 7/10

Pro shop Pro shop
Driving range Übungsplatz
Sheltered überdacht 12 mats - On grass auf Rasen yes -
Putting-green Putting-grün yes - Pitching-green Pitching-grün yes

HOTEL FACILITIES — HOTEL BESCHREIBUNG — 6/10

HOTELS HOTELS

Hotel Heuberg - 49 rooms, D € 95 - Garstedt 5 km
Tel (49) 040 - 528 070, Fax (49) 040 - 523 8067

Hotel Ausspann - 32 rooms, D € 90 - Schnelsen 6 km
Tel (49) 040 - 559 8700, Fax (49) 040 - 559 87060

Parkhotel - 78 rooms, D € 102 - Norderstedt 7 km
Tel (49) 040 - 5265 60, Fax (49) 040 - 5265 6400

RESTAURANTS RESTAURANTS

Golf Club Restaurant - on site - Tel (49) 040 - 550 8583

Montgomery Champs - Schnelsen 6 km
Tel (49) 040 - 559 79 10

Lutz und König - Niendorf 7 km - Tel (49) 040 - 555 99533

Winnerod

15 | 8 | 7

Michael Pinner, der früher für die Design-Firma von Jack Nicklaus arbeitete, ist es gelungenen in dem hügeligen Gelände nahe Giessen vorzügliche 18 Spielbahnen zu legen, die zum Teil herrliche Aussichten auf die Wälder des Taunus und des Vogelsbergs bieten. Trotz der zum Teil grossen Höhenunterschiede (für konditionsschwache Spieler empfehlen wir einen Golfwagen) schaffte es Pinner, dass man nur bei zwei Par-4-Löchern vom Abschlag die Fahne nicht sieht. angesichts der Topographie eine Meisterleistung. So ist die Spielstrategie immer klar zu erkennen, der Platz ist nicht hinterlistig. Alle Hindernisse, ob Bäume, Sträucher oder Wasser kommen ins Spiel, sind aber selten so bedrohlich, dass man verzweifelt nach einer Lösung sucht. Die Grüns sind relativ gross und nicht sonderlich gut verteidigt, doch die Schwierigkeit beim Anspielen der Putting-Oberfläche liegen mehr in der Wahl des richtigen Schlägers. Das eindrucksvolle Clubhaus befindet sich in alten renovierten Gebäuden des alten Landguts.

Michael Pinner, who used to work with Jack Nicklaus' course design business, got to grips with rather hilly terrain in a magnificent site presenting pretty views of the wonderful forest landscapes of Taunus and Vogelsberg. Despite some spectacular differences in altitude (a buggy is a serious option), Pinner succeeded in limiting the number of blind greens to two, which was quite some achievement. As all hazards are there to be seen, you can hardly accuse this course of back-stabbing and game strategy is obvious. Whether trees or bushes, fairway bunkers or water, hazards are well in play but seldom dangerous enough to leave you stuck for a solution. The greens are large, well-built and relatively unprotected, but the difficulties here lie elsewhere, starting with the choice of club to actually reach the putting surface. The club-house has been laid out in some impressive refurbished buildings. For high-handicappers, we would advise the front tees every time, or the additional 9-hole course.

Golfpark Winnerod — 1999

Parkstrasse 22
D - 35447 REISKIRCHEN-WINNEROD

Office Sekretariat (49) 06408 - 9513 0
Pro shop Pro shop (49) 06408 - 9513 62
Fax Fax (49) 06408 - 9513 13
Web www.golfpark.de
Situation Lage Giessen, 12 km
Annual closure Jährliche Schliessung no
Weekly closure Wöchentliche Schliessung Monday
(Montag): restaurant closed

Fees main season Preisliste hochsaison 18 holes

	Week days Woche	We/Bank holidays We/Feiertag
Individual Individuell	€ 40	€ 58
Couple Ehepaar	€ 80	€ 116

– 21 & Students: – 50%

Caddie Caddie no
Electric Trolley Elektrokarren yes
Buggy Elektrischer Wagen yes
Clubs Leihschläger yes
Credit cards Kreditkarten VISA - Eurocard

Access Zufahrt : Frankfurt: A 5 → Kassel, Exit (Ausfahrt) Reiskirchen. After Reiskirchen, left → Rabenau-Winnerod, 1,5 km → 'Golfplatz'.
Map 3 on page 353 Karte 3 Seite 353

GOLF COURSE — PLATZ 15/20

Site Lage
Maintenance Instandhaltung
Architect Architekt Michael Pinner
Type Typ hilly
Relief Begehbarkeit
Water in play Platz mit Wasser
Exp. to wind Wind ausgesetzt
Trees in play Platz mit Bäumen

Scorecard Scorekarte	Chp. Chp.	Mens Herren	Ladies Damen
Length Länge	6166	5765	5197
Par	72	72	72
Slope system	126	126	127

Advised golfing ability Empfohlene Spielstärke 0 12 24 36
Hcp required Min. Handicap 45 (36 We)

CLUB HOUSE & AMENITIES — KLUBHAUS UND NEBENGEBÄUDE 8/10

Pro shop Pro shop
Driving range Übungsplatz
Sheltered überdacht 8 mats - On grass auf Rasen yes - Putting-green Putting-grün yes - Pitching-green Pitching-grün yes

HOTEL FACILITIES — HOTEL BESCHREIBUNG 7/10

HOTELS HOTELS
Sporthotel - 47 rooms, D € 86- Grünberg 5 km
Tel (49) 06401 - 80 20, Fax (49) 06401 - 802 166

Alte Klostermühle - Lich 15 km
25 rooms, D € 110
Tel (49) 06404 - 919 00, Fax (49) 06404 - 919 091

Tandreas - 32 rooms, D € 110 - Giessen 12 km
Tel (49) 0641 - 940 70, Fax (49) 0641 - 940 7499

Steinsgarten - 126 rooms, D € 150 - Giessen 12 km
Tel (49) 0641 - 38 990, Fax (49) 0641 - 3899 200

RESTAURANTS RESTAURANTS
Tandreas - Giessen 12 km - Tel (49) 0641 - 940 70

WinstonGolf

16 | 7 | 6

Im Osten Deutschland eröffnen immer mehr Golfplätze – eine ideale Möglichkeit die herrliche Landschaft dieser Gegend zu erkunden. Das gilt ganz besonders für Mecklenburg-Vorpommern, ein Bundesland mit tausend Seen, dem Müritzsee und seinem Nationalpark nahe der vorzüglichen Plätze des Fleesensee resorts. Knapp 80 km westlich liegt der Platz von Winstongolf in einem noch erträglich hügeligen Gelände. Für den mühsamen Aufstieg zum 7. Abschlag entschädigt ein herrlicher Blick über den angrenzenden See. Es gibt keine verborgenen Hindernisse in diesem klassischen Layout mit vielen Wasserhindernisse. Die Grüns zeichnen einige starke Breaks aus. Der Platz nimmt den Spieler mit auf eine abwechslungsreiche Reise: es ist sehr guter, moderner Platz, der von den hinteren Abschlägen um einiges schwieriger ist – ganz wie es sein sollte. Der Platz war im September 2005 Gastgeber der deutschen Amateur-Meisterschaften für Damen urd Herren.

The eastern side of Germany is unveiling some magnificent landscapes. This is the case with Mecklenburg, a large region with 1,000 lakes which include the Müritzersee and its national park, a natural reserve and paradise for bird- and plant-lovers very close to the Fleesensee course. Some 50 miles further west close to the regional capital of Schwerin, this Winstongolf has just opened over very acceptable hilly terrain where one or two climbs may prove something of an ordeal; the walk up to the 7th tee reserves the pleasure of some glorious views over the neighbouring lake. There are no hidden traps here on what is a rather classical layout with the extensive use of water hazards and good quality greens with some sometimes surprisingly sharp breaks. The course interestingly grows in intensity from 1 to 18. A good, modern course, perhaps seriously more difficult from the back tees… which is only logical.

WinstonGolf GmbH — 2002
Kranichweg 1
D - 19065 VORBECK

Office	Sekretariat	(49) 03860 - 5020
Pro shop	Pro shop	(49) 03860 - 5020
Fax	Fax	(49) 03860 - 502 222
Web	www.winstongolf.de	
Situation	Lage	Schwerin, 23 km
Annual closure	Jährliche Schliessung	no
Weekly closure	Wöchentliche Schliessung	no

Fees main season Preisliste hochsaison	18 holes	
	Week days Woche	**We/Bank holidays** We/Feiertag
Individual Individuell	€ 37	€ 49
Couple Ehepaar	€ 74	€ 98

Caddie Caddie no — **Electric Trolley** Elektrokarren yes

Buggy Elektrischer Wagen yes — **Clubs** Leihschläger yes

Credit cards Kreditkarten
VISA - Eurocard - MasterCard

Access Zufahrt : On A426 Exit 12 (Ausfahrt), then A421, Exit Schwerin Ost, turn right. In Raben Steinfeld, turn right at traffic lights. After 2 km, right again → Golf. Follow the road (K5) through Godern, Gneven and Vorbeck. Golf just after Vorbeck. **Map 7 on page 361** Karte 7 Seite 361

GOLF COURSE — PLATZ — 16/20

Site	Lage	
Maintenance	Instandhaltung	
Architect	Architekt	Holger Rengstorf
Type	Typ	inland
Relief	Begehbarkeit	
Water in play	Platz mit Wasser	
Exp. to wind	Wind ausgesetzt	
Trees in play	Platz mit Bäumen	

Scorecard Scorekarte	**Chp.** Chp.	**Mens** Herren	**Ladies** Damen
Length Länge	6276	6015	5153
Par	72	72	72
Slope system	133	132	130

Advised golfing ability Empfohlene Spielstärke — 0 12 24 36

Hcp required Min. Handicap — 50

CLUB HOUSE & AMENITIES — KLUBHAUS UND NEBENGEBÄUDE — 7/10

Pro shop Pro shop

Driving range Übungsplatz

Sheltered überdacht 6 mats - On grass auf Rasen yes - Putting-green Putting-grün yes - Pitching-green Pitching-grün yes

HOTEL FACILITIES — HOTEL BESCHREIBUNG — 6/10

HOTELS HOTELS

Schloss Basthorst - Crivitz 3 km
45 rooms, D € 108
Tel (49) 03863 - 5250, Fax (49) 03863 - 525 555

Schloss Kaartz - Kaartz 18 km
17 rooms, D € 80
Tel (49) 038483 - 3080, Fax (49) 038483 - 30840

Niederländischer Hof - Schwerin 20 km
33 rooms, D € 129
Tel (49) 0385 - 591 100, Fax (49) 0385 -591 10999

RESTAURANTS RESTAURANTS

Schröter's - Schwerin 23 km - Tel (49) 0385 - 550 7698
Weinhaus Uhle - Schwerin 23 km - Tel (49) 0385 - 550 7698

Wittelsbacher

16	7	6

Unweit der Donau liegt dieser flache Platz in einer parkähnlichen Landschaft mit wunderschönen alten Bäumen, meist Eichen. Die Hauptschwierigkeit dieses Platzes liegt darin, diesen herrlichen Bäumen und dem extrem dicken Rough aus dem Weg zu gehen. Zudem erschweren drei Wasserhindernisse und 17 strategisch geschickt platzierte Fairway-Bunker das Spiel. Die gut gesicherten Grüns sind von herausragender Qualität. Sie sind von teilweise immenser Grösse, so dass man den einen oder anderen Drei-Putt einkalkulieren muss. Der Clubpräsident, seine Königliche Hoheit Herzog Max in Bayern, der Mitglied von Pine Valley, des R&A, Muirfield und Royal St. George's ist, besteht in bester schottischer Tradition darauf, dass die Fairways nicht künstlich bewässert werden und keine Entfernungsmarkierungen aufweisen. Imposant ist das moderne Clubhaus mit Wohnmöglichkeit und einem nahegelegene Dormi-Haus. Ein Platz, den man unbedingt spielen muss, wenn man im Grossraum München-Ingolstadt-Augsburg unterwegs ist.

In countryside along the Danube, this is a flat course surrounded by some really beautiful trees, mainly oak, which give the impression of a large English-style park. The main difficulty here is to stay away from these impressive trees and the heavy, thick rough. Three water hazards and 17 strategically placed fairway bunkers add to the difficulty. The greens are well defended and of excellent quality, but some are simply huge, so getting away without at least one 3-putt is a major feat. The Club president and de-facto owner, His Royal Highness Duke Max of Bavaria, who is a member of Pine Valley, the R & A, Muirfield and Royal St. George's, insists in the best Scottish traditions that there is no irrigation system for the fairways and no distance markers either. Guests can stay either at the ultra modern club-house or in the charming dormy-house located two minutes from the course. This is a course not to be missed, if you are in the greater Munich-Ingolstadt-Augsburg area.

Wittelsbacher Golfclub Rohrenfeld-Neuburg — 1988

Gut Rohrenfeld
D - 86633 NEUBURG/DONAU

Office	Sekretariat	(49) 08431 - 44 118
Pro shop	Pro shop	(49) 08431 - 44 118
Fax	Fax	(49) 08431 - 41 301
Web	www.wittelsbacher-golf.de	
Situation	Lage	Ingolstadt, 20 km
Annual closure	Jährliche Schliessung	no
Weekly closure	Wöchentliche Schliessung	no

Fees main season Preisliste hochsaison	Week days Woche	We/Bank holidays We/Feiertag
18 holes		
Individual Individuell	€ 45	€ 55
Couple Ehepaar	€ 90	€ 110

– 21 & Students: – 50%

Caddie Caddie no — **Electric Trolley** Elektrokarren yes
Buggy Elektrischer Wagen yes — **Clubs** Leihschläger yes
Credit cards Kreditkarten MasterCard

Access Zufahrt : München, A9 → Nürnberg. Exit (Ausf.) Manching B16 → Neuburg. Exit Rohrenfeld → Golf
Map 2 on page 350 Karte 2 Seite 350

GOLF COURSE — PLATZ 16/20

Site	Lage	
Maintenance	Instandhaltung	
Architect	Architekt	Dudok van Heel
Type	Typ	forest
Relief	Begehbarkeit	
Water in play	Platz mit Wasser	
Exp. to wind	Wind ausgesetzt	
Trees in play	Platz mit Bäumen	

Scorecard Scorekarte	Chp. Chp.	Mens Herren	Ladies Damen
Length Länge	6318	6113	5310
Par	72	72	72
Slope system	130	127	125

Advised golfing ability Empfohlene Spielstärke: 0 12 24 36
Hcp required Min. Handicap 36

CLUB HOUSE & AMENITIES — KLUBHAUS UND NEBENGEBÄUDE 7/10

Pro shop Pro shop
Driving range Übungsplatz
Sheltered überdacht 10 mats - On grass auf Rasen yes - Putting-green Putting-grün yes - Pitching-green Pitching-grün yes

HOTEL FACILITIES — HOTEL BESCHREIBUNG 6/10

HOTELS HOTELS

Am Fluss - 22 rooms, D € 90 - Neuburg 6 km
Tel (49) 08431 - 676 80, Fax (49) 08431 - 676 830

Bergbauer - 21 rooms, D € 85 - Neuburg 6 km
Tel (49) 08431 - 616 890, Fax (49) 08431 - 47 090

Romantik Hotel zum Klosterbräu - Neuburg-Bergen 12 km
24 rooms, D € 80
Tel (49) 08431 - 677 50, Fax (49) 08431 - 411 20

Blumenhotel - 98 rooms, D € 100 - Rain am Lech 20 km
Tel (49) 09090 - 760, Fax (49) 09090 - 76 400

RESTAURANTS RESTAURANTS

Arco Schlösschen - Neuburg 6 km - Tel (49) 08431 - 22 85
Im Stadttheater - Ingolstadt 20 km - Tel (49) 0841 - 93 5150

PEUGEOT

GREAT BRITAIN & IRELAND

While travel these days knows no frontiers, or at least very few, the heading "Great Britain and Ireland" lives on for four good reasons. Firstly geography, then the language, followed by the fact that the two countries stand for the history and tradition of golf, and finally for sporting reasons. The best players from both islands used to be selected for the Ryder Cup team in years gone by and still are for the Walker Cup and Curtis Cup matches against the United States. A fifth criterion might be unity of style in terms of golf courses, imposed, despite the variety of landscapes, by the pounding seas around each and every coastline. Seas which, miraculously, have left ample space for the great links courses of England, Scotland, Wales, Northern Ireland and the Republic of Ireland.

When you make choices you necessarily leave yourself open to criticism and amongst the some 3,000 eighteen-hole courses to be found in this home of golf, we will still stand accused of having overlooked a number of excellent layouts in Britain and Ireland. But we won't deny the fact that we have also given preference to the more specifically British style course, even though these days they may appear a little outdated in terms of yardage. In the same way, the scores given to club-houses were awarded in relation to the general standard of club-house found in the British Isles. Some may be considered very low compared to their counterparts in the United States, Japan and even continental Europe. We have considered warmth of atmosphere, respect for tradition and the "golfing" excellence of the site to be of greater importance than marble hallways, thick-pile carpets and gym rooms.

As a general rule, visitors need to be aware of certain local customs. First of all, driving ranges are still few and far between, even though the more recent courses are beginning to think differently. Here people learnt to play out on the course. If you want a few practice swings, bring a bag of balls with you in the boot of your car. Hit them and pick them up yourself on the area provided for practice. Out on the course, players from Europe will often be surprised at the speed of the game in the UK. Never hesitating to let people play through is one thing, but more importantly they should learn to speed up their own game. Last but by no means least, always pack a shirt, tie and jacket in your car. Most clubs impose the tie and jacket rule in the bar or restaurant or both, often in the evening but also during the day. So don't get caught out on that one. One last word: when measuring the length of all our courses we have consistently used the metric system, even though many courses which have gone metric sell you yardage books...

GRANDE BRETAGNE & IRLANDE

En matière de voyage, s'il n'y a plus de frontières, la notion de "Grande-Bretagne et Irlande" s'est maintenue pour quatre raisons. D'abord géographique, puis linguistique, ensuite parce que ces pays représentent l'histoire et la tradition, et enfin sportive : en golf, on unit les meilleurs joueurs des deux îles, autrefois pour disputer la Ryder Cup, aujourd'hui encore pour jouer la Walker Cup et la Curtis Cup contre les Etats-Unis. On pourrait ajouter en dernier lieu une unité de style de parcours, imposée en dépit des diversités des paysages par les assauts de l'océan, de tous côtés, qui ont par miracle laissé de grands espaces vierges pour y tracer les grands links d'Angleterre, d'Ecosse, du Pays de Galles, d'Irlande et d'Irlande du Nord.

Quand on fait des choix, on est forcément vulnérable aux critiques, et on nous reprochera toujours d'avoir "oublié" certains parcours, en Grande-Bretagne et Irlande, parmi les quelques 3.000 parcours de 18 trous que comptent ces berceaux du golf. Mais nous ne cacherons pas avoir privilégié les parcours les plus spécifiquement britanniques de style, même s'ils peuvent parfois paraître désuets par leur manque de longueur. De la même façon, les notes attribuées aux club-houses ont été attribuées en relation avec leur niveau général dans les îles britanniques : certains d'entre eux seraient jugés très modestes en comparaison avec leurs équivalents les plus luxueux aux Etats-Unis, au Japon, ou même sur le continent. Pour nous, la chaleur de l'ambiance, le respect de la tradition, la qualité "golfique" du lieu ont plus d'importance que le marbre, les moquettes et les salles de mise en forme.

En règle générale, les visiteurs doivent être informés de certaines coutumes locales. D'abord, les practices ou driving ranges sont encore rares, même si les récents parcours y pensent. Ici, on apprenait à jouer sur le parcours. Si vous souhaitez vous entraîner, ayez un sac de balles dans votre coffre, que vous ramasserez vous-même sur les zones prévues à cet effet. Les joueurs du continent peuvent être surpris par la rapidité de jeu sur les parcours. Ils doivent laisser passer les autres parties, mais aussi apprendre à accélérer leur propre rythme. Enfin, ayez toujours dans votre voiture un petit sac avec une chemise de ville, une cravate et une veste. Beaucoup de clubs imposent "tie and jacket" au bar, au restaurant, ou les deux, souvent le soir, mais aussi dans la journée. Vous ne serez pas pris au dépourvu.

Enfin, précisons que nous avons partout unifié les longueurs des parcours en utilisant le système métrique, même si beaucoup de parcours qui l'ont adopté vendent encore des "yardage books" où les distances sont en yards...

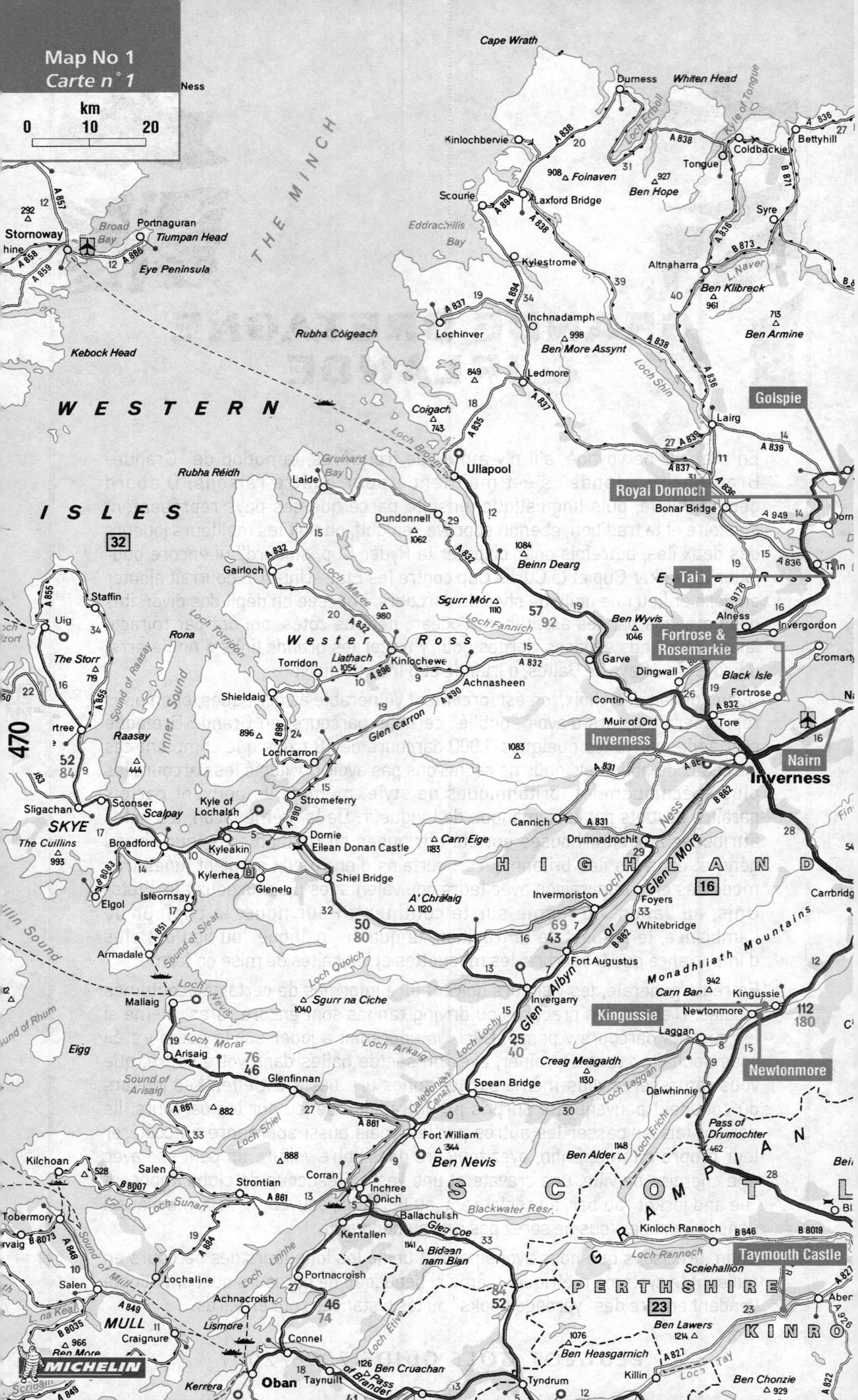

Map No 1
Carte n° 1
km
0
10
20
Cape Wrath
Durness
Whiten Head
Kyle of Tongue
Loch Eriboll
Bettyhill
Kinlochbervie
Coldbackie
Tongue
Foinaven
Ben Hope
Scourie
Laxford Bridge
Syre
Eddrachillis Bay
Kylestrome
Altnaharra
L. Naver
Ben Klibreck
THE MINCH
Ness
Stornoway
Broad Bay
Portnaguran
Tiumpan Head
Eye Peninsula
Inchnadamph
Lochinver
Rubha Còigeach
Ben More Assynt
Loch Shin
Ben Armine
Kebock Head
Ledmore
Coigach
WESTERN
ISLES
Golspie
Lairg
Loch Broom
Ullapool
Rubha Réidh
Gruinard Bay
Laide
Royal Dornoch
Bonar Bridge
Dundonnell
Beinn Dearg
Tain
Gairloch
Loch Maree
Sgurr Mór
Staffin
Uig
The Storr
Loch Torridon
Rona
Wester Ross
Loch Fannich
Ben Wyvis
Alness
Invergordon
Fortrose & Rosemarkie
Cromarty
Black Isle
Fortrose
Torridon
Liathach
Kinlochewe
Achnasheen
Garve
Dingwall
Contin
Shieldaig
Sound of Raasay
Inner Sound
Raasay
Glen Carron
Muir of Ord
Tore
Inverness
Nairn
Lochcarron
470
Stromeferry
Sligachan
Sconser
Scalpay
Kyle of Lochalsh
SKYE
The Cuillins
Broadford
Kyleakin
Dornie
Eilean Donan Castle
Carn Eige
Cannich
Drumnadrochit
Loch Ness
Glen More
HIGHLAND
Kylerhea
Glenelg
Shiel Bridge
Elgol
Isleornsay
A' Chràlaig
Invermoriston
Foyers
Whitebridge
Carrbridge
Sound of Sleat
Armadale
Loch Quoich
Fort Augustus
Monadhliath Mountains
Mallaig
Loch Nevis
Sgurr na Ciche
Invergarry
Glen Albyn
Carn Ban
Kingussie
Newtonmore
Sound of Rhum
Eigg
Loch Morar
Arisaig
Loch Arkaig
Loch Lochy
Laggan
Creag Meagaidh
Sound of Arisaig
Glenfinnan
Spean Bridge
Caledonian Canal
Loch Laggan
Dalwhinnie
Loch Ericht
Loch Shiel
Fort William
Ben Nevis
Ben Alder
Pass of Drumochter
Kilchoan
Salen
Strontian
Corran
Inchree
Onich
GRAMPIAN
Loch Sunart
Blackwater Resr.
Tobermory
Sound of Mull
Kentallen
Ballachulish
Glen Coe
Kinloch Rannoch
Bidean nam Bian
Loch Rannoch
Schiehallion
Taymouth Castle
Loch Linnhe
Portnacroish
Lochaline
PERTHSHIRE
L. na Keal
MULL
Achnacroish
Lismore
Loch Etive
Ben Lawers
KINRO
Craignure
Ben More
Connel
Ben Heasgarnich
Loch Tay
MICHELIN
Kerrera
Oban
Taynuilt
Pass of Brander
Ben Cruachan
Tyndrum
Killin
Ben Chonzie

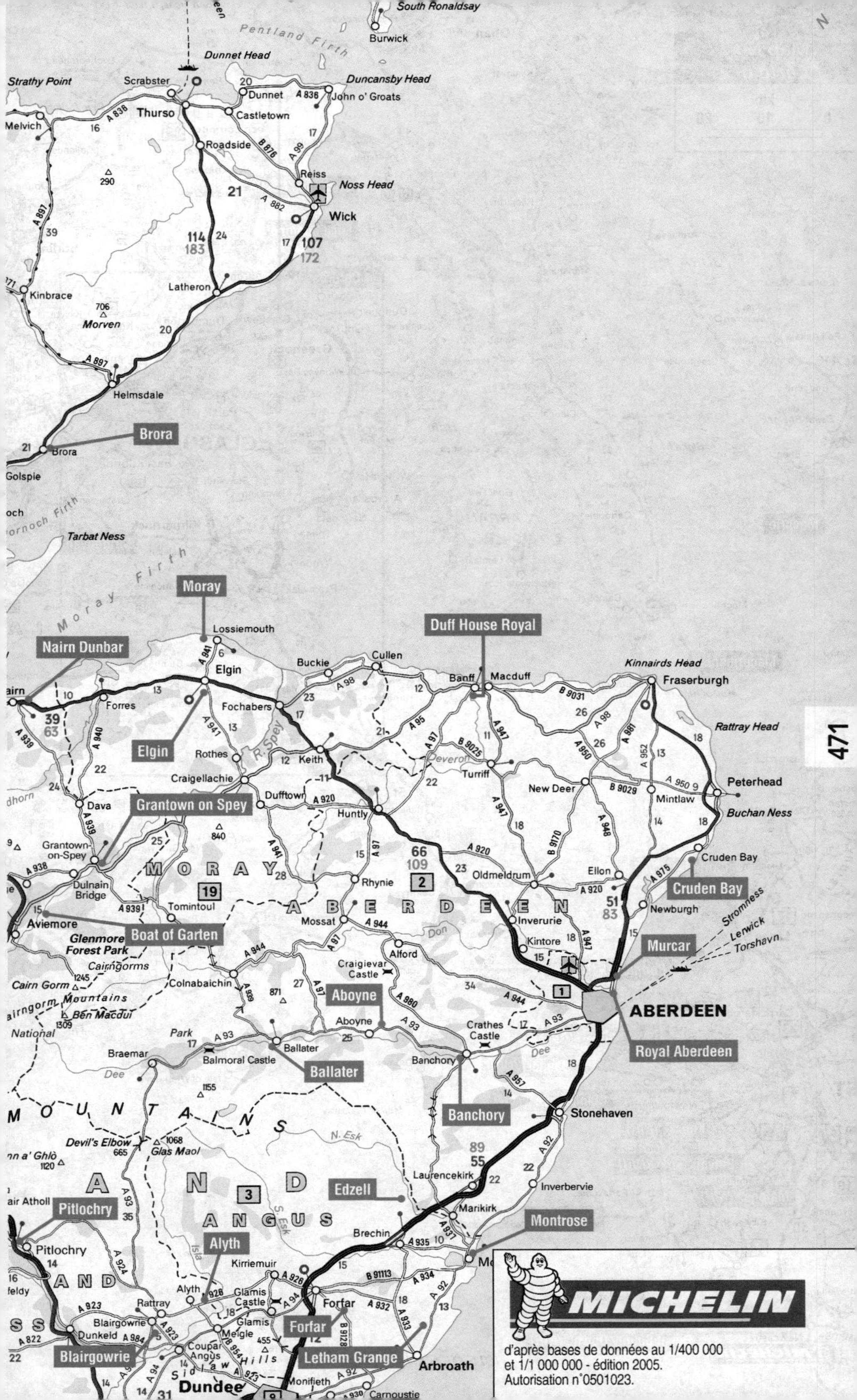

South Ronaldsay
Burwick
Pentland Firth
Dunnet Head
Strathy Point
Scrabster
Thurso
Dunnet
Duncansby Head
John o' Groats
Castletown
Melvich
Roadside
Reiss
Noss Head
Wick
Latheron
Kinbrace
Morven
Helmsdale
Brora
Golspie
Dornoch Firth
Tarbat Ness
Moray Firth
Moray
Nairn Dunbar
Lossiemouth
Elgin
Forres
Fochabers
Buckie
Cullen
Duff House Royal
Banff
Macduff
Kinnairds Head
Fraserburgh
Rattray Head
Peterhead
Buchan Ness
Keith
Rothes
Craigellachie
Dufftown
Huntly
Turriff
New Deer
Mintlaw
Dava
Grantown on Spey
Grantown-on-Spey
Dulnain Bridge
Aviemore
Boat of Garten
Tomintoul
MORAY
ABERDEEN
Rhynie
Mossat
Oldmeldrum
Ellon
Cruden Bay
Newburgh
Inverurie
Kintore
Murcar
Stromness
Lerwick
Torshavn
Alford
Craigievar Castle
Glenmore Forest Park
Cairngorms
Cairn Gorm
Cairngorm Mountains
Ben Macdui
National Park
Colnabaichin
Aboyne
ABERDEEN
Royal Aberdeen
Crathes Castle
Banchory
Braemar
Balmoral Castle
Ballater
Stonehaven
MOUNTAINS
Devil's Elbow
Glas Maol
Edzell
Laurencekirk
Inverbervie
Marikirk
ANGUS
Brechin
Montrose
Pitlochry
Alyth
Kirriemuir
Glamis Castle
Forfar
Rattray
Blairgowrie
Dunkeld
Meigle
Coupar Angus
Letham Grange
Arbroath
Sidlaw Hills
Dundee
Monifieth
Carnoustie
471
MICHELIN
d'après bases de données au 1/400 000
et 1/1 000 000 - édition 2005.
Autorisation n°0501023.

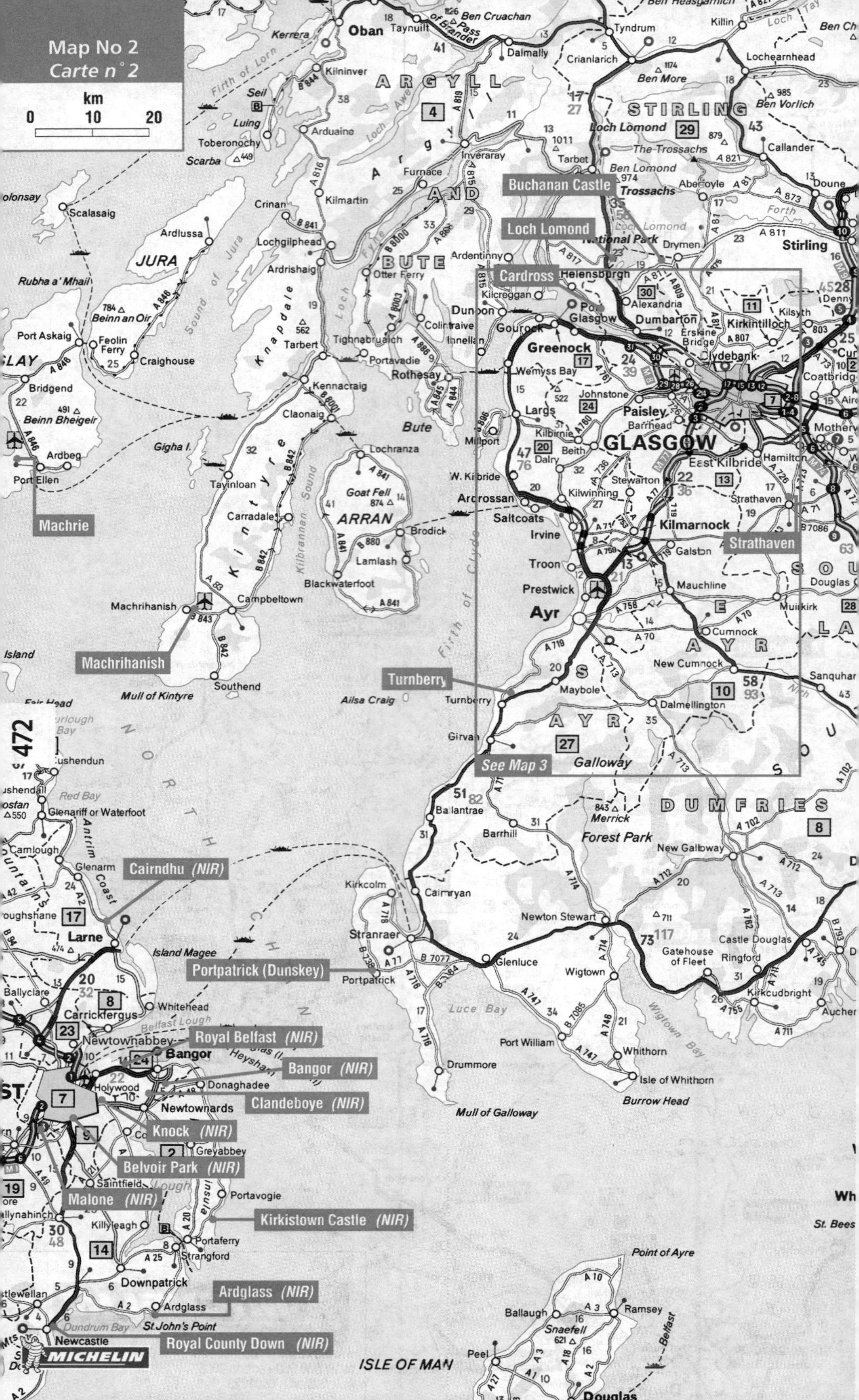
Map No 2
Carte n° 2
km
0 10 20
Buchanan Castle
Loch Lomond
Cardross
Machrie
Machrihanish
Turnberry
Strathaven
See Map 3
Cairndhu (NIR)
Portpatrick (Dunskey)
Royal Belfast (NIR)
Bangor (NIR)
Clandeboye (NIR)
Knock (NIR)
Belvoir Park (NIR)
Malone (NIR)
Kirkistown Castle (NIR)
Ardglass (NIR)
Royal County Down (NIR)
472
MICHELIN
Oban
Taynuilt
Ben Cruachan
Pass of Brander
Tyndrum
Killin
Dalmally
Crianlarich
Lochearnhead
Kerrera
Kilninver
Firth of Lorn
Seil
Luing
Arduaine
Toberonochy
Scarba
ARGYLL AND BUTE
Inveraray
Ben More
Ben Vorlich
STIRLING
Loch Lomond
The Trossachs
Callander
Tarbet
Ben Lomond
Aberfoyle
Doune
Stirling
Drymen
Furnace
Crinan
Kilmartin
Colonsay
Scalasaig
Ardlussa
JURA
Lochgilphead
Ardrishaig
Otter Ferry
Ardentinny
Helensburgh
Kilcreggan
Dunoon
Gourock
Port Glasgow
Dumbarton
Alexandria
Erskine Bridge
Kirkintilloch
Kilsyth
Denny
Clydebank
Coatbridge
Rubha a' Mhail
Beinn an Oir
Sound of Jura
Knapdale
Port Askaig
Feolin Ferry
Craighouse
Tarbert
Tighnabruaich
Colintraive
Innellan
Portavadie
Rothesay
Greenock
Wemyss Bay
Johnstone
Paisley
Barrhead
GLASGOW
ISLAY
Bridgend
Beinn Bheigeir
Ardbeg
Port Ellen
Kennacraig
Claonaig
Bute
Largs
Kilbirnie
Millport
Dalry
Beith
East Kilbride
Hamilton
Motherwell
Gigha I.
Lochranza
Tayinloan
Kintyre
Carradale
Kilbrannan Sound
Goat Fell
ARRAN
Brodick
Lamlash
Blackwaterfoot
W. Kilbride
Ardrossan
Saltcoats
Irvine
Kilwinning
Stewarton
Kilmarnock
Galston
Troon
Prestwick
Ayr
Mauchline
Muirkirk
Douglas
Cumnock
New Cumnock
Sanquhar
Machrihanish
Campbeltown
Southend
Mull of Kintyre
Island
Firth of Clyde
Ailsa Craig
Turnberry
Maybole
Dalmellington
Girvan
AYR
Galloway
Fair Head
Torr Head
Murlough Bay
Cushendun
Cushendall
Red Bay
Glenariff or Waterfoot
Antrim Mountains
Antrim Coast
Carnlough
Glenarm
Broughshane
Larne
Island Magee
Ballyclare
Whitehead
Carrickfergus
Belfast Lough
Newtownabbey
Bangor
Holywood
Donaghadee
Newtownards
Greyabbey
Saintfield
Ballynahinch
Killyleagh
Portavogie
Portaferry
Strangford
Downpatrick
Ardglass
St John's Point
Dundrum Bay
Newcastle
NORTH CHANNEL
Ballantrae
Barrhill
Merrick
Forest Park
DUMFRIES
New Galloway
Kirkcolm
Cairnryan
Stranraer
Portpatrick
Glenluce
Newton Stewart
Wigtown
Gatehouse of Fleet
Castle Douglas
Ringford
Kirkcudbright
Auchencairn
Luce Bay
Wigtown Bay
Port William
Whithorn
Isle of Whithorn
Burrow Head
Drummore
Mull of Galloway
Point of Ayre
Ramsey
Ballaugh
Snaefell
Peel
ISLE OF MAN
Douglas
Whitehaven
St. Bees

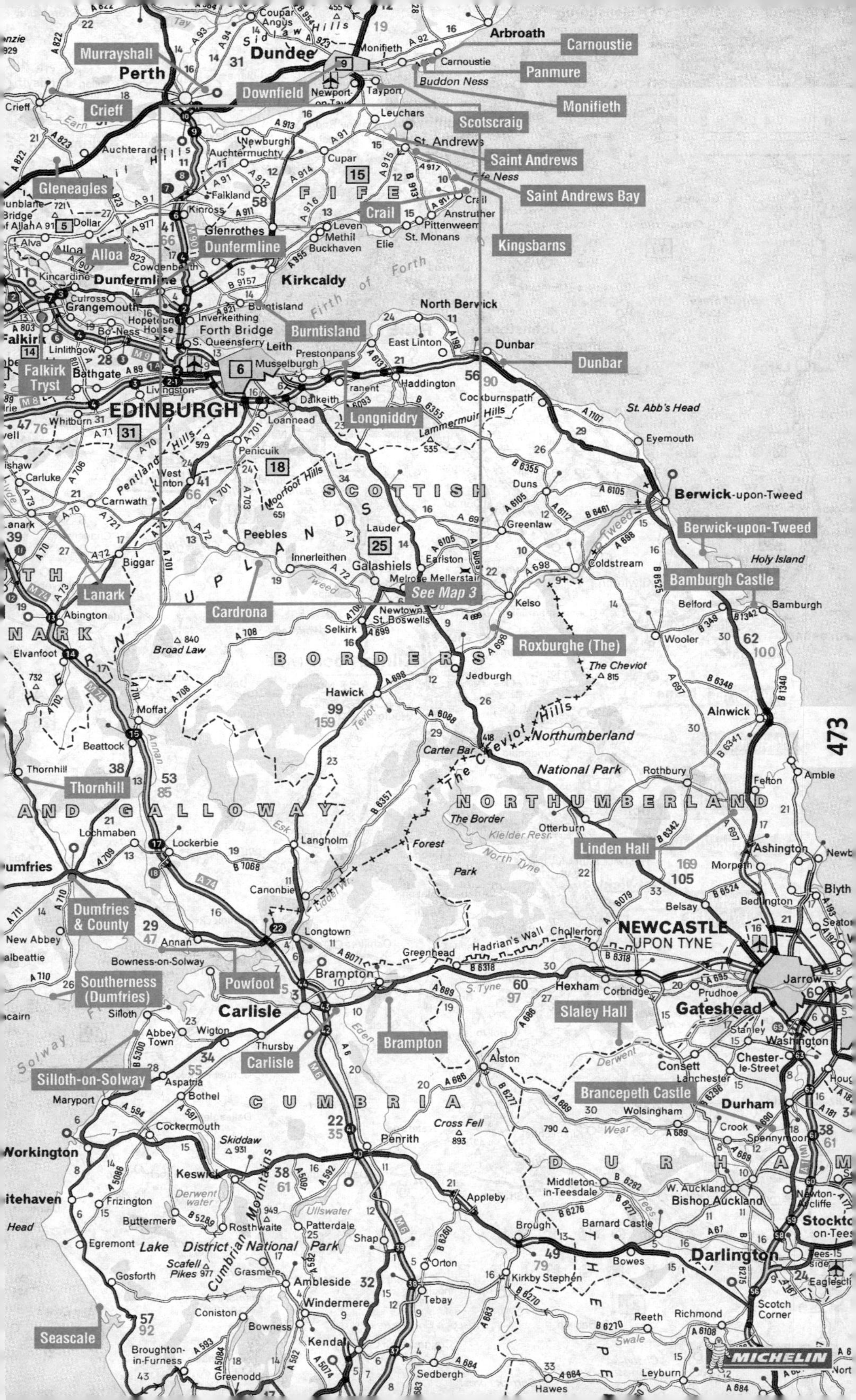

Murrayshall
Downfield
Carnoustie
Panmure
Monifieth
Crieff
Scotscraig
Saint Andrews
Saint Andrews Bay
Gleneagles
Crail
Kingsbarns
Alloa
Dunfermline
Burntisland
Dunbar
Falkirk Tryst
Longniddry
Berwick-upon-Tweed
Bamburgh Castle
See Map 3
Lanark
Cardrona
Roxburghe (The)
Thornhill
Linden Hall
Dumfries & County
Powfoot
Southerness (Dumfries)
Slaley Hall
Brampton
Carlisle
Silloth-on-Solway
Brancepeth Castle
Seascale
MICHELIN
Perth
Dundee
Arbroath
EDINBURGH
Kirkcaldy
Firth of Forth
SCOTTISH UPLANDS
BORDERS
Northumberland National Park
NORTHUMBERLAND
NEWCASTLE UPON TYNE
Gateshead
DUMFRIES AND GALLOWAY
CUMBRIA
DURHAM
Lake District National Park
Darlington

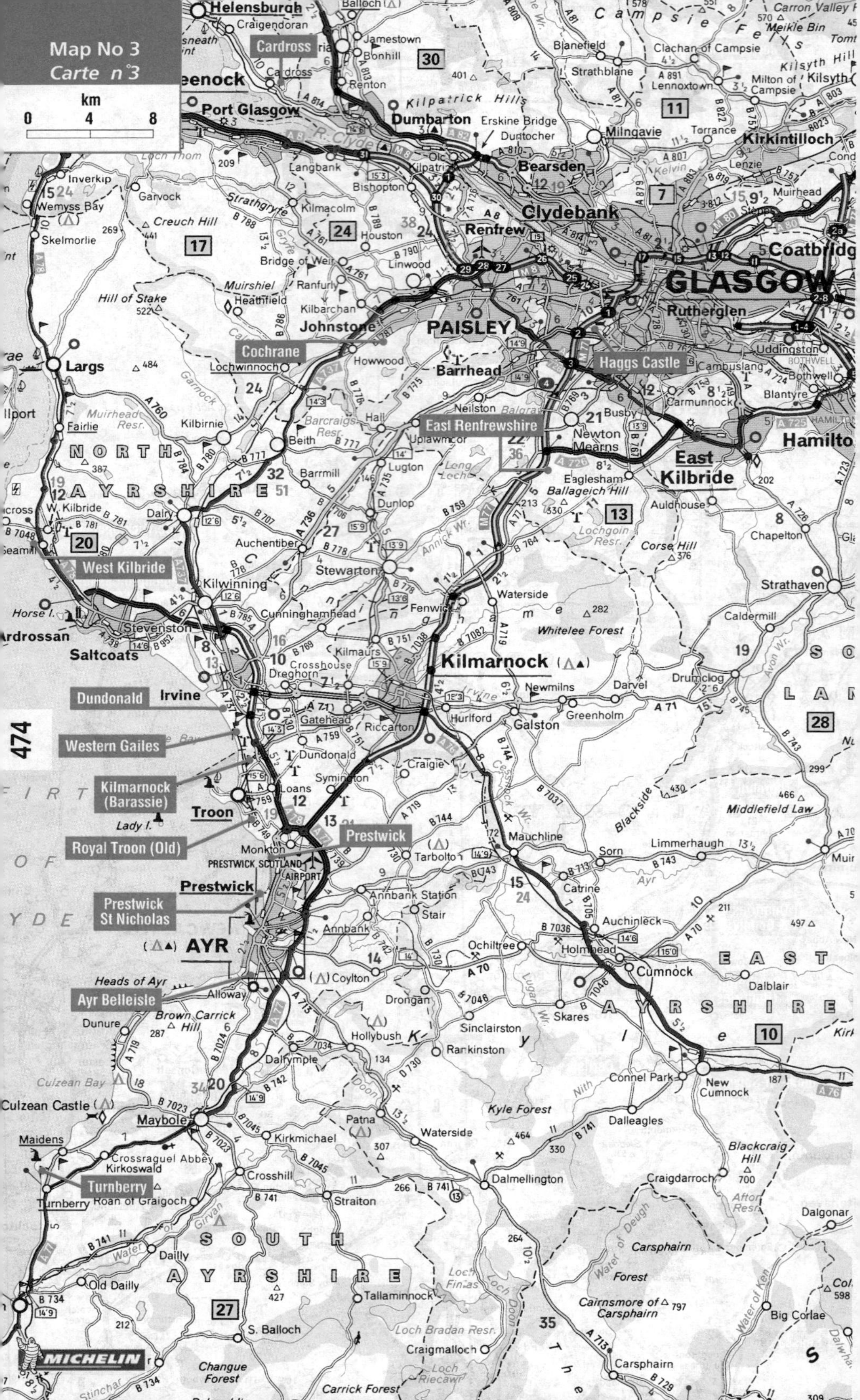

Map No 3
Carte n°3
km
0 4 8
Cardross
Cochrane
Haggs Castle
East Renfrewshire
West Kilbride
Dundonald
Western Gailes
Kilmarnock (Barassie)
Royal Troon (Old)
Prestwick
Prestwick St Nicholas
Ayr Belleisle
Turnberry
Helensburgh
Greenock
Port Glasgow
Dumbarton
Clydebank
Renfrew
Bearsden
Milngavie
Kirkintilloch
Coatbridge
GLASGOW
Rutherglen
PAISLEY
Johnstone
Barrhead
Largs
Kilbirnie
Beith
Dalry
Kilwinning
Stevenston
Ardrossan
Saltcoats
Irvine
Troon
Prestwick
AYR
Kilmarnock
Stewarton
East Kilbride
Hamilton
Strathaven
Mauchline
Cumnock
New Cumnock
Maybole
Girvan
Dalmellington
NORTH AYRSHIRE
EAST AYRSHIRE
SOUTH AYRSHIRE
PRESTWICK SCOTLAND AIRPORT
MICHELIN

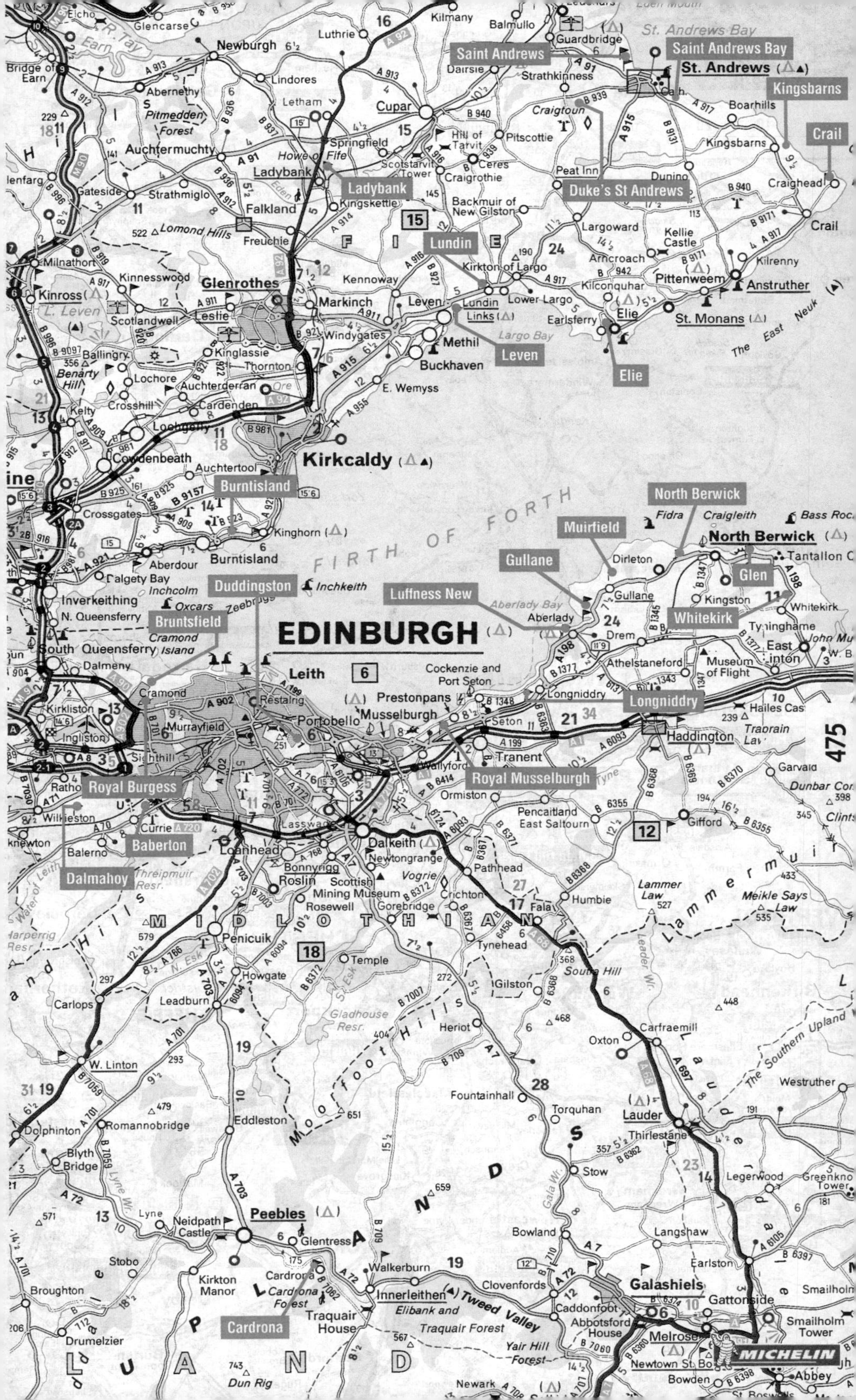

Saint Andrews
Saint Andrews Bay
St. Andrews
Kingsbarns
Crail
Duke's St Andrews
Ladybank
Lundin
Leven
Elie
Burntisland
North Berwick
Muirfield
Gullane
Glen
Luffness New
Whitekirk
Duddingston
Bruntsfield
Longniddry
Royal Musselburgh
Royal Burgess
Baberton
Dalmahoy
Cardrona
EDINBURGH
FIRTH OF FORTH
Kirkcaldy
Glenrothes
Cupar
Newburgh
Anstruther
Pittenweem
St. Monans
Leith
Musselburgh
Prestonpans
Tranent
Haddington
Dalkeith
Penicuik
Peebles
Innerleithen
Galashiels
Melrose
Lauder
Midlothian
Moorfoot Hills
Lammermuir
Tweed Valley
Inverkeithing
South Queensferry
Cowdenbeath
Kinross
Dunfermline
Aberlady
Dirleton
Traquair House
Abbotsford House
475
MICHELIN

Map No 4
Carte n° 4
km
0 10 20
476
Carlisle
Brampton
Slaley Hall
Brancepeth Castle
Seascale
Clitheroe
Fairhaven
Royal Lytham & St Anne's
Pleasington
Bolton Old Links
Huddersfield (Fixby)
Harrogate
Rudding Park
Pannal
Sand Moor
Ilkley
Moortown
Alwoodley
Moor Allerton
Woodsome Hall
Manchester
Royal Liverpool
Caldy
Mere
Wilmslow
Hallamshire
Reddish Vale
Lindrick
Cavendish
Prestbury
Carden Park
Coxmoor
Notts (Hollinwell)
Hawkstone Park
See Map 5
CUMBRIA
DURHAM
LANCASHIRE
CHESHIRE
DERBY
NORTH YORKS
Lake District National Park
Yorkshire Dales National Park
Peak District National Park
NEWCASTLE UPON TYNE
Gateshead
Durham
Darlington
Stockton-on-Tees
Barrow-in-Furness
Morecambe
Lancaster
Fleetwood
BLACKPOOL
Preston
Blackburn
Burnley
BRADFORD
LEEDS
Halifax
Huddersfield
Rochdale
Bolton
Wigan
Oldham
MANCHESTER
LIVERPOOL
Birkenhead
Warrington
Stockport
SHEFFIELD
Barnsley
Rotherham
Chesterfield
Chester
Wrexham / Wrecsam
Macclesfield
Crewe
STOKE-ON-TRENT
Derby
Stafford
Shrewsbury
MICHELIN

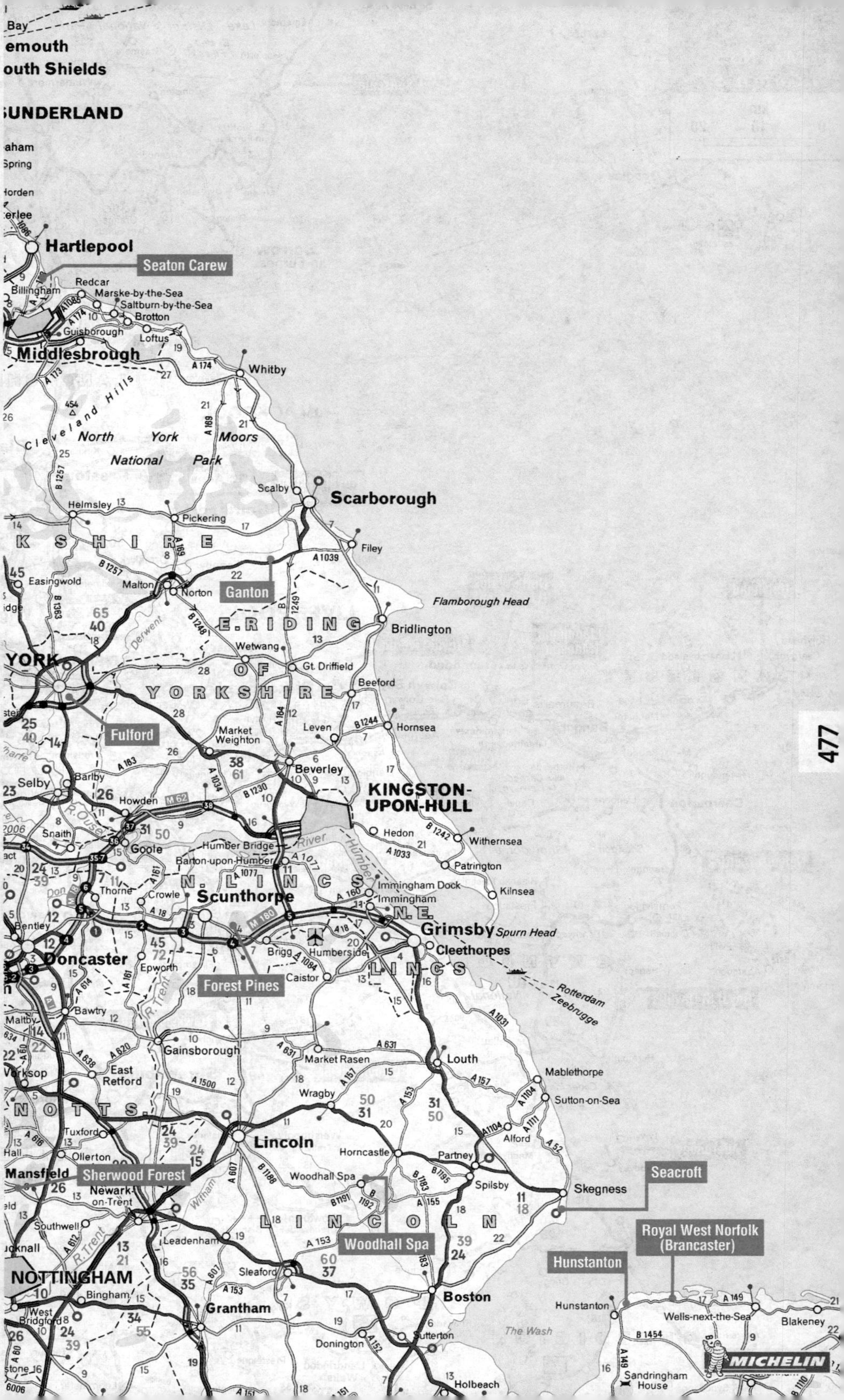
Bay
emouth
outh Shields
SUNDERLAND
aham
Spring
Horden
erlee
Hartlepool
Seaton Carew
Redcar
Billingham
Marske-by-the-Sea
Saltburn-by-the-Sea
Brotton
Guisborough
Loftus
Middlesbrough
Whitby
Cleveland Hills
North York Moors
National Park
Scalby
Scarborough
Helmsley
Pickering
Filey
Easingwold
Malton
Norton
Ganton
Flamborough Head
E. RIDING
OF
YORKSHIRE
Bridlington
Wetwang
Gt. Driffield
Beeford
YORK
Fulford
Leven
Hornsea
Market Weighton
Beverley
KINGSTON-UPON-HULL
Selby
Barlby
Howden
M 62
Snaith
Goole
Humber Bridge
Barton-upon-Humber
Hedon
Withernsea
Patrington
Kilnsea
River Humber
Immingham Dock
Immingham
N. LINCS
N.E. LINCS
Thorne
Crowle
Scunthorpe
Grimsby
Spurn Head
Cleethorpes
Bentley
Doncaster
Epworth
Brigg
Humberside
Caistor
Forest Pines
Rotterdam
Zeebrugge
Bawtry
Maltby
Gainsborough
Market Rasen
Louth
Worksop
East Retford
Mablethorpe
Sutton-on-Sea
NOTTS.
Wragby
Tuxford
Lincoln
Alford
Ollerton
Horncastle
Partney
Mansfield
Sherwood Forest
Newark-on-Trent
Woodhall Spa
Spilsby
Skegness
Seacroft
Southwell
LINCOLN
Leadenham
Royal West Norfolk (Brancaster)
Hunstanton
NOTTINGHAM
Sleaford
Boston
West Bridgford
Bingham
Grantham
Hunstanton
Wells-next-the-Sea
Blakeney
The Wash
Donington
Sutterton
Sandringham House
Holbeach
MICHELIN

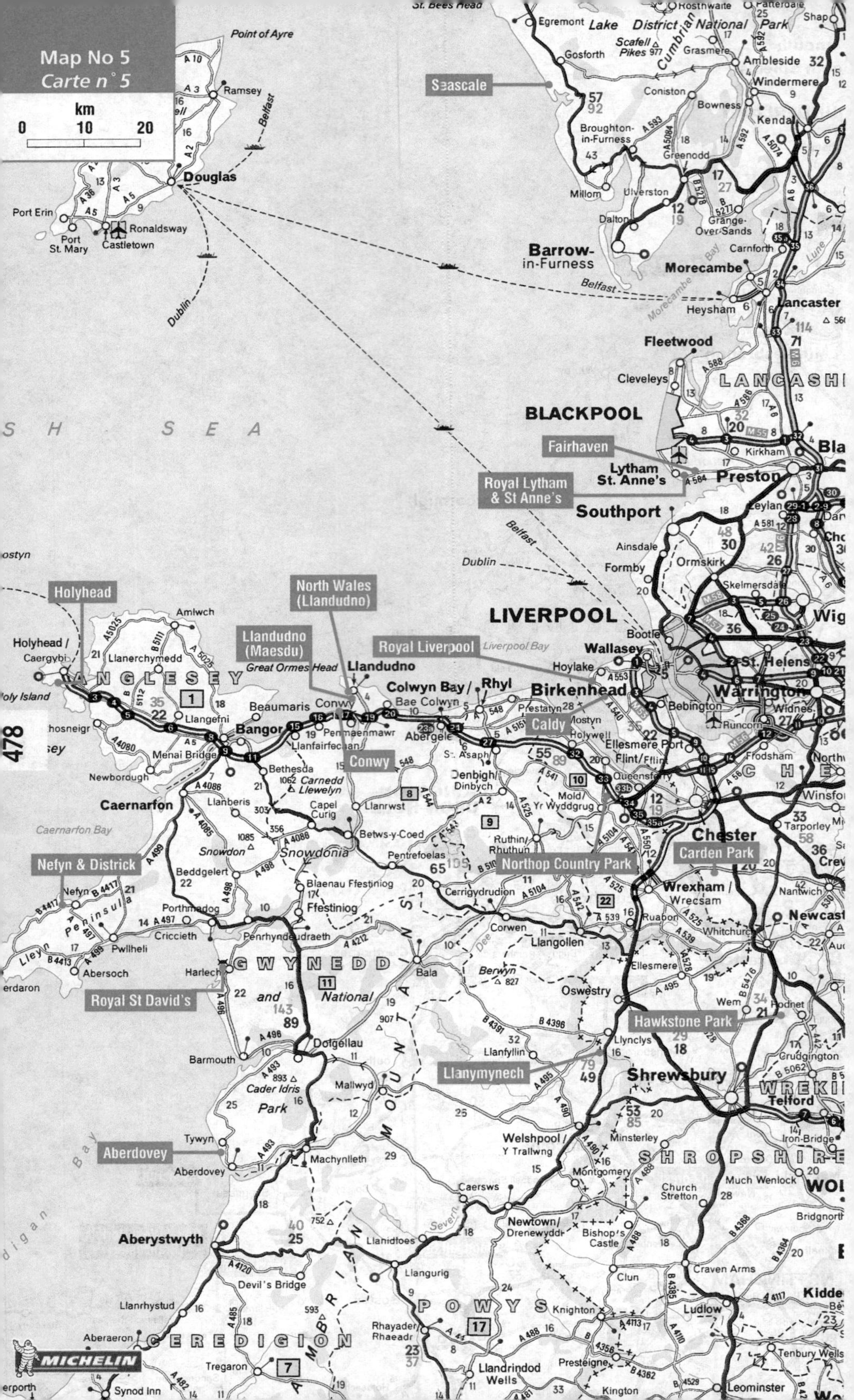

Map No 5
Carte n° 5
km
0 10 20
478
Seascale
Fairhaven
Royal Lytham & St Anne's
Holyhead
North Wales (Llandudno)
Llandudno (Maesdu)
Royal Liverpool
Conwy
Caldy
Northop Country Park
Carden Park
Nefyn & District
Royal St David's
Hawkstone Park
Llanymynech
Aberdovey
Point of Ayre
Ramsey
Douglas
Port Erin
Port St. Mary
Castletown
Ronaldsway
Belfast
Dublin
Egremont
Lake District National Park
Scafell Pikes 977
Gosforth
Ambleside
Grasmere
Windermere
Coniston
Bowness
Kendal
Broughton-in-Furness
Greenodd
Millom
Ulverston
Dalton
Grange-Over-Sands
Barrow-in-Furness
Carnforth
Morecambe
Morecambe Bay
Heysham
Lancaster
Fleetwood
Cleveleys
BLACKPOOL
LANCASHI
Kirkham
Preston
Lytham St. Anne's
Southport
Leylan
Ainsdale
Formby
Ormskirk
Skelmersdale
LIVERPOOL
Liverpool Bay
Bootle
Wallasey
Hoylake
Birkenhead
Bebington
St. Helens
Warrington
Widnes
Runcorn
Ellesmere Port
Frodsham
Amlwch
Holyhead / Caergybi
Llanerchymedd
ANGLESEY
Holy Island
Rhosneigr
Llangefni
Beaumaris
Bangor
Menai Bridge
Newborough
Caernarfon
Caernarfon Bay
Great Ormes Head
Llandudno
Conwy
Colwyn Bay / Bae Colwyn
Rhyl
Prestatyn
Mostyn
Holywell
Abergele
Penmaenmawr
Llanfairfechan
St. Asaph
Denbigh / Dinbych
Flint / Fflint
Queensferry
Mold / Yr Wyddgrug
Chester
Bethesda
Carnedd Llewelyn
Llanberis
Capel Curig
Llanrwst
Betws-y-Coed
Snowdon
Snowdonia
Beddgelert
Pentrefoelas
Ruthin / Rhuthun
Wrexham / Wrecsam
Ruabon
Blaenau Ffestiniog
Ffestiniog
Cerrigydrudion
Corwen
Llangollen
Nefyn
Lleyn Peninsula
Porthmadog
Criccieth
Penrhyndeudraeth
Pwllheli
Abersoch
Harlech
GWYNEDD
Bala
Berwyn 827
Oswestry
Ellesmere
Whitchurch
Wem
Hodnet
Tarporley
Winsford
Nantwich
Newcast
Snowdonia National Park
Barmouth
Dolgellau
Cader Idris
Mallwyd
Llanfyllin
Llynclys
Shrewsbury
Telford
WREKIN
Tywyn
Aberdovey
Machynlleth
Welshpool / Y Trallwng
Minsterley
Montgomery
SHROPSHIRE
Much Wenlock
Church Stretton
Iron-Bridge
Bridgnorth
Caersws
Newtown / Drenewydd
Bishop's Castle
Craven Arms
Clun
Aberystwyth
Llanidloes
Severn
Llangurig
Devil's Bridge
Llanrhystud
POWYS
Knighton
Ludlow
Rhayader / Rhaeadr
Aberaeron
CEREDIGION
CAMBRIAN MOUNTAINS
Tregaron
Llandrindod Wells
Presteigne
Kington
Leominster
Tenbury Wells
Synod Inn
MICHELIN

1 / 400 000
BLACKPOOL
Royal Lytham & St Anne's
Lytham St. Anne's
Fairhaven
PRESTON
Pleasington
BLACKBURN
Leyland
Chorley
SOUTHPORT
Royal Birkdale
Hillside
Southport & Ainsdale
Formby
Formby Point
Ormskirk
Skelmersdale
WIGAN
West Lancashire
Crosby
Bootle
Kirkby
ST. HELENS
Liverpool Bay
Wallasey
LIVERPOOL
Hoylake
Royal Liverpool
BIRKENHEAD
Caldy
Bebington
Widnes
WARRINGTON
LIVERPOOL JOHN LENNON AIRPORT
Runcorn
Ellesmere Port
Delamere Forest
Northop Country Park
CHESTER
Sandiway
Portal
Carden Park
Wrexham / Wrecsam
Nantwich
MICHELIN

Map No 6
Carte n° 6
km
0 10 20
Cardigan
Carmarthen
Tenby
Ashburnham
Pennard
Langland Bay
Saunton
Royal North Devon (Westward Ho)
Bude & North Cornwall
Bowood (Cornwall)
St Enodoc
Trevose
Perranporth
West Cornwall
Mullion
St Mellion
Thurlestone
Strumble Head
Pembrokeshire Coast National Park
St. David's Head
St. David's
PEMBROKESHIRE
St. Bride's Bay
Haverfordwest/ Hwlffordd
Milford Haven/ Aberdaugleddau
Pembroke Dock/ Doc Penfro
Pembroke
Neyland
Narberth
Fishguard / Abergwaun
Newport
Cardigan/ Aberteifi
Aberporth
New Quay
Aberaeron
Synod Inn
Tregaron
Lampeter
Newcastle Emlyn
Llandysul
Crymych
CARMARTHENSHIRE
Carmarthen Caerfyrddin
Whitland
St. Clears/ Sanclêr
Pendine
Saundersfoot
Tenby/ Dinbych-y-pysgod
St. Govan's Head
Rosslare
Carmarthen Bay
Kidwelly
Cross Hands
Burry Port
Llanelli
Pontarddulais
Swansea / Abertawe
Rhossili
Worms Head
Port Eynon
The Mumbles
Cork
BRISTOL CH
Lundy
Ilfracombe
Combe Martin
Croyde
Braunton
Barnstaple
Northam
Hartland Point
Clovelly
Bideford
Great Torrington
Kilkhampton
Bude
Stratton
Holsworthy
Winkleigh
Hatherleigh
Okehampton
High Willhays
Moretonhampstead
Dartmoor
Tintagel
Launceston
Camelford
Padstow
Wadebridge
Bodmin
CORNWALL
Tavistock
Callington
Princetown
Ashburton
Buckfastleigh
Newquay
Fraddon
Lostwithiel
Liskeard
Saltash
Plympton
Fowey
Looe
Polperro
Torpoint
Plymstock
PLYMOUTH
Modbury
Newton Ferrers
Salcombe
St. Austell
Mevagissey
Tregony
Truro
Redruth
Camborne
Penryn
Falmouth
St. Mawes
St. Ives
Hayle
Penzance
St. Just
Sennen
Land's End
St. Michael's Mount
Helston
Mount's Bay
St. Keverne
Lizard
Lizard Point
Santander
Roscoff
MICHELIN

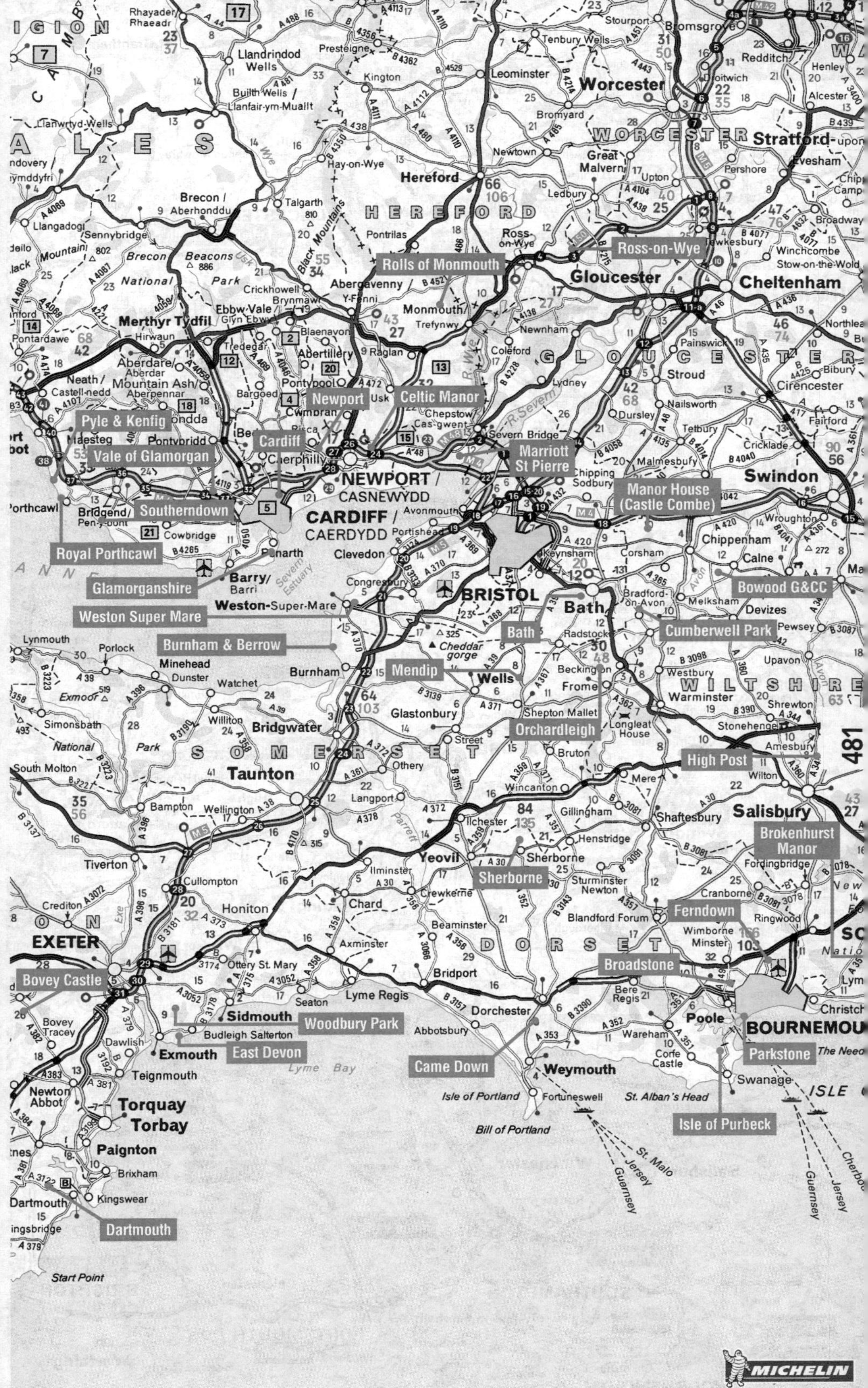

Rolls of Monmouth
Ross-on-Wye
Newport
Celtic Manor
Pyle & Kenfig
Cardiff
Vale of Glamorgan
Marriott St Pierre
Southerndown
Manor House (Castle Combe)
Royal Porthcawl
Glamorganshire
Bowood G&CC
Weston Super Mare
Bath
Cumberwell Park
Burnham & Berrow
Mendip
Orchardleigh
High Post
Brokenhurst Manor
Sherborne
Ferndown
Broadstone
Bovey Castle
Woodbury Park
East Devon
Came Down
Parkstone
Isle of Purbeck
Dartmouth
WALES
HEREFORD
GLOUCESTER
WORCESTER
WILTSHIRE
SOMERSET
DORSET
Hereford
Worcester
Stratford-upon
Gloucester
Cheltenham
Swindon
NEWPORT / CASNEWYDD
CARDIFF / CAERDYDD
BRISTOL
Bath
Salisbury
Taunton
EXETER
Torquay Torbay
Yeovil
Poole
BOURNEMOU
Weymouth
481
MICHELIN

Map No 7
Carte n° 7
km
0 10 20
482
Beau Desert
Little Aston
Whittington Heath
The Belfry
Luffenham Heath
Forest of Arden
Copt Heath
Warwickshire
Northamptonshire
Collingtree Park
John O'Gaunt
Tadmarton Heath
Woburn
The Grove
Ashridge
Berkhamsted
Huntercombe
Manor House (Castle Combe)
Frilford Heath
West Berkshire
Porters Park
Bowood G&CC
Swinley Forest
Royal Wimbledon
Berkshire (The)
Cumberwell Park
Newbury and Crookham
North Hants
Camberley Heath
Hankley Common
High Post
West Surrey
Blackmoor
Hindhead
Old Thorns
Mannings Heath
Liphook
Meon Valley
Brokenhurst Manor
West Sussex
Broadstone
Stoneham
Parkstone
Ferndown
Hayling
MICHELIN

Royal Cromer
Royal West Norfolk (Brancaster)
Hunstanton
Sheringham
King's Lynn
Thetford
Gog Magog
Thorpeness
Aldeburgh
Woodbridge
Ipswich
Felixstowe Ferry
Hertfordshire (The)
Thorndon Park
London Club
Prince's
Royal St George's
Royal Cinque Ports
Hever
Chart Hills
Royal Ashdown Forest
Crowborough Beacon
Rye
East Sussex National
Wimereux (F)
Boston
Hunstanton
Wells-next-the-Sea
Sheringham
Cromer
Blakeney
Holt
Mundesley
Sandringham House
Fakenham
North Walsham
Holbeach
Long Sutton
Spalding
Guist
Aylsham
Low Street
King's Lynn
NORFOLK
East Dereham
Crowland
Wisbech
Outwell
Swaffham
Acle
Great Yarmouth
Peterborough
Guyhirn
Downham Market
Stradsett
Wymondham
NORWICH
Gorleston-on-Sea
Whittlesey
March
Watton
Attleborough
Mundford
Chatteris
Brandon
Littleport
Bungay
Lowestoft
Beccles
Thetford
Harleston
Ely
Diss
Huntingdon
Earith
Soham
Scole
Halesworth
Southwold
St. Ives
Ixworth
Dennington
Yoxford
Newmarket
Bury St. Edmunds
Saxmundham
Leiston
Stowmarket
Cambridge
SUFFOLK
Aldeburgh
Lavenham
Haverhill
IPSWICH
Woodbridge
Saffron Walden
Clare
Royston
Sudbury
Hadleigh
Baldock
Finchingfield
Buntingford
Halstead
Felixstowe
Stansted
Puckeridge
Great Dunmow
Braintree
Harwich
Stevenage
The Naze
Hertford
Bishop's Stortford
ESSEX
Colchester
Walton-on-the-Naze
Ware
Witham
Esbjerg
Göteborg
Hoek van Holland
Hamburg
Sawbridgeworth
Brightlingsea
Frinton-on-Sea
Harlow
Clacton-on-Sea
Chelmsford
W. Mersea
Hoddesdon
Epping
Maldon
Bradwell-on-Sea
Brentwood
Billericay
Burnham-on-Crouch
Wickford
Rayleigh
Foulness Point
LONDON
Dagenham
Basildon
Southend-on-Sea
Benfleet
Grays Thurrock
Canvey Island
Dartford
Tilbury
Grain
Sheerness
Gravesend
Queenborough
Isle of Sheppey
Rochester
Leysdown-on-Sea
Birchington
Margate
Orpington
Swanley
Gillingham
Herne Bay
Croydon
Chatham
Whitstable
North Foreland
Broadstairs
Sittingbourne
Faversham
Ramsgate
Canterbury
Sandwich
Knole
Maidstone
Deal
Sevenoaks
Tonbridge
KENT
Southborough
Ashford
South Foreland
East Grinstead
Royal Tunbridge Wells
Biddenden
Terminal
Dover
Crowborough
Tenterden
Hythe
Folkestone
Tunnel-sous la Manche
Channel Tunnel
Heathfield
Uckfield
Calais
Burgess Hill
E. SUSSEX
New Romney
Lydd
Rye
Cap Blanc Nez
Wissant
Terminal
Winchelsea
Dungeness
Lewes
Battle
Cap Gris Nez
Guînes
Polegate
Bexhill
Hastings
Ardres
Marquise
Newhaven
Seaford
Eastbourne
Wimereux
Beachy Head
Boulogne
MICHELIN

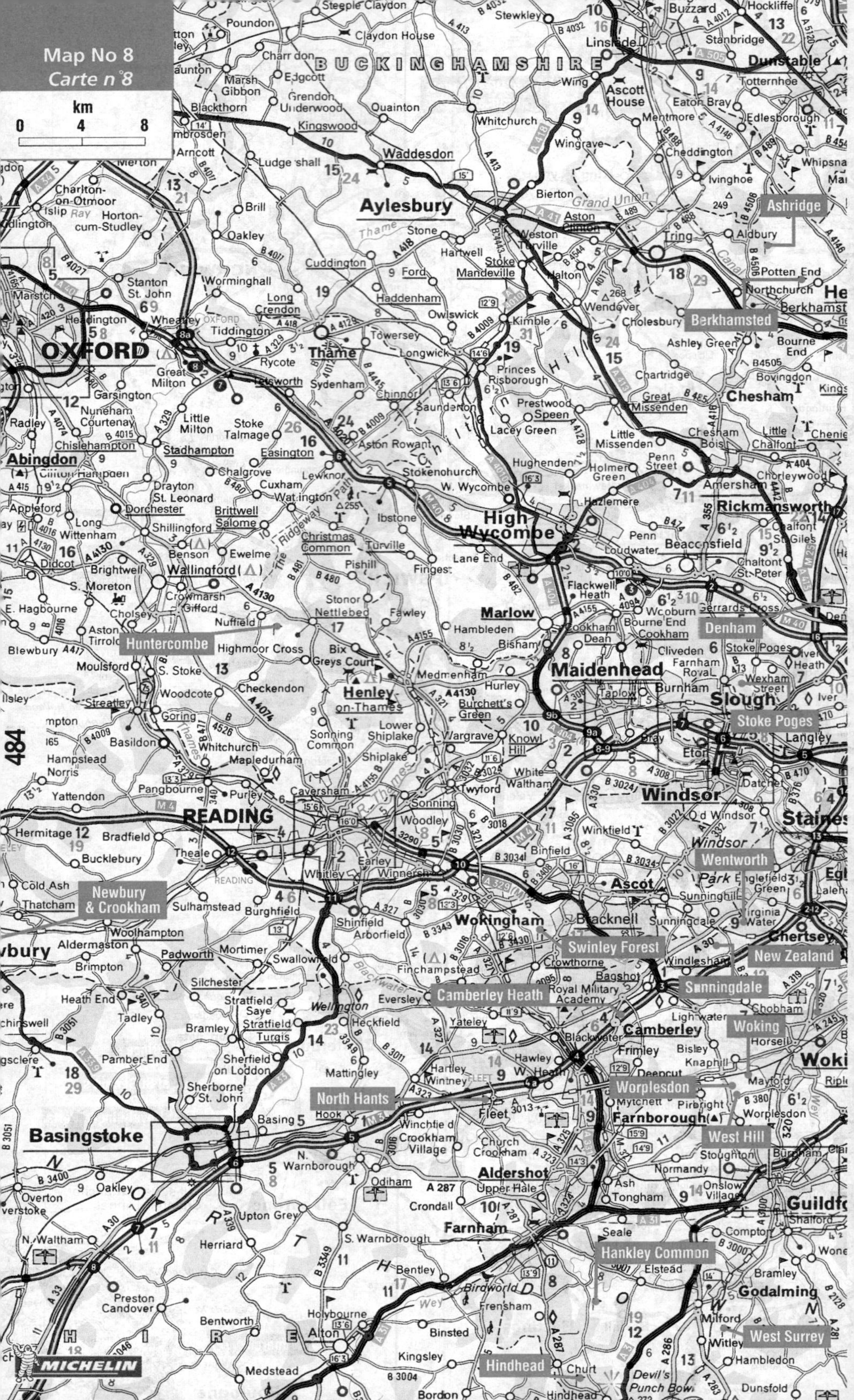
Map No 8
Carte n°8
km
0 4 8
BUCKINGHAMSHIRE
Aylesbury
OXFORD
Thame
High Wycombe
Marlow
Maidenhead
Slough
Windsor
READING
Henley-on-Thames
Wokingham
Bracknell
Ascot
Camberley
Farnborough
Aldershot
Farnham
Fleet
Basingstoke
Guildford
Godalming
Abingdon
Wallingford
Didcot
Dunstable
Tring
Berkhamsted
Chesham
Amersham
Beaconsfield
Rickmansworth
Staines
Chertsey
Woking
Alton
Ashridge
Berkhamsted
Huntercombe
Denham
Stoke Poges
Newbury & Crookham
Wentworth
Swinley Forest
New Zealand
Camberley Heath
Sunningdale
Woking
North Hants
Worplesdon
West Hill
Hankley Common
West Surrey
Hindhead
484
MICHELIN

LUTON
Stevenage
HERTFORDSHIRE
Bishop's Stortford
Hanbury Manor
Harpenden
Hertford
Ware
Welwyn Garden City
Hemel Hempstead
St. Albans
Hatfield
Hoddesdon
Harlow
Hertfordshire (The)
The Grove
Cheshunt
Epping
Potters Bar
Watford
Borehamwood
Bushey
Waltham Abbey
Loughton
Hadley Wood
Moor Park
Chigwell
Buckinghamshire (The)
LONDON
HAMMERSMITH
Royal Mid Surrey
HOUNSLOW
RICHMOND UPON THAMES
WANDSWORTH
LAMBETH
LEWISHAM
GREENWICH
BEXLEY
Dartford
Royal Wimbledon
Hampton Court
Walton-on-Thames
Esher
Weybridge
KINGSTON UPON THAMES
CROYDON
SUTTON
Ewell
Epsom
Banstead
Cobham
Leatherhead
Walton Heath
St George's Hill
Caterham
Sevenoaks
SURREY
Dorking
Reigate
Horley
Crawley
GATWICK AIRPORT
East Grinstead
Hever
Edenbridge
485
MICHELIN

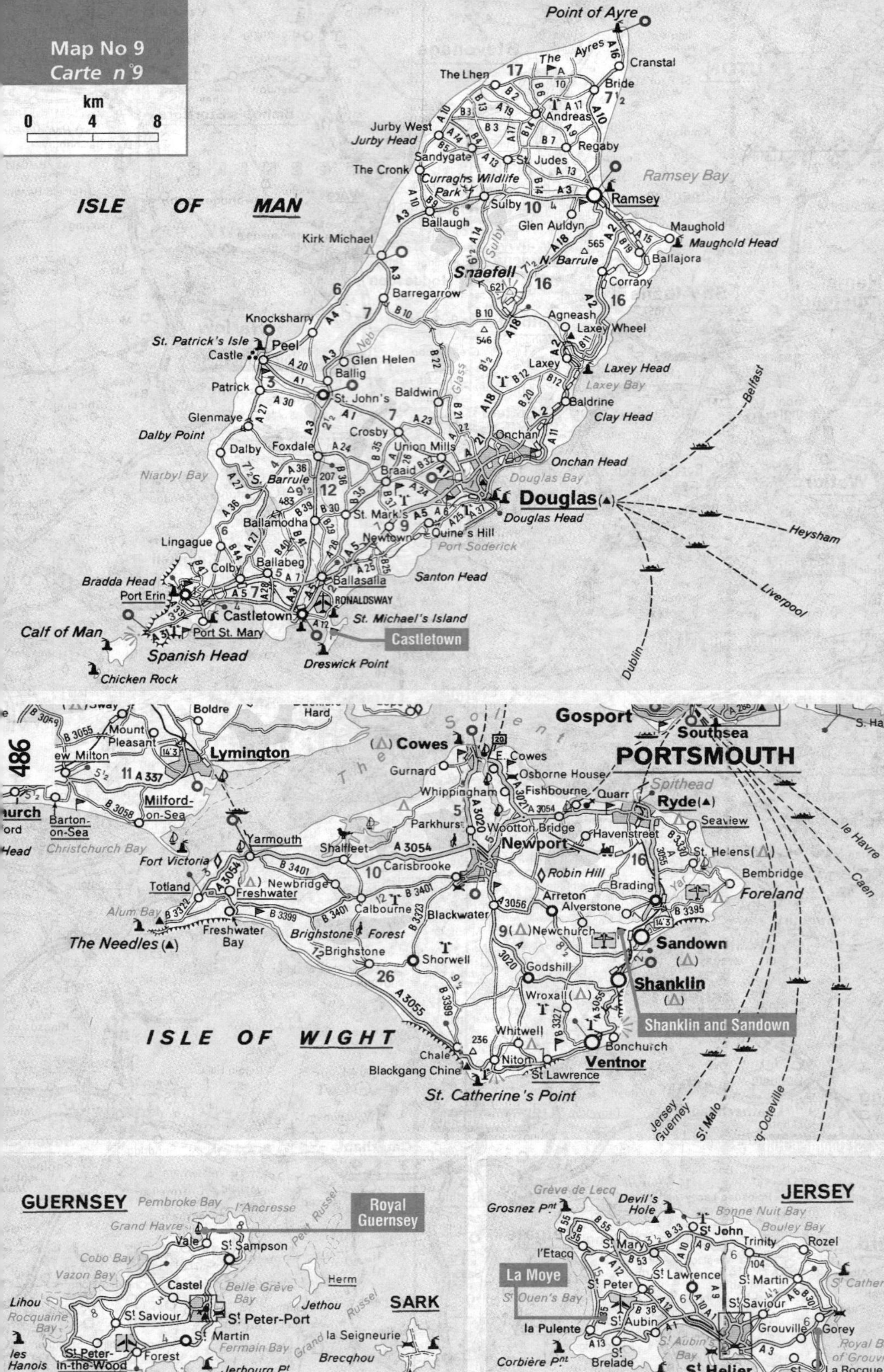

Map No 9
Carte n°9
km
0 4 8
ISLE OF MAN
Point of Ayre
The Ayres
Cranstal
Bride
The Lhen
Andreas
Jurby West
Jurby Head
Regaby
Sandygate
St. Judes
The Cronk
Curraghs Wildlife Park
Ramsey Bay
Ramsey
Sulby
Ballaugh
Glen Auldyn
Maughold
Maughold Head
Kirk Michael
N. Barrule
Ballajora
Snaefell
Corrany
Barregarrow
Agneash
Knocksharry
Laxey Wheel
St. Patrick's Isle
Peel
Castle
Laxey
Laxey Head
Laxey Bay
Glen Helen
Ballig
Patrick
St. John's
Baldwin
Baldrine
Clay Head
Glenmaye
Crosby
Dalby Point
Onchan
Dalby
Foxdale
Union Mills
Onchan Head
Niarbyl Bay
S. Barrule
Braaid
Douglas Bay
Douglas
Ballamodha
St. Mark's
Douglas Head
Quine's Hill
Newtown
Port Soderick
Lingague
Colby
Ballabeg
Ballasalla
Santon Head
Bradda Head
Port Erin
Ronaldsway
Castletown
St. Michael's Island
Calf of Man
Port St. Mary
Castletown
Spanish Head
Dreswick Point
Chicken Rock
Belfast
Heysham
Liverpool
Dublin
ISLE OF WIGHT
486
Sway
Boldre
Bucklers Hard
Gosport
Southsea
S. Hay
Mount Pleasant
New Milton
Lymington
Cowes
E. Cowes
PORTSMOUTH
The Solent
Gurnard
Osborne House
Spithead
Milford-on-Sea
Whippingham
Fishbourne
Quarr
Ryde
Christchurch
Barton-on-Sea
Parkhurst
Seaview
Christchurch Bay
Yarmouth
Shalfleet
Wootton Bridge
Havenstreet
Newport
St. Helens
le Havre
Fort Victoria
Carisbrooke
Robin Hill
Bembridge
Totland
Newbridge
Brading
Freshwater
Arreton
Foreland
Caen
Alum Bay
Calbourne
Blackwater
Alverstone
Freshwater Bay
Brighstone Forest
Newchurch
The Needles
Sandown
Brighstone
Shorwell
Godshill
Shanklin
Wroxall
Shanklin and Sandown
Whitwell
Bonchurch
Chale
Niton
Ventnor
Blackgang Chine
St Lawrence
St. Catherine's Point
Jersey
Guernsey
St. Malo
Cherbourg-Octeville
GUERNSEY
Pembroke Bay
l'Ancresse
Royal Guernsey
Grand Havre
Vale
St. Sampson
Petit Russel
Cobo Bay
Vazon Bay
Castel
Belle Grève Bay
Herm
Lihou
Rocquaine Bay
St. Saviour
Jethou
St. Peter-Port
SARK
St. Martin
Fermain Bay
la Seigneurie
les Hanois
St. Peter-in-the-Wood
Forest
Brecqhou
Jerbourg Pt.
Icart Point
Little Sark
la Coupée
MICHELIN
JERSEY
Grève de Lecq
Devil's Hole
Grosnez Pt.
Bonne Nuit Bay
Bouley Bay
St. John
Trinity
Rozel
St. Mary
l'Etacq
La Moye
St. Lawrence
St. Peter
St. Martin
St. Ouen's Bay
St. Catherine
St. Saviour
St. Aubin
la Pulente
Grouville
Gorey
St. Aubin's Bay
Royal Bay of Grouville
St. Brelade
Corbière Pt.
St. Helier
Noirmont Pt.
St. Clément
La Rocque
Green Island
Royal Jersey

CLASSIFICATION OF COURSES
CLASSEMENT DES PARCOURS

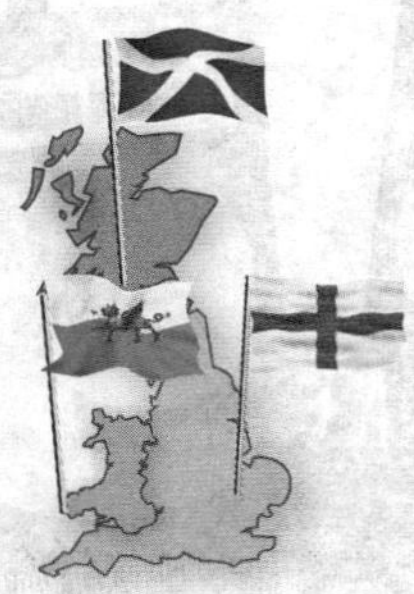

This classification gives priority consideration to the score awarded to the actual course.
Ce classement donne priorité à la note attribuée au parcours.

Eng England - **SCO** Scotland - **WAL** Wales
Within each score, the ranking is purely alphabetical

Course score / Note du parcours					Page
19	5	6	Carnoustie Championship	SCO	693
19	8	5	Ganton	ENG	548
19	8	7	Kingsbarns	SCO	724
19	7	6	Muirfield	SCO	739
19	7	7	Nairn	SCO	742
19	9	7	Royal Birkdale	ENG	604
19	7	7	Royal Dornoch Championship	SCO	755
19	7	6	Royal Porthcawl	WAL	799
19	7	5	Royal St George's	ENG	613
19	7	7	Royal Troon Old Course	SCO	757
19	9	7	Turnberry Ailsa Course	SCO	771
19	7	8	Woodhall Spa Hotchkin	ENG	669
18	7	7	Alwoodley	ENG	501
18	8	6	Blairgowrie Rosemount	SCO	684
18	7	6	Burnham & Berrow	ENG	521
18	6	8	Castletown	ENG	527
18	8	6	Chart Hills	ENG	529
18	7	6	Cruden Bay	SCO	697
18	8	7	Dundonald	SCO	705
18	8	7	East Sussex National East Course	ENG	539
18	7	6	Formby	ENG	545
18	8	7	Gleneagles King's	SCO	715
18	7	7	Hillside	ENG	560
18	6	6	Lindrick	ENG	572
18	8	6	Loch Lomond	SCO	730
18	6	4	Machrihanish	SCO	735
18	7	7	Moortown	ENG	585
18	6	7	North Berwick	SCO	745
18	6	6	Notts (Hollinwell)	ENG	591
18	6	7	Prestwick	SCO	750
18	7	8	Royal Aberdeen Balgownie Links	SCO	753
18	8	7	Royal Liverpool (Hoylake)	ENG	609
18	8	8	Royal Lytham & St Anne's	ENG	610
18	6	5	Royal St David's	WAL	800
18	7	5	Royal West Norfolk (Brancaster)	ENG	614
18	6	6	Rye	ENG	617
18	7	4	Saunton East Course	ENG	620
18	7	4	Silloth-on-Solway	ENG	629
18	6	4	Southerness	SCO	760
18	8	8	St Andrews Old Course	SCO	764
18	7	4	St Enodoc Church Course	ENG	632
18	7	7	St George's Hill	ENG	633
18	8	8	Sunningdale New Course	ENG	637
18	8	8	Sunningdale Old Course	ENG	638
18	8	9	The Grove	ENG	643
18	7	7	Walton Heath Old Course	ENG	651
18	8	7	Wentworth West Course	ENG	654
18	7	5	West Sussex	ENG	660
17	7	7	Aberdovey	WAL	779
17	8	7	Berkshire Blue Course	ENG	507
17	8	7	Berkshire) Red Course	ENG	508
17	6	6	Bowood G&CC	ENG	514
17	7	7	Broadstone	ENG	517
17	8	7	Buckinghamshire	ENG	519
17	8	8	Carden Park Nicklaus Course	ENG	525

CLASSIFICATION OF COURSES
CLASSEMENT DES PARCOURS

17	7	8	Cardrona	SCO	690
17	9	7	Celtic Manor Roman Road	WAL	784
17	8	8	Dalmahoy East Course	SCO	698
17	6	7	Downfield	SCO	699
17	6	7	East Devon	ENG	538
17	7	7	Ferndown Old Course	ENG	542
17	6	7	Forest Pines Forest + Pines	ENG	544
17	8	7	Gleneagles PGA Centenary	SCO	716
17	7	6	Gullane No 1	SCO	720
17	6	6	Hankley Common	ENG	553
17	8	7	Hayling	ENG	556
17	7	6	Hunstanton	ENG	563
17	7	6	Ilkley	ENG	565
17	6	7	Kilmarnock (Barassie)	SCO	723
17	7	8	La Moye	ENG	570
17	7	5	Ladybank	SCO	726
17	7	6	Liphook	ENG	573
17	7	8	Little Aston	ENG	574
17	7	5	Machrie	SCO	734
17	6	6	Monifieth	SCO	736
17	5	6	Montrose	SCO	737
17	5	6	Moray Old	SCO	738
17	6	5	Panmure	SCO	746
17	6	6	Pennard	WAL	796
17	8	7	The Roxburghe	SCO	752
17	6	5	Royal Cinque Ports	ENG	605
17	6	6	Royal North Devon (Westward Ho!)	ENG	612
17	7	4	Seacroft	ENG	622
17	5	4	Seascale	ENG	623
17	7	5	Seaton Carew	ENG	624
17	7	6	Sherwood Forest	ENG	628
17	5	5	Shiskine (Blackwaterfoot)	SCO	759
17	8	7	Slaley Hall Hunting Course	ENG	630
17	8	8	St Andrews New Course	SCO	763
17	7	8	St Andrews Bay Devlin Course	SCO	765
17	9	6	St Mellion Nicklaus Course	ENG	634
17	8	8	Stoke Park Golf Club	ENG	635
17	6	8	Swinley Forest	ENG	639
17	6	6	Tain	SCO	768
17	7	6	Tenby	WAL	802
17	7	7	Trevose Championship	ENG	648
17	8	7	Wentworth East Course	ENG	653
17	5	7	Western Gailes	SCO	774
17	7	7	Woburn Duke's Course	ENG	664
17	7	7	Woburn Marquess	ENG	665
17	6	6	Woking	ENG	666
17	7	6	Worplesdon	ENG	671
16	6	5	Ashburnham	WAL	780
16	7	6	Ashridge	ENG	502
16	5	7	Ayr (Belleisle)	SCO	679
16	7	7	Beau Desert	ENG	505
16	6	5	Blackmoor	ENG	510
16	7	6	Brampton	ENG	515
16	7	7	Caldy	ENG	522
16	6	6	Camberley Heath	ENG	523
16	7	7	Carlisle	ENG	526
16	7	7	Clitheroe	ENG	530
16	7	7	Cochrane Castle	SCO	694
16	7	7	Conwy	WAL	785
16	6	6	Copt Heath	ENG	532
16	7	6	Cumberwell Park	ENG	534
16	6	7	Delamere Forest	ENG	536
16	5	6	Dunbar	SCO	704
16	7	8	Fairhaven	ENG	540
16	6	5	Fortrose & Rosemarkie	SCO	713
16	7	8	Fulford	ENG	547
16	8	8	Hanbury Manor	ENG	552
16	6	7	High Post	ENG	559
16	7	5	Holyhead	WAL	787
16	7	7	Inverness	SCO	722
16	7	6	Isle of Purbeck	ENG	567
16	6	5	Lanark	SCO	727
16	6	5	Leven	SCO	729
16	8	5	Linden Hall	ENG	571
16	5	7	Llandudno (Maesdu)	WAL	789
16	4	6	Luffness New	SCO	732
16	7	7	Lundin	SCO	733
16	7	7	Manchester	ENG	577
16	8	6	Mannings Heath Waterfall Course	ENG	578
16	8	7	Moor Park High Course	ENG	584
16	7	5	Nefyn & District	WAL	792
16	6	7	New Zealand	ENG	587
16	7	6	North Hants	ENG	589
16	6	8	North Wales (Llandudno)	WAL	794
16	6	6	Northamptonshire	ENG	590
16	6	7	Pannal	ENG	594
16	7	8	Parkstone	ENG	595
16	8	6	Pleasington	ENG	597
16	6	4	Powfoot	SCO	749
16	8	7	Prestbury	ENG	599
16	6	7	Prestwick St Nicholas	SCO	751
16	7	5	Pyle & Kenfig	WAL	797
16	5	7	Reddish Vale	ENG	601
16	6	5	Rolls of Monmouth	WAL	798
16	7	6	Royal Ashdown Forest	ENG	603
16	7	8	Royal Burgess	SCO	754
16	7	8	Royal Jersey	ENG	608
16	8	7	Royal Musselburgh	SCO	756
16	5	7	Sandiway	ENG	619
16	6	6	Scotscraig	SCO	758
16	7	6	Sheringham	ENG	627
16	7	7	Southerndown	WAL	801

CLASSIFICATION OF COURSES
CLASSEMENT DES PARCOURS

16	7	7	Southport & Ainsdale	ENG	631
16	8	8	St Andrews Jubilee Course	SCO	762
16	9	8	The Belfry Brabazon	ENG	641
16	9	7	Turnberry Kintyre Course	SCO	772
16	8	7	Vale Hotel, Golf & Spa (Vale of Glamorgan) Wales National	WAL	803
16	7	7	Wallasey	ENG	649
16	7	7	Walton Heath New Course	ENG	650
16	7	6	West Cornwall	ENG	656
16	6	6	West Hill	ENG	657
16	7	6	West Kilbride	SCO	773
16	7	7	West Lancashire	ENG	658
16	6	7	Whittington Heath	ENG	662
15	7	5	Alloa	SCO	677
15	6	6	Ballater	SCO	681
15	7	6	Berkhamsted	ENG	506
15	6	5	Berwick-upon-Tweed	ENG	509
15	8	6	Blairgowrie Lansdowne	SCO	683
15	5	7	Bolton Old Links	ENG	511
15	8	6	Bovey Castle	ENG	512
15	7	6	Bowood (Cornwall)	ENG	513
15	6	5	Brancepeth Castle	ENG	516
15	6	6	Brokenhurst Manor	ENG	518
15	7	6	Brora	SCO	686
15	8	8	Bruntsfield	SCO	687
15	6	5	Bude & North Cornwall	ENG	520
15	6	5	Cavendish	ENG	528
15	8	7	Collingtree Park	ENG	531
15	6	6	Coxmoor	ENG	533
15	6	6	Crail Balcomie Links	SCO	695
15	7	7	Crieff Ferntower Course	SCO	696
15	9	6	Dartmouth	ENG	535
15	7	7	Denham	ENG	537
15	7	8	Duddingston	SCO	700
15	6	5	Duff House Royal	SCO	701
15	7	8	Duke's St Andrews	SCO	702
15	7	5	Dumfries & County	SCO	703
15	7	6	Dunfermline	SCO	706
15	6	8	East Renfrewshire	SCO	707
15	7	5	Elgin	SCO	709
15	6	6	Elie	SCO	710
15	8	8	Forest of Arden Arden	ENG	543
15	7	7	Frilford Heath Red Course	ENG	546
15	8	7	Gleneagles Queen's	SCO	717
15	7	8	Gog Magog Old Course	ENG	549
15	7	7	Hadley Wood	ENG	550
15	7	8	Haggs Castle	SCO	721
15	6	8	Hallamshire	ENG	551
15	7	7	Harrogate	ENG	554
15	8	7	Hawkstone Park Hawkstone	ENG	555
15	7	7	Hertfordshire (The)	ENG	557
15	7	6	Hindhead	ENG	561
15	6	7	Huddersfield (Fixby)	ENG	562
15	6	7	Huntercombe	ENG	564
15	7	7	Ipswich (Purdis Heath)	ENG	566
15	7	6	John O'Gaunt	ENG	568
15	6	5	King's Lynn	ENG	569
15	4	4	Kingussie	SCO	725
15	7	4	Letham Grange Old Course	SCO	728
15	9	7	London Golf Club International	ENG	575
15	8	7	Manor House (Castle Combe)	ENG	579
15	8	7	Marriott St Pierre Old Course	WAL	791
15	7	7	Mere	ENG	582
15	5	5	Mullion	ENG	586
15	6	6	Murcar	SCO	740
15	7	7	Nairn Dunbar	SCO	743
15	6	7	Newport	WAL	793
15	9	6	Northop Country Park	WAL	795
15	7	6	Orchardleigh	ENG	593
15	6	6	Perranporth	ENG	596
15	8	7	Portal Championship	ENG	598
15	6	6	Portpatrick (Dunskey)	SCO	748
15	6	4	Prince's Himalayas-Shore	ENG	600
15	7	6	Royal Cromer	ENG	606
15	7	7	Royal Guernsey	ENG	607
15	7	8	Royal Wimbledon	ENG	615
15	7	7	Sand Moor	ENG	618
15	7	4	Saunton West Course	ENG	621
15	7	6	Shanklin & Sandown	ENG	625
15	6	6	Sherborne	ENG	626
15	7	8	St Andrews Bay Torrance Course	SCO	766
15	7	8	Stoneham	ENG	636
15	6	6	Strathaven	SCO	767
15	9	8	The Belfry PGA National	ENG	642
15	7	4	Thetford	ENG	644
15	7	6	Thorndon Park	ENG	645
15	6	5	Thornhill	SCO	770
15	6	5	Thurlestone	ENG	647
15	7	8	Warwickshire	ENG	652
15	7	7	West Berkshire	ENG	655
15	7	6	West Surrey	ENG	659
15	6	7	Weston-Super-Mare	ENG	661
15	6	6	Whitekirk	SCO	775
15	7	6	Wilmslow	ENG	663
15	7	7	Woodbridge	ENG	667
15	9	6	Woodbury Park The Oaks	ENG	668
14	6	5	Aboyne	SCO	676
14	6	7	Aldeburgh	ENG	500
14	6	5	Alyth	SCO	678

CLASSIFICATION OF COURSES
CLASSEMENT DES PARCOURS

14	6	8	Baberton	SCO	680
14	5	5	Bamburgh Castle	ENG	503
14	7	7	Banchory	SCO	682
14	6	9	Bath	ENG	504
14	6	6	Boat of Garten	SCO	685
14	6	6	Buchanan Castle	SCO	688
14	6	6	Burntisland	SCO	689
14	5	6	Came Down	ENG	524
14	6	8	Cardiff	WAL	781
14	6	5	Cardigan	WAL	782
14	6	4	Cardross	SCO	691
14	7	4	Carmarthen	WAL	783
14	5	6	Carnoustie Burnside	SCO	692
14	6	3	Edzell	SCO	708
14	6	6	Felixstowe Ferry Martello Course	ENG	541
14	5	4	Forfar	SCO	712
14	7	7	Glamorganshire	WAL	786
14	7	6	Glen	SCO	714
14	5	4	Golspie	SCO	718
14	6	5	Grantown on Spey	SCO	719
14	8	7	Hever	ENG	558
14	7	7	Langland Bay	WAL	788
14	6	4	Llanymynech	WAL	790
14	7	5	Longniddry	SCO	731
14	6	5	Luffenham Heath	ENG	576
14	5	6	Mendip	ENG	580
14	8	7	Meon Valley Meon Course	ENG	581
14	6	7	Moor Allerton	ENG	583
14	7	7	Murrayshall	SCO	741
14	7	7	Newbury & Crookham	ENG	588
14	5	5	Newtonmore	SCO	744
14	7	7	Old Thorns	ENG	592
14	6	6	Pitlochry	SCO	747
14	5	6	Ross-on-Wye	ENG	602
14	8	8	Royal Mid-Surrey Outer	ENG	611
14	8	7	Rudding Park	ENG	616
14	8	8	St Andrews Eden Course	SCO	761
14	6	5	Tadmarton Heath	ENG	640
14	7	7	Thorpeness	ENG	646
14	7	6	Woodsome Hall	ENG	670
13	5	7	Falkirk Tryst	SCO	711
13	4	6	Taymouth Castle	SCO	769

HOTEL FACILITIES
ENVIRONNEMENT HOTELIER

This classification gives priority consideration to the score awarded to the hotel facilities.

Ce classement donne priorité à la note attribuée à l'environnement hôtelier.

Hotel facility score
Note de l'environnement hôtelier

Page

14	6	**9**	Bath	ENG	504
18	8	**9**	The Grove	ENG	643
14	6	**8**	Baberton	SCO	680
15	8	**8**	Bruntsfield	SCO	687
17	8	**8**	Carden Park Nicklaus Course	ENG	525
14	6	**8**	Cardiff	WAL	781
17	7	**8**	Cardrona	SCO	690
18	6	**8**	Castletown	ENG	527
17	8	**8**	Dalmahoy East Course	SCO	698
15	7	**8**	Duddingston	SCO	700
15	7	**8**	Duke's St Andrews	SCO	702
15	6	**8**	East Renfrewshire	SCO	707
16	7	**8**	Fairhaven	ENG	540
15	8	**8**	Forest of Arden Arden Course	ENG	543
16	7	**8**	Fulford	ENG	547
15	7	**8**	Gog Magog Old Course	ENG	549
15	7	**8**	Haggs Castle	SCO	721
15	6	**8**	Hallamshire	ENG	551
16	8	**8**	Hanbury Manor	ENG	552
17	7	**8**	La Moye	ENG	570
17	7	**8**	Little Aston	ENG	574
16	6	**8**	North Wales (Llandudno)	WAL	794

HOTEL FACILITIES
ENVIRONNEMENT HOTELIER

16	7	**8**	Parkstone	ENG	595
18	7	**8**	Royal Aberdeen Balgownie Links	SCO	753
16	7	**8**	Royal Burgess	SCO	754
16	7	**8**	Royal Jersey	ENG	608
18	8	**8**	Royal Lytham & St Anne's	ENG	610
14	8	**8**	Royal Mid-Surrey Outer	ENG	611
15	7	**8**	Royal Wimbledon	ENG	615
14	8	**8**	St Andrews Eden Course	SCO	761
16	8	**8**	St Andrews Jubilee Course	SCO	762
17	8	**8**	St Andrews New Course	SCO	763
18	8	**8**	St Andrews Old Course	SCO	764
17	7	**8**	St Andrews Bay Devlin	SCO	765
15	7	**8**	St Andrews Bay Torrance	SCO	766
17	8	**8**	Stoke Park Golf Club	ENG	635
15	7	**8**	Stoneham	ENG	636
18	8	**8**	Sunningdale New Course	ENG	637
18	8	**8**	Sunningdale Old Course	ENG	638
17	6	**8**	Swinley Forest	ENG	639
16	9	**8**	The Belfry Brabazon	ENG	641
15	9	**8**	The Belfry PGA National	ENG	642
15	7	**8**	Warwickshire	ENG	652
19	7	**8**	Woodhall Spa Hotchkin	ENG	669
17	7	**7**	Aberdovey	WAL	779
14	6	**7**	Aldeburgh	ENG	500
18	7	**7**	Alwoodley	ENG	501
16	5	**7**	Ayr (Belleisle)	SCO	679
14	7	**7**	Banchory	SCO	682
16	7	**7**	Beau Desert	ENG	505
17	8	**7**	Berkshire Blue Course	ENG	507
17	8	**7**	Berkshire Red Course	ENG	508
15	5	**7**	Bolton Old Links	ENG	511
17	7	**7**	Broadstone	ENG	517
17	8	**7**	Buckinghamshire	ENG	519
16	7	**7**	Caldy	ENG	522
16	7	**7**	Carlisle	ENG	526
17	9	**7**	Celtic Manor Roman Road	WAL	784
16	7	**7**	Clitheroe	ENG	530
16	7	**7**	Cochrane Castle	SCO	694
15	8	**7**	Collingtree Park	ENG	531
16	7	**7**	Conwy	WAL	785
15	7	**7**	Crieff Ferntower Course	SCO	696
16	6	**7**	Delamere Forest	ENG	536
15	7	**7**	Denham	ENG	537
17	6	**7**	Downfield	SCO	699
18	8	**7**	Dundonald	SCO	705
17	6	**7**	East Devon	ENG	538
18	8	**7**	East Sussex National East Course	ENG	539
13	5	**7**	Falkirk Tryst	SCO	711

17	7	**7**	Ferndown Old Course	ENG	542
17	6	**7**	Forest Pines Forest + Pines	ENG	544
15	7	**7**	Frilford Heath Red Course	ENG	546
14	7	**7**	Glamorganshire	WAL	786
18	8	**7**	Gleneagles King's	SCO	715
17	8	**7**	Gleneagles PGA Centenary	SCO	716
15	8	**7**	Gleneagles Queen's	SCO	717
15	7	**7**	Hadley Wood	ENG	550
15	7	**7**	Harrogate	ENG	554
15	8	**7**	Hawkstone Park Hawkstone	ENG	555
17	8	**7**	Hayling	ENG	556
15	7	**7**	Hertfordshire (The)	ENG	557
14	8	**7**	Hever	ENG	558
16	6	**7**	High Post	ENG	559
18	7	**7**	Hillside	ENG	560
15	6	**7**	Huddersfield (Fixby)	ENG	562
15	6	**7**	Huntercombe	ENG	564
16	7	**7**	Inverness	SCO	722
15	7	**7**	Ipswich (Purdis Heath)	ENG	566
17	6	**7**	Kilmarnock (Barassie)	SCO	723
19	8	**7**	Kingsbarns	SCO	724
14	7	**7**	Langland Bay	WAL	788
16	5	**7**	Llandudno (Maesdu)	WAL	789
15	9	**7**	London Golf Club International	ENG	575
16	7	**7**	Lundin	SCO	733
16	7	**7**	Manchester	ENG	577
15	8	**7**	Manor House (Castle Combe)	ENG	579
15	8	**7**	Marriott St Pierre Old	WAL	791
14	8	**7**	Meon Valley Meon Course	ENG	581
15	7	**7**	Mere	ENG	582
14	6	**7**	Moor Allerton	ENG	583
16	8	**7**	Moor Park High Course	ENG	584
18	7	**7**	Moortown	ENG	585
14	7	**7**	Murrayshall	SCO	741
19	7	**7**	Nairn	SCO	742
15	7	**7**	Nairn Dunbar	SCO	743
16	6	**7**	New Zealand	ENG	587
14	7	**7**	Newbury & Crookham	ENG	588
15	6	**7**	Newport	WAL	793
18	6	**7**	North Berwick	SCO	745
14	7	**7**	Old Thorns	ENG	592
16	6	**7**	Pannal	ENG	594
15	8	**7**	Portal Championship	ENG	598
16	8	**7**	Prestbury	ENG	599
18	6	**7**	Prestwick	SCO	750
16	6	**7**	Prestwick St Nicholas	SCO	751
16	5	**7**	Reddish Vale	ENG	601
17	8	**7**	Roxburghe (The)	SCO	752
19	9	**7**	Royal Birkdale	ENG	604
19	7	**7**	Royal Dornoch Championship	SCO	755
15	7	**7**	Royal Guernsey	ENG	607

18	8	**7**	Royal Liverpool (Hoylake)	ENG	609
16	8	**7**	Royal Musselburgh	SCO	756
19	7	**7**	Royal Troon Old Course	SCO	757
14	8	**7**	Rudding Park	ENG	616
15	7	**7**	Sand Moor	ENG	618
16	5	**7**	Sandiway	ENG	619
17	8	**7**	Slaley Hall Hunting Course	ENG	630
16	7	**7**	Southerndown	WAL	801
16	7	**7**	Southport & Ainsdale	ENG	631
18	7	**7**	St George's Hill	ENG	633
14	7	**7**	Thorpeness	ENG	646
17	7	**7**	Trevose Championship	ENG	648
19	9	**7**	Turnberry Ailsa Course	SCO	771
16	9	**7**	Turnberry Kintyre Course	SCO	772
16	8	**7**	Vale Hotel, Golf & Spa (Vale of Glamorgan) Wales National	WAL	803
16	7	**7**	Wallasey	ENG	649
16	7	**7**	Walton Heath New Course	ENG	650
18	7	**7**	Walton Heath Old Course	ENG	651
17	8	**7**	Wentworth East Course	ENG	653
18	8	**7**	Wentworth West Course	ENG	654
15	7	**7**	West Berkshire	ENG	655
16	7	**7**	West Lancashire	ENG	658
17	5	**7**	Western Gailes	SCO	774
15	6	**7**	Weston-Super-Mare	ENG	661
16	6	**7**	Whittington Heath	ENG	662
17	7	**7**	Woburn Duke's Course	ENG	664
17	7	**7**	Woburn Marquess	ENG	665
15	7	**7**	Woodbridge	ENG	667
16	7	**6**	Ashridge	ENG	502
15	6	**6**	Ballater	SCO	681
15	7	**6**	Berkhamsted	ENG	506
15	8	**6**	Blairgowrie Lansdowne	SCO	683
18	8	**6**	Blairgowrie Rosemount	SCO	684
14	6	**6**	Boat of Garten	SCO	685
15	8	**6**	Bovey Castle	ENG	512
15	7	**6**	Bowood (Cornwall)	ENG	513
17	6	**6**	Bowood G&CC	ENG	514
16	7	**6**	Brampton	ENG	515
15	6	**6**	Brokenhurst Manor	ENG	518
15	7	**6**	Brora	SCO	686
14	6	**6**	Buchanan Castle	SCO	688
18	7	**6**	Burnham & Berrow	ENG	521
14	6	**6**	Burntisland	SCO	689
16	6	**6**	Camberley Heath	ENG	523
14	5	**6**	Came Down	ENG	524
14	5	**6**	Carnoustie Burnside	SCO	692
19	5	**6**	Carnoustie Championship	SCO	693
18	8	**6**	Chart Hills	ENG	529
16	6	**6**	Copt Heath	ENG	532
15	6	**6**	Coxmoor	ENG	533
15	6	**6**	Crail Balcomie Links	SCO	695
18	7	**6**	Cruden Bay	SCO	697
16	7	**6**	Cumberwell Park	ENG	534
15	9	**6**	Dartmouth	ENG	535
16	5	**6**	Dunbar	SCO	704
15	7	**6**	Dunfermline	SCO	706
15	6	**6**	Elie	SCO	710
14	6	**6**	Felixstowe Ferry Martello Course	ENG	541
18	7	**6**	Formby	ENG	545
14	7	**6**	Glen	SCO	714
17	7	**6**	Gullane No 1	SCO	720
17	6	**6**	Hankley Common	ENG	553
15	7	**6**	Hindhead	ENG	561
17	7	**6**	Hunstanton	ENG	563
17	7	**6**	Ilkley	ENG	565
16	7	**6**	Isle of Purbeck	ENG	567
15	7	**6**	John O'Gaunt	ENG	568
18	6	**6**	Lindrick	ENG	572
17	7	**6**	Liphook	ENG	573
18	8	**6**	Loch Lomond	SCO	730
16	4	**6**	Luffness New	SCO	732
16	8	**6**	Mannings Heath Waterfall Course	ENG	578
14	5	**6**	Mendip	ENG	580
17	6	**6**	Monifieth	SCO	736
17	5	**6**	Montrose	SCO	737
17	5	**6**	Moray Old	SCO	738
19	7	**6**	Muirfield	SCO	739
15	6	**6**	Murcar	SCO	740
16	7	**6**	North Hants	ENG	589
16	6	**6**	Northamptonshire	ENG	590
15	9	**6**	Northop Country Park	WAL	795
18	6	**6**	Notts (Hollinwell)	ENG	591
15	7	**6**	Orchardleigh	ENG	593
17	6	**6**	Pennard	WAL	796
15	6	**6**	Perranporth	ENG	596
14	6	**6**	Pitlochry	SCO	747
16	8	**6**	Pleasington	ENG	597
15	6	**6**	Portpatrick (Dunskey)	SCO	748
14	5	**6**	Ross-on-Wye	ENG	602
16	7	**6**	Royal Ashdown Forest	ENG	603
15	7	**6**	Royal Cromer	ENG	606
17	6	**6**	Royal North Devon (Westward Ho!)	ENG	612
19	7	**6**	Royal Porthcawl	WAL	799
18	6	**6**	Rye	ENG	617
16	6	**6**	Scotscraig	SCO	758
15	7	**6**	Shanklin & Sandown	ENG	625
15	6	**6**	Sherborne	ENG	626
16	7	**6**	Sheringham	ENG	627
17	7	**6**	Sherwood Forest	ENG	628
17	9	**6**	St Mellion Nicklaus Course	ENG	634

HOTEL FACILITIES
ENVIRONNEMENT HOTELIER

15	6	**6**	Strathaven	SCO	767
17	6	**6**	Tain	SCO	768
13	4	**6**	Taymouth Castle	SCO	769
17	7	**6**	Tenby	WAL	802
15	7	**6**	Thorndon Park	ENG	645
16	7	**6**	West Cornwall	ENG	656
16	6	**6**	West Hill	ENG	657
16	7	**6**	West Kilbride	SCO	773
15	7	**6**	West Surrey	ENG	659
15	6	**6**	Whitekirk	SCO	775
15	7	**6**	Wilmslow	ENG	663
17	6	**6**	Woking	ENG	666
15	9	**6**	Woodbury Park The Oaks	ENG	668
14	7	**6**	Woodsome Hall	ENG	670
17	7	**6**	Worplesdon	ENG	671
14	6	**5**	Aboyne	SCO	676
15	7	**5**	Alloa	SCO	677
14	6	**5**	Alyth	SCO	678
16	6	**5**	Ashburnham	WAL	780
14	5	**5**	Bamburgh Castle	ENG	503
15	6	**5**	Berwick-upon-Tweed	ENG	509
16	6	**5**	Blackmoor	ENG	510
15	6	**5**	Brancepeth Castle	ENG	516
15	6	**5**	Bude & North Cornwall	ENG	520
14	6	**5**	Cardigan	WAL	782
15	6	**5**	Cavendish	ENG	528
15	6	**5**	Duff House Royal	SCO	701
15	7	**5**	Dumfries & County	SCO	703
15	7	**5**	Elgin	SCO	709
16	6	**5**	Fortrose & Rosemarkie	SCO	713
19	8	**5**	Ganton	ENG	548
14	6	**5**	Grantown on Spey	SCO	719
16	7	**5**	Holyhead	WAL	787
15	6	**5**	King's Lynn	ENG	569
17	7	**5**	Ladybank	SCO	726
16	6	**5**	Lanark	SCO	727
16	6	**5**	Leven	SCO	729
16	8	**5**	Linden Hall	ENG	571
14	7	**5**	Longniddry	SCO	731
14	6	**5**	Luffenham Heath	ENG	576
17	7	**5**	Machrie	SCO	734
15	5	**5**	Mullion	ENG	586
16	7	**5**	Nefyn & District	WAL	792
14	5	**5**	Newtonmore	SCO	744
17	6	**5**	Panmure	SCO	746
16	7	**5**	Pyle & Kenfig	WAL	797
16	6	**5**	Rolls of Monmouth (The)	WAL	798
17	6	**5**	Royal Cinque Ports	ENG	605
18	6	**5**	Royal St David's	WAL	800
19	7	**5**	Royal St George's	ENG	613
18	7	**5**	Royal West Norfolk (Brancaster)	ENG	614
17	7	**5**	Seaton Carew	ENG	624
17	5	**5**	Shiskine (Blackwaterfoot)	SCO	759
14	6	**5**	Tadmarton Heath	ENG	640
15	6	**5**	Thornhill	SCO	770
15	6	**5**	Thurlestone	ENG	647
18	7	**5**	West Sussex	ENG	660
14	6	**4**	Cardross	SCO	691
14	7	**4**	Carmarthen	WAL	783
14	5	**4**	Forfar	SCO	712
14	5	**4**	Golspie	SCO	718
15	4	**4**	Kingussie	SCO	725
15	7	**4**	Letham Grange Old Course	SCO	728
14	6	**4**	Llanymynech	WAL	790
18	6	**4**	Machrihanish	SCO	735
16	6	**4**	Powfoot	SCO	749
15	6	**4**	Prince's Himalayas-Shore	ENG	600
18	7	**4**	Saunton East Course	ENG	620
15	7	**4**	Saunton West Course	ENG	621
17	7	**4**	Seacroft	ENG	622
17	5	**4**	Seascale	ENG	623
18	7	**4**	Silloth-on-Solway	ENG	629
18	6	**4**	Southerness	SCO	760
18	7	**4**	St Enodoc Church Course	ENG	632
15	7	**4**	Thetford	ENG	644
14	6	**3**	Edzell	SCO	708

RECOMMENDED GOLFING STAY
SÉJOUR DE GOLF RECOMMANDÉ

Berkshire (The) Blue Course	ENG	**17**	8	7	507
Berkshire (The) Red Course	ENG	**17**	8	7	508
Blairgowrie Lansdowne	SCO	**15**	8	6	683
Blairgowrie Rosemount	SCO	**18**	8	6	684
Burnham & Berrow	ENG	**18**	7	6	521
Carden Park Nicklaus Course	ENG	**17**	8	8	525
Carnoustie Burnside	SCO	**14**	5	6	692
Carnoustie Championship	SCO	**19**	5	6	693
Celtic Manor Roman Road	WAL	**17**	9	7	784
Cumberwell Park	ENG	**16**	7	6	534
Dalmahoy East Course	SCO	**17**	8	8	698
East Sussex National East Course	ENG	**18**	8	7	539
Ferndown Old Course	ENG	**17**	7	7	542
Forest of Arden	ENG	**15**	8	8	543
Forest Pines Forest + Pines	ENG	**17**	6	7	544
Formby	ENG	**18**	7	6	545
Gleneagles King's	SCO	**18**	8	7	715
Gleneagles PGA Centenary	SCO	**17**	8	7	716
Gleneagles Queen's	SCO	**15**	8	7	717
Gullane No 1	SCO	**17**	7	6	720
Hawkstone Park Hawkstone	ENG	**15**	8	7	555
Hillside	ENG	**18**	7	7	560
Isle of Purbeck	ENG	**16**	7	6	567
John O'Gaunt	ENG	**15**	7	6	568
Machrihanish	SCO	**18**	6	4	735
Marriott St Pierre Old Course	WAL	**15**	8	7	791
Moray Old	SCO	**17**	5	6	738
Portal Championship	ENG	**15**	8	7	598
Pyle & Kenfig	WAL	**16**	7	5	797
Royal Ashdown Forest	ENG	**16**	7	6	603
Royal Birkdale (The)	ENG	**19**	9	7	604
Royal Cinque Ports	ENG	**17**	6	5	605
Royal Dornoch Championship	SCO	**19**	7	7	755
Royal St David's	WAL	**18**	6	5	800
Royal Troon Old Course	SCO	**19**	7	7	757
Saunton East Course	ENG	**18**	7	4	620
Saunton West Course	ENG	**15**	7	4	621
Slaley Hall Hunting Course	ENG	**17**	8	7	630
St Andrews Eden Course	SCO	**14**	8	8	761
St Andrews Jubilee Course	SCO	**16**	8	8	762
St Andrews New Course	SCO	**17**	8	8	763
St Andrews Old Course	SCO	**18**	8	8	764
St Andrews Bay Devlin	SCO	**17**	7	8	765
St Andrews Bay Torrance	SCO	**15**	7	8	766
St Enodoc Church Course	ENG	**18**	7	4	632
St Mellion Nicklaus Course	ENG	**17**	9	6	634
Stoke Park Golf Club	ENG	**17**	8	8	635
Sunningdale New Course	ENG	**18**	8	8	637
Sunningdale Old Course	ENG	**18**	8	8	638
The Belfry Brabazon	ENG	**16**	9	8	641
The Belfry PGA National	ENG	**15**	9	8	642
Trevose Championship	ENG	**17**	7	7	648
Turnberry Ailsa Course	SCO	**19**	9	7	771
Turnberry Kintyre Course	SCO	**16**	9	7	772
Walton Heath New Course	ENG	**16**	7	7	650
Walton Heath Old Course	ENG	**18**	7	7	651
Warwickshire (The)	ENG	**15**	7	8	652
Wentworth East Course	ENG	**17**	8	7	653
Wentworth West Course	ENG	**18**	8	7	654
Woburn Dukes Course	ENG	**17**	7	7	664
Woodhall Spa Hotchkin	ENG	**19**	7	8	669

RECOMMENDED HOLIDAYS
VACANCES RECOMMANDÉES

Gleneagles King's	SCO	**18**	8	7	715
Gleneagles PGA Centenary	SCO	**17**	8	7	716
Gleneagles Queen's	SCO	**15**	8	7	717
Hayling	ENG	**17**	8	7	556
La Moye	ENG	**17**	7	8	570
Langland Bay	WAL	**14**	7	7	788
Llandudno (Maesdu)	WAL	**16**	5	7	789
North Wales (Llandudno)	WAL	**16**	6	8	794
Pennard	WAL	**17**	6	6	796
Royal Guernsey	ENG	**15**	7	7	607
Royal Jersey	ENG	**16**	7	8	608

ANGLETERRE

ENGLAND

ENGLAND

For enthusiastic students of golf-course architecture, playing the game in England is sheer bliss, such is the diversity of style, landscape and terrain. First there are the great links courses in Kent, Suffolk and Norfolk along the English Channel and the North Sea, in the south-west through Devon and Cornwall and a string of beauties from Liverpool to Blackpool. Then the landscape changes sharply with the classic gorse and heather courses and the lush parks around London.

Here you will find courses designed by the likes of James Braid, Herbert Fowler, Alister Mackenzie or Harry S. Colt, perhaps the most consistently inspired architect of them all. Plus layouts by the more modern architects such as Jack Nicklaus or Dave Thomas and today's rising stars going by the names of Kyle Phillips or David McLay Kidd, who has designed the top-secret Queenwood course. Yet while England is one of the cradles of golf, only very few great courses have opened there in recent years, and even "The Grove", a very impressive piece of work, was a sort of tribute paid to the great architects of the golden age whose popularity never seems to wear thin, rather like Shakespeare or... the Beatles.

So, about a dozen courses make a first appearance in this guide but they are not necessarily new creations. They best express the wealth of golfing facilities which result in your preferring one layout before going on to another the next day. Golfers, too, can be such fickle customers.

There are some 1,900 courses in England, many of which are good. We do not claim to be 100% objective about this and some have certainly slipped through the net. But may our readers rest assured, all the courses included this year are, to coin a wine phrase, great vintages. You will find the greatest links, the top parkland courses, courses which are ranked amongst the best and also those little "gems" which we hope you will be proud to talk about to your friends. And if you happen to come across any others, please let us know. Whittling down the numbers to make our final choice was harder here than anywhere else.

ANGLETERRE

Pour les amateurs d'architecture de golf, jouer en Angleterre est un paradis, tant la diversité des styles, des paysages, des terrains est grande. On y trouve les grands links du Kent, du Suffolk et du Norfolk le long de la Manche et de la Mer du Nord, ou ceux – au sud-ouest – du Devon et de Cornouailles, et enfin un collier de merveilles de Liverpool à Blackpool. Mais on changera radicalement de paysages avec les classiques en terre de bruyère, les beaux parcs de la région de Londres.

On trouve des signatures comme celles de James Braid, Herbert Fowler, Alister Mackenzie, ou de Harry S. Colt, peut-être le plus constamment inspiré de tous. Mais aussi des modernes comme Jack Nicklaus ou Dave Thomas, et des vedettes de notre temps comme Kyle Phillips ou David McLay Kidd, signataire de l'ultra-secret Queenwood. Pourtant, si l'Angleterre est l'un des berceaux du golf, peu de grands parcours se sont ouverts depuis quelques années en Angleterre, et même "The Grove", si impressionnante réalisation était une sorte d'hommage aux grands architectes de l'Age d'or anglais dont on ne se lasse pas pas plus que de Shakespeare... ou des Beatles.

Ainsi, plus d'une dizaine de parcours font leur apparition dans ce guide, mais ils ne sont pas forcément très récents, ils expriment au mieux la richesse de l'offre, qui fait que l'on peut préférer un tracé avant de le remplacer le lendemain par un autre. Le golfeur est aussi un être volage.

L'Angleterre compte quelque 1.900 parcours, et beaucoup de bons parcours. Nous ne saurions ainsi prétendre à l'objectivité et certains autres bons tracés nous ont peut-être échappé, mais que les lecteurs soient rassurés, tous les parcours présentés sont, comme on dit en gastronomie, de "bonnes tables". On y trouve les plus grands links, les meilleurs "parkland", les parcours qui figurent dans les grands classements, mais vous découvrirez aussi quelques petits joyaux dont nous espérons que vous serez fier de parler ensuite à vos amis. Et si vous en découvrez encore d'autres, n'hésitez pas à nous le dire... Jamais plus qu'ici il n'a été difficile de faire un choix.

Aldeburgh

14	6	7

Music lovers might like to know that the English composer Benjamin Britten lived alongside this course for many years and that a music festival in his honour continues to be held every June in Aldeburgh's superb Snape Maltings.This course is not a grand tournament layout but it is a pleasant holiday course to be included in any golfing tour around this area. Just avoid coming here after any prolonged dry period because the fairways are not watered and can get very hard. With gorse and heather in the wings, the holes don't look all that wide and the wind will probably prompt you to play this as you would a links course. But don't let the attractive surroundings lower your concentration, either, as there is no shortage of difficulties waiting to make life really complicated. Luckily, inexperienced players can try the 9-hole "River" course to test their progress without getting lost in the heather.

Les amateurs de musique auront une pensée pour le compositeur Benjamin Britten, qui vécut longtemps à côté du golf et dont le festival de musique se perpétue en juin dans les superbes Snape Maltings d'Aldeburgh. Le présent parcours n'est pas un très grand tracé de championnat, mais il reste un parcours de vacances agréable à intégrer dans un festival de golf dans la région, en évitant toutefois les longues périodes de sécheresse car les fairways ne sont pas arrosés. Avec la présence de bruyère et d'ajoncs, les trous ne paraissent pas bien larges, et le vent incite à jouer comme sur des links. Et l'amabilité apparente du site ne doit pas inciter à baisser sa garde, car les difficultés ne manquent pas de compliquer la quiétude du golfeur. Heureusement pour les joueurs peu expérimentés, le 9 trous supplémentaire ("River Course") permet de s'aguerrir sans craindre de se perdre dans la bruyère.

Aldeburgh Golf Club — 1884

Saxmundham Road
ENG - ALDEBURGH, Suffolk IP15 5PE

Office Secrétariat (44) 01728 - 452 890
Pro shop Pro-shop (44) 01728 - 453 309
Fax Fax (44) 01728 - 452 937
Web www.aldeburghgolfclub.co.uk
Situation Situation Aldeburgh, 2 km
Ipswich (pop. 130 157), 38 km
Annual closure Fermeture annuelle no
Weekly closure Fermeture hebdomadaire no

Fees main season Tarifs haute saison — 18 holes

	Week days Semaine	We/Bank holidays We/Férié
Individual Individuel	£ 55	£ 65
Couple Couple	£ 110	£ 130

After 12:00 pm £ 45 and £ 55 (We)

Caddie Caddie no — **Electric Trolley** Chariot électrique no
Buggy Voiturette yes — **Clubs** Clubs yes
Credit cards Cartes de crédit
Visa - Mastercard (Pro shop goods only)

Access Accès : London A12. Ipswich → Felixstowe. Right unto A1094. Course on left of the road before entering Aldeburgh
Map 7 on page 483 Carte 7 Page 483

GOLF COURSE — PARCOURS 14/20

Site Site
Maintenance Entretien
Architect Architecte John Thompson, Willie Fernie
Type Type open country, heathland
Relief Relief
Water in play Eau en jeu
Exp. to wind Exposé au vent
Trees in play Arbres en jeu

Scorecard Carte de score	Chp. Chp.	Mens Mess.	Ladies Da.
Length Long.	5807	5547	5254
Par	68	68	74
Slope system	—	—	—

Advised golfing ability 0 12 24 36
Niveau de jeu recommandé
Hcp required Handicap exigé 24 Men, 28 Ladies

CLUB HOUSE & AMENITIES — CLUB HOUSE ET ANNEXES 6/10

Pro shop Pro-shop
Driving range Practice
Sheltered couvert no - On grass sur herbe yes - Putting-green putting-green yes - Pitching-green pitching green yes

HOTEL FACILITIES — ENVIRONNEMENT HOTELIER 7/10

HOTELS HÔTELS
Wentworth Hotel - 37 rooms, D £ 123 - Aldeburgh 2 km
Tel (44) 01728 - 452 312, Fax (44) 01728 - 454 343

White Lion - 38 rooms, D £ 154 - Aldeburgh 2 km
Tel (44) 01728 - 452 720, Fax (44) 01728 - 452 986

Brudenell - 42 rooms, D £ 130 - Aldeburgh 2 km
Tel (44) 01728 - 452 071, Fax (44) 01728 - 454 082

RESTAURANTS RESTAURANTS

Regatta - Aldeburgh 2 km - Tel (44) 01728 - 452 011

Lighthouse - Aldeburgh 2 km - Tel (44) 01728 - 453377

Alwoodley (The)

18	7	7

The comfortable club-house with its unusual little roof turrets completes what is a remarkable course and a true revelation for anyone who has never played here before. You have to admit that the partnering of Harry Colt and Alister Mackenzie will always appeal to connoisseurs. The greens were recently re-laid along the lines of the original layouts, but to modern American specifications. Likewise, several new tee-boxes have helped to restyle the course without changing any of the strategy involved in coping with hazards. Besides the trees (beautiful in autumn), which come into play only for the really bad shot, the heather and gorse of Wigton moor (always impossible to get out of) and especially bunkers create most of the trouble. On the fairways, finding sand can cost you half a shot. Around the greens, where access is tight, it can cost even more. A demanding course running out and in like a links but the fairest adversary you could hope for. You won't forget it in a long, long while.

Le confort du club-house avec ses toits étranges complète un parcours remarquable qui sera une révélation pour ceux qui l'ignorent. Il faut dire que l'association de Harry Colt et Alister MacKenzie ne peut laisser indifférent les connaisseurs. Les greens ont été récemment refaits suivant les dessins originaux, mais avec les spécifications américaines modernes. De même, quelques nouveaux départs ont permis d'adapter le parcours, sans rien changer à la stratégie par rapport aux obstacles. A côté des bois (superbes en automne) qui ne sont vraiment en jeu que pour les mauvais coups, la bruyère et les ajoncs de cette Lande de Wigton (il est toujours impossible de s'en extraire) et surtout les bunkers constituent l'essentiel des obstacles. Sur les fairways, ils coûtent cher. Près des greens, dont les ouvertures sont rendues assez étroites, ils peuvent en coûter plus encore. Ce parcours est exigeant, en aller-retour comme un links, et constitue l'adversaire le plus loyal qui soit. On s'en souviendra longtemps.

The Alwoodley Golf Club — 1907

Wigton Lane
ENG - LEEDS, Yorkshire LS17 8SA

Office Secrétariat (44) 0113 - 268 1680
Pro shop Pro-shop (44) 0113 - 268 9603
Fax Fax (44) 0113 - 293 9458
Web www.alwoodley.co.uk
Situation Situation Leeds (pop. 680 725), 8 km
Annual closure Fermeture annuelle no
Weekly closure Fermeture hebdomadaire

Fees main season Tarifs haute saison — Full day

	Week days Semaine	We/Bank holidays We/Férié
Individual Individuel	£ 65	£ 80
Couple Couple	£ 130	£ 160

Caddie Caddie yes — **Electric Trolley** Chariot électrique yes
Buggy Voiturette no — **Clubs** Clubs yes
Credit cards Cartes de crédit
VISA - MasterCard

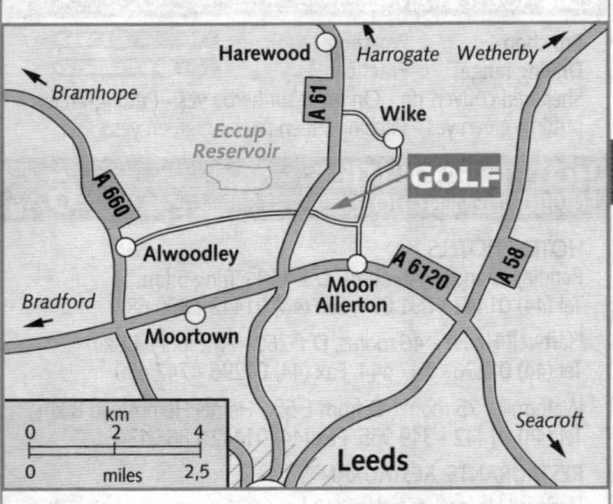

Access Accès : Turn off A61 (→ Harrogate) at traffic lights at Wigton Lane X-roads 8 km N of Leeds.
Map 4 on page 476 Carte 4 Page 476

GOLF COURSE — PARCOURS — 18/20

Site Site
Maintenance Entretien
Architect Architecte — Harry S. Colt, Alister Mackenzie
Type Type — heathland
Relief Relief
Water in play Eau en jeu
Exp. to wind Exposé au vent
Trees in play Arbres en jeu

Scorecard Carte de score	Chp. Chp.	Mens Mess.	Ladies Da.
Length Long.	6107	5690	5097
Par	71	70	73
Slope system	—	—	—

Advised golfing ability Niveau de jeu recommandé — 0 12 24 36
Hcp required Handicap exigé — no

CLUB HOUSE & AMENITIES — CLUB HOUSE ET ANNEXES — 7/10

Pro shop Pro-shop
Driving range Practice
Sheltered couvert practice area - On grass sur herbe yes - Putting-green putting-green yes - Pitching-green pitching green yes

HOTEL FACILITIES — ENVIRONNEMENT HOTELIER — 7/10

HOTELS HÔTELS
The Cottages - 5 rooms, D £ 54 - Bramhope 6 km
Tel (44) 0113 - 284 2754, Fax (44) 0113 - 203 7496

42 The Calls - 41 rooms, D £ 160 - Leeds 8 km
Tel (44) 0113 - 244 0099, Fax (44) 0113 - 234 4100

Queens - 199 rooms, D £ 140 - Leeds 8 km
Tel (44) 0113 - 243 1323, Fax (44) 0113 - 242 5154

RESTAURANTS RESTAURANTS
Pool Court at 42 - Leeds 8 km - Tel (44) 0113 - 244 4242
Leodis - Leeds 8 km - Tel (44) 0113 - 242 1010
Brasserie Forty Four - Leeds 8 km - Tel (44) 0113 - 234 3232

Ashridge

16 | 7 | 6

Not far from the Thames valley, the Chiltern Hills and Whipsnade zoo, the largest wildlife reserve in Europe, Ashridge sits right in the middle of this peaceful, wonderful countryside where the aristocrats of yesteryear built superb estates. The course was opened in 1932 and aside from some remodelling by Tom Simpson has undergone only minor changes since. Not even Henry Cotton, who was the club professional for many a year, could find anything to alter. In a superb parkland setting, the course is wonderfully classical in style with each hole having a distinctly individual character. The club founders obviously had the pleasure of week-end golfers in mind, and only the sometimes high rough represents any significant sort of difficulty. Yardages seem modest although some of the par 4s are designed to set a very serious challenge. A very good course for all players, male and female. As an added bonus you may spy a few herds of deer, a reminder of the distant past when this was a hunting estate, and you should undoubtedly enjoy the comfortable new club-house.

Non loin de la Tamise, des Chiltern Hills, ou de la réserve d'animaux sauvages de Whipsnade, la plus vaste d'Europe, Ashridge est situé au calme dans cette adorable campagne où les familles aristocrates ont bâti de superbes domaines. Depuis 1932, ce parcours n'a fait l'objet que de minimes modifications par Tom Simpson, et pas même d'Henry Cotton, qui fut longtemps le professionnel du club. Dans un superbe environnement de parc, le dessin est d'un classicisme réjouissant, chaque trou ayant pourtant un caractère individuel marqué. Les fondateurs du club ont visiblement pensé surtout au plaisir des amateurs en week-end : seul le rough haut et épais représente une difficulté importante. La longueur semble modeste, mais quelques par 4 présentent de sérieux défis par leur dessin. Un très bon parcours adapté à tous les joueurs... et joueuses ! En prime, quelques hardes de cervidés, témoins d'un passé de grandes chasses dans ce domaine, et un club-house tout neuf et confortable.

Ashridge Golf Club — 1932

Little Gaddesden
ENG - BERKHAMSTED, Herts HP4 1LY

Office	Secrétariat	(44) 01442 - 842 244
Pro shop	Pro-shop	(44) 01442 - 842 307
Fax	Fax	(44) 01442 - 843 770
Web		www.ashridgegolfclub.ltd.uk
Situation	Situation	Aylesbury, 11 km
Annual closure	Fermeture annuelle	no
Weekly closure	Fermeture hebdomadaire	no

Fees main season Tarifs haute saison	18 holes	
	Week days Semaine	**We/Bank holidays** We/Férié
Individual Individuel	£ 57	*
Couple Couple	£ 114	*

* Weekends: no visitors / Full weekdays: £ 79
No Ladies in spike bar

Caddie Caddie no **Electric Trolley** Chariot électrique yes

Buggy Voiturette no **Clubs** Clubs yes

Credit cards Cartes de crédit (Visa & Switch also for GF)
Visa - Eurocard - Mastercard - Switch

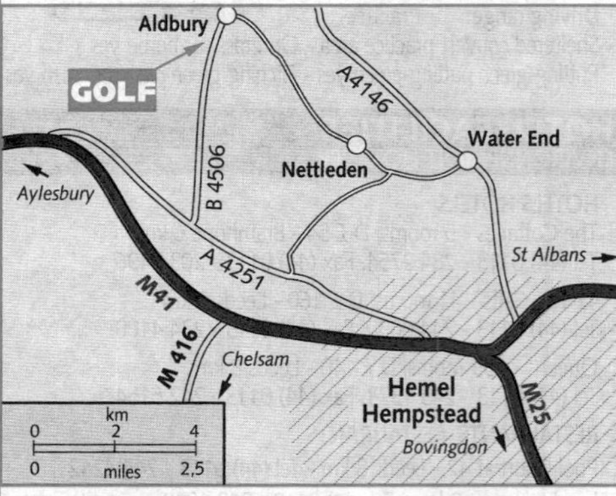

Access Accès : A41 to Berkhamsted. At Northchurch, turn right onto B4506.
Map 8 on page 484 Carte 8 Page 484

GOLF COURSE — PARCOURS — 16/20

Site	Site	
Maintenance	Entretien	
Architect	Architecte	Sir Guy Campbell, C.K. Hutchinson, Hotchkin
Type	Type	parkland
Relief	Relief	
Water in play	Eau en jeu	
Exp. to wind	Exposé au vent	
Trees in play	Arbres en jeu	

Scorecard Carte de score	**Chp.** Chp.	**Mens** Mess.	**Ladies** Da.
Length Long.	5892	5595	5100
Par	72	72	73
Slope system	—	—	—

Advised golfing ability Niveau de jeu recommandé: 0 12 24 36
Hcp required Handicap exigé: certificate

CLUB HOUSE & AMENITIES — CLUB HOUSE ET ANNEXES — 7/10

Pro shop Pro-shop
Driving range Practice
Sheltered couvert no - On grass sur herbe yes - Putting-green putting-green yes - Pitching-green pitching green yes

HOTEL FACILITIES — ENVIRONNEMENT HOTELIER — 6/10

HOTELS HÔTELS
Pendley Manor - 74 rooms, D £ 140 - Tring 5 km
Tel (44) 01442 - 891 891, Fax (44) 01442 - 890 687

Hartwell House - 46 rooms, D £ 260 - Aylesbury 12 km
Tel (44) 01296 - 747 444, Fax (44) 01296 - 747 450

Watermill - 75 rooms, D from £ 55 - Hemel Hempstead 8 km
Tel (44) 01442 - 349 955, Fax (44) 01442 - 866 130

RESTAURANTS RESTAURANTS
Hartwell House - Aylesbury 12 km
Tel (44) 01296 - 747 444
Pendley Manor - Tring 5 km
Tel (44) 01442 - 891 891

Bamburgh Castle

14	5	5

Of course this is not the world's greatest golf course, but how could anyone not marvel at this extraordinary location in a region that was a battleground for the Celts, the Scots, the English and the Vikings? At almost driving distance from the local St. Michael's Mount – Lindisfarne – standing in the shadow of the remains of a castle where the Kings of Northumbria were crowned, this course, or rather the 15th tee, provides a fabulous view over four different castles. Connoisseurs might object to the fact that the layout follows every nook and cranny of the terrain and that it is just placed on top of land rather than worked into it, but it will delight today's growing number of admirers of minimalist architecture. And while hardly a very strategic course, it is a most interesting challenge, at least when it comes to steering clear of verges, heather, gorse and tall grass dotted with wild flowers. Serious students of golf architecture will politely refrain from comment, while lovers of a course that sticks to its origins will be delighted. But everyone will be out of their seats to applaud the spectacle…

Bien sûr, ce n'est pas le plus grand parcours du monde, mais comment ne pas s'émerveiller de cette situation extraordinaire dans une région qui fut le champ de bataille des Celtes, des Ecossais, des Anglais et des Vikings. A portée de drive du Mont-Saint-Michel du lieu, Lindisfarne, à l'ombre des restes d'un château où les rois de Northumbria se faisaient couronner, ce parcours réserve au départ du 15 une vue sur quatre citadelles différentes. On objectera que le tracé suit les ondulations du terrain dans leurs tours et détours, qu'il est davantage posé dessus que vraiment travaillé, mais il plaira à ces fameux partisans (aujourd'hui) d'une architecture minimaliste. Par ailleurs, il n'est guère stratégique, mais pas moins intéressant, au moins pour éviter les bas-côtés, la bruyère, les ajoncs, les herbes hautes parsemées de fleurs sauvages. Les spécialistes de l'architecture se tairont poliment, les amoureux d'un golf près des origines se réjouiront. Et tout le monde se lèvera devant le spectacle !

Bamburgh Castle Golf Club — 1904

The Wynding
ENG - BAMBURGH, Northumberland NE69 7DE

Office	Secrétariat	(44) 01668 - 214 321
Pro shop	Pro-shop	(44) 01668 - 214 378
Fax	Fax	—
Web	www.bamburghcastlegolfclub.org	
Situation	Situation	Newcastle-upon-Tyne, 51 km
Annual closure	Fermeture annuelle	no
Weekly closure	Fermeture hebdomadaire	no

Fees main season Tarifs haute saison		18 holes
	Week days Semaine	We/Bank holidays We/Férié
Individual Individuel	£ 32	£ 37
Couple Couple	£ 64	£ 74

Full day: £ 45 / 50 (We)

Caddie Caddie no — **Electric Trolley** Chariot électrique no
Buggy Voiturette yes — **Clubs** Clubs yes
Credit cards Cartes de crédit
VISA - MasterCard

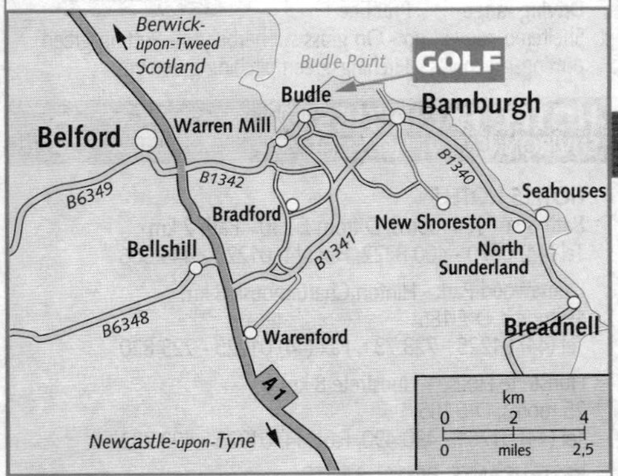

Access Accès : Newcastle-upon-Tyne A1 → Alnwick, then B1341 or 1342 to Bamburgh, golf close to Budle Point
Map 2 on page 473 Carte 2 Page 473

GOLF COURSE — PARCOURS — 14/20

Site	Site	
Maintenance	Entretien	
Architect	Architecte	George Rochester
Type	Type	seaside course
Relief	Relief	
Water in play	Eau en jeu	
Exp. to wind	Exposé au vent	
Trees in play	Arbres en jeu	

Scorecard Carte de score	Chp. Chp.	Mens Mess.	Ladies Da.
Length Long.	5060	4717	4589
Par	68	68	70
Slope system	—	—	—

Advised golfing ability / Niveau de jeu recommandé: 0 12 24 36
Hcp required / Handicap exigé: certificate

CLUB HOUSE & AMENITIES — CLUB HOUSE ET ANNEXES — 5/10

Pro shop Pro-shop
Driving range Practice
Sheltered couvert no - On grass sur herbe yes - Putting-green putting-green yes - Pitching-green pitching green no

HOTEL FACILITIES — ENVIRONNEMENT HOTELIER — 5/10

HOTELS HÔTELS
Lord Crewe Arms - 18 rooms, D £ 98 - Bamburgh, close
Tel (44) 01668 - 214 243, Fax (44) 01668 - 214 273

Waren House - 12 rooms, D £ 130 - Waren Mill 4 km
Tel (44) 01668 - 214 581, Fax (44) 01668 - 214 484

Olde Ship - 18 rooms, D £ 96- Seahouses 6 km
Tel (44) 01665 - 720 200, Fax (44) 01665 - 721 383

RESTAURANTS RESTAURANTS
Lord Crewe Arms - Bamburgh, close - Tel (44) 01668 - 214 243
Waren House - Waren Mill 4 km - Tel (44) 01668 - 214 581
Olde Ship - Seahouses 6 km - Tel (44) 01665 - 720 200

Bath

14	6	9

A famous Roman and Georgian spa city, Bath is one of those places that tourists just have to inspect – the optimum months being May-June, one of the best times to visit England anyway. Very busy at weekends, Bath has several good courses at hand, including this one, near to the interestingly named Sham Castle. Located on high ground (and providing some splendid views) the course is laid out over a former stone quarry where the soil is pleasant to walk and drains easily. Tips from the locals will help you negotiate a number of blind shots and some sloping fairways, avoid some disconcerting kicks and make allowance for wind that can blow your game away. Their help will only increase your enjoyment on what is a rather forgiving course for hackers and beginners, but where better players will need to keep their wits about them if they want to score as well as they hope to. Hardly a major championship course but one with real personality that is well worth getting to know. After your round, go visit the impressive Roman baths in the city centre.

Célèbre ville d'eau depuis les Romains, Bath est à visiter en mai-juin, l'une des plus belles périodes pour venir en Angleterre. Très fréquenté en week-end, Bath a plusieurs bons golfs, dont celui-ci, situé sur les hauteurs – avec de très belles vues – près du Sham Castle (château de l'Imposture!). Tracé sur le site d'anciennes carrières de pierre, il bénéficie d'un sol très agréable et bien drainant. L'aide des joueurs locaux vous aidera à bien négocier quelques coups aveugles et certains fairways en pente, éviter certains rebonds déconcertants, et tenir compte d'un vent qui peut être assez prononcé. Vous n'en apprécierez que mieux ce tracé assez indulgent pour les joueurs moyens ou peu expérimentés, mais les bons joueurs devront rester en éveil pour faire des scores à hauteur de leurs espérances, car les greens sont assez petits et souvent déconcertants. Sans être un parcours de championnat, il présente une personnalité à connaître. Ensuite, allez piquer une tête dans les Bains Romains de la ville.

Bath Golf Club — 1883/1937

Sham Castle, North Road
ENG - BATH, Somerset BA2 6JG

Office Secrétariat (44) 01225 - 463 834
Pro shop Pro-shop (44) 01225 - 466 953
Fax Fax (44) 01225 - 331 027
Web www.bathgolfclub.org.uk
Situation Situation Bristol (pop. 376 146), 20 km
Bath (pop. 78 689), 2 km

Annual closure Fermeture annuelle — no
Weekly closure Fermeture hebdomadaire — Christmas Day

Fees main season Tarifs haute saison	18 holes	
	Week days Semaine	**We/Bank holidays** We/Férié
Individual Individuel	£ 30	£ 36
Couple Couple	£ 60	£ 72

Caddie Caddie no — **Electric Trolley** Chariot électrique yes
Buggy Voiturette no — **Clubs** Clubs yes
Credit cards Cartes de crédit
Visa - Eurocard - Mastercard (Pro shop goods only)

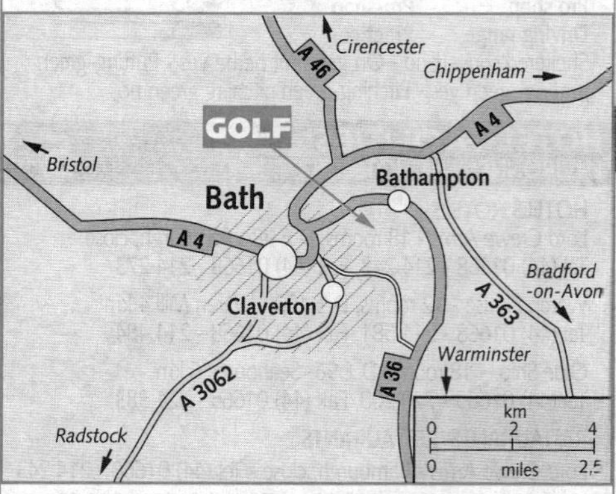

Access Accès : M4 or A36 to Bath. Warminster Road, up North Road, 0,7 km (800 yds) on left up hill. 2 km S of Bath.
Map 6 on page 481 Carte 6 Page 481

GOLF COURSE — PARCOURS — 14/20

Site Site
Maintenance Entretien
Architect Architecte — Harry S. Colt
Type Type — copse, open country
Relief Relief
Water in play Eau en jeu
Exp. to wind Exposé au vent
Trees in play Arbres en jeu

Scorecard Carte de score	Chp. Chp.	Mens Mess.	Ladies Da.
Length Long.	5795	5422	5243
Par	71	71	74
Slope system	—	—	—

Advised golfing ability Niveau de jeu recommandé — 0 12 24 36
Hcp required Handicap exigé — 28 Men, 36 Ladies

CLUB HOUSE & AMENITIES — CLUB HOUSE ET ANNEXES — 6/10

Pro shop Pro-shop
Driving range Practice
Sheltered couvert no - On grass sur herbe yes - Putting-green putting-green yes - Pitching-green pitching green yes

HOTEL FACILITIES — ENVIRONNEMENT HOTELIER — 9/10

HOTELS HÔTELS
Bath Spa - 104 rooms, D from £ 230 - Bath 2 km
Tel (44) 0870 - 400 8222, Fax (44) 01225 - 444 006

Homewood Park - Hinton Charterhouse 8 km
19 rooms, D £ 185
Tel (44) 01225 - 723 731, Fax (44) 01225 - 723 820

Hunstrete House - Hunstrete 8 km
25 rooms, D £ 185
Tel (44) 01761 - 490 490, Fax (44) 01225 - 490 732

RESTAURANTS RESTAURANTS
Mezza Luna - Bath 2 km - Tel (44) 01225 - 466 688
Hole in the Wall - Bath 2 km - Tel (44) 01225 - 425 242
Bath Priory - Bath 2 km - Tel (44) 01225 - 331922

Beau Desert

16	7	7

Opened in 1921 on the estate of Charles Paget, the Earl of Anglesey, Beau Desert is aptly named - not because of any similarity with the Sahara but because this is an idyllic golfing retreat. For French readers, the word "Beau" could very easily be replaced by "Elégant". This masterful Fowler layout embraces a magnificent setting. It strategically utilises the many trees and has bunkers that guard rather than frame greens (a little in the Harry Colt style). This is not a long course but it is narrow, so the choice of club off the tee is important. Most of the time a 3-wood or a long iron will do to get your ball into the right spot for approaching the greens. The rough is generously lined with heather and gorse, as is often the case on a classic heathland course such as this which easily soaks up the rain (rainfalls have been known to occur in this part of the world, even in a Desert). An amusing and little known course.

Ouvert en 1921 sur la propriété de Charles Paget, Marquis d'Anglesey, Beau Desert porte bien son nom. Sauf qu'il ne s'agit pas d'un quelconque Sahara mais plutôt d'un lieu de retraite idyllique. Et si l'on veut traduire "Beau" en français, ce sera le terme d'élégant que l'on utilisera. Le superbe dessin de Fowler s'est bien sûr adapté à un environnement magnifique, utilisant les nombreux arbres de manière stratégique, avec des bunkers qui gardent plus qu'ils n'encadrent (un peu dans le style de Colt). Ce parcours n'est pas bien long, mais il est étroit, ce qui oblige à bien réfléchir sur le club à jouer au départ. La plupart du temps, un bois 3 ou un long fer suffisent pour se placer en bonne position par rapport aux greens. La bruyère et les ajoncs garnissent généreusement les roughs, comme sur ces types de parcours classiques supportant bien la pluie, ce qui semble se produire de temps à autre dans ce pays, même dans un Desert. Un parcours amusant et méconnu.

Beau Desert Golf Club — 1921

Hazel Slade
ENG - CANNOCK, Staffs. WS12 5PJ

Office Secrétariat (44) 01543 - 422 626
Pro shop Pro-shop (44) 01543 - 422 492
Fax Fax (44) 01543 - 451 137
Web www.bdgc.co.uk
Situation Situation Birmingham, 25 km
Cannock (pop. 88 833), 5 km
Annual closure Fermeture annuelle no
Closed first two weeks of April
Weekly closure Fermeture hebdomadaire no

Fees main season Tarifs haute saison — Full day

	Week days / Semaine	We/Bank holidays / We/Férié
Individual Individuel	£ 45	£ 55
Couple Couple	£ 90	£ 110

Caddie Caddie no — **Electric Trolley** Chariot électrique yes
Buggy Voiturette no — **Clubs** Clubs no
Credit cards Cartes de crédit
VISA - Mastercard - AMEX (Pro shop only)

Access Accès : Birmingham, A452 N. A460 Cannock through Hednesford, right at signpost to Hazel Slade, and next left.
Map 7 on page 482 Carte 7 Page 482

GOLF COURSE — PARCOURS 16/20

Site Site
Maintenance Entretien
Architect Architecte Herbert Fowler
Type Type forest, heathland
Relief Relief
Water in play Eau en jeu
Exp. to wind Exposé au vent
Trees in play Arbres en jeu

Scorecard / Carte de score	Chp. / Chp.	Mens / Mess.	Ladies / Da.
Length Long.	5679	5365	4850
Par	71	70	71
Slope system	—	—	—

Advised golfing ability Niveau de jeu recommandé — 0 12 24 36
Hcp required Handicap exigé — certificate

CLUB HOUSE & AMENITIES — CLUB HOUSE ET ANNEXES 7/10

Pro shop Pro-shop
Driving range Practice
Sheltered couvert 10 bays - On grass sur herbe no - Putting-green putting-green yes - Pitching-green pitching green yes

HOTEL FACILITIES — ENVIRONNEMENT HOTELIER 7/10

HOTELS HÔTELS

Roman Way - 56 rooms, D £ 86 - Cannock 5 km
Tel (44) 01543 - 572 121, Fax (44) 01543 - 502 749

Jonathan's - 46 rooms, D £ 125 - Birmingham 25 km
Tel (44) 0121 - 429 3757, Fax (44) 0121 - 434 3107

Fairlawns - 50 rooms, D £ 125 - Aldridge 8 km
Tel (44) 01922 - 455 122, Fax (44) 01922 - 743 210

RESTAURANTS RESTAURANTS

Thrales - Lichfield 10 km - Tel (44) 01543 - 255 091

Chandlers Grande Brasserie - Lichfield 25 km
Tel (44) 01543 - 416688

Simpson's - Birmingham 25 km - Tel (44) 0121 - 454 3434

Berkhamsted

15	7	6

Berkhamsted is one of those courses that is close enough to London to be within easy reach and far enough away so as not to be over-crowded. Even so, you still need to call to book a tee-off time. The new club-house is cosy and comfortable while the landscape is attractive and similar to that at Ashridge, a few miles down the road. The one big difference is that Berkhamsted has no bunkers. This is logical enough in that bunkers traditionally were created by sheep and here there are no sheep, just horses in the woods and lots of people out walking. The absence of sand is largely made good by the absolute necessity to steer clear of the bushes and heather and by the dips that you might call swales, gulleys or grass bunkers. Getting out of them with the desired results is never easy, either. The greens are small and so emphasise the need for accuracy. Worth knowing.

Berkhamsted fait partie de ces clubs assez proches de Londres pour en faciliter l'accès, et assez éloignés pour ne pas être trop surchargés, bien qu'il soit toujours nécessaire de téléphoner à l'avance. Le club-house est à présent tout à fait confortable, le paysage séduisant assez proche de celui d'Ashridge, à quelques kilomètres. Mais avec une grande différence : ici, aucun bunker ! C'est bien logique, les bunkers étaient traditionnellement créés par des moutons, on ne trouve ici que des chevaux dans les bois, et beaucoup de promeneurs... Ce manque de sable est largement compensé par la nécessité impérative d'éviter les buissons et la bruyère, et par des dépressions que l'on peut appeler dépressions ou "bunkers d'herbe," dont il n'est pas facile de s'extraire avec des résultats garantis. Les greens sont petits, ce qui accentue la nécessité d'être précis. Un solide parcours à connaître.

Berkhamsted Golf Club 1890

The Common
ENG - BERKHAMSTED, Herts HP4 2QB

Office Secrétariat (44) 01442 - 865 832
Pro shop Pro-shop (44) 01442 - 865 851
Fax Fax (44) 01442 - 863 730
Web www.berkhamstedgolfclub.co.uk
Situation Situation Berkhamsted, 1.5 km
Hemel Hempstead (pop. 79 235), 8 km

Annual closure Fermeture annuelle no
Weekly closure Fermeture hebdomadaire no

Fees main season Tarifs haute saison 18 holes

	Week days Semaine	We/Bank holidays We/Férié
Individual Individuel	£ 37	£ 45
Couple Couple	£ 74	£ 90

Book in advance / Weekends: visitors after 11.30 am

Caddie Caddie no **Electric Trolley** Chariot électrique no
Buggy Voiturette no **Clubs** Clubs yes
Credit cards Cartes de crédit
Visa - Mastercard

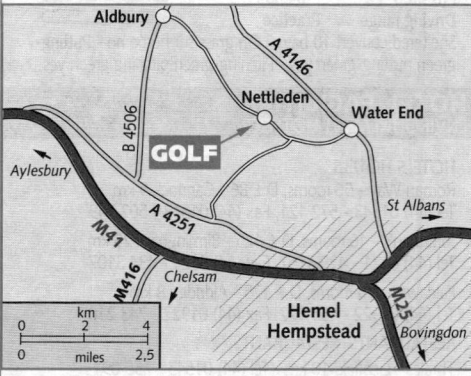

Access Accès : M1, Jct 8 to Hemel Hempstead. At roundabout, take Leighton Buzzard Road. After 4.5 km (3 m.) take Potten End. Turn on left. Golf 4.5 km on left.
Map 8 on page 484 Carte 8 Page 484

GOLF COURSE
PARCOURS 15/20

Site Site
Maintenance Entretien
Architect Architecte G.H. Gowring
Type Type inland, heathland
Relief Relief
Water in play Eau en jeu
Exp. to wind Exposé au vent
Trees in play Arbres en jeu

Scorecard Carte de score	Chp. Chp.	Mens Mess.	Ladies Da.
Length Long.	5945	5580	5161
Par	71	71	73
Slope system	—	—	—

Advised golfing ability 0 12 24 36
Niveau de jeu recommandé
Hcp required Handicap exigé certificate

CLUB HOUSE & AMENITIES
CLUB HOUSE ET ANNEXES 7/10

Pro shop Pro-shop
Driving range Practice
Sheltered couvert practice area - On grass sur herbe yes - Putting-green putting-green yes - Pitching-green pitching green yes

HOTEL FACILITIES
ENVIRONNEMENT HOTELIER 6/10

HOTELS HÔTELS
Pendley Manor - 74 rooms, D £ 140 - Tring 7 km
Tel (44) 01442 - 891 891, Fax (44) 01442 - 890 687

Hartwell House - Aylesbury 10 km
46 rooms, D £ 260
Tel (44) 01296 - 747 444, Fax (44) 01296 - 747 450

Watermill - Hemel Hempstead 8 km
75 rooms, D from £ 55
Tel (44) 01442 - 349 955, Fax (44) 01442 - 866 130

RESTAURANTS RESTAURANTS
Hartwell House - Aylesbury 10 km - Tel (44) 01296 - 747 444
Pendley Manor - Tring 7 km - Tel (44) 01442 - 891 891

Berkshire (The) *Blue Course*

17 | 8 | 7

As it is not always easy to choose between the Red and the Blue courses, play both either side of lunch. The club-house has lost nothing of its charm, retaining an ambience worthy of characters from a P.G. Wodehouse story. The trees, not quite so old but already venerable, are the main setting for this discreet course designed by Herbert Fowler, an equally discreet designer but a real connoisseur of golf (see also Saunton and Walton Heath). The other hazards are fewer in number but just as daunting, for example the heather-clad bunkers or the stream which crosses several fairways. Here you need every club in your bag, a sign of excellence if ever there was one. Green-keeping is always of the highest standard although without reaching the virtually fanatical levels of preparation that you see all too often these days. The Berkshire may not have a "royal" tag but at the very least could be termed "princely".

Comme il n'est pas possible de choisir vraiment entre les deux parcours du Berkshire, il faudra jouer les deux, avec une petite visite pour déjeuner à la mi-temps au club-house dont l'intérieur n'a pas perdu son atmosphère digne des histoires de P.G. Wodehouse. Les arbres (pas si anciens, mais déjà très vénérables) constituent le décor entourant ce parcours sobrement dessiné par Herbert Fowler, architecte discret, mais toujours aussi connaisseur du jeu de golf (voir aussi Saunton ou Walton Heath). Les autres obstacles ne sont pas très nombreux, mais sont toujours efficaces, comme les bunkers flanqués de bruyère ou le ruisseau traversant plusieurs fairways. Ici, on utilise tous les clubs du sac, c'est un signe de qualité. L'entretien y est de grande qualité, sans les excès de préparation quasi maniaque que l'on voit trop souvent aujourd'hui. Berkshire n'est peut-être plus "Royal," mais il vous offre un plaisir "princier", au minimum.

The Berkshire Golf Club — 1928

Swinley Road
ENG - ASCOT, Berks SL5 8AY

Office Secrétariat (44) 01344 - 621 495
Pro shop Pro-shop (44) 01344 - 622 351
Fax Fax —
Web —
Situation Situation Ascot (pop. 15 244), 3 km
Bracknell (pop. 50 325), 5 km
Annual closure Fermeture annuelle no
Weekly closure Fermeture hebdomadaire no

Fees main season / Tarifs haute saison	18 holes	
	Week days / Semaine	We/Bank holidays / We/Férié
Individual Individuel	£ 80	*
Couple Couple	£ 160	*

* No visitors at weekends / Booking essential / 36 holes weekdays: £ 110

Caddie Caddie on request **Electric Trolley** Chariot électrique no
Buggy Voiturette yes **Clubs** Clubs yes
Credit cards Cartes de crédit
Visa - Mastercard (Pro shop goods only)

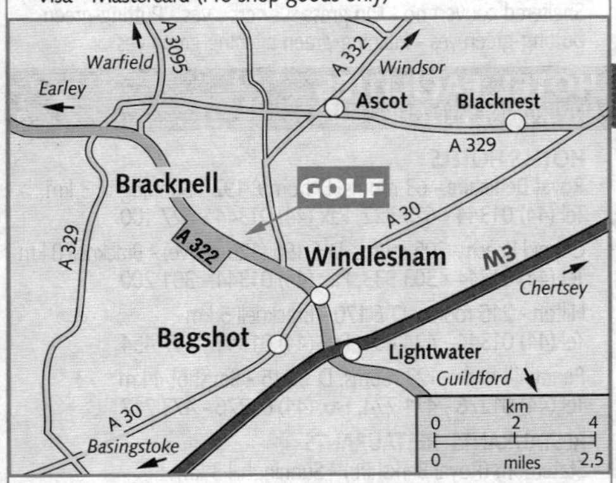

Access Accès : M3 Jct 3. A322 → Bracknell.
A332 on right → Ascot. Club-house 750 m. on left.
Map 8 on page 484 Carte 8 Page 484

GOLF COURSE — PARCOURS 17/20

Site Site
Maintenance Entretien
Architect Architecte Herbert Fowler
Type Type inland, forest
Relief Relief
Water in play Eau en jeu
Exp. to wind Exposé au vent
Trees in play Arbres en jeu

Scorecard / Carte de score	Chp. / Chp.	Mens / Mess.	Ladies / Da.
Length Long.	5635	5420	5077
Par	71	71	73
Slope system	—	—	—

Advised golfing ability / Niveau de jeu recommandé 0 12 24 36
Hcp required Handicap exigé letter from home club

CLUB HOUSE & AMENITIES — CLUB HOUSE ET ANNEXES 8/10

Pro shop Pro-shop
Driving range Practice
Sheltered couvert no - On grass sur herbe yes - Putting-green putting-green yes - Pitching-green pitching green yes

HOTEL FACILITIES — ENVIRONNEMENT HOTELIER 7/10

HOTELS HÔTELS
Royal Berkshire - 63 rooms, D from £ 192 - Sunninghill 3 km
Tel (44) 01344 - 623 322, Fax (44) 01344 - 627 100

Coppid Beech - 205 rooms, D £ 195 (125 at We) - Bracknell 8 km
Tel (44) 01344 - 303 333, Fax (44) 01344 - 301 200

Hilton - 215 rooms, D £ 170 - Bracknell 5 km
Tel (44) 01344 - 424 801, Fax (44) 01344 - 487 454

Pennyhill Park - 123 rooms, D £ 215 - Bagshot 4 km
Tel (44) 01276 - 471 774, Fax (44) 01276 - 473 217

RESTAURANTS RESTAURANTS
Stateroom (Royal Berkshire) - Sunninghill 3 km
Tel (44) 01344 - 623 322
Jade Fountain - Sunninghill 3 km - Tel (44) 01344 - 627 070
Ciao Ninety - Ascot 3 km - Tel (44) 01344 - 622 285

Berkshire (The) *Red Course*

17	8	7

If you have only ever played here once, you will probably be hard pushed to remember whether it was the Blue course or the Red. They are not quite twins but the similarities of landscape and in length can be confusing. Here is some valuable help: if you played six par 5s, six par 3s and six par 4s, then you played the Red course. You will need at least all those par 5s (some are trimmed to par 4s for certain top tournaments) to bag some birdies and recover what you will have almost certainly lost on the par 3s. They are all dangerous and making par can be a real problem should you miss the green. You need a steady game and some straight hitting to do well here, particularly with your longer irons. The pines, chestnut trees and birch trees certainly make for a pretty country setting, but you probably won't find them so appealing when you come to add up your score. And even if you do keep out of the trees, there is still the heather to contend with.

Si vous n'avez joué ici qu'une seule fois, vous avez peu de chances de vous souvenir si c'était le "Blue" ou le "Red." L'un ou l'autre ne sont sans doute pas aussi semblables que des jumeaux, mais même leurs similitudes de longueur peut ajouter à la confusion. Une indication précieuse : si vous avez joué six par 5, six par 3 et six par 4, c'était le "Red." Il faut au moins tous ces par 5 (certains sont ramenés en par 4 dans les grands tournois) pour attraper quelques birdies et récupérer ce que les par 3 vont sans doute vous coûter : ils sont tous dangereux et il est très problématique d'y faire le par si vous manquez le green. Il faut ici un jeu solide et bien droit, savoir bien taper les longs fers, car les pins, les châtaigniers et les bouleaux offrent peut-être un cadre bucolique, mais on ne les aime pas toujours autant quand on totalise les scores. Et les éviter ne signifie pas que l'on évitera la bruyère.

The Berkshire Golf Club — 1928

Swinley Road
ENG - ASCOT, Berks SL5 8AY

Office Secrétariat (44) 01344 - 621 495
Pro shop Pro-shop (44) 01344 - 622 351
Fax Fax —
Web —
Situation Situation Ascot (pop. 15 244), 3 km
Bracknell (pop. 50 325), 5 km
Annual closure Fermeture annuelle no
Weekly closure Fermeture hebdomadaire no

Fees main season Tarifs haute saison	18 holes	
	Week days Semaine	**We/Bank holidays** We/Férié
Individual Individuel	£ 80	*
Couple Couple	£ 160	*

* No visitors at weekends / Booking essential / 36 holes weekdays: £ 110

Caddie Caddie on request **Electric Trolley** Chariot électrique no
Buggy Voiturette yes **Clubs** Clubs yes
Credit cards Cartes de crédit
Visa - Mastercard (Pro shop goods only)

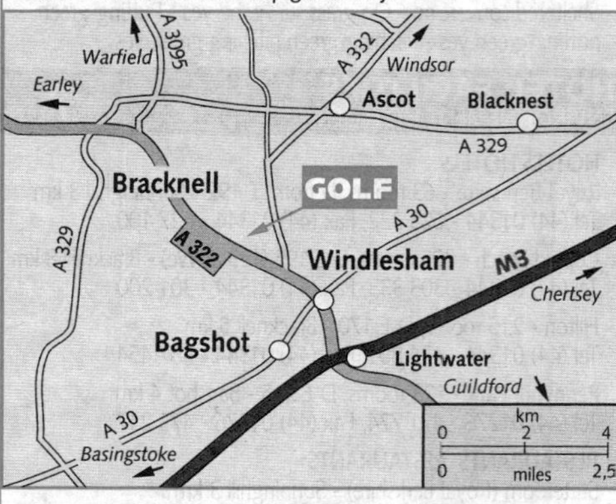

Access Accès : M3 Jct 3. A322 → Bracknell. A332 on right → Ascot. Club-house 750 m. on left.
Map 8 on page 484 Carte 8 Page 484

GOLF COURSE — PARCOURS 17/20

Site Site
Maintenance Entretien
Architect Architecte Herbert Fowler
Type Type inland, forest
Relief Relief
Water in play Eau en jeu
Exp. to wind Exposé au vent
Trees in play Arbres en jeu

Scorecard Carte de score	**Chp.** Chp.	**Mens** Mess.	**Ladies** Da.
Length Long.	5741	5525	5160
Par	72	72	73
Slope system	—	—	—

Advised golfing ability Niveau de jeu recommandé 0 12 24 36
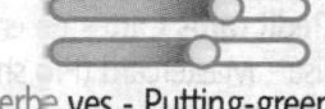
Hcp required Handicap exigé Letter from home club

CLUB HOUSE & AMENITIES — CLUB HOUSE ET ANNEXES 8/10

Pro shop Pro-shop
Driving range Practice
Sheltered couvert no - On grass sur herbe yes - Putting-green putting-green yes - Pitching-green pitching green yes

HOTEL FACILITIES — ENVIRONNEMENT HOTELIER 7/10

HOTELS HÔTELS
Royal Berkshire - 63 rooms, D from £ 192 - Sunninghill 3 km
Tel (44) 01344 - 623 322, Fax (44) 01344 - 627 100
Coppid Beech - 205 rooms, D £ 195 (125 at We) - Bracknell 8 km
Tel (44) 01344 - 303 333, Fax (44) 01344 - 301 200
Hilton - 215 rooms, D £ 170 - Bracknell 5 km
Tel (44) 01344 - 424 801, Fax (44) 01344 - 487 454
Pennyhill Park - 123 rooms, D £ 215 - Bagshot 4 km
Tel (44) 01276 - 471 774, Fax (44) 01276 - 473 217

RESTAURANTS RESTAURANTS
Stateroom (Royal Berkshire) - Sunninghill 3 km
Tel (44) 01344 - 623 322
Jade Fountain - Sunninghill 3 km - Tel (44) 01344 - 627 070
Ciao Ninety - Ascot 3 km - Tel (44) 01344 - 622 285

Berwick-upon-Tweed

15	6	5

A site of endless warring between the English and the Scots, Berwick-upon-Tweed brought peace between both sides and called in designers from both banks of the river Tweed to build a golf course. The site has an unpretentious look to it, an impression that lasts even as far as the club-house, which is simple, functional but hospitable. The course follows the same style with its two loops of nine holes (the outward nine go northward, the inward come back south) and generally flat terrain between Goswick dunes and the countryside. Other courses may be more spectacular, but its somewhat outdated simplicity, a site between the sea and countryside and the peaceful surroundings combine to create an appealing layout. It would be unthinkable not to play here when in the region or even when staying west of Edinburgh. Over the past two years, four greens have been re-laid and the addition of new tee-boxes has given the course a rather more "suitable" length.

Eternel théâtre des guerres entre les Ecossais et les Anglais, Berwick-upon-Tweed a fait la paix pour appeler des architectes des deux bords de la Tweed pour s'occuper du parcours. L'arrivée est sans prétention jusqu'au club-house simple, fonctionnel, accueillant. Le parcours est dans le même style, en deux boucles de neuf trous (l'aller vers le nord, le retour vers le sud) sur terrain généralement plat, entre les dunes de Goswick et la campagne. D'autres parcours sont plus spectaculaires, mais la simplicité un peu surannée de Berwick-upon-Tweed, une situation entre campagne et mer, la tranquillité de la région lui donnent un charme certain. Il est impensable de ne pas le jouer quand on passe à proximité, ou encore lorsque l'on fait un séjour à l'ouest d'Edimbourg. Depuis deux ans, quatre greens ont été refaits, et l'addition de nouveaux départs lui a donné une longueur plus "convenable".

Berwick-upon-Tweed Golf Club — 1890

Goswick, Beal
ENG - BERWICK-UPON-TWEED, Northumberland

Office	Secrétariat	(44) 01289 - 387 256
Pro shop	Pro-shop	(44) 01289 - 387 380
Fax	Fax	(44) 01289 - 387 334
Web	www.goswicklinksgc.co.uk	
Situation	Situation	Berwick-upon-Tweed, 7 km
Annual closure	Fermeture annuelle	no
Weekly closure	Fermeture hebdomadaire	no

Fees main season / Tarifs haute saison	Week days / Semaine	We/Bank holidays / We/Férié
	18 holes	
Individual Individuel	£ 30	£ 38
Couple Couple	£ 60	£ 76

Full day: £ 40 / £ 50 (We)

Caddie Caddie no — Electric Trolley Chariot électrique no

Buggy Voiturette yes — Clubs Clubs yes

Credit cards Cartes de crédit
Visa - Mastercard - Switch (Pro-shop only)

Access Accès : A1 → Berwick-upon-Tweed.

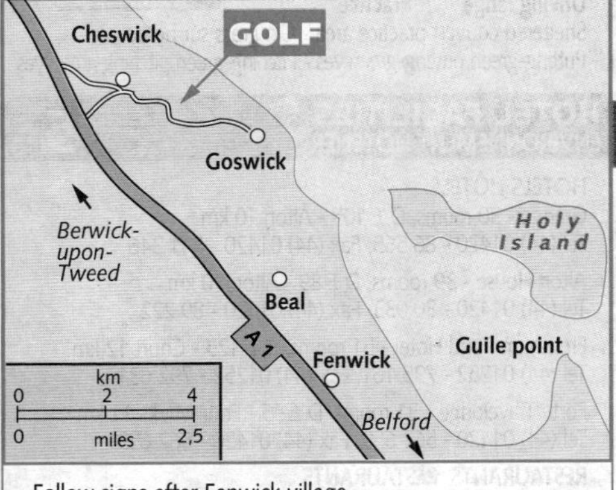

Follow signs after Fenwick village.
Map 2 on page 473 Carte 2 Page 473

GOLF COURSE — PARCOURS 15/20

Site	Site	
Maintenance	Entretien	
Architect	Architecte	James Braid, F. Pennink, D. Steel
Type	Type	links
Relief	Relief	
Water in play	Eau en jeu	
Exp. to wind	Exposé au vent	
Trees in play	Arbres en jeu	

Scorecard / Carte de score	Chp. / Chp.	Mens / Mess.	Ladies / Da.
Length Long.	5816	5665	5018
Par	72	72	74
Slope system	—	—	—

Advised golfing ability / Niveau de jeu recommandé: 0 12 24 36

Hcp required / Handicap exigé: certificate

CLUB HOUSE & AMENITIES — CLUB HOUSE ET ANNEXES 6/10

Pro shop — Pro-shop
Driving range — Practice
Sheltered couvert no - On grass sur herbe yes - Putting-green putting-green yes - Pitching-green pitching green yes

HOTEL FACILITIES — ENVIRONNEMENT HOTELIER 5/10

HOTELS HÔTELS

Marshall Meadows Country House - Berwick 10 km
19 rooms, D £ 115
Tel (44) 01289 - 331 133, Fax (44) 01289 - 331 438

Blue Bell Hotel - 17 rooms, D £ 90 - Belford 10 km
Tel (44) 01668 - 213 543, Fax (44) 01668 - 213 787

Queenshead - 6 rooms, D £ 75 - Berwick 10 km
Tel (44) 01289 - 307 852, Fax (44) 01289 - 307 858

Tillmouth Park - 14 rooms, D £ 125 - Cornhill-on-Tweed 25 km
Tel (44) 01890 - 882 255, Fax (44) 01890 - 882 540

RESTAURANTS RESTAURANTS

Marshall Meadows Country House - Berwick 10 km
Tel (44) 01289 - 331 133

Blackmoor

16	6	5

Golf is not really about preferring such and such a style of course design, as each has its great side and each its shortcomings. What makes golf such a rich game is the diversity of challenge thrown down to the player. Blackmoor is the perfect example of this, being a very carefully thought out and unassuming course without any visual gimmickry. Harry Colt placec the hazards, with emphasis as usual on fairness so you see exactly what needs to be done. Given the amcunt of land available, he preferred a good par 69 to a tricky par 72 and came up with a layout that you will want to play twice in the same day to savour every detail. There are a lot of ditches and wonderfully classical bunkers, heather and ubiquitous trees. That sort of description could apply to many other courses, we agree, but Blackmoor has real personality that you meet and feel out on the course. It is also more challenging than it looks and ends with some brilliant closing holes.

Il n'est pas question de préférer tel ou tel style d'architecture de golf, chacun a sa grandeur et ses défauts. La richesse du golf vient de cette diversité des défis offerts aux joueurs. Blackmoor est un parfait exemple d'une architecture mûrement pensée, mais sans aucun gadget visuel, sans prétention. Harry Colt était le maître du placement des obstacles, mais toujours dans un souci de franchise du parcours: on voit ce que l'on doit accomplir. Ici, compte tenu du terrain disponible, il a préféré un bon par 69 à un par 72 "tricky," et l'on aimera le jouer deux fois dans la journée pour mieux en savourer chaque détail. On trouve ici de nombreux fossés, mais surtout, de manière terriblement classique, les bunkers, la bruyère, les arbres omniprésents : c'est une description que l'on pourrait trouver ailleurs... La personnalité de Blackmoor, vous la trouverez avec votre jeu et votre sensibilité, sur un tracé plus exigeant qu'il n'y paraît, avec un très bon finale.

Blackmoor Golf Club — 1913

Firgrove Road
ENG - WHITEHILL, Hants GU35 9EH

Office Secrétariat (44) 01420 - 472 775
Pro shop Pro-shop (44) 01420 - 472 345
Fax Fax (44) 01420 - 487 666
Web www.blackmoorgolf.co.uk
Situation Situation Liphook, 10 km
Alton (pop. 16 356), 10 km

Annual closure Fermeture annuelle no
Weekly closure Fermeture hebdomadaire no

Fees main season Tarifs haute saison	18 holes	
	Week days Semaine	**We/Bank holidays** We/Férié
Individual Individuel	£ 37	*
Couple Couple	£ 74	*

* Weekends: only with member / Full day: £ 49

Caddie Caddie no — **Electric Trolley** Chariot électrique no
Buggy Voiturette no — **Clubs** Clubs no
Credit cards Cartes de crédit
VISA - MasterCard (not for green fees)

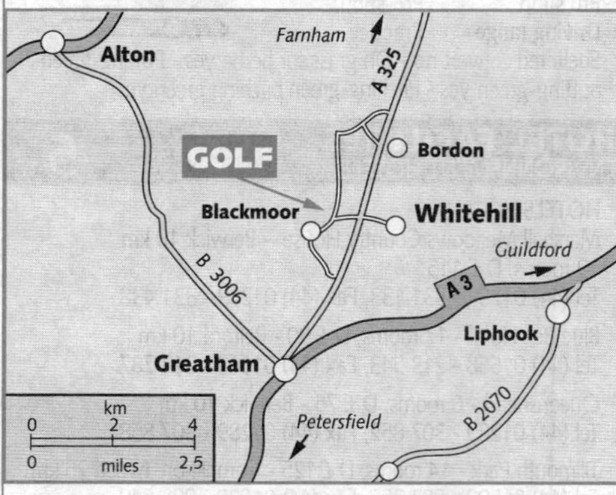

Access Accès : London A3, A31. At signs for Birdworld, A325. Pass Birdworld through Bordon. About 0.75 km out of Bordon, turn right to Blackmoor.
Map 7 on page 482 Carte 7 Page 482

GOLF COURSE — PARCOURS 16/20

Site Site
Maintenance Entretien
Architect Architecte Harry S. Colt
Type Type inland, heathland
Relief Relief
Water in play Eau en jeu
Exp. to wind Exposé au vent
Trees in play Arbres en jeu

Scorecard Carte de score	**Chp.** Chp.	**Mens** Mess.	**Ladies** Da.
Length Long.	5547	5350	5095
Par	69	69	72
Slope system	—	—	—

Advised golfing ability Niveau de jeu recommandé 0 12 24 36
Hcp required Handicap exigé 30

CLUB HOUSE & AMENITIES — CLUB HOUSE ET ANNEXES 6/10

Pro shop Pro-shop
Driving range Practice
Sheltered couvert practice area - On grass sur herbe yes - Putting-green putting-green yes - Pitching-green pitching green yes

HOTEL FACILITIES — ENVIRONNEMENT HOTELIER 5/10

HOTELS HÔTELS

Grange - 30 rooms, D £ 105 - Alton 10 km
Tel (44) 01420 - 86 565, Fax (44) 01420 - 541 346

Alton House - 39 rooms, D £ 89 - Alton 10 km
Tel (44) 01420 - 80 033, Fax (44) 01420 - 89 222

Frensham Pond Hotel - 51 rooms, D £ 125 - Churt 12 km
Tel (44) 01252 - 795 161, Fax (44) 01252 - 792 631

Forte Travelodge - 31 rooms, D £ 55 - Four Marks 11 km
Tel (44) 01420 - 562 659, Fax (44) 01420 - 562 659

RESTAURANTS RESTAURANTS

Yew Tree - Four Marks 15 km - Tel (44) 01256 - 389 224
Grange - Alton 10 km - Tel (44) 01420 - 86 565

Bolton Old Links

15 | 5 | 7

Despite the name, this course has neither the sub-soil nor the topography of a real links (it is laid out on the side of a hill). Close to Manchester, it is still a real change of surroundings for local players except for the few old factory chimneys you can see in the distance. Bolton Old Links actually lies in some pretty English countryside, full of trees, bushes and a few old flint walls, particularly on the 12th hole where there is also a ravine waiting to ruin your card. Note, too, the small and sloping greens on the short par 4s, and the overall difficulty of the putting surfaces in general (the 17th, for instance). Here lie the origins of some of the greens at Augusta, Alister Mackenzie being involved with both layouts. This is one of the region's finest tests of golf where, at least for the first time out, you shouldn't bother counting your score. Have fun, bearing in mind that the holes run in all directions and require a little forethought about exposure to the wind (a common factor here) and where it is coming from.

Ce n'est un vrai "links" ni par le sol, ni par le relief (il est à flanc de colline), mais on donna longtemps aux parcours cette dénomination, par extension. Situé près de Manchester, il est pourtant dépaysant, à part quelques cheminées d'usine au loin. Bolton Old Links est dans une jolie campagne anglaise, avec plein d'arbres et de buissons, quelques vieux murs de pierre, entre autres au 12, qui comprend également un ravin où votre score peut se perdre. A noter encore, la petite taille et les pentes des greens sur les par 4 courts, mais aussi leur difficulté générale (le 17...). On peut retrouver là l'origine du dessin de quelques greens d'Augusta, auxquels Alister Mackenzie a également si efficacement participé. C'est un des meilleurs tests de golf de la région. La première fois, on ne compte pas son score, et on s'amuse beaucoup. On remarquera que les trous vont dans toutes les directions, ce qui remet en question chaque coup selon le vent (qui n'est pas rare) et l'exposition des trous.

Bolton Old Links Golf Club — 1891

Chorley Old Road
ENG - BOLTON, Gtr Manchester BL1 5SU

Office	Secrétariat	(44) 01204 - 842 307
Pro shop	Pro-shop	(44) 01204 - 843 089
Fax	Fax	—
Web	www.boltonoldlinks.co.uk	
Situation	Situation	Bolton (pop. 258 584), 5 km
Annual closure	Fermeture annuelle	no
Weekly closure	Fermeture hebdomadaire	no

Fees main season Tarifs haute saison	Full day	
	Week days Semaine	**We/Bank holidays** We/Férié
Individual Individuel	£ 30	£ 40*
Couple Couple	£ 60	£ 80*

* Sunday, only with a reservation

Caddie Caddie no — **Electric Trolley** Chariot électrique no
Buggy Voiturette yes — **Clubs** Clubs no
Credit cards Cartes de crédit
Visa - Eurocard - Mastercard - AMEX - DC (Pro shop only)

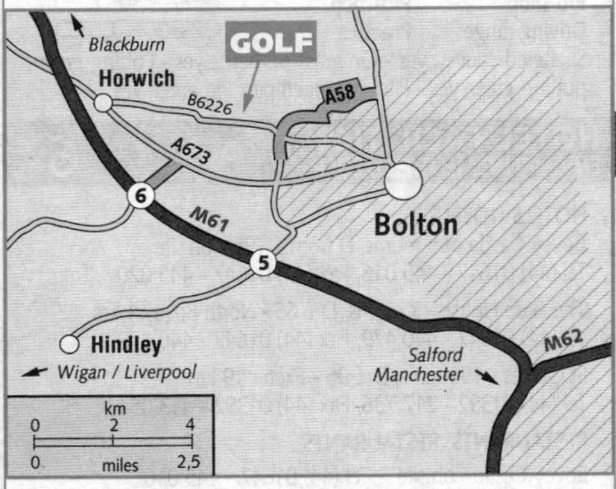

Access Accès : M61 Jct 5, A58 North, then B6226
Map 4 on page 476 Carte 4 Page 476

GOLF COURSE — PARCOURS — 15/20

Site	Site	
Maintenance	Entretien	
Architect	Architecte	Alister Mackenzie
Type	Type	inland, open country
Relief	Relief	
Water in play	Eau en jeu	
Exp. to wind	Exposé au vent	
Trees in play	Arbres en jeu	

Scorecard Carte de score	**Chp.** Chp.	**Mens** Mess.	**Ladies** Da.
Length Long.	5857	5540	5005
Par	72	70	74
Slope system	—	—	—

Advised golfing ability Niveau de jeu recommandé — 0 12 24 36
Hcp required Handicap exigé — certificate

CLUB HOUSE & AMENITIES — CLUB HOUSE ET ANNEXES — 5/10

Pro shop Pro-shop
Driving range Practice
Sheltered couvert 2 indoor nets - On grass sur herbe yes - Putting-green putting-green yes - Pitching-green pitching green no

HOTEL FACILITIES — ENVIRONNEMENT HOTELIER — 7/10

HOTELS HÔTELS
Bolton Moat House - 130 rooms, D from £ 99 - Bolton 5 km
Tel (44) 01204 - 879 988, Fax (44) 01204 - 380 777

Last Drop Village - 128 rooms, D £ 110 - Bromley Cross 5 km
Tel (44) 01204 - 591 131, Fax (44) 01204 - 304 122

New Pack Horse - 68 rooms, D £ 70 - Bolton 6 km
Tel (44) 01204 - 527 261, Fax (44) 01204 - 364 352

RESTAURANTS RESTAURANTS
Bolton Moat House - Bolton 5 km - Tel (44) 01204 - 383 338
Last Drop Village - Bromley Cross 5 km
Tel (44) 01204 - 591 131

Bovey Castle

15	8	6

This is "Hound of the Baskervilles" country on Dartmoor, the land of prehistoric remains, wild ponies, lingering mist, the charming village of Buckland-in-the-Moor, ruins, waterfalls and antique-dealers. Plus Bovey Castle, a manor-cum-hotel run like only the Engl sh know how with a multitude of things to do for people who don't like golf. Things like archery, horse-riding, fly-fishing, 4x4 driving… and other fun activities for children. This course, designed by J-F Abercromby, was seriously restyled by Steel and Mackenzie in 2003, but it happily winds its way through a most attractive landscape that features its fair share of rough ground and pretty water hazards. It is definitely not very long but a par 70 makes this a decent test for the average amateur golfer. And as the people who can afford to come here often have more money than top-rate golfing virtuosity, they will find this to be a varied and worthy adversary: 18 amusing and picturesque holes and simply sumptuous facilities for after the round.

Nous voici au pays du "Chien des Baskerville", dans la lande de Dartmoor où l'on trouve des vestiges préhistoriques, des poneys sauvages et heureux, de la brume, le charmant village de Buckland-in-the-Moor, des ruines et des cascades, des antiquaires. Et Bovey Castle, un manoir-hôtel comme seuls les anglais savent les faire avec une multitude d'activités pour ceux qui n'aiment pas le golf : tir à l'arc, équitation, pêche à la mouche, 4x4... et les enfants ne sont pas oubliés. Le présent parcours d'Abercromby a été sérieusement remanié par Steel et Mackenzie en 2003, et s'insinue avec bonheur dans un environnement aussi typique que superbe, assez escarpé par moments, avec quelques jolis obstacles d'eau. Il n'est pas très long, mais son par 70 en fait un test respectable pour les amateurs. Ceux qui peuvent venir ici ayant souvent plus de moyens qu'un très haut niveau golfique, ils trouveront là un adversaire varié, 18 trous amusants et pittoresques, et un 19ème trou tout à fait somptueux.

Bovey Castle — 1926

North Bovey
ENG - DARTMOOR NATIONAL PARK, Devon TQ13 8RE

Office	Secrétariat	(44) 01647 - 445 016
Pro shop	Pro-shop	(44) 01647 - 445 016
Fax	Fax	(44) 01647 - 445 020
Web		www.boveycastle.com
Situation	Situation	Exeter (pop. 106 775), 19 km
Annual closure	Fermeture annuelle	no
Weekly closure	Fermeture hebdomadaire	no

Fees main season / Tarifs haute saison	Week days / Semaine	We/Bank holidays / We/Férié
Full day		
Individual Individuel	£ 117,5	£ 117,5
Couple Couple	£ 235	£ 235

Caddie Caddie no — Electric Trolley Chariot électrique no
Buggy Voiturette yes — Clubs Clubs yes
Credit cards Cartes de crédit
VISA - MasterCard - AMEX

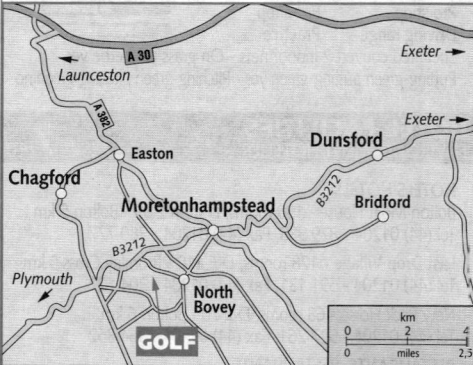

Access Accès : M5 to Exeter, Jct 31 onto the A30 (→ Okehampton). First exit to B3212 into Moretonhampsted (10 m./ 16 km). Go straight through Moretonhampsted → Postbridge. Bovey Castle 1,5 miles on the left.
Map 6 on page 480 Carte 6 Page 480

GOLF COURSE — PARCOURS 15/20

Site	Site	
Maintenance	Entretien	
Architect	Architecte	John Abercromby D. Steel, T. Mackenzie
Type	Type	hilly, moorland
Relief	Relief	
Water in play	Eau en jeu	
Exp. to wind	Exposé au vent	
Trees in play	Arbres en jeu	

Scorecard / Carte de score	Chp. / Chp.	Mens / Mess.	Ladies / Da.
Length Long.	6000	5670	5059
Par	70	70	68
Slope system	—	—	—

Advised golfing ability / Niveau de jeu recommandé: 0 12 24 36
Hcp required / Handicap exigé: no

CLUB HOUSE & AMENITIES — CLUB HOUSE ET ANNEXES 8/10

Pro shop — Pro-shop
Driving range — Practice
Sheltered couvert yes - On grass sur herbe yes - Putting-green putting-green yes - Pitching-green pitching green yes

HOTEL FACILITIES — ENVIRONNEMENT HOTELIER 6/10

HOTELS HÔTELS

Bovey Castle - 65 rooms, D from £ 195 - on site
Tel (44) 01647 - 445 016, Fax (44) 01647 - 445 020

The Gate House - 3 rooms, D £ 66 - North Bovey 1 km
Tel (44) 01647 - 440 479, Fax (44) 01647 - 440 479

St Olaves - 15 rooms, D £ 95 - Exeter 19 km
Tel (44) 01392 - 217 736, Fax (44) 01392 - 413 054

RESTAURANTS RESTAURANTS

Bovey Castle - on site - Tel (44) 01647 - 445 016
Michael Caines - Exeter 19 km - Tel (44) 01392 - 310 031

Bowood (Cornwall)

15 | 7 | 6

Although Cornwall is traditionally associated with great links courses, recent additions such as St Mellion have been designed in rather different landscapes. The same goes for Bowood (not to be confused with the Bowood in Wiltshire), a recent course opened in 1992. Laid out in what was once the Black Prince's hunting estate, there are a lot of trees, an unusual feature in Cornwall, many of which the designers have generously brought into play. The style is generally rather British (i.e. more subtle than 'in your face') although there are any number of water hazards in play that most beginners will find rather intimidating, particularly Allen's river on the 12th which has an island green. Having said that, the difficulties are not insurmountable as long as you can get the ball cleanly up in the air, especially on the 7th hole, a very long par 5. The club-house is huge with pretty views over a country landscape and provides 31 hotel rooms to cater to visitors, most of which overlook the course.

Si l'on associe la Cornouailles avec les grands links, c'est aller un peu vite car de récentes réalisations comme St Mellion se sont incrites dans des paysages tout différents. C'est le cas de ce Bowood (ne pas confondre avec celui du Wiltshire) ouvert en 1992. Situé dans un ancien domaine de chasse du Prince Noir, on y trouve beaucoup d'arbres (c'est inhabituel dans la région), généreusement mis en jeu par les architectes. Le style est resté assez britannique (le dessin est beaucoup plus subtil qu'agressif) bien qu'il y ait une multitude d'obstacles d'eau en jeu que les débutants trouveront intimidants, notamment la rivière Allen au 12 avec un green en île. Cela dit, les difficultés ne sont pas insurmontables... si l'on sait porter la balle, en particulier au 7, un très long par 5. Le club-house est immense, avec de jolies vues sur un paysage rural, et propose 31 chambres d'hôtel pour recevoir les visiteurs, dont la plupart dominent le parcours.

Bowood Golf Club — 1992

Valley Truckle, Lanteglos
ENG - CAMELFORD, Cornwall PL32 9RF

Office	Secrétariat	(44) 01840 - 213 017
Pro shop	Pro-shop	(44) 01840 - 213 017
Fax	Fax	(44) 01840 - 212 622
Web	www.bowoodpark.com	
Situation	Situation	Plymouth, 65 km

Newquay (pop. 7 390), 40 km

Annual closure	Fermeture annuelle	no
Weekly closure	Fermeture hebdomadaire	no

Fees main season Tarifs haute saison — 18 holes

	Week days Semaine	We/Bank holidays We/Férié
Individual Individuel	£ 30	£ 40
Couple Couple	£ 60	£ 80

Full day: £ 40 and £ 50 (We)

Caddie Caddie no — **Electric Trolley** Chariot électrique no
Buggy Voiturette yes — **Clubs** Clubs yes

Credit cards Cartes de crédit (Pro-shop goods & restaurant only) VISA - Eurocard - MasterCard - AMEX - DC

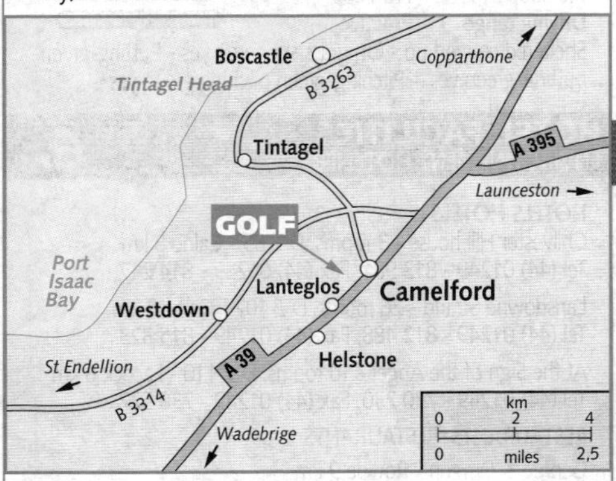

Access Accès : M5, Jct 31 (Exeter), then A30. After Launceston, A395, then A39 South through Camelford. 2 km (1 1/4 m.), turn right on B3266 → Tintagel. First left after garage.
Map 6 on page 480 Carte 6 Page 480

GOLF COURSE — PARCOURS — 15/20

Site	Site	
Maintenance	Entretien	
Architect	Architecte	Brian Huggett Knott/Bridge
Type	Type	copse, parkland
Relief	Relief	
Water in play	Eau en jeu	
Exp. to wind	Exposé au vent	
Trees in play	Arbres en jeu	

Scorecard Carte de score	Chp. Chp.	Mens Mess.	Ladies Da.
Length Long.	6090	5731	5188
Par	72	72	72
Slope system	—	—	—

Advised golfing ability Niveau de jeu recommandé — 0 12 24 36
Hcp required Handicap exigé — certificate

CLUB HOUSE & AMENITIES — CLUB HOUSE ET ANNEXES — 7/10

Pro shop Pro-shop
Driving range Practice
Sheltered couvert 9 bays - On grass sur herbe no - Putting-green putting-green yes - Pitching-green pitching green yes

HOTEL FACILITIES — ENVIRONNEMENT HOTELIER — 6/10

HOTELS HÔTELS

Wootons Country Hotel - 10 rooms, D £ 70- Tintagel 9 km
Tel (44) 01840 - 770 170, Fax (44) 01840 - 770 978

Bottreaux House - 8 rooms, D £ 80 - Boscastle 9 km
Tel (44) 01840 - 250 231, Fax (44) 01840 - 250 170

Wellington Hotel - 15 rooms, D £ 76 - Boscastle 12 km
Tel (44) 01840 - 250 202, Fax (44) 01840 - 250 621

Bowood Club-house - 23 rooms, D £ 78 - on site
Tel (44) 01840 - 213 017

RESTAURANTS RESTAURANTS

Port William - Tintagel 8 km - Tel (44) 01840 - 770 230
Bottreaux House - Boscastle 12 km - Tel (44) 01840 - 250 231

Bowood G&CC

17 | 6 | 6

Are today's course designers, we might ask, incapable of producing approaches to greens that call for the good old "bump 'n run" shot? Or do they go for the easier option of placing hazards that force players to pitch directly onto the greens? We're sorry that Dave Thomas was unable or chose not to preserve this very British feature here, but his style blends well with the modernity probably required for this sort of course. Bowood is an ambitious layout of a high standard overall where the par 5s are excellent, the greens remarkably well defended and where you need to play several rounds before understanding the ins and outs of a very imaginative layout. One word of advice, however: unless you drive straight and long, keep away from the back tees, play further forward and have fun. An impressive course which is exciting to play, but perhaps not for those continental Europeans who are looking for the traditional English approach to golf – right down to the worn tweeds and plus fours.

Les architectes d'aujourd'hui ne sauraient-ils plus dessiner des approches de greens permettant de faire les "bump 'n run" ? C'est plus difficile que de mettre des obstacles obligeant à faire des coups levés directement sur les greens. On regrette que Dave Thomas n'ait pas pu ou pas voulu conserver cet art très britannique, même si son style s'adapte bien à la modernité probablement souhaitée dans ce genre de réalisation. Bowood est un tracé ambitieux, de haute qualité générale, où les par 5 sont très réussis, où les greens sont remarquablement défendus, et où il faut jouer plusieurs fois avant de comprendre les subtilités d'un dessin très imaginatif. Un conseil cependant, ne partez pas des départs reculés, à moins de driver fort et droit. Choisissez de vous amuser, avant tout. Un ensemble impressionnant, passionnant à jouer, mais sans doute moins pour les continentaux qui vénèrent le côté old fashioned et tweed râpé, un peu rare ici.

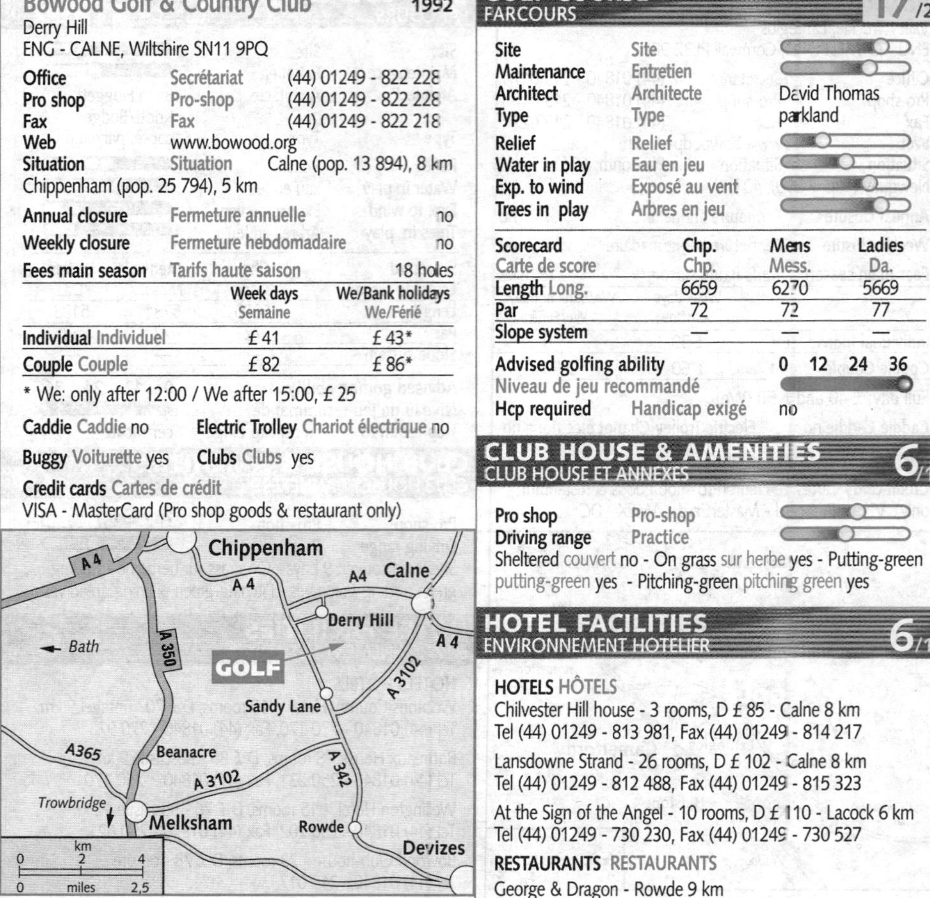

Bowood Golf & Country Club — 1992

Derry Hill
ENG - CALNE, Wiltshire SN11 9PQ

Office	Secrétariat	(44) 01249 - 822 228
Pro shop	Pro-shop	(44) 01249 - 822 228
Fax	Fax	(44) 01249 - 822 218
Web		www.bowood.org
Situation	Situation	Calne (pop. 13 894), 8 km

Chippenham (pop. 25 794), 5 km

Annual closure	Fermeture annuelle	no
Weekly closure	Fermeture hebdomadaire	no

Fees main season Tarifs haute saison	18 holes	
	Week days Semaine	We/Bank holidays We/Férié
Individual Individuel	£ 41	£ 43*
Couple Couple	£ 82	£ 86*

* We: only after 12:00 / We after 15:00, £ 25

Caddie Caddie no — **Electric Trolley** Chariot électrique no

Buggy Voiturette yes — **Clubs** Clubs yes

Credit cards Cartes de crédit
VISA - MasterCard (Pro shop goods & restaurant only)

Access Accès : M4 Exit 16, then A420, A3102 to Calne, then A4. At T-junction, turn left → Derry Hill, Golf on left side.
Map 6 on page 481 Carte 6 Page 481

GOLF COURSE — PARCOURS — 17/20

Site	Site	
Maintenance	Entretien	
Architect	Architecte	David Thomas
Type	Type	parkland
Relief	Relief	
Water in play	Eau en jeu	
Exp. to wind	Exposé au vent	
Trees in play	Arbres en jeu	

Scorecard Carte de score	Chp. Chp.	Mens Mess.	Ladies Da.
Length Long.	6659	6270	5669
Par	72	72	77
Slope system	—	—	—

Advised golfing ability Niveau de jeu recommandé — 0 12 24 36

Hcp required Handicap exigé — no

CLUB HOUSE & AMENITIES — CLUB HOUSE ET ANNEXES — 6/10

Pro shop Pro-shop
Driving range Practice
Sheltered couvert no - On grass sur herbe yes - Putting-green putting-green yes - Pitching-green pitching green yes

HOTEL FACILITIES — ENVIRONNEMENT HOTELIER — 6/10

HOTELS HÔTELS

Chilvester Hill house - 3 rooms, D £ 85 - Calne 8 km
Tel (44) 01249 - 813 981, Fax (44) 01249 - 814 217

Lansdowne Strand - 26 rooms, D £ 102 - Calne 8 km
Tel (44) 01249 - 812 488, Fax (44) 01249 - 815 323

At the Sign of the Angel - 10 rooms, D £ 110 - Lacock 6 km
Tel (44) 01249 - 730 230, Fax (44) 01249 - 730 527

RESTAURANTS RESTAURANTS

George & Dragon - Rowde 9 km
Tel (44) 01380 - 723 053

At the Sign of the Angel - Lacock 6 km
Tel (44) 01249 - 730 230

Brampton

16 | 7 | 6

Like nearby Carlisle, this is another little known "gem of a course." The real challenge is finding the opportunity to drive as far as this region and the intuition to stop off here. At 1,000 ft. above sea level, the course provides some splendid views over the Lake District peaks which soon soothe your sorely tested golfer's nerves. In fact the whole course gives an impression of peace and tranquillity. This is a typical James Braid layout, where the purity of style - there is nothing superfluous on this course - is plain to see: few fairway bunkers, careful thought required for each shot, punishment in keeping with the errors of your ways and just rewards for the good shot. You can pitch high balls into the greens but the wisest decision will always be to roll the ball up to the pin (or thereabouts). Fair (despite a few blind shots), and honestly straightforward, the course is rather hilly and at least looks tiring to play. We say "looks" because senior members walk it several times a week. A warm welcome here, both on the course and in the recently refurbished club-house.

Comme son voisin Carlisle, voici encore un petit joyau méconnu. Le plus difficile, c'est de trouver l'occasion de venir dans cette région, et l'intuition pour s'y arrêter. A 300 mètres d'altitude, Brampton offre des vues superbes sur les montagnes du Lake District, qui vous calmeront vite si vous êtes arrivé sur les nerfs. Tout comme le parcours vous donnera une sensation de paix. C'est un des plus typiques de James Braid. La pureté de son style, où rien n'est inutile, transparaît ici : peu de bunkers de fairway, une exigence de réflexion avant chaque coup, des punitions à la hauteur des fautes, et des récompenses pour les bons coups. Arrivés à proximité des greens, vous aurez la possibilité de faire des balles levées, mais la bonne décison consiste à la faire rouler. Franc (malgré quelques coups aveugles), direct et clair, ce parcours est assez accidenté et paraît fatigant, mais les membres seniors le jouent à pied plusieurs fois par semaine… Un club aussi accueillant que son club-house, récemment rénové.

Brampton Golf Club — 1920

Tarn Road
ENG - BRAMPTON, Cumbria CA8 1HN

Office	Secrétariat	(44) 016977 - 2255
Pro shop	Pro-shop	(44) 016977 - 2000
Fax	Fax	(44) 016977 - 41487
Web	www.bramptongolfclub.com	
Situation	Situation	Carlisle (pop. 100 562), 15 km
Annual closure	Fermeture annuelle	no
Weekly closure	Fermeture hebdomadaire	no
Fees main season	Tarifs haute saison	18 holes

	Week days Semaine	We/Bank holidays We/Férié
Individual Individuel	£ 26	£ 32
Couple Couple	£ 52	£ 64

Full day: £ 30 and £ 38 (We)

Caddie Caddie no **Electric Trolley** Chariot électrique yes

Buggy Voiturette yes (book before) **Clubs** Clubs yes

Credit cards Cartes de crédit
Visa - Mastercard - AMEX (Pro shop goods only)

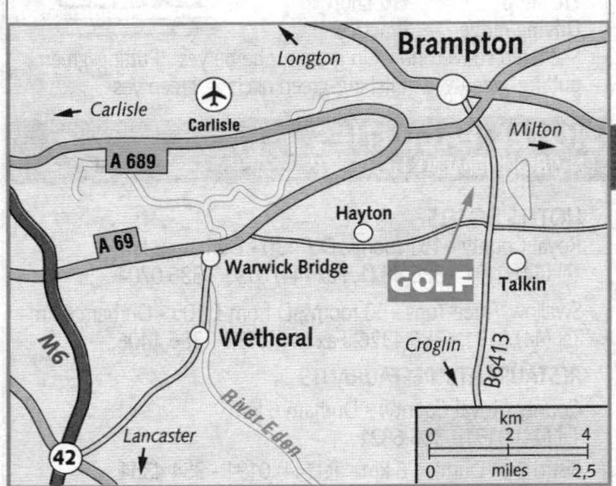

Access Accès : M6 to Carlisle. Jct 43, then A69. At Brampton, B6413 → Castle Carrock. Golf on right side.
Map 2 on page 473 Carte 2 Page 473

GOLF COURSE — PARCOURS — 16/20

Site	Site	
Maintenance	Entretien	
Architect	Architecte	James Braid
Type	Type	parkland
Relief	Relief	
Water in play	Eau en jeu	
Exp. to wind	Exposé au vent	
Trees in play	Arbres en jeu	

Scorecard Carte de score	Chp. Chp.	Mens Mess.	Ladies Da.
Length Long.	5766	5475	4930
Par	72	72	74
Slope system	—	—	—

Advised golfing ability — 0 12 24 36
Niveau de jeu recommandé

Hcp required Handicap exigé no

CLUB HOUSE & AMENITIES — CLUB HOUSE ET ANNEXES — 7/10

Pro shop Pro-shop
Driving range Practice

Sheltered couvert no - On grass sur herbe yes - Putting-green putting-green yes - Pitching-green pitching green yes

HOTEL FACILITIES — ENVIRONNEMENT HOTELIER — 6/10

HOTELS HÔTELS
Farlam Hall - 12 rooms, D £ 260 (w. dinner) - Brampton 3 km
Tel (44) 016977 - 46 234, Fax (44) 016977 - 46 683

Crown Hotel - 51 rooms, D from £ 110 - Wetheral 5 km
Tel (44) 01228 - 561 888, Fax (44) 01228 - 561 637

Crown + Mitre - 94 rooms, D £ 98 - Carlisle 15 km
Tel (44) 01228 - 525 491, Fax (44) 01228 - 514 553

RESTAURANTS RESTAURANTS
The Weary Sportsman (Pub) - Castle Carrock 5 km
Tel (44) 016977- 670 230

No 10 - Carlisle 15 km - Tel (44) 01228 - 524 183

Gallo Rosso - Carlisle 15 km - Tel (44) 01228 - 526 037

Brancepeth Castle

15 | 6 | 5

Before even thinking about a round of golf here, you come to this region to visit Durham, which has retained many vestiges of the Norman conquest, including a castle and an amazing cathedral which in many ways is quite unique. But this course is not to be outshone, laid out as it is around a castle flanked by a church, which both add to the majesty of what is a fine Harry Colt design. A good number of isolated trees make their presence very much felt and seem to detach themselves from the woods to make you bend the ball around them. A largé ravine is another hazard that has to be crossed three times over a wobbly bridge which surely could never take more than twenty players at a time. A very interesting and sometimes surprising course, where the finishing holes should be handled with the utmost care. The whole site is quite superb, so who could ask for more, Oliver?

Avant de venir pour le golf, on vient d'abord dans la région pour visiter Durham, qui conserve de multiples traces de la conquête normande, dont le château et surtout une cathédrale étonnante, avec certains aspects décoratifs uniques. Ce parcours n'est pas en reste, car il a trouvé place auprès d'un château flanqué de son église, ce qui apporte plus encore de majesté au beau dessin de Harry Colt. De nombreux arbres isolés sont bien présents, et se détachent parfois comme les gardes des bois environnants, obligeant à travailler souvent la balle. Un grand ravin a été également mis en jeu par l'architecte, et doit être traversé trois fois sur un pont qui ne peut sûrement pas supporter 50 personnes à la fois. Un parcours très intéressant, parfois surprenant, et dont les derniers trous doivent être considérés avec attention. L'endroit est superbe, que demander de plus ?

Brancepeth Castle Golf Club — 1924

Brancepeth Village
ENG - DURHAM, Durham DH7 8EA

Office	Secrétariat	(44) 0191 - 378 0075
Pro shop	Pro-shop	(44) 0191 - 378 0183
Fax	Fax	(44) 0191 - 378 3835
Web	—	
Situation	Situation	Durham (pop. 36 937), 6 km
Annual closure	Fermeture annuelle	no
Weekly closure	Fermeture hebdomadaire	no

Fees main season Tarifs haute saison — 18 holes

	Week days / Semaine	We/Bank holidays / We/Férié
Individual Individuel	£ 30	£ 40
Couple Couple	£ 60	£ 70

Full week day: £ 35

Caddie Caddie no — **Electric Trolley** Chariot électrique no

Buggy Voiturette no — **Clubs** Clubs no

Credit cards Cartes de crédit
VISA - Eurocard - MasterCard

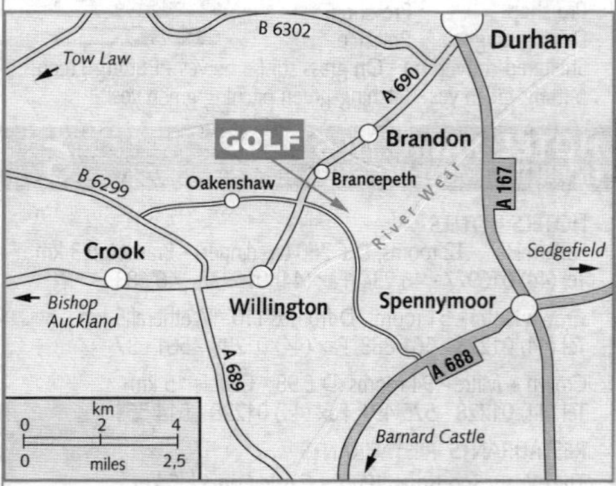

Access Accès : A1 (M) to Durham, then A690 → Crook.
Turn left at crossroads in Brancepeth village.
Take slip road left immediately before Castle gates.
Map 2 on page 473 Carte 2 Page 473

GOLF COURSE — PARCOURS — 15/20

Site	Site	
Maintenance	Entretien	
Architect	Architecte	Harry S. Colt
Type	Type	parkland
Relief	Relief	
Water in play	Eau en jeu	
Exp. to wind	Exposé au vent	
Trees in play	Arbres en jeu	

Scorecard / Carte de score	Chp. / Chp.	Mens / Mess.	Ladies / Da.
Length Long.	5720	5720	5312
Par	70	70	75
Slope system	—	—	—

Advised golfing ability Niveau de jeu recommandé: 0 12 24 36

Hcp required Handicap exigé: no

CLUB HOUSE & AMENITIES — CLUB HOUSE ET ANNEXES — 6/10

Pro shop Pro-shop
Driving range Practice
Sheltered couvert no - On grass sur herbe yes - Putting-green putting-green yes - Pitching-green pitching green yes

HOTEL FACILITIES — ENVIRONNEMENT HOTELIER — 5/10

HOTELS HÔTELS
Royal County - 151 rooms, D £ 130 - Durham 6 km
Tel (44) 0191 - 386 6821, Fax (44) 0191 - 386 0704

Swallow Three Tuns - 50 rooms, D from £ 105 - Durham 6 km
Tel (44) 0191 - 386 4326, Fax (44) 0191 - 386 1406

RESTAURANTS RESTAURANTS
County (Royal County) - Durham 6 km
Tel (44) 0191 - 386 6821

Bistro 21 - Durham 6 km - Tel (44) 0191 - 384 4354

The Seven Stars Inn - Shincliffe 5 km
Tel (44) 0191 - 384 8454

Broadstone

17	7	7

Some golfers have called Broadstone the Gleneagles of the south. This heather-clad terrain enhanced with pine, birch, oak, chestnut trees and rhododendrons, has kept the natural feel of Tom Dunn's original layout, although it was largely overhauled, perfected and re-touched by Harry Colt. Very little has been added since. Although the holes themselves are often flat, some of the hills are steep and tiring. Never easy to play, the course is a good test for every compartment of your game: length when you need it, accurate iron-play to the rather large but well defended greens, strategy for judging the right distance and flight to avoid the traps, including several dangerous water hazards. If that were not enough, you will also need an excellent short game to make up for mistakes, with lofted or bump 'n roll approach shots, and an acute sense of observation to make the most of the extremely useful experience of local players. Not forgetting your putting and a stop-off at the fountain on the 10th hole, one of the excellent features of a very likeable course.

Certains l'ont appelé le Gleneagles du sud. En terrain de bruyère, orné de pins, bouleaux, chênes, marronniers et rhododendrons, ce terrain a gardé l'esprit naturel du tracé de Tom Dunn, bien qu'il ait été largement bouleversé, perfectionné et affiné par Harry Colt. Depuis, il a très peu été modifié. Les trous y sont très souvent plats, mais certaines montées peuvent être assez fatigantes. Peu facile à jouer, c'est un bon test de tous les secteurs de son jeu : la longueur quand il faut porter assez loin la balle, la précision du jeu de fers vers des greens assez grands mais bien protégés, la stratégie quand il faut bien juger des distances et effets pour éviter les obstacles, dont quelques dangereux obstacles d'eau, le petit jeu pour rattraper toutes les fautes, avec des approches levées ou roulées suivant la situation, et l'observation pour tirer profit de l'expérience fort utile des joueurs locaux. N'oubliez pas votre putting ni de vous arrêter à la fontaine du 10, un des attraits d'une attachante réalisation.

Broadstone Dorset Golf Club — 1898

Wentworth Drive, Off Station Approach
ENG - BROADSTONE, Dorset BH18 8DQ

Office	Secrétariat	(44) 01202 - 692 595
Pro shop	Pro-shop	(44) 01202 - 692 835
Fax	Fax	(44) 01202 - 692 595
Web	www.broadstonegolfclub.com	
Situation	Situation	Poole, 7 km
Annual closure	Fermeture annuelle	no
Weekly closure	Fermeture hebdomadaire	no

Fees main season Tarifs haute saison — 18 holes

	Week days / Semaine	We/Bank holidays / We/Férié
Individual Individuel	£ 45	£ 55
Couple Couple	£ 90	£ 110

Weekdays: before 11:30 and after 14:00 /
We: after 14:30

Caddie Caddie no — **Electric Trolley** Chariot électrique yes

Buggy Voiturette no — **Clubs** Clubs yes (ask Pro)

Credit cards Cartes de crédit Visa - Mastercard

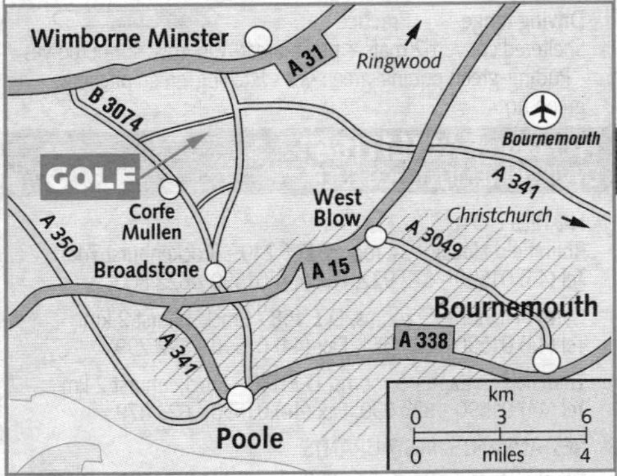

Access Accès : • M3, M27, A31, A349, then Dunyeats Road on the right.
• From Poole, B3074, Broadstone Links Road → Blandford, Golf on the right. **Map 6 on page 481** Carte 6 Page 481

GOLF COURSE — PARCOURS — 17/20

Site	Site	
Maintenance	Entretien	
Architect	Architecte	Tom Dunn, Harry S. Colt (1925)
Type	Type	heathland, hilly
Relief	Relief	
Water in play	Eau en jeu	
Exp. to wind	Exposé au vent	
Trees in play	Arbres en jeu	

Scorecard Carte de score	Chp. Chp.	Mens Mess.	Ladies Da.
Length Long.	5746	5547	4975
Par	70	70	72
Slope system	—	—	—

Advised golfing ability Niveau de jeu recommandé — 0 12 24 36

Hcp required Handicap exigé — Men 22, Ladies 30

CLUB HOUSE & AMENITIES — CLUB HOUSE ET ANNEXES — 7/10

Pro shop Pro-shop
Driving range Practice
Sheltered couvert no - On grass sur herbe yes - Putting-green putting-green yes - Pitching-green pitching green yes

HOTEL FACILITIES — ENVIRONNEMENT HOTELIER — 7/10

HOTELS HÔTELS

Mansion House - 32 rooms, D £ 135- Poole 6 km
Tel (44) 01202 - 685 666, Fax (44) 01202 - 665 709

Royal Bath - 140 rooms, D £ 175 - Bournemouth 8 km
Tel (44) 01202 - 555 555, Fax (44) 01202 - 554 158

Haven Hotel - 78 rooms, D from £ 180 - Poole 6 km
Tel (44) 01202 - 707 333, Fax (44) 01202 - 708 796

RESTAURANTS RESTAURANTS

La Roche (Haven Hotel) - Poole 6 km
Tel (44) 01202 - 707 333

John B's - Poole 6 km - Tel (44) 01202 - 672440

Isabel's - Poole 6 km - Tel (44) 01202 - 747 885

Brokenhurst Manor

15	6	6

Brokenhurst Manor is one of the rare "civilised" spots of the New Forest, one of the finest regions of England extending across a huge conserved expanse of moorland and oak forest, and once a hunting ground for William the Conqueror. The village of Brockenhurst is a starting point for hiking, bicycle rides and horse-trekking, or for playing golf on this course, reached after a very pleasant drive. There is no way you could imagine a course here without trees, and they are a beautiful sight and very much in play, so much so that players who can manœuvre the ball, in both directions, have a distinct advantage. As is often the case on a Harry Colt layout, the par 3s are magnificent and longer than they look. Another interesting and unusual aspect of this course is that it runs in three loops of 6 holes each, out and back to the club-house. Aside from the trees and bunkers, hazards include a stream which runs along seven holes. Although not really a championship course, you are guaranteed a great day's golfing with a few exciting glimpses of wild-life alongside the fairways.

Brokenhurst Manor est l'un des rares endroits "civilisés" de "New Forest", l'une des plus belles régions d'Angleterre, immense espace préservé de landes et de forêts de chênes, terrain de chasse de Guillaume le Conquérant. Et le village de Brockenhurst est une base de départs pour des randonnées. Ou pour jouer au golf sur ce parcours d'Harry Colt que l'on atteint après une route très plaisante. Ici, on ne pouvait imaginer un parcours sans arbres : ils sont à la fois très beaux visuellement, et très bien mis en jeu. Comme souvent chez Colt, les par 3 sont superbes, et plus longs qu'ils en ont l'air. Autre caractéristique intéressante et inhabituelle, les 18 trous forment trois boucles de six trous revenant au club-house, avec un cours d'eau qui se promène sur sept trous. Bien qu'il ne s'agisse pas vraiment d'un parcours de championnat, une bonne journée de golf est garantie, avec quelques aperçus passionnants sur la vie sauvage en lisière de parcours.

Brokenhurst Manor Golf Club — 1919

Sway Road
ENG - BROCKENHURST, Hants. SO42 7SG

Office	Secrétariat	(44) 01590 - 623 332
Pro shop	Pro-shop	(44) 01590 - 623 092
Fax	Fax	—
Web	www.brokenhurst-manor.org.uk	
Situation	Situation	Southampton, 23 km
Annual closure	Fermeture annuelle	no
Weekly closure	Fermeture hebdomadaire	no

Fees main season Tarifs haute saison — 18 holes

	Week days Semaine	We/Bank holidays We/Férié
Individual Individuel	£ 48	£ 58
Couple Couple	£ 96	£ 116

Caddie Caddie no — **Electric Trolley** Chariot électrique no
Buggy Voiturette no — **Clubs** Clubs no
Credit cards Cartes de crédit
VISA - MasterCard

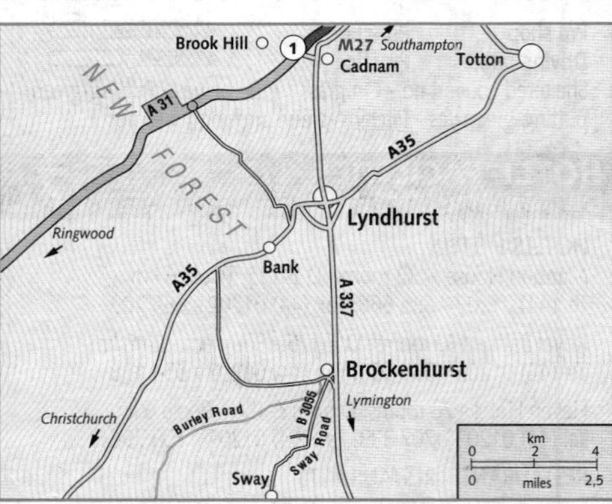

Access Accès : Southampton M27 → Bournemouth.
Exit 1 onto Lyndhurst. → Brockenhurst.
Golf on B0355 (Sway Road)
Map 7 on page 482 Carte 7 Page 482

GOLF COURSE — PARCOURS — 15/20

Site	Site	
Maintenance	Entretien	
Architect	Architecte	Harry S. Colt
Type	Type	inland
Relief	Relief	
Water in play	Eau en jeu	
Exp. to wind	Exposé au vent	
Trees in play	Arbres en jeu	

Scorecard Carte de score	Chp. Chp.	Mens Mess.	Ladies Da.
Length Long.	5600	5418	5000
Par	70	70	71
Slope system	—	—	—

Advised golfing ability Niveau de jeu recommandé — 0 12 24 36
Hcp required Handicap exigé — 24 Men, 36 Women

CLUB HOUSE & AMENITIES — CLUB HOUSE ET ANNEXES — 6/10

Pro shop Pro-shop
Driving range Practice
Sheltered couvert 2 mats + pract. area - On grass sur herbe yes - Putting-green putting-green yes - Pitching-green pitching green no

HOTEL FACILITIES — ENVIRONNEMENT HOTELIER — 6/10

HOTELS HÔTELS

Rhinefield House - 34 rooms, D £ 210 - Brockenhurst 7 km
Tel (44) 01590 - 622 922, Fax (44) 01590 - 622 800

Careys Manor - 79 rooms, D £ 158 - Brockenhurst 2 km
Tel (44) 01590 - 623 551, Fax (44) 01590 - 622 799

Thatched Cottage - 5 rooms, D £ 130 - Brockenhurst 2 km
Tel (44) 01590 - 623 090, Fax (44) 01590 - 623 479

RESTAURANTS RESTAURANTS

Simply Poussin - Brockenhurst 2 km - Tel (44) 01590 - 623 063
Thatched Cottage - Brockenhurst 2 km
Tel (44) 01590 - 623 090

Buckinghamshire (The)

17	8	7

This is one of those modern resorts that you find either very pretentious or very cosy. All that's missing is the obligatory fitness centre, but that will probably come. Having said that, you would never judge this John Jacobs course along that sort of criteria. The layout was created with much thought given to today's trends in professional and amateur golfing, forcing the player to take decisions as to the line of fire, the type of shot, whether to attack or whether to play safe. Choosing the right tee-boxes for your game is also an important decision. The woods, isolated trees, lakes (particularly on the 7th and 8th holes) and bunkers have been used, created or laid out as if geared to all these technical requirements. Dare we say it, here you get the impression of sitting an examination to ascertain your golf playing skills. As a wily craftsman himself, John Jacobs would not necessarily disagree. The course's shiny new glow is assuming a more mellow hue that makes it harder to date a course when mother nature reclaims her own.

Un de ces complexes actuels que l'on trouvera soit prétentieux, soit très confortable. Il n'y manque que l'inévitable unité de remise en forme, mais cela ne saurait tarder. Cela dit, le parcours dessiné par John Jacobs ne saurait être jugé sur des critères de ce genre ! Le tracé en a été fait avec beaucoup de réflexion sur les tendances des professionnels et des amateurs, il force à prendre des décisions sur la ligne de jeu, le type de coup, l'attaque ou la sécurité, il force même à choisir les départs adaptés à sa force du jour. Les bois, les arbres isolés, les lacs (aux 7 et 8 en particulier) et les bunkers ont été utilisés ou créés, ou disposés en fonction de ces exigences techniques. Aurez-vous un peu l'impression de passer un examen d'aptitude à jouer au golf ? Le fin technicien qu'est Jacobs ne dirait pas non. Les aspects un peu neufs commencent à prendre cette bonne patine qui fait peu à peu perdre leur "datation" aux parcours quand la nature reprend ses droits.

The Buckinghamshire Golf Club — 1992

Denham Court, Denham Court Drive
ENG - DENHAM, Bucks UB9 5BG

Office	Secrétariat	(44) 01895 - 835 777
Pro shop	Pro-shop	(44) 01895 - 835 777
Fax	Fax	(44) 01895 - 835 210
Web	www.buckinghamshiregc.com	
Situation	Situation	London, 25 km

Denham, 3 km

Annual closure	Fermeture annuelle	no
Weekly closure	Fermeture hebdomadaire	no
Fees main season	Tarifs haute saison	18 holes

	Week days / Semaine	We/Bank holidays / We/Férié
Individual Individuel	£ 90	£ 100*
Couple Couple	£ 180	£ 200*

* We: Friday, Saturday, Sunday

Caddie Caddie on request **Electric Trolley** Chariot électrique yes

Buggy Voiturette no **Clubs** Clubs yes

Credit cards Cartes de crédit
VISA - Eurocard - MasterCard - AMEX - DC

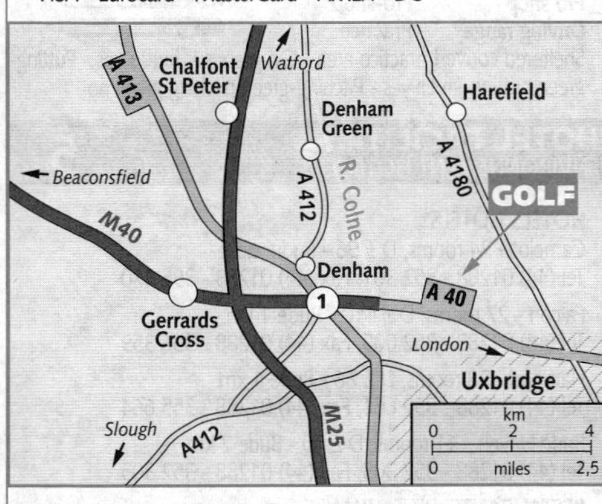

Access Accès : M40 Jct 1. Roundabout on A40, turn into Denham Court Drive, follow signs to the club.

Map 8 on page 484 Carte 8 Page 484

GOLF COURSE — PARCOURS — 17/20

Site	Site	
Maintenance	Entretien	
Architect	Architecte	John Jacobs
Type	Type	parkland
Relief	Relief	
Water in play	Eau en jeu	
Exp. to wind	Exposé au vent	
Trees in play	Arbres en jeu	

Scorecard / Carte de score	Chp. / Chp.	Mens / Mess.	Ladies / Da.
Length Long.	6192	5761	5123
Par	72	72	74
Slope system	—	—	—

Advised golfing ability / Niveau de jeu recommandé: 0 12 24 36

Hcp required Handicap exigé: no

CLUB HOUSE & AMENITIES — CLUB HOUSE ET ANNEXES — 8/10

Pro shop	Pro-shop
Driving range	Practice

Sheltered couvert - On grass sur herbe yes - Putting-green putting-green yes - Pitching-green pitching green yes

HOTEL FACILITIES — ENVIRONNEMENT HOTELIER — 7/10

HOTELS HÔTELS

De Vere Bull - Gerrards Cross 7 km
111 rooms, D from £ 100
Tel (44) 01753 - 885 995, Fax (44) 01753 - 885 504

Copthorne - 219 rooms, D £ 180 - Slough 12 km
Tel (44) 01753 - 516 222, Fax (44) 01753 - 516 237

Courtyard - 150 rooms, D £ 124 - Slough 12 km
Tel (44) 01753 - 551 551, Fax (44) 01753 - 553 333

RESTAURANTS RESTAURANTS

Etcetera - Gerrards Cross 5 km - Tel (44) 01753 - 880 888

Stoke's Brasserie - Stoke Poges 10 km
Tel (44) 01753 - 717 171

Bude & North Cornwall

15	6	5

Situated between Tintagel and the pretty harbour of Clovelly, Bude is a popular seaside resort and starting point for walks and treks, especially for bird-watchers who can take the path that runs along the coast. It is also home to a very pretty links course, almost touching the town, where the wind blows as usual and where you find the standard hazards and unpredictable kicks when the ground is dry. A few blind shots and greens add to the pleasure of discovering this course, particularly when you have given up any idea of keeping score. Good technique, good control with knock-down shots and an excellent short game are essential ingredients at Bude, the latter being helpful for short approaches or escapes from some typical links style bunkers. You won't find this course in the League of Champions, but the undulating, neatly mown fairways, generally excellent greens and a recently refurbished club-house make for total enjoyment. It is also excellent value for money.

Entre Tintagel et le joli port de Clovelly, Bude est un lieu de vacances balnéaires, mais il faut avoir le sang d'un Britannique pour aller se baigner. C'est aussi un point de départ de promenades, en particulier pour observer les oiseaux en parcourant le sentier qui longe toute la côte. C'est enfin le site d'un très joli links pratiquement en ville, où le vent joue son rôle, mais aussi les hasards de ce genre de parcours, avec des rebonds imprévisibles quand le sol est sec. Quelques coups et greens aveugles ajoutent au plaisir de la découverte, si l'on évite de compter le score. Une bonne technique, une bonne maîtrise des balles basses, un petit jeu excellent s'imposent, ce dernier aussi bien pour les approches roulées que pour s'extraire de quelques bunkers typiques. Bien sûr, Bude & North Cornwall ne joue pas dans la Ligue des Champions, mais les fairways ondulés et tondus courts, les greens généralement excellents, le club-house refait récemment garantissent un plaisir total. Et le rapport qualité/prix toujours excellent.

Bude & North Cornwall Golf Club — 1891

Burn View
ENG - BUDE, Cornwall EX23 8 DA

Office	Secrétariat	(44) 01288 - 352 006
Pro shop	Pro-shop	(44) 01288 - 353 635
Fax	Fax	(44) 01288 - 356 855
Web	www.budegolf.co.uk	
Situation	Situation	Exeter, 70 km
Annual closure	Fermeture annuelle	no
Weekly closure	Fermeture hebdomadaire	no

Fees main season Tarifs haute saison	Week days Semaine	We/Bank holidays We/Férié
	Full day	
Individual Individuel	£ 27	£ 27*
Couple Couple	£ 54	£ 54*

*After 14:30 Saturday and 12:30 Sunday, and 18 holes only

Caddie Caddie no — **Electric Trolley** Chariot électrique no

Buggy Voiturette no — **Clubs** Clubs yes

Credit cards Cartes de crédit
VISA - Eurocard - MasterCard (Pro shop goods only)

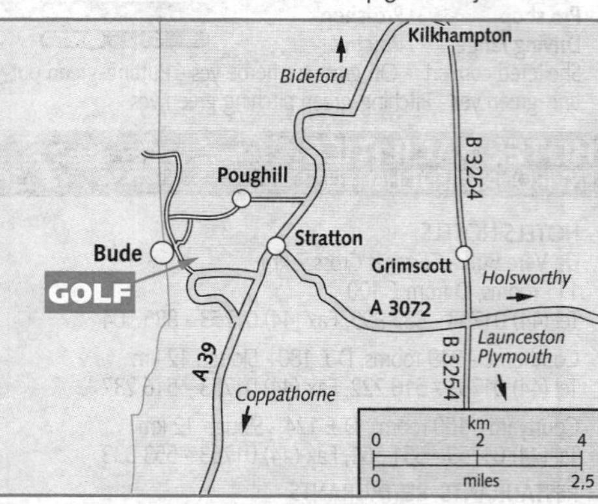

Access Accès : M5 Bristol → Exeter. Exit 27 → Tiverton, Barnstable on A39, then to Bude. Into town, Golf signposted.
Map 6 on page 480 Carte 6 Page 480

GOLF COURSE — PARCOURS — 15/20

Site	Site	
Maintenance	Entretien	
Architect	Architecte	Tom Dunn
Type	Type	seaside course, links
Relief	Relief	
Water in play	Eau en jeu	
Exp. to wind	Exposé au vent	
Trees in play	Arbres en jeu	

Scorecard Carte de score	Chp. Chp.	Mens Mess.	Ladies Da.
Length Long.	5452	5255	4841
Par	71	71	73
Slope system	—	—	—

Advised golfing ability Niveau de jeu recommandé — 0 12 24 36

Hcp required Handicap exigé — certificate

CLUB HOUSE & AMENITIES — CLUB HOUSE ET ANNEXES — 6/10

Pro shop Pro-shop
Driving range Practice
Sheltered couvert practice area - On grass sur herbe yes - Putting-green putting-green yes - Pitching-green pitching green no

HOTEL FACILITIES — ENVIRONNEMENT HOTELIER — 5/10

HOTELS HÔTELS

Camelot - 24 rooms, D £ 96 - Bude, close
Tel (44) 01288 - 352 361, Fax (44) 01288 - 355 470

Falcon - 27 rooms, D £ 110 - Bude 1 km
Tel (44) 01288 - 352 005, Fax (44) 01288 - 356 359

Hartland - 28 rooms, D £ 86 - Bude 1 km
Tel (44) 01288 - 355 661, Fax (44) 01288 - 355 664

Bude Haven - 11 rooms, D £ 70 - Bude 2 km
Tel (44) 01288 - 352 305, Fax (44) 01288 - 352 305

RESTAURANTS RESTAURANTS

Falcon - Bude 1 km - Tel (44) 01288 - 352 005
Atlantic House - Bude 1 km - Tel (44) 01288 - 352 451

Burnham & Berrow

18	7	6

Played for many a year by J.H. Taylor, this classic course has been profoundly altered throughout the 20th century, in particular to avoid hitting worshippers as they leave the church set in the middle of the course. The changes also cut out many of the blind shots, thereby reducing a little the glorious uncertainty of golf but giving the layout a more seamless feel as it winds, even sneaks, its way between majestic sand-dunes. In this protected space, plant-life is superb, especially the orchids, and as on many links courses there are very few water hazards (here on the 6th and behind the 13th holes). Dare we say it, these should only bother the higher handicappers. Generally speaking you have to hit the ball straight, as bushes, rough and bunkers await wayward drives, while hilly slopes and pot-bunkers snap up mis-hit approach shots. As the greens are small and steeply contoured, this is a great course for getting your short game together and one that has hosted a number of top tournaments.

Longtemps arpenté par J.H. Taylor, ce classique a été profondément modifié tout au long de ce siècle, en particulier pour éviter d'envoyer au paradis les fidèles de l'église au milieu du parcours. Les modifications ont aussi permis d'éliminer beaucoup de coups aveugles, retirant un peu de la glorieuse incertitude du golf, mais offrant plus de franchise au tracé, à présent mieux insinué, presque glissé entre des dunes majestueuses. Dans cet espace protégé, on trouve une flore sauvage superbe, notamment des orchidées. Comme sur la plupart des links, il y a peu d'obstacles d'eau (au 6 et derrière le 13), mais ils ne concernent que les handicaps élevés. En général, il faut placer la balle, car les buissons, le rough et les bunkers attendent les drives égarés, les mouvements de terrain et les pot bunkers happent les approches imprécises. Comme les greens sont petits et très mouvementés, on travaille son petit jeu sur ce grand parcours, qui a reçu nombre de grands championnats.

Burnham & Berrow Golf Club — 1890

St Christopher's Way
ENG - BURNHAM-ON-SEA, Somerset TA8 2PE

Office	Secrétariat	(44) 01278 - 785 760
Pro shop	Pro-shop	(44) 01278 - 785 760
Fax	Fax	(44) 01278 - 795 440
Web	www.burnhamandberrowgolfclub.co.uk	
Situation	Situation	Bristol, 50 km

Weston-Super-Mare, 8 km

Annual closure	Fermeture annuelle	no
Weekly closure	Fermeture hebdomadaire	no

Fees main season Tarifs haute saison		18 holes
	Week days Semaine	We/Bank holidays We/Férié
Individual Individuel	£ 45	£ 60*
Couple Couple	£ 90	£ 120*

Full week-days: £ 60 / * We: only 18 holes

Caddie Caddie on request **Electric Trolley** Chariot électrique yes

Buggy Voiturette no **Clubs** Clubs yes

Credit cards Cartes de crédit
Visa - Mastercard (Pro shop goods only)

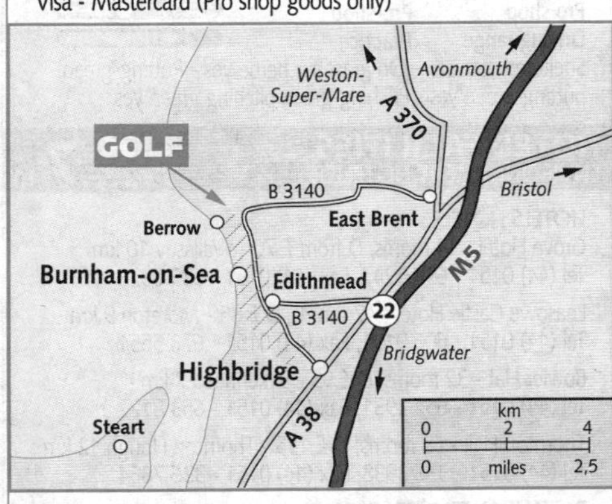

Access Accès : M5 Jct 22, 1,5 km (1 m.) N. of Burnham-on-Sea. Follow signs to Golf.
Map 6 on page 481 Carte 6 Page 481

GOLF COURSE — PARCOURS — 18/20

Site	Site	
Maintenance	Entretien	
Architect	Architecte	unknown
Type	Type	seaside course, links
Relief	Relief	
Water in play	Eau en jeu	
Exp. to wind	Exposé au vent	
Trees in play	Arbres en jeu	

Scorecard Carte de score	Chp. Chp.	Mens Mess.	Ladies Da.
Length Long.	6151	6012	5227
Par	71	71	74
Slope system	—	—	—

Advised golfing ability Niveau de jeu recommandé — 0 12 24 36

Hcp required Handicap exigé — 22 Men, 30 Ladies

CLUB HOUSE & AMENITIES — CLUB HOUSE ET ANNEXES — 7/10

Pro shop	Pro-shop
Driving range	Practice

Sheltered couvert no - On grass sur herbe yes - Putting-green putting-green yes - Pitching-green pitching green yes

HOTEL FACILITIES — ENVIRONNEMENT HOTELIER — 6/10

HOTELS HÔTELS

Dormy House - 4 rooms, D £ 80 - on site
Tel (44) 01278 - 785 760, Fax (44) 01278 - 795 440

Queenswood - Bude 8 km
19 rooms, D £ 95
Tel (44) 01934 - 416 141, Fax (44) 01934 - 621 759

Beachlands - Weston-Super-Mare 8 km
23 rooms, D £ 107
Tel (44) 01934 - 621 401, Fax (44) 01934 -621 966

RESTAURANTS RESTAURANTS

Duets - Weston-Super-Mare 8 km
Tel (44) 01934 - 413 428

Caldy

16 | 7 | 7

In a setting formed by the Dee estuary, Flintshire hills and Welsh mountains right in the background, the views from the course provide welcome inspiration, especially towards sun-set. Caldy is a mixture of sloping holes in a parkland setting and links-style seaside holes (3 to 10), and as such offers great variety of style without ever feeling too disparate. What's more, being less demanding and less uncompromising than its neighbour, Royal Liverpool, it is less intimidating for the average player. Having said that, the number of difficulties (trees, rough, water and sand) makes this a course to be reckoned with, even though the layout is clear and revealing enough for you to know exactly when and where to hit those magic shots. Although slightly hilly in places, no greens are blind but some are elevated, so make allowance for this when choosing your irons. On the down-side, there are no spectacular dunes to contend with, but this is offset by the excellence of drainage and work done to the greens (to USGA standards, if you please).

Le décor réunit l'estuaire de la Dee, les collines du Flintshire et les montagnes du Pays de Galles : de quoi inspirer le joueur, surtout au soleil couchant. Avec son mélange de trous en pente, d'esthétique de parc et de links (du 3 au 10), Caldy offre une superbe variété de styles, sans pour autant manquer d'homogénéité. De plus, n'étant pas aussi exigeant et brutal que son voisin Royal Liverpool, il intimidera moins le joueur moyen. Pourtant le nombre de difficultés (arbres, rough, eau, bunkers) oblige à réfléchir, mais comme on dispose de toutes les cartes en main - le parcours est d'une grande franchise générale - on peut jouer ses atouts au bon moment. En dépit d'un léger relief, on ne trouve pas de greens aveugles, mais certains étant en élévation, il faut bien choisir ses clubs. Si l'on peut regretter quelque chose, c'est l'absence de grandes dunes spectaculaires, bien compensée par la qualité des drainages, et du travail effectué sur les greens (aux normes USGA).

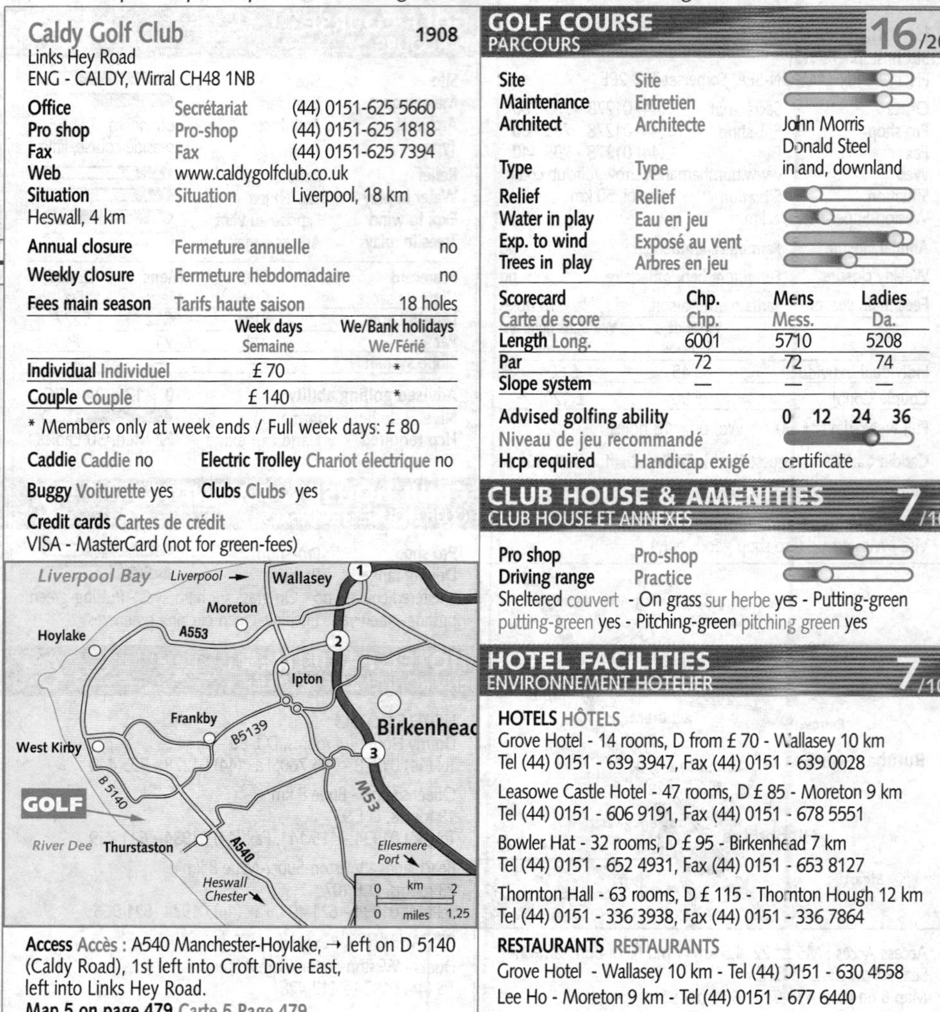

Caldy Golf Club — 1908

Links Hey Road
ENG - CALDY, Wirral CH48 1NB

Office	Secrétariat	(44) 0151-625 5660
Pro shop	Pro-shop	(44) 0151-625 1818
Fax	Fax	(44) 0151-625 7394
Web	www.caldygolfclub.co.uk	
Situation	Situation	Liverpool, 18 km

Heswall, 4 km

Annual closure	Fermeture annuelle	no
Weekly closure	Fermeture hebdomadaire	no

Fees main season Tarifs haute saison	18 holes	
	Week days Semaine	**We/Bank holidays** We/Férié
Individual Individuel	£ 70	*
Couple Couple	£ 140	*

* Members only at week ends / Full week days: £ 80

Caddie Caddie no — **Electric Trolley** Chariot électrique no

Buggy Voiturette yes — **Clubs** Clubs yes

Credit cards Cartes de crédit
VISA - MasterCard (not for green-fees)

Access Accès : A540 Manchester-Hoylake, → left on D 5140 (Caldy Road), 1st left into Croft Drive East, left into Links Hey Road.
Map 5 on page 479 Carte 5 Page 479

GOLF COURSE — PARCOURS — 16/20

Site	Site	
Maintenance	Entretien	
Architect	Architecte	John Morris, Donald Steel
Type	Type	inland, downland
Relief	Relief	
Water in play	Eau en jeu	
Exp. to wind	Exposé au vent	
Trees in play	Arbres en jeu	

Scorecard Carte de score	**Chp.** Chp.	**Mens** Mess.	**Ladies** Da.
Length Long.	6001	5710	5208
Par	72	72	74
Slope system	—	—	—

Advised golfing ability Niveau de jeu recommandé — 0 12 24 36

Hcp required Handicap exigé — certificate

CLUB HOUSE & AMENITIES — CLUB HOUSE ET ANNEXES — 7/10

Pro shop Pro-shop
Driving range Practice
Sheltered couvert - On grass sur herbe yes - Putting-green putting-green yes - Pitching-green pitching green yes

HOTEL FACILITIES — ENVIRONNEMENT HOTELIER — 7/10

HOTELS HÔTELS

Grove Hotel - 14 rooms, D from £ 70 - Wallasey 10 km
Tel (44) 0151 - 639 3947, Fax (44) 0151 - 639 0028

Leasowe Castle Hotel - 47 rooms, D £ 85 - Moreton 9 km
Tel (44) 0151 - 606 9191, Fax (44) 0151 - 678 5551

Bowler Hat - 32 rooms, D £ 95 - Birkenhead 7 km
Tel (44) 0151 - 652 4931, Fax (44) 0151 - 653 8127

Thornton Hall - 63 rooms, D £ 115 - Thornton Hough 12 km
Tel (44) 0151 - 336 3938, Fax (44) 0151 - 336 7864

RESTAURANTS RESTAURANTS

Grove Hotel - Wallasey 10 km - Tel (44) 0151 - 630 4558
Lee Ho - Moreton 9 km - Tel (44) 0151 - 677 6440

Camberley Heath

16	6	6

This golf-club, lying almost at the intersection between the counties of Surrey, Hampshire and Berkshire, has an impressive club-house from where you get some equally impressive views over a course which winds its way through trees and heather and which now has an automatic watering system. Virtually free of water hazards (except the 16th hole), this is a fine example of the exceptional skill of architect Harry Colt and his discreet but totally effective bunkering, the use of trees and natural slopes and the often multi-tiered putting surfaces where down-hill putts should be avoided at all costs. The terrain is hilly enough to get the better of tired legs, an important factor on a course where you will need every ounce of strength to cope with the last three holes, which are often decisive for your card. Depending on the tees you choose, the course can change to such an extent that we would recommend (for "friendly" rounds) changing from one day to the next to vary the fun and test your technique. All in all, a very clever layout.

Ce club, au croisement du Surrey, du Hampshire et du Berkshire, offre depuis son imposant club-house un panorama spectaculaire sur le parcours insinué dans les arbres et la bruyère, qui bénéficie de l'arrosage automatique. Pratiquement sans obstacle d'eau (sauf au 16), c'est un grand exemple de l'art exceptionnel de l'architecte Harry Colt, avec son placement sobre et efficace des bunkers, sa mise en jeu des arbres, son utilisation des pentes naturelles du terrain, et les contours fréquemment à plateaux des greens, où il convient absolument d'éviter les putts en descente. Assez accidenté, il éprouvera les jambes des moins résistants, alors que le jeu réclame ici de garder des forces jusqu'au bout : les trois derniers trous peuvent ainsi retourner le résultat d'une compétition. Suivant le choix des départs, le parcours peut changer à tel point que l'on conseillera (en partie amicale) d'en changer d'un jour à l'autre pour varier les plaisirs et tester sa technique sur ce tracé très intelligent.

Camberley Heath Golf Club — 1913

Golf Drive
ENG - CAMBERLEY, Surrey GU15 1JG

Office	Secrétariat	(44) 01276 - 23 258
Pro shop	Pro-shop	(44) 01276 - 27 905
Fax	Fax	(44) 01276 - 692 505
Web	www.camberleyheathgolfclub.co.uk	
Situation	Situation	London, 60 km
Camberley, 2 km		
Annual closure	Fermeture annuelle	no
Weekly closure	Fermeture hebdomadaire	no

Fees main season Tarifs haute saison	18 holes	
	Week days Semaine	We/Bank holidays We/Férié
Individual Individuel	£ 57	*
Couple Couple	£ 114	*

* Members only at week ends / Full week days: £ 74

Caddie Caddie £ 20 **Electric Trolley** Chariot électrique no

Buggy Voiturette £ 35 **Clubs** Clubs yes

Credit cards Cartes de crédit
Visa - Eurocard - Mastercard - AMEX

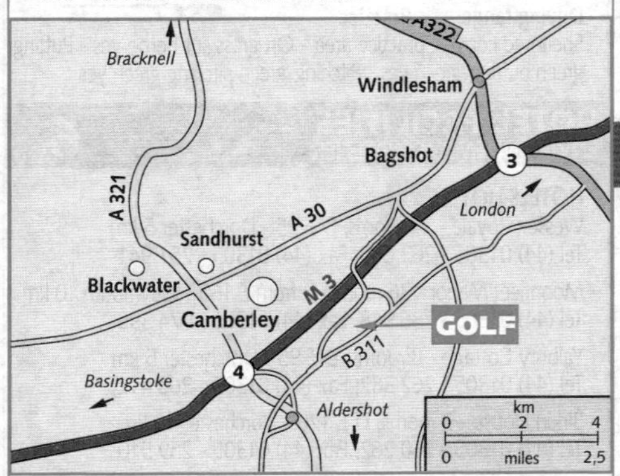

Access Accès : London M3 → Basingstoke. Exit 4 → Frimley. Turn left on Portsmouth Road.
Golf on the right at Golf Drive.
Map 8 on page 484 Carte 8 Page 484

GOLF COURSE — PARCOURS 16/20

Site	Site	
Maintenance	Entretien	
Architect	Architecte	Harry S. Colt
Type	Type	heathland, parkland
Relief	Relief	
Water in play	Eau en jeu	
Exp. to wind	Exposé au vent	
Trees in play	Arbres en jeu	

Scorecard Carte de score	Chp. Chp.	Mens Mess.	Ladies Da.
Length Long.	5670	5580	4950
Par	72	72	72
Slope system	—	—	—

Advised golfing ability Niveau de jeu recommandé 0 12 24 36

Hcp required Handicap exigé certificate

CLUB HOUSE & AMENITIES — CLUB HOUSE ET ANNEXES 6/10

Pro shop Pro-shop
Driving range Practice
Sheltered couvert - On grass sur herbe yes - Putting-green putting-green yes - Pitching-green pitching green yes

HOTEL FACILITIES — ENVIRONNEMENT HOTELIER 6/10

HOTELS HÔTELS

Frimley Hall - 86 rooms, D £ 170 - Camberley 3 km
Tel (44) 0870 - 400 8224, Fax (44) 01276 - 691 253

Toby Carvery and Lodge - 43 rooms, D £ 80 - Frimley 3 km
Tel (44) 01276 - 691 939, Fax (44) 01276 - 605 902

Pennyhill Park - 123 rooms, D £ 215 - Bagshot 5 km
Tel (44) 01276 - 471 774, Fax (44) 01276 - 473 217

RESTAURANTS RESTAURANTS

Pennyhill Park - Bagshot 5 km - Tel (44) 01276 - 471 774
Frimley Hall - Frimley 3 km - Tel (44) 0870 - 400 8224
Toby Carvery and Lodge - Frimley 3 km
Tel (44) 01276 - 691 939

Came Down

14	5	6

From Dorchester, it is just a short drive to the coast and Weymouth, a very old seaside resort where you can still see the vestiges of Maiden castle, a stone-age fortress. Even closer is the underrated Came Down golf club, a course designed by Tom Dunn, restyled by J.H. Taylor and fine-tuned by Harry Colt. Three top names in golf course design and three great connoisseurs of golf played at every level, indulgent for the less gifted, demanding for the smarter guys. Laid out on a hill, the course has a few climbs to negotiate but nothing too steep, and naturally reserves a few sloping lies. The advantage of this location is the view over the Dorset countryside and some wide open space where big-hitters can open their shoulders despite the risk of landing in some tall rough. You also have the wind to contend with, so keep the ball low and try to run it in. The greens are excellent but often very slick in summer.

De Dorchester, il faut quelques minutes pour rejoindre la côte et Weymouth, une très ancienne station balnéaire, ou voir les vestiges de Maiden Castle, une forteresse de l'Age de pierre. Il en faut encore moins pour jouer le parcours sous-estimé de Came Down, dessiné par Tom Dunn, revu par J.H. Taylor et peaufiné par Harry Colt. Trois grands noms de l'architecture, trois grands connaisseurs du jeu à tous les niveaux, indulgents pour les élèves peu doués, exigeants pour les premiers de la classe. Situé sur une colline, il réserve quelques moments de montées à pied mais sans rien d'excessif, et quelques positions de balle dans différentes pentes. Avantage de la situation, les points de vue sur la campagne du Dorset, et des espaces très ouverts où les frappeurs pourront se déchaîner, avec quelques risques présentés par les hauts roughs. Il faut aussi savoir jouer avec le vent, maîtriser les balles basses, et donc les approches roulées : les greens sont de bonne qualité, mais peuvent être très roulants en été.

Came Down Golf Club — 1904

ENG - CAME, DORCHESTER, Dorset DT2 8 NR

Office Secrétariat (44) 01305 - 813 494
Pro shop Pro-shop (44) 01305 - 812 670
Fax Fax (44) 01305 - 813 494
Web www.camedowngolfclub.co.uk
Situation Situation Weymouth, 10 km
Dorchester, 5 km
Annual closure Fermeture annuelle no
Weekly closure Fermeture hebdomadaire no
Fees main season Tarifs haute saison 18 holes

	Week days Semaine	We/Bank holidays We/Férié
Individual Individuel	£ 26	£ 30
Couple Couple	£ 52	£ 60

Prior booking essential

Caddie Caddie no — **Electric Trolley** Chariot électrique no
Buggy Voiturette yes — **Clubs** Clubs no
Credit cards Cartes de crédit
VISA - Eurocard - MasterCard (Pro shop goods only)

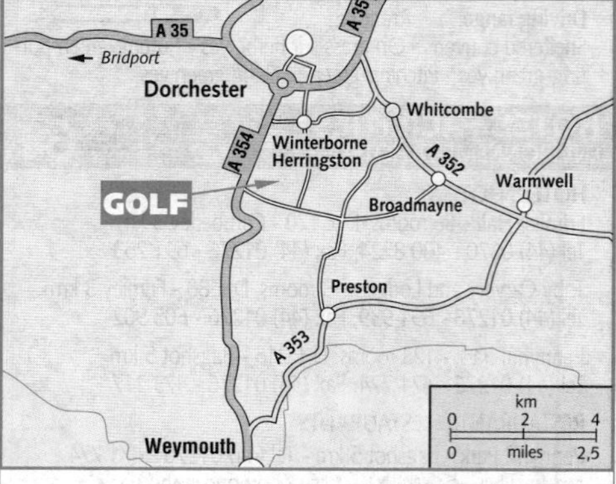

Access Accès : 5 km South of Dorchester. Take A354 head up hill. Keep on same road, club-house on right hand side.
Map 6 on page 481 Carte 6 Page 481

GOLF COURSE — PARCOURS — 14/20

Site Site
Maintenance Entretien
Architect Architecte — Tom Dunn , J.H. Taylor
Type Type — open country, hilly
Relief Relief
Water in play Eau en jeu
Exp. to wind Exposé au vent
Trees in play Arbres en jeu

Scorecard Carte de score	Chp. Chp.	Mens Mess.	Ladies Da.
Length Long.	5630	53'3	5011
Par	70	69	72
Slope system	—	—	—

Advised golfing ability Niveau de jeu recommandé — 0 12 24 36
Hcp required Handicap exigé — certificate

CLUB HOUSE & AMENITIES — CLUB HOUSE ET ANNEXES — 5/10

Pro shop Pro-shop
Driving range Practice
Sheltered couvert practice area - On grass sur herbe yes - Putting-green putting-green yes - Pitching-green pitching green yes

HOTEL FACILITIES — ENVIRONNEMENT HOTELIER — 6/10

HOTELS HÔTELS
Wessex Royale - 27 rooms, D £ 95 - Dorchester 5 km
Tel (44) 01305 - 262 660, Fax (44) 01305 - 251 941

Moonfleet Manor - 36 rooms, D from £ 160 - Weymouth 10 km
Tel (44) 01305 - 786 948, Fax (44) 01305 - 774 395

Yalbury Cottage - 8 rooms, D £ 95 - Dorchester 5 km
Tel (44) 01305 - 262 382, Fax (44) 01305 - 266 412

Birkin House - 9 rooms, D £ 120 - Dorchester 10 km
Tel (44) 01305 - 260 262, Fax (44) 01305 - 259 510

RESTAURANTS RESTAURANTS
Mock Turtle - Dorchester 5 km - Tel (44) 01305 - 264 011
Perry's - Weymouth 10 km - Tel (44) 01305 - 785 799
Yalbury Cottage - Dorchester 5 km - Tel (44) 01305 - 262 382

Carden Park *Nicklaus Course*

17 | 8 | 8

Steve Nicklaus (brother of Jack Nicklaus Junior) worked with his famous dad and designed his second course to date. The on-site hotel is also a great week-end destination, the only problem being the number of golfers here, compounded by the style of a course which is hardly conducive to quick play: water comes into play on more than half the holes. A meandering stream has resulted in double fairways on the 7th and 15th holes, where the risk you are about to take needs even more careful consideration than anywhere else on the course. This is Big Jack's famous "percentage golf". A few large trees complicate things still further, as do the very many bunkers, nearly all large but rather British in style. For once, the architect has not laid out his traditional bunkers with steep walls. Despite this hint of moderation, the course demands target golf, making it a tricky affair for lovers of bump 'n run shot or inveterate toppers of the ball who will prefer the more indulgent "Cheshire" course.

Après Jack Nicklaus Junior, c'est son frère Steve qui a travaillé avec papa sur ce second parcours du site (en date). L'hôtel sur place en a fait une bonne destination de week-end, mais il risque d'y avoir du monde, et le style du présent parcours ne favorise pas un jeu rapide, avec l'eau en jeu sur une dizaine de trous. Les méandres d'un cours d'eau ont permis de créer des doubles fairways au 7 et au 15, où l'on devra plus encore qu'ailleurs mesurer les risques avant de jouer : c'est le golf pourcentage cher à Nicklaus. Quelques grands arbres compliquent encore le jeu, ainsi que de nombreux bunkers, souvent grands mais de profils assez britanniques : pour une fois, l'architecte n'a pas trop plaqué ici ses bunkers traditionnels avec des parois abruptes. Malgré cette modération, ce parcours réclame un jeu de cible, ce qui le rend fort délicat pour les habitués du "bump n' run" et les joueurs sans grande expérience, qui préfèreront le "Cheshire course", plus indulgent.

Carden Park Hotel, Golf Resort & Spa — 1998

ENG - CHESTER, Ches. CH3 9DQ

Office Secrétariat (44) 01829 - 731 630
Pro shop Pro-shop (44) 01829 - 731 600
Fax Fax (44) 01829 - 731 629
Web www.devere-hotels.com
Situation Situation Nantwich, 15 km
Chester (pop. 115 971), 25 km
Annual closure Fermeture annuelle no
Weekly closure Fermeture hebdomadaire no

Fees main season Tarifs haute saison 18 holes

	Week days / Semaine	We/Bank holidays / We/Férié
Individual Individuel	£ 45	£ 45
Couple Couple	£ 90	£ 90

Caddie Caddie no — **Electric Trolley** Chariot électrique no
Buggy Voiturette yes — **Clubs** Clubs yes
Credit cards Cartes de crédit
VISA - Eurocard - MasterCard - AMEX - Switch - Solo

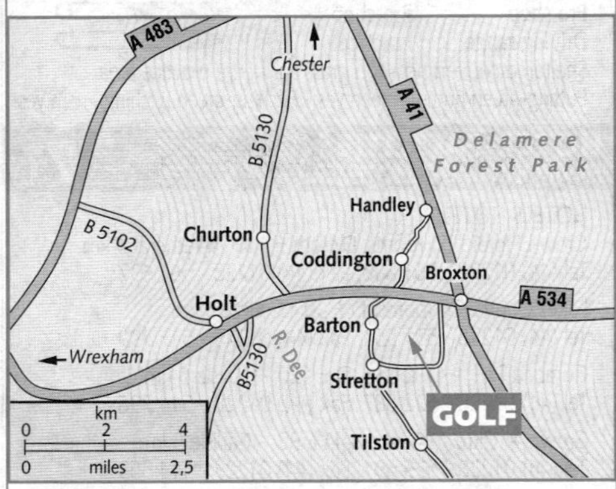

Access Accès : Chester, A41 → Whitchurch. Broxton roundabout, turn right onto A534 → Wrexham. Golf approx. 2.5 km (1.5 m) on left side.
Map 4 on page 476 Carte 4 Page 476

GOLF COURSE — PARCOURS 17/20

Site Site
Maintenance Entretien
Architect Architecte Jack Nicklaus, Steve Nicklaus
Type Type parkland, inland
Relief Relief
Water in play Eau en jeu
Exp. to wind Exposé au vent
Trees in play Arbres en jeu

Scorecard / Carte de score	Chp. / Chp.	Mens / Mess.	Ladies / Da.
Length Long.	6341	5672	4690
Par	72	72	72
Slope system	—	—	—

Advised golfing ability Niveau de jeu recommandé 0 12 24 36
Hcp required Handicap exigé no

CLUB HOUSE & AMENITIES — CLUB HOUSE ET ANNEXES 8/10

Pro shop Pro-shop
Driving range Practice
Sheltered couvert 13 bays - On grass sur herbe oppos. end of range - Putting-green putting-green yes (2) - Pitching-green pitching green yes

HOTEL FACILITIES — ENVIRONNEMENT HOTELIER 8/10

HOTELS HÔTELS
Carden Park Hotel - 192 rooms, D £ 138 - on site
Tel (44) 01829 - 731 000, Fax (44) 01829 - 731 032

Rowton Hall - Chester 10 km
38 rooms, D £ 150
Tel (44) 01244 - 335 262, Fax (44) 01244 - 335 464

Broxton Hall - 10 rooms, D £ 80 - near Chester 5 km
Tel (44) 01829 - 782 321, Fax (44) 01829 - 782 330

RESTAURANTS RESTAURANTS
Arkle - Chester 15 km - Tel (44) 01244 - 324 024
Crabwall Manor - Chester 15 km - Tel (44) 01244 - 851 666
Blue Bell - Chester 15 km - Tel (44) 01244 - 317 758

Carlisle

16 | 7 | 7

As you drive through northern England towards the great links courses of Ayrshire, forget the M6 motorway and keep to the A6, which crosses the breath-taking scenery of the Lake District and Hadrian's Wall. If it inspires you the way it inspired Keats, Wordsworth or Beatrix Potter, you could be in for a good day's golfing. The course at Carlisle leaves no-one indifferent, and as this a Tom Simpson design, no-one will be too surprised about that. You will find his trade-mark cross-bunkers (Simpson hated topped shots) and sharply contoured greens protected by bunkers on the one side, by bumps and hollows on the other, which offer their own particular brand of difficulty. Plus the never-ending need to think with a clear head on the length and direction of the ideal shot before choosing your club. The par 3s here are outstanding and the par 5s no less memorable. The only shortcoming might be the course's overall length, but hopefully would-be designers will think long and hard before making any alterations, except perhaps pushing a few tee-boxes further back.

En remontant du nord de l'Angleterre vers les grands links d'Ecosse, renoncez à la M6 au profit de l'A6, qui traverse les paysages sublimes du Lake District puis le Mur d'Hadrien. Vous y trouverez peut-être l'inspiration, comme Keats, Wordsworth ou Beatrix Potter. Au moins pour le golf, car Carlisle n'est pas un parcours qui laisse indifférent. La signature de Tom Simpson est une garantie. Vous y trouverez ses cross-bunkers car il haïssait les balles toppées, les greens parfois très mouvementés et souvent défendus d'un côté par les bunkers, et de l'autre par des creux et des bosses d'où il n'est guère plus facile de jouer, plus la nécessité de réfléchir sur la longueur et la direction du coup idéal avant de choisir un club. Les par 3 sont ici exceptionnels, les par 5 non moins mémorables. Seul défaut, un certain manque de longueur, mais il serait bien inutile de toucher quoi que ce soit sous prétexte de le "moderniser", sauf en reculant simplement quelques départs.

Carlisle Golf Club — 1909

Aglionby
ENG - CARLISLE, Cumbria CA4 8AG

Office Secrétariat (44) 01228 - 513 029
Pro shop Pro-shop (44) 01228 - 513 241
Fax Fax (44) 01228 - 513 303
Web www.carlislegolfclub.org
Situation Situation Carlisle (pop. 100 562), 3 km
Annual closure Fermeture annuelle no
Weekly closure Fermeture hebdomadaire no

Fees main season Tarifs haute saison	18 holes	
	Week days Semaine	**We/Bank holidays** We/Férié
Individual Individuel	£ 35	*
Couple Couple	£ 70	*

* No visitors at week-ends

Caddie Caddie no — **Electric Trolley** Chariot électrique yes
Buggy Voiturette yes — **Clubs** Clubs yes
Credit cards Cartes de crédit no

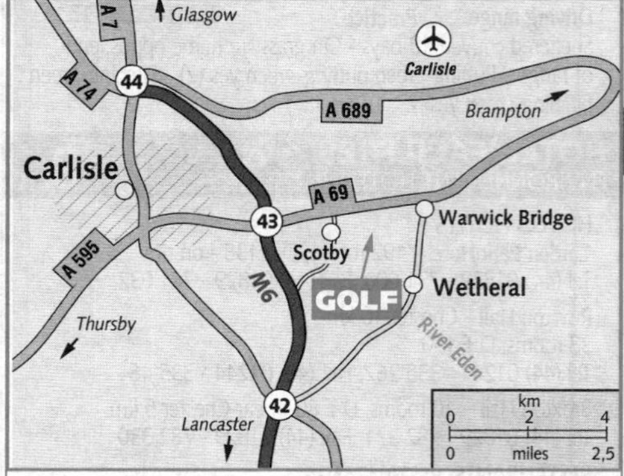

Access Accès : M6 Jct 43, A69 East, Golf 1 km on the right.
Map 2 on page 473 Carte 2 Page 473

GOLF COURSE — PARCOURS — 16/20

Site Site
Maintenance Entretien
Architect Architecte Tom Simpson, Mackenzie Ross
Type Type parkland
Relief Relief
Water in play Eau en jeu
Exp. to wind Exposé au vent
Trees in play Arbres en jeu

Scorecard Carte de score	**Chp.** Chp.	**Mens** Mess.	**Ladies** Da.
Length Long.	5601	5408	4945
Par	71	71	73
Slope system	—	—	—

Advised golfing ability Niveau de jeu recommandé 0 12 24 36
Hcp required Handicap exigé certificate

CLUB HOUSE & AMENITIES — CLUB HOUSE ET ANNEXES — 7/10

Pro shop Pro-shop
Driving range Practice
Sheltered couvert no - On grass sur herbe practice area -
Putting-green putting-green yes - Pitching-green pitching green yes

HOTEL FACILITIES — ENVIRONNEMENT HOTELIER — 7/10

HOTELS HÔTELS

Crown Hotel - 51 rooms, D from £ 110 - Wetheral 4 km
Tel (44) 01228 - 561 888, Fax (44) 01228 - 561 637

Lakes Court - 70 rooms, D £ 90 - Carlisle 5 km
Tel (44) 01228 - 531 951, Fax (44) 01228 - 547 799

Cumbria Park - 47 rooms, D £ 120 - Carlisle 5 km
Tel (44) 01228 - 522 887, Fax (44) 01228 - 514 796

Crown + Mitre - 94 rooms, D £ 98 - Carlisle 5 km
Tel (44) 01228 - 525 491, Fax (44) 01228 - 514 553

RESTAURANTS RESTAURANTS

No 10 - Carlisle 5 km - Tel (44) 01228 - 524 183
Crown Hotel - Wetheral 4 km - Tel (44) 01228 - 561 888

Castletown

18	6	8

In the middle of the Irish Sea, the Isle of Man is reached by ferry or by air from Blackpool. Castletown is located on a sort of triangular-shaped peninsula surrounded by the sea. They say that on the 17th hole, a sliced drive could end up in Ireland, Scotland, England or Wales. Whatever, this course is exposed to all winds and only the bunkers give any real shelter. Only a few small dunes and rocks give any relief to this flat, superbly-turfed landscape. The absence of any really high dunes also allows some splendid views over the cliffs, rocks and Irish sea. After the war, Mackenzie Ross brought Castletown back to life with all the talent he showed at Turnberry and even a touch of genius. This is a golfer's paradise on the edge of a rock, but it can be hell if ever a storm sets in and sends players scampering to seek refuge in the huge and very comfortable hotel on the course. We would recommend a visit here on a fine summer's day.

En plein milieu de la mer d'Irlande, l'Ile de Man est accessible par ferry ou par avion depuis Blackpool. Castletown est situé sur une sorte de presqu'île en forme de triangle cerné par la mer : on dit que du 17, un slice peut vous envoyer en Irlande, en Ecosse, en Angleterre ou au Pays de Galles. En tout cas, ce parcours est ouvert à tous les vents, et seuls les bunkers forment vraiment des abris. Quelques petites dunes et quelques rochers donnent un semblant de relief à ce paysage plat, mais au gazon superbe. Et l'absence de très hautes dunes permet d'offrir des vues superbes sur les falaises, les rochers et la mer d'Irlande. Après la guerre, Mackenzie Ross a rendu Castletown à la vie, avec autant de talent qu'à Turnberry, parfois même une forme de génie. C'est un paradis de golfeur sur un bout de rocher, que seule la tempête peut transformer en enfer, mais il ne reste plus alors qu'à se réfugier à l'hôtel sur le site, à la fois vaste et très confortable. Si l'on ne joue qu'une fois, on conseillera plutôt de venir par une belle journée d'été.

Castletown Golf Club — 1892

Fort Island
ENG - CASTLETOWN, Isle of Man

Office Secrétariat (44) 01624 - 822 220
Pro shop Pro-shop (44) 01624 - 822 211
Fax Fax (44) 01624 - 829 661
Web www.castletowngolflinks.co.uk
Situation Situation Castletown, 4.5 km
Douglas (pop. 22 214), 15 km

Annual closure Fermeture annuelle no
Weekly closure Fermeture hebdomadaire no

Fees main season Tarifs haute saison 18 holes

	Week days / Semaine	We/Bank holidays / We/Férié
Individual Individuel	£ 37	£ 43*
Couple Couple	£ 74	£ 86*

* We: Friday, Saturday, Sunday / After 15:00, £ 20

Caddie Caddie no — **Electric Trolley** Chariot électrique no
Buggy Voiturette yes — **Clubs** Clubs yes
Credit cards Cartes de crédit
VISA - Eurocard - MasterCard - AMEX - DC

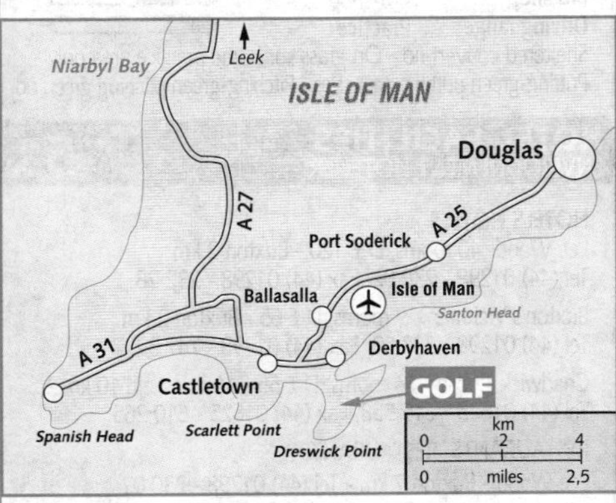

Access Accès : Close to airport
Map 9 on page 486 Carte 9 Page 486

GOLF COURSE — PARCOURS 18/20

Site Site
Maintenance Entretien
Architect Architecte Mackenzie Ross
Type Type seaside course, links
Relief Relief
Water in play Eau en jeu
Exp. to wind Exposé au vent
Trees in play Arbres en jeu

Scorecard / Carte de score	Chp. / Chp.	Mens / Mess.	Ladies / Da.
Length Long.	6040	5890	5072
Par	73	72	73
Slope system	–	–	–

Advised golfing ability 0 12 24 36
Niveau de jeu recommandé
Hcp required Handicap exigé certificate

CLUB HOUSE & AMENITIES — CLUB HOUSE ET ANNEXES 6/10

Pro shop Pro-shop
Driving range Practice
Sheltered couvert no - On grass sur herbe practice ground only - Putting-green putting-green yes - Pitching-green pitching green yes

HOTEL FACILITIES — ENVIRONNEMENT HOTELIER 8/10

HOTELS HÔTELS
Sefton- Douglas 15 km
100 rooms, D £ 100
Tel (44) 01624 - 645 500, Fax (44) 01624 - 676 004

Mount Murray - 90 rooms, D from £ 115 - Douglas 9 km
Tel (44) 01624 - 661 111, Fax (44) 01624 - 611 116

Empress - 102 rooms, D £ 75 - Douglas 15 km
Tel (44) 01624 - 661 155, Fax (44) 01624 - 673 554

RESTAURANTS RESTAURANTS
Chablis Cellar - Castletown 3 km - Tel (44) 01624 - 823 527
The Waterfront - Douglas 15 km - Tel (44) 01624 - 673 222
Blazers (Pub) - Douglas 15 km - Tel (44) 01624 - 673 222

Cavendish

15	6	5

This course could be a highlight of your first visit to Buxton, one of the gateways to the Peak District and a neo-classical spa town with a beautiful opera house that each year hosts a summer music festival. In a region where there could be more top-notch courses, this layout emerges as one of the best, even though it has been seriously underestimated in rankings published to date. A walk-over par 68? With five par 3s and only one par 5, birdie chances are rare, ostensibly because architect Alister Mackenzie has few peers when it comes to artful deception, varying his use of slopes, inclines and hazards (but no water). His layout harmonizes beautifully with the natural lie of the land, introducing pleasant changes of tempo and a few problems of strategy here and there. The test here is not one of length but of intelligence , with a very fine stretch from holes 8 to 11 and a tough closing hole. Without ever being as distinguished as Alwoodley or Moortown, this is one of the very good Mackenzie courses in Britain.

On découvrira en même temps que ce golf l'une des portes du parc national du Peak District, Buxton, une ville d'eau néo-classique avec un très bel opéra accueillant chaque été un festival de musique. Dans une région pas si fournie en bons parcours, celui-ci émerge au tout premier rang, quand bien même il serait sérieusement sous-estimé dans les palmarès. Facile, en par 68 ? Avec cinq pars 3 et un seul par 5, les occasions de birdie seront rares, car son architecte Alister Mackenzie s'y entendait comme personne pour tromper son monde, variant l'utilisation des pentes, des dévers, des obstacles (mais pas d'obstacles d'eau). Son tracé joue à merveille avec le paysage, avec des changements de rythme agréables, quelques problèmes de stratégie ici et là. Le test n'est pas ici la longueur, mais l'intelligence du dessin, avec un très beau passage du 8 au 11 et un difficile trou final. Sans être aussi distingué que Alwoodley ou Moortown, il s'agit là d'un des très bons Mackenzie de Grande-Bretagne.

Cavendish Golf Club — 1925

Gadley Lane
ENG - BUXTON, Derbyshire SX17 6XD

Office	Secrétariat	(44) 01298 - 797 08
Pro shop	Pro-shop	(44) 01298 - 797 08
Fax	Fax	—
Web	www.cavendishgolfcourse.com	
Situation	Situation	Manchester, 25 km
Annual closure	Fermeture annuelle	no
Weekly closure	Fermeture hebdomadaire	no
Fees main season	Tarifs haute saison	18 holes

	Week days Semaine	We/Bank holidays We/Férié
Individual Individuel	£ 30	£ 40
Couple Couple	£ 60	£ 80

Full week days: £ 40 / Juniors: – 50%

Caddie Caddie no — **Electric Trolley** Chariot électrique no

Buggy Voiturette no — **Clubs** Clubs yes

Credit cards Cartes de crédit
VISA - MasterCard

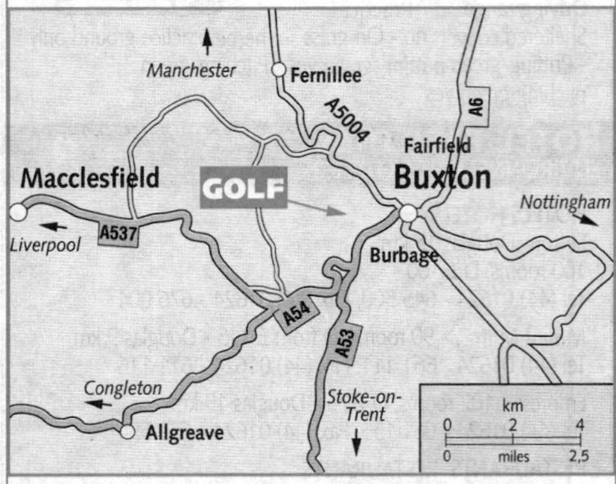

Access Accès : Manchester to Stockport, then → Buxton, A5004 to Buxton, then A53 → Leek, golf 2 km (well signposted)
Map 4 on page 476 Carte 4 Page 476

GOLF COURSE — PARCOURS 15/20

Site	Site	
Maintenance	Entretien	
Architect	Architecte	Alister Mackenzie
Type	Type	inland, parkland
Relief	Relief	
Water in play	Eau en jeu	
Exp. to wind	Exposé au vent	
Trees in play	Arbres en jeu	

Scorecard Carte de score	Chp. Chp.	Mens Mess.	Ladies Da.
Length Long.	5149	4980	4646
Par	68	68	72
Slope system	—	—	—

Advised golfing ability 0 12 24 36
Niveau de jeu recommandé
Hcp required Handicap exigé no

CLUB HOUSE & AMENITIES — CLUB HOUSE ET ANNEXES 6/10

Pro shop Pro-shop
Driving range Practice
Sheltered couvert no - On grass sur herbe practice area only -
Putting-green putting-green yes - Pitching-green pitching green no

HOTEL FACILITIES — ENVIRONNEMENT HOTELIER 5/10

HOTELS HÔTELS
Lee Wood- 40 rooms, D £ 120 - Buxton 2 km
Tel (44) 01298 - 230 02, Fax (44) 01298 - 232 28

Buxton's Victorian - 9 rooms, D £ 65 - Buxton 2 km
Tel (44) 01298 - 787 59, Fax (44) 01298 - 747 32

Chadwick House - 14 rooms, D £ 55 - Macclesfield 10 km
Tel (44) 01625 - 615 558, Fax (44) 01625 - 610 265

RESTAURANTS RESTAURANTS
Lee Wood - Buxton 2 km - Tel (44) 01298 - 230 02
White House - Prestbury 14 km - Tel (44) 01625 - 829 376

Chart Hills

18	8	6

They say you shouldn't always expect champions to be great course designers. Well here, Nick Faldo, backed by the excellent (and discreet) American specialist Steve Smyers, has produced a masterly layout. We admit that our very high score is intended more for experienced players, and many golfers find this course a little over-elaborate with a touch too much sand and water. Those who are afraid that their game might not be up to such a challenge should head shamelessly straight for the front tees. Only there will they learn how to tame a layout which is psychologically rather than really difficult. It was designed with brilliant, bold and uncompromising intelligence. Upholders of the British tradition for discreet courses will be a little surprised here, that's for sure, but you need visual and technical shocks such as this to keep your game moving.

On ne doit pas toujours espérer des champions qu'ils soient de grands architectes. Cependant, épaulé par l'excellent (et discret) spécialiste américain Steve Smyers, Nick Faldo a réussi un coup de maître et a depuis imposé un style. Certes, notre note très favorable pour Chart Hills est plutôt destinée aux joueurs expérimentés, car beaucoup de golfeurs trouvent ce parcours "trop dessiné," avec un rien trop de sable et un peu trop d'eau. Mais que ceux qui ont peur de ne pas avoir un jeu à la hauteur des défis présentés choisiront sans honte les départs avancés, ils apprendront à apprivoiser ce tracé plus difficile psychologiquement que réellement, conçu avec une brillante intelligence, avec hardiesse, sans concessions. Certes, les tenants de la tradition britannique d'une architecture discrète seront ici surpris, mais il faut des chocs visuels et techniques de ce genre pour progresser. La qualité générale de ce parcours et de ses installations est exceptionnelle.

Chart Hills Golf Club — 1993

Weeks Lane
ENG - BIDDENDEN, Kent TN27 8JX

Office	Secrétariat	(44) 01580 - 292 222
Pro shop	Pro-shop	(44) 01580 - 292 148
Fax	Fax	(44) 01580 - 292 233
Web	www.charthills.co.uk	
Situation	Situation	Ashford, 14 km

Maidstone (pop. 136 209), 20 km

Annual closure	Fermeture annuelle	no
Weekly closure	Fermeture hebdomadaire	no
Fees main season	Tarifs haute saison	18 holes

	Week days Semaine	We/Bank holidays We/Férié
Individual Individuel	£ 45	£ 68*
Couple Couple	£ 90	£ 136*

Week days: Monday → Friday morning /* We: visitors after 14:00

Caddie Caddie no — **Electric Trolley** Chariot électrique yes
Buggy Voiturette yes — **Clubs** Clubs yes

Credit cards Cartes de crédit
VISA - MasterCard - AMEX

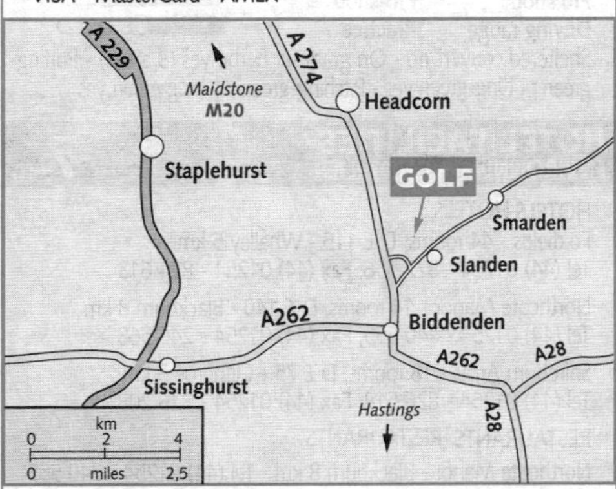

Access Accès : • M20, Jct 6 to Maidstone. A274 → Biddenden. After Headcorn, left at Petrol Station, signpost to Smarden • Ashford, A28 to Tenderden, A262 to Biddenden, A274 → Headcorn. **Map 7 on page 483** Carte 7 Page 483

GOLF COURSE — PARCOURS — 18/20

Site	Site	
Maintenance	Entretien	
Architect	Architecte	Nick Faldo, S. Smyers
Type	Type	parkland, open country
Relief	Relief	
Water in play	Eau en jeu	
Exp. to wind	Exposé au vent	
Trees in play	Arbres en jeu	

Scorecard Carte de score	Chp. Chp.	Mens Mess.	Ladies Da.
Length Long.	6375	5780	4980
Par	72	72	72
Slope system	—	—	—

Advised golfing ability Niveau de jeu recommandé: 0 12 24 36
Hcp required Handicap exigé: no

CLUB HOUSE & AMENITIES — CLUB HOUSE ET ANNEXES — 8/10

Pro shop Pro-shop
Driving range Practice
Sheltered couvert no - On grass sur herbe yes - Putting-green putting-green yes - Pitching-green pitching green yes (2)

HOTEL FACILITIES — ENVIRONNEMENT HOTELIER — 6/10

HOTELS HÔTELS

Eastwell Manor - 62 rooms, D £ 220 - Ashford 20 km
Tel (44) 01233 - 213 000, Fax (44) 01233 - 213 017

Ashford International - Ashford 14 km
201 rooms, D from £ 90
Tel (44) 01233 - 219 988, Fax (44) 01233 - 647 743

Pilgrims Rest - 29 rooms, D £ 75 - Ashford 14 km
Tel (44) 01233 - 636 863, Fax (44) 01233 - 610 119

RESTAURANTS RESTAURANTS

Three Chimneys - Biddenden 2 km - Tel (44) 01580 - 291 472
Alhambra (Ashford Intern.) - Goudhurst 20 km
Tel (44) 01233 - 219 988
Eastwell Manor - Ashford 14 km - Tel (44) 01233 - 213 000

Clitheroe

16 | 7 | 7

The course's location on the edge of the forest of Bowland in the Ribble Valley makes this an ideal site for a few days off the beaten track exploring rivers, old villages, a Roman camp and an abbey or two. Here, the fairways are carpeted with thick turf which prevents balls from ever rolling too far, trees abound but the fairways are wide and the rough not too severe. A few water hazards threaten and readily swallow up any miscued shots, but they are there to be seen and so won't cause any unpleasant surprises. As on many of James Braid's courses, a sharp short game is of the essence, as is skill in rolling the ball onto the greens. This is another course that deserves rehabilitation, even if its short yardage may not always be to the liking of golfers who hit the ball a long way. But as long-hitters sometimes tend to hook the ball, the out-of-bounds areas down the left on the front 9 will teach them a little respect. The course has changed very little and recent work has been devoted to the club-house.

La situation de ce club en bordure de la forêt de Bowland, au coeur de la Ribble Valley, en fait un site idéal pour quelques jours hors des sentiers battus, à la découverte des rivières et vieux villages, d'un camp romain ou d'une abbaye. Le parcours bénéficie d'un gazon fourni, ce qui évite aux balles de trop rouler. Les arbres sont très nombreux, mais les fairways sont larges et les roughs peu pénalisants. Quelques obstacles d'eau menacent ou retiennent quelques mauvais coups, mais ils sont bien visibles et ne sauraient causer de mauvaises surprises. De fait, comme sur de nombreux parcours de James Braid, il est essentiel d'avoir un bon petit jeu, en particulier savoir faire rouler la balle roulée. Encore un parcours à réhabiliter, même si sa longueur le fait regarder avec indifférence par les frappeurs. Comme ce sont souvent des "hockers," les hors-limites à gauche à l'aller leur apprendront le respect. Le parcours a peu changé, et les récents efforts ont surtout été consacrés au club-house.

Clitheroe Golf Club — 1932

Whalley Road
ENG - PENDLETON, Lancs BB7 1PP

Office Secrétariat (44) 01200 - 422 292
Pro shop Pro-shop (44) 01200 - 424 242
Fax Fax (44) 01200 - 422 292
Web www.clitheroegolfclub.com
Situation Situation Blackburn, 15 km
Clitheroe (pop. 13 548), 3 km

Annual closure Fermeture annuelle — no
Weekly closure Fermeture hebdomadaire — no
Fees main season Tarifs haute saison — 18 holes

	Week days / Semaine	We/Bank holidays / We/Férié
Individual Individuel	£ 33	£ 45
Couple Couple	£ 66	£ 90

Full week day, £ 38 (Friday £ 39) / 18 holes Friday £ 35

Caddie Caddie no — **Electric Trolley** Chariot électrique no
Buggy Voiturette no — **Clubs** Clubs no
Credit cards Cartes de crédit
VISA (Pro shop & restaurant only)

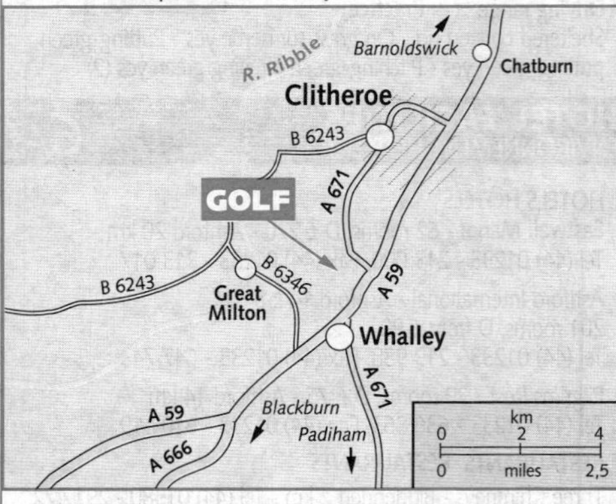

Access Accès : Blackburn, A666 then A59 → Clitheroe.
Golf 3 km on Whalley Road.
Map 4 on page 476 Carte 4 Page 476

GOLF COURSE — PARCOURS — 16/20

Site Site
Maintenance Entretien
Architect Architecte — James Braid
Type Type — parkland
Relief Relief
Water in play Eau en jeu
Exp. to wind Exposé au vent
Trees in play Arbres en jeu

Scorecard / Carte de score	Chp. / Chp.	Mens / Mess.	Ladies / Da.
Length Long.	5693	5490	4586
Par	71	71	74
Slope system	—	—	—

Advised golfing ability / Niveau de jeu recommandé — 0 12 24 36
Hcp required Handicap exigé — certificate

CLUB HOUSE & AMENITIES — CLUB HOUSE ET ANNEXES — 7/10

Pro shop Pro-shop
Driving range Practice
Sheltered couvert no - On grass sur herbe yes (3 areas) - Putting-green putting-green yes - Pitching-green pitching green yes

HOTEL FACILITIES — ENVIRONNEMENT HOTELIER — 7/10

HOTELS HÔTELS
Foxfields - 44 rooms, D £ 115 - Whalley 5 km
Tel (44) 01254 - 822 556, Fax (44) 01254 - 824 613

Northcote Manor - 14 rooms, D £ 140 - Blackburn 8 km
Tel (44) 01254 - 240 555, Fax (44) 01254 - 246 568

Shireburn Arms - 18 rooms, D £ 75 - Clitheroe 3 km
Tel (44) 01254 - 826 518, Fax (44) 01254 - 826 208

RESTAURANTS RESTAURANTS
Northcote Manor - Blackburn 8 km - Tel (44) 01254 - 240 555
The Longridge Restaurant - Longridge 18 km
Tel (44) 01772 - 784 969
Browns Bistro - Clitheroe 3 km - Tel (44) 01200 - 426 928
Inn at Whitewell - Clitheroe 3 km - Tel (44) 01200 - 448 222

Collingtree Park

15 | 8 | 7

A corner of the United States in England, a nice change of style for the English but continental Europeans might prefer a little more local colour. With water in play on eight of the 18 holes, numerous well-placed bunkers which lack the "feeling" of what a Simpson, a Colt or a Braid might have produced, and well-balanced difficulties geared to the very many different tee-boxes, Collingtree Park is a good, very pleasant and often very interesting American style course. It doesn't always blend into the surrounding landscape – but then the surroundings aren't exactly beautiful! Johnny Miller was a player who attacked golf courses and there wasn't a great deal of subtlety in his game and this trait appears to be reflected in his approach to course design. Somewhat surprisingly, Miller has succeeded in giving the last nine something of a links feel despite the water hazards. At all events, there is no disputing the excellence of practice facilities and services on offer.

Un coin d'Etats-Unis en Angleterre, c'est dépaysant pour les Anglais, mais les continentaux attendent plus de couleur locale. Avec de l'eau en jeu sur huit des 18 trous, des bunkers nombreux, et bien placés, mais aux formes moins "sensuelles" que les créations de Simpson, Braid ou Colt, des difficultés bien balancées suivant les différents (et nombreux) départs, Collingtree Park est un bon parcours à l'américaine, très agréable et souvent très intéressant. Son intégration à la nature environnante n'est pas toujours aussi complète qu'on le souhaiterait et les alentours procurent peu de chocs visuels. Johnny Miller a été un très grand attaquant, sans excès de subtilité et l'on retrouve cela dans son approche de l'architecture où l'on attendait peut-être davantage de lui... la surprise étant de le voir retrouver sur les neuf derniers trous un certain esprit des links, même avec des obstacles d'eau. Et, la qualité remarquable des installations d'entraînement et des services offerts reste incontestable.

Collingtree Park Golf Club — 1987

Windingbrook Lane
ENG - NORTHAMPTON NN4 0XN

Office	Secrétariat	(44) 01604 - 633 940
Pro shop	Pro-shop	(44) 01604 - 700 000
Fax	Fax	(44) 01604 - 702 600
Web	www.collingtreeparkgolf.com	
Situation	Situation	Northampton, 10 km
Annual closure	Fermeture annuelle	no
Weekly closure	Fermeture hebdomadaire	no

Fees main season Tarifs haute saison — 18 holes

	Week days Semaine	We/Bank holidays We/Férié
Individual Individuel	£ 50	£ 60*
Couple Couple	£ 100	£ 120*

* We: Friday, Saturday, Sunday

Caddie Caddie no — **Electric Trolley** Chariot électrique no
Buggy Voiturette yes — **Clubs** Clubs yes

Credit cards Cartes de crédit
VISA - Eurocard - MasterCard - AMEX - DC

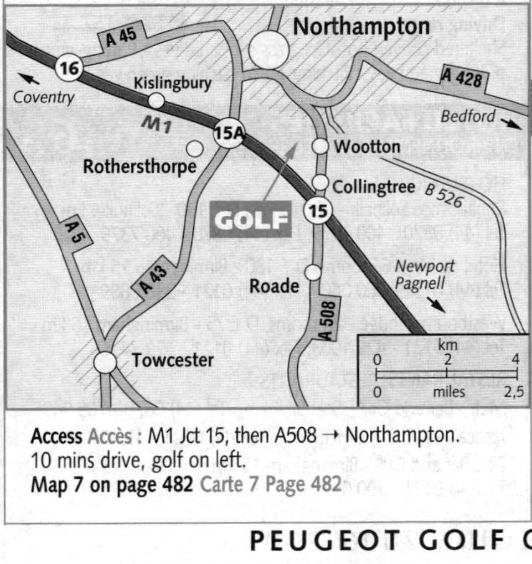

Access Accès : M1 Jct 15, then A508 → Northampton.
10 mins drive, golf on left.
Map 7 on page 482 Carte 7 Page 482

GOLF COURSE — PARCOURS — 15/20

Site	Site	
Maintenance	Entretien	
Architect	Architecte	Johnny Miller
Type	Type	parkland
Relief	Relief	
Water in play	Eau en jeu	
Exp. to wind	Exposé au vent	
Trees in play	Arbres en jeu	

Scorecard Carte de score	Chp. Chp.	Mens Mess.	Ladies Da.
Length Long.	6217	5598	4860
Par	72	72	73
Slope system	—	—	—

Advised golfing ability Niveau de jeu recommandé — 0 12 24 36
Hcp required Handicap exigé — certificate

CLUB HOUSE & AMENITIES — CLUB HOUSE ET ANNEXES — 8/10

Pro shop Pro-shop
Driving range Practice
Sheltered couvert 16 bays (floodlit) - On grass sur herbe yes - Putting-green putting-green yes - Pitching-green pitching green yes

HOTEL FACILITIES — ENVIRONNEMENT HOTELIER — 7/10

HOTELS HÔTELS
Hilton Northampton - 139 rooms, D £ 240 - Northampton 2 km
Tel (44) 01604 - 700 666, Fax (44) 01604 - 702 850

Northampton Marriott - Northampton 10 km
120 rooms, D from £ 135
Tel (44) 01604 - 768 700, Fax (44) 01604 - 769 011

Lime Trees - 27 rooms, D £ 85 - Northampton 10 km
Tel (44) 01604 - 632 188, Fax (44) 01604 - 233 012

RESTAURANTS RESTAURANTS
La Fontana (North. Marriott) - Northampton 10 km - Tel (44) 01604 - 768 700

The New French Partridge - Horton 7 km
Tel (44) 01604 - 870 033

Copt Heath

16 | 6 | 6

Although the Club will celebrate its centenary, its members haven't tired of investing in the future of the game by organizing each year the Peter McEvoy Trophy, a tournament played for young golfers. Geographically the course is ideally placed. The Midlands are indeed the heart of England as seen by the numbers of old stone or Tudor-style houses, museums of the industrial age, manors and monuments, not forgetting the string of gardens from Warwick to Cheltenham, the envy of many would-be gardeners who are more heavy-handed than green-fingered. And green is certainly the colour on show at Copt Heath, where green-keeping is almost an obsession, doubtless in homage to one of the crispest and most stylish designs ever produced by Harry Vardon and Harry Colt. There is nothing unusual about the layout , except maybe the classic and sensible blend of trees nicely in play, well-shaped bunkers and greens perfectly adjusted to the length and type of stroke you need to play. An elegant, strategic and varied course where every slip-up gets exactly what it deserves.

Certes, le club va fêter son centenaire, tout en jouant la carte de la jeunesse avec l'organisation chaque année du Peter McEvoy Trophy pour les juniors... Il est géographiquement bien placé car les Midlands sont le cœur de l'Angleterre et cela se voit par la quantité de vieilles maisons en pierre ou à colombages, de musées de l'âge industriel, de manoirs et monuments, sans oublier ce circuit de jardins de Warwick à Cheltenham qui fera pâlir de jalousie ceux qui ont la main plus lourde que verte. C'est d'ailleurs une couleur que l'on célèbre à Copt Heath, où l'entretien du parcours est presque maniaque, en hommage sans doute à l'un des plus purs dessins de Harry Vardon et Harry Colt. Il ne présente rien d'inhabituel, sinon le mélange classique et raisonné de mise en jeu des arbres, de bunkers bien sculptés, de greens exactement adaptés à la longueur et la nature du coup à jouer. Un tracé élégant, stratégique, varié, où la punition est toujours en juste proportion de l'erreur commise.

Copt Heath Golf Club — 1907

1220 Warwick Road, Knowle
ENG - KNOWLE, SOLLIHULL, W. Midlands B93 9LN

Office Secrétariat (44) 01564 - 772 650
Pro shop Pro-shop (44) 01564 - 776 155
Fax Fax (44) 01564 - 771 022
Web www.coptheath.co.uk
Situation Situation Birmingham, 15 km
Annual closure Fermeture annuelle no
Weekly closure Fermeture hebdomadaire no

Fees main season Tarifs haute saison — 18 holes

	Week days / Semaine	We/Bank holidays / We/Férié
Individual Individuel	£ 40	£ 40
Couple Couple	£ 80	£ 80

Fullday: £ 50 / We: ask before coming

Caddie Caddie no — **Electric Trolley** Chariot électrique no
Buggy Voiturette yes — **Clubs** Clubs no
Credit cards Cartes de crédit
VISA - MasterCard

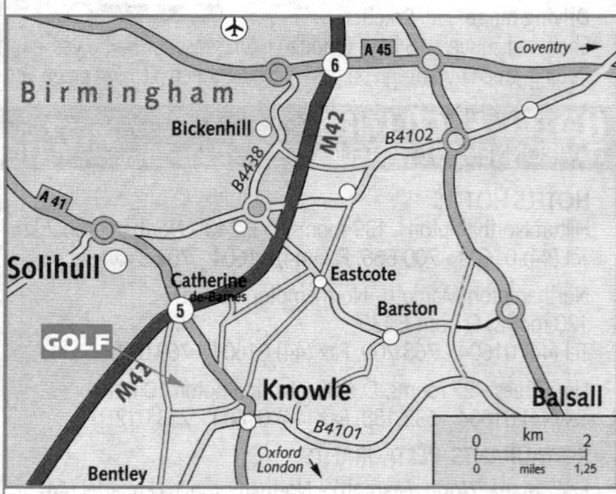

Access Accès : M42, Exit at Jct 5. The Club is south of the motorway (sign posted Knowle), around 800 yards from the motorway on your right.
Map 7 on page 482 Carte 7 Page 482

GOLF COURSE — PARCOURS 16/20

Site Site
Maintenance Entretien
Architect Architecte Harry Vardon, Harry S. Colt
Type Type parkland
Relief Relief
Water in play Eau en jeu
Exp. to wind Exposé au vent
Trees in play Arbres en jeu

Scorecard / Carte de score	Chp. / Chp.	Mens / Mess.	Ladies / Da.
Length Long.	5868	5530	5048
Par	71	71	73
Slope system	—	—	—

Advised golfing ability 0 12 24 36
Niveau de jeu recommandé
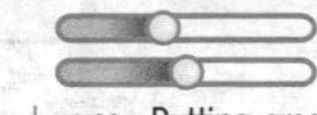
Hcp required Handicap exigé certificate

CLUB HOUSE & AMENITIES — CLUB HOUSE ET ANNEXES 6/10

Pro shop Pro-shop
Driving range Practice
Sheltered couvert no - On grass sur herbe yes - Putting-green putting-green yes - Pitching-green pitching green yes

HOTEL FACILITIES — ENVIRONNEMENT HOTELIER 6/10

HOTELS HÔTELS
Renaissance Solihull - 180 rooms, D £ 130 - Solihull 4 km
Tel (44) 0870 - 400 7279, Fax (44) 0870 - 400 7379

Hotel du Vin - 66 rooms, D £ 180 - Birmingham 15 km
Tel (44) 0121 - 200 0600, Fax (44) 0121 - 236 0889

Westbourne Lodge - 24 rooms, D £ 75 - Birmingham 15 km
Tel (44) 0121 - 429 1003, Fax (44) 0121 - 429 7436

RESTAURANTS RESTAURANTS
Metro Bar and Grill - Solihull 4 km - Tel (44) 0870 - 705 9495
Jessica's - Birmingham 15 km - Tel (44) 0121 - 455 0999
Zinc Bar and Grill - Birmingham 15 km
Tel (44) 0121 - 200 0620

Coxmoor

15	6	6

With Notts, Sherwood Forest and Coxmoor, this region has three no-nonsense courses, the latter being sited on attractive moorland,and hilly enough to test your fitness as well as your golfing skills. A good score is there for the taking as long as you avoid the traps on some of the dog-leg holes or carry a number of dangerous hazards, but there could be some mean surprises in store when you come to add up your score. Strategy here is even more important than the standard of your game and the hazards are generally in clear view from the many elevated tee-boxes. Very pleasant to play with the family or friends, there is an obvious parallel to be drawn with the many similar courses found in Surrey, the one reservation being the sameness of several holes which make some of them difficult to remember. The location of this course on one of the highest points of Nottinghamshire provides some remarkable vistas over the valleys of adjacent Leicestershire.

Entre Notts, Sherwood Forest et Coxmoor, cette région dispose de trois parcours peu contestables. Celui-ci est dans un bel espace de landes, assez accidenté pour tester la forme physique autant que golfique. Un bon score est à votre portée du moment que vous savez déjouer les pièges de certains doglegs ou survoler quelques obstacles dangereux, mais on peut avoir des surprises au moment de l'addition. La stratégie est ici encore plus importante que la qualité du jeu, et les obstacles sont généralement visibles car beaucoup de départs sont en hauteur. Très agréable à jouer avec des amis ou en famille, que ce soit en stroke-play ou en match-play, ce parcours est à mettre en parallèle avec de nombreux parcours similaires du Surrey, avec une petite restriction sur la similarité de plusieurs trous, qui gêne la précision des souvenirs. La situation du parcours sur l'un des sites les plus élevés du Nottinghamshire permet d'offrir des points de vue remarquables sur les vallons du Leicestershire voisin.

Coxmoor Golf Club — 1913

Coxmoor Road
ENG - SUTTON-IN- ASHFIELD, Notts. NG17 5LF

Office Secrétariat (44) 01623 - 557 359
Pro shop Pro-shop (44) 01623 - 559 906
Fax Fax (44) 01623 - 559 854
Web www.coxmoor.freeuk.com
Situation Situation Mansfield, 7 km
Annual closure Fermeture annuelle no
Weekly closure Fermeture hebdomadaire no

Fees main season Tarifs haute saison	18 holes	
	Week days Semaine	**We/Bank holidays** We/Férié
Individual Individuel	£ 40	*
Couple Couple	£ 80	*

* No visitors / Full week days: £ 55

Caddie Caddie no — **Electric Trolley** Chariot électrique no
Buggy Voiturette no — **Clubs** Clubs no

Credit cards Cartes de crédit
Visa - Eurocard - Mastercard (Pro shop & green fees)

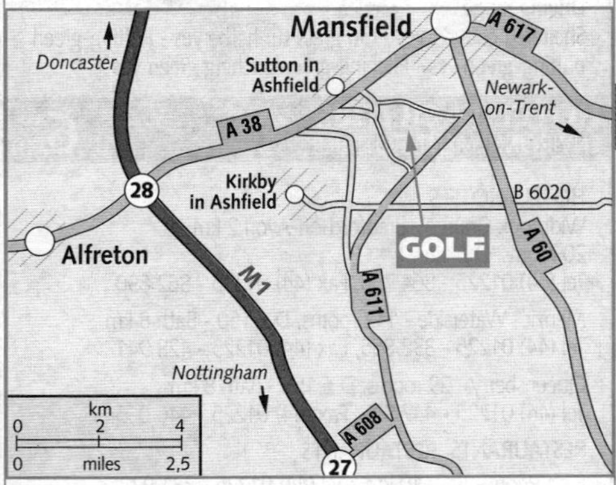

Access Accès : M1 Jct 27. A608 then A611 → Coxmoor
Map 4 on page 476 Carte 4 Page 476

GOLF COURSE — PARCOURS 15/20

Site Site
Maintenance Entretien
Architect Architecte unknown
Type Type parkland, heathland
Relief Relief
Water in play Eau en jeu
Exp. to wind Exposé au vent
Trees in play Arbres en jeu

Scorecard Carte de score	**Chp.** Chp.	**Mens** Mess.	**Ladies** Da.
Length Long.	5914	5626	4936
Par	73	73	74
Slope system	—	—	—

Advised golfing ability Niveau de jeu recommandé: 0 12 24 36
Hcp required Handicap exigé certificate

CLUB HOUSE & AMENITIES — CLUB HOUSE ET ANNEXES 6/10

Pro shop Pro-shop
Driving range Practice
Sheltered couvert practice area - On grass sur herbe yes - Putting-green putting-green yes - Pitching-green pitching green yes

HOTEL FACILITIES — ENVIRONNEMENT HOTELIER 6/10

HOTELS HÔTELS
Pine Lodge - 20 rooms, D £ 65 - Mansfield 4 km
Tel (44) 01623 - 622 308, Fax (44) 01623 - 656 819

Renaissance Derby - South Normanton 10 km
158 rooms, D £ 138
Tel (44) 01773 - 812 000, Fax (44) 01773 - 580 032

Royal Moat House - 210 rooms, D £ 135 - Nottingham 20 km
Tel (44) 0115 - 936 9988, Fax (44) 0115 - 969 1506

RESTAURANTS RESTAURANTS
Renaissance Derby - South Normanton 10 km
Tel (44) 01773 - 812 000

Restaurant Sat Bains - Nottingham 20 km
Tel (44) 0115 - 986 6566

Sonny's - Nottingham 20 km - Tel (44) 0115 - 947 3041

Cumberwell Park

16	7	6

From the back tees, this is a tough course with at least two par 5s that are virtually unreachable in two. The designer made up for this, though, by refusing those huge par 3s and preferring shorter but more technical holes. With four short par 4s, you'll find a good number of opportunities to scent some of those evasive birdies. Adrian Stiff has cleverly combined stress and relaxation. In doing so, he has made Cumberwell Park a very pleasant course to play over gently rolling landscape, dotted with elm and oak trees and crossed by a stream that is very much a part of your game. The greens have now been relaid to USGA standards. The terrain has been carefully contoured, without overdoing the visual side but with extra concern for enhancing the course within its environment. This promising layout is good value for money and its success has prompted the promoters to begin building a second course. The club-house extends a warm welcome and the practice facilities are well above the norm for the UK.

Des départs arrière, c'est un parcours solide, avec au moins deux par 5 pratiquement intouchables en deux, mais l'architecte a compensé en renonçant à ces par 3 interminables, au profit de petits trous plus techniques. Avec quatre par 4 courts, les occasions de birdie ne manqueront pas. Adrian Stiff a bien alterné la tension et la détente, ce qui rend Cumberwell Park très agréable à jouer, dans ce paysage gentiment vallonné et orné de chênes et de pins, où circule un cours d'eau bien mis en jeu. Les greens ont été très bien construits dans les normes de l'USGA. Le modelage du terrain a été fait avec soin, sans excès visuels, mais avec un bon souci de mettre en valeur le parcours dans son environnement. Cette réalisation prometteuse présente un bon rapport qualité/prix, et son succès a incité les promoteurs à entreprendre la construction d'un second parcours. Le club-house est accueillant, les installations de practice très au-dessus des normes britanniques.

Cumberwell Park Golf Club — 1994

ENG - BRADFORD-ON-AVON, Wiltshire, BA15 2PQ

Office	Secrétariat	(44) 01225 - 863 322
Pro shop	Pro-shop	(44) 01225 - 862 332
Fax	Fax	(44) 01225 - 868 160
Web	www.cumberwellpark.com	
Situation	Situation	Bath (pop. 78 689), 6 km
Annual closure	Fermeture annuelle	no
Weekly closure	Fermeture hebdomadaire	no
Fees main season	Tarifs haute saison	18 holes

	Week days Semaine	We/Bank holidays We/Férié
Individual Individuel	£ 27	£ 33
Couple Couple	£ 54	£ 66

Caddie Caddie no — **Electric Trolley** Chariot électrique no

Buggy Voiturette yes — **Clubs** Clubs yes (week days)

Credit cards Cartes de crédit

VISA - MasterCard (Pro shop goods & restaurant only)

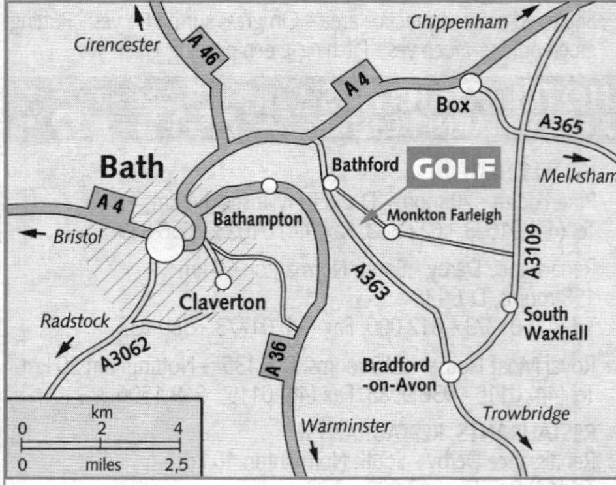

Access Accès : On A363 between Bathford and Bradford-on-Avon

Map 6 on page 481 Carte 6 Page 481

GOLF COURSE — PARCOURS — 16/20

Site	Site	
Maintenance	Entretien	
Architect	Architecte	Adrian Stiff
Type	Type	parkland
Relief	Relief	
Water in play	Eau en jeu	
Exp. to wind	Exposé au vent	
Trees in play	Arbres en jeu	

Scorecard Carte de score	Chp. Chp.	Mens Mess.	Ladies Da.
Length Long.	6218	5902	5070
Par	72	72	72
Slope system	—	—	—

Advised golfing ability / Niveau de jeu recommandé: 0 12 24 36

Hcp required — Handicap exigé: certificate

CLUB HOUSE & AMENITIES — CLUB HOUSE ET ANNEXES — 7/10

Pro shop — Pro-shop

Driving range — Practice

Sheltered couvert yes - On grass sur herbe yes - Putting-green putting-green yes - Pitching-green pitching green yes

HOTEL FACILITIES — ENVIRONNEMENT HOTELIER — 6/10

HOTELS HÔTELS

Widbrook Grange - Bradford-on-Avon 2 km
20 rooms, D £ 120
Tel (44) 01225 - 864 750, Fax (44) 01225 - 862 890

Menzies Waterside - 112 rooms, D £ 150 - Bath 8 km
Tel (44) 01225 - 338 855, Fax (44) 01225 - 428 941

Queensberry - 29 rooms, D £ 155 - Bath 8 km
Tel (44) 01225 - 447 928, Fax (44) 01225 - 446 065

RESTAURANTS RESTAURANTS

Bath Priory - Bath 10 km - Tel (44) 01225 - 331 922

Olive Tree (Queensberry) - Bath 8 km
Tel (44) 01225 - 447 928

Richmond Arms (pub) - Bath 8 km - Tel (44) 01225 - 316 725

Dartmouth

15	9	6

Together with Bowood, this is one of the most promising new courses in this very romantic region of moor-land and heath land. It is also as surprising as the gardens of neighbouring Torquay might appear to foreign visitors... they would do the French Riviera proud. This new course is an inland and rather hilly layout (buggy highly recommended, and the club has 30 for hire). Designer Jeremy Pern has created many very good courses on the continent of Europe (particularly in France) but this is probably one of his very best. He has used land very cleverly indeed, forcing players from the back-tees (this makes the course very long) to carry the ball a long way, particularly to clear the dozen or so water hazards. First time out, this is your typical match-play course. If it's too tough for you, try the 5,200 m Dartmouth Course. The club-house (with cottages) is remarkably well equipped with a pool, sauna, jacuzzi and gymnasium.

Avec Bowood, c'est l'une des réalisations prometteuses dans cette région très romantique aux paysages de landes, mais souvent aussi surprenante que les jardins de Torquay, dignes de la Riviéra française, à quelques kilomètres de Dartmouth, d'où partirent les navires des croisades. Ce nouveau parcours est à l'intérieur des terres, et assez accidenté pour ne pas avoir honte d'emprunter une voiturette. L'architecte Jeremy Pern a fait de nombreux très bons parcours sur le continent (en France notamment), et celui-ci est sans doute l'un de ses tout meilleurs, notamment par l'utilisation très intelligente du terrain, obligeant à porter loin la balle des départs arrière (il est alors très long), en particulier au-dessus des nombreux obstacles d'eau (une douzaine). La première fois, c'est un parcours de match-play typique. Et l'on peut toujours se contenter du Dartmouth Course, de 5200 m. Le club-house (avec cottages) est remarquablement équipé, avec piscine, sauna, jaccuzzi et gymnase.

Dartmouth Golf & Country Club — 1992

Blackawton
ENG - TOTNES, Devon TQ9 7 DE

Office Secrétariat (44) 01803 - 712 686
Pro shop Pro-shop (44) 01803 - 712 650
Fax Fax (44) 01803 - 712 628
Web www.dgcc.co.uk
Situation Situation Totnes, 12 km
Dartmouth (pop. 5 712), 4 km
Annual closure Fermeture annuelle no
Weekly closure Fermeture hebdomadaire no

Fees main season Tarifs haute saison	Full day	
	Week days Semaine	**We/Bank holidays** We/Férié
Individual Individuel	£ 35	£ 45
Couple Couple	£ 70	£ 90

After 17:00, £ 10 and £ 12 (We)

Caddie Caddie yes — **Electric Trolley** Chariot électrique yes
Buggy Voiturette yes — **Clubs** Clubs yes
Credit cards Cartes de crédit
VISA - MasterCard (Pro shop goods only)

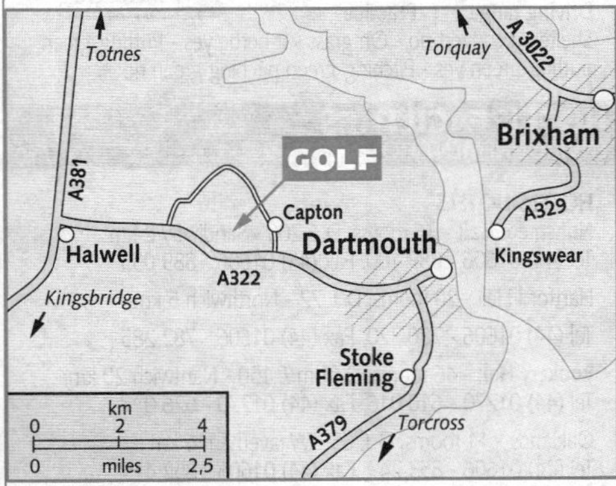

Access Accès : M5, then A380, A3022, A 379 then A3122.
Golf on right hand side.
Map 6 on page 481 Carte 6 Page 481

GOLF COURSE — PARCOURS 15/20

Site	Site	
Maintenance	Entretien	
Architect	Architecte	Jeremy Pern
Type	Type	parkland, hilly
Relief	Relief	
Water in play	Eau en jeu	
Exp. to wind	Exposé au vent	
Trees in play	Arbres en jeu	

Scorecard Carte de score	**Chp.** Chp.	**Mens** Mess.	**Ladies** Da.
Length Long.	6544	6064	5169
Par	72	72	73
Slope system	—	—	—

Advised golfing ability Niveau de jeu recommandé — 0 12 24 36
Hcp required Handicap exigé — certificate

CLUB HOUSE & AMENITIES — CLUB HOUSE ET ANNEXES 9/10

Pro shop Pro-shop
Driving range Practice
Sheltered couvert 4 bays - On grass sur herbe no - Putting-green putting-green yes - Pitching-green pitching green yes

HOTEL FACILITIES — ENVIRONNEMENT HOTELIER 6/10

HOTELS HÔTELS
Fingals (Old Coombe Farm) - Dittisham 6 km
11 rooms, D £ 100
Tel (44) 01803 - 722 398, Fax (44) 01803 - 722 401

Royal Castle - Dartmouth 8 km
25 rooms, D £ 155
Tel (44) 01803 - 833 033, Fax (44) 01803 - 835 445

Dart Marina - 49 rooms, D from £ 159 - Dartmouth 8 km
Tel (44) 01803 - 832 580, Fax (44) 01803 - 835 040

RESTAURANTS RESTAURANTS
Hooked - Dartmouth 8 km - Tel (44) 01803 - 832 022
Carved Angel - Dartmouth 8 km - Tel (44) 01803 - 832 465

Delamere Forest

16 | 6 | 7

Here we are at the traditional heart of England and this layout seems to be so symbolic of old English golf that even the card still uses the old term "bogey" instead of "par". It is rather as if the course were gently reminding you that you shouldn't expect miracles on the tougher holes. Let's forget that this should be a par 69 and be proud of playing to our handicap. The word forest should not scare you either, as this course is full of wide open spaces and beautiful views. Designed by Herbert Fowler, this is the perfect heath land course with just the right amount of trees, bunkers (sometimes very deep), heather, a splattering of water and the contours to test your legs and pose a few problems of awkwards stances and bounces. There is nothing easy about it, nothing impossible, either, and very few dog-legs. You can pitch your approach or, preferably, roll it onto the green. The golf course is built into and blends very comfortably with its surroundings.

C'est ici le coeur traditionnel de l'Angleterre, et ce parcours est comme le symbole des parcours de golf anglais, au point que la carte de score porte le terme "bogey" au lieu de par, comme pour souligner avec indulgence que l'on n'attend pas de miracles sur les trous difficiles. Oublions donc que ce devrait être un par 69, et soyons fier de jouer notre handicap. Le nom de Forest ne doit pas effrayer, car les grands espaces et les beaux points de vue ne manquent pas. Dessiné par Herbert Fowler, c'est le parfait parcours de terre de bruyère, avec les arbres qu'il faut, les bunkers qu'il faut (parfois très profonds), la bruyère bien sûr, quelques soupçons d'eau, des reliefs pour tester les jambes et poser quelques problèmes de stance et de rebonds. Rien de facile mais rien d'impossible, et assez peu de doglegs. On peut y jouer des coups levés, mais plutôt des balles roulées. Le golf est ici logé dans la nature, et s'y trouve bien à l'aise.

Delamere Forest Golf Club — 1910

Station Road, Delamere
ENG - NORTHWICH, Cheshire CW8 2JE

Office	Secrétariat	(44) 01606 - 883 800
Pro shop	Pro-shop	(44) 01606 - 883 307
Fax	Fax	(44) 01606 - 889 444
Web	www.delameregolf.co.uk	
Situation	Situation	Chester (pop.115 971), 23 km
Annual closure	Fermeture annuelle	no
Weekly closure	Fermeture hebdomadaire	no
Fees main season	Tarifs haute saison	18 holes

	Week days / Semaine	We/Bank holidays / We/Férié
Individual Individuel	£ 40	£ 60
Couple Couple	£ 80	£ 120

Full week day: £ 55

Caddie Caddie no — **Electric Trolley** Chariot électrique no
Buggy Voiturette no — **Clubs** Clubs yes
Credit cards Cartes de crédit no

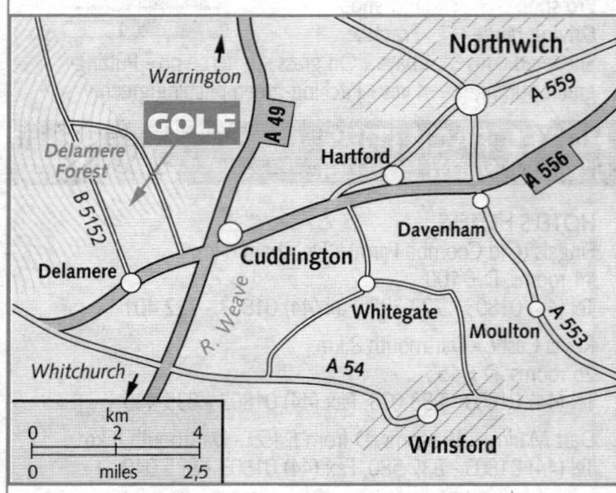

Access Accès : M6 Jct 19, then A556 → Chester. Golf on right side.
Map 4 on page 476 Carte 4 Page 476

GOLF COURSE — PARCOURS — 16/20

Site	Site	
Maintenance	Entretien	
Architect	Architecte	Herbert Fowler
Type	Type	parkland, heathland
Relief	Relief	
Water in play	Eau en jeu	
Exp. to wind	Exposé au vent	
Trees in play	Arbres en jeu	

Scorecard / Carte de score	Chp. / Chp.	Mens / Mess.	Ladies / Da.
Length Long.	5483	5483	4972
Par	72	72	72
Slope system	—	—	—

Advised golfing ability — Niveau de jeu recommandé: 0 12 24 36
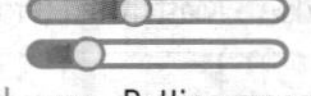
Hcp required Handicap exigé no

CLUB HOUSE & AMENITIES — CLUB HOUSE ET ANNEXES — 6/10

Pro shop Pro-shop
Driving range Practice
Sheltered couvert no - On grass sur herbe yes - Putting-green putting-green yes - Pitching-green pitching green no

HOTEL FACILITIES — ENVIRONNEMENT HOTELIER — 7/10

HOTELS HÔTELS

Nunsmere Hall - 36 rooms, D £ 200 - Sandiway 2 km
Tel (44) 01606 - 889 100, Fax (44) 01606 - 889 055

Hartford Hall - 20 rooms, D £ 72 - Northwich 5 km
Tel (44) 01606 - 780 320, Fax (44) 01606 - 782 285

Rookery Hall - 46 rooms, D from £ 150 - Nantwich 20 km
Tel (44) 01270 - 610 016, Fax (44) 01270 - 626 027

Oaklands - 11 rooms, D £ 65 - Weaverham 5 km
Tel (44) 01606 - 853 249, Fax (44) 01606 - 852 419

RESTAURANTS RESTAURANTS

Arkle - Chester 22 km - Tel (44) 01244 - 324 024
Albion Inn - Chester 22 km - Tel (44) 01244 - 340 345

Denham

15	7	7

Along with Aberdovey, this is one of the few golf courses to have its own railway station. It also has the type of club-house architecture (an impressive converted barn) that reminds you very much of a country residence, and, last but not least, is the type of course that makes you want to take up golf and continue playing for ever. There is nothing particularly spectacular about it, but no Harry Colt course is ever bland. Many of Colt's favourite design traits are in evidence at Denham: there are some cleverly placed bunkers but which never bar the entrance to greens (except on the 11th hole), trees but no forest, no hidden terrors, no heather to bury your ball in and no water hazards. It is also a nice length for players who will never hit it as far as Tiger Woods even if they do use high-tech drivers – although a booming drive is rewarded on the rather tricky 11th hole where you need a long tee-shot to get a view of the green nestling in a deep vale. A course is always an adversary, but this one is fair and most likeable.

C'est un des seuls golfs, avec Aberdovey, qui dispose de sa propre station de chemin de fer. Il a aussi ce genre de club-house dont l'architecture vous donne des idées de maison de campagne. Et c'est enfin le genre de parcours qui donne envie de commencer le golf, et de continuer à l'aimer au point de devenir un jour "oldest member" quelque part. Il n'a rien de très spectaculaire, mais un tracé de Harry Colt n'est jamais banal, et l'on retrouve quelques éléments typiques de ses autres parcours. Ici, il y a des bunkers bien placés mais pas en travers de la route du green, des arbres mais pas de forêt, rien d'horrible n'est caché, il n'y a pas de bruyère pour happer les balles, pas d'obstacles d'eau, et la longueur est favorable aux joueurs qui n'auront jamais la puissance de Tiger Woods, même avec un driver high-tech, sauf au 11, assez "tricky", où il faut un très long drive pour apercevoir le green niché dans une profonde vallée. Si le parcours est l'adversaire du golfeur, Denham est très amical !

Denham Golf Club — 1910

Tilehouse Lane
ENG - DENHAM, Bucks UB9 5DE

Office Secrétariat (44) 01895 - 832 022
Pro shop Pro-shop (44) 01895 - 832 801
Fax Fax (44) 01895 - 835 340
Web www.denhamgolfclub.co.uk
Situation Situation London, 25 km
Slough, 8 km
Annual closure Fermeture annuelle no
Weekly closure Fermeture hebdomadaire no

Fees main season Tarifs haute saison	18 holes	
	Week days Semaine	We/Bank holidays We/Férié
Individual Individuel	£ 50	*
Couple Couple	£ 100	*

* No visitors Friday and week-end

Caddie Caddie on request **Electric Trolley** Chariot électrique yes
Buggy Voiturette no **Clubs** Clubs yes
Credit cards Cartes de crédit
Visa - Mastercard (Pro shop goods only)

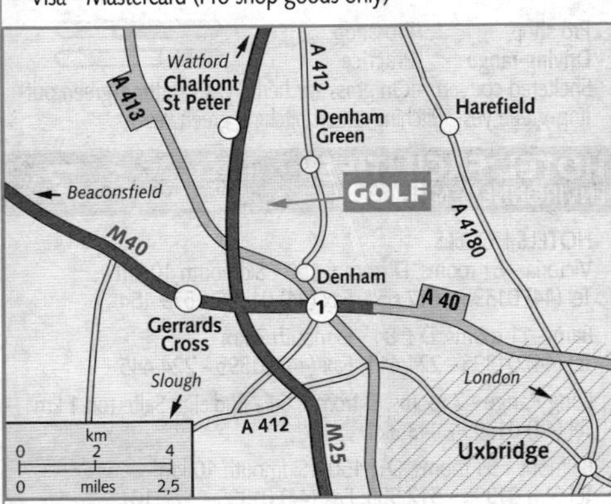

Access Accès : M40, Jct 1, A40 → Gerrards Cross, then A412 → Watford. 2nd left to club-house.
Map 8 on page 484 Carte 8 Page 484

GOLF COURSE — PARCOURS 15/20

Site Site
Maintenance Entretien
Architect Architecte Harry S. Colt
Type Type parkland
Relief Relief
Water in play Eau en jeu
Exp. to wind Exposé au vent
Trees in play Arbres en jeu

Scorecard Carte de score	Chp. Chp.	Mens Mess.	Ladies Da.
Length Long.	5806	5543	5014
Par	70	70	72
Slope system	—	—	—

Advised golfing ability Niveau de jeu recommandé 0 12 24 36
Hcp required Handicap exigé 28 Men, 36 Ladies

CLUB HOUSE & AMENITIES — CLUB HOUSE ET ANNEXES 7/10

Pro shop Pro-shop
Driving range Practice
Sheltered couvert practice area - On grass sur herbe yes - Putting-green putting-green yes - Pitching-green pitching green yes

HOTEL FACILITIES — ENVIRONNEMENT HOTELIER 7/10

HOTELS HÔTELS
De Vere Bull - Gerrards Cross 5 km
111 rooms, D from £ 100
Tel (44) 01753 - 885 995, Fax (44) 01753 - 885 504

Copthorne- 219 rooms, D £ 180 - Slough 11 km
Tel (44) 01753 - 516 222, Fax (44) 01753 - 516 237

Courtyard - 150 rooms, D £ 124 - Slough 11 km
Tel (44) 01753 - 551 551, Fax (44) 01753 - 553 333

RESTAURANTS RESTAURANTS
Etcetera - Gerrards Cross 3 km - Tel (44) 01753 - 880 888
Stoke's Brasserie - Stoke Poges 6 km
Tel (44) 01753 - 717 171

East Devon

17 | 6 | 7

A typical Surrey or Berkshire course transplanted to the West country. On the cliff tops here, you would think you were playing at Walton Heath or the Berkshire, complete with tall pine-trees, birch trees and gorse. The marine landscape is something of a bonus, as are the flowers in spring or the occasional pheasant and deer. Forgetting the unquestionable visual appeal, East Devon is a very good course where, from the back-tees, you need a good solid hit, a long carry and some basic skills in flighting the ball through the wind, as the normally harmless hazards can come dangerously into play. The course is not too hilly but there are four blind or semi-blind greens and two others that are elevated. Accurate players will relish the challenge but the higher-handicappers might not enjoy tangling with the gorse and heather on the tougher holes, especially as they often look tighter than they actually are. Their golfing superiors will have every opportunity to teach them a thing or two about the tactics of golf before enjoying some wonderful twilight scenery from the terrace.

On pourrait se croire dans le Surrey ou le Berkshire, quand la bruyère, les grands pins, les bouleaux, les buissons d'ajoncs rappellent Walton Heath ou The Berkshire : les paysages marins sont un supplément tout comme les fleurs au printemps, ou les faisans et les cervidés parfois. Tout plaisir visuel mis à part, c'est un très bon parcours, où il faut parfois porter solidement la balle depuis les départs arrière, travailler ses balles dans le vent car les obstacles normalement inoffensifs peuvent venir en jeu. Le relief n'est pas trop prononcé, mais quatre greens sont plus ou moins aveugles et deux autres en élévation. Les joueurs précis prendront du plaisir, mais les hauts handicaps risquent d'avoir quelques soucis avec la bruyère et les trous les plus difficiles, d'autant que les trous paraissent plus étroits qu'ils ne sont. Cela dit, leurs aînés en golf se feront un plaisir de les faire profiter de leur expérience tactique du jeu, avant de profiter du spectacle du soir sur la terrasse du club-house.

The East Devon Golf Club — 1902

North View Road
ENG - BUDLEIGH SALTERTON, Devon EX 9 6DR

Office	Secrétariat	(44) 01395 - 443 370
Pro shop	Pro-shop	(44) 01395 - 445 195
Fax	Fax	(44) 01395 - 445 547
Web	www.edgc.co.uk	
Situation	Situation	Exeter, 10 km
Annual closure	Fermeture annuelle	no
Weekly closure	Fermeture hebdomadaire	Monday
Fees main season	Tarifs haute saison	18 holes

	Week days Semaine	We/Bank holidays We/Férié
Individual Individuel	£ 36	£ 36*
Couple Couple	£ 72	£ 72*

* We: 18 holes only / Full week days: £ 45
No play before 9:00

Caddie Caddie no **Electric Trolley** Chariot électrique yes

Buggy Voiturette no **Clubs** Clubs yes

Credit cards Cartes de crédit
VISA - Eurocard - Mastercard (Pro shop only)

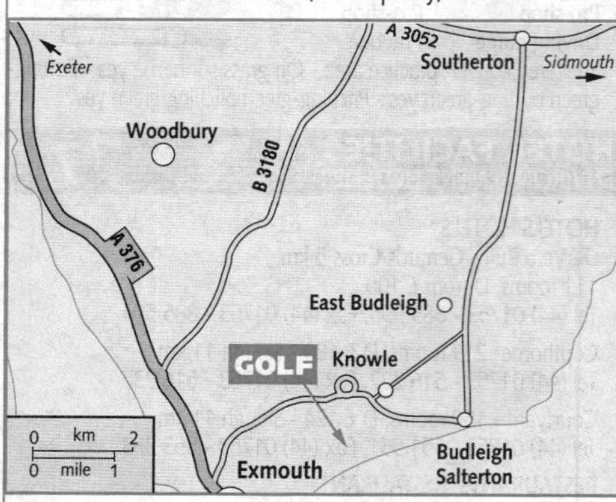

Access Accès : M5 Jct 30, Exmouth A370 onto B3179 Budleigh Satterton, to T Jct. Turn right onto B373C, then B3173. Club on the right hand side before town, on Links Road.
Map 6 on page 481 Carte 6 Page 481

GOLF COURSE — PARCOURS — 17/20

Site	Site	
Maintenance	Entretien	
Architect	Architecte	Harry S. Colt, James Braid
Type	Type	heathland, seaside
Relief	Relief	
Water in play	Eau en jeu	
Exp. to wind	Exposé au vent	
Trees in play	Arbres en jeu	

Scorecard Carte de score	Chp. Chp.	Mens Mess.	Ladies Da.
Length Long.	5616	5307	5090
Par	70	70	74
Slope system	—	—	—

Advised golfing ability / Niveau de jeu recommandé: 0 12 24 36
Hcp required Handicap exigé: certificate

CLUB HOUSE & AMENITIES — CLUB HOUSE ET ANNEXES — 6/10

Pro shop Pro-shop
Driving range Practice
Sheltered couvert - On grass sur herbe yes - Putting-green putting-green yes - Pitching-green pitching green yes

HOTEL FACILITIES — ENVIRONNEMENT HOTELIER — 7/10

HOTELS HÔTELS

Victoria - 61 rooms, D from £ 150 - Sidmouth 10 km
Tel (44) 01395 - 512 651, Fax (44) 01395 - 579 154

Barn - 11 rooms, D £ 84 - Exmouth 3 km
Tel (44) 01395 - 224 411, Fax (44) 01395 - 224 445

Long Range - 7 rooms, D from £ 64 - Budleigh Salterton 1 km
Tel (44) 01395 - 443 321

Belmont - 53 rooms, D £ 150 - Sidmouth 10 km
Tel (44) 01395 - 512 555, Fax (44) 01395 - 579 101

RESTAURANTS RESTAURANTS

The Seafood - Exmouth 3 km - Tel (44) 01395 - 269 459
Barn - Exmouth 3 km - Tel (44) 01395 - 224 411

East Sussex National *East Course* | 18 | 8 | 7

This is a 36-hole complex where the more intimate "West" course is reserved in principle for members (having said that, there are opportunities for green-fee golfers, so please enquire). The "East" course was planned as a tournament layout with mounds designed for spectators. Designed by the very talented Robert Cupp (he actually laid out both the courses here), the American style is never too loud and you can even sometimes roll your ball onto the green. The many different tee-boxes add to the variety and allow you to approach the course with the caution it deserves first time out, as some of the hazards are hard to spot and game strategy requires some careful thought. Start with a round of match-play, an excellent idea especially since the finishing holes are very impressive. The appeal of the site is supplemented by the on-site hotel, a superb driving range and a huge club-house.

Cet ensemble comprend 36 trous, mais le parcours "Ouest," plus intime, est a priori réservé aux membres, bien que certaines opportunités soient ouvertes (se renseigner). Celui-ci a été davantage conçu comme parcours de tournoi, avec des buttes prévues pour accueillir des spectateurs. Dessiné comme son voisin par le très talentueux Robert Cupp, le style américain n'est pourtant pas trop agressif, il est parfois même possible d'arriver en roulant sur les greens. La multiplicité des départs permet de renouveler chaque fois les plaisirs, mais aussi, la première fois, de reconnaître prudemment le parcours, car certains obstacles sont peu visibles, et la stratégie du jeu réclame aussi quelque réflexion. Commencer par jouer en match-play sera d'autant plus agréable que le "finish" est excellent. Pour situer la séduction du lieu, ajoutons l'hôtel sur place, un practice superbé et un vaste club-house.

East Sussex National 1990
Little Horsted
ENG - UCKFIELD, East Sussex TN22 5ES

Office Secrétariat (44) 01825 - 880 088
Pro shop Pro-shop (44) 01825 - 880 256
Fax Fax (44) 01825 - 880 066
Web www.eastsussexnational.co.uk
Situation Situation Lewes (pop. 15 376), 10 km
Uckfield (pop. 12 090), 3 km

Annual closure Fermeture annuelle no
Weekly closure Fermeture hebdomadaire no

Fees main season Tarifs haute saison	Week days Semaine	We/Bank holidays We/Férié
		18 holes
Individual Individuel	£ 45	£ 50
Couple Couple	£ 90	£ 100

Caddie Caddie on request **Electric Trolley** Chariot électrique no
Buggy Voiturette yes **Clubs** Clubs yes
Credit cards Cartes de crédit
VISA - MasterCard - AMEX

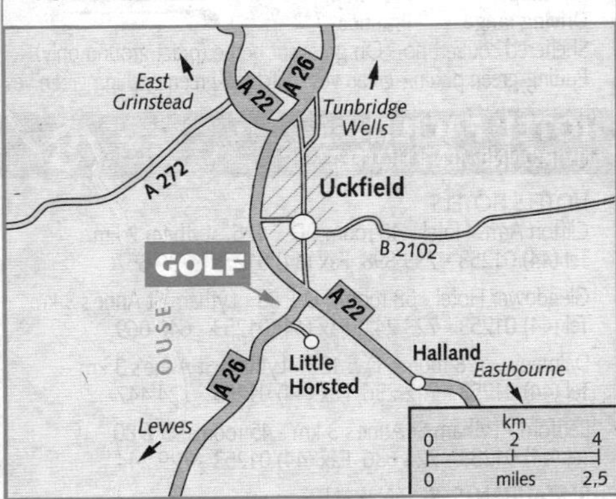

Access Accès : London, A23 then A22 through East Grinstead, Uckfield. Golf 4.5 km South of Uckfield on A22.
Map 7 on page 483 Carte 7 Page 483

GOLF COURSE — PARCOURS 18/20

Site Site
Maintenance Entretien
Architect Architecte Robert E. Cupp
Type Type open country
Relief Relief
Water in play Eau en jeu
Exp. to wind Exposé au vent
Trees in play Arbres en jeu

Scorecard Carte de score	Chp. Chp.	Mens Mess.	Ladies Da.
Length Long.	6424	6084	4764
Par	72	72	72
Slope system	—	—	—

Advised golfing ability Niveau de jeu recommandé 0 12 24 36
Hcp required Handicap exigé certificate

CLUB HOUSE & AMENITIES — CLUB HOUSE ET ANNEXES 8/10

Pro shop Pro-shop
Driving range Practice
Sheltered couvert no - On grass sur herbe yes - Putting-green putting-green yes - Pitching-green pitching green yes

HOTEL FACILITIES — ENVIRONNEMENT HOTELIER 7/10

HOTELS HÔTELS
Horsted Place Hotel - 20 rooms, D £ 145 - Uckfield, adjacent
Tel (44) 01825 - 750 581, Fax (44) 01825 - 750 459

Grand Hotel - 152 rooms, D from £ 135 - Eastbourne 17 km
Tel (44) 01323 - 412 345, Fax (44) 01323 - 412 233

Buxted Park - 44 rooms, D £ 145 - Uckfield 10 km
Tel (44) 01825 - 732 711, Fax (44) 01825 - 732 770

RESTAURANTS RESTAURANTS
Horsted Place Hotel - Uckfield a - Tel (44) 01825 - 750 581
Buxted Park - Uckfield 3 km - Tel (44) 01825 - 732 711
Mirabelle - Eastbourne 17 km - Tel (44) 01323 - 435 066

Fairhaven

16	7	8

Golfers who love lush green courses, neatly mown rough, soft greens and trees which shelter from the wind, and who like to get a tan in the process should avoid all the courses on this side of England. On this coast you play golf with all the clubs in your bag, with your head, your technical know-how, all the inspiration you can muster and with locals who will explain where you should hit the ball and where the greens and pins actually are. Although the course had to be shifted from its original site in 1924 to a slightly more inland location (this is not a real links course), Fairhaven is simply a great course, not really outstanding in terms of pure beauty, but honest, absorbing, exciting and very well maintained. There are others that have all these attributes but they don't have the pureness of style. To play well here, stick to the basics: hit it straight, hard and clean. Otherwise don't bother too much counting your strokes, take the gimmies or make full use of the strokes you are given. Make a point of playing here when you come to Royal Lytham.

Ceux qui aiment les parcours bien verts, les roughs bien tondus, les greens bien mous, les arbres qui abritent du vent, et bronzer en plus, doivent éviter tous les golfs de cette côte d'Angleterre. Ici, on joue au golf avec tous ses clubs et sa tête, avec son bagage technique, avec l'inspiration du moment et avec les joueurs du coin qui vont vous expliquer où sont les points cardinaux, s'il y a des drapeaux au bout des fairways, et où. Bien qu'il ait dû quitter son site initial en 1924 pour émigrer plus à l'intérieur (ce n'est pas un vrai links), Fairhaven est simplement un grand parcours, pas exceptionnel au sens esthétique, mais franc, absorbant, passionnant, très bien entretenu. Il en est d'autres qui ont toutes ces qualités, mais pas la pureté du style. Pour bien le jouer, revenez aux bases : taper droit, fort, franchement. Ou alors ne pas trop s'occuper de compter les coups, ceux que l'on donne et ceux que l'on reçoit. Ne pas oublier de jouer ici quand on vient à Royal Lytham !

Fairhaven Golf Club — 1922

Lytham Hall Park, Ansdell
ENG - LYTHAM ST ANNE'S, Lancs FY8 4JU

Office Secrétariat (44) 01253 - 736 741
Pro shop Pro-shop (44) 01253 - 736 976
Fax Fax (44) 01253 - 731 461
E-mail secretary@fairhaven.golf
Situation Situation Blackpool, 9 km
close to Lytham St Anne's (pop. 40 866)

Annual closure Fermeture annuelle — no
Weekly closure Fermeture hebdomadaire — no

Fees main season Tarifs haute saison — 18 holes

	Week days / Semaine	We/Bank holidays / We/Férié
Individual Individuel	£ 45	£ 50*
Couple Couple	£ 90	£ 100*

Full weekdays: £ 55 / * We: 18 holes only

Caddie Caddie no — **Electric Trolley** Chariot électrique no
Buggy Voiturette yes — **Clubs** Clubs yes
Credit cards Cartes de crédit
VISA - MasterCard

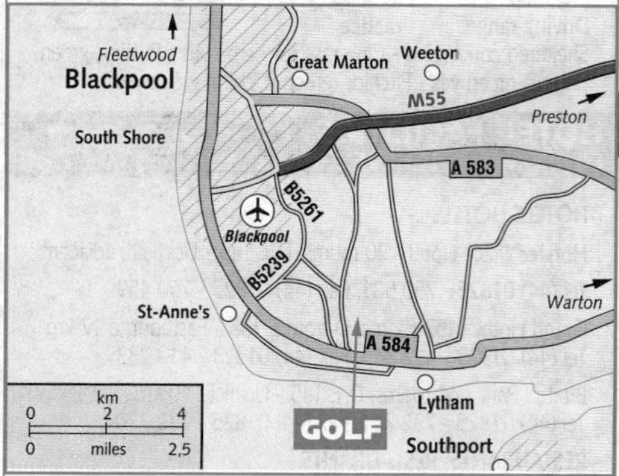

Access Accès : A584 (Blackpool Road). B5261
Next to rugby ground
Map 5 on page 479 Carte 5 Page 479

GOLF COURSE — PARCOURS 16/20

Site Site
Maintenance Entretien
Architect Architecte — James Braid, Jim Steer
Type Type — links
Relief Relief
Water in play Eau en jeu
Exp. to wind Exposé au vent
Trees in play Arbres en jeu

Scorecard / Carte de score	Chp. / Chp.	Mens / Mess.	Ladies / Da.
Length Long.	6195	5847	5386
Par	74	72	75
Slope system	—	—	—

Advised golfing ability / Niveau de jeu recommandé — 0 12 24 36
Hcp required Handicap exigé — 28 Men, 36 Ladies

CLUB HOUSE & AMENITIES — CLUB HOUSE ET ANNEXES 7/10

Pro shop Pro-shop
Driving range Practice
Sheltered couvert no - On grass sur herbe (pract.ground only) - Putting-green putting-green yes - Pitching-green pitching green yes

HOTEL FACILITIES — ENVIRONNEMENT HOTELIER 8/10

HOTELS HÔTELS
Clifton Arms Hotel - 48 rooms, D £ 125 - Lytham 2 km
Tel (44) 01253 - 739 898, Fax (44) 01253 - 730 657

Glendower Hotel - 58 rooms, D £ 88 - Lytham St Anne's 3 km
Tel (44) 01253 - 723 241, Fax (44) 01253 - 640 069

Dalmeny - 128 rooms, D £ 128 - Lytham St Anne's 3 km
Tel (44) 01253 - 712 236, Fax (44) 01253 - 724 447

Bedford - Lytham St Anne's 3 km - 45 rooms, D £ 80
Tel (44) 01253 - 724 636, Fax (44) 01253 - 729 244

RESTAURANTS RESTAURANTS
Pleasant Street Brasserie - Lytham 2 km - Tel (44) 01253 - 733 800
9 Clifton Street - Lytham 2 km - Tel (44) 01253 - 794 000
Tiggy's Italian - Lytham 2 km - Tel (44) 01253 - 714 714

Felixstowe Ferry *Martello Course* | 14 | 6 | 6

This is the fifth oldest club in England and a course little known to the majority of golfers on the continent. Yet this is a top notch links course, without the spectacular dunes of the west coast but slightly reminiscent of the courses in Scotland's East Lothian. Re-designed by Henry Cotton and Sir Guy Campbell after the second world war which left the site in ruins, Tom Dunn's original layout is now a challenge of the highest order despite being rather on the short side. Bisected by a road, the course's most interesting holes run along the sea-shore. These are the last six holes which make for a highly interesting finish, especially when the wind blows a little (and it does frequently!). A course to bravely go out and pitch into and a club where many top amateur golfers have honed their skills, the hard way (including the golf writer Bernard Darwin). This is a private club which readily welcomes outsiders onto its 9-hole par 35 course, an ideal layout for schooling beginners in the family and fun to play whilst awaiting a week-day tee-off time.

Le cinquième plus ancien club d'Angleterre, un parcours méconnu par les continentaux. C'est pourtant un links de qualité, sans les dunes spectaculaires de la côte ouest, mais qui n'est pas sans rappeler les parcours de l'East Lothian en Ecosse. Remodelé par Henry Cotton et Sir Guy Campbell, après la Seconde Guerre Mondiale qui l'avait laissé en ruines, le dessin de Tom Dunn reste aujourd'hui un challenge de premier ordre, même avec sa longueur réduite. Traversé par une route, il offre ses trous les plus intéressants le long de la mer, et ce sont justement les six derniers, ce qui permet un finale des plus excitants, quand le vent daigne souffler un peu (ce qui arrive). Un parcours à attaquer avec bravoure, où de nombreux bons amateurs ont été formés à la dure, y compris le grand écrivain de golf Bernard Darwin ! Club privé, il ouvre largement ses portes sur son parcours de 9 trous (par 35) idéal pour former les débutants de la famille, ou pour attendre les jours de semaine !

Felixstowe Ferry Golf Club — 1880

Ferry Road
ENG - FELIXSTOWE, Suffolk IP11 9RY

Office Secrétariat (44) 01394 - 286 834
Pro shop Pro-shop (44) 01394 - 283 975
Fax Fax (44) 01394 - 273 679
Web www.felixstoweferrygolf.co.uk
Situation Situation Felixstowe, 1 km
Ipswich (pop. 130 157), 18 km

Annual closure Fermeture annuelle — no
Weekly closure Fermeture hebdomadaire — no

Fees main season Tarifs haute saison	Full day	
	Week days Semaine	**We/Bank holidays** We/Férié
Individual Individuel	£ 35	£ 40
Couple Couple	£ 70	£ 80

Week days after 14:00, £ 25 / We: after 14:30 only

Caddie Caddie no — **Electric Trolley** Chariot électrique yes
Buggy Voiturette no — **Clubs** Clubs no

Credit cards Cartes de crédit
Visa - Mastercard - AMEX (Pro shop goods & green fees)

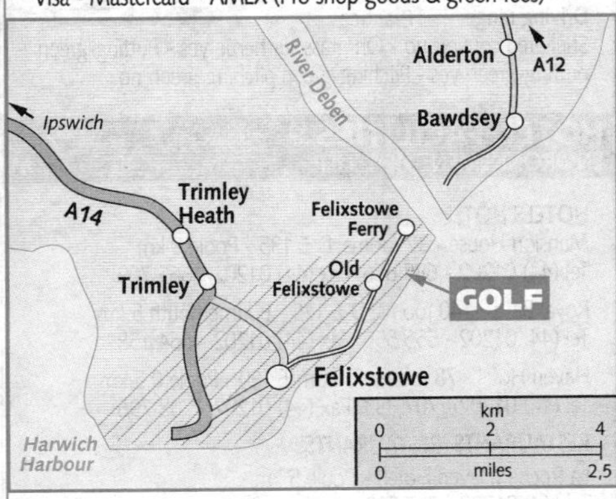

Access Accès : Ipswich, A14 → North Felixstowe. At beach, continue on the left. Course entrance on the right.
Map 7 on page 483 Carte 7 Page 483

GOLF COURSE — PARCOURS 14/20

Site	Site	
Maintenance	Entretien	
Architect	Architecte	Tom Dunn Henry Cotton (1947)
Type	Type	seaside course, links
Relief	Relief	
Water in play	Eau en jeu	
Exp. to wind	Exposé au vent	
Trees in play	Arbres en jeu	

Scorecard Carte de score	**Chp.** Chp.	**Mens** Mess.	**Ladies** Da.
Length Long.	5645	5562	4935
Par	72	72	72
Slope system	—	—	—

Advised golfing ability Niveau de jeu recommandé — 0 12 24 36
Hcp required Handicap exigé — certificate

CLUB HOUSE & AMENITIES — CLUB HOUSE ET ANNEXES 6/10

Pro shop Pro-shop
Driving range Practice
Sheltered couvert no - On grass sur herbe yes - Putting-green putting-green yes - Pitching-green pitching green yes

HOTEL FACILITIES — ENVIRONNEMENT HOTELIER 6/10

HOTELS HÔTELS
Orwell Hotel - 58 rooms, D £ 75 - Felixstowe 2 km
Tel (44) 01394 - 285 511, Fax (44) 01394 - 670 687

Waverley - 19 rooms, D £ 75 - Felixstowe 2 km
Tel (44) 01394 - 282 811, Fax (44) 01394 - 670 185

Marlborough - 48 rooms, D £ 65 - Felixstowe 2 km
Tel (44) 01394 - 285 621, Fax (44) 01394 - 670 724

RESTAURANTS RESTAURANTS
Orwell Hotel - Felixstowe 2 km - Tel (44) 01394 - 309955
St Peter's - Ipswich 18 km - Tel (44) 01473 - 210 810
Mortimer's Seafood Restaurant - Ipswich 18 km
Tel (44) 01473 - 230 225

Ferndown *Old Course*

17	7	7

With sand, heather, pine-trees and conifers, Ferndown is first and foremost a beautiful site with a simple but very functional club-house. Once a very dry course during rain-free summers, the course is now watered automatically so that you no longer get those infuriatingly unfair kicks left and right down the fairway, especially on the dog-legs. But be careful with Ferndown, because despite the impression of dealing with a fair and open course, some of the trees are more in play than you think and a number of ditches lie hidden in the rough. Heather, too, can make life a good deal more complicated. Low scores depend a lot on your driving, not only to avoid the dangerous fairway bunkers but also to get the ball in the right spot and have a good shot at the green. Although dose to Bournemouth, this is not just a simple holiday course but one that has staged some top tournaments in the past. Today it is a little short for the big boys, but ideal for "normal" golfers. The pleasant 9-hole "New Course" has alternative tee-boxes on each hole.

De sable et de bruyère, de pins et de sapins, Ferndown est d'abord un bel endroit, avec un club-house sans prétentions mais très fonctionnel. Autrefois très sec lors des étés sans pluie, il bénéficie maintenant d'un arrosage qui a retiré certains rebonds imprévus et souvent injustes, en particulier sur les nombreux doglegs. Il faut se méfier de ce parcours très franc en apparence, alors que certains arbres sont plus en jeu qu'ils ne paraissent, que des fossés se dissimulent dans les roughs. Et la bruyère complique le jeu. Les bons scores dépendent beaucoup du driving, non seulement pour éviter les dangereux bunkers de fairway, mais aussi placer la balle en bonne position pour attaquer les greens. Bien que proche de Bournemouth, il vaut bien mieux qu'un simple parcours de vacances. Il fut le théâtre de grandes compétitions: aujourd'hui un peu court pour les cogneurs, il est parfait pour les "joueurs normaux". Le plaisant "New Course" de 9 trous dispose de tees alternatifs sur chaque trou.

Ferndown Golf Club — 1914

119, Golf Links Road
ENG - FERNDOWN, Dorset BH22 8BU

Office Secrétariat (44) 01202 - 874 602
Pro shop Pro-shop (44) 01202 - 873 825
Fax Fax (44) 01202 - 873 926
Web www.ferndown-golf-club.co.uk
Situation Situation Poole (pop. 133 050), 5 km
Annual closure Fermeture annuelle no
Weekly closure Fermeture hebdomadaire Christmas Day

Fees main season Tarifs haute saison — 18 holes

	Week days / Semaine	We/Bank holidays / We/Férié
Individual Individuel	£ 60	£ 70
Couple Couple	£ 120	£ 140

Full days: £ 70 / £ 80 (weekends)

Caddie Caddie no — **Electric Trolley** Chariot électrique no
Buggy Voiturette yes — **Clubs** Clubs no
Credit cards Cartes de crédit
Visa - Eurocard - Mastercard - Amex (Pro shop goods only)

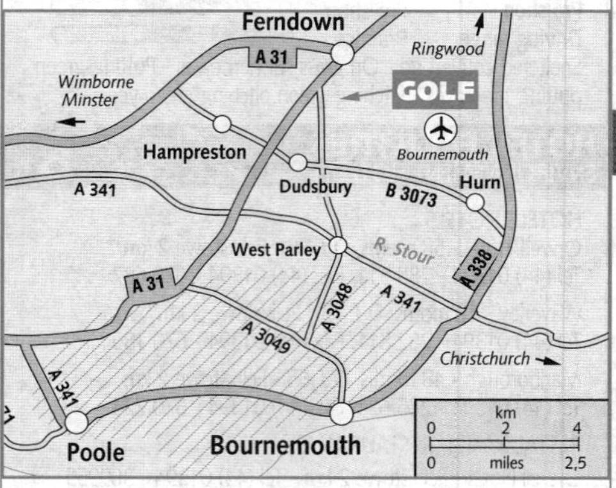

Access Accès : M3 last exit, then A31 to Trickett's Cross, then A348 to Ferndown, follow signs → Golf.
Map 6 on page 481 Carte 6 Page 481

GOLF COURSE — PARCOURS — 17/20

Site Site
Maintenance Entretien
Architect Architecte Harold Hilton
Type Type inland, heathland
Relief Relief
Water in play Eau en jeu
Exp. to wind Exposé au vent
Trees in play Arbres en jeu

Scorecard / Carte de score	Chp. / Chp.	Mens / Mess.	Ladies / Da.
Length Long.	5895	5651	5176
Par	71	71	72
Slope system	—	—	—

Advised golfing ability Niveau de jeu recommandé 0 12 24 36
Hcp required Handicap exigé 28 Men, 30 Ladies

CLUB HOUSE & AMENITIES — CLUB HOUSE ET ANNEXES — 7/10

Pro shop Pro-shop
Driving range Practice
Sheltered couvert no - On grass sur herbe yes - Putting-green putting-green yes - Pitching-green pitching green no

HOTEL FACILITIES — ENVIRONNEMENT HOTELIER — 7/10

HOTELS HÔTELS
Mansion House - 32 rooms, D £ 135 - Poole 8 km
Tel (44) 01202 - 685 666, Fax (44) 01202 - 665 709

Royal Bath - 140 rooms, D £ 175 - Bournemouth 5 km
Tel (44) 01202 - 555 555, Fax (44) 01202 - 554 158

Haven Hotel - 78 rooms, D from £ 180 - Poole 0,5 km
Tel (44) 01202 - 707 333, Fax (44) 01202 - 708 796

RESTAURANTS RESTAURANTS
La Roche (Haven Hotel) - Poole 5 km
Tel (44) 01202 - 707 333
John B's - Poole 5 km - Tel (44) 01202 - 672440
Isabel's - Poole - Tel (44) 01202 - 747 885

Forest of Arden *Arden Course*

15	8	8

The fine hotel today belongs to the Marriott Group, who manage the facility's two golf courses, 'the Arden' and 'the Aylesford'. The longer Arden Course is is technically a very interesting layout, especially for the better player, and one which has hosted the English Open. All in all, it is a very pleasant spot for a few days golfing with a group or with the family, even if you are playing with golfers of very different abilities. We would simply recommend avoiding the wetter months as the soil takes a long time to soak up surface water. The Arden Course was originally designed by Donald Steel but was subsequently renovated by European Golf Design. It features many different tee-boxes, and we would advise the yellow tees, at least for your first round unless you are a good player of long irons. A tricky course overall with quite a few water hazards – particularly at the 18th, which is a make-or-break finishing hole with the tee shot played over a lake – trees which neatly line the fairways and thick rough. A very professional golfing resort.

Le très bel hôtel appartient aujourd'hui au groupe Marriott, gestionnaire des deux parcours, "Aylesford" et "Arden" Ce dernier est le plus intéressant techniquement, en particulier pour les meilleurs joueurs, qui y ont notamment joué l'English Open. C'est ainsi un lieu très agréable pour passer quelques jours en groupe ou en famille, même si les niveaux de golf sont très différents. On recommandera simplement d'éviter les mois très humides, car le sol a du mal à évacuer les excès d'eau. Le "Arden" a été dessiné par Donald Steel, et largement remanié par European Golf Design. Parmi ses multiples départs, nous conseillerons les "jaunes," au moins la première fois, à moins d'être un solide joueur de longs fers et de savoir lever la balle. Assez "tricky" en général, avec pas mal d'obstacles d'eau – en particulier au 18, avec un lac qui vous oblige à passer ou à casser votre carte – des arbres sculptant bien les trous, un rough épais.

Marriott Forest of Arden Golf Club — 1970

Maxstoke Lane
ENG - MERIDEN, Warwicks. CV7 7HR

Office	Secrétariat	(44) 01676 - 522 335
Pro shop	Pro-shop	(44) 01676 - 526 113
Fax	Fax	(44) 01676 - 523 711
Web	www.mariotthotels.co.uk	
Situation	Situation	Coventry, 16 km

Birmingham (pop. 961 041), 24 km

Annual closure	Fermeture annuelle	no
Weekly closure	Fermeture hebdomadaire	no
Fees main season	Tarifs haute saison	18 holes

	Week days / Semaine	We/Bank holidays / We/Férié
Individual Individuel	£ 90	£ 100
Couple Couple	£ 180	£ 200

Caddie Caddie on request **Electric Trolley** Chariot électrique no
Buggy Voiturette yes **Clubs** Clubs yes
Credit cards Cartes de crédit
VISA - Eurocard - MasterCard - AMEX - DC

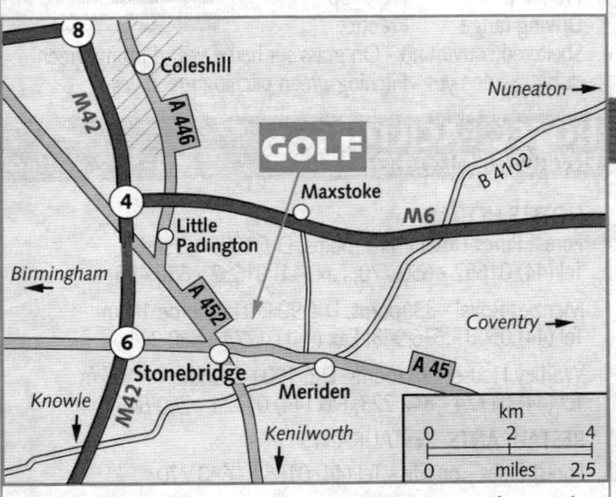

Access Accès : M42 Jct 6, then A45 → Coventry. After 1.5 km (1 m), left into Shepherds Lane, by "Little Chef". Golf 2 km on the left.
Map 7 on page 482 Carte 7 Page 482

GOLF COURSE — PARCOURS — 15/20

Site	Site	
Maintenance	Entretien	
Architect	Architecte	Donald Steel
Type	Type	parkland
Relief	Relief	
Water in play	Eau en jeu	
Exp. to wind	Exposé au vent	
Trees in play	Arbres en jeu	

Scorecard Carte de score	**Chp.** Chp.	**Mens** Mess.	**Ladies** Da.
Length Long.	6420	5867	5106
Par	72	72	72
Slope system	–	–	–

Advised golfing ability — Niveau de jeu recommandé: 0 12 24 36
Hcp required — Handicap exigé: 24 Men, 36 Ladies

CLUB HOUSE & AMENITIES — CLUB HOUSE ET ANNEXES — 8/10

Pro shop — Pro-shop
Driving range — Practice
Sheltered couvert 16 floodlight bays - On grass sur herbe no - Putting-green putting-green yes - Pitching-green pitching green yes

HOTEL FACILITIES — ENVIRONNEMENT HOTELIER — 8/10

HOTELS HÔTELS
Marriott Hotel - 214 rooms, D from £ 138 - on site
Tel (44) 01676 - 522 335, Fax (44) 01676 - 523 711

Manor (De Vere) - 112 rooms, D £ 145 - Meriden 3 km
Tel (44) 01676 - 522 735, Fax (44) 01676 - 522 186

Haigs - 23 rooms, D £ 108 - Balsall Common 6 km
Tel (44) 01676 - 533 004, Fax (44) 01676 - 535 132

Hilton Birmingham Metropole - 793 rooms, D £ 215
Nat. Ex. Centre, Birmingham 6 km
Tel (44) 0121 - 780 4242, Fax (44) 0121 - 780 3923

RESTAURANTS RESTAURANTS
La Toque d'Or - Birmingham 24 km - Tel (44) 0121 - 233 3655
The Broadwater - on site - Tel (44) 01676 - 522 335

Forest Pines *Forest + Pines*

17 | 6 | 7

It is easier than you might think to get a course all wrong. Not so here, where the impression is one of a site blessed by Mother Nature and given the able help of John Morgan. He had to know how to trace the right path through a forest, how to define an intelligent layout, adapt the course to players of different levels, individualise the holes whilst respecting overall harmony, bring hazards into play without penalising the good shots, and keep a few surprises in store so that it's fun to play again and again. There are courses with which you have an affair and courses which you embrace for life: Forest Pines would appear to be in the latter category, but we will wait a while to see whether it stays as good as it is right now as it comes of age. Opened in 1996, the site also features a good standard 9 hole course ("The Beeches") which every golfer should play if passing through. A resort not to be missed with a hotel run by BestWestern.

Il est plus facile qu'on ne le croit de rater un parcours. Ici, on peut avoir l'impression que Mère Nature a béni les lieux, mais John Morgan lui a aussi donné un coup de main. Il fallait savoir tracer la route dans la forêt, définir un itinéraire intelligent, adapter son parcours aux différents niveaux de jeu, individualiser les trous tout en conservant une harmonie générale, mettre en jeu les obstacles sans pénaliser les bons coups de golf, et réserver des surprises pour que le plaisir ne soit pas émoussé après la première fois. Il est des parcours avec lesquels on a une liaison et d'autres que l'on épouse. Celui-ci pourrait bien faire partie de la seconde catégorie, même si l'on attend encore un peu pour voir s'il garde sa qualité actuelle en prenant quelques rides. Ouvert en 1996, il proposet également un 9 trous de bonne facture ("Beeches"), qu'il serait dommage de ne pas jouer au passage, c'est un ensemble à connaître sans faute, avec un hôtel géré par BestWestern.

Forest Pines — 1996
Ermine Street, Broughton
ENG - BRIGG, Lincs DN20 04Q

Office	Secrétariat	(44) 01652 - 650 756
Pro shop	Pro-shop	(44) 01652 - 650 756
Fax	Fax	(44) 01652 - 650 495
Web	www.forestpines.co.uk	
Situation	Situation	Scunthorpe, 10 km
Annual closure	Fermeture annuelle	no
Weekly closure	Fermeture hebdomadaire	no
Fees main season	Tarifs haute saison	18 holes

	Week days Semaine	We/Bank holidays We/Férié
Individual Individuel	£ 40	£ 40
Couple Couple	£ 80	£ 80

Full days: £ 50

Caddie Caddie no — **Electric Trolley** Chariot électrique no
Buggy Voiturette yes — **Clubs** Clubs yes
Credit cards Cartes de crédit
VISA - Eurocard - MasterCard - AMEX

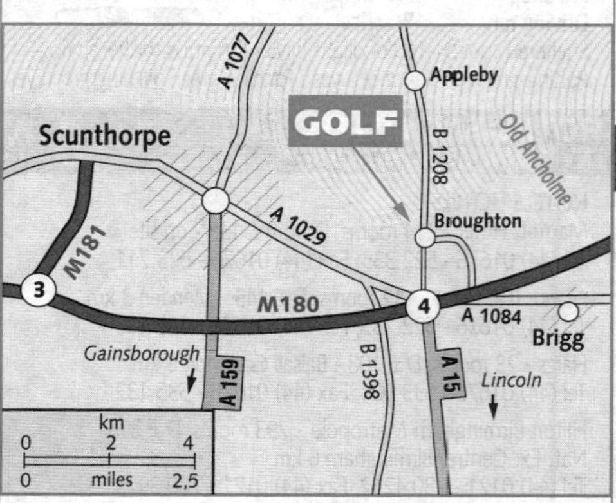

Access Accès : M1, M18 at Jct 32, then M180.
At Jct 4, Golf 2 km North
Map 4 on page 477 Carte 4 Page 477

GOLF COURSE — PARCOURS — 17/20

Site	Site	
Maintenance	Entretien	
Architect	Architecte	John Morgan
Type	Type	forest
Relief	Relief	
Water in play	Eau en jeu	
Exp. to wind	Exposé au vent	
Trees in play	Arbres en jeu	

Scorecard / Carte de score	Chp. / Chp.	Mens / Mess.	Ladies / Da.
Length Long.	6262	5920	5295
Par	73	73	74
Slope system	0	0	0

Advised golfing ability Niveau de jeu recommandé — 0 12 24 36
Hcp required Handicap exigé — no

CLUB HOUSE & AMENITIES — CLUB HOUSE ET ANNEXES — 6/10

Pro shop Pro-shop
Driving range Practice
Sheltered couvert no - On grass sur herbe yes - Putting-green putting-green yes - Pitching-green pitching green yes

HOTEL FACILITIES — ENVIRONNEMENT HOTELIER — 7/10

HOTELS HÔTELS
Forest Pines Hotel - 114 rooms, D £ 109 - on site
Tel (44) 01652 - 650 770, Fax (44) 01652 - 650 495

Menzies Royal - 33 rooms, D £ 90 - Scunthorpe 10 km
Tel (44) 0500 - 636 943, Fax (44) 01773 - 880 321

Wortley House - 38 rooms, D £ 100 - Scunthorpe 10 km
Tel (44) 01724 - 842 223, Fax (44) 01724 - 280 646

RESTAURANTS RESTAURANTS
Forest Pines - on site - Tel (44) 01652 - 650 770

Formby

18 | 7 | 6

It is considerably more easy to play here as a green-feer (the course is often deserted on weekdays) than to become a member. In this sort of golfing paradise, the latter is perfectly understandable. The layout, soil and dunes bear the hallmark of a links course, but there are trees on a good number of holes, meaning that the wind is not such an important factor as it can be on the region's other links courses. Donald Steel has recently lengthened the course but has taken nothing away from the highly strategic and penal placement of bunkers, laid out initially by Willie Park then improved upon by Harry Colt. Seen overall, this is a unique and exciting course which offers a permanent challenge. Bernard Darwin 1910 wrote: "It is one of those courses where the player's fate is entirely in his own hands. If he plays well everything will conspire to help him on his way, but he has got to play really well - good, sterling, honest golf". Playing here is a blissful experience, except perhaps for the ladies, who have their own adjacent course (a gem) and their own club-house...

Il est plus facile de jouer ici en visiteur (en semaine, c'est souvent désert) que d'y devenir membre. On comprend que ce soit difficile, car Formby est une sorte de paradis. Le dessin, le sol, les dunes sont ceux des links, mais les arbres y sont assez présents sur une bonne partie des trous pour que le vent ne soit pas un facteur aussi terriblement important que sur les autres links de la région. Donald Steel a récemment allongé le parcours, mais sans rien ôter du placement très stratégique et pénalisant des bunkers, établi par Willie Park d'abord, mais surtout par Harry Colt. Au total, le caractère de ce parcours est unique, le jeu passionnant, le challenge permanent. En 1910, Bernard darwin écrivait : "C'est l'un de ces parcours où vous êtes maître de votre destin. Si vous jouez bien, tout ira avec vous, mais il faut jouer un bon golf, solide, honnête." Rien n'a changé, on éprouve ici une impression de bonheur... Les Dames ont un parcours à elles (un petit bijou) et leur propre club-house...

Formby Golf Club — 1895

Freshfields
ENG - FORMBY, Lancs L37 1LQ

Office Secrétariat (44) 01704 - 872 164
Pro shop Pro-shop (44) 01704 - 873 090
Fax Fax (44) 01704 - 833 028
Web www.formbygolfclub.co.uk
Situation Situation Liverpool, 23 km
Southport (pop. 90 959), 8 km

Annual closure Fermeture annuelle — no
Weekly closure Fermeture hebdomadaire — no

Fees main season / Tarifs haute saison	Week days / Semaine	We/Bank holidays / We/Férié
		Full day
Individual Individuel	£ 85	£ 95*
Couple Couple	£ 170	£ 190*

* Saturday after 15:30 - Sunday after 14:30

Caddie Caddie on request **Electric Trolley** Chariot électrique no
Buggy Voiturette no **Clubs** Clubs no
Credit cards Cartes de crédit (Pro shop goods only)
VISA - Eurocard - MasterCard - AMEX - DC - JCB

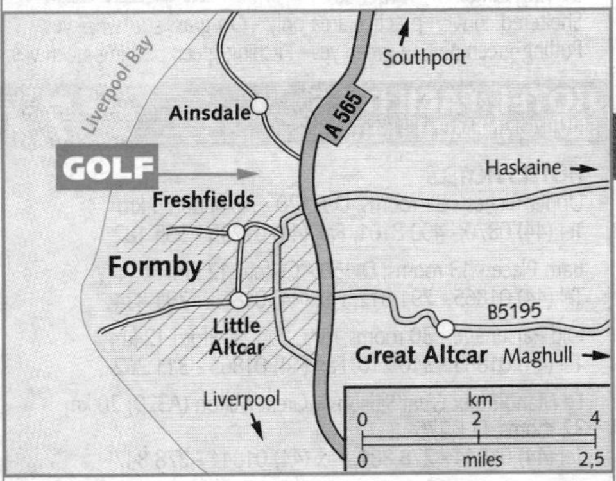

Access Accès : Off A565 Liverpool → Southport. Formby, green lane to Victoria Road (signposted), near Freshfields Rail Station.
Map 5 on page 479 Carte 5 Page 479

GOLF COURSE — PARCOURS — 18/20

Site Site
Maintenance Entretien
Architect Architecte — W. Park, H.S. Colt, F. Pennink, D. Steel
Type Type — links
Relief Relief
Water in play Eau en jeu
Exp. to wind Exposé au vent
Trees in play Arbres en jeu

Scorecard / Carte de score	Chp. / Chp.	Mens / Mess.	Ladies / Da.
Length Long.	6344	5708	5053
Par	72	72	73
Slope system	—	—	—

Advised golfing ability / Niveau de jeu recommandé — 0 12 24 36
Hcp required Handicap exigé — certificate

CLUB HOUSE & AMENITIES — CLUB HOUSE ET ANNEXES — 7/10

Pro shop Pro-shop
Driving range Practice
Sheltered couvert yes - On grass sur herbe yes - Putting-green putting-green no - Pitching-green pitching green yes

HOTEL FACILITIES — ENVIRONNEMENT HOTELIER — 6/10

HOTELS HÔTELS
Dormy House (Males only...) - Formby Golf Club, on site
6 rooms, D £ 264 (with 2 GF)
Tel (44) 01704 - 872 164, Fax (44) 01704 - 833 028

Scarisbrick - 88 rooms, D from £ 100 - Southport 10 km
Tel (44) 01704 - 543 000, Fax (44) 01704 - 533 335

Tree Tops Hotel - 11 rooms, D £ 105 - Formby 2 km
Tel (44) 01704 - 572 430, Fax (44) 01704 - 572 430

RESTAURANTS RESTAURANTS
60 Hope Street - Liverpool 18 km - Tel (44) 0151 - 707 6060
Est, Est, Est! - Formby 2 km - Tel (44) 01704 - 833 775
Tree Tops Hotel - Formby 2 km - Tel (44) 01704 - 572 430

Frilford Heath *Red Course*

15	7	7

Although the club has three 18-hole courses, the "Red Course" is still the one most people refer to. The first four holes (fairly recent additions to the layout and incorporated so as to bring the course closer to the club-house) are a little out of keeping with the rest, especially the bunkering, but the course quickly slips back into the typical style of J.H. Taylor (albeit restyled by J.H. Turner). This is a frequently hilly layout and tough going for the physically... and technically unfit golfer. As not all the trouble in store is visible at first sight, the tee-shot here is more important than ever for your final score. Strangely enough for a course as British in style and atmosphere as this one, you are better off hitting high balls (sometimes a risky business when the wind swirls between the trees) either to carry some well-placed fairway bunkers or to hit the well-guarded greens. An often under-estimated course but a class layout in a complex where the number of courses provides peaceful golfing in a busy neighbourhood. Some extensive refurbishing work has worked wonders for the club-house.

Ce club propose trois 18 trous dont le "Red Course" reste la référence. Certes, les quatre premiers trous sont récents afin d'aménager une grande quantité de départs et de greens près du club-house, et détonnent un peu, notamment pour ce qui est du bunkering, mais on retrouve vite le style de J.H. Taylor, révisé par J.H. Turner. Le parcours est assez accidenté, difficile pour les joueurs peu entraînés, physiquement... et techniquement. Toutes les difficultés ne sont pas visibles au premier coup d'oeil, alors que la qualité des drives conditionne généralement la qualité du score. Assez curieusement pour un parcours aussi britannique d'ambiance et de style, il vaut mieux faire des trajectoires hautes (aléatoires quand le vent tourbillonne dans les arbres), soit pour porter la balle au dessus de quelques bunkers de fairway bien placés, soit pour rejoindre des greens bien défendus. Un parcours souvent sous-estimé, mais de bonne classe. Le club-house vient d'être largement rénové.

Frilford Heath Golf Club — 1908

Frilford Heath
ENG - ABINGDON, Oxfordshire OX13 5NW

Office Secrétariat (44) 01865 - 390 864
Pro shop Pro-shop (44) 01865 - 390 887
Fax Fax (44) 01865 - 390 823
Web www.frilfordheath.co.uk
Situation Situation Oxford (pop. 110 103), 12 km
Abingdon (pop. 30 771), 5 km

Annual closure Fermeture annuelle — no
Weekly closure Fermeture hebdomadaire — no

Fees main season Tarifs haute saison	Week days Semaine	We/Bank holidays We/Férié
	Full day	
Individual Individuel	£ 55	£ 70
Couple Couple	£ 110	£ 140

Caddie Caddie no **Electric Trolley** Chariot électrique yes

Buggy Voiturette yes **Clubs** Clubs yes

Credit cards Cartes de crédit
VISA - MasterCard - AMEX - DC (Green fees & Pro shop only)

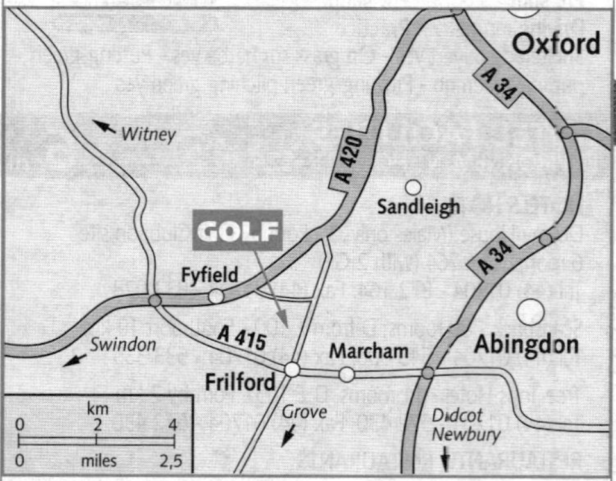

Access Accès : London, M40, A40 → Oxford, A4142 → Abingdon. A415 → Frilford, A338 on right hand side.
Map 7 on page 482 Carte 7 Page 482

GOLF COURSE — PARCOURS — 15/20

Site Site
Maintenance Entretien
Architect Architecte J.H. Taylor
Type Type heathland
Relief Relief
Water in play Eau en jeu
Exp. to wind Exposé au vent
Trees in play Arbres en jeu

Scorecard Carte de score	Chp. Chp.	Mens Mess.	Ladies Da.
Length Long.	6159	5931	5234
Par	73	73	73
Slope system	0	0	0

Advised golfing ability Niveau de jeu recommandé 0 12 24 36
Hcp required Handicap exigé certificate

CLUB HOUSE & AMENITIES — CLUB HOUSE ET ANNEXES — 7/10

Pro shop Pro-shop
Driving range Practice
Sheltered couvert practice area only - On grass sur herbe yes - Putting-green putting-green yes - Pitching-green pitching green yes

HOTEL FACILITIES — ENVIRONNEMENT HOTELIER — 7/10

HOTELS HÔTELS

Upper Riches - 31 rooms, D £ 120 - Abingdon 5 km
Tel (44) 0870 - 400 8101, Fax (44) 01235 - 555 182

Bath Place - 13 rooms, D 150 - Oxford 12 km
Tel (44) 01865 - 791 812, Fax (44) 01865 - 791 834

Old Parsonage - 30 rooms, D £ 155 - Oxford 12 km
Tel (44) 01865 - 310 210, Fax (44) 01865 - 311 262

Le Manoir aux Quat'Saisons - Great Milton (A329) 20 km
32 rooms, D £ 275
Tel (44) 01844 - 278 881, Fax (44) 01844 - 278 847

RESTAURANTS RESTAURANTS

Le Manoir aux Quat'Saisons - Great Milton (A329) 20 km
Tel (44) 01844 - 278 881

Gee's - Oxford 12 km - Tel (44) 01865 - 553 540

Fulford

16 | 7 | 8

The much admired course at Fulford has always been famed for its standard of green-keeping. This reputation was enhanced further by the staging here of the English Open and the Benson & Hedges International tournament in the past, not to mention Bernhard Langer's famous shot from a tree. Sure, the very low scores carded by the pros suggested that the course might now be a little short for them, but they were largely the result of their holing any number of putts. The greens have always been fast and true, adding to the pleasure of playing here, and the course is definitely long enough for most of us. This is a driver course, not power-wise but in terms of accuracy off the tee, as approach shots must be played from the right spot (bunkers are often on one side of the green only) and will vary according to pin positions. A tactical, technical and fair course for all levels, Fulford has retained its dominant position in York, a superb city to visit with a pedestrians-only centre. The club will be celebrating its centenary in 2006.

Fulford a toujours été renommé pour la qualité de son entretien. Et la venue au cours des précédentes décades de l'English Open comme celle du Benson & Hedges ont ensuite accentué cette réputation, avec un fameux coup de Bernard Langer depuis le haut d'un arbre.... Certes, les scores très bas des professionnels suggéraient que le parcours soit un peu "court" pour eux, mais ils rentraient aussi beaucoup de putts... Les greens sont toujours rapides et fermes, ce qui n'ajoute qu'un peu plus de plaisir, et le parcours est bien assez "long" pour la majorité d'entre nous. C'est un parcours de driver, pas en termes de puissance, mais de précision, car il faut aborder les greens dans un bon angle (bunkers souvent d'un seul côté), et qui peut varier selon les placements de drapeaux. Tactique et technique, franc et pour tous niveaux, Fulford conserve sa situation dominante à York, qui reste une superbe ville à visiter, avec son centre ville piétonnier. Le club fêtera son centenaire en 2006.

Fulford Golf Club — 1935

Hessington Lane
ENG - YORK, Yorkshire Y01 5DY

Office	Secrétariat	(44) 01904 - 413 579
Pro shop	Pro-shop	(44) 01904 - 412 882
Fax	Fax	(44) 01904 - 416 918
Web	www.fulfordgolfclub.co.uk	
Situation	Situation	York (pop. 98 745), 3 km
Annual closure	Fermeture annuelle	no
Weekly closure	Fermeture hebdomadaire	no

Fees main season Tarifs haute saison	18 holes	
	Week days Semaine	**We/Bank holidays** We/Férié
Individual Individuel	£ 50	£ 55*
Couple Couple	£ 100	£ 110*

Full week day: £ 65 / * Sunday only after 14:00

Caddie Caddie no — **Electric Trolley** Chariot électrique yes
Buggy Voiturette yes — **Clubs** Clubs no

Credit cards Cartes de crédit
VISA - MasterCard (Pro shop goods only)

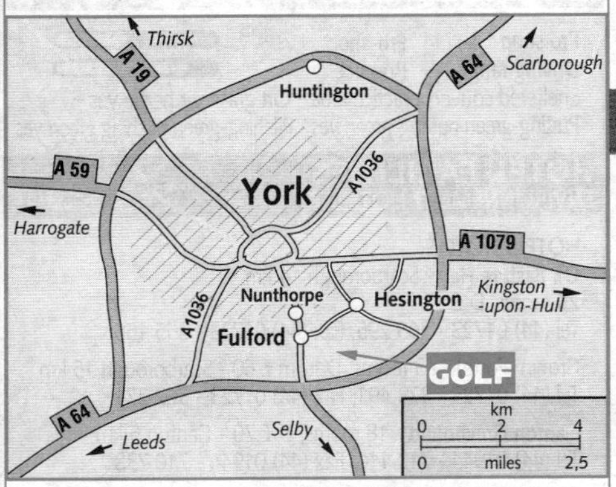

Access Accès : A19 → Fulford Village. Heslington Lane on left. Follow signs for University.
Map 4 on page 477 Carte 4 Page 477

GOLF COURSE — PARCOURS 16/20

Site	Site	
Maintenance	Entretien	
Architect	Architecte	Charles MacKenzie
Type	Type	parkland
Relief	Relief	
Water in play	Eau en jeu	
Exp. to wind	Exposé au vent	
Trees in play	Arbres en jeu	

Scorecard Carte de score	**Chp.** Chp.	**Mens** Mess.	**Ladies** Da.
Length Long.	6100	5698	4875
Par	72	72	74
Slope system	—	—	—

Advised golfing ability Niveau de jeu recommandé — 0 12 24 36
Hcp required Handicap exigé — 28 Men, 36 Ladies

CLUB HOUSE & AMENITIES — CLUB HOUSE ET ANNEXES 7/10

Pro shop Pro-shop
Driving range Practice
Sheltered couvert practice area - On grass sur herbe yes - Putting-green putting-green yes - Pitching-green pitching green yes

HOTEL FACILITIES — ENVIRONNEMENT HOTELIER 8/10

HOTELS HÔTELS
Middlethorpe Hall - 29 rooms, D £ 180 - York 2 km
Tel (44) 01904 - 641 241, Fax (44) 01904 - 620 176

York Pavilion - 57 rooms, D £ 130 - York 3 km
Tel (44) 01904 - 622 099, Fax (44) 01904 - 626 939

Novotel - 124 rooms, D £ 132 - York 3 km
Tel (44) 01904 - 611 660, Fax (44) 01904 - 610 925

RESTAURANTS RESTAURANTS
Melton's - York 3 km - Tel (44) 01904 - 634 341
Melton's Too - York 3 km - Tel (44) 01904 - 629 222
Blue Bicycle - York 3 km - Tel (44) 01904 - 673 990

Ganton

19 | 8 | 5

This is one of the very few inland courses to find favour with links enthusiasts. The sea must have stretched this far in times gone by because you can still find sea-shells in the sand and the soil is of the kind found on every links course. Located between the resort of Scarborough and the superb city of York (a former Viking stronghold), this is a sheer masterpiece of a course where Dunn, Vardon, Colt and C.K. Cotton all had a hand in its design. The links style is all the more obvious in that trees come into play only on a very few holes and on the outskirts. Elsewhere, the fairways are bordered by gorse bushes, tall grass and rough, while deep hungry bunkers snap up anything within reach. But all the hazards are there to be seen and the course is a fair if severe test. The slick greens are well-protected but leave the way open for bump 'n roll shots. As we were saying, all that is missing is the sea. With the Ryder Cup held here in 1949, the Curtis Cup in 2000 and the Walker Cup in 2003, Ganton is one of the finest match-play courses around, so it often comes down to the final hole.

C'est l'un des seuls "inland" à trouver grâce auprès des amoureux des links. La mer devait autrefois venir ici, car on a trouvé des coquillages dans le sable et le sol est celui des links. Entre la station balnéaire de Scarborough et la ville superbe d'York (ancienne place forte viking), voici un chef d'oeuvre absolu où Tom Dunn, Vardon, Colt et C.K. Cotton ont apporté leur contribution. Le style de links est d'autant plus flagrant que les arbres ne sont en jeu que sur de rares trous, et sur la périphérie du lieu. Ailleurs, les buissons, les grands roughs délimitent les fairways, de profonds bunkers pleins d'appétit attrapent tout ce qui passe à portée. Mais les obstacles sont bien en vue, le parcours est sévère mais juste. Les greens subtils et bien défendus laissent néanmoins la porte ouverte aux approches roulées. Il ne manque que la mer... Ryder Cup 1949, Curtis Cup 2000, Walker Cup 2003... Ganton est aussi un des grands parcours de match-play, qui se décident souvent au dernier trou..

Ganton Golf Club — 1891

Ganton
ENG - SCARBOROUGH, Yorkshire YO12 4PA

Office Secrétariat (44) 01944 - 710 329
Pro shop Pro-shop (44) 01944 - 710 260
Fax Fax (44) 01944 - 710 922
Web www.gantongolfclub.com
Situation Situation Scarborough, 15 km
Annual closure Fermeture annuelle 24/12→31/12
Weekly closure Fermeture hebdomadaire no

Fees main season Tarifs haute saison	Week days Semaine	We/Bank holidays We/Férié
		Full day
Individual Individuel	£ 68	£ 78
Couple Couple	£ 136	£ 156

Caddie Caddie on request **Electric Trolley** Chariot électrique yes
Buggy Voiturette medical resaons **Clubs** Clubs yes
Credit cards Cartes de crédit
VISA - MasterCard - Switch (Pro shop & green fees)

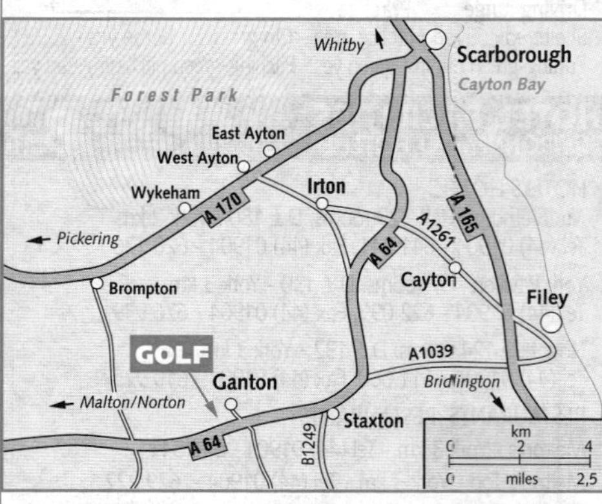

Access Accès : On A64 Leeds-York-Scarborough, 15 km before Scarborough
Map 4 on page 477 Carte 4 Page 477

GOLF COURSE — PARCOURS — 19/20

Site Site
Maintenance Entretien
Architect Architecte Tom Dunn, H. Vardon H S. Colt, CK Cotton
Type Type open country, heathland
Relief Relief
Water in play Eau en jeu
Exp. to wind Exposé au vent
Trees in play Arbres en jeu

Scorecard Carte de score	Chp. Chp.	Mens Mess.	Ladies Da.
Length Long.	6061	5827	5447
Par	73	73	75
Slope system	0	0	0

Advised golfing ability Niveau de jeu recommandé 0 12 24 36
Hcp required Handicap exigé 24 Men, 36 Ladies

CLUB HOUSE & AMENITIES — CLUB HOUSE ET ANNEXES — 8/10

Pro shop Pro-shop
Driving range Practice
Sheltered couvert practice area - On grass sur herbe yes - Putting-green putting-green yes - Pitching-green pitching green yes

HOTEL FACILITIES — ENVIRONNEMENT HOTELIER — 5/10

HOTELS HÔTELS
Ox Pasture Hall - Scarborough 14 km
23 rooms, D £ 95
Tel (44) 01723 - 365 295, Fax (44) 01723 - 355 156

Crown (Forte) - 83 rooms, D from £ 60 - Scarborough 15 km
Tel (44) 01723 - 373 491, Fax (44) 01723 - 362 271

Ganton Greyhound - 18 rooms, D £ 70 - Ganton 5 km
Tel (44) 01944 - 710 116, Fax (44) 01944 - 710 738

RESTAURANTS RESTAURANTS
Marmalade's - Scarborough 15 km - Tel (44) 01723 - 365 766
Lanterna - Scarborough 15 km - Tel (44) C1723 - 363 616

Gog Magog *Old Course*

15 | 7 | 8

The landscape in this part of the country is generally so flat that it could hardly have inspired early course designers who probably had little more than ploughs and wheelbarrows to shift earth. For want of golf courses, you will enjoy visiting Cambridge, Ely, Bury St. Edmunds or the Fens with their windmills. At the foot of the hills which bear the same name, Gog Magog is the exception to the rule and is laid out over some small hills which are easy to walk. The club has a long tradition of hospitality and also a second course, Wandlebury (by Martin Hawtree), which is longer and more "modern" if you will. This Old Course however has the greater charm and is the more demanding - especially savour the outstanding two-shot 16th). There are not too many trees but they are sometimes placed to block your second shot if the drive is not perfect. A fair and shortish course which rewards good shots, Gog Magog is pleasant to play with friends or with the family, whatever their level.

Le paysage de cette région est assez plat, ce qui ne pouvait guère inspirer les architectes des origines, qui ne disposaient que de charrues et brouettes pour modeler le terrain. Faute de nombreux parcours, la visite de Cambridge, d'Ely, de Bury St Edmunds ou les marais des Fens avec leurs moulins à vent est déjà un dépaysement. Au pied des Gog Magog Hills, qui lui ont donné son nom, Gog Magog est l'exception à la règle, et a trouvé place sur de petites collines assez aimables pour les jambes. Ce club à la longue tradition d'accueil offre un second parcours, Wandlebury, plus long et plus "moderne" si l'on veut, mais le Old Course est le plus charmeur et le plus exigeant (voir le 16, superbe par 4). Les arbres n'y sont pas trop nombreux, mais parfois placés pour bloquer les seconds coups si les drives n'ont pas été parfaits. Honnête, récompensant les bons coups de golf, c'est un parcours agréable pour jouer en famille ou avec des amis, quel que soit leur niveau.

The Gog Magog Golf Club — 1901

ENG - SHELFORD BOTTOM, Cambridgeshire CB2 4AB

Office	Secrétariat	(44) 01223 - 247 626
Pro shop	Pro-shop	(44) 01223 - 246 058
Fax	Fax	(44) 01223 - 414 990
Web	www.gogmagog.co.uk	
Situation	Situation	Cambridge, 4 km
Annual closure	Fermeture annuelle	no
Weekly closure	Fermeture hebdomadaire	no

Fees main season Tarifs haute saison	18 holes	
	Week days Semaine	We/Bank holidays We/Férié
Individual Individuel	£ 40	£ 60*
Couple Couple	£ 80	£ 120*

Full week day: £ 50 / Saturday after 15:30 & Sunday after 14:30, £ 40

Caddie Caddie no — **Electric Trolley** Chariot électrique yes

Buggy Voiturette yes — **Clubs** Clubs yes

Credit cards Cartes de crédit
Visa - Mastercard - AMEX (Pro shop goods only)

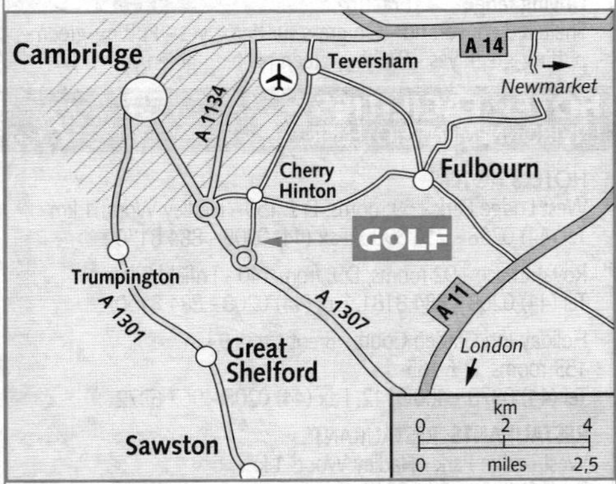

Access Accès : Cambridge A1307 SE. Second roundabout turn left → Fulbourn. Entrance 200 m on the right.
Map 7 on page 483 Carte 7 Page 483

GOLF COURSE — PARCOURS 15/20

Site	Site	
Maintenance	Entretien	
Architect	Architecte	F.W. Hawtree
Type	Type	inland, copse
Relief	Relief	
Water in play	Eau en jeu	
Exp. to wind	Exposé au vent	
Trees in play	Arbres en jeu	

Scorecard Carte de score	Chp. Chp.	Mens Mess.	Ladies Da.
Length Long.	5760	5565	5010
Par	70	70	71
Slope system	—	—	—

Advised golfing ability Niveau de jeu recommandé — 0 12 24 36

Hcp required Handicap exigé — certificate

CLUB HOUSE & AMENITIES — CLUB HOUSE ET ANNEXES 7/10

Pro shop Pro-shop
Driving range Practice
Sheltered couvert no - On grass sur herbe yes - Putting-green putting-green yes - Pitching-green pitching green yes

HOTEL FACILITIES — ENVIRONNEMENT HOTELIER 8/10

HOTELS HÔTELS

University Arms - 115 rooms, D £ 153 - Cambridge 4 km
Tel (44) 01223 - 351 241, Fax (44) 01223 - 315 256

Arundel House - 102 rooms, D £ 110 - Cambridge 4 km
Tel (44) 01223 - 367 701, Fax (44) 01223 - 367 721

Centennial - 39 rooms, D £ 96 - Cambridge 4 km
Tel (44) 01223 - 314 652, Fax (44) 01223 - 315 443

RESTAURANTS RESTAURANTS

Sycamore House - Little Shelford 3 km
Tel (44) 01223 - 843396

Midsummer House - Cambridge 4 km - Tel (44) 01223 - 69299

22 Chesterton Road - Cambridge 4 km
Tel (44) 01223 - 351 880

Hadley Wood

15 | 7 | 7

Whichever direction you're travelling, London just seems never-ending. The strangest thing is that you start finding golf courses where you would never expect them and, what's more, in calm secluded spots. Less than a mile from Cockfosters tube station, Hadley Wood is one such course, where a superb club-house is surrounded by flowers and bushes whose colours contrast sharply with the grey (or blue) skies. The same elegance and eye for detail are found in what is a very distinguished layout by Alister Mackenzie, landscaped like a garden and whose bunkers, streams and lakes look like items of decoration straight out of a magazine. But deceptive as ever, even the sweetest looking courses can prove deadly and easily end any hope of a good score. Testimony to the difficulties here is the fact that Hadley Wood is one of the qualifying courses for the British Open.

Que l'on aille dans n'importe quelle direction, Londres semble ne jamais finir. Le plus étrange est de parvenir à trouver beaucoup de golfs là où on ne penserait pas en chercher, et à les trouver dans des endroits calmes. Hadley Wood fait partie de ces sites privilégiés, à moins d'un mile du métro Cockfosters. Autour du superbe club-house, fleurs et arbustes témoignent une fois de plus d'un amour des végétaux coloriés qui tranchent avec le ciel gris (et d'ailleurs parfois bleu !). On retrouve cette élégance, ce souci du détail dans le tracé très distingué d'Alister Mackenzie, paysagé comme un jardin, où les bunkers, les petits cours d'eau et les lacs paraissent des éléments d'un décor pour magazine. Mais il faut se méfier des apparences, les dessins les plus évidents peuvent être meurtriers, du moins si l'on tente de faire un bon score. Témoin de ces difficultés, le fait qu'Hadley Wood figure parmi les parcours de qualification du British Open.

Hadley Wood Golf Club — 1922

Beech Hill
ENG - BARNET, Herts EN4 0JJ

Office	Secrétariat	(44) 0208 - 449 4328
Pro shop	Pro-shop	(44) 0208 - 449 3285
Fax	Fax	(44) 0208 - 364 8633
Web	www.hadleywoodgc.com	
Situation	Situation	London, 16 km
Annual closure	Fermeture annuelle	no
Weekly closure	Fermeture hebdomadaire	no

Fees main season Tarifs haute saison	Week days Semaine	We/Bank holidays We/Férié
		18 holes
Individual Individuel	£ 50	£ 55
Couple Couple	£ 100	£ 110

Full week days: £ 70 / * Sunday afternoon & 18 holes only

Caddie Caddie on request **Electric Trolley** Chariot électrique yes

Buggy Voiturette yes **Clubs** Clubs yes

Credit cards Cartes de crédit (extra charge/no credit cards in club-house) VISA - Eurocard - MasterCard - AMEX

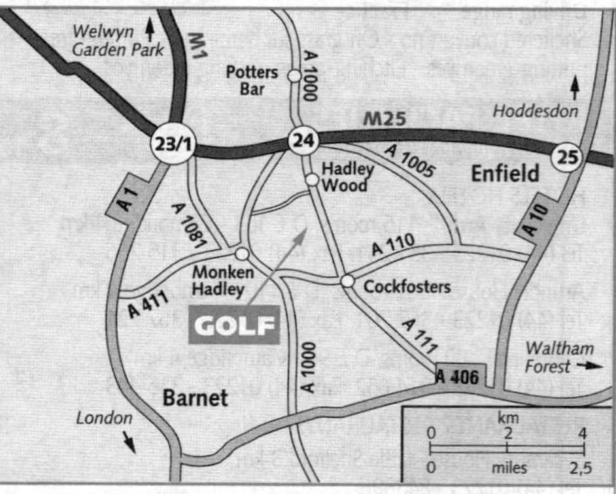

Access Accès : M25 Jct 24. A111 → Cockfosters.
3rd right into Beech Hill. Golf 400 m on left.
Map 8 on page 485 Carte 8 Page 485

GOLF COURSE — PARCOURS 15/20

Site	Site	
Maintenance	Entretien	
Architect	Architecte	Alister Mackenzie
Type	Type	parkland
Relief	Relief	
Water in play	Eau en jeu	
Exp. to wind	Exposé au vent	
Trees in play	Arbres en jeu	

Scorecard Carte de score	Chp. Chp.	Mens Mess.	Ladies Da.
Length Long.	5811	5612	4710
Par	72	72	73
Slope system	—	—	—

Advised golfing ability Niveau de jeu recommandé: 0 12 24 36

Hcp required Handicap exigé: certificate

CLUB HOUSE & AMENITIES — CLUB HOUSE ET ANNEXES 7/10

Pro shop Pro-shop
Driving range Practice
Sheltered couvert no - On grass sur herbe yes - Putting-green putting-green yes - Pitching-green pitching green yes

HOTEL FACILITIES — ENVIRONNEMENT HOTELIER 7/10

HOTELS HÔTELS

West Lodge Park - 59 rooms, D £ 150 - Hadley Wood 1 km
Tel (44) 0208 - 216 3900, Fax (44) 0208 - 884 8150

Royal Chace - 92 rooms, D £ from 140 - Enfield 3 km
Tel (44) 0208 - 884 8181, Fax (44) 0208 - 884 8150

Holiday Inn Garden Court - Brent Cross 9 km
153 rooms, D £ 165
Tel (44) 0870 - 400 9112, Fax (44) 0208 - 967 6372

RESTAURANTS RESTAURANTS

West Lodge Park - Hadley Wood 1 km
Tel (44) 0208 - 216 3900

The King's Head - Winchmore Hill 7 km
Tel (44) 0208 - 886 1988

The Cedar - Hadley Wood 1 km - Tel (44) 0208 - 216 3900

Hallamshire

15 | 6 | 8

As this is probably not the most touristic part of Yorkshire, the courses around Sheffield are played mostly by two types of golfer: the locals and large numbers of travelling businessmen. They definitely enjoy playing Hallamshire, which would certainly be better known if located in a more fashionable golfing county like Surrey. The anonymous architect certainly had talent to spare. This is a course of moorland and woods over rolling but easily walkable terrain, where, surprise, surprise, there is no water. The tall rough is out of play (or should be) and the turf lush and springy, so unless you are here in the middle of a drought you won't have to contend with bad kicks. There are a few blind holes here and there, but if you play with a local golfer from the club, he will guide you around and help you avoid any unpleasant surprises. Hallamshire is a well-balanced course where playing to your handicap is never a foregone conclusion, perhaps owing to a tendency to under-estimate the hazards and ignore the dangers behind a friendly exterior. A most respectable course.

Ce n'est certes pas la partie la plus touristique du Yorkshire, et les parcours aux alentours de Sheffield, mis à part les joueurs locaux, sont surtout fréquentés par les "businessmen" en déplacement. Ils apprécieront Hallamshire, dont la notoriété aurait été plus grande s'il avait par exemple été situé dans le Surrey, et l'architecte resté anonyme devait avoir pas mal de talent. Parcours de landes et de bois, dans un paysage animé mais facile à parcourir à pied, il est dénué d'obstacles d'eau, ce qui est rare de nos jours. Le haut rough n'est pas en jeu, le gazon bien souple, les surprises au rebond ne sont à craindre que par sécheresse. On trouve çà et là quelques coups aveugles, mais avec un bon "pilote" habitué du club, pas de mauvaises surprises non plus. Pourtant, il n'est pas si facile de jouer ici son handicap, peut être parce que l'on a tendance à en sous-estimer les difficultés, à ne pas sentir les dents derrière une amabilité de façade. Bien équilibré, c'est un parcours fort respectable.

Hallamshire Golf Club — 1897

The Club House
ENG - SANDYGATE, SHEFFIELD, S. Yorks. S10 44A

Office	Secrétariat	(44) 01142 - 302 153
Pro shop	Pro-shop	(44) 01142 - 305 222
Fax	Fax	(44) 01142 - 305 656
Web		www.hallamshiregolfclub.co.uk
Situation	Situation	Sheffield (pop. 501 202), 3 km
Annual closure	Fermeture annuelle	no
Weekly closure	Fermeture hebdomadaire	no

Fees main season Tarifs haute saison	18 holes	
	Week days Semaine	We/Bank holidays We/Férié
Individual Individuel	£ 45	£ 60
Couple Couple	£ 90	£ 120

Caddie Caddie yes **Electric Trolley** Chariot électrique yes

Buggy Voiturette no **Clubs** Clubs no

Credit cards Cartes de crédit
VISA - MasterCard - Switch (not for green fees)

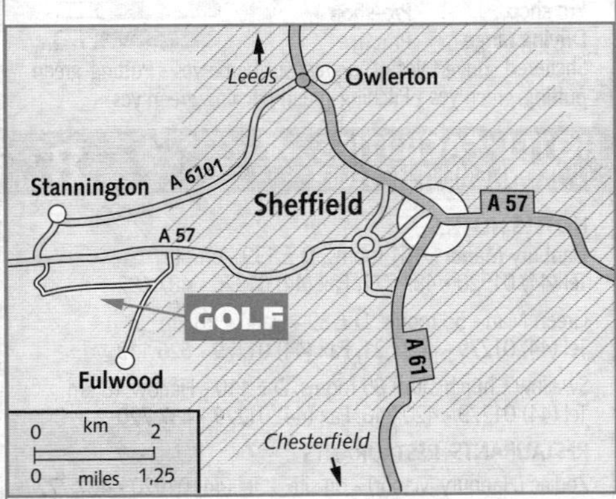

Access Accès : A57 from Sheffield city centre, left fork at Crosspool (pub), 1.5 km to the golf.
Map 4 on page 476 Carte 4 Page 476

GOLF COURSE — PARCOURS 15/20

Site	Site	
Maintenance	Entretien	
Architect	Architecte	unknown
Type	Type	parkland, hilly
Relief	Relief	
Water in play	Eau en jeu	
Exp. to wind	Exposé au vent	
Trees in play	Arbres en jeu	

Scorecard Carte de score	Chp. Chp.	Mens Mess.	Ladies Da.
Length Long.	5724	5292	5104
Par	71	71	74
Slope system	—	—	

Advised golfing ability Niveau de jeu recommandé: 0 12 24 36

Hcp required Handicap exigé: no

CLUB HOUSE & AMENITIES — CLUB HOUSE ET ANNEXES 6/10

Pro shop Pro-shop

Driving range Practice

Sheltered couvert no - On grass sur herbe yes - Putting-green putting-green yes - Pitching-green pitching green yes

HOTEL FACILITIES — ENVIRONNEMENT HOTELIER 8/10

HOTELS HÔTELS

Beauchief Hotel - 50 rooms, D £ 93 - Sheffield 4 km
Tel (44) 0114 - 262 0500, Fax (44) 0114 - 235 0197

Sheffield Park Hotel - Sheffield 8 km
95 rooms, D £ 115
Tel (44) 0114 - 282 9988, Fax (44) 0114 - 237 8140

Sheffield Marriott - 116 rooms, D £ 115 - Sheffield 4 km
Tel (44) 0114 - 258 3811, Fax (44) 0114 - 250 0138

RESTAURANTS RESTAURANTS

Thyme Out - Sheffield 4 km - Tel (44) 0114 - 266 6096
Rafters - Sheffield 4 km - Tel (44) 0114 - 230 4819
Slammers - Sheffield 4 km - Tel (44) 0114 - 268 0999

Hanbury Manor

16 | 8 | 8

This is the kind of luxury resort typically dished up at the end of the 20th century. Only members and hotel patrons can play here on an estate where Vardon earlier built nine holes. All nine have been totally restyled and included into the present 18-hole layout by Jack Nicklaus II. This is an amalgam between ancient and modern, and the association of Jacobean style buildings with other ' red-brick" affairs may raise more than a few eyebrows. Few people however can fail to be impressed by the collection of splendid specimen trees – many quite ancient – that are dotted across this blend of open park and wild country. The small lakes are not there for decoration and come into play on half a dozen holes. The overall style is American, even to the extent of a certain lack of subtlety here and there, but while this type of US-style park is none too common in Europe, they are a dime a dozen in the United States. A serious, modern golf-course, well thought through and well designed, very long but with loads of different tee-boxes. Ideal for a great week-end in silken sheets.

C'est le genre de resort de luxe que la fin du XXème siècle nous a apporté. Ici, seuls les membres et les résidents de l'hôtel peuvent évoluer, dans un domaine où Harry Vardon avait jadis construits 9 trous, totalement retravaillés et intégrés par Jack Nicklaus II dans l'actuel 18 trous. On est dans le mariage de l'ancien et du moderne, car l'alliance de bâtiments de style jacobéen avec d'autres de style un peu "brique rouge" peut faire grincer quelques dents. On se consolera avec quelques splendides spécimens d'arbres disséminés dans ce mariage d'un grand parc et d'une zone plus campagnarde. De petits lacs interviennent sur une demi-douzaine de trous. L'esthétique générale est américaine, jusque dans un certain manque de subtilité, mais si ce genre de parc US n'est pas si fréquent en Europe, il serait plus banal outre-Atlantique. Un sérieux parcours moderne, bien pensé et bien travaillé, très long mais avec plein de départs. Pour un bon week-end dans la soie...

Hanbury Manor Hotel & Country Club 1991

ENG - WARE, Herfordshire SG12 0SD

Office	Secrétariat	(44) 01920 - 487 722
Pro shop	Pro-shop	(44) 01920 - 885 000
Fax	Fax	(44) 01920 - 487 692
Web	www.hanbury-manor.com	
Situation	Situation	London, 40 km
Annual closure	Fermeture annuelle	no
Weekly closure	Fermeture hebdomadaire	no

552

Fees main season Tarifs haute saison — 18 holes

	Week days / Semaine	We/Bank holidays / We/Férié
Individual Individuel	*	*
Couple Couple	*	*

* Members & Hotel's guests only

Caddie Caddie no — **Electric Trolley** Chariot électrique no

Buggy Voiturette yes — **Clubs** Clubs yes

Credit cards Cartes de crédit
VISA - MasterCard - AMEX

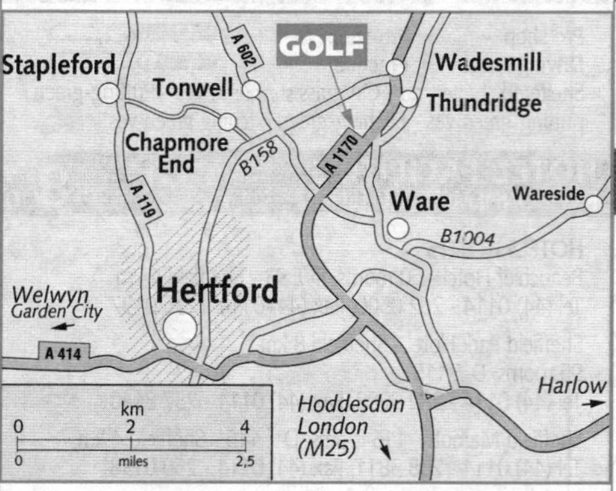

Access Accès : London A10 at the North Circular or J25 of M25. Head north → Hertford. Remain on A10 for 12 miles, past Hertford and Ware, then Exit → Thundridge/Wadesmill. Turn right at the roundabout, Hanbury Manor on left hand side just after Thundridge Road. **Map 8 on page 485** Carte 8 Page 485

GOLF COURSE
PARCOURS — **16/20**

Site	Site	
Maintenance	Entretien	
Architect	Architecte	Harry Vardon Jack Nicklaus II
Type	Type	parkland
Relief	Relief	
Water in play	Eau en jeu	
Exp. to wind	Exposé au vent	
Trees in play	Arbres en jeu	

Scorecard Carte de score	**Chp.** Chp.	**Mens** Mess.	**Ladies** Da.
Length Long.	6315	5960	4757
Par	72	72	72
Slope system	—	—	—

Advised golfing ability Niveau de jeu recommandé — 0 12 24 36

Hcp required Handicap exigé no

CLUB HOUSE & AMENITIES
CLUB HOUSE ET ANNEXES — **8/10**

Pro shop Pro-shop

Driving range Practice

Sheltered couvert yes - On grass sur herbe yes - Putting-green putting-green yes - Pitching-green pitching green yes

HOTEL FACILITIES
ENVIRONNEMENT HOTELIER — **8/10**

HOTELS HÔTELS

Hanbury Manor - 161 rooms, D £ 139 - on site
Tel (44) 01920 - 487 772, Fax (44) 01920 - 487 692

Green Man - 55 rooms, D £ 89 - Harlow 18 km
Tel (44) 01279 - 442 521, Fax (44) 01279 - 626 113

Swallow Churchgate - 85 rooms, D £ 110 - Harlow 18 km
Tel (44) 01279 - 420 246, Fax (44) 01279 - 437 720

RESTAURANTS RESTAURANTS

Zodiac (Hanbury Manor) - on site - Tel (44) 01920 - 487 772
Jacoby's (Pub) - Ware 2 km - Tel (44) 01920 - 469 181
The Hillside (Pub) - Hertford 6 km - Tel (44) 01992 - 554 556

Hankley Common

17	6	6

First of all a word of praise for the slick, very fast greens and their flawless maintenance. Might this be a tribute to Bobby Locke, one of the greatest putters of all time who for years lived right beside this course and rated it as comparable in quality to the country's top links courses? It used to be very dry in summer but now has automatic sprinklers which tend to lengthen the course and stress the need for long-hitting. Keep it straight, too, because the fairway bunkers snap up anything remotely off-line, and even if you miss the sand there's enough heather to keep you busy for longer than you would like, finding ways of getting your ball back into play. The felling of a number of trees has exposed the course to the wind and sometimes gives a part of the course an unexpected links feel, with all the technical challenge that entails. A final word for the beautiful finishing holes, especially the 18th, where our advice is always to take one club more than you think you need to hit the green. Then move on and enjoy the club-house which was extended and refurbished in 1999.

D'abord un mot pour les greens subtils, très rapides et d'un entretien irréprochable, comme en hommage à l'un des meilleurs putters de tous les temps, Bobby Locke, qui habita longtemps à côté d'ici et l'estimait d'une qualité comparable à celle des grands links du pays. Longtemps très sec en été, ce parcours bénéficie d'un arrosage automatique, qui l'a en quelque sorte "allongé," renforçant la nécessité d'être long, et droit car les nombreux bunkers de fairway accueillent avec le sourire les balles incertaines. Et quand on réussit à les passer, la bruyère peut les retenir à son tour. La disparition de nombreux arbres a exposé davantage les joueurs au vent, ce qui donne effectivement un caractère de links inattendu à certains trous, avec l'exigence technique que cela représente. A côté d'une faune sauvage très diverse, signalons, la beauté du finale, en particulier du 18ème trou: prenez un club de plus pour jouer le green, avant de retrouver un club-house agrandi et rénové en 1999.

Hankley Common Golf Club — 1895

Tilford Road, Tilford
ENG - FARNHAM, Surrey GU10 2DD

Office Secrétariat (44) 01252 - 792 493
Pro shop Pro-shop (44) 01252 - 797 717
Fax Fax (44) 01252 - 795 699
Web www.hankley.co.uk
Situation Situation Farnham (pop. 30 430), 6 km
Annual closure Fermeture annuelle no
Weekly closure Fermeture hebdomadaire no

Fees main season Tarifs haute saison — 18 holes

	Week days Semaine	We/Bank holidays We/Férié
Individual Individuel	£ 60	£ 75*
Couple Couple	£ 120	£ 150*

Full weekdays: £ 75 / * For 18 holes/Prior booking essential

Caddie Caddie no **Electric Trolley** Chariot électrique no

Buggy Voiturette no **Clubs** Clubs no

Credit cards Cartes de crédit
Visa - Eurocard - Mastercard - Switch (Pro shop goods only)

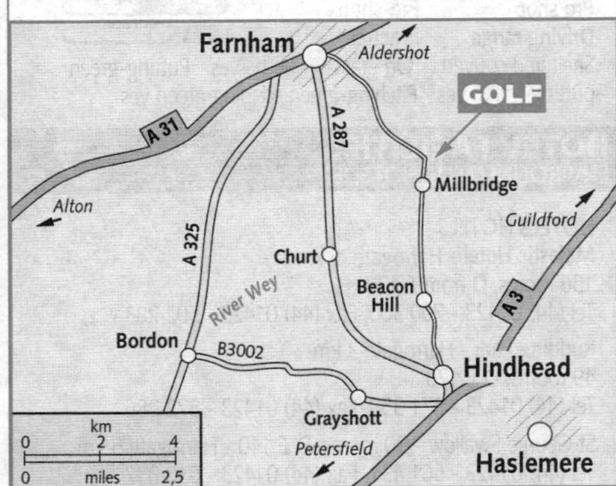

Access Accès : A3 (→ Portsmouth). After Devils Punch Bowl, turn right onto Tilford Road.
Golf Club is approx; 6 km (4 m) on the right.
Map 7 on page 482 Carte 7 Page 482

GOLF COURSE — PARCOURS — 17/20

Site Site
Maintenance Entretien
Architect Architecte — Charles Lawrie
Type Type — inland, heathland
Relief Relief
Water in play Eau en jeu
Exp. to wind Exposé au vent
Trees in play Arbres en jeu

Scorecard Carte de score	Chp. Chp.	Mens Mess.	Ladies Da.
Length Long.	5795	5503	5002
Par	71	71	72
Slope system	—	—	—

Advised golfing ability Niveau de jeu recommandé — 0 12 24 36
Hcp required Handicap exigé — certificate

CLUB HOUSE & AMENITIES — CLUB HOUSE ET ANNEXES — 6/10

Pro shop Pro-shop
Driving range Practice
Sheltered couvert no - On grass sur herbe yes - Putting-green putting-green yes - Pitching-green pitching green yes

HOTEL FACILITIES — ENVIRONNEMENT HOTELIER — 6/10

HOTELS HÔTELS
Bush (Forte Heritage) - Farnham 5 km
66 rooms, D from £ 150
Tel (44) 01252 - 715 237, Fax (44) 01252 - 733 530

Bishop's Table - 17 rooms, D £ 115 - Farnham 5 km
Tel (44) 01252 - 710 222, Fax (44) 01252 - 733 494

Farnham House - 25 rooms, D £ 89 - Farnham 5 km
Tel (44) 01252 - 716 908, Fax (44) 01252 - 722 583

RESTAURANTS RESTAURANTS
Bishop's Table - Farnham 5 km - Tel (44) 01252 - 710 222
Auberge de France - Haslemere 10 km
Tel (44) 01428 - 651 251
Vienna - Farnham 5 km - Tel (44) 01252 - 722 978

Harrogate

15 | 7 | 7

This course is close to Knaresborough, one of the oldest towns in the country. The superb surroundings in this region are further enhanced by the spa city of Harrogate, the Yorkshire Dales and the ruins of Fountains Abbey with its gardens and... fountains. There are several superb courses around here and this is one of them. With neighbouring Pannal, Harrogate is one of Sandy Herd's best layouts and a little advice was also given by Alistair MacKenzie. Here we are on woody terrain (the trees are never too dense) which is hilly enough to conceal one or two difficulties. In other words, strategy is never simple the first time out and errors of positioning or direction can easily require the use of every club you have available. Although not a terribly long or spectacular course, it is an excellent examination of talent and technique that connoisseurs of the game will appreciate on its merits.

Le présent parcours est tout proche de Knaresborough, une des plus vieilles villes du pays. La ville d'eau d'Harrogate, le Parc National des Yorkshire Dales, ou encore les ruines de l'Abbaye, les temples à l'antique et les jeux d'eau des jardins de Fountains Abbey ajoutent encore à l'agrément de l'environnement superbe de cette région. Elle est pourvue de plusieurs parcours de qualité et celui-ci ne détonne pas auprès d'eux. Avec son voisin Pannal, c'est un des meilleurs tracés de Sandy Herd. Et Alister MacKenzie a aussi prodigué ses conseils au club. Le terrain est boisé mais sans devoir inquiéter les claustrophobes, assez accidenté, ce qui dissimule quelques difficultés. La stratégie n'est alors pas évidente à la première visite, et les erreurs de placement ou de direction peuvent obliger à sortir tous les coups de son sac. Sans être un parcours long, ni très spectaculaire, c'est en fait un excellent examen du talent et de la technique, que les bons connaisseurs apprécieront à sa juste valeur.

Harrogate Golf Club — 1892

Forest Lane Head
ENG - HARROGATE, North Yorkshire HG2 7 TF

Office	Secrétariat	(44) 01423 - 862 999
Pro shop	Pro-shop	(44) 01423 - 862 547
Fax	Fax	(44) 01423 - 860 073
Web	www.harrogate-gc.co.uk	
Situation	Situation	Harrogate, 3 km
Annual closure	Fermeture annuelle	no
Weekly closure	Fermeture hebdomadaire	no

Fees main season Tarifs haute saison		Full day
	Week days Semaine	We/Bank holidays We/Férié
Individual Individuel	£ 36	£ 40
Couple Couple	£ 72	£ 80

Week-end after 14:30, £ 30

Caddie Caddie no — **Electric Trolley** Chariot électrique no

Buggy Voiturette yes — **Clubs** Clubs yes

Credit cards Cartes de crédit
VISA - Eurocard - MasterCard

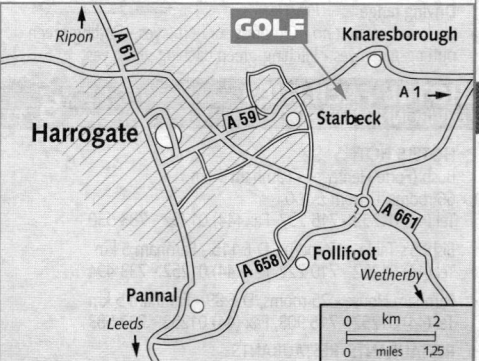

Access Accès : Harrogate, A 59 → Knaresborough.
Golf 3 km on right hand side
Map 4 on page 476 Carte 4 Page 476

GOLF COURSE — PARCOURS 15/20

Site	Site	
Maintenance	Entretien	
Architect	Architecte	Sandy Herd
Type	Type	parkland
Relief	Relief	
Water in play	Eau en jeu	
Exp. to wind	Exposé au vent	
Trees in play	Arbres en jeu	

Scorecard Carte de score	Chp. Chp.	Mens Mess.	Ladies Da.
Length Long.	5617	5483	5127
Par	69	69	72
Slope system	—	—	—

Advised golfing ability Niveau de jeu recommandé — 0 12 24 36
Hcp required Handicap exigé — certificate

CLUB HOUSE & AMENITIES — CLUB HOUSE ET ANNEXES 7/10

Pro shop Pro-shop
Driving range Practice
Sheltered couvert - On grass sur herbe yes - Putting-green putting-green yes - Pitching-green pitching green yes

HOTEL FACILITIES — ENVIRONNEMENT HOTELIER 7/10

HOTELS HÔTELS

Majestic Hotel - Harrogate 5 km
156 rooms, D from £ 120
Tel (44) 01423 - 700 300, Fax (44) 01423 - 502 283

Rudding Park - Harrogate 3 km
49 rooms, D £ 170
Tel (44) 01423 - 871 350, Fax (44) 01423 - 872 286

St George Swallow - 90 rooms, D £ 140 - Harrogate 5 km
Tel (44) 01423 - 561 431, Fax (44) 01423 - 530 037

RESTAURANTS RESTAURANTS

Villu Toots - Harrogate 5 km - Tel (44) 01423 - 705 805
Sasso - Harrogate 5 km - Tel (44) 01423 - 508 838

Hawkstone Park *Hawkstone*

15	8	7

A strange place where the "Follies" of Hawkstone Park could be a setting for a video game with caves, secret passages or little monuments, all hidden in lush vegetation. They also say that King Arthur is buried somewhere on this estate. What is certain is that Sandy Lyle learnt how to play here. Today, this is a real resort with a hotel and two courses, including the "Hawkstone", which was designed by James Braid with some of the greens in the style of Alister Mackenzie. The course was restored and adapted to the modern game by Brian Huggett, who also laid out the resort's other good 18-hole course, the "Windmill". Imaginative, sometimes spectacular, very well landscaped and blending perfectly with its environment, this is a course whose subtleties will probably appeal more to the better golfer. Non-golfers can always visit the pretty town of Shrewsbury in the footsteps of Cadfael, the hero of the medieval murder novels by Ellis Peters.

Etrange endroit où les "Follies" de Hawkstone Park pourraient servir de cadre à un jeu video avec grottes, passages secrets ou petits monuments, tous cachés dans une végétation très riche. On murmure que le Roi Arthur aurait été enterré sur ce domaine, mais la seule chose certaine, c'est que Sandy Lyle a appris le golf ici. C'est aujourd'hui un resort, avec hôtel et deux parcours, dont le "Hawkstone" est un James Braid avec certains greens à la Alister Mackenzie, restauré et adapté au jeu moderne par Brian Huggett, qui a également signé l'autre bon 18 trous du domaine, le "Windmill". Imaginatif, parfois spectaculaire, bien paysagé mais en même temps magnifiquement intégré à son environnement, c'est un parcours dont les joueurs d'un bon niveau apprécieront le plus les subtilités. Les autres pourront chercher dans la jolie ville de Shrewsbury les traces de Frère Cadfael, héros des romans policiers médiévaux d'Ellis Peters.

Hawkstone Park Hotel — 1920

Weston-under-Redcastle
ENG - SHREWSBURY, Shropshire SY4 5UY

Office	Secrétariat	(44) 01939 - 200 611
Pro shop	Pro-shop	(44) 01939 - 200 611
Fax	Fax	(44) 01939 - 200 311
Web	www.hawkstone.co.uk	
Situation	Situation	Shrewsbury, 19 km
Annual closure	Fermeture annuelle	no
Weekly closure	Fermeture hebdomadaire	no

Fees main season Tarifs haute saison	18 holes	
	Week days Semaine	**We/Bank holidays** We/Férié
Individual Individuel	£ 34	£ 44
Couple Couple	£ 68	£ 88

Full days: £ 50 / £ 60 (We)

Caddie Caddie on request **Electric Trolley** Chariot électrique no

Buggy Voiturette yes **Clubs** Clubs yes

Credit cards Cartes de crédit
VISA - Eurocard - MasterCard - AMEX

Access Accès : M6 Birmingham → Liverpool. Jct 10A through Telford, A5 → Shrewsbury. A49 North.
Follow signs for Hawkstone Historic Park
Map 5 on page 478 Carte 5 Page 478

GOLF COURSE — PARCOURS 15/20

Site	Site	
Maintenance	Entretien	
Architect	Architecte	James Braid
Type	Type	parkland
Relief	Relief	
Water in play	Eau en jeu	
Exp. to wind	Exposé au vent	
Trees in play	Arbres en jeu	

Scorecard Carte de score	**Chp.** Chp.	**Mens** Mess.	**Ladies** Da.
Length Long.	5842	5519	5153
Par	72	72	72
Slope system	—	—	—

Advised golfing ability / Niveau de jeu recommandé: 0 12 24 36

Hcp required Handicap exigé: certificate

CLUB HOUSE & AMENITIES — CLUB HOUSE ET ANNEXES 8/10

Pro shop Pro-shop
Driving range Practice
Sheltered couvert no - On grass sur herbe yes - Putting-green putting-green yes - Pitching-green pitching green yes

HOTEL FACILITIES — ENVIRONNEMENT HOTELIER 7/10

HOTELS HÔTELS

Hawkstone Park Hotel - 70 rooms, D £ 105 - on site
Tel (44) 01939 - 200 611, Fax (44) 01939 - 200 311

Albrighton Hall - 71 rooms, D £ 112 - Albrighton 12 km
Tel (44) 01939 - 291 000, Fax (44) 01939 - 291 123

Prince Rupert - 69 rooms, D £ 105 - Shrewsbury 19 km
Tel (44) 01743 - 499 955, Fax (44) 01743 - 357 306

RESTAURANTS RESTAURANTS

Hawkstone Park Hotel - on site
Tel (44) 01939 - 200 611

Sol - Shrewsbury 19 km - Tel (44) 01743 - 340 560

Hayling

17	8	7

Kent aside, the southern coast of England has very few genuine links courses. Rye (totally private) can claim the label, and so can Hayling, whose reputation is surprisingly modest, despite being designed by Tom Simpson, a hallmark of quality. As usual, the hazards are remarkably well located with the best route to the green always being the most dangerous (as with Donald Ross). At the same time visibility is 90% perfect so you can get to grips with the course from the first time out. The ever-changing conditions dictate a player's strategy and here you are adapting your game all the time, but that is one of the pleasures of golf. This easy-walking course is ideal for the holidays if you are not too concerned about your score. Close to the beach and a very rich nature reserve, Hayling merits a visit, especially now that an automatic sprinkler system softens fairways that used to get very hard in summer. There is also a new club-house (built in a yacht club style) with some pretty views over the sea.

A part le Kent, cette côte de l'Angleterre propose peu de vrais links. Rye peut prétendre en être un, mais aussi Hayling, dont la notoriété est étrangement réduite, en dépit de la signature de Tom Simpson, une garantie de qualité. Comme d'habitude avec lui, le placement des obstacles est remarquable, la meilleure route étant toujours la plus dangereuse (comme avec Donald Ross), et la visibilité est à 90 % parfaite, de manière à pouvoir entrer dans le vif du sujet dès la première visite. Les conditions de jeu et de vent dictent la stratégie, ce qui oblige à s'adapter sans cesse, mais c'est un des plaisirs du golf. Peu fatigant à marcher, c'est un parcours idéal pour les vacances, si l'on n'est pas trop soucieux de son score. Proche de la plage et d'une très riche réserve naturelle, Hayling mérite une visite, d'autant que l'arrosage automatique a adouci les fairways parfois durs et très roulants en été, et qu'un nouveau club-house (de style yacht-club) a été ouvert, offrant de jolies vues sur la mer.

Hayling Golf Club — 1883

Links Lane
ENG- HAYLING ISLAND, Hampshire PO11 0BX

Office	Secrétariat	(44) 023 - 9246 4446
Pro shop	Pro-shop	(44) 023 - 9246 4491
Fax	Fax	(44) 02392 - 461 119
Web	www.haylinggolf.co.uk	
Situation	Situation	Portsmouth, 15 km

Havant (pop. 46 510), 8 km

Annual closure	Fermeture annuelle	no
Weekly closure	Fermeture hebdomadaire	no

Fees main season Tarifs haute saison — 18 holes

	Week days Semaine	We/Bank holidays We/Férié
Individual Individuel	£ 45	£ 60
Couple Couple	£ 90	£ 120

Full week day: £ 60

Caddie Caddie no **Electric Trolley** Chariot électrique yes

Buggy Voiturette yes **Clubs** Clubs no

Credit cards Cartes de crédit
VISA - MasterCard (Pro shop goods only)

Fareham · Waterlooville · A3M · Chichester · M27 · 5 · Havant · 12 · A 27 · Duffield · A 3023 · Stoke · Portsmouth · Hayling Island · South Hayling · GOLF · 0 2 4 km · 0 2,5 miles

Access Accès : London, A3 → Portsmouth, A27 → Havant. A 3023 to Hayling Island. Seafront, turn right
Map 7 on page 482 Carte 7 Page 482

GOLF COURSE — PARCOURS — 17/20

Site	Site	
Maintenance	Entretien	
Architect	Architecte	J.H Taylor Tom Simpson
Type	Type	seaside course, links
Relief	Relief	
Water in play	Eau en jeu	
Exp. to wind	Exposé au vent	
Trees in play	Arbres en jeu	

Scorecard Carte de score	Chp. Chp.	Mens Mess.	Ladies Da.
Length Long.	5870	5675	5240
Par	71	71	73
Slope system	—	—	—

Advised golfing ability 0 12 24 36
Niveau de jeu recommandé
Hcp required Handicap exigé certificate

CLUB HOUSE & AMENITIES — CLUB HOUSE ET ANNEXES — 8/10

Pro shop Pro-shop
Driving range Practice

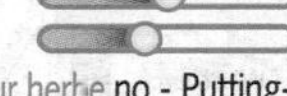

Sheltered couvert 2 mats - On grass sur herbe no - Putting-green putting-green yes - Pitching-green pitching green no

HOTEL FACILITIES — ENVIRONNEMENT HOTELIER — 7/10

HOTELS HÔTELS

Portsmouth Marriott - 174 rooms, D £ 108 - Portsmouth 15 km
Tel (44) 023 - 9238 3151, Fax (44) 023 - 9238 8701

Holiday Inn - 167 rooms, D £ 125 - Portsmouth 15 km
Tel (44) 0870 - 400 9065, Fax (44) 023 - 9275 6715

Seacrest - 26 rooms, D £ 75 - Portsmouth 15 km
Tel (44) 023 - 9273 3192, Fax (44) 023 - 9233 2523

RESTAURANTS RESTAURANTS

Bistro Montparnasse - Portsmouth 15 km
Tel (44) 023 - 9281 6754

Lemon Sole - Portsmouth 15 km - Tel (44) 023 - 9281 1303

Hertfordshire (The) 15 7 7

The Tudor style architecture of the listed club-house gives a pleasant if somewhat misleading first impression when you arrive here. You might expect an old-fashioned golf course but in fact you are met with excellent practice facilities and a very modern layout by Nicklaus Design, the company that Jack built whose staff includes Jack II, his son. Within a fairly confined area, the Nicklauus architectural approach is evident with well designed and often large bunkers, water which comes very much into play but which can be avoided, and huge, well-contoured greens. The front nine are very interesting, the back nine a little less so, although note the 15th, a spectacular and dangerous par 3 with a green almost entirely surrounded by water. The whole layout doubtless needs to mature a little with some of the wide open spaces more clearly defined by rough. Within easy reach of London, this very peacefully situated course deserves more than one visit.

L'architecture Tudor du club-house classé donne d'emblée une fallacieuse impression de majesté. On attendrait un parcours de grande tradition conservatrice. En fait, il y a ici de remarquables installations d'entraînement, et un parcours de dessin très moderne, créé par Nicklaus Design, la société du grand joueur et architecte américain, qui a glissé son fils Jack II dans l'équipe. On y trouve cependant, sur un espace assez réduit, la même approche stratégique, avec des bunkers très dessinés et souvent grands, des obstacles d'eau bien en jeu, mais dont il est possible (et conseillé) de ne pas trop s'approcher, des greens vastes et très travaillés. L'aller est très intéressant, le retour un peu moins, sauf le 15, spectaculaire et dangereux par 3 au green presque entouré d'eau. L'ensemble a besoin de mûrir, peut-être aussi de voir certains grands espaces bien dessinés par les roughs. Si proche de Londres, ce parcours très tranquille mérite plus qu'une visite.

The Hertfordshire Golf & Country Club 1995

Broxbournebury Mansion, White Stubbs Lane
ENG - BROXBOURNE, Herts EN10 7 PY

Office Secrétariat (44) 01992 - 466 666
Pro shop Pro-shop (44) 01992 - 466 666
Fax Fax (44) 01992 - 470 326
Web www.crown-golf.co.uk/thehertfordshire
Situation Situation Hertford (pop. 22 176), 8 km
Cheshunt (pop. 57 980), 5 km

Annual closure Fermeture annuelle no
Weekly closure Fermeture hebdomadaire no

Fees main season Tarifs haute saison	18 holes	
	Week days Semaine	We/Bank holidays We/Férié
Individual Individuel	£ 30	£ 35*
Couple Couple	£ 60	£ 70*

* We: visitors after 12:00 / Friday, £ 33
Week days: Monday → Thursday

Caddie Caddie no — **Electric Trolley** Chariot électrique no
Buggy Voiturette yes — **Clubs** Clubs yes
Credit cards Cartes de crédit VISA - MasterCard

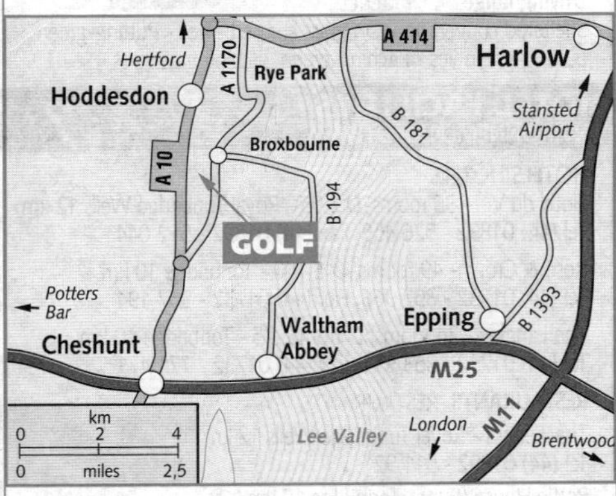

Access Accès : M25. At Jct 25 take A10 → Cambridge. Exit for Turnford, take A1170 to Bell Lane. Turn left, Bell Lane becomes White Stubbs Lane. Course on right.
Map 8 on page 485 Carte 8 Page 485

GOLF COURSE — PARCOURS 15/20

Site Site
Maintenance Entretien
Architect Architecte Nicklaus Design
Type Type parkland
Relief Relief
Water in play Eau en jeu
Exp. to wind Exposé au vent
Trees in play Arbres en jeu

Scorecard Carte de score	Chp. Chp.	Mens Mess.	Ladies Da.
Length Long.	5750	5403	4390
Par	70	70	70
Slope system	—	—	—

Advised golfing ability Niveau de jeu recommandé 0 12 24 36
Hcp required Handicap exigé 28 Men, 36 Ladies

CLUB HOUSE & AMENITIES — CLUB HOUSE ET ANNEXES 7/10

Pro shop Pro-shop
Driving range Practice
Sheltered couvert 30 bays - On grass sur herbe yes (May →Oct)
Putting-green putting-green yes
Pitching-green pitching green yes

HOTEL FACILITIES — ENVIRONNEMENT HOTELIER 7/10

HOTELS HÔTELS
Cheshunt Marriott - 143 rooms, D £ 119 - Cheshunt 4 km
Tel (44) 01992 - 451 245, Fax (44) 01992 - 440 120

Churchgate Manor - Old Harlow 12 km
85 rooms, D from £ 100
Tel (44) 01279 - 420 246, Fax (44) 01279 - 437 720

Harlow Moat House - 119 rooms, D from £ 120 - Harlow 10 km
Tel (44) 01279 - 829 988, Fax (44) 01279 - 635 094

Green Man - 55 rooms, D £ 90 - Harlow 9 km
Tel (44) 01279 - 442 521, Fax (44) 01279 - 626 113

RESTAURANTS RESTAURANTS
Cheshunt Marriott - Cheshunt 4 km - Tel (44) 01992 - 451 245

Hever

14 | 8 | 7

An impressive site and one of the more interesting new courses in the South-East of England which is now so easy to reach courtesy of Eurotunnel. The course, club-house and hotel have been laid out in the estate of a castle where Ann Boleyn spent her childhood before briefly becoming Henry VIII's second wife. An initial 9-hole course was laid out in the 1920s but the present course is an entirely recent creation. A stream is in play on almost one half of the course before running into the castle lake, but the hazard is psychologically rather than really dangerous. The trees are much more of a problem and those already on the estate have been supplemented by young plantations which will gradually make their presence felt in better defining the fairways and alter the course as the years go by. Generally speaking, the architect, Nicholson has made good use of existing features, particularly on the dog-legs, and has created enough variety for the course to be constantly enjoyable. Good work and a pretty place to spend a fine day's golfing.

Un site impressionnant, et l'un des bons parcours récents à connaître dans le sud-est de l'Angleterre, si facilement accessible par Eurotunnel. Le golf, le club-house et l'hôtel ont été créés dans le domaine d'un château où Ann Boleyn passa son enfance, avant d'être la seconde et passagère épouse d'Henry VIII. Un premier 9 trous fut construit dans les années 1920, mais le présent parcours a été une création complète. Il met en jeu sur près de la moitié des trous un cours d'eau se jetant dans le lac du château, mais cet obstacle est plus psychologique que vraiment dangereux. Les arbres le sont bien davantage, et ceux du parc ont été complétés par de jeunes plantations, qui viendront mieux délimiter les fairways et modifier le jeu. Nicholson a généralement fait bon usage des éléments existants, en particulier sur les doglegs, et donné assez de diversité pour que le plaisir soit constamment renouvelé. Du bon travail et un joli endroit pour passer une bonne journée de golf.

Hever Golf Club — 1993

ENG - HEVER, Kent TN8 7NG

Office	Secrétariat	(44) 01732 - 700 771
Pro shop	Pro-shop	(44) 01732 - 701 008
Fax	Fax	(44) 01732 - 700 775
Web	www.hevercastlegolfclub.co.uk	
Situation	Situation	Tonbridge, 10 km
Annual closure	Fermeture annuelle	no
Weekly closure	Fermeture hebdomadaire	no

Fees main season / Tarifs haute saison	Week days / Semaine	We/Bank holidays / We/Férié
		18 holes
Individual Individuel	£ 40	£ 60
Couple Couple	£ 70	£ 110

Visitors after 11.00 am on week-ends after 10:30 am on week days

Caddie Caddie no — Electric Trolley Chariot électrique no

Buggy Voiturette yes — Clubs Clubs yes

Credit cards Cartes de crédit
VISA - MasterCard - AMEX

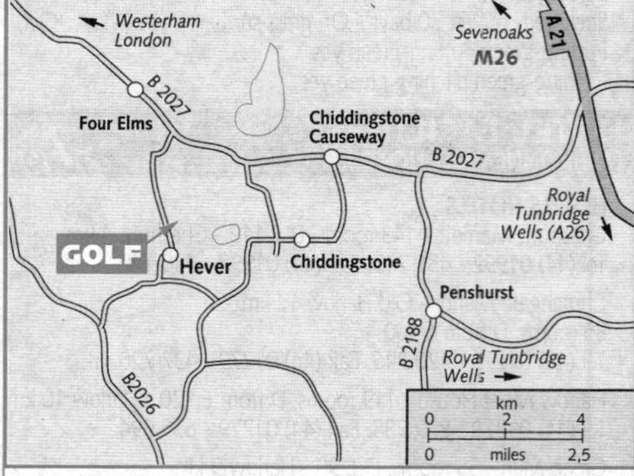

Access Accès : M25 Jct 6, A22, A25 → Sevenoaks. Limpsfield B269 to Crocham Hill, Four Elms, Bough Beech → Hever Castle

Map 7 on page 483 Carte 7 Page 483

GOLF COURSE / PARCOURS — 14/20

Site	Site	
Maintenance	Entretien	
Architect	Architecte	Peter Nicholson
Type	Type	parkland
Relief	Relief	
Water in play	Eau en jeu	
Exp. to wind	Exposé au vent	
Trees in play	Arbres en jeu	

Scorecard / Carte de score	Chp. / Chp.	Mens / Mess.	Ladies / Da.
Length Long.	6402	6085	5144
Par	72	72	73
Slope system	—	—	—

Advised golfing ability / Niveau de jeu recommandé: 0 12 24 36

Hcp required / Handicap exigé: certificate

CLUB HOUSE & AMENITIES / CLUB HOUSE ET ANNEXES — 8/10

Pro shop / Pro-shop

Driving range / Practice

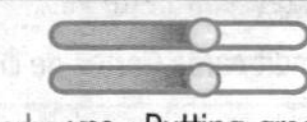

Sheltered couvert no - On grass sur herbe yes - Putting-green putting-green yes - Pitching-green pitching green yes

HOTEL FACILITIES / ENVIRONNEMENT HOTELIER — 7/10

HOTELS HÔTELS

Hotel du Vin - 35 rooms, D £ 95 - Royal Tunbridge Wells 12 km
Tel (44) 01892 - 526 455, Fax (44) 01892 - 512 044

Rose & Crown- 49 rooms, D £ 140 - Tonbridge 10 km
Tel (44) 01732 - 357 966, Fax (44) 01732 - 357 194

The Langley - 34 rooms, D from £ 75 - Tonbridge 10 km
Tel (44) 01732 - 353 311, Fax (44) 01732 - 771 471

RESTAURANTS RESTAURANTS

Thackeray's - Royal Tunbridge Wells 12 km
Tel (44) 01892 - 511 921

Bottle House (Pub) - Tonbridge 10 km
Tel (44) 01892 - 870 306

Right on the Green - Southborough 8 km
Tel (44) 01892 - 513 161

High Post

16 | 6 | 7

Here we are out in the country, with wild peacocks strutting around the club-house, jet fighters flying overhead to disturb your putting stroke, and an obligatory stop at tea-time to taste the delicious cakes. High Post is a hilly course which can be tough on the legs and on your score, but the chalky terrain drains well and doesn't get heavy after rain. The fairways are wide and the rough not too exacting, except when you get too close to the hawthorn bushes. High Post had a quiet and underrated profile until Peter Alliss drew attention to the course by rating the 9th hole as one of the 18 best holes in England. Amongst the par 4s the 16th also stands out with its long uphill climb. With only two par 5s here, birdies can be hard to come by. There are not many bunkers but they are well located, although the hollows and grassy sand-hills are often a tougher proposition than playing from sand.

Ici, on est à la campagne. Des paons sauvages se promènent autour du club-house, des avions de chasse vous dérangent quand vous puttez, il faut s'arrêter à l'heure du thé pour déguster quelques fameux Cakes. On monte et on descend, ce qui tire sur les jambes comme sur les scores, mais le terrain crayeux est bien draînant, ce qui évite un sol trop lourd par temps de pluie. Les fairways sont larges, les roughs pas trop pénalisants, sauf auprès des nombreux buissons d'aubépine. On pouvait croire que High Post allait poursuivre sa vie tranquille à l'écart des grandes histoires, quand Peter Alliss attira l'attention sur ce parcours, en classant son 9 parmi les 18 meilleurs trous d'Angleterre. Parmi les par 4, on distinguera aussi le 16, long et en montée. Et avec seulement deux par 5, les birdies ne sont pas donnés. Les bunkers sont assez peu nombreux, mais bien placés, et les dépressions ou buttes d'herbe sont souvent moins faciles à négocier que le sable.

High Post Golf Club — 1931

Great Durnford
ENG - SALISBURY, Wiltshire SP4 6AT

Office Secrétariat (44) 01722 - 782 356
Pro shop Pro-shop (44) 01722 - 782 219
Fax Fax (44) 01722 - 782 674
E-mail highpostgolfclub@lineone.net
Situation Situation Salisbury (pop. 105 318), 6 km
Annual closure Fermeture annuelle no
Weekly closure Fermeture hebdomadaire Restaurant: limited service on Mondays

Fees main season Tarifs haute saison	18 holes	
	Week days Semaine	**We/Bank holidays** We/Férié
Individual Individuel	£ 32	£ 42
Couple Couple	£ 64	£ 84

Caddie Caddie no — **Electric Trolley** Chariot électrique yes
Buggy Voiturette yes — **Clubs** Clubs no
Credit cards Cartes de crédit
Visa - Mastercard (Pro shop goods only)

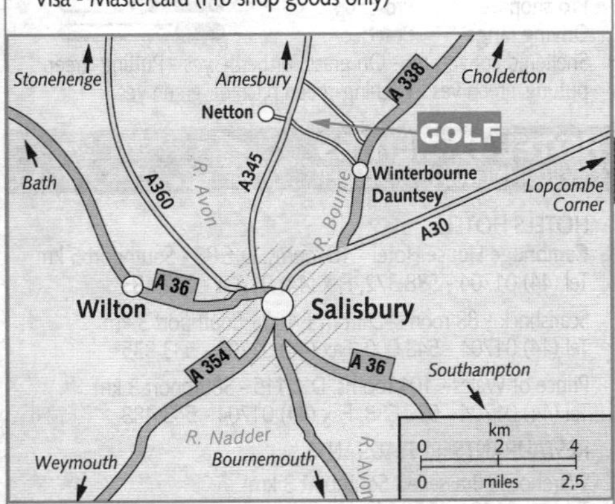

Access Accès : M3 to Southampton, then M27. Jct 2, A36 to Salisbury, then A345 → Amesbury. Golf on right side.
Map 6 on page 481 Carte 6 Page 481

GOLF COURSE — PARCOURS 16/20

Site Site
Maintenance Entretien
Architect Architecte Hawtree & Taylor
Type Type copse, open country
Relief Relief
Water in play Eau en jeu
Exp. to wind Exposé au vent
Trees in play Arbres en jeu

Scorecard Carte de score	**Chp.** Chp.	**Mens** Mess.	**Ladies** Da.
Length Long.	5738	5490	5172
Par	70	69	73
Slope system	—	—	—

Advised golfing ability Niveau de jeu recommandé 0 12 24 36
Hcp required Handicap exigé certificate

CLUB HOUSE & AMENITIES — CLUB HOUSE ET ANNEXES 6/10

Pro shop Pro-shop
Driving range Practice
Sheltered couvert no - On grass sur herbe yes - Putting-green putting-green yes - Pitching-green pitching green yes

HOTEL FACILITIES — ENVIRONNEMENT HOTELIER 7/10

HOTELS HÔTELS
Milford Hall - 35 rooms, D £ 120 - Salisbury 6 km
Tel (44) 01722 - 417 411, Fax (44) 01722 - 419 444

Red Lion Hotel - 51 rooms, D £ 129 - Salisbury 6 km
Tel (44) 01722 - 323 334, Fax (44) 01722 - 325 756

Rose and Crown - 28 rooms, D £ 140 - Harnham 8 km
Tel (44) 01722 - 399 955, Fax (44) 01722 - 339 816

RESTAURANTS RESTAURANTS
LXIX - Salisbury 6 km - Tel (44) 01722 - 340 000
Rose and Crown - Harnham 8 km - Tel (44) 01722 - 399 955
Grasmere House - Harnham 8 km - Tel (44) 01722 - 338 388

Hillside

18 | 7 | 7

A fairly modest course prior to 1962, Hillside took on a new dimension with the acquisition of some spectacular dune-land which Fred Hawtree fashioned and which became incorporated into the layout essentially from the 10th hole onward. A part of the course is lined by pine-trees, forming a rather unusual setting for a links course. The first holes run along the railway line and set a "down-the-middle" tone from the very beginning. The dunes and tall rough are more concentrated on the back nine (much praised by Jack Nicklaus) and the fairways run between the dune valleys. In such a dramatic landscape where the ever-changing wind can have such a diverse influence on the ball, it is not a bad idea to develop a low trajectory in order to stay on track. Featuring several quite elevated tee-boxes (giving some great views over the Irish Sea), Hillside looks very natural and is always pleasant to play and it is a joy to tread the springy seaside turf. It is certainly not the best known links course outside England but it is a must to play alongside neighbouring Birkdale.

Parcours modeste jusqu'en 1962, Hillside a pris une dimension nouvelle avec l'acquisition de dunes spectaculaires travaillées et incorporées au tracé par Fred Hawtree, essentiellement à partir du 10. De grands pins ornent une partie du parcours, comme un décor insolite posé sur un links. Les premiers trous longent la voie ferrée et annoncent qu'il sera impossible de se relâcher. Les dunes et hauts roughs sont davantage concentrés sur le retour (admiré par Nicklaus), les fairways glissant dans les vallées comme dans des amphithéâtres. Dans un paysage aussi divers où la direction du vent influe de manière déconcertante sur la balle, il faut savoir garder la balle basse pour rester en piste. Très soigné, rassurant avec ses départs souvent surélevés (de belles vues sur la mer d'Irlande), tout en conservant un aspect naturel, avec ce genre de sol de links si agréable à marcher et à jouer, Hillside n'est pas le plus connu des links hors des frontières, mais il est inévitable, à côté de son voisin Birkdale..

Hillside Golf Club — 1923

Hastings Road, Hillside
ENG - SOUTHPORT, Lancs PR8 2 LU

Office	Secrétariat	(44) 01704 - 567169
Pro shop	Pro-shop	(44) 01704 - 568360
Fax	Fax	(44) 01704 - 563192
Web	www.ukgolfer.org/clubs/hillside	
Situation	Situation	Liverpool, 28 km

Southport (pop. 90 959), 3 km

Annual closure	Fermeture annuelle	no
Weekly closure	Fermeture hebdomadaire	no

Fees main season Tarifs haute saison — 18 holes

	Week days / Semaine	We/Bank holidays / We/Férié
Individual Individuel	£ 65	£ 85
Couple Couple	£ 130	£ 170

Full week days: £ 85

Caddie Caddie no — **Electric Trolley** Chariot électrique no
Buggy Voiturette yes — **Clubs** Clubs no
Credit cards Cartes de crédit
VISA - MasterCard

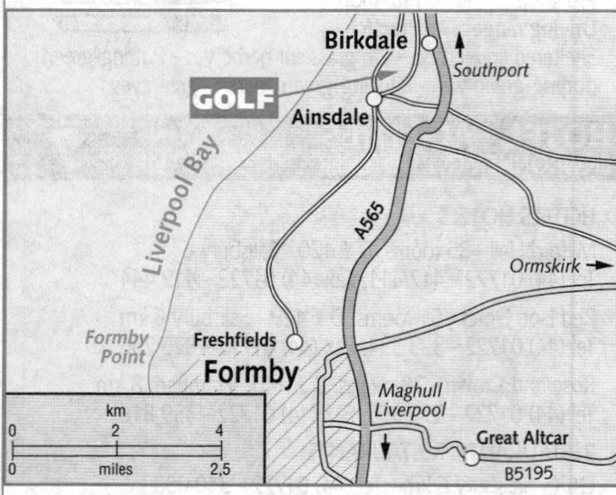

Access Accès : Off A565 Liverpool → Southport, between Hillside railway station and Royal Birkdale gates.
Map 5 on page 479 Carte 5 Page 479

GOLF COURSE — PARCOURS 18/20

Site	Site	
Maintenance	Entretien	
Architect	Architecte	Fred Hawtree
Type	Type	links
Relief	Relief	
Water in play	Eau en jeu	
Exp. to wind	Exposé au vent	
Trees in play	Arbres en jeu	

Scorecard Carte de score	Chp. Chp.	Mens Mess.	Ladies Da.
Length Long.	6165	5920	5345
Par	72	72	75
Slope system	—	—	—

Advised golfing ability Niveau de jeu recommandé — 0 12 24 36
Hcp required Handicap exigé — certificate

CLUB HOUSE & AMENITIES — CLUB HOUSE ET ANNEXES 7/10

Pro shop Pro-shop
Driving range Practice
Sheltered couvert no - On grass sur herbe yes - Putting-green putting-green yes - Pitching-green pitching green yes

HOTEL FACILITIES — ENVIRONNEMENT HOTELIER 7/10

HOTELS HÔTELS
Cambridge House Hotel - 16 rooms, D £ 83 - Southport 5 km
Tel (44) 01704 - 538 372, Fax (44) 01704 - 547 183

Scarisbrick - 88 rooms, D from £ 100 - Southport 3 km
Tel (44) 01704 - 543 000, Fax (44) 01704 - 533 335

Prince of Wales - 101 rooms, D £ 115 - Southport 3 km
Tel (44) 01704 - 536 688, Fax (44) 01704 - 543 488

RESTAURANTS RESTAURANTS
Warehouse Brasserie - Southport 3 km
Tel (44) 01704 - 544 662
Valentino's - Southport 3 km - Tel (44) 01704 - 541 252
Cloisters (Scarisbrick) - Southport 3 km
Tel (44) 01704 - 535 153

Hindhead

15	7	6

In this region of Surrey, Hindhead is one of a recommended threesome which includes Hankley Common and West Surrey. Set in a roller-coasting landscape the golf can however be a little tiring if you are pulling your own cart. Hindhead is a course of two contrasting halves, with the first 9 holes played in a valley dating from the ice age and the back 9 straddling the top of a hill. From a visual point of view the front 9 are more memorable, especially the 6th, a par-3 looking down steeply onto a well-protected green. Before your round, go and have a drink at the bar, enjoy the magnificent view over the 18th hole and listen to the locals explaining how to play the course. It all comes down to one pint of best bitter and two ideas: keep it straight and keep out of the heather. They could also tell you to avoid the trees and bushes as well, but one look is enough for that to go without saying. Spare one final thought for the club's founders, including Conan Doyle who lived close by next door to Bernard Shaw.

Dans cette région du Surrey, Hindhead fait partie d'un joli trio avec Hankley Common et West Surrey. Le paysage est campagnard, mais un peu fatigant s'il faut aussi tirer son chariot. Les deux parties du parcours sont très contrastées, les neuf premiers étant joués dans une vallée de l'ère glaciaire et les neuf derniers au sommet d'une colline. Visuellement, l'aller est plus mémorable, on se souviendra en particulier du 6, un par 3 au green en contrebas et très défendu. Avant de jouer, allez donc faire un tour au bar où les vues sur le 18 sont magnifiques, et où les locaux vous expliqueront la stratégie du parcours. Elle tient en une pinte et deux idées : restez droit et évitez la bruyère, les bois et buissons, cela va sans dire en jetant un seul coup d'oeil. Vous aurez enfin une pensée pour les fondateurs du club, parmi lesquels Conan Doyle, qui vivait à deux pas, voisin de Bernard Shaw. Un lieu qui inspire sans doute !

Hindhead Golf Club — 1904

Churt Road
ENG - HINDHEAD, Surrey GU26 6HX

Office Secrétariat (44) 01428 - 604 614
Pro shop Pro-shop (44) 01428 - 604 458
Fax Fax (44) 01428 - 608 508
Web www.the-hindhead-golf-club.co.uk
Situation Situation Haslemere (pop. 7 326), 4 km
Annual closure Fermeture annuelle no
Weekly closure Fermeture hebdomadaire no

Fees main season / Tarifs haute saison	Week days / Semaine	We/Bank holidays / We/Férié
18 holes		
Individual Individuel	£ 42	£ 55
Couple Couple	£ 84	£ 110

Full days: £ 52 / £ 65 (We)

Caddie Caddie no — **Electric Trolley** Chariot électrique yes
Buggy Voiturette no — **Clubs** Clubs no
Credit cards Cartes de crédit no

Access Accès : London, A3 (→ Portsmouth). Approx. 9 km (5 m) after Milford, turn right onto A287 → Hindhead, Farnham. After Beacon Hill, golf on right side.
Map 7 on page 482 Carte 7 Page 482

GOLF COURSE — PARCOURS — 15/20

Site Site
Maintenance Entretien
Architect Architecte J.H. Taylor
Type Type inland, heathland
Relief Relief
Water in play Eau en jeu
Exp. to wind Exposé au vent
Trees in play Arbres en jeu

Scorecard / Carte de score	Chp. / Chp.	Mens / Mess.	Ladies / Da.
Length Long.	5735	5520	4992
Par	70	69	72
Slope system	—	—	—

Advised golfing ability Niveau de jeu recommandé 0 12 24 36
Hcp required Handicap exigé certificate

CLUB HOUSE & AMENITIES — CLUB HOUSE ET ANNEXES — 7/10

Pro shop Pro-shop
Driving range Practice
Sheltered couvert 2 nets - On grass sur herbe yes - Putting-green putting-green yes - Pitching-green pitching green yes

HOTEL FACILITIES — ENVIRONNEMENT HOTELIER — 6/10

HOTELS HÔTELS
Pride of the Valley - 16 rooms, D £ 150 - Churt 2 km
Tel (44) 01428 - 605 799, Fax (44) 01428 - 605 875

Lythe Hill - 41 rooms, D £ 184 - Haslemere 6 km
Tel (44) 01428 - 651 251, Fax (44) 01428 - 644 131

Georgian - 53 rooms, D from £ 89 - Haslemere 4 km
Tel (44) 01428 - 656 644, Fax (44) 01428 - 645 600

RESTAURANTS RESTAURANTS
Undershaw - Hindhead 1 km - Tel (44) 01428 - 604 039
Flutes - Haslemere 4 km - Tel (44) 01428 - 645255
Auberge de France - Haslemere 4 km
Tel (44) 01428 - 651 251

Huddersfield (Fixby)

15	6	7

This was one of the centres of the great industrial revolution in the 19th century. Industries here included coal-mining, today illustrated by the Yorkshire Mining Museum, and textiles, one of the centres of which was Halifax a few miles down the road. If you are with the family, take the children to visit the Eureka Museum, a sort of living compendium of science. It might divert your (and their) attention from the many nearby golf courses, including the very underrated Huddersfield course, where Sandy Herd learnt how to play well enough to win the British Open in 1902. He must have been pretty fit, too, because this is a very hilly course. Also called Fixby, the layout is lined with trees and strategy is by no means simple as it is hard to judge the right distances and trajectories you need in order to find the optimum place for your drive so as to attack the greens. A classic layout where from the very first hole (a long par 4) you understand that only the good shots get their just desserts. Isn't that how it should be?

C'était une des grandes régions de la révolution industrielle au XIXème siècle. Un bassin minier illustré aujourd'hui par le Musée Minier du Yorkshire, une région de textile aussi, dont l'une des capitales était Halifax, à quelques kilomètres d'ici. En famille, vous mènerez aussi vos jeunes enfants au Musée Eureka, une sorte de livre vivant de la science. De quoi les (et vous) distraire de votre passion du golf exercée à Huddersfield, où le jeune Sandy Herd apprit un jeu qui le mena à la victoire au British Open 1902. Il a au moins acquis ici, sur un terrain bien accidenté, les jambes solides nécessaires à de bons appuis du swing. Appelé aussi Fixby, ce parcours est très boisé, la stratégie n'y est pas évidente tant il est difficile d'y juger des distances et des trajectoires nécessaires, pour placer les drives au bon endroit et pouvoir attaquer les greens. Un parcours au déroulement classique qui vous indique dès le 1 (très long par 4) que seuls les bons coups seront récompensés. C'est l'essentiel.

Fixby Golf Club — 1891

Fixby Hall, Lightridge Road
ENG - FIXBY, HUDDERSFIELD, W. Yorks. HD2 2EP

Office	Secrétariat	(44) 01484 - 426 203
Pro shop	Pro-shop	(44) 01484 - 426 463
Fax	Fax	(44) 01484 - 424 623
Web	www.huddersfield-golf.co.uk	
Situation	Situation	Huddersfield, 3 km
Annual closure	Fermeture annuelle	no
Weekly closure	Fermeture hebdomadaire	no

Fees main season Tarifs haute saison		18 holes
	Week days Semaine	We/Bank holidays We/Férié
Individual Individuel	£ 37	£ 47
Couple Couple	£ 74	£ 94

Full days: £ 47 / £ 57 (We)

Caddie Caddie no — **Electric Trolley** Chariot électrique yes

Buggy Voiturette yes — **Clubs** Clubs no

Credit cards Cartes de crédit
VISA - Eurocard - MasterCard (Pro shop goods only)

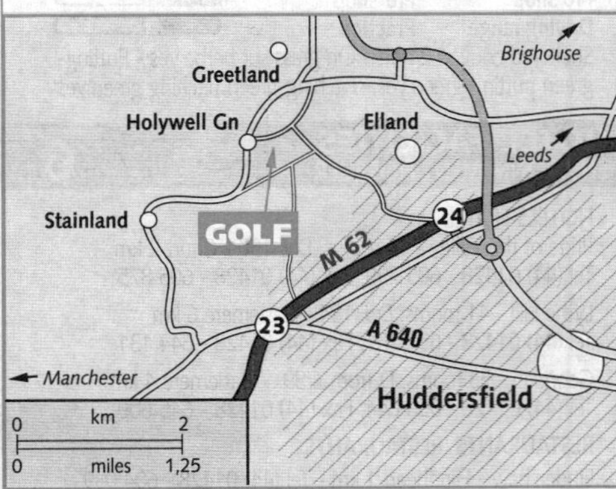

Access Accès : M62 Exit 24 to roundabout. 3rd exit → Brighouse. 1 km to lights, turn right. Turn right again onto Lightridge Road. Golf 500 m on right.
Map 4 on page 476 Carte 4 Page 476

GOLF COURSE — PARCOURS — 15/20

Site	Site	
Maintenance	Entretien	
Architect	Architecte	unknown
Type	Type	parkland, hilly
Relief	Relief	
Water in play	Eau en jeu	
Exp. to wind	Exposé au vent	
Trees in play	Arbres en jeu	

Scorecard Carte de score	Chp. Chp.	Mens Mess.	Ladies Da.
Length Long.	5825	5470	5020
Par	71	71	71
Slope system	—	—	—

Advised golfing ability Niveau de jeu recommandé: 0 12 24 36

Hcp required Handicap exigé: certificate

CLUB HOUSE & AMENITIES — CLUB HOUSE ET ANNEXES — 6/10

Pro shop Pro-shop
Driving range Practice
Sheltered couvert - On grass sur herbe yes - Putting-green putting-green yes - Pitching-green pitching green yes

HOTEL FACILITIES — ENVIRONNEMENT HOTELIER — 7/10

HOTELS HÔTELS

Hilton Nation - 114 rooms, D £ 90 - Huddersfield 5 km
Tel (44) 01422 - 375 431, Fax (44) 01422 - 310 067

The Lodge Hotel - 12 rooms, D £ 90 - Huddersfield 7 km
Tel (44) 01484 - 431 001, Fax (44) 01484 - 421 590

Old Golf House - Outlane/Huddersfield 3 km
52 rooms, D £ 90
Tel (44) 01422 - 379 311, Fax (44) 01422 - 372 694

RESTAURANTS RESTAURANTS

Weaver's Shed - Golcar 4 km - Tel (44) 01484 - 654 284
Brook's - Brighouse 5 km - Tel (44) 01484 - 715 284
Bradley's - Huddersfield 4 km - Tel (44) 01484 - 516 773

Hunstanton

17	7	6

To the majority of continental golfers (who are unfamiliar with England) East Anglia is the make of a 1960s family saloon. In fact it is a region comprising three counties and home to some of the country's finest links including Hunstanton, nestling in a superb landscape of dunes, wild grass and scrubby bushes. From the 4th to the 15th holes, after a comparatively placid start, the course winds in every direction - thus ensuring that the wind assaults the golfer from all angles and making that all-important judgment for each shot even more complicated. And just to prove once and for all that golf is an unfair game, this course boasts a famous par 3 hole with a blind green. In contrast, neither the sea nor the beach is out of bounds. Hunstanton plays host to major amateur tournaments, which is only fair dues for this often unorthodox and uplifting course. You might find it more enjoyable if you lose your scoring pencil. Now stretched to some 6,300 m, this is a genuinely formidable test, even if a golfer once holed-in-one here at the 16th hole, three days in succession!

Pour ceux qui ne connaissent guère l'Angleterre, l'East Anglia est le nom d'une voiture des années 1960. Mais on trouve dans cette région quelques-uns des plus beaux links du pays, dont Hunstanton, blotti dans un superbe paysage de dunes couronnées d'herbes folles et de buissons touffus. Du 4 au 15, après un départ assez calme, les trous ne cessent de tourner dans toutes les directions, ce qui n'est pas fait pour garder les idées en place, alors que c'est plus que nécessaire ici. Pour faire définitivement comprendre que le golf n'est pas un jeu juste, on trouve ici un fameux par 3 avec green aveugle. En revanche, ni la mer ni la plage ne sont hors limites. Hunstanton reçoit de grandes compétitions amateur, c'est justice, avec ce tracé souvent peu orthodoxe, exaltant et d'autant plus amusant que l'on oublie de noter le score. Porté à près de 6300 m, c'est un test encore plus redoutable, même si un joueur a fait trou-en-un sur le 16 trois jours de suite !

Hunstanton Golf Club — 1891

Golf Course Road
ENG - OLD HUNSTANTON, Norfolk PE36 6JQ

Office Secrétariat (44) 01485 - 532 811
Pro shop Pro-shop (44) 01485 - 532 751
Fax Fax (44) 01485 - 532 319
Web www.hunstantongolfclub.com
Situation Situation King's Lynn, 27 km
Hunstanton (pop. 4 736), 1 km
Annual closure Fermeture annuelle no
Weekly closure Fermeture hebdomadaire no
Fees main season Tarifs haute saison 18 holes

	Week days / Semaine	We/Bank holidays / We/Férié
Individual Individuel	£ 65	£ 75
Couple Couple	£ 130	£ 150

Caddie Caddie no — **Electric Trolley** Chariot électrique no
Buggy Voiturette yes — **Clubs** Clubs no
Credit cards Cartes de crédit
Visa - Mastercard (Pro shop goods only)

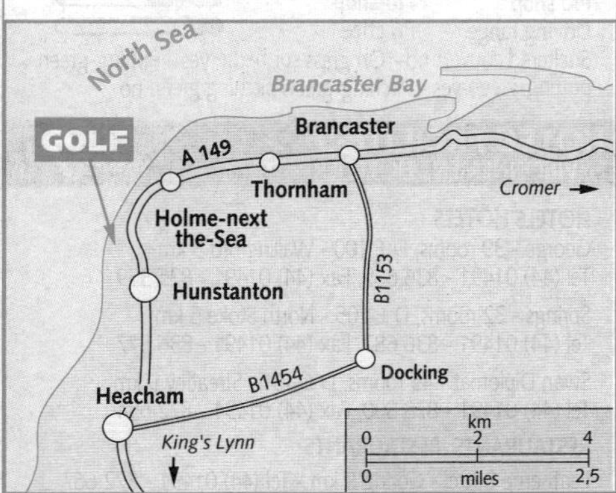

Access Accès : London M11. Cambridge A10 to King's Lynn. A149 North through Hunstanton to Old Hunstanton. Turn left → Golf course.
Map 4 on page 477 Carte 4 Page 477

GOLF COURSE / PARCOURS — 17/20

Site Site
Maintenance Entretien
Architect Architecte James Braid, George Fernie
Type Type seaside course, links
Relief Relief
Water in play Eau en jeu
Exp. to wind Exposé au vent
Trees in play Arbres en jeu

Scorecard / Carte de score	Chp. / Chp.	Mens / Mess.	Ladies / Da.
Length Long.	6220	5730	5415
Par	74	70	75
Slope system	—	—	—

Advised golfing ability Niveau de jeu recommandé 0 12 24 36
Hcp required Handicap exigé certificate

CLUB HOUSE & AMENITIES / CLUB HOUSE ET ANNEXES — 7/10

Pro shop Pro-shop
Driving range Practice
Sheltered couvert no - On grass sur herbe yes - Putting-green putting-green yes - Pitching-green pitching green no

HOTEL FACILITIES / ENVIRONNEMENT HOTELIER — 6/10

HOTELS HÔTELS
Le Strange Arms - 36 rooms, D £ 110 - Hunstanton 2 km
Tel (44) 01485 - 534 411, Fax (44) 01485 - 534 724

Congham Hall - 14 rooms, D £ 175 - Grimston 28 km
Tel (44) 01485 - 600 250, Fax (44) 01485 - 601 191

Hoste Arms - 36 rooms, D £ 114 - Burnham Market 15 km
Tel (44) 01328 - 738 777, Fax (44) 01328 - 730 103

RESTAURANTS RESTAURANTS
White Horse - Brancaster 6 km - Tel (44) 01485 - 210 262
The Restaurant (Hoste hotel) - Burnham Market 15 km
Tel (44) 01328 - 738 777
The Lord Nelson - Burnham Thorpe 16 km
Tel (44) 01328 - 738 241

Huntercombe

15 | 6 | 7

At the beginning of the century, Daimlers and then a bus would ferry players to and from Henley railway station. Those were the good old days when service and hospitality actually meant something. Huntercombe has become a members' course but green-feers can get on more easily than in the past. Here is a classic layout designed by Willie Park Jr. It features tightly cropped fairways and traversies through a landscape that is framed by heather and gorse, demanding an accurate and serious game where the only excuse for taking your eyes off the ball is the wonderful view over the plain of Oxford. A very well maintained, rather flat (except holes 2 and 3) and so very British course where slow players will find themselves in hot water. The club prefers twosomes or threesomes. While in the region, spend a good day out in Oxford and visit Blenheim Palace, birthplace of Winston Churchill, ancestral home of the Dukes of Marlborough and whose gardens were designed by Capability Brown.

Au début du siècle, des Daimler puis un autobus du club faisaient l'aller-retour jusqu'à la gare d'Henley pour amener et ramener les joueurs. C'était l'époque héroïque où le service voulait dire beaucoup. Huntercombe est devenu un golf de membres, mais l'accès y est plus facile que par le passé. Le tracé classique de Willie Park Jr est d'aussi excellente qualité que le gazon des fairways entre les bruyères et les ajoncs, il exige un jeu précis et sérieux, où on ne lèvera la tête que pour admirer de jolis panoramas sur la plaine d'Oxford. Un parcours très classique, assez plat (sauf les 2 et 3), bien préservé et terriblement britannique, où l'on chasse les escargots (golfeurs !) et où l'on joue à deux ou trois. Dans la région, il ne faudra pas oublier de passer une journée à Oxford et au Blenheim Palace où est né Winston Churchill, c'est le château des ducs de Marlborough, et les jardins créés par le grand paysagiste Capability Brown vous donneront quelques idées pour votre petite maison.

Huntercombe Golf Club — 1902

Nuffield
ENG - HENLEY-ON-THAMES, Oxon RG9 5SL

Office	Secrétariat	(44) 01491 - 641 207
Pro shop	Pro-shop	(44) 01491 - 641 241
Fax	Fax	(44) 01491 - 642 060
Web	www.huntercombegolfclub.co.uk	
Situation	Situation	Henley (pop. 10 058), 10 km

Wallingford (pop. 6 616), 5 km

Annual closure	Fermeture annuelle	no
Weekly closure	Fermeture hebdomadaire	no
Fees main season	Tarifs haute saison	18 holes

	Week days Semaine	We/Bank holidays We/Férié
Individual Individuel	£ 40	£ 60
Couple Couple	£ 80	£ 120

Full day: £ 60 and £ 75 (We)

Caddie Caddie no — **Electric Trolley** Chariot électrique yes

Buggy Voiturette yes — **Clubs** Clubs no

Credit cards Cartes de crédit
Visa - Eurocard - Mastercard

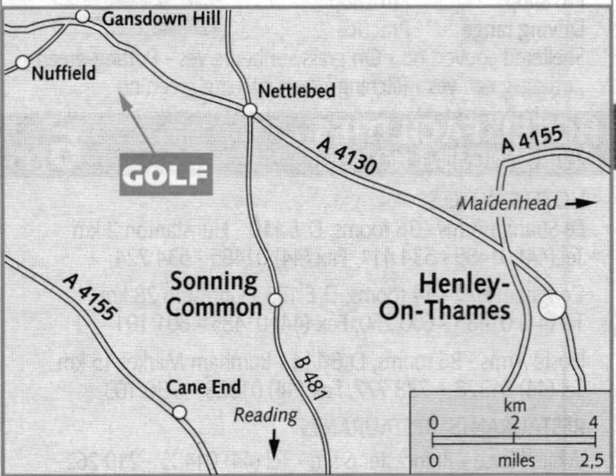

Access Accès : Leave M4 at Jct 8/9, A404, A4130 through Henley, → Oxford. Club-house on the left after 10 km (6 m.)
Map 8 on page 484 Carte 8 Page 484

GOLF COURSE — PARCOURS — 15/20

Site	Site	
Maintenance	Entretien	
Architect	Architecte	Willie Park Jr
Type	Type	heathland
Relief	Relief	
Water in play	Eau en jeu	
Exp. to wind	Exposé au vent	
Trees in play	Arbres en jeu	

Scorecard Carte de score	Chp. Chp.	Mens Mess.	Ladies Da.
Length Long.	5671	5493	5115
Par	70	70	72
Slope system	—	—	—

Advised golfing ability Niveau de jeu recommandé — 0 12 24 36

Hcp required Handicap exigé — certificate

CLUB HOUSE & AMENITIES — CLUB HOUSE ET ANNEXES — 6/10

Pro shop Pro-shop
Driving range Practice
Sheltered couvert no - On grass sur herbe yes - Putting-green putting-green yes - Pitching-green pitching green no

HOTEL FACILITIES — ENVIRONNEMENT HOTELIER — 7/10

HOTELS HÔTELS

George - 39 rooms, D £ 100 - Wallingford 5 km
Tel (44) 01491 - 836 665, Fax (44) 01491 - 825 359

Springs - 32 rooms, D £ 105 - North Stoke 5 km
Tel (44) 01491 - 836 687, Fax (44) 01491 - 836 877

Swan Diplomat - 45 rooms, D £ 161 - Streatley 9 km
Tel (44) 01491 - 878 800, Fax (44) 01491 - 872 554

RESTAURANTS RESTAURANTS

Leatherne Bottel - Goring 8 km - Tel (44) 01491 - 872 667

Beetle and Wedge - Moulsford 7 km
Tel (44) 01491 - 651 381

Springs - North Stoke 5 km - Tel (44) 01491 - 836 687

Ilkley

17 | 7 | 6

Welcome to the beautiful region of the Yorkshire Dales, where you can visit the Wharfe valley and Ilkley, Fountains Abbey and the town of Haworth, home to the Brontë sisters. While you are here, don't forget to play this superb course designed by Colt and Mackenzie, where the river Wharfe threatens your card on the first seven holes. Flat and laid out in picturesque landscape, every aspect of which comes into view as you progress, Ilkley is a charming course where nothing is easy but where nothing is impossible, either. Just avoid the trees, the fairway bunkers and the traps beside the greens. Nothing could be simpler! The green-side bunkers tend to obstruct the obvious approach route to what are generally excellent putting surfaces. A good score is by no means a certainty here, as there are only two par 5s offering up the chance of a birdie, in contrast with several long par 4s where you can easily waste precious strokes. Mark James, Gordon Brand and Colin Montgomerie are honorary members here and we envy them.

De cette très belle région, on retiendra le Parc National des Vallées du Yorkshire, dont celle de la Wharfe qui irrigue Ilkley, le très bel et très curieux ensemble religieux et aristocratique de Fountains Abbey, et la ville d'Haworth, foyer des soeurs Brontë. Et l'on n'oubliera pas de jouer ce superbe parcours, dessiné par Colt et Mackenzie, où la Wharfe vient en jeu sur sept trous (les premiers). Plat et dans un paysage pittoresque, dont on voit successivement tous les aspects depuis les différents trous, c'est un parcours de charme, où rien n'est facile, mais rien impossible. Il suffit d'éviter les arbres, les bunkers de fairway, les bunkers de greens qui ferment l'entrée de greens généralement en condition parfaite. Un bon score n'est pas donné d'avance car il n'y a que deux par 5 pour espérer des birdies, cinq par 3 et quelques longs par 4 pour gaspiller toutes ses réserves. Mark James, Gordon Brand et Colin Montgomerie sont membres d'honneur, on les envie.

Ilkley Golf Club — 1890

Middleton
ENG - ILKLEY, Yorkshire LS29 0BE

Office Secrétariat (44) 01943 - 600 214
Pro shop Pro-shop (44) 01943 - 607 463
Fax Fax (44) 01943 - 816 130
Web www.ilkleygolfclub.co.uk
Situation Situation Leeds, 25 km
Ilkley (pop. 13 530), 1.5 km

Annual closure Fermeture annuelle — no
Weekly closure Fermeture hebdomadaire — no
Fees main season Tarifs haute saison — 18 holes

	Week days / Semaine	We/Bank holidays / We/Férié
Individual Individuel	£ 42	£ 50
Couple Couple	£ 84	£ 100

Caddie Caddie on request **Electric Trolley** Chariot électrique yes
Buggy Voiturette no **Clubs** Clubs yes
Credit cards Cartes de crédit
VISA - MasterCard (£ 1 added charge for pro shop goods)

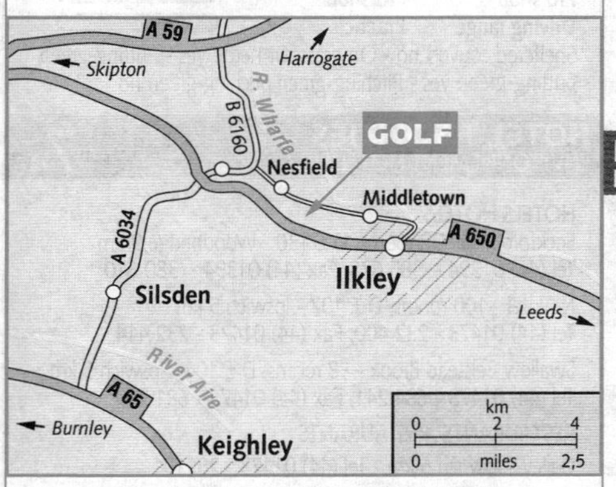

Access Accès : From Leeds, A660, then A65 W → Ilkley, Skipton. In Ilkley, turn right at town centre traffic lights and then second left.
Map 4 on page 476 Carte 4 Page 476

GOLF COURSE — PARCOURS 17/20

Site Site
Maintenance Entretien
Architect Architecte Harry S. Colt, Alister Mackenzie
Type Type parkland
Relief Relief
Water in play Eau en jeu
Exp. to wind Exposé au vent
Trees in play Arbres en jeu

Scorecard / Carte de score	Chp. / Chp.	Mens / Mess.	Ladies / Da.
Length Long.	5636	5357	5120
Par	69	69	73
Slope system	—	—	—

Advised golfing ability 0 12 24 36
Niveau de jeu recommandé
Hcp required Handicap exigé certificate

CLUB HOUSE & AMENITIES — CLUB HOUSE ET ANNEXES 7/10

Pro shop Pro-shop
Driving range Practice
Sheltered couvert no - On grass sur herbe yes - Putting-green putting-green yes (3) - Pitching-green pitching green yes (2)

HOTEL FACILITIES — ENVIRONNEMENT HOTELIER 6/10

HOTELS HÔTELS
Rombalds - 15 rooms, D £ 105 - Ilkley 1 km
Tel (44) 01943 - 603 201, Fax (44) 01943 - 816 586
The Crescent - 20 rooms, D from £ 100 - Ilkley 1 km
Tel (44) 01943 - 600 012, Fax (44) 01943 - 601 513
Rendez-vous - 75 rooms, D £ 100 - Skipton 12 km
Tel (44) 01756 - 700 100, Fax (44) 01756 - 700 107

RESTAURANTS RESTAURANTS
Box Tree - Ilkley 1 km - Tel (44) 01943 - 608 484
Mantra Restaurant - Burley-in-Wharfedale 5 km
Tel (44) 01943 - 864 602
The Crescent - Ilkley 1 km - Tel (44) 01943 - 600 012

Ipswich (Purdis Heath)

15	7	7

This is exactly the hide-out you dream of when the wind is too strong to attempt the links courses on the coast. It is also the opportunity to discover what is undoubtedly one of the most attractive inland courses in East Anglia. Often known as Purdis Heath, the course's rather modest reputation is surprising given that it was designed by James Braid (with contributions from Hawtree and Taylor). Even though the great man designed more than a hundred courses, he always succeeded in squeezing the very best out of the land or in creating an extraordinary challenge. Like on the 17th, a par 5 which would be quite harmless if he hadn't placed a few pot bunkers to make you wonder about the length of your second shot. If you decide to lay up, you have a tough third shot on your hands. Then there is the 4th hole where the green is hidden in a vale; if your drive is not just perfect, you have a blind second shot to contend with. Just a few examples to prove that nothing is given away here, and that "old" architects can still teach over-confident youngsters a thing or two.

C'est exactement le refuge dont on rêve quand le vent souffle trop pour aller sur les links de la côte. Et c'est l'occasion de découvrir l'un des meilleurs "inland" d'East Anglia. Généralement connu sous le nom de Purdis Heath, sa réputation modeste est d'autant plus surprenante qu'il a été dessiné par James Braid, auquel il faut ajouter Hawtree et Taylor. Même s'il a fait des centaines de parcours, Braid a toujours su tirer du terrain la quintessence, ou alors créer des défis inédits. Comme au 17, un par 5 qui serait anodin s'il n'avait placé quelques pot bunkers pour que l'on s'interroge sur la longueur du second coup : si on décide de rester court, le troisième coup ne sera pas facile ! Prenons le 4, un énorme par 4 où le green est caché dans un vallon : si le drive n'est pas exceptionnel, le second coup est aveugle. De rares exemples pour dire que rien n'est ici donné, que les "vieux" architectes peuvent encore donner des leçons aux jeunes stars trop sûres d'elles.

Ipswich Golf Club — 1895

Purdis Heath, Bucklesham Road
ENG - IPSWICH, Suffolk IP 3 88VQ

Office	Secrétariat	(44) 01473 - 728 941
Pro shop	Pro-shop	(44) 01473 - 724 017
Fax	Fax	(44) 01473 - 715 236
Web	www.ipswichgolfclub.com	
Situation	Situation	Ipswich (pop. 130 157), 5 km
Annual closure	Fermeture annuelle	no
Weekly closure	Fermeture hebdomadaire	no

Fees main season Tarifs haute saison	Week days Semaine	We/Bank holidays We/Férié
		Full day
Individual Individuel	£ 45	£ 50
Couple Couple	£ 90	£ 100

Afternoon: £ 35 and £ 40 (We)

Caddie Caddie no — **Electric Trolley** Chariot électrique no
Buggy Voiturette no — **Clubs** Clubs no
Credit cards Cartes de crédit
Visa - Mastercard (Pro shop goods only)

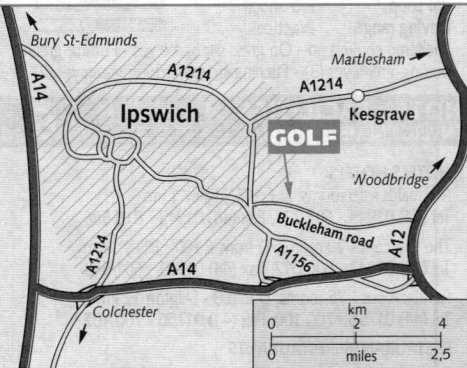

Access Accès : Ipswich A14 E. Left at roundabout by St Augustine's Church. Golf into Bucklesham Road
Map 7 on page 483 Carte 7 Page 483

GOLF COURSE — PARCOURS — 15/20

Site	Site	
Maintenance	Entretien	
Architect	Architecte	James Braid
Type	Type	inland, heathland
Relief	Relief	
Water in play	Eau en jeu	
Exp. to wind	Exposé au vent	
Trees in play	Arbres en jeu	

Scorecard Carte de score	Chp. Chp.	Mens Mess.	Ladies Da.
Length Long.	5792	5792	5172
Par	71	71	73
Slope system	—	—	—

Advised golfing ability / Niveau de jeu recommandé: 0 12 24 36
Hcp required Handicap exigé: certificate

CLUB HOUSE & AMENITIES — CLUB HOUSE ET ANNEXES — 7/10

Pro shop Pro-shop
Driving range Practice
Sheltered couvert no - On grass sur herbe yes - Putting-green putting-green yes - Pitching-green pitching green no

HOTEL FACILITIES — ENVIRONNEMENT HOTELIER — 7/10

HOTELS HÔTELS
Seckford Hall - 32 rooms, D £ 130 - Woodbridge 9 km
Tel (44) 01394 - 385 678, Fax (44) 01394 - 380 610

Novotel - 100 rooms, D £ 107 - Ipswich 5 km
Tel (44) 01473 - 232 400, Fax (44) 01473 - 232 414

Swallow Belstead Brook - 88 rooms, D £ 104 - Ipswich 5 km
Tel (44) 01473 - 684 241, Fax (44) 01473 - 681 249

RESTAURANTS RESTAURANTS
Galley - Ipswich 5 km - Tel (44) 01473 - 281131
Mortimer's Seafood Restaurant - Ipswich 5 km
Tel (44) 01473 - 230 225
St Peter's - Ipswich 5 km - Tel (44) 01473 - 210 810

Isle of Purbeck

16 | 7 | 6

This is the kind of course where the superb views add a point or two to the artistic score. In the distance are the busy south-coast resorts of Poole and Bournemouth, and the Solent. Here you have all the peace and quiet of superb country landscape on the edge of a natural reserve for plant and bird-lovers. By the way, Enid Blyton was one of the club's founders. The broom and heather add to the decoration and to the problems awaiting players who are wayward or blown off line by the wind. Strictly speaking this is not a links course but it does require the same skills of flighting and rolling the ball, of trying to outwit and outfox the course. A pretty site for a long weekend with a very pleasant club-house, warm welcome, excellent food and a classy additional 9 hole course where you can guiltlessly leave the less gifted members of the family while you go and tackle the "big boy".

C'est le genre de parcours où la qualité des vues donne une "note artistique" en plus. Au loin, les stations très fréquentées de Poole, Bournemouth, le Solent. Ici, c'est le calme dans un superbe paysage de campagne, en bordure d'une réserve naturelle pour amoureux de plantes et d'oiseaux. Enid Blyton (auteur du "Club des Cinq" et excellente joueuse) fut parmi les fondateurs du club. Les genêts et la bruyère y apportent un élément de décor, mais pas mal aussi de problèmes aux joueurs peu précis, ou emportés par le vent. Ce parcours n'est pas exactement un links dans son style d'architecture, mais il demande les mêmes qualités, savoir travailler la balle, la faire rouler comme il faut, avoir aussi un peu de ruse, être en quelque sorte plus intelligent que le parcours. Un joli lieu de long week-end, avec un club-house très agréable, un accueil chaleureux, une bonne cuisine et un 9 trous supplémentaire de bonne facture pour déposer sans scrupules les joueurs les moins compétents de la famille pendant que l'on affronte le "grand".

Isle of Purbeck Golf Club — 1892

ENG - SWANAGE, Dorset BH19 3AB

Office Secrétariat (44) 01929 - 450 354
Pro shop Pro-shop (44) 01929 - 450 354
Fax Fax (44) 01929 - 450 501
Web www.purbeckgolf.co.uk
Situation Situation Poole (pop. 133 050), 12 km
Swanage (pop. 9 037), 5 km

Annual closure Fermeture annuelle — no
Weekly closure Fermeture hebdomadaire — no

Fees main season Tarifs haute saison	Week days Semaine	We/Bank holidays We/Férié
18 holes		
Individual Individuel	£ 38	£ 43
Couple Couple	£ 76	£ 86

Full days: £ 46 / £ 49 (We)

Caddie Caddie no — **Electric Trolley** Chariot électrique no
Buggy Voiturette yes — **Clubs** Clubs yes
Credit cards Cartes de crédit
VISA - MasterCard

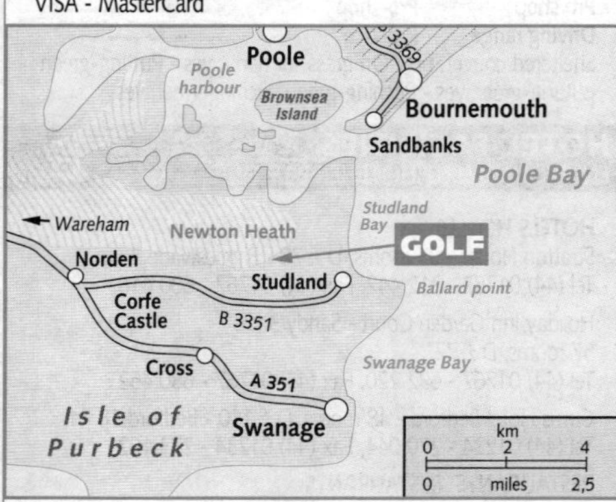

Access Accès : • Ferry from Sandbanks to Studland
• Poole, A351 through Wareham and B3351 → Studland
Map 6 on page 481 Carte 6 Page 481

GOLF COURSE — PARCOURS — 16/20

Site Site
Maintenance Entretien
Architect Architecte — Harry S. Colt
Type Type — seaside course, heathland
Relief Relief
Water in play Eau en jeu
Exp. to wind Exposé au vent
Trees in play Arbres en jeu

Scorecard Carte de score	Chp. Chp.	Mens Mess.	Ladies Da.
Length Long.	5730	5450	5080
Par	70	70	73
Slope system	—	—	—

Advised golfing ability Niveau de jeu recommandé — 0 12 24 36
Hcp required Handicap exigé — 28 Men, 36 Ladies

CLUB HOUSE & AMENITIES — CLUB HOUSE ET ANNEXES — 7/10

Pro shop Pro-shop
Driving range Practice
Sheltered couvert no - On grass sur herbe yes - Putting-green putting-green yes - Pitching-green pitching green yes

HOTEL FACILITIES — ENVIRONNEMENT HOTELIER — 6/10

HOTELS HÔTELS
Havenhurst - 17 rooms, D £ 74 - Swanage 5 km
Tel (44) 01929 - 424 224, Fax (44) 01929 - 422 173

Mortons House - 19 rooms, D £ 129 - Corfe Castle 5 km
Tel (44) 01929 - 480 988, Fax (44) 01929 - 480 280

Grand Hotel - 30 rooms, D £ 138 - Swanage 5 km
Tel (44) 01929 - 423 353, Fax (44) 01929 - 427 068

RESTAURANTS RESTAURANTS
Cauldron Bistro - Swanage 5 km - Tel (44) 01929 - 422 671
Bistro on the Beach - Bournemouth 15 km
Tel (44) 01202 - 431 473

567

John O'Gaunt

15	7	6

A great club, as British as they come, with two 18-hole courses and a huge and very comfortable club-house with old-style architecture straight out of a TV serial. John O'Gaunt is close enough to London to be within easy reach but far enough not to be too busy, at least during the week. The trees are magnificent (many are prime specimens) and give the courses a very mature park-like appearance. On.the main course, which was designed by Hawtree, a stream comes into play on a few holes to add a little spice. A classic layout which calls for no particular comment but which gives an impression of balance and fulfilment when you play it, especially for lovers of traditional courses that seem to have been around for ever. The other course, Carthagena, opened in 1981, is more of a heather-land course and was built by the ground staff.

Un grand club bien britannique comme on l'imagine, avec deux parcours de 18 trous et un gigantesque club-house à l'architecture ancienne digne d'une série policière télévisée, et parfaitement confortable. John O'Gaunt est assez proche de Londres pour être facilement accessible, mais assez loin pour ne pas être trop encombré, en tout cas en semaine. Les arbres y sont magnifiques (un bonheur pour les spécialistes), donnant une allure de parc qui convient bien à l'esthétique assez sobre de Hawtree, pour le parcours principal en tout cas, où une petite rivière en jeu sur quelques trous vient épicer le tracé. Très classique, c'est le genre de réalisation qui n'appelle pas de commentaires particuliers, mais donne une impression d'équilibre et de plénitude quand on le joue. Pour amoureux des bons parcours traditionnels qui donnent l'impression d'être là depuis toujours. L'autre parcours, Carthagena, inauguré en 1981, est plus proche d'un style de terre de bruyère, il a été construit par l'équipe du parcours..

John O'Gaunt Golf Club — 1948

Sutton Park
ENG - SANDY, Bedshire SG19 2LY

Office Secrétariat (44) 01767 - 260 360
Pro shop Pro-shop (44) 01767 - 260 094
Fax Fax (44) 01767 - 262 834
Web www.johnogauntgolfclub.co.uk
Situation Situation Cambridge, 35 km
Bedford (pop. 13 066), 18 km
Annual closure Fermeture annuelle no
Weekly closure Fermeture hebdomadaire no

Fees main season Tarifs haute saison	Week days Semaine	We/Bank holidays We/Férié
	18 holes	
Individual Individuel	£ 50	£ 60
Couple Couple	£ 100	£ 120

Caddie Caddie no — **Electric Trolley** Chariot électrique no
Buggy Voiturette yes — **Clubs** Clubs no
Credit cards Cartes de crédit no

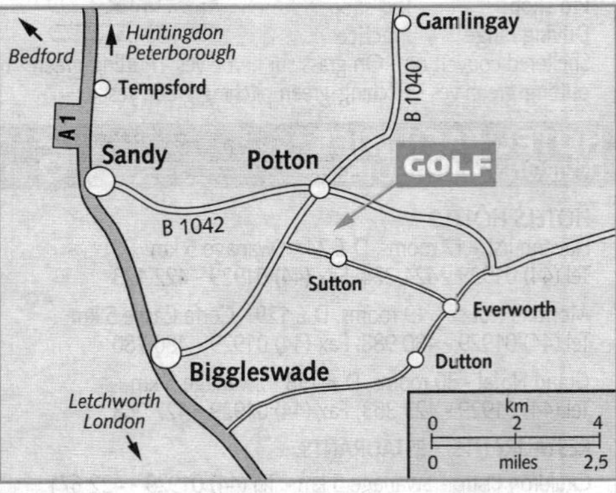

Access Accès : London A1 (M), then A1. At Biggleswade, turn on B1040 → Potton. Golf on right side before Potton.
Map 7 on page 482 Carte 7 Page 482

GOLF COURSE — PARCOURS 15/20

Site Site
Maintenance Entretien
Architect Architecte Fred Hawtree
Type Type parkland
Relief Relief
Water in play Eau en jeu
Exp. to wind Exposé au vent
Trees in play Arbres en jeu

Scorecard Carte de score	Chp. Chp.	Mens Mess.	Ladies Da.
Length Long.	5861	5593	5112
Par	71	71	75
Slope system	—	—	—

Advised golfing ability 0 12 24 36
Niveau de jeu recommandé
Hcp required Handicap exigé 28 Men, 36 Ladies

CLUB HOUSE & AMENITIES — CLUB HOUSE ET ANNEXES 7/10

Pro shop Pro-shop
Driving range Practice
Sheltered couvert no - On grass sur herbe yes - Putting-green putting-green yes - Pitching-green pitching green yes

HOTEL FACILITIES — ENVIRONNEMENT HOTELIER 6/10

HOTELS HÔTELS
Stratton House - 31 rooms, D £ 78 - Biggleswade 3 km
Tel (44) 01767 - 312 442, Fax (44) 01767 - 600 416

Holiday Inn Garden Court - Sandy 3 km
57 rooms, D £ 72
Tel (44) 01767 - 692 220, Fax (44) 01767 - 680 452

Corus Hotel Bedford - 48 rooms, D £ 110 - Bedford 18 km
Tel (44) 01234 - 270 044, Fax (44) 01234 - 273 102

RESTAURANTS RESTAURANTS
St Helena - Elstow (Bedford) 20 km - Tel (44) 01234 - 344 848
Corus Hotel restaurant - Bedford 16 km
Tel (44) 01767 - 270 044

King's Lynn

15	6	5

The presence of Sandringham House, where the royal family come to shoot or to spend Christmas – and which doubles up as a stately home open to visitors – has certainly something to do with the fact that three of the great links courses on this coast of East Anglia bear the royal seal... if you were wondering. Not so far away, this course was laid out through a forest at about the same time as Woburn, and should be played in more or less the same way: keep out of the woods and the bunkers and everything will be fine. Although the site is rather flat, there are some slopes to contend with, but by and large this is a course that should be played 'through the air' rather than along the ground. Big-hitters will be more tempted to let rip on the outward nine, strangely much longer than the back nine and which play even longer than they look. Strategy is pretty obvious from each tee, enough to let you immediately get to grips with a course where difficulties are fairly well balanced. This is a fine example of woodland golfing in a quiet, remote site.

Si on se demande pourquoi trois des grands links de cette côte de l'East Anglia ont droit au titre de "Royal", la présence de Sandringham House n'y est sans doute pas étrangère, où la famille royale vient chasser ou fêter Noël (c'est aussi un musée à visiter). A proximité, ce parcours tracé en forêt, à la même époque que Woburn et à jouer un peu de la même manière : évitez les bois, évitez les bunkers et tout ira bien. Bien que le site soit assez plat, le parcours n'est pas dénué de pentes, mais c'est principalement un golf à jouer "en l'air" plutôt que le long du sol. Les frappeurs seront davantage tentés de frapper à l'aller, curieusement beaucoup plus long que le retour, et qui "joue" encore plus long qu'il n'y paraît. Mais la stratégie est assez évidente pour chaque départ pour que l'on rentre immédiatement dans la discussion avec ce tracé aux difficultés bien équilibrées. Certes, ce n'est pas un très grand parcours, mais un bon exemple de style forestier, dans un site tranquille et reculé.

King's Lynn Golf Club — 1975

ENG - KING'S LYNN,
Norfolk PE31 6BD

Office	Secrétariat	(44) 01553 - 633 000
Pro shop	Pro-shop	(44) 01553 - 631 655
Fax	Fax	(44) 01553 - 631 036
Web		www.club-noticeboard.co.uk/kingslynn/
Situation	Situation	Cambridge, 50 km
Annual closure	Fermeture annuelle	no
Weekly closure	Fermeture hebdomadaire	no

Fees main season Tarifs haute saison	18 holes	
	Week days / Semaine	We/Bank holidays / We/Férié
Individual Individuel	£ 45	£ 55
Couple Couple	£ 90	£ 110

Caddie Caddie no — **Electric Trolley** Chariot électrique yes
Buggy Voiturette no — **Clubs** Clubs yes
Credit cards Cartes de crédit
VISA - MasterCard

Access Accès : North of Cambridge, A10 to King's Lynn. Golf north of the city on A 149
Map 7 on page 483 Carte 7 Page 483

GOLF COURSE — PARCOURS 15/20

Site	Site	
Maintenance	Entretien	
Architect	Architecte	Peter Alliss, Dave Thomas
Type	Type	forest
Relief	Relief	
Water in play	Eau en jeu	
Exp. to wind	Exposé au vent	
Trees in play	Arbres en jeu	

Scorecard Carte de score	Chp. Chp.	Mens Mess.	Ladies Da.
Length Long.	5949	5689	5205
Par	72	72	74
Slope system	—	—	—

Advised golfing ability Niveau de jeu recommandé: 0 12 24 36
Hcp required Handicap exigé: certificate

CLUB HOUSE & AMENITIES — CLUB HOUSE ET ANNEXES 6/10

Pro shop Pro-shop
Driving range Practice
Sheltered couvert no - On grass sur herbe practice area only - Putting-green putting-green yes - Pitching-green pitching green no

HOTEL FACILITIES — ENVIRONNEMENT HOTELIER 5/10

HOTELS HÔTELS
Congham Hall - Grimston 12 km
14 rooms, D £ 175
Tel (44) 01485 - 600 250, Fax (44) 01485 - 601 191

Premier Travel Inn - King's Lynn 6 km
40 rooms, D £ 48
Tel (44) 01485 - 772 221, Fax (44) 01485 - 775 827

Old Rectory - 4 rooms, D £ 48 - King's Lynn 2 km
Tel (44) 01485 - 768 544

RESTAURANTS RESTAURANTS
Congham Hall - Grimston 12 km - Tel (44) 01485 - 600 250
Rococo - King's Lynn 2 km - Tel (44) 01553 - 771 483

La Moye

17 | 7 | 8

Designed by James Braid, La Moye has been considerably lengthened over the years and refined to become the great tournament course of the Channel Islands and long-time home to the Jersey Open. Laid out over the dunes and rolling mounds on the promontory overlooking St Ouen's Bay, it provides outstanding views and a constantly entertaining challenge. Length and wind together don't make reaching the greens any easier, some of which are blind, all of which are well protected by bunkers or sandhills. In this setting, only a sharp short game can help save a normal score. If you don't understand how to roll the ball up to the pin ask the pro or some of the local players. During the long even ngs of May and early Summer, there are few places on earth where you can get so much pleasure out of golfing.... no matter how well or badly you are playing.

Dessiné par James Braid, La Moye a été considérablement allongé et modifié pour devenir le grand parcours de championnat des îles anglo-normandes, où s'est longtemps disputé le Jersey Open. Tracé sur les dunes et ondulations du promontoire dominant St Ouen's Bay, il offre un panorama exceptionnel et constitue un défi constamment intéressant. Cette longueur combinée au vent ne facilite pas l'accès aux greens, dont certains sont presque aveugles, et tous bien protégés par des bunkers ou les ondulations du terrain. Dans ces conditions, la qualité du petit jeu peut seule garantir un score correct, mais si on n'arrive pas à comprendre comment faire rouler la balle jusqu'au drapeau, il faut demander au pro ou aux joueurs locaux ! Au cours des longues fins de journée du mois de mai au début de l'été, il y a peu d'endroits où l'on puisse éprouver autant de plaisir à jouer au golf. Bien ou mal, peu importe.

La Moye Golf Club — 1902

La Moye
ENG - ST BRELADE, Jersey JE3 8GQ

Office	Secrétariat	(44) 01534 - 743 401
Pro shop	Pro-shop	(44) 01534 - 743 130
Fax	Fax	(44) 01534 - 747 289
Web	—	
Situation	Situation	St Aubin, 4 km

St Helier (pop. 28 123), 10 km

Annual closure	Fermeture annuelle	no
Weekly closure	Fermeture hebdomadaire	no
Fees main season	Tarifs haute saison	18 holes

	Week days / Semaine	We/Bank holidays / We/Férié
Individual Individuel	£ 55	£ 60*
Couple Couple	£ 110	£ 120*

* only after 2.30 pm at weekends

Caddie Caddie no — **Electric Trolley** Chariot électrique yes

Buggy Voiturette yes (04 → 10) **Clubs** Clubs yes

Credit cards Cartes de crédit
VISA - MasterCard

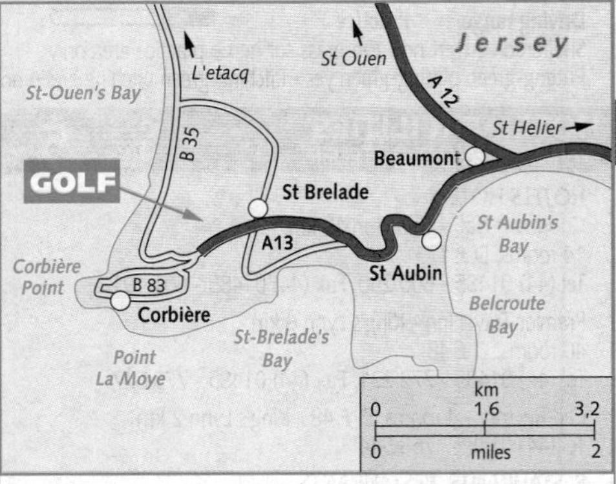

Access Accès : St Helier A1 through St Aubin, then A13 → St Brelade.
Map 9 on page 486 Carte 9 Page 486

GOLF COURSE — PARCOURS — 17/20

Site	Site	
Maintenance	Entretien	
Architect	Architecte	James Braid
Type	Type	seaside course, links
Relief	Relief	
Water in play	Eau en jeu	
Exp. to wind	Exposé au vent	
Trees in play	Arbres en jeu	

Scorecard / Carte de score	Chp. / Chp.	Mens / Mess.	Ladies / Da.
Length Long.	5998	5775	5320
Par	72	72	74
Slope system	—	—	—

Advised golfing ability 0 12 24 36
Niveau de jeu recommandé

Hcp required Handicap exigé 24 Men, 30 Ladies

CLUB HOUSE & AMENITIES — CLUB HOUSE ET ANNEXES — 7/10

Pro shop Pro-shop
Driving range Practice
Sheltered couvert 10 mats - On grass sur herbe no - Putting-green putting-green yes - Pitching-green pitching green yes

HOTEL FACILITIES — ENVIRONNEMENT HOTELIER — 8/10

HOTELS HÔTELS

L'Horizon- 106 rooms, D £ 130 - St Brelade's Bay 2 km
Tel (44) 01534 - 743 101, Fax (44) 01534 - 746 269

St Brelade's Bay- St Brelade's Bay 2 km
80 rooms, D from £ 110
Tel (44) 01534 - 746 141, Fax (44) 01534 - 747 278

Golden Sands - 62 rooms, D £ 100 - St Brelade's Bay 2 km
Tel (44) 01534 - 741241, Fax (44) 01534 - 499366

RESTAURANTS RESTAURANTS

The Grill (L'Horizon) - St Brelade's Bay 2 km
Tel (44) 01534 - 743 101

Sea Crest - Corbière 2 km - Tel (44) 01534 - 746 353

Old Court House Inn - St Aubin 4 km - Tel (44) 0134 - 746 433

Linden Hall

16 | 8 | 5

It was the superb hotel of the same name that added this 18-hole course to its estate. The owners love the end result, quite rightly so, and they have sensitively developed the magnificent historical manor. They wanted a course that was playable by all, always an extremely difficult task but one that Jonathan Gaunt managed to achieve. This is a fair course that you can get to grips with right away, as the thick rough and rather frequent hazards (ditches and lakes) only penalise the truly wayward shot. Only two holes really call for high pitching shots, and even then the distances involved are short. However the constant presence of water might scare off the higher-handicappers. Despite the course's relatively tender age, green-keeping is excellent on a site where everything has been done so very professionally. Pleasant to play, challenging from the back tees and set in a very peaceful part of the country where there is a lot to do and see, Linden Hall is one of the excellent surprises to have emerged in the past dozen or so years.

C'est le superbe hôtel du même nom qui a ajouté ce récent 18 trous à son domaine. Les propriétaires aiment leur réalisation, ils n'ont pas tort, ils ont développé le magnifique manoir historique. Ils voulaient un parcours jouable par tous, ce qui est toujours une tâche difficile, mais Jonathan Gaunt l'a bien remplie. D'abord, c'est un parcours franc, jouable directement, mais le rough épais, comme les assez nombreux obstacles d'eau (fossés et lacs) ne pénalisent que les coups lâchés. Seuls deux trous obligent vraiment à porter la balle, mais ce sont alors de petits coups. Cependant, cette présence insistante de l'eau peut effrayer. L'entretien est excellent en dépit de la relative jeunesse du parcours, mais les choses ont été faites très professionnellement. Plaisant à jouer, exigeant des départs arrière, situé dans une région très calme avec beaucoup de choses à faire et à voir, c'est une des très bonnes surprises de ces dernières décennies.

Linden Hall Hotel & Golf Club — 1997

ENG - LONGHORSLEY, Northumberland

Office Secrétariat (44) 01670 - 516 611
Pro shop Pro-shop (44) 01670 - 788 050
Fax Fax (44) 01670 - 788 544
Web www.lindenhall.co.uk
Situation Situation Morpeth, 10 km
Newcastle (pop. 259 541), 40 km
Annual closure Fermeture annuelle no
Weekly closure Fermeture hebdomadaire no

Fees main season Tarifs haute saison	18 holes	
	Week days Semaine	**We/Bank holidays** We/Férié
Individual Individuel	£ 30	£ 35
Couple Couple	£ 60	£ 70

Full days: £ 45 / £ 50 (We) / Reduced rates for hotel guests

Caddie Caddie no — **Electric Trolley** Chariot électrique no
Buggy Voiturette yes — **Clubs** Clubs yes
Credit cards Cartes de crédit
VISA - Eurocard - MasterCard - DC - JCB

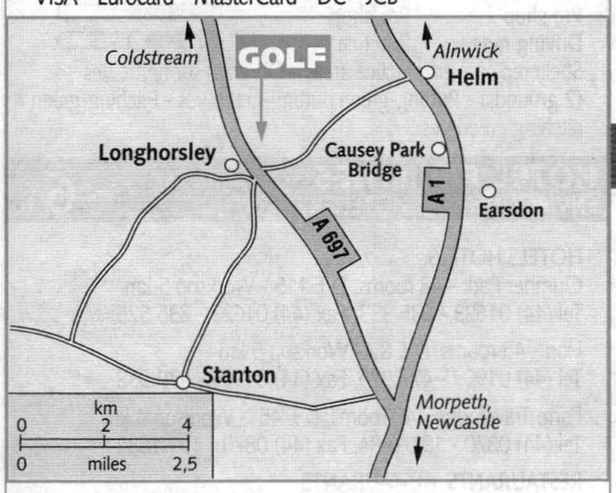

Access Accès : A1. After Morpeth, A697.
Golf at Longhorsley Village.
Map 2 on page 473 Carte 2 Page 473

GOLF COURSE — PARCOURS 16/20

Site Site
Maintenance Entretien
Architect Architecte Jonathan Gaunt
Type Type parkland
Relief Relief
Water in play Eau en jeu
Exp. to wind Exposé au vent
Trees in play Arbres en jeu

Scorecard Carte de score	**Chp.** Chp.	**Mens** Mess.	**Ladies** Da.
Length Long.	6128	5857	4977
Par	72	72	72
Slope system	—	—	—

Advised golfing ability Niveau de jeu recommandé 0 12 24 36
Hcp required Handicap exigé 24 Men, 36 Ladies

CLUB HOUSE & AMENITIES — CLUB HOUSE ET ANNEXES 8/10

Pro shop Pro-shop
Driving range Practice
Sheltered couvert 8 bays - On grass sur herbe yes Putting-green putting-green yes - Pitching-green pitching green yes

HOTEL FACILITIES — ENVIRONNEMENT HOTELIER 5/10

HOTELS HÔTELS
Linden Hall Hotel - on site
50 rooms, D £ 140
Tel (44) 01670 - 516 611, Fax (44) 01670 - 788 544

Thistleyhaugh Farm - 5 rooms, D £ 70 - Longhorsley 3 km
Tel (44) 01665 - 570 629, Fax (44) 01665 - 570 629

Orchard - 6 rooms, D £ 50 - Rothbury 15 km
Tel (44) 01669 - 620 684

RESTAURANTS RESTAURANTS
Linden Hall Hotel - on site
Tel (44) 01670 - 516 611

Lindrick

18 | 6 | 6

Lindrick was for a long while the last course where the American Ryder Cup team actually lost (1957)... How times have changed! Although Lindrick must now be considered a little too short for the most powerful pros, for amateurs, men or women, this is a magnificent test of golf in heather-land shorn of any trees to speak of. It demands a style of play similar to when playing on a links course. Driving is very important, if only to avoid the well-placed bunkers and especially the very tough and highly penalising rough with ball-eating bushes. But the fairways are so wonderfully groomed that you won't want to miss them. Original for its landscape, intelligent for its strategic layout, natural-looking, fun to play and rarely busy, Lindrick is a must that is very pleasant to play all year, even in winter. The club has also subscribed to an environment protection plan, which can only be good news.

Lindrick fut longtemps le dernier parcours à avoir vu l'équipe américaine perdre la Ryder Cup (en 1957). Les temps ont changé ! Il est aujourd'hui bien court pour les pros les plus puissants. Pour les amateurs, hommes ou femmes, c'est toutefois un magnifique test de golf en pleine terre de bruyère, avec assez peu d'arbres, qui demande un style de jeu assez analogue à celui des links. Le driving est très important, ne serait-ce que pour éviter les bunkers bien placés, mais surtout un rough très sévère, très pénalisant, avec en supplément des buissons mangeurs de balles. Mais les fairways sont d'une telle qualité que l'on serait assez stupide de les manquer ! Original par son paysage, intelligent par ses aspects stratégiques, naturel dans son aspect, amusant à apprivoiser, et rarement très fréquenté, Lindrick est un "must" très agréable toute l'année, même en hiver. Le club a aussi adhéré à un programme environnemental, on ne saurait que s'en réjouir.

572

Lindrick Golf Club — 1891

Lindrick
ENG - WORKSOP, Notts S81 8BH

Office	Secrétariat	(44) 01909 - 475 282
Pro shop	Pro-shop	(44) 01909 - 475 820
Fax	Fax	(44) 01909 - 488 685
Web	www.lindrickgolfclub.co.uk	
Situation	Situation	Sheffield, 20 km
Worksop, 5 km		
Annual closure	Fermeture annuelle	no
Weekly closure	Fermeture hebdomadaire	no

Fees main season Tarifs haute saison — 18 holes

	Week days / Semaine	We/Bank holidays / We/Férié
Individual Individuel	£ 50	£ 60*
Couple Couple	£ 100	£ 120*

* We: Sunday only after 14:30
Full week days: £ 60

Caddie Caddie no **Electric Trolley** Chariot électrique yes

Buggy Voiturette medical resaons **Clubs** Clubs yes

Credit cards Cartes de crédit
Visa - Mastercard - AMEX - DC (Pro shop only)

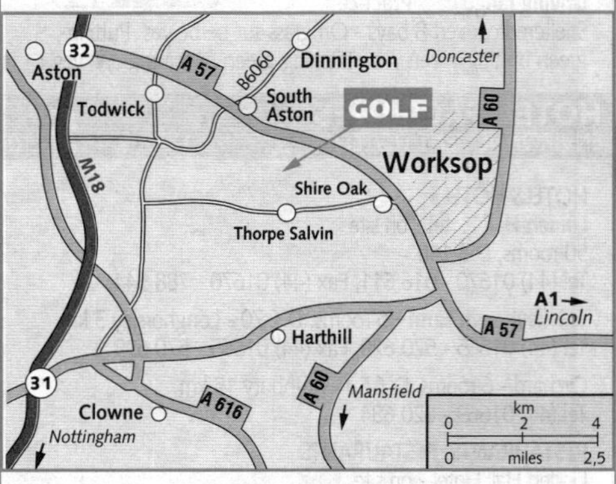

Access Accès : M1 Jct 31. A 57 East → Worksop.
Golf on right side after South Anston.
Map 4 on page 476 Carte 4 Page 476

GOLF COURSE — PARCOURS — 18/20

Site	Site	
Maintenance	Entretien	
Architect	Architecte	Tom Dunn, W. Park Herbert Fowler
Type	Type	inland, heathland
Relief	Relief	
Water in play	Eau en jeu	
Exp. to wind	Exposé au vent	
Trees in play	Arbres en jeu	

Scorecard Carte de score	Chp. Chp.	Mens Mess.	Ladies Da.
Length Long.	5945	5643	5195
Par	71	71	74
Slope system	—	—	—

Advised golfing ability Niveau de jeu recommandé — 0 12 24 36

Hcp required Handicap exigé — certificate

CLUB HOUSE & AMENITIES — CLUB HOUSE ET ANNEXES — 6/10

Pro shop Pro-shop

Driving range Practice

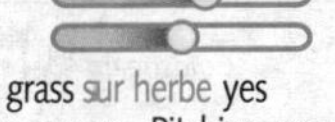

Sheltered couvert practice areas - On grass sur herbe yes (2 grounds) - Putting-green putting-green yes - Pitching-green pitching green yes

HOTEL FACILITIES — ENVIRONNEMENT HOTELIER — 6/10

HOTELS HÔTELS

Clumber Park - 48 rooms, D £ 115 - Worksop 5 km
Tel (44) 01623 - 835 333, Fax (44) 01623 - 835 525

Lion - 45 rooms, D £ 85 - Worksop 5 km
Tel (44) 01909 - 477 925, Fax (44) 01909 - 479 038

Forte Travelodge - 40 rooms, D £ 45 - Worksop 4 km
Tel (44) 0870 - 191 1684, Fax (44) 0870 - 191 1684

RESTAURANTS RESTAURANTS

Old Vicarage - Worfield 15 km - Tel (44) 01746 - 716 497

Limetree (Clumber Park) - Worksop 5 km
Tel (44) 01623 - 835 333

Liphook

17	7	6

Hampshire is one of those counties whose villages, landscape and greenery seem to symbolise the English countryside as seen in films. The drive to Liphook and the hospitality awaiting visitors in the club-house realises this mood and more. The designer has bent the course to match the landscape instead of the opposite, maybe because the excavators in service in the 1920s were not up to moving much earth. Liphook is a gem of a course and the hazards penalise absolutely every mis-hit shot. As they are almost invariably clearly visible, the sanction comes as no surprise. The charming landscape might make you think this to be a kindly course, but nothing could be further from the truth. You need to flight the ball and play with care or else resign yourself to trying to hack your ball out of the heather. Add to this subtle greens that are usually fast in summer and you have the full picture: Liphook is an exciting course whose visual discretion cleverly hides the real difficulties in store.

Le Hampshire est l'une de ces régions qui symbolisent par leurs villages, leur paysage, leur végétation ce qu'est la campagne anglaise, comme dans les films. L'arrivée au golf de Liphook, comme l'hospitalité du club-house vont dans le même sens. L'architecte a plié le parcours au paysage au lieu du contraire, mais il faut bien dire que, dans les années 20, les engins de terrassement ne permettaient pas de bouger beaucoup de terre. Liphook est un petit joyau, et les obstacles pénalisent absolument tous les coups manqués. Comme ils sont très visibles, on ne saurait en être surpris. Le charme du paysage peut faire penser à un parcours aimable. Ce n'est pas le cas, il faut savoir travailler la balle, jouer avec prudence, ou alors accepter de devoir sortir ses balles de la bruyère. Si l'on ajoute la subtilité des greens, généralement rapides en été, on aura compris qu'il s'agit d'un parcours passionnant, dont la sobriété visuelle cache bien les réelles difficultés.

Liphook Golf Club — 1922

Wheatsheaf Enclosure
ENG - LIPHOOK, Hants GU30 7EH

Office	Secrétariat	(44) 01428 - 723 271
Pro shop	Pro-shop	(44) 01428 - 723 271
Fax	Fax	(44) 01428 - 724 853
E-mail		liphookgolfclub@btinternet.com
Situation	Situation	Liphook, 2 km
Annual closure	Fermeture annuelle	no
Weekly closure	Fermeture hebdomadaire	no

Fees main season Tarifs haute saison — 18 holes

	Week days / Semaine	We/Bank holidays / We/Férié
Individual Individuel	£ 44	£ 55*
Couple Couple	£ 88	£ 110*

Full weekdays: £ 55 / Full Saturday : £ 66 /
* Sunday: £ 66 after 12:00 only

Caddie Caddie no — **Electric Trolley** Chariot électrique no

Buggy Voiturette yes — **Clubs** Clubs yes

Credit cards Cartes de crédit
Visa - Mastercard (Pro shop goods only)

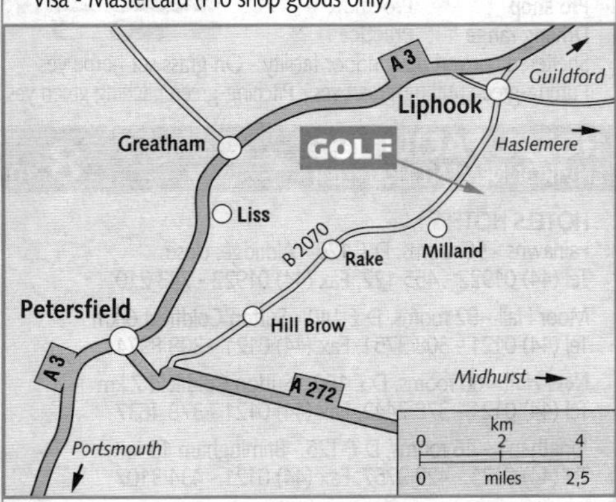

Access Accès : A3 London to Portsmouth. B2131, then B2070 (old A3). Golf on the right after Railway line
Map 7 on page 482 Carte 7 Page 482

GOLF COURSE — PARCOURS — 17/20

Site	Site	
Maintenance	Entretien	
Architect	Architecte	Arthur Croome
Type	Type	inland, heathland
Relief	Relief	
Water in play	Eau en jeu	
Exp. to wind	Exposé au vent	
Trees in play	Arbres en jeu	

Scorecard Carte de score	Chp. Chp.	Mens Mess.	Ladies Da.
Length Long.	5550	5270	4975
Par	70	70	72
Slope system	—	—	—

Advised golfing ability Niveau de jeu recommandé — 0 12 24 36

Hcp required Handicap exigé — certificate

CLUB HOUSE & AMENITIES — CLUB HOUSE ET ANNEXES — 7/10

Pro shop Pro-shop
Driving range Practice
Sheltered couvert 2 mats - On grass sur herbe no - Putting-green putting-green yes - Pitching-green pitching green yes

HOTEL FACILITIES — ENVIRONNEMENT HOTELIER — 6/10

HOTELS HÔTELS

Lythe Hill - 41 rooms, D £ 184 - Haslemere 10 km
Tel (44) 01428 - 651 251, Fax (44) 01428 - 644 131

Georgian - Haslemere 10 km
53 rooms, D from £ 89
Tel (44) 01428 - 656 644, Fax (44) 01428 - 645 600

Travelodge - 40 rooms, D £ 50 - Liphook 2 km
Tel (44) 0870 - 191 1544, Fax (44) 01428 - 727 619

RESTAURANTS RESTAURANTS

Auberge de France - Haslemere 10 km
Tel (44) 01428 - 651 251

Lythe Hill - Haslemere 10 km - Tel (44) 01428 - 651 251

Little Aston

17	7	8

While Little Aston is now approximately 100 years old there are few more attractive, or challenging, inland courses than this one. It is the perfect example of the best that British parkland courses can offer and one where just setting foot on the springy turf is an experience in itself. Despite its age, Little Aston has a young feeling about it and those who take up the challenge will soon dispel the myth that it is a little on the short side. Maybe it is short, compared with the modern day courses under construction, but what you see is what you get – there are no hidden hazards to contend with. They are clearly in view, especially the mammoth bunker which stretches across the full width of the 15th fairway, to escape from which is a sheer pleasure just as it is from the 100 or so fairway and greenside traps strategically placed around the course. There are water hazards, too, and together with the trees which line many of the fairways, there is not a weak hole on the course. Here you live and breathe a sense of sheer quality.

Bien que Little Aston soit presque centenaire, peu de parcours inland restent plus attrayants, ou exigeants. C'est un parfait exemple de ce style de parcours britanniques, et le seul fait de poser le pied sur le gazon est une expérience en soi. Malgré son âge, Little Aston n'a rien perdu de sa jeunesse et ceux qui pourraient un instant croire que ce tracé est trop court perdront vite leurs illusions. Peut-être manque-t-il de longueur en regard des références modernes, mais tous les obstacles sont clairement visibles et vous serez récompensé en fonction de vos efforts. Vous distinguerez particulièrement l'énorme bunker qui barre le fairway du 15, et dont le seul fait de sortir est un vrai plaisir, tout comme de la centaine d'autres bunkers de fairway ou de green placés de manière toujours stratégique. Peu d'eau en revanche, mais des arbres bordant les fairways. Sans aucun trou inférieur aux autres, on respire ici le sens de la mesure et le goût de la qualité.

Little Aston Golf Club — 1908

Streetly
ENG - SUTTON COLDFIELD, West Midlands B74 3AN

Office	Secrétariat	(44) 0121 - 353 2942
Pro shop	Pro-shop	(44) 0121 - 353 0330
Fax	Fax	(44) 0121 - 580 8387
Web	www.littleastongolf.co.uk	
Situation	Situation	Sutton Coldfield, 10 km
Annual closure	Fermeture annuelle	no
Weekly closure	Fermeture hebdomadaire	no

Fees main season Tarifs haute saison	18 holes	
	Week days Semaine	**We/Bank holidays** We/Férié
Individual Individuel	£ 63	£ 63*
Couple Couple	£ 126	£ 126*

* Sundays only for 18 holes / Full Week days: £ 78

Caddie Caddie yes — **Electric Trolley** Chariot électrique no
Buggy Voiturette yes — **Clubs** Clubs no
Credit cards Cartes de crédit VISA - MasterCard

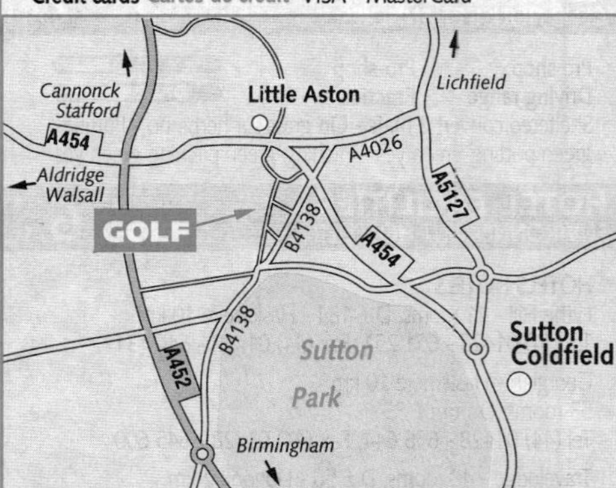

Access Accès : Birmingham A34 (Walsall Road). At Great Barr (Scott Arms pub), turn right at traffic lights → A4041. Go to the fifth roundabout (crossing A452) and take Chester Road (A 452) on the left. 2nd exit through the gates on the right, Roman Road (private road). Golf on left hand side.
Map 7 on page 482 Carte 7 Page 482

GOLF COURSE — PARCOURS — 17/20

Site	Site	
Maintenance	Entretien	
Architect	Architecte	Harry Vardon
Type	Type	inland, parkland
Relief	Relief	
Water in play	Eau en jeu	
Exp. to wind	Exposé au vent	
Trees in play	Arbres en jeu	

Scorecard Carte de score	**Chp.** Chp.	**Mens** Mess.	**Ladies** Da.
Length Long.	6003	5758	5179
Par	73	72	74
Slope system	—	—	—

Advised golfing ability Niveau de jeu recommandé: 0 12 24 36
Hcp required Handicap exigé: 24 Men, 36 Ladies

CLUB HOUSE & AMENITIES — CLUB HOUSE ET ANNEXES — 7/10

Pro shop Pro-shop
Driving range Practice
Sheltered couvert new indoor facility - On grass sur herbe yes
Putting-green putting-green yes - Pitching-green pitching green yes

HOTEL FACILITIES — ENVIRONNEMENT HOTELIER — 8/10

HOTELS HÔTELS

Fairlawns - 50 rooms, D £ 125 - Aldridge, close
Tel (44) 01922 - 455 122, Fax (44) 01922 - 743 210

Moor Hall - 82 rooms, D £ 140 - Sutton Coldfield 6 km
Tel (44) 0121 - 308 3751, Fax (44) 0121 - 308 8974

New Hall - 60 rooms, D £ 160 - Sutton Coldfield 7 km
Tel (44) 0121 - 378 2442, Fax (44) 0121 - 378 4637

Jonathan's - 46 rooms, D £ 125 - Brimingham 15 km
Tel (44) 0121 - 429 3757, Fax (44) 0121 - 434 3107

RESTAURANTS RESTAURANTS

Metro - Birmingham 15 km - Tel (44) 0121 - 200 1911
La Toque d'Or - Hockley 10 km - Tel (44) 0121 - 233 3655

London Golf Club *International* 15 | 9 | 7

These days, when you want to build a fashionable layout you call in someone like Jack Nicklaus to design it. This is what happened with the "Heritage Course", for members only, but this "International" course is more open, and was left to his Golden Bear company and architect Ron Kirby. The contrary might have been a more preferable option, opening the more demanding of the two courses to players with the ability to play it, but such golfers can seldom afford this kind of membership at a club that cares so much about being "exclusive". Having had our gripe, this course is excellent and still wide open, as the trees are young. The wide fairways give welcome breathing space and the huge greens require shots close to the pin to avoid three-putting. The key to a successful round lies with the second shot; the greens are stoutly guarded with sand-traps, and water hazards on four holes. The layout is certainly imaginative with holes giving good variety in length and difficulties, but with a green-fee this high you are entitled to expect something exceptional.

Quand on veut un ensemble à la mode, on demande à Jack Nicklaus de le dessiner. Il l'a fait pour le "Heritage Course" réservé aux membres et a laissé à son collaborateur Ron Kirby le tracé de cet "International". Il aurait été préférable de faire le contraire et d'ouvrir le plus exigeant des deux parcours aux joueurs susceptibles par leur niveau de jeu de le maîtriser, car ils ont rarement les moyens d'être membres dans un club qui se veut si exclusif. Cela dit, le présent parcours est d'excellente qualité, très ouvert car les arbres sont petits, avec des fairways larges permettant de se déchaîner, et de vastes greens où il faut viser le drapeau pour ne pas risquer trois putts : la clef du succès réside ici dans les seconds coups. Les défenses de greens sont solides, avec des bunkers ou des obstacles d'eau sur quatre trous. Certes, le dessin est imaginatif, les trous aussi variés en distance qu'en difficultés mais pour un montant de green-fee aussi élevé, on est en droit d'attendre l'exceptionnel.

The London Golf Club 1993

South Ash Manor Estate
ENG - ASH, near SEVENOAKS, Kent TN15 7EN

Office	Secrétariat	(44) 01474 - 879 899
Pro shop	Pro-shop	(44) 01474 - 879 899
Fax	Fax	(44) 01474 - 879 912
Web	www.londongolf.co.uk	
Situation	Situation	London, 42 km

Sevenoaks (pop. 19 617), 24 km

Annual closure Fermeture annuelle — no

Weekly closure Fermeture hebdomadaire — no

Fees main season Tarifs haute saison — 18 holes

	Week days / Semaine	We/Bank holidays / We/Férié
Individual Individuel	£ 80	£ 90
Couple Couple	£ 160	£ 180

Caddie Caddie on request **Electric Trolley** Chariot électrique yes

Buggy Voiturette yes **Clubs** Clubs yes

Credit cards Cartes de crédit
VISA - MasterCard - AMEX - Switch

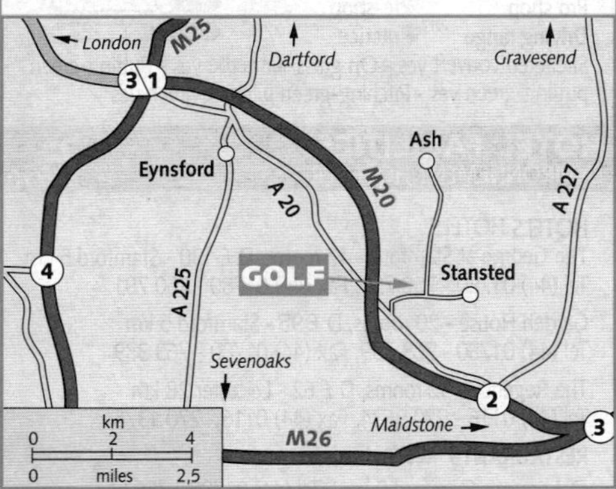

Access Accès : London M20 Exit 2. Turn left → West Kingsdown on A20. 3 km (2 m) on right, sign to Stansted and Golf course. Entrance 100 m on left.
Map 7 on page 483 Carte 7 Page 483

GOLF COURSE — PARCOURS 15/20

Site	Site	
Maintenance	Entretien	
Architect	Architecte	Ron Kirby/Golden Bear
Type	Type	open country, hilly
Relief	Relief	
Water in play	Eau en jeu	
Exp. to wind	Exposé au vent	
Trees in play	Arbres en jeu	

Scorecard Carte de score	Chp. Chp.	Mens Mess.	Ladies Da.
Length Long.	6305	5917	4945
Par	72	72	72
Slope system	—	—	—

Advised golfing ability Niveau de jeu recommandé — 0 12 24 36

Hcp required Handicap exigé — certificate

CLUB HOUSE & AMENITIES — CLUB HOUSE ET ANNEXES 9/10

Pro shop Pro-shop
Driving range Practice
Sheltered couvert 6 bays - On grass sur herbe yes - Putting-green putting-green yes - Pitching-green pitching green yes

HOTEL FACILITIES — ENVIRONNEMENT HOTELIER 7/10

HOTELS HÔTELS

Brands Hatch Place - 38 rooms, D £ 82 (golfers) - Fawkham 5 km
Tel (44) 01474 - 872 239, Fax (44) 01474 - 879 652

Brands Hatch Thistle - 121 rooms, D £ 147 - Brands Hatch 5 km
Tel (44) 01474 - 854 900, Fax (44) 01474 - 853 220

Forte Posthouse - 106 rooms, D £ 80 - Wrotham Heath 5 km
Tel (44) 01474 - 883 311, Fax (44) 01474 - 885 850

Anchor & Hope - 5 rooms, D £ 50 (w.breakfast) - Ash 2 km
Tel (44) 01474 - 872 382

RESTAURANTS RESTAURANTS

Brands Hatch Place - Fawkham 5 km
Tel (44) 01474 - 872 239

Club's restaurant - on site - Tel (44) 01474 - 879 899

Luffenham Heath

14	6	5

This charmingly peaceful corner of England attracts large numbers of nature lovers, walkers and hikers. And history-lovers will travel from afar to see the amazing Burghley House, a lordly manor dating back to the 16th century. A good excuse, we might add, to discover this course, today listed as a site of special scientific interest for the variety of plants, insects and birds that abound here. Traditional golf freaks will love this typical James Braid layout which, in its own modest way, is somewhat reminiscent of the top inland links courses like Gleneagles. It even features some good old cross-bunkers, a rarity indeed these days. A little tricky and sometimes a little devious, this short course calls for more thought than you might think. It is the kind of "old-fashioned" course that you don't visit with a noisy group of mates, rather with the family so as not to be too obtrusive. Next door is the little Medieval and Georgian town of Stamford, which houses the wax statue of a man weighing a full 52 stone (335 kg). Show it to the kids to put them off eating too many sweets.

Si ce n'est pour ses parcours, le Lincolnshire attire beaucoup de visiteurs et de randonneurs. Et les amateurs d'histoire viennent de loin visiter l'étonnante Burghley House, demeure seigneuriale du XVIème siècle. C'est le prétexte pour découvrir ce parcours classé d'intérêt scientifique spécial, à cause de la variété de plantes, d'insectes, d'oiseaux qui y abondent. Les amoureux de nature et de tradition golfique vont aimer ce James Braid typique, qui n'est pas sans rappeler – en toute modestie – les grands inland links comme Gleneagles. On y trouve même une rareté aujourd'hui, des cross-bunkers. Un peu tricky, pas toujours franc, ce tracé court mérite plus de réflexion qu'il n'y paraît. Le genre de golf "old-fashioned" où l'on ne vient pas en troupe bruyante, mais plutôt en famille pour ne pas trop déranger. A côté, la petite ville de Stamford, à la fois médiévale et georgienne. On y trouve la statue en cire d'une homme de 335 kg, à montrer aux enfants pour qu'ils lâchent leurs sucreries.

Luffenham Heath Golf Club — 1911

Ketton
ENG - STAMFORD, Lincolnshire PE9 3UU

Office Secrétariat (44) 01780 - 720 205
Pro shop Pro-shop (44) 01780 - 722 146
Fax Fax (44) 01780 - 722 146
Web www.luffenhamheath.co.uk
Situation Situation Leicester, 29 km
Stamford, 7 km

Annual closure Fermeture annuelle no
Weekly closure Fermeture hebdomadaire no

Fees main season Tarifs haute saison 18 holes

	Week days Semaine	We/Bank holidays We/Férié
Individual Individuel	£ 40*	£ 50
Couple Couple	£ 80*	£ 100

We: 10:30 → 12:00 & after 14:00
Juniors: £ 10 / * Not Tuesday

Caddie Caddie — **Electric Trolley** Chariot électrique yes
Buggy Voiturette no — **Clubs** Clubs no
Credit cards Cartes de crédit
VISA - MasterCard

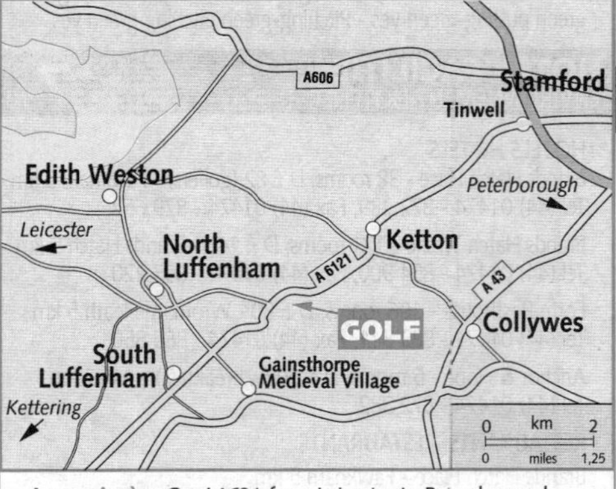

Access Accès : On A1621 from Leicester to Petersborough
Map 7 on page 482 Carte 7 Page 482

GOLF COURSE — PARCOURS 14/20

Site Site
Maintenance Entretien
Architect Architecte James Braid
Type Type heathland
Relief Relief
Water in play Eau en jeu
Exp. to wind Exposé au vent
Trees in play Arbres en jeu

Scorecard Carte de score	Chp. Chp.	Mens Mess.	Ladies Da.
Length Long.	5684	5405	5066
Par	70	69	71
Slope system	—	—	—

Advised golfing ability Niveau de jeu recommandé 0 12 24 36
Hcp required Handicap exigé certificate

CLUB HOUSE & AMENITIES — CLUB HOUSE ET ANNEXES 6/10

Pro shop Pro-shop
Driving range Practice
Sheltered couvert yes - On grass sur herbe yes - Putting-green putting-green yes - Pitching-green pitching green yes

HOTEL FACILITIES — ENVIRONNEMENT HOTELIER 5/10

HOTELS HÔTELS
The George at Stamford - 47 rooms, D £ 130 - Stamford 5 km
Tel (44) 01780 - 750 750, Fax (44) 01780 - 750 701

Garden House - 20 rooms, D £ 95 - Stamford 5 km
Tel (44) 01780 - 763 359, Fax (44) 01780 - 763 339

The Regency - 32 rooms, D £ 62 - Leicester 28 km
Tel (44) 0116 - 270 9634, Fax (44) 0116 - 270 1375

RESTAURANTS RESTAURANTS
Oakhouse - Stamford 5 km - Tel (44) 01780 - 756 565
The Olive Branch - Clipsham 20 km - Tel (44) 01780 - 410 355
The Jackson Stops Inn - Stretton 19 km
Tel (44) 01780 - 410 237

Manchester

16 | 7 | 7

Very close to the city of Manchester, this fine course is easy to play during the week, particularly in tandem with meetings where business and extreme pleasure mix very well indeed. The layout is not very long but the tee-boxes are well placed to provide each category of player with a good challenge, and the better players will have to think long and hard and play well to card any sort of sore. On an open moorland landscape which is unusual so close to a city, the course is very exposed to the wind which can become a major obstacle, particularly on the dog-leg holes, where, as on all Harry Colt courses, you need to think carefully about where to put your drive to get the right approach to greens protected by bushes, trees and bunkers. Strategy is to the fore again at the 12th, where hitting the driver will leave you a short approach shot but on a sloping lie, while a 2 iron will leave you on a flat part of the fairway but with a longer approach to the green. A rather hilly course (buggy recommended), Manchester offers fine views to make up for the difficulty of club selection.

Proche de Manchester, ce beau parcours est très accessible en semaine, notamment pour des réunions d'affaires joignant l'utile au très agréable. Le tracé n'est pas très long, et les départs assez bien placés pour offrir un bon "challenge" à toutes les catégories de joueurs, les meilleurs ayant quand même pas mal à réfléchir, et du travail à accomplir pour bien scorer. Dans son paysage de lande, assez inhabituel si près de la ville, ce parcours est très exposé au vent, qui peut devenir l'obstacle essentiel, notamment sur les doglegs où il faut réfléchir sur sa ligne pour avoir les greens ouverts, comme sur beaucoup de dessins d'Harry Colt. Ils sont protégés par des buissons, arbres et bunkers. Stratégie encore au 12, où jouer le drive vous fera jouer un second coup court, mais dans une pente, alors que jouer un fer du départ vous permettra d'avoir les pieds à plat, mais un coup plus long. Assez accidenté, Manchester offre de très belles vues, comme pour compenser la difficulté de sélection de clubs.

Manchester Golf Club — 1882

Hopwood Cottage, Middleton
ENG - MANCHESTER M24 2QP

Office	Secrétariat	(44) 0161 - 643 3202
Pro shop	Pro-shop	(44) 0161 - 643 2638
Fax	Fax	(44) 0161 - 643 9174
Web	www.mangc.co.uk	
Situation	Situation	Manchester, 10 km

Rochdale (pop. 202 164), 6 km

Annual closure Fermeture annuelle — no
Weekly closure Fermeture hebdomadaire — no

Fees main season Tarifs haute saison — 18 holes

	Week days / Semaine	We/Bank holidays / We/Férié
Individual Individuel	£ 25	*
Couple Couple	£ 50	*

Full week days: £ 40 / * We: members only

Caddie Caddie no — **Electric Trolley** Chariot électrique yes
Buggy Voiturette yes — **Clubs** Clubs no

Credit cards Cartes de crédit
VISA - Eurocard - MasterCard

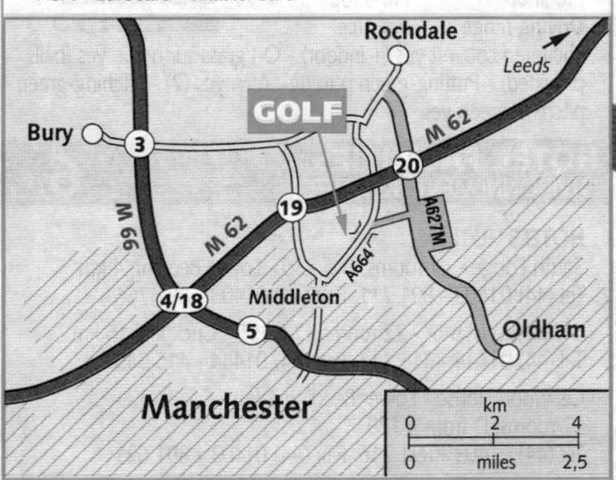

Access Accès : M62 Jct 20, then A627(M) → Oldham. First exit, follow A664 signs. Club on the right over humped back bridge.
Map 4 on page 476 Carte 4 Page 476

GOLF COURSE — PARCOURS — 16/20

Site	Site	
Maintenance	Entretien	
Architect	Architecte	Harry S. Colt
Type	Type	parkland, moorland
Relief	Relief	
Water in play	Eau en jeu	
Exp. to wind	Exposé au vent	
Trees in play	Arbres en jeu	

Scorecard Carte de score	Chp. / Chp.	Mens / Mess.	Ladies / Da.
Length Long.	5873	5660	5198
Par	72	72	74
Slope system	—	—	—

Advised golfing ability Niveau de jeu recommandé — 0 12 24 36
Hcp required Handicap exigé — certificate

CLUB HOUSE & AMENITIES — CLUB HOUSE ET ANNEXES — 7/10

Pro shop Pro-shop
Driving range Practice
Sheltered couvert no - On grass sur herbe yes - Putting-green putting-green yes - Pitching-green pitching green yes

HOTEL FACILITIES — ENVIRONNEMENT HOTELIER — 7/10

HOTELS HÔTELS

Royal Toby Lodge - 44 rooms, D £ 89 - Rochdale 7 km
Tel (44) 01706 - 861 861, Fax (44) 01706 - 868 428

Palace - 257 rooms, D £ 160- Manchester 10 km
Tel (44) 0161 - 288 1111, Fax (44) 0161 - 288 2222

Victoria and Albert - 158 rooms, D £ 135 - Manchester 10 km
Tel (44) 0161 - 832 1188, Fax (44) 0161 - 834 2484

RESTAURANTS RESTAURANTS

The French Restaurant - Manchester 10 km
Tel (44) 0161 - 236 3333

After Eight - Rochdale 7 km - Tel (44) 01706 - 646 432

Yang Sing (Chinese) - Manchester 10 km
Tel (44) 0161 - 236 2200

Mannings Heath *Waterfall Course*

16	8	6

One of England's finest inland courses and one that is constantly evolving. Ewan Murray has redesigned the greens to blend in better with the surrounding countryside and they are now to USGA specs and more suitable to handle the sometimes hard winters. Temporary greens are a thing of the past and a very effective drainage system makes golf good fun at anytime of the year. This is a steeply sloping course set in a magical corner of Sussex, so a buggy is recommended. Between the woods, the sections of heather and parkland, find time to admire the landscape and squirrels, they might give you some precious inspiration. Although not a long course, you need a good golfing brain to score well. Some drives have to be long enough to be able to see the green for the approach shot, while tee-shots on the par 3s need careful thought and execution: the 10th hole with its waterfall is a particularly memorable experience and gives its name to the course. The second and much newer "Kingfisher" course is pleasant but less testing. The club-house is splendid.

C'est l'un des meilleurs "inland" d'Angleterre, et en évolution permanente. Ewan Murray en a redessiné les greens aux spécifications de l'USGA pour mieux les adapter à la région. Ainsi, les greens d'hiver appartiennent au passé, et le drainage très efficace permet d'assurer de bonnes conditions de jeu en toutes saisons. Dans ce coin de campagne enchanteur du Sussex, ce parcours est assez accidenté pour conseiller un chariot électrique. Entre les bois, les parties de bruyère ou de parc, on doit se donner le temps d'admirer le paysage, et le jeu des écureuils : c'est un bon prétexte pour reprendre ses esprits car, en dépit de sa faible longueur, il ne s'agit pas de jouer sans cervelle. Certains drives doivent être assez longs pour pouvoir ensuite apercevoir le green, et les coups de départ bien calculés sur les par 3 : on retiendra en particulier le 10 avec sa cascade (qui a donné son nom au parcours). Le second parcours, Kingfisher, est plaisant, mais moins décisif. Le club-house est splendide.

578

Mannings Heath Golf Club — 1905

Fullers, Hammerspond Road, Mannings Heath
ENG - HORSHAM, W. Sussex RH13 6PG

Office	Secrétariat	(44) 01403 - 210 228
Pro shop	Pro-shop	(44) 01403 - 210 228
Fax	Fax	(44) 01403 - 270 974
Web	www.manningsheath.com	
Situation	Situation	Crawley, 12 km
Annual closure	Fermeture annuelle	no
Weekly closure	Fermeture hebdomadaire	no

Fees main season Tarifs haute saison	18 holes	
	Week days Semaine	**We/Bank holidays** We/Férié
Individual Individuel	£ 63	*
Couple Couple	£ 126	*

* Members only / Full week days: £ 75
Fridays: £ 73 for 18 holes, £ 90 full day

Caddie Caddie no — **Electric Trolley** Chariot électrique no
Buggy Voiturette yes — **Clubs** Clubs yes

Credit cards Cartes de crédit
VISA - MasterCard - AMEX

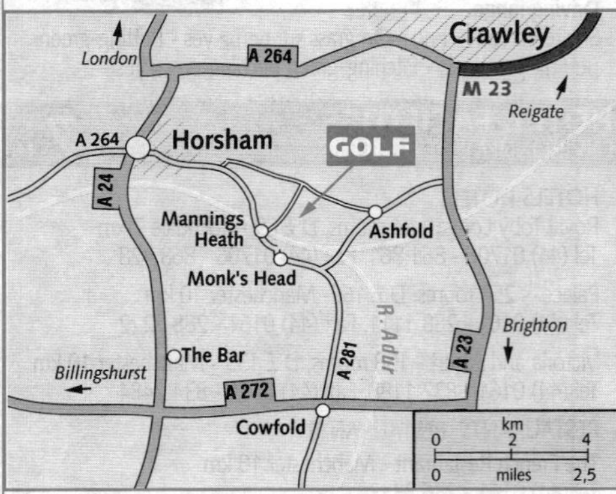

Access Accès : M23 Jct 11, through Pease Pottage to Grouse Lane (left hand side). 5 km (3.5 m.) to T junction, right and first left to Golf.
Map 7 on page 482 Carte 7 Page 482

GOLF COURSE — PARCOURS — 16/20

Site	Site	
Maintenance	Entretien	
Architect	Architecte	unknown
Type	Type	inland, heathland
Relief	Relief	
Water in play	Eau en jeu	
Exp. to wind	Exposé au vent	
Trees in play	Arbres en jeu	

Scorecard Carte de score	**Chp.** Chp.	**Mens** Mess.	**Ladies** Da.
Length Long.	5805	5460	4920
Par	73	71	73
Slope system	0	0	0

Advised golfing ability Niveau de jeu recommandé — 0 12 24 36
Hcp required Handicap exigé — certificate

CLUB HOUSE & AMENITIES — CLUB HOUSE ET ANNEXES — 8/10

Pro shop Pro-shop
Driving range Practice
Sheltered couvert yes (+ indoor) - On grass sur herbe yes (balls provided) - Putting-green putting-green yes (2) - Pitching-green pitching green yes

HOTEL FACILITIES — ENVIRONNEMENT HOTELIER — 6/10

HOTELS HÔTELS
South Lodge - 41 rooms, D £ 230 - Lower Beeding 4 km
Tel (44) 01403 - 891 711, Fax (44) 01403 - 891 766

Ockenden Manor - 22 rooms, D £ 155 - Cuckfield 15 km
Tel (44) 01444 - 416 111, Fax (44) 01444 - 415 549

Cisswood House - Lower Beeding 4 km
52 rooms, D from £ 120
Tel (44) 01403 - 891 216, Fax (44) 01403 - 891 621

RESTAURANTS RESTAURANTS
Ockenden Manor - Cuckfield 15 km - Tel (44) 01444 - 416 111
Cole's - Southwater 6 km - Tel (44) 01403 - 730 456

Manor House (Castle Combe) 15 8 7

It is no coincidence that there are so many buggies here. The superb views from the tee or green come courtesy of some roller-coaster landscape which makes this course something of an ordeal to walk. Designers Alliss and Clark followed the natural lie of the land and evidently had a lot of fun here, alternating pot bunkers or sprawling "sand-traps" and making extensive use of water hazards, particularly on the 18th (a tad artificial with its lakes and cascades). All these difficulties combine to make this a very testing layout. And the relatively short yardage doesn't mean much when you are constantly shooting uphill or downhill. A spectacular, exciting and, first time out, often a surprising course, it provides an experience that can properly be described as unique. You come here for a few days of leisure, staying if you can at Manor House, a pretty piece of architecture alongside hole N° 3 with all the most modern amenities. You can also play as a green-feer.

S'il y a autant de voiturettes ici, ce n'est pas par hasard. Les vues superbes du haut des départs ou des greens sont au prix de montagnes russes qui rendent le jeu à pied très éprouvant et la flotte de voiturettes très utile. Les architectes Alliss et Clark ont suivi les contours naturels et se sont bien amusés dans un tel espace, alternant les "pot" bunkers ou de longues étendues de sable, et faisant usage généreux des obstacles d'eau, en particulier au 18 (un peu artificiel avec ses lacs et cascades). Toutes ces difficultés réunies en font un tracé exigeant, et la longueur relativement faible ne veut pas dire grand chose avec ces changements incessants de niveau. Un parcours spectaculaire, souvent surprenant la première fois, parfois passionnant, et à classer à part. On vient ici passer quelques jours de plaisir, si l'on peut en logeant au Manor House Hotel, jolie pièce d'architecture le long du 3, avec le confort le plus moderne, mais on peut aussi jouer au green-fee.

Manor House (at Castle Combe) 1992

ENG - CASTLE COMBE, Wiltshire SN14 7 PL

Office Secrétariat (44) 01249 - 782 982
Pro shop Pro-shop (44) 01249 - 783 101
Fax Fax (44) 01249 - 782 992
Web www.exclusivehotels.co.uk
Situation Situation Bristol, 37 km
Bath (pop. 78 689), 18 km
Annual closure Fermeture annuelle no
Weekly closure Fermeture hebdomadaire no

Fees main season Tarifs haute saison	Week days Semaine	We/Bank holidays We/Férié
	18 holes	
Individual Individuel	£ 70	£ 85
Couple Couple	£ 140	£ 170

Caddie Caddie no — **Electric Trolley** Chariot électrique yes
Buggy Voiturette yes — **Clubs** Clubs yes
Credit cards Cartes de crédit (Pro shop goods & restaurant only) VISA - Eurocard - MasterCard

Access Accès : • M4 Jct 17, A350 → Chippenham, A420 on the right, then B4039 N of Castle Combe. • Bath: A46, A420 to Ford, then turn left to Castle Combe.
Map 6 on page 481 Carte 6 Page 481

GOLF COURSE — PARCOURS 15/20

Site Site
Maintenance Entretien
Architect Architecte Peter Alliss, Clive Clark
Type Type copse, parkland
Relief Relief
Water in play Eau en jeu
Exp. to wind Exposé au vent
Trees in play Arbres en jeu

Scorecard Carte de score	Chp. Chp.	Mens Mess.	Ladies Da.
Length Long.	5496	5298	4659
Par	73	71	72
Slope system	—	—	—

Advised golfing ability Niveau de jeu recommandé 0 12 24 36
Hcp required Handicap exigé 28 Men, 36 Ladies

CLUB HOUSE & AMENITIES — CLUB HOUSE ET ANNEXES 8/10

Pro shop Pro-shop
Driving range Practice
Sheltered couvert - On grass sur herbe yes - Putting-green putting-green yes - Pitching-green pitching green yes

HOTEL FACILITIES — ENVIRONNEMENT HOTELIER 7/10

HOTELS HÔTELS
Manor House Hotel - 48 rooms, D from £ 180 - on site
Tel (44) 01249 - 782 206, Fax (44) 01249 - 782 159

Castle Inn - 10 rooms, D £ 125 - Castle Combe 1 km
Tel (44) 01249 - 783 030, Fax (44) 01249 - 782 315

White Hart Inn - 11 rooms, D £ 80 - Ford 3 km
Tel (44) 01249 - 782 213, Fax (44) 01249 - 783 075

Crown Inn - 8 rooms, D £ 80 - Chippenham
Tel (44) 01249 - 782 229, Fax (44) 01249 - 782 337

RESTAURANTS RESTAURANTS
Manor House Hotel - on site - Tel (44) 01249 - 782 206
Crown Inn - Chippenham 8 km - Tel (44) 01249 - 782 229

Mendip

14	5	6

The highest point of this course is more than 1,000 ft. above sea-level from where - the members will tell you - you can see as far as Glastonbury and its abbey (you need good eyes), Exmoor (you need binoculars) and Wales. If they add America to the list, then you must be at the bar. But this is not too hilly a course and the turf is wonderfully springy underfoot. This adds comfort to the pleasure of playing a course where you are rarely on the flat, where you need to think, and where you need some good iron play and razor-sharp putting: the greens come in all shapes, sizes, slopes and contours. However they are seldom too tightly defended and front bunkers feature only on holes 17 and 18. Don't place too much faith in the overall yardage, either, as some of the par 4s are very long. Although minor details are always being tampered with, the 9 hole course by Vardon, later completed by Pennink, remained unchanged until 1988, when the purchase of new land took the par up to 71. The club-house is not the world's prettiest but the atmosphere inside is very friendly.

Le point haut du parcours est à plus de 300 mètres, d'où l'on voit – selon les membres – jusqu'à Glastonbury et son abbaye (avec de bons yeux), Exmoor (avec des jumelles) et le Pays de Galles. Si l'on évoque l'Amérique, c'est que vous êtes au bar. Pourtant, le parcours n'est pas trop accidenté, et le gazon est d'une rare souplesse, ce qui ajoute au plaisir d'un parcours où l'on a rarement les pieds à plat, où il faut un très bon jeu de fers et un putting affûté comme un rasoir, car les greens sont de formes, de tailles, et de reliefs variés. Cependant, leurs défenses ne sont pas trop serrées, et les bunkers ne sont frontaux que sur les 17 et 18. Attention à ne pas trop se fier à la longueur totale, certains par 4 sont longs. Tout en remaniant en permanence les détails, le dessin de 9 trous par Vardon, complété par Frank Pennink, est resté inchangé jusqu'en 1988, où l'achat de terrains a porté le par à 71. Le club-house n'est peut-être pas le plus joli du monde mais l'atmosphère y est très amicale.

Mendip Golf Club — 1909

Gurney Slade
ENG - BATH, Somerset BA3 4UT

Office	Secrétariat	(44) 01749 - 840 570
Pro shop	Pro-shop	(44) 01749 - 840 793
Fax	Fax	(44) 01749 - 841 439
Web	www.mendipgolf.co.uk	
Situation	Situation	Bristol, 38 km

Bath (pop. 78 689), 28 km

Annual closure	Fermeture annuelle	no
Weekly closure	Fermeture hebdomadaire	no

Fees main season Tarifs haute saison — 18 holes

	Week days / Semaine	We/Bank holidays / We/Férié
Individual Individuel	£ 27	£ 38
Couple Couple	£ 54	£ 76

Full week days: £ 33

Caddie Caddie no — **Electric Trolley** Chariot électrique no

Buggy Voiturette no — **Clubs** Clubs no

Credit cards Cartes de crédit
Visa - Mastercard (Pro shop goods only)

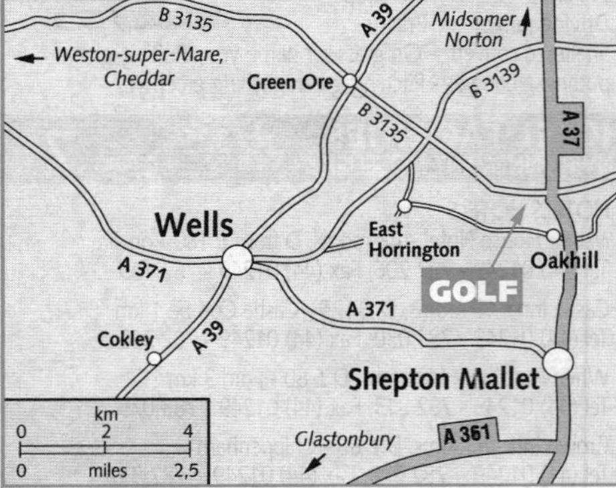

Access Accès : Bristol, A37 → Shepton Mallet, Golf 4.5 km (3 m.) before Shepton Mallet. From Bath, A367.
Map 6 on page 481 Carte 6 Page 481

GOLF COURSE — PARCOURS — 14/20

Site	Site	
Maintenance	Entretien	
Architect	Architecte	Harry Vardon Frank Pennink (1965)
Type	Type	open country
Relief	Relief	
Water in play	Eau en jeu	
Exp. to wind	Exposé au vent	
Trees in play	Arbres en jeu	

Scorecard / Carte de score	Chp. / Chp.	Mens / Mess.	Ladies / Da.
Length Long.	5833	5653	5452
Par	71	71	75
Slope system	—	—	—

Advised golfing ability / Niveau de jeu recommandé — 0 12 24 36

Hcp required — Handicap exigé — certificate

CLUB HOUSE & AMENITIES — CLUB HOUSE ET ANNEXES — 5/10

Pro shop — Pro-shop
Driving range — Practice

Sheltered couvert no - On grass sur herbe yes - Putting-green putting-green yes - Pitching-green pitching green yes

HOTEL FACILITIES — ENVIRONNEMENT HOTELIER — 6/10

HOTELS HÔTELS

Shrubbery - 10 rooms, D £ 85 - Shepton Mallet 5 km
Tel (44) 01749 - 346 671, Fax (44) 01749 - 346 581

Ston Easton Park - 22 rooms, D £ 185 - Ston Easton 6 km
Tel (44) 01761 - 241 631, Fax (44) 01749 - 241 377

Charlton House - 25 rooms, D £ 230 - Shepton Mallet 7 km
Tel (44) 01749 - 342 008, Fax (44) 01749 - 346 362

RESTAURANTS RESTAURANTS

Mulberry (Charlton House) - Shepton Mallet 7 km
Tel (44) 01749 - 342 008

Shrubbery - Shepton Mallet 5 km - Tel (44) 01749 - 346 671

Ston Easton Park - Ston Easton 6 km - Tel (44) 01761 - 241 631

Meon Valley *Meon Course*

14	8	7

This southern area of the Downs is a great site for walks and drives (behind the wheel), stretching out in the direction of Winchester, Chichester, Southampton, Beaulieu, Portsmouth and even the Isle of Wight. What's more, the course hotel is convenient and comfortable with an indoor swimming pool, sauna, fitness centre, etc. and has recently been refurbished. And as this "resort" also boasts a second 9-hole course (play it twice from two different sets of tee-box), a few days rest here is time well spent. On the Meon course, only real beginners might find the few small lakes a problem, but everyone should take extra care on the 12th and 18th holes. A ditch runs across a large section of the course but is not always that much in play. Elsewhere, a few isolated trees threaten the tee-shot; trees as a whole are generally in play and bunkers, although sparingly used, are very well positioned. This is an easily walkable and reassuringly short course which does not reveal all the trouble in store at first sight. You are well advised to use the yardage book.

Cette partie sud des "Downs" est un site de promenades, à pied, ou en voiture pour rayonner vers Winchester, Chichester, Southampton, Beaulieu, Portsmouth ou même l'Ile de Wight. L'hôtel sur le golf est pratique et confortable, avec piscine intérieure, sauna, centre de remise en forme, etc, il a récemment été rénové. Et comme ce "resort" comprend un autre 9 trous (jouez-le deux fois de départs très différents !), quelques jours de repos ici seront bien occupés. Sur le "Meon Course", seuls les débutants risquent d'être gênés par quelques petits lacs, mais tous devront s'en méfier au 12 et au 18. Un fossé parcourt une grande partie du terrain, sans être toujours dangereux. A part cela, quelques arbres isolés menacent certains tee-shots, l'ensemble des arbres étant en jeu, et des bunkers bien placés. Assez facile à jouer à pied, de longueur fort rassurante, ce parcours ne présente pas tous les obstacles au premier abord, il est conseillé de consulter le carnet de parcours.

Marriott Meon Valley Golf & CC — 1976

Sandy Lane
ENG - SHEDFIELD, SOUTHAMPTON SO32 2HQ

Office	Secrétariat	(44) 01329 - 833 455
Pro shop	Pro-shop	(44) 01329 - 836 832
Fax	Fax	(44) 01329 - 834 411
Web		www.marriott.com/sougs
Situation	Situation	Southampton, 18 km
Annual closure	Fermeture annuelle	no
Weekly closure	Fermeture hebdomadaire	no

Fees main season Tarifs haute saison	18 holes	
	Week days Semaine	**We/Bank holidays** We/Férié
Individual Individuel	£ 42	£ 50
Couple Couple	£ 84	£ 100

Caddie Caddie no — **Electric Trolley** Chariot électrique yes
Buggy Voiturette yes — **Clubs** Clubs yes
Credit cards Cartes de crédit
VISA - MasterCard - AMEX - DC - Switch

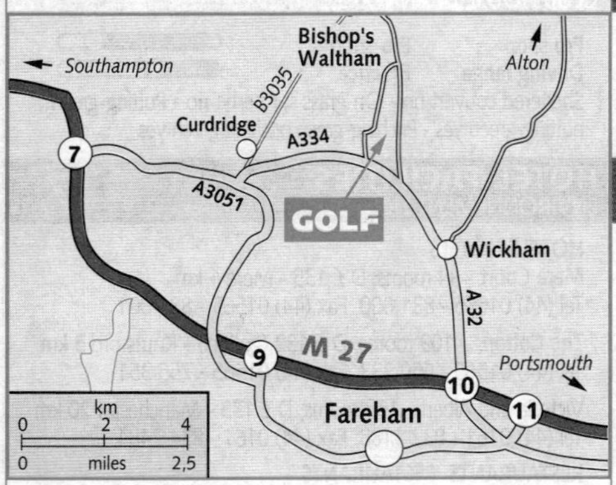

Access Accès : London M3 onto Southampton, then M27 → Portsmouth. Exit Jct 7, first exit for Botley (A334). → Wickham. On passing Wickham Vineyard, Sandy Lane is the next turning on your left.
Map 7 on page 482 Carte 7 Page 482

GOLF COURSE — PARCOURS 14/20

Site	Site	
Maintenance	Entretien	
Architect	Architecte	Hamilton Stutt
Type	Type	parkland
Relief	Relief	
Water in play	Eau en jeu	
Exp. to wind	Exposé au vent	
Trees in play	Arbres en jeu	

Scorecard Carte de score	**Chp.** Chp.	**Mens** Mess.	**Ladies** Da.
Length Long.	5868	5488	5049
Par	71	71	73
Slope system	—	—	—

Advised golfing ability Niveau de jeu recommandé: 0 12 24 36
Hcp required Handicap exigé: certificate

CLUB HOUSE & AMENITIES — CLUB HOUSE ET ANNEXES 8/10

Pro shop Pro-shop
Driving range Practice
Sheltered couvert 5 bays - On grass sur herbe yes - Putting-green putting-green yes - Pitching-green pitching green yes

HOTEL FACILITIES — ENVIRONNEMENT HOTELIER 7/10

HOTELS HÔTELS

Marriott Meon Valley Hotel - 113 rooms, D £ 138 - on site
Tel (44) 01329 - 833 455, Fax (44) 01329 - 834 411

Old House - 9 rooms, D from £ 75 - Wickham 3 km
Tel (44) 01329 - 833 049, Fax (44) 01329 - 833 672

Botley Park - 130 rooms, D £ 150 - Botley 8 km
Tel (44) 01489 - 780 888, Fax (44) 01489 - 789 242

RESTAURANTS RESTAURANTS

Treetops (Marriott Hotel) - Shedfield on site
Tel (44) 01329 - 833 455

Old House - Wickham 3 km - Tel (44) 01329 - 833 049

Kings Head - Wickham 3 km - Tel (44) 01329 - 832 123

Mere

15 | 7 | 7

Mere was revived in 1985 by the Boler family when the club-house was completely overhauled (adding swimming pools, sauna, tennis courts, etc.) and a building fitted out for seminars and weddings. Out on the course, an extensive tree-planting program was begun, new tee-boxes designed and a new green laid on the 18th hole. The face-lift carried out by ground staff has "modernised" the original design by Braid and Duncan - you don't have to love the water hazards on the 7th and 8th holes - and generally enhanced the site with a more challenging finish to the course. Some rolling landscape adds a little variety to the layout where there is a pleasant mix of tight and wider holes. Putting and approach shots can be a tricky business on some of the multi-tiered greens. Your best bet here is to pitch onto the greens rather than roll the ball. This is one of the most accomplished courses in the region south of Manchester, a fair test and always a pleasure to play but only on week-days for visitors.

Mere (synonyme de lac) a été réveillé en 1985 par la famille Boler, avec une refonte totale du club-house (piscines, sauna, tennis, etc), l'aménagement d'un bâtiment pour séminaires et mariages et, sur le parcours, la plantation de nombreux arbres, de nouveaux départs, un nouveau green au 18. Ce rajeunissement a un peu "modernisé" le dessin original de Braid et de Duncan - on peut ne pas adorer les obstacles d'eau du 7 et du 8 - mais c'était au profit de l'embellissement général du site, et du renforcement d'un finale très exigeant. Quelques ondulations apportent de la variété au terrain, où le tracé alterne agréablement les trous étroits et les espaces plus larges. Le putting et les approches sont intéressants et délicats à apprécier sur certains greens à plateaux : en général, on devra ici privilégier les coups levés. C'est une des réalisations les plus achevées au sud de Manchester, et le parcours d'une grande franchise reste un plaisir à jouer, en semaine pour les visiteurs.

Mere Golf & Country Club 1934

Chester Road, Mere
ENG - KNUTSFORD, Cheshire WA16 6LJ

Office Secrétariat (44) 01565 - 830 155
Pro shop Pro-shop (44) 01565 - 830 155
Fax Fax (44) 01565 - 830 713
Web www.meregolf.co.uk
Situation Situation Manchester, 20 km
Knutsford, 3 km

Annual closure Fermeture annuelle no
Weekly closure Fermeture hebdomadaire no

Fees main season Tarifs haute saison	Full day	
	Week days Semaine	**We/Bank holidays** We/Férié
Individual Individuel	£ 70	*
Couple Couple	£ 140	*

* Fridays and week-ends: members only

Caddie Caddie on request **Electric Trolley** Chariot électrique no
Buggy Voiturette yes **Clubs** Clubs yes
Credit cards Cartes de crédit
VISA - Eurocard - MasterCard - AMEX - DC

Manchester
Stretford
Warrington
Stockport Manchester
Stockport
M 56
A 556
A 50
A 5034
Bucklow Hill
Rostherne
M 6
Mere
GOLF
Northwich
Birmingham
Macclesfield
km 0 2 4
miles 0 2,5

Access Accès : Manchester, M56 Jct 7. A556 S → Northwich. Golf on left side before A50.
Map 4 on page 476 Carte 4 Page 476

GOLF COURSE
PARCOURS 15/20

Site Site
Maintenance Entretien
Architect Architecte James Braid, George Duncan
Type Type parkland
Relief Relief
Water in play Eau en jeu
Exp. to wind Exposé au vent
Trees in play Arbres en jeu

Scorecard Carte de score	**Chp.** Chp.	**Mens** Mess.	**Ladies** Da.
Length Long.	6135	5910	5192
Par	71	71	74
Slope system	—	—	—

Advised golfing ability Niveau de jeu recommandé 0 12 24 36
Hcp required Handicap exigé certificate

CLUB HOUSE & AMENITIES
CLUB HOUSE ET ANNEXES 7/10

Pro shop Pro-shop
Driving range Practice
Sheltered couvert no - On grass sur herbe no - Putting-green putting-green yes - Pitching-green pitching green yes

HOTEL FACILITIES
ENVIRONNEMENT HOTELIER 7/10

HOTELS HÔTELS
Mere Court - 34 rooms, D £ 135 - Mere 1 km
Tel (44) 01565 - 831 000, Fax (44) 01565 - 831 001

The Cottons - 109 rooms, D £ 132 (golfers) - Knutsford 3 km
Tel (44) 01565 - 650 333, Fax (44) 01565 - 755 351

Victoria and Albert - 158 rooms, D £ 135 - Manchester 20 km
Tel (44) 0161 - 832 1188, Fax (44) 0161 - 834 2484

RESTAURANTS RESTAURANTS
Belle Epoque Brasserie - Knutsford 4 km
Tel (44) 01565 - 633 060

The Market - Manchester 20 km - Tel (44) 0161 - 834 3743

Magnolia (Cottons) - Knutsford 3 km
Tel (44) 01565 - 650 333

Moor Allerton

14 | 6 | 7

With Moortown, Sand Moor and Alwoodley, Moor Allerton is the fourth member of a remarkable crop of courses just to the north of Leeds. Here, though, contrary to the typical Yorkshire moor landscape of the three others, the style is much more that of a parkland course. In 1971, the work carried out by Robert Trent Jones effected the creation of 27 holes in an American style far removed from the original layout of 1923. Hazards come in the form of trees and bunkers (well designed and located) completed by strategically placed stretches of water. To score well you will have to produce a whole range of shots, meaning that the lesser player could have a hard time of things. A few holes stick in the memory, and although there are other, more spectacular courses in the world, this one deserves a round or two. The 20,000 trees planted in recent years will obviously change the course considerably.

Avec Moortown, Sand Moor et Alwoodley, Moor Allerton constitue le quatrième élément d'un quatuor remarquable au nord de Leeds. Mais, contrairement aux trois premiers, typiques de la lande du Yorkshire, celui-ci revêt une esthétique beaucoup plus nette de parc. En 1971, le travail de Robert Trent Jones a été une véritable recréation de 27 trous avec un caractère résolument américain bien éloigné du parcours original créé en 1923, au moins pour ce qui est des aspects stratégiques. Les obstacles sont constitués par les arbres et les bunkers (très bien dessinés et placés), et complétés par quelques pièces d'eau tout aussi soigneusement placées. Il faudra développer ici toute une panoplie de coups de golf pour bien scorer, et les joueurs peu expérimentés s'y sentiront moins à l'aise que les autres. Quelques trous marquent bien la mémoire, et s'il existe à l'évidence des parcours globalement plus mémorables, celui-ci mérite d'être joué et apprécié. 20.000 arbres plantés au cours des dernières années vont modifier notablement le lieu.

Moor Allerton Golf Club — 1923

Coal Road
ENG - WIKE, LEEDS, West Yorks. LS17 9NH

Office Secrétariat (44) 01132 - 661 154
Pro shop Pro-shop (44) 01132 - 665 209
Fax Fax (44) 01132 - 680 589
Web www.magc.co.uk
Situation Situation Leeds (pop. 680 725), 5 km
Annual closure Fermeture annuelle no
Weekly closure Fermeture hebdomadaire no

Fees main season Tarifs haute saison 18 holes

	Week days / Semaine	We/Bank holidays / We/Férié
Individual Individuel	£ 52	£ 62
Couple Couple	£ 104	£ 124

Caddie Caddie on request
Electric Trolley Chariot électrique yes
Buggy Voiturette yes **Clubs** Clubs yes
Credit cards Cartes de crédit
VISA - Eurocard - MasterCard (Pro shop goods only)

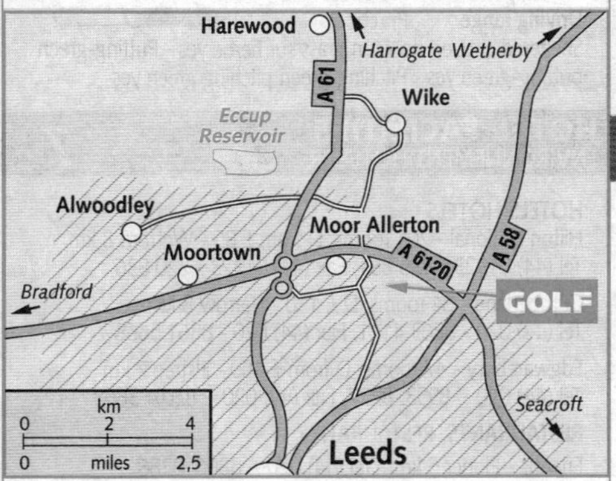

Access Accès : Leeds, A 61 → Harrogate, then A621 → Moor Allerton
Map 4 on page 476 Carte 4 Page 476

GOLF COURSE — PARCOURS 14/20

Site Site
Maintenance Entretien
Architect Architecte Robert Trent Jones
Type Type parkland
Relief Relief
Water in play Eau en jeu
Exp. to wind Exposé au vent
Trees in play Arbres en jeu

Scorecard / Carte de score	Chp. / Chp.	Mens / Mess.	Ladies / Da.
Length Long.	6157	5949	5184
Par	72	72	73
Slope system	—	—	—

Advised golfing ability 0 12 24 36
Niveau de jeu recommandé
Hcp required Handicap exigé no

CLUB HOUSE & AMENITIES — CLUB HOUSE ET ANNEXES 6/10

Pro shop Pro-shop
Driving range Practice
Sheltered couvert 7 bays - On grass sur herbe yes - Putting-green putting-green yes (2) - Pitching-green pitching green no

HOTEL FACILITIES — ENVIRONNEMENT HOTELIER 7/10

HOTELS HÔTELS
Haleys Hote - 28 rooms, D £ 140l - Headingley 4 km
Tel (44) 0113 - 278 4446, Fax (44) 0113 - 275 3342

Weetwood Hall - Leeds 6 km
106 rooms, D £ 130
Tel (44) 0113 - 230 6000, Fax (44) 0113 - 230 6095

42 The Calls - 41 rooms, D £ 160 - Leeds 6 km
Tel (44) 0113 - 244 0099, Fax (44) 0113 - 234 4100

RESTAURANTS RESTAURANTS
Leodis Brasserie - Leeds 6 km - Tel (44) 0113 - 242 1010
Brasserie Forty Four - Leeds 6 km - Tel (44) 0113 - 234 3232
The Calls Grill - Leeds 6 km - Tel (44) 0113 - 245 3870

Moor Park *High Course*

16	8	7

Originally there were three courses here, two of which have survived beneath the impressive and even intimidating shadows of the historic club-house. The shirt and tie rule is so obvious here that you're surprised to see people actually dressed in casual wear on the course. The "West Course" is on the short side but goes very well with the Championship "High" course, where from the 2nd hole onward you realise you'll need some sort of bearings or benchmarks if you are ever going to card a good score. The yardage book will come in handy for knowing where you should put your drive and for identifying the gardens where your ball should not go (especially on the front 9). A Harry Colt course is never a dull affair and this is no exception to the rule. The last nine holes are particularly memorable with three par 3s more than worthy of the designer's reputation. This is most definitely not the place where you can see that golf has become a sport for all and sundry, but it is a mighty fine course nonetheless.

Au départ, il y avait trois parcours, dont deux sont restés sous l'ombre impressionnante, et même intimidante d'un club-house historique où le port d'une cravate paraît tellement évident qu'on la gardera pour jouer (au cas où). Le "West Course" est assez court, mais constitue un bon complément au "High Course," où dès le 2, on comprend qu'il va falloir trouver ses marques pour espérer un score décent. Le "yardage book" ne sera pas inutile pour savoir où poser le drive, et pour identifier (surtout à l'aller) les jardins où il ne faut pas envoyer sa balle. Un parcours dessiné par Harry Colt n'est jamais indifférent, et celui-ci ne fait pas exception à la règle. On gardera un souvenir particulier des neuf derniers trous, avec trois par 3 à la hauteur de la réputation de l'architecte. Certes, ce n'est pas vraiment le lieu où l'on puisse constater que le golf est réellement devenu un sport démocratique, mais c'est vraiment un bon parcours !

Moor Park Golf Club — 1923

ENG - RICKMANSWORTH, Herts WD31QN

Office	Secrétariat	(44) 01923 - 773 146
Pro shop	Pro-shop	(44) 01923 - 721 673
Fax	Fax	(44) 01923 - 777 109
Web	www.moorparkgc.co.uk	
Situation	Situation	London, 35 km

Watford (pop. 74 566), 8 km

Annual closure	Fermeture annuelle	no
Weekly closure	Fermeture hebdomadaire	no

Fees main season Tarifs haute saison — 18 holes

	Week days Semaine	We/Bank holidays We/Férié
Individual Individuel	£ 77,50	*
Couple Couple	£ 155	*

Full week days: £ 105 (Booking essential)
* No visitors at week ends

Caddie Caddie on request **Electric Trolley** Chariot électrique yes
Buggy Voiturette yes **Clubs** Clubs yes
Credit cards Cartes de crédit Visa - Mastercard

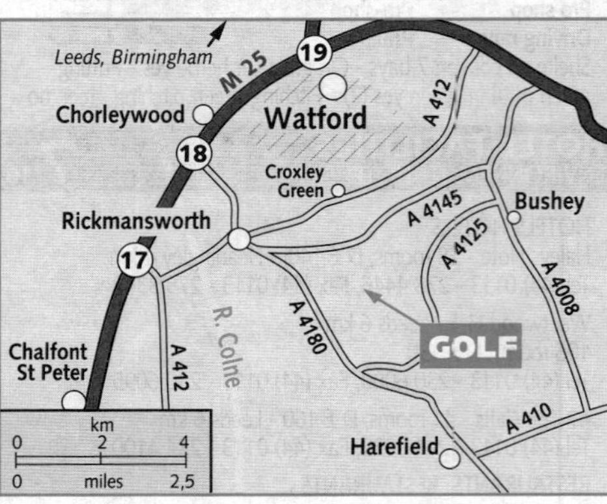

Access Accès : London, M4 Jct 3, A312, A4180, A404 → Rickmansworth, Golf on the right.
Map 8 on page 484 Carte 8 Page 484

GOLF COURSE — PARCOURS 16/20

Site	Site	
Maintenance	Entretien	
Architect	Architecte	Harry S. Colt
Type	Type	parkland
Relief	Relief	
Water in play	Eau en jeu	
Exp. to wind	Exposé au vent	
Trees in play	Arbres en jeu	

Scorecard Carte de score	Chp. Chp.	Mens Mess.	Ladies Da.
Length Long.	6045	5735	5130
Par	72	72	73
Slope system	—	—	—

Advised golfing ability Niveau de jeu recommandé — 0 12 24 36
Hcp required Handicap exigé — certificate

CLUB HOUSE & AMENITIES — CLUB HOUSE ET ANNEXES 8/10

Pro shop Pro-shop
Driving range Practice
Sheltered couvert no - On grass sur herbe yes - Putting-green putting-green yes - Pitching-green pitching green yes

HOTEL FACILITIES — ENVIRONNEMENT HOTELIER 7/10

HOTELS HÔTELS

Hilton National - 201 rooms, D from £ 85 - Watford 8 km
Tel (44) 01923 - 235 881, Fax (44) 01923 - 220 836

Cumberland - 84 rooms, D £ 110 - Harrow 8 km
Tel (44) 020 - 8863 4111, Fax (44) 020 - 8861 5668

Edgwarebury - 47 rooms, D from £ 100 - Elstree 7 km
Tel (44) 020 - 8953 8227, Fax (44) 020 - 8207 3668

RESTAURANTS RESTAURANTS

Friends - Pinner 5 km - Tel (44) 020 - 8866 0286
Trattoria Sorrentina - Harrow 8 km - Tel (44) 020 - 8427 9411

Moortown

18	7	7

Together with Alwoodley and Sand Moor (Moor Allerton is much more modern), you have three great classic courses close to Leeds, which is not the prettiest of English cities but is in a region that has a lot to be said for it, particularly the nearby city of York. At least 16 holes of the present course were designed by Alister Mackenzie, while the last two were added in 1989, giving the whole layout more than respectable yardage and leaving the original style untouched. Classic, well-landscaped and with huge greens in excellent condition, the course gives nothing away. By the same token, it doesn't steal strokes either. At Moortown you score what you deserve and score well only if you hit it straight. The Ryder Cup was played here for the first time in England (in 1929), as was a particular English Amateur Championship, where one player had to hit his third shot on the 18th from inside the club-house bar. A good place to go, but only after you have sunk that final putt.

Avec The Alwoodley et Sand Moor (Moor Allerton est beaucoup plus moderne), voici un fameux trio de parcours classiques voisins, à proximité de Leeds, qui n'est sans doute pas la plus belle ville d'Angleterre, mais la région ne manque pas de séductions, en particulier avec York. Le présent parcours a été dessiné par Alister Mackenzie. Du moins 16 trous, car deux nouveaux trous ont été ajoutés en 1989, permettant d'afficher maintenant une longueur fort respectable. Le style original n'en a pas été modifié. Classique, bien paysagé, avec de vastes greens généralement excellents, ce parcours ne fait certes pas de cadeaux, mais il ne vole non plus personne : on y fait le score que l'on mérite, si l'on a démontré la précision obligatoire ici. La Ryder Cup 1929 s'y est disputée pour la première fois en Grande-Bretagne, tout comme un English Amateur où un joueur dut taper son troisième coup du 18 depuis l'intérieur du bar. On comprend qu'il y soit allé, il est bien agréable.

Moortown Golf Club — 1909

Harrogate Road
ENG - LEEDS, W. Yorkshire LS17 7DB

Office	Secrétariat	(44) 0113 - 268 6521
Pro shop	Pro-shop	(44) 0113 - 268 3636
Fax	Fax	(44) 0113 - 268 0986
Web		www.moortown-gc.co.uk
Situation	Situation	Leeds (pop. 680 722), 8 km
Annual closure	Fermeture annuelle	no
Weekly closure	Fermeture hebdomadaire	no

Fees main season / Tarifs haute saison	Week days / Semaine	We/Bank holidays / We/Férié
		Full day
Individual Individuel	£ 65	£ 75
Couple Couple	£ 130	£ 150

Caddie Caddie no — Electric Trolley Chariot électrique yes
Buggy Voiturette yes — Clubs Clubs yes
Credit cards Cartes de crédit no

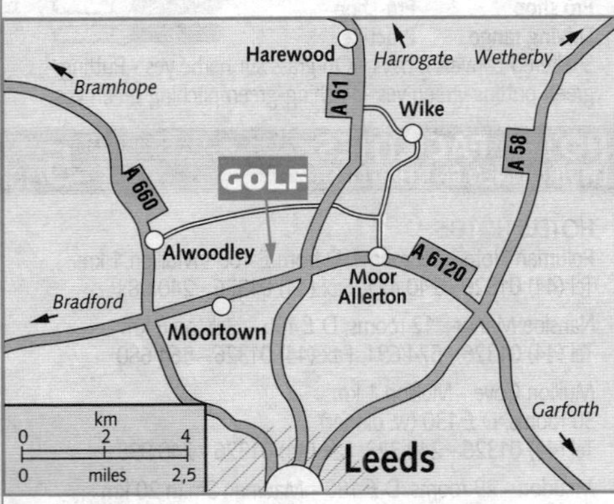

Access Accès : On A61 approx. 8 km (5 m.) N of Leeds
Map 4 on page 476 Carte 4 Page 476

GOLF COURSE — PARCOURS — 18/20

Site	Site	
Maintenance	Entretien	
Architect	Architecte	Alister Mackenzie
Type	Type	inland, moorland
Relief	Relief	
Water in play	Eau en jeu	
Exp. to wind	Exposé au vent	
Trees in play	Arbres en jeu	

Scorecard / Carte de score	Chp. / Chp.	Mens / Mess.	Ladies / Da.
Length Long.	6390	5883	5398
Par	71	72	75
Slope system	—	—	—

Advised golfing ability / Niveau de jeu recommandé: 0 12 24 36
Hcp required / Handicap exigé: certificate

CLUB HOUSE & AMENITIES — CLUB HOUSE ET ANNEXES — 7/10

Pro shop — Pro-shop
Driving range — Practice

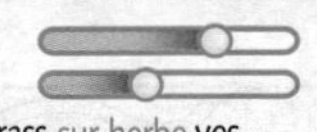

Sheltered couvert practice area - On grass sur herbe yes - Putting-green putting-green yes - Pitching-green pitching green yes

HOTEL FACILITIES — ENVIRONNEMENT HOTELIER — 7/10

HOTELS HÔTELS

The Cottages - 5 rooms, D £ 54 - Bramhope 5 km
Tel (44) 0113 - 284 2754, Fax (44) 0113 - 203 7496

42 The Calls - 41 rooms, D £ 160 - Leeds 8 km
Tel (44) 0113 - 244 0099, Fax (44) 0113 - 234 4100

Haleys Hotel - 28 rooms, D £ 140 - Headingley 8 km
Tel (44) 0113 - 278 4446, Fax (44) 0113 - 275 3342

Queens - 199 rooms, D £ 140 - Leeds 6 km
Tel (44) 0113 - 243 1323, Fax (44) 0113 - 242 5154

RESTAURANTS RESTAURANTS

Pool Court at 42 - Leeds 8 km - Tel (44) 0113 - 244 4242
Leodis - Leeds 8 km - Tel (44) 0113 - 242 1010
Brasserie Forty Four - Leeds 8 km - Tel (44) 0113 - 234 3232

Mullion

15 | 5 | 5

Before teeing it up on this, the southernmost course in England, you will have already enjoyed a very warm welcome and splendid views. The sea is a sight to behold on windy cays, when you are better off playing cards than golf, because on this huge, wide open space the wind can wreak havoc. Having said that, the weather is often fine down here and lovers of the open air and inventive golf, even if they are only average golfers, will have a great time. It might take some of them a while to reach the greens but they always get there in the end because no shot is impossible. Although a part of the course may feel a little spongy underfoot with the huge reed-beds (particularly along the 7th hole), most of the terrain is sandy and the grass excellent. A few dips and hillocks conceal the foot of the pin on occasions but the course in still very fair and open. The good holes include the 6th, the 7th lined with cross-bunkers and the 10th, a par 4 which can be terrifying to play in a head-wind. This is one of those courses where the golfer really feels very close to nature.

Avant d'aborder le parcours le plus septentrional d'Angleterre, on aura remarqué l'accueil très amical, et un panorama splendide sur les falaises et la mer, grandiose les jours de tempête : dans un espace aussi vaste, le vent peut se déchaîner. Mais il y a aussi beaucoup de beaux jours où les amateurs de grand air et d'un golf inventif s'en donneront à coeur joie, même si leur niveau de golf est moyen : s'il leur faut bien des coups pour arriver au green, aucun d'eux n'est impossible. Une partie du terrain peut parfois être spongieuse avec de vastes roselières (le long du 7 en particulier), la plus grande partie du parcours est sablonneuse, et le gazon excellent. Quelques vallonnements dissimulent certains pieds des drapeaux, mais le parcours est néanmoins d'une grande franchise. On y retiendra parmi bien des bons trous les 6, le 7 avec ses cross-bunkers, le 10 un par 4, qui peut être terrible par vent contraire. Un parcours où le sentiment de communion avec la nature est très fort.

Mullion Golf Club — 1895

ENG - CURY, HELSTON, Cornwall TR12 7BP

Office	Secrétariat	(44) 01326 - 240 685
Pro shop	Pro-shop	(44) 01326 - 241 176
Fax	Fax	(44) 01326 - 241 527
Web	www.mulliongolfclub.net	
Situation	Situation	Falmouth, 25 km
Annual closure	Fermeture annuelle	no
Weekly closure	Fermeture hebdomadaire	no
Fees main season	Tarifs haute saison	18 holes

	Week days / Semaine	We/Bank holidays / We/Férié
Individual Individuel	£ 30	£ 35
Couple Couple	£ 60	£ 70

Caddie Caddie no — **Electric Trolley** Chariot électrique yes

Buggy Voiturette yes — **Clubs** Clubs yes

Credit cards Cartes de crédit no

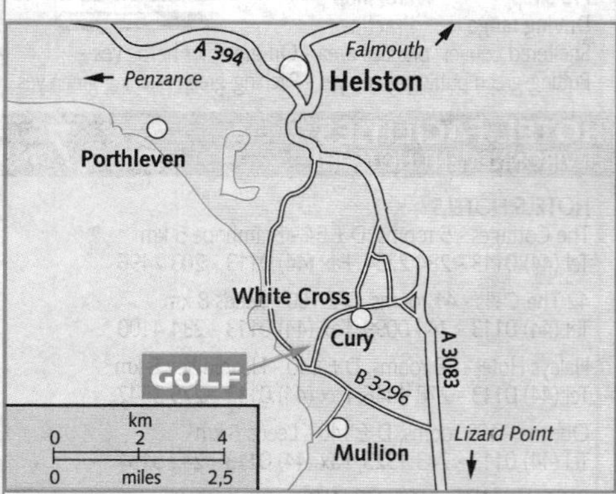

Access Accès : M4, M5 South, A30 → Penzance, → Helston. → Mullion. Follow signs to Golf course.

Map 6 on page 480 Carte 6 Page 480

GOLF COURSE — PARCOURS — 15/20

Site	Site	
Maintenance	Entretien	
Architect	Architecte	William Side
Type	Type	seaside course, open country
Relief	Relief	
Water in play	Eau en jeu	
Exp. to wind	Exposé au vent	
Trees in play	Arbres en jeu	

Scorecard / Carte de score	Chp. / Chp.	Mens / Mess.	Ladies / Da.
Length Long.	5475	5312	4899
Par	70	70	72
Slope system	—	—	—

Advised golfing ability / Niveau de jeu recommandé: 0 12 24 36

Hcp required — Handicap exigé — certificate

CLUB HOUSE & AMENITIES — CLUB HOUSE ET ANNEXES — 5/10

Pro shop — Pro-shop

Driving range — Practice

Sheltered couvert 2 bays - On grass sur herbe yes - Putting-green putting-green yes - Pitching-green pitching green yes

HOTEL FACILITIES — ENVIRONNEMENT HOTELIER — 5/10

HOTELS HÔTELS

Polurrian Hotel - 39 rooms, D from £ 160 - Mullion 1 km
Tel (44) 01326 - 240 421, Fax (44) 01326 - 240 083

Nansloe Manor - 12 rooms, D £ 195 - Helston 8 km
Tel (44) 01326 - 574 691, Fax (44) 01326 - 564 680

Mullion Cove - Mullion 1 km
30 rooms, D £ 130 (w. dinner)
Tel (44) 01326 - 240 328, Fax (44) 01326 - 240 998

Meudon - 29 rooms, D £ 180 - Mawnan Smith 20 km
Tel (44) 01326 - 250 541, Fax (44) 01326 - 250 543

RESTAURANTS RESTAURANTS

Halzephron Inn - Gunwalloe 3 km - Tel (44) 01326 - 240 406

New Zealand

16 | 6 | 7

This little gem with an odd name has kept a low profile amongst the wealth of golf-courses that grace this part of the country. It must have been hidden in a time and space warp and the members here clearly live in their own happy little hidden world. A little neglected on account of its shortness, it is still more than a match for many of the longer and more "fashionable" layouts. It was designed by Tom Simpson, which defines the excellence of this course almost by default. Invariably you will need to choose the right side of the fairway for an easier second shot into smallish but well-defended greens, and the drive is sometimes threatened by encroaching heather, but you seldom need to bring out the big guns anyway. Don't go thinking that this is an easy course: it is demandingly honest and you will need to be on top of your game to cope with the subtler aspects of Simpson-style golfing. It is the sort of wonderful old course full of bunkers that you imagine being played by a number of eccentric old characters à la P.G. Wodehouse.

Ce club au curieux nom est resté une sorte de joyau caché au milieu de la couronne de golfs de cette région. Sans doute était-il caché dans une distorsion de l'espace-temps et ses membres vivent manifestement aussi heureux que cachés. Un peu négligé parce qu'il est très court, il vaut pourtant bien des tracés plus longs et plus "fashionable". Son architecte est Tom Simpson, c'est dire par défaut la qualité du tracé, où il faudra choisir le bon côté du fairway pour faciliter ses approches vers des greens pas immenses et bien défendus. Les drives sont parfois menacés par les avancées gloutonnes de la bruyère, mais il est rarement utile de sortir la grosse artillerie. Que l'on n'aie pas l'impression que ce tracé est facile : il est franc, mais il faut un jeu bien patiné pour se sortir des subtilités du dessin. Le genre de bon vieux parcours adorable plein de bunkers sur lequel on imagine bien voir évoluer quelques personnages excentriques de P.G. Wodehouse.

New Zealand Golf Club — 1931

Woodham Lane
ENG - ADDLESTONE, Surrey KT15 3QD

Office	Secrétariat	(44) 01932 - 345 049
Pro shop	Pro-shop	(44) 01932 - 349 619
Fax	Fax	(44) 01932 - 342 891
Web	www.nzgc.org	
Situation	Situation	London, 40 km
Annual closure	Fermeture annuelle	no
Weekly closure	Fermeture hebdomadaire	no

Fees main season Tarifs haute saison	18 holes	
	Week days / Semaine	We/Bank holidays / We/Férié
Individual Individuel	£ 55	*
Couple Couple	£ 110	*

* No visitors at We

Caddie Caddie no — **Electric Trolley** Chariot électrique no
Buggy Voiturette no — **Clubs** Clubs no
Credit cards Cartes de crédit
VISA - MasterCard

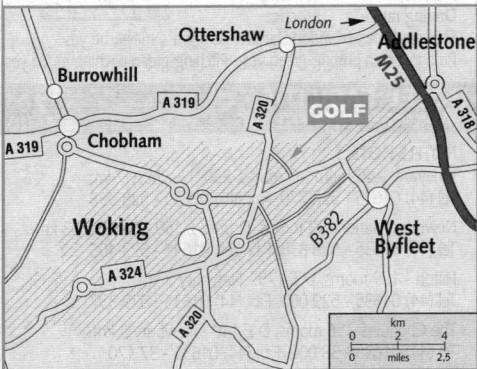

Ottershaw
London →
Addlestone
M25
Burrowhill
A 319
A 320
GOLF
A 318
A 319
Chobham
Woking
B382
West Byfleet
A 324
A 320
km 0 2 4
0 miles 2,5

Access Accès : London M25 Exit 10 → A245 → West Byfleet. Golf at the junction off Woodham Lane and Sheerwater Road
Map 8 on page 484 Carte 8 Page 484

GOLF COURSE — PARCOURS — 16/20

Site	Site	
Maintenance	Entretien	
Architect	Architecte	Tom Simpson
Type	Type	heathland, parkland
Relief	Relief	
Water in play	Eau en jeu	
Exp. to wind	Exposé au vent	
Trees in play	Arbres en jeu	

Scorecard Carte de score	Chp. Chp.	Mens Mess.	Ladies Da.
Length Long.	5468	5468	5038
Par	68	68	72
Slope system	—	—	—

Advised golfing ability 0 12 24 36
Niveau de jeu recommandé
Hcp required Handicap exigé certificate

CLUB HOUSE & AMENITIES — CLUB HOUSE ET ANNEXES — 6/10

Pro shop Pro-shop
Driving range Practice
Sheltered couvert - On grass sur herbe practice area only
Putting-green putting-green yes - Pitching-green pitching green

HOTEL FACILITIES — ENVIRONNEMENT HOTELIER — 7/10

HOTELS HÔTELS
Oatlands Park - 144 rooms, D £ 207 - Weybridge 6 km
Tel (44) 01932 - 847 242, Fax (44) 01932 - 842 252

The Ship Inn - Weybridge 6 km
39 rooms, D £ 140
Tel (44) 01932 - 848 364, Fax (44) 01932 - 857 153

Holiday Inn - Woking 3 km
161 rooms, D £ 175
Tel (44) 01483 - 221 000, Fax (44) 01483 - 221 021

RESTAURANTS RESTAURANTS
Zinfandel - Chobham 5 km - Tel (44) 01276 - 858 491
Drake's - Ripley 5 km - Tel (44) 01483 - 224 777
Casa Romana - Weybridge 6 km - Tel (44) 01932 - 223 543

Newbury & Crookham

14 | 7 | 7

Horse-racing enthusiasts will already have heard of Newbury, whose racecourse is visible from the 17th hole. But despite being so close, the ground here is far from flat although easy enough to walk. The club was founded in 1873, making it one of the oldest in England, and is still popular and busy enough to be closed to non-members on week-ends. The present course was laid out in 1923 and like many of the courses from that period, Newbury & Crookham has a lot of trees and the course is fairly short by today's standards. However despite the present lack of yardage this is definitely not a course to be taken lightly. It is a very pretty challenge with several holes of the highest order defended by some very well-placed bunkers. There is an obvious need to put your drive in the right place and we would recommend this as a "disciplinary" course for "sprayers". The trees and thick rough will soon get them back on the straight and narrow. The club-house is small and not the most cheerful place in the world, but the food is good.

Les amateurs de chevaux connaissent Newbury pour son hippodrome, que l'on aperçoit du 17. Malgré ce voisinage, le terrain n'est pas plat, même s'il est facile à jouer à pied. Le club a été fondé en 1873, ce qui en fait l'un des clubs de golf les plus anciens d'Angleterre, et qui reste très fréquenté car il n'est pas possible d'y jouer en week-end. Le parcours actuel a été tracé en 1923. Comme beaucoup de parcours de cette époque, il est abondamment pourvu d'arbres, et son dessin n'a guère été que rajeuni. Cependant, son manque de longueur actuel ne doit pas le faire sous-estimer… C'est un très joli challenge, avec plusieurs trous de premier ordre, défendus par des bunkers très bien disposés, et la nécessité de placer correctement les drives est évidente : on recommande un petit séjour "disciplinaire" pour les "arroseurs": les arbres, mais aussi un rougn épais sauront redresser leurs trajectoires. Le club-house est petit et pas très gai, mais la table est très correcte.

Newbury & Crookham Golf Club 1873/1923

Burysbank Road, Greenham
ENG - NEWBURY, Berks RG19 8BZ

Office Secrétariat (44) 01635 - 40 035
Pro shop Pro-shop (44) 01635 - 31 201
Fax Fax (44) 01635 - 40 045
Web www.newburygolf.co.uk
Situation Situation Newbury, 3 km
Reading (pop. 128 877), 25 km

Annual closure Fermeture annuelle no
Weekly closure Fermeture hebdomadaire no

Fees main season Tarifs haute saison 18 holes

	Week days Semaine	We/Bank holidays We/Férié
Individual Individuel	£ 35	*
Couple Couple	£ 70	*

Full week days: £ 40 / * No visitors at week-ends

Caddie Caddie no — **Electric Trolley** Chariot électrique no
Buggy Voiturette no — **Clubs** Clubs no

Credit cards Cartes de crédit
Visa - Mastercard (2,5 % surcharge in the bar & restaurant)

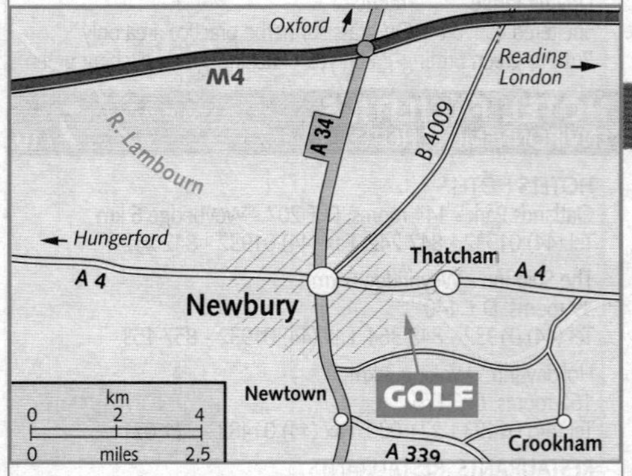

Access Accès : London, M4. Jct 13, A34 South through Newbury. Turn into Newbury Retall Park, 2.5 km SE of Newbury. Golf on left.
Map 7 on page 482 Carte 7 Page 482

GOLF COURSE
PARCOURS **14/20**

Site Site
Maintenance Entretien
Architect Architecte J.H. Turner
Type Type parkland
Relief Relief
Water in play Eau en jeu
Exp. to wind Exposé au vent
Trees in play Arbres en jeu

Scorecard Carte de score	Chp. Chp.	Mens Mess.	Ladies Da.
Length Long.	5346	5141	4745
Par	69	69	70
Slope system	—	—	—

Advised golfing ability Niveau de jeu recommandé 0 12 24 36
Hcp required Handicap exigé certificate

CLUB HOUSE & AMENITIES
CLUB HOUSE ET ANNEXES **7/10**

Pro shop Pro-shop
Driving range Practice
Sheltered couvert indoor facility - On grass sur herbe yes
Putting-green putting-green yes - Pitching-green pitching green yes

HOTEL FACILITIES
ENVIRONNEMENT HOTELIER **7/10**

HOTELS HÔTELS
Vineyard - 49 rooms, D from £ 250- Newbury 7 km
Tel (44) 01635 - 528 770, Fax (44) 01635 - 528 398

Newbury Manor - 33 rooms, D from £ 150 - Newbury 3 km
Tel (44) 01635 - 528 838, Fax (44) 01635 - 523 406

Hilton - 109 rooms, D £ 175 - Newbury 3 km
Tel (44) 01635 - 529 000, Fax (44) 01635 - 529 337

The Chequers - 56 rooms, D £ 140 - Newbury 3 km
Tel (44) 01635 - 38 000, Fax (44) 01635 - 37 170

RESTAURANTS RESTAURANTS
Vineyard - Newbury 7 km - Tel (44) 01635 - 528 770
The Red House (Pub) - Newbury 7 km
Tel (44) 01635 - 582 017

North Hants

16 | 7 | 6

With Blackmoor and Liphook, North Hants completes an excellent clan of courses in a very beautiful part of Hampshire where Harry Colt, Arthur Croome and here James Braid have left their mark. The three are very similar in style, each having been hewn out of the heather and woods. With Braid, a very great champion in his time, there is always serious emphasis on making each hole different so that the whole course forms a comprehensive examination of a player's ability. If you want to score well, you will need to manœuvre the ball both ways and while there are few dog-legs here, there is always a right side and a wrong side of the fairway, depending on pin positions. As the greens are very large and protected in proportion to the theoretical length of the approach shot, you will need to be accurate and confident. High-handicappers might not feel all that comfortable here but the majority of amateurs will have a lot of fun. North Hants looks great and plays great.

North Hants forme avec Blackmoor et Liphook une excellente famille de parcours dans cette très belle région du Hampshire, où Harry Colt, Arthur Croome et (ici) James Braid ont apposé leur sceau. Les trois sont de styles assez similaires, car la bruyère et les bois constituaient la matière à travailler. Avec Braid, qui était un très grand champion, on a toujours un grand souci de différencier chaque trou, afin que l'ensemble constitue un examen complet du joueur. Si l'on veut très bien scorer, il faut travailler la balle dans tous les sens. Et s'il y a très peu de doglegs, il y a toujours un "bon" côté du fairway suivant la position du drapeau. Comme les greens sont très grands et protégés en proportion de la longueur théorique du deuxième coup, il faudra être précis et sûr de soi. Les handicaps élevés ne seront pas très à l'aise, mais la majorité des amateurs prendra beaucoup de plaisir. North Hants est un beau et bon classique.

North Hants Golf Club — 1904

Minley Road
ENG - FLEET, Hants GU13 8BR

Office	Secrétariat	(44) 01252 - 616 443
Pro shop	Pro-shop	(44) 01252 - 616 655
Fax	Fax	(44) 01252 - 811 627
Web	www.northhantsgolf.co.uk	
Situation	Situation	Fleet, 1 km

Camberley (pop. 46 120), 4 km

Annual closure	Fermeture annuelle	no
Weekly closure	Fermeture hebdomadaire	no
Fees main season	Tarifs haute saison	18 holes

	Week days / Semaine	We/Bank holidays / We/Férié
Individual Individuel	£ 40	*
Couple Couple	£ 80	*

* Weekends: only as a guest of member / Full day: £ 55

Caddie Caddie no — **Electric Trolley** Chariot électrique no
Buggy Voiturette no — **Clubs** Clubs no

Credit cards Cartes de crédit
VISA - Eurocard - MasterCard (Pro shop goods only)

A 30
Camberley
London
4
A 327
M3
Hartley Wintney
B3013
A4
A 325
A 327
A3013
Fleet
Winchester
Farnborough
GOLF
A 323
km 0 2 4
0 miles 2,5
Farnham
Aldershot

Access Accès : London M3 Jct 4A → Fleet
Map 8 on page 484 Carte 8 Page 484

GOLF COURSE — PARCOURS 16/20

Site	Site	
Maintenance	Entretien	
Architect	Architecte	James Braid
Type	Type	inland, heathland
Relief	Relief	
Water in play	Eau en jeu	
Exp. to wind	Exposé au vent	
Trees in play	Arbres en jeu	

Scorecard Carte de score	Chp. Chp.	Mens Mess.	Ladies Da.
Length Long.	5631	5480	4905
Par	69	69	71
Slope system	—	—	—

Advised golfing ability Niveau de jeu recommandé — 0 12 24 36
Hcp required Handicap exigé — 24

CLUB HOUSE & AMENITIES — CLUB HOUSE ET ANNEXES 7/10

Pro shop Pro-shop
Driving range Practice
Sheltered couvert no - On grass sur herbe yes - Putting-green putting-green yes - Pitching-green pitching green no

HOTEL FACILITIES — ENVIRONNEMENT HOTELIER 6/10

HOTELS HÔTELS

Frimley Hall - Camberley 6 km
86 rooms, D £ 170
Tel (44) 0870 - 400 8224, Fax (44) 01276 - 691 253

Premier Travel Inn - Farnborough 6 km
40 rooms, D £ 50
Tel (44) 01252 - 546 654, Fax (44) 01252 - 546 427

Falcon - 30 rooms, D £ 110 - Farnborough 6 km
Tel (44) 01252 - 545 378, Fax (44) 01252 - 522 539

RESTAURANTS RESTAURANTS

Wings Cottage - Farnborough 6 km - Tel (44) 01252 - 544 141
Lismoyne - Fleet 4 km - Tel (44) 01252 - 628 555

Northamptonshire

16	6	6

If it were to be found near London and not in the middle of nowhere (apologies to the local inhabitants), there is no doubt that this course – a classic heathland layout from Harry Colt in his early style – would be ranked in the British top 100. Under-estimated through being little known or unknown, NC is still one of the finest examples of this style of architecture, the most spectacular demonstration of which are the bunkers, placed and designed to perfection. The grief of ending up in one is quickly compensated by the pleasure of putting on greens that are as subtle as they are perfectly well defended. When the pins are teasingly placed in the corners, you are in for some very interesting short-game situations. Total yardage is respectable for a par 70 and, while driving is never severely demanding, you are straightaway challenged as the course starts out with a very stern par 4, followed by a hazardous stretch between holes N° 10 and 14. It all ends with a par 5 and a good birdie opportunity to celebrate at the bar… with a nice pint of mineral water, of course.

S'il se trouvait près de Londres et non pas de Nulle Part (pardon à ses habitants), ce parcours – un classique "heathland" de Harry Colt première manière – serait dans le Top-100 britannique. Sous-estimé parce que mal connu, c'est pourtant l'un des meilleurs exemples du style de l'architecte, et les bunkers du lieu en sont la démonstration la plus spectaculaire, par leur position et leur dessin. Le regret de s'y trouver sera vite compensé par le plaisir de putter sur des greens aussi subtils que bien protégés. Et quand les drapeaux sont un peu rangés dans les coins, les situations de petit jeu peuvent s'avérer très intéressantes. La longueur de ce parcours est très honorable pour un par 70, et si le driving présente peu de danger, on peut vite prendre peur car on commence par un très solide par 4, avec un passage dangereux du 10 au 14 (derrière la voie ferrée), pour finir avec un par 5 qui réserve une belle chance de birdie à fêter au bar... avec une bonne pinte d'eau minérale bien sûr.

Northamptonshire County Golf Club 1910

Golf Lane, Church Brampton
ENG - NORTHAMPTON, Northamptonshire NN6 8AZ

Office	Secrétariat	(44) 01604 - 843 025
Pro shop	Pro-shop	(44) 01604 - 842 226
Fax	Fax	(44) 01604 - 843 463
Web	www.countygolfclub.org.uk	
Situation	Situation	Northampton, 6 km
Annual closure	Fermeture annuelle	no
Weekly closure	Fermeture hebdomadaire	no
Fees main season	Tarifs haute saison	18 holes

	Week days Semaine	We/Bank holidays We/Férié
Individual Individuel	£ 40	*
Couple Couple	£ 80	*

* Not at We / Full week days: £ 60

Caddie Caddie no — **Electric Trolley** Chariot électrique no
Buggy Voiturette yes — **Clubs** Clubs yes
Credit cards Cartes de crédit
VISA - MasterCard

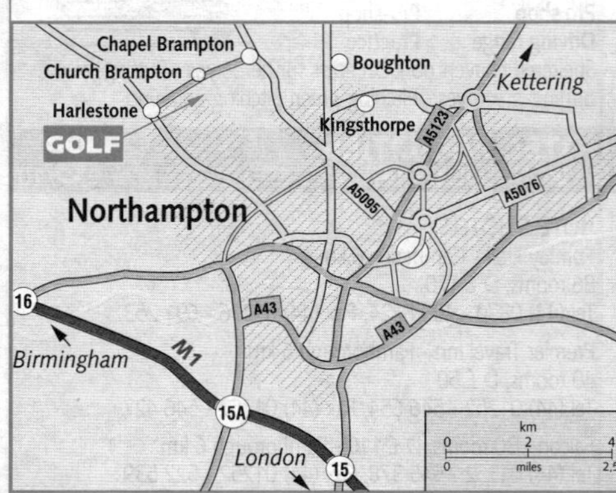

Access Accès : Northampton, A 428 NW. After Harlestone, turn right → Church Brampton, golf on right hand side
Map 7 on page 482 Carte 7 Page 482

GOLF COURSE — PARCOURS 16/20

Site	Site	
Maintenance	Entretien	
Architect	Architecte	Harry S. Colt
Type	Type	heathland
Relief	Relief	
Water in play	Eau en jeu	
Exp. to wind	Exposé au vent	
Trees in play	Arbres en jeu	

Scorecard Carte de score	Chp. Chp.	Mens Mess.	Ladies Da.
Length Long.	5884	5604	5247
Par	70	70	70
Slope system	—	—	—

Advised golfing ability / Niveau de jeu recommandé: 0 12 24 36
Hcp required / Handicap exigé: certificate

CLUB HOUSE & AMENITIES — CLUB HOUSE ET ANNEXES 6/10

Pro shop Pro-shop
Driving range Practice
Sheltered couvert no - On grass sur herbe practice area only - Putting-green putting-green yes - Pitching-green pitching green

HOTEL FACILITIES — ENVIRONNEMENT HOTELIER 6/10

HOTELS HÔTELS
Broomhill Country House - 13 rooms, D £ 95 - Spratton 5 km
Tel (44) 01604 - 845 959, Fax (44) 01604 - 845 834

Northampton Marriott - Northampton 12 km
120 rooms, D from £ 135
Tel (44) 01604 - 768 700, Fax (44) 01604 - 769 011

Hilton Northampton - Northampton 12 km
139 rooms, D £ 240
Tel (44) 01604 - 700 666, Fax (44) 01604 - 702 850

RESTAURANTS RESTAURANTS
Broomhill Country House - Spratton 5 km
Tel (44) 01604 - 845 959
Mediterraneo (Marriott) - Northampton 12 km
Tel (44) 0870 - 400 7252

Notts (Hollinwell)

18	6	6

The magnificent course at Hollinwell is often referred to as one of the best inland challenges in England. It is in a superb setting deep in the countryside with a good old club-house the way we all like them. Designed by Willie Park Jr., and given bunkers by J.H. Taylor, this splendidly modeled course is typical of a heath land layout that plots its way through silver birches and oak trees. There is hardly any water to speak of, but where there is it poses a threat to every card. Tackle the eighth hole from the back tee and you will see what we mean. From the back tees in fact, the course is the sort of monster generally reserved for the more talented players who have the ability to flight the ball. It is more forgiving from the front tees, which for the ladies in particular are even too far forward. One of Hollinwell's greatest attributes is that it is a course for the purist, prompting a rhythm of play where there is no place for poor shots after a fairly benevolent opening hole. You are never called upon to play the same shot twice running, which is why members and visitors love playing here.

Ce magnifique parcours est souvent cité en référence parmi les très grands parcours "inland" d'Angleterre, dans un paysage magnifique, avec un bon vieux club-house comme on les aime. Dessiné par Willie Park Jr., le bunkering ayant ensuite été fait par J.H. Taylor, c'est un parcours bien modelé et typique des terres de bruyère, insinué entre les bouleaux blancs et les chênes. L'eau y est peu abondante, mais elle pose alors bien des problèmes pour les scores. Jouez le 8 des départs arrière et vous comprendrez ! En règle générale, c'est une sorte de monstre, et jouer du fond est réservé aux joueurs de haut niveau qui savent manoeuvrer la balle. Le parcours est plus doux des départs avancés – un peu trop pour les dames. Notts est aussi un très grand parcours par le rythme qu'il impose, parce qu'il ne supporte pas les coups médiocres après un premier trou indulgent, et parce que l'on ne joue jamais deux fois le même coup deux fois de suite. Membres et visiteurs s'y régalent...

Notts Golf Club Hollinwell — 1887

Hollinwell, Derby Road
ENG - KIRBY-IN-ASHFIELD, Notts NG17 7QR

Office Secrétariat (44) 01623 - 753 225
Pro shop Pro-shop (44) 01623 - 753 087
Fax Fax (44) 01623 - 753 655
Web www.nottsgolfclub.co.uk
Situation Situation Nottingham, 20 km
Annual closure Fermeture annuelle no
Weekly closure Fermeture hebdomadaire no

Fees main season Tarifs haute saison		18 holes
	Week days Semaine	**We/Bank holidays** We/Férié
Individual Individuel	£ 60	£ 60
Couple Couple	£ 120	£ 120

Full day: £ 90

Caddie Caddie on request **Electric Trolley** Chariot électrique yes
Buggy Voiturette yes **Clubs** Clubs on request
Credit cards Cartes de crédit
Visa - Mastercard (Pro Shop goods only)

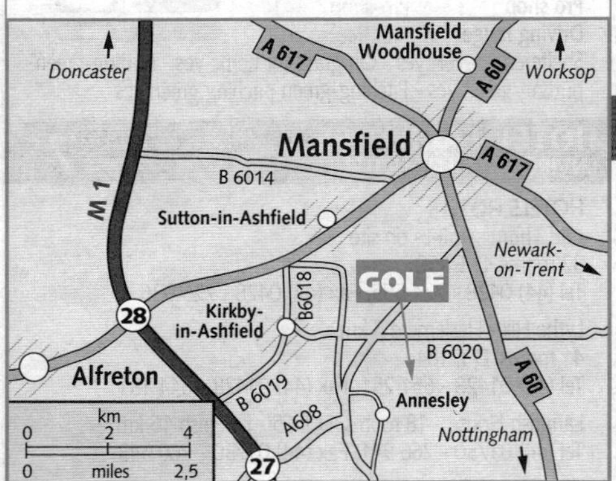

Access Accès : M1 Jct 27. A608 then A611 → Kirby, Mansfield. Golf 3 km on the right.
Map 4 on page 476 Carte 4 Page 476

GOLF COURSE — 18/20
PARCOURS

Site Site
Maintenance Entretien
Architect Architecte Willie Park Jr.
Type Type inland
Relief Relief
Water in play Eau en jeu
Exp. to wind Exposé au vent
Trees in play Arbres en jeu

Scorecard Carte de score	Chp. Chp.	Mens Mess.	Ladies Da.
Length Long.	6398	6250	5187
Par	72	72	74
Slope system	—	—	—

Advised golfing ability Niveau de jeu recommandé 0 12 24 36
Hcp required Handicap exigé certificate

CLUB HOUSE & AMENITIES — 6/10
CLUB HOUSE ET ANNEXES

Pro shop Pro-shop
Driving range Practice
Sheltered couvert practice area - On grass sur herbe yes - Putting-green putting-green yes - Pitching-green pitching green yes

HOTEL FACILITIES — 6/10
ENVIRONNEMENT HOTELIER

HOTELS HÔTELS
Pine Lodge - 20 rooms, D £ 65 - Mansfield 8 km
Tel (44) 01623 - 622 308, Fax (44) 01623 - 656 819

Renaissance Derby - South Normanton 8 km
158 rooms, D £ 138
Tel (44) 01773 - 812 000, Fax (44) 01773 - 580 032

Royal Moat House - 210 rooms, D £ 135 - Nottingham 20 km
Tel (44) 0115 - 936 9988, Fax (44) 0115 - 969 1506

RESTAURANTS RESTAURANTS
Renaissance Derby - South Normanton 8 km
Tel (44) 01773 - 812 000
Restaurant Sat Bains - Nottingham 20 km
Tel (44) 0115 - 986 6566
Sonny's - Nottingham 20 km - Tel (44) 0115 - 947 3041

Old Thorns

14	7	7

The Kosaido group, which owns Old Thorns, is also the proprietor of Ambrosiano in Italy, the Dusseldorf International and Les Bordes in France, one of the finest courses in continental Europe. Old Thorns was laid out in 1981 by Dave Thomas and Peter Alliss in an attractive, not to say spectacular, site where trees abound. It is a good and honest test of golf without ever being truly stunning. The most surprising aspect is the water, given that generally speaking water hazards are few and far between on moor-land. You will have to keep your wits about you to keep out of them. Another surprise is that the course is not so long, despite being a fairly recent layout. The objective was certainly not to scare away long-hitters. However, Old Thorns is also a good course for people who are looking not only for a good golf course… The restaurant, hotel, general ambience, tennis courts and beauty care centre are all pleasant and relaxing facilities. When dad is playing golf, mum never gets bored.

Le groupe Kosaido est propriétaire d'Old Thorns, d'Ambrosiano en Italie, de Dusseldorf International et des Bordes en France, l'un des tout meilleurs parcours en Europe continentale. Celui-ci a été créé en 1981 par Dave Thomas et Peter Alliss dans un site attrayant, sinon spectaculaire, abondamment arboré . C'est un bon et honnête test de golf, sans être vraiment spectaculaire. Ce sont les obstacles d'eau les plus étonnants, dans la mesure où il n'y en a généralement peu ou pas dans les terres de bruyère. Il ne faudra d'ailleurs rien négliger pour les éviter. Au passage, on peut être surpris que le parcours ne soit pas si long – car il est récent, l'objectif n'était sans doute pas de chasser les longs frappeurs. Mais c'est aussi un bon parcours pour ceux qui ne recherchent pas seulement un bon parcours ! Le restaurant, l'hôtel, l'ambiance générale, le tennis, le centre de soins de beauté sont à la fois plaisants et relaxants. Quand Monsieur est au golf, Madame ne s'ennuiera pas.

Old Thorns Hotel, Golf & CC — 1981

Grigg's Green
ENG - LIPHOOK, Hampshire GU30 7PE

Office Secrétariat (44) 0428 - 724 555
Pro shop Pro-shop (44) 0428 - 724 555
Fax Fax (44) 0428 - 725 036
Web www.oldthorns.com
Situation Situation London, 85 km
Annual closure Fermeture annuelle no
Weekly closure Fermeture hebdomadaire no

Fees main season Tarifs haute saison — 18 holes

	Week days / Semaine	We/Bank holidays / We/Férié
Individual Individuel	£ 55	£ 75
Couple Couple	£ 110	£ 150

After 15:00, £ 20 / 30 (We)

Caddie Caddie no — **Electric Trolley** Chariot électrique no
Buggy Voiturette yes — **Clubs** Clubs yes
Credit cards Cartes de crédit
VISA - MasterCard - AMEX

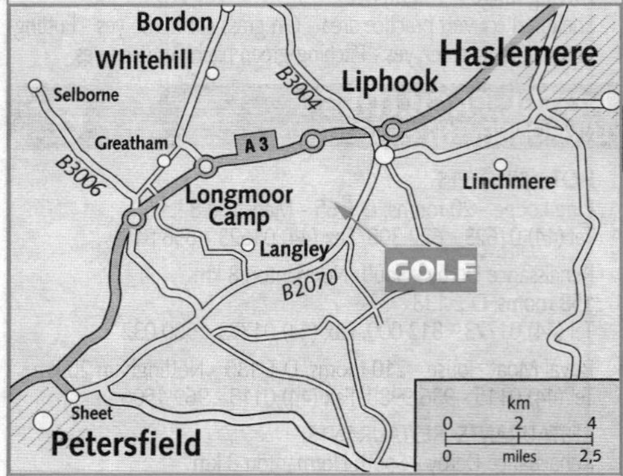

Access Accès : London A3 → Portsmouth. Exit Liphook, then Longmoor Road. Golf 2 km after Liphook
Map 7 on page 482 Carte 7 Page 482

GOLF COURSE — PARCOURS — 14/20

Site Site
Maintenance Entretien
Architect Architecte — Peter Alliss, Dave Thomas
Type Type — heathland, parkland
Relief Relief
Water in play Eau en jeu
Exp. to wind Exposé au vent
Trees in play Arbres en jeu

Scorecard / Carte de score	Chp. / Chp.	Mens / Mess.	Ladies / Da.
Length Long.	5815	5415	4842
Par	72	72	73
Slope system	—	—	—

Advised golfing ability Niveau de jeu recommandé — 0 12 24 36
Hcp required Handicap exigé — no

CLUB HOUSE & AMENITIES — CLUB HOUSE ET ANNEXES — 7/10

Pro shop Pro-shop
Driving range Practice
Sheltered couvert yes - On grass sur herbe yes - Putting-green putting-green yes - Pitching-green pitching green yes

HOTEL FACILITIES — ENVIRONNEMENT HOTELIER — 7/10

HOTELS HÔTELS
Old Thorns Hotel - on site
32 rooms, D £ 150
Tel (44) 0428 - 724 555, Fax (44) 0428 - 725 036

Lythe Hill - Haslemere 7 km
41 rooms, D £ 184
Tel (44) 01428 - 651 251, Fax (44) 01428 - 644 131

Langrish House - 18 rooms, D £ 65 - Langrish 15 km
Tel (44) 01730 - 266 941, Fax (44) 01730 - 260 543

RESTAURANTS RESTAURANTS
Old Thorns Hotel - on site - Tel (44) 0428 - 724 555
JSW (Watkins) - Petersfield 15 km - Tel (44) 01730 - 262 030
Mulchrone's - Petersfield 15 km - Tel (44) 0428 - 231 295

Orchardleigh

15 | 7 | 6

Close to Bath, this is an ambitious resort with plans for a second course, a hotel, swimming pool and tennis courts all set within a listed Victorian manor. Designed by Brian Huggett with the help of Peter McEvoy, it is a course you will want to get to know. A little on the hilly side with a lot of water in play on six holes, Orchardleigh is a blatantly American style course calling for some "target golf" to hit the greens. We are a far cry from the traditional "down to earth" game, but the demands of present-day golfers and the nature of available sites mean that is the way golf seems to be moving in England. So there are few trees in play but a lot of fairway bunkers, as dangerous as water for high-handicappers (which is a bit of shame). On a peaceful site rich in wildlife and neatly landscaped, this is a sound layout which from a technical angle is very interesting to discover and play.

A proximité de Bath, c'est un complexe ambitieux, avec un projet de second parcours, un hôtel, une piscine et des tennis, mais le tout dans l'environnement d'un petit manoir victorien classé… d'où nombre de problèmes! Dessiné par Brian Huggett avec l'aide de Peter McEvoy c'est un parcours à connaître. Assez vallonné, mais sans excès, il présente beaucoup d'obstacles d'eau (en jeu sur un tiers des trous), ce qui donne à l'évidence un style américain que la nécessité de jouer du "jeu de cibles" vers les greens accentue encore. Nous sommes loin du "jeu à terre" de la tradition, mais l'exigence des golfeurs d'aujourd'hui, comme la nature des terrains disponibles imposent cette tendance : on trouve ainsi peu d'arbres en jeu, mais de nombreux bunkers de fairway, aussi dangereux que l'eau pour les hauts handicaps (c'est un peu dommage). Dans un site tranquille, riche en vie sauvage et bien paysagé, c'est une solide réalisation, techniquement très intéressante à découvrir et jouer.

Orchardleigh Golf Club — 1996

Near Frome
ENG - BATH, Somerset BA11 2PH

Office Secrétariat (44) 01373 - 454 200
Pro shop Pro-shop (44) 01373 - 454 200
Fax Fax (44) 01373 - 454 202
Web www.orchardleighgolf.co.uk
Situation Situation Frome, 3.5 km
Bath (pop. 78 689), 18 km

Annual closure Fermeture annuelle no
Weekly closure Fermeture hebdomadaire no

Fees main season Tarifs haute saison	18 holes	
	Week days Semaine	**We/Bank holidays** We/Férié
Individual Individuel	£ 30	£ 40
Couple Couple	£ 60	£ 80

Full week days: £ 40

Caddie Caddie on request **Electric Trolley** Chariot électrique no
Buggy Voiturette yes **Clubs** Clubs yes
Credit cards Cartes de crédit
VISA - MasterCard

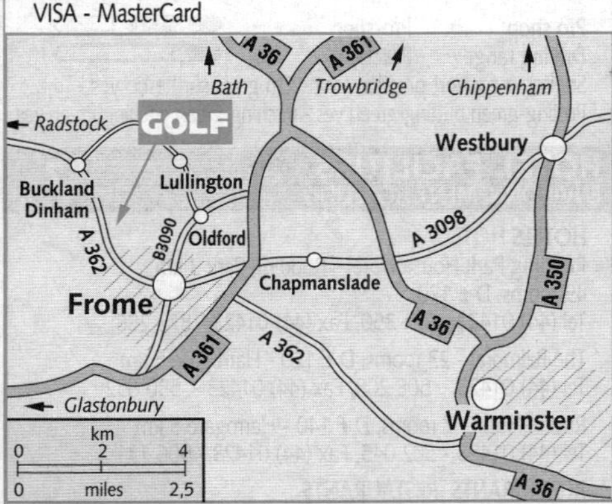

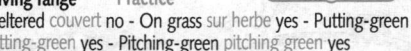

Access Accès : M4 Jct 18, A46 to Bath, then A36 to Frome then A362 → Radstock. 3.5 km NW of Frome, main entrance on right side, before village of Buckland Dinham.
Map 6 on page 481 Carte 6 Page 481

GOLF COURSE — PARCOURS 15/20

Site Site
Maintenance Entretien
Architect Architecte Brian Huggett
Type Type inland, parkland
Relief Relief
Water in play Eau en jeu
Exp. to wind Exposé au vent
Trees in play Arbres en jeu

Scorecard Carte de score	**Chp.** Chp.	**Mens** Mess.	**Ladies** Da.
Length Long.	6198	5691	5026
Par	72	72	73
Slope system	—	—	—

Advised golfing ability Niveau de jeu recommandé 0 12 24 36
Hcp required Handicap exigé no

CLUB HOUSE & AMENITIES — CLUB HOUSE ET ANNEXES 7/10

Pro shop Pro-shop
Driving range Practice
Sheltered couvert no - **On grass** sur herbe yes - **Putting-green** putting-green yes - **Pitching-green** pitching green yes

HOTEL FACILITIES — ENVIRONNEMENT HOTELIER 6/10

HOTELS HÔTELS
Babington House - 27 rooms, D £ 285 - Frome 1 km
Tel (44) 01373 - 812 266, Fax (44) 01373 - 812 112

Royal Crescent - 45 rooms, D £ 290- Bath 18 km
Tel (44) 01225 - 823 333, Fax (44) 01225 - 447 427

Bloomfield House - 6 rooms, D from £ 100 - Bath 18 km
Tel (44) 01225 - 420 105, Fax (44) 01225 - 481 958

RESTAURANTS RESTAURANTS
Mulberry (Charlton House) - Shepton Mallet 12 km
Tel (44) 01749 - 342 008
Babington House - Frome 1 km - Tel (44) 01373 - 812 266
Bowlish House - Shepton Mallet 12 km
Tel (44) 01749 - 342 022

Pannal

16 | 6 | 7

Yorkshire has more delights to offer than just Yorkshire pudding (which for non-English readers is a sort of batter pastry served with roast-beef especially on a Sunday). There are also excellent golf courses, some majestic scenery, castles and abbeys aplenty and the hot springs of Harrogate, which were particularly popular before the first world war. But before trying out the city's superb baths, spend a day on this very fine course, laid out on a plateau overlooking the region originally laid out by Sandy Herd then restyled by Charles MacKenzie in 1935. This is a typical Yorkshire moorland course, very exposed to the wind but with a lot of trees. The difficulties lie with the thickness of the rough and your score will depend more than usual on how well you drive. Despite the slopes, the course is not tiring to walk, only one green and one drive are blind and only a few elevated greens call for high approach shots. Otherwise you can practice your newly acquired art of rolling the ball onto the green. Green-keeping is very good, the club-house elegant and cosy.

Qu'on le sache, le Yorkshire Pudding n'est pas un dessert, mais une pâte à choux servie avec le rôti du dimanche. Le Yorkshire a d'autre spécialités, dont les châteaux et abbayes, les bons golfs et les sources thermales à Harrogate, très en activité avant la Grande Guerre. Avant de vous remettre au superbe Sauna Turc de la ville, vous pourrez vous dépenser sur ce très beau parcours, dessiné sur un plateau dominant la région par Sandy Herd et retravaillé en 1935 par Charles Mackenzie. C'est un parcours typique des landes du Comté, très exposé au vent, mais bien arboré. Les difficultés principales tiennent à la densité du rough, et la qualité du drive commande celle du score. En dépit du relief, le parcours n'est pas épuisant, on ne trouve qu'un seul drive et un seul green aveugles, et seules quelques greens surélevés qui appellent des balles levées. Autrement, on peut se livrer à l'amour des balles tendues et des approches roulées. L'entretien est excellent, le club-house élégant et chaleureux.

Pannal Golf Club — 1906

Follifoot Road
ENG - HARROGATE, Yorkshire HG3 1ES

Office Secrétariat (44) 01423 - 872 628
Pro shop Pro-shop (44) 01423 - 872 620
Fax Fax (44) 01423 - 870 043
Web www.pannalgc.co.uk
Situation Situation Leeds, 21 km
Harrogate (pop. 143 530), 4 km

Annual closure Fermeture annuelle — no
Weekly closure Fermeture hebdomadaire — no

Fees main season Tarifs haute saison — 18 holes

	Week days / Semaine	We/Bank holidays / We/Férié
Individual Individuel	£ 41	£ 51
Couple Couple	£ 82	£ 102

Full week days: £ 50

Caddie Caddie no — **Electric Trolley** Chariot électrique yes
Buggy Voiturette no — **Clubs** Clubs no

Credit cards Cartes de crédit
VISA - Eurocard - MasterCard (Pro shop & green fees)

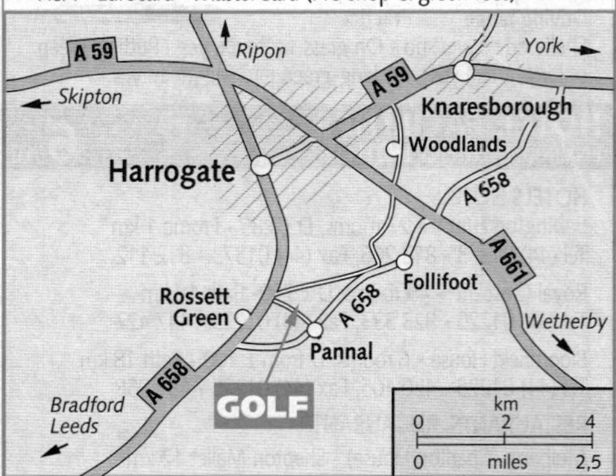

Access Accès : A61 Leeds → Harrogate.
Map 4 on page 476 Carte 4 Page 476

GOLF COURSE — PARCOURS 16/20

Site Site
Maintenance Entretien
Architect Architecte — Sandy Herd, Charles MacKenzie
Type Type — moorland
Relief Relief
Water in play Eau en jeu
Exp. to wind Exposé au vent
Trees in play Arbres en jeu

Scorecard / Carte de score	Chp. / Chp.	Mens / Mess.	Ladies / Da.
Length Long.	5960	5808	5237
Par	72	72	74
Slope system	—	—	—

Advised golfing ability Niveau de jeu recommandé — 0 12 24 36
Hcp required Handicap exigé — 24 Men, 28 Ladies

CLUB HOUSE & AMENITIES — CLUB HOUSE ET ANNEXES 6/10

Pro shop Pro-shop
Driving range Practice
Sheltered couvert practice area - On grass sur herbe yes - Putting-green putting-green yes - Pitching-green pitching green yes

HOTEL FACILITIES — ENVIRONNEMENT HOTELIER 7/10

HOTELS HÔTELS
Rudding Park House Hotel - Rudding Park 3 km
49 rooms, D £ 170
Tel (44) 01423 - 871 350, Fax (44) 01423 - 872 286

The Balmoral - 23 rooms, D £ 120 - Harrogate 5 km
Tel (44) 01423 - 508 208, Fax (44) 01423 - 530 652

Ruskin Hotel - 7 rooms, D £ 140 - Harrogate 5 km
Tel (44) 01423 - 502 045, Fax (44) 01423 - 506 131

RESTAURANTS RESTAURANTS
The Boar's Head - Harrogate 5 km - Tel (44) 01423 - 771 888
Clocktower Brasserie - Rudding Park 3 km
Tel (44) 01423 - 872 100
Drum & Monkey - Harrogate 5 km - Tel (44) 01423 - 502 650

Parkstone

16 | 7 | 8

The best time to come here is in late Spring to see how the rhododendrons add colour to the picturesque landscape of heather and pine, or to listen to the ducks quacking as your ball splashes into its watery grave. Parkstone is virtually in town, between Poole and Bournemouth, one of England's most popular seaside resorts. But everything is tranquil in a pretty setting where you feel so privileged to be walking the fairways that it is almost unthinkable not to play well. Yet Willie Park and Harry Colt used their combined talents to set traps and decorate their work of art with heather from where a decent recovery is nigh on impossible. High-handicappers will certainly not consider this to be a holiday course, but after all there is something to be said for being thrown in at the deep end. They'll learn that this is a good course and if they make it to the 18th (a big par 3) they will do the same as everyone else, take one shot more than they expected. The loss (and planned removal) of many trees has opened up the course a little and made the wind a more dominant factor.

Il faut venir au printemps quand les rhododendrons ajoutent leurs couleurs de fête au paysage de bruyères et de pins, et les canards leurs cris de joie quand les balles de golf font des ronds dans l'eau. Parkstone est pratiquement en ville, entre Poole et Bournemouth, une des stations balnéaires les plus fréquentées d'Angleterre. Mais on est ici au calme, dans un joli paysage où il est impossible de mal jouer tant on a le sentiment d'être privilégié. Pourtant, Willie Park et Harry Colt se sont ingéniés à tendre des pièges, à décorer leur oeuvre de bruyère dont il est impossible de sortir dignement. Les handicaps un peu élevés ne vont pas trouver qu'il s'agisse d'un parcours de vacances, mais après tout, il faut d'abord apprendre à nager, même au golf. Qu'ils apprennent seulement ce qu'est un bon parcours. Au 18 (un gros par 3), ils feront comme tout le monde, un coup de plus qu'ils n'espérent. La perte de nombreux arbres a donné au vent un rôle inusité, mais ils seront remplacés..

Parkstone Golf Club — 1910

Links Road, Parkstone
ENG - POOLE, Dorset BH14 9QS

Office Secrétariat (44) 01202 - 707 138
Pro shop Pro-shop (44) 01202 - 708 092
Fax Fax (44) 01202 - 706 027
Web www.parkstonegolfclub.co.uk
Situation Situation Poole, 2 km
Bournemouth (pop. 151 302), 3 km

Annual closure Fermeture annuelle — no
Weekly closure Fermeture hebdomadaire — no

Fees main season Tarifs haute saison — 18 holes

	Week days Semaine	We/Bank holidays We/Férié
Individual Individuel	£ 50	£ 60
Couple Couple	£ 100	£ 120

Full days: £ 75 and £ 85 (We)

Caddie Caddie no — **Electric Trolley** Chariot électrique yes
Buggy Voiturette no — **Clubs** Clubs yes

Credit cards Cartes de crédit
VISA - MasterCard (Pro shop & Green fees)

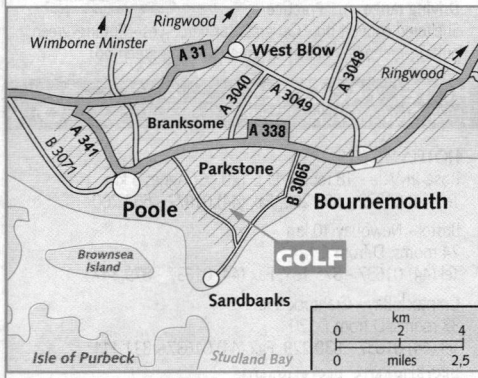

Access Accès : A35 Bournemouth → Poole.
Turn left on St Osmunds Road
Map 6 on page 481 Carte 6 Page 481

GOLF COURSE — PARCOURS 16/20

Site Site
Maintenance Entretien
Architect Architecte — Willie Park, James Braid
Type Type — forest, heathland
Relief Relief
Water in play Eau en jeu
Exp. to wind Exposé au vent
Trees in play Arbres en jeu

Scorecard Carte de score	Chp. Chp.	Mens Mess.	Ladies Da.
Length Long.	5690	5405	4952
Par	72	71	71
Slope system	—	—	—

Advised golfing ability Niveau de jeu recommandé — 0 12 24 36
Hcp required Handicap exigé — certificate

CLUB HOUSE & AMENITIES — CLUB HOUSE ET ANNEXES 7/10

Pro shop Pro-shop
Driving range Practice
Sheltered couvert yes - On grass sur herbe yes - Putting-green putting-green yes - Pitching-green pitching green yes

HOTEL FACILITIES — ENVIRONNEMENT HOTELIER 8/10

HOTELS HÔTELS
Haven - 77 rooms, D from £ 185 - Sandbanks 2 km
Tel (44) 01202 - 707 333, Fax (44) 01202 - 708 796

Mansion House - 32 rooms, D £ 135 - Poole 2 km
Tel (44) 01202 - 685 666, Fax (44) 01202 - 665 709

East Cliff Court - 67 rooms, D £ 140 - Bournemouth 2 km
Tel (44) 01202 - 554 545, Fax (44) 01202 - 557 456

Miramar - 43 rooms, D £ 120 - Bournemouth 2 km
Tel (44) 01202 - 556 581, Fax (44) 01202 - 291 242

RESTAURANTS RESTAURANTS
La Roche - Sandbanks 2 km - Tel (44) 01202 - 707 333
Benjamin's (Mansion H.) - Poole 2 km - Tel (44) 01202 - 685 666

Perranporth

15 | 6 | 6

The cliffs and reefs of the west coast of Cornwall sometimes give way to little bays and fine beaches, such as here and the neighbouring holiday resort of Newquay, a surfer's paradise. It's also pretty good for golfers, too, who should make it along here and visit a links course that is almost capable of being mentioned in the same breath as St Enodoc and Trevose. You are in for a relatively easy round if you don't stray from the fairways, but it's a big "if". The "short stuff" is very tight, hilly (with dips, bumps, mounds and hillocks) and difficult to hit. After climbing up the dunes, you now find yourself in long grass from where good scoring can pose something of a problem. At first glance you might think this an easy course, as there are very few bunkers. Paradoxically it is easier for mid-handicappers than it is for better players, who often prefer to play their approach shots out of sand rather than in thick grass. The club-house has been refurbished and in the absence of an on-site hotel a number of well-equipped caravans are available to golfers.

Les falaises et écueils de la côte de Cornouailles laissent parfois place à de petites criques et même des plages, où se trouvent des stations de vacances comme Newquay, paradis des surfeurs, mais aussi des golfeurs, qui se doivent de venir ici comme à St Enodoc et Trevose. Si l'on ne quitte pas les fairways, le jeu y sera relativement aisé. Mais ils sont très étroits, mouvementés (des creux et des bosses, des petites buttes et monticules), et on s'en écarte un peu trop facilement. Après avoir grimpé dans les dunes, on se retrouve alors dans des herbes bien hautes, d'où un bon score devient problématique. En apparence, il s'agit d'un parcours facile, car les bunkers sont peu nombreux : il est paradoxalement plus rassurant pour les handicaps moyens que pour les bons, qui préfèrent souvent jouer leurs balles dans le sable que dans l'herbe haute... Le club-house a été rénové, et, faute d'hôtel sur place, des caravanes bien équipées sont à disposition des golfeurs !

Perranporth Golf Club — 1929

The Clubhouse, Budnic Hill
ENG - PERRANPORTH, Cornwall TR6 0AB

Office	Secrétariat	(44) 01872 - 573 701
Pro shop	Pro-shop	(44) 01872 - 572 317
Fax	Fax	(44) 01872 - 573 701
Web	www.perranporthgolfclub.co.uk	
Situation	Situation	Truro, 15 km

Newquay (pop. 17 390), 10 km

Annual closure	Fermeture annuelle	no
Weekly closure	Fermeture hebdomadaire	no
Fees main season	Tarifs haute saison	18 holes

	Week days / Semaine	We/Bank holidays / We/Férié
Individual Individuel	£ 30	£ 35
Couple Couple	£ 60	£ 70

Full days: £ 35 / £ 40 (We)

Caddie Caddie no — **Electric Trolley** Chariot électrique no

Buggy Voiturette no — **Clubs** Clubs yes

Credit cards Cartes de crédit
VISA - Eurocard - MasterCard (Pro shop goods only)

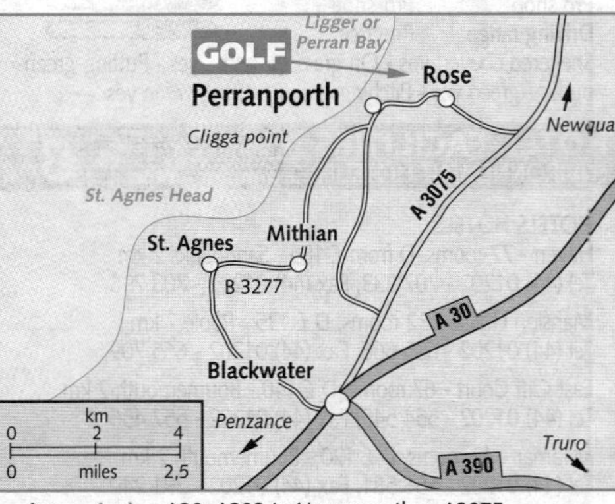

Access Accès : A30, A392 to Newquay, then A3075. At Goonhavern, B3285. Golf on edge of Perranporth, next to beach
Map 6 on page 480 Carte 6 Page 480

GOLF COURSE — PARCOURS — 15/20

Site	Site	
Maintenance	Entretien	
Architect	Architecte	James Braid
Type	Type	seaside course, links
Relief	Relief	
Water in play	Eau en jeu	
Exp. to wind	Exposé au vent	
Trees in play	Arbres en jeu	

Scorecard / Carte de score	Chp. / Chp.	Mens / Mess.	Ladies / Da.
Length Long.	5722	5460	4880
Par	72	72	72
Slope system	—	—	—

Advised golfing ability / Niveau de jeu recommandé — 0 12 24 36

Hcp required Handicap exigé — certificate

CLUB HOUSE & AMENITIES — CLUB HOUSE ET ANNEXES — 6/10

Pro shop Pro-shop
Driving range Practice
Sheltered couvert no - On grass sur herbe yes - Putting-green putting-green yes - Pitching-green pitching green no

HOTEL FACILITIES — ENVIRONNEMENT HOTELIER — 6/10

HOTELS HÔTELS

Rose-in-Vale - 18 rooms, D £ 120 - St Agnes 5 km
Tel (44) 01872 - 552 202, Fax (44) 01872 - 552 700

Bristol - Newquay 10 km
74 rooms, D from £ 124
Tel (44) 01637 - 875 181, Fax (44) 01637 - 879 347

Crantock Bay - Crantock 5 km
33 rooms, D from £ 120
Tel (44) 01637 - 830 229, Fax (44) 01637 - 831 111

RESTAURANTS RESTAURANTS

Pennypots - Truro 15 km - Tel (44) 01209 - 820 347
Saffron - Truro 15 km - Tel (44) 01872 - 263 771

Pleasington

16 | 8 | 6

This is one the region's great parkland courses and in 1997 treated itself to an impressively sized and much-needed new club-house. Between plateaus and valleys (or both on the 7th), you are confronted with a lot of trees, particularly on the 16th (a par 3) which you have to hit over in order to reach the green. Elsewhere they are rarely in play, except for slicers. The other hazards are the heather and the many large bunkers. Once again, a good score here means you really did play well. You may be lucky once, but rarely twice. Because of the technical challenge here, inexperienced players can expect to sweat a little, so stableford, match-play or a scramble game might be a more enjoyable option. This is indeed an excellent course for match-play golf, the design bearing testimony to the not too distant day and age when match-play was the formula used by all amateur golfers. The general excellence of green-keeping makes a visit here something we would eagerly recommend, despite the proximity of some pretty good links courses.

C'est un des grands parcours "de parc" de cette région, qui s'est offert en 1997 un vaste club-house devenu nécessaire. Entre plateaux et vallées (le 7 associe les deux), on trouve beaucoup d'arbres dans ce site de campagne, notamment un au 16 (par 3), qu'il faut survoler pour atteindre le green, mais ils sont rarement très en jeu... sauf pour les sliceurs. Les autres auront plutôt de la bruyère, de grands et nombreux bunkers. Un bon score est forcément la preuve d'un bon jeu. Ici, on peut avoir de la chance une fois, mais rarement deux. En raison de ses exigences techniques, les joueurs peu expérimentés doivent s'attendre à souffrir, on leur conseillera donc le stableford, le match-play... ou le scramble ! Car c'est un excellent parcours de match-play, témoin d'une époque pas si lointaine où il s'agissait de la formule de jeu des amateurs. La qualité générale de l'entretien permet de recommander une visite, même si de grands links sont à proximité.

Pleasington Golf Club — 1891

Pleasington
ENG - BLACKBURN, Lancs BB2 5JF

Office Secrétariat (44) 01254 - 202 177
Pro shop Pro-shop (44) 01254 - 201 630
Fax Fax (44) 01254 - 201 028
Web www.pleasington-golf.co.uk
Situation Situation Preston, 10 km
Blackburn (pop. 136 612), 5 km

Annual closure Fermeture annuelle: no
Weekly closure Fermeture hebdomadaire: no

Fees main season Tarifs haute saison	18 holes	
	Week days Semaine	We/Bank holidays We/Férié
Individual Individuel	£ 45	£ 45
Couple Couple	£ 90	£ 90

Caddie Caddie no — **Electric Trolley** Chariot électrique no
Buggy Voiturette no — **Clubs** Clubs yes
Credit cards Cartes de crédit no

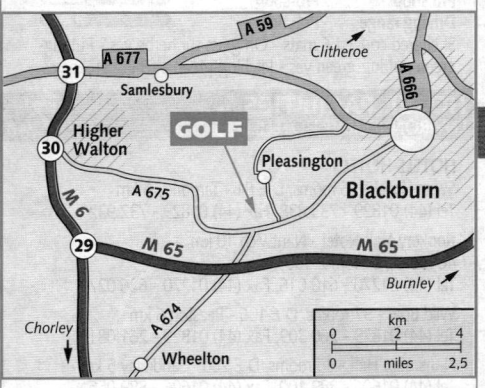

Access Accès : M61 → Preston Jct 9, then M65 → Blackburn. Jct 3, then A674 → Blackburn, to Pleasington Lane. Golf 200 m from Pleasington Station.
Map 5 on page 479 Carte 5 Page 479

GOLF COURSE — PARCOURS 16/20

Site Site
Maintenance Entretien
Architect Architecte: George Low, Sandy Herd
Type Type: parkland, heathland
Relief Relief
Water in play Eau en jeu
Exp. to wind Exposé au vent
Trees in play Arbres en jeu

Scorecard Carte de score	Chp. Chp.	Mens Mess.	Ladies Da.
Length Long.	5816	5816	5217
Par	71	71	74
Slope system	—	—	—

Advised golfing ability Niveau de jeu recommandé: 0 12 24 36
Hcp required Handicap exigé: certificate

CLUB HOUSE & AMENITIES — CLUB HOUSE ET ANNEXES 8/10

Pro shop Pro-shop
Driving range Practice
Sheltered couvert no - On grass sur herbe practice range only - Putting-green putting-green yes - Pitching-green pitching green yes

HOTEL FACILITIES — ENVIRONNEMENT HOTELIER 6/10

HOTELS HÔTELS
Swallow Preston Hotel - Samlesbury 3 km
78 rooms, D £ 90
Tel (44) 01772 - 877 351, Fax (44) 01772 - 877 424

Preston Marriott - Broughton 10 km
150 rooms, D from £ 90
Tel (44) 1772 - 864 087, Fax (44) 1772 - 861 728

Millstone - 23 rooms, D from £ 94 - Mellor 6 km
Tel (44) 01254 - 813 333, Fax (44) 01254 - 812 628

RESTAURANTS RESTAURANTS
Simpley Heathcotes - Preston 10 km - Tel (44) 01772 - 252 732
Campions - Samlesbury 6 km - Tel (44) 01772 - 877 641
Golf Club - on site - Tel (44) 01254 - 202 177

Portal *Championship*

15 | 8 | 7

They needed a big club-house here (although the extraordinary design is arguably a little over the top) to cater for the number of players on the two 18 hole courses (the second course is the Old Oaklands Golf Club). The Championship Course (1989), probably one of Donald Steel's best, is hilly enough for us to recommend a buggy to keep all your strength for playing golf (you will need it). The existing lie of the land was used and enhanced to great effect, completed by some shifting of earth that never clashes with landscape where the impression is more that of a park than open countryside. A little decoration never does any harm, like the little waterfalls on the 15th hole or the plants on the 6th. Owing to the length of this course, you will be hard pushed to play it twice in one day, so you will be pleased to learn that all the hazards are clearly visible. To avoid them, though, you will have to pitch the ball in high, sometimes flighting it both ways. One big golfing factory but a fine course too.

Il fallait un club-house imposant (son design est un peu too much !) pour s'accommoder de la fréquentation sur deux 18 trous et un 9 trous (le second parcours est l'ancien Oaklands Golf Club). Le Championship Course (1989) est probablement une des meilleures réalisations de Donald Steel, mais on conseillera l'usage d'une voiturette afin de garder assez de forces pour jouer au golf. Le terrain existant a été très bien utilisé et mis en valeur, et complété de mouvements qui ne heurtent jamais un paysage quand même plus proche du parc que de la campagne. Un peu de décoration ne nuit pas, comme les petites cascades du 15 ou les plantations du 6. Comme on jouera difficilement deux fois dans la journée en raison de la longueur du parcours, il faut savoir que tous les obstacles sont bien visibles, mais qu'il vaut mieux savoir bien lever la balle, et parfois la travailler pour réussir. Une grande usine à golf, mais une belle réalisation.

Portal Golf Club — 1989

Cobblers Cross
ENG - TARPORLEY, Cheshire CW6 0DJ

Office	Secrétariat	(44) 01829 - 733 933
Pro shop	Pro-shop	(44) 01829 - 733 933
Fax	Fax	(44) 01829 - 733 928
Web	www.portalgolf.co.uk	
Situation	Situation	Chester (pop. 115 971), 16 km
Annual closure	Fermeture annuelle	no
Weekly closure	Fermeture hebdomadaire	no

Fees main season Tarifs haute saison — 18 holes

	Week days Semaine	We/Bank holidays We/Férié
Individual Individuel	£ 70	£ 70
Couple Couple	£ 140	£ 140

Caddie Caddie no — **Electric Trolley** Chariot électrique no

Buggy Voiturette yes — **Clubs** Clubs on request

Credit cards Cartes de crédit
VISA - Eurocard - MasterCard - AMEX - DC

598

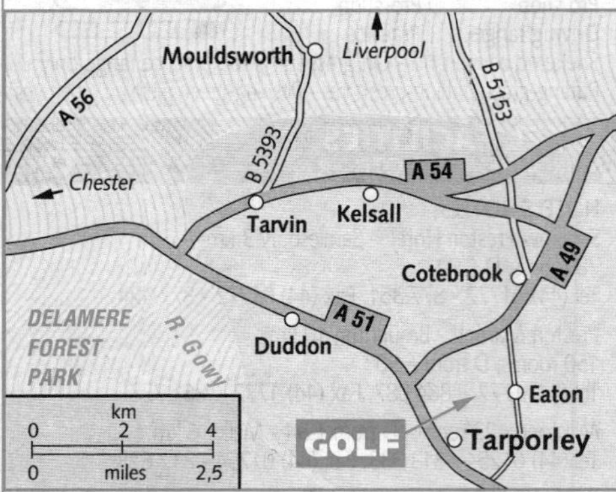

Access Accès : Chester A51, then A49. 1 km (0.5 m) north of Tarporley.
Map 4 on page 476 Carte 4 Page 476

GOLF COURSE — PARCOURS — 15/20

Site	Site	
Maintenance	Entretien	
Architect	Architecte	Donald Steel
Type	Type	parkland
Relief	Relief	
Water in play	Eau en jeu	
Exp. to wind	Exposé au vent	
Trees in play	Arbres en jeu	

Scorecard Carte de score	Chp. Chp.	Mens Mess.	Ladies Da.
Length Long.	6333	5854	5362
Par	73	73	73
Slope system	—	—	—

Advised golfing ability Niveau de jeu recommandé: 0 12 24 36
Hcp required Handicap exigé: no

CLUB HOUSE & AMENITIES — CLUB HOUSE ET ANNEXES — 8/10

Pro shop Pro-shop
Driving range Practice
Sheltered couvert 6 mats - On grass sur herbe yes - Putting-green putting-green yes - Pitching-green pitching green yes

HOTEL FACILITIES — ENVIRONNEMENT HOTELIER — 7/10

HOTELS HÔTELS
Swan Hotel - 16 rooms, D £ 81 - Tarporley 5 km
Tel (44) 01829 - 733 838, Fax (44) 01829 - 732 932

Rookery Hall Hotel - Nantwich 10 km
46 rooms, D from £ 150
Tel (44) 01270 - 610 016, Fax (44) 01270 - 626 027

Wild Boar - 37 rooms, D £ 106 - Beeston 6 km
Tel (44) 01829 - 260 309, Fax (44) 01829 - 261 081

Nunsmere Hall - 36 rooms, D £ 200 - Sandiway 5 km
Tel (44) 01606 - 889 100, Fax (44) 01606 - 889 055

RESTAURANTS RESTAURANTS
Swan Hotel - Tarporley 5 km - Tel (44) 01829 - 733 838
Blue Bell - Chester 15 km - Tel (44) 01244 - 317 758

Prestbury

16	8	7

The sterling efforts of the course's green-keepers only add to the pleasure of playing one of the very few moorland courses designed by Harry Colt. A huge planting programme has enhanced the course both visually and in terms of giving each hole clearer definition over wide open space. Colt didn't do much to the terrain, he just used it with his usual brilliance, and you might be surprised by some of the sloping fairways which make shots harder to judge. You need an accurate driver here, but the essential challenge lies in hitting some very-well defended greens which are sometimes tiered, sometimes terraced owing to the lie of the land. There are not too many bunkers but they are all usefully placed. You need to play every shot in the book, in every direction. Basically you will want at least one good shot per hole (and some good putts) so you don't have much breathing space. A very sound course that makes an impression on all who play it, although visitors can only tee-off during the week. The ideal time would be a fine Autumn afternoon.

Le travail des greenkeepers ne fait qu'ajouter au plaisir d'évoluer sur l'un des seuls dessins de Harry Colt en paysage de lande, auquel un énorme programme de plantations a donné à la fois beauté visuelle et définition des trous dans l'espace. Colt n'a pas beaucoup touché au terrain, il l'a utilisé avec son génie habituel, et certaines inclinaisons des fairways pourront surprendre, et fausser le jugement. Il faut être précis au drive, mais le travail essentiel est dans les approches de greens très protégés, parfois en plateau ou en balcons en raison des mouvements du terrain. Le nombre de bunkers n'est pas très élevé, mais ils sont tous utiles. Il faut alors savoir jouer tous les coups, et dans tous les sens : un seul bon coup de golf par trou (et de bons putts) est un strict minimum, ce qui ne laisse guère respirer. C'est un solide parcours qui ne laissera pas indifférent, mais on ne peut le jouer qu'en semaine. A voir par un bel après-midi d'automne.

Prestbury Golf Club — 1921

Macclesfield Road
ENG - PRESTBURY, Cheshire SK10 4BJ

Office Secrétariat (44) 01625 - 828 241
Pro shop Pro-shop (44) 01625 - 828 242
Fax Fax (44) 01625 - 828 241
Web www.prestburygolfclub.com
Situation Situation Macclesfield, 3 km
Manchester (pop. 404 861), 25 km

Annual closure Fermeture annuelle — no
Weekly closure Fermeture hebdomadaire — no

Fees main season Tarifs haute saison — Full day

	Week days Semaine	We/Bank holidays We/Férié
Individual Individuel	£ 45	*
Couple Couple	£ 90	*

* No visitors at week-ends

Caddie Caddie on request **Electric Trolley** Chariot électrique yes
Buggy Voiturette no **Clubs** Clubs yes
Credit cards Cartes de crédit (Pro shop goods only)
VISA - Eurocard - MasterCard - AMEX - DC

Manchester
A 34
A 538
A 523
Mottram St-Andrew
Alderley Edge
Prestbury
B 5087
Nether Alderley
Tytherington
GOLF
Knutsford
A 537
Macclesfield
Stoke-on-Trent
km 0 2 4
miles 0 2,5

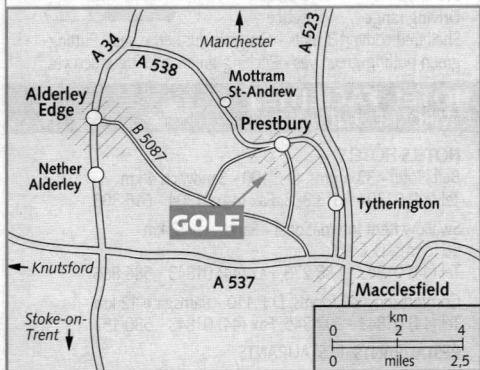

Access Accès : 3 km NW of Macclesfield on A538 off A523.
Map 4 on page 476 Carte 4 Page 476

GOLF COURSE — PARCOURS 16/20

Site Site
Maintenance Entretien
Architect Architecte Harry S. Colt, John Morrison
Type Type inland, open country
Relief Relief
Water in play Eau en jeu
Exp. to wind Exposé au vent
Trees in play Arbres en jeu

Scorecard Carte de score	Chp. Chp.	Mens Mess.	Ladies Da.
Length Long.	5723	5528	4917
Par	71	71	74
Slope system	—	—	—

Advised golfing ability Niveau de jeu recommandé 0 12 24 36
Hcp required Handicap exigé no

CLUB HOUSE & AMENITIES — CLUB HOUSE ET ANNEXES 8/10

Pro shop Pro-shop
Driving range Practice
Sheltered couvert no - On grass sur herbe yes - Putting-green putting-green yes - Pitching-green pitching green yes

HOTEL FACILITIES — ENVIRONNEMENT HOTELIER 7/10

HOTELS HÔTELS
White House Manor - 11 rooms, D £ 120 - Prestbury 1 km
Tel (44) 01625 - 829 376, Fax (44) 01625 - 828 627

The Bridge Hotel - Prestbury 1 km
23 rooms, D £ 90
Tel (44) 01625 - 829 326, Fax (44) 01625 - 827 557

Shrigley Hall - 150 rooms, D £ 130 - Adlington 5 km
Tel (44) 01625 - 575 757, Fax (44) 01625 - 573 323

RESTAURANTS RESTAURANTS
White House - Prestbury 1 km - Tel (44) 01625 - 829 376
The Bridge Hotel - Prestbury 1 km - Tel (44) 01625 - 829 326
Church House Inn - Bollington 2 km - Tel (44) 01625 - 574 014

Prince's *Himalayas-Shore*

15 | 6 | 4

Restoration work and alterations since the war, the arranging of the course into 3 nine-hole loops (but all 27 run parallel) and a commitment to making this a course more for your average golfer have somewhat undermined the original layout by Campbell and Morrison. The fairways are wider than they used to be and the bunkers and greens are smaller, thereby reducing the risk of 3-putts. The most interesting combination is certainly 'Shore-Himalayas' which, and this is no coincidence, embraces most of the original layout and features a number of horribly deep bunkers. Perhaps intimidated by the neighbouring and aristocratic Royal St. George's and Royal Cinque Ports, a number of less experienced golfers will enjoy their first taste of links golfing here without getting too much of a bloody nose. And of course if the wind blows (often a cross-wind here) Prince's can be long and tough. But all the same, the better players will still find this challenge a little less demanding and exciting than it might have been. The club-house is modern with good facilities and fine views.

Les restaurations de l'après-guerre, la disposition en trois boucles de neuf trous, l'adaptation aux handicaps moyens ont quelque peu affaibli le dessin original de Campbell et Morrison. Les fairways sont plus larges qu'autrefois, les bunkers souvent plus petits, tout comme les greens : on n'y risque plus trois putts. La combinaison la plus intéressante est incontestablement "Shore-Himalayas" où l'on trouve, ce n'est pas un hasard, la majorité du tracé d'origine, et enfin quelques bunkers aux redoutables profondeurs. Certes, intimidés par le voisin et aristocratique Royal St George's ou Royal Cinque Ports, certains golfeurs peu aguerris aimeront faire leur expérience des links ici, sans trop se casser les dents. Certes, si le vent souffle (souvent en travers), Prince's peut être long et difficile. Il n'empêche que les meilleurs joueurs trouveront le défi un peu moins exigeant qu'il pourrait l'être. Le club-house est moderne avec de belles vues, les équipements convenables.

Prince's Golf Club — 1904

ENG - SANDWICH BAY, Kent CT13 9QB

Office Secrétariat (44) 01304 - 611 118
Pro shop Pro-shop (44) 01304 - 613 797
Fax Fax (44) 01304 - 612 000
Web www.princesgolfclub.co.uk
Situation Situation Deal (pop. 28 504), 10 km
Sandwich (pop. 4 729), 4 km

Annual closure Fermeture annuelle no
Weekly closure Fermeture hebdomadaire no

Fees main season Tarifs haute saison 18 holes

	Week days Semaine	We/Bank holidays We/Férié
Individual Individuel	£ 60	£ 70
Couple Couple	£ 120	£ 140

Full days: £ 80 and £ 90 (We)

Caddie Caddie no — **Electric Trolley** Chariot électrique no
Buggy Voiturette yes — **Clubs** Clubs yes
Credit cards Cartes de crédit
VISA - MasterCard - DC

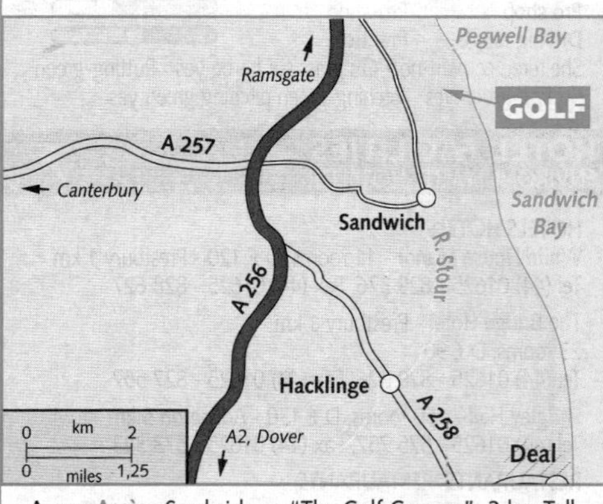

Access Accès : Sandwich, → "The Golf Courses". 3 km Toll gate into Sandwich Bay Estate, left 1 km and left again. Continue 2 km along seafront.
Map 7 on page 483 Carte 7 Page 483

GOLF COURSE — PARCOURS 15/20

Site Site
Maintenance Entretien
Architect Architecte Sir Guy Campbell, John Morrison
Type Type seaside course, links
Relief Relief
Water in play Eau en jeu
Exp. to wind Exposé au vent
Trees in play Arbres en jeu

Scorecard Carte de score	Chp. Chp.	Mens Mess.	Ladies Da.
Length Long.	5860	5614	5260
Par	71	71	73
Slope system	0	0	0

Advised golfing ability 0 12 24 36
Niveau de jeu recommandé
Hcp required Handicap exigé no

CLUB HOUSE & AMENITIES — CLUB HOUSE ET ANNEXES 6/10

Pro shop Pro-shop
Driving range Practice
Sheltered couvert 3 mats - On grass sur herbe yes - Putting-green putting-green yes - Pitching-green pitching green yes

HOTEL FACILITIES — ENVIRONNEMENT HOTELIER 4/10

HOTELS HÔTELS
Bell Hotel - 33 rooms, D £ 100 - Sandwich 4 km
Tel (44) 01304 - 613 388, Fax (44) 01304 - 615 308

Swallow Kent International - Sandwich 12 km
56 rooms, D £ 100
Tel (44) 01843 - 588 276, Fax (44) 01843 - 586 866

Comfort Inn - 44 rooms, D £ 110 - Ramsgate 12 km
Tel (44) 01843 - 592 345, Fax (44) 01843 - 580 157

RESTAURANTS RESTAURANTS
Blazing Donkey - Ham, Sandwich 7 km
Tel (44) 01304 - 617362

Dunkerleys Restaurant - Deal 10 km - Tel (44) 01304 - 375016

Hare & Hounds - Deal 10 km - Tel (44) 01304 - 365 429

Reddish Vale

16	5	7

In a part residential and part industrial area, this course is a golfing oasis, so well concealed that you easily understand why so many people have never noticed it. It has also undergone a recent new plantation programme that was no more necessary than the committee who took a decision aimed primarily at staking out their own territory. This is your typical self-sufficient course, simply laid out following the natural lie of the land. Architect Alister Mackenzie, here at the height of his powers, used all his skill to vary the difficulties which call for every shot in the book. A little while after, during the Great War, he was to develop a number of camouflage and optical illusion techniques, some of which can already be seen here. He was helped by some intriguing topography in the shape of vales and dales, where there was no need to conceal bunkers designed to trap players. Neither too long nor too hard, this is a course for the connoisseur, whose only regret will be the less than immaculate green-keeping. This vintage Mackenzie course certainly deserves it.

Dans une zone à la fois résidentielle et industrielle, ce parcours constitue une oasis, à ce point cachée que l'on comprend aisément qu'elle soit restée inaperçue de beaucoup. Et le parcours a récemment fait l'objet de plantations aussi peu nécessaires que le comité qui a décidé de marquer son territoire. C'est pourtant un tracé qui se suffit à lui-même, suivant naturellement les ondulations du terrain. Son auteur, Alister Mackenzie au meilleur de sa forme, a utilisé toutes les variantes de son art pour alterner les difficultés, qui réclament tous les coups de golf. Peu de temps après, il devait pendant la Grande Guerre mettre au point des procédés de camouflage et de trompe-l'œil que l'on trouve déjà ici, aidé par une topographie capricieuse, des hauts et des bas où il n'est pas nécessaire de loger des bunkers pour piéger les joueurs. Ni long, ni très difficile, c'est un parcours pour connaisseurs, dont on regrette qu'il ne bénéficie pas d'un entretien immaculé. Ce Mackenzie pur malt le mérite.

Reddish Vale Golf Club — 1912

Southcliffe Road, Reddish
ENG - STOCKPORT, Cheshire, SK5 7EE

Office	Secrétariat	(44) 0161 - 480 2359
Pro shop	Pro-shop	(44) 0161 - 480 2359
Fax	Fax	(44) 0161 - 480 2359
Web	www.rvgc.co.uk	
Situation	Situation	Manchester, 20 km

Stockport, 3 km

Annual closure	Fermeture annuelle	no
Weekly closure	Fermeture hebdomadaire	no

Fees main season / Tarifs haute saison	18 holes	
	Week days / Semaine	We/Bank holidays / We/Férié
Individual Individuel	£ 40	*
Couple Couple	£ 80	*

* No visitors at We / Juniors: £ 8

Caddie Caddie no — Electric Trolley Chariot électrique no

Buggy Voiturette no — Clubs Clubs yes

Credit cards Cartes de crédit
VISA - MasterCard

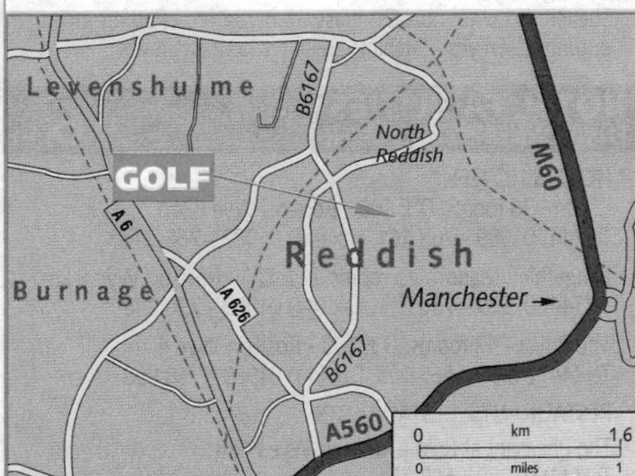

Access Accès : M60 Exit Jct 25. Take Tiviot Way to roundabout, then follow Sandy Lane until signposts to the club

Map 4 on page 476 Carte 4 Page 476

GOLF COURSE — PARCOURS — 16/20

Site	Site	
Maintenance	Entretien	
Architect	Architecte	Alister Mackenzie
Type	Type	hilly, moorland
Relief	Relief	
Water in play	Eau en jeu	
Exp. to wind	Exposé au vent	
Trees in play	Arbres en jeu	

Scorecard / Carte de score	Chp. / Chp.	Mens / Mess.	Ladies / Da.
Length Long.	5478	5306	5148
Par	69	69	73
Slope system	—	—	—

Advised golfing ability / Niveau de jeu recommandé: 0 12 24 36

Hcp required — Handicap exigé — no

CLUB HOUSE & AMENITIES — CLUB HOUSE ET ANNEXES — 5/10

Pro shop — Pro-shop
Driving range — Practice
Sheltered couvert no - On grass sur herbe yes - Putting-green putting-green yes - Pitching-green pitching green yes

HOTEL FACILITIES — ENVIRONNEMENT HOTELIER — 7/10

HOTELS HÔTELS

Didsbury House - 27 rooms, D £ 145 - Didsbury 5 km
Tel (44) 0161 - 448 2200, Fax (44) 0161 - 448 2525

Eleven Didsbury Park - 20 rooms, D £ 185 - Didsbury 7 km
Tel (44) 0161 - 448 7711, Fax (44) 0161 - 448 8282

Rossetti - 61 rooms, D £ 155 - Manchester 7 km
Tel (44) 0161 - 247 7744, Fax (44) 0161 - 247 7747

RESTAURANTS RESTAURANTS

River Room - Manchester 7 km - Tel (44) 0161 - 827 4003

That Café - Levenshulme-Stockport 3 km
Tel (44) 0161 - 432 4672

Ross-on-Wye

14	5	6

Driving up from London, you will have stopped off at Stratford-upon-Avon (the birthplace of Shakespeare) and then at Gloucester to visit the cathedral and the docks that have now been transformed into a museum. As you pursue your cultural trek on to Hereford, home of the world's first map (in the cathedral), you drive along the very beautiful Wye valley and stop off in the pretty town that has given its name to this discreet and perhaps a little too unassuming golf course. It was laid out in 1964 in a forest with literally thousands of trees, especially birch, which make this pleasant course such a beautiful site with its small, interesting and very well protected greens. There are a few blind shots but overall this is a very fair course with clearly identifiable hazards. Devoid of traps, well maintained and very pleasant to play, Ross-on-Wye extends a simple but very friendly welcome to green-feers.

Venant de Londres, vous vous serez arrêté à Stratford-upon-Avon (ville natale de Shakespeare), puis à Gloucester pour visiter la cathédrale et les docks transformés en musée. Avant de poursuivre votre quête culturelle à Hereford où l'on trouve la première carte du monde (à la cathédrale), vous devez passer par la très belle vallée de la Wye et vous arrêter dans la jolie ville qui a donné son nom à ce parcours discret, et dont on aimerait parfois que son caractère soit plus affirmé. Il date de 1964, a été tracé dans une forêt composée de millions d'arbres, en particulier de bouleaux, qui donnent une grande beauté à ce plaisant parcours, avec de petits greens animés et bien défendus. On trouve quelques coups aveugles, mais l'ensemble est néanmoins très franc, avec des obstacles clairement identifiables. Sans pièges, bien entretenu, très agréable à jouer, Ross-on-Wye bénéficie également d'un accueil simple, mais très amical.

Ross-on-Wye Golf Club — 1964

Two Park, Gorsley
ENG - ROSS-ON-WYE, Hereford HR9 7UT

Office	Secrétariat	(44) 01989 - 720 267
Pro shop	Pro-shop	(44) 01989 - 720 439
Fax	Fax	(44) 01989 - 720 212
Web	www.therossonwyegolfclub.co.uk	
Situation	Situation	Ross-on-Wye, 5 km

Gloucester (pop. 101 608), 20 km

Annual closure	Fermeture annuelle	no
Weekly closure	Fermeture hebdomadaire	no

Fees main season Tarifs haute saison — Full day

	Week days / Semaine	We/Bank holidays / We/Férié
Individual Individuel	£ 50	£ 50
Couple Couple	£ 100	£ 100

Caddie Caddie no — **Electric Trolley** Chariot électrique yes
Buggy Voiturette yes — **Clubs** Clubs no
Credit cards Cartes de crédit
VISA - MasterCard

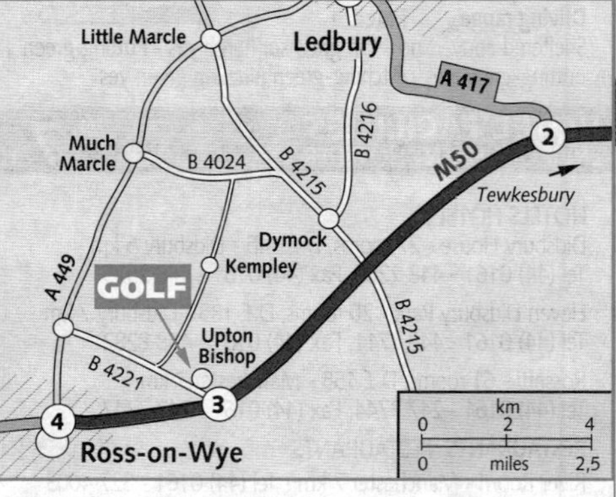

Access Accès : Adjacent Jct 3 of M50.
Map 6 on page 481 Carte 6 Page 481

GOLF COURSE — PARCOURS — 14/20

Site	Site	
Maintenance	Entretien	
Architect	Architecte	C.K. Cotton
Type	Type	parkland
Relief	Relief	
Water in play	Eau en jeu	
Exp. to wind	Exposé au vent	
Trees in play	Arbres en jeu	

Scorecard / Carte de score	Chp. / Chp.	Mens / Mess.	Ladies / Da.
Length Long.	5897	5443	5130
Par	72	72	73
Slope system	—	—	—

Advised golfing ability / Niveau de jeu recommandé — 0 12 24 36
Hcp required — Handicap exigé — certificate

CLUB HOUSE & AMENITIES — CLUB HOUSE ET ANNEXES — 5/10

Pro shop	Pro-shop
Driving range	Practice

Sheltered couvert no - On grass sur herbe yes - Putting-green putting-green yes - Pitching-green pitching green yes

HOTEL FACILITIES — ENVIRONNEMENT HOTELIER — 6/10

HOTELS HÔTELS

Chase - 36 rooms, D £ 105 - Ross-on-Wye 6 km
Tel (44) 01989 - 763 161, Fax (44) 01989 - 768 330

Pengethley Manor - 25 rooms, D £ 120 - Ross-on-Wye 8 km
Tel (44) 01989 - 730 211, Fax (44) 01989 - 730 238

The Royal - 42 rooms, D £ 100 - Ross-on-Wye 4 km
Tel (44) 01989 - 565 105, Fax (44) 01989 - 768 058

RESTAURANTS RESTAURANTS

The Pheasant at Ross - Ross-on-Wye 6 km
Tel (44) 01989 - 565 751

The Lough Pool Inn (Pub) - Ross-on-Wye 6 Km
Tel (44) 1989 - 730 236

Le Champignon Sauvage - Cheltenham 30 km
Tel (44) 01242 - 573 449

Royal Ashdown Forest

16	7	6

Players who hate getting in and getting out of sand can die happy here, as there is not a single bunker in sight. So it could claim to be the most natural course around, as no-one has ever seen a bunker on wholly natural terrain except perhaps on links courses where grazing sheep once helped to fashion the layout. This was the result of an administrative ban but has now become a sort of coquetry. But don't be too relieved, as there is no shortage of difficulties elsewhere: there are encroaching pine and birch trees, a stream on several holes, and heather, which is even more dangerous than water and often has to be carried with your drive or even your second shot (on the 12th). As a general rule, and with a couple of exceptions, members will tell you to hit the ball high into the greens, which are rather large, very quick in summer and slope in all directions. A pretty course and a superbly atmospheric club-house, plus a second course (West Course) which is shorter and easier.

Bonheur, disent les golfeurs qui détestent aller dans le sable et plus encore en sortir. Il n'y a pas ici un seul bunker, c'est donc le parcours le plus naturel qui soit, car qui a vu des bunkers naturels dans le monde, sinon dans les jardins d'enfant et sur les links authentiques où paissent les moutons ? C'était le résultat d'une interdiction administrative, c'est devenu une sorte de coquetterie du club. Que l'on ne soit pas trop vite soulagé, les difficultés ne manquent pas : les pins et les bouleaux d'abord, un cours d'eau sur plusieurs trous, la bruyère encore, bien plus pénalisante que l'eau, dont il faut souvent franchir des étendues au drive ou même au second coup (au 12). En règle générale, les membres vous souffleront qu'il faut ici lever la balle, sauf pour approcher un ou deux greens. Ceux-ci sont assez grands, avec des pentes dans tous les sens, et très rapides en été. Un joli parcours, avec un club-house plein d'atmosphère, et un second parcours (West Course), plus court et abordable.

Royal Ashdown Forest Golf Club — 1989

Chapel Lane, Forest Row
ENG - EAST GRINSTEAD, East Sussex RH18 5LR

Office	Secrétariat	(44) 01342 - 822 018
Pro shop	Pro-shop	(44) 01342 - 822 247
Fax	Fax	(44) 01342 - 825 211
Web	www.royalashdown.co.uk	
Situation	Situation	East Grinstead, 8 km
Annual closure	Fermeture annuelle	no
Weekly closure	Fermeture hebdomadaire	no

Fees main season / Tarifs haute saison	Week days / Semaine	We/Bank holidays / We/Férié
	18 holes	
Individual Individuel	£ 50	£ 70
Couple Couple	£ 100	£ 140

Full week days: £ 70

Caddie Caddie yes — Electric Trolley Chariot électrique no
Buggy Voiturette no — Clubs Clubs yes

Credit cards Cartes de crédit
VISA - Eurocard - MasterCard (Pro Shop only)

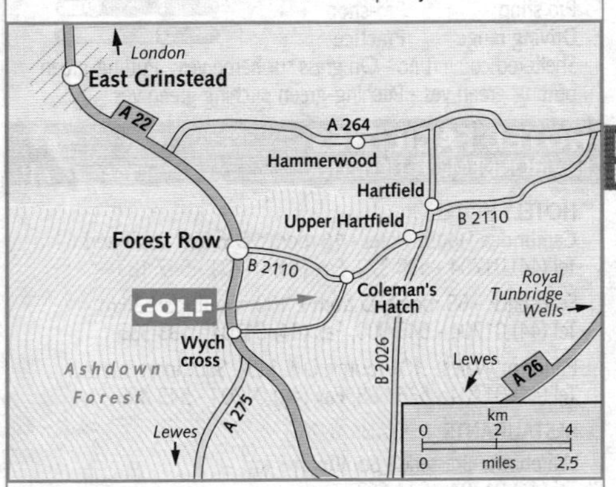

Access Accès : M25 Jct 6 then A22 South through East Grinstead. At Forest Row, turn left into B2110. 0.8 km (1/2 m.) right into Chapel Lane. Top of hill turn left.
Map 7 on page 483 Carte 7 Page 483

GOLF COURSE / PARCOURS — 16/20

Site	Site	
Maintenance	Entretien	
Architect	Architecte	Archdeacon Scott
Type	Type	inland, heathland
Relief	Relief	
Water in play	Eau en jeu	
Exp. to wind	Exposé au vent	
Trees in play	Arbres en jeu	

Scorecard / Carte de score	Chp. / Chp.	Mens / Mess.	Ladies / Da.
Length Long.	5712	5675	5032
Par	72	72	73
Slope system	—	—	—

Advised golfing ability / Niveau de jeu recommandé: 0 12 24 36
Hcp required / Handicap exigé: certificate

CLUB HOUSE & AMENITIES / CLUB HOUSE ET ANNEXES — 7/10

Pro shop / Pro-shop
Driving range / Practice
Sheltered couvert no - On grass sur herbe yes - Putting-green putting-green yes - Pitching-green pitching green yes

HOTEL FACILITIES / ENVIRONNEMENT HOTELIER — 6/10

HOTELS HÔTELS

Ashdown Park - 106 rooms, D £ 165 - Wych Cross 3 km
Tel (44) 01342 - 824 988, Fax (44) 01342 - 826 206

Gravetye Manor - East Grinstead 8 km
18 rooms, D £ 210
Tel (44) 01342 - 810 567, Fax (44) 01342 - 810 080

Langshott Manor - 22 rooms, D £ 190- Horley 12 km
Tel (44) 01293 - 786 680, Fax (44) 01293 - 783 905

RESTAURANTS RESTAURANTS

Gravetye Manor - East Grinstead 8 km
Tel (44) 01342 - 810 567

Chequers Inn - Forest Row 2 km - Tel (44) 01342 - 823 333

Royal Birkdale (The)

19 | 9 | 7

Royal Birkdale has hosted every top tournament: the Open, the Ryder, Walker and Curtis Cups, and the Ladies Open. It has done so more than others probably because this is an open and honest course where you can draw up your strategy according to the wind and not to the imponderables that create the "rough justice" charm of other links. Here, if you stay on the fairway you will avoid any blind shots. If you stray onto the surrounding dunes, you can end up in some very nasty situations indeed. This is a course for the technician and artist, not the big-hitter. Thomson, Watson, Trevino, Miller and Mark O'Meara have all won here, as did Arnold Palmer, a more strategically refined golfer than some might believe. There is no point in describing what could easily fill a whole book. Suffice it to say that Birkdale is unforgettable and that, like a dinner in a top hotel, this immerse pleasure comes at a price. So make it a full day's golfing and hope to play from the back tees.

Royal Birkdale a reçu toutes les grandes compétitions : le British Open, la Ryder Cup, la Walker Cup, la Curtis Cup, le British Ladies Open... Plus que d'autres sans doute, parce que sa franchise permet d'établir la stratégie en fonction du vent, et non des impondérables qui font le charme d'autres links, mais pas toujours dans la justice ! Pas de coups aveugles ici, du moins si l'on reste sur le fairway, car les dunes et le rough alentour peuvent vous imposer des situations peu confortables. Ce n'est pas un parcours de frappeur, mais de technicien, d'artiste du travail de la balle: Thomson, Watson, Trevino, Miller et Mark O'Meara ont gagné ici, mais aussi Arnold Palmer, plus fin stratège qu'on ne le croit. Inutile de décrire ce qui prendrait un livre entier, disons seulement que Birkdale est inoubliable, que cet immense plaisir se paie cher, comme un dîner dans un trois étoiles. Alors, prenez la journée et espérez pouvoir jouer du fond...

The Royal Birkdale Golf Club — 1897

Waterloo Road
ENG - SOUTHPORT, Lancs PR8 2LX

Office	Secrétariat	(44) 01704 - 567 920
Pro shop	Pro-shop	(44) 01704 - 568 857
Fax	Fax	(44) 01704 - 562 327
Web	www.royalbirkdale.com	
Situation	Situation	Liverpool, 30 km

Southport (pop. 90 959), 1.5 km

Annual closure	Fermeture annuelle	no
Weekly closure	Fermeture hebdomadaire	no
Fees main season	Tarifs haute saison	18 holes

	Week days / Semaine	We/Bank holidays / We/Férié
Individual Individuel	£ 130	£ 155*
Couple Couple	£ 260	£ 310*

* Sunday only / Full week days: £ 165

Caddie Caddie on request **Electric Trolley** Chariot électrique yes

Buggy Voiturette no **Clubs** Clubs yes

Credit cards Cartes de crédit
VISA - Eurocard - MasterCard - AMEX (Pro shop goods only)

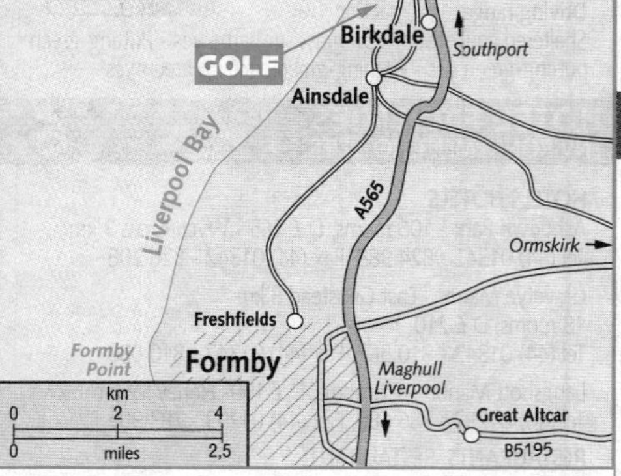

Access Accès : A565 Liverpool → Southport, 1.5 km (1 m.) before Southport.
Map 5 on page 479 Carte 5 Page 479

GOLF COURSE — PARCOURS 19/20

Site	Site	
Maintenance	Entretien	
Architect	Architecte	F.W. Hawtree, J.H. Taylor
Type	Type	links
Relief	Relief	
Water in play	Eau en jeu	
Exp. to wind	Exposé au vent	
Trees in play	Arbres en jeu	

Scorecard / Carte de score	Chp. / Chp.	Mens / Mess.	Ladies / Da.
Length Long.	6290	6021	5195
Par	70	72	75
Slope system	—	—	—

Advised golfing ability 0 12 24 36
Niveau de jeu recommandé
Hcp required Handicap exigé certificate

CLUB HOUSE & AMENITIES — CLUB HOUSE ET ANNEXES 9/10

Pro shop Pro-shop
Driving range Practice
Sheltered couvert no - On grass sur herbe yes - Putting-green putting-green yes - Pitching-green pitching green yes

HOTEL FACILITIES — ENVIRONNEMENT HOTELIER 7/10

HOTELS HÔTELS
Cambridge House Hotel - 16 rooms, D £ 83 - Southport 6 km
Tel (44) 01704 - 538 372, Fax (44) 01704 - 547 183

Scarisbrick - 88 rooms, D from £ 100 - Southport 3 km
Tel (44) 01704 - 543 000, Fax (44) 01704 - 533 335

Prince of Wales - 101 rooms, D £ 115 - Southport 3 km
Tel (44) 01704 - 536 688, Fax (44) 01704 - 543 488

RESTAURANTS RESTAURANTS
Warehouse Brasserie - Southport 3 km
Tel (44) 01704 - 544 662
Valentino's - Southport 3 km - Tel (44) 01704 - 541 252
Cloisters (Scarisbrick) - Southport 3 km
Tel (44) 01704 - 535 153

Royal Cinque Ports

17 | 6 | 5

Here you are a sliced drive away from the sea but you hardly ever see it. Deal (the course's other name) needs this barrier of sand hills to protect the course from the sea-water which is deadly for turf. On a narrow strip of land, dotted with a few dunes and flanked by a little road and houses, you'd think it almost impossible to lay-out such a marvellous course, brought back to life after each world war. Less majestic than Royal St. George's but more constantly demanding and unflinching than Prince's, Deal requires a degree of wisdom that comes from long years of golfing to admit, for example, that on a particular day a particular shot will need three or even four clubs more. Highly strategic and full of small pot bunkers, this is a lively, clever and smart course which should make you a more intelligent golfer, or else leave you feeling a real fool. A number of top architects have brushed up RCP and the club's present consultant is Donald Steel.

Ici, on est à deux pas de la mer, mais on ne la voit pratiquement jamais. Il faut ce cordon de dunes pour protéger "Deal" (comme on le nomme aussi) des assauts d'eau salée, mortelle pour les gazons. Sur cette étroite langue de terre à peine animée par quelques dunes, longée par une petite route et des maisons, on aurait peine à imaginer pouvoir loger un aussi merveilleux parcours, ressuscité après chaque guerre mondiale. Moins majestueux que St George's, plus constamment exigeant et farouche que Prince's, Deal réclame la sagesse que donne une longue pratique, pour admettre par exemple qu'il faut aujourd'hui trois ou quatre clubs de plus à cause du vent. Hautement stratégique, plein de petits bunkers où seul un mouton peut tenir, c'est un parcours vivant, astucieux et malin, d'où on sort intelligent, ou définitivement stupide. Nombre de grands architectes s'y sont penchés, Donald Steel est aujourd'hui le conseiller du club.

Royal Cinque Ports Golf Club — 1892

Golf Road
ENG - DEAL, Kent

Office Secrétariat (44) 01304 - 374 007
Pro shop Pro-shop (44) 01304 - 374 170
Fax Fax (44) 01304 - 379 530
Web www.royalcinqueports.com
Situation Situation Sandwich (pop. 4 729), 8 km adjacent to Deal (pop.28 504)
Annual closure Fermeture annuelle no
Weekly closure Fermeture hebdomadaire no

Fees main season Tarifs haute saison 18 holes

	Week days / Semaine	We/Bank holidays / We/Férié
Individual Individuel	£ 85	£ 85
Couple Couple	£ 170	£ 170

Full days: £ 95 / £ 105 (We)

Caddie Caddie on request **Electric Trolley** Chariot électrique yes
Buggy Voiturette yes **Clubs** Clubs yes
Credit cards Cartes de crédit
VISA - MasterCard (also AMEX at Pro shop)

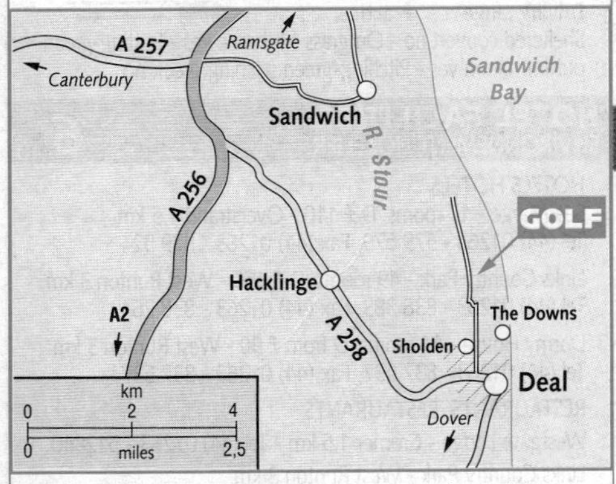

Access Accès : A2, A258 to Deal. Seafront to the end. Turn left and right into Golf Road
Map 7 on page 483 Carte 7 Page 483

GOLF COURSE — PARCOURS 17/20

Site Site
Maintenance Entretien
Architect Architecte Tom Dunn, Sir Guy Campbell
Type Type seaside course, links
Relief Relief
Water in play Eau en jeu
Exp. to wind Exposé au vent
Trees in play Arbres en jeu

Scorecard / Carte de score	Chp. / Chp.	Mens / Mess.	Ladies / Da.
Length Long.	6080	5835	5105
Par	72	70	74
Slope system	—	—	—

Advised golfing ability Niveau de jeu recommandé 0 12 24 36
Hcp required Handicap exigé certificate

CLUB HOUSE & AMENITIES — CLUB HOUSE ET ANNEXES 6/10

Pro shop Pro-shop
Driving range Practice
Sheltered couvert no - On grass sur herbe yes - Putting-green putting-green yes - Pitching-green pitching green yes

HOTEL FACILITIES — ENVIRONNEMENT HOTELIER 5/10

HOTELS HÔTELS
Royal - 18 rooms, D £ 80 - Deal 1 km
Tel (44) 01304 - 375 555, Fax (44) 01304 - 372 270
Bell Hotel - 33 rooms, D £ 100 - Sandwich 7 km
Tel (44) 01304 - 613 388, Fax (44) 01304 - 615 308
Wallet's Court - 16 rooms, D £ 119 - St Margaret's Bay 8 km
Tel (44) 01304 - 852 424, Fax (44) 01304 - 853 430

RESTAURANTS RESTAURANTS
Dunkerleys Restaurant - Deal 1 km - Tel (44) 01304 - 375016
Boathouse Brasserie (Royal) - Deal 1 km
Tel (44) 01304 - 375 555
Chequers Inn - on site - Tel (44) 01304 - 636 288

Royal Cromer

15 | 7 | 6

Royal Cromer enjoys a select location between Yarmouth and Brancaster. 'Select' firstly for its site atop cliffs which alternate with sandy dunes right down the coastline and afford some superb views. Secondly in historical terms, because this is where they thought up the idea of the Curtis Cup between the top British and American ladies. And last but by no means least for the course, which although not a links has the same sort of difficulties including gorse bushes, wind and beautiful bunkering for which we suspect Harry Colt was largely responsible. You need to keep your wits about ycu as some of the elevation changes are surprising. Although not quite in the same league as its illustrious neighbours and without the visual appeal you get with dunes on a true links course (although the closing ho es are great), this layout is well worth a thoroughly serious visit. While you are here, make the most of your time and see the very pretty old cathedral city of Norwich.

Entre Yarmouth et Brancaster, Royal Cromer s'est fait une place de choix. Par sa situation d'abord, au sommet des falaises qui alternent sur toute la côte avec les sites dunaires, et qui offrent des vues superbes. Par l'histoire aussi, car c'est là qu'est née l'idée de la future Curtis Cup, entre les meilleures dames amateur de Grande-Bretagne et des USA. Par le parcours enfin, qui n'est pas un links, mais dont les difficultés en sont bien proches, avec les buissons d'ajoncs, le vent, un "bunkering" de toute beauté, dont on soupçonne Harry Colt d'être largement responsable. Il faudra aussi de l'astuce, car les mouvements du terrain sont parfois importants. Sans être tout à fait au niveau de ses illustres voisins de la région, sans avoir toujours cette animation visuelle que donnent les dunes sur les links authentiques (mais le finale est beau), ce parcours mérite une visite approfondie et sérieuse. Et tant que vous êtes là, profitez-en pour visiter la très jolie vieille ville de Norwich.

Royal Cromer Golf Club — 1888

Overstrand Road
ENG - CROMER, Norfolk NR27 0JH

Office Secrétariat (44) 01263 - 512 884
Pro shop Pro-shop (44) 01263 - 512 267
Fax Fax (44) 01263 - 512 430
Web www.royalcromergolfclub.com
Situation Situation Norwich, 32 km
Cromer (pop. 5 025), 1.5 km
Annual closure Fermeture annuelle no
Weekly closure Fermeture hebdomadaire no

Fees main season Tarifs haute saison — Full day

	Week days Semaine	We/Bank holidays We/Férié
Individual Individuel	£ 45	£ 55
Couple Couple	£ 90	£ 110

Caddie Caddie no — **Electric Trolley** Chariot électrique yes
Buggy Voiturette yes — **Clubs** Clubs yes
Credit cards Cartes de crédit
VISA - MasterCard (Pro shop & Bar)

Access Accès : Norwich, A149. In Cromer, turn right on Coast Road past lighthouse.
Map 7 on page 483 Carte 7 Page 483

GOLF COURSE — PARCOURS — 15/20

Site Site
Maintenance Entretien
Architect Architecte — Harry S. Colt
Type Type — seaside course, open country
Relief Relief
Water in play Eau en jeu
Exp. to wind Exposé au vent
Trees in play Arbres en jeu

Scorecard Carte de score	Chp. Chp.	Mens Mess.	Ladies Da.
Length Long.	5802	5652	5233
Par	72	72	74
Slope system	—	—	—

Advised golfing ability Niveau de jeu recommandé — 0 12 24 36
Hcp required Handicap exigé — certificate

CLUB HOUSE & AMENITIES — CLUB HOUSE ET ANNEXES — 7/10

Pro shop Pro-shop
Driving range Practice
Sheltered couvert no - On grass sur herbe yes - Putting-green putting-green yes - Pitching-green pitching green no

HOTEL FACILITIES — ENVIRONNEMENT HOTELIER — 6/10

HOTELS HÔTELS
Sea Marge - 17 rooms, D £ 110 - Overstrand 1.5 km
Tel (44) 01263 - 579 579, Fax (44) 01263 - 579 524

Links Country Park - 49 rooms, D £ 150 - West Runton 3 km
Tel (44) 01263 - 838 383, Fax (44) 01263 - 838 264

Dormy House - 14 rooms, D from £ 90 - West Runton 3 km
Tel (44) 01263 - 837 537, Fax (44) 01263 - 837 537

RESTAURANTS RESTAURANTS
Westgate Lodge - Cromer 1.5 km - Tel (44) 01263 - 512840
Links Country Park - West Runton 3 km
Tel (44) 01263 - 838383
Dales Country House - Sheringham 7 km
Tel (44) 01263 - 824 555

Royal Guernsey

15	7	7

The Channel Islands are a curious blend of things English and French, with food coming under the latter influence (happily for the French). But golfing here is very British, as seen with this course. Firstly, given the incredible number of players who walk these fairways, Royal Guernsey is very well maintained (but often very dry in Summer). Then it requires good golfing skills and experience of playing in the wind, a capricious element here often changing directions several times in one round This traditional links course looks as natural as ever despite a number of restyling operations, particularly from Mackenzie Ross and Fred Hawtree. As a bonus, you get splendid views over the sea, the gardens close to the club-house... and the cows. Enjoy in a holiday mood.

Les îles anglo-normandes (Channel Islands) présentent un curieux mélange d'anglais et de français, cette dernière influence étant aussi sensible (heureusement) sur la cuisine locale. Mais le golf est bien britannique, ce parcours en est l'illustration. D'abord, compte-tenu du nombre incroyable de joueurs qui y passent, il est bien entretenu (mais souvent très sec en été), ensuite, il réclame un jeu très aguerri et une bonne expérience du vent, car celui-ci est capricieux et peut changer plusieurs fois de sens pendant une partie. Dans ces conditions, on n'abîme pas trop les petits greens, que l'on rejoint moins vite qu'on le voudrait. Parcours de links traditionnel, il continue à paraître naturel, malgré de nombreuses révisions, surtout de Mackenzie Ross et Fred Hawtree. En prime, les vues sont magnifiques, sur la mer, sur les jardins près du club-house... et sur les vaches. A déguster dans un esprit de vacances.

Royal Guernsey Golf Club — 1890

L'Ancresse
ENG - VALE, Guernsey, Channel Islands

Office	Secrétariat	(44) 01481 - 246 523
Pro shop	Pro-shop	(44) 01481 - 245 070
Fax	Fax	(44) 01481 - 243 960
Web	www.royalguernseygolfclub.com	
Situation	Situation	St Peter Port, 4.5 km
Annual closure	Fermeture annuelle	no
Weekly closure	Fermeture hebdomadaire	no

Fees main season Tarifs haute saison	Week days Semaine	We/Bank holidays We/Férié
		Full day
Individual Individuel	£ 45	*
Couple Couple	£ 90	*

* Thursday, Saturday afternoon & Sunday: members & guests only

Caddie Caddie no **Electric Trolley** Chariot électrique no

Buggy Voiturette no **Clubs** Clubs yes

Credit cards Cartes de crédit
VISA - MasterCard (Pro shop goods only)

Access Accès : Near Pembroke Bay, north of the island
Map 9 on page 486 Carte 9 Page 486

GOLF COURSE — PARCOURS — 15/20

Site	Site	
Maintenance	Entretien	
Architect	Architecte	unknown
Type	Type	seaside course, links
Relief	Relief	
Water in play	Eau en jeu	
Exp. to wind	Exposé au vent	
Trees in play	Arbres en jeu	

Scorecard Carte de score	Chp. Chp.	Mens Mess.	Ladies Da.
Length Long.	5585	5585	5005
Par	70	70	72
Slope system	—	—	—

Advised golfing ability Niveau de jeu recommandé: 0 12 24 36

Hcp required Handicap exigé: certificate

CLUB HOUSE & AMENITIES — CLUB HOUSE ET ANNEXES — 7/10

Pro shop Pro-shop
Driving range Practice
Sheltered couvert 10 bays - On grass sur herbe no - Putting-green putting-green yes - Pitching-green pitching green yes

HOTEL FACILITIES — ENVIRONNEMENT HOTELIER — 7/10

HOTELS HÔTELS

De Havelet - 34 rooms, D £ 120 - St Peter Port 5 km
Tel (44) 01481 - 722 199, Fax (44) 01481 - 714 057

St Pierre Park - 131 rooms, D £ 170 - St Peter Port 5 km
Tel (44) 01481 - 728 282, Fax (44) 01481 - 712 041

La Frégate - 13 rooms, D from £ 135- St Peter Port 5 km
Tel (44) 01481 - 724624, Fax (44) 01481 - 720443

RESTAURANTS RESTAURANTS

The Absolute End - St Peter Port 5 km
Tel (44) 01481 - 723 822

Wellington Boot - St Peter Port 5 km
Tel (44) 01481 - 722 199

Café du Moulin - St Peter in the Wood 12 km
Tel (44) 01481 - 265 944

Royal Jersey

16	7	8

Harry Vardon was born next door, just before fellow Channel Islander Ted Ray. Add to that the fact that more recently Tommy Horton learnt how to play here and that is maybe a record number of champions for a club that has recently celebrated its 125th anniversary. The views from the impressive clubhouse are simply magnificent on a course which is a real paradise for golfers, especially players who can produce shots while interpreting every change in land level and get their distances right. In this respect, you are almost better off trusting your eyes than the yardage book. There is no par 4 longer than 400 yards (360 metres), there are five par 3s and only two par 5s at the beginning, doubtless to get you off to a happy start. The plot thickens thereafter with numerous hazards all very well positioned, the deadliest being the sea, the ultimate slicer's graveyard. Royal Jersey is very busy in Summer but playable all year because of the warm climate. The best times are Spring and Autumn, which are sheer magic.

Harry Vardon est né à côté d'ici, précédant Ted Ray. Si on ajoute que, plus récemment, Tommy Horton a appris le golf ici, voici un record de champions pour un seul club, qui vient de fêter ses 125 ans. Les vues sont magnifiques depuis l'impressionnant clubhouse sur ce véritable paradis pour ceux qui savent fabriquer des coups de golf, en interprétant tous les changements de niveau du terrain, notamment pour les distances. A ce propos, il est presque plus sûr de se fier à ses yeux qu'au carnet de parcours. Aucun par 4 ne dépasse 360 mètres (400 yards), il y a cinq par 3 et seulement deux par 5 placés dès le début, sans doute pour commencer avec le sourire. Les choses sérieuses commencent alors, avec des obstacles nombreux, très bien placés, le plus redoutable étant la mer, en tout cas pour les sliceurs. Très fréquenté en été, Royal Jersey est jouable toute l'année en raison de la douceur du climat, mais on préférera encore le printemps et l'automne, simplement sublimes.

Royal Jersey Golf Club — 1878

ENG - GROUVILLE, Jersey JE3 9BD

Office Secrétariat (44) 01534 - 854 416
Pro shop Pro-shop (44) 01534 - 852 234
Fax Fax (44) 01534 - 854 684
Web www.royaljersey.com
Situation Situation Gorey, 1 km
St Helier (pop. 28 123), 7 km

Annual closure Fermeture annuelle no
Weekly closure Fermeture hebdomadaire no

Fees main season Tarifs haute saison	18 holes	
	Week days Semaine	**We/Bank holidays** We/Férié
Individual Individuel	£ 50	£ 50*
Couple Couple	£ 100	£ 100*

* Visitors after 14:30 at week-ends

Caddie Caddie no — **Electric Trolley** Chariot électrique yes
Buggy Voiturette yes — **Clubs** Clubs yes
Credit cards Cartes de crédit
VISA - Eurocard - MasterCard - DC (Pro shop goods only)

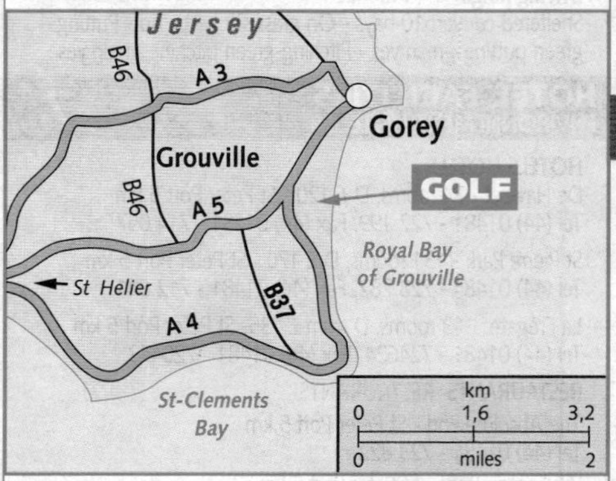

Access Accès : St Helier, A3 → Gorey. Turn right on A4.
Map 9 on page 486 Carte 9 Page 486

GOLF COURSE — PARCOURS — 16/20

Site Site
Maintenance Entretien
Architect Architecte F.W. Brewster
Type Type seaside course, links
Relief Relief
Water in play Eau en jeu
Exp. to wind Exposé au vent
Trees in play Arbres en jeu

Scorecard Carte de score	**Chp.** Chp.	**Mens** Mess.	**Ladies** Da.
Length Long.	5480	5480	4890
Par	70	70	71
Slope system	—	—	—

Advised golfing ability Niveau de jeu recommandé 0 12 24 36
Hcp required Handicap exigé 28 Men, 36 Ladies

CLUB HOUSE & AMENITIES — CLUB HOUSE ET ANNEXES — 7/10

Pro shop Pro-shop
Driving range Practice
Sheltered couvert no - On grass sur herbe no - Putting-green putting-green yes - Pitching-green pitching green no

HOTEL FACILITIES — ENVIRONNEMENT HOTELIER — 8/10

HOTELS HÔTELS
Longueville Manor - St Saviour/St Helier 6 km
28 rooms, D £ 240
Tel (44) 01534 - 725 501, Fax (44) 01534 - 731 613

Old Court House - 58 rooms, D £ 130 - Gorey 1 km
Tel (44) 01534 - 854 444, Fax (44) 01534 - 853 587

De Vere Grand - 114 rooms, D £ 150 - St Helier 7 km
Tel (44) 01534 - 722 301, Fax (44) 01534 - 737 815

RESTAURANTS RESTAURANTS
Longueville Manor - St Saviour 6 km - Tel (44) 01534 - 725 501
Jersey Pottery - Gorey 1 km - Tel (44) 01534 - 851119
La Petite Pomme - St Helier 7 km - Tel (44) 01534 - 766 608
Suma's - Gorey 1 km - Tel (44) 01534 - 853 291

Royal Liverpool (Hoylake)

18	8	7

Royal Liverpool makes its long overdue return to the Open Championship rota 2006. Few courses are as flat as this and yet because of the course's complexity the services of a caddy are strongly recommended. Although you can barely see the sea, the wind is always a problem. The same goes for OB, some of which is inside the course, on hole N° 1 for example (it will not play as the first during the Open). This poses an immediate threat if the wind is in the wrong direction. Hoylake is said to be a match for Carnoustie in terms of difficulty and it is hard to argue with that, even when playing in fine weather. The golfer needs patience, imagination and skill to produce shots you will never find in the instruction manual, particularly on the less spectacular holes where you might be tempted to drop your guard. Surrounded by houses, Royal Liverpool may not be the most attractive of courses but don't be lulled into a false sense of security…you need to be on top of your game to meet the challenge and understand exactly what this magnificent course is all about.

Royal Liverpool célèbre le retour du parcours parmi les hôtes du British Open. Ce sera en 2006. Peu de parcours sont aussi plats que celui-ci, et vous êtes fortement incités à engager un caddie. Bien que l'on ne voit pas la mer, le vent pose toujours des problèmes, de même que les hors-limites. Certains sont même internes, comme au 1 par exemple : attention si le vent ne souffle pas du bon côté. On dit que Hoylake tient tête à Carnoustie en matière de difficulté et ce n'est pas faux, même par beau temps. Il faut ici de la patience et de l'imagination, savoir improviser, inventer des coups qui ne sont pas dans les livres… surtout sur les trous les moins spectaculaires, où l'on aurait tendance à baisser sa garde. Entouré de maisons, Royal Liverpool n'est sans doute pas le parcours de golf le plus séduisant, mais ne vous laissez pas porter par une impression de sécurité. Il faut être au sommet de son jeu pour relever ses défis et comprendre de quoi ce parcours est capable.

Royal Liverpool Golf Club — 1869

Meols Drive, Hoylake
ENG - WIRRAL, Cheshire L47 4AL

Office Secrétariat (44) 0151 - 632 3101
Pro shop Pro-shop (44) 0151 - 632 5868
Fax Fax (44) 0151 - 632 6737
Web www.royal-liverpool-golf.com
Situation Situation Wallasey, 5 km
Liverpool (pop. 452 450), 16 km
Annual closure Fermeture annuelle no
Weekly closure Fermeture hebdomadaire no

Fees main season Tarifs haute saison	18 holes	
	Week days Semaine	We/Bank holidays We/Férié
Individual Individuel	£ 100	£ 150
Couple Couple	£ 200	£ 300

Full week days: £ 150

Caddie Caddie yes **Electric Trolley** Chariot électrique no
Buggy Voiturette no **Clubs** Clubs yes

Credit cards Cartes de crédit
VISA - Eurocard - MasterCard - AMEX - DC - JCB

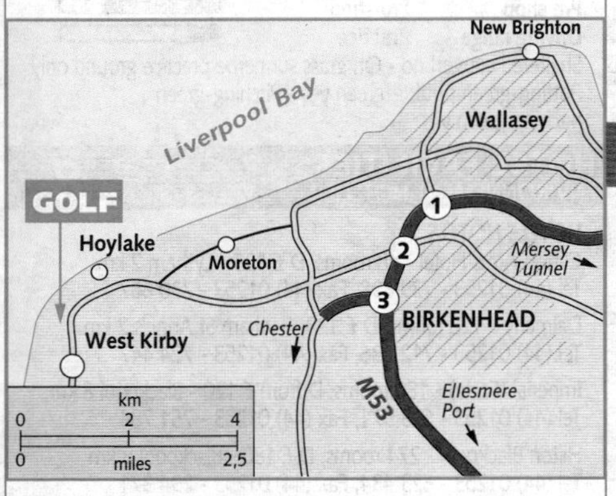

Access Accès : A551/A553 to Hoylake.
Map 5 on page 479 Carte 5 Page 479

GOLF COURSE — PARCOURS 18/20

Site Site
Maintenance Entretien
Architect Architecte Jack Morris
Type Type links
Relief Relief
Water in play Eau en jeu
Exp. to wind Exposé au vent
Trees in play Arbres en jeu

Scorecard Carte de score	Chp. Chp.	Mens Mess.	Ladies Da.
Length Long.	6345	6139	5180
Par	72	72	74
Slope system	—	—	—

Advised golfing ability Niveau de jeu recommandé 0 12 24 36
Hcp required Handicap exigé Men 24, Ladies 36

CLUB HOUSE & AMENITIES — CLUB HOUSE ET ANNEXES 8/10

Pro shop Pro-shop
Driving range Practice
Sheltered couvert no - On grass sur herbe yes (pract. fairway) - Putting-green putting-green yes - Pitching-green pitching green yes

HOTEL FACILITIES — ENVIRONNEMENT HOTELIER 7/10

HOTELS HÔTELS

Grove Hotel - 14 rooms, D from £ 70 - Wallasey 6 km
Tel (44) 0151 - 639 3947, Fax (44) 0151 - 639 0028

Leasowe Castle Hotel - 47 rooms, D £ 85- Moreton 4 km
Tel (44) 0151 - 606 9191, Fax (44) 0151 - 678 5551

Bowler Hat - 32 rooms, D £ 95 - Birkenhead 8 km
Tel (44) 0151 - 652 4931, Fax (44) 0151 - 653 8127

Thornton Hall - 63 rooms, D £ 115 - Thornton Hough 5 km
Tel (44) 0151 - 336 3938, Fax (44) 0151 - 336 7864

RESTAURANTS RESTAURANTS

Grove Hotel - Wallasey 6 km - Tel (44) 0151 - 630 4558
Lee Ho - Moreton 4 km - Tel (44) 0151 - 677 6440

Royal Lytham & St Anne's

18	8	8

Like nearby Fairhaven, Royal Lytham doesn't look the most spectacular of courses at first sight, nor the most isolated. It is surrounded by houses and a railway line and has no sea-views. In fact you might think it has done everything to avoid any superfluous cosmetic appearance. But this is a golfer's course, and when the wind howls it is a real monster, almost on a par with Carnoustie, the most brutal of all British courses. Fowler, Colt and Simpson joined forces to make this the ultimate test, the obligatory final examination which was later to be fine-tuned by C.K. Cotton. Pure and tough, every hazard is visible but you need to play here fifty times or more to become familiar with them all. Course maintenance is excellent and the greens are slick but prone to push balls towards the deep bunkers. Thinking about it, this style of austerity does have its own special appeal. For the British Open in 2001 won by David Duval, 14 bunkers were added by Stan Eby taking the total to 196. Come here with all the sand-wedges you can muster.

Comme Fairhaven, Royal Lytham ne donne pas d'emblée l'impression la plus spectaculaire, ni celle de l'isolement que proposent souvent les golfs. Entouré par les maisons, la voie ferrée et sans vue sur la mer, c'est un parcours dont on pourrait croire qu'il a évité tout aspect décoratif superflu. C'est un parcours pour golfeurs. Avec le vent, c'est un monstre, l'égal presque de Carnoustie, le plus brutal des parcours de Grande-Bretagne. Fowler, Colt et Simpson se sont alliés pour en faire un test absolu, un examen de passage inévitable, C.K. Cotton l'a enfin peaufiné. Pur, dur, il dévoile tous ses obstacles, mais il faut jouer cinquante fois pour bien assimiler. L'entretien est excellent, les greens subtils, mais ils rejettent volontiers la balle vers de profonds bunkers. Finalement, une telle austérité ne manque pas de charme. Pour le British Open 2001 remporté par David Duval, 14 nouveaux bunkers avaient été ajoutés par Stan Eby, portant le total à 196. On peut venir ici avec une brassée de sandwedges...

Royal Lytham & St Anne's Golf Club 1896

St Patrick's Road South
ENG - LYTHAM, Lancs FY8 3LQ

Office Secrétariat (44) 01253 - 724 206
Pro shop Pro-shop (44) 01253 - 720 094
Fax Fax (44) 01253 - 780 946
Web www.royallytham.org
Situation Situation Blackpool (pop. 146 069), 8 km
Annual closure Fermeture annuelle no
Weekly closure Fermeture hebdomadaire no

Fees main season Tarifs haute saison	18 holes	
	Week days Semaine	**We/Bank holidays** We/Férié
Individual Individuel	£ 110	*
Couple Couple	£ 220	*

* Visitors Monday and Thursday only

Caddie Caddie on request **Electric Trolley** Chariot électrique no
Buggy Voiturette no **Clubs** Clubs no
Credit cards Cartes de crédit
VISA - MasterCard

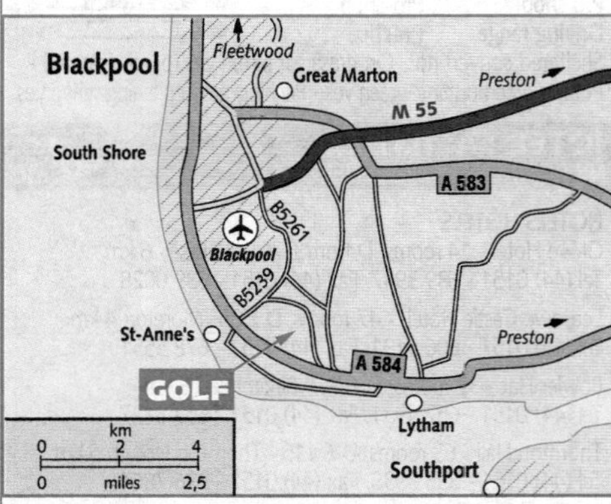

Access Accès : 1 km from centre of St Anne's
Map 5 on page 479 Carte 5 Page 479

GOLF COURSE 18/20
PARCOURS

Site Site
Maintenance Entretien
Architect Architecte H. Fowler, H.S. Colt, T.Simpson, C.K.Cotton
Type Type links
Relief Relief
Water in play Eau en jeu
Exp. to wind Exposé au vent
Trees in play Arbres en jeu

Scorecard Carte de score	**Chp.** Chp.	**Mens** Mess.	**Ladies** Da.
Length Long.	6202	6011	5232
Par	71	71	75
Slope system	—	—	—

Advised golfing ability 0 12 24 36
Niveau de jeu recommandé
Hcp required Handicap exigé 21 Men, 30 Ladies

CLUB HOUSE & AMENITIES 8/10
CLUB HOUSE ET ANNEXES

Pro shop Pro-shop
Driving range Practice
Sheltered couvert no - On grass sur herbe practice ground only
Putting-green putting-green yes - Pitching-green pitching green yes

HOTEL FACILITIES 8/10
ENVIRONNEMENT HOTELIER

HOTELS HÔTELS
Clifton Arms Hotel - 48 rooms, D £ 125 - Lytham 2 km
Tel (44) 01253 - 739 898, Fax (44) 01253 - 730 657

Dalmeny - 128 rooms, D £ 128 - Lytham St Anne's 2 km
Tel (44) 01253 - 712 236, Fax (44) 01253 - 724 447

Imperial (Forte) - 180 rooms, D from £ 120 - Blackpool 8 km
Tel (44) 01253 - 623 971, Fax (44) 01253 - 751 784

Hilton Blackpool - 274 rooms, D £ 180 - Blackpool 8 km
Tel (44) 01253 - 623 434, Fax (44) 01253 - 294 371

RESTAURANTS RESTAURANTS
September Brasserie - Blackpool 8 km - Tel (44) 01253 - 623 282
Cromwellian - Kirkham 13 km - Tel (44) 01772 - 685 680

Royal Mid-Surrey *Outer*

14	8	8

With two courses (including the "Inner" course which is not quite as good), this is one of the great clubs close to London. Unfortunately it lies directly beneath a London Heathrow flight path and so, even though located in a residential area, is less tranquil than it might have been. There is a warm welcome for visitors during the week, a none too frequent occurrence in this part of the country, and the club-house is well worth inspecting to view an impressive collection of golfing memorabilia. This generally flat course, designed by J.H. Taylor, is historically important but has no outstanding difficulty, even though lack of yardage is offset by a par 69 and some very tough rough might test a few weak wrists. Except holes 1 (a long par 3) and 17, this is a very decent course for enjoying your golf even when your swing is not quite in the groove. The recent automatic watering system has considerably improved the course's overall condition during prolonged periods of dry weather.

Avec deux parcours, dont le "Inner" est moins intéressant, c'est un des grands clubs près de Londres, mais aussi sur le passage des avions d'Heathrow, ce qui perturbe un endroit autrement très calme, bien qu'il soit situé dans une zone résidentielle. L'accueil est agréable en semaine, ce n'est pas forcément si fréquent dans la région, et le club-house mérite une visite, pour la belle collection de souvenirs de golf qui faisaient de l'ancien un petit musée. Généralement plat, le parcours de J.H. Taylor n'offre pas de difficultés particulières, même si son manque de longueur est compensé par un par de 69, et si quelques zones de rough peuvent inquiéter les poignets fragiles. Mis à part le 1 (long par 3) et le 17, c'est un très honorable parcours pour se faire plaisir même quand on n'est pas dans son meilleur swing. L'arrosage automatique a beaucoup amélioré son entretien dans les périodes de sécheresse.

Royal Mid-Surrey Golf Club — 1892

Old Deer Park
ENG - RICHMOND, Surrey TW9 2SB

Office Secrétariat (44) 020 - 8940 1894
Pro shop Pro-shop (44) 020 - 8939 0148
Fax Fax (44) 020 - 8939 0150
Web www.rmsgc.co.uk
Situation Situation London, 15 km
Richmond, 1 km
Annual closure Fermeture annuelle no
Weekly closure Fermeture hebdomadaire no

Fees main season Tarifs haute saison — Full day

	Week days Semaine	We/Bank holidays We/Férié
Individual Individuel	£ 75	*
Couple Couple	£ 150	*

* Week-ends: members only / Week days after 13:00, £ 50

Caddie Caddie on request **Electric Trolley** Chariot électrique yes
Buggy Voiturette yes **Clubs** Clubs yes
Credit cards Cartes de crédit
Visa - Mastercard - Switch - Delta (Pro shop only)

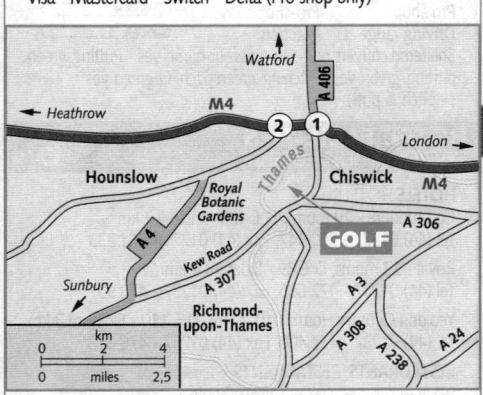

Access Accès : A316, 300 m before Richmond roundabout → London (close to Royal Botanic Gardens).
Map 8 on page 485 Carte 8 Page 485

GOLF COURSE — PARCOURS 14/20

Site Site
Maintenance Entretien
Architect Architecte J.H. Taylor
Type Type parkland
Relief Relief
Water in play Eau en jeu
Exp. to wind Exposé au vent
Trees in play Arbres en jeu

Scorecard Carte de score	Chp. Chp.	Mens Mess.	Ladies Da.
Length Long.	5747	5450	5231
Par	69	69	73
Slope system	—	—	—

Advised golfing ability Niveau de jeu recommandé 0 12 24 36
Hcp required Handicap exigé Men 28, 36 Ladies

CLUB HOUSE & AMENITIES — CLUB HOUSE ET ANNEXES 8/10

Pro shop Pro-shop
Driving range Practice
Sheltered couvert 4 indoor nets - On grass sur herbe yes - Putting-green putting-green yes - Pitching-green pitching green yes (2)

HOTEL FACILITIES — ENVIRONNEMENT HOTELIER 8/10

HOTELS HÔTELS
Petersham - 61 rooms, D £ 170 - Richmond 2 km
Tel (44) 020 - 8940 7471, Fax (44) 020 - 8939 1098

Richmond Gate - 68 rooms, D from £ 150 - Richmond 2 km
Tel (44) 020 - 8940 0061, Fax (44) 020 - 8332 0354

Richmond Hill - 138 rooms, D £ 155 - Richmond 2 km
Tel (44) 020 - 8940 2247, Fax (44) 020 - 8940 5424

RESTAURANTS RESTAURANTS
Nightingales (Petersham Hotel) - Richmond 2 km
Tel (44) 020 - 8939 1084
McClements - Twickenham 1 km - Tel (44) 020 - 8744 9610

Royal North Devon (Westward Ho!) 17 6 6

This is the oldest links course in England. If you are disappointed when you set eyes on the flat-looking terrain, you certainly won't be once you are out on the course. It might look gentle and simplistic but it doesn't play that way. Consider the following range of challenges, for example: tight fairways, invisible ditches, small deep bunkers sometimes lined with railway sleepers, very well protected greens where the approach is sometimes blind and rough with sea-gorse where it is nigh on impossible to get the ball back onto the fairway. Sheep crop the grass and bleat at the top of your back-swing, and then there is the wind. If you can keep the ball low, if you know your strengths and weaknesses, if you stay humble in your ambitions and if someone accompanies you around this huge open space, you can spend a great day and get the impression of having walked around a piece of golfing history. The club-house (1892) is virtually as old as the club and has a sort of mini-museum which every child should see.

Le plus vieux links d'Angleterre. L'arrivée à "Westward Ho!" peut paraître décevante tant le terrain est sans relief, mais votre partie ne va pas en manquer : c'est beaucoup moins tranquille qu'il n'y paraît. D'abord, les difficultés : fairways étroits, fossés invisibles, bunkers petits et profonds, parfois bordés de traverses, greens très défendus et dont l'entrée est parfois aveugle, dans les roughs et buissons de joncs marins d'où il est impossible de sortir. Des moutons broutent le gazon et bêlent quand vous êtes en haut du backswing. Il y a aussi du vent. Si vous savez jouer des balles basses, si vous connaissez bien vos forces et vos faiblesses, si vous envisagez humblement ce parcours, et si quelqu'un vous oriente dans cet immense espace, vous passerez une merveilleuse journée en ayant l'impression d'avoir mis vos pas dans l'histoire. Le club-house (1892) est quasiment aussi ancien que le club, on y trouve un véritable petit musée à montrer aux petits jeunes qui ne connaissent pas l'histoire.

Royal North Devon Golf Club — 1864

Golf Links Road, Westward Ho!
ENG - BIDEFORD, Devon EX39 7HD

Office Secrétariat (44) 01237 - 473 817
Pro shop Pro-shop (44) 01237 - 477 598
Fax Fax (44) 01237 - 473 456
Web www.royalnorthdevongolfclub.co.uk
Situation Situation Barnstaple, 12 km
Bideford (pop. 13 070), 4 km

Annual closure Fermeture annuelle no
Weekly closure Fermeture hebdomadaire no

Fees main season Tarifs haute saison 18 holes

	Week days Semaine	We/Bank holidays We/Férié
Individual Individuel	£ 38	£ 44
Couple Couple	£ 76	£ 88

Full days: £ 44 and £ 50 (We)

Caddie Caddie no — **Electric Trolley** Chariot électrique no
Buggy Voiturette no — **Clubs** Clubs yes

Credit cards Cartes de crédit
VISA - Eurocard - MasterCard (except bar)

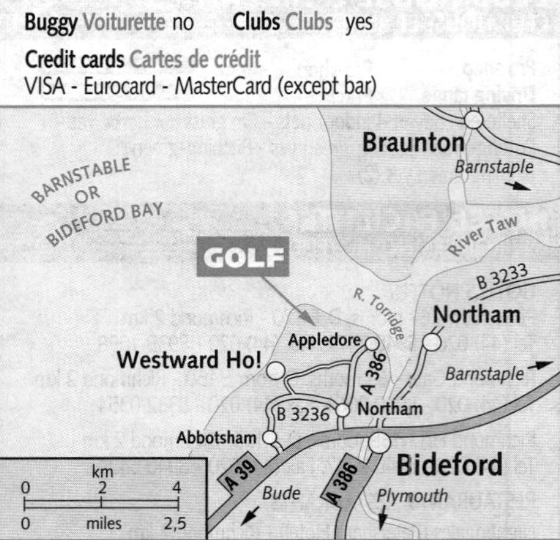

Access Accès : M5 Exit 27, A361 to Barnstaple, then A39 through Northam, take road down Bone Hill past Post Office, keep on left, club-house ahead on hill.
Map 6 on page 480 Carte 6 Page 480

GOLF COURSE — PARCOURS 17/20

Site Site
Maintenance Entretien
Architect Architecte — Old Tom Morris
Type Type — links
Relief Relief
Water in play Eau en jeu
Exp. to wind Exposé au vent
Trees in play Arbres en jeu

Scorecard Carte de score	Chp. Chp.	Mens Mess.	Ladies Da.
Length Long.	5990	5758	5137
Par	71	72	73
Slope system	—	—	—

Advised golfing ability Niveau de jeu recommandé — 0 12 24 36
Hcp required Handicap exigé — certificate

CLUB HOUSE & AMENITIES — CLUB HOUSE ET ANNEXES 6/10

Pro shop Pro-shop
Driving range Practice
Sheltered couvert no - On grass sur herbe yes - Putting-green putting-green yes - Pitching-green pitching green yes (+ pitch & putt)

HOTEL FACILITIES — ENVIRONNEMENT HOTELIER 6/10

HOTELS HÔTELS
Commodore - 20 rooms, D £ 120 - Instow 7 km
Tel (44) 01271 - 860 347, Fax (44) 01271 - 861 233

Royal - 32 rooms, D £ 89 - Bideford 4 km
Tel (44) 01237 - 472 005, Fax (44) 01237 - 478 957

Yeoldon Country House - 10 rooms, D £ 110 - Bideford 3 km
Tel (44) 01237 - 474 400, Fax (44) 01237 - 476 618

RESTAURANTS RESTAURANTS
Yeoldon Country House - Bideford 3 km
Tel (44) 01237 - 474 400
Halmpstone Manor - Barnstaple 10 km
Tel (44) 01271 - 830 321

Royal St George's

19 | 7 | 5

This is the sort of masterpiece that defies description. If a golf course is to be an adversary offering the toughest resistance to every shot and yet still giving the player the opportunity to shine – sometimes forcing him (or her) to take a longer route to get a better shot at the target – then this is the ultimate challenge. If it can be said to provoke even the hardiest golfer before breaking them completely but at the same time, respecting the wise and the knowledgeable, then Royal St George's is the greatest of them all. If we had to find one fault with this regular venue for the British Open, it would be that not all the hazards are clearly visible. Even if you have seen the course on TV, you have to play it several times to uncover its secret but this is a privilege largely reserved for members. Although the course is open during the week, we would advise visitors to play with a member to savour to the full what it has to offer. Lengthened still further for the British Open in 2003, the course showed how well it resists new technologies. Even the world's very best came to grief.

C'est le genre de chef d'oeuvre qui échappe à toute description. Si un parcours de golf est un adversaire qui se défend contre tous les coups, offre des chances de briller à son adversaire, oblige parfois à contourner son objectif pour mieux y revenir ensuite, c'est le meilleur de tous. S'il faut provoquer les téméraires pour mieux les détruire, respecter les sages et les savants, Royal St George's est l'un des très grands. S'il est un seul défaut à ce links où le British Open revient régulièrement, c'est que tous les obstacles ne sont pas clairement visibles : même si vous l'avez vu à la TV, il faut le jouer souvent pour en découvrir les secrets, c'est un privilège largement réservé aux membres. Bien que le parcours soit ouvert en semaine, on conseille aux visiteurs de jouer avec eux, ou au moins avec un caddie. Le plaisir n'en sera que plus grand. Plus encore allongé, le parcours a montré au British Open 2003 à quel point il peut résister aux technologies, en cassant les griffes des plus grands.

Royal St George's Golf Club — 1887

ENG - SANDWICH, Kent CT13 9PB

Office Secrétariat (44) 01304 - 613 090
Pro shop Pro-shop (44) 01304 - 615 236
Fax Fax (44) 01304 - 611 245
Web www.royalstgeorges.com
Situation Situation Sandwich, 2 km, Deal, 7 km
Annual closure Fermeture annuelle no
Weekly closure Fermeture hebdomadaire no

Fees main season Tarifs haute saison	18 holes	
	Week days Semaine	We/Bank holidays We/Férié
Individual Individuel	£ 115	*
Couple Couple	£ 230	*

* We: members only
Week days: Monday, Tuesday, Thursday

Caddie Caddie on request **Electric Trolley** Chariot électrique no
Buggy Voiturette no **Clubs** Clubs yes
Credit cards Cartes de crédit
Visa - Mastercard (Pro shop goods only)

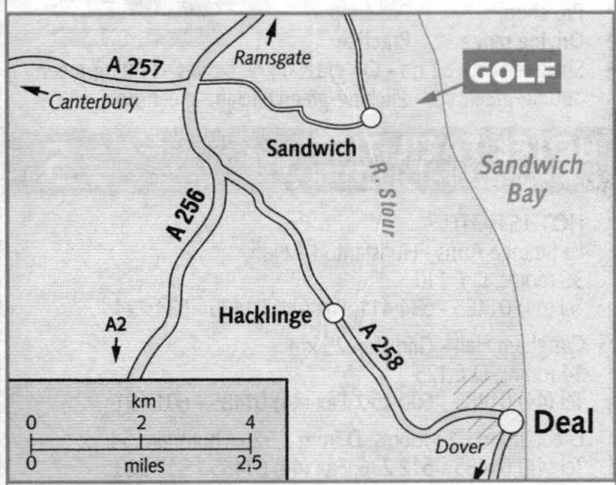

Access Accès : Sandwich → "Golf Courses". 1 km along Sandown Road. Club drive on left after last houses
Map 7 on page 483 Carte 7 Page 483

GOLF COURSE — PARCOURS 19/20

Site Site
Maintenance Entretien
Architect Architecte Dr W. Laidlaw Purves
Type Type seaside course, links
Relief Relief
Water in play Eau en jeu
Exp. to wind Exposé au vent
Trees in play Arbres en jeu

Scorecard Carte de score	Chp. Chp.	Mens Mess.	Ladies Da.
Length Long.	6174	5904	—
Par	70	70	—
Slope system	—	—	—

Advised golfing ability Niveau de jeu recommandé 0 12 24 36
Hcp required Handicap exigé 18

CLUB HOUSE & AMENITIES — CLUB HOUSE ET ANNEXES 7/10

Pro shop Pro-shop
Driving range Practice
Sheltered couvert no - On grass sur herbe yes - Putting-green putting-green yes - Pitching-green pitching green yes

HOTEL FACILITIES — ENVIRONNEMENT HOTELIER 5/10

HOTELS HÔTELS
Bell Hotel - 33 rooms, D £ 100 - Sandwich
Tel (44) 01304 - 613 388, Fax (44) 01304 - 615 308
Swallow Kent International - Sandwich
56 rooms, D £ 100
Tel (44) 01843 - 588 276, Fax (44) 01843 - 586 866
Blazing Donkey Country Hotel - Sandwich
22 rooms, D £ 125 (w. dinner)
Tel (44) 01304 - 617 362, Fax (44) 01304 - 615 264

RESTAURANTS RESTAURANTS
Dunkerleys Restaurant - Deal 7 km - Tel (44) 01304 - 375016
George and Dragon Inn - Sandwich
Tel (44) 01304 - 613 106

Royal West Norfolk (Brancaster) 18 7 5

Don't be put off savouring one of the most intriguing courses you are ever likely to visit by the fact that, at high tide, the sea floods the roadway that leads to the car park. If you are one of those golfers who are attracted by nature, wildlife and seaside vegetation, this course is for you, set in a landscape of dunes and salt-marshes which are home to a host of wild animals. Brancaster is famous for its railway sleeper bunkers and its fiendishly slick greens, which are tough to putt on and tough to hit as they are small and often demand a long-iron approach shot to reach them. In typical links fashion, there are nine holes out and nine holes in – and if the wind blows the differences will become apparent. The course can be so daunting that it is far preferable to play match-play, with drinks at the bar afterwards the stakes. By the way, once in there in front of the inviting fire which always burns in the lounge, you will be tempted to stay for ever. Old and charming Brancaster is a place where time has stood still, which is why you should feel so privileged to be there.

Ne refusez pas de visiter l'un des parcours les plus étonnants que vous puissiez jouer parce que, à marée haute, la mer inonde la route qui conduit au club. Si vous êtes de ces amoureux de la nature, de la flore et de la faune, ce parcours est pour vous, dans un paysage de dunes et de marais salés, qui abritent une vie sauvage très riche. Royal West Norfolk est célèbre pour ses terribles bunkers renforcés par des traverses de chemin de fer, mais aussi pour des greens diaboliques, difficiles à toucher car ils sont petits, difficiles à putter, et l'on doit souvent les attaquer avec de longs fers. Comme sur les vrais links, le dernier trou de l'aller ne revient pas au club house, et quand le vent souffle, vous sentirez la différence. Ce parcours est si exigeant qu'il vaut mieux le jouer en match-play, avec un enjeu à consommer au club-house, devant l'éternel feu de bois dans la cheminée où il fait bon rester. Ici, tout est ancien et beau, le temps s'est arrêté, c'est pourquoi on s'y sent aussi privilégié.

Royal West Norfolk Golf Club — 1892

ENG - BRANCASTER, Norfolk PE31 8 AY

Office	Secrétariat	(44) 01485 - 210 087
Pro shop	Pro-shop	(44) 01485 - 210 616
Fax	Fax	(44) 01485 - 210 087
Web	—	
Situation	Situation	King's Lynn, 30 km
Annual closure	Fermeture annuelle	no
Weekly closure	Fermeture hebdomadaire	no

Fees main season / Tarifs haute saison	Week days / Semaine	We/Bank holidays / We/Férié
		Full day
Individual Individuel	£ 70	£ 80
Couple Couple	£ 140	£ 160

Caddie Caddie on request Electric Trolley Chariot électrique no

Buggy Voiturette no Clubs Clubs yes

Credit cards Cartes de crédit
Visa - Mastercard (Pro shop goods & green fees)

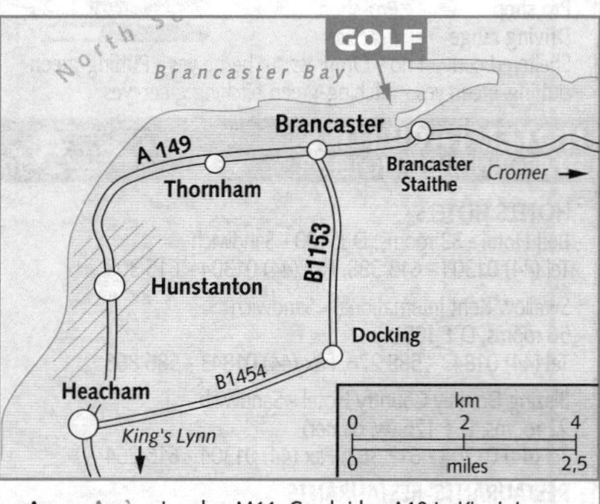

Access Accès : London M11. Cambridge A10 to King's Lynn. A149 North through Hunstanton to Brancaster. Turn left into Beach Road, continue across marsh.
Map 4 on page 477 Carte 4 Page 477

GOLF COURSE / PARCOURS — 18/20

Site	Site	
Maintenance	Entretien	
Architect	Architecte	Holcombe Ingleby, Horace Hutchinson
Type	Type	seaside course, links
Relief	Relief	
Water in play	Eau en jeu	
Exp. to wind	Exposé au vent	
Trees in play	Arbres en jeu	

Scorecard / Carte de score	Chp. / Chp.	Mens / Mess.	Ladies / Da.
Length Long.	5785	5785	5334
Par	71	71	75
Slope system	—	—	—

Advised golfing ability / Niveau de jeu recommandé: 0 12 24 36

Hcp required / Handicap exigé: certificate

CLUB HOUSE & AMENITIES / CLUB HOUSE ET ANNEXES — 7/10

Pro shop — Pro-shop
Driving range — Practice
Sheltered couvert no - On grass sur herbe yes - Putting-green putting-green yes - Pitching-green pitching green no

HOTEL FACILITIES / ENVIRONNEMENT HOTELIER — 5/10

HOTELS HÔTELS

Le Strange Arms - Hunstanton 12 km
36 rooms, D £ 110
Tel (44) 01485 - 534 411, Fax (44) 01485 - 534 724

Congham Hall - Grimston 25 km
14 rooms, D £ 175
Tel (44) 01485 - 600 250, Fax (44) 01485 - 601 191

Lifeboat Inn - 13 rooms, D from £ 92 - Thornham 5 km
Tel (44) 01485 - 512 236, Fax (44) 01485 - 512 323

RESTAURANTS RESTAURANTS

The White Horse - Brancaster 2 km
Tel (44) 01485 - 210 262

Royal Wimbledon

15	7	8

Being a very private club (but open to green-fees on week days) and having been upstaged by other, slightly newer courses a little further out of town, Royal Wimbledon probably doesn't have the reputation it deserves. Yet this is the second oldest course in England, although restyled by Willie Park and then by Harry Colt, whose layouts always appeal one way or the other. The course is rather hilly but for some reason the club does not provide buggies. Luckily, the 18 holes are on the short side, so at least you will be hitting short irons into greens defended by some formidable bunkers, always well placed and often deep. The par 3s, holes 5, 13 and 17, fall into this category. To add to the pleasure of this challenge, the putting surfaces are also remarkably well designed and excellent in quality. And you will have all the time in the world to practice your putting stroke on a famous and equally remarkable practice green, rather like at St Andrews. The club will willingly show visitors some very comprehensive historical documents about the course.

Parce qu'il s'agit d'un club privé, parce qu'il a été éclipsé par d'autres golfs plus éloignés, plus campagnards aussi, Royal Wimbledon n'a pas la réputation qu'il mérite. Il s'agit pourtant du second golf créé en Angleterre, mais il a été largement remanié par Willie Park, puis Harry Colt, dont aucun parcours ne laisse indifférent. Il est assez accidenté mais les voiturettes n'étant sans doute pas assez "royales", il n'y en a pas. Heureusement, les 18 trous sont assez courts, car il vaut mieux attaquer les greens avec de petits clubs : les bunkers de défense sont redoutables, bien placés et parfois très profonds. Les par 3 n° 5, 13 et 17 sont notamment très défendus. Pour ajouter encore au plaisir, les greens sont remarquablement dessinés et de très bonne qualité de surface. On a tout le loisir de s'y entraîner sur un célèbre et remarquable putting-green, utilisé pour des compétitions spécifiques, à l'instar de celui de St Andrews. Le club vous montrera volontiers son historique très documenté.

Royal Wimbledon Golf Club — 1870

Camp Road
ENG - WIMBLEDON SW19

Office Secrétariat (44) 020 - 8946 2125
Pro shop Pro-shop (44) 020 - 8946 4606
Fax Fax (44) 020 - 8944 8652
Web www.rwgc.co.uk
Situation Situation London, 14 km
Annual closure Fermeture annuelle no
Weekly closure Fermeture hebdomadaire no

Fees main season Tarifs haute saison	18 holes	
	Week days Semaine	**We/Bank holidays** We/Férié
Individual Individuel	£ 60	*
Couple Couple	£ 120	*

* Members only / Full week days: £ 85

Caddie Caddie on request **Electric Trolley** Chariot électrique yes
Buggy Voiturette no **Clubs** Clubs yes
Credit cards Cartes de crédit (Pro shop goods only)
VISA - Eurocard - MasterCard - AMEX - DC

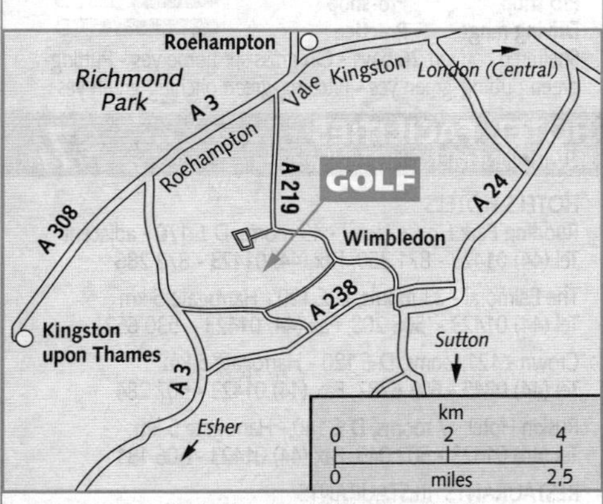

Access Accès : Central London, Fulham Road (A304) → Putney, then Putney Hill, A219 → Caesar's Camp. Golf at Wimbledon Common.
Map 8 on page 485 Carte 8 Page 485

GOLF COURSE — PARCOURS 15/20

Site Site
Maintenance Entretien
Architect Architecte W. Park, H S. Colt
Type Type inland, parkland
Relief Relief
Water in play Eau en jeu
Exp. to wind Exposé au vent
Trees in play Arbres en jeu

Scorecard Carte de score	**Chp.** Chp.	**Mens** Mess.	**Ladies** Da.
Length Long.	5712	5712	5015
Par	70	70	72
Slope system	—	—	—

Advised golfing ability Niveau de jeu recommandé 0 12 24 36

Hcp required Handicap exigé certificate

CLUB HOUSE & AMENITIES — CLUB HOUSE ET ANNEXES 7/10

Pro shop Pro-shop
Driving range Practice
Sheltered couvert - **On grass** sur herbe yes - **Putting-green** putting-green yes - **Pitching-green** pitching green yes

HOTEL FACILITIES — ENVIRONNEMENT HOTELIER 8/10

HOTELS HÔTELS

Cannizaro House - 45 rooms, D £ 241 - Wimbledon, close
Tel (44) 020 - 8879 1464, Fax (44) 020 - 8879 7338

Forte Travelodge - 32 rooms, D £ 95 - Morden 5 km
Tel (44) 020 - 8640 8227, Fax (44) 020 - 8640 8227

Kingston Lodge - Kingston-upon-Thames 2 km
63 rooms, D £ 145
Tel (44) 020 - 8541 4481, Fax (44) 020 - 8547 1013

RESTAURANTS RESTAURANTS

Gravier's - Kingston-upon-Thames 4 km
Tel (44) 020 - 8547 1121

Sonny's - Barnes 5 km - Tel (44) 020 - 8748 0393

Restaurant at the Petersham - Richmond 6 km
Tel (44) 020 - 8939 1084

Rudding Park

14 | 8 | 7

Faced with very strict planning controls, the course architect was required to make a choice between giving up the ghost or simple ingenuity. Designer Martin Hawtree chose the second option and here has produced one of his best courses in a park that was created by the celebrated Humphrey Repton in the 18th century. As no bunkers were allowed except in wooded areas, there are very few greenside traps but the edges of the putting surfaces are well contoured with slopes and hollows and the trees are brought into play to be more strategic than decorative. As far as your game is concerned, approach shots are tricky and putting calls for some inspired play. Water has also been cleverly brought into the frame, although on several holes the ladies may have problems carrying it. It will be interesting to see how this interesting project matures, and the hotel on site is not only pleasant but also regularly receives awards. Cottages are also available for rent.

Devant des règlements administratifs stricts, on laissé le choix à Martin Hawtree entre l'abandon et l'ingéniosité. Il a choisi la deuxième solution et produit là un de ses meilleurs ouvrages, à partir d'un parc dessiné par le célèbre Humphrey Repton au 18è siècle. Comme il était interdit de placer des bunkers sauf dans les zones boisées, on ne trouve ici que très peu de bunkers de greens, mais les alentours des surfaces de putting sont modelés en reliefs et en creux, et les arbres mis en jeu de manière encore plus stratégique que décorative. Sur le plan du jeu, les approches sont beaucoup plus délicates, et les greens très modelés demandent de l'inspiration. Les obstacles d'eau ont aussi été mis en jeu avec intelligence, mais certaines dames auront peut-être du mal à les franchir sur certains trous en portant la balle. On suit avec intérêt l'évolution de ce projet intéressant, et l'hôtel sur place est non seulement agréable mais régulièrement distingué. Des cottages sont également disponibles à la location.

Rudding Park Golf Club — 1995

Rudding Park, Follifoot
ENG - HARROGATE, Yorkshire HG3 1DJ

Office	Secrétariat	(44) 01423 - 872 100
Pro shop	Pro-shop	(44) 01254 - 872 100
Fax	Fax	(44) 01254 - 873 011
Web	www.ruddingpark.com	
Situation	Situation	Harrogate, 5 km
Annual closure	Fermeture annuelle	no
Weekly closure	Fermeture hebdomadaire	no

Fees main season Tarifs haute saison — 18 holes

	Week days / Semaine	We/Bank holidays / We/Férié
Individual Individuel	£ 29,50	£ 35*
Couple Couple	£ 59	£ 70*

Full days: £ 40 / £ 50 (We)
* We: Friday → Sunday

Caddie Caddie no **Electric Trolley** Chariot électrique yes
Buggy Voiturette yes **Clubs** Clubs yes
Credit cards Cartes de crédit
VISA - Eurocard - MasterCard - AMEX - JCB

Access Accès : Leeds → Harrogate on A61, then A658 (Harrogate by-pass), follow brown tourist signs for Rudding Park.
Map 4 on page 476 Carte 4 Page 476

GOLF COURSE — PARCOURS — 14/20

Site	Site	
Maintenance	Entretien	
Architect	Architecte	Martin Hawtree
Type	Type	parkland
Relief	Relief	
Water in play	Eau en jeu	
Exp. to wind	Exposé au vent	
Trees in play	Arbres en jeu	

Scorecard Carte de score	Chp. Chp.	Mens Mess.	Ladies Da.
Length Long.	6184	5873	5167
Par	72	72	72
Slope system	0	0	0

Advised golfing ability Niveau de jeu recommandé — 0 12 24 36
Hcp required Handicap exigé — 28 Men, 36 Ladies

CLUB HOUSE & AMENITIES — CLUB HOUSE ET ANNEXES — 8/10

Pro shop Pro-shop
Driving range Practice
Sheltered couvert 26 bays - On grass sur herbe yes - Putting-green putting-green yes - Pitching-green pitching green yes

HOTEL FACILITIES — ENVIRONNEMENT HOTELIER — 7/10

HOTELS HÔTELS

Rudding Park House Hotel - 49 rooms, D £ 170 - adjacent
Tel (44) 01423 - 871 350, Fax (44) 01423 - 872 286

The Balmoral - 23 rooms, D £ 120 - Harrogate 5 km
Tel (44) 01423 - 508 208, Fax (44) 01423 - 530 652

Crown - 121 rooms, D £ 120 - Harrogate 5 km
Tel (44) 0845 - 602 6787, Fax (44) 01423 - 502 284

Ruskin Hotel - 7 rooms, D £ 140 - Harrogate 5 km
Tel (44) 01423 - 502 045, Fax (44) 01423 - 506 131

RESTAURANTS RESTAURANTS

The Boar's Head - Harrogate 5 km - Tel (44) 01423 - 771 888
Clocktower Brasserie - Rudding Park - Tel (44) 01423 - 872 100
Drum & Monkey - Harrogate 5 km - Tel (44) 01423 - 502 650

Rye

18 | 6 | 6

A masterpiece of links golf architecture on a par with the nearby courses at Sandwich and Deal. It is also a formidable test of golf with a par 68, which seems harmless enough until you actually read the scorecard. There is only one par 5 and that is hole No 1, suggesting that the architect wanted to get the birdie holes out of the way from the word go. This is followed by five par 3s with tiered greens stretching from 140 to almost 200 metres, and twelve par 4s, half of which are close to 400 metres. Add a few blind shots and a touch of wind then save your best for the closing holes, which finish with a magnificent 18th hole. You don't have much chance to relax here, with the first headache being the choice of club, compounded by the obligation not only to carry fourteen clubs but also to be able to play each one in ten different ways. Rye is a must, but the club is so private that it is virtually impossible to get on, but you never know. Maybe in the pretty medieval town of the same name (also well worth a visit) you will run into a club member. If you do, treat him nice.

Un chef-d'œuvre de l'architecture de links, au même titre que ses (proches) voisins de Deal et Sandwich. C'est aussi un redoutable test de golf, avec un par 68 qui paraît anodin tant que l'on ne regarde pas la carte de score. Un seul par 5 ici, le premier trou, comme pour régler tout de suite l'affaire des trous à birdie, mais cinq par 3 étagés entre 140 et 200 mètres, et douze par 4, dont la moitié flirte avec les 400 mètres. Ajoutez quelques coups aveugles, le vent, et un finale culminant dans un 18 de toute beauté. On ne trouvera guère ici d'occasions de se reposer, la migraine commençant dès le choix du club, accentuée par l'obligation d'en avoir non seulement quatorze, mais aussi dix manières de jouer chacun d'entre eux. Il faut jouer Rye, et c'est presque impossible tant le club est privé. Mais peut-être rencontrerez-vous dans la jolie petite ville médiévale du même nom un membre du club. Si cela vous arrive, traitez-le bien !

Rye Golf Club — 1894

Camber
ENG - RYE, East Sussex TN31 7QS

Office	Front desk	(44) 01797 - 225 241
Pro shop	Pro shop	(44) 01797 - 225 218
Fax	Fax	(44) 01797 - 228 419
Web	—	
Situation	Location	Rye (pop. 3708), 6 km
Annual closure	Annual closing	no
Weekly closure	Weekly closing	no

Fees main season Fees main season	18 holes	
	Week days Week days	**We/Bank holidays** We/Legal holidays
Individual Single player	*	*
Couple Couple	*	*

* Strictly for members and their guests / or introduction of a member

Caddie Caddie no — **Electric Trolley** Electric trolley no

Buggy Buggy no — **Clubs** Clubs no

Credit cards Credit cards
Pro shop only

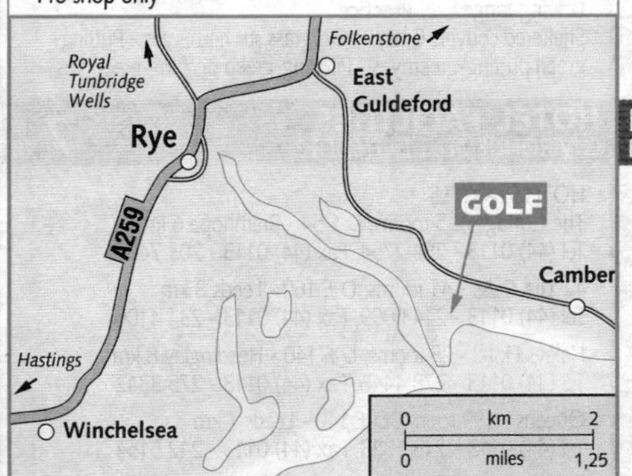

Access Access : A259 Hastings → Folkestone. After Rye, turn right → Camber. After 5 km, golf on right hand side.
Map 7 on page 483 Map 7 Page 483

GOLF COURSE — PARCOURS — 18/20

Site	Site	
Maintenance	Upkeep	
Architect	Designer(s)	Harry S. Colt
Type	Type	links, seaside course
Relief	Relief	
Water in play	Water in play	
Exp. to wind	Exposed to wind	
Trees in play	Trees in play	

Scorecard Scorecard	**Chp.** Chp.	**Mens** Men	**Ladies** Women
Length Length	5680	5680	4914
Par	68	68	73
Slope system	—	—	—

Advised golfing ability Recommended golfing ability — 0 12 24 36

Hcp required Hcp required — no

CLUB HOUSE & AMENITIES — CLUB HOUSE ET ANNEXES — 6/10

Pro shop Pro shop
Driving range Driving range
Sheltered Sheltered practice area - On grass On grass yes - Putting-green Putting-green yes - Pitching-green Pitching-green yes

HOTEL FACILITIES — ENVIRONNEMENT HOTELIER — 6/10

HOTELS HOTELS

Mermaid Inn - 31 rooms, D £ 160 - Rye 6 km
Tel (44) 01797 - 223 065, Fax (44) 01797 - 225 069

George - 22 rooms, D £ 90 - Rye 6 km
Tel (44) 01797 - 222 114, Fax (44) 01797 - 224 065

Broomhill Lodge - Rye 6 km
12 rooms, D £ 90
Tel (44) 01797 - 280 421, Fax (44) 01797 - 280 402

RESTAURANTS RESTAURANTS

Mermaid Inn - Rye 6 km - Tel (44) 01797 - 223 065
Flushing Inn - Rye 6 km - Tel (44) 01797 - 223 292
Landgate Bistro - Rye 6 km - Tel (44) 01797 - 222 829

Sand Moor

15	7	7

Modern club-houses unquestionably lack the charm of their older counterparts but they are more comfortable. Following this same modern trend, many clubs have also laid out driving ranges like here to cater to the ever greater number of players. In 1961, Sand Moor was given a face-lift and at the same time re-styled, adhering most respectfully to the original layout of Alister MacKenzie on one side of Alwoodley Lane. The land is rather hilly, but as the use of buggies requires a medical certificate we will simply recommend an electric trolley. Laid out over moorland, the feeling of space here is very pleasant and the rough not too hard on your game, but some of the stands of trees and carefully placed fairway bunkers do their job very well. We noted the excellence of the par 3s on what is a very good test of golf, albeit now a little on the short side for the better players.

Les club-houses modernes manquent sans doute un peu du charme des anciens, mais ils ont gagné en confort. De même, bien des clubs comme celui-ci ont aménagé de véritables espaces d'entraînement, ne serait-ce que pour répondre à la demande des joueurs. En 1961, Sand Moor s'est ainsi rajeuni et en a profité pour réaménager – avec beaucoup de respect d'ailleurs – le tracé original d'Alister Mackenzie d'un seul côté d'Alwoodley Lane. Le terrain est assez accidenté, mais seul un certificat médical permettant de jouer en voiturette, on conseillera le chariot électrique. En terre de lande, la sensation d'espace est ici très agréable, le rough n'est pas trop pénalisant, mais certains bouquets d'arbres et des bunkers de fairway judicieusement placés ne manquent pas de jouer leur rôle. A remarquer enfin, la qualité des pars 3. Un très bon test de golf, un peu court aujourd'hui pour les meilleurs joueurs.

Sand Moor Golf Club — 1926

Alwoodley Lane
ENG - LEEDS, W. Yorkshire LS17 7DJ

Office Secrétariat (44) 0113 - 268 5180
Pro shop Pro-shop (44) 0113 - 268 3925
Fax Fax (44) 0113 - 266 1105
Web www.sandmoorgolf.co.uk
Situation Situation Leeds (pop. 680 722), 8 km
Annual closure Fermeture annuelle no
Weekly closure Fermeture hebdomadaire no

618

Fees main season Tarifs haute saison	18 holes	
	Week days Semaine	We/Bank holidays We/Férié
Individual Individuel	£ 40	£ 50
Couple Couple	£ 80	£ 100

Caddie Caddie no — **Electric Trolley** Chariot électrique yes
Buggy Voiturette no — **Clubs** Clubs on request

Credit cards Cartes de crédit
VISA - Eurocard - MasterCard - Switch
(+4% for green fees, not in club-house)

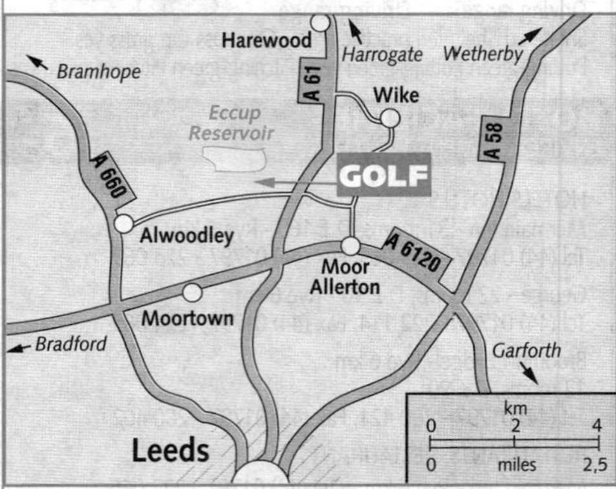

Access Accès : Leeds, A61 North, left into Alwoodley Lane, Golf 0.8 km (1/2 m.) on right hand side.
Map 4 on page 476 Carte 4 Page 476

GOLF COURSE — PARCOURS 15/20

Site Site
Maintenance Entretien
Architect Architecte Alister Mackenzie
Type Type parkland
Relief Relief
Water in play Eau en jeu
Exp. to wind Exposé au vent
Trees in play Arbres en jeu

Scorecard Carte de score	Chp. Chp.	Mens Mess.	Ladies Da.
Length Long.	5851	5454	5092
Par	71	71	73
Slope system	—	—	—

Advised golfing ability Niveau de jeu recommandé 0 12 24 36
Hcp required Handicap exigé certificate

CLUB HOUSE & AMENITIES — CLUB HOUSE ET ANNEXES 7/10

Pro shop Pro-shop
Driving range Practice
Sheltered couvert 6 bays - On grass sur herbe yes - Putting-green putting-green yes - Pitching-green pitching green yes

HOTEL FACILITIES — ENVIRONNEMENT HOTELIER 7/10

HOTELS HÔTELS
The Cottages - 5 rooms, D £ 54 - Bramhope 6 km
Tel (44) 0113 - 284 2754, Fax (44) 0113 - 203 7496

42 The Calls - 41 rooms, D £ 160 - Leeds 8 km
Tel (44) 0113 - 244 0099, Fax (44) 0113 - 234 4100

Haleys Hotel - 28 rooms, D £ 140 - Headingley 8 km
Tel (44) 0113 - 278 4446, Fax (44) 0113 - 275 3342

Queens - 199 rooms, D £ 140 - Leeds 7 km
Tel (44) 0113 - 243 1323, Fax (44) 0113 - 242 5154

RESTAURANTS RESTAURANTS
Pool Court at 42 - Leeds 8 km - Tel (44) 0113 - 244 4242
Leodis - Leeds 8 km - Tel (44) 0113 - 242 1010
Brasserie Forty Four - Leeds 8 km - Tel (44) 0113 - 234 3232

Sandiway

16 | 5 | 7

Sandiway stands in a little compact group of courses to the east of Chester, the others being Mere and the similarly styled Delamere Forest. If Sandiway was in the western suburbs of London it would surely be better known than it is, but there again for a golfer there is something gratifying about being able to talk about little gems that no-one else has ever set eyes upon. With lots of trees lining sloping fairways, keeping your ball in play is anything but easy, so think twice before taking the driver out of the bag. This very varied course demands good tactics and skill in flighting the ball... at least when it comes to getting out of trouble. A very pretty course and a very intelligent one, too, which demands the same quality from the people who play it. The club-house is pleasant but unassuming in the pure English countryside style as pictured by "continentals".

Sandiway tient bien sa place dans un petit groupe compact à l'est de Chester, qui comprend également Mere et Delamere Forest, le second nommé lui étant le plus comparable par son paysage et son style. Sans nul doute, s'il était dans la banlieue ouest de Londres, ce parcours serait bien plus connu, mais, pour un golfeur, c'est très gratifiant de pouvoir parler des trésors que les autres n'ont jamais vu ! Avec beaucoup d'arbres délimitant les trous, et des fairways souvent en pente, il n'est pas évident d'y garder sa balle en sécurité, il faudra donc réfléchir avant d'empoigner son driver. Très varié, ce parcours exige une tactique solide et souvent de savoir travailler la balle... au moins pour s'extraire des problèmes. Ce très joli parcours est d'une grande intelligence, il en demande aussi aux joueurs. Le club-house est agréable et sans prétention, dans le pur style de campagne anglaise que les "continentaux" imaginent.

Sandiway Golf Club — 1921

Chester Road, Sandiway
ENG - NORTHWICH, Cheshire CW8 20 J

Office Secrétariat (44) 01606 - 883 247
Pro shop Pro-shop (44) 01606 - 883 180
Fax Fax (44) 01606 - 888 548
Web www.sandiwaygolf.co.uk
Situation Situation Northwich, 6 km
Chester (pop. 115 971), 25 km

Annual closure Fermeture annuelle: no
Weekly closure Fermeture hebdomadaire: no

Fees main season Tarifs haute saison	18 holes	
	Week days Semaine	**We/Bank holidays** We/Férié
Individual Individuel	£ 45	£ 60
Couple Couple	£ 90	£ 120

Full week days: £ 55

Caddie Caddie no — **Electric Trolley** Chariot électrique yes
Buggy Voiturette no — **Clubs** Clubs no

Credit cards Cartes de crédit
VISA - Eurocard - MasterCard - AMEX (Pro shop goods only)

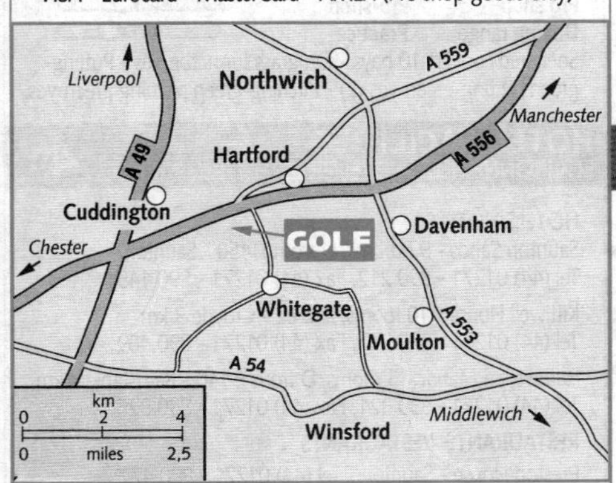

Access Accès : Manchester M56. Jct 7, A556 → Northwich, Chester. Golf on left side after Northwich.
Map 4 on page 476 Carte 4 Page 476

GOLF COURSE — PARCOURS — 16/20

Site Site
Maintenance Entretien
Architect Architecte: Ted Ray
Type Type: parkland
Relief Relief
Water in play Eau en jeu
Exp. to wind Exposé au vent
Trees in play Arbres en jeu

Scorecard Carte de score	**Chp.** Chp.	**Mens** Mess.	**Ladies** Da.
Length Long.	5791	5438	5071
Par	70	70	73
Slope system	—	—	—

Advised golfing ability Niveau de jeu recommandé: 0 12 24 36
Hcp required Handicap exigé: certificate

CLUB HOUSE & AMENITIES — CLUB HOUSE ET ANNEXES — 5/10

Pro shop Pro-shop
Driving range Practice
Sheltered couvert no - On grass sur herbe only practice ground - Putting-green putting-green yes - Pitching-green pitching green yes

HOTEL FACILITIES — ENVIRONNEMENT HOTELIER — 7/10

HOTELS HÔTELS
Nunsmere Hall - 36 rooms, D £ 200 - Sandiway 2 km
Tel (44) 01606 - 889 100, Fax (44) 01606 - 889 055

Rookery Hall - 46 rooms, D from £ 150 - Nantwich 20 km
Tel (44) 01270 - 610 016, Fax (44) 01270 - 626 027

Hartford Hall - 20 rooms, D £ 72 - Northwich 4 km
Tel (44) 01606 - 780 320, Fax (44) 01606 - 782 285

Tall Trees Lodge - 20 rooms, D £ 43 - Weaverham 3 km
Tel (44) 01606 - 790 824, Fax (44) 01606 - 791 330

RESTAURANTS RESTAURANTS
Nunsmere Hall - Sandiway 2 km - Tel (44) 01606 - 889 100
Rookery Hall - Nantwich 20 km - Tel (44) 01270 - 610 016

Saunton *East Course*

18 | 7 | 4

Saunton does not carry the Royal Seal but if it did it would be well deserved. Harry Vardon dreamed of retiring here, but he was a mere six-time Open champion, wasn't he? As such he must have appreciated the amazing balance of the East course, the more fluent of the two Saunton layouts. If you play from the back tees, the first four holes will most likely cause irreparable damage to your card. Likewise, if you don't watch out, the last five will finish it off completely. The other holes are perhaps not quite so devastating, but the worst danger here is being caught off-guard. Winding between magnificent dunes with sheltered greens, all 18 holes at Saunton (running in all directions, by the way) make for fantastic golf if you play from the tees that suit your level. The humbler you are, the more fun you will have, especially since the greens are real beauties. To quote Henry Longhurst, this is "the finest course never to have hosted the Open Championship".

Si Saunton n'a pas eu droit à l'annoblissement, il ne le mérite pas moins : Harry Vardon rêvait de s'y retirer, mais c'était un sextuple vainqueur du British... Comme tel, il dut apprécier le rythme étonnant de ce parcours Est, le plus éloquent des deux. Quand vous jouez des départs arrière, les quatre premiers trous vont dévorer votre carte, comme les cinq derniers la détruiront définitivement si vous n'y restez pas attentif. Les autres trous sont peut-être moins brutaux, mais le pire danger serait de baisser la garde. Insinués entre des dunes magnifiques, les greens bien à l'abri, les trous de Saunton (orientés dans toutes les directions) apportent un plaisir fou, si l'on joue des départs correspondant à son niveau : plus vous serez humble, plus vous prendrez du plaisir. Et d'autant plus que les greens sont un véritable régal. Quand Henry Longhurst disait que c'était le meilleur parcours à n'avoir jamais accueilli le British Open, il exagérait à peine, même si l'on peut toujours argumenter.

Saunton Golf Club — 1897

Saunton
ENG - BRAUNTON EX33 1LG

Office	Secrétariat	(44) 01271 - 812 436
Pro shop	Pro-shop	(44) 01271 - 812 436
Fax	Fax	(44) 01271 - 814 241
Web	www.sauntongolf.co.uk	
Situation	Situation	Barnstaple, 10 km
Annual closure	Fermeture annuelle	no
Weekly closure	Fermeture hebdomadaire	no
Fees main season	Tarifs haute saison	18 holes

	Week days Semaine	We/Bank holidays We/Férié
Individual Individuel	£ 55	£ 55
Couple Couple	£ 110	£ 110

£ 75 for one round on each course / Tee times limited at We

Caddie Caddie on request **Electric Trolley** Chariot électrique yes

Buggy Voiturette yes **Clubs** Clubs yes

Credit cards Cartes de crédit
VISA - MasterCard

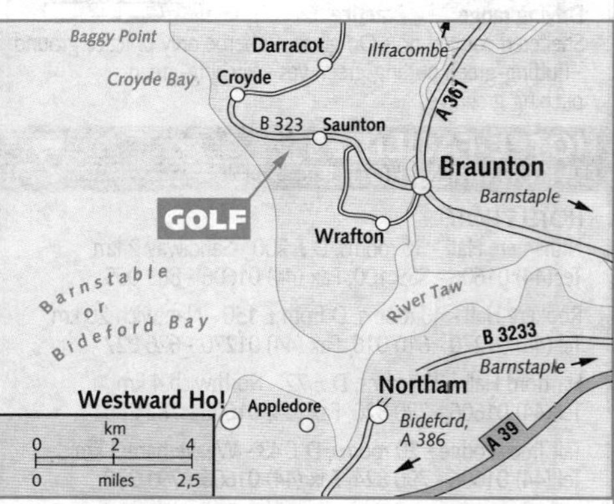

Access Accès : M5 Jct 27, then A361 to Barnstaple, then A361 to Braunton. Follow signs to Saunton, golf on the left.
Map 6 on page 480 Carte 6 Page 480

GOLF COURSE — PARCOURS — 18/20

Site	Site	
Maintenance	Entretien	
Architect	Architecte	Herbert Fowler
Type	Type	seaside course, links
Relief	Relief	
Water in play	Eau en jeu	
Exp. to wind	Exposé au vent	
Trees in play	Arbres en jeu	

Scorecard Carte de score	Chp. Chp.	Mens Mess.	Ladies Da.
Length Long.	6123	5800	4555
Par	73	71	74
Slope system	—	—	—

Advised golfing ability Niveau de jeu recommandé: 0 12 24 36

Hcp required Handicap exigé: certificate

CLUB HOUSE & AMENITIES — CLUB HOUSE ET ANNEXES — 7/10

Pro shop Pro-shop
Driving range Practice
Sheltered couvert 10 bays - On grass sur herbe yes - Putting-green putting-green yes (2) - Pitching-green pitching green yes

HOTEL FACILITIES — ENVIRONNEMENT HOTELIER — 4/10

HOTELS HÔTELS

Saunton Sands - 92 rooms, D from £ 150 - Saunton
Tel (44) 01271 - 890 212, Fax (44) 01271 - 890 145

Kittiwell House - 10 rooms, D £ 82 - Croyde 3 km
Tel (44) 01271 - 890 247, Fax (44) 01271 - 890 469

Halmstope Manor - 5 rooms, D from £ 140 - Barnstaple 8 km
Tel (44) 01271 - 830 321, Fax (44) 01271 - 830 826

RESTAURANTS RESTAURANTS

Preston House - Saunton - Tel (44) 01271 - 890 472

The White Leaf - Croyde 3 km - Tel (44) 01271 - 890 266

Saunton *West Course*

15	7	4

Much more recently constructed than the neighboring East course, Saunton West is a little like the petulant young kid in the family who lacks the good graces of his older brother but whose rowdy behaviour and language are easily forgiven because he is so nice. In other words, this course definitely does not have the subtle greatness of its neighbour but it is still a class act. Laid out amidst sand-dunes, it has taken lessons in classical architecture and even reserves a few blind shots here and there along with some unpredictable terrain and the accompanying awkward bounces that modern players find so irksome but which fascinate lovers of traditional golf. More exhilarating and exciting than the East, the one major shortcoming is its lack of yardage, hence a rightful feeling of frustration for the long-hitting golfer. Not so, though, for mid-handicappers, who will be delighted with this links course that should suit them down to the ground. In this respect the two courses at Saunton are complementary. Of course, the eldest inherits the prestige title, but isn't that how it is in all families?

Bien plus récent que l'East, c'est un peu comme le petit dernier de la famille, moins raisonnable que l'aîné, plus turbulent, et on lui pardonne un comportement et un langage sans souci d'élégance parce qu'il est trop mignon. Autrement dit, ce parcours n'a sans doute pas la subtile grandeur de son voisin, mais il ne manque pas de qualités. Situé au milieu des dunes, il a pris des leçons d'architecture classique, et réserve même ces coups aveugles çà et là, ces reliefs et rebonds imprévisibles qui agacent les joueurs modernes et ravissent les amoureux des traditions. Plus excitant et exaltant que l'East, il souffre cependant d'un gros défaut, c'est d'être bien court, d'où la juste frustration des frappeurs, que n'éprouveront pas les joueurs moyens, ravis de ce links à leur taille. En ce sens, les deux parcours de Saunton se complètent magnifiquement. Bien sûr, c'est l'aîné qui hérite du titre prestigieux, mais c'est le cas dans toutes les familles, non ?

Saunton Golf Club — 1975

Saunton
ENG - BRAUNTON EX33 1LG

Office	Secrétariat	(44) 01271 - 812 436
Pro shop	Pro-shop	(44) 01271 - 812 436
Fax	Fax	(44) 01271 - 814 241
Web	www.sauntongolf.co.uk	
Situation	Situation	Barnstaple, 10 km
Annual closure	Fermeture annuelle	no
Weekly closure	Fermeture hebdomadaire	no
Fees main season	Tarifs haute saison	18 holes

	Week days Semaine	We/Bank holidays We/Férié
Individual Individuel	£ 55	£ 55
Couple Couple	£ 110	£ 110

£ 75 for one round on each course / Tee times limited at We

Caddie Caddie on request **Electric Trolley** Chariot électrique yes

Buggy Voiturette yes **Clubs** Clubs yes

Credit cards Cartes de crédit
VISA - MasterCard

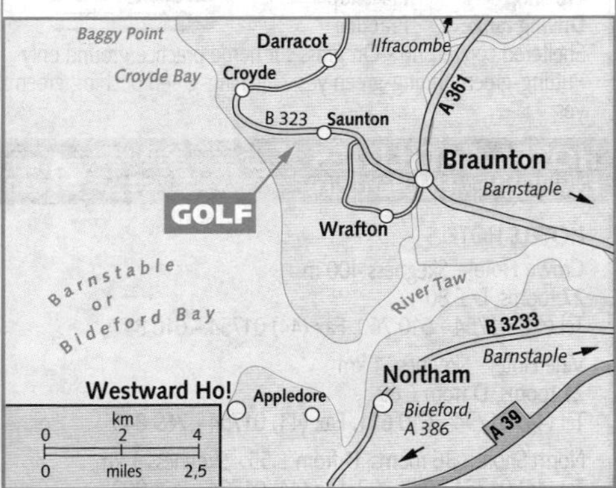

Access Accès : M5 Jct 27, then A361 to Barnstaple, then A361 to Braunton. Follow signs to Saunton, golf on the left.
Map 6 on page 480 Carte 6 Page 480

GOLF COURSE — PARCOURS 15/20

Site	Site	
Maintenance	Entretien	
Architect	Architecte	Frank Pennink
Type	Type	links
Relief	Relief	
Water in play	Eau en jeu	
Exp. to wind	Exposé au vent	
Trees in play	Arbres en jeu	

Scorecard Carte de score	**Chp.** Chp.	**Mens** Mess.	**Ladies** Da.
Length Long.	5763	5525	4808
Par	71	71	71
Slope system	—	—	—

Advised golfing ability Niveau de jeu recommandé — 0 12 24 36

Hcp required Handicap exigé — certificate

CLUB HOUSE & AMENITIES — CLUB HOUSE ET ANNEXES 7/10

Pro shop Pro-shop
Driving range Practice
Sheltered couvert 10 bays - On grass sur herbe yes - Putting-green putting-green yes (2) - Pitching-green pitching green yes

HOTEL FACILITIES — ENVIRONNEMENT HOTELIER 4/10

HOTELS HÔTELS
Saunton Sands - 92 rooms, D from £ 150 - Saunton
Tel (44) 01271 - 890 212, Fax (44) 01271 - 890 145

Kittiwell House - 10 rooms, D £ 82 - Croyde 3 km
Tel (44) 01271 - 890 247, Fax (44) 01271 - 890 469

Halmstope Manor - 5 rooms, D from £ 140 - Barnstaple 8 km
Tel (44) 01271 - 830 321, Fax (44) 01271 - 830 826

RESTAURANTS RESTAURANTS
Preston House - Saunton - Tel (44) 01271 - 890 472
The White Leaf - Croyde 3 km - Tel (44) 01271 - 890 266

Seacroft

17	7	4

Moving northwards along the English coast, this is the only real links course between Hunstanton and Seaton Carew in Teeside where the area is not so bad as it is often said. The landscape at Seacroft will hardly have you gasping with admiration but it is agreeable enough to give this course a pleasant setting. All the holes are neatly laid out in single file, out and in, over two levels separated by dunes, except the disorderly 6th hole. This makes club selection a little easier when the wind is howling and forces you to hit low shots. In fine weather you can hit any shot, which makes life easier for those of you who like to hit the ball high. Whatever, the very strategic placing of the 75 bunkers here plus some very thick undergrowth require a clear-cut tactical approach to every round, but the hazards are visible enough for you to do so with the exception of the odd blind shot. Varied, very authentic and traditional, this is a course you should try.

En remontant la côte, c'est le seul vrai links après Hunstanton, et le suivant sera Seaton Carew, dans un environnement peu séduisant qui lui a fait trop de tort. Les paysages de Seacroft ne vous arracheront pas des cris d'admiration, mais ils sont assez plaisants pour offrir un décor agréable au parcours. Tous les trous sont sagement rangés en file indienne sur deux niveaux séparés par des dunes, en aller et retour, mis à part un indiscipliné, le 6. Cet ordre facilite le choix de clubs quand il y a du vent, qui seul vous obligera aux balles basses. Par beau temps, tous les coups sont permis, ce qui peut faciliter le travail de ceux qui savent surtout lever la balle. En tous les cas, le placement très stratégique des 75 bunkers, la densité de la végétation impliquent de bien définir la tactique de jeu, mais les obstacles sont assez visibles pour ce faire, à l'exception de rares coups aveugles. Varié, très authentique et traditionnel, c'est un parcours à découvrir.

Seacroft Golf Club — 1895

Drummond Road
ENG - SKEGNESS, Lincolnshire PE25 3AU

Office	Secrétariat	(44) 01754 - 763 020
Pro shop	Pro-shop	(44) 01754 - 769 624
Fax	Fax	(44) 01754 - 763 020
Web	www.seacroft-golfclub.co.uk	
Situation	Situation	Skegness, 1.5 km

Boston (pop. 53 226), 30 km

Annual closure Fermeture annuelle — no
Weekly closure Fermeture hebdomadaire — Christmas Day

Fees main season Tarifs haute saison — 18 holes

	Week days / Semaine	We/Bank holidays / We/Férié
Individual Individuel	£ 35	£ 40
Couple Couple	£ 70	£ 80

Full days: £ 45 / £ 50 (We)

Caddie Caddie no — **Electric Trolley** Chariot électrique no
Buggy Voiturette yes — **Clubs** Clubs no
Credit cards Cartes de crédit (Pro shop goods only)
VISA - Eurocard - MasterCard - AMEX - DC

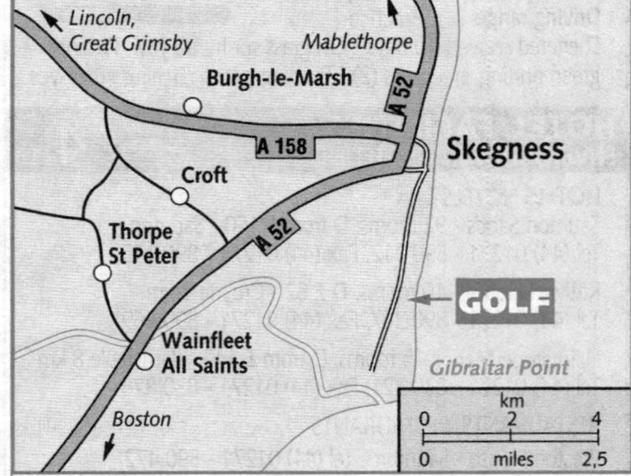

Access Accès : A52 to Skegness. 1.5 km S of Skegness alongside Gibraltar Road Bird Sanctuary.
Map 4 on page 477 Carte 4 Page 477

GOLF COURSE — PARCOURS — 17/20

Site	Site	
Maintenance	Entretien	
Architect	Architecte	Tom Dunn
Type	Type	seaside course, links
Relief	Relief	
Water in play	Eau en jeu	
Exp. to wind	Exposé au vent	
Trees in play	Arbres en jeu	

Scorecard Carte de score	Chp. Chp.	Mens Mess.	Ladies Da.
Length Long.	5831	5421	5275
Par	71	71	73
Slope system	—	—	—

Advised golfing ability Niveau de jeu recommandé — 0 12 24 36
Hcp required Handicap exigé — 28 Men, 36 Ladies

CLUB HOUSE & AMENITIES — CLUB HOUSE ET ANNEXES — 7/10

Pro shop Pro-shop
Driving range Practice
Sheltered couvert no - On grass sur herbe practice ground only
Putting-green putting-green yes - Pitching-green pitching green yes

HOTEL FACILITIES — ENVIRONNEMENT HOTELIER — 4/10

HOTELS HÔTELS

Crown Hotel - Skegness 400 m
27 rooms, D £ 80
Tel (44) 01754 - 610 760, Fax (44) 01754 - 610 847

Vine Hotel - Skegness 1 km
21 rooms, D from £ 69
Tel (44) 01754 - 610 611, Fax (44) 01754 - 769 845

North Shore - 36 rooms, D from £ 55 - Skegness 1 km
Tel (44) 01754 - 763 298, Fax (44) 01754 - 761 902

RESTAURANTS RESTAURANTS

Crown Hotel - Skegness 400 m - Tel (44) 01754 - 610 760

Seascale

17 | 5 | 4

A strange place where the Sellafield power station ought to give golfers at least the energy to turn their backs on the cooling towers. When you think of how much flak golf courses get from some environmentalists, it makes you wonder why they don't protect courses from this sort of eyesore. But at least you can feast your eyes on the distant hills of the Lake District or even closer,the Irish Sea and the Isle of Man. Seascale is a hidden gem, away from the world and off the beaten track. You can talk about this course in glowing terms, no-one will ever argue. An imposing but subtle layout, and unusual in that the railway line runs between the course and the sea, Seascale is anything but a fashionable course. Switching between sand-dunes and smoothly rolling fairways, it is a course to severely test any player's capacity for invention and adaptability. As on every links course, you either act positively or suffer the consequences, depending on the state of your game. If you do not know Seascale, then enter it now into your list of best little-known courses.

La centrale électrique de Sellafield devrait surtout donner l'énergie aux golfeurs de lui tourner le dos. Quand on sait à quel point on peut ennuyer les golfs avec les problèmes d'environnement, pourquoi ne pas préserver aussi les golfs des pollutions visuelles ? Mais on peut au moins tourner les yeux vers les collines du Lake District ou (plus proches) la mer d'Irlande et l'Ile de Man ! Seascale est un joyau caché, à l'écart du monde et des sentiers battus et, quand vous en parlerez avec émotion, personne ne viendra vous contredire. Puissant et subtil, assez curieux dans la mesure où le chemin de fer passe entre le golf et la mer, Seascale est tout sauf un parcours "fashionable." Entre les dunes et de calmes ondulations de fairways, il met en oeuvre la capacité d'invention et d'adaptation des joueurs. Comme sur les links, on agit ou on subit, suivant sa forme du moment. Si vous ne le connaissez pas, c'est un parcours à inscrire à votre tableau de chasse des meilleurs parcours méconnus.

Seascale Golf Club — 1893

The Banks
ENG - SEASCALE, Cumbria CA20 1QL

Office	Secrétariat	(44) 01946 - 728 202
Pro shop	Pro-shop	(44) 01946 - 721 779
Fax	Fax	(44) 01946 - 728 202
Web	www.seascalegolfclub.org	
Situation	Situation	Barrow-in-Furness, 45 km
Annual closure	Fermeture annuelle	no
Weekly closure	Fermeture hebdomadaire	no

Fees main season Tarifs haute saison	18 holes	
	Week days Semaine	**We/Bank holidays** We/Férié
Individual Individuel	£ 25	£ 30
Couple Couple	£ 50	£ 60

Full day: £ 30 / £ 33 (We)

Caddie Caddie no — **Electric Trolley** Chariot électrique no
Buggy Voiturette no — **Clubs** Clubs yes
Credit cards Cartes de crédit no

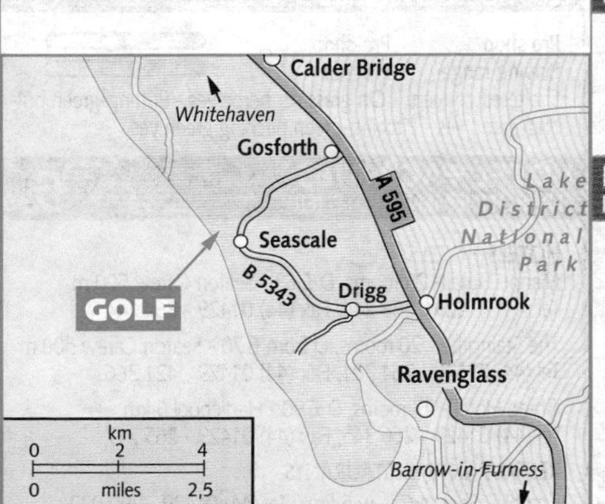

Access Accès : M6 Jct 36, A590 → Barrow-in-Furness. At Greenodd, A5092, then A595 to Seascale. Golf N. of village (can't miss it!)
Map 4 on page 476 Carte 4 Page 476

GOLF COURSE — PARCOURS — 17/20

Site	Site	
Maintenance	Entretien	
Architect	Architecte	Willie Campbell
Type	Type	links
Relief	Relief	
Water in play	Eau en jeu	
Exp. to wind	Exposé au vent	
Trees in play	Arbres en jeu	

Scorecard Carte de score	**Chp.** Chp.	**Mens** Mess.	**Ladies** Da.
Length Long.	5840	5554	5226
Par	71	71	74
Slope system	—	—	—

Advised golfing ability Niveau de jeu recommandé: 0 12 24 36
Hcp required Handicap exigé: certificate

CLUB HOUSE & AMENITIES — CLUB HOUSE ET ANNEXES — 5/10

Pro shop Pro-shop
Driving range Practice
Sheltered couvert no - On grass sur herbe yes - Putting-green putting-green yes - Pitching-green pitching green yes

HOTEL FACILITIES — ENVIRONNEMENT HOTELIER — 4/10

HOTELS HÔTELS
Westlakes - Gosforth 4 km
9 rooms, D from £ 75
Tel (44) 019467 - 25 221, Fax (44) 019467 - 25 099

Low Wood Hall Hotel - Nether Wasdale 10 km
1210 rooms, D from £ 70
Tel (44) 019467 - 26 100, Fax (44) 019467 - 26 111

RESTAURANTS RESTAURANTS
Westlakes - Gosforth 4 km - Tel (44) 019467 - 25 221
Low Wood Hall Hotel - Nether Wasdale 10 km
Tel (44) 019467 - 26 100

Seaton Carew

17	7	5

The industrial surroundings are certainly not the most pleasant setting for a golf course, but no keen golfer can afford to miss playing this course and getting to grips with the wile and cunning of Alister MacKenzie, the layout's devilishly clever architect. The four holes added by Frank Pennink for spice and variety were laid out in the same spirit. Although rather flat, the course comprises several clusters of sand-dunes just to bother the inaccurate hitter, plus the thickets, bushes and buckthorns that go with them. For all the qualities of this championship course, it is not what you woud call intimidating, especially the outward nine. Lesser players might prefer to watch how their betters negotiate the back nine, where certain shots calls for good ball-striking and long carries. This is particularly true on the 17th, probably the toughest hole of all (and the most cunningly conceived) with a terribly difficult approach shot to an elevated green made harder by the wind.

Certes, l'environnement industriel n'est pas des plus réjouissants, mais aucun golfeur acharné ne saurait passer à côté de ce parcours sans affronter les astuces et les ruses d'Alister Mackenzie, son diabolique architecte. Et les quatre trous ajoutés par Frank Pennink, pour varier les plaisirs, ont été créés dans le même esprit. Assez plat, il comprend néanmoins, pour mieux ennuyer le golfeur imprécis, quelques groupes de dunes, avec les arbustes touffus, les buissons et les nerpruns qui vont avec. En dépit de ses qualités de parcours de championnat, il n'est pourtant pas intimidant, en particulier l'aller. Les joueurs peu expérimentés regarderont plutôt leurs «maîtres» négocier le retour, où certains coups demandent des balles solides, bien portées. Notamment le 17, sans doute le trou le plus délicat (et le plus pervers) de Seaton Carew, par son approche des plus difficiles d'un green surélévé. Et le vent s'y amuse...

Seaton Carew Golf Club — 1925

Tees Road
ENG - HARTLEPOOL, Cleveland TS25 1DE

Office Secrétariat (44) 01429 - 261 040
Pro shop Pro-shop (44) 01429 - 890 660
Fax Fax (44) 01429 - 267 952
Web www.seatoncarewgolf.co.uk
Situation Situation Middlesbrough, 10 km

Annual closure Fermeture annuelle no
Weekly closure Fermeture hebdomadaire no

Fees main season Tarifs haute saison		Full day
	Week days Semaine	**We/Bank holidays** We/Férié
Individual Individuel	£ 34	£ 44
Couple Couple	£ 68	£ 88

Caddie Caddie no — **Electric Trolley** Chariot électrique yes
Buggy Voiturette yes — **Clubs** Clubs yes

Credit cards Cartes de crédit
VISA - MasterCard - AMEX - DC (not for green fees)

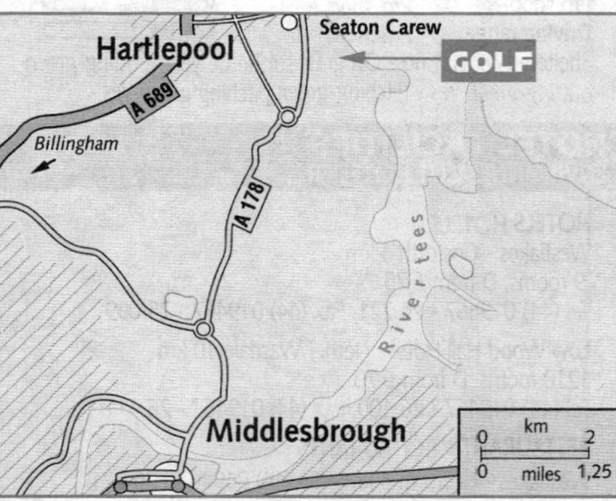

Access Accès : On Coast Road (A178) South of Hartlepool
Map 4 on page 477 Carte 4 Page 477

GOLF COURSE — PARCOURS — 17/20

Site Site
Maintenance Entretien
Architect Architecte — Dr McCuaig (1874), Alister Mackenzie
Type Type — links, seaside course
Relief Relief
Water in play Eau en jeu
Exp. to wind Exposé au vent
Trees in play Arbres en jeu

Scorecard Carte de score	**Chp.** Chp.	**Mens** Mess.	**Ladies** Da.
Length Long.	6170	5941	4951
Par	73	73	73
Slope system	—	—	—

Advised golfing ability Niveau de jeu recommandé — 0 12 24 36
Hcp required Handicap exigé — certificate

CLUB HOUSE & AMENITIES — CLUB HOUSE ET ANNEXES — 7/10

Pro shop Pro-shop
Driving range Practice
Sheltered couvert - On grass sur herbe yes - Putting-green putting-green yes - Pitching-green pitching green yes

HOTEL FACILITIES — ENVIRONNEMENT HOTELIER — 5/10

HOTELS HÔTELS

Marine Hotel - 25 rooms, D £ 63 - Seaton Carew 500 m
Tel (44) 01429 - 266 244, Fax (44) 01429 - 364 144

The Staincliffe - 20 rooms, D from £ 70 - Seaton Carew 500 m
Tel (44) 01429 - 264 301, Fax (44) 01429 - 421 366

Grand Hotel - 47 rooms, D £ 90 - Hartlepool 5 km
Tel (44) 01429 - 266 345, Fax (44) 01429 - 265 217

RESTAURANTS RESTAURANTS

Krimo's - Seaton Carew 5 km - Tel (44) 01429 - 290 022
Al Syros - Hartlepool 2 km - Tel (44) 01429 - 272 525
Portofinos - Hartlepool 3 km - Tel (44) 01429 - 266 166

Shanklin & Sandown

15 | 7 | 6

Shanklin & Sandown is the best of the seven courses on the Isle of Wight. It is short, naturally, as designers at the turn of the century weren't obsessed with length and so didn't build courses merely to cater for the small percentage of big hitters; they appreciated that wind can really bother simply anyone, whether blowing with or against the ball. A part of this layout is similar to a links ourse, another part is more inland in style with some impressive heather and broom. Despite a distinctly hilly character, there are only three blind drives, otherwise playing strategy is clear. The sole element of chance emanates from the stance and lie, sometimes difficult to negotiate for players who are used to flat courses. With tight fairways and well placed bunkers, we would recommend this course to players who have some control over their ball. Beginners here could easily spend all day looking for theirs.

Shanklin & Sandown se détache parmi les sept parcours de l'Ile de Wight. Il est bien sûr assez court, mais les architectes du début du siècle étaient des sages. Ils n'ignoraient pas que les bons frappeurs existaient déjà, mais qu'ils étaient loin d'être les plus nombreux, ils savaient aussi que le vent avait tendance à gêner tout le monde, qu'il soit contre ou avec. Ce parcours comporte une partie apparentée aux links et une partie "inland" avec une très belle végétation de bruyère et de genêts. On ne trouve ici, en dépit d'un certain relief, que trois drives aveugles. Autrement, la stratégie à mettre en oeuvre est assez claire, la part de hasard étant préservée par des stances parfois difficiles pour ceux qui jouent habituellement les pieds à plat. Avec ses fairways étroits et ses bunkers bien placés, on le recommendera à ceux qui savent déjà contrôler la balle car les débutants peuvent passer la journée à chercher la leur !

Shanklin & Sandown Golf Club — 1900

The Fairway Lake
ENG - SANDOWN, Isle of Wight PO36 9 PR

Office	Secrétariat	(44) 01983 - 403 217
Pro shop	Pro-shop	(44) 01983 - 404 424
Fax	Fax	(44) 01983 - 403 007
Web	www.ssgolfclub.com	
Situation	Situation	Isle of Wight
Annual closure	Fermeture annuelle	no
Weekly closure	Fermeture hebdomadaire	no

Fees main season Tarifs haute saison	18 holes	
	Week days Semaine	**We/Bank holidays** We/Férié
Individual Individuel	£ 29,5	£ 35
Couple Couple	£ 59	£ 70

Saturday: only after 13:00 / Sunday: after 9:30

Caddie Caddie no — **Electric Trolley** Chariot électrique yes

Buggy Voiturette no — **Clubs** Clubs yes

Credit cards Cartes de crédit
VISA - MasterCard (Pro shop goods only)

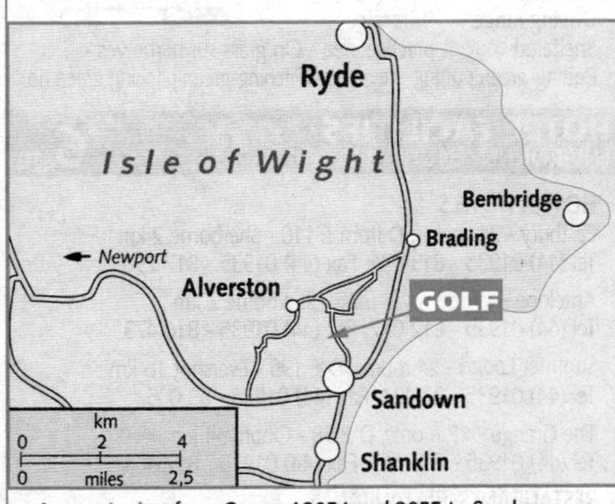

Access Accès : from Cowes A3054 and 3055 to Sandown. Avenue Road on left, then Broadway, Lake Hill on the right, The Fairway on the right.
Map 9 on page 486 Carte 9 Page 486

GOLF COURSE — PARCOURS — 15/20

Site	Site	
Maintenance	Entretien	
Architect	Architecte	James Braid, M. Cowper
Type	Type	links, parkland
Relief	Relief	
Water in play	Eau en jeu	
Exp. to wind	Exposé au vent	
Trees in play	Arbres en jeu	

Scorecard Carte de score	**Chp.** Chp.	**Mens** Mess.	**Ladies** Da.
Length Long.	5456	5223	4960
Par	70	70	72
Slope system	—	—	—

Advised golfing ability Niveau de jeu recommandé: 0 12 24 36
Hcp required Handicap exigé: certificate

CLUB HOUSE & AMENITIES — CLUB HOUSE ET ANNEXES — 7/10

Pro shop Pro-shop
Driving range Practice
Sheltered couvert no - On grass sur herbe yes - Putting-green putting-green yes - Pitching-green pitching green yes

HOTEL FACILITIES — ENVIRONNEMENT HOTELIER — 6/10

HOTELS HÔTELS

Brunswick - 35 rooms, D £ 100 - Shanklin 2 km
Tel (44) 01983 - 863 245, Fax (44) 01983 - 863 398

Royal Hotel - 55 rooms, D £ 140 - Ventnor 6 km
Tel (44) 01983 - 852 186, Fax (44) 01983 - 855 395

Bourne Hall Country - 31 rooms, D £ 120 - Shanklin 2 km
Tel (44) 01983 - 862 820, Fax (44) 01983 - 865 138

Rylstone Manor - 9 rooms, D £ 96 - Shanklin 2 km
Tel (44) 01983 - 862 806, Fax (44) 01983 - 862 806

RESTAURANTS RESTAURANTS

Bourne Hall Country - Shanklin 2 km - Tel (44) 01983 - 862820
Royal Hotel - Ventnor 6 km - Tel (44) 01983 - 852 186

Sherborne

15 | 6 | 6

This course, about a mile from the city of Sherborne, is testimony to the design skills of James Braid over a country landscape. It was completed in 1936 and built upon a rough layout dating from 1894. The course is not too hilly but the natural contours are put to good use and pose a few questions, particularly on the sloping fairways of holes 6 and 13. The five par 3s are all excellent holes. The greens are average in size, never blind but do have some stiff slopes at the front on half a dozen holes. This is a fair test, quite scenic and a good family course. For a little culture after your round, drive into town. In the 16th century, the transformation of Sherborne Abbey into a school led to the building being saved at a time when Henry VIII's break with Rome was resulting in the dissolution of monasteries and often the destruction of some of Britain's finest landmarks.

Ce parcours à deux kilomètres de Sherborne reste un bon témoignage de l'architecture de James Braid en paysage de campagne, réalisé en 1936 à partir d'un tracé ébauché en 1894. Les reliefs ne sont pas très importants mais ils sont bien utilisés et permettent d'apporter quelques éléments d'interrogation, en particulier avec les fairways en pente au 6 et au 13. A remarquer aussi, la qualité des cinq par 3. Les greens sont de taille moyenne, jamais aveugles mais avec des pentes sévères en début de surface, sur une demi-douzaine de trous. Aucun green n'est aveugle, ce qui confirme la franchise de ce bon parcours familial. Pour la culture, on ira en ville : au XVIè siècle la transformation de l'abbaye de Sherborne en école a permis de la préserver, après que la rupture d'Henry VIII avec Rome ait eu pour conséquence la dissolution des monastères, leur abandon et souvent la destruction de monuments magnifiques dans toute la Grande-Bretagne.

Sherborne Golf Club — 1894/1936

Higher Clatcombe
ENG - SHERBORNE, Dorset DT9 4RN

Office Secrétariat (44) 01935 - 814 431
Pro shop Pro-shop (44) 01935 - 812 274
Fax Fax (44) 01935 - 814 218
Web sherbornegc
Situation Situation Yeovil (pop. 28 317), 10 km
Sherborne (pop. 7 606), 2 km
Annual closure Fermeture annuelle no
Weekly closure Fermeture hebdomadaire no

Fees main season Tarifs haute saison — 18 holes

	Week days Semaine	We/Bank holidays We/Férié
Individual Individuel	£ 25	£ 36
Couple Couple	£ 50	£ 72

Full day: £ 30

Caddie Caddie no — **Electric Trolley** Chariot électrique no
Buggy Voiturette no — **Clubs** Clubs ask Pro
Credit cards Cartes de crédit
VISA - MasterCard (Pro shop goods only)

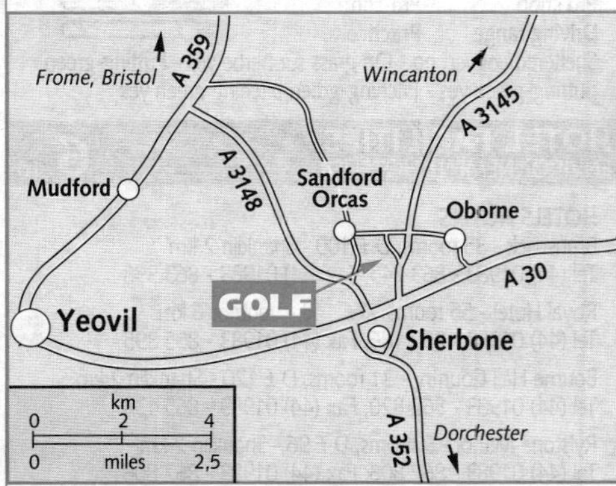

Access Accès : • London M3, Jct 8, A303 to Wincanter, A357 then B3145 → Sherborne. • Bristol A37 to Yeovil, A30 to Sherborne, then B3145 → Wincanton.
Map 6 on page 481 Carte 6 Page 481

GOLF COURSE — PARCOURS — 15/20

Site Site
Maintenance Entretien
Architect Architecte James Braid
Type Type parkland
Relief Relief
Water in play Eau en jeu
Exp. to wind Exposé au vent
Trees in play Arbres en jeu

Scorecard Carte de score	Chp. Chp.	Mens Mess.	Ladies Da.
Length Long.	5377	5220	5018
Par	70	70	73
Slope system	—	—	—

Advised golfing ability Niveau de jeu recommandé 0 12 24 36
Hcp required Handicap exigé certificate

CLUB HOUSE & AMENITIES — CLUB HOUSE ET ANNEXES — 6/10

Pro shop Pro-shop
Driving range Practice
Sheltered couvert practice area - On grass sur herbe yes - Putting-green putting-green yes - Pitching-green pitching green no

HOTEL FACILITIES — ENVIRONNEMENT HOTELIER — 6/10

HOTELS HÔTELS
Eastbury - 21 rooms, D from £ 110 - Sherborne 2 km
Tel (44) 01935 - 813 131, Fax (44) 01935 - 817 296

Antelope - 19 rooms, D £ 75 - Sherborne 2 km
Tel (44) 01935 - 812 077, Fax (44) 01935 - 816 473

Summer Lodge - 24 rooms, D £ 195 - Evershot 16 km
Tel (44) 01935 - 83 424, Fax (44) 01935 - 83 005

The Grange - 18 rooms, D £ 98 - Oborne 4 km
Tel (44) 01935 - 813 463, Fax (44) 01935 - 817 464

RESTAURANTS RESTAURANTS
Eastbury - Sherborne 2 km - Tel (44) 01935 - 813 131
The Grange - Oborne 4 km - Tel (44) 01935 - 813 463
Little Barwick House - Barwick 5 km - Tel (44) 01935 - 423 902

Sheringham

16 | 7 | 6

Less well known than Royal West Norfolk and Hunstanton, Sheringham (together with Royal Cromer) is one of the excellent quartet of courses along this magnificent northern coast of East Anglia. Once you have actually found the entrance to the course, some of the views from the top of chalk cliffs are quite magnificent (the club is especially proud of the view from the 5th tee). This is not a links course but the wind plays an important role as the fairways roll and turn and there are few dunes to offer any shelter. The professionals find Sheringham a little on the short side (we've heard that one before) but the course is looked upon with the greatest respect by the best amateur golfers, for whom the need to improvise and shape shots is an even more essential factor than length. Bunkers play a key role in the definition of each hole and in strategy, but so do the encroaching heather and gorse. At least there are no hidden traps on this Tom Dunn layout (created in 1891) and it is perhaps this fairness which merits our greatest respect.

Moins connu que Royal West Norfolk et Hunstanton, Sheringham est avec Royal Cromer l'un des excellents parcours de cette magnifique côte nord de l'East Anglia, et offre des vues exceptionnelles, du haut de ses falaises de craie (on est fier ici du panorama depuis le tee du 5)... une fois que l'on a trouvé l'entrée du golf. Bien sûr, ce n'est pas un links, mais le vent y joue un rôle encore plus important : les fairways sont bien animés, mais il n'y a pas beaucoup de dunes pour s'en abriter ! Les professionnels le trouvent un peu court (c'est un air connu), mais c'est un tracé hautement respecté par les meilleurs amateurs, pour qui la nécessité de savoir créer des coups de golf est un facteur plus essentiel que la distance. Les bunkers jouent un rôle important dans la définition des trous et la stratégie, mais peut-être plus encore les buissons d'ajoncs et de bruyère. Au moins n'y a t-il aucun piège caché sur ce dessin de Tom Dunn (en 1891), et cette honnêteté mérite le plus grand respect.

Sheringham Golf Club — 1891

Weybourne Road
ENG - SHERINGHAM, Norfolk NR26 8HG

Office Secrétariat (44) 01263 - 823 488
Pro shop Pro-shop (44) 01263 - 822 980
Fax Fax (44) 01263 - 826 129
Web www.sheringhamgolfclub.co.uk
Situation Situation Norwich, 35 km
Cromer (pop. 5 025), 8 km

Annual closure Fermeture annuelle — no
Weekly closure Fermeture hebdomadaire — no

Fees main season Tarifs haute saison — Full day

	Week days Semaine	We/Bank holidays We/Férié
Individual Individuel	£ 45	£ 60
Couple Couple	£ 90	£ 120

Same charge for 18 holes / Week days = Sunday → Friday

Caddie Caddie on request **Electric Trolley** Chariot électrique no

Buggy Voiturette yes **Clubs** Clubs yes

Credit cards Cartes de crédit
Visa - Mastercard (Pro shop goods only)

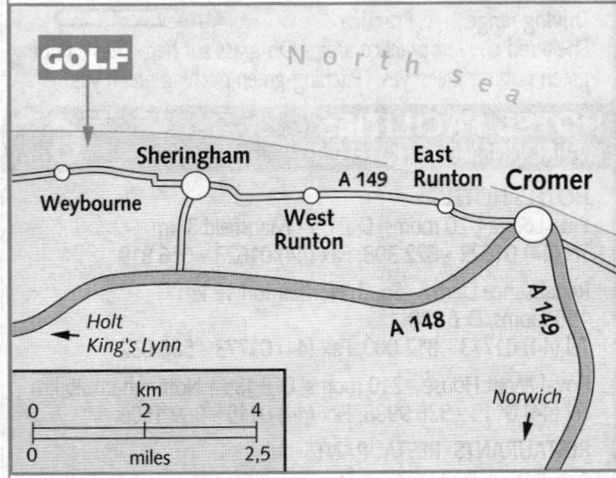

Access Accès : Norwich, A140 N to Cromer. A149 W through Sheringham, Golf on the right opposite Mobil Garage
Map 7 on page 483 Carte 7 Page 483

GOLF COURSE — PARCOURS — 16/20

Site Site
Maintenance Entretien
Architect Architecte — Tom Dunn
Type Type — seaside course, open country
Relief Relief
Water in play Eau en jeu
Exp. to wind Exposé au vent
Trees in play Arbres en jeu

Scorecard Carte de score	Chp. Chp.	Mens Mess.	Ladies Da.
Length Long.	5817	5485	5256
Par	71	71	73
Slope system	—	—	—

Advised golfing ability Niveau de jeu recommandé — 0 12 24 36
Hcp required Handicap exigé — certificate

CLUB HOUSE & AMENITIES — CLUB HOUSE ET ANNEXES — 7/10

Pro shop Pro-shop
Driving range Practice
Sheltered couvert no - On grass sur herbe yes - Putting-green putting-green yes - Pitching-green pitching green yes

HOTEL FACILITIES — ENVIRONNEMENT HOTELIER — 6/10

HOTELS HÔTELS
Beaumaris Hotel - 21 rooms, D £ 96 - Sheringham 5 km
Tel (44) 01263 - 822 370, Fax (44) 01263 - 821 421

Links Country Park - West Runton 6 km
49 rooms, D £ 150
Tel (44) 01263 - 838 383, Fax (44) 01263 - 838 264

Beeches Hotel - 36 rooms, D from £ 95 - Norwich 35 km
Tel (44) 01603 - 621 167, Fax (44) 01603 - 620 151

RESTAURANTS RESTAURANTS
Adlard's - Norwich 35 km - Tel (44) 01603 -633522
Mad Moose Arms (Pub) - Norwich 35 km
Tel (44) 01603 - 627 687

Sherwood Forest

17	7	6

Here we are in Robin Hood country where you can visit the cities of Nottingham and Lincoln and what is left of Sherwood Forest. As you might expect, trees are the main feature on this course and they play a major role throughout. It will be surprising if you don't have to play at least one swirling recovery to get back onto the fairway (the undergrowth is cut back short). Otherwise Harry Colt and James Braid have laid out bunkers as effectively as usual, including around the greens which can be approached in different ways according to their line of defence. A rather traditional layout but with a back 9 that can mess up your score. Having spent many years in the shadow of Notts Golf Club (Hollinwell), this hilly course deserves a little limelight of its own.

Nous voici dans le monde de Robin des Bois. Entre une visite à Nottingham et une excursion vers Lincoln, la forêt de Sherwood n'est plus inquiétante que pour les imaginations d'enfants. Comme on pouvait s'y attendre, les arbres constituent l'essentiel du décor de ce parcours, mais un décor qui joue les rôles principaux. Il serait étonnant que vous n'ayiez jamais à jouer de balles à effet pour vous en extraire (les sous-bois sont bien dégagés). Autrement, Harry Colt et James Braid ont développé leur jeu de bunkers toujours aussi efficace, y compris autour des greens. Ceux-ci peuvent cependant être attaqués de différentes manières, selon les lignes de défense. Un tracé assez traditionnel, mais la difficulté du retour peut perturber le score. Longtemps à l'ombre du Notts Golf Club (Hollinwell), ce parcours très vallonné mérite d'être placé sous une meilleure lumière.

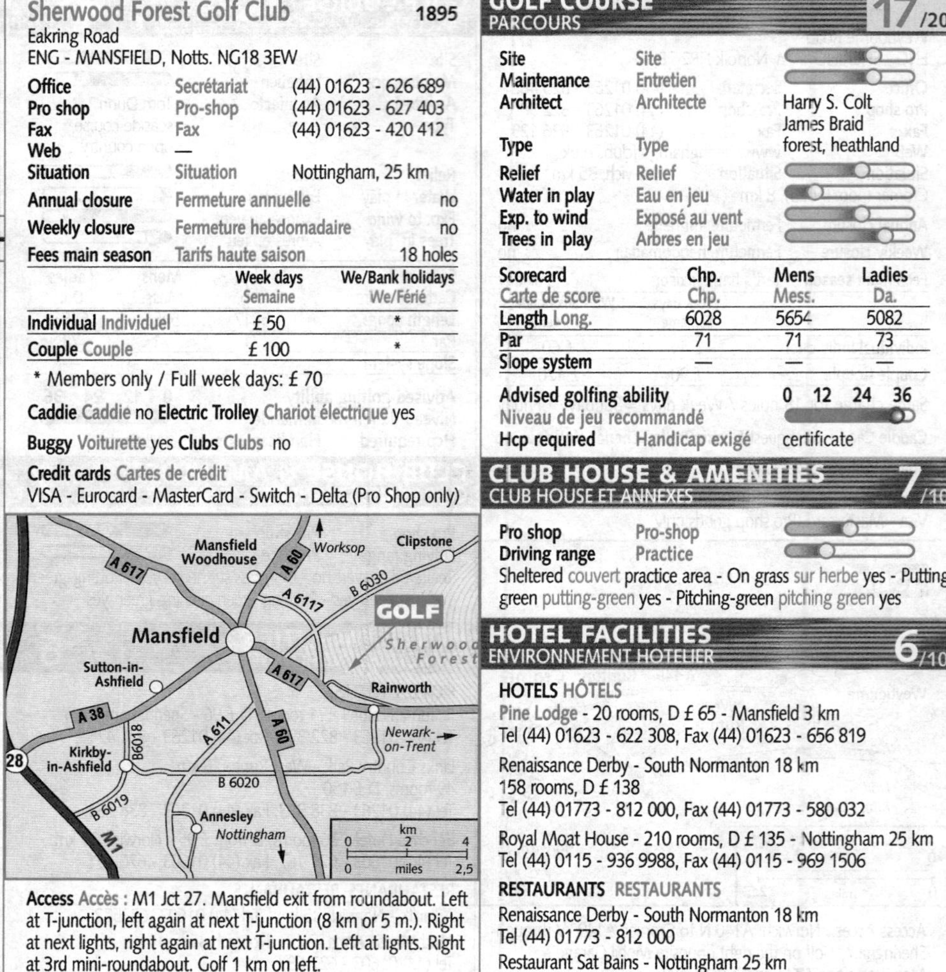

Sherwood Forest Golf Club 1895
Eakring Road
ENG - MANSFIELD, Notts. NG18 3EW

Office	Secrétariat	(44) 01623 - 626 689
Pro shop	Pro-shop	(44) 01623 - 627 403
Fax	Fax	(44) 01623 - 420 412
Web	—	
Situation	Situation	Nottingham, 25 km
Annual closure	Fermeture annuelle	no
Weekly closure	Fermeture hebdomadaire	no
Fees main season	Tarifs haute saison	18 holes

	Week days Semaine	We/Bank holidays We/Férié
Individual Individuel	£ 50	*
Couple Couple	£ 100	*

* Members only / Full week days: £ 70

Caddie Caddie no **Electric Trolley** Chariot électrique yes

Buggy Voiturette yes **Clubs** Clubs no

Credit cards Cartes de crédit
VISA - Eurocard - MasterCard - Switch - Delta (Pro Shop only)

Access Accès : M1 Jct 27. Mansfield exit from roundabout. Left at T-junction, left again at next T-junction (8 km or 5 m.). Right at next lights, right again at next T-junction. Left at lights. Right at 3rd mini-roundabout. Golf 1 km on left.
Map 4 on page 477 Carte 4 Page 477

GOLF COURSE
PARCOURS — **17**/20

Site	Site	
Maintenance	Entretien	
Architect	Architecte	Harry S. Colt James Braid
Type	Type	forest, heathland
Relief	Relief	
Water in play	Eau en jeu	
Exp. to wind	Exposé au vent	
Trees in play	Arbres en jeu	

Scorecard Carte de score	Chp. Chp.	Mens Mess.	Ladies Da.
Length Long.	6028	5654	5082
Par	71	71	73
Slope system	—	—	—

Advised golfing ability 0 12 24 36
Niveau de jeu recommandé
Hcp required Handicap exigé certificate

CLUB HOUSE & AMENITIES
CLUB HOUSE ET ANNEXES — **7**/10

Pro shop Pro-shop
Driving range Practice
Sheltered couvert practice area - On grass sur herbe yes - Putting-green putting-green yes - Pitching-green pitching green yes

HOTEL FACILITIES
ENVIRONNEMENT HOTELIER — **6**/10

HOTELS HÔTELS
Pine Lodge - 20 rooms, D £ 65 - Mansfield 3 km
Tel (44) 01623 - 622 308, Fax (44) 01623 - 656 819

Renaissance Derby - South Normanton 18 km
158 rooms, D £ 138
Tel (44) 01773 - 812 000, Fax (44) 01773 - 580 032

Royal Moat House - 210 rooms, D £ 135 - Nottingham 25 km
Tel (44) 0115 - 936 9988, Fax (44) 0115 - 969 1506

RESTAURANTS RESTAURANTS
Renaissance Derby - South Normanton 18 km
Tel (44) 01773 - 812 000
Restaurant Sat Bains - Nottingham 25 km
Tel (44) 0115 - 986 6566

Silloth-on-Solway

18	7	4

A course to take in on your way from Liverpool to Scotland or from Glasgow to England, together with Southerness just opposite on the other side of Solway Firth. Keep looking in this direction, too, because the industrial complex nearby is something of an eyesore. The course's location in the middle of nowhere has kept Silloth from staging any top tournaments, but this does have it advantages: being a quiet course and frequented mostly only by the inhabitants of Carlisle, its overall condition is simply marvellous. It has its enthusiasts, who rate this amongst their top-five links courses and understandably so. The well-contoured fairways rarely have you standing on flat ground, some fairway bunkers have been replaced by heather and gorse, the approaches to greens are tight and putting surfaces are tricky. The course was laid out over a very varied landscape of dunes with lush vegetation. Play it before it becomes too fashionable and raise your glass to Cecil Leitch, one of Silloth's own and the greatest lady player of her day back in the early 20th century.

Un parcours à inclure dans un voyage de Liverpool vers l'Ecosse, avec celui de Southerness, juste en face, de l'autre côté du Solway Firth. Regardez plutôt de ce côté, car le complexe industriel à proximité n'est pas beau. Parce qu'il est à l'écart de tout, Silloth n' pas reçu de grands championnats, mais il y a un avantage : peu fréquenté, sinon par les locaux, il est dans un état généralement merveilleux. Ses amoureux le classent dans leur "Top 5" des links, et on les comprend. Les fairways bien modelés vous mettent rarement à plat, quelques bunkers de fairway ont été remplacés par la bruyère et les ajoncs, les entrées de greens sont étroites, leurs surfaces subtiles. Le parcours a été tracé dans un paysage de dunes aussi varié que possible, avec una abondante végétation à déguster lors des floraisons. Un parcours où l'on a envie de rester, à jouer avant qu'il ne devienne à la mode, avant de boire au souvenir de Cecil Leitch, la plus grand joueuse de son temps, au début du XXè siècle.

Silloth-on-Solway Golf Club — 1892

ENG - SILLOTH-ON-SOLWAY, Cumbria CA5 4AT

Office Secrétariat (44) 016973 - 31 304
Pro shop Pro-shop (44) 016973 - 32 404
Fax Fax (44) 016973 - 31 782
Web www.sillothgolfclub.co.uk
Situation Situation Carlisle, 40 km
Annual closure Fermeture annuelle no
Weekly closure Fermeture hebdomadaire no

Fees main season Tarifs haute saison	Week days Semaine	We/Bank holidays We/Férie
18 holes		
Individual Individuel	£ 33	£ 45
Couple Couple	£ 66	£ 90

Full week days: also £ 33

Caddie Caddie no — **Electric Trolley** Chariot électrique yes
Buggy Voiturette no — **Clubs** Clubs yes
Credit cards Cartes de crédit
VISA - Eurocard - MasterCard (Pro shop only)

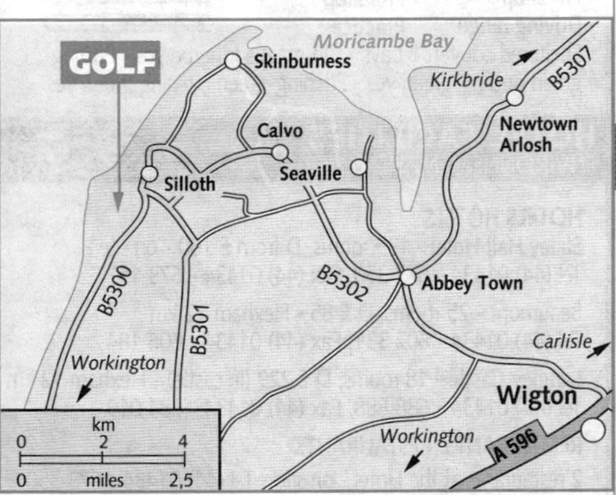

Access Accès : M6 to Carlisle, then A595 & A596. At Wigton, B5302 to Silloth Promenade. Go right 200 m.
Map 2 on page 473 Carte 2 Page 473

GOLF COURSE — PARCOURS — 18/20

Site Site
Maintenance Entretien
Architect Architecte Willie Park
Type Type links
Relief Relief
Water in play Eau en jeu
Exp. to wind Exposé au vent
Trees in play Arbres en jeu

Scorecard Carte de score	Chp. Chp.	Mens Mess.	Ladies Da.
Length Long.	5952	5721	5203
Par	72	72	75
Slope system	—	—	—

Advised golfing ability Niveau de jeu recommandé 0 12 24 36
Hcp required Handicap exigé certificate

CLUB HOUSE & AMENITIES — CLUB HOUSE ET ANNEXES — 7/10

Pro shop Pro-shop
Driving range Practice
Sheltered couvert no - On grass sur herbe yes - Putting-green putting-green yes - Pitching-green pitching green yes

HOTEL FACILITIES — ENVIRONNEMENT HOTELIER — 4/10

HOTELS HÔTELS
Silloth Golf Hotel - Silloth, 200 m
22 rooms, D £ 98
Tel (44) 016973 - 31 438, Fax (44) 016973 - 32 582

The Skinburness - Silloth, close
26 rooms, D £ 90 (w. dinner)
Tel (44) 016973 - 32 332, Fax (44) 016973 - 32 549

Crown + Mitre - Carlisle 40 km
94 rooms, D £ 98
Tel (44) 01228 - 525 491, Fax (44) 01228 - 514 553

RESTAURANTS RESTAURANTS
The Skinburness - Silloth close - Tel (44) 016973 - 32 332

629

Slaley Hall *Hunting Course*

17	8	7

The Woburn of the north or the Gleneagles of the south, it doesn't matter either way. Slaley Hall is one of those courses that has brought life to a region where good courses were comparatively few and far between. The vegetation is typical of the north, with a good number of pine-trees lining the fairways or adding dark colour to contrast with the lighter greens of the fairways and putting surfaces, the sand in the bunkers and the lakes. Familiar colours to golfers, certainly, but here they just look smarter than anywhere else. The many different playing options add variety to the fun of playing here; you can change the complexion of the course by switching tee-boxes but still keep the same panoply of hazards, including fairway bunkers whose shape (Dave Thomas style) gives this magnificent English style park a little American touch. If you are feeling tired after the very challenging finishing holes, the club-house and hotel offer all the facilities of a major golfing resort, enhanced still further with a second course that is shorter and easier.

Woburn du nord ou Gleneagles du sud, peu importe, Slaley Hall fait partie, des golfs qui ont un peu réveillé une région assez pauvre en grands parcours. La végétation est néanmoins plus typique du nord, avec les nombreux sapins bordant les fairways ou fournissant des couleurs sombres harmonisées à celles des greens et des fairways, au sable des bunkers et aux lacs. Ce sont des couleurs familières aux golfeurs, mais ici plus soignées que partout ailleurs. De multiples options de jeu permettent de varier les plaisirs : d'un jour à l'autre, changez de difficultés en changeant de tees, tout en conservant une panoplie d'obstacles, les formes des bunkers de fairway (à la Dave Thomas !) apportant une touche américaine à ce beau parc à l'anglaise. Si vous êtes un peu fatigué après un finale exigeant, le club-house et l'hôtel offrent tous les services d'un grand "resort", encore amélioré avec son second parcours, plus court et accessible.

Slaley Hall Hotel & Golf Club — 1988

Slaley
ENG - HEXHAM, Northumberland NE47 0BY

Office Secrétariat (44) 01434 - 673 350
Pro shop Pro-shop (44) 01434 - 673 154
Fax Fax (44) 01434 - 673 152
Web www.devereonline.co.uk/hotel_slaley/golf.htm
Situation Situation Hexham, 15 km
Annual closure Fermeture annuelle no
Weekly closure Fermeture hebdomadaire no

Fees main season Tarifs haute saison	18 holes	
	Week days Semaine	We/Bank holidays We/Férié
Individual Individuel	£ 65	£ 65*
Couple Couple	£ 130	£ 130*

Full week days: £ 100
* We: play alternates between the 2 courses

Caddie Caddie no — **Electric Trolley** Chariot électrique no
Buggy Voiturette yes — **Clubs** Clubs yes
Credit cards Cartes de crédit
VISA - Eurocard - MasterCard - AMEX - DC

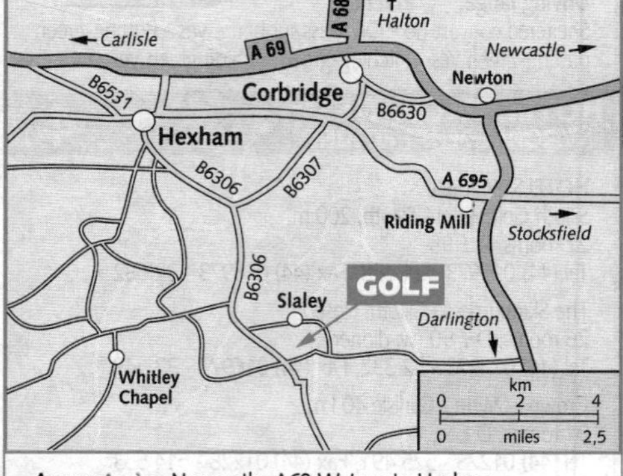

Access Accès : Newcastle, A69 W, turn to Hexham, then B6306 to Slaley.
Map 2 on page 473 Carte 2 Page 473

GOLF COURSE — PARCOURS 17/20

Site Site
Maintenance Entretien
Architect Architecte David Thomas
Type Type parkland
Relief Relief
Water in play Eau en jeu
Exp. to wind Exposé au vent
Trees in play Arbres en jeu

Scorecard Carte de score	Chp. Chp.	Mens Mess.	Ladies Da.
Length Long.	6320	6085	5255
Par	72	72	75
Slope system	—	—	—

Advised golfing ability Niveau de jeu recommandé 0 12 24 36
Hcp required Handicap exigé 24 Men, 36 Ladies

CLUB HOUSE & AMENITIES — CLUB HOUSE ET ANNEXES 8/10

Pro shop Pro-shop
Driving range Practice
Sheltered couvert 8 bays - On grass sur herbe yes - Putting-green putting-green yes - Pitching-green pitching green yes

HOTEL FACILITIES — ENVIRONNEMENT HOTELIER 7/10

HOTELS HÔTELS
Slaley Hall Hotel - 139 rooms, D from £ 160 - on site
Tel (44) 01434 - 673 350, Fax (44) 01434 - 673 152

Beaumont - 25 rooms, D £ 85 - Hexham 12 km
Tel (44) 01434 - 602 331, Fax (44) 01434 - 606 184

Langley Castle - 18 rooms, D £ 229 (in castle) - Hexham 12 km
Tel (44) 01434 - 688 888, Fax (44) 01434 - 684 019

RESTAURANTS RESTAURANTS
2 restaurants at the Hotel - on site - Tel (44) 01434 - 673 350
Josephine (Langley Castle) - Hexham 10 km
Tel (44) 01434 - 688 888
Ramblers Country House - Corbridge 15 km
Tel (44) 01434 - 632 424

Southport & Ainsdale

16 | 7 | 7

Although it has staged the Ryder Cup and the British Ladies Open, this course has suffered from being overshadowed by its towering neighbours Birkdale and Hillside, although actually it can look them both squarely in the eye as it has assets of a different nature. Of course it may look short, but only to the better players. For the rest of us intimidated by its glorious neighbours it has yardage enough, especially since driving these tight fairways is never easy. The route to the greens is never very wide, either, and calls for bump 'n run shots in classic style (although this does not make the task any easier for golfers who have learnt to hit greens with towering iron shots). By contrast, game strategy will vary with the wind and always be clear: you see exactly what needs to be done. Whether you play here twice or a hundred times, it is always as exciting as that very first day in an elegant, traditional and warm atmosphere.

Bien qu'il ait reçu la Ryder Cup et le British Ladies Open, ce parcours a souffert de l'ombre de ses puissants voisins, Birkdale et Hillside, mais sans vraiment devoir leur envier grand-chose, car ses armes sont différentes. Il peut bien sûr paraître court, mais seulement aux meilleurs joueurs : il est bien assez long pour la plupart d'entre nous, intimidés par ses glorieux voisins, en particulier parce que le drive sur ces fairways étroits n'est guère facile. Les entrées de greens ne sont pas toujours très larges, mais on doit les approcher en roulant, de manière classique, mais cela ne facilite pas non plus la tâche à ceux qui ont appris à jouer autrement, en portant la balle. En revanche, la stratégie peut varier en fonction du vent, mais elle apparaît toujours clairement : on voit exactement ce que l'on doit faire. Que l'on joue deux fois ou cent fois, le plaisir est comme au premier jour dans ce club à l'ambiance élégante, traditionnelle et chaleureuse.

Southport & Ainsdale Golf Club — 1922

Bradshaws Lane, Ainsdale
ENG - SOUTHPORT, Lancs PR8 3LG

Office Secrétariat (44) 01704 - 578 000
Pro shop Pro-shop (44) 01704 - 577 316
Fax Fax (44) 01704 - 570 896
Web www.sandagolfclub.co.uk
Situation Situation Southport, 5 km - Liverpool (pop. 452 450), 26 km
Annual closure Fermeture annuelle — no
Weekly closure Fermeture hebdomadaire — no

Fees main season Tarifs haute saison — 18 holes

	Week days / Semaine	We/Bank holidays / We/Férié
Individual Individuel	£ 60	£ 75*
Couple Couple	£ 120	£ 150*

* Limited access at week-ends / Full week days: £ 75

Caddie Caddie on request **Electric Trolley** Chariot électrique yes
Buggy Voiturette yes **Clubs** Clubs yes
Credit cards Cartes de crédit
VISA - Eurocard - MasterCard - DC - JCB

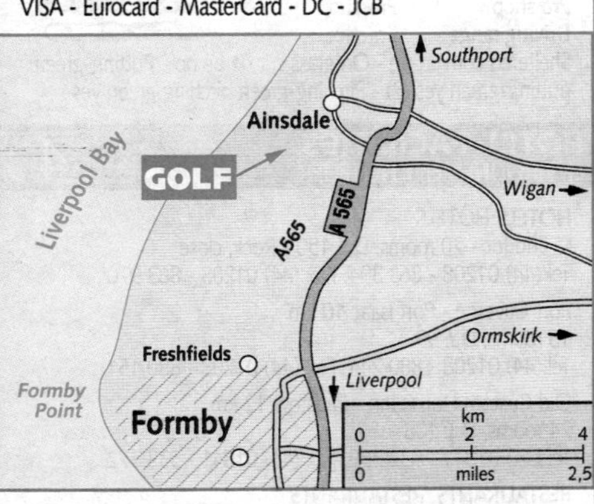

Access Accès : A565 Liverpool → Southport. Ainsdale Village centre, turn left on Bradswhaws Lane
Map 5 on page 479 Carte 5 Page 479

GOLF COURSE — PARCOURS — 16/20

Site Site
Maintenance Entretien
Architect Architecte — James Braid
Type Type — links
Relief Relief
Water in play Eau en jeu
Exp. to wind Exposé au vent
Trees in play Arbres en jeu

Scorecard / Carte de score	Chp. / Chp.	Mens / Mess.	Ladies / Da.
Length Long.	6075	5688	5073
Par	72	71	74
Slope system	—	—	—

Advised golfing ability Niveau de jeu recommandé — 0 12 24 36
Hcp required Handicap exigé — 28 Men, 36 Ladies

CLUB HOUSE & AMENITIES — CLUB HOUSE ET ANNEXES — 7/10

Pro shop Pro-shop
Driving range Practice
Sheltered couvert no - **On grass** sur herbe yes - **Putting-green** putting-green yes - **Pitching-green** pitching green yes

HOTEL FACILITIES — ENVIRONNEMENT HOTELIER — 7/10

HOTELS HÔTELS
Cambridge House Hotel - 16 rooms, D £ 88 - Southport 6 km
Tel (44) 01704 - 538 372, Fax (44) 01704 - 547 183

Scarisbrick - 88 rooms, D from £ 100 - Southport 5 km
Tel (44) 01704 - 543 000, Fax (44) 01704 - 533 335

Prince of Wales - 101 rooms, D £ 115 - Southport 5 km
Tel (44) 01704 - 536 688, Fax (44) 01704 - 543 488

RESTAURANTS RESTAURANTS
Warehouse Brasserie - Southport 5 km
Tel (44) 01704 - 544 662
Valentino's - Southport 5 km - Tel (44) 01704 - 541 252
Cloisters (Scarisbrick) - Southport 5 km
Tel (44) 01704 - 535 153

St Enodoc *Church Course*

18 | 7 | 4

You will remember three things about this course: the wonderful views over the Cornish coast and the Camel estuary, the little church on the 10th hole dug out of the sand 60 years ago, and Himalayas, a giant hill-shaped bunker standing some 80 feet high where you watch golfers walk up and down in a vain attempt to get their ball back in the fairway. But this is not the only hill over steeply undulating terrain, which can be tiring for the fainter-hearted. The fourth thing you may well remember is your score. Some greens are difficult to reach other than with lofted shots, meaning that good scores go to good players as you often need to be long and straight to get a clear view of the green. Beginners will spend their time in the dunes and the very thick rough. St Enodoc is a superb golfing arena with special mention going to the renovation of bunkering, and to the final holes where you play for the match and an excellent meal in the club-house. A rare and wonderful golfing treat.

Vous vous souviendrez au moins de trois choses : les vues magnifiques sur la côte de Cornouailles et le Camel Estuary, la petite église au 10, tirée du sable il y a 60 ans, et l'Himalaya, gigantesque bunker en forme de colline de 25 mètres de haut, d'où il est distrayant de regarder les joueurs monter et descendre sans parvenir à sortir leur balle. Mais ce n'est pas la seule colline d'un terrain très mouvementé, parfois assez fatigant pour les plus faibles. Un quatrième souvenir sera votre score. Certains greens sont difficiles à atteindre autrement qu'avec des balles levées, ce qui réserve les bons scores aux bons joueurs, et il faut souvent être long et droit pour avoir la vue sur les greens. Les débutants passeront leur vie dans les dunes et dans les roughs très épais. St Enodoc est une superbe arène pour jouer, avec une mention particulière pour la rénovation du bunkering et pour les derniers trous quand on y joue le match et un très bon repas au club-house.

St Enodoc Golf Club — 1890

Rock
ENG - WADEBRIDGE, Cornwall PL2T 6LD

Office	Secrétariat	(44) 01208 - 863 216
Pro shop	Pro-shop	(44) 01208 - 862 402
Fax	Fax	(44) 01208 - 862 976
E-mail	stenodocgolfclub@tiscali.co.uk	
Situation	Situation	Bodmin, 32 km

Wadebridge, 10 km

Annual closure Fermeture annuelle — no
Weekly closure Fermeture hebdomadaire — no

Fees main season Tarifs haute saison	18 holes	
	Week days Semaine	We/Bank holidays We/Férié
Individual Individuel	£ 45	£ 55
Couple Couple	£ 90	£ 110

Full day (except Saturday): £ 65

Caddie Caddie no — **Electric Trolley** Chariot électrique yes
Buggy Voiturette no — **Clubs** Clubs yes

Credit cards Cartes de crédit
Visa - Eurocard (Pro shop goods only)

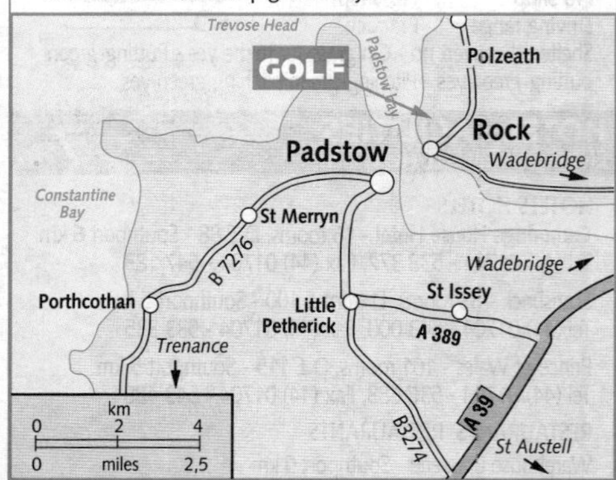

Access Accès : A30 Exeter to Bodmin, then A389 to Wadebridge, follow signs to Rock, drive through Rock, past Boat Club and Matiner's pub, sharp right uphill to Clubhouse (signposted) **Map 6 on page 480** Carte 6 Page 480

GOLF COURSE — PARCOURS — 18/20

Site	Site	
Maintenance	Entretien	
Architect	Architecte	James Braid
Type	Type	seaside course, links
Relief	Relief	
Water in play	Eau en jeu	
Exp. to wind	Exposé au vent	
Trees in play	Arbres en jeu	

Scorecard Carte de score	Chp. Chp.	Mens Mess.	Ladies Da.
Length Long.	5800	5450	5115
Par	69	69	73
Slope system	—	—	—

Advised golfing ability Niveau de jeu recommandé — 0 12 24 36
Hcp required Handicap exigé — certificate

CLUB HOUSE & AMENITIES — CLUB HOUSE ET ANNEXES — 7/10

Pro shop Pro-shop
Driving range Practice
Sheltered couvert no - On grass sur herbe no - Putting-green putting-green yes (2) - Pitching-green pitching green yes

HOTEL FACILITIES — ENVIRONNEMENT HOTELIER — 4/10

HOTELS HÔTELS
St Enodoc - 20 rooms, D £ 150 - Rock, close
Tel (44) 01208 - 863 394, Fax (44) 01208 - 863 970

Port Gaverne - Port Isaac 10 km
16 rooms, D £ 99
Tel (44) 01208 - 880 244, Fax (44) 01208 - 880 151

Old Custom House Inn - Padstow 12 km
24 rooms, D £ 108
Tel (44) 01841 - 532 359, Fax (44) 01841 - 533 372

RESTAURANTS RESTAURANTS
Porthilly Grill (St Enodoc) - St Kew, close
Tel (44) 01208 - 863 394
The Seafood - Padstow 12 km - Tel (44) 01841 - 532 700

St George's Hill

18	7	7

Come and play here in late May or early June. If your game lets you down you'll probably find some consolation in the rhododendrons in full bloom, whose colours contrast with the purple heather, silver birch and pines to produce a wonderful setting for a superb course designed by Harry Shapland Colt. For those of you who are not as fit as you were, this is a very hilly course. If you run out of puff, make it back to the club-house and admire the superb views. Once out on the course, the changes of elevation and the slopes call for a little reconnoitring before hoping to card a good score, especially since the greens are very quick, full of breaks and sometimes multi-tiered. A few blind drives or tee-shots to steeply sloping fairways also require extreme accuracy. St George's Hill is not only picturesque, it is also one of the country's finest inland courses. A sort of grand classic which actually defies any real comment.

Venez donc fin mai ou début juin. Si votre jeu vous a déçu, vous vous consolerez à la vue des rhododendrons en pleine floraison, dont les couleurs s'ajoutent aux bruyères pourpres, aux bouleaux blancs, aux pins et aux sapins pour offrir un cadre somptueux au superbe dessin de Harry Colt. Hélas pour ceux qui n'ont pas une excellente forme, ce parcours est très physique. Ils pourront toujours rester au club-house, qui offre des vues superbes. Quant au parcours, ses changements de niveaux et ses pentes exigent une petite reconnaissance préalable avant d'espérer un bon score, d'autant plus que les greens sont rapides, très mouvementés, parfois à plusieurs plateaux. Quelques drives aveugles ou vers des fairways en dévers demandent aussi beaucoup de précision. St George's Hill n'est pas seulement pittoresque, c'est aussi un des meilleurs parcours "inland" du pays. Une sorte de classique qui défie les commentaires, en fait !

St George's Hill Golf Club — 1912

Golf Club Road, St George's Hill
ENG - WEYBRIDGE, Surrey KT13 0NL

Office	Secrétariat	(44) 01932 - 847 758
Pro shop	Pro-shop	(44) 01932 - 843 523
Fax	Fax	(44) 01932 - 821 564
Web	www.stgeorgeshillgolfclub.co.uk	
Situation	Situation	Weybridge, 1 km
Annual closure	Fermeture annuelle	no
Weekly closure	Fermeture hebdomadaire	no

Fees main season Tarifs haute saison	18 holes	
	Week days Semaine	**We/Bank holidays** We/Férié
Individual Individuel	£ 90	*
Couple Couple	£ 180	*

* Members only / Full week day: £ 120 / Week days: Wednesday, Thursday, Friday

Caddie Caddie on request **Electric Trolley** Chariot électrique yes

Buggy Voiturette no **Clubs** Clubs yes

Credit cards Cartes de crédit (Pro Shop goods only)
VISA - Eurocard - MasterCard - AMEX - JCB

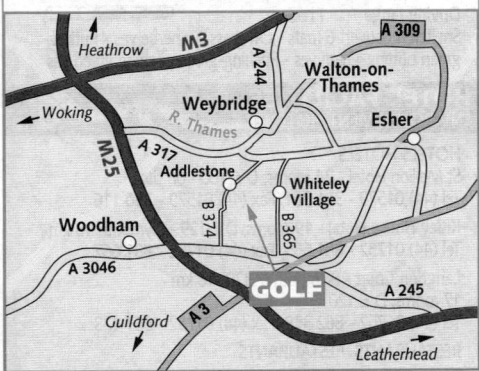

Access Accès : London A3. Cobham Bridge A245 (Byfleet Road). After 2 km (1.2 m.), B374 (Brooklands Road) on right. Golf on right (Golf Club Road).

Map 8 on page 485 Carte 8 Page 485

GOLF COURSE — PARCOURS — 18/20

Site	Site	
Maintenance	Entretien	
Architect	Architecte	Harry S. Colt
Type	Type	inland, parkland
Relief	Relief	
Water in play	Eau en jeu	
Exp. to wind	Exposé au vent	
Trees in play	Arbres en jeu	

Scorecard Carte de score	**Chp.** Chp.	**Mens** Mess.	**Ladies** Da.
Length Long.	5960	5960	5020
Par	70	70	72
Slope system	—	—	—

Advised golfing ability Niveau de jeu recommandé: 0 12 24 36

Hcp required Handicap exigé: certificate

CLUB HOUSE & AMENITIES — CLUB HOUSE ET ANNEXES — 7/10

Pro shop	Pro-shop
Driving range	Practice

Sheltered couvert no - On grass sur herbe yes - Putting-green putting-green yes - Pitching-green pitching green no

HOTEL FACILITIES — ENVIRONNEMENT HOTELIER — 7/10

HOTELS HÔTELS

Oatlands Park - 144 rooms, D £ 207 - Weybridge 3 km
Tel (44) 01932 - 847 242, Fax (44) 01932 - 842 252

The Ship Inn - 39 rooms, D £ 140- Weybridge 1 km
Tel (44) 01932 - 848 364, Fax (44) 01932 - 857 153

Hilton National - 158 rooms, D £ 189 - Cobham 3 km
Tel (44) 01932 - 864 471, Fax (44) 01932 - 868 017

RESTAURANTS RESTAURANTS

Casa Romana - Weybridge 1 km - Tel (44) 01932 - 223 543

Le Petit Pierrot - Esher-Claygate 6 km
Tel (44) 01372 - 465 105

Good Earth - Esher 4 km - Tel (44) 01932 - 462 489

St Mellion *Nicklaus Course*

17	9	6

This is a Jack Nicklaus course and golfers who know his style in the United States will recognise the way in which he has moulded the Cornish countryside to fit his requirements. Turning around a hill which is the setting for another 18 hole course, St Mellion is exposed to all winds and weathers which make the course even more difficult than usual. Let's be honest here: even from the front tees this course will be beyond most average players. The bunkers, lakes and the often small, multi-tiered greens are impressive and sufficiently demanding to put off many visitors. Equally true though is the fact that it mellows a little more each time you play it. This is a course you cannot pass by, especially given the club's outstanding facilities, but it is not exactly what you would call a holiday course and there is little local colour to talk of. A must to play to form your own opinion and test the state of your game. Recent drainage work has erased a few earlier shortcomings.

D'accord, St Mellion est signé Jack Nicklaus. Ceux qui connaissent ses parcours aux USA reconnaîtront qu'il a su plier le paysage de Cornouailles à ses volontés. Tournant autour d'une colline où est logé un autre 18 trous, celui-ci est exposé à tous les vents, ce qui renforce encore sa difficulté. Disons-le franchement, même des départs avancés, ce parcours n'est pas à la portée des joueurs moyens. Les bunkers, les lacs et les greens souvent minuscules (beaucoup à plateaux) impressionnent assez pour refroidir le visiteur. Il est vrai que ce parcours s'adoucit à mesure qu'on le joue. Il est impossible d'ignorer ce golf, d'autant que les équipements sont remarquables, mais ce n'est pas exactement un parcours de vacances, et l'on cherchera vainement une couleur vraiment locale. A connaître pour se faire une opinion. Et tester son jeu. Avec les bénéfices d'un drainage qui a gommé bien des défauts...

St Mellion International — 1987

St Mellion
ENG - SALTASH, Cornwall PL12 6 SD

Office	Secrétariat	(44) 01579 - 351 351
Pro shop	Pro-shop	(44) 01579 - 352 002
Fax	Fax	(44) 01579 - 350 537
Web	www.crown-golf.co.uk	
Situation	Situation	Plymouth, 16 km
Annual closure	Fermeture annuelle	no
Weekly closure	Fermeture hebdomadaire	no

Fees main season Tarifs haute saison	Week days Semaine	We/Bank holidays We/Férié
		18 holes
Individual Individuel	£ 57	£ 57
Couple Couple	£ 114	£ 114

Full days: £ 80

Caddie Caddie no — **Electric Trolley** Chariot électrique no

Buggy Voiturette £ 18 /18 holes **Clubs** Clubs yes

Credit cards Cartes de crédit (Pro shop goods & restaurant only) VISA - MasterCard - AMEX

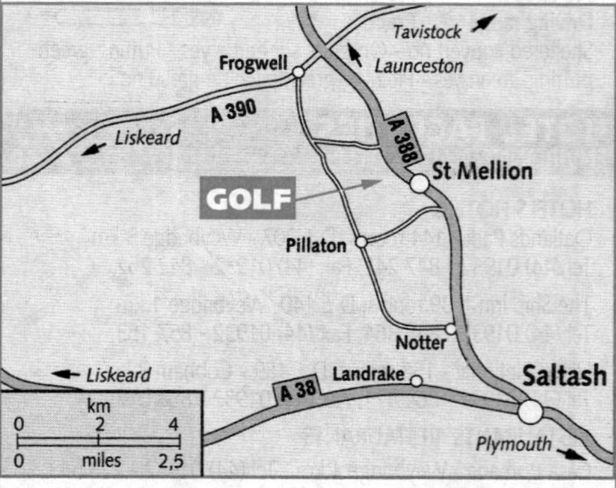

Access Accès : M5 then A38 to Saltash, then A388 to St Mellion. Golf signposted.
Map 6 on page 480 Carte 6 Page 480

GOLF COURSE — PARCOURS 17/20

Site	Site	
Maintenance	Entretien	
Architect	Architecte	Jack Nicklaus
Type	Type	parkland, open country
Relief	Relief	
Water in play	Eau en jeu	
Exp. to wind	Exposé au vent	
Trees in play	Arbres en jeu	

Scorecard Carte de score	Chp. Chp.	Mens Mess.	Ladies Da.
Length Long.	6080	5846	5146
Par	72	72	73
Slope system	—	—	—

Advised golfing ability Niveau de jeu recommandé — 0 12 24 36

Hcp required Handicap exigé no

CLUB HOUSE & AMENITIES — CLUB HOUSE ET ANNEXES 9/10

Pro shop Pro-shop
Driving range Practice
Sheltered couvert 6 mats - **On grass** sur herbe yes - **Putting-green** putting-green yes - **Pitching-green** pitching green yes

HOTEL FACILITIES — ENVIRONNEMENT HOTELIER 6/10

HOTELS HÔTELS
St Mellion Hotel - 24 rooms, D £ 100 - on site
Tel (44) 01579 - 351 351, Fax (44) 01579 - 350 116

Kitley House Hotel - 19 rooms, D £ 129 - Plymouth 18 km
Tel (44) 01752 - 881 555, Fax (44) 01752 - 881 667

Langdon Court - Plymouth (A379) 18 km
17 rooms, D £ 120
Tel (44) 01752 - 862 358, Fax (44) 01752 - 863 428

RESTAURANTS RESTAURANTS
Tanners - Plymouth 16 km - Tel (44) 01752 - 252 001
Danescombe - Calstock 16 km - Tel (44) 01822 - 832 414
Kitley House Hotel - Plymouth 18 km
Tel (44) 01752 - 881 555

Stoke Park Golf Club

17 | 8 | 8

Agreed, at this price the week-end green-fee is a little high but we suppose they have to find some sort of deterrent. The most surprising thing here is not the price nor the lavish club-house, re-designed to cater for the addition of a new 9-hole course, sumptuous hotel rooms and a swimming pool. No, what really surprises the visitor is the absence of heather found on every other course in the region virtually without exception. Here we are golfing in the purest "park-land" style, where fairways lined with splendid trees meander through terrain that only Harry Colt could have turned into such a clever course. Everyone talks about the 7th hole, an exemplary par 3 which apparently served as a model for the 12th at Augusta, but the rest are no less exciting. With Colt you always have to weigh up the pros and cons of each shot, look twice and avoid the plethora of hazards. If you want to talk about your round, there are some excellent restaurants in the club-house.

D'accord, à ce prix en week-end, c'est un peu cher, mais le tarif doit être surtout dissuasif ! Ce qui est le plus surprenant ici, ce n'est pas cela, ni le club-house, bien refait, avec un nouveau 9 trous, un très bel hôtel et une piscine. Ce qui est le plus surprenant, c'est qu'il n'y a pas ici de bruyère, comme dans tous les parcours de la région, pratiquement sans exception. Nous sommes dans le style "parkland" le plus pur, avec des fairways décorés d'arbres splendides, dans un espace dont seul un Harry Colt pouvait tirer un parcours d'une telle intelligence. On parle toujours du 7, un par 3 exemplaire qui aurait été le modèle du 12 d'Augusta, mais les autres ne sont pas moins passionnants à envisager. Avec Colt, il faut toujours regarder à deux fois, éviter l'abondance d'obstacles, il faut toujours peser le pour et le contre de chaque coup. Pour en discuter, il y a d'excellents restaurants au club-house...

Stoke Park Golf Club — 1908

North Drive, Park Road, Stoke Poges
ENG - SLOUGH, Bucks SL2 4PG

Office	Secrétariat	(44) 01753 - 717 171
Pro shop	Pro-shop	(44) 01753 - 717 172
Fax	Fax	(44) 01753 - 717 194
Web	www.stokeparkclub.com	
Situation	Situation	Slough (pop. 101 066), 3 km
Annual closure	Fermeture annuelle	no
Weekly closure	Fermeture hebdomadaire	no

Fees main season Tarifs haute saison	18 holes	
	Week days Semaine	**We/Bank holidays** We/Férié
Individual Individuel	£ 125	£ 200
Couple Couple	£ 250	£ 400

Caddie Caddie no — **Electric Trolley** Chariot électrique yes
Buggy Voiturette yes — **Clubs** Clubs yes

Credit cards Cartes de crédit
VISA - Eurocard - MasterCard - AMEX - DC - JCB

Access Accès : M4 Jct 6 at Slough, A355 → Beaconsfield. At double mini roundabout in Farnham Royal turn right into Park Road.
Map 8 on page 484 Carte 8 Page 484

GOLF COURSE — PARCOURS — 17/20

Site	Site	
Maintenance	Entretien	
Architect	Architecte	Harry S. Colt
Type	Type	parkland
Relief	Relief	
Water in play	Eau en jeu	
Exp. to wind	Exposé au vent	
Trees in play	Arbres en jeu	

Scorecard Carte de score	**Chp.** Chp.	**Mens** Mess.	**Ladies** Da.
Length Long.	6003	5682	5280
Par	71	71	74
Slope system	—	—	—

Advised golfing ability Niveau de jeu recommandé — 0 12 24 36
Hcp required Handicap exigé — 28 Men, 36 Ladies

CLUB HOUSE & AMENITIES — CLUB HOUSE ET ANNEXES — 8/10

Pro shop Pro-shop
Driving range Practice
Sheltered couvert no - On grass sur herbe yes - Putting-green putting-green yes - Pitching-green pitching green yes

HOTEL FACILITIES — ENVIRONNEMENT HOTELIER — 8/10

HOTELS HÔTELS

Stoke Park - 21 rooms, D from £ 270 - on site
Tel (44) 01753 - 717171, Fax (44) 01753 - 717181

Copthorne - 219 rooms, D £ 180 - Slough 5 km
Tel (44) 01753 - 516 222, Fax (44) 01753 - 516 237

Courtyard - 150 rooms, D £ 124 - Slough 5 km
Tel (44) 01753 - 551 551, Fax (44) 01753 - 553 333

Burnham Beeches - 80 rooms, D from £ 110 - Burnham 4 km
Tel (44) 01628 - 429 955, Fax (44) 01628 - 603 994

RESTAURANTS RESTAURANTS

Waldo's - Taplow 6 km - Tel (44) 01628 - 668 561
Club house (3 restaurants) - on site - Tel (44) 01753 - 717171

Stoneham

15	7	8

A lack of yardage did not prevent Stoneham from staging the first British Masters in 1946 or the Brabazon Trophy in 1993. We'll simply say that this is a good par 70 for golfers who know the course well and pay more attention to their overall score, rather than concentrating on playing to par on each individual hole. Whatever, the fairway bunkers should not bother too many players as their placement largely reflects a bygone age and perhaps many should be moved to restore their original purpose. The main hazards are now the heather and gorse-bushes together with the slopes and hills on a site that can be tiring to walk on a number of holes (the 3rd and 18th). This course poses enough problems for us to recommend it first and foremost to experienced players, who will appreciate the severity of the challenge. Last but not least, although so close to the port of Southampton, the course is a haven of peace and quiet.

Son manque de longueur n'a pas empêché Stoneham de recevoir le premier British Masters en 1946, ainsi que le Brabazon Trophy en 1993. Nous dirons simplement que c'est un bon par 70 pour ceux qui le connaissent bien et font plus attention au par total qu'au par de chaque trou. En tout cas, les bunkers de fairway ne gêneront pas grand monde car ils ne sont plus beaucoup en jeu et il faudrait maintenant les déplacer pour leur restituer leur fonction originelle. Ce sont la bruyère et les buissons d'ajoncs qui sont maintenant les obstacles principaux, avec les changements de niveau ou même les ondulations d'un terrain assez fatigant sur quelques trous (3 et 18). Ce parcours pose assez de problèmes pour qu'on le conseille d'abord aux joueurs expérimentés, qui apprécieront la rigueur sans concession du défi présenté. Enfin, si près du port de Southampton, on est ici parfaitement au calme.

Stoneham Golf Club — 1908

Monks Wood Close
ENG - SOUTHAMPTON, Hampshire SO16 3TT

Office	Secrétariat	(44) 023 - 8076 9272
Pro shop	Pro-shop	(44) 023 - 8076 8397
Fax	Fax	(44) 023 - 8076 6320
Web	www.stonehamgolfclub.org.co.uk	
Situation	Situation	in Southampton
Annual closure	Fermeture annuelle	no
Weekly closure	Fermeture hebdomadaire	no

Fees main season Tarifs haute saison	18 holes	
	Week days Semaine	We/Bank holidays We/Férié
Individual Individuel	£ 40	£ 50
Couple Couple	£ 80	£ 100

Full days: £ 45 / £ 60 (We)

Caddie Caddie no — **Electric Trolley** Chariot électrique no

Buggy Voiturette no — **Clubs** Clubs no

Credit cards Cartes de crédit
Visa - Mastercard (Pro shop goods only)

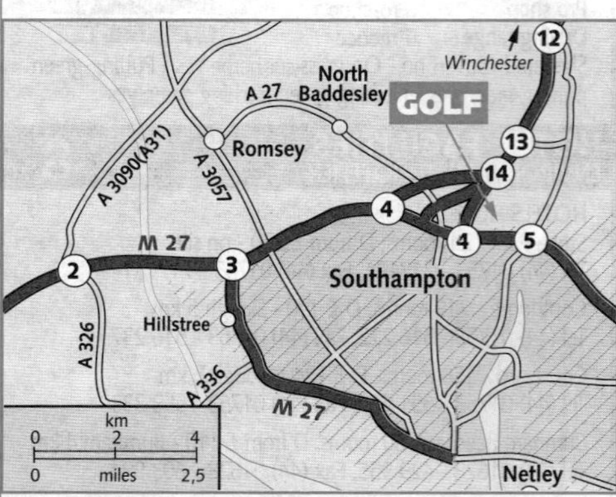

Access Accès : M27 Jct 5. Drive towards Southampton. Turn right at first traffic lights on A27 (Bassett Green Road). 1.2 km, turn right into Golf Club.
Map 7 on page 482 Carte 7 Page 482

GOLF COURSE — PARCOURS — 15/20

Site	Site	
Maintenance	Entretien	
Architect	Architecte	Willie Park
Type	Type	inland, heathland
Relief	Relief	
Water in play	Eau en jeu	
Exp. to wind	Exposé au vent	
Trees in play	Arbres en jeu	

Scorecard Carte de score	Chp. Chp.	Mens Mess.	Ladies Da.
Length Long.	5680	5360	4809
Par	72	72	71
Slope system	—	—	—

Advised golfing ability Niveau de jeu recommandé — 0 12 24 36

Hcp required Handicap exigé — certificate

CLUB HOUSE & AMENITIES — CLUB HOUSE ET ANNEXES — 7/10

Pro shop Pro-shop
Driving range Practice
Sheltered couvert 2 mats - On grass sur herbe no - Putting-green putting-green yes - Pitching-green pitching green yes

HOTEL FACILITIES — ENVIRONNEMENT HOTELIER — 8/10

HOTELS HÔTELS

Botleigh Grange - 56 rooms, D £ 135 - Southampton 5 km
Tel (44) 01489 - 787 700, Fax (44) 01489 - 788 535

De Vere Grand Harbour - Southampton 4 km
172 rooms, D from £ 176
Tel (44) 023 - 8063 3033, Fax (44) 023 - 8063 3066

Highfield House - Southampton 4 km
66 rooms, D from £ 110
Tel (44) 023 - 8035 9955, Fax (44) 023 - 8058 3910

RESTAURANTS RESTAURANTS

Botley Grange - Southampton 5 km - Tel (44) 01489 - 787 700
Prezzo - Romney 12 km - Tel (44) 01794 - 517 353
White Star Dining Rooms (Pub) - Southampton 5 km
Tel (44) 02380 - 821 990

Sunningdale *New Course*

18 | 8 | 8

When you find two great courses at the same Club, you always have a slight preference. But don't be disappointed if you cannot play the "Old" course, its "New" counterpart is just as good and some excellent players even prefer it. If you forget the less enchanting and more "manly" landscape, the "New" course has a lot to be said for it. It allows more aggressive driving although placing the ball is still crucially important – as is avoiding the fairway bunkers (the edges of which are very high), a very dangerous pond on the 15th and a few wicked ditches. Your ironwork will have to be up to scratch, too, to hit the right spot on greens which readily shrug off any mis-hit approach shots. Technical and tactical, lovely to walk but not so easy to score on, this is one of Harry Colt's vintage courses and one of his best. If possible, spend a whole day here at this very chic Club so you can play the two excellent courses.

Quand on trouve deux grands parcours dans le même golf, on a toujours une légère inclination. Que ceux qui ne pourraient jouer le "Old" ne soient pas déçus, le "New" est d'une qualité très comparable, certains excellents joueurs le préférant même. Si l'on fait abstraction d'un paysage moins charmeur, plus "viril," le New ne manque pas d'arguments. Il autorise des drives plus agressifs, mais le placement de la balle reste aussi crucial que la nécessité d'éviter les bunkers de fairway (leurs rebords sont très hauts), une mare très dangereuse au 15 et quelques fossés pernicieux. Il faut garder un excellent jeu de fers pour placer la balle en bonne position sur les greens, qui rejettent sans hésiter les balles un peu approximatives. Technique, tactique, très agréable à marcher, pas facile à scorer, c'est un des bons crus de son architecte Harry Colt, et l'un de ses meilleurs enfants. Si possible, passez la journée pour jouer les deux excellents parcours de ce club très chic.

Sunningdale Golf Club — 1922

Ridgemount Road
ENG - SUNNINGDALE, Berks SL5 9RW

Office	Secrétariat	(44) 013 - 4462 1681
Pro shop	Pro-shop	(44) 013 - 4462 0128
Fax	Fax	(44) 013 - 4462 4154
Web		—
Situation	Situation	Ascot, 5 km
Annual closure	Fermeture annuelle	no
Weekly closure	Fermeture hebdomadaire	no

Fees main season Tarifs haute saison	18 holes	
	Week days Semaine	We/Bank holidays We/Férié
Individual Individuel	£ 110	*
Couple Couple	£ 220	*

Full week days: £ 180 (Old + New)
* Visitors from Monday to Thursday only

Caddie Caddie on request **Electric Trolley** Chariot électrique no

Buggy Voiturette no **Clubs** Clubs no

Credit cards Cartes de crédit
VISA - MasterCard (Pro shop & green fees only)

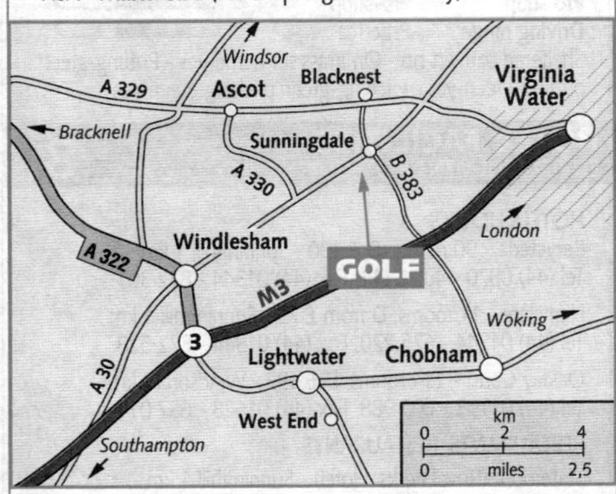

Access Accès : London, A30. 1st left after Sunningdale level crossing. Club 300 m on left.
Map 8 on page 484 Carte 8 Page 484

GOLF COURSE — PARCOURS — 18/20

Site	Site	
Maintenance	Entretien	
Architect	Architecte	Harry S. Colt
Type	Type	forest, heathland
Relief	Relief	
Water in play	Eau en jeu	
Exp. to wind	Exposé au vent	
Trees in play	Arbres en jeu	

Scorecard Carte de score	Chp. Chp.	Mens Mess.	Ladies Da.
Length Long.	6022	5798	5256
Par	71	71	74
Slope system	—	—	—

Advised golfing ability Niveau de jeu recommandé — 0 12 24 36

Hcp required Handicap exigé — 18 Men, 24 Ladies

CLUB HOUSE & AMENITIES — CLUB HOUSE ET ANNEXES — 8/10

Pro shop Pro-shop
Driving range Practice
Sheltered couvert no - On grass sur herbe yes - Putting-green putting-green yes - Pitching-green pitching green yes

HOTEL FACILITIES — ENVIRONNEMENT HOTELIER — 8/10

HOTELS HÔTELS

Berystede - 90 rooms, D £ 190 - Sunninghill 1 km
Tel (44) 0870 - 400 8111, Fax (44) 01344 - 872 301

Highclere - 11 rooms, D from £ 75 - Sunninghill 1 km
Tel (44) 01344 - 625 220, Fax (44) 01344 - 872 528

Oakley Court - 114 rooms, D £ 192 - Windsor 12 km
Tel (44) 01753 - 609 988, Fax (44) 01628 - 637 011

RESTAURANTS RESTAURANTS

Stateroom (Royal Berks. Hotel) - Sunninghill 1 km
Tel (44) 01344 - 623 322

Ciao Ninety - Ascot 3 km - Tel (44) 01344 - 622 285

Jade Fountain - Sunninghill 1 km - Tel (44) 01344 - 627 070

Sunningdale *Old Course*

18	8	8

This is one of those courses where the impression of space unfolding before you is as inviting as it is deceptive. In a magnificent setting, the trees are a sight to behold and are enhanced by heather which has invaded all the rough. When in flower it all looks wonderful, although you might wish you'd never set eyes on it when trying to hack your ball back onto the fairway. Laid out on ideal sandy soil, Sunningdale may lack yardage but is still a model of course design. This is one of Willie Park's masterpieces, such is the need for accuracy and inspiration, for a constant choice of tactics and for control over the full panoply of shots, particularly near the greens. But on a fine day when the ball rolls and rolls and when the greens are at their sublime best, scores can be flattering. This "Old Lady" has boundless charm and appeal.

C'est l'un des parcours où l'impression d'espace devant soi invite au jeu, mais elle peut être aussi trompeuse que la séduction du lieu. Les arbres sont un spectacle, mis en valeur par la bruyère qui envahit tous les roughs, magnifique quand elle prend ses couleurs, impossible quand il faut en déloger sa balle. Construit sur cette terre sablonneuse qui fait de si bons golfs, Sunningdale manque peut-être de longueur, mais reste un modèle d'architecture, et l'un des chefs-d'oeuvre de Willie Park, tant il réclame de précision et d'inspiration, tant il offre constamment des choix tactiques, tant il oblige à disposer de la gamme complète des coups de golf, notamment au petit jeu. Mais en un beau jour d'été où les balles n'en finissent pas de rouler, et où les greens sont à leur sommet, les scores peuvent être flatteurs. Cette "Old Lady" sait toujours se laisser séduire.

Sunningdale Golf Club — 1901

Ridgemount Road
ENG - SUNNINGDALE, Berks SL5 9RW

Office	Secrétariat	(44) 013 - 4462 1681
Pro shop	Pro-shop	(44) 013 - 4462 0128
Fax	Fax	(44) 013 - 4462 4154
Web	—	
Situation	Situation	Ascot, 5 km
Annual closure	Fermeture annuelle	no
Weekly closure	Fermeture hebdomadaire	no

Fees main season Tarifs haute saison — 18 holes

	Week days Semaine	We/Bank holidays We/Férié
Individual Individuel	£ 145	*
Couple Couple	£ 290	*

Full week days: £ 185 (Old + New)
* Visitors from Monday to Thursday only

Caddie Caddie on request **Electric Trolley** Chariot électrique no

Buggy Voiturette no **Clubs** Clubs no

Credit cards Cartes de crédit
VISA - MasterCard (Pro shop & green fees only)

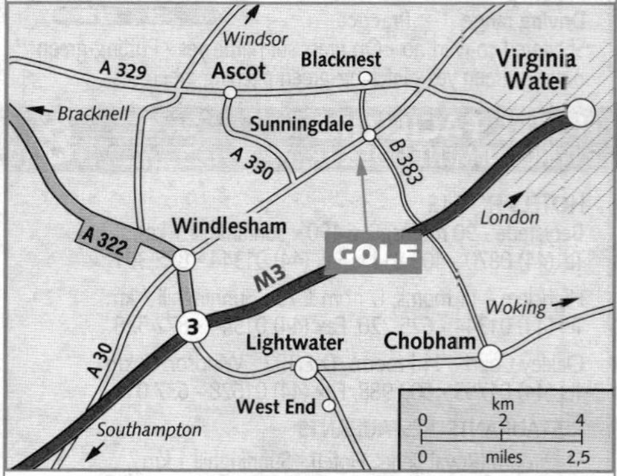

Access Accès : London, A30. 1st left after Sunningdale level crossing. Club 300 m on left.
Map 8 on page 484 Carte 8 Page 484

GOLF COURSE — PARCOURS — 18/20

Site	Site	
Maintenance	Entretien	
Architect	Architecte	Willie Park
Type	Type	forest, heathland
Relief	Relief	
Water in play	Eau en jeu	
Exp. to wind	Exposé au vent	
Trees in play	Arbres en jeu	

Scorecard Carte de score	Chp. Chp.	Mens Mess.	Ladies Da.
Length Long.	5948	5707	5242
Par	72	70	74
Slope system	—	—	—

Advised golfing ability Niveau de jeu recommandé — 0 12 24 36

Hcp required Handicap exigé — 18 Men, 24 Ladies

CLUB HOUSE & AMENITIES — CLUB HOUSE ET ANNEXES — 8/10

Pro shop	Pro-shop
Driving range	Practice

Sheltered couvert no - On grass sur herbe yes - Putting-green putting-green yes - Pitching-green pitching green yes

HOTEL FACILITIES — ENVIRONNEMENT HOTELIER — 8/10

HOTELS HÔTELS

Berystede - 90 rooms, D £ 190 - Sunninghill 1 km
Tel (44) 0870 - 400 8111, Fax (44) 01344 - 872 301

Highclere - 11 rooms, D from £ 75 - Sunninghill 1 km
Tel (44) 01344 - 625 220, Fax (44) 01344 - 872 528

Oakley Court - 114 rooms, D £ 192 - Windsor 12 km
Tel (44) 01753 - 609 988, Fax (44) 01628 - 637 011

RESTAURANTS RESTAURANTS

Stateroom (Royal Berks. Hotel) - Sunninghill 1 km
Tel (44) 01344 - 623 322

Ciao Ninety - Ascot 3 km - Tel (44) 01344 - 622 285

Jade Fountain - Sunninghill 1 km - Tel (44) 01344 - 627 070

Swinley Forest

17	6	8

A striking feature is the impression of wide open space despite the impressive mass of pine trees: the fairways are indeed wide and only hugely mis-hit drives can cause real problems for the second shot. Having said that, you will need to be more accurate if you want to hit the greens from the best position and stay on the putting surface, as uncannily they tend to pick out the well-hit shots and reject the rest. As usual with Harry Colt, the tee-boxes, bunkers and greens are at once carefully designed and well-positioned. Here more than ever, try not to count those golfing birdies before they are hatched; granted, the course is not long but it is a par 69 with five par 3s and some long par 4s, the kind of holes which add to your score rather than lower it. Last but not least, we should emphasize that this is a gentleman's club (no Ryder cup here!) where ladies and dogs are nonetheless welcome and where the rules of admission may be relaxed with a prior telephone call to the Secretary.

L'impression d'espace ouvert est frappante, en dépit de la masse imposante des pins : les fairways sont effectivement larges, et seuls les drives très égarés peuvent vous préoccuper pour le second coup. Cela dit, il convient d'être plus précis si l'on veut attaquer les greens en bonne position, et y rester, car ils ont assez tendance à trier les bonnes balles et rejeter les moins bonnes. Comme d'habitude avec Harry Colt, les départs comme les bunkers de fairway et de green sont soignés dans leur dessin comme dans leur placement. Il convient aussi de ne pas préjuger de son score avant de l'avoir fait : le parcours n'est pas long, mais c'est un par 69, avec 5 par 3 et quelques longs par 4, le genre de trous qui font les additions plus que les soustractions. Soulignons que c'est un club très "gentlemen" où femmes et chiens sont néanmoins bienvenus, et que les règles d'entrée peuvent s'assouplir avec un coup de téléphone au Secretary..

Swinley Forest Golf Club — 1909

Coronation Road
ENG - ASCOT, Berkshire SL9 5LE

Office	Secrétariat	(44) 01344 - 874 979
Pro shop	Pro-shop	(44) 01344 - 874 811
Fax	Fax	(44) 01344 - 874 733
E-mail	swinleyfgc@aol.com	
Situation	Situation	Ascot, 5 km
Annual closure	Fermeture annuelle	no
Weekly closure	Fermeture hebdomadaire	no
Fees main season	Tarifs haute saison	18 holes

	Week days Semaine	We/Bank holidays We/Férié
Individual Individuel	£ 110	*
Couple Couple	£ 220	*

* Members only

Caddie Caddie yes — **Electric Trolley** Chariot électrique no
Buggy Voiturette yes — **Clubs** Clubs yes
Credit cards Cartes de crédit
Visa - Mastercard - AMEX

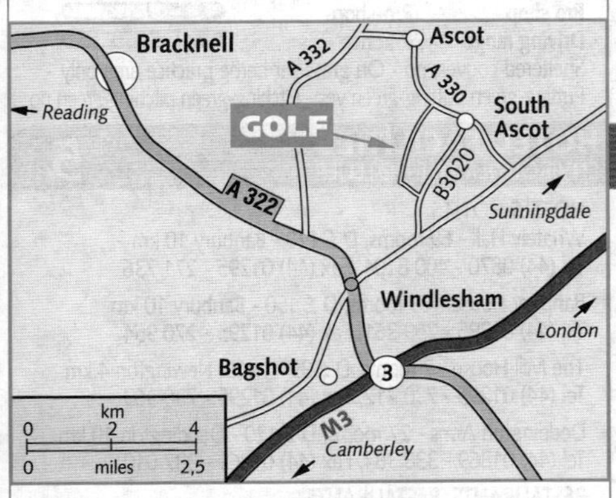

Access Accès : London A30. After Sunningdale, turn right on B3020 and left into Coronation Road. Golf course 1 km on left.
Map 8 on page 484 Carte 8 Page 484

GOLF COURSE — PARCOURS — 17/20

Site	Site	
Maintenance	Entretien	
Architect	Architecte	Harry S. Colt
Type	Type	inland, forest
Relief	Relief	
Water in play	Eau en jeu	
Exp. to wind	Exposé au vent	
Trees in play	Arbres en jeu	

Scorecard Carte de score	Chp. Chp.	Mens Mess.	Ladies Da.
Length Long.	5441	5176	4451
Par	69	68	68
Slope system	—	—	—

Advised golfing ability — Niveau de jeu recommandé: 0 12 24 36
Hcp required — Handicap exigé: Secretary's discretion

CLUB HOUSE & AMENITIES — CLUB HOUSE ET ANNEXES — 6/10

Pro shop Pro-shop
Driving range Practice
Sheltered couvert no - On grass sur herbe yes - Putting-green putting-green yes - Pitching-green pitching green yes

HOTEL FACILITIES — ENVIRONNEMENT HOTELIER — 8/10

HOTELS HÔTELS
Berystede - 90 rooms, D £ 190 - Sunninghill 1 km
Tel (44) 0870 - 400 8111, Fax (44) 01344 - 872 301

Highclere - 11 rooms, D from £ 75 - Sunninghill 1 km
Tel (44) 01344 - 625 220, Fax (44) 01344 - 872 528

Oakley Court - 114 rooms, D £ 192 - Windsor 12 km
Tel (44) 01753 - 609 988, Fax (44) 01628 - 637 011

RESTAURANTS RESTAURANTS
Stateroom (Royal Berks. Hotel) - Sunninghill 1 km
Tel (44) 01344 - 623 322
Ciao Ninety - Ascot 3 km - Tel (44) 01344 - 622 285
Jade Fountain - Sunninghill 1 km - Tel (44) 01344 - 627 070

Tadmarton Heath

14	6	5

On the road from Oxford to Birmingham, driving up the Thames valley, a pretty little stop-off to taste local pastries and admire the famous cross of Banbury market and, a few miles on in the middle of the countryside see what looks like a pretty and charming B&B but which is in fact the club-house of Tadmarton Heath, made from Costwold flint. As the name suggests, there is heather here and gorse too – especially on the back nine – and they combine to ensure that this course is as tight as it is short. A splendid sight when the gorse is in full bloom. And let's not talk about the windier days, a frequent feature of the weather and which can make those "little" holes devilishly hard to reach. In addition, the layout includes a few features in the Ganton style, albeit on a smaller scale, which is hardly surprising when you learn that both courses were designed by a one Harry Vardon. In his day and age you had to make do with fairly basic equipment: here today, many approach shots call for virtuosity that not even an armful of wedges in every shape and size could ever buy.

Sur la route d'Oxford à Birmingham, en remontant la Tamise, une petite halte pour déguster une galette et admirer la croix du marché de Banbury. Quelques kilomètres de plus en pleine campagne, on distinguera ce qui ressemble à un joli B&B plein de charme, le club-house de Tadmarton Heath, en pierre des Costwolds. Son nom l'affirme, il y a de la bruyère et assez d'ajoncs – surtout au retour – pour rendre ce parcours aussi étroit qu'il est court. Et splendide aussi quand tous les buissons d'ajoncs sont en fleur ! Et ne parlons pas des jours où souffle le vent, ils sont fréquents et rendent bien des "petits" trous inaccessibles. En plus, on a ici en réduction quelques coups de pinceau "à la Ganton", ce n'est guère étonnant quand leur dénominateur commun s'appelle Harry Vardon. En son temps, il fallait se débrouiller avec un matériel imparfait : bien des approches demandent ici une virtuosité que l'on n'achète pas avec la collection complète des wedges.

Tadmarton Heath Golf Club — 1922

Wiggington
ENG - BANBURY, Oxfordshire OX15 5HL

Office	Secrétariat	(44) 01608 - 737 278
Pro shop	Pro-shop	(44) 01608 - 730 047
Fax	Fax	(44) 01608 - 730 542
Web	www.thgolfclub.f9.co.uk	
Situation	Situation	Birmingham, 45 km
Annual closure	Fermeture annuelle	no
Weekly closure	Fermeture hebdomadaire	no

Fees main season Tarifs haute saison	Week days Semaine	We/Bank holidays We/Férié
		Full day
Individual Individuel	£ 45	£ 50
Couple Couple	£ 90	£ 100

Week days after 12:30, £ 35 /
We after 12:00 (18 holes only), £ 40

Caddie Caddie no — **Electric Trolley** Chariot électrique no
Buggy Voiturette yes — **Clubs** Clubs yes
Credit cards Cartes de crédit
VISA - MasterCard

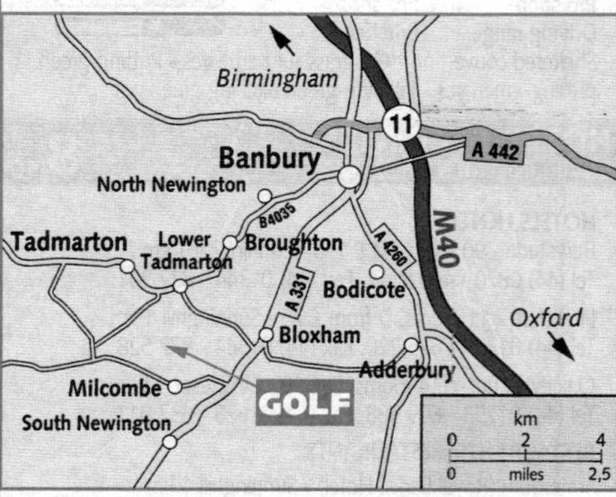

Access Accès : M40 London-Birmingham. Exit 11 to Banbury then A381 → Chipping Norton. Golf on right hand side
Map 7 on page 482 Carte 7 Page 482

GOLF COURSE — PARCOURS — 14/20

Site	Site	
Maintenance	Entretien	
Architect	Architecte	Harry Vardon C.K. Hutchinson
Type	Type	heathland
Relief	Relief	
Water in play	Eau en jeu	
Exp. to wind	Exposé au vent	
Trees in play	Arbres en jeu	

Scorecard Carte de score	Chp. Chp.	Mens Mess.	Ladies Da.
Length Long.	5326	5326	4891
Par	69	69	72
Slope system	—	—	—

Advised golfing ability Niveau de jeu recommandé — 0 12 24 36
Hcp required Handicap exigé — certificate

CLUB HOUSE & AMENITIES — CLUB HOUSE ET ANNEXES — 6/10

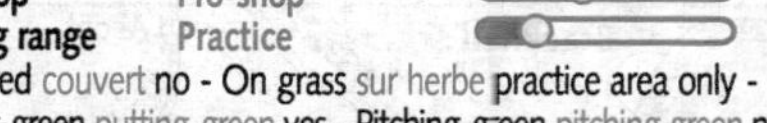

Pro shop Pro-shop
Driving range Practice
Sheltered couvert no - On grass sur herbe practice area only - Putting-green putting-green yes - Pitching-green pitching green no

HOTEL FACILITIES — ENVIRONNEMENT HOTELIER — 5/10

HOTELS HÔTELS

Whately Hall - 69 rooms, D £ 110 - Banbury 10 km
Tel (44) 0870 - 400 8104, Fax (44) 01295 - 271 736

Banbury House - 63 rooms, D £ 150 - Banbury 10 km
Tel (44) 01295 - 259 361, Fax (44) 01295 - 270 954

The Mill House - 7 rooms, D £ 99 - North Newington 4 km
Tel (44) 01295 - 730 212, Fax (44) 01295 - 730 363

Deddington Arms - 27 rooms, D £ 120 - Deddington 10 km
Tel (44) 01869 - 338 364, Fax (44) 01869 - 337 010

RESTAURANTS RESTAURANTS

Whately Hall - Banbury 10 km - Tel (44) 0870 - 400 8104
Inn at Sibford Gower (Pub) - Sibford Gower 5 km
Tel (44) 01295 - 788 808

The Belfry *Brabazon*

16	9	8

With so many attractive and challenging courses in Britain, if you don't know how important money and politics are in the choice of Ryder Cup sites then you won't understand why this course has hosted the event four times. The Belfry must be an extraordinary place: Brabazon is a good, but not exceptional parkland course. In contrast to the way the course is set up for the pros, the rough is kept cropped most of the time to speed up play and these flat 18 holes lose something of their character and appeal. Actually, two holes here have built the course's reputation: the 10th, a driveable par 4 from the front tees (remember the Ryder Cup) but which most amateurs try to reach from the back. And the 18th, a remarkable high-risk par 4 where the bogey is generally greeted with glee. The course was designed by Dave Thomas and Peter Alliss thirty years ago and has matured nicely alongside a luxury hotel and two other courses.

Avec une telle quantité de grands parcours britanniques, si l'on ne sait pas à quel point l'argent et la politique sont essentiels dans le choix des sites de la Ryder Cup, on ne comprend pas pourquoi ce parcours a reçu tant de fois cette épreuve mythique. Il s'agit d'un "resort" de remarquable qualité générale car le "Brabazon Course" est un bon, mais pas un grand "parkland". Contrairement à ce qui se passe pour les pros, le rough est soigneusement tondu la plupart du temps pour accélérer le jeu, et ces 18 trous perdent une partie de leur définition, comme de leur intérêt. En fait, deux trous ici ont fait la réputation du parcours, le 10, drivable des départs rouges (comme en Ryder Cup), mais que tous les amateurs essaient de driver des départs arrière, et le 18, remarquable par 4 à hauts risques, où un bogey est souvent suffisant pour gagner un match. Ce parcours a été construit par Dave Thomas et Peter Alliss il y a trente ans, il a bien évolué, aux côtés d'un hôtel de luxe et de deux autres parcours.

The Belfry — 1977

ENG - WISHAW, North Warwickshire B76 9PR

Office	Secrétariat	(44) 01675 - 470 301
Pro shop	Pro-shop	(44) 01675 - 470 301
Fax	Fax	(44) 01675 - 470 178
Web	www.devereonline.co.uk	
Situation	Situation	Birmingham, 10 km
Annual closure	Fermeture annuelle	no
Weekly closure	Fermeture hebdomadaire	no

Fees main season Tarifs haute saison	18 holes	
	Week days Semaine	**We/Bank holidays** We/Férié
Individual Individuel	£ 140	£ 140
Couple Couple	£ 280	£ 280

Special rate if staying at The Belfry Hotel

Caddie Caddie yes — **Electric Trolley** Chariot électrique no

Buggy Voiturette yes — **Clubs** Clubs yes

Credit cards Cartes de crédit
VISA - Eurocard - MasterCard - AMEX - DC

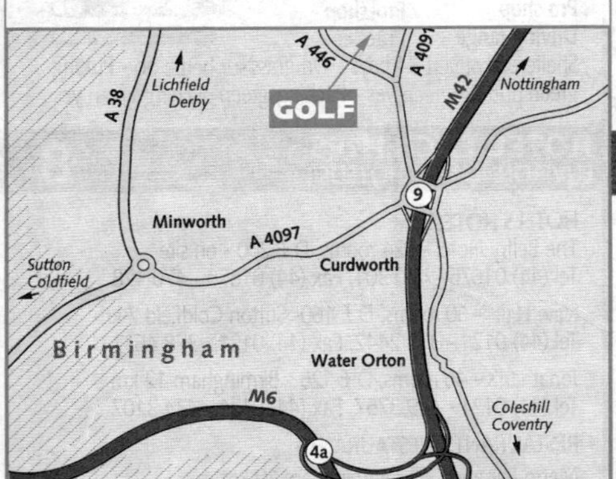

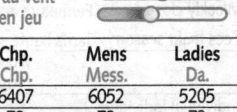

Access Accès : From London: M42 Exit 9. Follow signs to Belfry
From Birmingham: A38 to M6, then M42 North at Jct 4A.
Exit 9 on M42. Follow signs to Belfry.
Map 7 on page 482 Carte 7 Page 482

GOLF COURSE — PARCOURS — 16/20

Site	Site	
Maintenance	Entretien	
Architect	Architecte	Peter Alliss Dave Thomas
Type	Type	open country, parkland
Relief	Relief	
Water in play	Eau en jeu	
Exp. to wind	Exposé au vent	
Trees in play	Arbres en jeu	

Scorecard Carte de score	**Chp.** Chp.	**Mens** Mess.	**Ladies** Da.
Length Long.	6407	6052	5205
Par	72	72	73
Slope system	—	—	—

Advised golfing ability Niveau de jeu recommandé: 0 12 24 36

Hcp required Handicap exigé: 24 Men, 32 Women

CLUB HOUSE & AMENITIES — CLUB HOUSE ET ANNEXES — 9/10

Pro shop Pro-shop
Driving range Practice
Sheltered couvert 34 bays - On grass sur herbe no - Putting-green putting-green yes - Pitching-green pitching green yes

HOTEL FACILITIES — ENVIRONNEMENT HOTELIER — 8/10

HOTELS HÔTELS

The Belfry Hotel - 324 rooms, D £ 200 - on site
Tel (44) 01675 - 470 301, Fax (44) 01675 - 470 178

New Hall - 60 rooms, D £ 160- Sutton Coldfield 7 km
Tel (44) 0121 - 378 2442, Fax (44) 0121 - 378 4637

Jonathan's - 46 rooms, D £ 125 - Birmingham 12 km
Tel (44) 0121 - 429 3757, Fax (44) 0121 - 434 3107

RESTAURANTS RESTAURANTS

Metro Bar and Grill - Birmingham 10 km
Tel (44) 0121 - 200 1911

La Toque d'Or - Hockley 10 km - Tel (44) 0121 - 233 3655

French Restaurant - on site
Tel (44) 01675 - 470 301

The Belfry *PGA National*

15	9	8

When the powers-that-be at The Belfry decided a few years ago to build a third course – to complement the famous Brabazon and lesser know Derby – a distinctly modern American design concept was selected for the PGA National with an abundance of water coming into play on land that hardly lends itself to a golf course. To avoid too much trouble with the water we strongly advise visitors to play off the front tees, particularly at the fourth and eighth holes where it is especially easy for a drive to find a watery grave. The bunkers have been particularly well designed by architect Dave Thomas and decisively brought into play, although some greens can still be reached with a good old bump-and-run shot. The course is getting better as it matures and will improve even further when the thousands of saplings that have been planted grow a little more. For those who like a course to be pleasing on the eye there is one downside – the monstrous electricity pylons are a blot on the landscape.

Lorsque les maîtres du Belfry ont décidé il y a quelques années de construire un troisième parcours, en plus du Brabazon et du Derby, le concept général de ce PGA National a été d'adopter un style résolument américain, avec quantité d'obstacles d'eau, sur un terrain difficilement adaptable à un parcours de golf. Pour éviter ces problèmes avec l'eau, nous ne saurions trop recommander aux visiteurs de jouer des départs avancés, particulièrement au 4 et au 8, spécialement destinés à noyer les drives inconsidérés. Les bunkers ont été particulièrement bien dessinés par Dave Thomas, et mis résolument en jeu bien que certains greens puissent encore être attaqués en faisant rouler sa balle. Ce parcours vieillit plutôt bien et ne saurait que continuer dans cette voie lorsque les milliers de plantations auront grandi. Ceux qui aiment la plénitude du spectacle lorsqu'ils jouent au golf distingueront ici un bémol, les pylones de lignes à haute tension.

The Belfry — 1997

ENG - WISHAW, North Warwickshire B76 9PR

Office Secrétariat (44) 01675 - 470 301
Pro shop Pro-shop (44) 01675 - 470 301
Fax Fax (44) 01675 - 470 178
Web www.devereonline.co.uk
Situation Situation Birmingham, 10 km
Annual closure Fermeture annuelle no
Weekly closure Fermeture hebdomadaire no

Fees main season / Tarifs haute saison	Week days / Semaine	We/Bank holidays / We/Férié
18 holes		
Individual Individuel	£ 75	£ 75
Couple Couple	£ 150	£ 150

Special rate if staying at The Belfry Hotel

Caddie Caddie yes — **Electric Trolley** Chariot électrique no
Buggy Voiturette yes — **Clubs** Clubs yes
Credit cards Cartes de crédit
VISA - Eurocard - MasterCard - AMEX - DC

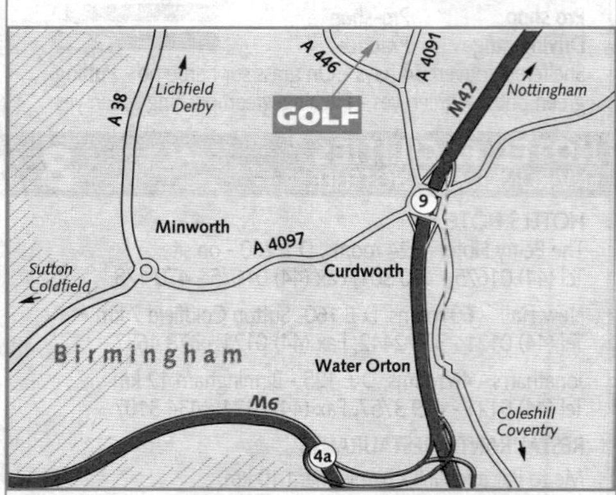

Access Accès : From London: M42 Exit 9. Follow signs to Belfry
From Birmingham: A38 to M6, then M42 North at Jct 4A.
Exit 9 on M42. Follow signs to Belfry.
Map 7 on page 482 Carte 7 Page 482

GOLF COURSE — PARCOURS — 15/20

Site Site
Maintenance Entretien
Architect Architecte — Dave Thomas
Type Type — open country, parkland
Relief Relief
Water in play Eau en jeu
Exp. to wind Exposé au vent
Trees in play Arbres en jeu

Scorecard / Carte de score	Chp. / Chp.	Mens / Mess.	Ladies / Da.
Length Long.	6365	6064	5175
Par	71	70	73
Slope system	—	—	—

Advised golfing ability Niveau de jeu recommandé — 0 12 24 36

Hcp required Handicap exigé — 24 Men, 32 Women

CLUB HOUSE & AMENITIES — CLUB HOUSE ET ANNEXES — 9/10

Pro shop Pro-shop
Driving range Practice
Sheltered couvert 34 bays - On grass sur herbe no - Putting-green putting-green yes - Pitching-green pitching green yes

HOTEL FACILITIES — ENVIRONNEMENT HOTELIER — 8/10

HOTELS HÔTELS
The Belfry Hotel - 324 rooms, D £ 200 - on site
Tel (44) 01675 - 470 301, Fax (44) 01675 - 470 178

New Hall - 60 rooms, D £ 160- Sutton Coldfield 7 km
Tel (44) 0121 - 378 2442, Fax (44) 0121 - 378 4637

Jonathan's - 46 rooms, D £ 125 - Birmingham 12 km
Tel (44) 0121 - 429 3757, Fax (44) 0121 - 434 3107

RESTAURANTS RESTAURANTS
Metro Bar and Grill - Birmingham 10 km
Tel (44) 0121 - 200 1911
La Toque d'Or - Hockley 10 km - Tel (44) 0121 - 233 3655
French Restaurant - on site
Tel (44) 01675 - 470 301

The Grove

18 | 8 | 9

This is one of Europe's most ambitious resorts: a 5-star plus facility half an hour from London with a luxurious hotel that caters for major social functions as well as itinerant golfers plus an 18-hole course manicured by 20 green-keepers. Architect Kyle Phillips, now an established star in course design, resisted the temptation to create too flashy a course and set about paying a serious tribute to the great architects of the past. Harry Colt would have been delighted to see his style evoked in the subtle shaping of the landscape and the often deceptive bunker placing. Phillips has revisited the art of cloaking perspective and trompe l'œil worthy of Alister Mackenzie. This is a severe test of talent with a certain emphasis on the chip shot that is so often overlooked on modern courses. An ability to shape the shot and strategic intelligence are as important here as the power game. A connoisseur's course whose excellence is unveiled as you play it, testing for the finest exponents of the game but never humbling for the common mortal, all wrapped in absolute elegance.

C'est l'un des complexes les plus ambitieux d'Europe. Une pluie d'étoiles à 30 minutes de Londres, avec un hôtel de luxe aussi bien destiné aux grandes réceptions qu'à accueillir les golfeurs, et un 18 trous entretenu par 20 jardiniers. Son architecte Kyle Phillips, désormais bien connu, a refusé la tentation d'un design "flashy" et rendu un hommage appuyé aux grands auteurs du passé. Harry Colt n'aurait pas renié le jeu subtil des mouvements de terrain, ni le placement parfois trompeur des bunkers. Phillips a retrouvé aussi un certain art du camouflage des perspectives et du trompe-l'œil digne d'Alister Mackenzie. On ajoutera l'examen des talents, avec une insistance sur le chipping, si souvent négligé sur les parcours modernes. De fait, la qualité du travail de balle et l'intelligence stratégique sont ici les égaux de la force de frappe. Un parcours de connaisseur dont les qualités se révèlent à mesure qu'on le joue, exigeant pour les meilleurs, mais jamais humiliant pour les autres, et d'une extrême élégance.

Chandler's Cross — 2003

ENG - RICKMANSWORTH, Hertforshire WD3 4TG

Office Secrétariat (44) 01923 - 807 807
Pro shop Pro-shop (44) 01923 - 807 807
Fax Fax (44) 01923 - 294 268
Web www.thegrove.co.uk
Situation Situation London, 28 km
Annual closure Fermeture annuelle no
Weekly closure Fermeture hebdomadaire no

Fees main season Tarifs haute saison	18 holes	
	Week days Semaine	We/Bank holidays We/Férié
Individual Individuel	£ 130	£ 130
Couple Couple	£ 260	£ 260

Special rates for Hotel guests / Spring & Autumn, £ 100

Caddie Caddie no — **Electric Trolley** Chariot électrique no
Buggy Voiturette yes — **Clubs** Clubs no
Credit cards Cartes de crédit
VISA - Eurocard - Mastercard - AMEX - DC - JCB

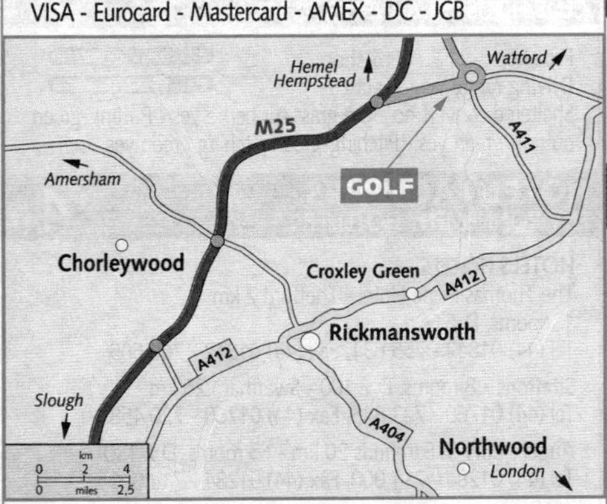

Access Accès : • M25 East → Junction 19, 3rd exit at first roundabout. • M25 West, → Junction 20, turn left, 2nd exit at first roundabout. 1/2 mile on A41 (Hempstead Road) turn right onto Grove Mill Lane. The Grove 1 m. on your right.
Map 8 on page 484 Carte 8 Page 484

GOLF COURSE — PARCOURS — 18/20

Site Site
Maintenance Entretien
Architect Architecte Kyle Phillips
Type Type inland, parkland
Relief Relief
Water in play Eau en jeu
Exp. to wind Exposé au vent
Trees in play Arbres en jeu

Scorecard Carte de score	Chp. Chp.	Mens Mess.	Ladies Da.
Length Long.	6453	6090	4957
Par	72	72	72
Slope system	—	—	—

Advised golfing ability Niveau de jeu recommandé 0 12 24 36
Hcp required Handicap exigé 24

CLUB HOUSE & AMENITIES — CLUB HOUSE ET ANNEXES — 8/10

Pro shop Pro-shop
Driving range Practice
Sheltered couvert Shelters over grass - On grass sur herbe yes - Putting-green putting-green yes - Pitching-green pitching green yes

HOTEL FACILITIES — ENVIRONNEMENT HOTELIER — 9/10

HOTELS HÔTELS
The Grove - on site
227 rooms, D from £ 230
Tel (44) 01923 - 807 807, Fax (44) 01923 - 221 008

Two Brewers Inn - 20 rooms, D £ 100 - Chipperfield 8 km
Tel (44) 01923 - 265 266, Fax (44) 01923 - 261 884

Hilton Watford - 201 rooms, D from £ 81 - Watford 4 km
Tel (44) 01923 - 235 881, Fax (44) 01923 - 220 836

RESTAURANTS RESTAURANTS
St James - Bushey 7 km - Tel (44) 02089 - 502 480
3 restaurants at The Grove - on site - Tel (44) 01923 - 807 807
Viceroy - Abbots Langley 12 km - Tel (44) 01923 - 262 163

Thetford

15	7	4

In between visits to the pretty Georgian town of Swaffham, the national stud-farm of Newmarket, the Neolithic site of Grimes Graves and the beautiful medieval town of Norwich, you might find the time to play this 1912 course which was restyled and lengthened by Donald Steel in 1985. A pity perhaps that the fairways are so wide, but they do prompt the bigger-hitters to open their shoulders and dispatch their ball into the waiting fairway bunkers. There are trees, of course, but not all that close to the fairways. When they do come close, it is to complicate your second shot. Very pretty, calm, well-balanced and with pleasant springy turf over sandy sub-soil, Thetford is not the course of the century but it does enable golfers of all levels to play together very easily. For the less experienced player, however, we would shamelessly recommend the front tees.

Entre les visites de la jolie ville georgienne de Swaffham, du haras national de Newmarket, du site néolithique de Grimes Graves et de la belle ville médiévale de Norwich, il vous restera probablement quelques heures pour jouer ce parcours de 1912, mais remodelé et allongé par Donald Steel en 1985. On regrette que les fairways soient très larges, mais ils incitent les frappeurs à se déchaîner... et à expédier leurs balles dans les bunkers de fairway ! Certes, on trouve aussi des arbres, mais ils ne sont pas très proches des fairways, et quand ils le sont, c'est plutôt pour gêner les seconds coups. Très joli, très calme, bien équilibré, avec un gazon très agréable sur un sol de sable et de tourbe, Thetford n'est pas le parcours du siècle, mais il permet au moins à tous les niveaux d'évoluer en bonne harmonie. On conseillera cependant aux joueurs peu expérimentés de choisir sans honte les départs avancés.

Thetford Golf Club — 1912

Brandon Road
ENG - THETFORD, Norfolk IP24 3NE

Office Secrétariat (44) 01842 - 752 258
Pro shop Pro-shop (44) 01842 - 752 662
Fax Fax (44) 01842 - 766 212
Web www.club-noticeboard.co.uk/thetford/
Situation Situation Cambridge, 50 km
Annual closure Fermeture annuelle no
Weekly closure Fermeture hebdomadaire no

Fees main season Tarifs haute saison	Week days Semaine	We/Bank holidays We/Férié
	18 holes	
Individual Individuel	£ 30	£ 30*
Couple Couple	£ 60	£ 60*

* After 13:00 / Full week days £ 40

Caddie Caddie no — **Electric Trolley** Chariot électrique no
Buggy Voiturette no — **Clubs** Clubs no
Credit cards Cartes de crédit
Visa - Mastercard - AMEX (Pro shop goods only)

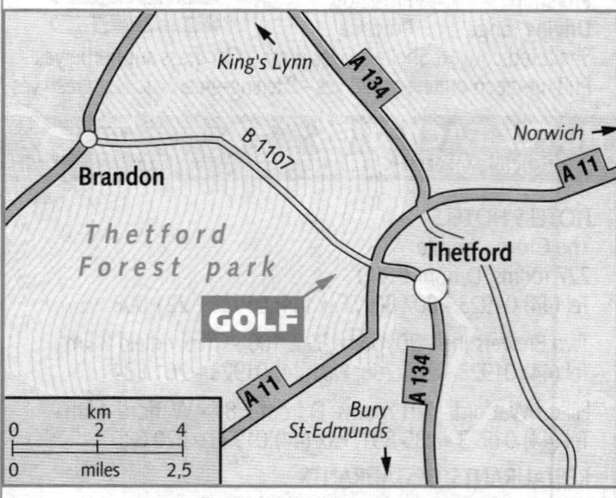

Access Accès : London M11. Jct 9, A11 → Norwich.
Thetford Bypass B1107 → Brandon, Golf 500 m on the left.
Map 7 on page 483 Carte 7 Page 483

GOLF COURSE — PARCOURS — 15/20

Site Site
Maintenance Entretien
Architect Architecte — C.H. Mayo, Donald Steel (1985)
Type Type — inland, forest
Relief Relief
Water in play Eau en jeu
Exp. to wind Exposé au vent
Trees in play Arbres en jeu

Scorecard Carte de score	Chp. Chp.	Mens Mess.	Ladies Da.
Length Long.	6190	5970	5405
Par	72	72	74
Slope system	—	—	—

Advised golfing ability Niveau de jeu recommandé — 0 12 24 36
Hcp required Handicap exigé — certificate

CLUB HOUSE & AMENITIES — CLUB HOUSE ET ANNEXES — 7/10

Pro shop Pro-shop
Driving range Practice
Sheltered couvert no - On grass sur herbe yes - Putting-green putting-green yes - Pitching-green pitching green yes

HOTEL FACILITIES — ENVIRONNEMENT HOTELIER — 4/10

HOTELS HÔTELS
The Thomas Paine Hotel - Thetford 2 km
13 rooms, D £ 66
Tel (44) 01842 - 755 631, Fax (44) 01842 - 766 505

Strattons - 8 rooms, D £ 100 - Swaffham 25 km
Tel (44) 01760 - 723 845, Fax (44) 01760 - 720 458

Angel - Bury St Edmunds 20 km - 65 rooms, D £ 130
Tel (44) 01284 - 714 000, Fax (44) 01284 - 714 001

RESTAURANTS RESTAURANTS
Angel - Bury St Edmunds 20 km - Tel (44) 01284 - 714 000
Strattons - Swaffham 25 km - Tel (44) 01760 - 723 845
Theobalds - Ixworth 17 km - Tel (44) 01359 - 231 707

Thorndon Park

15 | 7 | 6

Essex is not really a golfing county like Surrey, for example, on the other side of London. But some of the courses here do stand out, including this one, laid out in 1920 over a former hunting estate. Thorndon Park features a gigantic neo-classical mansion, one that would surely serve as an impressive and characterful club-house, although rather disappointingly the actual 19th hole is more modern and less imposing. This is one of the hundreds of courses designed by Harry Colt and it is as intelligent in its layout, as imaginative in its use of the land and as fair and open as the others, with a few superb fairways amidst ancient oaks and other trees. When you realise how few technical resources they had at the time (1920), it makes you think how much many modern designers could learn from this style of layout. Of course, like many British courses from another age, this one lacks length, but the vast majority of players won't complain. A course for everyone, even the best.

L'Essex n'est pas vraiment une région à golf comme le Surrey par exemple, de l'autre côté de Londres. Mais quelques parcours se distinguent comme celui-ci, créé en 1920 dans un ancien domaine de chasse orné d'une gigantesque bâtisse néo-classique que l'on dénomme "mansion," que l'on aurait volontiers vu transformer en club-house de caractère, il est malheureusement plus moderne et moins imposant. C'est un parcours parmi les centaines créés par Harry Colt, il est aussi intelligent dans son déroulement, imaginatif dans son utilisation du terrain, aussi franc et honnête que les autres, avec quelques superbes fairways au milieu des arbres, dont quelques chênes plusieurs fois centenaires. Quand on imagine le manque de moyens techniques à l'époque (1920), bien des architectes modernes devraient y prendre des leçons. Bien sûr, comme la plupart des parcours britanniques d'autrefois, il manque de longueur, mais l'immense majorité des joueurs ne s'en plaindra pas.

Thorndon Park Golf Club — 1920

Ingrave
ENG - BRENTWOOD, Essex CM13 3RH

Office	Secrétariat	(44) 01277 - 811 666
Pro shop	Pro-shop	(44) 01277 - 810 736
Fax	Fax	(44) 01277 - 810 645
Web	www.thorndonparkgolfclub.com	
Situation	Situation	London, 35 km
Annual closure	Fermeture annuelle	no
Weekly closure	Fermeture hebdomadaire	no

Fees main season Tarifs haute saison — 18 holes

	Week days Semaine	We/Bank holidays We/Férié
Individual Individuel	£ 40	*
Couple Couple	£ 80	*

Full week days: £ 55 (Booking essential)
* Members only at week-ends

Caddie Caddie no — **Electric Trolley** Chariot électrique no
Buggy Voiturette no — **Clubs** Clubs yes
Credit cards Cartes de crédit
Visa - Mastercard (Pro shop goods only)

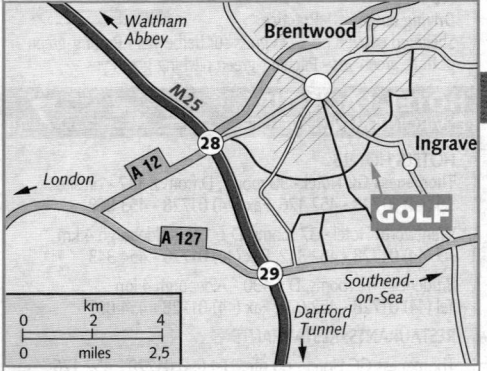

Access Accès : London E, A11 then A12 to Brentwood. A 128 SE → East Horndon. Golf on the right.
Map 7 on page 483 Carte 7 Page 483

GOLF COURSE — 15/20
PARCOURS

Site	Site	
Maintenance	Entretien	
Architect	Architecte	Harry S. Colt
Type	Type	parkland, inland
Relief	Relief	
Water in play	Eau en jeu	
Exp. to wind	Exposé au vent	
Trees in play	Arbres en jeu	

Scorecard Carte de score	Chp. Chp.	Mens Mess.	Ladies Da.
Length Long.	5845	5620	4580
Par	71	71	72
Slope system	—	—	—

Advised golfing ability Niveau de jeu recommandé — 0 12 24 36
Hcp required Handicap exigé — certificate

CLUB HOUSE & AMENITIES — 7/10
CLUB HOUSE ET ANNEXES

Pro shop Pro-shop
Driving range Practice
Sheltered couvert no - On grass sur herbe yes - Putting-green putting-green yes - Pitching-green pitching green no

HOTEL FACILITIES — 6/10
ENVIRONNEMENT HOTELIER

HOTELS HÔTELS
Marygreen Manor - 44 rooms, D £ 145 - Brentwood 6 km
Tel (44) 01277 - 225 252, Fax (44) 01277 - 262 809

Pontlands Park - Great Baddow (Chelmsford) 9 km
36 rooms, D £ 105
Tel (44) 01245 - 476 444, Fax (44) 01245 - 478 393

Travelodge - 22 rooms, D £ 53 - East Horndon 4 km
Tel (44) 01277 - 810 819, Fax (44) 01277 - 810 819

Posthouse Brentwood - 145 rooms, D £ 129 - Brentwood 5 km
Tel (44) 0870 - 400 9012, Fax (44) 01277 - 264 264

RESTAURANTS RESTAURANTS
Marygreen Manor - Brentwood 6 km - Tel (44) 01277 - 225 252
Posthouse Brentwood - Tel (44) 0870 - 400 9012

Thorpeness

14	7	7

Thorpeness is just outside Aldeburgh, not far from Minsmere nature reserve in Dunwich, where you can watch an incredible variety of birds. The hotel-club-house is excellent and makes this a fine destination, especially since there is an abundance of good courses round and about (Ipswich, Aldeburgh, Woodbridge, Felixstowe Ferry, etc.). This one was initially designed in 1923 by James Braid and slightly re-shaped in 1965. Here, you keep out of the heather and avoid the lupins, very pretty when in flower but not the ideal place to put your ball. An uncomplicated layout, not too demanding for the average golfer, but one which requires good placing of the ball, so don't think twice about playing an iron off the tee (except perhaps on the half dozen or so long par 4s). Other landmarks to cap a very pleasant day's golfing are a wind-mill, a curious "house in the clouds", an unsightly nuclear power station in the distance and a hotel to watch it all happen.

Thorpeness est juste à l'extérieur d'Aldeburgh, non loin de la réserve naturelle de Minsmere à Dunwich, d'où l'on peut observer une incroyable variété d'oiseaux. L'Hôtel-club-house est de grande qualité, ce qui en fait une destination tout à fait agréable, d'autant que les bons parcours alentour ne manquent pas (Ipswich, Aldeburgh, Woodbridge, Felixstowe Ferry...). Celui-ci a été dessiné par James Braid en 1923, et légèrement retouché vers 1965. On veillera à éviter les bruyères et les buissons de lupin, très jolis en fleur, mais dont il vaut mieux ne pas s'approcher avec une balle de golf. Ce tracé sans histoires, préparé pour faciliter les choses, nécessite avant tout un bon placement : il ne faut pas hésiter à jouer des fers au départ, sauf sur la demi-douzaine de longs par 4. Pour décorer une très agréable journée, un moulin à vent, un curieuse "maison dans les nuages," et une centrale nucléaire au loin, pas bien belle. Et un hôtel pour observer tout cela.

Thorpeness Golf Club — 1923

ENG - THORPENESS, Suffolk IP16 4NH

Office Secrétariat (44) 01728 - 452 176
Pro shop Pro-shop (44) 01728 - 454 926
Fax Fax (44) 01728 - 453 868
Web www.thorpeness.co.uk
Situation Situation Ipswich, 39 km
Aldeburgh (pop. 2 654), 3 km
Annual closure Fermeture annuelle no
Weekly closure Fermeture hebdomadaire no

Fees main season Tarifs haute saison — Full day

	Week days Semaine	We/Bank holidays We/Férié
Individual Individuel	£ 33	£ 38
Couple Couple	£ 66	£ 76

Caddie Caddie no — **Electric Trolley** Chariot électrique yes
Buggy Voiturette yes — **Clubs** Clubs no
Credit cards Cartes de crédit
VISA - MasterCard

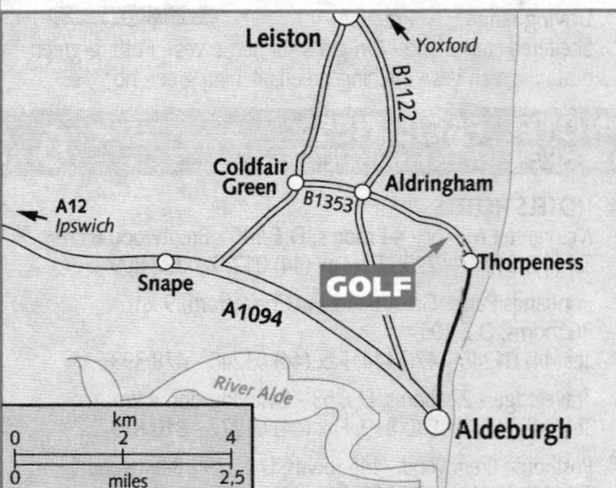

Access Accès : Ipswich A12 → Saxmundham. Turn right on B119 → Leiston. At Leiston, turn right on B1353
Map 7 on page 483 Carte 7 Page 483

GOLF COURSE — PARCOURS — 14/20

Site Site
Maintenance Entretien
Architect Architecte — James Braid
Type Type — seaside course, open country
Relief Relief
Water in play Eau en jeu
Exp. to wind Exposé au vent
Trees in play Arbres en jeu

Scorecard Carte de score	Chp. Chp.	Mens Mess.	Ladies Da.
Length Long.	5645	5674	4922
Par	69	69	74
Slope system	—	—	—

Advised golfing ability Niveau de jeu recommandé — 0 12 24 36
Hcp required Handicap exigé — certificate

CLUB HOUSE & AMENITIES — CLUB HOUSE ET ANNEXES — 7/10

Pro shop Pro-shop
Driving range Practice
Sheltered couvert no - On grass sur herbe yes - Putting-green putting-green yes - Pitching-green pitching green yes

HOTEL FACILITIES — ENVIRONNEMENT HOTELIER — 7/10

HOTELS HÔTELS
Thorpeness GC Hotel - 30 rooms, D from £ 112 - on site
Tel (44) 01728 - 452 176, Fax (44) 01728 - 453 868

Wentworth Hotel - 37 rooms, D £ 123 - Aldeburgh 4 km
Tel (44) 01728 - 452 312, Fax (44) 01728 - 454 343

Brudenell - 42 rooms, D £ 130 - Aldeburgh 4 km
Tel (44) 01728 - 452 071, Fax (44) 01728 - 454 082

RESTAURANTS RESTAURANTS
Thorpeness GC Hotel - on site - Tel (44) 01728 - 452 176
The Lighthouse - Aldeburgh 4 km - Tel (44) 01728 - 453 377

Thurlestone

15	6	5

This is a magnificent spot where you savour every moment along a rugged coastline with rocky cliffs and pounding waves. This course is beside the sea but most of the holes are pretty high up. Only the dunes are missing to make this a text-book links course, although the sandy soil is just right and the layout well worthy of the label. After much hesitation, the original short 9 hole course was extended and altered by Harry Colt; the back 9 are 1,000 yards longer than the front 9 and they have added a good deal of zip to the course. The first seven holes are short, rather treacherous and very technical in style, while the remainder are longer and more open but still to be played with care and caution when the wind blows. In windy weather, low punchers of the ball will have fun while the others can always divide their score by two and simply admire the surrounding landscape.

C'est un magnifique endroit à savourer chaque instant le long d'une côte tourmentée, avec d'impressionnantes falaises où la mer livre ses assauts. Ce parcours est situé en bordure de mer, mais la plupart des trous sont bien en hauteur. Il ne manque que les dunes pour en faire un links comme dans les livres, mais le sol sablonneux a la qualité requise, et le dessin est à la hauteur. Après bien des hésitations, les premiers 9 trous originaux furent modifiés et agrandis par Harry Colt : le retour est près de 1000 mètres plus long que l'aller et ils ont donné de la vigueur au tracé. Les sept premiers trous sont courts, assez traîtres et très techniques, les suivants plus longs et ouverts, à négocier avec attention et prudence quand le vent souffle. Les "puncheurs" de balles pourront alors s'y régaler, les autres diviseront leur score par deux, à moins de se contenter d'admirer le paysage ou de visiter la région.

Thurlestone Golf Club — 1897

Thurlestone
ENG - KINGSBRIDGE, S. Devon TQ7 3NZ

Office Secrétariat (44) 01548 - 560 405
Pro shop Pro-shop (44) 01548 - 560 715
Fax Fax (44) 01548 - 562 149
Web www.thurlestonegc.co.uk
Situation Situation Kingsbridge, 6 km
Annual closure Fermeture annuelle no
Weekly closure Fermeture hebdomadaire no

Fees main season / Tarifs haute saison	Week days / Semaine	We/Bank holidays / We/Férié
Full day		
Individual Individuel	£ 36	£ 36
Couple Couple	£ 72	£ 72

Caddie Caddie no — **Electric Trolley** Chariot électrique yes
Buggy Voiturette no — **Clubs** Clubs yes

Credit cards Cartes de crédit
Visa - Mastercard (Pro shop goods & Green fees)

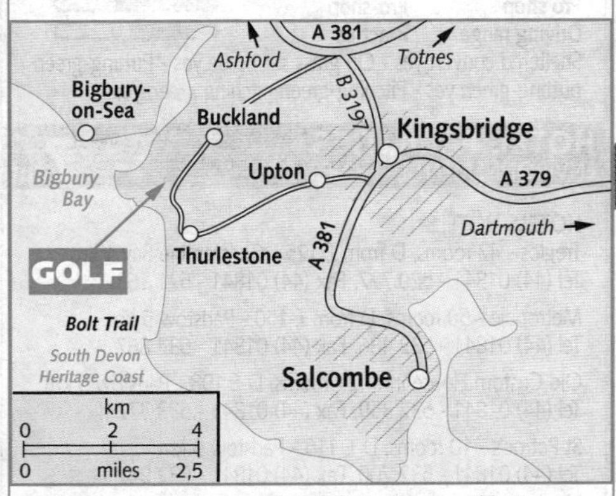

Access Accès : M5, then A38, A382 to Newton Abbott, then A381 through Totnes and Kingsbridge.
In Sutton, → South Milton and Thurlestone. Follow signs.
Map 6 on page 480 Carte 6 Page 480

GOLF COURSE — PARCOURS 15/20

Site Site
Maintenance Entretien
Architect Architecte Harry S. Colt
Type Type seaside course, open country
Relief Relief
Water in play Eau en jeu
Exp. to wind Exposé au vent
Trees in play Arbres en jeu

Scorecard / Carte de score	Chp. / Chp.	Mens / Mess.	Ladies / Da.
Length Long.	5770	5626	5086
Par	71	70	73
Slope system	—	—	—

Advised golfing ability / Niveau de jeu recommandé: 0 12 24 36
Hcp required Handicap exigé 28 Men, 45 Ladies

CLUB HOUSE & AMENITIES — CLUB HOUSE ET ANNEXES 6/10

Pro shop Pro-shop
Driving range Practice
Sheltered couvert no - On grass sur herbe yes - Putting-green putting-green yes - Pitching-green pitching green yes

HOTEL FACILITIES — ENVIRONNEMENT HOTELIER 5/10

HOTELS HÔTELS
Thurlestone Hotel - 64 rooms, D from £ 184 - on site
Tel (44) 01548 - 560 382, Fax (44) 01548 - 561 069

Buckland-Tout-Saints - 12 rooms, D from £ 70 - Kingsbridge 6 km
Tel (44) 01548 - 853 055, Fax (44) 01548 - 856 261

Marine - 53 rooms, D £ 200 (w. dinner)- Salcombe 10 km
Tel (44) 01548 - 844 444, Fax (44) 01548 - 843 109

RESTAURANTS RESTAURANTS
Restaurant 42 - Salcombe 10 km - Tel (44) 01548 - 843 408
Sloop Inn (Pub) - Bantham 2 km - Tel (44) 01548 - 560 489
Margaret Amelia (Thurlestone) - on site
Tel (44) 01548 - 560 382

Trevose *Championship*

17 | 7 | 7

If the fairways were generally narrowed and the rough allowed to grow taller, Trevose would be much more difficult. But this is first and foremost a holiday location, where regular golfers return each year with their children. The kids eventually get to play the "big" 18-hole course after cutting their teeth on the two 9-holers. Spectacular, charming and technically strong, Trevose is a course for golfers of all levels that even the best players never grow tired of. This Harry Colt layout is highly strategic and very honest, even though not all the hazards are visible, but there are seldom any really unpleasant surprises. They say that a friendly atmosphere adds to the pleasure of playing golf and that is certainly true here, even when the wind blows. From start to finish (and, yes, the clubhouse is excellent) Trevose is a magical place for golfers. And to think that King Arthur met Merlin the Wizard nearby.

Avec des fairways plus étroits, un rough aussi sauvage que les sommets des dunes, Trevose serait bien plus difficile encore. Mais c'est d'abord un lieu de vacances, où les habitués reviennent chaque année, avec les enfants qui finissent un jour par passer au "grand" 18 trous après avoir débuté et pris de l'expérience sur les deux 9 trous. Spectaculaire, plein de charme, techniquement puissant, Trevose est un parcours pour tous les niveaux, où les meilleurs ne s'ennuient jamais. Le dessin de Harry Colt est très stratégique et très franc, même si les obstacles ne sont pas tous bien visibles, mais on a rarement de mauvaises surprises. On dit qu'une atmosphère amicale contribue au plaisir du jeu, c'est bien le cas ici, même avec le vent. Du départ au restaurant du club-house, c'est un lieu magique. Normal, le Roi Arthur aurait rencontré l'Enchanteur Merlin dans les environs.

Trevose Golf & Country Club — 1925

Constantine Bay
ENG - PADSTOW, Cornwall PL28 8J13

Office	Secrétariat	(44) 01841 - 520 208
Pro shop	Pro-shop	(44) 01841 - 520 261
Fax	Fax	(44) 01841 - 521 057
Web	www.trevose-gc.co.uk	
Situation	Situation	Padstow (pop. 4 250), 6 km
Annual closure	Fermeture annuelle	no
Weekly closure	Fermeture hebdomadaire	no

Fees main season Tarifs haute saison	Full day	
	Week days Semaine	**We/Bank holidays** We/Férié
Individual Individuel	£ 50	£ 50
Couple Couple	£ 100	£ 100

Caddie Caddie no — **Electric Trolley** Chariot électrique no
Buggy Voiturette yes — **Clubs** Clubs yes
Credit cards Cartes de crédit
VISA - MasterCard

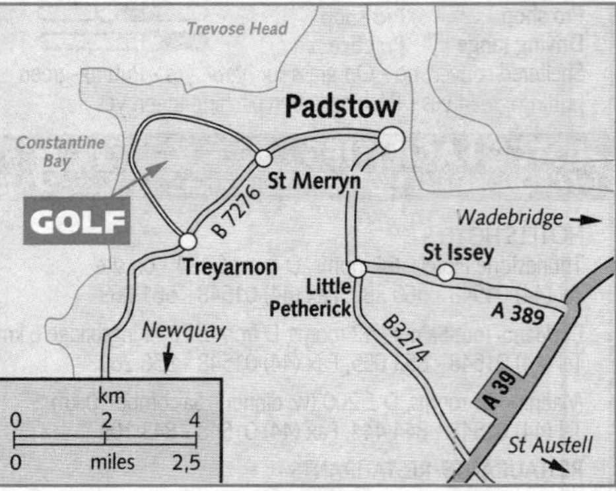

Access Accès : M5 Exit 31, then A30 (→ Exeter) through Bodwin, then B3274 on right after Victoria → Padstow. → St Merryn. Follow signs to golf.
Map 6 on page 480 Carte 6 Page 480

GOLF COURSE — PARCOURS — 17/20

Site	Site	
Maintenance	Entretien	
Architect	Architecte	Harry S. Colt
Type	Type	seaside course, links
Relief	Relief	
Water in play	Eau en jeu	
Exp. to wind	Exposé au vent	
Trees in play	Arbres en jeu	

Scorecard Carte de score	**Chp.** Chp.	**Mens** Mess.	**Ladies** Da.
Length Long.	6177	5569	5238
Par	72	71	73
Slope system	—	—	—

Advised golfing ability — 0 12 24 36
Niveau de jeu recommandé
Hcp required — Handicap exigé — 28 Men, 36 Ladies

CLUB HOUSE & AMENITIES — CLUB HOUSE ET ANNEXES — 7/10

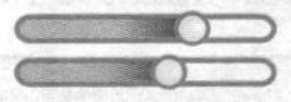

Pro shop — Pro-shop
Driving range — Practice
Sheltered couvert yes - On grass sur herbe yes - Putting-green putting-green yes - Pitching-green pitching green yes

HOTEL FACILITIES — ENVIRONNEMENT HOTELIER — 7/10

HOTELS HÔTELS

Treglos - 42 rooms, D from £ 125 - Constantine Bay 1 km
Tel (44) 01841 - 520 727, Fax (44) 01841 - 521 163

Metropole - 50 rooms, D from £ 150 - Padstow 5 km
Tel (44) 01841 - 532 486, Fax (44) 01841 - 532 867

Old Custom House Inn - 24 rooms, D £ 108 - Padstow 5 km
Tel (44) 01841 - 532 359, Fax (44) 01841 - 533 372

St Petroc's - 10 rooms, D £ 115 - Padstow 5 km
Tel (44) 01841 - 532 700, Fax (44) 01841 - 532 942

RESTAURANTS RESTAURANTS

Seafood - Padstow 5 km - Tel (44) 01841 - 532 485
St Petroc's Bistro - Padstow 5 km - Tel (44) 01841 - 532 700

Wallasey

16	7	7

With coastal erosion having washed away three of the original holes and the problems of ownership which caused some bad blood and the need to borrow less favourable terrain, the course has evolved considerably since its creation. Today, everything seems to have settled down. Laid out on more hilly landscape than its (near) neighbour Hoylake, Wallasey requires a lot of serious thought as to where to place your drive in order to attack the greens from the best position and keep well away from the dunes, bushes and fairway bunkers. The pleasure you get from hitting good recovery shots on this sort of course is such that you might almost stray off the straight and narrow deliberately in order to add to your fond memories. So try match-play, or the stableford points system, the eponymous inventor of which came from Wallasey and certainly knew a thing or two about the problems of counting a score once you reach a certain number. His portrait hangs in the club-house bar while the original of the famous portrait of Bobby Jones of Augusta fame is in the lounge.

L'érosion de la côte ayant supprimé trois des trous originaux, des problèmes de propriété ayant empoisonné le club, le parcours a évolué depuis sa création, devant emprunter des terrains moins favorables, mais tout cela semble résolu. Dans un paysage plus mouvementé que celui de son (presque) voisin Royal Liverpool, Wallasey demande quelque réflexion sur le placement des drives afin d'attaquer les greens en bonne position, et ne pas se retrouver dans les dunes, les buissons, les bunkers de fairway - peu nombreux mais pénalisants. Cela dit, le plaisir de réussir les recoveries sur ce genre de parcours est tel que l'on pourrait presque faire exprès de s'égarer pour se fabriquer des souvenirs ! Alors, jouez en match-play, ou en stableford, son inventeur éponyme venait d'ici, il savait donc à quoi s'en tenir sur la difficulté de compter à partir d'un certain chiffre. Son portrait est au bar du club-house, et l'original du célèbre portrait de Bobby Jones d'Augusta est au salon…

Wallasey Golf Club — 1891

Bayswater Road
ENG - WALLASEY, Cheshire L45 8LA

Office	Secrétariat	(44) 0151 - 691 1024
Pro shop	Pro-shop	(44) 0151 - 638 3888
Fax	Fax	(44) 0151 - 638 8988
Web	www.wallaseygolfclub.com	
Situation	Situation	Liverpool, 5 km
Annual closure	Fermeture annuelle	no
Weekly closure	Fermeture hebdomadaire	no

Fees main season Tarifs haute saison	18 holes	
	Week days Semaine	**We/Bank holidays** We/Férié
Individual Individuel	£ 70	£ 85
Couple Couple	£ 140	£ 170

Full days: £ 80 / £ 85 (We)

Caddie Caddie on request **Electric Trolley** Chariot électrique no

Buggy Voiturette no **Clubs** Clubs no

Credit cards Cartes de crédit (Pro shop goods only)
VISA - Eurocard - MasterCard - AMEX - DC

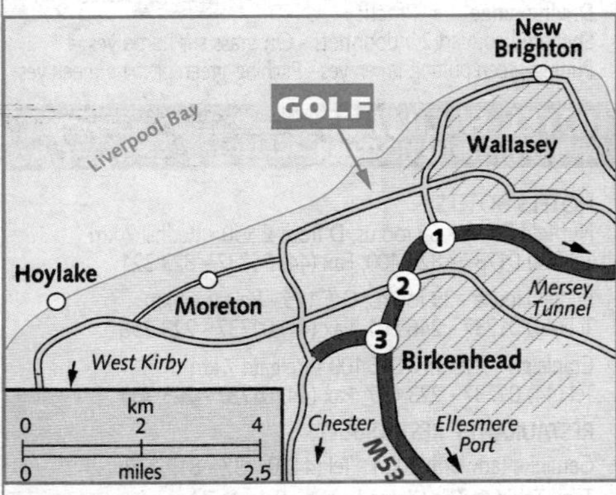

Access Accès : Liverpool, Wallasey tunnel to Jct 1. Follow signs to New Brighton. Golf on A 551.

Map 5 on page 479 Carte 5 Page 479

GOLF COURSE — PARCOURS 16/20

Site	Site	
Maintenance	Entretien	
Architect	Architecte	Tom Morris, J. Braid Taylor, Hawtree...
Type	Type	seaside course, links
Relief	Relief	
Water in play	Eau en jeu	
Exp. to wind	Exposé au vent	
Trees in play	Arbres en jeu	

Scorecard Carte de score	**Chp.** Chp.	**Mens** Mess.	**Ladies** Da.
Length Long.	5991	5691	5257
Par	72	72	74
Slope system	—	—	—

Advised golfing ability Niveau de jeu recommandé: 0 12 24 36

Hcp required Handicap exigé: certificate

CLUB HOUSE & AMENITIES — CLUB HOUSE ET ANNEXES 7/10

Pro shop Pro-shop
Driving range Practice
Sheltered couvert no - On grass sur herbe no - Putting-green putting-green yes - Pitching-green pitching green yes

HOTEL FACILITIES — ENVIRONNEMENT HOTELIER 7/10

HOTELS HÔTELS

Grove Hotel - 14 rooms, D from £ 70 - Wallasey 2 km
Tel (44) 0151 - 639 3947, Fax (44) 0151 - 639 0028

Leasowe Castle Hotel - 47 rooms, D £ 85 - Moreton 2 km
Tel (44) 0151 - 606 9191, Fax (44) 0151 - 678 5551

Bowler Hat - 32 rooms, D £ 95- Birkenhead 3 km
Tel (44) 0151 - 652 4931, Fax (44) 0151 - 653 8127

Thornton Hall - 63 rooms, D £ 115- Thornton Hough 10 km
Tel (44) 0151 - 336 3938, Fax (44) 0151 - 336 7864

RESTAURANTS RESTAURANTS

Grove Hotel - Wallasey 2 km - Tel (44) 0151 - 630 4558
Lee Ho - Moreton 2 km - Tel (44) 0151 - 677 6440

Walton Heath *New Course*

16 | 7 | 7

The history of Walton Heath is closely tied to politics, with many members being Ministers (including Winston Churchill in his younger days) or Peers. The Prince of Wales was club captain in 1935, but apparently that was not enough for the club to receive the royal seal. The two courses here were built one after the other on ideal soil with a lot of space, even so close to London, but sandy, heather-studded terrain was of no use to farmers in those days. The wind can be an important factor here, as the course is high up. There are some trees but they don't detract from a great feeling of openness, nor do they relieve the anxiety as you eye the ubiquitous heather and wonder how on earth anyone could ever get out of there. It is especially dangerous on the 12th hole, where you need a long drive to have any hope of reaching a very well-protected green. Although this "New" course is not easy, the members will tell you that it is two shots easier than its "Old" neighbour. We suggest you check that out for yourself.

L'histoire de Walton Heath est étroitement liée à la politique, avec quantité de membres ministres, dont Winston Churchill, ou appartenant à la Chambre des Lords. Le Prince de Galles en a été capitaine en 1935, sans que le club en soit anobli pour autant. Les parcours ont été construits successivement, sur un sol idéal, avec de l'espace, même à proximité de Londres car les terres de bruyère sablonneuses étaient inutilisables pour l'agriculture. Le vent y est un facteur important, car nous sommes ici en hauteur. Malgré les quelques arbres, on éprouve une grande sensation d'espace, avec un soupçon d'inquiétude devant l'omniprésence de la bruyère, dont aucun traité ne vous enseigne comment en sortir. Elle est spécialement dangereuse au 12, où il faut un long drive pour espérer toucher le green très défendu. Bien que ce "New" ne soit pas facile, les membres vous diront qu'il est de deux coups plus facile que le "Old." A vérifier par vous-même au cours d'une journée bien remplie…

Walton Heath Golf Club — 1907

Deans Lane, Walton-on-the-Hill
ENG - TADWORTH, Surrey, KT20 7TP

Office Secrétariat (44) 01737 - 812 380
Pro shop Pro-shop (44) 01737 - 812 152
Fax Fax (44) 01737 - 814 225
Web www.whgc.co.uk
Situation Situation Epsom, 5 km

Annual closure Fermeture annuelle no
Weekly closure Fermeture hebdomadaire no

Fees main season Tarifs haute saison 18 holes

	Week days / Semaine	We/Bank holidays / We/Férié
Individual Individuel	£ 90	£ 100*
Couple Couple	£ 180	£ 200*

* After 11:30 / Week days after 11:30, £ 80

Caddie Caddie on request **Electric Trolley** Chariot électrique no

Buggy Voiturette no **Clubs** Clubs yes

Credit cards Cartes de crédit
VISA - Eurocard - MasterCard - AMEX

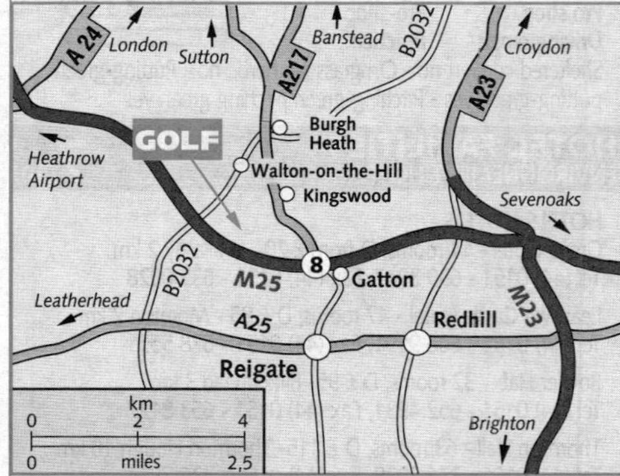

Access Accès : M25 Jct 8. A217 → Sutton. After 3 km (2 m.) B270 into Mill Lane, then left along B2032. Deans Lane on the right after 1.5 km (1 m.).
Map 8 on page 485 Carte 8 Page 485

GOLF COURSE — PARCOURS 16/20

Site Site
Maintenance Entretien
Architect Architecte Herbert Fowler
Type Type inland, heathland
Relief Relief
Water in play Eau en jeu
Exp. to wind Exposé au vent
Trees in play Arbres en jeu

Scorecard / Carte de score	Chp. / Chp.	Mens / Mess.	Ladies / Da.
Length Long.	6255	5952	5328
Par	72	72	74
Slope system	—	—	—

Advised golfing ability Niveau de jeu recommandé 0 12 24 36
Hcp required Handicap exigé certificate

CLUB HOUSE & AMENITIES — CLUB HOUSE ET ANNEXES 7/10

Pro shop Pro-shop
Driving range Practice
Sheltered couvert 2 indoor nets - On grass sur herbe yes - Putting-green putting-green yes - Pitching-green pitching green yes

HOTEL FACILITIES — ENVIRONNEMENT HOTELIER 7/10

HOTELS HÔTELS
Nutfield Priory - 60 rooms, D from £ 150 - Redhill 7 km
Tel (44) 01737 - 824 400, Fax (44) 01737 - 823 321

Bridge House - 39 rooms, D £ 125 - Reigate 4 km
Tel (44) 01737 - 246 801, Fax (44) 01737 - 223 756

Cranleigh - 9 rooms, D £ 100 - Reigate 7 km
Tel (44) 01737 - 223 417, Fax (44) 01737 - 223 734

RESTAURANTS RESTAURANTS
Gemini - Tadworth 2 km - Tel (44) 01737 - 812 179

Tony Tobin @ The Dining Room - Reigate 7 km
Tel (44) 01737 - 226 650

La Barbe - Reigate 7 km - Tel (44) 01737 - 241 966

Walton Heath *Old Course*

18	7	7

Herbert Fowler designed the courses for this club where James Braid was the first professional. He was here for 50 years and although his name does not figure as the course architect, it would be hard to imagine him never having retouched the original layout here and there, or never having given others the benefit of his invaluable advice. With the crisp, firm turf, the old-fashioned styled layout and even the sensation of space, you might think yourself on a links course if it weren't for the pine, birch and oak trees, and the heather. And when the wind blows, the illusion is complete. The wide, deep bunkers are a feature you'll remember for many a month as they fashion and shape the holes to perfection and attract any ball sailing slightly off course. The greens are fast, fair and particularly well defended. A difficult course with its very own distinct character, but every golfer will improve his game here as long as he remembers the one basic rule of golf... humility. The lengthening of holes over the years has made this a stiffer challenge still.

Herbert Fowler a dessiné les parcours de ce club dont James Braid a été le premier professionnel. Il y est resté pendant plus de 50 ans, et si son nom n'apparaît pas comme "architecte", on imagine mal qu'il n'ait jamais eu à retoucher çà et là le dessin originel, ou à donner quelques précieux conseils. Par la qualité du gazon comme par le dessin ou même la sensation d'espace, on pourait se croire sur un links, n'était la présence de pins, de bouleaux, de chênes et de bruyère. Et quand le vent souffle (c'est le plus haut point du Surrey), l'illusion est complète. Les bunkers larges et profonds sont un élément dont on se souvient, tant ils dessinent les trous à la perfection, tout en attirant les balles un peu trop écartées. Les greens sont rapides, francs, et surtout très défendus. C'est un parcours difficile, au caractère bien marqué, mais tous les joueurs y feront des progrès s'ils l'abordent avec modestie. L'allongement des trous au cours des années a durci encore le challenge.

Walton Heath Golf Club — 1903

Deans Lane, Walton-on-the-Hill
ENG - TADWORTH, Surrey, KT20 7TP

Office	Secrétariat	(44) 01737 - 812 380
Pro shop	Pro-shop	(44) 01737 - 812 152
Fax	Fax	(44) 01737 - 814 225
Web	www.whgc.co.uk	
Situation	Situation	Epsom, 5 km
Annual closure	Fermeture annuelle	no
Weekly closure	Fermeture hebdomadaire	no

Fees main season Tarifs haute saison — 18 holes

	Week days / Semaine	We/Bank holidays / We/Férié
Individual Individuel	£ 90	£ 100*
Couple Couple	£ 180	£ 200*

* After 11:30 / Week days after 11:30, £ 80

Caddie Caddie on request **Electric Trolley** Chariot électrique no

Buggy Voiturette no **Clubs** Clubs yes

Credit cards Cartes de crédit
VISA - Eurocard - MasterCard - AMEX

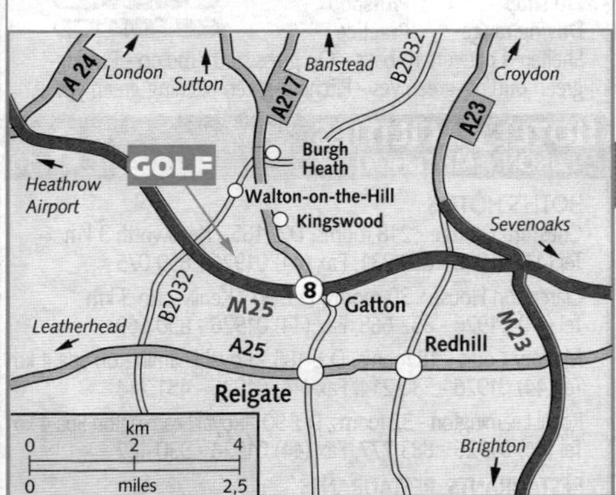

Access Accès : M25 Jct 8. A217 → Sutton. After 3 km (2 m.) B270 into Mill Lane, then left along B2032. Deans Lane on the right after 1.5 km (1 m.).
Map 8 on page 485 Carte 8 Page 485

GOLF COURSE — 18/20
PARCOURS

Site	Site	
Maintenance	Entretien	
Architect	Architecte	Herbert Fowler
Type	Type	inland, heathland
Relief	Relief	
Water in play	Eau en jeu	
Exp. to wind	Exposé au vent	
Trees in play	Arbres en jeu	

Scorecard / Carte de score	Chp. / Chp.	Mens / Mess.	Ladies / Da.
Length Long.	6320	6136	5346
Par	72	72	74
Slope system	—	—	—

Advised golfing ability 0 12 24 36
Niveau de jeu recommandé
Hcp required Handicap exigé — certificate

CLUB HOUSE & AMENITIES — 7/10
CLUB HOUSE ET ANNEXES

Pro shop Pro-shop
Driving range Practice
Sheltered couvert 2 indoor nets - On grass sur herbe yes - Putting-green putting-green yes - Pitching-green pitching green yes

HOTEL FACILITIES — 7/10
ENVIRONNEMENT HOTELIER

HOTELS HÔTELS

Nutfield Priory - 60 rooms, D from £ 150 - Redhill 7 km
Tel (44) 01737 - 824 400, Fax (44) 01737 - 823 321

Bridge House - 39 rooms, D £ 125 - Reigate 4 km
Tel (44) 01737 - 246 801, Fax (44) 01737 - 223 756

Cranleigh - 9 rooms, D £ 100 - Reigate 7 km
Tel (44) 01737 - 223 417, Fax (44) 01737 - 223 734

RESTAURANTS RESTAURANTS

Gemini - Tadworth 2 km - Tel (44) 01737 - 812 179

Tony Tobin @ The Dining Room - Reigate 7 km
Tel (44) 01737 - 226 650

La Barbe - Reigate 7 km - Tel (44) 01737 - 241 966

Warwickshire (The)

15	7	8

This is a complex of four inter-combinable nine-hole courses in four different styles (links, woodland, park and "American"). The East and North courses are rather hilly, the South and West courses are simply sloping. Karl Litten's design is in fact unashamedly American everywhere you look with a lot of dangerous water hazards (except on the North where there are more trees). Carefully placing your shots is important and if you are an attacking player you should trust your instinct as any hesitation can cost you dearly. The greens must be attacked with high shots, but they are often quite firm and so can cause problems for average-players. The length of each hole is such that we would suggest the forward tees for all except the very good player, and would recommend beginners head for the pitch 'n putt course. With a very flexible combination of courses, spectacular golf and very modern facilities, this is a very well designed resort but is more functional than hospitable. Our advice: rent a buggy and shoot 36 holes.

C'est un ensemble de quatre fois neuf trous combinables, de quatre styles différents ("américain", links, bois, et parc) l'Est et le Nord étant assez accidentés, le Sud et l'Ouest simplement ondulés. L'architecture de Karl Litten est partout américaine sans honte, avec beaucoup d'obstacles d'eau dangereux (sauf le Nord, plus arboré). Il est partout nécessaire de bien placer la balle, mais aussi d'attaquer sans réserves si on a ce caractère, car les hésitations ne pardonnent pas. Les greens doivent être attaqués comme des cibles, mais ils sont souvent fermes et ne facilitent pas la tâche des joueurs moyens. La longueur de chacun des neuf trous incite à ne recommander les départs arrière qu'aux très bons amateurs, et à conseiller aux presque débutants d'aller sur le parcours de par 3. Flexible dans ses combinaisons, spectaculaire, avec des équipements très modernes, c'est un ensemble très bien conçu, mais plus fonctionnel que chaleureux. Notre conseil : 36 trous en voiturette.

The Warwickshire — 1993

Leek Wootton
ENG - WARWICK, Warwickshire CV35 7QT

Office Secrétariat (44) 01926 - 409 409
Pro shop Pro-shop (44) 01926 - 409 409
Fax Fax (44) 01926 - 408 409
Web www.theclubcompany.com
Situation Situation Warwick, 5 km
Coventry (pop. 294 387), 13 km

Annual closure Fermeture annuelle — no
Weekly closure Fermeture hebdomadaire — no

Fees main season Tarifs haute saison	18 holes	
	Week days Semaine	**We/Bank holidays** We/Férié
Individual Individuel	£ 42,50	£ 52,50*
Couple Couple	£ 85	£ 105*

We: Friday → Sunday

Caddie Caddie no — **Electric Trolley** Chariot électrique no
Buggy Voiturette yes — **Clubs** Clubs yes
Credit cards Cartes de crédit
VISA - Eurocard - MasterCard - AMEX

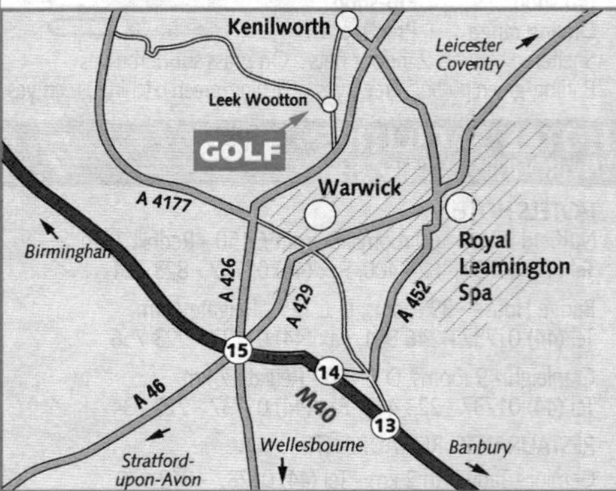

Access Accès : M40 Jct 15, then A46 → Coventry. Follow signs to Leek Wootton (B4115).
Map 7 on page 483 Carte 7 Page 483

GOLF COURSE — PARCOURS — 15/20

Site Site
Maintenance Entretien
Architect Architecte — Karl Litten
Type Type — parkland
Relief Relief
Water in play Eau en jeu
Exp. to wind Exposé au vent
Trees in play Arbres en jeu

Scorecard Carte de score	**Chp.** Chp.	**Mens** Mess.	**Ladies** Da.
Length Long.	6500	6000	5000
Par	72	72	72
Slope system	—	—	—

Advised golfing ability Niveau de jeu recommandé — 0 12 24 36
Hcp required Handicap exigé — no

CLUB HOUSE & AMENITIES — CLUB HOUSE ET ANNEXES — 7/10

Pro shop Pro-shop
Driving range Practice
Sheltered couvert 10 bays - On grass sur herbe no - Putting-green putting-green yes - Pitching-green pitching green yes

HOTEL FACILITIES — ENVIRONNEMENT HOTELIER — 8/10

HOTELS HÔTELS
Chesford Grange - 218 rooms, D £ 165 - Kenilworth 3 km
Tel (44) 01926 - 859 331, Fax (44) 01926 - 859 075

Clarendon House - 30 rooms, D £ 90 - Kenilworth 3 km
Tel (44) 01926 - 857 668, Fax (44) 01926 - 850 669

Mallory Court - 18 rooms, D £ 185 - Royal Leamington Spa 4 km
Tel (44) 01926 - 330 214, Fax (44) 01926 - 451 714

Royal Leamington - 32 rooms, D £ 90 - Royal Leamington Spa 4 km
Tel (44) 01926 - 883 777, Fax (44) 01926 - 330 467

RESTAURANTS RESTAURANTS
Simply Simpson's - Kenilworth 4 km - Tel (44) 01926 - 864 567
Bosquet - Kenilworth 4 km - Tel (44) 01926 - 852 463
Mallory Court - Royal Leamington Spa 4 km
Tel (44) 01926 - 330 214

Wentworth *East Course*

17	8	7

If Wentworth's Burma Road is a trifle tough to tackle, then head for the East Course. It is a real gem! This was the first course laid out by Harry Colt at Wentworth and many prefer it to the exertions of its more illustrious neighbour, particularly as it is not long enough to put a premium on big hitting. But don't run away with the idea that this course is a push over. Far from it. Each and every hole has its own characteristics but there is not enough trouble to cause even the higher handicapper too many problems. One distinct advantage the East course has over the West is that it is far more pleasant to walk on as it is built on a sand-based sub-soil which gives it a real feel of heath land at its best. It is a course that has been in the shadow of its neighbour for far too long and undoubtedly makes a valuable contribution to the big (but expensive!) complex that Wentworth has now become. Unfortunately the third and most recently built course – the Edinburgh – does not have the same appeal as the other two courses.

Si le parcours Burma Road est un peu difficile à maîtriser, faites connaissance avec le East Course, un petit bijou ! Ce fut le premier des parcours dessinés par Harry Colt à Wentworth, et beaucoup le préfèrent à son illustre voisin, notamment parce qu'il n'exige pas des drives de mammouth. Mais ne croyez pas que ce soit un jeu d'enfant de le maîtriser, loin de là. Chacun des trous a ses caractéristiques propres, mais il n'y a pas assez de pièges cachés ou d'obstacles insurmontables pour compromettre les chances des jouers moyens. Un de ses avantages sur le West Course, c'est que le sol y est plus agréable (il est plus sablonneux), ce qui lui donne un esprit de terrain de bruyère coloré et très plaisant. Ce parcours a été trop longtemps sous-estimé par rapport à son voisin, mais il contribue beaucoup à ce qu'est devenu Wentworth. Malheureusement, le troisième parcours de ce complexe, "Edinburgh", ne présente pas les mêmes séductions que les autres.

Wentworth Golf Club — 1924

Wentworth Drive
ENG - VIRGINIA WATER, Surrey GU25 4 LS

Office	Secrétariat	(44) 01344 - 842 201
Pro shop	Pro-shop	(44) 01344 - 843 353
Fax	Fax	(44) 01344 - 842 804
Web		www.wentworthclub.com
Situation	Situation	Ascot, 7 km
Annual closure	Fermeture annuelle	no
Weekly closure	Fermeture hebdomadaire	no

Fees main season Tarifs haute saison	18 holes	
	Week days Semaine	**We/Bank holidays** We/Férié
Individual Individuel	£ 125	£ 125*
Couple Couple	£ 250	£ 250*

* Members only, or players using Wentworth accomodation

Caddie Caddie on request **Electric Trolley** Chariot électrique no

Buggy Voiturette yes **Clubs** Clubs yes

Credit cards Cartes de crédit
VISA - Eurocard - MasterCard - AMEX - DC

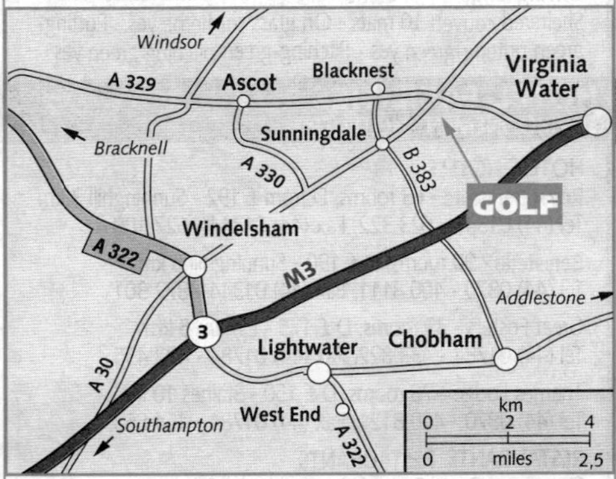

Access Accès : London, A30. Left road opposite A329 turning to Ascot.
Map 8 on page 484 Carte 8 Page 484

GOLF COURSE — PARCOURS — 17/20

Site	Site	
Maintenance	Entretien	
Architect	Architecte	Harry S. Colt
Type	Type	inland, forest
Relief	Relief	
Water in play	Eau en jeu	
Exp. to wind	Exposé au vent	
Trees in play	Arbres en jeu	

Scorecard Carte de score	**Chp.** Chp.	**Mens** Mess.	**Ladies** Da.
Length Long.	5558	5354	4855
Par	68	68	72
Slope system	—	—	—

Advised golfing ability Niveau de jeu recommandé: 0 12 24 36

Hcp required Handicap exigé: 28 Men, 36 Ladies

CLUB HOUSE & AMENITIES — CLUB HOUSE ET ANNEXES — 8/10

Pro shop Pro-shop
Driving range Practice
Sheltered couvert 10 mats - On grass sur herbe yes - Putting-green putting-green yes - Pitching-green pitching green yes

HOTEL FACILITIES — ENVIRONNEMENT HOTELIER — 7/10

HOTELS HÔTELS

Royal Berkshire - 63 rooms, D from £ 192 - Sunninghill 3 km
Tel (44) 01344 - 623 322, Fax (44) 01344 - 627 100

Berystede - 90 rooms, D £ 190 - Sunninghill 5 km
Tel (44) 0870 - 400 8111, Fax (44) 01344 - 872 301

Great Fosters - 39 rooms, D £ 175 - Egham 5 km
Tel (44) 01784 - 433 822, Fax (44) 01784 - 472 455

Thames Lodge - 78 rooms, D £ 150 - Staines 10 km
Tel (44) 0870 - 400 8121, Fax (44) 01784 - 454 858

RESTAURANTS RESTAURANTS

Stateroom (Royal Berkshire) - Sunninghill 3 km
Tel (44) 01344 - 623 322

Left Bank (Runnymede Hotel) - Egham 5 km
Tel (44) 01784 - 437 400

Wentworth *West Course*

18 | 8 | 7

Wentworth's West course – or the Burma Road as it is known – is familiar to most people as the venue of European Championships as seen on TV. It is set in an exclusive stockbroker belt on the outskirts of London and one of the joys of playing the course is admiring the multi-million pound properties surrounding it. But don't waste time if you are intent on playing your best golf because this is the sort of course which demands your full attention. It is a great test of golf and it is important to rely on the course planner to identify the problems it poses, especially when it comes to spotting the ditches, which are not particularly visible and, like all the other hazards, are very cleverly placed. You really do need an all-round game to survive the 13th, 14th and 15th holes and the two closing par 5s are not as easy as you might imagine. The green fee is such that you need to turn up in good shape to really enjoy a full day's golf, or else take advantage of the special rates from October (autumn is a fabulous time to play here) to March.

Ce parcours (appelé aussi Burma Road) est de ceux que la télévision a rendus familiers, grâce aux tournois européens. Il se situe dans un espace résidentiel très huppé, et l'un des plaisirs du lieu est de pouvoir parfois admirer de superbes maisons. Mais revenez vite au jeu car ce parcours demande une attention de tous les instants. C'est un grand test de golf, et le carnet de parcours sera fort utile pour identifier les difficultés, notamment des fossés pas très visibles, avec un placement d'obstacles d'une subtilité exceptionnelle. Il faut un jeu absolument complet dans le délicat passage du 13 au 15 et les deux par 5 clôturant ce parcours ne sont pas si faciles qu'on pourrait l'imaginer. Le 17 avec son hors-limites à gauche et un fairway en dévers, et le 18 avec un fossé traversant le fairway. Le prix du green-fee est tellement élevé qu'il faut être en forme pour vraiment savourer sa journée, ou alors profiter de tarifs spéciaux d'octobre (l'automne est ici splendide) à mars.

Wentworth Golf Club — 1926

Wentworth Drive
ENG - VIRGINIA WATER, Surrey GU25 4 LS

Office	Secrétariat	(44) 01344 - 842 201
Pro shop	Pro-shop	(44) 01344 - 843 353
Fax	Fax	(44) 01344 - 842 804
Web	www.wentworthclub.com	
Situation	Situation	Ascot, 7 km
Annual closure	Fermeture annuelle	no
Weekly closure	Fermeture hebdomadaire	no

Fees main season Tarifs haute saison — 18 holes

	Week days / Semaine	We/Bank holidays / We/Férié
Individual Individuel	£ 260	£ 260*
Couple Couple	£ 520	£ 520*

* Members only, or players using Wentworth accomodation

Caddie Caddie on request **Electric Trolley** Chariot électrique no

Buggy Voiturette yes **Clubs** Clubs yes

Credit cards Cartes de crédit
VISA - Eurocard - MasterCard - AMEX - DC

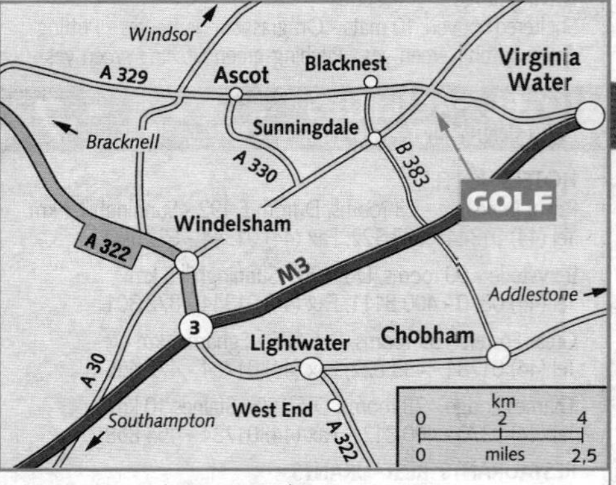

VISA - Eurocard - MasterCard - AMEX - DC
Access Accès : London, A30. Left road opposite A329 turning to Ascot.
Map 8 on page 484 Carte 8 Page 484

GOLF COURSE — PARCOURS — 18/20

Site	Site	
Maintenance	Entretien	
Architect	Architecte	Harry S. Colt
Type	Type	inland, forest
Relief	Relief	
Water in play	Eau en jeu	
Exp. to wind	Exposé au vent	
Trees in play	Arbres en jeu	

Scorecard / Carte de score	Chp. / Chp.	Mens / Mess.	Ladies / Da.
Length Long.	6261	6008	5440
Par	73	73	75
Slope system	—	—	—

Advised golfing ability Niveau de jeu recommandé — 0 12 24 36

Hcp required Handicap exigé — 24 Men, 32 Ladies

CLUB HOUSE & AMENITIES — CLUB HOUSE ET ANNEXES — 8/10

Pro shop Pro-shop
Driving range Practice
Sheltered couvert 10 mats - On grass sur herbe yes - Putting-green putting-green yes - Pitching-green pitching green yes

HOTEL FACILITIES — ENVIRONNEMENT HOTELIER — 7/10

HOTELS HÔTELS

Royal Berkshire - 63 rooms, D from £ 192 - Sunninghill 3 km
Tel (44) 01344 - 623 322, Fax (44) 01344 - 627 100

Berystede - 90 rooms, D £ 190 - Sunninghil l 5 km
Tel (44) 0870 - 400 8111, Fax (44) 01344 - 872 301

Great Fosters - 39 rooms, D £ 175 - Egham 5 km
Tel (44) 01784 - 433 822, Fax (44) 01784 - 472 455

Thames Lodge - 78 rooms, D £ 150 - Staines 10 km
Tel (44) 0870 - 400 8121, Fax (44) 01784 - 454 858

RESTAURANTS RESTAURANTS

Stateroom (Royal Berkshire) - Sunninghill 3 km
Tel (44) 01344 - 623 322

Left Bank (Runnymede Hotel) - Egham 5 km
Tel (44) 01784 - 437 400

West Berkshire

15	7	7

Without wishing to appear reactionary, not all of us are too keen on the modern trend of building super-long golf courses (just because today's professional golfers hit it for miles). Here at West Berkshire the par 5s are nothing less and on the 5th hole, a full 635 yards, it is virtually impossible to hit the green in regulation when the wind blows (and it often does) or when the ground is damp (it happens). Fortunately the medal tees bring everything down to more human proportions but there must be a happy medium somewhere for good golfers who don't have to be huge-hitters. It is a pity that such an ambitious facility with some magnificent views seems to have overlooked the average golfer's pleasure of playing the game. Having said that, the terrain is not very hilly, the par is 74 and the green-fee affordable. Golfers will appreciate this very interesting and often captivating layout (perhaps more so in a buggy) when competing with friends more than with the course.

Sans être un vieux réactionnaire, on peut ne pas apprécier la tentation moderne des parcours super longs, sous prétexte que les grands pros tapent à des kilomètres. Ici, tous les par 5 le sont vraiment, mais le trou n°5 atteignant 570 mètres (635 yards), il est quasiment impossible d'en atteindre le green en régulation quand le vent est là (ce qui n'est pas rare) ou le sol humide (ce qui arrive). Heureusement, les départs "normaux" (medal tees) ramènent les trous à des proportions normales, mais il y a sans doute un juste milieu pour les golfeurs qui ne sont pas des athlètes. Il est dommage qu'un équipement aussi ambitieux, offrant des vues magnifiques, ait parfois négligé le plaisir du joueur moyen. Cela dit, le terrain n'est pas très accidenté, le par est de 74, le green-fee assez abordable et on appréciera (davantage en voiturette ?) ce tracé intéressant et souvent captivant, en dehors de tout esprit de compétition pour le handicap, sauf bien sûr avec les amis.

West Berkshire Golf Club — 1978

Chaddleworth
ENG - NEWBURY, Berks RG16 0HS

Office	Secrétariat	(44) 01488 - 638 574
Pro shop	Pro-shop	(44) 01488 - 638 851
Fax	Fax	(44) 01488 - 638 781
Web	in construction	
Situation	Situation	Newbury, 8 km
Annual closure	Fermeture annuelle	no
Weekly closure	Fermeture hebdomadaire	Christmas Day

Fees main season Tarifs haute saison — 18 holes

	Week days Semaine	We/Bank holidays We/Férié
Individual Individuel	£ 27	£ 38*
Couple Couple	£ 54	£ 76*

Full week days: £ 38 / * Week-ends: with members only

Caddie Caddie no — **Electric Trolley** Chariot électrique no
Buggy Voiturette yes — **Clubs** Clubs no
Credit cards Cartes de crédit
VISA - MasterCard

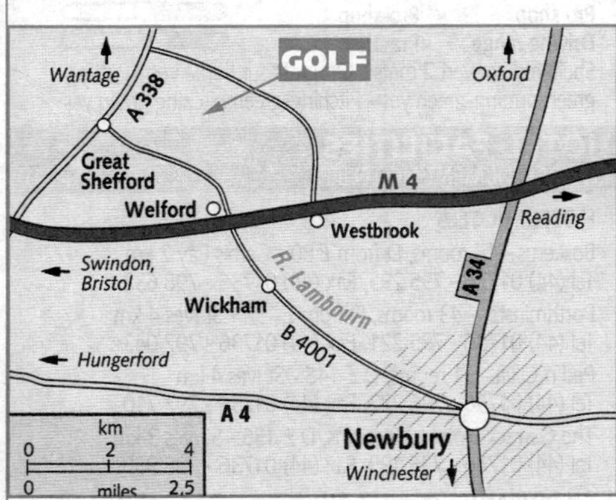

Access Accès : London M4. Jct 14 A338, → RAF Welford, club-house on right.
Map 7 on page 482 Carte 7 Page 482

GOLF COURSE PARCOURS — 15/20

Site	Site	
Maintenance	Entretien	
Architect	Architecte	John Stagg
Type	Type	open country
Relief	Relief	
Water in play	Eau en jeu	
Exp. to wind	Exposé au vent	
Trees in play	Arbres en jeu	

Scorecard Carte de score	**Chp.** Chp.	**Mens** Mess.	**Ladies** Da.
Length Long.	6353	5618	5200
Par	73	73	74
Slope system	—	—	—

Advised golfing ability Niveau de jeu recommandé — 0 12 24 36
Hcp required Handicap exigé — no

CLUB HOUSE & AMENITIES CLUB HOUSE ET ANNEXES — 7/10

Pro shop Pro-shop
Driving range Practice
Sheltered couvert no - On grass sur herbe yes - Putting-green putting-green yes - Pitching-green pitching green yes

HOTEL FACILITIES ENVIRONNEMENT HOTELIER — 7/10

HOTELS HÔTELS

Vineyard - 49 rooms, D from £ 250 - Newbury 7 km
Tel (44) 01635 - 528 770, Fax (44) 01635 - 528 398

Marshgate Cottage - 10 rooms, D £ 65 - Hungerford 8 km
Tel (44) 01488 - 682 307, Fax (44) 01488 - 685 475

Hilton Newbury - 109 rooms, D £ 175 - Newbury 8 km
Tel (44) 01635 - 529 000, Fax (44) 01635 - 529 337

The Bear - 41 rooms, D from £ 75 - Hungerford 7 km
Tel (44) 01488 - 682 512, Fax (44) 01488 - 684 357

RESTAURANTS RESTAURANTS

Vineyard - Newbury 7 km - Tel (44) 01635 - 528 770
Red House - Marsh Benham 6 km - Tel (44) 01635 - 582 017

West Cornwall

16 | 7 | 6

On the first hole at West Cornwall, you understand the religious and sporting nature of the game of golf as you line up your drive on the steeple of the village church, the birthplace of Jim Barnes, one of the few British golfers to have won both the British and the US Opens. The course has not changed much since his time. It is rather short and not always perfectly fair in that the sloping terrain can easily draw your ball off the fairway. At the same time the railway line exerts a strange attraction on slicers over four holes. Once you are out of "Calamity Corner", where two par 3s and a short par 4 (holes 5 to 7) have ruined many a card, you will need a cool head for the remaining 11 holes in the dunes, up until the 18th, where you are in for a gentle downhill landing. A very natural and imaginative layout, West Cornwall is one of those little known courses you will want to explore before visiting the pretty fishing village of St Ives, and its population of artists.

Le premier trou de West Cornwall permet de comprendre la nature religieuse et sportive du golf, il faut s'aligner sur le clocher de l'église du village où est né Jim Barnes, l'un des rares Britanniques à avoir remporté le British et l'US Open. Et le parcours n'a pas dû changer beaucoup depuis. Assez court, il n'est pas toujours d'une parfaite franchise, car les pentes peuvent sortir la balle du fairway, et la voie ferrée attire étrangement les sliceurs sur quatre trous. Une fois sorti indemne de "Calamity Corner," où deux par 3 et un minuscule par 4 (du 5 au 7) ont détruit bien des cartes, il faut garder son sang-froid pour les onze trous restant, toujours dans les dunes, et jusqu'au 18, un atterrissage en douceur et en descente. Très naturel et imaginatif, West Cornwall fait partie de ces parcours méconnus à découvrir, avant de visiter St Ives, joli village de pêcheurs et d'artistes.

West Cornwall Golf Club — 1889

Church Lane, Lelant
ENG - ST IVES, Cornwall TR26 3D2

Office	Secrétariat	(44) 01736 - 753 401
Pro shop	Pro-shop	(44) 01736 - 753 177
Fax	Fax	(44) 01736 - 753 401
Web	www.westcornwallgolfclub.co.uk	
Situation	Situation	Penzance, 16 km

St Ives (pop. 7 254), 3 km

Annual closure	Fermeture annuelle	no
Weekly closure	Fermeture hebdomadaire	no

Fees main season Tarifs haute saison — 18 holes

	Week days / Semaine	We/Bank holidays / We/Férié
Individual Individuel	£ 28	£ 33
Couple Couple	£ 56	£ 66

Caddie Caddie no **Electric Trolley** Chariot électrique yes

Buggy Voiturette no **Clubs** Clubs yes

Credit cards Cartes de crédit
Visa - Eurocard - Mastercard (Pro shop goods only)

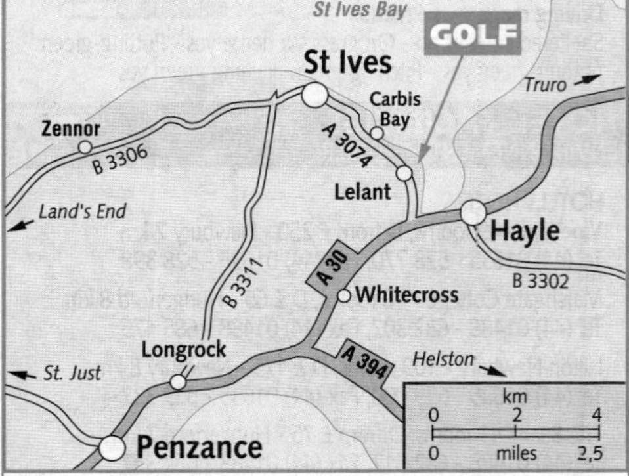

Access Accès : A30 to Hayle, then A3074 (Golf signposted)
Map 6 on page 480 Carte 6 Page 480

GOLF COURSE — PARCOURS — 16/20

Site	Site	
Maintenance	Entretien	
Architect	Architecte	Reverend Tyack, vicar of Lelant...
Type	Type	seaside course, links
Relief	Relief	
Water in play	Eau en jeu	
Exp. to wind	Exposé au vent	
Trees in play	Arbres en jeu	

Scorecard Carte de score	Chp. Chp.	Mens Mess.	Ladies Da.
Length Long.	5354	5180	4890
Par	69	69	73
Slope system	—	—	—

Advised golfing ability Niveau de jeu recommandé — 0 12 24 36
Hcp required Handicap exigé — 28 Men, 36 Ladies

CLUB HOUSE & AMENITIES — CLUB HOUSE ET ANNEXES — 7/10

Pro shop Pro-shop
Driving range Practice
Sheltered couvert 2 mats - On grass sur herbe yes - Putting-green putting-green yes - Pitching-green pitching green yes

HOTEL FACILITIES — ENVIRONNEMENT HOTELIER — 6/10

HOTELS HÔTELS

Boskerris - 16 rooms, D from £ 80 - Carbis Bay 2 km
Tel (44) 01736 - 795 295, Fax (44) 01736 - 798 632

Porthminster - 43 rooms, D from £ 130 - St Ives 4 km
Tel (44) 01736 - 795 221, Fax (44) 01736 - 797 043

Ped'n Olva - 31 rooms, D £ 146 - St Ives 4 km
Tel (44) 01736 - 796 222, Fax (44) 01736 - 797 710

The Garrack Hotel - 18 rooms, D £ 136 - St Ives 3 km
Tel (44) 01736 - 796 199, Fax (44) 01736 - 798 955

RESTAURANTS RESTAURANTS

Russets - St Ives 4 km - Tel (44) 01736 - 794 700
Alfresco - St Ives 3 km - Tel (44) 01736 - 793 737
Blue Fish - St Ives 3 km - Tel (44) 01736 - 794 204

West Hill

16 | 6 | 6

This is the third of a compact threesome of courses, the other two being virtual neighbours Woking and Worplesdon. All three are classic heathland courses although each has its own personality. We suppose you are bound to prefer one of the three but each to his own, as they say. West Hill is very short and only moderately contoured over land strewn with pines, birch and conifers. The heather narrows the fairways and even cuts them in two on the 5th and 17th holes, two par 5s where that age-old decision arises once again: do I carry the hazard or lay up short? In fact the whole course calls for constant thought on the best way of driving, hitting the second shot and approaching the greens. This is why it is always such fun to play. Or sometimes difficult, like the 15th hole, a wonderful par 3. The bunkers were recently upgraded and the course is all the better for it. A natural and well-landscaped layout whose sandy soil drains easily, West Hill has inimitable charm, matched only perhaps by the other two "Ws"...

C'est le troisième d'un trio compact, avec Woking et Worplesdon, pratiquement voisins. Comme s'il s'agissait de trois parcours d'un même club, alors que chacun a préservé sa personnalité. Que l'on préfère l'un à l'autre est inévitable, mais "chacun a son goût." West Hill est très court, avec un relief très modéré, et un espace arboré de pins, de bouleaux et de sapins. La bruyère rétrécit les fairways, et vient parfois même les interrompre comme au 5 et au 17, deux par 5 où il faut prendre la décision de risquer de passer ou de rester court. L'ensemble du parcours demande une réflexion constante sur la meilleure façon de driver, de jouer le second coup, d'approcher, c'est pourquoi il reste aussi amusant. Ou parfois difficile, comme au 15, un superbe par 3. Le travail entrepris sur l'ensemble des bunkers est maintenant achevé, pour le meilleur. Naturel et bien paysagé, bien draînant avec son sol sablonneux, West Hill a un charme inimitable, sauf par les deux autres "W," peut-être...

West Hill Golf Club — 1909

Bagshot Road
ENG - BROOKWOOD, Surrey GU24 0BH

Office	Secrétariat	(44) 01483 - 474 365
Pro shop	Pro-shop	(44) 01483 - 473 172
Fax	Fax	(44) 01483 - 474 252
Web	www.westhill-golfclub.co.uk	
Situation	Situation	Guildford, 8 km
Annual closure	Fermeture annuelle	no
Weekly closure	Fermeture hebdomadaire	no

Fees main season Tarifs haute saison — 18 holes

	Week days / Semaine	We/Bank holidays / We/Férié
Individual Individuel	£ 50	*
Couple Couple	£ 100	*

* Week-ends: members only / Full week days: £ 80

Caddie Caddie on request **Electric Trolley** Chariot électrique no

Buggy Voiturette yes **Clubs** Clubs yes

Credit cards Cartes de crédit
VISA - Eurocard - AMEX (Pro shop only)

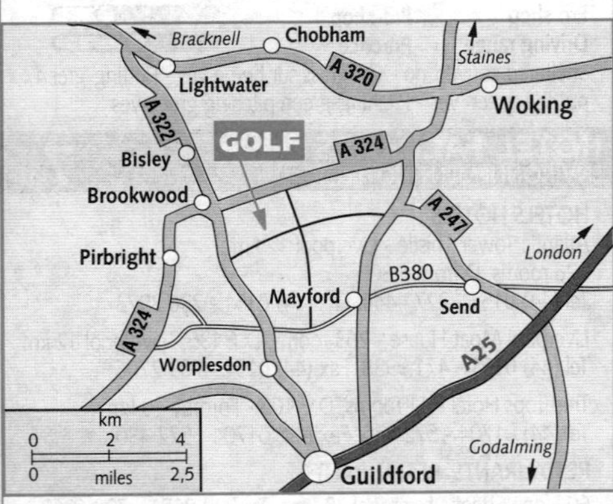

Access Accès : London A3 → Guildford. At Cobham, A245 on right. Through Woking. At Brookwood, turn left on A322 → Guildford. Entrance on left next to railway bridge.
Map 8 on page 484 Carte 8 Page 484

GOLF COURSE — PARCOURS 16/20

Site	Site	
Maintenance	Entretien	
Architect	Architecte	Willie Park Jack White
Type	Type	inland, heathland
Relief	Relief	
Water in play	Eau en jeu	
Exp. to wind	Exposé au vent	
Trees in play	Arbres en jeu	

Scorecard / Carte de score	Chp. / Chp.	Mens / Mess.	Ladies / Da.
Length Long.	5731	5731	5096
Par	69	69	74
Slope system	—	—	—

Advised golfing ability Niveau de jeu recommandé — 0 12 24 36

Hcp required Handicap exigé — certificate

CLUB HOUSE & AMENITIES — CLUB HOUSE ET ANNEXES 6/10

Pro shop Pro-shop
Driving range Practice
Sheltered couvert 2 mats - On grass sur herbe yes - Putting-green putting-green yes - Pitching-green pitching green no

HOTEL FACILITIES — ENVIRONNEMENT HOTELIER 6/10

HOTELS HÔTELS

Angel Posting House - Guildford 8 km
21 rooms, D £ 150
Tel (44) 01483 - 564 555, Fax (44) 01483 - 533 770

Posthouse Guildford - Guildford 8 km
161 rooms, D from £ 120
Tel (44) 0870 - 400 9036, Fax (44) 01483 - 302 960

The Manor - 45 rooms, D from £ 92 - Guildford 8 km
Tel (44) 01483 - 222 624, Fax (44) 01483 - 211 389

RESTAURANTS RESTAURANTS

Drake's Restaurant - Ripley 10 km - Tel (44) 01483 - 224 777
Café de Paris - Guildford 8 km - Tel (44) 01483 - 534 896

West Lancashire

16 | 7 | 7

Although West Lancashire is undoubtedly one of the great courses on this coast, it has seldom staged top tournaments. The views over the Mersey estuary and the Welsh mountains are superb from the club-house, yet are less visible from the actual course, which lies sheltered behind a line of dunes. This is not a very hilly course, a fact that tends to give it an air of austerity but also its very own personality. What's more, this impression of infinity makes it very difficult to judge distances. It is already a tough task choosing the right club for the wind avoiding bunkers, many of which just swallow up your ball, and getting to grips with firm, subtle and very slick greens. But despite everything, game strategy is pretty obvious even though a few hazards are hard to spot from the tee-boxes. The same cannot be said for the club-house which is certainly very comfortable but looks more like the corporate HQ of a computer company than what you would expect from a course of such nobility.

West Lancashire figure sans conteste parmi les grands links, alors qu'il a rarement reçu de grandes épreuves. Du club-house, les vues sont superbes sur l'estuaire de la Mersey et les montagnes du Pays de Galles, mais on les voit peu du parcours, à l'abri derrière un cordon de dunes. Le relief n'est pas ici très prononcé, ce qui lui donne un caractère d'austérité, mais aussi sa personnalité. De plus, cette impression d'infinité rend très difficile le jugement des distances : il est déjà délicat de choisir les bons clubs en fonction du vent, d'éviter les bunkers, dont beaucoup sont d'une grande voracité, de négocier des greens fermes, subtils et très rapides. La stratégie est malgré tout assez évidente, alors que certains obstacles sont peu visibles des départs. Moins que le club-house, certes très confortable, mais plus proche du siège d'une société d'informatique que de ce que l'on attend d'un parcours de vraie noblesse.

West Lancashire Golf Club — 1873

Hall Road West, Blundellsands
ENG - LIVERPOOL, Lancs L23 8SZ

Office	Secrétariat	(44) 0151 - 924 1076
Pro shop	Pro-shop	(44) 0151 - 924 5662
Fax	Fax	(44) 0151 - 931 4448
Web	www.westlancashiregolf.co.uk	
Situation	Situation	Liverpool, 14 km
Annual closure	Fermeture annuelle	no
Weekly closure	Fermeture hebdomadaire	no

Fees main season Tarifs haute saison — 18 holes

	Week days / Semaine	We/Bank holidays / We/Férié
Individual Individuel	£ 60	£ 80
Couple Couple	£ 120	£ 160

Full days: £ 75 and £ 95 (We)

Caddie Caddie on request **Electric Trolley** Chariot électrique yes

Buggy Voiturette no **Clubs** Clubs yes

Credit cards Cartes de crédit
VISA - Eurocard - MasterCard (Pro shop goods only)

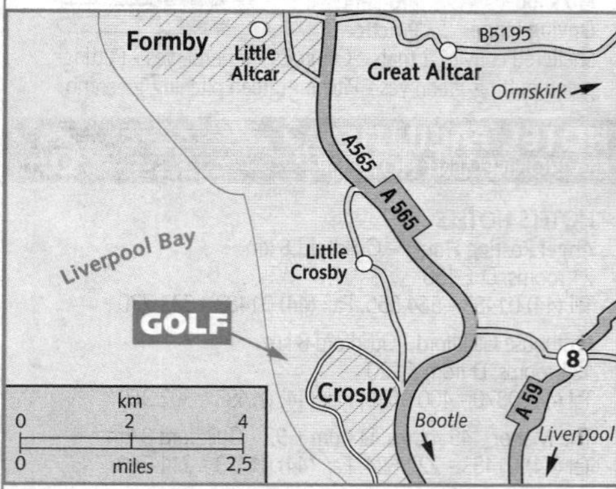

Access Accès : Liverpool, A565 to Crosby. +Follow signs to club by Hall Road Rail Station
Map 5 on page 479 Carte 5 Page 479

GOLF COURSE — PARCOURS 16/20

Site	Site	
Maintenance	Entretien	
Architect	Architecte	Unknown C.K Cotton (1960)
Type	Type	links
Relief	Relief	
Water in play	Eau en jeu	
Exp. to wind	Exposé au vent	
Trees in play	Arbres en jeu	

Scorecard / Carte de score	Chp. / Chp.	Mens / Mess.	Ladies / Da.
Length Long.	6086	5594	5135
Par	72	70	73
Slope system	—	—	—

Advised golfing ability 0 12 24 36
Niveau de jeu recommandé
Hcp required Handicap exigé 28 Men, 36 Ladies

CLUB HOUSE & AMENITIES — CLUB HOUSE ET ANNEXES 7/10

Pro shop Pro-shop
Driving range Practice
Sheltered couvert no - On grass sur herbe yes - Putting-green putting-green yes - Pitching-green pitching green yes

HOTEL FACILITIES — ENVIRONNEMENT HOTELIER 7/10

HOTELS HÔTELS

Atlantic Tower Thistle - Liverpool 12 km
226 rooms, D from £ 80
Tel (44) 0151 - 227 4444, Fax (44) 0151 - 236 3973

Liverpool Moat House - 263 rooms, D £ 135 - Liverpool 12 km
Tel (44) 0151 - 471 9988, Fax (44) 0151 - 709 2706

Tree Tops Hotel - 11 rooms, D £ 105 - Formby 10 km
Tel (44) 01704 - 572 430, Fax (44) 01704 - 572 430

RESTAURANTS RESTAURANTS

60 Hope Street - Liverpool 12 km - Tel (44) 0151 - 707 6060
Everyman Bistro - Liverpool 13 km - Tel (44) 0151 - 708 9545
Simply Heathcote's - Liverpool 15 km
Tel (44) 0151 - 236 3536

West Surrey

15 | 7 | 6

West Surrey is one of those courses where you soon start feeling excited about your game as all the hazards and the tactics you need to overcome them are crystal clear. This is important, because placing the drive is of prime importance if you want a relatively simple approach shot. So players who are playing to form should card their handicap and perhaps even better if they excel on the greens. The re-laying of all the greens (completed in 2002) to USGA specs, the lengthening of several holes with new tee-boxes and automatic sprinklers have literally transformed this course. It has become fairer and the rough, reserved for shots way off target, is long and thick enough for a wedge to be the only option. Having said that and apart from trees, there are not many other hazards to contend with. With a longer outward 9 but tighter back 9, there is something for every kind of player, and the long-hitters who keep out of the trees will enjoy a number of birdie opportunities on the par 5s.

West Surrey est de ces parcours où l'on éprouve vite de bonnes sensations, parce que les obstacles sont aussi visibles que la tactique à mettre en oeuvre. C'est important car le placement du drive est essentiel pour garantir un second coup assez facile. Ceux qui sont à leur bon niveau joueront normalement leur handicap, et mieux même s'ils sont inspirés sur les greens. Le remplacement (achevé en 2002) de tous ces greens par des surfaces aux spécifications USGA, l'allongement de plusieurs trous avec la construction de nouveaux départ et l'arrosage automatique ont littéralement transformé ce parcours. Il est devenu beaucoup plus franc et les roughs longs et épais dont on ne peut sortir qu'avec un wedge sont réservés aux joueurs erratiques. Cela dit, mis à part les arbres, il y a peu d'autres obstacles. Avec un aller plus long, mais un retour plus étroit, tous les types de joueurs sont bien servis, et les longs frappeurs sachant éviter les arbres trouveront de belles occasions de birdies sur les par 5.

West Surrey Golf Club — 1910

Enton Green
ENG - GODALMING, Surrey GU8 5AF

Office	Secrétariat	(44) 01483 - 421 275
Pro shop	Pro-shop	(44) 01483 - 417 278
Fax	Fax	(44) 01483 - 415 419
Web	www.wsgc.co.uk	
Situation	Situation	Guildford, 6 km
Annual closure	Fermeture annuelle	no
Weekly closure	Fermeture hebdomadaire	no

Tuesday 08 → 12

Fees main season Tarifs haute saison	Week days Semaine	We/Bank holidays We/Férié
		18 holes
Individual Individuel	£ 40	£ 50
Couple Couple	£ 80	£ 100

Full days: £ 60 and £ 70 (We) /Restrictions at week-ends

Caddie Caddie no — **Electric Trolley** Chariot électrique yes

Buggy Voiturette yes — **Clubs** Clubs yes

Credit cards Cartes de crédit
VISA - Eurocard - MasterCard (not for green fees)

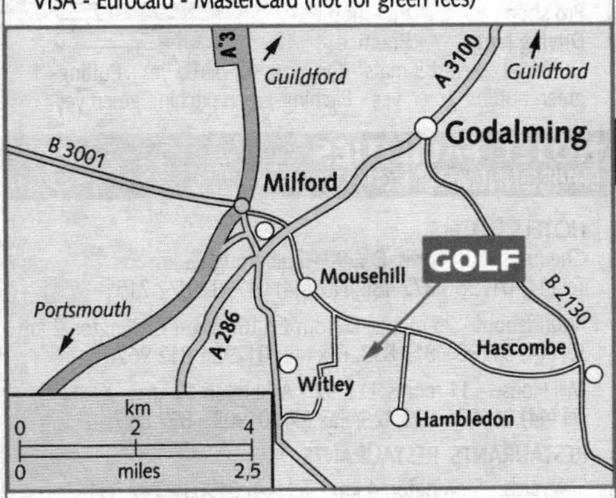

Access Accès : A3 (→ Portsmouth) through Guildford. Turn left to Milford. At traffic lights turn left onto A 3100 (→Portsmouth). Right onto Station Lane. Golf 3 km down (2 m.) on right side. **Map 8 on page 484** Carte 8 Page 484

GOLF COURSE — PARCOURS — 15/20

Site	Site	
Maintenance	Entretien	
Architect	Architecte	Herbert Fowler
Type	Type	parkland
Relief	Relief	
Water in play	Eau en jeu	
Exp. to wind	Exposé au vent	
Trees in play	Arbres en jeu	

Scorecard Carte de score	Chp. Chp.	Mens Mess.	Ladies Da.
Length Long.	5842	5633	4970
Par	71	71	72
Slope system	—	—	—

Advised golfing ability Niveau de jeu recommandé — 0 12 24 36

Hcp required Handicap exigé — certificate

CLUB HOUSE & AMENITIES — CLUB HOUSE ET ANNEXES — 7/10

Pro shop Pro-shop
Driving range Practice
Sheltered couvert no - On grass sur herbe yes (summer) - Putting-green putting-green yes - Pitching-green pitching green yes

HOTEL FACILITIES — ENVIRONNEMENT HOTELIER — 6/10

HOTELS HÔTELS

Devil's Punchbowl - Hindhead 8 km
31 rooms, D from £ 80
Tel (44) 01428 - 606 565, Fax (44) 01428 - 605 713

The Manor - 45 rooms, D from £ 92 - Guildford 7 km
Tel (44) 01483 - 222 624, Fax (44) 01483 - 211 389

Angel Posting House and Livery - Guildford 7 km
21 rooms, D £ 150
Tel (44) 01483 - 564 555, Fax (44) 01483 - 533 770

RESTAURANTS RESTAURANTS

White Horse - Hascombe 3 km - Tel (44) 01483 - 208 258
Café de Paris - Guildford 7 km - Tel (44) 01483 - 34 896
Cambio (Italian) - Guildford 3 km - Tel (44) 01483 - 577 702

West Sussex

18	7	5

The good news for most amateurs is that West Sussex is not a long course and the sub-soil is sandy and ideal for playing golf on. The bad news is that there is only one par 5, hole N°1, where your swing might not quite be in the right groove to hit the green in two and start off with a welcome birdie. Then there are a number of holes where you will hope to get by unscathed, for example the 6th and 15th, two tough par 3s where you need to carry water, and the 16th, a beautiful par 4 whose green looks depressingly tiny beyond a wide ravine. Here, you have every opportunity to shoot a good round as long as your game is in tip-top condition, and although the greens are very well protected, there is often an easy way in. You need to play every shot there is, one at a time, firstly in your mind, then with your club. This absolute gem of a course does not have the recognition it deserves, but the people here seem to have opted for the quiet life, preferring to leave the limelight for others.

Les bonnes nouvelles pour la plupart des amateurs, c'est que West Sussex n'est pas bien long, et que son sol sablonneux est idéal pour jouer au golf ! La mauvaise, c'est qu'il y a un seul par 5, et c'est le 1, où l'on n'est généralement pas assez assoupli pour vraiment attaquer le green en deux et commencer par un birdie. Car il y aura ensuite quelques trous dont il faut sortir indemne, comme le 6 et le 15, deux solides par 3 où il faut passer l'eau, ou le 16, très beau par 4 dont le green paraît minuscule au delà d'un large ravin. Autrement, il est ici beaucoup d'occasions de réussir si l'on a amené son meilleur jeu, d'autant que les greens sont bien protégés, mais qu'ils laissent très souvent une ouverture. Il faut ici savoir jouer tous les coups, et un seul à la fois, d'abord avec sa tête puis avec son club. Ce merveilleux petit bijou n'a pas la notoriété qu'il mérite, mais, ici, on a choisi de vivre tranquille, sans souci des projecteurs trop violents.

West Sussex Golf Club — 1931

ENG - PULBOROUGH, West Sussex RH20 2EN

Office	Secrétariat	(44) 01798 - 872 563
Pro shop	Pro-shop	(44) 01798 - 872 426
Fax	Fax	(44) 01798 - 872 033
Web	www.westsussexgolf.co.uk	
Situation	Situation	Brighton, 25 km
Annual closure	Fermeture annuelle	no
Weekly closure	Fermeture hebdomadaire	no

Fees main season Tarifs haute saison	18 holes	
	Week days Semaine	We/Bank holidays We/Férié
Individual Individuel	£ 65	*
Couple Couple	£ 130	*

Full week days: £ 80 / * No visitors on Friday & week-ends

Caddie Caddie no — **Electric Trolley** Chariot électrique no

Buggy Voiturette yes — **Clubs** Clubs yes

Credit cards Cartes de crédit
VISA - MasterCard (Pro shop goods only)

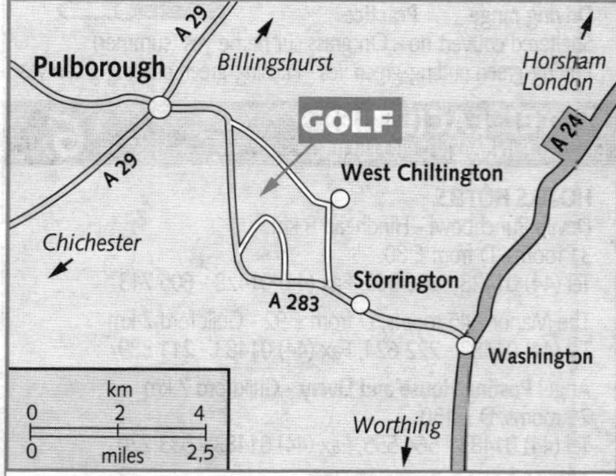

Access Accès : M25 Jct 9, A24 → Worthing. At Washington, A283 on the right through Storrington → Pulborough. Golf course on the right.
Map 7 on page 482 Carte 7 Page 482

GOLF COURSE — PARCOURS — 18/20

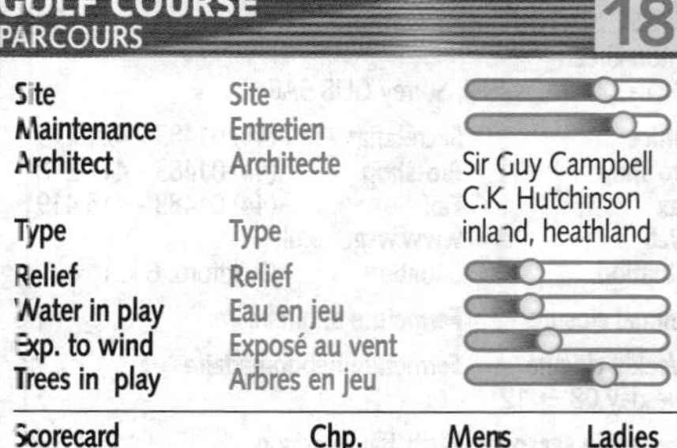

Site	Site	
Maintenance	Entretien	
Architect	Architecte	Sir Guy Campbell C.K. Hutchinson
Type	Type	inland, heathland
Relief	Relief	
Water in play	Eau en jeu	
Exp. to wind	Exposé au vent	
Trees in play	Arbres en jeu	

Scorecard Carte de score	**Chp.** Chp.	**Mens** Mess.	**Ladies** Da.
Length Long.	5600	5320	5020
Par	68	68	73
Slope system	—	—	—

Advised golfing ability — 0 12 24 36
Niveau de jeu recommandé

Hcp required Handicap exigé — certificate

CLUB HOUSE & AMENITIES — CLUB HOUSE ET ANNEXES — 7/10

Pro shop Pro-shop
Driving range Practice
Sheltered couvert 3 mats - On grass sur herbe yes - Putting-green putting-green yes - Pitching-green pitching green yes

HOTEL FACILITIES — ENVIRONNEMENT HOTELIER — 5/10

HOTELS HÔTELS

Chequers - 10 rooms, D £ 90 - Pulborough 3 km
Tel (44) 01798 - 872 486, Fax (44) 01798 - 872 715

Roundabout - 25 rooms, D from £ 116 - West Chiltington 2 km
Tel (44) 01798 - 813 838, Fax (44) 01798 - 812 962

Mill House - 11 rooms, D £ 92 - Ashington 10 km
Tel (44) 01903 - 892 426, Fax (44) 01903 - 892 855

RESTAURANTS RESTAURANTS

Sawyards - Storrington 4 km - Tel (44) 01903 - 742 331
Old Forge - Storrington 4 km - Tel (44) 01903 - 743 402
Roundabout Hotel - West Chiltington 2 km
Tel (44) 01798 - 813 838

Weston-Super-Mare

15 | 6 | 7

The beginning of the course is not so simple, between the sand-dunes lining one side of the course and out-of-bounds on the other. If the wind is blowing, don't go for the pin because you will be asking for trouble. The 15th is also surprising, because you have to cut the ball over an out-of-bounds area. If you really want to enjoy the course first time out, try and get a round with some local players so they can tell you about the pitfalls that are not always clearly in view. For example, the rough is never the same from one season to the next and even disappears altogether in the winter. Facing the Welsh coast, Weston-Super-Mare provides some spectacular views over the Bristol Channel but also leaves the course exposed to the wind. What is more, the general flatness of the course means you can easily play 36 holes in a day when on holiday. Similar to Saunton in style but without offering quite the same challenge, this is a course in the grand links tradition.

Le début du parcours n'est pas si simple, entre les dunes qui forment l'une des limites du parcours et le hors-limites de l'autre côté. S'il y a du vent, ne jouez pas directement les drapeaux, vous risquez des problèmes. Le 15 est aussi surprenant, où il faut couper au-dessus du hors-limites. Si vous voulez bien profiter du parcours lors de sa découverte, essayez donc de faire une partie avec des joueurs locaux, ils vous en apprendront les pièges pas toujours bien visibles, notamment que le rough n'est jamais le même suivant la saison, et qu'il est absent en hiver. Mais il est vrai que l'on vient rarement ici en cette période de l'année. En face du Pays de Galles, Weston-Super-Mare offre des vues spectaculaires sur le Bristol Channel, mais ce privilège s'accompagne de l'exposition au vent. En revanche, son absence de relief en fait un parcours idéal pour jouer 36 trous en vacances. Assez proche par son style de Saunton, sans prétendre à son exigence, c'est un parcours de grande tradition de links.

Weston-Super-Mare Golf Club — 1892

Uphill Road North
ENG - WESTON-SUPER-MARE, Bristol BS23 4NQ

Office	Secrétariat	(44) 01934 - 626 968
Pro shop	Pro-shop	(44) 01934 - 633 360
Fax	Fax	(44) 01934 - 621 300
Web	www.wsmgolfclub.com	
Situation	Situation	Bristol, 23 km
Annual closure	Fermeture annuelle	no
Weekly closure	Fermeture hebdomadaire	no
Fees main season	Tarifs haute saison	18 holes

	Week days / Semaine	We/Bank holidays / We/Férié
Individual Individuel	£ 36	£ 36
Couple Couple	£ 72	£ 72

Full days: £ 48 and £ 48 (We)

Caddie Caddie no

Electric Trolley Chariot électrique no (but batteries)

Buggy Voiturette no **Clubs** Clubs no

Credit cards Cartes de crédit
Visa - Mastercard (Pro shop goods only)

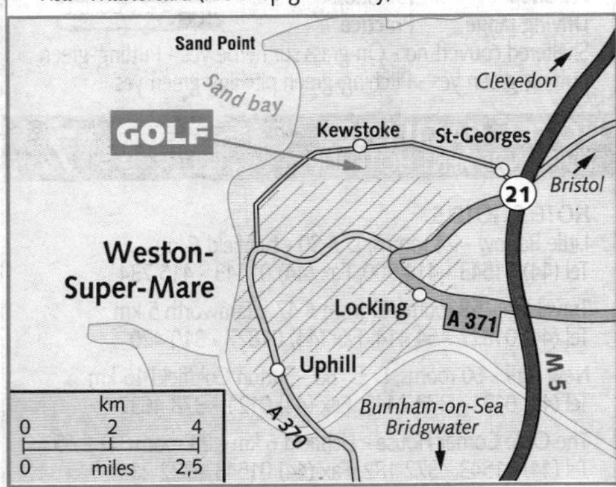

Access Accès : • M5 Jct 21, then A370 to Weston-Super-Mare. Follow signs. • From Bristol centre, A370.
Map 6 on page 481 Carte 6 Page 481

GOLF COURSE — PARCOURS 15/20

Site	Site	
Maintenance	Entretien	
Architect	Architecte	Tom Dunn
Type	Type	seaside course, links
Relief	Relief	
Water in play	Eau en jeu	
Exp. to wind	Exposé au vent	
Trees in play	Arbres en jeu	

Scorecard Carte de score	Chp. Chp.	Mens Mess.	Ladies Da.
Length Long.	5651	5540	5006
Par	70	70	72
Slope system	—	—	—

Advised golfing ability Niveau de jeu recommandé: 0 12 24 36

Hcp required Handicap exigé: certificate

CLUB HOUSE & AMENITIES — CLUB HOUSE ET ANNEXES 6/10

Pro shop Pro-shop
Driving range Practice
Sheltered couvert no - On grass sur herbe yes - Putting-green putting-green yes - Pitching-green pitching green yes

HOTEL FACILITIES — ENVIRONNEMENT HOTELIER 7/10

HOTELS HÔTELS

Beachlands - 23 rooms, D £ 107 - Weston-Super-Mare adjacent
Tel (44) 01934 - 621 401, Fax (44) 01934 -621 966

Queenswood - 19 rooms, D £ 95 - Weston-super-Mare 2 km
Tel (44) 01934 - 416 141, Fax (44) 01934 - 621 759

Commodore - Weston-Super-Mare 2 km
19 rooms, D from £ 85
Tel (44) 01934 - 415 778, Fax (44) 01934 - 636 483

RESTAURANTS RESTAURANTS

Duets - Weston-Super-Mare 3 km - Tel (44) 01934 - 413 428

Claremont Vaults - Weston-Super-Mare 2 km
Tel (44) 01934 - 629 503

Whittington Heath

16	6	7

This is the kind of course you would like to keep to yourself but one which has hosted some top and even international amateur tournaments. Very much underrated and often completely unknown, it is a sort of delectable gem that long-hitters will look down upon until they reach the 14th tee. For a heathland course the site is relatively unspectacular, however the layout was designed by Harry Colt, who knew a thing or two about teasing dog-legs. Missing the open side of the fairway calls for some golfing acrobatics through or over the trees, or some sheepish save-shots back into play. If you score well it's because you thought it out well. The greens are well defended, distinctly well contoured, pretty huge and a pleasure to putt on. What lingers here is an impression of happiness, of having discovered something personal, but which you have to share with others...

C'est le genre de parcours que l'on aimerait garder pour soi, mais qui a accueilli de bonnes compétitions amateurs, même internationales. Très sous-estimé, souvent complètement ignoré, c'est une sorte de délicieux petit bijou que les longs frappeurs regarderont de haut jusqu'au moment où ils parviendront au départ du 14. Pour un site de terre de bruyère il n'est pas spécialement impressionnant, mais le tracé est signé Harry Colt, qui savait notamment faire des doglegs provoquants, où manquer l'ouverture oblige à des coups d'acrobate, ou encore à des retours penauds en sécurité sur le fairway. Et si l'on a bien scoré, c'est que l'on a bien pensé. Bien défendus, très travaillés, et plutôt vastes, les greens sont un plaisir à négocier. C'est cette impression de bonheur qui reste ici, d'avoir découvert quelque chose, même si on est loin d'être le seul...

Whittington Heath Golf Club — 1886

Tamworth Road
ENG - LICHFIELD, Staffs WS14 9PW

Office	Secrétariat	(44) 01543 - 432 317
Pro shop	Pro-shop	(44) 01543 - 432 261
Fax	Fax	(44) 01543 - 433 962
Web	www.whittingtonheathgc.co.uk	
Situation	Situation	Birmingham, 20 km
Annual closure	Fermeture annuelle	no
Weekly closure	Fermeture hebdomadaire	no

Fees main season Tarifs haute saison	18 holes	
	Week days / Semaine	We/Bank holidays / We/Férié
Individual Individuel	£ 35	*
Couple Couple	£ 70	*

Full week days: £ 50 / * Week-ends: members only

Caddie Caddie no — **Electric Trolley** Chariot électrique yes
Buggy Voiturette no — **Clubs** Clubs no

Credit cards Cartes de crédit
Visa - Mastercard (Pro shop & green fees)

Access Accès : On A51, 4 km from Lichfield Station
Map 7 on page 482 Carte 7 Page 482

GOLF COURSE — PARCOURS — 16/20

Site	Site	
Maintenance	Entretien	
Architect	Architecte	Harry S. Colt
Type	Type	inland, heathland
Relief	Relief	
Water in play	Eau en jeu	
Exp. to wind	Exposé au vent	
Trees in play	Arbres en jeu	

Scorecard / Carte de score	Chp. / Chp.	Mens / Mess.	Ladies / Da.
Length Long.	5841	5542	5117
Par	70	70	72
Slope system	—	—	—

Advised golfing ability / Niveau de jeu recommandé: 0 12 24 36
Hcp required Handicap exigé: certificate

CLUB HOUSE & AMENITIES — CLUB HOUSE ET ANNEXES — 6/10

Pro shop	Pro-shop
Driving range	Practice

Sheltered couvert no - On grass sur herbe yes - Putting-green putting-green yes - Pitching-green pitching green yes

HOTEL FACILITIES — ENVIRONNEMENT HOTELIER — 7/10

HOTELS HÔTELS

Little Barrow - 24 rooms, D £ 80 - Lichfield 6 km
Tel (44) 01543 - 414 500, Fax (44) 01543 - 415 734

Travel Inn - 58 rooms, D from £ 47 - Tamworth 5 km
Tel (44) 01827 - 54 414, Fax (44) 01827 - 310 420

New Hall - 60 rooms, D £ 160 - Sutton Coldfield 15 km
Tel (44) 0121 - 378 2442, Fax (44) 0121 - 378 4637

The Olde Corner House - Lichfield 6 km - 23 rooms, D £ 65
Tel (44) 01543 - 372 182, Fax (44) 01543 - 372 211

RESTAURANTS RESTAURANTS

Thrales - Lichfield 6 km - Tel (44) 01543 - 255 091
New Hall - Sutton Coldfield 15 km - Tel (44) 0121 - 378 2442

Wilmslow

15	7	6

Golf at Wilmslow is a civilized affair with distinct disdain for the ostentatious. Although there is a pleasantly old-fashioned feel to the course, maintenance is definitely modern and probably the best in the region. It is generally set up in such a way as to not intimidate the less experienced players whilst providing a respectable challenge for low-handicappers. They can start by attempting to drive the green on hole N°1, cutting the corner of this par 4 by hitting it over the trees. The most surprising thing here is the unity of style, even though a dozen or so architects have altered the layout in their own way, from James Braid to Tom Simpson to Fred Hawtree to Dave Thomas. At least no-one thought of removing the many cross-bunkers that modern-day architects hardly know how to use or even simply place any more, even though they never think twice about blocking your path with water. A course with all the components of a good test of golf, but above all, Wilmslow is an honest course that neither flatters the hacker nor demands too much of single-figure handicappers.

Dans un paysage typique du Cheshire rural, le golf à Wilmslow est chose civilisée, dédaignant toute ostentation. Bien que l'on ait ici une sensation agréablement "old fashion", rien de tel dans l'entretien du parcours, l'un des meilleurs de la région sur ce plan. Il est généralement préparé de manière à ne pas intimider le joueur peu aguerri, tout en offrant des défis respectables aux meilleurs. Le plus surprenant ici est l'unité de style, bien qu'une bonne dizaine d'architectes se soient penchés sur ce dessin, de James Braid à Tom Simpson, de Fred Hawtree à Dave Thomas. Au moins personne n'aura songé à en effacer les nombreux "cross-bunkers" que les architectes modernes ne savent plus guère mettre en œuvre, ou simplement placer, alors qu'ils hésitent si peu à barrer votre route avec de l'eau ! Un parcours avec tous les éléments d'un bon test, et par dessus tout un parcours à l'échelle humaine, ni pour faire briller les mauvais joueurs à bon compte, ni pour demander l'impossible aux bons.

Wilmslow Golf Club — 1903

Great Warford, Mobberley
ENG - KNUTSFORD, Cheshire WA16 7AY

Office	Secrétariat	(44) 01565 - 872 148
Pro shop	Pro-shop	(44) 01565 - 873 620
Fax	Fax	(44) 01565 - 874 255
Web	www.wilmslowgolfclub.co.uk	
Situation	Situation	Manchester, 20 km
Annual closure	Fermeture annuelle	no
Weekly closure	Fermeture hebdomadaire	no

Fees main season Tarifs haute saison	Week days Semaine	We/Bank holidays We/Férié
		18 holes
Individual Individuel	£ 45	£ 55
Couple Couple	£ 90	£ 110

Full day: £ 55 and £ 65 (We)

Caddie Caddie no — Electric Trolley Chariot électrique yes

Buggy Voiturette yes — Clubs Clubs yes

Credit cards Cartes de crédit
VISA - Eurocard (Pro shop goods only)

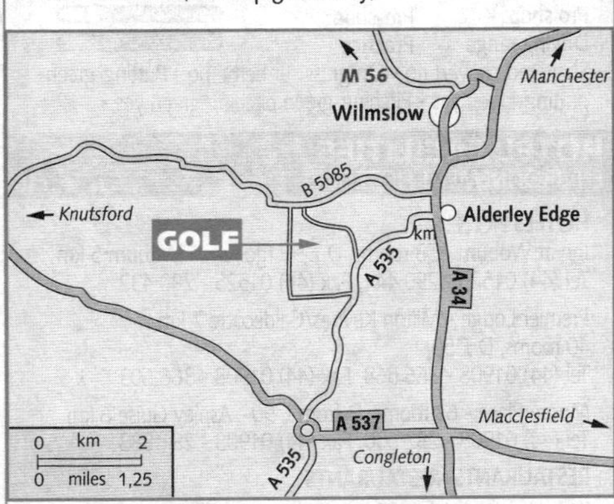

Access Accès : Manchester A34 onto Wilmslow, then B5085 → Mobberley, Knutsford, turn left → David Lewis Centre for Epilepsy, Golf course on left hand side.

Map 4 on page 476 Carte 4 Page 476

GOLF COURSE — PARCOURS — 15/20

Site	Site	
Maintenance	Entretien	
Architect	Architecte	S. Herd, J. Braid T. Simpson, G.Duncan...
Type	Type	inland, open country
Relief	Relief	
Water in play	Eau en jeu	
Exp. to wind	Exposé au vent	
Trees in play	Arbres en jeu	

Scorecard Carte de score	Chp. Chp.	Mens Mess.	Ladies Da.
Length Long.	6044	6044	5293
Par	72	72	74
Slope system	—	—	—

Advised golfing ability — Niveau de jeu recommandé: 0 12 24 36

Hcp required — Handicap exigé: certificate

CLUB HOUSE & AMENITIES — CLUB HOUSE ET ANNEXES — 7/10

Pro shop — Pro-shop
Driving range — Practice
Sheltered couvert practice area - On grass sur herbe yes - Putting-green putting-green yes - Pitching-green pitching green yes

HOTEL FACILITIES — ENVIRONNEMENT HOTELIER — 6/10

HOTELS HÔTELS

Stanneylands - 31 rooms, D £ 110 - Wilmslow 5 km
Tel (44) 01625 - 525 225, Fax (44) 01625 - 537 282

Mottram Hall Hotel - Wilmslow/Prestbury 8 km
132 rooms, D from £ 145
Tel (44) 01625 - 828 135, Fax (44) 01625 - 829 284

Alderley Edge Hotel - 52 rooms, D £ 140 - Alderley Edge 2 km
Tel (44) 01625 - 583 033, Fax (44) 01625 - 586 343

RESTAURANTS RESTAURANTS

Belle Epoque - Knutsford 3 km - Tel (44) 01565 - 633 060
The Alderley - Alderley Edge 2 km - Tel (44) 01625 - 583 033
The Wizard - Alderley Edge 2 km - Tel (44) 01625 - 584 000

Woburn *Duke'-s Course*

17 | 7 | 7

In a very elegant setting with an equally comfortable clubhouse, all three courses at Woburn are pleasantly sited well away from the noise of the outside world. The Duchess course is above average but not in the same league as the Duke's or Marquess courses which have been made famous by their staging televised professional tournaments. Except for the first few holes, and the occasional requirement to drive over a ravine. this is a rather flat layout which winds its way through a beautiful old forest of pine and chestnut trees, sufficiently in play for the rough to be fairly inconsequential. The sandy soil makes for pleasant golfing all the year round, enhanced by the excellence of the greens, which are never easy to read. The holes all have a distinct individual character but without detracting from a pleasant unity of style. The back-tees are for very good players only, especially from the 13th onward, where some of the par-4s are quite formidable.

D'une grande élégance générale et avec un confortable club-house, l'ensemble des trois parcours de Woburn bénéficie d'une situation bien à l'écart du monde. Le parcours "Duchess" est certes honorable, mais ne saurait lutter avec le "Duke's" et le "Marquess", rendu célèbre par les tournois télévisés. Assez plat, sauf dans ses premiers trous, il est insinué dans une belle et ancienne forêt, où dominent les pins et les châtaigniers, assez présents dans le jeu pour que les roughs ne soient pas nécessaires ni difficiles. Le sol sablonneux le rend très agréable à jouer toute l'année, et la qualité des greens, pas faciles à lire, augmente encore ce plaisir. Les trous sont bien individualisés, tout en offrant une bonne unité de style. On ne conseillera les départs arrière qu'aux très bons joueurs, surtout à partir du 13, où quelques par 4 sont redoutables.

Woburn Golf & Country Club — 1976

Bow Brickhill
ENG - MILTON KEYNES, Bucks MK17 9 LJ

Office	Secrétariat	(44) 01908 - 370 756
Pro shop	Pro-shop	(44) 01908 - 626 600
Fax	Fax	(44) 01908 - 378 436
Web	www.woburngolf.com	
Situation	Situation	Milton Keynes, 10 km
Annual closure	Fermeture annuelle	no
Weekly closure	Fermeture hebdomadaire	Christmas Day
Fees main season	Tarifs haute saison	18 holes

	Week days Semaine	We/Bank holidays We/Férié
Individual Individuel	£ 66	*
Couple Couple	£ 132	*

Full week day with lunch Duke + Marquess: £ 150 /
* Week-ends: members only

Caddie Caddie no — **Electric Trolley** Chariot électrique yes
Buggy Voiturette yes — **Clubs** Clubs yes
Credit cards Cartes de crédit
VISA - MasterCard - AMEX

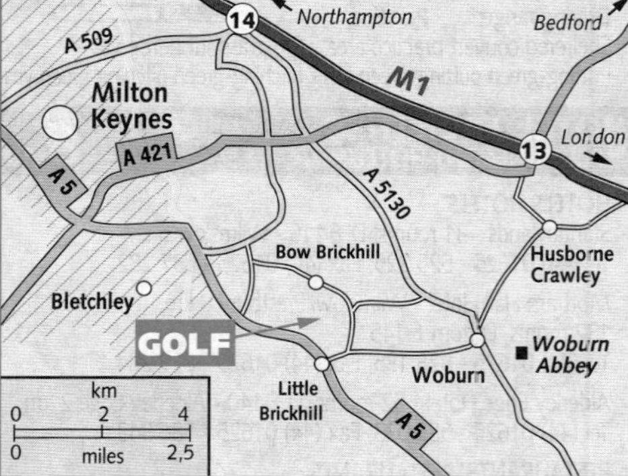

Access Accès : London M1 North. Jct 13 into Woburn Sands. Left to Woburn. After 0.75 km (1/2 m), right at sign.
Map 7 on page 482 Carte 7 Page 482

GOLF COURSE — PARCOURS 17/20

Site	Site	
Maintenance	Entretien	
Architect	Architecte	Charles Lawrie
Type	Type	inland, forest
Relief	Relief	
Water in play	Eau en jeu	
Exp. to wind	Exposé au vent	
Trees in play	Arbres en jeu	

Scorecard Carte de score	Chp. Chp.	Mens Mess.	Ladies Da.
Length Long.	6264	5898	5454
Par	72	72	75
Slope system	—	—	—

Advised golfing ability Niveau de jeu recommandé — 0 12 24 36
Hcp required Handicap exigé — 24 Men, 36 Ladies

CLUB HOUSE & AMENITIES — CLUB HOUSE ET ANNEXES 7/10

Pro shop Pro-shop
Driving range Practice
Sheltered couvert no - On grass sur herbe no - Putting-green putting-green yes - Pitching-green pitching green yes

HOTEL FACILITIES — ENVIRONNEMENT HOTELIER 7/10

HOTELS HÔTELS
Inn at Woburn - 58 rooms, D £ 99 (golfers) - Woburn 5 km
Tel (44) 01525 - 290 441, Fax (44) 01525 - 290 432

Premier Lodge - Milton Keynes/Caldecotte 7 km
40 rooms, D £ 50
Tel (44) 01908 - 366 568, Fax (44) 01908 - 366 603

Moore Place - 63 rooms, D from £ 90 - Aspley Guise 6 km
Tel (44) 01908 - 282 000, Fax (44) 01908 - 281 888

RESTAURANTS RESTAURANTS
Paris House - Woburn 5 km - Tel (44) 01525 - 290 692
The Birch (Pub) - Woburn 5 km - Tel (44) 01525 - 290 295
Bell Inn - Woburn 5 km - Tel (44) 01525 - 290 280

Woburn *Marquess*

17	7	7

With the famous Duke's and Duchess courses already well established, it was difficult to believe that it was possible to create something so different, yet equally alluring, as the Marquess course. All three grace this huge estate and are well away from the noise of the nearby M1 motorway. The layout of the Marquess puts more emphasis on driving, despite the fact that the fairways are generally wider than on the other courses. It possesses a charm and character of its own, lined as it is with pine, oak, chestnut, beech and spruce trees, some of which have stood majestically there for hundreds of years. What makes it so challenging is the fact that many of the trees come into play, demanding flighted shots to manœuvre the ball around interesting dog-legged holes. The greens are huge, well contoured and have been cleverly constructed to provide some tantalising pin positions. Green surrounds, too, call upon the golfer to exercise plenty of care and imagination before executing a shot.

Après les Duke's et Duchess, il était difficile d'imaginer qu'il soit possible de créer un autre parcours aussi différent, mais avec autant d'allure que ce Marquess Course. Tous trois ont trouvé place dans une immense propriété, à l'écart du bruit de l'autoroute M1 toute proche. Ce "Marquess" met l'accent sur le driving, bien que les fairways soient notablement plus larges que sur les autres tracés. Son charme et son caractère, c'est d'abord un environnement de pins, chênes, châtaigniers hêtres ou épicéas, dont certains ont plusieurs centaines d'années. Certains d'eux se détachent de l'arrière-plan forestier pour venir interférer sur le jeu, obligeant à travailler la balle ou à mesurer les risques sur les dog legs. Les greens sont assez vastes et bien travaillés, avec pas mal de positions intéressantes de drapeaux. Leurs alentours ont été bien travaillés, ce qui oblige à une certaine imagination pour jouer les approches.

Woburn Golf & Country Club — 1999

Bow Brickhill
ENG - MILTON KEYNES, Bucks MK17 9 LJ

Office	Secrétariat	(44) 01908 - 370 756
Pro shop	Pro-shop	(44) 01908 - 626 600
Fax	Fax	(44) 01908 - 378 436
Web	www.woburngolf.com	
Situation	Situation	Milton Keynes, 10 km
Annual closure	Fermeture annuelle	no
Weekly closure	Fermeture hebdomadaire	no

Fees main season Tarifs haute saison — 18 holes

	Week days / Semaine	We/Bank holidays / We/Férié
Individual Individuel	£ 95	*
Couple Couple	£ 190	*

Full week day with lunch Duke + Marquess: £ 150 /
* Week-ends: members only

Caddie Caddie no **Electric Trolley** Chariot électrique yes

Buggy Voiturette yes **Clubs** Clubs yes

Credit cards Cartes de crédit
VISA - MasterCard - AMEX

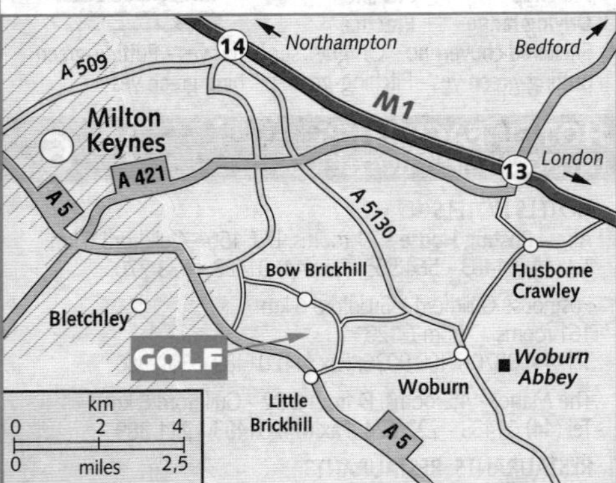

Access Accès : London M1 North. Jct 13 into Woburn Sands. Left to Woburn. After 0.75 km (1/2 m), right at sign.
Map 7 on page 482 Carte 7 Page 482

GOLF COURSE — PARCOURS — 17/20

Site	Site	
Maintenance	Entretien	
Architect	Architecte	P. Alliss, C. Clark, R. McMurray, A. Hay
Type	Type	inland, forest
Relief	Relief	
Water in play	Eau en jeu	
Exp. to wind	Exposé au vent	
Trees in play	Arbres en jeu	

Scorecard Carte de score	Chp. Chp.	Mens Mess.	Ladies Da.
Length Long.	6493	6070	5248
Par	72	72	72
Slope system	—	—	—

Advised golfing ability Niveau de jeu recommandé — 0 12 24 36

Hcp required Handicap exigé — 24 Men, 36 Ladies

CLUB HOUSE & AMENITIES — CLUB HOUSE ET ANNEXES — 7/10

Pro shop Pro-shop
Driving range Practice
Sheltered couvert no - On grass sur herbe no - Putting-green putting-green yes - Pitching-green pitching green yes

HOTEL FACILITIES — ENVIRONNEMENT HOTELIER — 7/10

HOTELS HÔTELS

Inn at Woburn - 58 rooms, D £ 99 (golfers) - Woburn 5 km
Tel (44) 01525 - 290 441, Fax (44) 01525 - 290 432

Premier Lodge - Milton Keynes/Caldecotte 7 km
40 rooms, D £ 50
Tel (44) 01908 - 366 568, Fax (44) 01908 - 366 603

Moore Place - 63 rooms, D from £ 90 - Aspley Guise 6 km
Tel (44) 01908 - 282 000, Fax (44) 01908 - 281 888

RESTAURANTS RESTAURANTS

Paris House - Woburn 5 km - Tel (44) 01525 - 290 692

The Birch (Pub) - Woburn 5 km - Tel (44) 01525 - 290 295

Bell Inn - Woburn 5 km - Tel (44) 01525 - 290 280

Woking

17 | 6 | 6

The oldest of the threesome of "Ws" (being adjacent to West Hill and Worplesdon) it would be wrong to imagine that all three offer an identical challenge, because they each have their own personality. Here it all starts with the club-house, as British as a cricket pavilion where you drink tea after your round, and it culminates with a plethora of spectacularly contoured putting surfaces. Otherwise the landscape is the same as on the other two courses, with heather just about everywhere you look. Isn't it about time someone invented a special "heather wedge" to help get balls back onto the fairway? And heather it is that puts the most pressure on your tee-shot here, where apprehension will always be your worst enemy. Add to this first class bunkering and medium-sized greens that are often so boldly contoured that it takes time and patience to figure them out and you realise that although a very fair proposition, Woking is a difficult course for carding a good score. A charming site, but watch out for its bite...

Avec West Hill et Worplesdon, ce sont de faux triplés. Mais si l'on imagine jouer trois fois le même parcours ou écrire trois fois le même texte, on se trompe, chacun a son propre caractère. Celui-ci commence par son club-house, à ce point British que l'on imagine ces pavillons de cricket où l'on boit le thé en fin de la partie, et culmine dans une pléthore de greens très modelés. Sinon, le paysage est analogue, avec une omniprésente bruyère : il faudra bien inventer un jour un "heather wedge" pour en sortir! C'est d'ailleurs cette possibilité qui met tant de pression sur les coups de départ : en golf aussi, la peur est mauvaise conseillère. Et si l'on ajoute un bunkering de premier ordre, ainsi que des greens de taille moyenne, mais d'une telle subtilité dans leurs contours qu'il faut du temps et de la patience pour les comprendre, on se doute que, en dépit de sa franchise, Woking n'est pas un parcours évident à scorer. Derrière le charme du lieu, il y a de solides mâchoires.

Woking Golf Club — 1893

Pond Road, Hook Heath
ENG - WOKING, Surrey GU22 0JZ

Office	Secrétariat	(44) 01483 - 760 053
Pro shop	Pro-shop	(44) 01483 - 769 582
Fax	Fax	(44) 01483 - 772 441
E-mail	wokinggolfclub@talk21.com	
Situation	Situation	Guildford, 6 km

London Centre, 48 km

Annual closure	Fermeture annuelle	no
Weekly closure	Fermeture hebdomadaire	no

666

Fees main season Tarifs haute saison	18 holes	
	Week days Semaine	We/Bank holidays We/Férié
Individual Individuel	£ 60	*
Couple Couple	£ 120	*

* Week-ends: members only

Caddie Caddie on request **Electric Trolley** Chariot électrique yes

Buggy Voiturette yes **Clubs** Clubs yes

Credit cards Cartes de crédit no

Chobham
Staines
Bracknell
Lightwater
A 320
A 322
Woking
GOLF
Bisley
A 324
Brookwood
A 247
London
Pirbright
B380
Mayford
Send
A 324
A 3
Worplesdon
km 0 2 4
0 miles 2,5
Godalming
Guildford

Access Accès : London A3 → Guildford. At Cobham, A245 on right. Through Woking. → St Johns Village. Hollibank Road, turn right into Golf Club Road. Entrance on right at end.

Map 8 on page 484 Carte 8 Page 484

GOLF COURSE — PARCOURS — 17/20

Site	Site	
Maintenance	Entretien	
Architect	Architecte	Tom Dunn
Type	Type	inland, heathland
Relief	Relief	
Water in play	Eau en jeu	
Exp. to wind	Exposé au vent	
Trees in play	Arbres en jeu	

Scorecard Carte de score	Chp. Chp.	Mens Mess.	Ladies Da.
Length Long.	5706	5361	5055
Par	70	70	73
Slope system	—	—	—

Advised golfing ability 0 12 24 36
Niveau de jeu recommandé
Hcp required Handicap exigé certificate

CLUB HOUSE & AMENITIES — CLUB HOUSE ET ANNEXES — 6/10

Pro shop Pro-shop
Driving range Practice

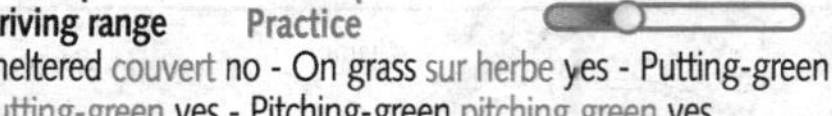

Sheltered couvert no - On grass sur herbe yes - Putting-green putting-green yes - Pitching-green pitching green yes

HOTEL FACILITIES — ENVIRONNEMENT HOTELIER — 6/10

HOTELS HÔTELS

Angel Posting House - 21 rooms, D £ 150 - Guildford 6 km
Tel (44) 01483 - 564 555, Fax (44) 01483 - 533 770

Posthouse Guildford - Guildford 6 km
161 rooms, D from £ 120
Tel (44) 0870 - 400 9036, Fax (44) 01483 - 302 960

The Manor - 45 rooms, D from £ 92 - Guildford 6 km
Tel (44) 01483 - 222 624, Fax (44) 01483 - 211 389

RESTAURANTS RESTAURANTS

Drake's Restaurant - Ripley 6 km - Tel (44) 01483 - 224 777

Café de Paris - Guildford 6 km
Tel (44) 01483 - 534 896

Woodbridge

15	7	7

Founded in 1893, Woodbridge has since moved with the times and got equipped with a modern club-house in the early 1970s. Once much wider, the course has become a lot tighter as the trees have grown, a factor rarely given full consideration but one which can significantly change a designer's original intentions. A lot of courses should be studying the question right now. As it happens, the trees at Woodbridge hardly make it the ideal course for wayward hitters or beginners, unless they can master a 1 iron off the tee, which for the latter at least is hardly likely. This is a pity because here you have a very good test of golf where many holes widen out after the driving area and things get a little easier if you stay out of the heather. Those of you who can flight the ball either way will enjoy Woodbridge, a fine course, an excellent test but never an ordeal and quiet during the week. Very pleasant to play with the family for fun. An additional 9-hole course completes the picture in a region that few tourists know about.

Fondé en 1893, Woodbridge a évolué avec le temps, et s'est doté d'un club-house moderne vers 1970. Autrefois large, le parcours est devenu beaucoup plus étroit avec la croissance des arbres : c'est un élément rarement pris en compte, alors qu'il peut beaucoup modifier les intentions des architectes. Cette question doit en tout cas se poser pour beaucoup de parcours. En l'occurrence, ce détail empêche de conseiller Woodbridge aux frappeurs pas trop précis et aux débutants, à moins qu'ils ne soient des maîtres du fer 1, ce qui serait étonnant, du moins chez les débutants. C'est dommage car c'est un très bon test de golf, beaucoup de trous s'élargissent après la zone de drive, et les choses vont mieux si l'on a évité la bruyère. Les travailleurs de balle s'amuseront beaucoup sur ce beau parcours, un bon test sans être une bataille, très tranquille en semaine et très agréable à jouer en famille, pour le plaisir. Un 9 trous complète bien cet équipement dans une région assez peu connue des touristes.

Woodbridge Golf Club — 1893

Bromeswell Heath
ENG - WOODBRIDGE, Suffolk IP12 2PF

Office	Secrétariat	(44) 01394 - 382 038
Pro shop	Pro-shop	(44) 01394 - 383 213
Fax	Fax	(44) 01394 - 382 392
Web	www.woodbridgegolfclub.co.uk	
Situation	Situation	Aldeburgh, 15 km
Annual closure	Fermeture annuelle	no
Weekly closure	Fermeture hebdomadaire	no

Fees main season Tarifs haute saison	Week days Semaine	We/Bank holidays We/Férié
18 holes		
Individual Individuel	£ 42	*
Couple Couple	£ 84	*

* Week-ends: members only

Caddie Caddie no — **Electric Trolley** Chariot électrique no

Buggy Voiturette no — **Clubs** Clubs yes, on request

Credit cards Cartes de crédit
Visa - Mastercard (Pro Shop goods only)

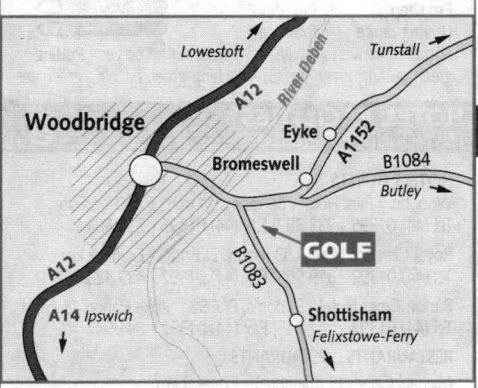

Lowestoft
Tunstall
River Deben
A12
Woodbridge
Eyke
A1152
Bromeswell
B1084
Butley
GOLF
B1083
A12
A14 Ipswich
Shottisham
Felixstowe-Ferry

Access Accès : Ipswich A12. At Woodbridge, B1084 through Melton. Over bridge. Left at roundabout.
Golf course 200 m on the right.
Map 7 on page 483 Carte 7 Page 483

GOLF COURSE — PARCOURS 15/20

Site	Site	
Maintenance	Entretien	
Architect	Architecte	F.W. Hawtree
Type	Type	inland, heathland
Relief	Relief	
Water in play	Eau en jeu	
Exp. to wind	Exposé au vent	
Trees in play	Arbres en jeu	

Scorecard Carte de score	Chp. Chp.	Mens Mess.	Ladies Da.
Length Long.	5670	5456	5137
Par	70	70	73
Slope system	—	—	—

Advised golfing ability Niveau de jeu recommandé: 0 12 24 36

Hcp required Handicap exigé: certificate

CLUB HOUSE & AMENITIES — CLUB HOUSE ET ANNEXES 7/10

Pro shop Pro-shop
Driving range Practice
Sheltered couvert no - On grass sur herbe yes - Putting-green putting-green yes - Pitching-green pitching green yes

HOTEL FACILITIES — ENVIRONNEMENT HOTELIER 7/10

HOTELS HÔTELS

Seckford Hall - 32 rooms, D £ 130 - Woodbridge 3 km
Tel (44) 01394 - 385 678, Fax (44) 01394 - 380 610

Ufford Park - 44 rooms, D from £ 110 - Woodbridge 3 km
Tel (44) 01394 - 383 555, Fax (44) 01394 - 383 582

Salthouse Harbor - 43 rooms, D £ 120 - Ipswich 7 km
Tel (44) 01473 - 226 789, Fax (44) 01473 - 226 927

RESTAURANTS RESTAURANTS

Seckford Hall - Woodbridge 3 km - Tel (44) 01394 - 385678
Ufford Park - Woodbridge 3 km - Tel (44) 01394 - 383555
The Captain's Table - Woodbridge 3 km
Tel (44) 01394 - 383 145

Woodbury Park *The Oaks*

15	9	6

As this course is famed for its association with Nigel Mansell, it is only logical to drive around it rather than walk. It is actually pretty hilly but it won't wear you out, at least not physically. Mentally, chronic hookers might find their ball in deep trouble on at least one half of the holes. Opened in 1992, this course is really starting to mature, although the well-wooded countryside has retained its typical Devonshire landscape. Holes through the woods alternate with holes over open space where water hazards beckon (on 7 holes). Add to this some pretty huge and deep bunkers with high lips and excellent greens laid to USGA standards and you can feel a very distinct American influence where you seldom get the chance to roll the ball onto the putting surface. This is a very interesting test where you should play from the tee-boxes designed for your level of ability. Beginners will certainly feel more comfortable on the neighbouring 9-holer, unless they prefer a little fishing, the swimming pool, tennis courts or aerobics available in this very well equipped resort.

Comme ce golf est associé à Nigel Mansell, il est assez logique de le jouer en voiture ! Il est effectivement assez accidenté mais pas épuisant, sauf mentalement pour les spécialistes du hook, qui risquent la sortie de route sur une bonne moitié des trous. Ouvert en 1992, le 18 trous commence à acquérir vraiment sa maturité, et le paysage bien boisé a gardé son style de campagne typique du Devon. Il alterne les trous très boisés et les espaces plus ouverts, où les obstacles d'eau sont dangereux (sur sept trous). Si l'on ajoute les bunkers plutôt vastes, profonds avec des faces très relevées, et des greens aux normes USGA de très bonne qualité, on a ici une sensation très nette d'influence américaine, et il est rarement possible de faire rouler la balle. C'est un test très intéressant, si l'on joue les départs à son niveau. Les débutants seront plus à l'aise sur le 9 trous voisin, à moins de se livrer aux plaisirs de la pêche, de la piscine, du tennis ou de l'aréobic que propose ce club très bien équipé.

Woodbury Park Golf & Country Club 1992

Woodbury Castle, Woodbury
ENG - EXETER EX5 1JJ

Office	Secrétariat	(44) 01395 - 233 382
Pro shop	Pro-shop	(44) 01395 - 233 500
Fax	Fax	(44) 01395 - 233 384
Web	www.woodburypark.co.uk	
Situation	Situation	Exeter, 9 km
Annual closure	Fermeture annuelle	no
Weekly closure	Fermeture hebdomadaire	no

Fees main season Tarifs haute saison — 18 holes

	Week days Semaine	We/Bank holidays We/Férié
Individual Individuel	£ 45	£ 55
Couple Couple	£ 90	£ 110

Full days: £ 60 / £ 80 (We)

Caddie Caddie no — **Electric Trolley** Chariot électrique yes

Buggy Voiturette yes — **Clubs** Clubs yes

Credit cards Cartes de crédit
VISA - MasterCard

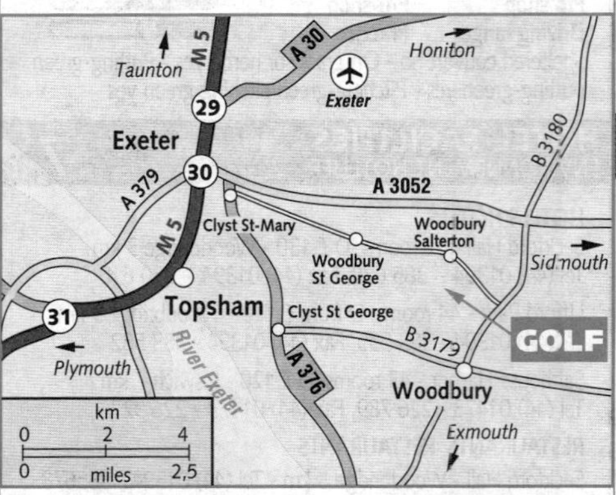

Access Accès : M5 Jct 30. A376 to Sidmouth/Exmouth. Take A3052 to Sidmouth. Turn right at Half Way House Inn.

Map 6 on page 481 Carte 6 Page 481

GOLF COURSE 15/20
PARCOURS

Site	Site	
Maintenance	Entretien	
Architect	Architecte	J. Hamilton Stutt
Type	Type	inland, parkland
Relief	Relief	
Water in play	Eau en jeu	
Exp. to wind	Exposé au vent	
Trees in play	Arbres en jeu	

Scorecard Carte de score	Chp. Chp.	Mens Mess.	Ladies Da.
Length Long.	6583	5921	5109
Par	72	72	73
Slope system	—	—	—

Advised golfing ability Niveau de jeu recommandé — 0 12 24 36

Hcp required Handicap exigé — certificate

CLUB HOUSE & AMENITIES 9/10
CLUB HOUSE ET ANNEXES

Pro shop Pro-shop
Driving range Practice

Sheltered couvert 18 bays - On grass sur herbe yes - Putting-green putting-green yes (3) - Pitching-green pitching green yes

HOTEL FACILITIES 6/10
ENVIRONNEMENT HOTELIER

HOTELS HÔTELS

Woodbury Park Hotel - 56 rooms, D from £ 150 - on site
Tel (44) 01395 - 233 382, Fax (44) 01395 - 233 384

Royal Clarence Hotel - 53 rooms, D £ 110 - Exeter 9 km
Tel (44) 01392 - 319 955, Fax (44) 01392 - 439 423

Barton Cross Hotel - 9 rooms, D £ 98 - Stoke Canon 15 km
Tel (44) 01392 - 841 245, Fax (44) 01392 - 841 942

RESTAURANTS RESTAURANTS

Michael Caines (R. Clarence) - Exeter 9 km
Tel (44) 01392 - 310 031

Barton Cross Hotel - Exeter 15 km - Tel (44) 01392 - 841 245

Brazz - Exeter 9 km - Tel (44) 01392 - 252 525

Woodhall Spa *Hotchkin*

19	7	8

Although situated in a fairly remote part of England, Woodhall Spa is a very important leisure and holiday centre, like a sort of wood-strewn oasis in the middle of the Lincolnshire countryside. It is similar to Pinehurst in the United States and accordingly has recently added a second 18-hole course designed by Donald Steel in a more American style. The century old Hotchkin course is regularly ranked amongst the best in Britain. Originally laid out by Vardon and Colt amidst pines, birch-trees and heather on sandy soil, it was re-designed by the then owner, Neil Hotchkin, before he sold the course to the EGU to be transformed into the National Golf Centre. The number one requirement is to keep your drive in play and the ball alive in order to square up to some of the toughest second shots you could imagine. You must then avoid the bunkers, where you might well spend quite some time, especially on the par 3s. Beginners will be better off here watching or carrying someone's bag. For experienced golfers, Woodhall Spa is a must-visit.

Dans un coin reculé du pays, Woodhall Spa est un centre de loisirs et de vacances important, comme une oasis boisée au milieu de la campagne du Lincolnshire, à l'instar de Pinehurst aux USA. Un second parcours a été dessiné par Donald Steel dans un style plus américain, mais le "centenaire" Hotchkin est régulièrement classé parmi les meilleurs de Grande-Bretagne. Tracé par Vardon et Colt dans les pins, les bouleaux et la bruyère, sur un sol sablonneux idéal, il a été redessiné par le propriétaire d'alors, Neil Hotchkin, avant d'être cédé à l'English Golf Union qui en a fait son centre d'entraînement national. Il exige d'abord de garder la balle en jeu au départ, afin d'être encore vivant pour affronter quelques-uns des deuxièmes coups les plus difficiles qui soient où il importe d'éviter des bunkers où l'on peut rester longtemps, notamment sur les par 3. Les débutants apprendront beaucoup en portant le sac des chevronnés. Un must.

Woodhall Spa Golf Club — 1905

The Broadway
ENG - WOODHALL SPA, Lincolnshire LN10 6PU

Office	Secrétariat	(44) 01526 - 352 511
Pro shop	Pro-shop	(44) 01526 - 352 511
Fax	Fax	(44) 01526 - 351 817
Web	www.woodhallspagolf.com	
Situation	Situation	Lincoln, 21 km
Annual closure	Fermeture annuelle	no
Weekly closure	Fermeture hebdomadaire	no

Fees main season Tarifs haute saison	18 holes	
	Week days Semaine	**We/Bank holidays** We/Férié
Individual Individuel	£ 65	£ 65
Couple Couple	£ 130	£ 130

Full day: £ 100 / EGU affiliated clubs members: £ 55 and £ 90

Caddie Caddie no — **Electric Trolley** Chariot électrique yes
Buggy Voiturette no — **Clubs** Clubs no

Credit cards Cartes de crédit
VISA - Eurocard - MasterCard - Switch

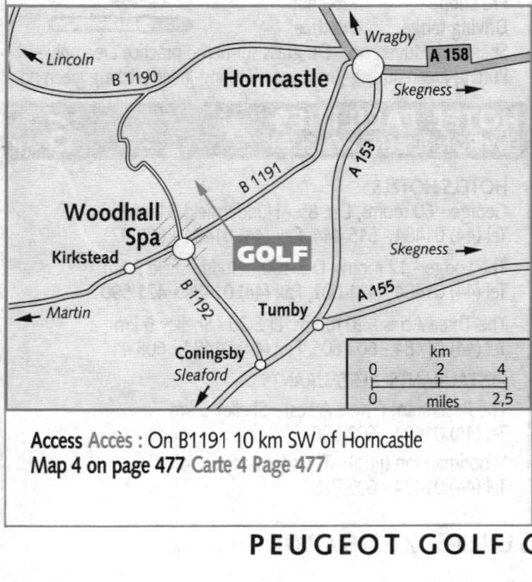

Access Accès : On B1191 10 km SW of Horncastle
Map 4 on page 477 Carte 4 Page 477

GOLF COURSE — PARCOURS — 19/20

Site	Site	
Maintenance	Entretien	
Architect	Architecte	H. S. Colt, H.Vardon, Col. S.V. Hotchkin
Type	Type	inland, heathland
Relief	Relief	
Water in play	Eau en jeu	
Exp. to wind	Exposé au vent	
Trees in play	Arbres en jeu	

Scorecard Carte de score	**Chp.** Chp.	**Mens** Mess.	**Ladies** Da.
Length Long.	6250	5897	5203
Par	73	71	73
Slope system	—	—	—

Advised golfing ability Niveau de jeu recommandé: 0 12 24 36
Hcp required Handicap exigé: 24 Men, 36 Ladies

CLUB HOUSE & AMENITIES — CLUB HOUSE ET ANNEXES — 7/10

Pro shop Pro-shop
Driving range Practice
Sheltered couvert 20 bays (floodlit) - On grass sur herbe no - Putting-green putting-green yes - Pitching-green pitching green yes

HOTEL FACILITIES — ENVIRONNEMENT HOTELIER — 8/10

HOTELS HÔTELS
Golf Hotel - 50 rooms, D from £ 75 - Woodhall Spa 2 km
Tel (44) 01526 - 353 535, Fax (44) 01526 - 353 096
Petwood House Hotel - 53 rooms, D £ 130- Woodhall Spa 2 km
Tel (44) 01526 - 352 411, Fax (44) 01526 - 353 473
Dower House - 9 rooms, D from £ 110 - Woodhall Spa 1 km
Tel (44) 01526 - 352 588, Fax (44) 01526 - 354 045
Washingborough Hall - Lincoln/Washingborough 20 km
12 rooms, D from £ 90
Tel (44) 01522 - 790 340, Fax (44) 01522 - 792 936

RESTAURANTS RESTAURANTS
The Magpies - Horncastle 10 km - Tel (44) 01507 - 527 004
Washingborough Hall - Tel (44) 01522 - 790 340

Woodsome Hall

14 | 7 | 6

The elegant manor which dates back to at least the 16th century is now a club-house that would make the most fitting backdrop to a Hercule Poirot murder investigation. The site is superb with huge oak and beech trees and a dash of rhododendrons, which make this a typical parkland course where neither the terrain nor the hazards are too severe or overdone. This is certainly not an Alwoodley or Ganton, but it is one of those Yorkshire courses where you like to spend a little time without wasting it. It is not a long course but it is a varied test for players who can flight the ball. A few stretches of water pleasantly enhance the landscape and your round but here again, nothing excessive. The architects have laid out a sound course, with James Braid adding a little zest of strategic detail to make this a round of golf you won't grow tired of. A bit of a relaxing day out for the long-hitters but a stern test for golfers who are unaware of, or unable to exploit, the newest technologies in golfing equipment. In other words, the majority.

L'élégant manoir qui remonte au moins au XVIème siècle est devenu un club-house que l'on imagine bien dans quelque enquête d'Hercule Poirot. Le site est superbe, avec de grands chênes et hêtres, une touche de rhododendrons, qui en font un "parkland" typique (avec quelques aspects de landes), où rien n'est exagéré, ni les reliefs, ni les difficultés. Ce n'est sans doute pas Alwoodley ou Ganton, mais c'est l'un des parcours du Yorkshire où l'on aimera passer son temps, sans jamais le perdre. Le parcours n'est pas bien long, mais c'est un test très varié pour les manieurs de balles. Quelques petits cours d'eau agrémentent le paysage et le jeu, mais là encore, rien d'excessif. Les architectes ont créé un dessin solide, James Braid ajoutant le zeste de détails stratégiques qui font que l'on ne se lasse pas de ce parcours. Assez reposant pour les joueurs longs, il offre une belle résistance à ceux qui ne savent pas – ou ne peuvent pas – utiliser au maximum les technologies nouvelles. Ils sont nombreux.

Woodsome Hall Golf Club 1922

Woodsome, Fenay Bridge
ENG - HUDDERSFIELD, West Yorkshire HD8 0LQ

Office	Secrétariat	(44) 01484 - 602 739
Pro shop	Pro-shop	(44) 01484 - 602 034
Fax	Fax	—
Web	www.woodsome.co.uk	
Situation	Situation	Huddersfield, 8 km
Annual closure	Fermeture annuelle	no
Weekly closure	Fermeture hebdomadaire	no

Fees main season Tarifs haute saison	Week days Semaine	We/Bank holidays We/Férié
	18 holes	
Individual Individuel	£ 33	£ 43
Couple Couple	£ 66	£ 86

Full day: £ 43 / 53 (We) / Juniors: £ 15

Caddie Caddie no — **Electric Trolley** Chariot électrique no
Buggy Voiturette no — **Clubs** Clubs no
Credit cards Cartes de crédit
VISA - MasterCard

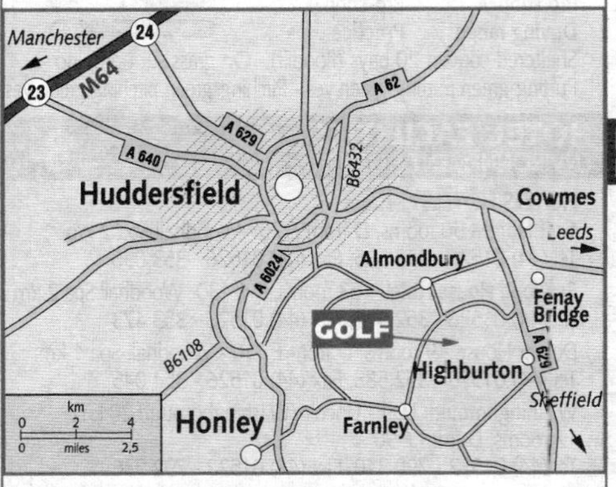

Access Accès : Huddersfield, A629 → Sheffield, turn right → Farnley Tyas/Honley, → Almondbury
Map 4 on page 476 Carte 4 Page 476

GOLF COURSE
PARCOURS — **14**/20

Site	Site	
Maintenance	Entretien	
Architect	Architecte	W. Button James Braid
Type	Type	parkland
Relief	Relief	
Water in play	Eau en jeu	
Exp. to wind	Exposé au vent	
Trees in play	Arbres en jeu	

Scorecard Carte de score	Chp. Chp.	Mens Mess.	Ladies Da.
Length Long.	5545	5260	5068
Par	70	70	73
Slope system	—	—	—

Advised golfing ability Niveau de jeu recommandé — 0 12 24 36
Hcp required Handicap exigé — certificate

CLUB HOUSE & AMENITIES
CLUB HOUSE ET ANNEXES — **7**/10

Pro shop Pro-shop
Driving range Practice
Sheltered couvert no - On grass sur herbe practice area only - Putting-green putting-green yes - Pitching-green pitching green no

HOTEL FACILITIES
ENVIRONNEMENT HOTELIER — **6**/10

HOTELS HÔTELS

George - 60 rooms, D £ 85 - Huddersfield 6 km
Tel (44) 01484 - 515 444, Fax (44) 01484 - 602 971

The Lodge - 12 rooms, D £ 100 - Huddersfield 9 km
Tel (44) 01484 - 431 001, Fax (44) 01484 - 421 590

The Three Acres - 20 rooms, D £ 80 - Shelley 5 km
Tel (44) 01484 - 602 606, Fax (44) 01484 - 608 411

RESTAURANTS RESTAURANTS

The Restaurant (Three Acres) - Shelley 5 km
Tel (44) 01484 - 602 606

Woodman Inn (Pub) - Thunder Bridge 4 km
Tel (44) 01484 - 605 778

Worplesdon

17	7	6

This is the third of the three "Ws" around Woking designed by John Abercromby, who worked with, amongst others, the inimitable Tom Simpson. On arriving you notice the winding first hole and the beautiful houses around the course. You never grow tired of that impression of privilege you get from playing golf over wide open spaces. A watering system has further enhanced green-keeping and the greens are very well defended by steep-sloping, heather framed bunkers which can cause all sorts of problems for high-handicappers who tend to top their sand-wedge shots. Putting surfaces are also very slick, so you'd better stay on the right side of the slopes and the right tier of the multi-tiered greens. If you are looking for a brilliant score, the pin placements here will dictate game strategy. While West Hill and Woking are, in a way, courses where the tee-shot is all-important, Worplesdon calls for excellence on your second shot. Choosing between the three would be like having to refuse the starter, main course or dessert in a good restaurant...

C'est le troisième de la trinité de Woking, cette fois dessiné par John Abercromby, qui a travaillé notamment avec Tom Simpson. En arrivant, on remarque d'une part les méandres du premier trou, et la beauté des maisons environnantes. Comment être insensible à cette sensation de privilège que donne le golf dans de beaux espaces ? Et l'arrosage a fait encore progresser l'entretien. On remarquera d'abord la bonne défense assurée par les bunkers, dont les faces sont assez abruptes et garnies de bruyère pour gêner tous ces amateurs qui ont tendance à topper leurs sorties ! Les greens sont souvent très rapides, ce qui implique d'être du bon côté des pentes et sur le bon plateau. Le placement des drapeaux va en fait dicter toute la stratégie si l'on veut faire un score brillant. Si West Hill et Woking sont, un peu, des parcours de mise en jeu, Worplesdon est un parcours de seconds coups. On ne choisira pas plus qu'on ne refuse l'entrée, le plat ou le dessert dans un bon restaurant...

Worplesdon Golf Club — 1908

Heath House Road
ENG - WOKING, Surrey GU22 0RA

Office	Secrétariat	(44) 01483 - 472 277
Pro shop	Pro-shop	(44) 01483 - 473 287
Fax	Fax	(44) 01483 - 473 303
Web	www.worplesdongc.co.uk	
Situation	Situation	Guildford, 6 km
Annual closure	Fermeture annuelle	no
Weekly closure	Fermeture hebdomadaire	no

Fees main season Tarifs haute saison	18 holes	
	Week days Semaine	**We/Bank holidays** We/Férié
Individual Individuel	£ 60	*
Couple Couple	£ 120	*

* Week-ends: members only / Full week days: £ 80

Caddie Caddie on request **Electric Trolley** Chariot électrique no

Buggy Voiturette no **Clubs** Clubs yes

Credit cards Cartes de crédit
VISA - Eurocard

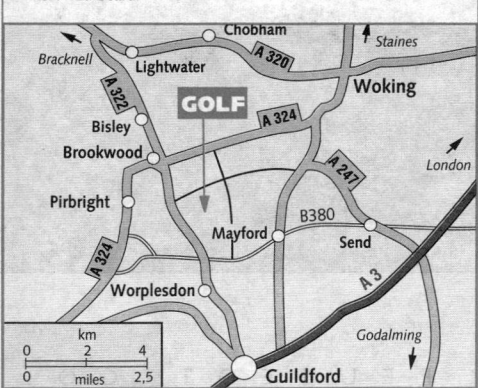

Access Accès : London A3 → Guildford. At Cobham, A245 on right. At Woking, A320 → Guildford, Afeter railway bridge, turn left into Heath House. Golf entrance on right.
Map 8 on page 484 Carte 8 Page 484

GOLF COURSE — PARCOURS 17/20

Site	Site	
Maintenance	Entretien	
Architect	Architecte	John Abercromby
Type	Type	inland, heathland
Relief	Relief	
Water in play	Eau en jeu	
Exp. to wind	Exposé au vent	
Trees in play	Arbres en jeu	

Scorecard Carte de score	**Chp.** Chp.	**Mens** Mess.	**Ladies** Da.
Length Long.	5760	5760	5040
Par	71	71	73
Slope system	—	—	—

Advised golfing ability Niveau de jeu recommandé: 0 12 24 36
Hcp required Handicap exigé: 20 Men, 30 Ladies

CLUB HOUSE & AMENITIES — CLUB HOUSE ET ANNEXES 7/10

Pro shop Pro-shop
Driving range Practice
Sheltered couvert no - On grass sur herbe yes (own balls) - Putting-green putting-green yes - Pitching-green pitching green yes

HOTEL FACILITIES — ENVIRONNEMENT HOTELIER 6/10

HOTELS HÔTELS

Angel Posting House - Guildford 6 km
21 rooms, D £ 150
Tel (44) 01483 - 564 555, Fax (44) 01483 - 533 770

Posthouse Guildford - Guildford 6 km
161 rooms, D from £ 120
Tel (44) 0870 - 400 9036, Fax (44) 01483 - 302 960

The Manor - 45 rooms, D from £ 92- Guildford 6 km
Tel (44) 01483 - 222 624, Fax (44) 01483 - 211 389

RESTAURANTS RESTAURANTS

Drake's Restaurant - Ripley 10 km - Tel (44) 01483 - 224 777
Café de Paris - Guildford 6 km - Tel (44) 01483 - 534 896

SCOTLAND

Dundonald

SCOTLAND

As a country, Scotland is a small in terms of land surface but quite exceptional when it comes to golf, with courses sometimes laid out one after the other in an uninterrupted sequence on either side of the country. There are huge clusters of links courses on both the east and the west coasts of Ayrshire. Here you will also find some lesser known gems not only around Glasgow and Edinburgh but also between Aberdeen and Inverness. But besides the links courses – Scotland's pride and joy – we have also elected a number of inland clubs, some of which have been laid out over areas of immense beauty, for example in the Highlands. Naturally, some people might consider their yardage to be bordering on the "ridiculous" by today's standards, but they are certainly more than a match for your average long-hitter who in many cases is not quite so clever when holding a wedge in his hands.

We could quite easily have included "North Inch" in Perth, a course that was played by King James VI in 1603, or again Askernish on the isle of South Uist, but at the risk of opting for history or unusual surroundings we have kept with Shiskine in Blackwaterfoot. With just 12 holes this is the most untypical of all our choices and in actual fact is the icing on the cake, being the 1001st course in the Peugeot Golf Guide. It remains an amazing reference in course design and for the game of golf. After all, it is always most useful to reiterate the fundamentals of course design or at least recall past references at a time when the temptation from America or influence from the top modern English clubs has pushed green-fees upward, and when golf in Scotland has always been and most of the time always will be a game for everyone. None of the country's 265,000 registered players will argue with that.

After ambitious projects like Loch Lomond, others have followed suit and are included this year, for instance Dundonald, which every day reserves some tee-times to the public at large. Archerfiel on the other hand preferred to be omitted. A lot of money has been invested in these new layouts, but the lure of sunnier climes and changes of season are the same as ever and players have to adapt whatever their means or resources. In Scotland, golf courses have always been created by Mother Nature helped by the genius of a few brilliant architects and golf is a shining light for all. Some courses are snow-bound in Winter, it sometimes rains and the wind can wreak havoc. But while the best time to play is from April to September, you can tee-off virtually all year... just don't forget to pack a few thick sweaters.

You don't come to Scotland the way you would fly to the Caribbean or to play the American way. At Kingsbarns, Kyle Phillips successfully combined as never before the spirit behind links golfing and today's modern techniques. It is another architect, David McLay Kidd who will be extending golfing facilities at the "real" St Andrews with a seventh course. This is not really a links course but we can trust him to uphold the proud traditions of Scotland the Brave.

ÉCOSSE

L'Ecosse est un petit pays en superficie mais un exceptionnel pays de golf, où les 546 parcours peuvent se succéder de manière ininterrompue sur les grandes concentrations de links des côtes Est comme de la côte de l'Ayrshire à l'Ouest. Mais vous trouverez aussi de petites merveilles moins connues, non seulement à proximité de Glasgow et d'Edimbourg, mais aussi d'Aberdeen à Inverness. En dehors des links qui ont fait la gloire de l'Ecosse, nous avons aussi choisi de vous présenter des parcours " inland", dont la plupart ont été comme posés sur des espaces d'une intense beauté, comme dans les Highlands. Bien sûr, on pourra estimer leur longueur parfois désuète, mais en ramener un bon score n'est pas à la portée du premier cogneur venu, souvent bien gauche avec un wedge en mains.

Sans aucun doute, comme nous sommes au cœur du golf, nous aurions presque pu inclure le "North Inch" de Perth, sur un terrain où a joué le roi James VI en 1603, ou encore Askernish dans l'île de South Uist, mais, quitte à être historique ou dépaysant, nous avons maintenu Shiskine à Blackwaterfoot. Avec ses 12 trous, ce parcours est atypique parmi tous nos 18 trous, mais c'est en fait la cerise sur le gâteau, le 1001ème parcours du Peugeot Golf Guide. Et c'est surtout une étonnante référence d'architecture et de jeu, car il n'est pas inutile de rappeler les fondamentaux du dessin de parcours, ou tout au moins les grands témoignages du passé, à l'heure où les fastes à l'américaine ou les grands clubs modernes anglais ont poussé les green-fees vers le haut. Le golf en Ecosse a toujours été un jeu pour tous, et le reste, fort heureusement, la plupart du temps, pour ses 265.000 pratiquants officiels.

Après des réalisations ambitieuses comme Loch Lomond, d'autres ont suivi, qui figurent ici comme Dundonald, qui s'ouvre au public moins d'une heure (de départs) par jour. Archerfiel en revanche a souhaité être ignoré. Beaucoup d'argent est investi dans ces nouvelles réalisations, mais la course du soleil et le rythme des saisons n'ont guère changé, et les joueurs doivent s'y adapter quels que soient leurs moyens. En Ecosse, les golfs ont toujours été faits par la nature et quelques architectes de génie, le soleil du golf brille pour tous, certains parcours sont enneigés en hiver, la pluie tombe parfois, le vent souffle aussi, et si la meilleure saison va d'avril à septembre, on peut jouer pratiquement toute l'année... avec de gros pulls dans la valise.

On vient ici pour jouer au golf, pour respirer le golf, vivre le golf. On ne vient pas en Ecosse comme dans les Caraïbes, ou pour retrouver l'Amérique. A Kingsbarns, Kyle Phillips avait su associer comme jamais l'esprit des links et les techniques de notre temps. C'est un autre architecte, David McLay Kidd qui va élargir l'offre du "vrai" St Andrews avec un septième parcours. Ce ne sera pas vraiment un links, mais on peut lui faire confiance pour maintenir les traditions de panache "d'Ecosse la brave".

Aboyne

14 | 6 | 5

There is no shortage of golf courses in the region of Deeside, each one having its own character often shaped by the setting and original or successive architects. Aboyne is a real park which dates back to the beginning of the 1880s but whose final layout is from the 1990s. On the edge of the course, holes run around a small hill and these slight slopes from the 11th to the 14th holes take us into more rocky countryside. Reassuringly, particularly for your game strategy, the course is free of hidden hazards as no-one likes to fall into that sort of trap the first time they play a new course. There are though just a few elevated or tiered greens that might cause you trouble. Generally speaking, Aboyne is a little similar to Ballater, only with a little more variety in hole layout. The views are as spectacular as the wildlife that has found refuge here.

Cette région du Deeside ne manque pas de parcours de golf, chacun ayant son propre caractère, souvent fonction de l'environnement, mais aussi des architectes originaux ou successifs. Aboyne est un véritable parc sans trop de relief, qui remonte au début des années 1880, mais dont le tracé définitif date des années 1990. A l'extrémité du parcours, les trous tournent autour d'une petite colline et ces quelques reliefs du 11 au 14 nous amènent dans un paysage de lande rocailleuse. Quand on joue un parcours pour la première fois, il n'est pas toujours agréable d'être piégé par des obstacles cachés, mais ici, ce n'est pas le cas, ce qui peut rassurer sur la stratégie à mettre en oeuvre. Seuls quelques greens surélevés, ou à plateau peuvent causer quelques surprises. En règle général, Aboyne est un peu similaire de caractère avec Ballater, mais avec un peu plus de variété de dessin des trous. Les vues sont aussi spectaculaires que la faune qui y a trouvé refuge.

Aboyne Golf Club — 1883

Formaston Park
SCO - ABOYNE, Aberdeenshire AB34 5 HE

Office	Secrétariat	(44) 013398 -870 78
Pro shop	Pro-shop	(44) 013398 -863 28
Fax	Fax	(44) 013398 -875 92
Web	www.aboynegolfclub.co.uk	
Situation	Situation	Aberdeen, 48 km

Banchory (pop. 6 230), 19 km

Annual closure	Fermeture annuelle	no
Weekly closure	Fermeture hebdomadaire	no
Fees main season	Tarifs haute saison	18 holes

	Week days Semaine	We/Bank holidays We/Férié
Individual Individuel	£ 20	£ 40
Couple Couple	£ 40	£ 80

Full days: £ 25 - £ 30 (We)

Caddie Caddie on request **Electric Trolley** Chariot électrique no

Buggy Voiturette yes **Clubs** Clubs yes

Credit cards Cartes de crédit
Eurocard - MasterCard

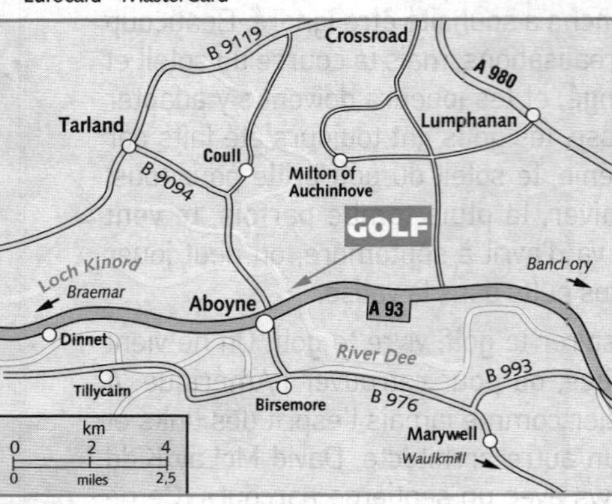

Access Accès : Aberdeen, A93. In Aboyne, turn off to right at club entrance.

Map 1 on page 471 Carte 1 Page 471

GOLF COURSE — PARCOURS — 14/20

Site	Site	
Maintenance	Entretien	
Architect	Architecte	Archie Simpson
Type	Type	parkland
Relief	Relief	
Water in play	Eau en jeu	
Exp. to wind	Exposé au vent	
Trees in play	Arbres en jeu	

Scorecard Carte de score	Chp. Chp.	Mens Mess.	Ladies Da.
Length Long.	5447	5112	4906
Par	68	67	72
Slope system	—	—	—

Advised golfing ability Niveau de jeu recommandé: 0 12 24 36

Hcp required Handicap exigé: no

CLUB HOUSE & AMENITIES — CLUB HOUSE ET ANNEXES — 6/10

Pro shop Pro-shop
Driving range Practice
Sheltered couvert no - On grass sur herbe no - Putting-green putting-green yes - Pitching-green pitching green yes

HOTEL FACILITIES — ENVIRONNEMENT HOTELIER — 5/10

HOTELS HÔTELS
Struan Hall - 3 rooms, D £ 64 - Aboyne, close
Tel (44) 013398 - 87 241, Fax (44) 013398 - 87 241
Hilton Craigendarroch - Ballater 14 km
45 rooms, D £ 150 (w. dinner)
Tel (44) 013397 - 55 858, Fax (44) 013397 - 55 447
Darroch Learg - 12 rooms, D £ 237 (w. dinner) - Ballater 14 km
Tel (44) 013397 - 55 443, Fax (44) 013397 - 55 252

RESTAURANTS RESTAURANTS
The Boat Inn (Pub) - Aboyne close - Tel (44) 01339 - 886 137
Conservatory (Darroch Learg) - Ballater 14 km
Tel (44) 01339 - 755 443
Green Inn - Ballater 14 km - Tel (44) 013397 - 55 701

Alloa

15 | 7 | 5

Alloa is one of a bunch of very good inland courses in Scotland, in a region little known by golfing tourists, or at any rate on the fringe of itineraries proposed by tour operators. You shouldn't pass through here without stopping off and playing this fine course, once again restyled by James Braid. Where hasn't the man left his mark in Scotland? If you are a "collector" of James Braid courses, you will recognize his strategic placing of bunkers denoting an astute knowledge of both the game at the highest level and of average players' abilities, a rare feature from a former champion such as he. While there are courses for driving and courses for approach shots, this one demands both to reach greens which are sometimes elevated and even blind and call for special care. Make a note, too, of the very challenging closing stretch between the 15th and 18th holes, comprising two par 3s and two par 4s, all four of which are very long. This is a hilly course so physical fitness will help.

Alloa fait partie du petit peloton des très bons parcours "inland" d'Ecosse, dans une région assez peu connue des touristes golfiques, en tout cas en marge des circuits de tour-operators. Mais il serait dommage de passer dans les environs sans connaître cette belle réalisation, une fois de plus remaniée par James Braid, mais où celui-ci n'est-il pas intervenu? Si vous "collectionnez" tous ses parcours, vous retrouverez ici un placement stratégique des obstacles, dénotant une connaissance aiguë du jeu au plus haut niveau mais aussi des joueurs moyens, ce qui est plus rare de la part d'un ancien champion comme lui. S'il est des parcours de drives et des parcours de "seconds coups," celui-ci exige autant des départs aux greens, avec une attention particulière pour attaquer ces derniers, parfois surélevés, voire aveugles. A noter aussi, le passage très exigeant du 15 au 18, avec deux longs pars 3 et deux longs pars 4. Le relief du parcours est bien marqué, attention à votre forme physique.

Alloa Golf Club — 1891

Schawpark
SCO - SAUCHIE, Clackmannanshire FK10 3AX

Office	Secrétariat	(44) 01259 - 722 745
Pro shop	Pro-shop	(44) 01259 - 724 476
Fax	Fax	(44) 01259 - 218 796
Web	www.alloagolfclub.co.uk	
Situation	Situation	Dunfermline, 24 km
Annual closure	Fermeture annuelle	no
Weekly closure	Fermeture hebdomadaire	no

Fees main season Tarifs haute saison	18 holes	
	Week days Semaine	We/Bank holidays We/Férié
Individual Individuel	£ 26	£ 30
Couple Couple	£ 52	£ 60

Full days: £ 36 - £ 40 (We)

Caddie Caddie no — **Electric Trolley** Chariot électrique yes
Buggy Voiturette no — **Clubs** Clubs no
Credit cards Cartes de crédit
VISA - Eurocard - MasterCard - AMEX - DC

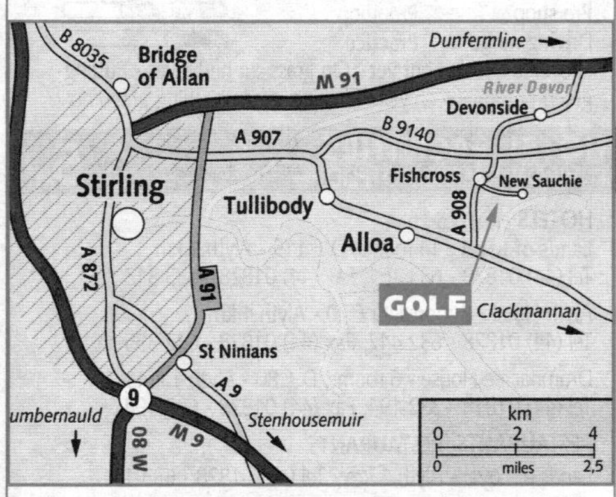

Access Accès : Edinburgh, A90, A907 to Dunfermline and Alloa. Turn right onto A908. course on the right in the village of Sauchie.
Map 2 on page 473 Carte 2 Page 473

GOLF COURSE — PARCOURS — 15/20

Site	Site	
Maintenance	Entretien	
Architect	Architecte	James Braid
Type	Type	parkland
Relief	Relief	
Water in play	Eau en jeu	
Exp. to wind	Exposé au vent	
Trees in play	Arbres en jeu	

Scorecard Carte de score	Chp. Chp.	Mens Mess.	Ladies Da.
Length Long.	5610	5395	4910
Par	70	69	73
Slope system	—	—	—

Advised golfing ability Niveau de jeu recommandé — 0 12 24 36
Hcp required Handicap exigé — no

CLUB HOUSE & AMENITIES — CLUB HOUSE ET ANNEXES — 7/10

Pro shop Pro-shop
Driving range Practice
Sheltered couvert no - On grass sur herbe yes - Putting-green putting-green yes - Pitching-green pitching green yes

HOTEL FACILITIES — ENVIRONNEMENT HOTELIER — 5/10

HOTELS HÔTELS
Dunmar House Hotel - 9 rooms, D £ 65 - Alloa 5 km
Tel (44) 01259 - 214 339, Fax (44) 01259 - 210 970
Park Lodge - 9 rooms, D £ 95 - Stirling 12 km
Tel (44) 01786 - 474 862, Fax (44) 01786 - 449 748
Ashgrove House - Stirling 12 km
3 rooms, D £ 80
Tel (44) 01786 - 472 640, Fax (44) 01786 - 472 640

RESTAURANTS RESTAURANTS
Olivia's Restaurant - Stirling 12 km - Tel (44) 01786 - 446 277
Unicorn Inn - Kincardine 6 km - Tel (44) 01259 - 730 704

Alyth

14	6	5

Within the immediate vicinity of Blairgowrie, Dundee and Perth, the Alyth course does not have the fame it deserves, partly because fame today comes through hosting top tournaments. This course now is too short for that but is way above average in terms of appeal, enhanced further by such a quiet location. With good, well protected greens, endless trees and heather edging the fairways and dangerous bunkers, Alyth requires great accuracy more than distance off the tee and is ideal for getting your ironwork into good shape. Hole N°5 in particular has its fair share of difficulties with two ditches and OB. A number of other very good holes and some superb views over the Perthshire countryside add extra appeal to a guaranteed good day's golfing without too much suffering. The region of Angus also offers a variety facilities for leisure and excursions.

A proximité immédiate de Blairgowrie, Dundee et Perth, le parcours d'Alyth n'a pas connu la notoriété qu'il mérite, en partie parce qu'elle se fait aujourd'hui en accueillant de grands tournois alors que celui-ci est resté dans l'ombre. Certes, ce parcours est aujourd'hui trop court pour les très grandes épreuves, mais son intérêt est nettement au-dessus de la moyenne et sa situation tranquille ajoute au plaisir. Avec de bons greens correctement défendus contre les assauts, des arbres nombreux et la bruyère bordant les fairways, des bunkers dangereux, il demande une grande précision plus que de la distance au drive, et c'est idéal pour travailler son jeu de fers. On notera en particulier les difficultés du 5, avec deux fossés et un hors-limites. D'autres très bons trous et des vues superbes sur la campagne du Perthshire ajoutent un intérêt supplémentaire à une bonne journée de golf garantie sans souffrances. Et cette région de l'Angus offre de multiples opportunités de loisirs et d'excursions.

Alyth Golf Club — 1894

Pitcrocknie
SCO - ALYTH, Perthshire PH10 7AB

Office	Secrétariat	(44) 01828 - 632 268
Pro shop	Pro-shop	(44) 01828 - 633 411
Fax	Fax	(44) 01828 - 633 491
Web	www.alythgolfclub.co.uk	
Situation	Situation	Blairgowrie, 5 km

Dundee (pop. 165 873), 24 km

Annual closure	Fermeture annuelle	nc
Weekly closure	Fermeture hebdomadaire	nc
Fees main season	Tarifs haute saison	18 holes

	Week days / Semaine	We/Bank holidays / We/Férié
Individual Individuel	£ 22	£ 30
Couple Couple	£ 44	£ 60

Full day: £ 33 / £ 45 (We)

Caddie Caddie on request **Electric Trolley** Chariot électrique yes
Buggy Voiturette yes **Clubs** Clubs no
Credit cards Cartes de crédit no

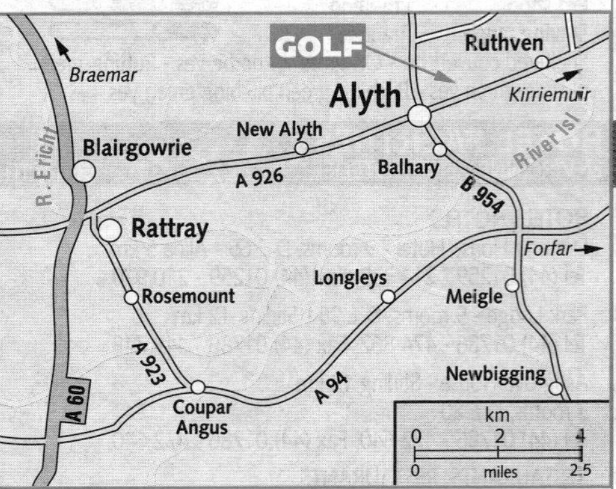

Access Accès : Edinburgh M90, Exit 11 → Perth, then A94 through Coupar to Meigle. Turn right on B954. Golf 1.5 km (1 m.) before Alyth.
Map 1 on page 471 Carte 1 Page 471

GOLF COURSE / PARCOURS — 14/20

Site	Site	
Maintenance	Entretien	
Architect	Architecte	Tom Morris, James Braid
Type	Type	heathland
Relief	Relief	
Water in play	Eau en jeu	
Exp. to wind	Exposé au vent	
Trees in play	Arbres en jeu	

Scorecard Carte de score	Chp. Chp.	Mens Mess.	Ladies Da.
Length Long.	5646	5409	4770
Par	70	70	71
Slope system	—	—	—

Advised golfing ability Niveau de jeu recommandé: 0 12 24 36
Hcp required Handicap exigé: certificate

CLUB HOUSE & AMENITIES / CLUB HOUSE ET ANNEXES — 6/10

Pro shop Pro-shop
Driving range Practice
Sheltered couvert not yet - **On grass** sur herbe yes - **Putting-green** putting-green yes - **Pitching-green** pitching green no

HOTEL FACILITIES / ENVIRONNEMENT HOTELIER — 5/10

HOTELS HÔTELS
Lands of Loyal - 14 rooms, D £ 119 - Alyth 1 km
Tel (44) 01828 - 633 151, Fax (44) 01828 - 633 313

Alyth Hotel - 8 rooms, D £ 70 - Alyth 1 km
Tel (44) 01828 - 632 447, Fax (44) 01828 - 632 355

Drumnacree House - 6 rooms, D £ 80 - Alyth 1 km
Tel (44) 01828 - 632 194, Fax (44) 01828 - 632 194

RESTAURANTS RESTAURANTS
Lands of Loyal - Alyth 1 km - Tel (44) 01828 - 633 151
Roundhouse restaurant - Bridgend of Lintrathen 8 km
Tel (44) 01575 - 560 340

Ayr (Belleisle)

16 | 5 | 7

Most of the visitors to this region head for Prestwick, Royal Troon and Turnberry and might easily neglect a number of little gems of which this is a typical example. Designed by James Braid (who else?) in 1927 to meet the huge demand for new courses, Belleisle was laid out in a public park close to the sea but without the features of a links. This is nonetheless a challenging course with a lot of character where there is something almost odd about the views over the sea in the setting of trees. With no hidden dangers, golfing can be enjoyed without fear as long as you choose the right clubs and the right way of playing them. The weather will decide whether you aim high or low, but beware the long par 4s and the meanders of Curtecan Burn. An ideal course for week-end golfing when the "big" courses are too crowded, too exclusive or too expensive...

La plupart des visiteurs de la région se concentrent sur Prestwick, Royal Troon et Turnberry, et risquent de négliger quelques petits joyaux de moindre réputation. En voici un exemple typique. Dessiné par James Braid en 1927 pour satisfaire une demande galopante de nouveaux parcours, Belleisle a été créé dans un parc public proche de la mer, mais sans les caractéristiques des links. Il n'empêche qu'il s'agit d'un parcours exigeant, avec beaucoup de caractère, où certains points de vue sur l'eau ont quelque chose d'étrange dans cet environnement d'arbres. Sans dissimuler aucun de ses dangers, ce parcours peut être immédiatement dégusté sans crainte, du moment que l'on y choisit à la fois les bons clubs et la bonne manière de s'en servir. Suivant le temps, on pourra y jouer balles roulées ou balles levées, en se méfiant des longs pars 4 et des méandres du Curtecan Burn. Idéal pour jouer en week-end quand les "grands" sont trop encombrés, très difficiles d'accès, ou beaucoup trop chers pour un budget limité.

Belleisle Golf Course — 1927

Belleisle Park, Doonfoot Road
SCO - AYR, Ayrshire KA7 4DU

Office	Secrétariat	(44) 01292 - 441 258
Pro shop	Pro-shop	(44) 01292 - 441 314
Fax	Fax	(44) 01292 - 442 632
Web	www.golfsouthayrshire.com	
Situation	Situation	Ayr (pop. 47 872), 1 km
Annual closure	Fermeture annuelle	no
Weekly closure	Fermeture hebdomadaire	no

Fees main season Tarifs haute saison	18 holes	
	Week days Semaine	**We/Bank holidays** We/Férié
Individual Individuel	£ 18,5	£ 20
Couple Couple	£ 37	£ 40

Full days: £ 26 - £ 30 (We)

Caddie Caddie on request **Electric Trolley** Chariot électrique no

Buggy Voiturette no **Clubs** Clubs yes

Credit cards Cartes de crédit
VISA - Eurocard - MasterCard

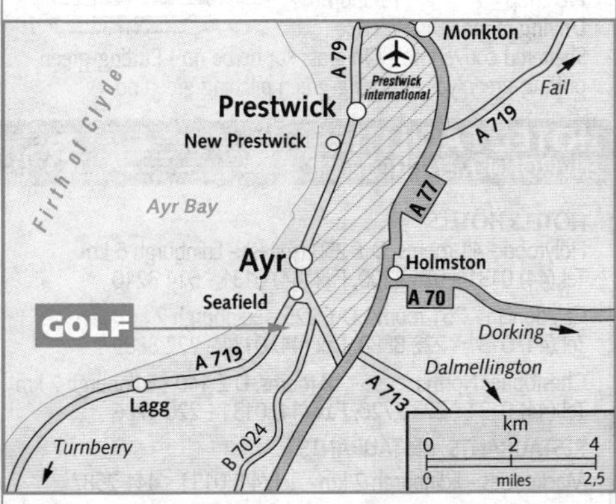

Access Accès : 1 km south of Ayr in Belleisle Park
Map 3 on page 474 Carte 3 Page 474

GOLF COURSE — PARCOURS — 16/20

Site	Site	
Maintenance	Entretien	
Architect	Architecte	James Braid
Type	Type	parkland
Relief	Relief	
Water in play	Eau en jeu	
Exp. to wind	Exposé au vent	
Trees in play	Arbres en jeu	

Scorecard Carte de score	**Chp.** Chp.	**Mens** Mess.	**Ladies** Da.
Length Long.	5855	5509	5150
Par	71	71	74
Slope system	—	—	—

Advised golfing ability Niveau de jeu recommandé — 0 12 24 36

Hcp required Handicap exigé — no

CLUB HOUSE & AMENITIES — CLUB HOUSE ET ANNEXES — 5/10

Pro shop Pro-shop

Driving range Practice

Sheltered couvert no - On grass sur herbe yes - Putting-green putting-green yes - Pitching-green pitching green no

HOTEL FACILITIES — ENVIRONNEMENT HOTELIER — 7/10

HOTELS HÔTELS

Fairfield House - 44 rooms, D £ 175 - Ayr 3 km
Tel (44) 01292 - 267 461, Fax (44) 01292 - 261 456

Savoy Park - 15 rooms, D £ 75 - Ayr 2 km
Tel (44) 01292 - 266 112, Fax (44) 01292 - 611 488

Brig O'Doon - 5 rooms, D £ 120 - Alloway 2 km
Tel (44) 01292 - 442 466, Fax (44) 01292 - 441 999

RESTAURANTS RESTAURANTS

Fouters - Ayr 3 km - Tel (44) 01292 - 261 391

Fleur de Lys (Fairfield House) - Ayr 3 km
Tel (44) 01292 - 267 461

Baberton

14 | 6 | 8

While the family is visiting Edinburgh or doing some shopping, you'll have the time and clear conscience to play 18 holes at Baberton to the south-west of the city. This is where the first steel shafts were invented, and the originals complete with patents are still kept in the club-house. Created in 1893 and designed by the great Wille Park Jr., this is no longer a tournament course but some of the par 4s and par 3s are anything but easy. Without being really dangerous, the trees, bunkers and ditches are in play just enough to bother average players, who make up the major share of green-feers here during the week. The trees are particularly beautiful especially in their Autumn colours, when we visited. Don't be surprised if you're late getting back, as the club-house extends a warm welcome to all. The best idea would be for the family to come and meet you here in a club where Sky TV commentator and excellent golfer Ewan Murray learnt how to play.

Pendant que la famille fait du shopping ou visite Edimbourg, à quelques kilomètres,vous avez la conscience tranquille et tout votre temps pour faire 18 trous à Baberton, au sud-ouest de la ville. C'est ici qu'est né le manche de club en acier, dont les originaux et les brevets sont conservés au club-house. Fondé en 1893 et dessiné par le grand Willie Park Jr., ce n'est plus aujourd'hui un parcours de championnat, bien que certains de ses par 4 et ses cinq par 3 ne soient pas des plus faciles. Sans être vaiment dangereux, les arbres, les bunkers et les fossés sont assez en jeu pour inquiéter le joueur moyen, qui fournit l'essentiel de la clientèle extérieure en semaine. Les arbres sont ici particulièrement beaux, spécialement dans leurs teintes d'automne. Et si vous êtes en retard pour rejoindre les vôtres, vous avez une excuse, le club-house est accueillant. En fait, la bonne idée, c'est de vous donner rendez-vous directement ici, dans un club où a été formé l'excellent joueur et commentateur sur Sky TV Ewan Murray.

Baberton Golf Club — 1893

50 Baberton Avenue, Juniper Green
SCO - EDINBURGH EH14 5DU

Office	Secrétariat	(44) 0131 - 453 4911
Pro shop	Pro-shop	(44) 0131 - 453 3555
Fax	Fax	(44) 0131 - 453 4678
Web	www.baberton.co.uk	
Situation	Situation	Edinburgh, 9 km
Annual closure	Fermeture annuelle	no
Weekly closure	Fermeture hebdomadaire	no

Fees main season Tarifs haute saison	18 holes	
	Week days Semaine	**We/Bank holidays** We/Férié
Individual Individuel	£ 22	£ 25
Couple Couple	£ 44	£ 50

Full day: £ 32 / £ 35 (We)

Caddie Caddie no — **Electric Trolley** Chariot électrique no

Buggy Voiturette no — **Clubs** Clubs yes

Credit cards Cartes de crédit no

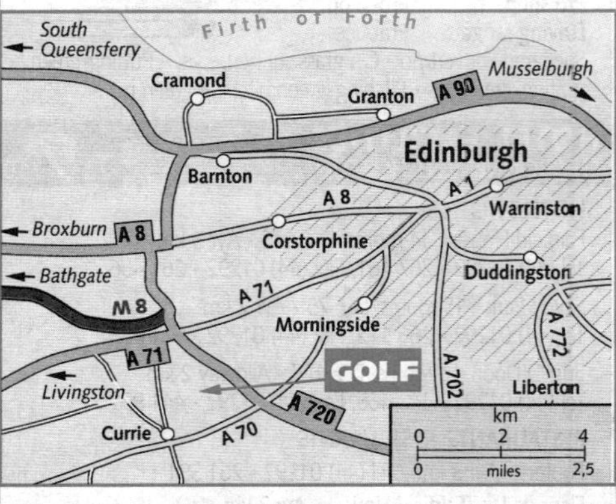

Access Accès : Edinburgh A70 Slateford Road and Lanark Road until by-pass (A720), Juniper Green and Baberton Junction.
Map 3 on page 475 Carte 3 Page 475

GOLF COURSE — PARCOURS — 14/20

Site	Site	
Maintenance	Entretien	
Architect	Architecte	Willie Park Jr.
Type	Type	parkland
Relief	Relief	
Water in play	Eau en jeu	
Exp. to wind	Exposé au vent	
Trees in play	Arbres en jeu	

Scorecard Carte de score	Chp. Chp.	Mens Mess.	Ladies Da.
Length Long.	5617	5347	5034
Par	69	69	72
Slope system	—	—	—

Advised golfing ability Niveau de jeu recommandé — 0 12 24 36

Hcp required Handicap exigé — no

CLUB HOUSE & AMENITIES — CLUB HOUSE ET ANNEXES — 6/10

Pro shop Pro-shop
Driving range Practice
Sheltered couvert no - On grass sur herbe no - Putting-green putting-green yes - Pitching-green pitching green no

HOTEL FACILITIES — ENVIRONNEMENT HOTELIER — 8/10

HOTELS HÔTELS

Holyrood - 41 rooms, D £ 250 (suites) - Edinburgh 5 km
Tel (44) 0131 - 524 3200, Fax (44) 0131 - 524 3210

Caledonian - 251 rooms, D £ 225 - Edinburgh 7 km
Tel (44) 0131 - 222 8888, Fax (44) 0131 - 222 8889

Christopher North House - 18 rooms, D £ 140 - Edinburgh 7 km
Tel (44) 0131 - 225 2720, Fax (44) 0131 - 220 4706

RESTAURANTS RESTAURANTS

Mackenzies - Edinburgh 2 km - Tel (44) 0131 - 441 2587

Indian Cavalry Club - Edinburgh 5 km
Tel (44) 0131 - 228 3282

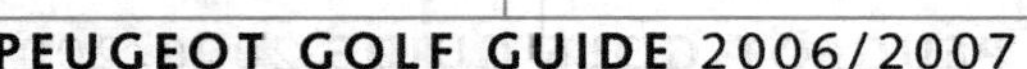

Ballater

15	6	6

Here we are just a few miles from Balmoral Castle, the Royal Family's summer residence, in a very beautiful region of the Highlands surrounded by hills along the banks of the river Dee, which borders the course and collects many a mis-hit golf ball. The area is more popular for tourism than golf, or even for fishing or hunting from Spring to late Autumn only, as at 2,000 ft. above sea level the winter weather always has the final say. The course is rather hilly especially with the slopes created by streams (river terraces running along the ancient flood plain) but it is never too exhausting to walk on a soft carpet of grass, which winds its way through heather, broom and trees. James Braid and Harry Vardon added their personal touch to a very pleasant layout, where the land has been used very intelligently. This may not be the world's most difficult course but playing here certainly is time well spent.

Nous ne sommes qu'à quelques kilomètres du château de Balmoral, la résidence d'été de la famille royale, dans une très belle région des Highlands entourée de collines, en bordure de la rivière Dee qui sert de limite au parcours et recueille bien des balles égarées. On vient généralement ici davantage pour le tourisme que pour le golf, très souvent pour la pêche et la chasse, à partir du printemps et jusqu'à la fin de l'automne, car nous sommes tout de même à 600 mètres d'altitude et l'hiver peut être précoce. Les reliefs du parcours sont assez prononcés, en particulier avec les ondulations créées par les cours d'eau (soit des terrasses qui parcourent l'ancien lit majeur), mais l'ensemble n'est pas épuisant, grâce à un gazon très fourni, insinué dans la bruyère, les genêts et les arbres. James Braid et Harry Vardon ont apporté leur touche personnelle à un dessin très agréable, où le terrain a été utilisé avec beaucoup d'à-propos. Ce n'est peut-être pas le parcours le plus difficile du monde, mais on n'y perdra jamais son temps.

Ballater Golf Club — 1892

Victoria Road
SCO - BALLATER, Aberdeenshire AB35 5QX

Office	Secrétariat	(44) 013397 - 55 567
Pro shop	Pro-shop	(44) 013397 - 55 658
Fax	Fax	—
Web	www.ballatergolfclub.co.uk	
Situation	Situation	Aberdeen, 67 km
Annual closure	Fermeture annuelle	no
Weekly closure	Fermeture hebdomadaire	no

Chances of snow in winter months

Fees main season Tarifs haute saison — 18 holes

	Week days / Semaine	We/Bank holidays / We/Férié
Individual Individuel	£ 23	£ 27
Couple Couple	£ 46	£ 54

Full day: £ 30 / £ 38 (We)

Caddie Caddie on request **Electric Trolley** Chariot électrique yes

Buggy Voiturette yes **Clubs** Clubs yes

Credit cards Cartes de crédit
VISA - MasterCard - Switch

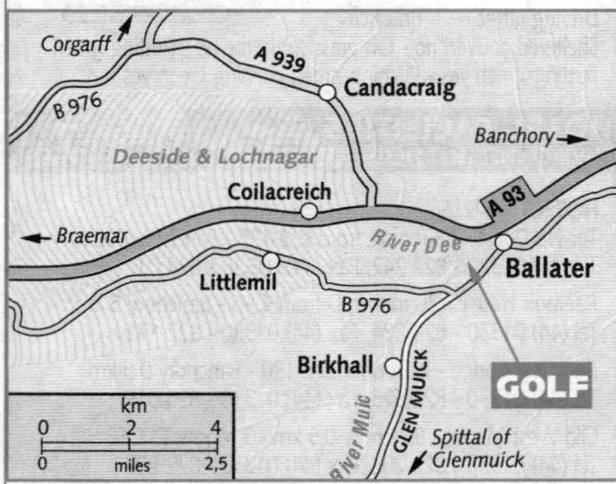

Access Accès : Aberdeen, A93 West → Ballater, Balmoral Castle
Map 1 on page 471 Carte 1 Page 471

GOLF COURSE — PARCOURS — 15/20

Site	Site	
Maintenance	Entretien	
Architect	Architecte	James Braid, H. Vardon
Type	Type	parkland
Relief	Relief	
Water in play	Eau en jeu	
Exp. to wind	Exposé au vent	
Trees in play	Arbres en jeu	

Scorecard Carte de score	Chp. Chp.	Mens Mess.	Ladies Da.
Length Long.	5638	5545	5278
Par	70	70	71
Slope system	—	—	—

Advised golfing ability Niveau de jeu recommandé — 0 12 24 36
Hcp required Handicap exigé — no

CLUB HOUSE & AMENITIES — CLUB HOUSE ET ANNEXES — 6/10

Pro shop	Pro-shop
Driving range	Practice

Sheltered couvert no - On grass sur herbe no - Putting-green putting-green no - Pitching-green pitching green no

HOTEL FACILITIES — ENVIRONNEMENT HOTELIER — 6/10

HOTELS HÔTELS
Hilton Craigendarroch - Ballater
45 rooms, D £ 150 (w. dinner)
Tel (44) 013397 - 55 858, Fax (44) 013397 - 55 447

Darroch Leargh - 18 rooms, D £ 237 (w. dinner) - Ballater
Tel (44) 01339 - 755 443, Fax (44) 01339 - 755 252

Balgonie Country House - 9 rooms, D £ 140 - Ballater
Tel (44) 01339 - 755 482, Fax (44) 01339 - 755 482

RESTAURANTS RESTAURANTS
Oaks - Ballater - Tel (44) 013397 - 55 858
Green Inn - Ballater - Tel (44) 013397 - 55 701
Conservatory (Darroch Leargh) - Ballater
Tel (44) 01339 - 755 443

Banchory

14 | 7 | 7

Starting out from Aberdeen, the A93 runs up the Grampian mountains alongside the river Dee. You won't be alone in making this climb, the salmon have been doing it for centuries, as you will probably see from the Brigg O'Feugh, an 18th century bridge on the edge of the village of Banchory. The splendours of Royal Deeside include this golf course, which lies right alongside the river. Recently remodelled by Scottish golf course architect John Souter, this is a combination of wide open space and tree-lined fairways. Big-hitting is not always an essential virtue on this ideal holiday course, but the par 3s are long (except the 16th) and tricky. The best is certainly hole N°12 (180 yards/162 metres) with OB to the left and a burn in front of the green. There are also half a dozen or so short par 4s that are fun to play. Non-golfers have lots to do in this region and can even take an indiscreet look at Balmoral Castle, the Queen's summer residence.

En partant d'Aberdeen, la A93 s'enfonce dans les Grampians, en longeant la rivière Dee. Vous ne serez pas seul à remonter, les saumons le font aussi depuis des siècles, comme on peut les apercevoir du Brigg o'Feugh, un pont du XVIIIè siècle en limite du village de Banchory. Parmi les splendeurs du Royal Deeside, ce parcours qui longe la rivière, récemment remanié par l'architecte écossais John Souter, il associe les espaces ouverts avec des fairways bordés d'arbres. La force de frappe n'est pas une qualité obligatoire sur ce parcours idéal pour des vacances, mais les par 3 sont longs (sauf le 16) et délicats. Le meilleur d'entre eux est sans doute le 12, de 162 mètres (180 yards), avec hors-limites à gauche et un "burn" devant le green. On remarquera aussi une demi-douzaine de courts par 4 très amusants. Quant aux non golfeurs, ils ne manqueront pas de sources d'intérêt dans cette région, et jetteront un coup d'œil indiscret sur le Château de Balmoral, résidence d'été de la Reine.

Banchory Golf Club — 1905

Kinneskie Road
SCO - BANCHORY AB31 5TA

Office	Secrétariat	(44) 01330 - 822 365
Pro shop	Pro-shop	(44) 01330 - 822 447
Fax	Fax	(44) 01330 - 822 491
Web	www.banchorygolfclub.co.uk	
Situation	Situation	Aberdeen, 29 km
Annual closure	Fermeture annuelle	no
Weekly closure	Fermeture hebdomadaire	no

Fees main season Tarifs haute saison — 18 holes

	Week days / Semaine	We/Bank holidays / We/Férié
Individual Individuel	£ 22	£ 22
Couple Couple	£ 44	£ 44

Full day: £ 30

Caddie Caddie no — **Electric Trolley** Chariot électrique yes

Buggy Voiturette yes — **Clubs** Clubs yes

Credit cards Cartes de crédit yes

Access Accès : Aberdeen, A93, Golf in village centre.

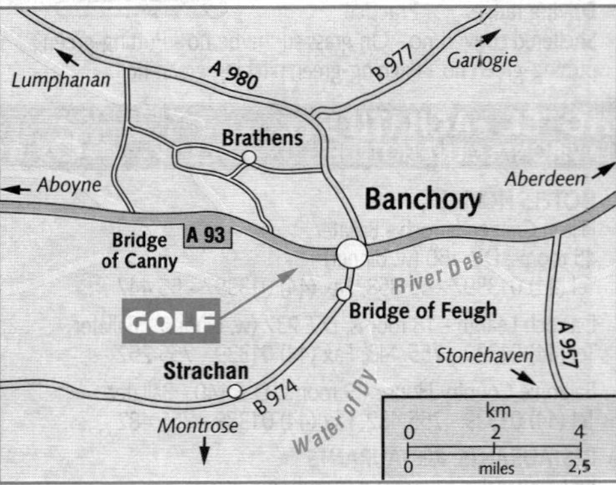

Map 1 on page 471 Carte 1 Page 471

GOLF COURSE — PARCOURS — 14/20

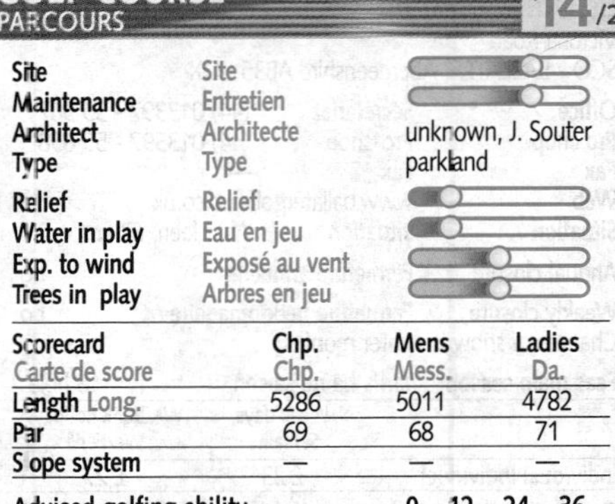

Site	Site	
Maintenance	Entretien	
Architect	Architecte	unknown, J. Souter
Type	Type	parkland
Relief	Relief	
Water in play	Eau en jeu	
Exp. to wind	Exposé au vent	
Trees in play	Arbres en jeu	

Scorecard / Carte de score	Chp. / Chp.	Mens / Mess.	Ladies / Da.
Length Long.	5286	5011	4782
Par	69	68	71
Slope system	—	—	—

Advised golfing ability — Niveau de jeu recommandé: 0 12 24 36

Hcp required — Handicap exigé: no

CLUB HOUSE & AMENITIES — CLUB HOUSE ET ANNEXES — 7/10

Pro shop Pro-shop
Driving range Practice

Sheltered couvert no - On grass sur herbe no - Putting-green putting-green yes - Pitching-green pitching green yes

HOTEL FACILITIES — ENVIRONNEMENT HOTELIER — 7/10

HOTELS HÔTELS

Tor-Na-Coille - 23 rooms, from D £ 125 - Banchory 500 m
Tel (44) 01330 - 822 242, Fax (44) 01330 - 824 012

Raemoir House - 20 rooms, D from £ 95 - Banchory 5 km
Tel (44) 01330 - 824 884, Fax (44) 01330 - 822 171

Banchory Lodge - 22 rooms, D £ 130 - Banchory 0.5 km
Tel (44) 01330 - 822 625, Fax (44) 01330 - 825 019

Old West Manse - Banchory 0,5 km - 3 rooms, D £ 60
Tel (44) 01330 - 822 202, Fax (44) 01330 - 822 202

RESTAURANTS RESTAURANTS

The Milton - Crathes 6 km - Tel (44) 01330 - 844 566
Watsons - Banchory 500 m - Tel (44) 01330 - 822 242

Blairgowrie *Lansdowne*

15 | 8 | 6

In a magnificent and highly reputed resort located in some of Scotland's finest countryside, this course designed by Thomas and Alliss in 1974 brought a welcome alternative to the famous Rosemount course. There is of course a definite American influence in this layout spread over very flat and thickly treed landscape (pine and silver birch in particular). The fairways are narrow and then the heather makes things a little more complicated on either side, but the designers have often left a few open corridors to the greens to make things easier for Scottish golfers who are not always experts at lofting the ball. We would have liked a little more breathing space for the tee-shot, as players who are neither too long nor too straight will have a tough time if they choose to play from the back tees. The course has aged well even though some might find this still just a touch artificial.

Dans ce magnifique ensemble d'excellente réputation, situé dans un des très beaux paysages d'Ecosse, ce parcours de Dave Thomas et Peter Alliss a apporté en 1974 une alternative bienvenue au fameux Rosemount Course. Bien sûr, on trouve une certaine influence américaine dans leur dessin tracé dans un paysage très plat, généreusement boisé (surtout des pins et des bouleaux argentés). Les fairways sont étroits, la bruyère complique ensuite les choses de part et d'autre, mais les architectes ont souvent laissé quelques passages en ouverture des greens pour faciliter le travail des joueurs écossais pas toujours habitués aux balles levées. On aimerait parfois une plus grande sensation d'espace au moment de driver, car les joueurs ni très longs, ni très droits souffriront s'ils choisissent les départs reculés. Le parcours a bien vieilli, mais on peut toujours le trouver un rien artificiel.

Blairgowrie Golf Club — 1974

Rosemount
SCO - BLAIRGOWRIE, Perthshire PH10 6LG

Office Secrétariat (44) 01250 - 872 622
Pro shop Pro-shop (44) 01250 - 873 116
Fax Fax (44) 01250 - 875 451
Web www.theblairgowriegolfclub.co.uk
Situation Situation Perth, 35 km

Annual closure Fermeture annuelle no
Weekly closure Fermeture hebdomadaire no

Fees main season Tarifs haute saison	18 holes	
	Week days / Semaine	We/Bank holidays / We/Férié
Individual Individuel	£ 50	£ 50
Couple Couple	£ 100	£ 100

Day ticket for a round on both courses: £ 80

Caddie Caddie on request **Electric Trolley** Chariot électrique yes
Buggy Voiturette yes **Clubs** Clubs yes
Credit cards Cartes de crédit
VISA - Eurocard - MasterCard

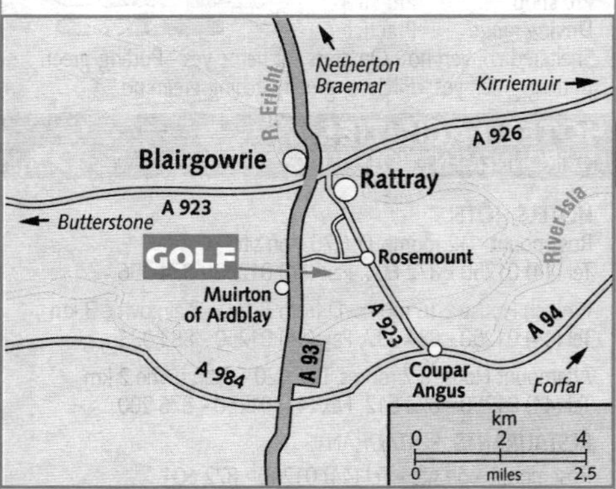

Access Accès : Edinburgh M90 to Perth, then A93 → Blairgowrie (golf 2 km South of Blairgowrie)
Map 1 on page 471 Carte 1 Page 471

GOLF COURSE — PARCOURS 15/20

Site Site
Maintenance Entretien
Architect Architecte Dave Thomas, Peter Alliss
Type Type heathland, inland
Relief Relief
Water in play Eau en jeu
Exp. to wind Exposé au vent
Trees in play Arbres en jeu

Scorecard / Carte de score	Chp. / Chp.	Mens / Mess.	Ladies / Da.
Length Long.	6290	5805	5420
Par	72	71	73
Slope system	—	—	—

Advised golfing ability Niveau de jeu recommandé 0 12 24 36
Hcp required Handicap exigé 28 Men, 36 Ladies

CLUB HOUSE & AMENITIES — CLUB HOUSE ET ANNEXES 8/10

Pro shop Pro-shop
Driving range Practice
Sheltered couvert no - On grass sur herbe yes - Putting-green putting-green yes - Pitching-green pitching green no

HOTEL FACILITIES — ENVIRONNEMENT HOTELIER 6/10

HOTELS HÔTELS
Rosemount - 12 rooms, D £ 70 - on site
Tel (44) 01250 - 872 604, Fax (44) 01250 - 874 496

Kinloch House - 16 rooms, D from £ 150 - Blairgowrie 3 km
Tel (44) 01250 - 884 237, Fax (44) 01250 - 884 333

Altamount House - 7 rooms, D £ 120 - Blairgowrie 2 km
Tel (44) 01250 - 873 512, Fax (44) 01250 - 876 200

RESTAURANTS RESTAURANTS
Rosemount - on site - Tel (44) 01250 - 872 604
Altamount House (book before) - Blairgowrie 2 km
Tel (44) 01250 - 873 512

Blairgowrie *Rosemount*

18 | 8 | 6

For many golfers this is one of the best British inland courses. It's a pity they had to sacrifice two or three holes to cater to the building of the Lansdowne course but James Braid had already altered the original layout by Alister MacKenzie. Despite this, Rosemount has lost nothing of its charm and of the marvellous feeling of tranquillity you get when playing here, as each hole is clearly separated from the others by a thick row of trees. The wildlife and flora add to the beauty of the spot, particularly in Autumn, and to this excellent course where you need to play in every direction. Beneath its kindly exterior, Rosemount cleverly conceals perhaps not the hazards but at least its difficulties, like for example hole N° 17, a superb par 3. And as it is never tiring to play, it is worth more than the one visit. The course has hosted a great many top tournaments in its time and it was here that Greg Norman recorded his first win on the European Tour in 1977.

C'est pour beaucoup de connaisseurs l'un des meilleurs parcours "inland" de Grande-Bretagne. On regrette un peu que deux ou trois trous aient été sacrifiés au moment de la construction du Lansdowne Course, mais James Braid avait déjà retouché auparavant le travail original d'Alister MacKenzie. Rosemount n'a rien perdu pour autant de son charme, et de la merveilleuse sensation de paix qu'on y éprouve, chaque trou étant nettement séparé des autres par d'épais rideaux d'arbres. La vie sauvage et la flore ajoutent encore à la beauté du lieu, notamment en automne. Qui plus est, c'est un excellent parcours où il faut savoir jouer dans tous les sens, et qui cache bien sous des dehors souriants, sinon ses obstacles, du moins ses difficultés, comme au 17, un superbe par 3 par exemple. Comme Rosemount n'est pas non plus fatigant à jouer, il mérite bien mieux qu'une simple visite. D'ailleurs, il a reçu de nombreux tournois, et fut notamment le cadre de la première victoire de Greg Norman sur le circuit européen, en 1977...

Blairgowrie Golf Club — 1889

Rosemount
SCO - BLAIRGOWRIE, Perthshire PH10 6LG

Office Secrétariat (44) 01250 - 872 622
Pro shop Pro-shop (44) 01250 - 873 116
Fax Fax (44) 01250 - 875 451
Web www.theblairgowriegolfclub.co.uk
Situation Situation Perth, 35 km
Annual closure Fermeture annuelle no
Weekly closure Fermeture hebdomadaire no

Fees main season Tarifs haute saison	18 holes	
	Week days Semaine	**We/Bank holidays** We/Férié
Individual Individuel	£ 65	£ 65
Couple Couple	£ 130	£ 130

Day ticket for a round on both courses: £ 80

Caddie Caddie on request **Electric Trolley** Chariot électrique yes
Buggy Voiturette yes **Clubs** Clubs yes
Credit cards Cartes de crédit
VISA - Eurocard - MasterCard

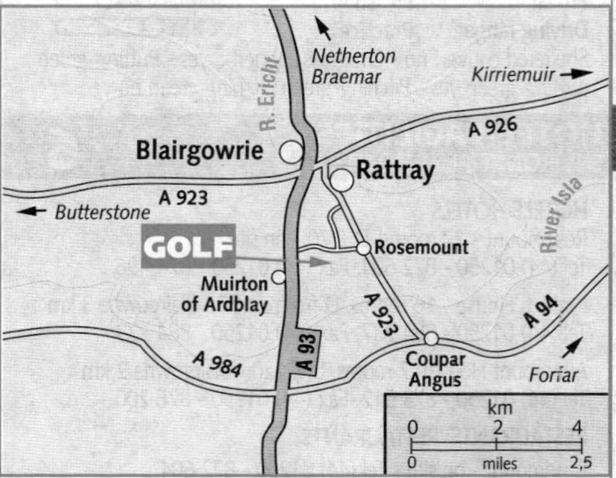

Access Accès : Edinburgh M90 to Perth, then A93 → Blairgowrie (golf 2 km South of Blairgowrie)
Map 1 on page 471 Carte 1 Page 471

GOLF COURSE — PARCOURS 18/20

Site Site
Maintenance Entretien
Architect Architecte Alister Mackenzie, James Braid
Type Type heathland, inland
Relief Relief
Water in play Eau en jeu
Exp. to wind Exposé au vent
Trees in play Arbres en jeu

Scorecard Carte de score	**Chp.** Chp.	**Mens** Mess.	**Ladies** Da.
Length Long.	6014	5693	5445
Par	72	70	74
Slope system	—	—	—

Advised golfing ability Niveau de jeu recommandé 0 12 24 36
Hcp required Handicap exigé 28 Men, 36 Ladies

CLUB HOUSE & AMENITIES — CLUB HOUSE ET ANNEXES 8/10

Pro shop Pro-shop
Driving range Practice
Sheltered couvert no - On grass sur herbe yes - Putting-green putting-green yes - Pitching-green pitching green no

HOTEL FACILITIES — ENVIRONNEMENT HOTELIER 6/10

HOTELS HÔTELS
Rosemount - 12 rooms, D £ 70 - on site
Tel (44) 01250 - 872 604, Fax (44) 01250 - 874 496

Kinloch House - 16 rooms, D from £ 150 - Blairgowrie 3 km
Tel (44) 01250 - 884 237, Fax (44) 01250 - 884 333

Altamount House - 7 rooms, D £ 120 - Blairgowrie 2 km
Tel (44) 01250 - 873 512, Fax (44) 01250 - 876 200

RESTAURANTS RESTAURANTS
Rosemount - on site - Tel (44) 01250 - 872 604
Altamount House (book before) - Blairgowrie 2 km
Tel (44) 01250 - 873 512

Boat of Garten

14 | 6 | 6

Within the immediate vicinity of a wildlife reserve designed to protect white-tailed eagles and just a few miles down the road from the ski resort of Aviemore (where the steam train is a popular attraction), Boat of Garten is a sort of gateway to the Cairngorms, with splendid views and some of the highest peaks in the UK. The flora and fauna in this region are well worth the trip anyway, but the local distilleries are also popular with visitors. The golf course winds its way through gently undulating heath-land but is easy to walk, and its overall excellence makes it more than just an added distraction or excuse to admire the spectacular vistas. The rolling fairways often present hanging lies in the manner of seaside golf courses. James Braid's layout is first class and the 6th hole is one of the most memorable in all of Scottish golf. It's the perfect holiday course, as the many foreign tourists who have discovered it, almost by accident, know so very well.

A proximité immédiate d'une réserve naturelle créée pour protéger les orfraies, et à quelques kilomètres de la station de ski d'Aviemore, reliée par un charmant train à vapeur, Boat of Garten est une sorte de porte d'entrée dans les Cairngorns (avec des vues splendides), qui figurent parmi les plus hautes montagnes de Grande-Bretagne. La flore et la faune de cette région valent largement le déplacement, mais les distilleries locales sont tout aussi appréciées par les visiteurs. Facile à jouer à pied, le parcours de Boat of Garten se déroule dans un site aimablement accidenté mais sans excès, et sa qualité générale en fait plus qu'une distraction annexe ou un prétexte à admirer de spectaculaires panoramas. Les fairways présentent souvent des ondulations dignes des golfs de bord de mer, et le dessin de James Braid est globalement de première qualité, notamment au 6, l'un des meilleurs trous de toute l'Ecosse. Un parcours de vacances, mais de bonnes vacances. Les touristes étrangers qui l'ont découvert presque par hasard le savent bien.

Boat of Garten Golf Club — 1932

SCO - BOAT OF GARTEN, Inverness-shire PH24 3BQ

Office Secrétariat (44) 01479 - 831 282
Pro shop Pro-shop (44) 01479 - 831 282
Fax Fax (44) 01479 - 831 523
Web www.boatgolf.com
Situation Situation Inverness, 48 km
Aviemore, 8 km
Annual closure Fermeture annuelle 1/11→1/4
Weekly closure Fermeture hebdomadaire no

Fees main season Tarifs haute saison 18 holes

	Week days Semaine	We/Bank holidays We/Férié
Individual Individuel	£ 30	£ 35
Couple Couple	£ 60	£ 70

Full day: £ 40 - £ 45 (We)

Caddie Caddie on request **Electric Trolley** Chariot électrique yes
Buggy Voiturette yes **Clubs** Clubs yes
Credit cards Cartes de crédit
VISA - MasterCard - Delta - JCB

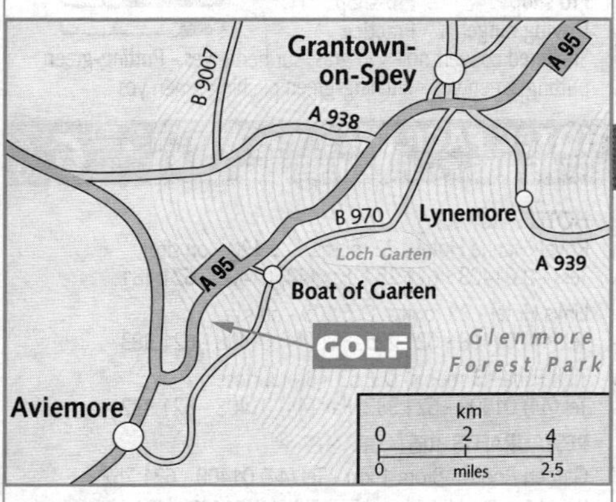

Access Accès : Inverness, A9 and A95. 12 km North of Aviemore. Follow signs to village.
Map 1 on page 471 Carte 1 Page 471

GOLF COURSE — PARCOURS 14/20

Site Site
Maintenance Entretien
Architect Architecte James Braid
Type Type heathland
Relief Relief
Water in play Eau en jeu
Exp. to wind Exposé au vent
Trees in play Arbres en jeu

Scorecard Carte de score	Chp. Chp.	Mens Mess.	Ladies Da.
Length Long.	5373	5165	4707
Par	70	70	72
Slope system	—	—	—

Advised golfing ability Niveau de jeu recommandé 0 12 24 36
Hcp required Handicap exigé certificate

CLUB HOUSE & AMENITIES — CLUB HOUSE ET ANNEXES 6/10

Pro shop Pro-shop
Driving range Practice
Sheltered couvert no - On grass sur herbe no - Putting-green putting-green yes - Pitching-green pitching green yes

HOTEL FACILITIES — ENVIRONNEMENT HOTELIER 6/10

HOTELS HÔTELS

The Boat Hotel - 26 rooms, D from £ 120 - Boat of Garten 1 km
Tel (44) 01479 - 831 258, Fax (44) 01479 - 831 414

Muckrach Lodge - Dulnain Bridge 3 km
14 rooms, D from £ 130
Tel (44) 01479 - 851 257, Fax (44) 01479 - 851 325

Auchendean Lodge - 5 rooms, D £ 98 - Dulnain Bridge 3 km
Tel (44) 01479 - 851 347

RESTAURANTS RESTAURANTS

The Boat Hotel - Boat of Garten 1 km
Tel (44) 01479 - 831 258

Muckrach Lodge - Dulnain Bridge 3 km
Tel (44) 01479 - 851 257

Brora

15 | 7 | 6

This course is found no further than the end of the world, a little after Dornoch and Golspie, where the length of the days in summer could almost let you play all three in the same day. Brora is one of the great traditional links, fine-tuned in 1924 after a design by James Braid. Electric fences (fixed obstructions) protect all the greens from the sheep employed to keep the grass cropped. The tee-boxes and greens are often elevated, built between dunes of between 5 and 12 metres high, and the texture of the turf is particularly pleasant, especially for putting. Although rather short, Brora is not an easy course, even though sometimes you might prefer slightly more penalizing rough (especially for the guys you're playing with) and the par 3s run in all directions and so call for careful thought. This is a club of perfect hospitality, with some spectacular views (hole N°2 for example) and where the 19th hole is both reward and consolation. More should be said about this side of Brora to people who are not curious enough to come and discover the course.

Ce n'est pas plus loin que le bout du monde, un peu après Dornoch et Golspie, là où la longueur des journées de début d'été vous permettraient presque de jouer les trois le même jour. Brora est un des grands links traditionnels, peaufiné en 1924 d'après un dessin de James Braid. Des clôtures électriques (obstructions inamovibles) préservent chaque green des moutons chargés de tondre. Les départs et greens sont souvent surélevés, construits entre des dunes de 5 à 12 mètres de haut, la texture du gazon particulièrement agréable, notamment au putting. Bien qu'assez court, Brora n'est pas un parcours facile, même si l'on souhaiterait parfois (pour ses adversaires !) un rough plus pénalisant, et les pars 3 vont dans toutes les directions, ce qui oblige à la réflexion. Un club à la parfaite hospitalité, avec des vues superbes (du 2 par exemple), où le 19ème trou est à la fois récompense et consolation, dont on aimera parler à ceux qui ne sont pas assez curieux pour connaître ce parcours.

Brora Golf Club — 1891

Golf Road
SCO - BRORA, Highland KW9 6QS

Office	Secrétariat	(44) 01408 - 621 417
Pro shop	Pro-shop	(44) 01408 - 621 473
Fax	Fax	(44) 01408 - 622 157
Web	www.broragolf.co.uk	
Situation	Situation	Inverness, 85 km
Annual closure	Fermeture annuelle	no
Weekly closure	Fermeture hebdomadaire	no

Fees main season Tarifs haute saison — 18 holes

	Week days / Semaine	We/Bank holidays / We/Férié
Individual Individuel	£ 30	£ 35
Couple Couple	£ 60	£ 70

Second round on the same day: £ 5

Caddie Caddie on request **Electric Trolley** Chariot électrique yes

Buggy Voiturette yes **Clubs** Clubs yes

Credit cards Cartes de crédit
VISA - Access - Delta

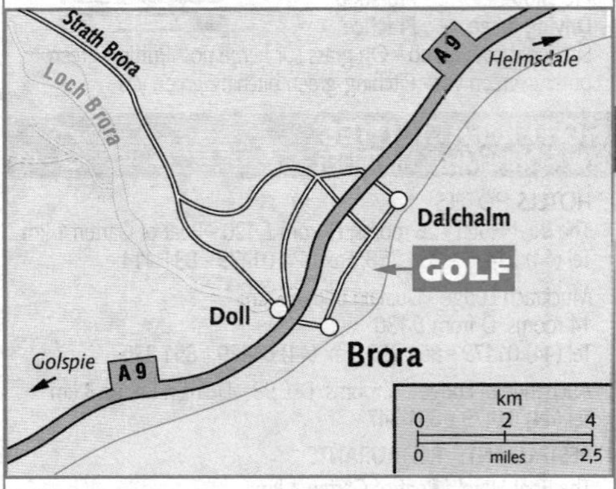

Access Accès : Inverness, A9 to the North
Map 1 on page 471 Carte 1 Page 471

GOLF COURSE — PARCOURS 15/20

Site	Site	
Maintenance	Entretien	
Architect	Architecte	James Braid
Type	Type	links
Relief	Relief	
Water in play	Eau en jeu	
Exp. to wind	Exposé au vent	
Trees in play	Arbres en jeu	

Scorecard / Carte de score	Chp. / Chp.	Mens / Mess.	Ladies / Da.
Length Long.	5499	5285	4746
Par	69	69	70
Slope system	—	—	—

Advised golfing ability / Niveau de jeu recommandé: 0 12 24 36

Hcp required Handicap exigé: no

CLUB HOUSE & AMENITIES — CLUB HOUSE ET ANNEXES 7/10

Pro shop Pro-shop
Driving range Practice
Sheltered couvert no - On grass sur herbe yes - Putting-green putting-green yes - Pitching-green pitching green yes

HOTEL FACILITIES — ENVIRONNEMENT HOTELIER 6/10

HOTELS HÔTELS

Royal Marine Hotel - 22 rooms, D £ 120 - on site
Tel (44) 01408 - 621 252, Fax (44) 01408 - 621 181

Links Hotel - 22 rooms, D £ 100 - on site
Tel (44) 01408 - 621 225, Fax (44) 01408 - 621 383

Tigh Fada - 3 rooms, D £ 53 - Brora, close
Tel (44) 01408 - 621 332, Fax (44) 01408 - 621 332

RESTAURANTS RESTAURANTS

Garden Room - Brora 1 km - Tel (44) 01408 - 621 252
Royal Marine Hotel - on site - Tel (44) 01408 - 621 252
Brora Golf Club - on site - Tel (44) 01408 - 621 417

Bruntsfield

15 | 8 | 8

For many continental Europeans, playing golf virtually in town is a unique experience. This club used to be right in the middle of Edinburgh but has since moved to the outskirts, where space is a little less cramped and some magnificent views are to be had over the Firth of Forth. Willie Park and the great Alistair Mackenzie are responsible for a very pleasant layout at the edge of some hills but where steep slopes were avoided, reviewed and altered by Hawtree between 1972 and 1974. This park-style course is generally in excellent condition with immaculate fairways and greens which, although not over-sized, are contoured in sometimes the most disconcerting way. In addition to traditional bunkers, trees are often a dangerous hazard if you play without thinking. This course is a good test for everyone before they square up to more formidable ordeals on either side of the Forth. Of special note: the top-notch green-keeping, a warm welcome from members and an excellent restaurant.

Pour bien des continentaux, jouer au golf quasiment en ville est une expérience unique. Ce club était autrefois en plein milieu d'Edimbourg, mais il a émigré à la périphérie, moins à l'étroit, mais en bénéficiant ainsi de vues magnifiques sur le Firth of Forth. Willie Park et le grand Alister Mackenzie sont responsables d'un tracé très plaisant, en bordure de collines, mais où les fortes pentes ont été évitées, revu et corrigé par Hawtree de 1972 à 1974. Ce véritable parc est généralement en excellente condition, avec des fairways impeccables et des greens pas très vastes, mais aux modelages parfois déconcertants. En plus des bunkers traditionnels, les arbres constituent souvent des obstacles dangereux, si l'on ne réfléchit pas assez. C'est un bon test pour tous, avant d'affronter des adversaires plus redoutables, d'un côté ou de l'autre du Forth. A signaler enfin, la qualité de l'entretien et de l'accueil des membres, l'excellence du restaurant.

Bruntsfield Links Golfing Society — 1898

32 Barnton Avenue
SCO - EDINBURGH EH4 6JH

Office Secrétariat (44) 0131 - 336 1479
Pro shop Pro-shop (44) 0131 - 336 4050
Fax Fax (44) 0131 - 336 5538
Web www.sol.co.uk/b/bruntsfieldlinks
Situation Situation Edinburgh, 5 km
Annual closure Fermeture annuelle no
Weekly closure Fermeture hebdomadaire no

Fees main season Tarifs haute saison	18 holes	
	Week days Semaine	**We/Bank holidays** We/Férié
Individual Individuel	£ 42	£ 47
Couple Couple	£ 84	£ 94

Full day: £ 60 - £ 65 (We)

Caddie Caddie no — **Electric Trolley** Chariot électrique no
Buggy Voiturette yes — **Clubs** Clubs yes
Credit cards Cartes de crédit
VISA - MasterCard (Pro Shop only)

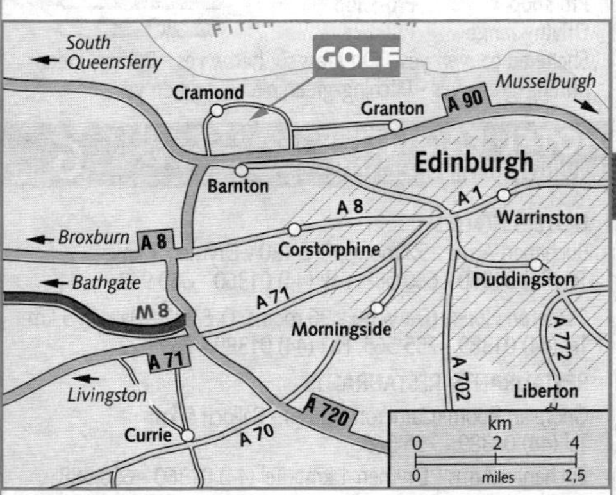

Access Accès : Edinburgh centre, A90 West (Queenferry Road) Right into Quality St and Crammond Road South, then left into Barnton Avenue.
Map 3 on page 475 Carte 3 Page 475

GOLF COURSE — PARCOURS — 15/20

Site Site
Maintenance Entretien
Architect Architecte — Willie Park, Alister Mackenzie
Type Type — parkland
Relief Relief
Water in play Eau en jeu
Exp. to wind Exposé au vent
Trees in play Arbres en jeu

Scorecard Carte de score	**Chp.** Chp.	**Mens** Mess.	**Ladies** Da.
Length Long.	5830	5560	5007
Par	71	70	70
Slope system	—	—	—

Advised golfing ability Niveau de jeu recommandé — 0 12 24 36
Hcp required Handicap exigé 36

CLUB HOUSE & AMENITIES — CLUB HOUSE ET ANNEXES — 8/10

Pro shop Pro-shop
Driving range Practice
Sheltered couvert members only - On grass sur herbe members only Putting-green putting-green yes - Pitching-green pitching green yes

HOTEL FACILITIES — ENVIRONNEMENT HOTELIER — 8/10

HOTELS HÔTELS
The Howard - 18 rooms, D from £ 220 - Edinburgh 3 km
Tel (44) 0131 - 557 3500, Fax (44) 0131 - 557 6515

The Roxburghe - 198 rooms, D £ 210 - Edinburgh 3 km
Tel (44) 0131 - 240 5500, Fax (44) 0131 - 240 5555

Lodge - 10 rooms, D £ 125 - Edinburgh 5 km
Tel (44) 0131 - 337 3682, Fax (44) 0131 - 313 1700

RESTAURANTS RESTAURANTS
The Melrose (Roxburghe) - Edinburgh 3 km
Tel (44) 0131 - 240 5500
Restaurant Martin Wishart - Edimbourg 6 km
Tel (44) 0131 - 553 3557

Buchanan Castle

14 | 6 | 6

While Donald Ross or Tom Simpson might define their designer art as the straight hole, James Braid prefers the dog-leg. Here on the former training grounds for the horses of the Dukes of Montrose, Braid designed a good dozen of them. They have been shortened somewhat since to cater to members who found the layout a little too long and difficult – there were eight par 5s at the time. The site is almost flat and so easy on the legs, but keep away from the thick rough, which looks harmless enough but can be really sticky in wet weather. The river Endrick, although theoretically out of reach for normal shots (although that was not always the case), seems to attract balls like a magnet and it is true that your average hacker is pretty good at going where he never wanted to. Since this course is close to Loch Lomond, Scotland's most private course, come and dream here. You will be made most welcome.

Si l'aboutissement de l'art de Donald Ross ou de Tom Simpson en tant qu'architectes, c'est le trou rectiligne, celui de James Braid, c'est le dog-leg. Ici, sur les anciennes pistes d'entraînement des chevaux des Ducs de Montrose, il en a dessiné une bonne douzaine. Un peu raccourcis depuis, car on estimait que son tracé était trop long et trop difficile pour les membres, il y avait alors huit pars 5 ! Le terrain est pratiquement plat, ce qui le rend facile à marcher, mais il vaut mieux ne pas se risquer dans les roughs, apparemment anodins, mais très difficiles quand le temps est à la pluie. Mais rien n'oblige à y aller ! La rivière Endrick est théoriquement hors de portée des coups normaux (ce ne fut pas toujours le cas), mais elle semble avoir un effet magnétique, tant il est vrai que les golfeurs moyens réussissent surtout à aller là où ils ne veulent pas aller. Comme ce parcours est proche de Loch Lomond, le club le plus fermé d'Ecosse, venez rêver ici, vous serez les bienvenus.

Buchanan Castle Golf Club — 1936

SCO - DRYMEN, Glasgow G63 0HY

Office	Secrétariat	(44) 01360 - 660 307
Pro shop	Pro-shop	(44) 01360 - 660 330
Fax	Fax	(44) 01360 - 660 993
Web	www.buchanancastlegolfclub.com	
Situation	Situation	Glasgow, 29 km
Annual closure	Fermeture annuelle	no
Weekly closure	Fermeture hebdomadaire	no

Fees main season Tarifs haute saison — 18 holes

	Week days Semaine	We/Bank holidays We/Férié
Individual Individuel	£ 38	£ 48
Couple Couple	£ 76	£ 96

We: ask before coming / Full day: £ 48
(We on request)

Caddie Caddie no **Electric Trolley** Chariot électrique on request

Buggy Voiturette yes **Clubs** Clubs yes

Credit cards Cartes de crédit no

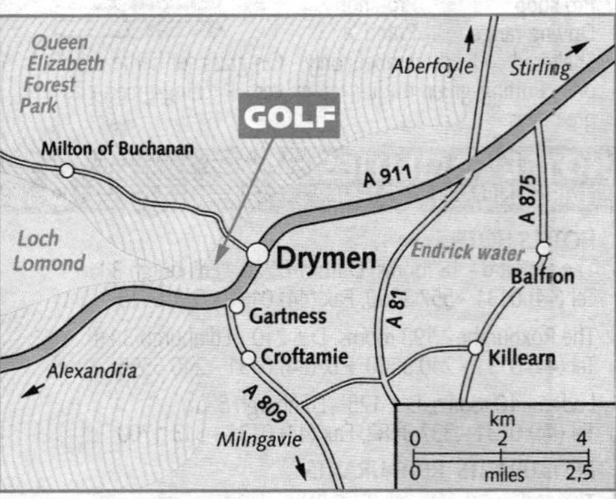

Access Accès : Glasgow, A81 to Milngavie, then A809, A811, off the A811 → Drymen, Golf just South of Drymen.

Map 2 on page 472 Carte 2 Page 472

GOLF COURSE — PARCOURS — 14/20

Site	Site	
Maintenance	Entretien	
Architect	Architecte	James Braid
Type	Type	parkland
Relief	Relief	
Water in play	Eau en jeu	
Exp. to wind	Exposé au vent	
Trees in play	Arbres en jeu	

Scorecard Carte de score	Chp. Chp.	Mens Mess.	Ladies Da.
Length Long.	5529	5157	4786
Par	70	68	71
Slope system	—	—	—

Advised golfing ability Niveau de jeu recommandé — 0 12 24 36

Hcp required Handicap exigé — 26 Men, 36 Ladies

CLUB HOUSE & AMENITIES — CLUB HOUSE ET ANNEXES — 6/10

Pro shop Pro-shop
Driving range Practice

Sheltered couvert yes - On grass sur herbe yes - Putting-green putting-green yes - Pitching-green pitching green yes

HOTEL FACILITIES — ENVIRONNEMENT HOTELIER — 6/10

HOTELS HÔTELS

Buchanan Arms - 52 rooms, D £ 130 - Drymen 1 km
Tel (44) 01360 - 660 588, Fax (44) 01360 - 660 943

Cameron House (De Vere) - 96 rooms, D £ 242 - Balloch 5 km
Tel (44) 01389 - 755 565, Fax (44) 01389 - 759 522

RESTAURANTS RESTAURANTS

Georgian Room (Cameron House) - Balloch 5 km
Tel (44) 01389 - 755 565

Buchanan Arms - Drymen 1 km - Tel (44) 01360 - 660 588

Breakers (Cameron House) - Balloch 5 km
Tel (44) 01360 - 755 565

Burntisland

14	6	6

The club was founded in 1797 but the course dates back to the end of the 19th century. Laid out by Willie Park Jr., it was restyled by the inevitable James Braid. At the time, this was one of the few courses to open on a Sunday. Built on a little hill overlooking the Firth of Forth, it is still very walkable but a number of elevated greens call for very careful club selection. Likewise, the natural topography has been used with great skill, as you might expect from the afore-mentioned architects. Besides the many links courses along the coast leading up to Saint Andrews, Burntisland provides the alternative of a parkland style which is highly satisfactory to look at and to play. A candidly open course when the wind stays away, it can turn nasty when the weather gets rough, as all the holes seem to be laid out in different directions. So on a windy day this is a good test for technique and for your nerves. The club-house is modern, functional and unpretentious with a warm welcome.

Le Club a été fondé en 1797 mais le parcours date de la fin du XIXème siècle. Tracé par Willie Park Jr., il a été remanié par l'inévitable James Braid. A l'époque, c'était l'un des seul parcours du pays ouvert le dimanche. Il est construit sur une petite colline dominant le Firth of Forth, mais reste tout à fait jouable à pied. Cependant, quelques greens en élévation exigent un choix de club très exact. De même, les contours du terrain ont été utilisés avec beaucoup de savoir-faire, comme on peut l'attendre de tels architectes. A côté des nombreux links de la côte menant jusqu'à St Andrews, Burntisland offre l'alternative d'une esthétique "parkland" très satisfaisante visuellement et golfiquement. Assez franc quand il n'y pas de vent, ce parcours peut devenir plus méchant s'il souffle, car les trous changent sans cesse d'orientation. C'est alors un bon test pour la technique et les nerfs. Le club-house est moderne, fonctionnel et sans prétention, l'accueil chaleureux.

Burntisland Golf House — 1898

Dodhead
SCO - BURNTISLAND, Fife KY3 9HS

Office	Secrétariat	(44) 01592 - 874 093
Pro shop	Pro-shop	(44) 01592 - 872 116
Fax	Fax	(44) 01592 - 873 247
E-mail	wktbghc@ aol.com	
Situation	Situation	Edinburgh, 35 km
Annual closure	Fermeture annuelle	no
Weekly closure	Fermeture hebdomadaire	no
Fees main season	Tarifs haute saison	18 holes

	Week days Semaine	We/Bank holidays We/Férié
Individual Individuel	£ 25	£ 35
Couple Couple	£ 50	£ 70

Full days: £ 35 / £ 40 (We)

Caddie Caddie on request **Electric Trolley** Chariot électrique yes

Buggy Voiturette yes **Clubs** Clubs yes

Credit cards Cartes de crédit
VISA - MasterCard - JCB

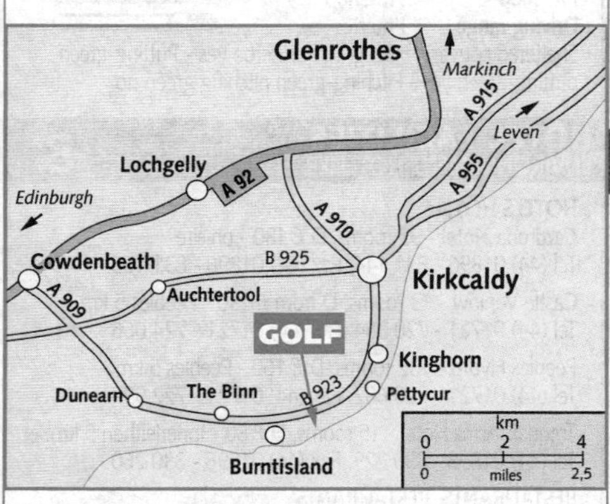

Access Accès : Edinburgh, M90 Jct 1, A921 → Kirkcaldy, Golf on B923, 1.5 km (1 m.) East of Burntisland.
Map 3 on page 475 Carte 3 Page 475

GOLF COURSE — PARCOURS — 14/20

Site	Site	
Maintenance	Entretien	
Architect	Architecte	Willie Park Jr.
Type	Type	parkland
Re,lief	Relief	
Water in play	Eau en jeu	
Exp. to wind	Exposé au vent	
Trees in play	Arbres en jeu	

Scorecard Carte de score	Chp. Chp.	Mens Mess.	Ladies Da.
Length Long.	5430	5020	4635
Par	70	69	70
Slope system	—	—	—

Advised golfing ability Niveau de jeu recommandé: 0 12 24 36
Hcp required Handicap exigé: certificate

CLUB HOUSE & AMENITIES — CLUB HOUSE ET ANNEXES — 6/10

Pro shop	Pro-shop
Driving range	Practice

Sheltered couvert no - On grass sur herbe no - Putting-green putting-green yes - Pitching-green pitching green yes

HOTEL FACILITIES — ENVIRONNEMENT HOTELIER — 6/10

HOTELS HÔTELS

Kingswood - 12 rooms, D from £ 85 - Burntisland 1.5 km
Tel (44) 01592 - 872 329, Fax (44) 01592 - 873 123

Balbirnie House - 30 rooms, D £ 190 - Markinch, Leven 15 km
Tel (44) 01592 - 610 066, Fax (44) 01592 - 610 529

Rescobie - 10 rooms, D £ 100 - Leslie 15 km
Tel (44) 01592 - 749 555, Fax (44) 01592 - 620 231

Garvock House - 12 rooms, D £ 120 - Dunfermline 15 km
Tel (44) 01383 - 621 067, Fax (44) 01383 - 621 168

RESTAURANTS RESTAURANTS

Rescobie - Leslie 15 km - Tel (44) 01592 - 749 555

Kingswood - Burntisland 1.5 km - Tel (44) 01592 - 872 329

Cardrona

17 | 7 | 8

The Borders of Scotland have always been a slightly arid region of the Home of Golf in terms of the number of courses available to the visitor. However, the balance has been significantly redressed by the opening of The Roxburghe and now the new Cardrona Golf & Country Club near Peebles. Set in the heart of spectacular rolling countryside with the famous salmon river, the Tweed, snaking its way through the layout, this Dave Thomas design is a very welcome addition to Scotland's inventory of very fine courses. It is a part parkland, part woodland setting and mostly flat with the layout of the holes following the run of the river. It is a course very much in harmony with its surroundings and, with large and cleverly contoured greens, an excellent challenge for all levels of players. Cardrona is part of a 100 bedroom Macdonald hotel, leisure club, spa and outdoor activity centre and a perfect base not only for golf but fishing and hill walking.

Cette région des Borders, au sud d'Edimbourg, a toujours été une sorte de désert dans la patrie du golf, en termes de nombre de parcours. Cependant, l'équilibre a commencé à se rétablir avec l'ouverture de The Roxburghe et à présent de ce nouveau Cardrona Golf & Country Club près de Peebles. Situé au cœur d'un paysage spectaculaire et légèrement mouvementé, parcouru par la Tweed, fameuse rivière à saumons, ce tracé de Dave Thomas est une addition bienvenue à l'inventaire des bons parcours d'Ecosse. En partie dans un parc, en partie dans les bois, il est généralement plat, les trous suivant le cours de la rivière. Ce parcours épouse le paysage environnant avec un grand souci d'harmonie et, avec des greens bien dimensionnés et dessinés avec intelligence, c'est un excellent "adversaire" pour les joueurs de tous niveaux. On trouve sur le site un hôtel Macdonald de 100 chambres, un club de loisirs, un spa et des activités multiples : c'est idéal aussi bien pour le golf que pour la pêche ou les balades dans la campagne et les collines.

Cardrona Hotel, Golf & Country Club — 2001

SCO - CARDRONA, Peebles, EH45 6LZ

Office	Secrétariat	(44) 01896 - 833 600
Pro shop	Pro-shop	(44) 01896 - 833 701
Fax	Fax	(44) 01896 - 831 166
Web	www.cardrona-hotel.com	
Situation	Situation	Edinburgh, 38 km
Annual closure	Fermeture annuelle	no
Weekly closure	Fermeture hebdomadaire	no

Fees main season Tarifs haute saison	18 holes	
	Week days Semaine	We/Bank holidays We/Férié
Individual Individuel	£ 50	£ 70
Couple Couple	£ 100	£ 140

Caddie Caddie no — **Electric Trolley** Chariot électrique no

Buggy Voiturette yes — **Clubs** Clubs yes

Credit cards Cartes de crédit
VISA - Eurocard - AMEX - DC

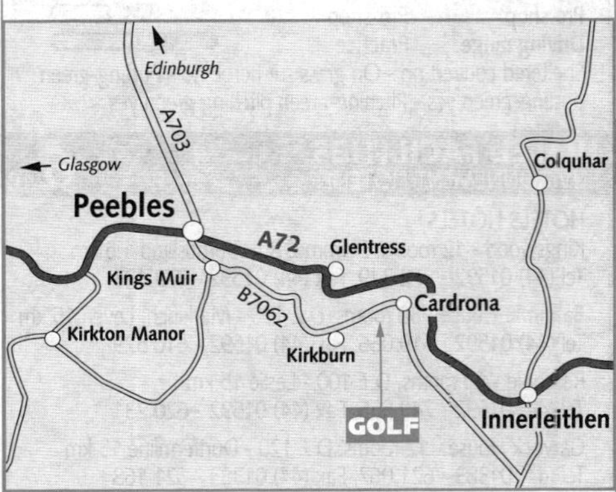

Access Accès : A702, left onto Seafield Moor Road, A701, B7026, A6094. Turn left onto A703 (Edinburgh Road). Next roundabout, Innerleithen Road (A72). Turn right Horsbrugh Frd. Next roundabout 1st exit. **Map 3 on page 475** Carte 3 Page 475

GOLF COURSE — PARCOURS — 17/20

Site	Site	
Maintenance	Entretien	
Architect	Architecte	Dave Thomas
Type	Type	parkland
Relief	Relief	
Water in play	Eau en jeu	
Exp. to wind	Exposé au vent	
Trees in play	Arbres en jeu	

Scorecard Carte de score	Chp. Chp.	Mens Mess.	Ladies Da.
Length Long.	6171	5900	5526
Par	72	72	72
Slope system	—	—	—

Advised golfing ability / Niveau de jeu recommandé: 0 12 24 36

Hcp required Handicap exigé: no

CLUB HOUSE & AMENITIES — CLUB HOUSE ET ANNEXES — 7/10

Pro shop Pro-shop
Driving range Practice
Sheltered couvert - On grass sur herbe yes - Putting-green putting-green yes - Pitching-green pitching green no

HOTEL FACILITIES — ENVIRONNEMENT HOTELIER — 8/10

HOTELS HÔTELS

Cardrona Hotel - 99 rooms, D £ 180 - on site
Tel (44) 01896 - 831 144, Fax (44) 01896 - 831 166

Castle Venlow - 13 rooms, D from £ 130 - Peebles 5 km
Tel (44) 01721 - 720 384, Fax (44) 01721 - 724 066

Peebles Hydro - 132 rooms, D £ 160 - Peebles 5 km
Tel (44) 01721 - 720 602, Fax (44) 01721 - 722 999

Traquair Arms Hotel - 15 rooms, D £ 80 - Innerleithen 5 km
Tel (44) 01896 - 830 229, Fax (44) 01896 - 830 260

RESTAURANTS RESTAURANTS

Renwick's Restaurant - on site - Tel (44) 01896 - 831 144
Sunflower - Peebles 5 km - Tel (44) 01721 - 722 420
Traquair Arms Hotel - Innerleithen 5 km - Tel (44) 01896 - 830 229

Cardross

14	6	4

To the south of Loch Lomond, this course provides some pretty views over the Firth of Clyde and the countryside around Dumbarton. Laid out in an undulating parkland landscape, it is a good test of golf for players of all abilities, even though the course is hardly the latest thing in modern golf design. Strategic bunkering is a feature of this course which because of its sandy sub-soil and good drainage allows play throughout the year. Although the club was founded in 1895, the site of the present course dates back to 1904 when Willie Fernie from Troon first laid it out. It was subsequently amended by master architect James Braid in 1921, but without any change to the spirit of this old and respectable golf club. Other clubs in the region certainly are more famous and probably have more spectacular courses than this (and higher green-fees, too !), but with its superb turf, fine greens and subtle qualities it is not only a good challenge but also a beautiful place to play golf.

Au sud du Loch Lomond, ce parcours offre de jolis panoramas sur le Firth of Clyde et la campagne de Dumbarton. Tracé dans un paysage de parc modérément accidenté, c'est un bon test de golf pour les joueurs de tous niveaux, même s'il ne représente pas le tout dernier modernisme à la mode. Ce sont d'ailleurs de classiques et nombreux bunkers qui sont la principale difficulté. Le sous-sol sablonneux assure un bon drainage, ce qui permet de jouer facilement toute l'année. Le club a été fondé en 1895 mais le parcours construit en 1904 par Willie Fernie, de Troon, et les changements apportés depuis (par James Braid en 1921) n'ont pas modifié l'esprit de ce vieux et respectable Club de golf. Certes, d'autres Clubs de la région ont acquis plus de célébrité, avec des parcours plus spectaculaires (et aussi des green-fees plus élevés !), mais la densité du gazon, la qualité des greens et les subtilités du dessin en font un bel endroit où jouer au golf.

Cardross Golf Club — 1895

Main Road
SCO - CARDROSS, Dumbarton G82 5LB

Office Secrétariat (44) 01389 - 841 754
Pro shop Pro-shop (44) 01389 - 841 350
Fax Fax (44) 01389 -842 162
Web www.cardross.com
Situation Situation Glasgow, 30 km
Dumbarton, 8 km
Annual closure Fermeture annuelle no
Weekly closure Fermeture hebdomadaire no

Fees main season Tarifs haute saison	18 holes	
	Week days Semaine	We/Bank holidays We/Férié
Individual Individuel	£ 30	*
Couple Couple	£ 60	*

* No visitors at week-ends
Full week day: £ 45 / Juniors (Under 18 : – 50%)

Caddie Caddie on request **Electric Trolley** Chariot électrique no
Buggy Voiturette no **Clubs** Clubs yes
Credit cards Cartes de crédit VISA

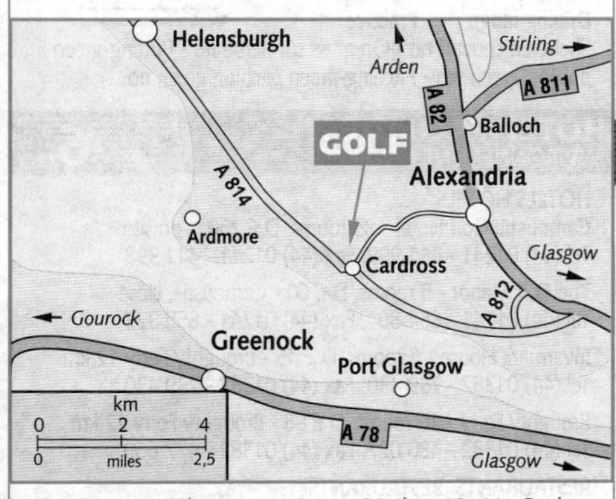

Access Accès : Glasgow, M8 Exit Jct 30, then A814 to Cardross
Map 3 on page 474 Carte 3 Page 474

GOLF COURSE — PARCOURS 14/20

Site Site
Maintenance Entretien
Architect Architecte Willie Fernie, James Braid
Type Type parkland
Relief Relief
Water in play Eau en jeu
Exp. to wind Exposé au vent
Trees in play Arbres en jeu

Scorecard / Carte de score	Chp. / Chp.	Mens / Mess.	Ladies / Da.
Length Long.	5887	5607	5273
Par	71	71	75
Slope system	—	—	—

Advised golfing ability 0 12 24 36
Niveau de jeu recommandé
Hcp required Handicap exigé no

CLUB HOUSE & AMENITIES — CLUB HOUSE ET ANNEXES 6/10

Pro shop Pro-shop
Driving range Practice
Sheltered couvert no - On grass sur herbe yes - Putting-green putting-green yes - Pitching-green pitching green yes

HOTEL FACILITIES — ENVIRONNEMENT HOTELIER 4/10

HOTELS HÔTELS
Kirkton House - 6 rooms, D £ 79 - Cardross 1.5 km
Tel (44) 01389 - 841 951, Fax (44) 01389 - 841 868

Balloch Hotel - 10 rooms, D £ 60 - Balloch, close
Tel (44) 01389 - 752 579, Fax (44) 01389 - 755 604

Travelodge - 32 rooms, D £ 65 - Dumbarton 8 km
Tel (44) 0870 - 191 1633, Fax (44) 01389 - 765 202

RESTAURANTS RESTAURANTS
Abbotsford Hotel - Dumbarton 9 km
Tel (44) 01389 - 733 304
Smolletts - Balloch 7 km - Tel (44) 01389 - 755 565

Carnoustie *Burnside*

14 | 5 | 6

Of course you don't come here only to play this "Burnside Course", but if you consider this simply as a warm-up round before playing the Championship course, then watch out: this is not a layout for beginners. It is certainly much shorter than its prestigious older companion but does have enough difficulties for it to hold its head high. It is laid out in a similar setting, the only blemish being that it runs alongside the railway track. Bunkers form the main line of defence, but there is also a number of trees which accentuates the countryside appearance found here and there on the Championship course. On a site that could contain in all almost a dozen courses, this layout more than does itself justice. And the appeal of the environment benefits from the hotel opened for the memorable return of the British Open in 1999. We might also emphasize the importance of professionals from Carnoustie in the history of golf. Many emigrated to the United States, including a one Stewart Maiden, who taught Bobby Jones how to play.

On ne vient pas ici pour jouer ce "Burnside Course", mais s'il s'agit de s'échauffer avant de jouer le "Championship", méfiance car ce n'est pas un parcours pour débutants. Il est certes beaucoup plus court que son prestigieux aîné, mais présente assez de difficultés pour garder la tête haute. Il est d'ailleurs situé dans un environnement similaire, son seul défaut étant de longer davantage la voie ferrée. Les bunkers constituent la défense essentielle, avec aussi pas mal d'arbres, ce qui accentue un aspect campagne que l'on retrouve çà et là sur le "Championship." Dans un site qui pourrait contenir une bonne dizaine de parcours, celui-ci est plus qu'honorable. Et la séduction autrefois incertaine de l'environnement a bénéficié de l'ouverture de l'hôtel lors du retour mémorable du British Open à Carnoustie en 1999. On soulignera enfin l'importance des professionnels de Carnoustie dans l'histoire du golf. Beaucoup ont émigré aux USA, dont Stewart Maiden, professeur de... Bobby Jones.

Carnoustie Golf Links — 1914

Links Parade
SCO- CARNOUSTIE, Angus, DD7 7JE

Office	Secrétariat	(44) 01241 - 853 789
Pro shop	Pro-shop	(44) 01241 - 411 986
Fax	Fax	(44) 01241 - 852 720
Web	www.carnoustiegolflinks.co.uk	
Situation	Situation	Abroath, 9 km

Dundee (pop. 165 873), 17 km

Annual closure	Fermeture annuelle	no
Weekly closure	Fermeture hebdomadaire	no
Fees main season	Tarifs haute saison	18 holes

	Week days / Semaine	We/Bank holidays / We/Férié
Individual Individuel	£ 31	£ 31
Couple Couple	£ 62	£ 62

Caddie Caddie yes — **Electric Trolley** Chariot électrique yes
Buggy Voiturette no — **Clubs** Clubs yes
Credit cards Cartes de crédit
VISA - Eurocard - MasterCard - AMEX

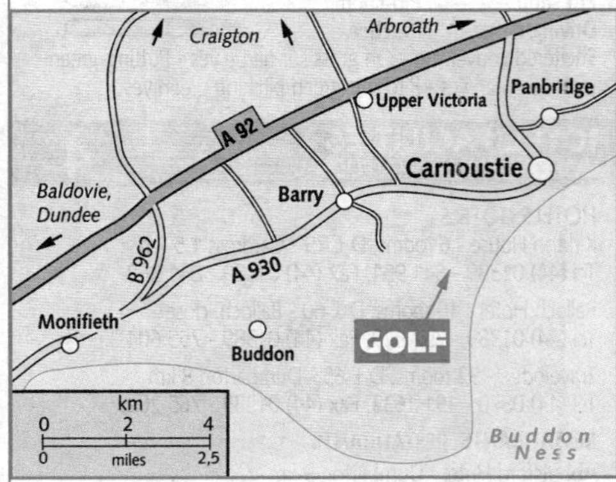

Access Accès : Dundee, A92 and A930
Map 2 on page 473 Carte 2 Page 473

GOLF COURSE — PARCOURS — 14/20

Site	Site	
Maintenance	Entretien	
Architect	Architecte	unknown
Type	Type	links
Relief	Relief	
Water in play	Eau en jeu	
Exp. to wind	Exposé au vent	
Trees in play	Arbres en jeu	

Scorecard / Carte de score	Chp. / Chp.	Mens / Mess.	Ladies / Da.
Length Long.	5420	5420	4860
Par	68	68	72
Slope system	—	—	—

Advised golfing ability Niveau de jeu recommandé: 0 12 24 36
Hcp required Handicap exigé: no

CLUB HOUSE & AMENITIES — CLUB HOUSE ET ANNEXES — 5/10

Pro shop Pro-shop
Driving range Practice
Sheltered couvert no - On grass sur herbe no - Putting-green putting-green yes - Pitching-green pitching green no

HOTEL FACILITIES — ENVIRONNEMENT HOTELIER — 6/10

HOTELS HÔTELS
Carnoustie Golf Hotel - 85 rooms, D £ 250 - on site
Tel (44) 01241 - 411 999, Fax (44) 01241 - 411 998

The Old Manor - 5 rooms, D £ 60 - Carnoustie, close
Tel (44) 01241 - 854 804, Fax (44) 01241 - 855 327

Invermark House - 5 rooms, D £ 45 - Broughty Ferry 12 km
Tel (44) 01382 - 739 430, Fax (44) 01382 - 739 430

Broughty Ferry - 16 rooms, D £ 88 - Broughty Ferry 12 km
Tel (44) 01382 - 480 027, Fax (44) 01382 - 477 660

RESTAURANTS RESTAURANTS
11 Park Avenue - Carnoustie 3 km - Tel (44) 01241 - 853 336
Café Montmartre (French) - Broughty Ferry 12 km
Tel (44) 01382 - 739 313

Carnoustie *Championship*

19	5	6

The British Open at Carnoustie had honoured legendary golfers such as Armour, Cotton, Hogan, Player and Watson before history smiled wryly at the misadventures of Jean van de Velde in 1999 and Paul Lawrie's surprise win. Carnoustie is a dangerous course, and contrary to many links courses which really bare their teeth only in strong winds, this one is very difficult even in calm weather. When the wind does blow it can be a real brute. There are no large dunes here, just a sort of space where the sea looks to have quietly receded to leave room for a few strips of turf, streams, bushes, a little scrub and long grass. Architects have successively added a few wicked bunkers, very tricky greens and optical illusions that make club choice very difficult. If you survive the first 15 holes, the last three can easily finish you off. For this inhuman greatness, some prefer Carnoustie to the Old Course at St Andrews. There is certainly very little in it

Le British Open à Carnoustie avait couronné des légendes telles que Armour, Cotton, Ben Hogan, Gary Player et Tom Watson avant que l'histoire prenne un visage sardonique en 1999 avec les mésaventures de Jean van de Velde et la victoire surprise de Paul Lawrie. Carnoustie est un parcours dangereux : au contraire de beaucoup de links qui ne prennent leur vraie dimension que dans un vent violent, celui-ci est très difficile même quand il n'y en a pas. Et s'il souffle, il devient carrément une brute. Pas de grandes dunes ici, mais une sorte d'espace d'où la mer se serait retirée doucement pour laisser place à des vagues de gazon, quelques ruisseaux, aux buissons, à de rares arbustes, aux longues herbes. Les architectes y ont successivement ajouté quelques bunkers très méchants, des greens d'une grande subtilité, et des illusions d'optique qui rendent très difficile le choix de clubs. Et si l'on a survécu à quinze trous, les trois derniers peuvent vous achever. Pour cette grandeur inhumaine, certains préfèrent Carnoustie au "Old Course" de St Andrews... Il n'est certes pas inférieur.

Carnoustie Golf Links — 1842

Links Parade
SCO- CARNOUSTIE, Angus, DD7 7JE

Office	Secrétariat	(44) 01241 - 853 789
Pro shop	Pro-shop	(44) 01241 - 411 986
Fax	Fax	(44) 01241 - 852 720
Web	www.carnoustiegolflinks.co.uk	
Situation	Situation	Abroath, 9 km

Dundee (pop. 165 873), 17 km

Annual closure	Fermeture annuelle	no
Weekly closure	Fermeture hebdomadaire	no
Fees main season	Tarifs haute saison	18 holes

	Week days Semaine	We/Bank holidays We/Férié
Individual Individuel	£ 98	£ 98
Couple Couple	£ 196	£ 196

Caddie Caddie yes — **Electric Trolley** Chariot électrique yes
Buggy Voiturette no — **Clubs** Clubs yes
Credit cards Cartes de crédit
VISA - Eurocard - MasterCard - AMEX

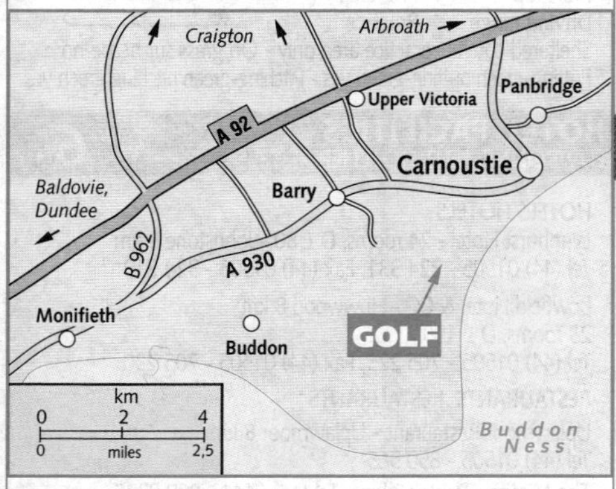

Access Accès : Dundee, A92 and A930
Map 2 on page 473 Carte 2 Page 473

GOLF COURSE — PARCOURS 19/20

Site	Site	
Maintenance	Entretien	
Architect	Architecte	Tom Morris, James Braid
Type	Type	links, seaside course
Relief	Relief	
Water in play	Eau en jeu	
Exp. to wind	Exposé au vent	
Trees in play	Arbres en jeu	

Scorecard Carte de score	Chp. Chp.	Mens Mess.	Ladies Da.
Length Long.	6247	6023	5514
Par	70	70	73
Slope system	144	142	—

Advised golfing ability Niveau de jeu recommandé — 0 12 24 36
Hcp required Handicap exigé — 28 Men, 36 Ladies

CLUB HOUSE & AMENITIES — CLUB HOUSE ET ANNEXES 5/10

Pro shop Pro-shop
Driving range Practice
Sheltered couvert no - On grass sur herbe no - Putting-green putting-green yes - Pitching-green pitching green no

HOTEL FACILITIES — ENVIRONNEMENT HOTELIER 6/10

HOTELS HÔTELS

Carnoustie Golf Hotel - 85 rooms, D £ 250 - on site
Tel (44) 01241 - 411 999, Fax (44) 01241 - 411 998

The Old Manor - 5 rooms, D £ 60 - Carnoustie, close
Tel (44) 01241 - 854 804, Fax (44) 01241 - 855 327

Invermark House - 5 rooms, D £ 45 - Broughty Ferry 12 km
Tel (44) 01382 - 739 430, Fax (44) 01382 - 739 430

Broughty Ferry - 16 rooms, D £ 88 - Broughty Ferry 12 km
Tel (44) 01382 - 480 027, Fax (44) 01382 - 477 660

RESTAURANTS RESTAURANTS

11 Park Avenue - Carnoustie 3 km - Tel (44) 01241 - 853 336
Café Montmartre (French) - Broughty Ferry 12 km
Tel (44) 01382 - 739 313

Cochrane Castle

16	7	6

It was Charlie Hunter, the professional and green-keeper at Old Prestwick, who designed Cochrane Castle in 1895. In 1949, the Town Council reclaimed eight holes for building purposes and new land had to be found. From 1950 onwards, there were so many changes that people talked about this as a course with "greens-on-wheels". Yet the course survived and what it may lack in modernism it more than makes up for in charm. Small, distinctly contoured greens, a challenging outward nine and five blind holes are the major features. The need is often to keep the ball low against the wind because the course is exposed, but there is the compensation of a number of splendid views over Ben Lomond and, from the 3rd fairway, even the peaks of the Isle of Arran on a clear day. It is not a likely venue for a future Ryder Cup but it is great fun and makes for pleasant recreation and good exercise (you will need a sturdy pair of legs) before moving onto the coast to confront the stiffer challenges awaiting on the top links courses.

C'est Charlie Hunter, pro et greenkeeper à Old Prestwick qui dessina Cochrane Castle en 1895. En 1949, le Town Council en récupéra huit trous pour bâtir et il fallut retrouver du terrain. A partir de 1950, il y eut tant de changements qu'on en parlait comme d'un parcours avec des "greens à roulettes", mais il a su résister et ne manque pas de charme, à défaut de modernisme. De petits greens très modelés, une première partie de parcours exigeante et cinq trous aveugles en sont les traits marquants. Il faut savoir garder la balle basse contre le vent car le parcours est exposé, avec l'avantage certain de pouvoir offrir quelques belles vues sur le Ben Lomond et même les sommets de l'île d'Arran quand le temps est clair (du fairway du 3). Certes, il ne s'agit pas d'un immense tracé, mais il est très amusant, et constitue une plaisante récréation et une bonne mise en jambes (il faut les avoir quand même solides) avant d'aller vers la côte affronter les challenges plus décisifs que sont les grands links.

Cochrane Castle Golf Club — 1895

Scott Avenue, Craigston
SCO - JOHNSTONE PA5 0HF

Office	Secrétariat	(44) 01505 - 320 146
Pro shop	Pro-shop	(44) 01505 - 328 465
Fax	Fax	(44) 01505 - 325 338
E-mail		secretary@cochranecastle.scottishgolf.com
Situation	Situation	Glasgow, 8 km
Annual closure	Fermeture annuelle	no
Weekly closure	Fermeture hebdomadaire	no

Fees main season Tarifs haute saison — 18 holes

	Week days / Semaine	We/Bank holidays / We/Férié
Individual Individuel	£ 22	*
Couple Couple	£ 44	*

* Members & their guests only

Caddie Caddie no — **Electric Trolley** Chariot électrique no
Buggy Voiturette no — **Clubs** Clubs no
Credit cards Cartes de crédit no

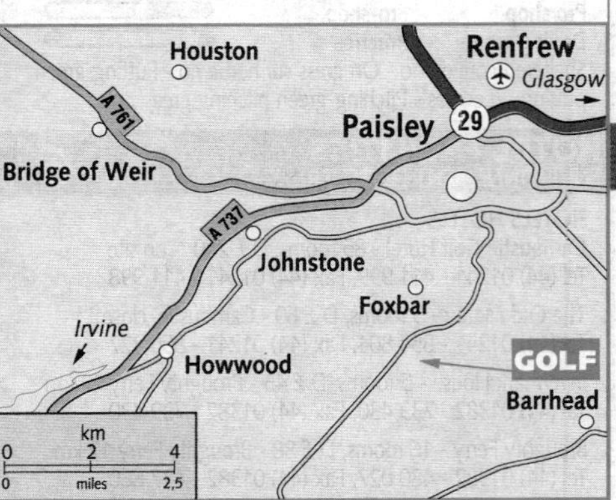

Access Accès : 1 km south of Beith Road, Johnstone
Map 3 on page 474 Carte 3 Page 474

GOLF COURSE — PARCOURS — 16/20

Site	Site	
Maintenance	Entretien	
Architect	Architecte	Charlie Hunter
Type	Type	parkland
Relief	Relief	
Water in play	Eau en jeu	
Exp. to wind	Exposé au vent	
Trees in play	Arbres en jeu	

Scorecard / Carte de score	Chp. / Chp.	Mens / Mess.	Ladies / Da.
Length Long.	5663	5394	4855
Par	71	70	72
Slope system	—	—	—

Advised golfing ability 0 12 24 36
Niveau de jeu recommandé
Hcp required Handicap exigé 36

CLUB HOUSE & AMENITIES — CLUB HOUSE ET ANNEXES — 7/10

Pro shop Pro-shop
Driving range Practice
Sheltered couvert practice area only - On grass sur herbe no
Putting-green putting-green yes - Pitching-green pitching green yes

HOTEL FACILITIES — ENVIRONNEMENT HOTELIER — 6/10

HOTELS HÔTELS

Lynnhurst Hotel - 24 rooms, D £ 80 - Johnstone 1 km
Tel (44) 01505 - 324 331, Fax (44) 01505 - 324 219

Bowfield Hotel & CC - Howwood 8 km
23 rooms, D £ 150
Tel (44) 01505 - 705 225, Fax (44) 01505 - 705 230

RESTAURANTS RESTAURANTS

Uplawmoor Restaurant - Uplawmoor 8 km
Tel (44) 01505 - 850 565

The Mirage - Paisley 3 km - Tel (44) 0141 - 889 9325

Ubiquitous Chip - Glasgow 8 km - Tel (44) 0141 - 334 5007

Crail *Balcomie Links*

15	6	6

The Balcomie Links in the ancient burgh of Crail not far from St Andrews itself, is one of Scotland's finest golfing treasures. This is not one of the country's longest courses but it is one of its most popular and draws visitors from every corner of the world, year after year, to enjoy a very special challenge to add to wonderful views across St Andrews Bay. Several fairways wind their way along golden sandy beaches and rocky outcrops along the Forth foreshore. The club itself is the seventh oldest in the world, having been founded in 1786. It may be an old club, but it is very modern in its thinking and outlook. The club brought in American architect Gil Hanse to build a second course in Crail - the Craighead Links. This is a different animal altogether from the Balcomie course, and already has earned a reputation for its severity of challenge and for depth of its rough.

Construit dans le "burgh" de Crail, non loin de St Andrews, Balcomie Links n'est pas l'un des plus longs parcours du pays, mais sa popularité lui attire des visiteurs du monde entier, venus relever ses nombreux défis, tout en admirant le merveilleux spectacle de St Andrews Bay. Le relief de la côte Est de l'Ecosse est moins mouvementé que celui de la côte Ouest, soumise à toutes les tempêtes, mais on trouvera plusieurs trous le long de plages dorées ponctuées d'affleurements rocheux le long du rivage du Forth. Le reste du parcours, plus "inland," n'est pas moins exposé au vent, il est assez intéressant pour que l'on reste concentré jusqu'à la fin. Crail est le septième plus ancien club de l'histoire du golf (il a été fondé en 1786), mais son ancienneté ne l'empêche pas d'être parmi les plus accueillants de tout le pays, et il ne refuse pas la modernité. Ainsi, Crail a demandé à l'architecte américain Gil Hanse de construire un second 18 trous, Craighead Links. Dans un autre style que Balcomie Links, il a conquis sa réputation par son exigence, et aussi la densité de ses roughs.

Crail Golfing Society — 1895

Balcomie Clubhouse, Fifeness
SCO - CRAIL, Fife KY10 3XN

Office	Secrétariat	(44) 01333 - 450 686
Pro shop	Pro-shop	(44) 01333 - 450 960
Fax	Fax	(44) 01333 - 450 416
Web	www.crailgolfingsociety.co.uk	
Situation	Situation	St Andrews, 14 km
Annual closure	Fermeture annuelle	no
Weekly closure	Fermeture hebdomadaire	no

Fees main season Tarifs haute saison — 18 holes

	Week days / Semaine	We/Bank holidays / We/Férié
Individual Individuel	£ 40	£ 50
Couple Couple	£ 80	£ 100

Full day: £65 - £78 (We)

Caddie Caddie on request **Electric Trolley** Chariot électrique yes

Buggy Voiturette medical reasons only **Clubs** Clubs yes

Credit cards Cartes de crédit
VISA - Eurocard - MasterCard - JCB

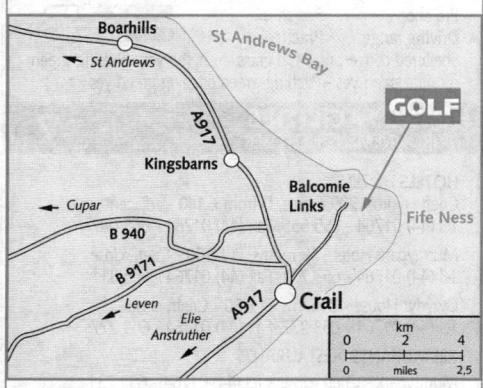

Access Accès : Edinburgh A92 to Kirkcaldy, then A915 through Leven, B942 and A 917 through Crail until Golf Hotel, turn right → Golf.
Map 2 on page 473 Carte 2 Page 473

GOLF COURSE — PARCOURS — 15/20

Site	Site	
Maintenance	Entretien	
Architect	Architecte	Tom Morris
Type	Type	links
Relief	Relief	
Water in play	Eau en jeu	
Exp. to wind	Exposé au vent	
Trees in play	Arbres en jeu	

Scorecard / Carte de score	Chp. / Chp.	Mens / Mess.	Ladies / Da.
Length Long.	5330	4908	4707
Par	69	67	70
Slope system	—	—	—

Advised golfing ability / Niveau de jeu recommandé: 0 12 24 36
Hcp required / Handicap exigé: no

CLUB HOUSE & AMENITIES — CLUB HOUSE ET ANNEXES — 6/10

Pro shop Pro-shop
Driving range Practice
Sheltered couvert no - On grass sur herbe no - Putting-green putting-green yes - Pitching-green pitching green no

HOTEL FACILITIES — ENVIRONNEMENT HOTELIER — 6/10

HOTELS HÔTELS
Balcomie Links - 15 rooms, D £ 90 - Crail 1 km
Tel (44) 01333 - 450 237, Fax (44) 01333 - 450 540

Croma - 10 rooms, D £ 55 - Crail 1 km
Tel (44) 01333 - 450 239, Fax (44) 01333 - 4514333

Smuggler's Innx - 9 rooms, D £ 70 - Crail 1 km
Tel (44) 01333 - 310 506, Fax (44) 01333 - 312 706

RESTAURANTS RESTAURANTS
The Cellar - Anstruther 6 km - Tel (44) 01333 - 310 378
Haven - Anstruther 6 km - Tel (44) 01333 - 310 574

Crieff *Ferntower Course* | 15 | 7 | 7

Set in the dramatic countryside of Perthshire, Crieff Golf Club was established in 1891 and was recently voted the 29th best golfing facility in Britain by Golf World magazine. There are magnificent views over the Strathearn Valley from a course that has hosted many significant events over the years. Old Tom Morris laid out the original nine-hole course which was extended to 18 by Robert Simpson at the beginning of the First World War. James Braid made alterations to the layout in the 1920s but very little now remains of the changes he recommended following extensive alterations to the Ferntower course and the creation of the nine-hole Dornock course. The Ferntower Course in its present layout only dates back to 1980. Most golfers will need to shape their shots or choose the right strategy with due consideration given to the slopes. Familiarity with the layout is a big advantage here. Visitors are assured of a warm and hospitable welcome.

Le golf de Crieff a été récemment distingué parmi les sites de golf en Grande-Bretagne par le magazine Golf World. Depuis le parcours, on profite de vues magnifiques sur la Strathearn Valley. Old Tom Morris lui-même a tracé le 9-trous original, porté à 18 trous par Robert Simpson au début de la Première Guerre Mondiale. James Braid a aussi effectué un certain nombre de modifications dans les années 1920, mais il reste peu de choses de ces éléments d'origine, suite à la modification du tracé du Ferntower Course et de la construction d'un 9-trous supplémentaire, le Dornock Course. Les travaux définitifs ont été achevés en 1980, mais ils ont été assez bien menés pour que l'on n'ait pas trop de disparités de style. Les pentes doivent d'ailleurs souvent être prises en considération pour établir une stratégie efficace, comme pour choisir les meilleures trajectoires. Il est utile de jouer plusieurs fois pour bien comprendre ce tracé, mais on le fera avec plaisir quand on constate la qualité de la réception et de l'accueil.

Crieff Golf Club — 1891

Perth Road
SCO - CRIEFF, Perthshire PH7 3LR

Office	Secrétariat	(44) 01764 - 652 397
Pro shop	Pro-shop	(44) 01764 - 652 909
Fax	Fax	(44) 01764 - 655 096
Web	www.crieffgolf.co.uk	
Situation	Situation	Perth, 27 km
Annual closure	Fermeture annuelle	no
Weekly closure	Fermeture hebdomadaire	no

Fees main season Tarifs haute saison — 18 holes

	Week days Semaine	We/Bank holidays We/Férié
Individual Individuel	£ 30	£ 40
Couple Couple	£ 60	£ 80

Caddie Caddie no — **Electric Trolley** Chariot électrique no

Buggy Voiturette yes — **Clubs** Clubs yes

Credit cards Cartes de crédit
VISA - Mastercard - Access (only in Pro shop)

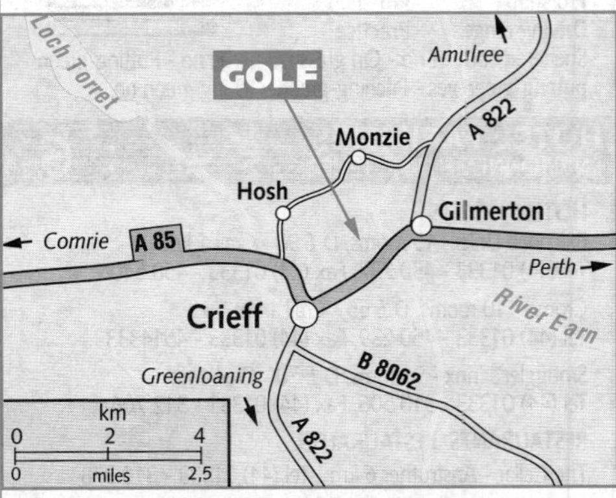

Access Accès : Edinburgh M90 to Perth, then A85 → Crieff. Golf on right at the edge of town.
Map 2 on page 473 Carte 2 Page 473

GOLF COURSE — PARCOURS 15/20

Site	Site	
Maintenance	Entretien	
Architect	Architecte	Bob Simpson, James Braid
Type	Type	parkland
Relief	Relief	
Water in play	Eau en jeu	
Exp. to wind	Exposé au vent	
Trees in play	Arbres en jeu	

Scorecard Carte de score	Chp. Chp.	Mens Mess.	Ladies Da.
Length Long.	5830	5830	5830
Par	71	71	76
Slope system	—	—	—

Advised golfing ability Niveau de jeu recommandé — 0 12 24 36

Hcp required Handicap exigé — certificate

CLUB HOUSE & AMENITIES — CLUB HOUSE ET ANNEXES 7/10

Pro shop Pro-shop
Driving range Practice
Sheltered couvert no - On grass sur herbe yes - Putting-green putting-green yes - Pitching-green pitching green yes

HOTEL FACILITIES — ENVIRONNEMENT HOTELIER 7/10

HOTELS HÔTELS
Crieff Hydro - 209 rooms, D from £ 140 - adjacent
Tel (44) 01764 - 655 555, Fax (44) 01764 - 653 087

Murraypark Hotel - 19 rooms, D £ 100 - Crieff, close
Tel (44) 01764 - 653 731, Fax (44) 01764 - 655 311

Gwydyr House - 8 rooms, D £ 80 - Crieff, close
Tel (44) 01764 - 653 277, Fax (44) 01764 - 653 277

RESTAURANTS RESTAURANTS
Murraypark - Crieff, close - Tel (44) 01764 - 653 731
The Bank - Crieff, close - Tel (44) 01764 - 656 575

Cruden Bay

18	7	6

This is one of the very few Tom Simpson courses in Scotland, a masterpiece on a par with County Louth, another hidden gem but this time in Ireland. They say that Slain Castle in the background inspired Bram Stoker for his Dracula. Well you'll find drama enough here and maybe blood on your card too when the wind starts to blow and the architect, as if in a game of chess, takes your pieces one by one as the course unwinds. You will find every challenge to test your game: subtle, well-protected greens, which must be approached from the right slant (see the 13th), strategic fairway bunkers, deep green-side bunkers, burns, blind shots, majestic long holes or teasing shorter ones. There was once a grand hotel on this site, whose course was one of the facilities built by the Great North of Scotland Railway Company, but it was demolished. This might explain the relative anonymity from which Cruden Bay deserves to emerge... but don't tell anybody.

C'est un des seuls parcours de Tom Simpson en Ecosse, un véritable chef-d'oeuvre à mettre à côté de County Louth, lui aussi un des joyaux cachés du golf, mais d'Irlande cette fois. On dit que Slain Castle, en arrière plan du lieu, a inspiré Bram Stoker pour son "Dracula." Nul doute qu'il y aura aussi des drames et du sang sur les cartes de score quand le vent souffle un peu, et que la patiente partie d'échec de l'architecte avec les joueurs tourne à la déconfiture de ceux-ci. Greens subtils et bien défendus, et qu'il faut à tout prix attaquer selon le bon angle (voir le 13), bunkers de fairway stratégiques, profonds bunkers de green, petits "burns" piégeux, coups aveugles, longs trous majestueux ou petits trous provocants : on a ici tous les défis pour mettre son jeu à l'épreuve. Il y avait autrefois un grand hôtel sur place, dont ce parcours était l'un des équipements construits par les chemins de fer d'Ecosse (Great North of Scotland Railway Company). Il a été détruit, ce qui explique le relatif anonymat dont Cruden Bay mérite de sortir. Mais n'en parlez à personne...

Cruden Bay Golf Club — 1899

Aulton Road, Cruden Bay
SCO - PETERHEAD, Aberdeenshire AB42 0NN

Office Secrétariat (44) 01779 - 812 285
Pro shop Pro-shop (44) 01779 - 812 414
Fax Fax (44) 01779 - 812 945
Web www.crudenbaygolfclub.co.uk
Situation Situation Peterhead, 12 km
Aberdeen (pop. 204 885), 40 km

Annual closure Fermeture annuelle no
Weekly closure Fermeture hebdomadaire no

Fees main season Tarifs haute saison	18 holes	
	Week days Semaine	We/Bank holidays We/Férié
Individual Individuel	£ 55	£ 65
Couple Couple	£ 110	£ 130

Some week-end restrictions: ask before

Caddie Caddie on request **Electric Trolley** Chariot électrique yes
Buggy Voiturette no **Clubs** Clubs yes
Credit cards Cartes de crédit VISA - MasterCard

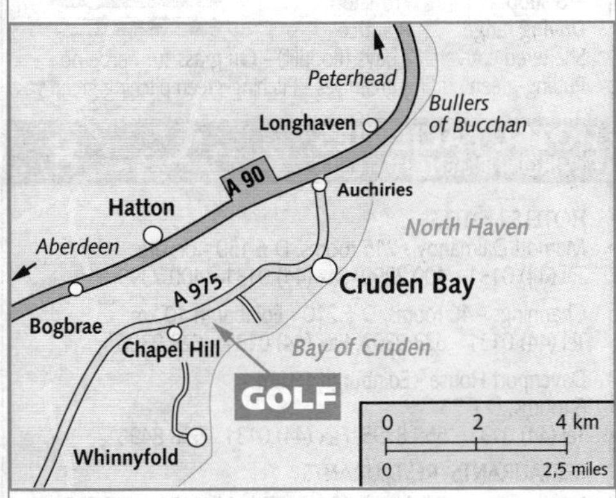

Access Accès : A92 through Aberdeen, then A975 → Peterhead to Cruden Bay.
Map 1 on page 473 Carte 1 Page 473

GOLF COURSE — PARCOURS 18/20

Site Site
Maintenance Entretien
Architect Architecte Tom Simpson
Type Type links
Relief Relief
Water in play Eau en jeu
Exp. to wind Exposé au vent
Trees in play Arbres en jeu

Scorecard Carte de score	Chp. Chp.	Mens Mess.	Ladies Da.
Length Long.	5752	5371	5126
Par	70	70	74
Slope system	—	—	—

Advised golfing ability Niveau de jeu recommandé 0 12 24 36
Hcp required Handicap exigé certificate

CLUB HOUSE & AMENITIES — CLUB HOUSE ET ANNEXES 7/10

Pro shop Pro-shop
Driving range Practice
Sheltered couvert 10 mats - On grass sur herbe yes - Putting-green putting-green yes - Pitching-green pitching green yes

HOTEL FACILITIES — ENVIRONNEMENT HOTELIER 6/10

HOTELS HÔTELS
Waterside Inn - Peterhead 13 km
69 rooms, D £ 100
Tel (44) 01779 - 471 121, Fax (44) 01779 - 470 670

Udny Arms - Newburgh 10 km
26 rooms, D £ 105
Tel (44) 01358 - 789 444, Fax (44) 01779 - 789 012

Ardoe House - 113 rooms, D £ 160 - Aberdeeen 35 km
Tel (44) 01224 - 860 600, Fax (44) 01224 - 860 644

RESTAURANTS RESTAURANTS
Udny Arms - Newburgh 10 km - Tel (44) 01358 - 789 444
Waterside Inn - Peterhead 13 km - Tel (44) 01779 - 471 121

Dalmahoy *East Course*

17 | 8 | 8

With two 18-hole courses, one of which is in the international league, this golfing complex controlled by Marriott is a very high class resort with a full-facility hotel, particularly for non-golfers (tennis, swimming pool, fitness, etc.). The East Course, designed by James Braid, has played host to some major tournaments, including the Solheim Cup in 1992. Although some aspects of the course are reminiscent of a links, here we are in a beautiful park where trees are important not so much as dangerous hazards but for outlining the holes. Water comes into play but only on two holes. So really if you drive straight you're half-way there, but only half-way. You need some accurate ironwork to hit the well-protected greens, so a few rudiments of target golf will more than come in handy. A good test of golf.

Avec deux parcours de 18 trous, dont un de classe internationale, cet ensemble contrôlé par Marriott est devenu un complexe de tout premier ordre avec un hôtel très bien équipé, notamment pour les non-golfeurs, qui auront de quoi s'occcuper en vous attendant: tennis, piscine, mise en forme, etc... Dessiné par James Braid, l'East Course a accueilli de grandes épreuves, dont la Solheim Cup en 1992. Bien que certains aspects puissent rappeler les links, nous sommes ici dans un parc de toute beauté, où les arbres jouent un certain rôle, mais ils définissent plus les trous qu'ils ne constituent des obstacles dangereux. L'eau n'est en jeu que sur deux trous. De fait, si l'on drive bien, on aura fait une bonne partie du chemin vers un bon score, mais c'est loin d'être suffisant : il faut être d'autant plus précis que les greens sont bien défendus, ce qui exige parfois de connaître les secrets du "target golf". Un bon test de golf.

Marriott Dalmahoy Golf & Country Club 1927
Kirknewton
SCO - EDINBURGH EH27 8EB

Office	Secrétariat	(44) 0131 - 333 1845
Pro shop	Pro-shop	(44) 0131 - 333 1845
Fax	Fax	(44) 0131 - 333 1433
Web	www.marriott.com	
Situation	Situation	Edinburgh, 12 km
Annual closure	Fermeture annuelle	no
Weekly closure	Fermeture hebdomadaire	no

Fees main season Tarifs haute saison	18 holes	
	Week days Semaine	**We/Bank holidays** We/Férié
Individual Individuel	£ 65	£ 80
Couple Couple	£ 130	£ 160

Prices for non residents

Caddie Caddie on request **Electric Trolley** Chariot électrique no

Buggy Voiturette yes **Clubs** Clubs yes

Credit cards Cartes de crédit
VISA - Eurocard - MasterCard - AMEX - DC

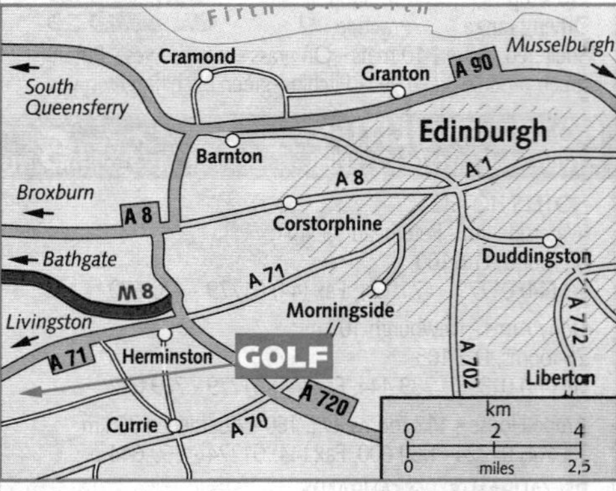

Access Accès : From Edinburgh, on A 71 → Livingston
Map 3 on page 475 Carte 3 Page 475

GOLF COURSE
PARCOURS — 17/20

Site	Site	
Maintenance	Entretien	
Architect	Architecte	James Braid
Type	Type	parkland
Relief	Relief	
Water in play	Eau en jeu	
Exp. to wind	Exposé au vent	
Trees in play	Arbres en jeu	

Scorecard Carte de score	**Chp.** Chp.	**Mens** Mess.	**Ladies** Da.
Length Long.	6030	5836	5356
Par	72	71	75
Slope system	—	—	—

Advised golfing ability 0 12 24 36
Niveau de jeu recommandé
Hcp required Handicap exigé certificate

CLUB HOUSE & AMENITIES
CLUB HOUSE ET ANNEXES — 8/10

Pro shop Pro-shop
Driving range Practice
Sheltered couvert 12 bays (floodlit) - On grass sur herbe no - Putting-green putting-green yes - Pitching-green pitching green yes

HOTEL FACILITIES
ENVIRONNEMENT HOTELIER — 8/10

HOTELS HÔTELS
Marriott Dalmahoy - 215 rooms, D £ 150 - on site
Tel (44) 0131 - 400 7299, Fax (44) 0131 - 400 7399

Channings - 46 rooms, D £ 210 - Edinburgh 10 km
Tel (44) 0131 - 623 9302, Fax (44) 0131 - 623 9306

Davenport House - Edinburgh 10 km
6 rooms, D £ 75
Tel (44) 0131 - 558 8495, Fax (44) 0131 - 558 8496

RESTAURANTS RESTAURANTS
Number One - Edinburgh 12 km - Tel (44) 0131 - 622 8831
Yumi (Japanese) - Edinburgh 9 km - Tel (44) 0131 - 337 2173
Channings - Edinburgh 10 km - Tel (44) 0131 - 623 9302

Downfield

17 | 6 | 7

Located in the north-west confines of Dundee, Downfield is without a doubt one of the very great British inland courses, even though it is still little known outside of Scotland and even less so to players from continental Europe. If you are in the region it would be a great pity to miss it. James Braid has designed an uncompromising challenge in an already very heavily wooded area comprising about a hundred different varieties of tree. The course's park style means that the ball doesn't roll much, so each yard of the course – which was updated in 1964 - really counts on your card. Only good drivers can hope to get a good score, as long they keep on the straight and narrow. But short-game experts will feel very welcome here, as will wildlife lovers, as fox, water fowl, squirrels, deer and birds of prey live abound. At an equal distance from St Andrews and Carnoustie, this is an excellent stop-over and a serious test of golf, more sheltered from the wind than its neighbours.

Situé aux limites nord-ouest de Dundee, Downfield est sans conteste un des très bons parcours "inland" de Grande-Bretagne, bien qu'il reste peu connu en dehors des limites de l'Ecosse, et ne parlons même pas des joueurs du continent. Mais il serait fort dommage de le négliger si l'on passe dans les environs. James Braid a créé un défi sans compromis dans un espace boisé de centaines d'espèces. La nature de parc implique que la balle roule peu sur les fairways, et chaque mètre de ce parcours – révisé en 1964 – compte sur la carte. Seuls les bons drivers peuvent espérer un score honorable, du moment qu'ils parviennent à ne pas trop s'égarer. Mais les maîtres du petit jeu sont aussi les bienvenus ici, ainsi que les amateurs de faune sauvage: renards, gibier d'eau, écureuils, cervidés, rapaces vivent ici heureux. A égale distance de Carnoustie et de St Andrews, voici une halte de qualité, et un sérieux test de golf... plus à l'abri du vent que ses deux presque voisins.

Downfield Golf Club — 1932

Turnberry Avenue
SCO - DUNDEE DD2 3QP

Office	Secrétariat	(44) 01382 - 825 595
Pro shop	Pro-shop	(44) 01382 - 889 246
Fax	Fax	(44) 01382 - 813 111
Web	www.downfieldgolf.co.uk	
Situation	Situation	Dundee, 3 km
Annual closure	Fermeture annuelle	no
Weekly closure	Fermeture hebdomadaire	no
Fees main season	Tarifs haute saison	18 holes

	Week days / Semaine	We/Bank holidays / We/Férié
Individual Individuel	£ 38	£ 40
Couple Couple	£ 76	£ 80

Caddie Caddie yes — **Electric Trolley** Chariot électrique yes

Buggy Voiturette yes — **Clubs** Clubs yes

Credit cards Cartes de crédit yes

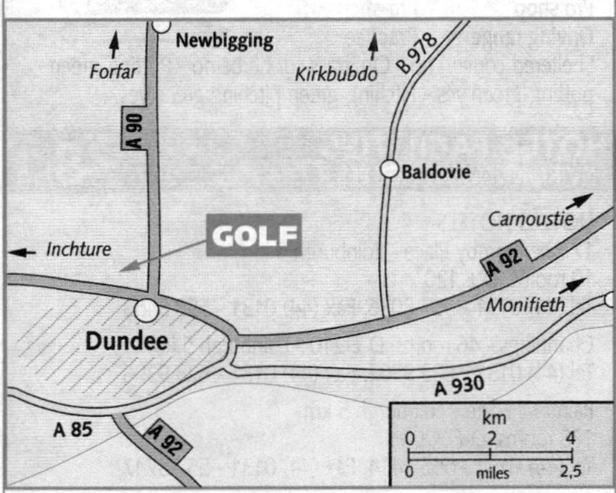

Access Accès : In Dundee, A90 Kingsway (Ring Road. A923 Coupar Angus Road. 50 m, right Faraday St, 1st left on Harrison Rd. 200 m, T junction, left onto Dalamhoy Dr. 400 m, left.

Map 1 on page 471 Carte 1 Page 471

GOLF COURSE — PARCOURS — 17/20

Site	Site	
Maintenance	Entretien	
Architect	Architecte	James Braid
Type	Type	parkland
Relief	Relief	
Water in play	Eau en jeu	
Exp. to wind	Exposé au vent	
Trees in play	Arbres en jeu	

Scorecard Carte de score	Chp. Chp.	Mens Mess.	Ladies Da.
Length Long.	6208	5702	5330
Par	73	70	74
Slope system	—	—	—

Advised golfing ability Niveau de jeu recommandé: 0 12 24 36

Hcp required Handicap exigé: no

CLUB HOUSE & AMENITIES — CLUB HOUSE ET ANNEXES — 6/10

Pro shop Pro-shop

Driving range Practice

Sheltered couvert no - On grass sur herbe yes - Putting-green putting-green yes - Pitching-green pitching green yes

HOTEL FACILITIES — ENVIRONNEMENT HOTELIER — 7/10

HOTELS HÔTELS

Swallow Hotel - Dundee 3 km
103 rooms, D from £ 70
Tel (44) 01382 - 641 122, Fax (44) 01382 - 568 340

Hilton Dundee - 129 rooms, D £ 120 - Dundee 5 km
Tel (44) 01382 - 229 271, Fax (44) 01382 - 200 072

Queens Hotel - Dundee 5 km
52 rooms, D from £ 80
Tel (44) 01382 - 322 515, Fax (44) 01382 - 202 668

RESTAURANTS RESTAURANTS

Birkhill Inn - Dundee 2 km - Tel (44) 01382 - 581 297
Beefeater - Dundee 5 km - Tel (44) 01382 - 561 115
Raffles - Dundee 4 km - Tel (44) 01382 - 226 344

Duddingston

15	7	8

One of the good Edinburgh courses, of which there are several dozen. The club has a good sporting reputation with an encouraging policy for young golfers that is none too common in the often crowded big city clubs. Located immediately behind Arthur's Seat to the east of the castle, this is a park course with the meanders of Braid's burn to make life a misery for golfers who like a round without hazards. The trees are also dangerously in play when there are no fairway bunkers. This moderately hilly course is well worth playing, especially since the architects kept the cohorts of average players very much in mind - this was often the case in olden days, even though the tough par 4s here are no walk-over. A very pleasant course and a hospitable club, but only on week days. The club is currently building a new £1.4 million club-house due for completion at the end of 2005, which will offer facilities ahead of most golf clubs in the Lothians.

L'un des bons parcours d'Edimbourg, qui en compte plusieurs dizaines pratiquement en ville. Celui-ci s'est fait une bonne réputation sportive, avec une politique en direction des jeunes, pas toujours si courante dans les grands clubs citadins, souvent très fréquentés. Situé immédiatement derrière Arthur's Seat, à l'est du château, c'est un golf de parc, avec les méandres du Braid's burn pour empoisonner la vie de ceux qui aiment la vie sans obstacles. Et les arbres viennent aussi dangereusement en jeu quand les bunkers de fairway manquent à l'appel. D'un relief modéré, c'est un parcours à connaître, d'autant que les architectes n'ont jamais perdu de vue les armées de joueurs moyens auxquels on pensait beaucoup autrefois, bien que la difficulté des pars 4 ne soit pas négligeable. Un parcours très plaisant, et un club accueillant, mais seulement en semaine. Un nouveau club-house d'1,4 millions de £ doit être inauguré fin 2005, avec des équipements de premier plan par rapport aux golfs du Lothian.

Duddingston Golf Club — 1895

Duddingston Road West
SCO - EDINBURGH EH15 3QD

Office	Secrétariat	(44) 0131 - 661 7688
Pro shop	Pro-shop	(44) 0131 - 661 4301
Fax	Fax	(44) 0131 - 652 6057
Web		www.duddingston-golf-club.com
Situation	Situation	Edinburgh, 3 km
Annual closure	Fermeture annuelle	no
Weekly closure	Fermeture hebdomadaire	no
Fees main season	Tarifs haute saison	18 holes

	Week days Semaine	We/Bank holidays We/Férié
Individual Individuel	£ 29	£ 29
Couple Couple	£ 58	£ 58

Caddie Caddie no — Electric Trolley Chariot électrique yes

Buggy Voiturette yes — Clubs Clubs yes

Credit cards Cartes de crédit yes

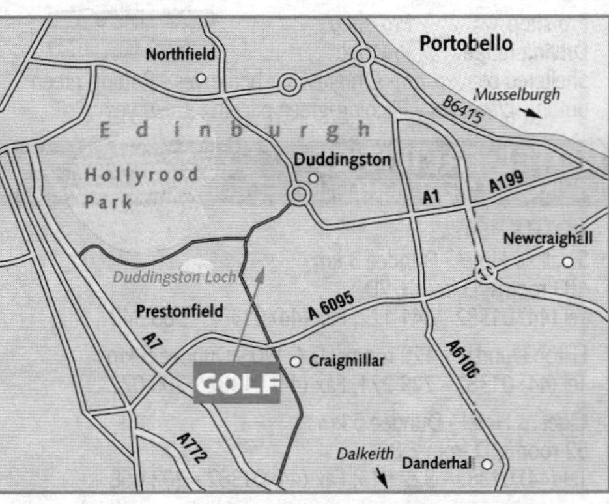

Access Accès : Edinburgh Princes Street, Regent Road, London Road, turn off right to Willowbrae Road, right to Duddingston Road West (near Duddingston Loch).
Map 3 on page 475 Carte 3 Page 475

GOLF COURSE — PARCOURS — 15/20

Site	Site	
Maintenance	Entretien	
Architect	Architecte	Willie Park
Type	Type	parkland
Relief	Relief	
Water in play	Eau en jeu	
Exp. to wind	Exposé au vent	
Trees in play	Arbres en jeu	

Scorecard Carte de score	Chp. Chp.	Mens Mess.	Ladies Da.
Length Long.	5937	5687	5087
Par	72	72	72
Slope system	—	—	—

Advised golfing ability / Niveau de jeu recommandé: 0 12 24 36

Hcp required — Handicap exigé — no

CLUB HOUSE & AMENITIES — CLUB HOUSE ET ANNEXES — 7/10

Pro shop — Pro-shop
Driving range — Practice
Sheltered couvert no - On grass sur herbe no - Putting-green putting-green yes - Pitching-green pitching green yes

HOTEL FACILITIES — ENVIRONNEMENT HOTELIER — 8/10

HOTELS HÔTELS

17 Abercromby Place - Edinburgh 5 km
10 rooms, D £ 120
Tel (44) 0131 - 557 8036, Fax (44) 0131 - 558 3453

Channings - 46 rooms, D £ 210 - Edinburgh 5 km
Tel (44) 0131 - 623 9302, Fax (44) 0131 - 623 9306

Balmoral Forte - Edinburgh 5 km
188 rooms, D £ 290
Tel (44) 0131 - 556 2414, Fax (44) 0131 - 557 3747

RESTAURANTS RESTAURANTS

Vintners Room - Edinburgh 5 km - Tel (44) 0131 - 554 6767
The Marque - Edinburgh 5 km - Tel (44) 0131 - 466 6660
Oloroso - Edinburgh 5 km - Tel (44) 0131 - 226 7614

Duff House Royal

15 | 6 | 5

There are courses you play in tournaments and courses you prefer for a bright stroll. This, of course, is one of the latter, where enjoyment comes first. Although architect Alister MacKenzie also laid out great championship courses like Augusta and Cypress Point, here, in restyling the 1910 James Braid layout, he was looking above all else to satisfy golfers of all levels. The difficulties are there, certainly (clever bunkering, trees) but they are never insurmountable or unavoidable. So you can hope to reach the green without too much to-do, keeping to your handicap on rather flat terrain, but be careful not to waste those precious handicap strokes: the greens are often two-tiered with tricky slopes and are well protected. The river Deveron can also cause a few headaches, as it comes into play for drives off the 7th, 16th and 17th tees. The club-house offers some very pleasant views.

Il y a des parcours pour s'affronter en compétition et d'autres plus propices à d'intelligentes balades. Celui-ci fait évidemment partie de la seconde catégorie, celle du golf-plaisir avant tout. Certes, l'architecte Alister MacKenzie a aussi créé Augusta et Cypress Point, immenses parcours de championnats, mais, en repensant le tracé de James Braid de 1910, il a surtout cherché ici à satisfaire tous les niveaux. Les difficultés sont présentes avec un bunkering intelligent, des arbres, mais jamais insurmontables ou impossibles à éviter. On peut ainsi espérer arriver paisiblement jusqu'au green en utilisant sagement ses points de handicap sur un terrain assez plat, mais il faut rester attentif à ne pas les gâcher : les greens sont souvent ici à double plateau, avec des pentes subtiles. Ils sont aussi bien protégés. La rivière Deveron peut aussi causer quelques soucis, elle est en jeu sur les drives du 7, du 16 et du 17. Les vues depuis le club-house sont très plaisantes.

Duff House Royal — 1909
The Barnyards
SCO - BANFF, AB45 3SX

Office	Secrétariat	(44) 01261 - 812 062
Pro shop	Pro-shop	(44) 01261 - 812 075
Fax	Fax	(44) 01261 - 812 224
Web	www.theduffhouseroyalgolfclub.co.uk	
Situation	Situation	Banff (pop. 4 402), 1 km
Annual closure	Fermeture annuelle	no
Weekly closure	Fermeture hebdomadaire	no
Fees main season	Tarifs haute saison	18 holes

	Week days / Semaine	We/Bank holidays / We/Férié
Individual Individuel	£ 25	£ 32
Couple Couple	£ 50	£ 64

Full days: £ 25 - £ 30 (We)

Caddie Caddie yes — **Electric Trolley** Chariot électrique yes

Buggy Voiturette no — **Clubs** Clubs yes

Credit cards Cartes de crédit yes

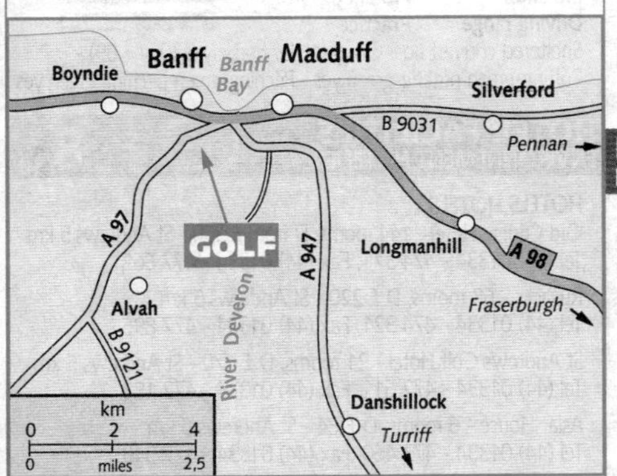

Access Accès : Aberdeen, A947 → Banff and Macduff. In Macduff, cross the river Deveron, course next to the bridge, up the rise towards Banff.
Map 1 on page 471 Carte 1 Page 471

GOLF COURSE — PARCOURS — 15/20

Site	Site	
Maintenance	Entretien	
Architect	Architecte	Alister Mackenzie
Type	Type	parkland
Relief	Relief	
Water in play	Eau en jeu	
Exp. to wind	Exposé au vent	
Trees in play	Arbres en jeu	

Scorecard Carte de score	Chp. / Chp.	Mens / Mess.	Ladies / Da.
Length Long.	5665	5665	5665
Par	69	69	69
Slope system	—	—	—

Advised golfing ability / Niveau de jeu recommandé: 0 12 24 36

Hcp required / Handicap exigé: no

CLUB HOUSE & AMENITIES — CLUB HOUSE ET ANNEXES — 6/10

Pro shop Pro-shop
Driving range Practice
Sheltered couvert no - **On grass** sur herbe no - **Putting-green** putting-green yes - **Pitching-green** pitching green no

HOTEL FACILITIES — ENVIRONNEMENT HOTELIER — 5/10

HOTELS HÔTELS
The Orchard - 5 rooms, D £ 56 - Banff 1 km
Tel (44) 01261 - 812 146, Fax (44) 01261 - 812 146

Fife Lodge - Banff 1 km
7 rooms, D £ 75
Tel (44) 01261 - 812 436, Fax (44) 01261 - 812 636

Banff Springs Hotel - Banff 1.5 km
31 rooms, D £ 97
Tel (44) 01261 - 812 881, Fax (44) 01261 - 815 546

RESTAURANTS RESTAURANTS
Banff Springs Hotel - Banff 1.5 km - Tel (44) 01261 - 812 881

Duke's St Andrews

15 | 7 | 8

Five times British Open winner Peter Thomson designed this course at the request of the Old Course Hotel. It was intended for hotel patrons owing to the problem of getting firm guaranteed tee-off times on the adjacent Old Course (the hotel has recently been purchased by the American Kohler, the owner of Whistling Straits). Contrary to its illustrious neighbour, the Duke's Course is 3 miles inland and very different in character. It is situated on high land in a park of over 330 acres and offers some magnificent views over the old town of St Andrews and the mountains to the north beyond the bay of St Andrews. Owing to the steep slopes and distances between green and next tee, we would advise a buggy, something that would certainly be seen as sacrilege on the "real" St Andrews. Difficult, intelligent and well landscaped, the Duke's is a solid test of golf, best played from the front tees. Facilities here are top quality.

Cinq fois vainqueur du British Open, Peter Thomson a dessiné ce parcours à la demande du Old Course Hotel et à l'intention de ses clients, en raison de la difficulté d'obtenir des départs garantis sur le "Old Course" jouxtant cet hôtel, racheté récemment par l'Américain Kohler, créateur de Whistling Straits. Contrairement à son illustre voisin, le "Duke's" est un parcours intérieur situé à 5 km de la mer, et d'un caractère très différent. Il a été tracé sur un terrain élevé, dans un parc de plus de 150 hectares (330 acres) et propose des vues magnifiques sur la vieille ville de St Andrews, et sur les montagnes au nord au delà de la baie de St Andrews. A cause du relief et des distances entre greens et départs, on conseillera l'usage de la voiturette, qui serait une hérésie sur le "vrai" St Andrews. Bien mieux qu'une solution de rechange ou un ersatz, difficile, intelligent, bien paysagé, le "Duke's" propose un solide test de golf, où l'on conseillera les départs avancés. Les équipements du lieu sont de haute qualité.

The Duke's Golf Club — 1995

Craigton
SCO - ST ANDREWS, Fife KY16 8NS

Office	Secrétariat	(44) 01334 - 474 371
Pro shop	Pro-shop	(44) 01334 - 474 371
Fax	Fax	(44) 01334 - 477 668
Web	www.oldcoursehotel.co.uk	
Situation	Situation	St Andrews, 5 km
Annual closure	Fermeture annuelle	no
Weekly closure	Fermeture hebdomadaire	no
Fees main season	Tarifs haute saison	18 holes

	Week days Semaine	We/Bank holidays We/Férié
Individual Individuel	£ 65	£ 75
Couple Couple	£ 130	£ 150

Caddie Caddie no — **Electric Trolley** Chariot électrique no
Buggy Voiturette yes — **Clubs** Clubs yes

Credit cards Cartes de crédit
VISA - Eurocard - MasterCard - AMEX - DC - JCB

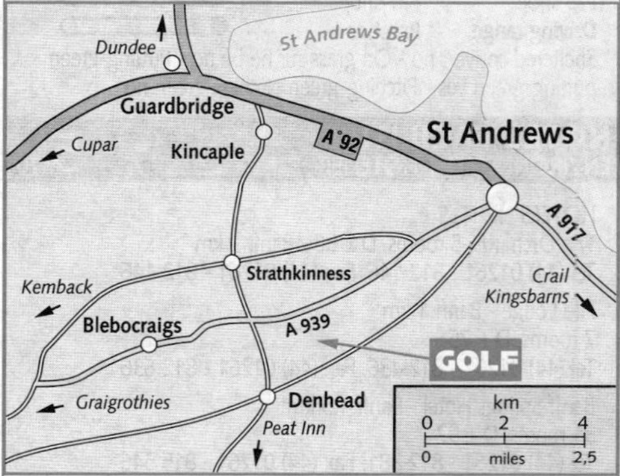

Access Accès : A91 → St Andrews through Guardbridge, then right to Strathkinness, go through towards Craigtoun (on left). Follow signs to Craigtoun Country Park).
Map 3 on page 475 Carte 3 Page 475

GOLF COURSE — PARCOURS — 15/20

Site	Site	
Maintenance	Entretien	
Architect	Architecte	Peter Thomson
Type	Type	parkland
Relief	Relief	
Water in play	Eau en jeu	
Exp. to wind	Exposé au vent	
Trees in play	Arbres en jeu	

Scorecard Carte de score	Chp. Chp.	Mens Mess.	Ladies Da.
Length Long.	6616	6145	5528
Par	72	72	72
Slope system	127	127	127

Advised golfing ability — Niveau de jeu recommandé — 0 12 24 36
Hcp required — Handicap exigé — 36

CLUB HOUSE & AMENITIES — CLUB HOUSE ET ANNEXES — 7/10

Pro shop Pro-shop
Driving range Practice
Sheltered couvert no - On grass sur herbe yes (05 → 09) - Putting-green putting-green yes - Pitching-green pitching green yes

HOTEL FACILITIES — ENVIRONNEMENT HOTELIER — 8/10

HOTELS HÔTELS

Old Course Hotel - 144 rooms, D from £ 350 - St Andrews 5 km
Tel (44) 01334 - 474 371, Fax (44) 01334 - 477 668

Rusacks - 68 rooms, D £ 220 - St Andrews 5 km
Tel (44) 01334 - 474 321, Fax (44) 01334 - 477 896

St Andrews Golf Hotel - 21 rooms, D £ 170 - St Andrews 5 km
Tel (44) 01334 - 472 611, Fax (44) 01334 - 472 188

Aslar House - 6 rooms, D £ 84 - St Andrews 5 km
Tel (44) 01334 - 473 460, Fax (44) 01334 - 477 540

RESTAURANTS RESTAURANTS

The Cellar - Ansruther 12 km - Tel (44) 01333 - 477 540
The Peat Inn - Peat Inn 8 km - Tel (44) 01334 - 840 206
Vine Leaf Garden - St Andrews 5 km - Tel (44) 1334 - 477 497

Dumfries & County

15 | 7 | 5

This is one of the best courses in south-west Scotland, a region too often neglected by foreign tourists. Off the beaten track, Dumfries & County is generally in excellent condition and very pleasant on the eye with the river Nith alongside the course. This adds a pastoral note to a very tree-bound landscape. Designed by Willie Fernie in two loops each returning to the club-house, this is one of those collection of courses which will probably never mark the history of golf design but which you are glad to have played. An unpretentious layout which was restyled after WWII and substantially replanted, it is happy to be just a rather difficult course to test the average player, kind enough not to put off the rather less experienced golfer and clever enough to tease expert golfers. The one hole no-one will forget is the tiny 14th, a par-3.

C'est un des meilleurs parcours du sud-ouest de l'Ecosse, une région trop souvent négligée par les touristes étrangers. Hors des sentiers battus, Dumfries & County est généralement en excellente condition, et très plaisant visuellement, où la rivière Nith, le long du terrain, ajoute une note pastorale à un paysage très arboré. Dessiné par Willie Fernie en deux bouclers revenant au club-house, il fait partie de cet ensemble de golfs qui ne marqueront sans doute pas l'histoire de l'architecture de golf, mais que l'on est heureux de connaître et surtout d'avoir joué. Sans prétention aucune,ayant fait l'objet de remaniements après la dernière guerre, et de nombreuses plantations, il tire satisfaction d'être un parcours assez difficile pour tester les joueurs moyens, assez aimable pour ne pas rebuter les joueurs peu expérimentés, assez astucieux pour provoquer les golfeurs experts. Ils garderont au minimum le souvenir du minuscule 14, un par 3.

Dumfries & County Golf Club — 1912

Nunfields, Edinburgh Road
SCO - DUMFRIES DG1 1JX

Office Secrétariat (44) 01387 - 253 585
Pro shop Pro-shop (44) 01387 - 268 918
Fax Fax (44) 01387 - 253 585
Web www.thecounty.org.uk
Situation Situation Dumfries, 1.5 km
Annual closure Fermeture annuelle no
Weekly closure Fermeture hebdomadaire no

Fees main season Tarifs haute saison	18 holes	
	Week days Semaine	**We/Bank holidays** We/Férié
Individual Individuel	£ 28	£ 34
Couple Couple	£ 56	£ 68

Restrictions at week-ends during summer months

Caddie Caddie no — **Electric Trolley** Chariot électrique yes
Buggy Voiturette yes — **Clubs** Clubs yes
Credit cards Cartes de crédit yes (Pro Shop only)

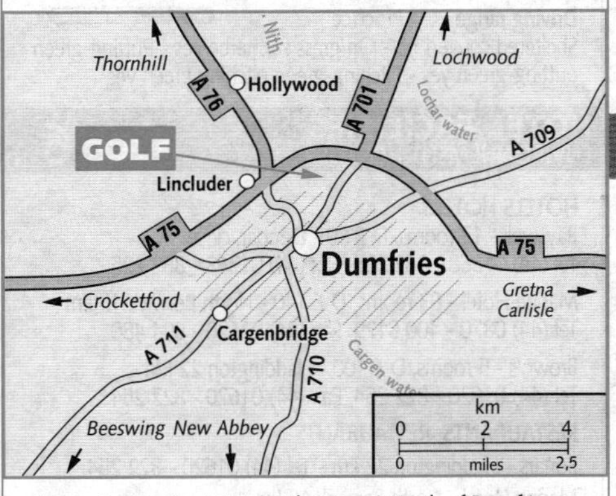

Access Accès : On A701, 1.5 km (1 m.) North of Dumfries
Map 1 on page 471 Carte 1 Page 471

GOLF COURSE — PARCOURS 15/20

Site Site
Maintenance Entretien
Architect Architecte Willie Fernie
Type Type parkland
Relief Relief
Water in play Eau en jeu
Exp. to wind Exposé au vent
Trees in play Arbres en jeu

Scorecard Carte de score	**Chp.** Chp.	**Mens** Mess.	**Ladies** Da.
Length Long.	5418	5418	4954
Par	68	68	72
Slope system	0	0	0

Hcp required Handicap exigé no

CLUB HOUSE & AMENITIES — CLUB HOUSE ET ANNEXES 7/10

Pro shop Pro-shop
Driving range Practice
Sheltered couvert no - On grass sur herbe yes - Putting-green putting-green yes - Pitching-green pitching green no

HOTEL FACILITIES — ENVIRONNEMENT HOTELIER 5/10

HOTELS HÔTELS
Cairndale - 91 rooms, D £ 149 - Dumfries 2 km
Tel (44) 01387 - 254 111, Fax (44) 01387 - 250 555
Station - 32 rooms, D £ 110 - Dumfries 1.5 km
Tel (44) 01387 - 254 316, Fax (44) 01387 - 250 388
Redbank House - 5 rooms, D £ 60 - Dumfries 4 km
Tel (44) 01387 - 247 034, Fax (44) 01387 - 266 220

RESTAURANTS RESTAURANTS
Golf restaurant - on site - Tel (44) 01387 - 253 585
Cairndale - Dumfries 2 km - Tel (44) 01387 - 254 111
Plumed Horse - Crossmichael 20 km
Tel (44) 01556 - 670 333

Dunbar

16 | 5 | 6

One of the classic courses of East Lothian, which nestles on a narrow strip of land along a rocky seashore hardly big enough for two fairways but still reserving some superb views over the Firth of Forth, May Island and the coastline of Fife. This means that you have not only the sea but also a wall and out-of-bounds to contend with, so when the wind blows you just might feel you haven't a friend on earth. In this case do what all amateurs used to do and go around in match-play, a very exciting format on this type of course. The most memorable part of the course is from the 7th to the 16th holes, as the holes close to the club-house are rather squeezed together. This is where the Firth of Forth becomes the North Sea and the view of this mass of water adds to the pleasure of playing golf in the bracing sea-air, all in a friendly atmosphere.

C'est un des parcours classiques de l'East Lothian, blotti sur une étroite bande le long d'un rivage rocheux, avec à peine assez de place pour placer deux fairways côte-à-côte, mais assez pour réserver des vues superbes sur le Firth of Forth, la May Island et les contours du Fife. Ce qui implique non seulement que la mer est en jeu, mais aussi qu'il y ait un mur et des hors-limites. Autrement dit, les jours de vent, les joueurs peuvent avoir l'impression de n'avoir que des adversaires et que tout se ligue contre eux, surtout si leur swing n'est pas au mieux. On leur conseillera alors de se réfugier dans la formule de tous les amateurs d'autrefois, le match-play, toujours très excitant sur des parcours de ce style. Ici, on retiendra particulièrement le passage du 7 au 16, les trous à proximité immédiate du club-house étant plus resserrés. C'est ici que le Firth of Forth devient vraiment la Mer du Nord, et la vue de cette immensité ajoute encore au plaisir du jeu de golf dans un air vivifiant, et dans une atmosphère amicale.

Dunbar Golf Club — 1856

East Links
SCO - DUNBAR, East Lothian, EH42 1LL

Office	Secrétariat	(44) 01368 - 862 317
Pro shop	Pro-shop	(44) 01368 - 862 086
Fax	Fax	(44) 01368 - 865 202
Web	www.dunbar-golfclub.co.uk	
Situation	Situation	Edinburgh, 48 km
Annual closure	Fermeture annuelle	no
Weekly closure	Fermeture hebdomadaire	no

Fees main season Tarifs haute saison — 18 holes

	Week days / Semaine	We/Bank holidays / We/Férié
Individual Individuel	£ 43	£ 53
Couple Couple	£ 86	£ 106

Caddie Caddie yes — **Electric Trolley** Chariot électrique yes
Buggy Voiturette yes — **Clubs** Clubs yes
Credit cards Cartes de crédit
VISA - MasterCard

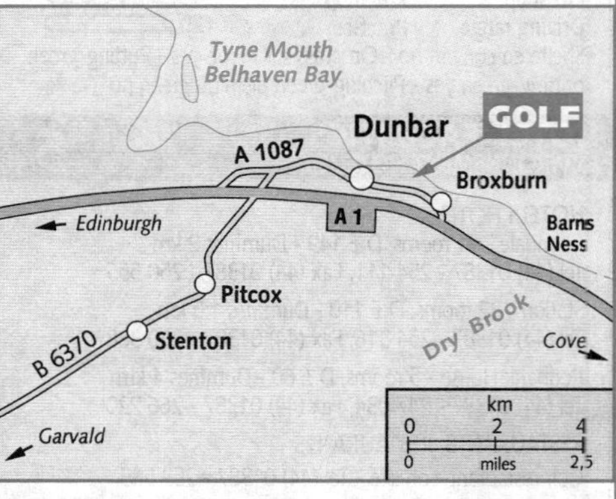

Access Accès : 1 km East of Dunbar on A1 and A1087
Map 2 on page 473 Carte 2 Page 473

GOLF COURSE — PARCOURS 16/20

Site	Site	
Maintenance	Entretien	
Architect	Architecte	Tom Morris
Type	Type	seaside course
Relief	Relief	
Water in play	Eau en jeu	
Exp. to wind	Exposé au vent	
Trees in play	Arbres en jeu	

Scorecard / Carte de score	Chp. / Chp.	Mens / Mess.	Ladies / Da.
Length Long.	5848	5848	5848
Par	71	71	74
Slope system	—	—	—

Advised golfing ability / Niveau de jeu recommandé — 0 12 24 36
Hcp required — Handicap exigé — certificate

CLUB HOUSE & AMENITIES — CLUB HOUSE ET ANNEXES 5/10

Pro shop — Pro-shop
Driving range — Practice
Sheltered couvert no - On grass sur herbe yes - Putting-green putting-green yes - Pitching-green pitching green yes

HOTEL FACILITIES — ENVIRONNEMENT HOTELIER 6/10

HOTELS HÔTELS
Bayswell - 13 rooms, D £ 80 - Dunbar, close
Tel (44) 01368 - 862 225, Fax (44) 01368 - 862 225

Marine Hotel - 83 rooms, D £ 140 - North Berwick 15 km
Tel (44) 0870 - 400 8129, Fax (44) 01620 - 894 480

Brown's - 5 rooms, D £ 100 - Haddington 22 km
Tel (44) 01620 - 822 254, Fax (44) 01620 - 822 254

RESTAURANTS RESTAURANTS
Bonars - Haddington 22 km - Tel (44) 01620 - 822 254
Marine Hotel - North Berwick 15 km
Tel (44) 01620 - 892 406
Bayswell Hotel - Dunbar, close - Tel (44) 01368 - 862 225

Dundonald

18	8	7

This new links course is the seaside outpost of the very exclusive international members' club at Loch Lomond. It lies at the heart of that great stretch of classic links land on the Ayrshire coast centred around Prestwick and Royal Troon. When the Loch Lomond owners bought the site they changed the name from Southern Gailes to Dundonald and it was expected that the course would be just as private and inaccessible to the public as Loch Lomond. But Dundonald has not retreated entirely behind closed doors. The outside world is being given the chance to sample this spectacular layout created by Kyle Phillips, designer of the famous Kingsbarns Links near St Andrews in Fife. However, only four tee times per day are being allocated to visitors and there is likely to be a steady demand for them. Kyle Philips has been true to the style of the classic links courses that surround Dundonald and it is hard to imagine that this course is so young and yet so mature. Huge and sometimes severely contoured greens and clever bunkering are the hallmarks of this excellent design.

Au cœur d'une grande série de links classiques de l'Ayrshire, c'est l'avant-poste en bord de mer du très exclusif Loch Lomond GC. Les nouveaux propriétaires ont modifié son nom de Southern Gailes à Dundonald, et l'on pensait qu'il serait aussi privé que Loch Lomond. Mais ce parcours aussi exigeant que spectaculaire n'a pas été dissimulé aux yeux du monde, et quatre départs par jour sont réservés aux visiteurs extérieurs. Il est dû au crayon de Kyle Phillips, l'auteur célébré de Kingsbarns, et Dundonald ne lui est pas inférieur. L'architecte a bien sûr emprunté avec panache tous les habits des grands links de la côte, et l'on imagine mal que ce parcours soit si jeune et déjà si "mature", tant ses formes ont été soignées, qu'il s'agisse des bunkers, des contours de fairway ou des greens vastes et nettement modelés. Ici, la nature ayant déjà fait une part du travail, il ne fallait plus qu'un architecte cultivé pour produire une belle œuvre d'art, sans copier rien ni personne.

Dundonald Golf Club — 2003

Ayr Road
SCO - IRVINE, KA11 5BF

Office	Secrétariat	(44) 01294 - 314 000
Pro shop	Pro-shop	(44) 01294 - 314 006
Fax	Fax	(44) 01294 - 314 001
Web	www.lochlomond.com	
Situation	Situation	Troon, 8 km
Annual closure	Fermeture annuelle	no
Weekly closure	Fermeture hebdomadaire	no

Fees main season Tarifs haute saison	18 holes	
	Week days Semaine	**We/Bank holidays** We/Férié
Individual Individuel	£ 95	£ 95
Couple Couple	£ 190	£ 190

Caddie Caddie yes — **Electric Trolley** Chariot électrique no

Buggy Voiturette no — **Clubs** Clubs yes

Credit cards Cartes de crédit
VISA - MasterCard - AMEX - DC

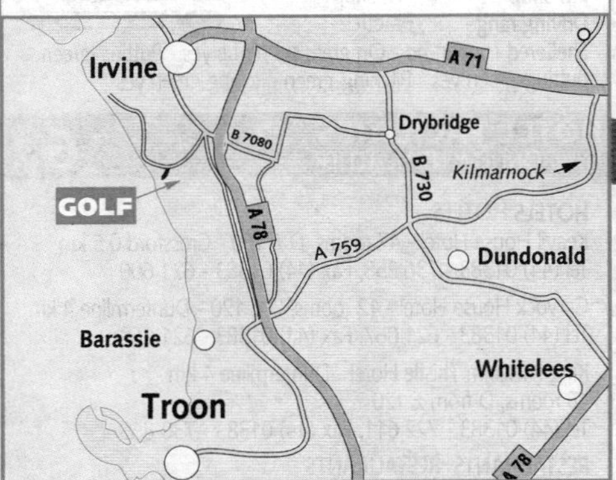

Access Accès : On A78, 3 km South of Jct with A71
Map 3 on page 474 Carte 3 Page 474

GOLF COURSE — PARCOURS — 18/20

Site	Site	
Maintenance	Entretien	
Architect	Architecte	Kyle Phillips
Type	Type	links, seaside
Relief	Relief	
Water in play	Eau en jeu	
Exp. to wind	Exposé au vent	
Trees in play	Arbres en jeu	

Scorecard Carte de score	**Chp.** Chp.	**Mens** Mess.	**Ladies** Da.
Length Long.	6675	6186	5102
Par	72	72	72
Slope system	—	138	131

Advised golfing ability Niveau de jeu recommandé: 0 12 24 36
Hcp required Handicap exigé

CLUB HOUSE & AMENITIES — CLUB HOUSE ET ANNEXES — 8/10

Pro shop Pro-shop
Driving range Practice
Sheltered couvert no - On grass sur herbe yes - Putting-green putting-green yes - Pitching-green pitching green yes

HOTEL FACILITIES — ENVIRONNEMENT HOTELIER — 7/10

HOTELS HÔTELS
The Gailes Lodge - 40 rooms, D £ 60 - Gailes 1 km
Tel (44) 01294 – 204 040, Fax 44) 01294 – 204 047

Marine Highland - 89 rooms, D £ 140 - Troon 5 km
Tel (44) 01292 - 314 444, Fax (44) 01292 - 316 922

Lochgreen House - Troon 5 km
44 rooms, D £ 110
Tel (44) 01292 - 313 343, Fax (44) 01292 - 318 661

RESTAURANTS RESTAURANTS
Highgrove House - Troon 3 km - Tel (44) 01292 - 312 511
The Oyster Bar - Troon 5 km - Tel (44) 01292 - 319 339

Dunfermline

15 | 7 | 6

This city was the capital of Scotland up until 1603 and still carries the vestiges of its prestigious past. Now while the kingdom of Fife is famous for its links, shaped by nature over several hundred years, this particular course is an inland layout which has much to be said for it but without quite the same nobility. Tradition here goes back more than 110 years, and although the course was constructed at the beginning of the 1950s, no great change was made to the 600 year-old club-house. Trees and bunkers form the traditional hazards of a well-balanced course which is moderately hilly and fun for all. In short, this may not be a top class design but the watchword here is always fun. A major refurbishment of the club-house locker room facilities has provided an additional first class locker room for the exclusive use of visitors, but although functional, this modern extension is hardly what you might call appealing.

La ville fut la capitale de l'Ecosse jusqu'en 1603, et conserve les vestiges d'un aussi prestigieux passé. Mais si le royaume de Fife est célèbre par ses links patinés depuis des siècles par la nature, le présent parcours "inland" ne manque pas de qualités non plus, sans prétendre pour autant à tant de noblesse. Sa tradition remonte à plus de 110 ans, et bien que le parcours lui-même ait été créé au début des années 1950, l'on a peu touché au club-house, qui date, lui, de plus de six cent ans. Les arbres et les bunkers forment les obstacles traditionnels d'un parcours bien équilibré dans ses difficultés, modérément mouvementé, amusant pour tous les niveaux. Bref, un modèle de golf "middle-of-the-road," que l'on pourrait parfois avoir envie de violenter un peu, mais le maître mot est ici le plaisir. Un rafraîchissement important du club-house a offert aux visiteurs de très beaux vestiaires, mais, pour être fonctionnelle, cette extension moderne n'est pas des plus séduisantes.

Dunfermline Golf Club — 1887

Pitfirrane, Crossford
SCO - DUNFERMLINE, Fife KY12 8QW

Office	Secrétariat	(44) 01383 - 723 534
Pro shop	Pro-shop	(44) 01383 - 729 061
Fax	Fax	(44) 01383 - 723 547
E-mail	secretary@dunfermlinegolfclub.com	
Situation	Situation	Edinburgh, 27 km

Dunfermline (pop.29 436), 3 km

Annual closure	Fermeture annuelle	no
Weekly closure	Fermeture hebdomadaire	no
Fees main season	Tarifs haute saison	18 holes

	Week days / Semaine	We/Bank holidays / We/Férié
Individual Individuel	£ 27	£ 35*
Couple Couple	£ 54	£ 70*

* Sundays only

Caddy Caddie no — **Electric Trolley** Chariot électrique yes
Buggy Voiturette yes — **Clubs** Clubs yes
Credit cards Cartes de crédit no

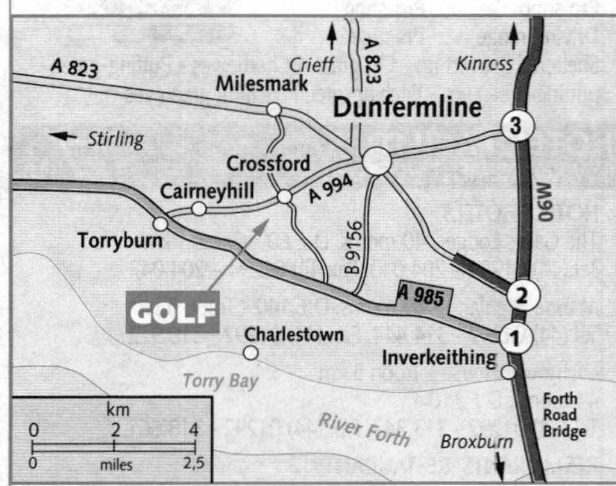

Access Accès : On A994, West of Dunfermline
Map 2 on page 473 Carte 2 Page 473

GOLF COURSE — PARCOURS 15/20

Site	Site	
Maintenance	Entretien	
Architect	Architecte	Stutt & Co
Type	Type	parkland
Relief	Relief	
Water in play	Eau en jeu	
Exp. to wind	Exposé au vent	
Trees in play	Arbres en jeu	

Scorecard Carte de score	Chp. Chp.	Mens Mess.	Ladies Da.
Length Long.	5575	5263	4917
Par	72	70	72
Slope system	—	—	—

Advised golfing ability Niveau de jeu recommandé: 0 12 24 36
Hcp required Handicap exigé: certificate

CLUB HOUSE & AMENITIES — CLUB HOUSE ET ANNEXES 7/10

Pro shop Pro-shop
Driving range Practice
Sheltered couvert no - On grass sur herbe yes - Putting-green putting-green yes - Pitching-green pitching green yes

HOTEL FACILITIES — ENVIRONNEMENT HOTELIER 6/10

HOTELS HÔTELS

Keavil House Hotel - 47 rooms, D £ 150 - Crossford 0.5 km
Te (44) 01383 - 736 258, Fax (44) 01383 - 621 600

Garvock House Hotel - 12 rooms, D £ 120 - Dunfermline 4 km
Te (44) 01383 - 621 067, Fax (44) 01383 - 621 168

King Malcolm Thistle Hotel - Dunfermline 4 km
48 rooms, D from £ 120
Te (44) 01383 - 722 611, Fax (44) 01383 - 730 865

RESTAURANTS RESTAURANTS

Keavil House Hotel - Crossford 0.5 km
Te (44) 01383 - 736 258

King Malcolm - Dunfermline 4 km - Tel (44) 01383 - 722 611

East Renfrewshire

15 | 6 | 8

Although close to Glasgow, this course is located away from any residential area and its location at almost 660 feet gives some magnificent views over Glasgow and the hills of the southern highlands. We are out in the country on Scottish moorland with its typical covering of whin (gorse) and heather, many trees which outline the fairways (originally there were none at all) and a stream that crosses the course, running down the side of the fairways and sometimes cutting across them at strategic distances. This was only to be expected from James Braid. It is very easy to see your ball end up there if you don't give enough thought to flight and roll. Mid-handicappers, though, can always choose a line of flight without too many risks, although the experts will be keen to flex their muscles. In a word, a good score here is not as easy as all that. The club-house is spacious but the course crowded enough for us to advise you to book your tee-off time in advance.

Bien qu'il soit proche de Glasgow, ce parcours est situé en dehors de toute zone résidentielle, et sa situation à près de 200 mètres d'altitude offre des vues imprenables sur Glasgow et les collines du sud des Highlands. Nous sommes à la campagne, dans la lande écossaise, avec une végétation typique d'ajoncs et de bruyère, de nombreux arbres qui définissent les fairways (il n'y en avait pas à l'origine), mais aussi un ruisseau qui parcourt l'espace, longeant les fairways ou venant les interrompre, de manière stratégique, ccomme on pouvait l'attendre de James Braid. Il est très facile d'y voir les balles y terminer leur course si l'on n'a pas réfléchi un peu sur leur portée et leur roulement. Cependant, les handicaps moyens peuvent toujours choisir des lignes de jeu sans grands risques, alors que les experts voudront montrer leurs muscles. Bref, il n'est pas si facile de scorer ici. Le club-house est spacieux, mais le parcours assez fréquenté pour que l'on conseille de réserver les départs à l'avance.

East Renfrewshire Golf Course — 1923

Pilmuir, Newton Mearns
SCO - GLASGOW G77 6RT

Office	Secrétariat	(44) 01355 - 500 256
Pro shop	Pro-shop	(44) 01355 - 500 206
Fax	Fax	(44) 01355 - 500 323
E-mail		secretary@eastrengolfclub.co.uk
Situation	Situation	Glasgow, 15 km
Annual closure	Fermeture annuelle	no
Weekly closure	Fermeture hebdomadaire	no

Fees main season Tarifs haute saison — 18 holes

	Week days Semaine	We/Bank holidays We/Férié
Individual Individuel	£ 40	£ 50
Couple Couple	£ 80	£ 100

Full week day: £ 50

Caddy Caddie no — **Electric Trolley** Chariot électrique no

Buggy Voiturette no — **Clubs** Clubs no

Credit cards Cartes de crédit
VISA - Eurocard - MasterCard - AMEX - DC

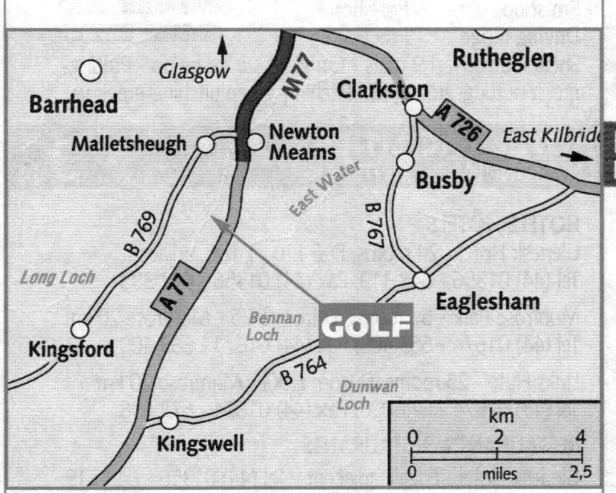

Access Accès : Glasgow M8 and M77/A77 → Kilmarnock. Club on the right shortly after Newton Mearns.
Map 3 on page 474 Carte 3 Page 474

GOLF COURSE — PARCOURS — 15/20

Site	Site	
Maintenance	Entretien	
Architect	Architecte	James Braid
Type	Type	inland, moorland
Relief	Relief	
Water in play	Eau en jeu	
Exp. to wind	Exposé au vent	
Trees in play	Arbres en jeu	

Scorecard Carte de score	Chp. Chp.	Mens Mess.	Ladies Da.
Length Long.	5577	5577	4668
Par	70	70	71
Slope system	—	—	—

Advised golfing ability Niveau de jeu recommandé — 0 12 24 36

Hcp required Handicap exigé — certificate

CLUB HOUSE & AMENITIES — CLUB HOUSE ET ANNEXES — 6/10

Pro shop Pro-shop
Driving range Practice
Sheltered couvert no - On grass sur herbe yes - Putting-green putting-green yes - Pitching-green pitching green yes

HOTEL FACILITIES — ENVIRONNEMENT HOTELIER — 8/10

HOTELS HÔTELS

Glasgow Hilton - 319 rooms, D £ 190 - Glasgow 15 km
Tel (44) 0141 - 204 5555, Fax (44) 0141 - 204 5004

One Devonshire Gardens - Glasgow 15 km
35 rooms, D from £ 145
Tel (44) 0141 - 339 2001, Fax (44) 0141 - 337 1663

Bewley's - 103 rooms, D £ 59 - Glasgow 15 km
Tel (44) 0141 - 353 0800, Fax (44) 0141 - 353 0900

RESTAURANTS RESTAURANTS

One Devonshire Gardens - Glasgow 15 km
Tel (44) 0141 - 339 2001

Buttery - Glasgow 15 km - Tel (44) 0141 - 221 8188

No Sixteen - Glasgow 15 km - Tel (44) 0141 - 339 2544

Edzell

14	6	3

This course is located virtually in town, or should we say village, as Edzell has often been voted "the best preserved village in Scotland". It was certainly one of the most stylishly frequented for many a year, as princes and maharajahs would come here for the fishing and hunting at the edge of the Highlands, and certainly to play this course designed in 1895 by Bob Simpson of Carnoustie and updated by Braid in 1933. Laid out over gorse-land, this is a gem of a course, with a wide variety of holes, small, well-kept greens, soft fairways and hazards of all shapes and sizes, including bunkers, a steep-banked river and trees. This is one of the places in Scotland where you can still feel "out of time", as you are so far away from the main roads. We didn't expect a Japanese-style club-house on this kind of course; what really matters was hospitality, and here you found that a plenty, but a £300,000 club-house refurbishment has been completed. And the 9-hole West Water Course opened in 2001 is now well established.

Ce parcours est pratiquement situé dans le village d'Edzell, souvent élu comme "le village le mieux préservé d'Ecosse." Il fut longtemps aussi le "mieux" fréquenté, car princes et maharadjahs venaient ici pêcher, chasser en bordure des Highlands, et sans doute aussi jouer sur ce parcours créé en 1895 par Bob Simpson de Carnoustie et révisé par Braid en 1933. Tracé en terre de bruyère, c'est un petit bijou, avec des trous très variés, de petits greens bien entretenus, des fairways souples et des obstacles en tous genres, depuis les bunkers jusqu'à la rivière et ses rives abruptes en passant par les bois. C'est un des endroits d'Ecosse où l'on peut le plus se croire hors du temps, parce qu'on se retrouve aussi à l'écart des grandes routes. Dans ce genre de golf, l'on n'attendait pas un club-house à la japonaise, l'essentiel était dans la chaleur de l'accueil. Mais une rénovation du club-house a été effectuée, que l'on ajoutera au plaisir de trouver ici un 9 trous supplémentaire depuis quelques années.

The Edzell Golf Club — 1895

High Street
SCO - EDZELL, by Brechin, Tayside DD9 7TF

Office	Secrétariat	(44) 01356 - 647 283
Pro shop	Pro-shop	(44) 01356 - 648 462
Fax	Fax	(44) 01356 - 648 094
Web	www.edzellgolfclub.net	
Situation	Situation	Brechin, 8 km Montrose (pop. 8 473), 20 km
Annual closure	Fermeture annuelle	no
Weekly closure	Fermeture hebdomadaire	no

Fees main season Tarifs haute saison — 18 holes

	Week days Semaine	We/Bank holidays We/Férié
Individual Individuel	£ 28	£ 34
Couple Couple	£ 56	£ 68

Full week day: £ 35

Caddy Caddie no — **Electric Trolley** Chariot électrique no
Buggy Voiturette yes — **Clubs** Clubs yes
Credit cards Cartes de crédit yes

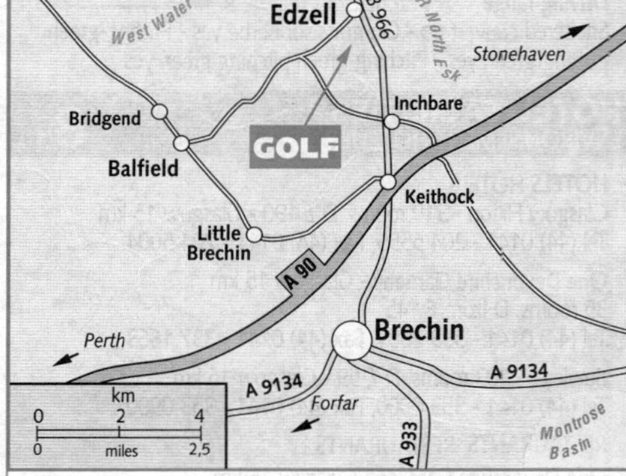

Access Accès : Dundee A90. After Brechin, B966 to Edzell. Golf alongside main entrance to village.
Map 1 on page 471 Carte 1 Page 471

GOLF COURSE — PARCOURS 14/20

Site	Site	
Maintenance	Entretien	
Architect	Architecte	Bob Simpson
Type	Type	heathland, parkland
Relief	Relief	
Water in play	Eau en jeu	
Exp. to wind	Exposé au vent	
Trees in play	Arbres en jeu	

Scorecard Carte de score	Chp. Chp.	Mens Mess.	Ladies Da.
Length Long.	5822	5525	5064
Par	71	71	74
Slope system	—	—	—

Advised golfing ability Niveau de jeu recommandé — 0 12 24 36
Hcp required Handicap exigé — no

CLUB HOUSE & AMENITIES — CLUB HOUSE ET ANNEXES 6/10

Pro shop Pro-shop
Driving range Practice
Sheltered couvert 9 mats - On grass sur herbe no - Putting-green putting-green yes - Pitching-green pitching green yes

HOTEL FACILITIES — ENVIRONNEMENT HOTELIER 3/10

HOTELS HÔTELS

Glenesk Hotel - 24 rooms, D £ 110 - Edzell, adjacent
Tel (44) 01356 - 648 319, Fax (44) 01356 - 647 333

Montrose Park - 57 rooms, D from £ 75 - Montrose 20 km
Tel (44) 01674 - 663 400, Fax (44) 01674 - 663 400

Links Hotel - 25 rooms, D from £ 90 - Montrose 20 km
Tel (44) 01674 - 671 000, Fax (44) 01674 - 672 698

RESTAURANTS RESTAURANTS

Glenesk Hotel - Edzell, adjacent - Tel (44) 01356 - 648 319

Elgin

15 | 7 | 5

This course has the enviable reputation of being one of the best inland courses in northern Scotland; it was upgraded to 18 holes in 1924 with an immediate effect on the course's popularity (a special bus service had to be opened to meet demand). At all events it is a very good test of golf, and although its length may seem a little outdated, there is only the one par 5 and this can often dash any hope of carding a good score. Precision is at a premium here, but hazards are in good view and so can help you recover an efficient game strategy. Eight of the par-4s are longer than 390 yards, so you can understand Elgin's reputation for being a serious examination of every green-feer's talent. For want of beating any records, you can always enjoy the view over the old city of Elgin to the north (well worth a visit) and to the south the superb Cairngorm Mountains (well worth exploring). The present club-house was opened in what was a former smallpox hospital.

Ce parcours a la réputation enviable d'être l'un des meilleurs parcours "inlands" du nord de l'Ecosse, il fut étendu à 18 trous en 1924, avec un succès de fréquentation immédiat (on créa même une ligne de bus pour y accéder). C'est en tout cas un très bon test de golf, et si sa longueur peut le faire paraître désuet, ce n'est après tout qu'un par 69, qui ne comporte qu'un seul par 5, ce qui complique bien souvent l'espérance d'un bon score. Il faut être ici très précis, mais les obstacles sont assez en vue pour établir rapidement une stratégie efficace. Huit des par 4 mesurant plus de 360 mètres, on comprend que la réputation d'Elgin soit aussi d'être un sérieux examen du talent des visiteurs. A défaut de battre tous les records, ceux-ci pourront se livrer à la contemplation du panorama sur la vieille cité d'Elgin au nord (à visiter) et, au sud, sur les superbes Cairngorm Mountains (à explorer). L'actuel club-house a été créé dans les bâtiments de l'ancien hôpital contre la variole.

Elgin Golf Club — 1926

Birnie Road
SCO - ELGIN, Moray IV30 3SX

Office	Secrétariat	(44) 01343 - 542 338
Pro shop	Pro-shop	(44) 01343 - 542 884
Fax	Fax	(44) 01343 - 542 341
Web	www.elgingolfclub.com	
Situation	Situation	Elgin (pop. 11 855), 1 km

Inverness (pop. 62 186), 62 km

Annual closure Fermeture annuelle — no

Weekly closure Fermeture hebdomadaire — no

Fees main season Tarifs haute saison — 18 holes

	Week days Semaine	We/Bank holidays We/Férié
Individual Individuel	£ 28	£ 28
Couple Couple	£ 56	£ 56

Caddy Caddie yes — **Electric Trolley** Chariot électrique yes

Buggy Voiturette yes — **Clubs** Clubs yes

Credit cards Cartes de crédit yes

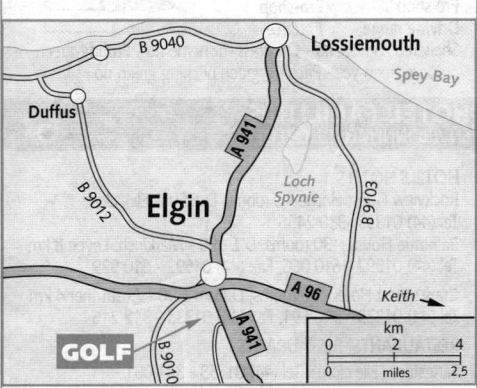

Access Accès : Aberdeen or Inverness A96 to Elgin.
Golf on A941 just South of town limits
Map 1 on page 471 Carte 1 Page 471

GOLF COURSE — PARCOURS — 15/20

Site	Site	
Maintenance	Entretien	
Architect	Architecte	John MacPherson
Type	Type	parkland
Relief	Relief	
Water in play	Eau en jeu	
Exp. to wind	Exposé au vent	
Trees in play	Arbres en jeu	

Scorecard / Carte de score	**Chp.** / Chp.	**Mens** / Mess.	**Ladies** / Da.
Length Long.	5834	5608	5290
Par	69	69	74
Slope system	—	—	—

Advised golfing ability / Niveau de jeu recommandé — 0 12 24 36

Hcp required Handicap exigé — no

CLUB HOUSE & AMENITIES — CLUB HOUSE ET ANNEXES — 7/10

Pro shop Pro-shop
Driving range Practice
Sheltered couvert 16 mats - On grass sur herbe no - Putting-green putting-green yes - Pitching-green pitching green no

HOTEL FACILITIES — ENVIRONNEMENT HOTELIER — 5/10

HOTELS HÔTELS
Mansion House - Elgin 1 km
23 rooms, D £ 165
Tel (44) 01343 - 548 811, Fax (44) 01343 - 547 916

Mansefield House - Elgin 1 km
40 rooms, D £ 90
Tel (44) 01343 - 540 883, Fax (44) 01343 - 552 491

The Croft - 3 rooms, D £ 60 - Elgin 2 km
Tel (44) 01343 - 546 004, Fax (44) 01343 - 546 004

RESTAURANTS RESTAURANTS
Mansion House - Elgin 1 km - Tel (44) 01343 - 548 811
Mansefield House - Elgin 1 km - Tel (44) 01343 - 540 883

Elie

15	6	6

This is where James Braid learnt his golf, and you can understand why he became such a great champion and such a good course architect. Elie is a delightful course, as picturesque as they come with a number of rural features that will stay for ever, notably its location virtually in the middle of the village. But if you get the impression you are in for a pleasure cruise, watch out. The traps here are as frequent as the number of shots that, although not completely blind, do raise a few questions and eye-brows. Exposure to the wind is so fierce that there is no point in worrying about the theoretical par for each hole. It changes from one day to the next. Likewise you'll learn how to bump and run the ball by asking the locals who are always willing to give advice. One of the region's most amusing courses. If the going gets really tough, stop and have a chat with the seals on the 11th tee…

C'est ici que James Braid a appris le golf, l'on comprend qu'il soit devenu un si grand champion, et un si bon architecte. Elie est un délicieux parcours, aussi pittoresque que possible, avec certains aspects rustiques à préserver, notamment sa situation quasiment au milieu du village. Mais si l'on a l'impression de s'y livrer à une partie de plaisir, il faut méfiance garder. Les pièges sont ici aussi nombreux que les coups sinon aveugles (il y en a, comme le drive du 1), du moins bien soulignés de points d'interrogation. L'exposition au vent est tellement importante qu'il ne faut surtout pas se soucier du par théorique de chaque trou, il change d'un jour à l'autre. De même on y apprendra à faire rouler la balle, en demandant aux joueurs locaux, qui n'hésitent jamais à livrer leurs bons conseils (parfois très personnels)... avec l'accent. L'un des plus amusants parcours de la région. Et si vous ne parvenez pas à déjouer ses pièges, allez demander conseil aux phoques au départ du 11.

Golf House Club Elie — 1875

SCO - ELIE, LEVEN, Fife, KY9 1AS

Office Secrétariat (44) 01333 - 330 301
Pro shop Pro-shop (44) 01333 - 330 955
Fax Fax (44) 01333 - 330 895
Web www.valuegolf.co.uk/html/golf_course_map.html
Situation Situation St Andrews, 19 km
Annual closure Fermeture annuelle no
Weekly closure Fermeture hebdomadaire no

Fees main season Tarifs haute saison	18 holes	
	Week days Semaine	**We/Bank holidays** We/Férié
Individual Individuel	£ 50	£ 60
Couple Couple	£ 100	£ 120

Full days: £ 70 / £ 80 (We)

Caddy Caddie on request **Electric Trolley** Chariot électrique yes
Buggy Voiturette no **Clubs** Clubs yes
Credit cards Cartes de crédit yes

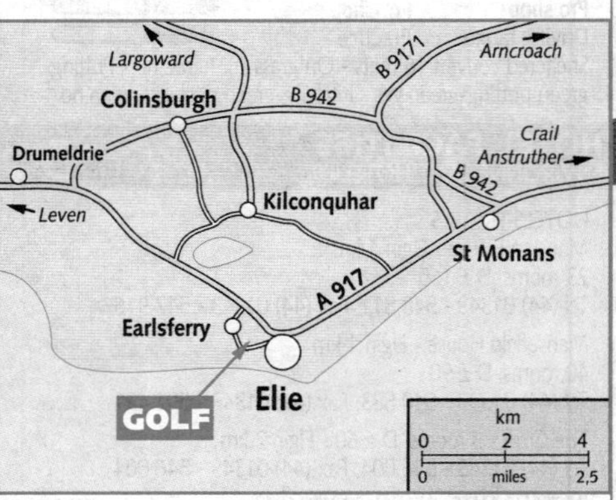

Access Accès : Edinburgh M90, A92 to Kirkcaldy. then A917. Golf 8 km in the centre of village.
Map 3 on page 475 Carte 3 Page 475

GOLF COURSE — PARCOURS 15/20

Site Site
Maintenance Entretien
Architect Architecte unknown
Type Type links
Relief Relief
Water in play Eau en jeu
Exp. to wind Exposé au vent
Trees in play Arbres en jeu

Scorecard Carte de score	**Chp.** Chp.	**Mens** Mess.	**Ladies** Da.
Length Long.	5697	5697	5697
Par	70	70	75
Slope system	—	—	—

Advised golfing ability Niveau de jeu recommandé 0 12 24 36
Hcp required Handicap exigé certificate

CLUB HOUSE & AMENITIES — CLUB HOUSE ET ANNEXES 6/10

Pro shop Pro-shop
Driving range Practice
Sheltered couvert no - **On grass** sur herbe no - **Putting-green** putting-green yes - **Pitching-green** pitching green no

HOTEL FACILITIES — ENVIRONNEMENT HOTELIER 6/10

HOTELS HÔTELS
Rockview Guest House - 6 rooms, D £ 50 - Elie, close
Tel (44) 01333 -330 2456
Balbirnie House - 30 rooms, D £ 190 - Markinch, Leven 8 km
Tel (44) 01592 - 610 066, Fax (44) 01592 - 610 529
Craw's Nest Hotel - 50 rooms, D from £ 90 - Anstruther 4 km
Tel (44) 01333 - 310 691, Fax (44) 01333 - 312 216

RESTAURANTS RESTAURANTS
Sangsters - Elie close - Tel (44) 01333 - 331 001
Cellar - Anstruther 4 km - Tel (44) 01333 - 310 378
Ship Inn - Elie close - Tel (44) 01333 - 330 246

Falkirk Tryst

13	5	7

This is not the most engaging site for golf. With a cricket pitch right in the middle, here you have the two most mysterious games ever invented by man sitting side by side. The course was built over several stages on flat terrain in the village of Larbert. The first three holes form a sort of loop. From N° 4 to N° 10 (plus the 18th), you have another set of holes, then a third running from hole number 11 to 17. On this course, where the rhythm of the layout is strange to say the least, the par 3s are called "short holes", even though two of them are in the region of 200 yards and the three others never shorter than 165 yards. By contrast, two of the three par 5s provide a reasonable opportunity for a birdie. When it comes to counting your score, you will see that playing to your handicap is anything but easy, an annoying state of affairs when considering how flat and short the course is overall. Lovers of spectacular courses probably would not play here every day, but a round from time to time is always time well spent.

Ce n'est pas le site le plus engageant. Avec un terrain de cricket au milieu de ce golf, voici côte-à-côte les deux jeux les plus mystérieux que l'homme ait inventé. Le parcours a été créé en plusieurs temps sur cet espace plat dans le village de Larbert. Les trois premiers trous forment une boucle. Du 4 au 10 (avec le 18), nous avons encore un autre ensemble, le troisième allant du 11 au 17. Dans cette réalisation au rythme un peu étrange, les par 3 sont appelés "short holes" en anglais, ils n'ont rien de court, deux d'entre eux dépassent les 180 mètres, les trois autres ne sont jamais inférieurs à 150 mètres. Deux des trois par 5 fournissent néanmoins de raisonnables occasions de birdie. A l'heure des comptes, il n'est guère facile de jouer son handicap, ce qui est d'autant plus vexant que le terrain est plat et l'ensemble plutôt court. Certes, les amateurs de parcours spectaculaires ne joueront pas ici tous les jours, mais une visite de temps en temps n'est jamais du temps perdu.

Falkirk Tryst Golf Club **1885**

86 Burn,head Road
SCO - LARBERT, Stirlingshire FK5 4BD

Office	Secrétariat	(44) 01324 - 562 415
Pro shop	Pro-shop	(44) 01324 - 562 091
Fax	Fax	—
Web	—	
Situation	Situation	Edinburgh, 40 km
Annual closure	Fermeture annuelle	no
Weekly closure	Fermeture hebdomadaire	no

Fees main season Tarifs haute saison		full day
	Week days Semaine	**We/Bank holidays** We/Férié
Individual Individuel	£ 18	*
Couple Couple	£ 36	*

* No visitors at week-ends / Full week days: £ 27

Caddy Caddie no — **Electric Trolley** Chariot électrique yes
Buggy Voiturette no — **Clubs** Clubs yes
Credit cards Cartes de crédit no

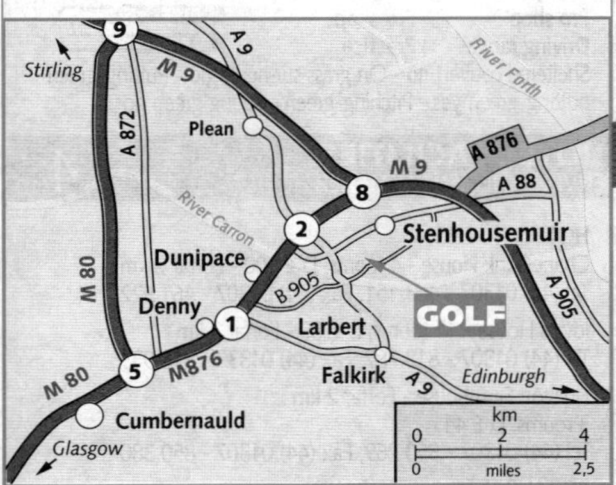

Access Accès : On A88. Access from M876 (from West), A9 from North and South, M9 and A905 from East.
Map 2 on page 473 Carte 2 Page 473

GOLF COURSE
PARCOURS — **13**/20

Site	Site	
Maintenance	Entretien	
Architect	Architecte	unknown
Type	Type	inland, links
Relief	Relief	
Water in play	Eau en jeu	
Exp. to wind	Exposé au vent	
Trees in play	Arbres en jeu	

Scorecard Carte de score	**Chp.** Chp.	**Mens** Mess.	**Ladies** Da.
Length Long.	5532	5112	4993
Par	70	67	71
Slope system	—	—	—

Advised golfing ability Niveau de jeu recommandé: 0 12 24 36
Hcp required Handicap exigé: no

CLUB HOUSE & AMENITIES
CLUB HOUSE ET ANNEXES — **5**/10

Pro shop Pro-shop
Driving range Practice
Sheltered couvert no - On grass sur herbe no - Putting-green putting-green yes - Pitching-green pitching green yes

HOTEL FACILITIES
ENVIRONNEMENT HOTELIER — **7**/10

HOTELS HÔTELS
MacDonald Inchyra - 107 rooms, D £ 150 - Falkirk 5 km
Tel (44) 01324 - 711 911, Fax (44) 01324 - 716 134

Airth Castle - 122 rooms, D £ 195 - Airth 5 km
Tel (44) 01324 - 831 411, Fax (44) 01324 - 831 419

Grange Manor - 36 rooms, D £ 135 - Falkirk 3 km
Tel (44) 01324 - 474 836, Fax (44) 01324 - 665 861

Topps Farm - 8 rooms, D £ 50 - Denny 5 km
Tel (44) 01324 - 822 471, Fax (44) 01324 - 823 099

RESTAURANTS RESTAURANTS
Priory (MacDonald Inchyra) - Falkirk 5 km
Tel (44) 01324 - 711 911

Forfar

14 | 5 | 4

Old Tom Morris came from St Andrews to lay out the first nine holes of this course in beautiful woody landscape dotted with heather at the heart of Angus. In 1925, the Club asked James Braid to upgrade the course to 18 holes, which he did for the princely sum of £10. At that rate you can understand why the man travelled Scotland far and wide, designing hundreds of courses and managing to earn his living as a golf-course architect. Today, the course has been enhanced by some tall pine-trees, but you can still feel Tom Morris' beloved springy turf underfoot and contouring worthy of the finest links. Not a long course - although it is only a par 69 with just the one par 5 - it is still exciting to play, especially the par 3s and a number of blind shots for a few extra thrills. Of further note are two long par 4s, the 12th (440 yards) and the 15th, called "Braid's Best", which says it all. If you are in the region, Forfar is well worth a visit.

Old Tom Morris vint de St Andrews pour tracer les neuf premiers trous de ce parcours dans un beau paysage boisé et parsemé de bruyère, au cœur de l'Angus. En 1925, le club demanda à James Braid de le porter à 18 trous, ce qu'il fit pour la modique somme de dix livres. A ce tarif, on comprend qu'il ait sillonné l'Ecosse pour dessiner une multitude de parcours et parvenir à gagner sa vie d'architecte de golf ! Aujourd'hui, de grands pins viennent agrémenter le tracé, mais on y trouve toujours ce sol élastique que Tom Morris aimait tant, et des contours qui ne dépareraient pas sur un links. De longueur assez modeste - mais c'est un par 69 avec un seul par 5 - il n'en est pas moins passionnant à jouer, en particulier avec ses très beaux par 3, et quelques coups aveugles pour donner un peu d'émotions. On signalera aussi deux longs par 4, le 12, avec 400 mètres, ainsi que le 15, "Braid's Best", c'est tout dire. Si vous êtes dans la région, Forfar mérite bien une halte.

Forfar Golf Club — 1871

Cunning Hill, Arbroath Road
SCO - FORFAR, Angus DD8 2RL

Office Secrétariat (44) 01307 - 463 773
Pro shop Pro-shop (44) 01307 - 465 683
Fax Fax (44) 01307 - 468 495
Web www.forfargolfclub.com
Situation Situation Dundee, 27 km
Forfar (pop. 14 159), 2.5 km
Annual closure Fermeture annuelle no
Weekly closure Fermeture hebdomadaire no

Fees main season Tarifs haute saison — 18 holes

	Week days / Semaine	We/Bank holidays / We/Férié
Individual Individuel	£ 24	£ 24*
Couple Couple	£ 48	£ 48*

* Members only Saturday morning / Full day: £ 30 (We)

Caddy Caddie no — **Electric Trolley** Chariot électrique yes
Buggy Voiturette no — **Clubs** Clubs no
Credit cards Cartes de crédit yes

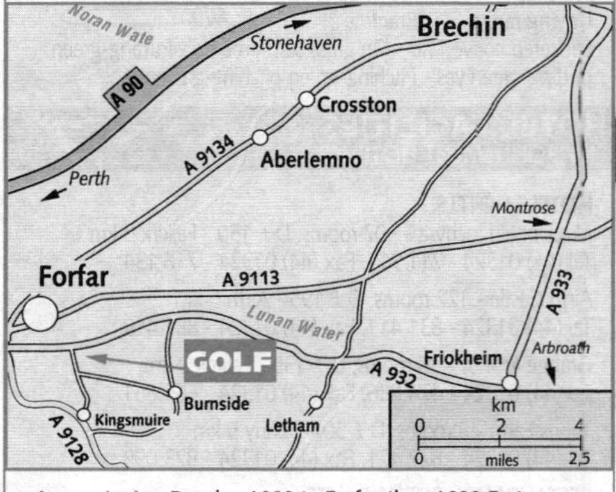

Noran Water
Stonehaven
Brechin
A 90
Crosston
A 9134
Aberlemno
Perth
Montrose
Forfar
A 9113
A 933
Lunan Water
GOLF
Friokheim
Arbroath
A 932
Burnside
Kingsmuire
Letham
A 9128
km 0 2 4
0 miles 2,5

Access Accès : Dundee A929 to Forfar, then A932 East
Map 1 on page 471 Carte 1 Page 471

GOLF COURSE — PARCOURS — 14/20

Site Site
Maintenance Entretien
Architect Architecte — Tom Morris, James Braid
Type Type — heathland
Relief Relief
Water in play Eau en jeu
Exp. to wind Exposé au vent
Trees in play Arbres en jeu

Scorecard / Carte de score	Chp. / Chp.	Mens / Mess.	Ladies / Da.
Length Long.	5547	5261	4970
Par	69	69	72
Slope system	—	—	—

Advised golfing ability Niveau de jeu recommandé — 0 12 24 36
Hcp required Handicap exigé — certificate

CLUB HOUSE & AMENITIES — CLUB HOUSE ET ANNEXES — 5/10

Pro shop Pro-shop
Driving range Practice
Sheltered couvert no - On grass sur herbe no - Putting-green putting-green yes - Pitching-green pitching green no

HOTEL FACILITIES — ENVIRONNEMENT HOTELIER — 4/10

HOTELS HÔTELS
Chapelbank House - 4 rooms, D £ 100 - Forfar 2 km
Tel (44) 01307 - 463 151, Fax (44) 01307 - 461 922

Idvies House - 11 rooms, D £ 80 - Forfar 2 km
Tel (44) 01307 - 818 787, Fax (44) 01333 - 818 933

Finavon Farmhouse - Forfar 2 km
3 rooms, D £ 44
Tel (44) 01307 - 850 269, Fax (44) 01307 - 850 380

RESTAURANTS RESTAURANTS
Chapelbank House - Forfar 2 km - Tel (44) 01307 - 463 151
August Moon - Forfar 2 km - Tel (44) 01307 - 468 688

Fortrose & Rosemarkie

16 | 6 | 5

This delightful course is sited on a promontory on Black Isle and gives a magnificent view over Cromarty Firth. Its shortish length might make you feel that only accuracy is of any importance here, and that's true if the wind keeps low, which is rare. Twice restyled by James Braid, it uses the land in remarkable fashion and is extremely dangerous in the way the sea comes into play on eight holes. Heather, too, is a threat, not to mention some astute bunkering and smallish greens. You will need a broad pair of shoulders to keep your score down on an off-day, but you don't have to keep score. Doubtless a little kinder than its neighbours Royal Dornoch and Nairn, this gently rolling course is magic for everyone, and remarkable value for money with, as a bonus, the spectacle of the dolphins in the Firth. On the 17th, watch out for the stone marking the tomb of the "last" Scottish witch. Was she really the last?

Ce délicieux parcours au nom magnifique est situé sur un promontoire sur la Black Isle et offre un spectacle magnifique sur le Cromarty Firth. Sa longueur très modérée pourrait faire croire que seule va compter la précision. C'est vrai si le vent ne souffle pas, ce qui est bien rare. Révisé à deux reprises par James Braid, il utilise le terrain de manière remarquable, et met en jeu la mer de manière fort dangereuse sur huit trous, ou encore la bruyère, sans compter que les bunkers sont bien placés et les greens pas bien grands. Il faut certes avoir les épaules larges pour serrer le score quand le jeu n'est pas au rendez-vous... mais après tout, on n'est pas toujours obligé de compter les coups. Moins brutal sans doute que ses voisins Royal Dornoch et Nairn, ce parcours aimablement ondulé est un régal pour tous, avec un rapport qualité/prix remarquable, et en prime le spectacle des dauphins dans le Firth. A remarquer enfin au 17, la pierre marquant la tombe de la "dernière" sorcière d'Ecosse. La dernière, vraiment ?

Fortrose & Rosemarkie — 1888

Ness Road East, Fortrose
SCO - BLACK ISLE, Ross-shire IV10 8SE

Office	Secrétariat	(44) 01381 - 620 529
Pro shop	Pro-shop	(44) 01381 - 620 733
Fax	Fax	(44) 01381 - 621 328
Web	www.fortrosegolfclub.co.uk	
Situation	Situation	Inverness, 21 km
Annual closure	Fermeture annuelle	no
Weekly closure	Fermeture hebdomadaire	no

Fees main season Tarifs haute saison — 18 holes

	Week days / Semaine	We/Bank holidays / We/Férié
Individual Individuel	£ 25	£ 30
Couple Couple	£ 50	£ 60

Full day: £ 35 - £ 40 (We)

Caddy Caddie no — **Electric Trolley** Chariot électrique no

Buggy Voiturette yes — **Clubs** Clubs yes

Credit cards Cartes de crédit
VISA - MasterCard

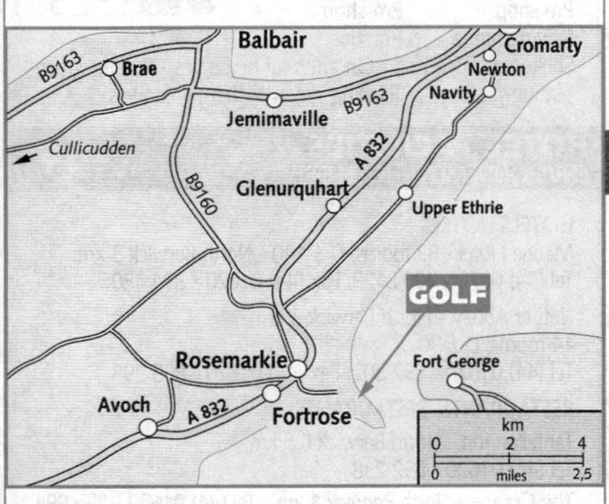

Access Accès : Inverness, A9 North to Tore.
At roundabout, A382 to Fortrose

Map 1 on page 470 Carte 1 Page 470

GOLF COURSE — PARCOURS — 16/20

Site	Site	
Maintenance	Entretien	
Architect	Architecte	James Braid
Type	Type	links
Relief	Relief	
Water in play	Eau en jeu	
Exp. to wind	Exposé au vent	
Trees in play	Arbres en jeu	

Scorecard / Carte de score	Chp. / Chp.	Mens / Mess.	Ladies / Da.
Length Long.	5295	5000	4824
Par	71	71	71
Slope system	—	—	—

Advised golfing ability 0 12 24 36
Niveau de jeu recommandé

Hcp required Handicap exigé — 28 Men, 36 Ladies

CLUB HOUSE & AMENITIES — CLUB HOUSE ET ANNEXES — 6/10

Pro shop Pro-shop
Driving range Practice

Sheltered couvert no - On grass sur herbe no - Putting-green putting-green yes - Pitching-green pitching green no

HOTEL FACILITIES — ENVIRONNEMENT HOTELIER — 5/10

HOTELS HÔTELS

Royal - 10 rooms, D £ 60 - Cromarty 15 km
Tel (44) 01381 - 600 217

Bunchrew House Hotel - 14 rooms, D £ 160 - Inverness 25 km
Tel (44) 0163 - 234 917, Fax (44) 0163 - 710 620

Culloden House - 28 rooms, D £ 200 - Culloden 23 km
Tel (44) 01463 - 790 461, Fax (44) 01463 - 792 181

RESTAURANTS RESTAURANTS

Chez Christophe - Inverness 25 km - Tel (44) 01463 - 717 126
Culloden House - Inverness 23 km - Tel (44) 01463 - 790 461
Bunchrew House Hotel - Inverness 25 km
Tel (44) 0163 - 234 917

Glen

14	7	6

A few miles from Gullane and Muirfield, this is the "East Links" of North Berwick, less well known than its neighbour doubtless because it is less of a complete links and has several inland holes. It is laid out over two levels but is still easy on the legs. Designed at the turn of the century and tastefully restyled by MacKenzie Ross with a considerate thought for al players, it offers some splendid views over the Firth of Forth and over the famous bird reserve of Bass Rock in the open sea. It is not over-long (compared as always with today's standards) but is still a stiff test of golf, especially with the wind which, although not too blustery, is never far away. Green-feers will at the very least remember the drive from the 18th tee, from a severely elevated tee, the excitement of a number of blind shots, and the 13th, a "postage stamp" par 3 with sea all around, worthy of the famous 7th hole at Pebble Beach.

A quelques kilomètres de Gullane et Muirfield, c'était le "East Links" de North Berwick, moins connu que son voisin, sans doute parce qu'il a un caractère moins totalement "links", avec plusieurs trous nettement "inland." Construit sur deux niveaux, il n'est pas fatigant à jouer. Créé au début du siècle, remanié par Mackenzie Ross avec beaucoup de goût et de souci d'adaptation à tous les joueurs, il propose de superbes vues sur le Firth of Forth et sur la fameuse réserve d'oiseaux du Bass Rock, au large. Bien qu'il ne soit pas très long (toujours en regard des célèbres critères modernes), c'est néanmoins un solide test de jeu, spécialement avec le vent, pas toujours violent, mais toujours présent. Les visiteurs garderont d'ici au moins le souvenir du drive du 18, depuis un départ très en hauteur, celui de quelques émotions sur certains coups aveugles et le 13, un par 3 "timbre-poste" étranglé par la mer et digne du célèbre trou n°7 de Pebble Beach.

Glen Golf Club — 1906

Tantallon Terrace
SCO - NORTH BERWICK, East Lothian EH39 4LE

Office Secrétariat (44) 01620 - 892 726
Pro shop Pro-shop (44) 01620 - 892 726
Fax Fax (44) 01620 - 895 447
Web www.glengolfclub.co.uk
Situation Situation Edinburgh, 25 km
Annual closure Fermeture annuelle no
Weekly closure Fermeture hebdomadaire no

Fees main season Tarifs haute saison	18 holes	
	Week days Semaine	We/Bank holidays We/Férié
Individual Individuel	£ 25	£ 38
Couple Couple	£ 50	£ 76

Caddy Caddie on request **Electric Trolley** Chariot électrique yes
Buggy Voiturette no **Clubs** Clubs yes
Credit cards Cartes de crédit VISA - Mastercard

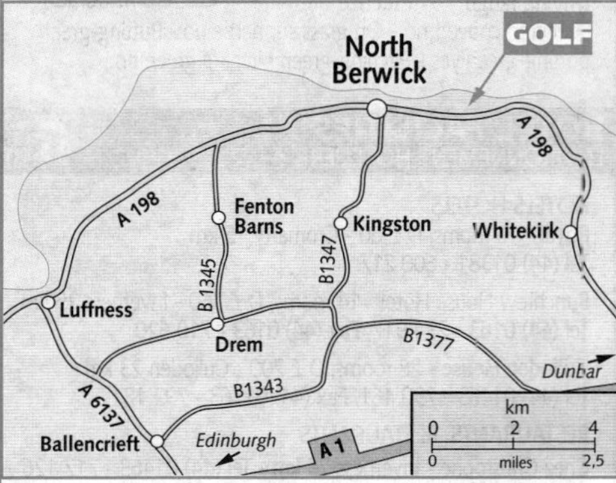

Access Accès : East of North Berwick town.
Follow seafront road from harbour. Course signposted.
Map 3 on page 475 Carte 3 Page 475

GOLF COURSE — PARCOURS — 14/20

Site Site
Maintenance Entretien
Architect Architecte Mackenzie Ross
Type Type seaside course
Relief Relief
Water in play Eau en jeu
Exp. to wind Exposé au vent
Trees in play Arbres en jeu

Scorecard Carte de score	Chp. Chp.	Mens Mess.	Ladies Da.
Length Long.	5485	5251	5039
Par	70	70	72
Slope system	—	—	—

Advised golfing ability Niveau de jeu recommandé 0 12 24 36
Hcp required Handicap exigé no

CLUB HOUSE & AMENITIES — CLUB HOUSE ET ANNEXES — 7/10

Pro shop Pro-shop
Driving range Practice
Sheltered couvert no - On grass sur herbe yes - Putting-green putting-green yes - Pitching-green pitching green yes

HOTEL FACILITIES — ENVIRONNEMENT HOTELIER — 6/10

HOTELS HÔTELS
Marine Hotel - 83 rooms, D £ 140 - North Berwick 3 km
Tel (44) 0870 - 400 8129, Fax (44) 01620 - 894 480

Nether Abbey - North Berwick 3 km
14 rooms, D £ 90
Tel (44) 01620 - 892 802, Fax (44) 01620 - 895 298

RESTAURANTS RESTAURANTS
Tantallon Inn - North Berwick 0.5 km
Tel (44) 01620 - 892 238
The Grange - North Berwick 1 km - Tel (44) 01620 - 895 894

Gleneagles *King's*

18	8	7

You come here as a true golfing fanatic, and to hell with the cost. The Gleneagles Hotel, an absolute must, is a genuine palace hotel in an idyllic region of the Highlands. At the end of the first world war, James Braid designed the first two 18-hole courses - the King's and Queen's - while the third, the PGA Centenary, was laid out by Jack Nicklaus. The King's Course is without a doubt the finest of the three, magnificently crafted from the surrounding landscape, winding its way through trees, bushes and hills and teeming with wildlife. The course has one essential quality, namely the variety of holes and a sort of indefinable logic in its balance. The artistry in the shapes of greens and bunkers only adds to the visual and technical pleasure of playing this challenging, very technical and remarkably well-groomed course. Exposure to the wind may vary considerably, depending on how protected the fairways are.

On vient ici en passionné du golf, en décidant de ne pas compter ses sous. Le Gleneagles Hotel, point de passage obligatoire, est un véritable palace, dans une région idyllique des Highlands. A la fin de la première Guerre Mondiale, James Braid dessina les deux premiers 18 trous, le King's et le Queen's, le troisième, le PGA Centenary, ayant été créé par Jack Nicklaus. Le premier nommé reste sans doute le plus savoureux des trois. Magnifiquement sculpté dans la campagne environnante, insinué au milieu des arbres, des buissons, des collines, parcourus d'une vie animale intense, il a une qualité essentielle, la variété des trous et une sorte de logique indéfinissable de rythme. Et la sensualité des formes des greens ou des bunkers ne fait qu'ajouter au plaisir visuel et technique de ce parcours exigeant, très technique, remarquablement entretenu. L'exposition au vent peut varier considérablement, suivant que les fairways sont ou non protégés.

Gleneagles Hotel & Golf Courses — 1919

Gleneagles Hotel
SCO - AUCHTERARDER, Perthshire PH3 1NF

Office	Secrétariat	(44) 01764 - 662 231
Pro shop	Pro-shop	(44) 01764 - 694 362
Fax	Fax	(44) 01764 - 662 134
Web	www.gleneagles.com	
Situation	Situation	Perth, 30 km
Annual closure	Fermeture annuelle	no
Weekly closure	Fermeture hebdomadaire	no

Fees main season Tarifs haute saison	Week days Semaine	We/Bank holidays We/Férié
	18 holes	
Individual Individuel	£ 110	£ 110
Couple Couple	£ 220	£ 220

Residents greenfees: £ 90

Caddy Caddie yes — **Electric Trolley** Chariot électrique no
Buggy Voiturette yes — **Clubs** Clubs yes

Credit cards Cartes de crédit
VISA - Eurocard - MasterCard - AMEX - DC - JCB

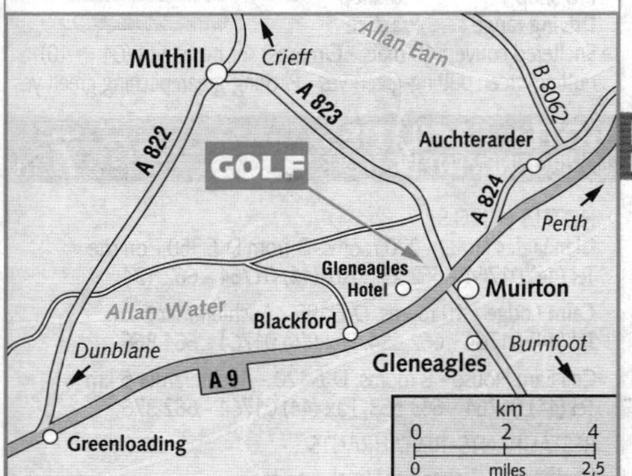

Access Accès : • Glasgow A80, M9, A9. Turn left at junction with A823 signed Crieff & Gleneagles • Edinburgh M90. Jct 2, then A823 through Dunfermline, → Crieff.
Map 2 on page 473 Carte 2 Page 473

GOLF COURSE — PARCOURS — 18/20

Site	Site	
Maintenance	Entretien	
Architect	Architecte	James Braid
Type	Type	moorland
Relief	Relief	
Water in play	Eau en jeu	
Exp. to wind	Exposé au vent	
Trees in play	Arbres en jeu	

Scorecard Carte de score	Chp. Chp.	Mens Mess.	Ladies Da.
Length Long.	6111	5824	5286
Par	70	70	75
Slope system	—	—	—

Advised golfing ability Niveau de jeu recommandé: 0 12 24 36
Hcp required Handicap exigé: no

CLUB HOUSE & AMENITIES — CLUB HOUSE ET ANNEXES — 8/10

Pro shop Pro-shop
Driving range Practice
Sheltered couvert 10 mats - On grass sur herbe yes (04 → 10) - Putting-green putting-green yes - Pitching-green pitching green yes

HOTEL FACILITIES — ENVIRONNEMENT HOTELIER — 7/10

HOTELS HÔTELS
Gleneagles Hotel - 270 rooms, D from D £ 350 - on site
Tel (44) 01764 - 662 231, Fax (44) 01764 - 662 134

Cairn Lodge - 10 rooms, D £ 190 - Auchterarder 5 km
Tel (44) 01764 - 662 634, Fax (44) 01764 - 664 866

Coll Earn House - 8 rooms, D £ 120 - Auchterarder 5 km
Tel (44) 01764 - 663 553, Fax (44) 01764 - 662 376

RESTAURANTS RESTAURANTS
Strathearn - Gleneagles Hotel on site
Tel (44) 01764 - 662 231
The Club - on site - Tel (44) 01764 - 694 359
Restaurant Andrew Fairlie - on site - Tel (44) 01764 - 694 267

Gleneagles *PGA Centenary*

17 | 8 | 7

This course was built to complement the King's and Queen's courses. It was designed by Jack Nicklaus and clearly aimed at appealing to the American visitors who visit the internationally famous hotel. Created as a venue for championship golf, it has natural amphitheatres round every hole which not only create a sense of grandeur but also excellent viewing areas for spectators. The course is memorable for its dramatic and open views of the nearby Ochil Hills and Glendevon. Five tees on each hole make it both the longest and the shortest playing course at the resort, to accommodate all levels of ability. The course is of an excellent strategic standard, even though Nicklaus was visibly thinking more of the proficient golfer than the less experienced hacker. The superb setting will silence even those people who feel that the difference in style with the other two courses is over the top. With the 2014 Ryder Cup on the distant horizon, the course is currently undergoing a few changes led by David McLay Kidd.

Ce parcours a été construit pour compléter le King's et le Queen's. Dessiné par Jack Nicklaus, il est visiblement destiné aux visiteurs américains qui adorent ce célèbre hôtel. Conçu pour recevoir des championnats, il est entouré d'amphithéâtres naturels, qui ne créent pas seulement un sentiment de grandeur, mais offrent aussi une excellente visibilité aux spectateurs. Les vues des Ochil Hills et du Glendevon ajoutent encore du prestige au lieu. Cinq tees de départ permettent d'en faire le parcours le plus long comme le plus court du domaine, pour accommoder tous les niveaux de jeu. Son dessin assez américain, et parfois un peu artificiel dans ce paysage, est d'une grande qualité stratégique, même si Nicklaus a visiblement plus pensé aux bons joueurs qu'aux moins expérimentés. L'environnement fera taire même ceux qui estiment la différence esthétique excessive par rapport aux deux autres parcours. En vue de la Ryder Cup 2014, il fait l'objet de modifications par David McLay Kidd.

Gleneagles Hotel & Golf Courses — 1993

Gleneagles Hotel
SCO - AUCHTERARDER, Perthshire PH3 1NF

Office Secrétariat (44) 01764 - 662 231
Pro shop Pro-shop (44) 01764 - 694 362
Fax Fax (44) 01764 - 662 134
Web www.gleneagles.com
Situation Situation Edinburgh, 85 km
Perth (pop. 123 495), 30 km

Annual closure Fermeture annuelle no
Weekly closure Fermeture hebdomadaire no

Fees main season Tarifs haute saison	full day	
	Week days Semaine	We/Bank holidays We/Férié
Individual Individuel	£ 110	£ 110
Couple Couple	£ 220	£ 220

Residents greenfees: £ 90

Caddie Caddie yes — **Electric Trolley** Chariot électrique no
Buggy Voiturette yes — **Clubs** Clubs yes
Credit cards Cartes de crédit
VISA - Eurocard - MasterCard - AMEX - DC - JCB

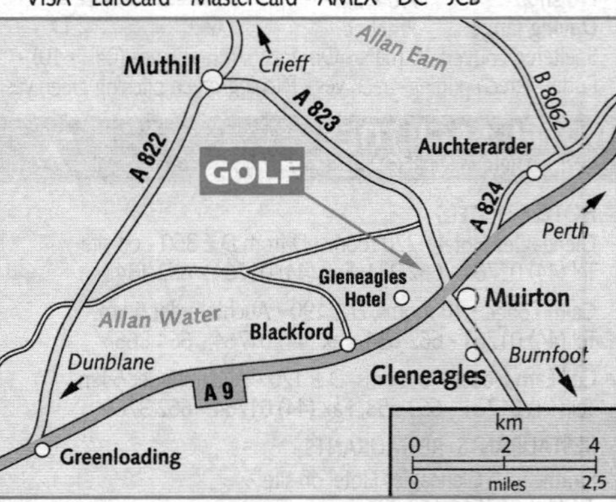

Access Accès : • Glasgow A80, M9, A9. Turn left at junction with A823 signed Crieff & Gleneagles • Edinburgh M90. Jct 2, then A823 through Dunfermline, → Crieff.
Map 2 on page 473 Carte 2 Page 473

GOLF COURSE — PARCOURS 17/20

Site Site
Maintenance Entretien
Architect Architecte Jack Nicklaus
Type Type moorland
Relief Relief
Water in play Eau en jeu
Exp. to wind Exposé au vent
Trees in play Arbres en jeu

Scorecard Carte de score	Chp. Chp.	Mens Mess.	Ladies Da.
Length Long.	6380	5521	5128
Par	72	72	72
Slope system	—	—	—

Advised golfing ability Niveau de jeu recommandé 0 12 24 36
Hcp required Handicap exigé no

CLUB HOUSE & AMENITIES — CLUB HOUSE ET ANNEXES 8/10

Pro shop Pro-shop
Driving range Practice
Sheltered couvert 10 mats - On grass sur herbe yes (04 → 10)
Putting-green putting-green yes - Pitching-green pitching green yes

HOTEL FACILITIES — ENVIRONNEMENT HOTELIER 7/10

HOTELS HÔTELS
Gleneagles Hotel - 270 rooms, D from D £ 350 - on site
Tel (44) 01764 - 662 231, Fax (44) 01764 - 662 134

Cairn Lodge - 10 rooms, D £ 190 - Auchterarder 5 km
Tel (44) 01764 - 662 634, Fax (44) 01764 - 664 866

Coll Earn House - 8 rooms, D £ 120 - Auchterarder 5 km
Tel (44) 01764 - 663 553, Fax (44) 01764 - 662 376

RESTAURANTS RESTAURANTS
Strathearn - Gleneagles Hotel, on site
Tel (44) 01764 - 662 231
The Club - on site - Tel (44) 01764 - 694 359
Restaurant Andrew Fairlie - on site - Tel (44) 01764 - 694 267

Gleneagles *Queen's*

15 | 8 | 7

The Queen's course has rather lived in the shadow of its more famous sister, the King's course over the years, but this beautifully designed James Braid layout is a wonderful golf course in its own right. Were it standing on its own in another location, it would undoubtedly have received far more acclaim than it already has. It is not as long or ultimately taxing as its sister courses, but it still represents a wonderful challenge and shares the magical surroundings of this very special venue. There are many fine and demanding holes here enhanced with attractive stretches of water. And while it is more reassuring because it offers less resistance to good golfers, it is still essential playing when you are here. From Spring to late Autumn, when the sun is shining in this corner of Perthshire, there are few more idyllic spots to be found in the whole of world golf.

Dans un grand ensemble de parcours, il y a souvent un parcours que l'on réserve aux moins bons joueurs, ou qui figure comme un repos pour le guerrier. Le "Queen's" a vécu longtemps dans l'ombre de son voisin le "King's", mais le splendide tracé de James Braid mérite à lui seul le déplacement. N'importe où ailleurs, ce très bon parcours aurait été bien plus acclamé qu'il ne l'a été jusqu'ici. Il n'est pas aussi long, aussi difficile, aussi exposé que ses deux compagnons, mais ce n'en est pas moins bien mieux qu'un faire-valoir. Dans le même environnement sublime, on trouve ici de nombreux trous très exigeants, rehaussés visuellement par des points d'eau. Et s'il rassure par une moindre résistance aux efforts, il n'en est pas moins incontournable quand on se trouve ici. Du printemps à la fin de l'automne, il y a peu de plus beaux endroits au monde que cette région du Perthshire pour séjourner et jouer au golf, même si l'on trouve ailleurs de plus grands chefs-d'oeuvre encore au plan technique.

Gleneagles Hotel & Golf Courses — 1917

Gleneagles Hotel
SCO - AUCHTERARDER, Perthshire PH3 1NF

Office Secrétariat (44) 01764 - 662 231
Pro shop Pro-shop (44) 01764 - 694 362
Fax Fax (44) 01764 - 662 134
Web www.gleneagles.com
Situation Situation Edinburgh, 85 km
Perth (pop. 123 495), 30 km
Annual closure Fermeture annuelle no
Weekly closure Fermeture hebdomadaire no

Fees main season Tarifs haute saison	full day	
	Week days Semaine	**We/Bank holidays** We/Férié
Individual Individuel	£ 110	£ 110
Couple Couple	£ 220	£ 220

Residents greenfees: £ 90

Caddie Caddie yes — **Electric Trolley** Chariot électrique no
Buggy Voiturette yes — **Clubs** Clubs yes
Credit cards Cartes de crédit
VISA - Eurocard - MasterCard - AMEX - DC - JCB

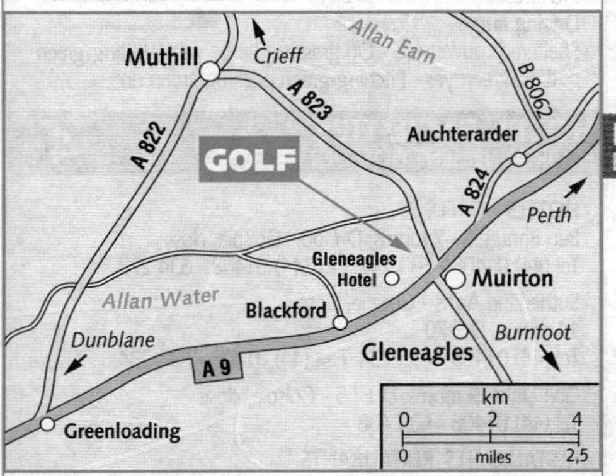

Access Accès : • Glasgow A80, M9, A9. Turn left at junction with A823 signed Crieff & Gleneagles • Edinburgh M90. Jct 2, then A823 through Dunfermline, → Crieff.
Map 2 on page 473 Carte 2 Page 473

GOLF COURSE — PARCOURS 15/20

Site Site
Maintenance Entretien
Architect Architecte James Braid
Type Type moorland
Relief Relief
Water in play Eau en jeu
Exp. to wind Exposé au vent
Trees in play Arbres en jeu

Scorecard Carte de score	**Chp.** Chp.	**Mens** Mess.	**Ladies** Da.
Length Long.	5369	5094	4946
Par	68	68	74
Slope system	—	—	—

Advised golfing ability Niveau de jeu recommandé 0 12 24 36
Hcp required Handicap exigé no

CLUB HOUSE & AMENITIES — CLUB HOUSE ET ANNEXES 8/10

Pro shop Pro-shop
Driving range Practice
Sheltered couvert 10 mats - On grass sur herbe yes (04 → 10)
Putting-green putting-green yes - Pitching-green pitching green yes

HOTEL FACILITIES — ENVIRONNEMENT HOTELIER 7/10

HOTELS HÔTELS
Gleneagles Hotel - 270 rooms, D from D £ 350 - on site
Tel (44) 01764 - 662 231, Fax (44) 01764 - 662 134

Cairn Lodge - 10 rooms, D £ 190 - Auchterarder 5 km
Tel (44) 01764 - 662 634, Fax (44) 01764 - 664 866

Coll Earn House - 8 rooms, D £ 120 - Auchterarder 5 km
Tel (44) 01764 - 663 553, Fax (44) 01764 - 662 376

RESTAURANTS RESTAURANTS
Strathearn - Gleneagles Hotel, on site
Tel (44) 01764 - 662 231
The Club - on site - Tel (44) 01764 - 694 359
Restaurant Andrew Fairlie - on site - Tel (44) 01764 - 694 267

Golspie

14	5	4

Lying at the foot of Ben Cragghie in the Highlands, Golspie is particularly interesting for the shape and layout of the course. Over limited space, you start off virtually in a park before moving on to pure links holes (not necessarily the best), then into woods and heather before returning to park landscape. Once again, James Braid has worked wonders with a variety of styles that call for the utmost versatility. There is no shortage of interesting holes of all shapes and sizes, with some very long and very short par 4s, five par 3s and two par 5s. A very pleasant course to play on holiday, far from the crowds who flock to more fashionable and less remote venues, Golspie also offers some beautiful views over the coast, north and south. A word should go to the excellent green-keeping despite only very few staff working on the course. Play here in Summer, when the wind keeps away, before playing Brora, Tain and Dornoch.

Situé au pied du Ben Cragghie dans les Highlands, Golspie est particulièrement intéressant en raison de sa conformation. Sur un espace restreint, on part quasiment d'un parc pour passer ensuite par des trous de pur links (ce ne sont pas forcément les meilleurs comme on pourrait l'imaginer), puis dans les bois, la bruyère et enfin revenir au parc. Une fois de plus, James Braid a tiré un excellent parti de cette variété d'esthétiques, qui demandent de grandes qualités d'adaptation. Les trous intéressants ne manquent pas ici, dans tous les genres car on trouve des longs par 4 mais aussi de très courts, cinq par 3 et deux pars 5. Très agréable à jouer en vacances, loin de la foule qui choisit des endroits plus à la mode, ou moins lointains, Golspie offre en outre des vues très belles sur la côte, au nord comme au sud. On signalera enfin l'excellente qualité de l'entretien, malgré un personnel très restreint. A jouer en été, quand le vent est amical, et avant de jouer Brora, Tain et Dornoch.

Golspie Golf Club — 1889

Ferry Road
SCO - GOLSPIE, Sutherland KW10 6ST

Office	Secrétariat	(44) 01408 - 633 266
Pro shop	Pro-shop	(44) 01408 - 633 266
Fax	Fax	(44) 01408 - 633 393
Web	www.golspie-golf-club.co.uk	
Situation	Situation	Inverness, 80 km

Dornoch (pop. 2 042), 18 km

Annual closure	Fermeture annuelle	no
Weekly closure	Fermeture hebdomadaire	no
Fees main season	Tarifs haute saison	18 holes

	Week days Semaine	We/Bank holidays We/Férié
Individual Individuel	£ 25	£ 25
Couple Couple	£ 50	£ 50

Full day: £ 40

Caddie Caddie on request **Electric Trolley** Chariot électrique no

Buggy Voiturette yes **Clubs** Clubs yes

Credit cards Cartes de crédit
VISA - MasterCard - Switch - Delta

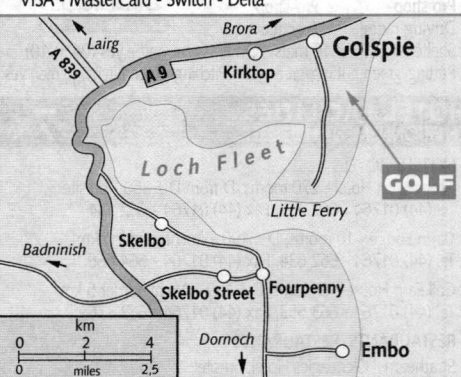

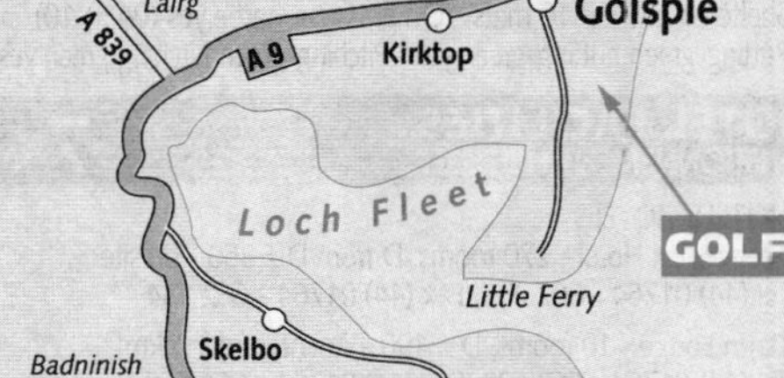

Access Accès : Off the main A9, at south entry to Golspie, turn right 150m after crossing Railway Bridge.
Golf Course on the Links along sea-side.
Map 1 on page 471 Carte 1 Page 471

GOLF COURSE — PARCOURS — 14/20

Site	Site	
Maintenance	Entretien	
Architect	Architecte	James Braid
Type	Type	links, parkland
Relief	Relief	
Water in play	Eau en jeu	
Exp. to wind	Exposé au vent	
Trees in play	Arbres en jeu	

Scorecard Carte de score	Chp. Chp.	Mens Mess.	Ladies Da.
Length Long.	5477	5206	4789
Par	68	68	71
Slope system	—	—	—

Advised golfing ability Niveau de jeu recommandé: 0 12 24 36

Hcp required Handicap exigé: certificate

CLUB HOUSE & AMENITIES — CLUB HOUSE ET ANNEXES — 5/10

Pro shop	Pro-shop
Driving range	Practice

Sheltered couvert n,o - On grass sur herbe yes - Putting-green putting-green yes - Pitching-green pitching green no

HOTEL FACILITIES — ENVIRONNEMENT HOTELIER — 4/10

HOTELS HÔTELS

Ben Bhraggie - 7 rooms, D £ 50 - Golspie, close
Tel (44) 01408 - 633 242, Fax (44) 01408 - 634 277

Sutherland Arms - Golspie, close
14 rooms, D £ 70
Tel (44) 01408 - 633 234, Fax (44) 01408 - 633 234

Golf Links- 9 rooms, D £ 55 - Golspie, close
Tel (44) 01408 - 633 408

RESTAURANTS RESTAURANTS

Taste Buds - Golspie, close - Tel (44) 01408 - 633 022

Grantown on Spey

14	6	5

This is the kind of course you want to show those golfers who know only the links courses in Scotland. But why go and play mountain courses, you may ask? Firstly because they are located in superb, untamed regions (with some beautiful wildlife to admire) and then because they are flat enough not to tire the legs of people who spend the rest of the year behind a desk. And perhaps you'll find more things to do outside golf (for non-golfers) in the Highlands than beside the sea. Close to Boat of Garten, Aviemore and the Cairngorms National Park, this course was designed by Willie Park and James Braid. It has no needless complications, is very short (even for a par 68), is quick to play and is approachable by golfers of all levels. A dozen holes are spread over a park and the six holes from 7 to 12 run through hillier terrain. The best players might find it a little on the easy side, but there is nothing to stop them from trying to beat the course record (60), or play more than once.

Le genre de parcours à mettre sous les yeux de ceux qui ne connaissent de l'Ecosse que les paysages de links. Pourquoi aller jouer ses parcours de montagne? D'abord parce qu'ils se trouvent dans des régions superbes et sauvages (avec une faune merveilleuse à observer), ensuite parce qu'ils sont souvent, paradoxalement, assez plats pour ne pas effrayer ceux qui passent leur vie dans un bureau. Parce que l'on trouve peut-être plus d'activités annexes (pour ceux qui ne jouent pas) dans les Highlands qu'en bord de mer. A proximité de Boat of Garten, d'Aviemore et du Parc National des Cairngorms, ce parcours de Willie Park et Braid est sans complications inutiles, très court (même pour un par 68), rapide à jouer et bien adapté à tous les niveaux. 12 de ses trous se déroulent dans un parc, les six trous du 7 au 12 sur un terrain plus accidenté. Les meilleurs le trouveront un peu limité, mais qui les empêche de tenter de battre le record (60), et de le jouer plusieurs fois !

Grantown on Spey Golf Club — 1890

Golf Course Road
SCO - GRANTOWN ON SPEY, Morayshire PH26 3HY

Office Secrétariat (44) 01479 - 872 079
Pro shop Pro-shop (44) 01479 - 872 079
Fax Fax (44) 01479 - 873 725
Web www.grantownonspeygolfclub.co.uk
Situation Situation Inverness, 56 km

Annual closure Fermeture annuelle no
club-house closed 11 → 03 inclusive

Weekly closure Fermeture hebdomadaire no

Fees main season / Tarifs haute saison	Full day	
	Week days / Semaine	We/Bank holidays / We/Férié
Individual Individuel	£ 20	£ 25
Couple Couple	£ 40	£ 50

Caddie Caddie no **Electric Trolley** Chariot électrique no

Buggy Voiturette yes **Clubs** Clubs yes

Credit cards Cartes de crédit
VISA - Eurocard - MasterCard

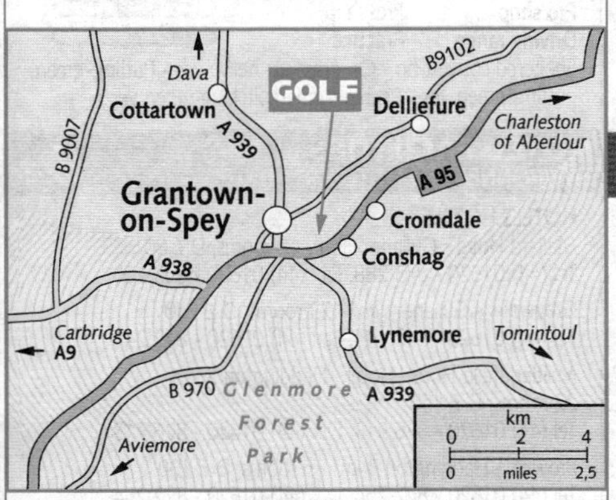

Access Accès : Inverness, A9, A938 & A95 to Grantown.
Course lies off the road to Nairn and Forres, on NE side of Grantown
Map 1 on page 471 Carte 1 Page 471

GOLF COURSE — PARCOURS — 14/20

Site Site
Maintenance Entretien
Architect Architecte A.C. Brown, W. Park, James Braid
Type Type parkland
Relief Relief
Water in play Eau en jeu
Exp. to wind Exposé au vent
Trees in play Arbres en jeu

Scorecard / Carte de score	Chp. / Chp.	Mens / Mess.	Ladies / Da.
Length Long.	5198	4930	4801
Par	70	69	72
Slope system	—	—	—

Advised golfing ability Niveau de jeu recommandé 0 12 24 36
Hcp required Handicap exigé no

CLUB HOUSE & AMENITIES — CLUB HOUSE ET ANNEXES — 6/10

Pro shop Pro-shop
Driving range Practice
Sheltered couvert no - On grass sur herbe no - Putting-green putting-green yes - Pitching-green pitching green no

HOTEL FACILITIES — ENVIRONNEMENT HOTELIER — 5/10

HOTELS HÔTELS
Muckrach Lodge - Dulnain Bridge 5 km
14 rooms, D from £ 130
Tel (44) 01479 - 851 257, Fax (44) 01479 - 851 325

Culdearn House - Grantown 0.5 km
7 rooms, D £ 170 (w. dinner)
Tel (44) 01479 - 872 106, Fax (44) 01479 - 873 641

Ravenscourt House - 7 rooms, D £ 75 - Grantown 0.5 km
Tel (44) 01479 - 872 286, Fax (44) 01479 - 873 260

RESTAURANTS RESTAURANTS
Craggan Mill - Grantown 0.5 km - Tel (44) 01479 - 872 288
La Taverna - Aviemore 22 km - Tel (44) 01479 - 810 683

Gullane *No 1*

17	7	6

Of the three courses at Gullane, the N° 1 is unquestionably the most spectacular and the most challenging in golfing terms, although its two neighbours are a pleasant alternative on holiday and still of an excellent standard. The less experienced members of the family or group will find them very much to their liking. The slow climb along an impressive hill takes you gradually up above the Firth of Forth until you can make out the famous Muirfield links not far away. From the 7th tee you can even see as far as Edinburgh. But Gullane is much more than an observatory. Wide open spaces, where only the tall rough can break the feeling of immensity, accommodate a high class course (hole N° 3 is outstanding) where the work of anonymous architects consisted primarily in laying out the greens, digging the bunkers (often deep) and leaving time do the rest. If you want to enjoy rather than endure this often austere course, which could have inspired some of today's "minimalist" architects, give it your best shot(s).

Des trois parcours de Gullane, voici le plus spectaculaire et le plus exigeant au plan golfique, bien que ses deux voisins constituent une alternative heureuse en vacances, de bonne qualité golfique. Ils séduiront par leur plus grande amabilité les membres moins expérimentés de la famille ou du groupe. La lente montée le long d'une imposante colline permet de s'élever peu à peu au-dessus du Firth of Forth, jusqu'à distinguer non loin les fameux links de Muirfield. On peut même voir jusqu'à Edinburgh depuis le départ du 7. Mais Gullane est bien plus qu'un observatoire. Les vastes espaces, où seul le haut rough peut rompre le sentiment d'immensité, accueillent un parcours de haute volée (avec un sommet, le 3), où le travail anonyme des architectes a surtout consisté à aménager les greens, creuser les bunkers (souvent profonds) et laisser faire le temps. Ici, sur ce tracé souvent austère, qui peut inspirer les architectes "minimalistes" de notre temps, on exprime tout son golf, ou alors on le subit.

Gullane Golf Club — 1844

West Links Road
SCO - GULLANE, East Lothian EH31 2BB

Office Secrétariat (44) 01620 - 842 255
Pro shop Pro-shop (44) 01620 - 843 111
Fax Fax (44) 01620 - 842 327
Web www.gullanegolfclub.com
Situation Situation Edinburgh, 29 km
Annual closure Fermeture annuelle no
Weekly closure Fermeture hebdomadaire no

Fees main season Tarifs haute saison	Week days Semaine	We/Bank holidays We/Férié
	18 holes	
Individual Individuel	£ 80	£ 90
Couple Couple	£ 160	£ 180

Full week days: £ 100

Caddie Caddie on request **Electric Trolley** Chariot électrique no
Buggy Voiturette yes **Clubs** Clubs yes
Credit cards Cartes de crédit
VISA - Eurocard - MasterCard - AMEX

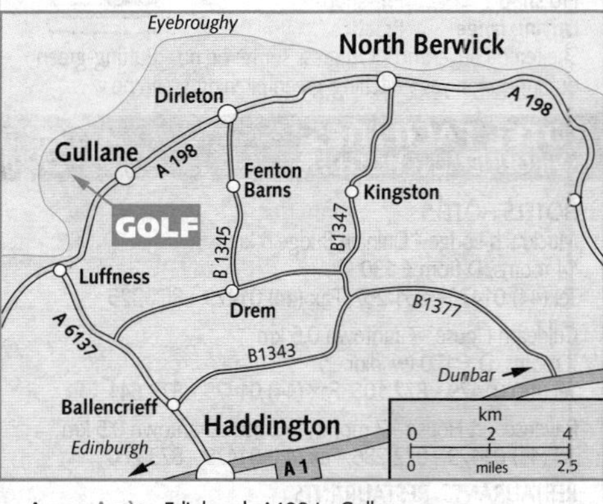

Access Accès : Edinburgh A198 to Gullane
Map 3 on page 475 Carte 3 Page 475

GOLF COURSE — PARCOURS 17/20

Site Site
Maintenance Entretien
Architect Architecte unknown
Type Type seaside course, links
Relief Relief
Water in play Eau en jeu
Exp. to wind Exposé au vent
Trees in play Arbres en jeu

Scorecard Carte de score	Chp. Chp.	Mens Mess.	Ladies Da.
Length Long.	5884	5530	5530
Par	71	71	75
Slope system	—	—	—

Advised golfing ability Niveau de jeu recommandé 0 12 24 36
Hcp required Handicap exigé 24 Men, 30 Ladies

CLUB HOUSE & AMENITIES — CLUB HOUSE ET ANNEXES 7/10

Pro shop Pro-shop
Driving range Practice
Sheltered couvert no - On grass sur herbe yes - Putting-green putting-green yes - Pitching-green pitching green yes

HOTEL FACILITIES — ENVIRONNEMENT HOTELIER 6/10

HOTELS HÔTELS
Mallard Hotel - Gullane 2 km - 18 rooms, D £ 80
Tel (44) 01620 - 843 288, Fax (44) 01620 - 843 200

Greywalls - Gullane 1 km - 23 rooms, D £ 230
Tel (44) 01620 - 842 144, Fax (44) 01620 - 842 241

Maitlandfield House Hotel - Haddington 3 km
22 rooms, D £ 150
Tel (44) 01620 - 826 513, Fax (44) 01620 - 826 713

Brown's - Haddington 3 km - 5 rooms, D £ 100
Tel (44) 01620 - 822 254, Fax (44) 01620 - 822 254

RESTAURANTS RESTAURANTS
La Potinière - Gullane 1 km - Tel (44) 01620 - 843 214
Greywalls - Gullane 1 km - Tel (44) 01620 - 842 144

Haggs Castle

15	7	8

The fine layout of this well-known Glaswegian club unwinds between rows of fully grown trees a few miles to the south-west of the city centre. It is one of the easiest-to-reach courses around Glasgow, useful to know in that although a private club, it willingly welcomes visitors during the week. Of course it doesn't offer the array of technical challenges found on the great championship courses but it has often been used for some very high level tournaments which testify to its status. The Scottish Open was one such before it moved on to Gleneagles and then Carnoustie. Good drivers will feel easy here, the others will need all their expertise to reach the well-protected greens which pitch well. There are very few bump 'n run shots to be played here, rather more in the American target golf style, despite the very British nature of the course overall.

Le beau tracé de ce club bien connu de Glasgow s'étire entre des rangées d'arbres bien adultes, à quelques kilomètres au sud-ouest du centre ville. C'est un des golfs de Glasgow les plus faciles d'accès. Et d'autant plus que, bien qu'il soit privé, il accueille volontiers les visteurs en semaine. Certes, le parcours ne présente pas la variété des défis techniques des plus grands parcours de championnat, mais il a souvent été utilisé pour de très bonnes épreuves, ce qui témoigne de son rang : nous ne citerons que le Scottish Open, qui émigra ensuite à Gleneagles puis à Carnoustie. Les bons drivers y seront ici à l'aise. Les autres devront témoigner de virtuosité pour rejoindre des greens bien protégés, mais qui tiennent bien la balle. Ici, peu de "bump'n run," mais plutôt un jeu de cible à l'américaine, malgré le caractère général très britannique de l'ensemble.

Haggs Castle Golf Club — 1910
70 Dumbreck Road
SCO - GLASGOW G41 4SN

Office	Secrétariat	(44) 0141 - 427 1157
Pro shop	Pro-shop	(44) 0141 - 427 3355
Fax	Fax	(44) 0141 - 427 1157
E-mail	secretary@haggscastlegolfclub.com	
Situation	Situation	Glasgow, 5 km
Annual closure	Fermeture annuelle	no
Weekly closure	Fermeture hebdomadaire	no
Fees main season	Tarifs haute saison	18 holes

	Week days Semaine	We/Bank holidays We/Férié
Individual Individuel	£ 40	*
Couple Couple	£ 80	*

No visitors at week-ends

Caddie Caddie on request **Electric Trolley** Chariot électrique no
Buggy Voiturette on request **Clubs** Clubs on request
Credit cards Cartes de crédit yes

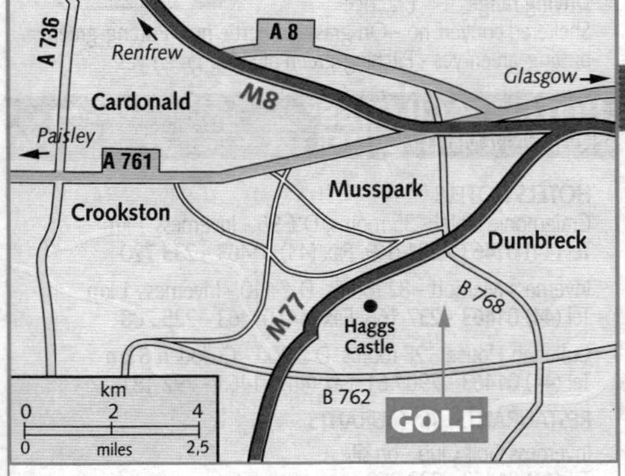

Access Accès : A7 end of Jct 1 off M77. SW of Glasgow city centre.
Map 3 on page 474 Carte 3 Page 474

GOLF COURSE — PARCOURS 15/20

Site	Site	
Maintenance	Entretien	
Architect	Architecte	unknown
Type	Type	parkland
Relief	Relief	
Water in play	Eau en jeu	
Exp. to wind	Exposé au vent	
Trees in play	Arbres en jeu	

Scorecard Carte de score	Chp. Chp.	Mens Mess.	Ladies Da.
Length Long.	5876	5475	5041
Par	72	70	73
Slope system	—	—	—

Advised golfing ability Niveau de jeu recommandé — 0 12 24 36
Hcp required Handicap exigé — certificate

CLUB HOUSE & AMENITIES — CLUB HOUSE ET ANNEXES 7/10

Pro shop Pro-shop
Driving range Practice
Sheltered couvert no - On grass sur herbe yes - Putting-green putting-green yes - Pitching-green pitching green yes

HOTEL FACILITIES — ENVIRONNEMENT HOTELIER 8/10

HOTELS HÔTELS
One Devonshire Gardens - Glasgow 5 km
35 rooms, D from £ 145
Tel (44) 0141 - 339 2001, Fax (44) 0141 - 337 1663

Glasgow Hilton - 319 rooms, D £ 190 - Glasgow 5 km
Tel (44) 0141 - 204 5555, Fax (44) 0141 - 204 5004

Sherbrooke Castle - 21 rooms, D £ 120 - Glasgow 5 km
Tel (44) 0141 - 427 4227, Fax (44) 0141 - 427 5685

RESTAURANTS RESTAURANTS
One Devonshire Gardens - Glasgow 5 km
Tel (44) 0141 - 339 2001
The Restaurant at Corinthian - Glasgow 5 km
Tel (44) 0141 - 552 1101
Café Gandolfi - Glasgow 5 km - Tel (44) 0141 - 552 6813

Inverness

16 | 7 | 7

The completion of a new, first-rate club-house has provided an additional argument for this often underrated course in the capital of the Scottish highlands. The site is excellent with views over the hills on either side of Loch Ness, and the occasional glimpse over Moray Firth. The course is lined by any number of trees (not always as tall as you might imagine), the fairways are generously wide and it takes a pretty wild mis-hit to reach the tall rough. On this moderately hilly terrain, there is only one really blind shot, from the 16th tee. Otherwise the layout is very frank and hides nothing. Pleasant to play in normal weather, it can turn nasty under championship conditions, when a tough round can turn distinctly nightmarish on the 14th, one of the toughest par 4s in the north of Scotland. Inverness certainly does not have the layout or setting to claim parity with Nairn or Dornoch, but in its own style it can and does hold its head high.

La réalisation d'un nouveau club-house de premier ordre a apporté un argument de plus à ce parcours souvent sous-estimé, celui de la capitale des Highlands. Le site est de grande qualité, avec les vues sur les collines de part et d'autre du Loch Ness, et des aperçus sur le Firth de temps à autre. De nombreux arbres longent le parcours, pas toujours immenses d'ailleurs, les fairways sont de largeur généreuse, et il faut faire des efforts pour s'égarer dans le haut rough. Sur ce terrain modérément accidenté, on ne trouve qu'un seul coup vraiment aveugle, au drive du 16. Sinon, le dessin est d'une grande franchise. Agréable en temps normal, il peut montrer les dents en conditions de championnat, culminant au 14, l'un des par 4 les plus difficiles du nord de l'Ecosse. Certes, Inverness ne prétend ni par son dessin, ni par son cadre à être l'égal de Nairn ou de Dornoch, mais dans son propre style, il peut tenir la tête haute.

Inverness Golf Club — 1908

Culcabock
SCO - INVERNESS IV2 3XQ

Office	Secrétariat	(44) 01463 - 239 882
Pro shop	Pro-shop	(44) 01463 - 231 989
Fax	Fax	(44) 01463 - 240 616
Web	www.invernessgolfclub.co.uk	
Situation	Situation	Inverness, 1.5 km
Annual closure	Fermeture annuelle	no
Weekly closure	Fermeture hebdomadaire	no
Fees main season	Tarifs haute saison	18 holes

	Week days / Semaine	We/Bank holidays / We/Férié
Individual Individuel	£ 33	£ 33
Couple Couple	£ 66	£ 66

Full day: £ 42

Caddie Caddie on request **Electric Trolley** Chariot électrique no

Buggy Voiturette yes **Clubs** Clubs yes

Credit cards Cartes de crédit yes

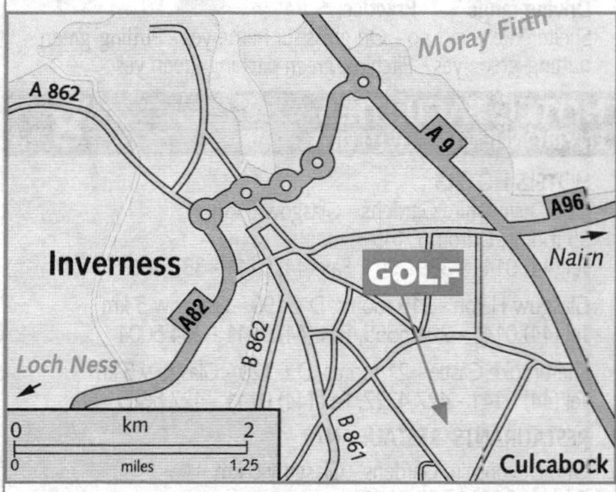

Access Accès : A9 North. First turn off → Inverness. Roundabout, turn right (5th exit). Next roundabout, Club on left.
Map 1 on page 470 Carte 1 Page 470

GOLF COURSE — PARCOURS — 16/20

Site	Site	
Maintenance	Entretien	
Architect	Architecte	unknown
Type	Type	park
Relief	Relief	
Water in play	Eau en jeu	
Exp. to wind	Exposé au vent	
Trees in play	Arbres en jeu	

Scorecard Carte de score	Chp. Chp.	Mens Mess.	Ladies Da.
Length Long.	5700	5204	5068
Par	69	67	72
Slope system	—	—	—

Advised golfing ability Niveau de jeu recommandé: 0 12 24 36

Hcp required Handicap exigé 35

CLUB HOUSE & AMENITIES — CLUB HOUSE ET ANNEXES — 7/10

Pro shop Pro-shop
Driving range Practice
Sheltered couvert no - On grass sur herbe no - Putting-green putting-green yes - Pitching-green pitching green yes

HOTEL FACILITIES — ENVIRONNEMENT HOTELIER — 7/10

HOTELS HÔTELS

Craigmonie Hotel - 35 rooms, D £ 95 - Inverness 1 km
Tel (44) 01463 - 231 649, Fax (44) 01463 - 233 720

Inverness Marriott - 82 rooms, D £ 110 - Inverness 1 km
Tel (44) 01463 - 237 166, Fax (44) 01463 - 225 208

Culloden House - 28 rooms, D £ 200 - Culloden 6 km
Tel (44) 01463 - 790 461, Fax (44) 01463 - 792 181

RESTAURANTS RESTAURANTS

Inverness Golf Club - on site
Tel (44) 01463 - 233 259
Culloden House - Culloden 6 km - Tel (44) 01463 - 790 461

Kilmarnock (Barassie)

17	6	7

Much closer to the holiday resort of Troon than to Kilmarnock, Barassie is also much more than a friendly leisure course. Although near the sea it often feels like an inland course, but don't let that fool you. This is an impressive challenge even for the best players and each visit is the opportunity to discover new surprises and enjoy it again and again. A few blind shots add a little spice to the fun and the difficulties are evenly spread around the course. You'll need the full range of shots here to see you home, but then again you do on virtually every course of this type. Testimony to the excellence of this layout is the fact that this is one of the courses for the final qualification rounds when the British Open is played at Troon. It has also hosted some of the greatest amateur tournaments. Essential visiting when in this region that is spoilt for great courses.

Bien plus près de la station de vacances de Troon que de Kilmarnock, Barassie est beaucoup plus qu'un aimable parcours de loisirs. Bien qu'il soit proche de la mer, il offre parfois la sensation d'être un vrai parcours "inland," mais il ne faut pas se laisser piéger : il présente un imposant défi, même aux meilleurs, et chaque visite est l'occasion de surprises, et d'un plaisir renouvelé. Quelques coups aveugles ajoutent un peu de piment, les difficultés sont très bien équilibrées, et il faudra toute la panoplie de coups du sac pour en sortir, mais c'est pratiquement le cas sur tous les parcours de ce type. Témoin de sa qualité, c'est l'un des parcours des ultimes qualifications quand le British Open se joue à Royal Troon, il a aussi été le site de grandes compétitions amateurs. A ne pas oublier d'inscrire dans son itinéraire lorsque l'on vient dans cette région richissime en grands golfs.

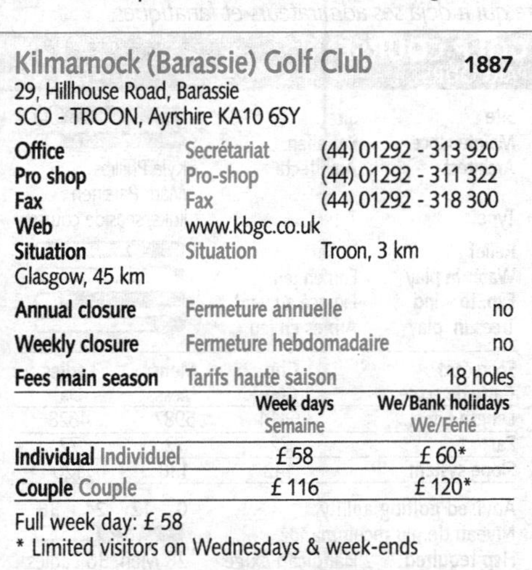

Kilmarnock (Barassie) Golf Club 1887
29, Hillhouse Road, Barassie
SCO - TROON, Ayrshire KA10 6SY

Office Secrétariat (44) 01292 - 313 920
Pro shop Pro-shop (44) 01292 - 311 322
Fax Fax (44) 01292 - 318 300
Web www.kbgc.co.uk
Situation Situation Troon, 3 km
Glasgow, 45 km
Annual closure Fermeture annuelle no
Weekly closure Fermeture hebdomadaire no

Fees main season Tarifs haute saison		18 holes
	Week days Semaine	**We/Bank holidays** We/Férié
Individual Individuel	£ 58	£ 60*
Couple Couple	£ 116	£ 120*

Full week day: £ 58
* Limited visitors on Wednesdays & week-ends

Caddie Caddie no **Electric Trolley** Chariot électrique no
Buggy Voiturette no **Clubs** Clubs no
Credit cards Cartes de crédit yes

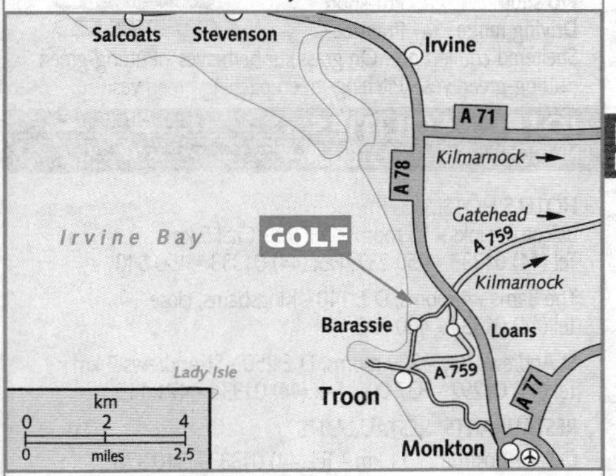

Access Accès : On A78 3 km N of Troon, opposite Barassie railway station
Map 3 on page 474 Carte 3 Page 474

GOLF COURSE 17/20
PARCOURS

Site Site
Maintenance Entretien
Architect Architecte Theodore Moon
Type Type links
Relief Relief
Water in play Eau en jeu
Exp. to wind Exposé au vent
Trees in play Arbres en jeu

Scorecard Carte de score	**Chp.** Chp.	**Mens** Mess.	**Ladies** Da.
Length Long.	6203	5902	5511
Par	72	72	74
Slope system	—	—	—

Advised golfing ability 0 12 24 36
Niveau de jeu recommandé
Hcp required Handicap exigé certificate

CLUB HOUSE & AMENITIES 6/10
CLUB HOUSE ET ANNEXES

Pro shop Pro-shop
Driving range Practice
Sheltered couvert no - On grass sur herbe yes - Putting-green putting-green yes - Pitching-green pitching green no

HOTEL FACILITIES 7/10
ENVIRONNEMENT HOTELIER

HOTELS HÔTELS
Piersland House - 30 rooms, D from £ 130 - Troon 3 km
Tel (44) 01292 - 314 747, Fax (44) 01292 - 315 613

Lochgreen House - 44 rooms, D £ 110 - Troon 3 km
Tel (44) 01292 - 313 343, Fax (44) 01292 - 318 661

Marine Highland - 89 rooms, D £ 140 - Troon 3 km
Tel (44) 01292 - 314 444, Fax (44) 01292 - 316 922

RESTAURANTS RESTAURANTS
Restaurant 1820 (Piersland) - Troon 3 km
Tel (44) 01292 - 314 747
Highgrove House - Troon 3 km - Tel (44) 01292 - 312 511
The Oyster Bar - Troon 3 km - Tel (44) 01292 - 319 339

Kingsbarns

19 | 8 | 7

Mark Parsinen and Art Dunkley called in Kyle Phillips to design this genuine masterpiece. They have proven that it is possible to blend the classic early days of golf course architecture with the technology of the modern age. Kingsbarns has everything of a real links course without ever going over the top: just formidable bunkers, bushes and sometimes fearful rough, a few ditches running down to the sea and crossing your path, and greens which hug the natural terrain. The out and in design is reminiscent of Saint Andrews but with a sense of space found more at courses like Muirfield or Carnoustie, all made better by the fact that almost every hole overlooks the sea. Then there is the sheer variety of holes which blend to form a coherent whole, the golfing challenge and excellence of realizations (this is pure links turf). As the site is one of the last capable of hosting a real links course, they could neither damage nor undermine it. Kingsbarns is an authentic masterly achievement that has already gained an international reputation and a devoted following.

Mark Parsinen et Art Dunkley ont fait appel à Kyle Phillips pour créer cet authentique chef-d'œuvre, prouvant qu'il était parfaitement possible d'associer la grande tradition classique avec les technologies modernes. On trouve ainsi tous les composants des vrais links, sans que ce soit un catalogue : bunkers redoutables, buissons et rough très dangereux, quelques fossés qui vont vers la mer et croisent votre route, des greens qui épousent le terrain. La forme aller-retour est réminiscente de St Andrews, mais avec un sens de l'espace que l'on trouve davantage à Muirfield ou Carnoustie, accentué par le fait qu'on domine la mer pratiquement partout. Ajoutons la diversité des trous, harmonieusement fondus dans un ensemble cohérent, l'exigence du jeu à fournir, la qualité de la réalisation (un vrai gazon de links). Le site étant l'un des derniers à pouvoir accueillir un links, il ne fallait ni l'endommager, ni l'affaiblir. Kingsbarns est un coup de maître qui a déjà ses admirateurs et fanatiques.

Kingsbarns Golf Links — 2001

SCO - KINGSBARNS, Fife KY16 8QD

Office Secrétariat (44) 01334 - 460 860
Pro shop Pro-shop (44) 01334 - 460 865
Fax Fax (44) 01334 - 460 877
Web www.kingsbarns.com
Situation Situation St Andrews, 10 km
Annual closure Fermeture annuelle 30/11→1/4
Weekly closure Fermeture hebdomadaire no

Fees main season Tarifs haute saison	18 holes	
	Week days Semaine	**We/Bank holidays** We/Férié
Individual Individuel	£ 145	£ 145
Couple Couple	£ 290	£ 290

£ 50 for Fife residents/Full day: £ 200

Caddie Caddie yes — **Electric Trolley** Chariot électrique no
Buggy Voiturette no — **Clubs** Clubs yes
Credit cards Cartes de crédit
VISA - MasterCard - Switch - AMEX

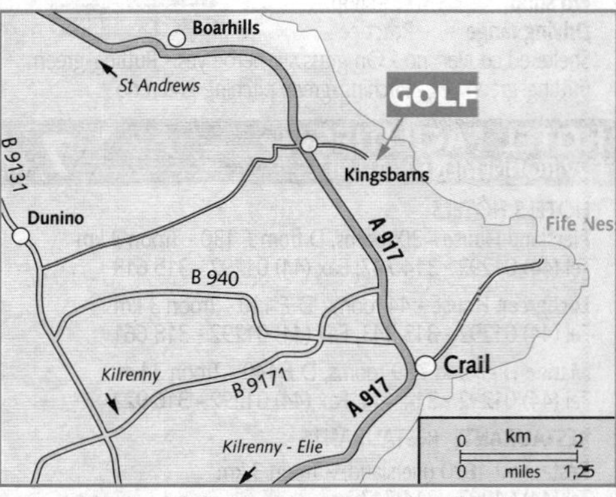

Access Accès : Edinburgh, M90, Jct 8, A92 to St Andrews, A917 → Crail. After village of Kingsbarns, 750 m, golf on the left hand side
Map 3 on page 475 Carte 3 Page 475

GOLF COURSE — PARCOURS 19/20

Site Site
Maintenance Entretien
Architect Architecte — Kyle Phillips, Mark Parsinen
Type Type — links, seaside course
Relief Relief
Water in play Eau en jeu
Exp. to wind Exposé au vent
Trees in play Arbres en jeu

Scorecard Carte de score	**Chp.** Chp.	**Mens** Mess.	**Ladies** Da.
Length Long.	6414	5987	4628
Par	72	72	72
Slope system	142	136	126

Advised golfing ability Niveau de jeu recommandé — 0 12 24 36
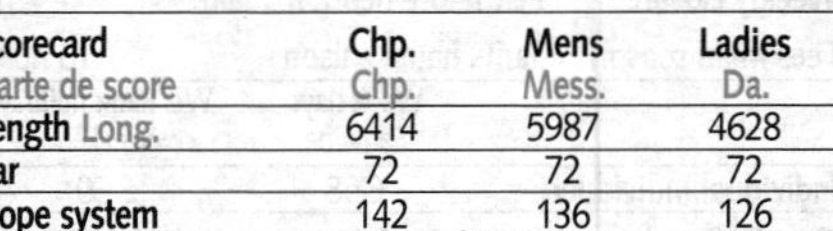
Hcp required Handicap exigé — 28 Men, 36 Ladies

CLUB HOUSE & AMENITIES — CLUB HOUSE ET ANNEXES 8/10

Pro shop Pro-shop
Driving range Practice
Sheltered couvert no - On grass sur herbe yes - Putting-green putting-green yes - Pitching-green pitching green yes

HOTEL FACILITIES — ENVIRONNEMENT HOTELIER 7/10

HOTELS HÔTELS

Balcomie Links - 15 rooms, D £ 90 - Crail 5 km
Tel (44) 01333 - 450 237, Fax (44) 01333 - 450 540

The Barns - 4 rooms, D £ 140 - Kingsbarns, close
Tel (44) 01334 - 460 820

St Andrews Bay - 209 rooms, D £ 250 - St Andrews 7 km
Tel (44) 01292 - 837 000, Fax (44) 01334 - 471 115

RESTAURANTS RESTAURANTS

Cellar - Anstruther 11 km - Tel (44) 01333 - 310 378
The Barns - Kingsbarns, close - Tel (44) 01334 - 460 820
The Peat Inn - Peat Inn 12 km - Tel (44) 01334 - 840 206

Kingussie

15	4	4

This Highlands course, located at 1,000 ft. above sea level, provides some breath-taking views over Speyside and the Cairngorms. The river Gynack crosses the course and comes into play on several occasions. Kingussie was originally designed on farmland, and Harry Vardon has made so much out of it that you'd willingly believe he had shifted tons of earth. He was unable to avoid a few blind shots over rather hilly terrain, but they are few and far between. The course is not really too tiring, either, as only holes N°4 and 8 have a few steepish slopes; the designer was a great champion and knew what can be asked of an amateur golfer. On this terrain of peat and moor-land, the ball never rolls much so the course plays every yard of its length. With a charming setting and warm welcome, Kingussie is a good holiday course with excellent value for money to boot.

Situé à environ 300 mètres d'altitude, ce parcours des Highlands offre de vastes panoramas sur le Speyside et les montagnes des Cairngorms. La rivière Gynack parcourt le site, venant en jeu sur quelques trous. A l'origine, ce parcours a été dessiné sur un terrain réservé à l'élevage, et Harry Vardon en a tiré un tel parti que l'on pourrait croire qu'il a déplacé des tonnes de terre. Dans un espace assez accidenté, il n'a pu éviter quelques coups aveugles, mais ils sont bien rares. De plus, on ne peut pas dire que ce parcours soit épuisant, seuls les trous n° 4 et 8 réservent quelques montées accentuées : l'architecte était un grand champion, il savait ce qu'on peut demander à un amateur. Sur ce terrain de tourbe et de lande, la balle ne roule jamais beaucoup, ce qui rend à peine plus long ce parcours. Le charme de l'environnement, comme l'accueil font de Kingussie un bon golf de vacances, avec un excellent rapport qualité-prix.

Kingussie Golf Club — 1891

Gynack Road
SCO - KINGUSSIE, Inverness-shire PH21 1LR

Office	Secrétariat	(44) 01540 - 661 600
Pro shop	Pro-shop	(44) 01540 - 661 600
Fax	Fax	(44) 01540 - 662 066
Web	www.kingussie-golf.co.uk	
Situation	Situation	Aviemore, 20 km
Annual closure	Fermeture annuelle	no

Chances of snow during winter months

Weekly closure	Fermeture hebdomadaire	no
Fees main season	Tarifs haute saison	full day

	Week days / Semaine	We/Bank holidays / We/Férié
Individual Individuel	£ 22	£ 24
Couple Couple	£ 44	£ 48

Caddie Caddie no — **Electric Trolley** Chariot électrique no
Buggy Voiturette yes — **Clubs** Clubs yes
Credit cards Cartes de crédit yes

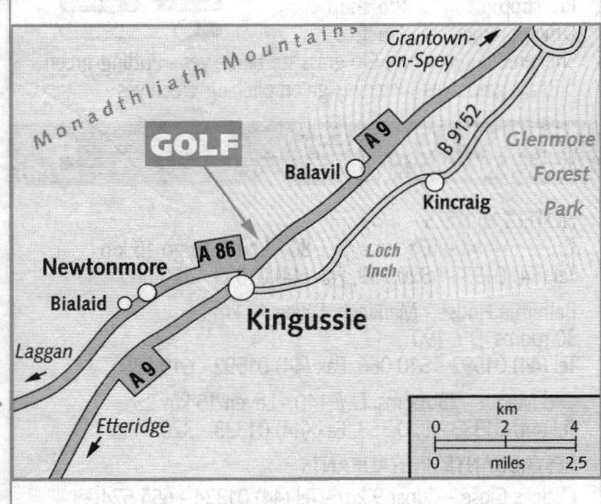

Access Accès : Just off main A9
Map 1 on page 470 Carte 1 Page 470

GOLF COURSE — PARCOURS — 15/20

Site	Site	
Maintenance	Entretien	
Architect	Architecte	Harry Vardon
Type	Type	hilly
Relief	Relief	
Water in play	Eau en jeu	
Exp. to wind	Exposé au vent	
Trees in play	Arbres en jeu	

Scorecard Carte de score	Chp. Chp.	Mens Mess.	Ladies Da.
Length Long.	5115	4813	4575
Par	67	67	73
Slope system	—	—	—

Advised golfing ability Niveau de jeu recommandé: 0 12 24 36
Hcp required Handicap exigé: no

CLUB HOUSE & AMENITIES — CLUB HOUSE ET ANNEXES — 4/10

Pro shop Pro-shop
Driving range Practice
Sheltered couvert no - On grass sur herbe yes - Putting-green putting-green yes - Pitching-green pitching green yes

HOTEL FACILITIES — ENVIRONNEMENT HOTELIER — 4/10

HOTELS HÔTELS

Scot House - 9 rooms, D from £ 75 - Kingussie, close
Tel (44) 01540 - 661 351, Fax (44) 01540 - 661 111

Columba House - 11 rooms, D £ 90 - Kingussie, close
Tel (44) 01540 - 661 402, Fax (44) 01540 - 661 652

Hermitage - 5 rooms, D £ 60 - Kingussie, close
Tel (44) 01540 - 662 137, Fax (44) 01540 - 662 177

RESTAURANTS RESTAURANTS

The Cross (booking essential) - Kingussie, close
Tel (44) 01540 - 661 166
Scot House - Kingussie, close - Tel (44) 01540 - 661 351

Ladybank

17	7	5

Although not a links, Ladybank is used as a qualifying course for the British Open when held at St Andrews. In other words it is deservedly held in high esteem by the game's governing bodies and provides a stiff test. Amidst pine-trees, heather and gorse, it is an idyllic site with enough wildlife to break anyone's concentration, but this is a technical challenge of the highest order. Accuracy is at a premium as you are best advised to keep well away from the formidable rough here where you can lose balls, clubs and perhaps even players too! But while good players may suffer, the humbler hacker can get by with a minimum of careful thought. With superb use of the land, pleasantly contoured fairways, increasingly rare red squirrels and well-defended greens where there is always one safe way in, Ladybank really is worth the trip.

Bien qu'il ne s'agisse pas d'un links, Ladybank est utilisé comme parcours de qualification pour le British Open quand il a lieu à St Andrews. C'est dire qu'il est tenu en haute estime par les pouvoirs sportifs et qu'il propose un test éloquent. Il le mérite amplement. Au milieu des pins, de la bruyère et des ajoncs, il constitue aussi un site idyllique où s'épanouit la vie sauvage. On y perdrait facilement sa concentration, mais c'est un défi technique de première grandeur. La précision d'abord est essentielle, car il vaut mieux ne pas s'égarer dans les roughs redoutables où l'on perd les balles, les clubs et sans doute aussi les joueurs ! Mais si les bons joueurs peuvent souffrir, les joueurs plus humbles et modestes tireront leur épingle du jeu avec un minimum de réflexion. Par sa superbe utilisation du terrain, son relief agréable, ses greens bien défendus mais qui laissent toujours une porte ouverte, ses écureuils rouges bien rares aujourd'hui en Grande-Bretagne, Ladybank mérite vraiment le détour.

Ladybank Golf Club — 1879

Annsmuir
SCO - LADYBANK, Fife KY7 7RA

Office	Secrétariat	(44) 01337 - 830 814
Pro shop	Pro-shop	(44) 01337 - 830 725
Fax	Fax	(44) 01337 - 831 505
Web	www.ladybankgolf.co.uk	
Situation	Situation	Cupar, 9 km
Annual closure	Fermeture annuelle	no
Weekly closure	Fermeture hebdomadaire	no

Fees main season Tarifs haute saison	18 holes	
	Week days Semaine	We/Bank holidays We/Férié
Individual Individuel	£ 40	£ 45
Couple Couple	£ 80	£ 90

Full day: £ 50

Caddie Caddie no **Electric Trolley** Chariot électrique no

Buggy Voiturette yes (4) **Clubs** Clubs on request

Credit cards Cartes de crédit VISA - MasterCard

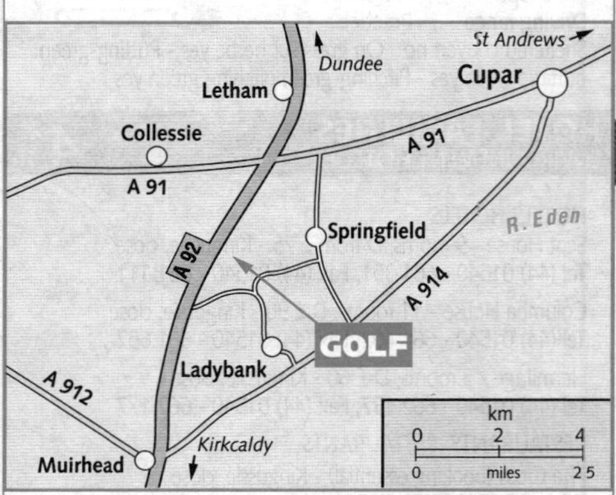

Access Accès : Just off the A92, between Glenrothes and Dundee

Map 3 on page 475 Carte 3 Page 475

GOLF COURSE — PARCOURS 17/20

Site	Site	
Maintenance	Entretien	
Architect	Architecte	Tom Morris
Type	Type	heathland
Relief	Relief	
Water in play	Eau en jeu	
Exp. to wind	Exposé au vent	
Trees in play	Arbres en jeu	

Scorecard Carte de score	Chp. Chp.	Mens Mess.	Ladies Da.
Length Long.	6079	5670	5330
Par	71	71	71
Slope system	—	—	—

Advised golfing ability Niveau de jeu recommandé: 0 12 24 36

Hcp required Handicap exigé: certificate

CLUB HOUSE & AMENITIES — CLUB HOUSE ET ANNEXES 7/10

Pro shop Pro-shop
Driving range Practice
Sheltered couvert no - On grass sur herbe yes - Putting-green putting-green yes - Pitching-green pitching green yes

HOTEL FACILITIES — ENVIRONNEMENT HOTELIER 5/10

HOTELS HÔTELS

Crusoe Hotel - 16 rooms, D £ 80 - Lower Largo 15 km
Tel (44) 01333 - 320 759, Fax (44) 01333 - 320 865

Balbirnie House - Markinch, Leven 10 km
30 rooms, D £ 190
Tel (44) 01592 - 610 066, Fax (44) 01592 - 610 529

Old Manor - 23 rooms, D £ 140 - Leven 15 km
Tel (44) 01333 - 320 368, Fax (44) 01333 - 320 911

RESTAURANTS RESTAURANTS

Ostler's Close - Cupar 9 km - Tel (44) 01334 - 655 574
Balbinie House - Markinch, Leven 10 km
Tel (44) 01592 - 610 066

Lanark

16	6	5

They say that the total length of courses designed by James Braid exceeds the combined length and width of Great Britain. That's probably true inasmuch as he basically retouched a lot of existing courses. This layout was designed by Old Tom Morris, another prolific designer, but at the time "golf architecture" was primarily a question of laying out the route of the course and the position of bunkers and greens. The course was then completed by the work of nature. At some 650 feet above sea-level, Lanark is one of those courses where golf seems always to have been a part of the scene on land of glacial sand, heather and moorland which make such excellent playing surfaces. Not overly long, moderately hilly and with only one or two blind shots, this is a no-nonsense course and a serious test for all levels. A genuinely hidden treasure of Scottish golf.

On dit que la longueur totale des parcours dessinés par James Braid totalise plus de la longueur et de la largeur de la Grande-Bretagne. C'est probablement vrai, dans la mesure où il en a dessiné beaucoup, mais il a essentiellement retouché beaucoup de parcours existants. Celui-ci avait été tracé par Old Tom Morris, lui aussi architecte très prolifique : mais, à son époque, l'architecture de golf consistait avant tout à définir l'itinéraire du parcours, l'emplacement des greens et bunkers. Un parcours devait s'arranger avec la nature. A 200 mètres d'altitude, Lanark est l'un de ces sites où le golf paraît avoir toujours été présent, en terre de sables glaciaires, de bruyère et de lande qui fait de bons tapis de jeu. Pas trop long, avec un relief modéré, et seulement un ou deux coups aveugles, c'est un parcours sans autres histoires que celles que l'on y fait, un test sérieux pour tous niveaux. Un petit bijou bien caché du golf écossais.

Lanark Golf Club — 1851

The Moor, Whiteless Road
SCO - LANARK, ML11 7RX

Office	Secrétariat	(44) 01555 - 663 219
Pro shop	Pro-shop	(44) 01555 - 661 456
Fax	Fax	—
Web	www.lanarkgolfclub.co.uk	
Situation	Situation	Lanark, 1 km
Annual closure	Fermeture annuelle	no
Weekly closure	Fermeture hebdomadaire	no

Fees main season Tarifs haute saison — 18 holes

	Week days Semaine	We/Bank holidays We/Férié
Individual Individuel	£ 35	*
Couple Couple	£ 70	*

Full week days: £ 45 / * No visitors at week-ends

Caddie Caddie no — **Electric Trolley** Chariot électrique no
Buggy Voiturette yes — **Clubs** Clubs no
Credit cards Cartes de crédit no

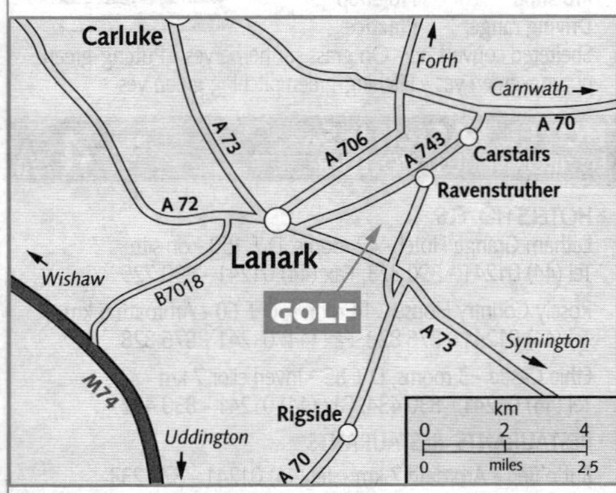

Access Accès : • Edinburgh, A71, then A706 to Lanark
• Glasgow, M74 and A72 to Lanark
Map 2 on page 473 Carte 2 Page 473

GOLF COURSE — PARCOURS — 16/20

Site	Site	
Maintenance	Entretien	
Architect	Architecte	Tom Morris James Braid
Type	Type	moorland
Relief	Relief	
Water in play	Eau en jeu	
Exp. to wind	Exposé au vent	
Trees in play	Arbres en jeu	

Scorecard Carte de score	Chp. Chp.	Mens Mess.	Ladies Da.
Length Long.	5845	5570	5330
Par	70	70	74
Slope system	—	—	—

Advised golfing ability Niveau de jeu recommandé — 0 12 24 36
Hcp required Handicap exigé — certificate

CLUB HOUSE & AMENITIES — CLUB HOUSE ET ANNEXES — 6/10

Pro shop Pro-shop
Driving range Practice
Sheltered couvert no - On grass sur herbe no - Putting-green putting-green yes - Pitching-green pitching green no

HOTEL FACILITIES — ENVIRONNEMENT HOTELIER — 5/10

HOTELS HÔTELS

Shieldhill Castle - 16 rooms, D £ 150 - Biggar 15 km
Tel (44) 01899 - 220 035, Fax (44) 01899 - 221 092

Cartland Bridge - 18 rooms, D £ 100 - Lanark 2 km
Tel (44) 01555 - 664 426, Fax (44) 01555 - 663 773

New Lanark Mill - New Lanark 2 km
40 rooms, D £ 110
Tel (44) 01555 - 667 200, Fax (44) 01555 - 667 222

RESTAURANTS RESTAURANTS

La Vigna - Lanark 2 km - Tel (44) 01555 - 664 320
Crown Tavern - Lanark 2 km - Tel (44) 01555 - 662 465
Shieldhill Castle - Biggar 15 km - Tel (44) 01899 - 220 035

Letham Grange *Old Course*

15 | 7 | 4

This course was opened in 1987 at the foot of the splendid Letham Grange Hotel and was designed by gentleman farmer Ken Smith, who drew his inspiration from the Augusta National course, hoping that one day this might become known as the Scottish Augusta. In actual fact there are very few similarities but this is nonetheless a pretty and rather challenging layout with fairways that are sometime flanked by trees and other times more open, and a few rather dangerous water hazards. The course is rather hilly in places, which means a few blind shots. Target golf is virtually an obligation here, and this is why you don't always get the impression of playing in Scotland. But despite everything, it is fun playing here with friends of all levels, of whom the least experienced will probably enjoy more the second Glen course, a shorter par 68 of 5,528 yards.

Ce parcours a été ouvert en 1987 au pied du splendide Letham Grange Hotel, et dessiné par Ken Smith, un gentleman farmer qui s'inspira d'Augusta National en espérant que ce parcours pourrait un jour être appelé le "Augusta d'Ecosse". Sans vouloir le chagriner, on trouve peu de ressemblances avec le parcours du Masters, mais il s'agit malgré tout d'un joli tracé, assez exigeant, aux fairways parfois bordés d'arbres, parfois dans un espace plus ouvert, avec quelques obstacles d'eau assez dangereux. Le relief est parfois assez prononcé, ce qui implique quelques coups aveugles. Ici, le target golf est quasiment une obligation, c'est pourquoi on n'a pas forcément l'impression de se trouver en Ecosse. Malgré tout, on aura plaisir à évoluer ici avec des amis de tous niveaux, dont les moins expérimentés aimeront jouer le second parcours, le Glen Course, bien plus court avec ses 5000 mètres et son par 68.

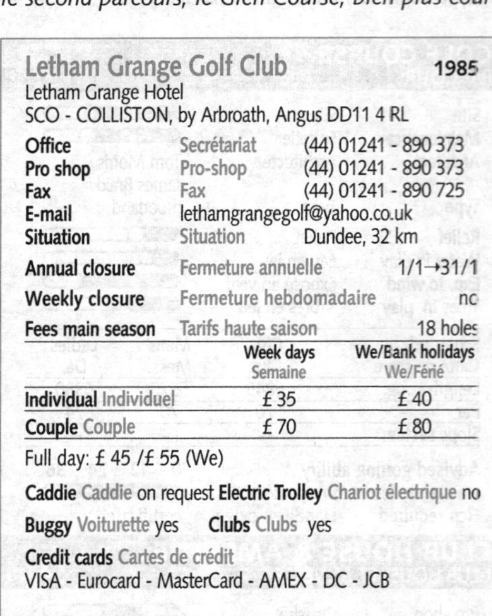

Letham Grange Golf Club — 1985

Letham Grange Hotel
SCO - COLLISTON, by Arbroath, Angus DD11 4 RL

Office	Secrétariat	(44) 01241 - 890 373
Pro shop	Pro-shop	(44) 01241 - 890 373
Fax	Fax	(44) 01241 - 890 725
E-mail	lethamgrangegolf@yahoo.co.uk	
Situation	Situation	Dundee, 32 km
Annual closure	Fermeture annuelle	1/1→31/1
Weekly closure	Fermeture hebdomadaire	no

Fees main season Tarifs haute saison		18 holes
	Week days Semaine	We/Bank holidays We/Férié
Individual Individuel	£ 35	£ 40
Couple Couple	£ 70	£ 80

Full day: £ 45 /£ 55 (We)

Caddie Caddie on request **Electric Trolley** Chariot électrique no

Buggy Voiturette yes **Clubs** Clubs yes

Credit cards Cartes de crédit
VISA - Eurocard - MasterCard - AMEX - DC - JCB

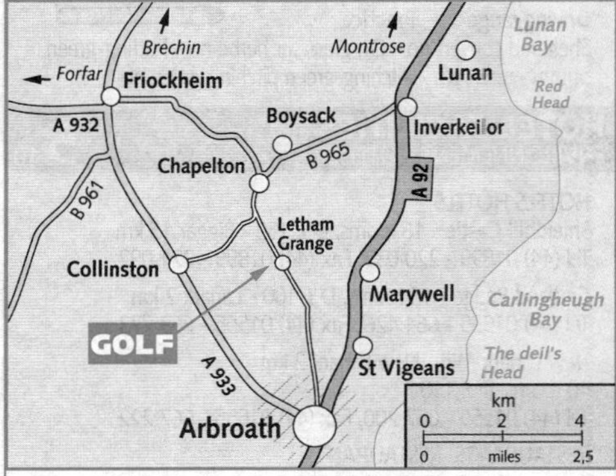

Access Accès : 8 km N of Arbroath just off A92.
Well signposted.
Map 1 on page 471 Carte 1 Page 471

GOLF COURSE — 15/20
PARCOURS

Site	Site	
Maintenance	Entretien	
Architect	Architecte	D. Steel, GK. Smith
Type	Type	parkland
Relief	Relief	
Water in play	Eau en jeu	
Exp. to wind	Exposé au vent	
Trees in play	Arbres en jeu	

Scorecard Carte de score	Chp. Chp.	Mens Mess.	Ladies Da.
Length Long.	6341	5777	5254
Par	73	73	75
Slope system	—	—	—

Advised golfing ability Niveau de jeu recommandé — 0 12 24 36

Hcp required Handicap exigé no

CLUB HOUSE & AMENITIES — 7/10
CLUB HOUSE ET ANNEXES

Pro shop Pro-shop
Driving range Practice
Sheltered couvert no - On grass sur herbe yes - Putting-green putting-green yes - Pitching-green pitching green yes

HOTEL FACILITIES — 4/10
ENVIRONNEMENT HOTELIER

HOTELS HÔTELS

Letham Grange Hotel - 42 rooms, D £ 150 - on site
Tel (44) 01241 - 890 373, Fax (44) 01241 - 890 725

Rosely Country House - 14 rooms, D £ 60 - Arbroath 5 km
Tel (44) 01241 - 876 828, Fax (44) 01241 - 876 828

Ethie Castle - 3 rooms, D £ 85 - Inverkeilor 7 km
Tel (44) 01241 - 830 434, Fax (44) 01241 - 830 432

RESTAURANTS RESTAURANTS

But'n'Ben - Arbroath 7 km - Tel (44) 01241 - 877 233

Leven

16 | 6 | 5

The original course was shared with the Lundin Golf Club. But when the railways arrived in the region, the course was split nine holes on one side and nine on the other, with each club creating an extra nine holes. So instead of one good course, here we have two, as adjacent now as they were in the past. Most of the holes at Leven are pure links style, but two or three are close to the heather-bound inland courses that are so common in both Scotland and England. Here again the wind has a say in things, because Leven is distinctly vulnerable when played in fine weather by long-hitters and skilled technicians. In this case even the least experienced players will have fun, the last few holes notwithstanding. The least they should do is avoid the deep fairway bunkers and the sand around the green, and stay focused until the very end, as the Scoonie Burn can scupper your round just as easily as the burn on the 18th hole at Carnoustie. This has always been one of the finest closing stretches in the game, one to conclude a great day's golfing.

A l'arrivée du chemin de fer dans la région, le parcours original a été partagé en deux entre Leven et Lundin. Chacun a donc dû créer de son côté neuf autres trous. Au lieu d'un seul bon parcours, en voilà deux, toujours mitoyens. La plupart des trous de Leven ont un caractère de pur links, mais deux ou trois sont assez proches des parcours inland de bruyère, que l'on trouve en Ecosse comme en Angleterre. C'est toujours le vent qui fait la différence, car Leven s'avère fragile face aux solides frappeurs et aux bons techniciens quand le temps est beau. Alors, même les moins expérimentés y trouveront leur plaisir, mais les derniers trous peuvent leur créer des problèmes. Qu'ils évitent en tous cas les profonds bunkers de fairway comme ceux qui défendent les greens. Et qu'ils ne baissent pas la garde avant le 18, car le Scoonie Burn y joue un rôle un peu analogue à celui du burn du 18 de Carnoustie. C'est depuis toujours l'une des meilleures conclusions à une belle journée de golf.

Leven Golfing Society — 1846

P.O. Box 14609, Links Road
SCO - LEVEN, Fife KY9 1LG

Office	Secrétariat	(44) 01333 - 424 229
Pro shop	Pro-shop	no Pro Shop
Fax	Fax	(44) 01333 - 424 229
Web	www.leven-links.com	
Situation	Situation	St Andrews, 20 km
Annual closure	Fermeture annuelle	no
Weekly closure	Fermeture hebdomadaire	no

Fees main season Tarifs haute saison	18 holes	
	Week days Semaine	We/Bank holidays We/Férié
Individual Individuel	£ 37	£ 45
Couple Couple	£ 74	£ 90

Caddie Caddie no — **Electric Trolley** Chariot électrique no

Buggy Voiturette no — **Clubs** Clubs no

Credit cards Cartes de crédit no

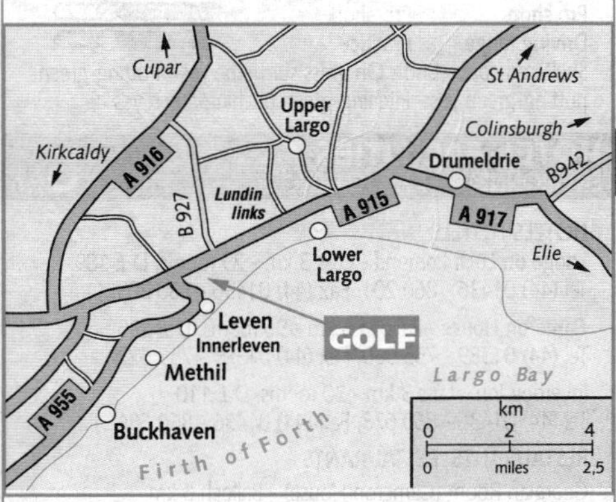

Access Accès : Edinburgh, M90 then A92 (Jct3), A955.
Golf East of Leven, on Promenade.
Map 3 on page 475 Carte 3 Page 475

GOLF COURSE — PARCOURS — 16/20

Site	Site	
Maintenance	Entretien	
Architect	Architecte	unknown
Type	Type	links, seaside course
Relief	Relief	
Water in play	Eau en jeu	
Exp. to wind	Exposé au vent	
Trees in play	Arbres en jeu	

Scorecard Carte de score	Chp. Chp.	Mens Mess.	Ladies Da.
Length Long.	5785	5544	5181
Par	71	69	73
Slope system	—	—	—

Advised golfing ability Niveau de jeu recommandé: 0 12 24 36

Hcp required Handicap exigé: no

CLUB HOUSE & AMENITIES — CLUB HOUSE ET ANNEXES — 6/10

Pro shop Pro-shop
Driving range Practice
Sheltered couvert no - On grass sur herbe no - Putting-green putting-green yes - Pitching-green pitching green no

HOTEL FACILITIES — ENVIRONNEMENT HOTELIER — 5/10

HOTELS HÔTELS

Old Manor Hotel - Lundin Links 3 km
23 rooms, D £ 150
Tel (44) 01333 - 320 368, Fax (44) 01333 - 320 911

Crusoe Hotel - 16 rooms, D £ 90 - Lundin Links 3 km
Tel (44) 01333 - 320 759, Fax (44) 01333 - 320 865

Lundin Links Hotel - 21 rooms, D £ 99 - Lundin 3 km
Tel (44) 01333 - 320 207, Fax (44) 01333 - 320 930

RESTAURANTS RESTAURANTS

Old Manor Hotel - Lundin Links 3 km
Tel (44) 01333 - 320 368

The Peat Inn - Peat Inn 5 km - Tel (44) 01334 - 840 206

Loch Lomond

18	8	6

Loch Lomond is the preserve of a mainly international membership who play here only occasionally. Alone or with their guests, they enjoy the privilege of strolling down the quiet fairways of one of the world's most beautiful courses. This has definitely raised a few eyebrows in Scotland, a country where golf has always been considered the right of all and not the (happy) few. In between time, professional tournaments have made the course familiar to TV viewers. This is a course of the highest standard, at once open and challenging, spectacular and blending beautifully into the landscape, long and technically hard work in a setting that has successfully preserved the natural flora and fauna. There are though one or two minor flaws, like the way the course suffers in rainy weather and a style that is a little too American for this part of the world. We have respect enough for the course architects, but have they shown enough respect for the bonnie heart of Scotland? Tom Weiskopf believes that this course is his lasting memorial to golf. So who are we to argue?

Loch Lomond est la chasse gardée de membres venant du monde entier, qui ne jouent ici que de temps à autre. Seuls, avec leurs invités, ils ont le droit de fouler les fairways tranquilles de l'un des plus beaux parcours du monde. Ainsi, le club a encouru quelques critiques en Ecosse, pays où le droit de jouer au golf est considéré comme le droit de tous, et non de "happy few", mais la Solheim Cup et le Scottish Open l'on fait largement connaître aux téléspectateurs. A la fois franc et exigeant, spectaculaire et bien insinué dans le paysage, long et technique, c'est un parcours du plus haut niveau, qui a su aussi préserver la faune et la flore du lieu. On y trouvera quelques bémols, une certaine fragilité par temps de pluie, et un style peut-être un peu trop américain pour le lieu. Nous respectons les architectes, ont-t-il assez respecté l'âme du pays ? De son côté, Tom Weiskopf estime que c'est sa meilleure contribution au golf. Pourquoi en discuter ?

Loch Lomond Golf Club — 1993

Rossdu House
SCO - LUSS, Dunbartonshire G83 8NT

Office	Secrétariat	(44) 01436 - 655 555
Pro shop	Pro-shop	(44) 01436 - 655 555
Fax	Fax	(44) 01436 - 655 500
Web	www.lochlomond.com	
Situation	Situation	Glasgow, 35 km
Annual closure	Fermeture annuelle	no
Weekly closure	Fermeture hebdomadaire	no

Fees main season Tarifs haute saison — 18 holes

	Week days / Semaine	We/Bank holidays / We/Férié
Individual Individuel	*	*
Couple Couple	*	*

* Strictly for members and their guests

Caddie Caddie on request **Electric Trolley** Chariot électrique no

Buggy Voiturette yes **Clubs** Clubs no

Credit cards Cartes de crédit
VISA - Eurocard - MasterCard - AMEX - DC

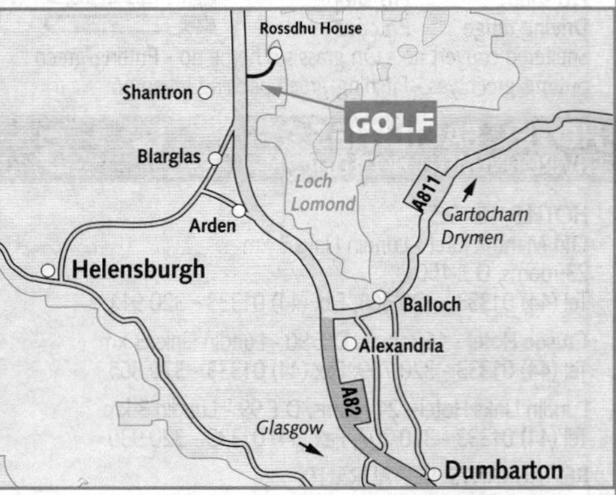

Access Accès : Glasgow, go to Erskine Bridge, A82 → Alexandria, Luss. After Alexandria, golf on right hand side.
Map 2 on page 472 Carte 2 Page 472

GOLF COURSE — PARCOURS 18/20

Site	Site	
Maintenance	Entretien	
Architect	Architecte	Tom Weiskopf Jay Morrish
Type	Type	parkland
Relief	Relief	
Water in play	Eau en jeu	
Exp. to wind	Exposé au vent	
Trees in play	Arbres en jeu	

Scorecard Carte de score	Chp. Chp.	Mens Mess.	Ladies Da.
Length Long.	6420	6057	5036
Par	71	72	74
Slope system	—	—	—

Advised golfing ability Niveau de jeu recommandé — 0 12 24 36

Hcp required Handicap exigé — no

CLUB HOUSE & AMENITIES — CLUB HOUSE ET ANNEXES 8/10

Pro shop Pro-shop
Driving range Practice
Sheltered couvert no - On grass sur herbe yes - Putting-green putting-green yes - Pitching-green pitching green yes

HOTEL FACILITIES — ENVIRONNEMENT HOTELIER 6/10

HOTELS HÔTELS

Lodge on Loch Lomond - Luss 3 km - 29 rooms, D £ 189
Tel (44) 01436 - 860 201, Fax (44) 01436 - 860 203

Cameron House - Balloch 6 km - 96 rooms, D £ 235
Tel (44) 01389 - 755 565, Fax (44) 01389 - 759 522

Inverbeg Inn - Luss 3 km - 20 rooms, D £ 110
Tel (44) 01436 - 860 678, Fax (44) 01436 - 860 686

RESTAURANTS RESTAURANTS

Georgian Room (Cameron House) - Balloch 6 km
Tel (44) 01389 - 755 565

Lodge on Loch Lomond - Luss 3 km - Tel (44) 01436 - 860 201

Inverbeg Inn - Luss 3 km - Tel (44) 01436 - 860 678

Longniddry

14	7	5

Legend has it that Mary Queen of Scots played golf "over the fields of Seton" in 1567 in the vicinity of the present course, shortly after the death of her husband Lord Darnley. The original course here was designed by Harry Colt some 350 years later, and formally opened for play in 1922. James Braid and MacKenzie Ross made alterations to the course which in more recent times has undergone another makeover, this time at the hands of architect Donald Steel. Many of the cross-bunkers from the original design have now been relocated further from the teeing areas to take account of advances in technology. The course is now less penal for the bogey golfer and more challenging for the scratch player. It always gives an impression of tranquillity, beauty and elegance, and a breath-taking view over the Firth of Forth. It is as much parkland as links, and is unusual in not having any par 5 holes, even if some of the long par 4s could be considered as such. The greens are good and receptive to well-hit approach shots, whether pitched or rolled.

Mary Reine d'Ecosse aurait joué au golf dans les environs en 1567, au lendemain de la mort de son mari Lord Darnley. 350 ans plus tard, Harry Colt dessina le parcours original, retouché ensuite par James Braid et Mackenzie Ross. Récemment, l'architecte Donald Steel a été chargé de réviser le tracé, notamment en reportant un certain nombre de "cross-bunkers" plus loin des départs, pour mieux répondre aux défis du matériel de golf. Le parcours pénalise moins les joueurs moyens, et davantage les meilleurs. Il n'a rien perdu de son atmosphère de calme, de beauté et d'élégance. Avec sa vue imprenable sur le Firth of Forth, Longniddry est aussi bien un parc qu'un links, il a aussi la particularité de ne pas avoir de par 5 à proprement parler, même si certains longs par 4 pourraient prétendre à ce titre. Les greens, de bonne qualité, sont réceptifs à des approches bien jouées, éventuellement roulées, on peut seulement regretter que certains greens à double plateau aient disparu.

Longniddry Golf Club — 1921

SCO - LONGNIDDRY, East Lothian EH32 0NL

Office	Secrétariat	(44) 01875 - 852 141
Pro shop	Pro-shop	(44) 01875 - 852 228
Fax	Fax	(44) 01875 - 853 371
Web	www.longniddrygolfclub.co.uk	
Situation	Situation	Edinburgh, 19 km
Annual closure	Fermeture annuelle	no
Weekly closure	Fermeture hebdomadaire	no

Fees main season Tarifs haute saison	Week days Semaine	We/Bank holidays We/Férié
Individual Individuel	£ 35	£ 45
Couple Couple	£ 70	£ 90

18 holes

Full week days: £ 50

Caddie Caddie on request **Electric Trolley** Chariot électrique yes

Buggy Voiturette yes **Clubs** Clubs on request

Credit cards Cartes de crédit
VISA - MasterCard - AMEX

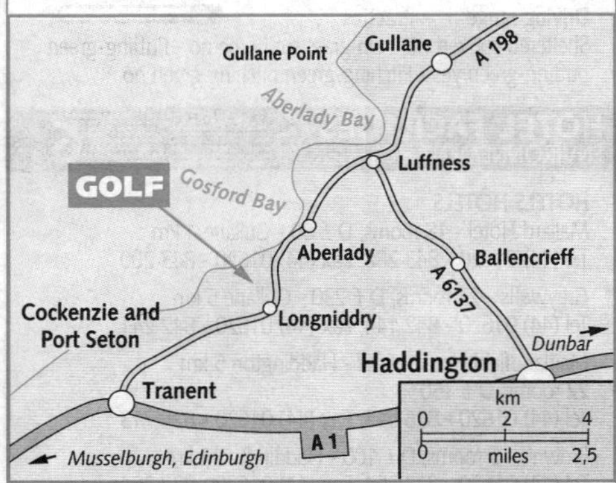

Access Accès : Edinburgh, A1, A198. Course reached via Links Road at South of the village.

Map 3 on page 475 Carte 3 Page 475

GOLF COURSE — PARCOURS — 14/20

Site	Site	
Maintenance	Entretien	
Architect	Architecte	Harry S. Colt, J.Braid, Mackenzie Ross
Type	Type	parkland
Relief	Relief	
Water in play	Eau en jeu	
Exp. to wind	Exposé au vent	
Trees in play	Arbres en jeu	

Scorecard Carte de score	Chp. Chp.	Mens Mess.	Ladies Da.
Length Long.	5634	5425	5207
Par	68	68	73
Slope system	—	—	—

Advised golfing ability Niveau de jeu recommandé — 0 12 24 36

Hcp required Handicap exigé — 28 Men, 36 Ladies

CLUB HOUSE & AMENITIES — CLUB HOUSE ET ANNEXES — 7/10

Pro shop	Pro-shop
Driving range	Practice

Sheltered couvert no - On grass sur herbe yes - Putting-green putting-green yes - Pitching-green pitching green yes

HOTEL FACILITIES — ENVIRONNEMENT HOTELIER — 5/10

HOTELS HÔTELS

Mallard Hotel - Gullane 10 km - 18 rooms, D £ 80
Tel (44) 01620 - 843 288, Fax (44) 01620 - 843 200

Brown's - Haddington 12 km - 5 rooms, D £ 100
Tel (44) 01620 - 822 254, Fax (44) 01620 - 822 254

Maitlandfield House Hotel - Haddington 12 km
22 rooms, D £ 150
Tel (44) 01620 - 826 513, Fax (44) 01620 - 826 713

RESTAURANTS RESTAURANTS

Greywalls Hotel - Gullane 10 km - Tel (44) 01620 - 842 144
Brown's - Haddington - Tel (44) 01620 - 822 254

Luffness New

16	4	6

Arriving here, you seem to be carrying on from Gullane in a whole cluster of courses the equivalent of which is to be found only at St Andrews or Pinehurst. Although Luffness New is not as well known as its neighbours or even nearby Muirfield, it is a course of great character which is always in perfect condition (the greens are famous for this). It rewards the good shots and punishes the bad ones, the way it should be but not always is. There is virtually no water to speak of, but the wet stuff is replaced by top-notch bunkering. The wind is an important factor but the direction changes at almost every hole, while formidable and omnipresent rough patiently awaits the slightest mis-hit. The highlights include a few long par 4s and hole N°4, a par 5 of 531 yards that is far trickier than it looks. When all is said and done, carding a good score here is the sign of a talented player. Should this quality be in short supply, you'll still have a lot of fun.

En arrivant ici, on se retrouve dans la continuité des parcours de Gullane, et dans une véritable galaxie dont on ne retrouve l'équivalent qu'à St Andrews ou, plus encore, Pinehurst. Bien que Luffness New n'ait pas la notoriété de ses voisins ou, plus encore, de Muirfield tout proche, c'est un parcours de caractère fort, toujours en bon état (ses greens sont célèbres), qui récompense les bons coups et punit les mauvais, ce qui devrait toujours être le cas, mais n'est pas si fréquent. L'eau y est pratiquement absente, mais elle est remplacée par un bunkering de premier ordre. Le vent y est un facteur important, mais l'orientation change pratiquement à chaque trou et un rough aussi redoutable qu'omniprésent attend patiemment vos moindres erreurs. Parmi les sommets du lieu, on notera quelques longs pars 4, et le 4, un par 5 de 480 mètres (531 yards) plus délicat qu'il n'y paraît. Tous comptes faits, signer un bon score ici est une preuve de talent. Si l'on manque de cette qualité première, on s'y amusera aussi beaucoup.

Luffness New Golf Club — 1894

SCO - ABERLADY EH32 0QA

Office	Secrétariat	(44) 01620 - 843 336
Pro shop	Pro-shop	—
Fax	Fax	(44) 01620 - 842 933
Web	www.luffnessgolf.com	
Situation	Situation	Edinburgh, 27 km
Annual closure	Fermeture annuelle	no
Weekly closure	Fermeture hebdomadaire	no

Fees main season Tarifs haute saison	18 holes	
	Week days Semaine	**We/Bank holidays** We/Férié
Individual Individuel	£ 45	*
Couple Couple	£ 90	*

Full week day: £ 65 /* No visitors at week-ends / Restrictions for Ladies (ask)

Caddie Caddie no **Electric Trolley** Chariot électrique no

Buggy Voiturette no **Clubs** Clubs no

Credit cards Cartes de crédit yes

Access Accès : Edinburgh A1. Near Tranent, A198 through Longniddry and Aberlady. Turn off right to Luffness club-house.

Map 3 on page 475 Carte 3 Page 475

GOLF COURSE — PARCOURS — 16/20

Site	Site	
Maintenance	Entretien	
Architect	Architecte	Tom Morris
Type	Type	links
Relief	Relief	
Water in play	Eau en jeu	
Exp. to wind	Exposé au vent	
Trees in play	Arbres en jeu	

Scorecard Carte de score	**Chp.** Chp.	**Mens** Mess.	**Ladies** Da.
Length Long.	5510	5510	5510
Par	69	69	73
Slope system	—	—	—

Advised golfing ability Niveau de jeu recommandé: 0 12 24 36

Hcp required Handicap exigé: certificate

CLUB HOUSE & AMENITIES — CLUB HOUSE ET ANNEXES — 4/10

Pro shop Pro-shop

Driving range Practice

Sheltered couvert no - On grass sur herbe no - Putting-green putting-green yes - Pitching-green pitching green no

HOTEL FACILITIES — ENVIRONNEMENT HOTELIER — 6/10

HOTELS HÔTELS

Mallard Hotel - 18 rooms, D £ 80 - Gullane 4 km
Tel (44) 01620 - 843 288, Fax (44) 01620 - 843 200

Greywalls - 23 rooms, D £ 230 - Gullane 5 km
Tel (44) 01620 - 842 144, Fax (44) 01620 - 842 241

Maitlandfield House Hotel - Haddington 5 km
22 rooms, D £ 150
Tel (44) 01620 - 826 513, Fax (44) 01620 - 826 713

Brown's - 5 rooms, D £ 100 - Haddington 4 km
Tel (44) 01620 - 822 254, Fax (44) 01620 - 822 254

RESTAURANTS RESTAURANTS

La Potinière - Gullane 5 km - Tel (44) 01620 - 843 214
Greywalls - Gullane 4 km - Tel (44) 01620 - 842 144

Lundin

16	7	7

The twin brother to Leven Links, Lundin was born when each course took 9 holes and went their own way up to 18. Don't wait for the annual tournament that brings both courses together, just try and play this course which originated beside the sea. Restyled like so many other courses by James Braid, this is a good old links - there is even an old railway track running through the middle - used for the qualifying rounds for the British Open. You'll find some holes in heathland, particularly the 12th and 13th holes and especially the 14th, from where the view over the whole course and the Firth of Forth is impressive indeed, from the confines of Edinburgh to Muirfield, just opposite. Out on the fairways, the major hazard is of course the wind, and while there is now an automatic irrigation system, we can only hope that it is not over-used. Soft terrain kills a little of the subtlety and unpredictable nature of a links course and requires less creativity from the golfer. The club-house has been recently refurbished at great expense and been given a welcome facelift.

Frère jumeau de Leven Links, Lundin est né d'une scission en 1868, chacun gardant neuf trous et complétant son parcours. N'attendez pas la compétition annuelle qui les réunit, essayez aussi de jouer ce parcours des origines le long de la mer. Remodelé comme bien d'autres par James Braid, c'est un vrai bon links (avec même une ancienne voie ferrée au milieu) utilisé pour les qualifications du British Open. Mais on y trouve aussi des trous en terrain de bruyère, en particulier au 12 et au 13, et surtout au 14 d'où la vue est impressionnante sur l'esemble du présent parcours, sur le Firth of Forth, des confins d'Edimbourg à Muirfield, en face. Le vent est bien sûr le principal obstacle, mais s'il y a l'arrosage automatique, on peut souhaiter qu'il ne soit pas trop utilisé, car un terrain mou retire beaucoup de leur subtilité et de leur caractère imprévisible aux links, et exige moins de créativité. Le club-house vient de subir une fort coûteuse cure de jeunesse tout à fait bienvenue.

Lundin Golf Club — 1868

Golf Road
SCO - LUNDIN LINKS, Fife KY8 6BA

Office	Secrétariat	(44) 01333 - 320 202
Pro shop	Pro-shop	(44) 01333 - 320 051
Fax	Fax	(44) 01333 - 329 743
Web	www.lundingolfclub.co.uk	
Situation	Situation	Kirkcaldy, 17 km

St Andrews (pop. 11 136), 20 km

Annual closure	Fermeture annuelle	no
Weekly closure	Fermeture hebdomadaire	no

Fees main season Tarifs haute saison	Week days Semaine	We/Bank holidays We/Férié
	18 holes	
Individual Individuel	£ 42	£ 50*
Couple Couple	£ 84	£ 100*

Full week days: £ 50 /* Saturday: after 2.30 pm
Limited access on Sundays.

Caddie Caddie on request **Electric Trolley** Chariot électrique no

Buggy Voiturette no **Clubs** Clubs no

Credit cards Cartes de crédit yes

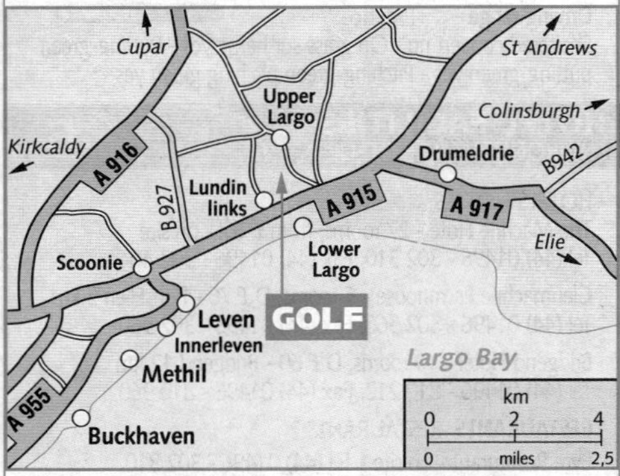

Access Accès : Edinburgh A92 and A915. In the village of Lundin Links on the sea front, turn right at the Royal Bank of Scotland, thereafter first right and second left.

Map 3 on page 475 Carte 3 Page 475

GOLF COURSE — PARCOURS 16/20

Site	Site	
Maintenance	Entretien	
Architect	Architecte	James Braid
Type	Type	links
Relief	Relief	
Water in play	Eau en jeu	
Exp. to wind	Exposé au vent	
Trees in play	Arbres en jeu	

Scorecard Carte de score	Chp. Chp.	Mens Mess.	Ladies Da.
Length Long.	5823	5610	5183
Par	71	71	73
Slope system	—	—	—

Advised golfing ability Niveau de jeu recommandé: 0 12 24 36

Hcp required Handicap exigé: certificate

CLUB HOUSE & AMENITIES — CLUB HOUSE ET ANNEXES 7/10

Pro shop	Pro-shop
Driving range	Practice

Sheltered couvert no - On grass sur herbe yes - Putting-green putting-green yes - Pitching-green pitching green no

HOTEL FACILITIES — ENVIRONNEMENT HOTELIER 7/10

HOTELS HÔTELS

Old Manor Hotel - Lundin Links, close
23 rooms, D £ 150
Tel (44) 01333 - 320 368, Fax (44) 01333 - 320 911

Crusoe Hotel - 16 rooms, D £ 90 - Lundin Links, close
Tel (44) 01333 - 320 759, Fax (44) 01333 - 320 865

Lundin Links Hotel - 21 rooms, D £ 99 - Lundin, close
Tel (44) 01333 - 320 207, Fax (44) 01333 - 320 930

RESTAURANTS RESTAURANTS

Old Manor Hotel - Lundin Links 0.4 km
Tel (44) 01333 - 320 368

The Peat Inn - Peat Inn 12 km - Tel (44) 01334 - 840 206

Machrie

17	7	5

So far away from the "civilized" world, this course, where designer Willie Campbell worked wonders, could but adapt to existing terrain. With a 100-year-old hotel or small cottages, there is no shortage of accommodation or pleasure facilities, aided by some exceptional pure malt whiskies smoked over a peat fire – the speciality of the Isle of Islay – and even tastier when drunk after some wholesome sporting exercise. The beaches are superb and the views equally magnificent and romantic. The fairways lie like a carpet above Langland Bay and form nothing less than a good, pure and authentic golf course which can be as friendly in mild conditions as it is hostile in rougher weather. Playing this course is a real treat, as is the post-round lunch or dinner in the club-house restaurant to celebrate. There are few places in the world that feel so "different" to what you know already as Machrie. You can get here by boat, but it's a long haul, or by plane in a quick hop from Glasgow for a trip back in time that you will not forget.

Autant à l'écart du monde "civilisé", ce parcours ne pouvait que s'adapter au terrain, et l'architecte Willie Campbell en a tiré des merveilles. Avec un hôtel plus que centenaire ou de petits cottages, le lieu ne manque pas de possibilités d'accueil, ni de plaisirs : on y distille alentour d'exceptionnels whiskies pur malt fumés à la tourbe (la spécialité de l'Isle of Islay), que l'on dégustera après s'être livré à de saines activités sportives. Les plages sont superbes, les vues magnifiques, romantiques. Le parcours est posé comme un tapis sur le sol au-dessus de Langland Bay, c'est un pur, vrai et bon parcours de golf, il peut s'avérer aussi aimable que difficile selon les caprices du temps. C'est un vrai bonheur de le jouer et de le célébrer ensuite au restaurant du club-house. Peu d'endroits au monde sont si "différents" de tout ce que l'on connaît. On peut y aller en bateau mais c'est long, ou alors en avion : c'est un saut de puce depuis Glasgow, un saut dans le temps que l'on n'oubliera pas.

Machrie Hotel & Golf Links — 1891

Western Cottage, Port Ellen
SCO - ISLE OF ISLAY, PA427 AN

Office	Secrétariat	(44) 01496 - 302 310
Pro shop	Pro-shop	(44) 01496 - 302 310
Fax	Fax	(44) 01496 - 302 404
Web	www.machrie.com	
Situation	Situation	Port Ellen (Isle of Islay)
Annual closure	Fermeture annuelle	no
Weekly closure	Fermeture hebdomadaire	no

Fees main season Tarifs haute saison	18 holes	
	Week days Semaine	**We/Bank holidays** We/Férié
Individual Individuel	£ 42	£ 42
Couple Couple	£ 84	£ 84

Full day: £ 57 (after 9.00 at week-ends)

Caddie Caddie on request **Electric Trolley** Chariot électrique no

Buggy Voiturette no **Clubs** Clubs yes

Credit cards Cartes de crédit
VISA - Eurocard - MasterCard - AMEX

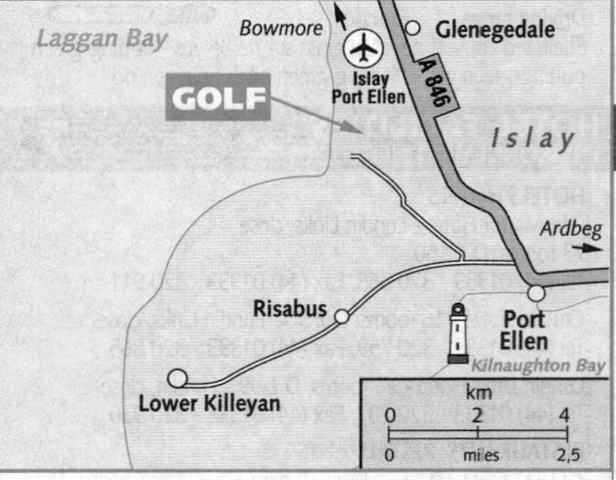

Access Accès : • By Plane, 25 mn from Glasgow (twice daily flights)
• Road & Ferry, 5 hrs from Glasgow
Map 2 on page 472 Carte 2 Page 472

GOLF COURSE — 17/20
PARCOURS

Site	Site	
Maintenance	Entretien	
Architect	Architecte	Willie Campbell, Donald Steel
Type	Type	links
Relief	Relief	
Water in play	Eau en jeu	
Exp. to wind	Exposé au vent	
Trees in play	Arbres en jeu	

Scorecard Carte de score	**Chp.** Chp.	**Mens** Mess.	**Ladies** Da.
Length Long.	5783	5398	4696
Par	71	71	70
Slope system	—	—	—

Advised golfing ability Niveau de jeu recommandé: 0 12 24 36
Hcp required Handicap exigé: no

CLUB HOUSE & AMENITIES — 7/10
CLUB HOUSE ET ANNEXES

Pro shop Pro-shop
Driving range Practice
Sheltered couvert no - On grass sur herbe yes - Putting-green putting-green yes - Pitching-green pitching green yes

HOTEL FACILITIES — 5/10
ENVIRONNEMENT HOTELIER

HOTELS HÔTELS
The Machrie Hote - 27 rooms, from £ 65l - on site
Tel (44) 01496 - 302 310, Fax (44) 01496 - 302 404

Glenmachrie Farmhouse - 5 rooms, D £ 76 - Port Ellen 5 km
Tel (44) 01496 - 302 560, Fax (44) 01496 - 302 560

Bridgend Hotel - 10 rooms, D £ 60 - Bridgend 12 km
Tel (44) 01496 - 810 212, Fax (44) 01496 - 810 960

RESTAURANTS RESTAURANTS
Byre Restaurant - on site - Tel (44) 01496 - 302 310
The Harbour Inn - Bowmore 7 km - Tel (44) 01496 - 810 330

Machrihanish

18	6	4

The road you take to reach here is as long as it is picturesque, the only problem being that you can't stay for ever. The course is superb, as are the distilleries and the hospitality of the inhabitants of Kintyre here at the ends of the world. So step into this wide open space "created by the Almighty to play golf", as Old Tom Morris would say, who knew a good sales pitch when he saw one and could design a course or two. He obviously lent our Good Lord a hand here to make this marvellous test of golf between the dunes and the foot of the hills. With a simply beautiful first hole, a par 4 over the sea, where the men will envy the ladies. For the fairer sex this is a par 5, for many male players too. You won't regret a single second of your visit here, especially now that a new course by David McLay Kidd will shortly be up and running.

La route pour arriver ici est aussi longue que splendide. Le seul problème est qu'il faut ensuite repartir. S'arracher à Machrihanish est d'autant plus dur que si le parcours est superbe, les distilleries ne le sont pas moins, et l'accueil des habitants du Kintyre d'autant plus agréable que l'on est au bout de l'ancien monde, et du monde tout court. Alors, immergez-vous dans un espace "créé par le Tout-Puissant pour jouer au golf" comme disait Old Tom Morris qui avait le sens du commerce, et du dessin de golf aussi. Car il est évidemment venu en aide au Seigneur pour en faire un merveilleux test de golf entre les dunes et le pied des collines. Avec un premier trou de toute beauté, un par 4 à jouer au-dessus de la mer où les hommes jalouseront les dames : c'est pour elles un par 5... pour beaucoup d'hommes aussi ! Le parcours a été dessiné par Old Tom Morris, remanié au cours des années, sans rien abandonner de ses qualités et de ses charmes. Vous ne regretterez rien du voyage, d'autant qu'un nouveau parcours de David McLay Kidd vous y attend bientôt.

Machrihanish Golf Club — 1876

Machrihanish
SCO - CAMPBELTOWN, Argyll PA28 6PT

Office	Secrétariat	(44) 01586 - 810 213
Pro shop	Pro-shop	(44) 01586 - 810 277
Fax	Fax	(44) 01586 - 810 221
Web	www.machgolf.com	
Situation	Situation	Campbeltown, 8 km
Annual closure	Fermeture annuelle	no
Weekly closure	Fermeture hebdomadaire	no

Fees main season Tarifs haute saison	18 holes	
	Week days Semaine	**We/Bank holidays** We/Férié
Individual Individuel	£ 40*	£ 50
Couple Couple	£ 80*	£ 100

* Week days: Sunday to Friday
Full day, £ 50 - £ 75 (Saturday)

Caddie Caddie on request **Electric Trolley** Chariot électrique no

Buggy Voiturette no **Clubs** Clubs yes

Credit cards Cartes de crédit
VISA - MasterCard

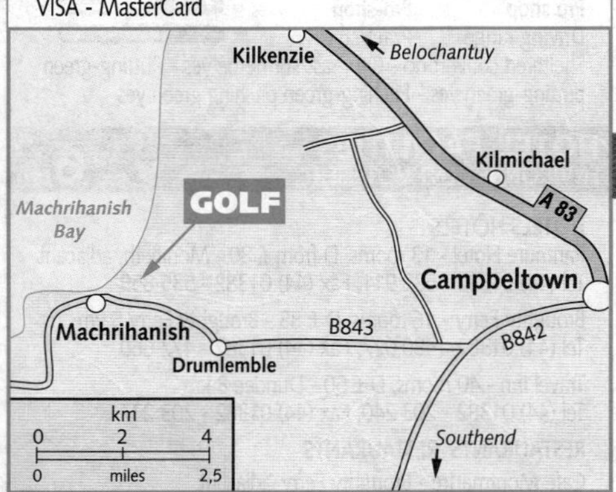

Access Accès : • By air: from Glasgow, 15 mn flight to Machrihanish Airport. • By car: 3 hrs drive by A82, A83, via Tarbet, Inverraray... or Ferry to Isle of Arran, and to Claonaig.
Map 2 on page 472 Carte 2 Page 472

GOLF COURSE — PARCOURS 18/20

Site	Site	
Maintenance	Entretien	
Architect	Architecte	Tom Morris
Type	Type	links
Relief	Relief	
Water in play	Eau en jeu	
Exp. to wind	Exposé au vent	
Trees in play	Arbres en jeu	

Scorecard Carte de score	**Chp.** Chp.	**Mens** Mess.	**Ladies** Da.
Length Long.	5670	5425	5025
Par	70	70	72
Slope system	—	—	—

Advised golfing ability Niveau de jeu recommandé — 0 12 24 36

Hcp required Handicap exigé no

CLUB HOUSE & AMENITIES — CLUB HOUSE ET ANNEXES 6/10

Pro shop Pro-shop
Driving range Practice
Sheltered couvert no - On grass sur herbe yes - Putting-green putting-green yes - Pitching-green pitching green yes

HOTEL FACILITIES — ENVIRONNEMENT HOTELIER 4/10

HOTELS HÔTELS

Craigard House - 8 rooms, D £ 110 - Campbeltown 8 km
Tel (44) 01586 - 554 242, Fax (44) 01586 - 551 137

Seafield - 9 rooms, D £ 60 - Campbeltown 8 km
Tel (44) 01586 - 554 385, Fax (44) 01586 - 552 741

Ardell House - 10 rooms, D £ 62 - Machrihanish, close
Tel (44) 01586 - 810 235, Fax (44) 01586 - 810 235

RESTAURANTS RESTAURANTS

Seafield - Campbeltown 8 km - Tel (44) 01586 - 554 385

Craigard House - Campbeltown 8 km
Tel (44) 01586 - 554 242

Monifieth

17	6	6

We know that golf was played here in the first half of the 17th century when certain Parishioners were banned from playing golf on the Sabbath. It was not the game's fault, more their absence from morning service. But the first signs of a real course really date from 1850. Like nearby Carnoustie, the course is shared by five different clubs, as is the Ashludie Course, a little more modest and restful but nonetheless interesting. The wide open spaces of the "great" course naturally leave it exposed to the wind, but anything else would come as a great surprise. Classic and discreet in design with no hidden traps, Monifieth is respectable in length and deserves to be better known outside Scotland. This is one of the best surprises that any visitor could hope to find on the east coast. A course for connoisseurs but pleasant for players of all levels, now even better after some discreet and very careful renovation work.

On sait que le golf a été pratiqué ici dès la première moitié du XVIIème siècle, où certains paroissiens furent interdits de golf le jour du Seigneur. Le sport n'était pas en jeu, mais l'absence à la messe. Mais les premiers signes d'un véritable parcours ne remontent pas plus loin que 1850. Comme les tout proches parcours de Carnoustie, celui-ci est partagé par cinq clubs différents, de même que le "Ashludie Course", plus modeste et reposant, mais néanmoins intéressant. Les vastes espaces où s'épanouit le "grand" parcours l'exposent bien sûr au vent, mais c'est le contraire qui serait étonnant. D'une architecture classique et sobre, sans pièges dissimulés, et d'une longueur très respectable, Monifieth mériterait de connaître une meilleure notoriété hors des frontières, et c'est l'une des meilleures surprises que les visiteurs pourront trouver de ce côté de l'Ecosse. Un parcours pour connaisseurs, mais agréable à tous niveaux de jeu, qui a fait l'objet d'une rénovation discrète et attentive.

Monifieth Golf Club — 1850

Medal Starter's Box, Princes Street
SCO - MONIFIETH, Dundee DD5 4AW

Office	Secrétariat	(44) 01382 - 535 553
Pro shop	Pro-shop	(44) 01382 - 532 945
Fax	Fax	(44) 01382 - 535 816
Web	www.monifiethgolf.co.uk	
Situation	Situation	Dundee, 8 km
Annual closure	Fermeture annuelle	no
Weekly closure	Fermeture hebdomadaire	no
Fees main season	Tarifs haute saison	18 holes

	Week days Semaine	We/Bank holidays We/Férié
Individual Individuel	£ 38	£ 48
Couple Couple	£ 75	£ 96

Full day: £ 65 / £ 75 (week-ends)

Caddie Caddie on request **Electric Trolley** Chariot électrique no

Buggy Voiturette yes **Clubs** Clubs yes

Credit cards Cartes de crédit no

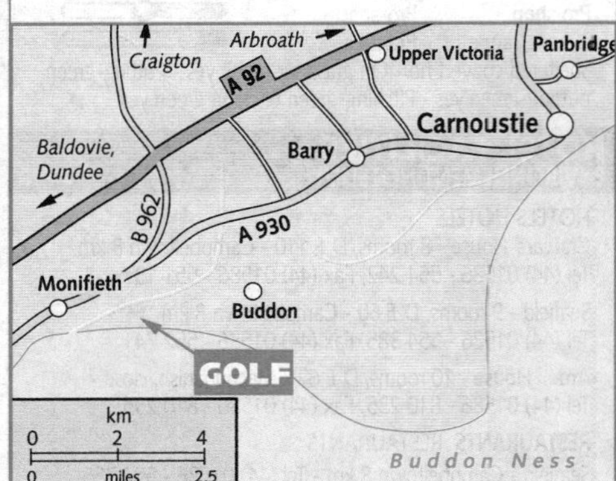

Access Accès : 8 km East of Dundee on coast road (A930)
Map 2 on page 473 Carte 2 Page 473

Map 2 on page 473 Carte 2 Page 473

GOLF COURSE — PARCOURS — 17/20

Site	Site	
Maintenance	Entretien	
Architect	Architecte	unknown
Type	Type	links
Relief	Relief	
Water in play	Eau en jeu	
Exp. to wind	Exposé au vent	
Trees in play	Arbres en jeu	

Scorecard Carte de score	Chp. Chp.	Mens Mess.	Ladies Da.
Length Long.	6056	5877	5361
Par	71	71	73
Slope system	—	—	—

Advised golfing ability Niveau de jeu recommandé: 0 12 24 36

Hcp required Handicap exigé: certificate

CLUB HOUSE & AMENITIES — CLUB HOUSE ET ANNEXES — 6/10

Pro shop Pro-shop
Driving range Practice
Sheltered couvert no - On grass sur herbe yes - Putting-green putting-green yes - Pitching-green pitching green yes

HOTEL FACILITIES — ENVIRONNEMENT HOTELIER — 6/10

HOTELS HÔTELS

Panmure Hotel - 13 rooms, D from £ 80 - Monifieth, adjacent
Tel (44) 01382 - 532 911, Fax (44) 01382 - 535 859

Broughty Ferry - 16 rooms, D £ 88 - Broughty Ferry 5 km
Tel (44) 01382 - 480 027, Fax (44) 01382 - 477 660

Travel Inn - 40 rooms, D £ 50 - Dundee 8 km
Tel (44) 01382 - 203 240, Fax (44) 01382 - 203 237

RESTAURANTS RESTAURANTS

Cafe Montmartre - Broughty Ferry, adjacent
Tel (44) 01382 - 739 313

L'Auberge - Broughty Ferry 5 km - Tel (44) 01382 - 730 890

Bombay Brasserie (Indian) - Broughty Ferry 5 km
Tel (44) 01382 - 480 027

Montrose

17	5	6

A great classic shared by three golf clubs, as is Carnoustie a few miles down the coast. If the history books are right, then this is the 5th oldest golf course in the world and golf has been played on the grounds of the Earl of Montrose since the 16th century. It is true that there is tradition in the air here, with a tinge of austerity as well. Here you'll find all the finest components that go to make up a great links course: deep bunkers, wonderfully soft soil, bushes and towering dunes covered by wild grass that shape the winding fairways and greens. Very reasonable in length, although this can change in a matter of minutes when the wind blows, this excellent course (complemented by the little Broomfield Course) has been a little neglected for the benefit of more powerful neighbours, but the course is so steeped in history (very few alterations have been made since the original layout by Willie Park Jr. in 1903) that it should be a part of your own experience.

Un grand classique partagé par trois clubs de golf, comme Carnoustie, quelques kilomètres plus bas sur la côte. L'histoire voudrait que ce soit le cinquième club du monde, et que l'on ait joué sur ces terres du Marquis de Montrose depuis le XVIè siècle. Il est vrai que l'on respire ici la tradition, non sans une certaine austérité. On trouve ici à l'état pur ce qui fait la grandeur des links, de profonds bunkers, un sol merveilleusement souple, des buissons, de hautes dunes envahies d'herbes folles entre lesquelles s'insinuent les fairways et les greens. De longueur très raisonnable, mais que le vent peut bien sûr métamorphoser d'un instant à l'autre, cet excellent parcours (complété par le petit Broomfield Course) a été un peu négligé au profit de puissants voisins, mais il témoigne de toute une histoire (il a été peu modifié depuis son tracé par Willie Park Jr. en 1903) et doit faire partie de la vôtre.

Montrose Golf Links Ltd — 1562

Traill Drive
SCO - MONTROSE, Angus DD10 8SW

Office Secrétariat (44) 01674 - 672 932
Pro shop Pro-shop (44) 01674 - 672 634
Fax Fax (44) 01674 - 671 800
Web www.montroselinks.co.uk
Situation Situation Dundee, 35 km
Annual closure Fermeture annuelle no
Weekly closure Fermeture hebdomadaire no

Fees main season Tarifs haute saison	18 holes	
	Week days Semaine	**We/Bank holidays** We/Férié
Individual Individuel	£ 40	£ 44*
Couple Couple	£ 80	£ 88*

* Saturdays: visitors between 2.45 and 3.38 pm only
Full day: £50 - £58 (We)

Caddie Caddie no **Electric Trolley** Chariot électrique no

Buggy Voiturette no **Clubs** Clubs yes

Credit cards Cartes de crédit
VISA - MasterCard - JCB

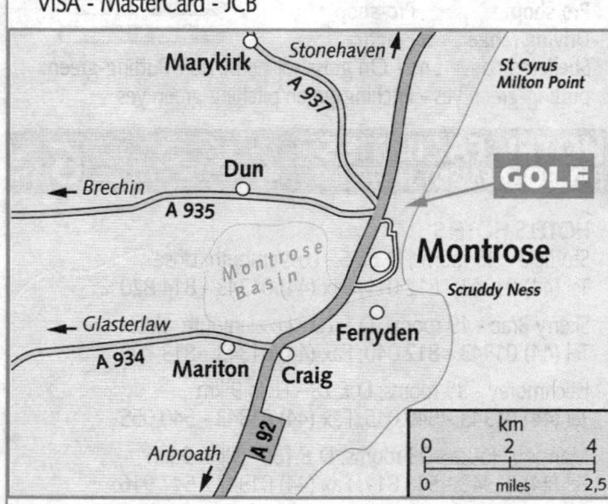

Access Accès : A90, turn off at Brechin and follow A935 to Montrose. Golf 0.8 km (1/2 m) from town centre.
Map 1 on page 471 Carte 1 Page 471

GOLF COURSE — PARCOURS — 17/20

Site Site
Maintenance Entretien
Architect Architecte Willie Park Jr.
Type Type links
Relief Relief
Water in play Eau en jeu
Exp. to wind Exposé au vent
Trees in play Arbres en jeu

Scorecard Carte de score	**Chp.** Chp.	**Mens** Mess.	**Ladies** Da.
Length Long.	5837	5490	5060
Par	71	71	73
Slope system	—	—	

Advised golfing ability Niveau de jeu recommandé 0 12 24 36
Hcp required Handicap exigé certificate

CLUB HOUSE & AMENITIES — CLUB HOUSE ET ANNEXES — 5/10

Pro shop Pro-shop
Driving range Practice
Sheltered couvert no - On grass sur herbe no - Putting-green putting-green yes - Pitching-green pitching green yes

HOTEL FACILITIES — ENVIRONNEMENT HOTELIER — 6/10

HOTELS HÔTELS

Montrose Park - 57 rooms, D from £ 75 - Montrose 1 km
Tel (44) 01674 - 663 400, Fax (44) 01674 - 663 400

Links Hotel - Montrose 1 km
25 rooms, D from £ 90
Tel (44) 01674 - 671 000, Fax (44) 01674 - 672 698

Oaklands - 7 rooms, D £ 40 - Montrose 1 km
Tel (44) 01674 - 672 018, Fax (44) 01674 - 672 018

RESTAURANTS RESTAURANTS

Montrose Park - Montrose 1 km - Tel (44) 01674 - 663 400

Moray *Old*

17 | 5 | 6

This is not the best known links in Scotland but it is a good one. Firstly for its antiquated charm, because like the Old Course at St Andrews, it starts and ends in town, in Lossiemouth, the name by which the course is also sometimes known. Founded by a group of whisky distillers, a large part of this "old" course was designed by Old Tom Morris although patient changes have given the layout its present-day look, custom-made for the requirements of modern golf. Players of all levels will enjoy this course, and the less experienced golfers can get acquainted with the subtle side of links golf without too much to worry about. Moray is also home to the "New Course", upgraded to 18 holes by Henry Cotton in 1979, a very pleasant layout but without the cachet of its "old" stable-mate. The main difficulties are small greens and narrow fairways. We would also emphasize the mildness of the climate here and the superb views over the Moray Firth. Highly recommended.

Ce n'est pas le plus connu des links d'Ecosse, mais ce n'est pas le moindre. Par son charme désuet d'abord : comme le Old Course de St Andrews, il commence et s'achève en ville, à Lossiemouth, qui lui a donné parfois son nom. Fondé par des distillateurs de whisky, le "Old" a en grande partie été conçu par Old Tom Morris, mais de patientes modifications lui ont donné son visage actuel, parfaitement adapté aux exigences du golf moderne. Cependant, les joueurs de tous niveaux y prendront plaisir, et les moins expérimentés pourront s'y familiariser avec les subtilités du golf de links sans être trop intimidés. De plus, on trouve également à Moray le "New Course" transformé en 18 trous par Henry Cotton en 1979, très agréable mais moins empreint de grandeur que le "Old". De petits greens et d'étroits fairways en constituent la principale difficulté. On soulignera enfin la douceur du climat local, et les vues superbes sur le Moray Firth. Visite conseillée !

Moray Golf Club — 1889

Stotfield Road
SCO - LOSSIEMOUTH, Moray JV31 6QS

Office	Secrétariat	(44) 01343 - 812 018
Pro shop	Pro-shop	(44) 01343 - 813 330
Fax	Fax	(44) 01343 - 815 102
Web	www.moraygolf.co.uk	
Situation	Situation	Elgin, 9 km
Annual closure	Fermeture annuelle	no
Weekly closure	Fermeture hebdomadaire	no

Fees main season Tarifs haute saison	18 holes	
	Week days Semaine	**We/Bank holidays** We/Férié
Individual Individuel	£ 40	£ 50
Couple Couple	£ 80	£ 100

Full days: £ 55 - £ 70 (week-ends) / One week: £ 150

Caddie Caddie on request **Electric Trolley** Chariot électrique yes

Buggy Voiturette no **Clubs** Clubs yes

Credit cards Cartes de crédit only pro-shop

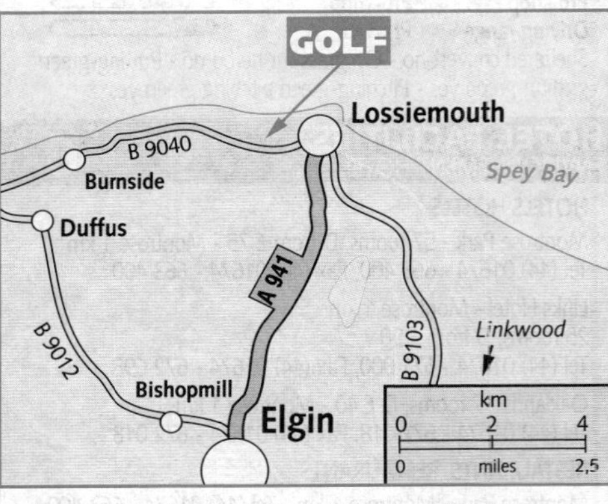

Access Accès : Inverness, A96 to Elgin, then A941 North.
Map 1 on page 471 Carte 1 Page 471

GOLF COURSE — PARCOURS 17/20

Site	Site	
Maintenance	Entretien	
Architect	Architecte	Tom Morris
Type	Type	links
Relief	Relief	
Water in play	Eau en jeu	
Exp. to wind	Exposé au vent	
Trees in play	Arbres en jeu	

Scorecard Carte de score	**Chp.** Chp.	**Mens** Mess.	**Ladies** Da.
Length Long.	6124	6015	5591
Par	71	70	75
Slope system	—	—	—

Advised golfing ability Niveau de jeu recommandé: 0 12 24 36

Hcp required Handicap exigé 24

CLUB HOUSE & AMENITIES — CLUB HOUSE ET ANNEXES 5/10

Pro shop Pro-shop
Driving range Practice
Sheltered couvert no - **On grass** sur herbe no - **Putting-green** putting-green yes - **Pitching-green** pitching green yes

HOTEL FACILITIES — ENVIRONNEMENT HOTELIER 6/10

HOTELS HÔTELS

Stotfield - 45 rooms, D £ 76 - Lossiemouth, close
Tel (44) 01343 - 812 011, Fax (44) 01343 - 814 820

Skerry Brae - 19 rooms, D £ 70 - Lossiemouth, close
Tel (44) 01343 - 812 040, Fax (44) 01343 - 813 708

Laichmoray - 35 rooms, D £ 78 - Elgin 9 km
Tel (44) 01343 - 540 045, Fax (44) 01343 - 540 055

Mansion House - 23 rooms, D £ 165 - Elgin 9 km
Tel (44) 01343 - 548 811, Fax (44) 01343 - 547 916

RESTAURANTS RESTAURANTS

Stotfield - Lossiemouth, close - Tel (44) 01343 - 812 011
Mansion House - Elgin 9 km - Tel (44) 01343 - 548 811

Muirfield

19 | 7 | 6

The course of the Honourable Company of Edinburgh Golfers, who drew up the first collection of the rules of golf, is first and foremost one of the great courses used for the British Open. Winners here include Nicklaus, Trevino, Faldo and Els, four players of very different talent, suggesting that great courses adapt to all styles of play. While there are no spectacular dunes and no sea in the immediate vicinity for this to be labelled a reference links course, the thick and very tall rough, deep bunkering that reflects a shrewd golfing mind, narrow (but welcoming) fairways and tricky greens where you need magic fingers, make it a golfing reference, full stop. The course asks a lot of players when it comes to shaping the right shot. A good hit is rewarded but any flaw is a shortcut to disaster. This is a great test of golf, the club-house is superb, historically very instructive and a great place to eat, but the welcome is perhaps more distinguished than warm.

Le parcours de l'Honourable Company of Edinburgh Golfers, qui a établi le premier recueil de règles de golf est surtout l'un des grands parcours du British Open, où ont triomphé notamment Nicklaus, Trevino, Faldo et Els, quatre hommes aux talents dissemblables, comme quoi les grands golfs s'adaptent à tous les types de jeu. S'il manque de dunes spectaculaires et de proximité immédiate de la mer pour être un links de référence, les roughs épais et très hauts, de profonds bunkers placés avec une très grande connaissance du jeu, des fairways étroits (mais accueillants), des greens subtils où il faut avoir des doigts de fée en font une référence. Ici, on exige beaucoup du joueur afin qu'il fasse le coup qui convient. Un bon coup est récompensé, mais toute défaillance amène un désastre. Un grand test de golf. Le club-house est superbe, historiquement très instructif, et la table excellente. L'accueil est plus distingué que vraiment chaleureux.

The Honourable Company of Edinburgh Golfers — 1891

Muirfield
SCO - GULLANE, E. Lothian, EH31 2EG

Office	Secrétariat	(44) 01620 - 842 123
Pro shop	Pro-shop	no Pro shop
Fax	Fax	(44) 01620 - 842 977
E-mail		hceg@muirfield.org.uk
Situation	Situation	Edinburgh, 30 km
Annual closure	Fermeture annuelle	no
Weekly closure	Fermeture hebdomadaire	no

Fees main season Tarifs haute saison	18 holes	
	Week days Semaine	**We/Bank holidays** We/Férié
Individual Individuel	£ 120	*
Couple Couple	£ 240	*

* No visitors at week-ends

Caddie Caddie on request **Electric Trolley** Chariot électrique no
Buggy Voiturette limited use **Clubs** Clubs no
Credit cards Cartes de crédit VISA - MasterCard

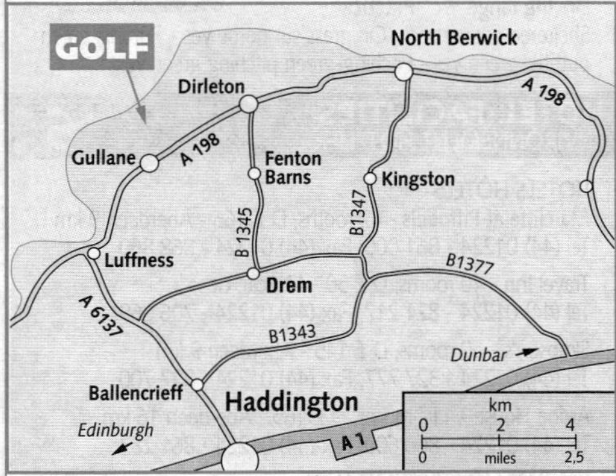

Access Accès : Edinburgh A198 along Firth of Forth.
Turn left at the end of Gullane, follow signs to Greywalls Hotel.
Map 3 on page 475 Carte 3 Page 475

GOLF COURSE — PARCOURS 19/20

Site	Site	
Maintenance	Entretien	
Architect	Architecte	Tom Morris Harry S. Colt
Type	Type	links
Relief	Relief	
Water in play	Eau en jeu	
Exp. to wind	Exposé au vent	
Trees in play	Arbres en jeu	

Scorecard Carte de score	**Chp.** Chp.	**Mens** Mess.	**Ladies** Da.
Length Long.	6336	6007	—
Par	73	73	
Slope system	—	—	

Advised golfing ability Niveau de jeu recommandé: 0 12 24 36
Hcp required Handicap exigé: certificate

CLUB HOUSE & AMENITIES — CLUB HOUSE ET ANNEXES 7/10

Pro shop Pro-shop
Driving range Practice
Sheltered couvert new practice ground - On grass sur herbe yes -
Putting-green putting-green yes - Pitching-green pitching green yes

HOTEL FACILITIES — ENVIRONNEMENT HOTELIER 6/10

HOTELS HÔTELS
Greywalls - 23 rooms, D £ 230 - Gullane, adjacent
Tel (44) 01620 - 842 144, Fax (44) 01620 - 842 241

Marine Hotel - North Berwick 8 km
83 rooms, D £ 140
Tel (44) 0870 - 400 8129, Fax (44) 01620 - 894 480

Maitlandfield House Hotel - Haddington 3 km
22 rooms, D £ 150
Tel (44) 01620 - 826 513, Fax (44) 01620 - 826 713

RESTAURANTS RESTAURANTS
Greywalls - Gullane, adjacent - Tel (44) 01620 - 842 144

Murcar

15	6	6

Murcar lies next door to Royal Aberdeen but although it may never have the Royal seal, there are many who rate it just as highly as its more famous neighbour. But if they say that mongrels are a tougher species than pedigrees, then Murcar is definitely a course not to be missed. It is a first class challenge even when the wind does not blow and must never be taken lightly. Not quite as long as Royal Aberdeen, the terrain is similar in many ways. There are three par 3s, two par 5s and 13 par 4s. The latter include a group of short par 4s that are devilishly tricky and often produce as many bogeys as pars for the unwary. Naturally you won't find the tremendous challenges that await you on the monster courses in Scotland, but Murcar deserves much more than just a quick look. It should be on everyone's itinerary in this part of Scotland, which has an abundance of great courses. Recent work on the course has now brought it back to excellent condition.

Murcar jouxte le parcours de Royal Aberdeen et n'a pas eu droit à l'anoblissement. Mais si on dit que les bâtards sont les plus vigoureux, Murcar est effectivement un parcours à ne pas manquer. C'est un défi de premier ordre à relever, à ne jamais prendre à la légère, même quand le vent ne souffle pas. A peine plus court que son voisin, il s'en rapproche par de nombreux aspects. La distribution des trous est assez inhabituelle, avec trois par 3, deux par 5 et treize par 4, dont ces démoniaques petits trous techniques que l'on croit pouvoir driver et qui vous mettent à genoux. Certes, l'on n'attendra pas ici d'aussi formidables défis que dans le groupe des grands monstres d'Ecosse, mais Murcar mérite beaucoup mieux qu'un simple regard. Il devrait figurer sur l'itinéraire de tout golfeur voyageant dans cette partie d'Ecosse, qui ne manque pas de grands parcours, d'autant que la poursuite des améliorations récentes lui ont rendu sa qualité d'entretien.

Murcar Golf Club — 1909

Bridge of Don
SCO - ABERDEEN, Aberdeenshire AB23 8BD

Office	Secrétariat	(44) 01224 - 704 354
Pro shop	Pro-shop	(44) 01224 - 704 370
Fax	Fax	(44) 01224 - 704 354
Web	www.murcar.co.uk	
Situation	Situation	Aberdeen, 8 km
Annual closure	Fermeture annuelle	no
Weekly closure	Fermeture hebdomadaire	no

Fees main season Tarifs haute saison	18 holes	
	Week days Semaine	**We/Bank holidays** We/Férié
Individual Individuel	£ 55	£ 65
Couple Couple	£ 110	£ 130

Caddie Caddie on request **Electric Trolley** Chariot électrique no

Buggy Voiturette no **Clubs** Clubs yes

Credit cards Cartes de crédit yes

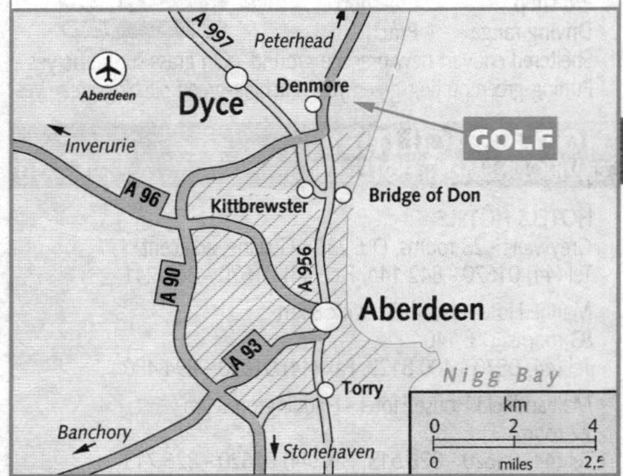

Access Accès : Aberdeen, A90 Aberdeen - Fraserburgh road. Signposted to right.
Map 1 on page 471 Carte 1 Page 471

GOLF COURSE — PARCOURS — 15/20

Site	Site	
Maintenance	Entretien	
Architect	Architecte	Archie Simpson James Braid
Type	Type	links
Relief	Relief	
Water in play	Eau en jeu	
Exp. to wind	Exposé au vent	
Trees in play	Arbres en jeu	

Scorecard Carte de score	**Chp.** Chp.	**Mens** Mess.	**Ladies** Da.
Length Long.	5784	5348	5092
Par	71	71	71
Slope system	—	—	—

Advised golfing ability Niveau de jeu recommandé — 0 12 24 36

Hcp required Handicap exigé — certificate

CLUB HOUSE & AMENITIES — CLUB HOUSE ET ANNEXES — 6/10

Pro shop Pro-shop
Driving range Practice
Sheltered couvert no - On grass sur herbe yes - Putting-green putting-green yes - Pitching-green pitching green yes

HOTEL FACILITIES — ENVIRONNEMENT HOTELIER — 6/10

HOTELS HÔTELS

Marcliffe at Piffodels - 42 rooms, D £ 165 - Aberdeen 9 km
Tel (44) 01224 - 861 000, Fax (44) 01224 - 868 860

Travel Inn - 40 rooms, D £ 50 - Murcar, close
Tel (44) 01224 - 821 217, Fax (44) 01224 - 706 869

Simpson's - 50 rooms, D £ 145 - Aberdeen 9 km
Tel (44) 01224 - 327 777, Fax (44) 01224 - 327 700

Ardoe House - 117 rooms, D £ 165 - Aberdeen 16 km
Tel (44) 01224 - 860 600, Fax (44) 01224 - 861 283

RESTAURANTS RESTAURANTS

Brasserie - Aberdeen 8 km - Tel (44) 01224 - 327 799
Silver Darling - Aberdeen 8 km - Tel (44) 01224 - 576 229

Murrayshall

14 | 7 | 7

Located in a well-forested setting not far from Perth, this country course was opened in 1981 and has quickly built up an excellent reputation among local players for its pleasant site, the hazards and the challenge of playing here. This is by no means an easy course but is one of those layouts which quickly help you forget a bad score. If your card is bad, there's no blaming the course. Game strategy is obvious from the first time out, the clearly demarcated fairways clearly show in which direction you should be headed, difficulties are evenly spread around the course with just the right balance of stress and relaxation, and the greens are well designed and protected. Spread over some 300 acres of land, this is one of the best-equipped golf clubs you can find, with a real driving range, a very comfortable hotel and a second 18-hole course (Lynedoch) designed by Hamilton Stutt.

Situé dans un environnement bien boisé non loin de Perth, ce parcours campagnard né en 1981 s'est vite bâti une excellente réputation parmi les joueurs de la région, en raison de l'agrément du site, mais aussi des difficultés présentées et du "challenge" offert. Ce n'est certes pas un parcours facile, mais il fait partie de ceux qui vous font vite oublier un mauvais score. En tout cas, on ne pourra pas en accuser le parcours. La stratégie de jeu y est assez évidente dès la première visite, les fairways nettement délimités indiquent parfaitement la route à suivre, les difficultés sont bien réparties, avec ce qu'il faut de tension et de détente, les greens sont bien dessinés et bien défendus. Situé dans un espace de près de 200 hectares, (350 acres) le club est l'un des mieux équipés que l'on puisse trouver, notamment avec un vrai practice, un hôtel très confortable et un autre 18 trous (Lynedoch Course, par 69) dessiné par Hamilton Stutt.

Murrayshall Golf Club — 1981

Murrayshall Country House Hotel
SCO - SCONE, Perthshire PH2 7PH

Office	Secrétariat	(44) 01738 - 551 171
Pro shop	Pro-shop	(44) 01738 - 554 804
Fax	Fax	(44) 01738 - 552 595
Web	www.murrayshall.com	
Situation	Situation	Perth, 8 km
Annual closure	Fermeture annuelle	no
Weekly closure	Fermeture hebdomadaire	no

Fees main season Tarifs haute saison — 18 holes

	Week days Semaine	We/Bank holidays We/Férié
Individual Individuel	£ 35	£ 40
Couple Couple	£ 70	£ 80

Full days: £ 40 - £ 45 (week-ends)

Caddie Caddie on request **Electric Trolley** Chariot électrique yes

Buggy Voiturette yes **Clubs** Clubs yes

Credit cards Cartes de crédit
VISA - Eurocard - MasterCard - AMEX

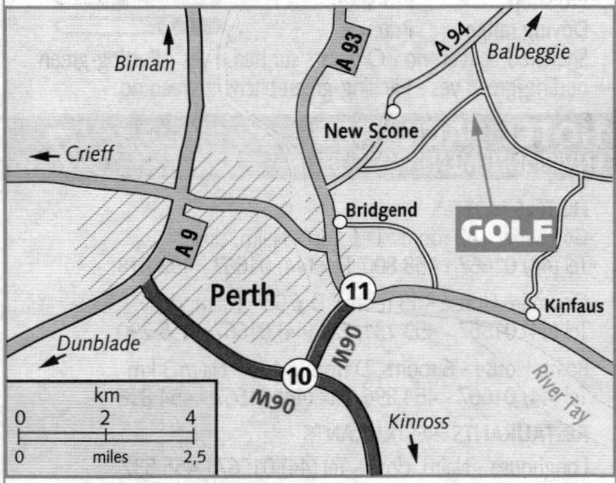

Access Accès : Edinburgh M90 to Perth, then A94 → Coupar Angus, Golf at Scone.

Map 2 on page 473 Carte 2 Page 473

GOLF COURSE — PARCOURS — 14/20

Site	Site	
Maintenance	Entretien	
Architect	Architecte	Hamilton Stutt
Type	Type	parkland
Relief	Relief	
Water in play	Eau en jeu	
Exp. to wind	Exposé au vent	
Trees in play	Arbres en jeu	

Scorecard Carte de score	**Chp.** Chp.	**Mens** Mess.	**Ladies** Da.
Length Long.	5797	5540	4786
Par	73	73	73
Slope system	—	—	—

Advised golfing ability Niveau de jeu recommandé — 0 12 24 36

Hcp required Handicap exigé — no

CLUB HOUSE & AMENITIES — CLUB HOUSE ET ANNEXES — 7/10

Pro shop Pro-shop
Driving range Practice
Sheltered couvert 11 mats - On grass sur herbe no - Putting-green putting-green yes - Pitching-green pitching green yes

HOTEL FACILITIES — ENVIRONNEMENT HOTELIER — 7/10

HOTELS HÔTELS

Murrayshall Country House - on site
41 rooms, D £ 170 (w. dinner)
Tel (44) 01738 - 551 171, Fax (44) 01738 - 552 595

Kinfauns Castle - 16 rooms, D £ 125 - Perth 12 km
Tel (44) 01738 - 620 777, Fax (44) 01738 - 620 778

Newmiln (18th century mansion) - Guildtown 4 km
8 rooms, Ask for details
Tel (44) 01738 - 552 364, Fax (44) 01738 - 553 505

RESTAURANTS RESTAURANTS

Old Masters (Murrayshall) - on site - Tel (44) 01738 - 551 171
Let's Eat - Perth 8 km - Tel (44) 01738 - 643 377
63 Tay Street - Perth 8 km - Tel (44) 01738 - 441 451

Nairn

19 | 7 | 7

This is one of the great links of Scotland, i.e. of the world, and for many a year was one of the country's best guarded secrets. The heather, broom and gorse complete a fine collection of hazards preying on your ball once you have avoided the traps along the Moray Firth that is in sight on each hole. On the whole Nairn is a remarkable sporting challenge, notably with greens that are often firm, very quick and devilishly well-contoured. If you add James Braid's high class bunkering and the need for carefully thought-out strategy, you'll understand that you don't drive past without stopping off a day or three to test your game on the long golfing road that leads the visitor from Aberdeen to Inverness then to Dornoch and beyond. The landscape is maybe plainer than on other courses in the region, but it is also a little more sheltered, if that is the right word. Another masterpiece in Scotland...

C'est l'un des plus grands links d'Ecosse, c'est-à-dire du monde... et ce fut longtemps l'un de ses secrets les mieux gardés. Il a depuis conquis la gloire, et connu l'affluence des connaisseurs. La bruyère, les genêts et les ajoncs complètent une belle collection d'entraves à la liberté des balles, une fois que l'on a déjoué les pièges le long du Moray Firth, que l'on voit depuis chaque trou. Mais Nairn est dans l'ensemble un défi sportif remarquable, avec notamment des greens souvent fermes, très rapides, aux contours parfois diaboliques. Si l'on ajoute la contribution majeure de James Braid, un "bunkering" de haute volée, la nécessité d'une stratégie réfléchie, on aura compris que l'on ne saurait passer devant la porte de Nairn sans s'arrêter un bon moment pour tester sa forme, sur la longue route golfique menant d'Aberdeen à Inverness puis Dornoch et au-delà. Le paysage est moins mouvementé que sur d'autres parcours de la région, mais il est aussi un peu plus abrité... si l'on peut dire. Un autre chef-d'œuvre d'Ecosse.

Nairn Golf Club — 1887

Seabank Road
SCO - NAIRN, IV12 4HB

Office	Secrétariat	(44) 01667 - 453 208
Pro shop	Pro-shop	(44) 01667 - 452 787
Fax	Fax	(44) 01667 - 456 328
Web	www.nairngolfclub.co.uk	
Situation	Situation	Inverness, 24 km
Annual closure	Fermeture annuelle	no
Weekly closure	Fermeture hebdomadaire	no

Full catering: only 04 → 10 inclusive

Fees main season Tarifs haute saison — 18 holes

	Week days / Semaine	We/Bank holidays / We/Férié
Individual Individuel	£ 75	£ 75
Couple Couple	£ 150	£ 150

Caddie Caddie on request **Electric Trolley** Chariot électrique no

Buggy Voiturette no **Clubs** Clubs yes

Credit cards Cartes de crédit
VISA - MasterCard - AMEX

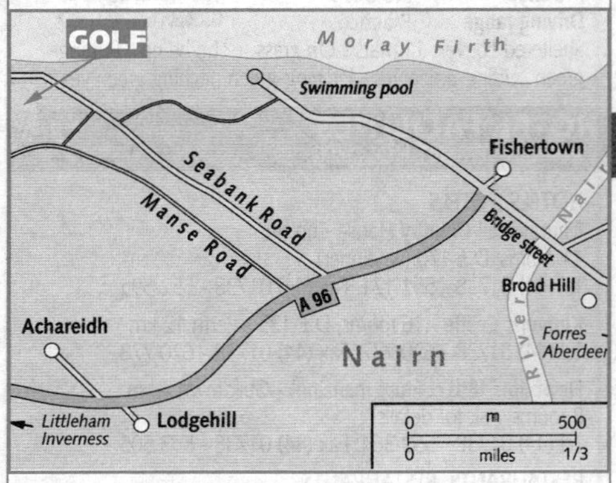

Access Accès : Off A96 Inverness to Nairn road. Golf to the West of town centre.
Map 1 on page 471 Carte 1 Page 471

GOLF COURSE — PARCOURS — 19/20

Site	Site	
Maintenance	Entretien	
Architect	Architecte	Tom Morris, James Braid
Type	Type	links
Relief	Relief	
Water in play	Eau en jeu	
Exp. to wind	Exposé au vent	
Trees in play	Arbres en jeu	

Scorecard Carte de score	Chp. Chp.	Mens Mess.	Ladies Da.
Length Long.	6035	5787	5162
Par	72	71	75
Slope system	—	—	—

Advised golfing ability Niveau de jeu recommandé — 0 12 24 36

Hcp required Handicap exigé — certificate

CLUB HOUSE & AMENITIES — CLUB HOUSE ET ANNEXES — 7/10

Pro shop Pro-shop
Driving range Practice
Sheltered couvert no - On grass sur herbe yes - Putting-green putting-green yes - Pitching-green pitching green no

HOTEL FACILITIES — ENVIRONNEMENT HOTELIER — 7/10

HOTELS HÔTELS

Golf View - 42 rooms, D £ 140 - Nairn, close
Tel (44) 01667 - 458 800, Fax (44) 01667 - 458 818

Claymore House - 13 rooms, D £ 95 - Nairn, close
Tel (44) 01667 - 453 731, Fax (44) 01667 - 455 290

Boath House - 6 rooms, D from £ 150 - Nairn 3 km
Tel (44) 01667 - 454 896, Fax (44) 01667 - 454 896

RESTAURANTS RESTAURANTS

Longhouse - Nairn, close - Tel (44) 01667 - 455 532
Golf View Hotel - Nairn, close - Tel (44) 01667 - 452 301
Cawdor Tavern - Nairn, close - Tel (44) 01667 - 404 777

Nairn Dunbar

15	7	7

The Nairn Dunbar Golf Club perhaps lives slightly in the shadow of its more widely known sister on the other side of town, but this beautiful links course should not be left off the visitor's itinerary, even if he is pressed for time. Lying close to the sea and the estuary, it has been cleverly tailored to the site with a distinct flair for invention. It is long enough to test the best players and yet is perfectly enjoyable for all standards of players. Accuracy is the key here because of the high stands of gorse that line many of the fairways. It is a course that demands the use of every club in the bag and the gorse has the added advantage of creating a wonderful feeling of solitude on most of the holes. This is a very friendly club and there are fine views across the links from the magnificent new club-house, plus a new driving range and practice facilities. Among many fine holes, the wonderful par four 10th remains firmly in the memory for most visitors to this delightful stretch of Morayshire coastline.

Ce parcours vit peut-être dans l'ombre de son célèbre cousin situé de l'autre côté de la ville, mais il serait très dommage pour le golfeur, même pressé, de ne pas l'inclure dans son itinéraire. Près de la mer et de l'embouchure de la rivière, il a été adapté au site avec beaucoup d'esprit d'invention. Assez long pour exiger beaucoup des meilleurs joueurs, il reste parfaitement agréable pour tous les autres. Il demande la maîtrise de tous les clubs du sac et la précision y est essentielle en raison de la végétation qui longe la plupart des trous, ce qui a par ailleurs l'avantage de donner aux joueurs une merveilleuse sensation d'isolement. Le club est très accueillant, et l'on profite avec plus de plaisir encore de vues magnifiques depuis le nouveau et superbe club-house, et aussi des nouvelles installations de practice et de petit jeu. Parmi bien d'autres trous, le 10, un formidable par 4, restera sans aucun doute dans la mémoire des visiteurs de cette merveilleuse région de la côte du Morayshire.

Nairn Dunbar Golf Club — 1899

Lochloy Road
SCO - NAIRN, IV12 5AE

Office	Secrétariat	(44) 01667 - 452 741
Pro shop	Pro-shop	(44) 01667 - 453 964
Fax	Fax	(44) 01667 - 456 897
Web	www.nairndunbar.com	
Situation	Situation	Inverness, 25 km
Annual closure	Fermeture annuelle	no
Weekly closure	Fermeture hebdomadaire	no

Fees main season Tarifs haute saison — 18 holes

	Week days / Semaine	We/Bank holidays / We/Férié
Individual Individuel	£ 40	£ 48
Couple Couple	£ 80	£ 96

Full Day: £55 - £65 (We)

Caddie Caddie on request **Electric Trolley** Chariot électrique no

Buggy Voiturette yes **Clubs** Clubs yes

Credit cards Cartes de crédit VISA - Access

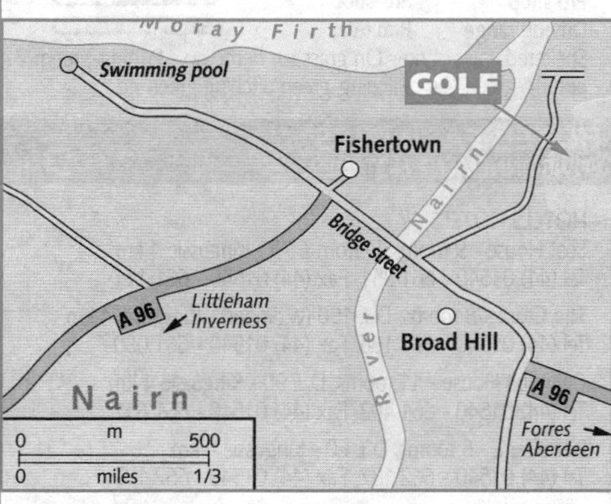

Access Accès : Inverness A96 through Nairn. Golf at the end of town.
Map 1 on page 471 Carte 1 Page 471

GOLF COURSE — PARCOURS — 15/20

Site	Site	
Maintenance	Entretien	
Architect	Architecte	unknown
Type	Type	links
Relief	Relief	
Water in play	Eau en jeu	
Exp. to wind	Exposé au vent	
Trees in play	Arbres en jeu	

Scorecard / Carte de score	Chp. / Chp.	Mens / Mess.	Ladies / Da.
Length Long.	6183	5749	5254
Par	72	72	75
Slope system	139	135	—

Advised golfing ability Niveau de jeu recommandé — 0 12 24 36

Hcp required Handicap exigé — no

CLUB HOUSE & AMENITIES — CLUB HOUSE ET ANNEXES — 7/10

Pro shop Pro-shop
Driving range Practice
Sheltered couvert no - On grass sur herbe no - Putting-green putting-green yes - Pitching-green pitching green yes

HOTEL FACILITIES — ENVIRONNEMENT HOTELIER — 7/10

HOTELS HÔTELS

Golf View - 42 rooms, D £ 140 - Nairn, close
Tel (44) 01667 - 458 800, Fax (44) 01667 - 458 818

Newton Hotel - Nairn 4 km
56 rooms, D from £ 160
Tel (44) 01667 - 453 144, Fax (44) 01667 - 454 026

Greenlawns - Nairn, close
7 rooms, D £ 60
Tel (44) 01667 - 452 738, Fax (44) 01667 - 452 738

RESTAURANTS RESTAURANTS

The Classroom - Nairn, close - Tel (44) 01667 - 455 999
Golf View - Nairn, close - Tel (44) 01667 - 452 301

Newtonmore

14	5	5

The neighbour to Kingussie and a good complementary course to play when spending a few days in the beautiful region of the Cairngorms. A large part of the course is laid out in the plain of the river Spey, which runs alongside several holes. The first and last two holes are on higher land with heather that is fortunately cut back, while the others run through heavier and flatter terrain generously lined with copses of conifers. Over the years, James Braid's original layout has been lengthened but this is by no means a monster. The different holes are well designed with a certain emphasis on variety, but there is nothing to get too excited about. The bottom-line is that this is a very pleasant course for holidays and the family in a magnificent setting. The club-house is not over-large but Scottish hospitality means everything here. People will also point out with some delight the surprising number of lefties amongst the club members. Explain that if you will.

C'est le voisin de Kingussie, et un bon complément quand on passe quelques jours dans cette belle région des Cairngorms. Le parcours est situé en grande partie dans la plaine de la rivière Spey, qui longe plusieurs trous. Les deux premiers et deux derniers trous se trouvent plus en hauteur, en terre de bruyère assez dégagée, alors que les autres trous, en terrain plus lourd et plus plat, sont généreusement boisés de bosquets de conifères. Au fil des ans, le parcours original de James Braid a été allongé, sans être pour autant un monstre, bien loin de là. Les différents trous sont bien dessinés, avec un certain souci de variété, mais les émotions restent assez limitées. En fait, il s'agit d'un très agréable parcours à faire en vacances et en famille, dans un cadre magnifique. Le club-house n'est pas grand, mais l'hospitalité écossaise n'y est pas un vain mot. On vous y signalera avec délectation la proportion surprenante de joueurs gauchers dans le club, que vous tenterez vainement d'expliquer.

Newtonmore Golf Club — 1893

Golf Course Road
SCO - NEWTONMORE, Highland PH20 1AT

Office	Secrétariat	(44) 01540 - 673 328
Pro shop	Pro-shop	(44) 01540 - 673 878
Fax	Fax	(44) 01540 - 673 878
Web	www.newtonmoregolf.com	
Situation	Situation	Inverness, 68 km

Kingussie (pop. 1 298), 4 km

Annual closure	Fermeture annuelle	no
Weekly closure	Fermeture hebdomadaire	no
Fees main season	Tarifs haute saison	18 holes

	Week days Semaine	We/Bank holidays We/Férié
Individual Individuel	£ 16	£ 25
Couple Couple	£ 32	£ 50

Caddie Caddie on request **Electric Trolley** Chariot électrique no

Buggy Voiturette yes **Clubs** Clubs yes

Credit cards Cartes de crédit
CISA - Eurocard - MasterCard - DC

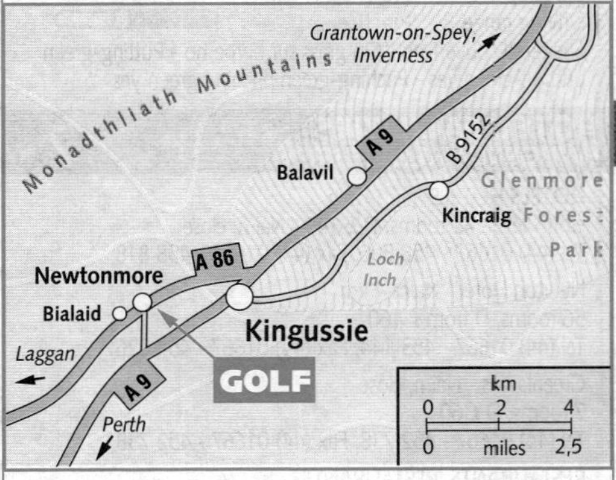

Access Accès : Inverness, A9 through Kingussie. Golf 100 m from centre of Newtonmore
Map 1 on page 472 Carte 1 Page 472

GOLF COURSE PARCOURS — 14/20

Site	Site	
Maintenance	Entretien	
Architect	Architecte	James Braid
Type	Type	inland
Relief	Relief	
Water in play	Eau en jeu	
Exp. to wind	Exposé au vent	
Trees in play	Arbres en jeu	

Scorecard Carte de score	Chp. Chp.	Mens Mess.	Ladies Da.
Length Long.	5487	4950	4813
Par	70	67	73
Slope system	—	—	—

Advised golfing ability Niveau de jeu recommandé — 0 12 24 36

Hcp required Handicap exigé — no

CLUB HOUSE & AMENITIES CLUB HOUSE ET ANNEXES — 5/10

Pro shop	Pro-shop
Driving range	Practice

Sheltered couvert no - On grass sur herbe no - Putting-green putting-green yes - Pitching-green pitching green no

HOTEL FACILITIES ENVIRONNEMENT HOTELIER — 5/10

HOTELS HÔTELS

Scot House - 9 rooms, D from £ 75 - Kingussie 4 km
Tel (44) 01540 - 661 351, Fax (44) 01540 - 661 111

The Cross - 8 rooms, D £ 190 (w.dinner) - Kingussie 4 km
Tel (44) 01540 - 661 166, Fax (44) 01540 - 661 080

Columba House - 11 rooms, D £ 90 - Kingussie 4 km
Tel (44) 01540 - 661 402, Fax (44) 01540 - 661 652

Hermitage - 5 rooms, D £ 60 - Kingussie 4 km
Tel (44) 01540 - 662 137, Fax (44) 01540 - 662 177

RESTAURANTS RESTAURANTS

Restaurants and pubs at Kingussie

North Berwick

18	6	7

This is probably one of the courses that is closest to the origins of the game, where you start off along the beach trying to avoid passers-by who watch without a smile. It's then onto a wide strip of land with a few, reasonably high dunes, and a wall you'll have to get over one day to reach the green. Although this is flattish terrain, there are a few blind holes, and despite Ben Sayers, who oversaw a number of alterations in 1932, North Berwick was modelled by mother nature and the sands of time. They did, however, need an architect (unknown) to build "Perfection (a par 4) and the famous "Redan", a diabolical par 3 endlessly imitated by all course architects. At once archaic and very modern, seemingly friendly but ferocious when the wind blows (any high ball can be disastrous), North Berwick slowly unveils its secrets which you can only discover with a good measure of patience and humility. A truly exciting experience.

C'est probablement l'un des parcours les plus proches des origines, où l'on commence le long de la plage en essayant d'éviter les promeneurs qui vous regardent sans rire, on se promène ensuite dans une large bande de terrain avec quelques dunes pas trop hautes. Il y a un mur au-dessus duquel il faudra passer un jour pour atteindre le green. Il y a quelques coups aveugles, malgré que le terrain soit assez plat. Bien que Ben Sayers en ait supervisé les modifications en 1932, ce sont la nature et les siècles qui ont modelé North Berwick, bien qu'il ait fallu un architecte (inconnu) pour faire le "Perfection" (par 4) et le célèbre "Redan", par 3 diabolique copié à l'infini par tous les architectes de golf. A la fois archaïque et très moderne, apparemment aimable et sauvage quand le vent le balaie (toute balle haute provoque un désastre), North Berwick révèle lentement ses secrets. Il faut savoir les découvrir avec patience et humilité. Passionnant.

North Berwick Golf Club — 1832

New Club House, Beach Road
SCO - NORTH BERWICK, East Lothian, EH39 4BB

Office Secrétariat (44) 01620 - 892 135
Pro shop Pro-shop (44) 01620 - 893 233
Fax Fax (44) 01620 - 893 274
Web www.northberwickgolfclub.com
Situation Situation Edinburgh, 37 km
Annual closure Fermeture annuelle no
Weekly closure Fermeture hebdomadaire no

Fees main season Tarifs haute saison	18 holes	
	Week days Semaine	**We/Bank holidays** We/Férié
Individual Individuel	£ 55	£ 75
Couple Couple	£ 110	£ 150

Full week days: £ 80

Caddie Caddie on request **Electric Trolley** Chariot électrique no

Buggy Voiturette no **Clubs** Clubs yes

Credit cards Cartes de crédit
VISA - MasterCard

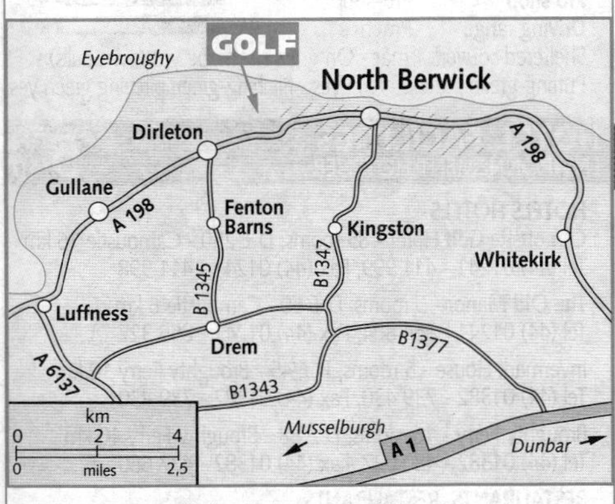

Access Accès : Edinburgh, by-pass and A1 → Berwick upon Tweed. Exit for A198, follow to North Berwick.
Map 3 on page 475 Carte 3 Page 475

GOLF COURSE — PARCOURS 18/20

Site Site
Maintenance Entretien
Architect Architecte unknown
Type Type links
Relief Relief
Water in play Eau en jeu
Exp. to wind Exposé au vent
Trees in play Arbres en jeu

Scorecard Carte de score	Chp. Chp.	Mens Mess.	Ladies Da.
Length Long.	5842	5490	5233
Par	71	70	74
Slope system	—	—	—

Advised golfing ability 0 12 24 36
Niveau de jeu recommandé
Hcp required Handicap exigé 25 Men, 35 Ladies

CLUB HOUSE & AMENITIES — CLUB HOUSE ET ANNEXES 6/10

Pro shop Pro-shop
Driving range Practice
Sheltered couvert no - On grass sur herbe yes - Putting-green putting-green yes - Pitching-green pitching green no

HOTEL FACILITIES — ENVIRONNEMENT HOTELIER 7/10

HOTELS HÔTELS
Marine Hotel - 83 rooms, D £ 140 - North Berwick adjacent
Tel (44) 0870 - 400 8129, Fax (44) 01620 - 894 480

Nether Abbey - North Berwick, close
14 rooms, D £ 90
Tel (44) 01620 - 892 802, Fax (44) 01620 - 895 298

Beach Lodge - 3 rooms, D £ 70 - North Berwick
Tel (44) 01620 - 892 257

RESTAURANTS RESTAURANTS
Marine Hotel - North Berwick adjacent
Tel (44) 01620 - 892 406
The Grange - North Berwick, close - Tel (44) 01620 - 895 894

Panmure

17	6	5

Although it has paled somewhat in the shadow of neighbouring Carnoustie, Panmure (like the other neighbour Monifieth) does not fall far short from featuring in the same class. Anywhere else it would be very highly rated, so take advantage of your stay in the region to play it. In a rather hilly landscape, sometimes even dotted with oddly-shaped dunes, you'll have to be pretty hot with your bump and run shots, regardless of wind direction, in order to control the flight of your shots even though from first reading the card you might think that the course has nothing over-difficult to offer. The greens are extremely well protected and the putting surface is always tricky but never impossible. A classic and very forthright links to which access is restricted on weekends but where a warm welcome awaits the visitor on week days. It is also the course where Ben Hogan came to get accustomed to the grass of links courses, and to the "small ball" used in Britain at the time, before playing the British Open. The pot-bunker on the 6th hole is a part of his heritage.

Bien qu'il ait un peu pâli du puissant voisinage de Carnoustie, il manque peu de chose à Panmure (tout comme à Monifieth, son autre voisin) pour figurer dans la même classe. Partout ailleurs, il serait hautement considéré : profitez d'être dans la région pour le découvrir. Dans un paysage mouvementé, parfois même orné de petites dunes de formes curieuses, il vous faudra savoir faire rouler la balle, que le vent soit dans n'importe quel sens, pour bien contrôler vos trajectoires de balles, même si la lecture de la carte peut faire penser que les difficultés ne sont pas immenses. Les greens sont très bien défendus, leurs surfaces subtiles mais sans exagérations. Un links classique d'une grande franchise, où l'accès est limité en week-end, mais l'accueil chaleureux en semaine. C'est celui dont Ben Hogan dût profiter lorsqu'il vint ici s'habituer au terrain et à l'herbe des links et à la "petite balle" anglaise d'autrefois en vue du British Open. Le pot-bunker du 6 est son héritage.

Panmure Golf Club — 1845

Barry
SCO- CARNOUSTIE, Angus DD7 7RT

Office Secrétariat (44) 01241 - 855 120
Pro shop Pro-shop (44) 01241 - 852 460
Fax Fax (44) 01241 - 859 737
Web www.panmuregolfclub.co.uk
Situation Situation Dundee, 16 km
Annual closure Fermeture annuelle no
Weekly closure Fermeture hebdomadaire no

Fees main season Tarifs haute saison 18 holes

	Week days Semaine	We/Bank holidays We/Férié
Individual Individuel	£ 50	£ 50*
Couple Couple	£ 100	£ 100*

* Saturday after 16.00 / Sunday: restricted times
Full week day: £ 65

Caddie Caddie on request **Electric Trolley** Chariot électrique no
Buggy Voiturette yes **Clubs** Clubs yes
Credit cards Cartes de crédit
VISA - Eurocard - MasterCard - JCB

Arbroath
Craigton
Panbridge
Upper Victoria
A 92
Carnoustie
Baldovie, Dundee
Barry
B 962
A 930
Monifieth
Buddon
GOLF
km 0 2 4
0 miles 2,5
Buddon Ness

Access Accès : Dundee A930 to Barry Village. Golf 1 km
Map 2 on page 473 Carte 2 Page 473

GOLF COURSE — PARCOURS — 17/20

Site Site
Maintenance Entretien
Architect Architecte unknown
Type Type links
Relief Relief
Water in play Eau en jeu
Exp. to wind Exposé au vent
Trees in play Arbres en jeu

Scorecard Carte de score	Chp. Chp.	Mens Mess.	Ladies Da.
Length Long.	5925	5538	5215
Par	70	70	73
Slope system	—	—	—

Advised golfing ability Niveau de jeu recommandé 0 12 24 36
Hcp required Handicap exigé no

CLUB HOUSE & AMENITIES — CLUB HOUSE ET ANNEXES — 6/10

Pro shop Pro-shop
Driving range Practice
Sheltered couvert 1 mat - On grass sur herbe yes (own balls) - Putting-green putting-green yes - Pitching-green pitching green yes

HOTEL FACILITIES — ENVIRONNEMENT HOTELIER — 5/10

HOTELS HÔTELS
Carnoustie Golf Hotel - 85 rooms, D £ 250 - Carnoustie 16 km
Tel (44) 01241 - 411 999, Fax (44) 01241 - 411 998

The Old Manor - 5 rooms, D £ 60 - Carnoustie 6 km
Tel (44) 01241 - 854 804, Fax (44) 01241 - 855 327

Invermark House - 5 rooms, D £ 45 - Broughty Ferry 10 km
Tel (44) 01382 - 739 430, Fax (44) 01382 - 739 430

Broughty Ferry - 16 rooms, D £ 88 - Broughty Ferry 10 km
Tel (44) 01382 - 480 027, Fax (44) 01382 - 477 660

RESTAURANTS RESTAURANTS
11 Park Avenue - Carnoustie 3 km - Tel (44) 01241 - 853 336
Café Montmartre (French) - Broughty Ferry 10 km
Tel (44) 01382 - 739 313

Pitlochry

14	6	6

A visit here in Winter – to an area known as Scottish Switzerland – would probably come as something as a surprise, as even at a moderate altitude snow is not rare. This little town, one of Queen Victoria's favourite destinations, is surrounded by hills edged with pine-trees and looks its best in Summer, when nature and the course are in full bloom and the salmon are on their way up to Loch Faskally. Accommodation here is both extensive and good standard and there is even a theatre. Designed by Willie Fernie then restyled by Cecil Hutchinson in the 1920s, the actual course lies on a hill above Pitlochry, and although the first few holes are something of a climb, the layout soon levels out and the view from the top of the course really is worth the effort. Slopes have been used so intelligently that you don't always notice them, and while tee-boxes and greens are frequently at the same level, you'll find a few surprises in store as you progress from one to the other. Interestingly, the bunkers here contain quartz sand.

Venir par ici en hiver – dans ce que l'on appelle la Suisse Ecossaise – pourrait bien vous surprendre. Même à une altitude modérée, il n'est pas rare d'y voir de la neige. Les collines bordées de pins entourent la petite ville, que la reine Victoria adorait. Il faut venir ici en été, quand la végétation est à sa plénitude, et que les saumons remontent le Loch Faskally. L'hébergement est ici aussi abondant que de qualité, on trouve même un théâtre. Dessiné par Willie Fernie, et retravaillé par Cecil Hutchinson dans les années 1920, ce parcours est situé sur une colline au-dessus de Pitlochry, le début est physiquement assez difficile, mais les choses s'arrangent rapidement, et la vue du haut du parcours valait cet effort. On ne remarque pas toujours les pentes, car elles sont intelligemment utilisées, les départs et les greens sont fréquemment au même niveau, mais on peut trouver quelques surprises entre les deux. A remarquer, le sable de quartz dans les bunkers.

Pitlochry Golf Club — 1909

Golf Course Road
SCO - PITLOCHRY, PH16 5QY

Office	Secrétariat	(44) 01796 - 472 314
Pro shop	Pro-shop	(44) 01796 - 472 792
Fax	Fax	(44) 01796 - 473 947
Web	www.pitlochrygolf.co.uk	
Situation	Situation	Perth, 45 km
Annual closure	Fermeture annuelle	no

Chances of snow during winter months

Weekly closure	Fermeture hebdomadaire	no
Fees main season	Tarifs haute saison	18 holes

	Week days / Semaine	We/Bank holidays / We/Férié
Individual Individuel	£ 24	£ 30
Couple Couple	£ 48	£ 60

Full day (week days): £ 24

Caddie Caddie no — **Electric Trolley** Chariot électrique yes

Buggy Voiturette no — **Clubs** Clubs yes

Credit cards Cartes de crédit yes

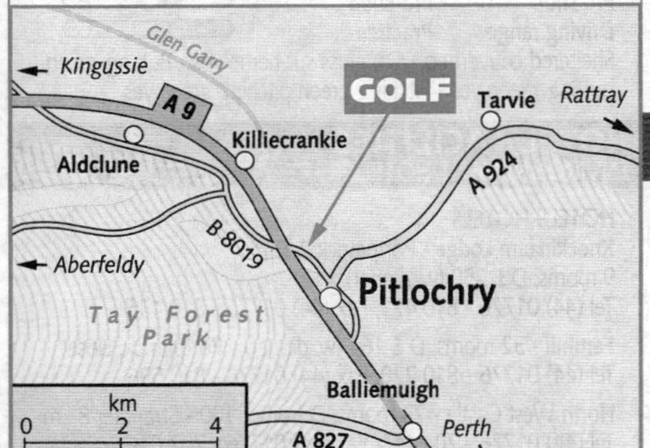

Access Accès : Edinburgh M90 then A9 to Pitlochry.
Turn uphill at sign in middle of town.

Map 1 on page 471 Carte 1 Page 471

GOLF COURSE — PARCOURS — 14/20

Site	Site	
Maintenance	Entretien	
Architect	Architecte	Willie Fernie
Type	Type	parkland, mountain
Relief	Relief	
Water in play	Eau en jeu	
Exp. to wind	Exposé au vent	
Trees in play	Arbres en jeu	

Scorecard Carte de score	Chp. Chp.	Mens Mess.	Ladies Da.
Length Long.	5290	5290	5290
Par	69	69	72
Slope system	—	—	—

Advised golfing ability / Niveau de jeu recommandé: 0 12 24 36

Hcp required — Handicap exigé — certificate

CLUB HOUSE & AMENITIES — CLUB HOUSE ET ANNEXES — 6/10

Pro shop	Pro-shop
Driving range	Practice

Sheltered couvert no - On grass sur herbe yes - Putting-green putting-green yes - Pitching-green pitching green no

HOTEL FACILITIES — ENVIRONNEMENT HOTELIER — 6/10

HOTELS HÔTELS

Pine Trees - 20 rooms, D £ 142 (w. dinner) - Pitlochry, close
Tel (44) 01796 - 472 121, Fax (44) 01796 - 472 460

Dundarave - 7 rooms, D £ 56 - Pitlochry, close
Tel (44) 01796 - 473 109, Fax (44) 01796 - 473 109

Green Park - 39 rooms, D £ 146 (w. dinner) - Pitlochry, close
Tel (44) 01796 - 473 248, Fax (44) 01796 - 473 520

RESTAURANTS RESTAURANTS

East Haugh House - Pitlochry 4 km - Tel (44) 01796 - 473 121

Portpatrick (Dunskey)

15 | 6 | 6

This course dominates the little village of Portpatrick from atop the cliffs overlooking the Irish sea, with views stretching tc the distant Isle of Man, the Irish coast and the Mull of Kintyre. Although close to the ocean, this is not a dunes links, although the scrub and bushes are just as dangerous. Because of its location it is very exposed to the prevailing south-westerlies, and of course overcoming, or at least accepting, this element is essential, particularly when it comes to club selection. Make full allowance for side-winds or head-winds or any possible combination of the two. This is a pretty spot to spend a holiday, especially as the little 9-holer is ideal for beginners to cut their teeth or even for non-golfers in the family to hit a ball or two. It is also the opportunity to discover a little known region of Scotland.

Ce parcours domine le petit village de Portpatrick du haut des falaises dominant la mer d'Irlande, avec des vues dans le lointain sur l'Ile de Man, la côte irlandaise et le Mull of Kintyre. Il est proche de l'océan, mais ce n'est pas un links dans les dunes, bien que les bosquets et arbustes y jouent un rôle identique. A cause de sa situation, il est très exposé aux vents dominants de sud-ouest. Bien sûr, savoir maîtriser - ou au moins accepter - cet élément est ici une nécessité, notamment au moment du choix des clubs : prévoir large par vent contre ou latéral, ou toutes combinaisons imaginables des deux. C'est un joli endroit où passer pendant les vacances, d'autant que le petit 9-trous est idéal pour aguerrir les débutants, voire initier les non-golfeurs de la famille. C'est aussi l'occasion de découvrir une région peu connue d'Ecosse.

Portpatrick Golf Club — 1903

Golf Course Road,
SCO - PORTPATRICK, STRANRAER, Wigtownshire DG9 8TB

Office	Secrétariat	(44) 01776 - 810 273
Pro shop	Pro-shop	(44) 01776 - 810 273
Fax	Fax	(44) 01776 - 810 811
Web	www.portpatrickgolfclub.co.uk	
Situation	Situation	Stranraer, 8 km
Annual closure	Fermeture annuelle	no
Weekly closure	Fermeture hebdomadaire	no

Fees main season Tarifs haute saison — 18 holes

	Week days Semaine	We/Bank holidays We/Férié
Individual Individuel	£ 30	£ 35
Couple Couple	£ 60	£ 70

Full days: £ 40 - £ 45 (We)

Caddie Caddie on request

Electric Trolley Chariot électrique on request

Buggy Voiturette on request **Clubs** Clubs yes

Credit cards Cartes de crédit VISA - MasterCard

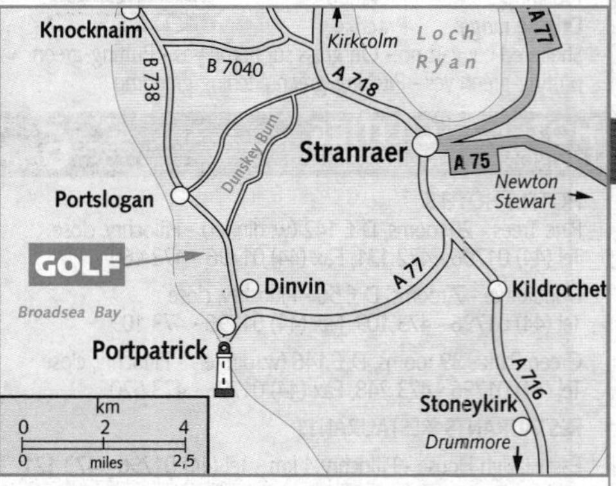

Access Accès : Glasgow, A77 through Ayr, Turnberry, to Stranraer, then A716 and A77 to Portpatrick.
Map 2 on page 472 Carte 2 Page 472

GOLF COURSE — PARCOURS — 15/20

Site	Site	
Maintenance	Entretien	
Architect	Architecte	C.W. Hunter
Type	Type	seaside course, parkland
Relief	Relief	
Water in play	Eau en jeu	
Exp. to wind	Exposé au vent	
Trees in play	Arbres en jeu	

Scorecard Carte de score	Chp. Chp.	Mens Mess.	Ladies Da.
Length Long.	5401	5061	4707
Par	70	70	70
Slope system	—	—	—

Advised golfing ability Niveau de jeu recommandé — 0 12 24 36

Hcp required Handicap exigé — 24 Men, 36 Ladies

CLUB HOUSE & AMENITIES — CLUB HOUSE ET ANNEXES — 6/10

Pro shop Pro-shop

Driving range Practice

Sheltered couvert no - On grass sur herbe yes - Putting-green putting-green yes - Pitching-green pitching green yes

HOTEL FACILITIES — ENVIRONNEMENT HOTELIER — 6/10

HOTELS HÔTELS

Knockinaam Lodge - Portpatrick 2 km
9 rooms, D £ 250 (w. dinner)
Tel (44) 01776 - 810 471, Fax (44) 01776 - 810 435

Fernhill - 32 rooms, D £ 164 (w. dinner) - Portpatrick, close
Tel (44) 01776 - 810 220, Fax (44) 01776 - 810 596

North West Castle - 73 rooms, D from £ 100 - Stranraer 8 km
Tel (44) 01776 - 704 413, Fax (44) 01776 - 702 646

RESTAURANTS RESTAURANTS

Knockinaam Lodge - Portpatrick 2 km
Tel (44) 01776 - 810 471

Campbells - Portpatrick 2 km - Tel (44) 01776 - 810 314

Powfoot

16	6	4

It has often been said that the finest turf in the world is to be found close to Solway Firth. Whatever, the grass at Powfoot does nothing to undermine that claim. And although the course is not specifically a links, the type of soil here means you play it as if it were. There is a lot of gorse to worry wayward hitters, although the fairways are wide enough for players to open their shoulders, as long as the wind behaves itself. Mid- and high-handicappers can rest assured: this is a friendly layout and they shouldn't be over-awed by the one or two blind shots. The surprises in store from off-target shots are more often pleasant than unpleasant. The better players will need to think harder to keep the ball straight and avoid the very many bunkers, which were laid out by James Braid. Need we say more? Excellent golfing.

On a souvent dit que l'on trouvait les meilleurs gazons du monde près du Solway Firth. Celui de Powfoot prouve en tout cas que ce n'est pas faux. Et bien que le parcours ne soit pas spécifiquement un links, la nature du sol fait qu'on le joue comme tel. Les ajoncs sont ici abondants pour inquiéter les joueurs imprécis, mais les fairways sont assez larges pour qu'ils oublient leurs craintes, tant que le vent ne souffle pas trop... Que les joueurs de handicap moyen ou élevé se rassurent, c'est un tracé des plus amicaux, et les quelques coups aveugles ne devraient pas trop les préoccuper : ils auront plus de bonnes surprises que de mauvaises avec leurs écarts imprévus ! Les meilleurs joueurs devront réfléchir davantage à garder la balle assez droite, à éviter les nombreux bunkers : James Braid les a disposés, il n'est pas nécessaire d'en dire plus. Une halte de qualité.

Powfoot Golf Club — 1903

Cummertrees
SCO - ANNAN, Dumfriesshire DG12 5QE

Office	Secrétariat	(44) 01461 - 700 276
Pro shop	Pro-shop	(44) 01461 - 700 327
Fax	Fax	(44) 01461 - 700 276
Web	www.powfoot.com	
Situation	Situation	Dumfries, 19 km
Annual closure	Fermeture annuelle	no
Weekly closure	Fermeture hebdomadaire	no

Fees main season Tarifs haute saison	Week days Semaine	We/Bank holidays We/Férié
		18 holes
Individual Individuel	£ 25	£ 26
Couple Couple	£ 50	£ 52

* Saturday: members only / Full week day: £ 32

Caddie Caddie no — **Electric Trolley** Chariot électrique no

Buggy Voiturette no — **Clubs** Clubs no

Credit cards Cartes de crédit VISA - JCB - Switch

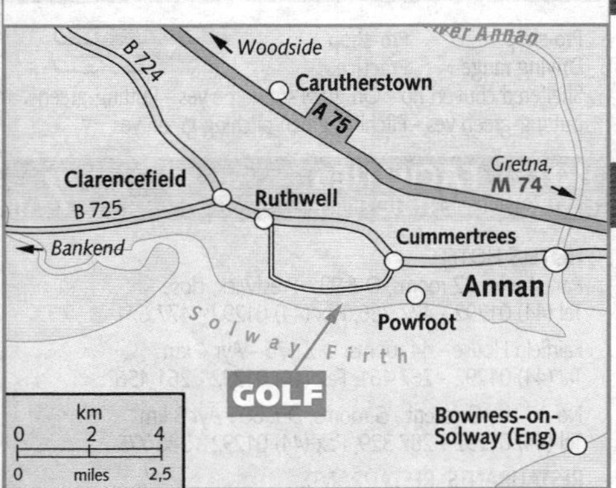

Access Accès : Glasgow, M74 and A74. Exit 18 after Lockerbie, B723 → Annan. B724 on right before Annan → Cummertrees. After 5 km (3 m.), pass under railway bridge, turn sharp left → Golf.

Map 2 on page 473 Carte 2 Page 473

GOLF COURSE — PARCOURS — 16/20

Site	Site	
Maintenance	Entretien	
Architect	Architecte	James Braid
Type	Type	links
Relief	Relief	
Water in play	Eau en jeu	
Exp. to wind	Exposé au vent	
Trees in play	Arbres en jeu	

Scorecard Carte de score	Chp. Chp.	Mens Mess.	Ladies Da.
Length Long.	5710	5475	5010
Par	70	70	74
Slope system	—	—	—

Advised golfing ability Niveau de jeu recommandé: 0 12 24 36

Hcp required Handicap exigé: no

CLUB HOUSE & AMENITIES — CLUB HOUSE ET ANNEXES — 6/10

Pro shop Pro-shop
Driving range Practice

Sheltered couvert ,o - On grass sur herbe yes - Putting-green putting-green yes - Pitching-green pitching green yes

HOTEL FACILITIES — ENVIRONNEMENT HOTELIER — 4/10

HOTELS HÔTELS

Cairndale - 91 rooms, D £ 149 - Dumfries 15 km
Tel (44) 01387 - 254 111, Fax (44) 01387 - 250 555

Station - 32 rooms, D £ 110 - Dumfries 15 km
Tel (44) 01387 - 254 316, Fax (44) 01387 - 250 388

Redbank House - 5 rooms, D £ 60 - Dumfries 15 km
Tel (44) 01387 - 247 034, Fax (44) 01387 - 266 220

RESTAURANTS RESTAURANTS

Cairndale - Dumfries 15 km - Tel (44) 01387 - 254 111

The Bistro (Station) - Dumfries 15 km
Tel (44) 01387 - 254 316

Prestwick

18	6	7

This was the first course used for the British Open but was withdrawn from the course rotation in 1925 for being too short and perhaps, too, for a number of eccentric features such as the blind par-3 fifth hole or the second shot on the 17th, where the green is nowhere to be seen. But no lover of authentic golf will miss playing this delightful and one-of-a-kind links course which is kept in excellent condition. Like many courses in Scotland, it unwinds between a railway track and the sea. It has been lengthened since the days when there were only twelve holes but this has added to the course's variety if not its unity. The bunkers here are particularly tough, especially the famous Cardinal, which cuts hole N°3 in two. While the original architect remains unknown, there is every likelihood that Tom Morris and Charlie Hunter were involved in some way or another. Prestwick thrives on hospitality (on week days) and memories of the past that you can't and won't miss in the club-house.

Ce fut le premier parcours du British Open, mais il fut retiré de la rotation des parcours en 1925, pour sa longueur insuffisante, mais peut-être aussi quelques aspects excentriques comme le 5, un par 3 aveugle, ou le second coup du 17, où le green n'est pas plus visible. Mais aucun amoureux de golf authentique ne manquera de jouer ce links savoureux et unique en son genre, où l'entretien est d'excellente qualité. Comme beaucoup de parcours en Ecosse, il se déroule entre la voie ferrée et la mer. Il a été allongé depuis l'époque où il ne comptait que 12 trous, mais cela a contribué à ajouter à sa variété, sinon à son unité. Les bunkers ici sont particulièrement féroces, notamment le fameux Cardinal, qui coupe le 3 en deux parties. Si l'architecte original est resté inconnu, il est probable que Tom Morris et Charlie Hunter y ont mis leur patte. Prestwick cultive l'hospitalité (en semaine) et les souvenirs des temps passés, que vous ne manquerez pas au club-house.

Prestwick Golf Club — 1851

2 Links Road
SCO - PRESTWICK, Ayrshire KA9 1QG

Office	Secrétariat	(44) 01292 - 477 404
Pro shop	Pro-shop	(44) 01292 - 479 483
Fax	Fax	(44) 01292 - 477 255
Web	www.prestwickgc.co.uk	
Situation	Situation	Ayr, 4 km
Annual closure	Fermeture annuelle	no
Weekly closure	Fermeture hebdomadaire	no

Fees main season Tarifs haute saison — 18 holes

	Week days Semaine	We/Bank holidays We/Férié
Individual Individuel	£ 100	*
Couple Couple	£ 200	*

* Some tee times on Sundays only: £125 for 18 holes
Full week days: £ 150

Caddie Caddie on request **Electric Trolley** Chariot électrique yes
Buggy Voiturette no **Clubs** Clubs yes
Credit cards Cartes de crédit
VISA - MasterCard - AMEX (Pro shop)

Access Accès : A77, take road to Prestwick, Golf adjacent to railway station
Map 3 on page 474 Carte 3 Page 474

GOLF COURSE — PARCOURS — 18/20

Site	Site	
Maintenance	Entretien	
Architect	Architecte	unknown
Type	Type	links
Relief	Relief	
Water in play	Eau en jeu	
Exp. to wind	Exposé au vent	
Trees in play	Arbres en jeu	

Scorecard Carte de score	Chp. Chp.	Mens Mess.	Ladies Da.
Length Long.	6068	6068	5074
Par	71	71	74
Slope system	—	—	—

Advised golfing ability Niveau de jeu recommandé — 0 12 24 36
Hcp required Handicap exigé — certificate

CLUB HOUSE & AMENITIES — CLUB HOUSE ET ANNEXES — 6/10

Pro shop Pro-shop
Driving range Practice
Sheltered couvert no - **On grass** sur herbe yes - **Putting-green** putting-green yes - **Pitching-green** pitching green yes

HOTEL FACILITIES — ENVIRONNEMENT HOTELIER — 7/10

HOTELS HÔTELS

Parkstone - 22 rooms, D £ 93 - Prestwick, close
Tel (44) 01292 - 477 286, Fax (44) 01292 - 477 671

Fairfield House - 44 rooms, D £ 175 - Ayr 4 km
Tel (44) 01292 - 267 461, Fax (44) 01292 - 261 456

No 26 The Crescent - 5 rooms, D £ 60 - Ayr 3 km
Tel (44) 01292 - 287 329, Fax (44) 01292 - 286 779

RESTAURANTS RESTAURANTS

Elliots - Prestwick, close - Tel (44) 01292 - 677 677
The Ivy House - Alloway 8 km - Tel (44) 01655 - 442 336

Prestwick St Nicholas

16	6	7

The reputation of the other Prestwick course has doubtless helped keep this course out of the limelight. That might be so with non-Scots, but the local players know that this is not just another course but one that should be included when making an intelligent and exhaustive survey of good courses in Ayrshire. This is a genuine typical Scottish links laid out between the sea and a railway line, both of which come into play depending on where the wind is blowing from. While some of the natural bunkers can keep you out of the wind, you'll have to get out of them sooner or later to affront the tricky slopes of the huge greens, which are often firm and slick. With difficulties spread evenly over the 18 holes, don't put too much faith in the lengths written on the card. You can certainly play to your handicap here, but it is certainly no gimme. Even if your card is looking good after fifteen holes, slicers better watch out for the last three holes, where OB looms on the right.

La réputation de l'autre Prestwick a sans doute maintenu celui-ci dans une certaine obscurité, au moins auprès des étrangers car les joueurs de la région savent qu'il ne s'agit pas là d'un parcours indifférent, à inclure dans une exploration intelligente et exhaustive des bons parcours de l'Ayrshire. Il s'agit là d'un vrai et typique "Scottish links," situé entre la mer et le chemin de fer, qui viennent tous deux en jeu selon que le vent souffle d'un côté ou de l'autre. Et si certains bunkers naturels vous fourniront un abri, il faudra pourtant bien en sortir un jour pour affronter les subtils reliefs de greens vastes, souvent fermes et bien roulants. Avec des difficultés bien réparties tout au long des 18 trous, il ne faut pas se fier aux longueurs inscrites sur la carte. Certes, on peut jouer ici son handicap, mais ce n'est pas donné d'avance. Et si le score est bon après quinze trous, méfiance avec les trois derniers, bordés de hors-limites pour sliceurs !

Prestwick St Nicholas Golf Club — 1892

Grangemuir Road
SCO - PRESTWICK, Ayrshire KA9 1SN

Office	Secrétariat	(44) 01292 - 477 608
Pro shop	Pro-shop	(44) 01292 - 473 904
Fax	Fax	(44) 01292 - 473 900
Web	www.prestwickstnicholas.com	
Situation	Situation	Glasgow, 51 km
Annual closure	Fermeture annuelle	no
Weekly closure	Fermeture hebdomadaire	no

Fees main season Tarifs haute saison		18 holes
	Week days Semaine	We/Bank holidays We/Férié
Individual Individuel	£ 45	£ 50*
Couple Couple	£ 90	£ 100*

Full week days: £ 60 /
* Visitors at week-ends: Sunday afternoon only

Caddie Caddie on request **Electric Trolley** Chariot électrique no
Buggy Voiturette no **Clubs** Clubs yes
Credit cards Cartes de crédit yes

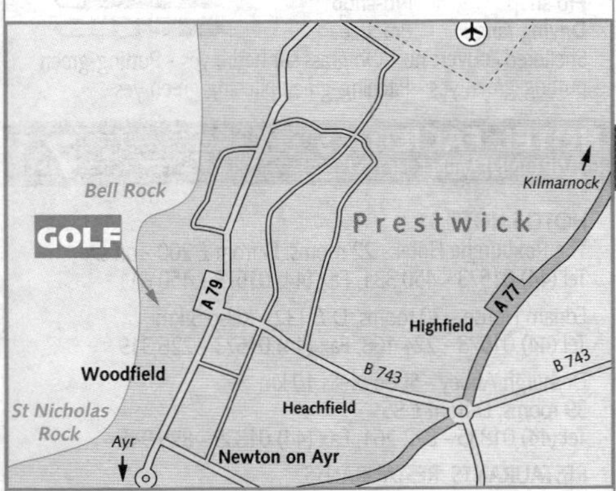

Access Accès : Glasgow, A77 to Prestwick
Map 3 on page 474 Carte 3 Page 474

GOLF COURSE
PARCOURS — 16/20

Site	Site	
Maintenance	Entretien	
Architect	Architecte	Charles Hunter James Allan
Type	Type	links
Relief	Relief	
Water in play	Eau en jeu	
Exp. to wind	Exposé au vent	
Trees in play	Arbres en jeu	

Scorecard Carte de score	Chp. Chp.	Mens Mess.	Ladies Da.
Length Long.	5416	5416	4836
Par	69	69	70
Slope system	—	—	—

Advised golfing ability Niveau de jeu recommandé — 0 12 24 36
Hcp required Handicap exigé — no

CLUB HOUSE & AMENITIES
CLUB HOUSE ET ANNEXES — 6/10

Pro shop Pro-shop
Driving range Practice
Sheltered couvert no driving range - On grass sur herbe no - Putting-green putting-green yes - Pitching-green pitching green yes

HOTEL FACILITIES
ENVIRONNEMENT HOTELIER — 7/10

HOTELS HÔTELS
Carlton Toby - 35 rooms, D £ 85 - Prestwick, close
Tel (44) 01292 - 476 811, Fax (44) 01292 - 474 845

Fairfield House - 44 rooms, D £ 175 - Ayr 4 km
Tel (44) 01292 - 267 461, Fax (44) 01292 - 261 456

Pickwick - 15 rooms, D £ 70 - Ayr 4 km
Tel (44) 01292 - 260 111, Fax (44) 01292 - 285 348

Brig O'Doon House - 5 rooms, D £ 120 - Alloway 9 km
Tel (44) 01292 - 442 466, Fax (44) 01292 - 441 999

RESTAURANTS RESTAURANTS
Elliotts - Prestwick, close - Tel (44) 01292 - 677 677

Roxburghe (The)

17	8	7

The Duke and Duchess of Roxburghe were personally involved in the decoration and style of the Roxburghe Hotel and everyone should visit their "home sweet home", i.e. the hundreds of rooms in the Floors Castle. Fishing, clay pigeon-shooting, riding and tennis are some of the activities on offer on this estate located very close to the English border, plus an 18-hole course designed by Dave Thomas alongside a river, following the natural relief of the estate and alternating stretches in the forest and the attractive park (the course is not always easy to walk). Modern in style, it demands target golf more than your usual bump and run shots to avoid the many different hazards. These include the architect's usual deep bunkers and water that comes into play on two of the tricky par 3s. A high-class location for a sporting holiday in very pretty countryside, now further enhanced as the course matures. Last but not least are the excellent practice facilities, which are none too common in Scotland.

Le Duc et la Duchesse de Roxburghe ont mis eux-même la main à la décoration de l'hôtel Roxburghe, et l'on ne manquera pas de visiter leur "sweet home", c'est-à-dire les centaines de pièces du Floors Castle. Pêche, tir au pigeon d'argile, équitation et tennis sont quelques-unes des activités proposées dans ce domaine tout proche de la frontière avec l'Angleterre, auxquelles s'ajoute un 18 trous dessiné par Dave Thomas en bordure de rivière. Il suivit les reliefs naturels du domaine et alterne passages en forêt et esthétique de parc (le parcours n'est pas toujours facile à marcher). De style moderne, il exige un jeu de cible plus que des coups roulés, avec de multiples obstacles, notamment les profonds bunkers caractéristiques de l'architecte, ou l'eau en jeu sur deux des délicats pars 3. C'est un lieu de vacances sportives de très bonne facture, dans un très joli paysage, avec un parcours qui a bien évolué. On ajoutera un très beau practice, ce qui n'est pas si fréquent en Ecosse !

The Roxburghe Golf Course — 1997

The Roxburghe Hotel
SCO - KELSO, Roxburghshire TD5 8JZ

Office	Secrétariat	(44) 01573 - 450 331
Pro shop	Pro-shop	(44) 01573 - 450 333
Fax	Fax	(44) 01573 - 450 611
Web	www.roxburghe.net	
Situation	Situation	Kelso, 5 km
Annual closure	Fermeture annuelle	no
Weekly closure	Fermeture hebdomadaire	no

Fees main season Tarifs haute saison — 18 holes

	Week days Semaine	We/Bank holidays We/Férié
Individual Individuel	£ 60	£ 60
Couple Couple	£ 120	£ 120

Caddie Caddie on request **Electric Trolley** Chariot électrique yes

Buggy Voiturette yes **Clubs** Clubs yes

Credit cards Cartes de crédit
VISA - MasterCard - DC

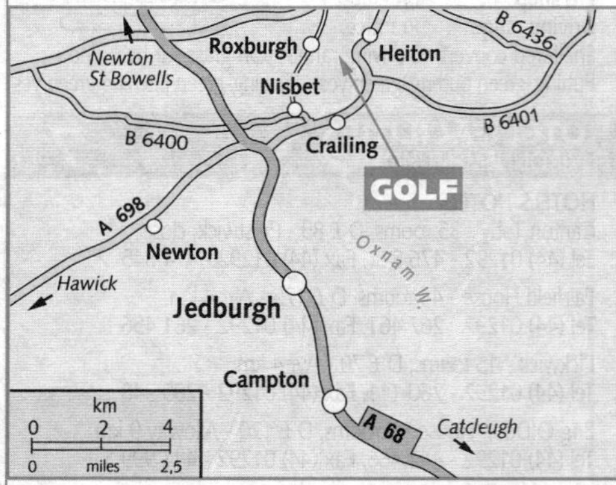

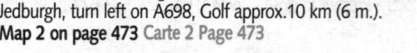

Access Accès : Edinburgh A68. After St Boswells and before Jedburgh, turn left on A698, Golf approx.10 km (6 m.).
Map 2 on page 473 Carte 2 Page 473

GOLF COURSE — PARCOURS — 17/20

Site	Site	
Maintenance	Entretien	
Architect	Architecte	Dave Thomas
Type	Type	parkland
Relief	Relief	
Water in play	Eau en jeu	
Exp. to wind	Exposé au vent	
Trees in play	Arbres en jeu	

Scorecard Carte de score	Chp. Chp.	Mens Mess.	Ladies Da.
Length Long.	6400	6232	5094
Par	72	72	72
Slope system	140	139	0

Advised golfing ability 0 12 24 36
Niveau de jeu recommandé
Hcp required Handicap exigé 24

CLUB HOUSE & AMENITIES — CLUB HOUSE ET ANNEXES — 8/10

Pro shop	Pro-shop
Driving range	Practice

Sheltered couvert no - **On grass** sur herbe yes - **Putting-green** putting-green yes - **Pitching-green** pitching green yes

HOTEL FACILITIES — ENVIRONNEMENT HOTELIER — 7/10

HOTELS HÔTELS

The Roxburghe Hotel - 22 rooms, D from £ 200 - on site
Tel (44) 01573 - 450 331, Fax (44) 01573 - 450 611

Ednam House - 30 rooms, D £ 132 - Kelso 5 km
Tel (44) 01573 - 224 168, Fax (44) 01573 - 226 319

Dryburgh Abbey - St Boswells 10 km
39 rooms, D from £ 85
Tel (44) 01835 - 822 261, Fax (44) 01835 - 823 945

RESTAURANTS RESTAURANTS

The Roxburghe - on site - Tel (44) 01573 - 450 331
Queens Bistro - Kelso 5 km - Tel (44) 01573 - 228 899

Royal Aberdeen *Balgownie Links*

18	7	8

A page of golf was written here, less than 2 miles from the "city of granite". Royal Aberdeen originated in 1780, was the world's sixth golf club and the first to adopt the 5-minute rule when looking for your ball. You probably won't lose yours as long as you play "Balgownie" (its more familiar name) carefully, avoid the bushes and tall grass and, in a word, stay in the fairway. You'll probably have a tougher time distinguishing some of the fairways amongst the dunes, avoiding the ten bunkers on the 8th hole, keeping a solid swing when the wind blows a little too hard, or remembering to turn around at the 9th, as the holes that naturally continue belong to Murcar. Originally designed by Robert and Archie Simpson from Carnoustie, it was altered by Braid and today Donald Steel is the club's consultant. A little off the beaten golf-trotter track, this is one of the great classics for every links-collector, fun to come back to every time.

A seulement trois km de la "ville de granit" s'est tournée une page du golf : le Royal Aberdeen trouve ses origines en 1780, c'est le sixième club du monde et le premier à avoir adopté la règle de cinq minutes pour chercher une balle. Mais on ne risque pas trop d'en perdre si l'on joue sagement "Balgownie" (comme on le connaît mieux), en évitant les buissons et les hautes herbes. Bref si l'on ne quitte pas le fairway. On perdra davantage la tête à repérer certains fairways parmi les dunes, à éviter les dix bunkers du 8, à garder un swing solide quand le vent souffle un peu trop fort, ou si l'on oublie de revenir en arrière au 9 : les trous qui suivent naturellement appartiennent au parcours de Murcar. Originellement dessiné par Robert et Archie Simpson de Carnoustie, il a été modifié par Braid, Donald Steel étant aujourd'hui le conseiller du club. Un peu en dehors des sentiers touristiques du golf, c'est un des grands classiques quand on fait la collection des links. Et c'est toujours un plaisir d'y revenir.

Royal Aberdeen Golf Club — 1888

Balgownie, Links Road, Bridge of Don
SCO- ABERDEEN AB23 8AT

Office	Secrétariat	(44) 01224 - 702 571
Pro shop	Pro-shop	(44) 01224 - 702 221
Fax	Fax	(44) 01224 - 826 591
Web	www.royalaberdeengolf.com	
Situation	Situation	Aberdeen, 3 km
Annual closure	Fermeture annuelle	no
Weekly closure	Fermeture hebdomadaire	no

Fees main season Tarifs haute saison — 18 holes

	Week days Semaine	We/Bank holidays We/Férié
Individual Individuel	£ 85	£ 95*
Couple Couple	£ 170	£ 190*

* after 15.30 / Full week days: £ 120

Caddie Caddie on request **Electric Trolley** Chariot électrique yes

Buggy Voiturette no **Clubs** Clubs yes

Credit cards Cartes de crédit
VISA - MasterCard - Switch

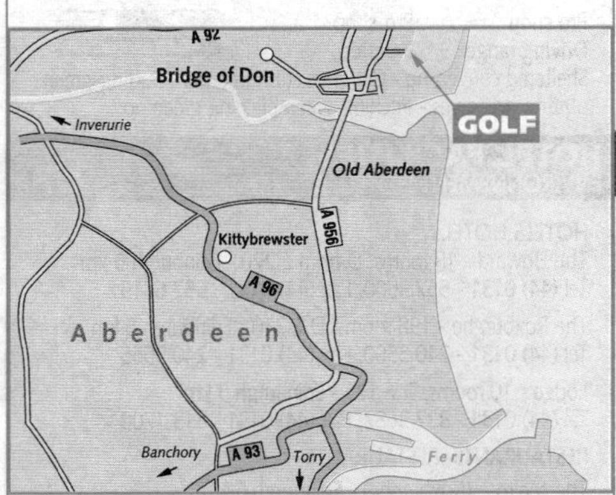

Access Accès : 3 km N of Aberdeen on A92. Cross River Don, on right at first traffic lights, on Links Road to golf course.
Map 1 on page 471 Carte 1 Page 471

GOLF COURSE — PARCOURS — 18/20

Site	Site	
Maintenance	Entretien	
Architect	Architecte	Bob et Archie Simpson James Braid
Type	Type	links
Relief	Relief	
Water in play	Eau en jeu	
Exp. to wind	Exposé au vent	
Trees in play	Arbres en jeu	

Scorecard Carte de score	Chp. Chp.	Mens Mess.	Ladies Da.
Length Long.	6257	5971	5464
Par	71	71	71
Slope system	—	—	—

Advised golfing ability Niveau de jeu recommandé — 0 12 24 36

Hcp required Handicap exigé 24

CLUB HOUSE & AMENITIES — CLUB HOUSE ET ANNEXES — 7/10

Pro shop Pro-shop
Driving range Practice
Sheltered couvert no - On grass sur herbe no - Putting-green putting-green yes - Pitching-green pitching green yes

HOTEL FACILITIES — ENVIRONNEMENT HOTELIER — 8/10

HOTELS HÔTELS
Marcliffe at Piffodels - 42 rooms, D £ 165 - Aberdeen 6 km
Tel (44) 01224 - 861 000, Fax (44) 01224 - 868 860

Travel Inn - 40 rooms, D £ 50 - Murcar 3 km
Tel (44) 01224 - 821 217, Fax (44) 01224 - 706 869

Simpson's - 50 rooms, D £ 145 - Aberdeen 6 km
Tel (44) 01224 - 327 777, Fax (44) 01224 - 327 700

Ardoe House - 117 rooms, D £ 165 - Aberdeen 5 km
Tel (44) 01224 - 860 600, Fax (44) 01224 - 861 283

RESTAURANTS RESTAURANTS
Brasserie - Aberdeen 5 km - Tel (44) 01224 - 327 799
Silver Darling - Aberdeen 5 km - Tel (44) 01224 - 576 229

Royal Burgess

16 | 7 | 8

This club was formed in 1735 and played the Brunstfield Links behind Edinburgh Castle. Today it lies adjoined to the Brunstfield Club (whose history runs parallel to this club) in the north-west of the city in magnificently laid out park landscape. The work of Old Tom Morris and then James Braid after 1945 (his bunkering is always so effective), this "Barnton" course has its own very personal character with alternating old trees and young saplings standing alone or in clumps. You cannot miss seeing the finest examples because they are right in play. Accuracy is recommended, needless to say, as for many golfers this is a "second-shot" course where you have to be so efficient to hit the greens or save your score when you miss them. The putting surfaces are such a pleasure to play that sometimes you would like to putt a little more often. Well worth knowing, but not easy to get on.

Ce club a été formé en 1735, et aurait eu comme parcours original les Bruntsfield Links derrière le Château d'Edinburgh. Toujours est-il qu'il est aujourd'hui mitoyen au Club de Bruntsfield (dont l'histoire est parallèle), au nord-ouest de la ville, et dans un paysage de parc magnifiquement sculpté. Dû aux crayons bien connus de Old Tom Morris, puis de James Braid après 1945 (son bunkering est toujours efficace), ce parcours de "Barnton" possède un caractère très personnel, avec son alternance d'arbres anciens et de jeunes pousses, solitaires ou en bosquets. On ne peut pas en manquer les plus beaux exemplaires, ils sont bien en jeu. Inutile de dire que la précision est recommandée, car c'est pour beaucoup un parcours "de seconds coups," tant il faut être efficace pour rejoindre les greens, et pour sauver le score quand on les a manqués. Les surfaces de putting sont d'ailleurs un tel régal que l'on aimerait devoir faire plein de putts ! A connaître, mais l'accès n'y est pas facile.

Royal Burgess Golfing Society of Edinburgh — 1894

181 Whitehouse Road, Barnton
SCO - EDINBURGH EH4 6BY

Office	Secrétariat	(44) 0131 - 339 2075
Pro shop	Pro-shop	(44) 0131 - 339 6474
Fax	Fax	(44) 0131 - 339 3712
Web	www.royalburgess.co.uk	
Situation	Situation	Edinburgh centre, 5 km
Annual closure	Fermeture annuelle	no
Weekly closure	Fermeture hebdomadaire	no
Fees main season	Tarifs haute saison	18 holes

	Week days / Semaine	We/Bank holidays / We/Férié
Individual Individuel	£ 65	*
Couple Couple	£ 130	*

* Week-ends: members only / Restrictions for Ladies (ask before)

Caddie Caddie no — **Electric Trolley** Chariot électrique no
Buggy Voiturette no — **Clubs** Clubs yes
Credit cards Cartes de crédit yes

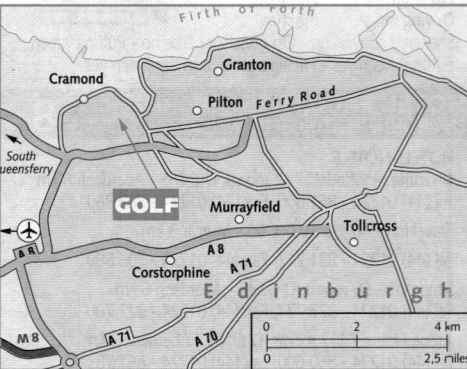

Access Accès : On Queensferry Road (A90). Turn right at traffic lights at junction of Barnton and Whitehouse Road.
Map 3 on page 475 Carte 3 Page 475

GOLF COURSE — PARCOURS — 16/20

Site	Site	
Maintenance	Entretien	
Architect	Architecte	Tom Morris, James Braid
Type	Type	parkland
Relief	Relief	
Water in play	Eau en jeu	
Exp. to wind	Exposé au vent	
Trees in play	Arbres en jeu	

Scorecard / Carte de score	Chp. / Chp.	Mens / Mess.	Ladies / Da.
Length Long.	5930	5587	—
Par	71	71	—
Slope system	—	—	—

Advised golfing ability Niveau de jeu recommandé: 0 12 24 36
Hcp required Handicap exigé: 24

CLUB HOUSE & AMENITIES — CLUB HOUSE ET ANNEXES — 7/10

Pro shop Pro-shop
Driving range Practice
Sheltered couvert no - On grass sur herbe yes - Putting-green putting-green yes - Pitching-green pitching green no

HOTEL FACILITIES — ENVIRONNEMENT HOTELIER — 8/10

HOTELS HÔTELS

The Howard - 18 rooms, D from £ 220 - Edinburgh 5 km
Tel (44) 0131 - 557 3500, Fax (44) 0131 - 557 6515

The Roxburghe - 198 rooms, D £ 210 - Edinburgh 5 km
Tel (44) 0131 - 240 5500, Fax (44) 0131 - 240 5555

Lodge - 10 rooms, D £ 125 - Edinburgh 5 km
Tel (44) 0131 - 337 3682, Fax (44) 0131 - 313 1700

RESTAURANTS RESTAURANTS

The Melrose (Roxburghe) - Edinburgh 5 km
Tel (44) 0131 - 240 5500

Restaurant Martin Wishart - Edimbourg 5 km
Tel (44) 0131 - 553 3557

Royal Dornoch *Championship*

19 | 7 | 7

Golf has been played here since about 1616, but it was Old Tom Morris and particularly the admirable Donald Ross who had the honour of really designing the course before John Sutherland added the final gloss. For untamed natural beauty and the challenge it offers any player, Royal Dornoch is one of the world's greatest courses. Carefully placing the drive is crucial here in order to get a clear shot at the greens, an element of play that was to be emulated a little later at Pinehurst 2. And no wonder, it was designed by Donald Ross. Located away from any large towns, this is a haven of peace and tranquillity in a unique atmosphere where you can chew long and hard over your technical flaws and the philosophy of golf. In fact it is only this isolation that has kept this gem of a course from being on the British Open rotation. In July you might often see some of the top champions who come here to re-acclimatize themselves to links golfing, the be-all and end-all for every true golfer. These connoisseurs include the likes of Watson and Ben Crenshaw.

Le golf a été pratiqué sur le site depuis 1616 environ, mais ce fut à Old Tom Morris et surtout à l'admirable Donald Ross que revinrent l'honneur de dessiner vraiment le parcours, plus tard peaufiné par John Sutherland. Pour sa beauté sauvage et naturelle, pour les défis qu'il présente aux joueurs, Royal Dornoch est un des plus grands parcours au monde. Le placement du drive y est crucial pour attaquer les greens en bonne position, comme ce sera plus tard le cas à Pinehurst 2... dessiné par Donald Ross. A l'écart des grandes villes, c'est un havre de paix à l'atmosphère unique où l'on peut méditer sur ses faiblesses techniques et la philosophie du jeu, et seul cet isolement a pu empêcher cette merveille d'être l'un des parcours du British Open. En juillet, il n'est pas rare d'y croiser de grands champions, venus se réacclimater au jeu sur les links, l'alpha et l'oméga du vrai golfeur. Parmi ces connaisseurs, Tom Watson et Ben Crenshaw, deux amoureux de "Dornoch".

Royal Dornoch Golf Club — 1877

Golf Road
SCO - DORNOCH, Sutherland IV25 3LW

Office	Secrétariat	(44) 01862 - 810 219
Pro shop	Pro-shop	(44) 01862 - 810 902
Fax	Fax	(44) 01862 - 810 792
Web	www.royaldornoch.com	
Situation	Situation	Inverness, 72 km
Annual closure	Fermeture annuelle	no
Weekly closure	Fermeture hebdomadaire	no

Fees main season Tarifs haute saison	18 holes	
	Week days Semaine	We/Bank holidays We/Férié
Individual Individuel	£ 72	£ 82
Couple Couple	£ 144	£ 164

GF £ 76 for Championship + Struie courses

Caddie Caddie on request **Electric Trolley** Chariot électrique yes

Buggy Voiturette yes **Clubs** Clubs yes

Credit cards Cartes de crédit
VISA - MasterCard

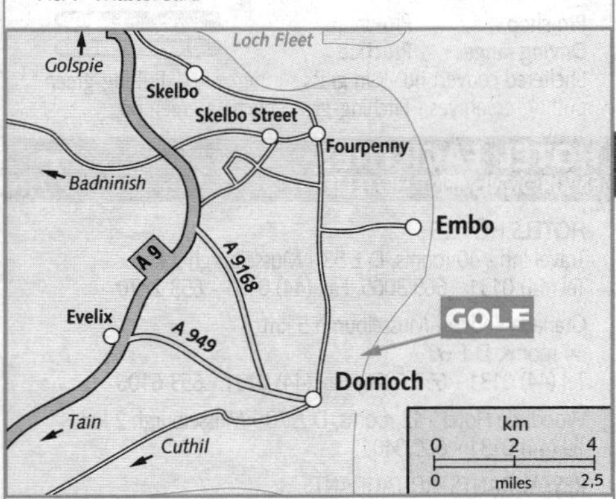

Access Accès : Inverness A9 North → Wick.
Golf on A949 to the east of the town.
Map 1 on page 470 Carte 1 Page 470

GOLF COURSE
PARCOURS — 19/20

Site	Site	
Maintenance	Entretien	
Architect	Architecte	Tom Morris Donald Ross
Type	Type	links
Relief	Relief	
Water in play	Eau en jeu	
Exp. to wind	Exposé au vent	
Trees in play	Arbres en jeu	

Scorecard Carte de score	Chp. Chp.	Mens Mess.	Ladies Da.
Length Long.	5927	5630	5420
Par	70	70	76
Slope system	—	—	—

Advised golfing ability Niveau de jeu recommandé — 0 12 24 36

Hcp required Handicap exigé — 24 Men, 35 Ladies

CLUB HOUSE & AMENITIES
CLUB HOUSE ET ANNEXES — 7/10

Pro shop Pro-shop
Driving range Practice
Sheltered couvert no - On grass sur herbe yes - Putting-green putting-green yes - Pitching-green pitching green yes

HOTEL FACILITIES
ENVIRONNEMENT HOTELIER — 7/10

HOTELS HÔTELS
The Eagle Hotel - 9 rooms, D from £ 90 - Dornoch, close
Tel (44) 01862 - 810 008, Fax (44) 01862 - 811 355

Dornoch Castle - 18 rooms, D from £ 95 - Dornoch, close
Tel (44) 01862 - 810 216, Fax (44) 01862 - 810 981

Royal Golf Hotel - 25 rooms, D from £ 200 - Dornoch, close
Tel (44) 01862 - 810 283, Fax (44) 01862 - 810 923

Burghfield House - 50 rooms, D £ 90 - Dornoch, close
Tel (44) 01862 - 810 212, Fax (44) 01862 - 810 404

RESTAURANTS RESTAURANTS
Morangie House Hotel - Tain 10 km - Tel (44) 01862 - 892 281
2 Quail - Dornoch, close - Tel (44) 01862 - 811 811

Royal Musselburgh

16 | 8 | 7

The club was founded in 1774 but we imagine that golf was played at the Old Musselburgh long before that. That course still exists but its original tenants left on the one hand to form the Muirfield club and on the other to open this course in 1926. This is not a links but a park course laid out around a majestic barony used as the club-house. James Braid designed the first layout, but in 1939 the Club asked Mungo Park to suggest some alterations. The very many trees form impressive lines of defence completed by some very effective bunkering to swallow any wayward shot. This is not a long course but there is only one par 5, something that generally speaking bothers the long-hitters on the look-out for "easy" birdies. A well-balanced course and a pleasant alternative when you have had enough of wind howling over the dunes.

Le Club a été fondé en 1774, mais on présume que le "Old Musselburgh" avait vu jouer au golf bien avant. Il existe toujours mais ses premiers locataires sont partis d'un côté créer Muirfield, et de l'autre celui-ci, en 1926. Il ne s'agit pas d'un links, mais d'un golf de parc, autour d'une majestueuse baronnie utilisée comme club-house. James Braid créa le premier tracé, mais le Club demanda en 1939 à Mungo Park de suggérer quelques modifications du parcours. Les nombreux arbres forment des défenses imposantes, complétées par un bunkering très efficace pour recueillir les coups un peu égarés. Ce n'est certes pas un parcours bien long, mais n'est guère plus facile à scorer car il n'a qu'un seul par 5, ce qui gêne en général beaucoup les frappeurs en quête de birdies faciles. Bien équilibré, c'est une bonne alternative quand on est un peu saoûlé par le vent dans les dunes.

Royal Musselburgh Golf Club — 1926

Prestongrange House
SCO - PRESTONPANS, East Lothian EH32 9RP

Office	Secrétariat	(44) 01875 - 810 276
Pro shop	Pro-shop	(44) 01875 - 810 139
Fax	Fax	(44) 01875 - 810 276
Web	www.royalmusselburgh.co.uk	
Situation	Situation	Edinburgh, 13 km
Annual closure	Fermeture annuelle	no
Weekly closure	Fermeture hebdomadaire	no

Fees main season Tarifs haute saison — 18 holes

	Week days / Semaine	We/Bank holidays / We/Férié
Individual Individuel	£ 28	£ 35
Couple Couple	£ 56	£ 70

Full days: £ 38 (Monday, Thursday, Friday morning)
No visitors Friday afternoon

Caddie Caddie on request **Electric Trolley** Chariot électrique yes

Buggy Voiturette yes **Clubs** Clubs yes

Credit cards Cartes de crédit Pro Shop only

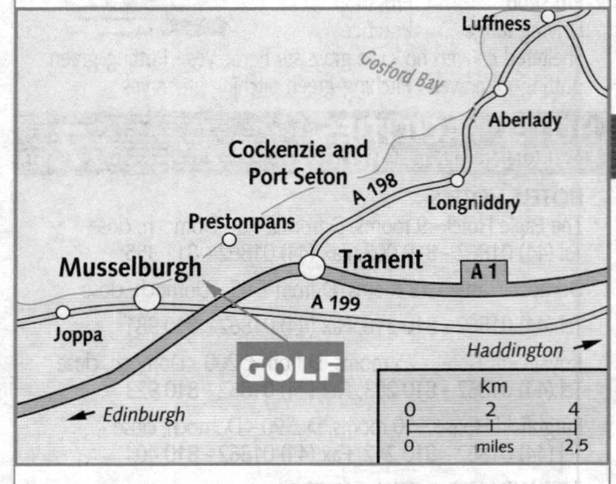

Access Accès : 13 km East of Edinburgh on B361 → North Berwick.
Map 3 on page 475 Carte 3 Page 475

GOLF COURSE — PARCOURS — 16/20

Site	Site	
Maintenance	Entretien	
Architect	Architecte	James Braid Mungo Park
Type	Type	parkland
Relief	Relief	
Water in play	Eau en jeu	
Exp. to wind	Exposé au vent	
Trees in play	Arbres en jeu	

Scorecard Carte de score	Chp. Chp.	Mens Mess.	Ladies Da.
Length Long.	5701	5346	5048
Par	70	70	72
Slope system	—	—	—

Advised golfing ability Niveau de jeu recommandé — 0 12 24 36
Hcp required Handicap exigé — certificate

CLUB HOUSE & AMENITIES — CLUB HOUSE ET ANNEXES — 8/10

Pro shop Pro-shop
Driving range Practice
Sheltered couvert no - On grass sur herbe no - Putting-green putting-green yes - Pitching-green pitching green no

HOTEL FACILITIES — ENVIRONNEMENT HOTELIER — 7/10

HOTELS HÔTELS

Travel Inn - 40 rooms, D £ 53 - Musselburgh 2 km
Tel (44) 0131 - 665 3005, Fax (44) 0131 - 653 2270

Granada Lodge - Musselburgh 5 km
44 rooms, D £ 60
Tel (44) 0131 - 653 6070, Fax (44) 0131 - 653 6106

Woodside Hotel - 12 rooms, D £ 70 - Musselburgh 2 km
Tel (44) 0131 - 665 0404

RESTAURANTS RESTAURANTS

Woodside Hotel - Musselburgh 2 km
Tel (44) 0131 - 665 0404
Caprice - Musselburgh 2 km - Tel (44) 0131 - 665 2991

Royal Troon *Old Course*

19 | 7 | 7

This course is the most remarkable of the five courses around Troon and has staged many a British Open. It also offers magnificent views of the Firth of Clyde towards the Isle of Arran and the Mull of Kintyre, lulling you into a false sense of tranquillity. On this tremendous links course, the outward 9 may seem comparatively easy, but the back 9 is one of the most horrendous in the world of golf. It is the wind that makes all the difference, especially as here it is often a side wind adding even more spice to the course. At the famous "postage-stamp" hole, the green can seem more like a pin-head when the wind is playing tricks. All those golfers who love Castles in Spain, huge trees bathed in sunlight and flattering scores can be on their way. Sure there's the Gulf Stream nearby, and sure you'll see more impressive dunes elsewhere, but this is no place for the mild or meek-hearted. Each hole here has hundreds of tales to tell, and maybe soon yours too. Warm up for the ordeal by playing the smaller Portland Course.

Ce parcours est le plus remarquable des cinq parcours autour de Troon, et a été le théâtre de nombreux British Open. Il offre des vues magnifiques au-delà du Firth of Clyde vers l'Ile d'Arran et le Mull of Kintyre, dans une trompeuse tranquillité. Sur ce formidable links, l'aller peut paraître assez facile et le retour un des plus féroces au monde. Mais le vent fera la différence, d'autant qu'il est souvent en travers, et ajoute encore à l'intérêt du parcours : au fameux "Postage Stamp", le green est encore plus petit qu'un timbre-poste quand il souffle. Que ceux qui aiment les châteaux en Espagne, les grands arbres baignés de soleil et les scores flatteurs passent leur chemin. Certes, le Gulf Stream passe par ici, certes, les dunes peuvent être encore plus impressionnantes ailleurs, mais on n'est pas ici au royaume de la douceur. Chaque trou de ce parcours pourrait raconter des centaines d'histoires... avec bientôt la vôtre. On peut s'échauffer sur le petit "Portland Course".

Royal Troon Golf Club — 1878

SCO - TROON, Ayrshire KA10 6EP

Office	Secrétariat	(44) 01292 - 311 555
Pro shop	Pro-shop	(44) 01292 - 313 281
Fax	Fax	(44) 01292 - 318 204
Web	www.royaltroon.co.uk	
Situation	Situation	Ayr, 20 km
Annual closure	Fermeture annuelle	no
Weekly closure	Fermeture hebdomadaire	no

Fees main season Tarifs haute saison — 18 holes

	Week days / Semaine	We/Bank holidays / We/Férié
Individual Individuel	£ 200	*
Couple Couple	£ 400	*

* Visitors: Monday, Tuesday, Thursday only.
GF includes coffee, lunch + 1 round

Caddie Caddie on request **Electric Trolley** Chariot électrique no

Buggy Voiturette no **Clubs** Clubs yes

Credit cards Cartes de crédit
VISA - Mastercard (Greenfees & Proshop only)

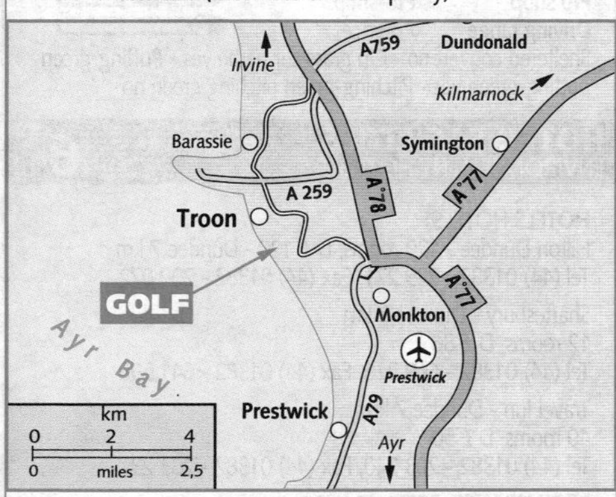

Access Accès : On B749 between Pretswick and Troon
Map 3 on page 474 Carte 3 Page 474

GOLF COURSE — PARCOURS — 19/20

Site	Site	
Maintenance	Entretien	
Architect	Architecte	Willie Fernie
Type	Type	links
Relief	Relief	
Water in play	Eau en jeu	
Exp. to wind	Exposé au vent	
Trees in play	Arbres en jeu	

Scorecard Carte de score	Chp. Chp.	Mens Mess.	Ladies Da.
Length Long.	6562	6070	5606
Par	71	71	75
Slope system	—	—	—

Advised golfing ability Niveau de jeu recommandé — 0 12 24 36

Hcp required Handicap exigé — 20 Men / 30 Ladies

CLUB HOUSE & AMENITIES — CLUB HOUSE ET ANNEXES — 7/10

Pro shop Pro-shop
Driving range Practice
Sheltered couvert practice area - On grass sur herbe yes - Putting-green putting-green yes - Pitching-green pitching green yes

HOTEL FACILITIES — ENVIRONNEMENT HOTELIER — 7/10

HOTELS HÔTELS

Marine Highland - 89 rooms, D £ 140 - Troon, close
Tel (44) 01292 - 314 444, Fax (44) 01292 - 316 922

Piersland House - 30 rooms, D from £ 130 - Troon, close
Tel (44) 01292 - 314 747, Fax (44) 01292 - 315 613

Travel Inn - 40 rooms, D £ 40 - Prestwick 4 km
Tel (44) 01292 - 678 262

RESTAURANTS RESTAURANTS

Highgrove House - Troon 3 km - Tel (44) 01292 - 312 511
Scotts - Troon Yacht Haven 4 km - Tel (44) 01292 - 315 315

Scotscraig

16 | 6 | 6

This is one of Scotland's oldest courses and the 13th oldest in the world. Its reputation has not really benefited from the closeness of St Andrews, at least not with outsiders. The road that gets you here is nothing special, but when you reach the course, all that changes. A little links but also very much an inland course with quite a few trees, heather and often the obligation to sky the ball rather than roll it in, this is a course that is none too tiring to play but one which requires a lot of concentration and precision-hitting to play well. The wind plays a vital role, it must be said, but so do the deep bunkers and the well-contoured greens which, like the course as a whole, are in good condition. Scotscraig has been used as a qualifying course for the British Open, which speaks volumes for its quality as a test of golf, but this doesn't stop less experienced players from having a go themselves; they won't necessarily be staring disaster in the face at each turn.

C'est un des plus anciens golfs d'Ecosse et le 13ème du monde, dont la réputation n'a pas vraiment bénéficié de la proximité de St Andrews, en tout cas auprès des étrangers à la région. La route d'arrivée n'est pas merveilleuse, mais tout change dès que l'on arrive. Un peu links, mais aussi beaucoup inland avec pas mal d'arbres, de la bruyère et la nécessité – souvent – de porter la balle au lieu de la faire rouler. C'est un parcours peu fatigant à jouer mais qui demande beaucoup d'attention et de précision pour être maîtrisé. Le vent y joue un rôle essentiel, faut-il le dire, mais aussi les profonds bunkers, les greens bien modelés et généralement en bon état, comme le parcours. Scotscraig a été utilisé comme parcours qualificatif pour le British Open, c'est le signe de sa qualité de test, mais que cela n'empêche pas les joueurs moins expérimentés de l'affronter sans trop risquer les catastrophes.

Scotscraig Golf Club — 1817

Golf Road
SCO - TAYPORT, Fife DD6 9DZ

Office	Secrétariat	(44) 01382 - 552 515
Pro shop	Pro-shop	(44) 01382 - 552 855
Fax	Fax	(44) 01382 - 553 130
E-mail		scotscraig@scottishgolf.com
Situation	Situation	St Andrews, 16 km
Annual closure	Fermeture annuelle	no
Weekly closure	Fermeture hebdomadaire	no

Fees main season Tarifs haute saison — 18 holes

	Week days / Semaine	We/Bank holidays / We/Férié
Individual Individuel	£ 44	£ 50
Couple Couple	£ 88	£ 100

Full week days: £ 44

Caddie Caddie on request **Electric Trolley** Chariot électrique yes

Buggy Voiturette yes **Clubs** Clubs yes

Credit cards Cartes de crédit
VISA - Mastercard - AMEX

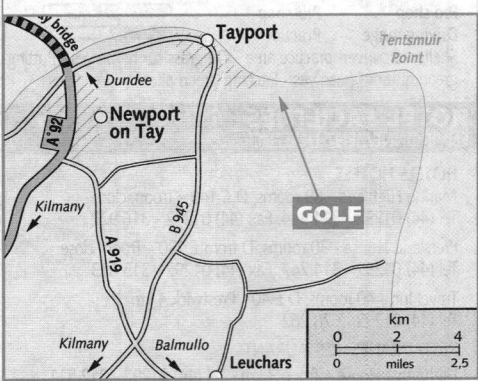

Access Accès : Edinburgh, M90 Jct 3, then A92 and A914 → Dundee. Before Tay Bridge, turn right to Tayport on B945. Golf signposted to left in Tayport.
Map 2 on page 473 Carte 2 Page 473

GOLF COURSE — PARCOURS — 16/20

Site	Site	
Maintenance	Entretien	
Architect	Architecte	James Braid
Type	Type	links, heathland
Relief	Relief	
Water in play	Eau en jeu	
Exp. to wind	Exposé au vent	
Trees in play	Arbres en jeu	

Scorecard / Carte de score	Chp. / Chp.	Mens / Mess.	Ladies / Da.
Length Long.	5960	5960	5960
Par	69	69	74
Slope system	—	—	—

Advised golfing ability / Niveau de jeu recommandé: 0 12 24 36

Hcp required Handicap exigé: certificate

CLUB HOUSE & AMENITIES — CLUB HOUSE ET ANNEXES — 6/10

Pro shop Pro-shop
Driving range Practice
Sheltered couvert no - **On grass** sur herbe yes - **Putting-green** putting-green yes - **Pitching-green** pitching green no

HOTEL FACILITIES — ENVIRONNEMENT HOTELIER — 6/10

HOTELS HÔTELS

Hilton Dundee - 129 rooms, D £ 120 - Dundee 7 km
Tel (44) 01382 - 229 271, Fax (44) 01382 - 200 072

Shaftesbury - Dundee 7 km
12 rooms, D £ 86
Tel (44) 01382 - 669 216, Fax (44) 01382 - 641 598

Travel Inn - Dundee 7 km
40 rooms, D £ 50
Tel (44) 01382 - 203 240, Fax (44) 01382 - 203 237

RESTAURANTS RESTAURANTS

Hilton Dundee - Dundee 7 km - Tel (44) 01382 - 229 271

Shiskine (Blackwaterfoot)

17	5	5

This is the one exception to our rule of featuring only 18-hole courses. Shiskine has only twelve but it is one of the most frequently visited courses by the world's golf architects, rather like a precious testimony to days gone by. There were once 18 holes courtesy of Willie Park, but after 1918 the new holes never re-opened. There is one blind shot on virtually each hole and signals in every direction telling players when it is safe to play. This is golf in its original pure style and enjoyment (but also with its own idiosyncrasies). The sheep are there to crop the sprinkler-free fairways, which haven't changed at all since the course first opened. That was when Willie Fernie brought the very best out of a space of land without even the most primitive excavator to call on. The greens are amazingly good, when you finally reach them. You need to play here a hundred times in order to fully understand the ins and outs of the course, but who's objecting.

Ce parcours est la seule exception à notre règle de ne signaler que des parcours de 18 trous. Le Shiskine n'a que douze trous, mais c'est un des parcours les plus visités par les architectes du monde entier, comme s'il s'agissait d'un témoignage précieux d'un temps révolu. Il en compta cependant 18 grâce à Willie Park, mais les nouveaux trous ne furent jamais réouverts après 1918. On trouve un coup aveugle sur pratiquement chaque trou, et des signaux dans tous les sens pour préciser aux joueurs quand ils peuvent jouer en toute sécurité. C'est ici le golf dans sa pureté et son plaisir originels (mais aussi ses excès baroques), avec des moutons pour tondre des fairways sans arrosage, qui n'ont pas bougé depuis la création. Alors, Willie Fernie avait tiré la quintessence d'un espace où il ne disposait pas du moindre engin de terrassement. Les greens y sont d'une surprenante qualité... quand on y parvient enfin. Il faut jouer ici cent fois pour comprendre toutes les astuces, mais on ne demande que çà.

Shiskine Golf & Tennis Club — 1896

Shiskine
SCO - BLACKWATERFOOT, Isle of Arran KA27 8 HA

Office	Secrétariat	(44) 01770 - 860 226
Pro shop	Pro-shop	(44) 01770 - 860 226
Fax	Fax	(44) 01770 - 860 205
Web	www.shiskinegolf.com	
Situation	Situation	Isle of Arran
Annual closure	Fermeture annuelle	no
Weekly closure	Fermeture hebdomadaire	no
Fees main season	Tarifs haute saison	12 holes round

	Week days Semaine	We/Bank holidays We/Férié
Individual Individuel	£ 15	£ 19
Couple Couple	£ 30	£ 38

Full Day: £25 - £30 (We)

Caddie Caddie no — **Electric Trolley** Chariot électrique no
Buggy Voiturette yes — **Clubs** Clubs yes
Credit cards Cartes de crédit yes

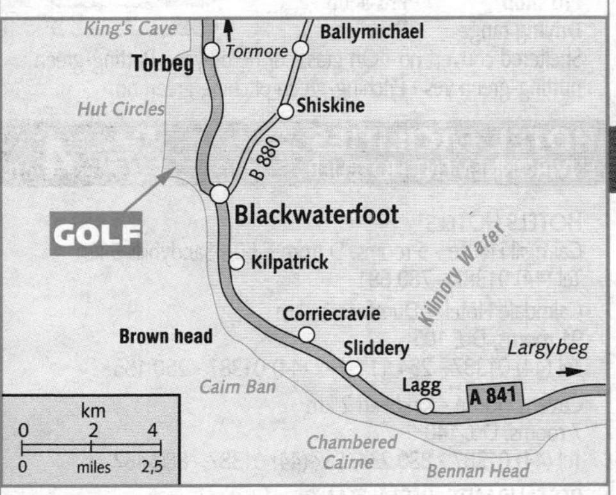

Access Accès : Ferry from Ardrossan to Brodick. Cross island via String Road (20 km) to village of Blackwaterfoot.
Map 2 on page 472 Carte 2 Page 472

GOLF COURSE
PARCOURS — 17/20

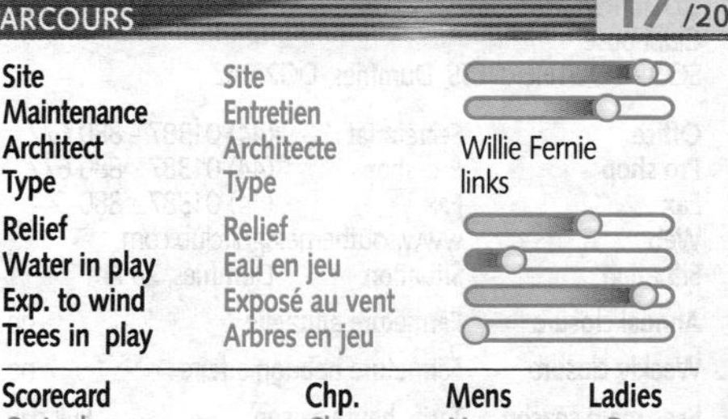

Site	Site	
Maintenance	Entretien	
Architect	Architecte	Willie Fernie
Type	Type	links
Relief	Relief	
Water in play	Eau en jeu	
Exp. to wind	Exposé au vent	
Trees in play	Arbres en jeu	

Scorecard Carte de score	Chp. Chp.	Mens Mess.	Ladies Da.
Length Long.	2745	2745	2561
Par	42	42	44
Slope system	—	—	—

Advised golfing ability Niveau de jeu recommandé — 0 12 24 36
Hcp required Handicap exigé — no

CLUB HOUSE & AMENITIES
CLUB HOUSE ET ANNEXES — 5/10

Pro shop Pro-shop
Driving range Practice
Sheltered couvert no - On grass sur herbe no - Putting-green putting-green yes - Pitching-green pitching green no

HOTEL FACILITIES
ENVIRONNEMENT HOTELIER — 5/10

HOTELS HÔTELS

Kinloch Hotel - 50 rooms, D £ 85 - Blackwaterfoot 1 km
Tel (44) 01770 - 860 444, Fax (44) 01770 - 860 447

Auchrannie Country House - Brodick 20 km
28 rooms, D £ 129
Tel (44) 01770 - 302 234, Fax (44) 01770 - 302 812

Kilmichael Country House - 7 rooms, D £ 135 - Brodick 20 km
Tel (44) 01770 - 302 219, Fax (44) 01770 - 302 068

Dunvegan House - 9 rooms, D £ 70 - Brodick 20 km
Tel (44) 01770 - 302 811, Fax (44) 01770 - 302 811

RESTAURANTS RESTAURANTS

Carraigh Mhor - Lamlash 22 km - Tel (44) 01770 - 600 453

Southerness

18 | 6 | 4

A course for connoisseurs off the traditional golfing trail but your journey will be more than rewarded by a superb day out. This is one of the most recent links to date in Scotland, designed by Mackenzie Ross while he was working on Turnberry. The excellence of the design, very elaborate despite the course's natural look, quickly caught the attention of the better players, who appreciate the distinctive layout and the variety of challenge, with a special mention for the 12th, one of the finest par 4s in Scotland. Golfing here can be very enjoyable when the weather is fine, but that doesn't happen all that often. What's more, the holes are always running in different directions, thus calling for constant improvisation. Generally flat with only a few welcome slopes and difficulties that are always visible, this course is well worth the trip, especially now that the recent restyling of bunkers and generally excellent green-keeping have worked wonders for the course.

Un golf de connaisseurs, à l'écart des sentiers traditionnels, mais le déplacement sera récompensé par une superbe journée. C'est l'un des derniers en date des links d'Ecosse, dessiné par Mackenzie Ross alors qu'il ressuscitait Turnberry au même moment. La qualité du dessin, très travaillé malgré son apparence naturelle, a vite attiré l'attention des bons joueurs. Ils apprécient la distinction du tracé, la diversité des défis proposés, avec une mention particulière pour le 12, un des plus beaux par 4 d'Ecosse. Le golf peut ici être très plaisant quand le temps est calme, mais ce n'est pas si fréquent. De plus, les trous vont dans des directions toujours différentes, ce qui oblige à un sens constant de l'improvisation. Généralement plat, avec quelques ondulations bienvenues, mais des difficultés toujours visibles, ce parcours vaut le voyage, d'autant que la récente rénovation des bunkers et la qualité de l'entretien en général lui ont fait le plus grand bien.

Southerness Golf Club — 1947

Clubhouse
SCO - SOUTHERNESS, Dumfries, DG2 8AZ

Office	Secrétariat	(44) 01387 - 880 677
Pro shop	Pro-shop	(44) 01387 - 880 677
Fax	Fax	(44) 01387 - 880 644
Web	www.southernessgolfclub.com	
Situation	Situation	Dumfries, 24 km
Annual closure	Fermeture annuelle	no
Weekly closure	Fermeture hebdomadaire	no

Fees main season Tarifs haute saison	Full day	
	Week days Semaine	**We/Bank holidays** We/Férié
Individual Individuel	£ 42	£ 52
Couple Couple	£ 84	£ 104

Caddie Caddie on request **Electric Trolley** Chariot électrique no

Buggy Voiturette no **Clubs** Clubs no

Credit cards Cartes de crédit
VISA - Eurocard - MasterCard

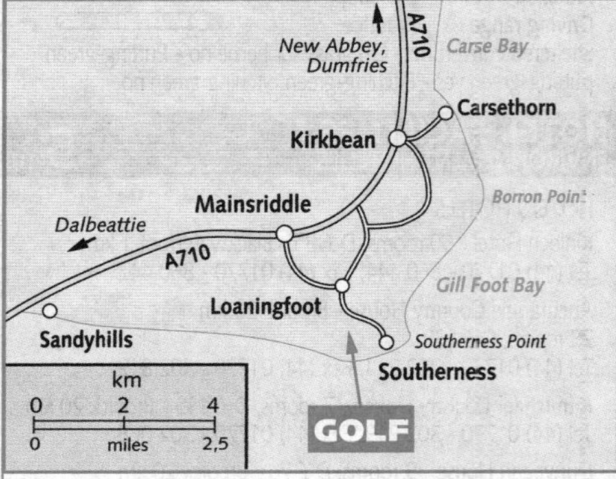

Access Accès : Glasgow M74 to Abbington. Edinburgh A702 to Abington. Then A74 to Beattock and A701 to Dumfries. Then A710. After Kirkbean, left to Southerness.
Map 2 on page 473 Carte 2 Page 473

GOLF COURSE — PARCOURS — 18/20

Site	Site	
Maintenance	Entretien	
Architect	Architecte	Mackenzie Ross
Type	Type	links
Relief	Relief	
Water in play	Eau en jeu	
Exp. to wind	Exposé au vent	
Trees in play	Arbres en jeu	

Scorecard Carte de score	**Chp.** Chp.	**Mens** Mess.	**Ladies** Da.
Length Long.	5975	5556	5116
Par	69	69	73
Slope system	—	—	—

Advised golfing ability Niveau de jeu recommandé — 0 12 24 36
Hcp required Handicap exigé 28

CLUB HOUSE & AMENITIES — CLUB HOUSE ET ANNEXES — 6/10

Pro shop Pro-shop
Driving range Practice
Sheltered couvert no - On grass sur herbe yes - Putting-green putting-green yes - Pitching-green pitching green no

HOTEL FACILITIES — ENVIRONNEMENT HOTELIER — 4/10

HOTELS HÔTELS
Cairngill House - 5 rooms, D from £ 50 - Sandyhills 5 km
Tel (44) 01387 - 780 681
Cairndale Hotel - Dumfries 24 km
91 rooms, D £ 105
Tel (44) 01387 - 254 111, Fax (44) 01387 - 250 155
Cavens House - Kirkbean 2 km
7 rooms, D £ 140
Tel (44) 01387 - 880 234, Fax (44) 01387 - 880 467

RESTAURANTS RESTAURANTS
Cavens House - Kirkbeans 2 km - Tel (44) 01387 - 880 234

St Andrews *Eden Course*

14 | 8 | 8

Notably shorter than its three most prestigious neighbours, the Eden Course is a most respectable course and probably, if not the most forthright then at least the least difficult of the three to figure out first time around, even though the wind will always be there to make things a little harder. This is a more conventional course, laid out in two loops of 9 holes, but the hazards are intelligently placed with a good number of remarkably well-located bunkers from which average players will find escaping a little less harrowing than on the other courses around here. Don't underestimate this Harry Colt layout, it can be fun playing here when everyone else is swarming over the other courses of the golf factory that St Andrews has now become. By the way, a new "branch" will be opening shortly, the future "N°7" designed by David McLay Kidd.

Notablement plus court que ses trois voisins les plus prestigieux, l'Eden Course est cependant un parcours plus qu'honorable. C'est probablement, sinon le plus franc des trois, du moins le moins difficile à déchiffrer au premier abord, même si le vent vient tout autant y compliquer les choses. De fait, c'est un parcours plus conventionnel, au point même d'avoir deux boucles de 9 trous, mais les obstacles sont intelligemment placés, les bunkers sont assez nombreux et remarquablement placés, mais les joueurs moyens pourront en sortir un jour (ce n'est pas toujours facile sur les autres parcours du site !). Il ne faut pas sous-estimer ce tracé de Harry Colt, et le plaisir de jouer ici n'est pas négligeable quand tout le monde s'agite dans les autres ateliers de cette véritable usine à golf qu'est le St Andrews Links. Il va d'ailleurs ouvrir une nouvelle succursale avec le prochain "N°7" dont le dessin a été confié à David McLay Kidd.

St Andrews Links — 1914

Pilmour House
SCO - ST ANDREWS, Fife, KY16 9SF

Office	Secrétariat	(44) 01334 - 466 666
Pro shop	Pro-shop	(44) 01334 - 466 666
Fax	Fax	(44) 01334 - 477 036
Web	www.standrews.org.uk	
Situation	Situation	Dundee, 30 km
Annual closure	Fermeture annuelle	no
Weekly closure	Fermeture hebdomadaire	no

Fees main season Tarifs haute saison	18 holes	
	Week days Semaine	We/Bank holidays We/Férié
Individual Individuel	£ 33	£ 33
Couple Couple	£ 66	£ 66

Under 16/ £ 16 (week days)

Caddie Caddie yes **Electric Trolley** Chariot électrique no
Buggy Voiturette medical reasons **Clubs** Clubs yes

Credit cards Cartes de crédit
VISA - Eurocard - MasterCard - AMEX

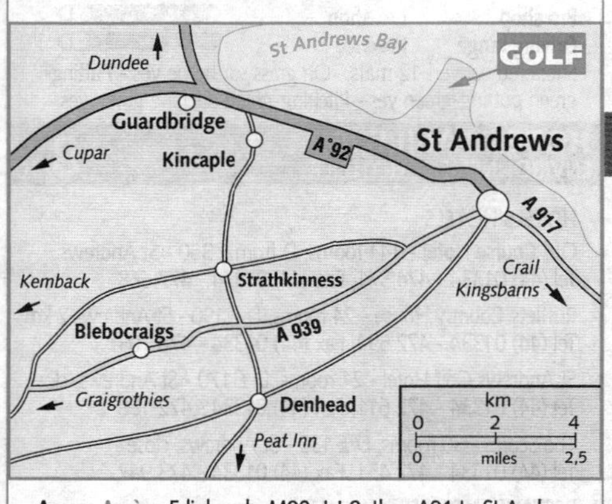

Access Accès : Edinburgh, M90, Jct 8, then A91 to St Andrews.
Map 3 on page 475 Carte 3 Page 475

GOLF COURSE — PARCOURS 14/20

Site	Site	
Maintenance	Entretien	
Architect	Architecte	Harry S. Colt
Type	Type	links
Relief	Relief	
Water in play	Eau en jeu	
Exp. to wind	Exposé au vent	
Trees in play	Arbres en jeu	

Scorecard Carte de score	Chp. Chp.	Mens Mess.	Ladies Da.
Length Long.	5662	5632	4986
Par	70	70	73
Slope system	—	—	—

Advised golfing ability Niveau de jeu recommandé: 0 12 24 36
Hcp required Handicap exigé: no

CLUB HOUSE & AMENITIES — CLUB HOUSE ET ANNEXES 8/10

Pro shop Pro-shop
Driving range Practice
Sheltered couvert 12 mats - **On grass** sur herbe yes - **Putting-green** putting-green yes - **Pitching-green** pitching green yes

HOTEL FACILITIES — ENVIRONNEMENT HOTELIER 8/10

HOTELS HÔTELS

Old Course Hotel - St Andrews, close
144 rooms, D from £ 350
Tel (44) 01334 - 474 371, Fax (44) 01334 - 477 668

Rufflets Country House - 24 rooms, D £ 190 - St Andrews 2 km
Tel (44) 01334 - 472 594, Fax (44) 01334 - 478 703

St Andrews Golf Hotel - 21 rooms, D £ 170 - St Andrews, close
Tel (44) 01334 - 472 611, Fax (44) 01334 - 472 188

The Scores - 30 rooms, D £ 130 - St Andrews, close
Tel (44) 01334 - 472 451, Fax (44) 01334 - 473 947

RESTAURANTS RESTAURANTS

The Peat Inn - Peat Inn 8 km - Tel (44) 01334 - 840 206
Grange Inn - St Andrews 2 km - Tel (44) 01334 - 472 670

St Andrews *Jubilee Course*

16	8	8

Having celebrated its centenary in 1997, the Jubilee Course has been given a recent face-lift and is now the longest course at St Andrews (pending the next two new courses, most likely). Don't look at this course as a foil for the others around here, as some people feel that this is the hardest of the lot. Although laid out in a single stretch with no return to the club-house at the 9th, there are no double fairways. The course is a little more hilly (but only very moderately so) and gives some pretty view-points in a region which overall is rather flat. There is little in the way of vegetation on the holes close to the sea if you exclude tall grass, but this layout requires accurate driving and a lot of concentration. Like the others, the course is run by the St Andrews Links Trust, which built a very well equipped club-house open to all. Needless to say any trip should be organized in advance, especially between April and September.

Centenaire en 1997, le "Jubilee" a bénéficié d'une récente cure de rajeunissement qui en a fait le plus long (en attendant les deux prochains sans doute) des parcours de St Andrews, à ne pas considérer comme un faire-valoir, certains le considèrent même comme le plus difficile de tous. On ne trouve pas ici les fameux double fairways, bien que le parcours se déroule aussi d'un seul trait, sans retour au club-house au 9. On trouve aussi davantage de relief (il reste très limité !), et donc quelques jolis points de vue assez rares dans une région somme toute peu accidentée. Les trous proches de la mer ont une végétation assez limitée, les hautes herbes mises à part, mais l'ensemble demande des drives précis, et généralement beaucoup d'attention. Comme les autres, ce parcours est géré par le St Andrews Links Trust, qui a construit un club-house très bien équipé, et ouvert à tous. Inutile de dire qu'il est nécessaire d'organiser son voyage à l'avance, surtout d'avril à septembre.

St Andrews Links — 1897

Pilmour House
SCO - ST ANDREWS, Fife, KY16 9SF

Office	Secrétariat	(44) 01334 - 466 666
Pro shop	Pro-shop	(44) 01334 - 466 666
Fax	Fax	(44) 01334 - 477 036
Web	www.standrews.org.uk	
Situation	Situation	Dundee, 30 km
Annual closure	Fermeture annuelle	no
Weekly closure	Fermeture hebdomadaire	no

Fees main season Tarifs haute saison — 18 holes

	Week days / Semaine	We/Bank holidays / We/Férié
Individual Individuel	£ 55	£ 55
Couple Couple	£ 110	£ 110

Under 16: £ 22 (Week days)

Caddie Caddie yes — **Electric Trolley** Chariot électrique no

Buggy Voiturette medical reasons — **Clubs** Clubs yes

Credit cards Cartes de crédit
VISA - Eurocard - MasterCard - AMEX

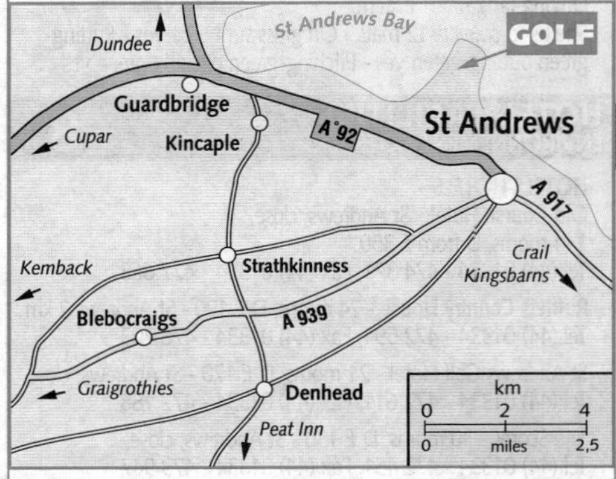

Access Accès : Edinburgh, M90, Jct 8, then A91 to St Andrews.
Map 3 on page 475 Carte 3 Page 475

GOLF COURSE — PARCOURS — 16/20

Site	Site	
Maintenance	Entretien	
Architect	Architecte	John Angus, T. Morris Auchterlonie, Steel
Type	Type	links
Relief	Relief	
Water in play	Eau en jeu	
Exp. to wind	Exposé au vent	
Trees in play	Arbres en jeu	

Scorecard Carte de score	Chp. Chp.	Mens Mess.	Ladies Da.
Length Long.	6162	5872	5444
Par	72	72	74
Slope system	—	—	—

Advised golfing ability Niveau de jeu recommandé — 0 12 24 36
Hcp required Handicap exigé — no

CLUB HOUSE & AMENITIES — CLUB HOUSE ET ANNEXES — 8/10

Pro shop Pro-shop
Driving range Practice
Sheltered couvert 12 mats - On grass sur herbe yes - Putting-green putting-green yes - Pitching-green pitching green yes

HOTEL FACILITIES — ENVIRONNEMENT HOTELIER — 8/10

HOTELS HÔTELS

Old Course Hotel - 144 rooms, D from £ 350 - St Andrews
Tel (44) 01334 - 474 371, Fax (44) 01334 - 477 668

Rufflets Country House - 24 rooms, D £ 190 - St Andrews 2 km
Tel (44) 01334 - 472 594, Fax (44) 01334 - 478 703

St Andrews Golf Hotel - 21 rooms, D £ 170 - St Andrews, close
Tel (44) 01334 - 472 611, Fax (44) 01334 - 472 188

The Scores - 30 rooms, D £ 130 - St Andrews, close
Tel (44) 01334 - 472 451, Fax (44) 01334 - 473 947

RESTAURANTS RESTAURANTS

The Peat Inn - Peat Inn 8 km - Tel (44) 01334 - 840 206
Grange Inn - St Andrews 2 km - Tel (44) 01334 - 472 670

St Andrews *New Course*

17 | 8 | 8

Fortunately, there are several other excellent golf courses at St Andrews when it is impossible to play the Old Course. The New Course is one of them and does not settle for playing second fiddle to its illustrious neighbour. Some local players even consider this their favourite course. At all events it is a very demanding layout, rather similar to the Old Course in its general physiognomy and the way it demands technical skill and powers of invention. Here you don't play the club you need for such and such a distance, rather the club that will roll the ball up to the pin. Hazard-wise there are no trees, naturally, only threatening thick gorse and bunkers like those on the Old Course, which collect any ball coming their way. The greens are huge and undulating and the turf a pleasure to walk and play on. To give it an "Old Course" flavour, there is a double fairway and a double green (for the 3rd and 15th holes) - recognition at last for the architect David Honeyman, Tom Morris' right-hand man.

Quand il est impossible de jouer le "Old Course", il reste d'excellents autres parcours à St Andrews. Le "New" est de ceux-là, et bien plus qu'un faire-valoir pour son voisin géographique immédiat. Cetains joueurs locaux en font leur favori ! C'est en tout cas un parcours exigeant, assez proche de son aîné pour sa physionomie générale et pour les qualités techniques et l'invention qu'il réclame. Ici, on ne joue pas le club qu'il faut pour telle distance, mais celui qui fera arriver la balle en roulant jusqu'au drapeau. Côté obstacles, pas d'arbres bien sûr, mais des ajoncs menaçants et denses, et aussi des bunkers comme ceux du "Old", qui recueillent toutes les balles qui passent aux alentours. Les greens sont vastes et ondulés, et le gazon un plaisir à fouler et à jouer. Pour un parfum de "Old", il y aussi un fairway partagé et un double green (pour le 3 et le 15). On sortira enfin de l'oubli l'assistant de Tom Morris pour ses parcours, David Honeyman.

St Andrews Links **1895**
Pilmour House
SCO - ST ANDREWS, Fife, KY16 9SF

Office	Secrétariat	(44) 01334 - 466 666
Pro shop	Pro-shop	(44) 01334 - 466 666
Fax	Fax	(44) 01334 - 477 036
Web	www.standrews.org.uk	
Situation	Situation	Dundee, 30 km
Annual closure	Fermeture annuelle	no
Weekly closure	Fermeture hebdomadaire	no

Fees main season Tarifs haute saison	Week days Semaine	We/Bank holidays We/Férié
	18 holes	
Individual Individuel	£ 55	£ 55
Couple Couple	£ 110	£ 110

Under 16: £ 25 (Week days)

Caddie Caddie yes — **Electric Trolley** Chariot électrique no

Buggy Voiturette medical reasons **Clubs** Clubs yes

Credit cards Cartes de crédit
VISA - Eurocard - MasterCard - AMEX

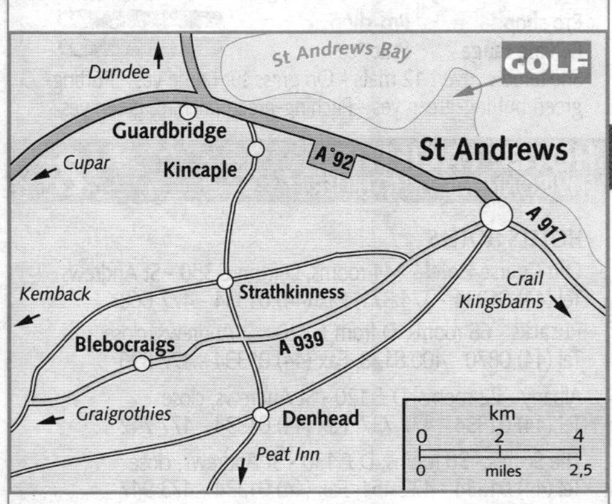

Access Accès : Edinburgh, M90, Jct 8, then A91 to St Andrews.
Map 3 on page 475 Carte 3 Page 475

GOLF COURSE
PARCOURS — **17**/20

Site	Site	
Maintenance	Entretien	
Architect	Architecte	W. Hall Blyth Tom Morris
Type	Type	links
Relief	Relief	
Water in play	Eau en jeu	
Exp. to wind	Exposé au vent	
Trees in play	Arbres en jeu	

Scorecard Carte de score	Chp. Chp.	Mens Mess.	Ladies Da.
Length Long.	6036	5815	5477
Par	71	71	75
Slope system	—	—	—

Advised golfing ability Niveau de jeu recommandé — 0 12 24 36

Hcp required Handicap exigé — no

CLUB HOUSE & AMENITIES
CLUB HOUSE ET ANNEXES — **8**/10

Pro shop Pro-shop
Driving range Practice
Sheltered couvert 12 mats - On grass sur herbe yes - Putting-green putting-green yes - Pitching-green pitching green yes

HOTEL FACILITIES
ENVIRONNEMENT HOTELIER — **8**/10

HOTELS HÔTELS

Rusacks - St Andrews, close
68 rooms, D from £ 220
Tel (44) 0870 - 400 8128, Fax (44) 01334 - 477 896

Rufflets Country House - 24 rooms, D £ 190 - St Andrews 2 km
Tel (44) 01334 - 472 594, Fax (44) 01334 - 478 703

St Andrews Golf Hotel - 21 rooms, D £ 170 - St Andrews, close
Tel (44) 01334 - 472 611, Fax (44) 01334 - 472 188

18 Queens Terrace - 4 rooms, D £ 80 - St Andrews, close
Tel (44) 01334 - 478 849, Fax (44) 01334 - 470 283

RESTAURANTS RESTAURANTS

The Peat Inn - Peat Inn 8 km - Tel (44) 01334 - 840 206
Grange Inn - St Andrews 2 km - Tel (44) 01334 - 472 670

St Andrews *Old Course*

18 | 8 | 8

Is there anything left to write about the Old Course? The world's most famous venue is a public course even though you do need to be patient if you want to play here. It is well thought of to say that this is the greatest course in the British Isles, so often in the public eye that when you come here for the first time you get the impression you have already played it. Be wise and take a caddy, as the devilish subtleties, traps, double fairways and double greens make every decision a tough one. The work of no real architect, the Old Course has been shaped by the passing centuries, the wind, champions and green-keepers. The atmosphere alone is enough to intimidate or even terrorize amateurs stepping onto the first tee. But if you disregard the "religiousness" of this hallowed site there are, dare we say it, many more challenging links courses when the weather is calm (may the gods of golf forgive us). No-one knows when the Old Course was first invented, but it will happen to you one day, even if you play it the other way around, the way they used to.

Est-il encore possible d'écrire sur l'Old Course ? Le plus célèbre parcours du monde, est un golf public, même s'il faut de la patience pour pouvoir le jouer. Il est bien vu de dire que c'est le plus grand parcours des Iles Britanniques, tellement montré qu'on a l'impression de déjà l'avoir joué quand on vient pour la première fois. Mais il reste prudent de prendre un caddie car ses diaboliques subtilités, ses pièges, ses double fairways et double greens rendent difficiles toutes les décisions. Sans véritable architecte, le "Old" a été admirablement façonné par les siècles, le vent, les champions, les green-keepers, et rien que son atmosphère rend les amateurs sinon terrorisés, du moins intimidés au départ du 1. Si l'on fait abstraction de la "religiosité du lieu", il est des links bien plus exigeants, quand le temps est calme. Mais a t-on le droit de le dire sans aller en enfer? L'Old Course est inévitable, sa date d'invention est inconnue, et on le joue même à l'envers de temps en temps, comme autrefois...

St Andrews Links — 1754

Pilmour House
SCO - ST ANDREWS, Fife, KY16 9SF

Office	Secrétariat	(44) 01334 - 466 666
Pro shop	Pro-shop	(44) 01334 - 466 666
Fax	Fax	(44) 01334 - 477 036
Web	www.standrews.org.uk	
Situation	Situation	Dundee, 30 km
Annual closure	Fermeture annuelle	no
Weekly closure	Fermeture hebdomadaire	Sunday

Fees main season Tarifs haute saison	18 holes	
	Week days Semaine	We/Bank holidays We/Férié
Individual Individuel	£ 115	£ 115*
Couple Couple	£ 230	£ 230*

* No play on Sunday

Caddie Caddie yes **Electric Trolley** Chariot électrique no
Buggy Voiturette medical reasons **Clubs** Clubs yes
Credit cards Cartes de crédit
VISA - Eurocard - MasterCard - AMEX

Access Accès : Edinburgh, M90, Jct 8, then A91 to St Andrews.
Map 3 on page 475 Carte 3 Page 475

GOLF COURSE — PARCOURS 18/20

Site	Site	
Maintenance	Entretien	
Architect	Architecte	unknown
Type	Type	links
Relief	Relief	
Water in play	Eau en jeu	
Exp. to wind	Exposé au vent	
Trees in play	Arbres en jeu	

Scorecard Carte de score	Chp. Chp.	Mens Mess.	Ladies Da.
Length Long.	6300	5838	5513
Par	72	72	76
Slope system	—	—	—

Advised golfing ability Niveau de jeu recommandé: 0 12 24 36
Hcp required Handicap exigé: 24 Men, 36 Ladies

CLUB HOUSE & AMENITIES — CLUB HOUSE ET ANNEXES 8/10

Pro shop Pro-shop
Driving range Practice
Sheltered couvert 12 mats - On grass sur herbe yes - Putting-green putting-green yes - Pitching-green pitching green yes

HOTEL FACILITIES — ENVIRONNEMENT HOTELIER 8/10

HOTELS HÔTELS

Old Course Hotel - 144 rooms, D from £ 350 - St Andrews
Tel (44) 01334 - 474 371, Fax (44) 01334 - 477 668

Rusacks - 68 rooms, D from £ 220 - St Andrews, close
Tel (44) 0870 - 400 8128, Fax (44) 01334 - 477 896

Albany - 22 rooms, D £ 120 - St Andrews, close
Tel (44) 01334 - 477 737, Fax (44) 01334 - 477 742

The Scores - 30 rooms, D £ 130 - St Andrews, close
Tel (44) 01334 - 472 451, Fax (44) 01334 - 473 947

RESTAURANTS RESTAURANTS

The Peat Inn - Peat Inn 8 km - Tel (44) 01334 - 840 206
Grange Inn - St Andrews 2 km - Tel (44) 01334 - 472 670

St Andrews Bay *Devlin Course*

17 | 7 | 8

The recently opened Devlin Course at St Andrews Bay is a perfect complement to the other Bay course designed by Sam Torrance and Gene Sarazen. Australian Bruce Devlin was the architect and was given a wonderful rugged cliff-top location to weave his magic. Already being acclaimed as a substantial test of golf even for the top professionals, the Devlin begins innocently enough but the walk to the 7th tee heralds the start of the roller coaster ride up, over and around the rugged wilderness of Kittock's Den. These ridge holes open up to the panorama of the white water crashing on the rocky shoreline below across St Andrews Bay to the Grampian mountains which dominate the horizon. This is an exposed setting with the wind a constant factor, but the elevation provides truly memorable views and the site for a spectacular cliff-top club-house which serves excellent food.

Le tout récent Devlin Course de St Andrews Bay est un parfait complément à l'autre parcours du site, créé par Sam Torrance et Gene Sarazen. L'australien Bruce Devlin en a été l'architecte et lui a donné un tracé superbe en haut d'une falaise. Déjà largement reconnu comme un test majeur par les meilleurs professionnels, le Devlin commence doucement, jusqu'à l'arrivée au départ du 7 qui donne le signal de départ d'une grande chevauchée par monts et par vaux, dans le site sauvage de Kittock's Den. Ces trous en bordure de falaise ouvrent sur le spectacle des vagues s'écrasant sur les rochers menant de St Andrews Bay aux Grampians qui dominent l'horizon. Dans un site aussi exposé, le vent est évidemment un facteur essentiel, mais on en oublie les inconvénients tant le panorama est mémorable. Bien sûr, le club-house se devait d'occuper une position dominante, où l'on pourra apprécier l'excellent restaurant.

St Andrews Bay Golf Resort & Spa — 2002

SCO - ST ANDREWS, Fife KY16 8 PN

Office	Secrétariat	(44) 01334 - 837 000
Pro shop	Pro-shop	(44) 01334 - 837 000
Fax	Fax	(44) 01334 - 471 115
Web	www.standrewsbay.com	
Situation	Situation	St Andrews, 3 km
Annual closure	Fermeture annuelle	no
Weekly closure	Fermeture hebdomadaire	no

Fees main season Tarifs haute saison		18 holes
	Week days Semaine	**We/Bank holidays** We/Férié
Individual Individuel	£ 95	£ 95
Couple Couple	£ 190	£ 190

Residents: £ 75

Caddie Caddie yes — **Electric Trolley** Chariot électrique no

Buggy Voiturette no — **Clubs** Clubs yes

Credit cards Cartes de crédit

VISA - Eurocard - MasterCard - AMEX - DC

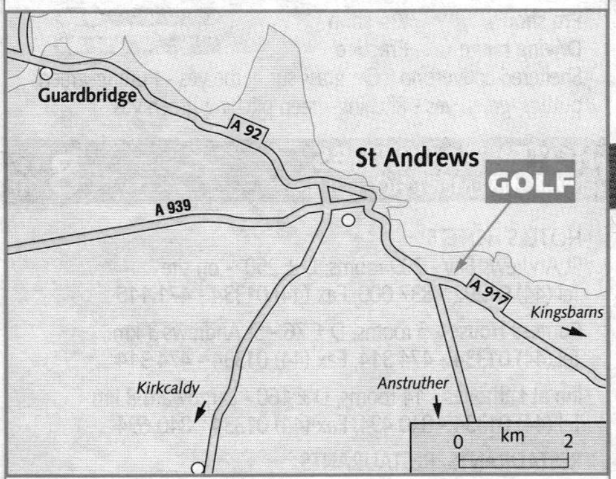

Access Accès : Edinburgh A90 unto Forth Road Bridge, M90 Exit 3 then A92 → Kirkcaldy. And A915 to St Andrews, Largo Road, Lamond Drive. Turn right onto A917 → Crail. Golf 2 km (1.5) on the left.

Map 3 on page 475 Carte 3 Page 475

GOLF COURSE — PARCOURS — 17/20

Site	Site	
Maintenance	Entretien	
Architect	Architecte	Bruce Devlin
Type	Type	cliff-top
Relief	Relief	
Water in play	Eau en jeu	
Exp. to wind	Exposé au vent	
Trees in play	Arbres en jeu	

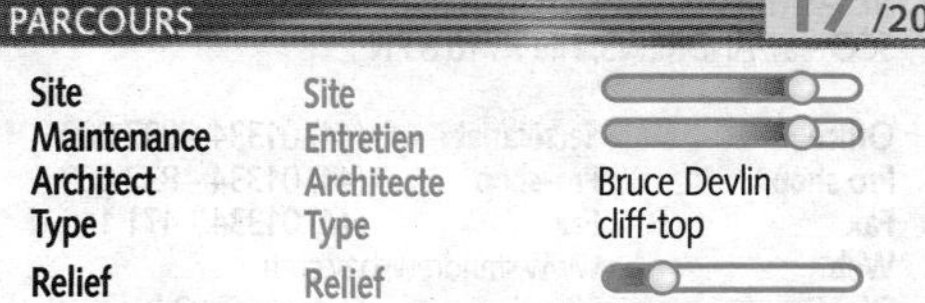

Scorecard Carte de score	**Chp.** Chp.	**Mens** Mess.	**Ladies** Da.
Length Long.	6683	5951	4676
Par	72	72	72
Slope system	—	—	—

Advised golfing ability Niveau de jeu recommandé — 0 12 24 36

Hcp required Handicap exigé — no

CLUB HOUSE & AMENITIES — CLUB HOUSE ET ANNEXES — 7/10

Pro shop Pro-shop
Driving range Practice
Sheltered couvert no - On grass sur herbe yes - Putting-green putting-green yes - Pitching-green pitching green yes

HOTEL FACILITIES — ENVIRONNEMENT HOTELIER — 8/10

HOTELS HÔTELS

St Andrews Bay - 209 rooms, D £ 250 - on site
Tel (44) 01292 - 837 000, Fax (44) 01334 - 471 115

Burness House - 5 rooms, D £ 76 - St Andrews 3 km
Tel (44) 01334 - 474 314, Fax (44) 01334 - 474 314

Inn at Lathones - 14 rooms, D £ 160 - Largoward 8 km
Tel (44) 01334 - 840 494, Fax (44) 01334 - 840 694

RESTAURANTS RESTAURANTS

The Dolls House - St Andrews 6 km - Tel (44) 01334 - 477 422
Inn at Lathones - Largoward 8 km - Tel (44) 01334 - 840 494
The Peat Inn (book first) - Peat Inn 6 km
Tel (44) 01334 - 840 206

St Andrews Bay *Torrance Course*

15 | 7 | 8

The St Andrews Bay Golf Resort and Spa just outside the Home of Golf was the vision of Don and Nancy Panoz, founders of Chateau Elan Hotels and Resorts. They discovered a wonderful cliff-top setting overlooking St Andrews and brought in former Ryder Cup Captain Sam Torrance to design the first course with legendary professional Gene Sarazen, who sadly did not live to see the project completed. The Torrance course initially works its way around the imposing new hotel and has wonderful views from a dramatic cliff-top setting. It is, however, a very fine challenge and offers dramatic views across St Andrews Bay and over the Auld Grey Toon itself. The decision to use rye grass for the courses ensures that it is vividly green all the year around. Large, undulating greens put a premium on steady putting.

A quelques kilomètres de la capitale mondiale du golf, le St Andrews Bay Golf Resort and Spa était le rêve de Don et Nancy Panoz, fondateurs des hôtels et resorts Château Elan, aux Etats-Unis. Ils ont trouvé ce site au sommet d'une falaise dominant St Andrews et ont demandé à Sam Torrance, alors capitaine de l'équipe de Ryder Cup, de dessiner le premier de deux parcours avec Gene Sarazen, professionnel légendaire qui devait malheureusement disparaître avant de voir ce projet achevé. Le parcours Torrance est situé dans un cadre exceptionnel, il se déroule autour de l'imposant hôtel et propose des points de vue exceptionnels depuis sa position sur la falaise, bien qu'il ne s'agisse pas exactement d'un parcours en bord de mer. Cependant, il s'agit d'un test de golf de première grandeur, offrent en supplément de vues superbes sur St Andrews et l'Auld Grey Toon. La décision de semer le parcours en rye grass garantit qu'il reste vert toute l'année. La dimension et le profil des greens montre qu'il faut ici savoir bien putter.

St Andrews Bay Golf Resort & Spa — 2001

SCO - ST ANDREWS, Fife KY16 8 PN

Office	Secrétariat	(44) 01334 - 837 000
Pro shop	Pro-shop	(44) 01334 - 837 000
Fax	Fax	(44) 01334 - 471 115
Web	www.standrewsbay.com	
Situation	Situation	St Andrews, 3 km
Annual closure	Fermeture annuelle	no
Weekly closure	Fermeture hebdomadaire	no

Fees main season Tarifs haute saison	18 holes	
	Week days Semaine	**We/Bank holidays** We/Férié
Individual Individuel	£ 95	£ 95
Couple Couple	£ 190	£ 190

Residents: £ 75

Caddie Caddie yes — **Electric Trolley** Chariot électrique no

Buggy Voiturette no — **Clubs** Clubs yes

Credit cards Cartes de crédit
VISA - Eurocard - MasterCard - AMEX - DC

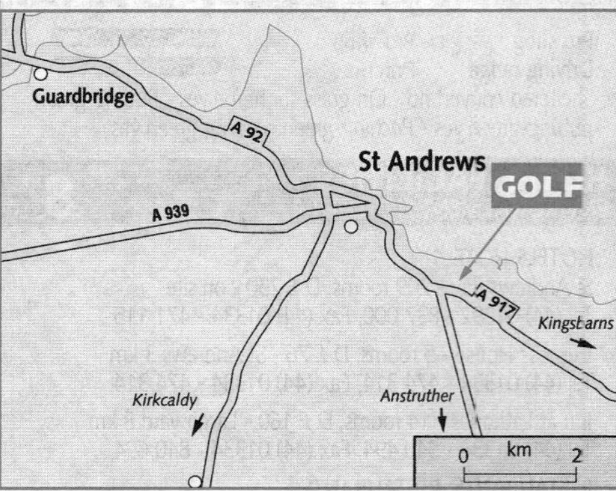

Access Accès : Edinburgh A90 unto Forth Road Bridge, M90 Exit 3 then A92 → Kirkcaldy. And A915 to St Andrews, Largo Road, Lamond Drive. Turn right onto A917 → Crail. Golf 2 km (1.5) on the left.
Map 3 on page 475 Carte 3 Page 475

GOLF COURSE — PARCOURS 15/20

Site	Site	
Maintenance	Entretien	
Architect	Architecte	Sam Torrance
Type	Type	cliff-top
Relief	Relief	
Water in play	Eau en jeu	
Exp. to wind	Exposé au vent	
Trees in play	Arbres en jeu	

Scorecard Carte de score	**Chp.** Chp.	**Mens** Mess.	**Ladies** Da.
Length Long.	6334	6010	5509
Par	72	72	72
Slope system	—	—	—

Advised golfing ability Niveau de jeu recommandé — 0 12 24 36

Hcp required Handicap exigé — no

CLUB HOUSE & AMENITIES — CLUB HOUSE ET ANNEXES 7/10

Pro shop Pro-shop
Driving range Practice
Sheltered couvert no - On grass sur herbe yes - Putting-green putting-green yes - Pitching-green pitching green yes

HOTEL FACILITIES — ENVIRONNEMENT HOTELIER 8/10

HOTELS HÔTELS

St Andrews Bay - 209 rooms, D £ 250 - on site
Tel (44) 01292 - 837 000, Fax (44) 01334 - 471 115

Burness House - 5 rooms, D £ 76 - St Andrews 3 km
Tel (44) 01334 - 474 314, Fax (44) 01334 - 474 314

Inn at Lathones - 14 rooms, D £ 160 - Largoward 8 km
Tel (44) 01334 - 840 494, Fax (44) 01334 - 840 694

RESTAURANTS RESTAURANTS

The Dolls House - St Andrews 6 km - Tel (44) 01334 - 477 422

Inn at Lathones - Largoward 8 km - Tel (44) 01334 - 840 494

The Peat Inn (book first) - Peat Inn 6 km
Tel (44) 01334 - 840 206

Strathaven

15 | 6 | 6

Located some 22 miles from Glasgow, this is one of those gems tucked away in the west of Scotland. It is an inland course which winds its way through fir trees and long established woodland. It also reserves some magnificent views over the town and the Kype Hills. This Willie Fernie layout was extended to 18 holes in 1965 in a fashion that is very much in keeping with the original course; the unity of style is to be commended. Bunkers are strategically located and the rough very penalizing, both of which call for careful game strategy. For many, this is a course for accurate drivers, sometimes a little treacherous, which needs to be played several times over with a fair dose of flair before getting to grips with the traps and appreciating its many qualities. Even when you reach the very tricky greens, you are still not through because you need a magic putter here to pick up strokes. Many high-level tournaments have been played at Strathaven, a token of the course's overall excellence.

A quelques 45 km de Glasgow, c'est un des petits bijoux cachés à l'ouest de l'Ecosse, et un parcours "inland" dont le dessin s'insinue entre les sapins et un paysage boisé. Il réserve des vues magnifiques sur la ville et les Kype Hills. Le tracé de Willie Fernie a été porté à 18 trous en 1965, dans un style qui reste très cohérent avec l'original, on peut s'en féliciter pour l'unité de style. Les bunkers sont stratégiquement placés et le rough très pénalisant, ce qui oblige à bien réfléchir sur la tactique à mettre en oeuvre. C'est pour beaucoup un parcours de drives précis, parfois un peu traître, il faut jouer plusieurs fois et avoir un peu de flair pour en comprendre à la fois les pièges et en savourer toutes les qualités. Et une fois arrivé sur des greens très subtils, le travail n'est pas fini, il faut un toucher d'orfèvre pour y gagner des points. De nombreux bons tournois ont été disputés ici, c'est une véritable marque de qualité.

Strathaven Golf Club — 1908

Overton Avenue, Glasgow Road
SCO - STRATHAVEN, Strathclyde, ML10 6NL

Office Secrétariat (44) 01357 - 520 421
Pro shop Pro-shop (44) 01357 - 521 812
Fax Fax (44) 01357 - 520 539
E-mail info@strathavengc.com
Situation Situation East Kilbride, 12 km
Annual closure Fermeture annuelle no
Weekly closure Fermeture hebdomadaire no

Fees main season Tarifs haute saison	18 holes	
	Week days Semaine	We/Bank holidays We/Férié
Individual Individuel	£ 27	*
Couple Couple	£ 54	*

* Week-ends: members only / Full week days: £ 37

Caddie Caddie no — **Electric Trolley** Chariot électrique no
Buggy Voiturette yes — **Clubs** Clubs no
Credit cards Cartes de crédit no

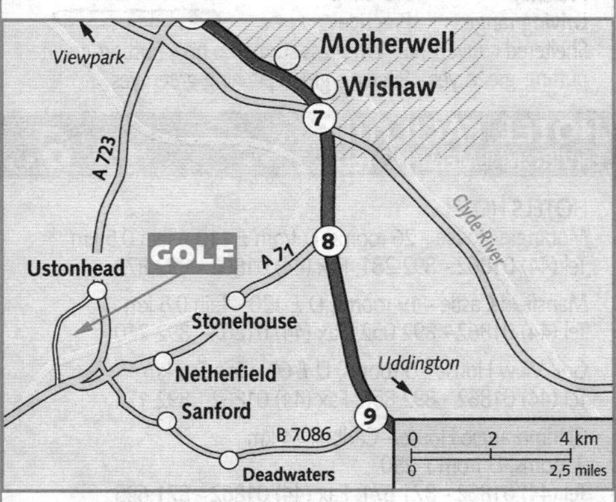

Access Accès : Glasgow, A726.
Golf in the outskirts of Strathaven city.
Map 2 on page 472 Carte 2 Page 472

GOLF COURSE — PARCOURS 15/20

Site Site
Maintenance Entretien
Architect Architecte Willie Fernie, J.R. Stutt
Type Type parkland
Relief Relief
Water in play Eau en jeu
Exp. to wind Exposé au vent
Trees in play Arbres en jeu

Scorecard Carte de score	Chp. Chp.	Mens Mess.	Ladies Da.
Length Long.	5665	5665	5066
Par	71	71	73
Slope system	—	—	—

Advised golfing ability Niveau de jeu recommandé 0 12 24 36
Hcp required Handicap exigé 28 Men, 36 Ladies

CLUB HOUSE & AMENITIES — CLUB HOUSE ET ANNEXES 6/10

Pro shop Pro-shop
Driving range Practice
Sheltered couvert no - On grass sur herbe no - Putting-green putting-green yes - Pitching-green pitching green no

HOTEL FACILITIES — ENVIRONNEMENT HOTELIER 6/10

HOTELS HÔTELS
Strathaven Hotel - Strathaven 2 km
22 rooms, D £ 90
Tel (44) 01357 - 521 778, Fax (44) 01357 - 520 789

Crutherland Country House - East Kilbride 5 km
75 rooms, D £ 170
Tel (44) 01355 - 577 000, Fax (44) 01355 - 220 855

Bruce - 68 rooms, D £ 90 - East Kilbride 2 km
Tel (44) 01355 - 229 771, Fax (44) 01355 - 242 216

RESTAURANTS RESTAURANTS
Hilton East Kilbride - East Kilbride 5 km
Tel (44) 01355 - 236 300
Waterside Inn - Strathaven

Tain

17	6	6

Although it doesn't have the aura of Dornoch, Tain is worth much more than just a casual visit. All the more so in that green-keeping here is on a par with that found at "posher" courses. The site is superb and very quiet with some spectacular views over the mountains and Dornoch Firth. The sheltered location actually results in relatively clement winter weather. The alternating heather and links holes produce a variety of landscapes, but playing here always requires a shrewd brain. Nothing is given away and players constantly have to adapt to new problems. The greens are never very large and the tricky breaks can be disastrous if you're not really careful. Holes N° 3 and N° 17 regularly figure amongst the frequent publications of "the greatest holes in golf". The new club-house should enhance still further the enjoyment of playing here, especially considering the excellent value for money and warm welcome.

Sans avoir l'aura de Dornoch, Tain mérite néanmoins bien plus qu'un regard distrait. Et d'autant plus que l'entretien rivalise généralement avec celui de parcours plus huppés. Le site en est superbe et très tranquille, avec des vues spectaculaires sur les montagnes et le Dornoch Firth et sa situation abritée lui assure des hivers (relativement) cléments. L'alternance de trous de links et de trous dans la bruyère apporte une variété de paysages, mais le jeu doit constamment être réfléchi. Rien n'est donné, et le joueur doit sans cesse s'adapter à de nouveaux problèmes. Les greens ne sont jamais très grands, et leurs subtiles ondulations peuvent provoquer des désastres si l'on n'y prête pas attention. Les trous 3 et 17 figurent régulièrement dans les sélections de grands trous de golf. Le nouveau club-house devrait augmenter encore le plaisir que l'on éprouve ici, d'autant que le rapport qualité-prix-accueil est très favorable !

Tain Golf Club — 1890

Chapel Road
SCO - TAIN, Ross-shire, IV19 1JE

Office	Secrétariat	(44) 01862 - 892 314
Pro shop	Pro-shop	(44) 01862 - 893 313
Fax	Fax	(44) 01862 - 892 099
Web		www.tain-golfclub.co.uk
Situation	Situation	Tain (pop. 4 540), 1 km

Inverness (pop. 62 186), 56 km

Annual closure	Fermeture annuelle	no
Weekly closure	Fermeture hebdomadaire	no

Fees main season Tarifs haute saison — 18 holes

	Week days Semaine	We/Bank holidays We/Férié
Individual Individuel	£ 36	£ 44
Couple Couple	£ 72	£ 88

Full Day: £44 / £54 (We)

Caddie Caddie on request **Electric Trolley** Chariot électrique yes

Buggy Voiturette yes **Clubs** Clubs yes

Credit cards Cartes de crédit VISA - MasterCard

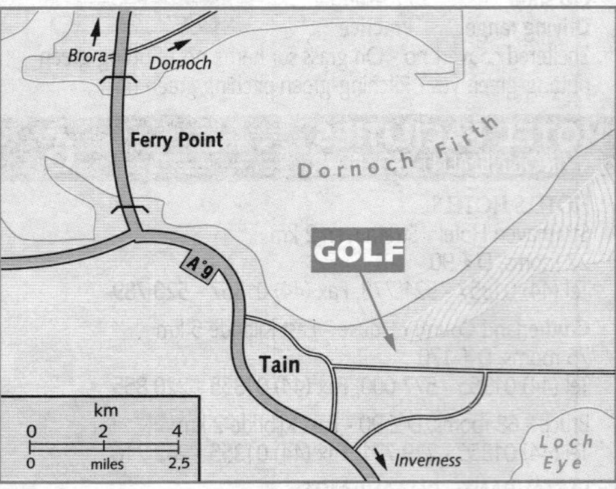

Access Accès : Inverness, A9 → Dornoch to Tain. From Tain town centre, down Castle Brae over railway, past cemetery

Map 1 on page 470 Carte 1 Page 470

GOLF COURSE — PARCOURS — 17/20

Site	Site	
Maintenance	Entretien	
Architect	Architecte	Tom Morris
Type	Type	links, heathland
Relief	Relief	
Water in play	Eau en jeu	
Exp. to wind	Exposé au vent	
Trees in play	Arbres en jeu	

Scorecard Carte de score	Chp. Chp.	Mens Mess.	Ladies Da.
Length Long.	5764	5500	5090
Par	70	70	73
Slope system	—	—	—

Advised golfing ability Niveau de jeu recommandé — 0 12 24 36

Hcp required Handicap exigé — no

CLUB HOUSE & AMENITIES — CLUB HOUSE ET ANNEXES — 6/10

Pro shop Pro-shop
Driving range Practice
Sheltered couvert no - **On grass** sur herbe no - **Putting-green** putting-green yes - **Pitching-green** pitching green yes

HOTEL FACILITIES — ENVIRONNEMENT HOTELIER — 6/10

HOTELS HÔTELS
Morangie House - 26 rooms, D from £ 110 - Tain 0.5 km
Tel (44) 01862 - 892 281, Fax (44) 01862 - 892 872

Mansfield Castle - 19 rooms, D £ 120 - Tain 0.5 km
Tel (44) 01862 - 892 052, Fax (44) 01862 - 892 260

Golf View House - 5 rooms, D £ 60 - Tain 0.5 km
Tel (44) 01862 - 892 856, Fax (44) 01862 - 892 172

Glenmorangie House - Cadboll 14 km
9 rooms, D from £ 230
Tel (44) 01862 - 871 671, Fax (44) 01862 - 871 625

RESTAURANTS RESTAURANTS
Morangie Hotel - Tain 0.5 km - Tel (44) 01862 - 892 281
Mansfield Castle - Tain 0.5 km - Tel (44) 01862 - 892 052

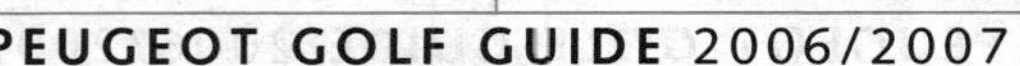

Taymouth Castle

13	4	6

This course is located in the alluvial plain on the banks of the river Tay, right next to the Loch of the same name. James Braid made the best possible use of limited space and restricted potential for contouring generally flat terrain. But even he was hard put to avoid a number of up and down holes and a hint of monotony. Whenever the course moves on to higher ground, the standard of the holes follows suit. In such an attractive region as this, the landscape is an added value of prime importance with the surrounding woods and hills. As the winter months are pretty wet here, even by Scottish standards, the best time to play is in summer or early autumn, for the colours. Most of the very many trees line and define the fairways, but some interfere to the point where they may be considered as hazards. Hit the ball in the right direction off the tee to keep out of trouble. This is not a great course, but there are few others in the immediate neighbourhood and, when all is said and done, this is a good layout despite the overall sobriety.

Ce parcours est situé dans la plaine alluviale au bord de la rivière Tay, et tout près du Loch. James Braid a tiré le meilleur parti possible d'un espace assez limité et de possibilités restreintes de modelage d'un terrain généralement plat. Mais il lui était difficile d'éviter un certain nombre d'allers et retours et une légère monotonie. Dès que le parcours s'élève un peu, la qualité des trous fait de même. Dans une région aussi attrayante, le paysage est une valeur ajoutée de premier ordre, avec les bois et les collines environnants. Les mois d'hiver étant assez humides - même pour un Ecossais - on viendra ici en été ou en début d'automne, pour les couleurs. La plupart des nombreux arbres longent et définissent les fairways, mais certains empiètent assez pour prendre le statut d'obstacles : il est alors sage de bien étudier la trajectoire des coups de départ. En définitive, ce n'est pas un "grand" parcours, mais il y en a peu dans les environs immédiats, et celui-ci est de qualité, dans sa sobriété.

Taymouth Castle Golf Course **1923**
Kenmore
SCO - ABERFELDY, Perthshire PH15 2NT

Office Secrétariat (44) 01887 - 830 228
Pro shop Pro-shop (44) 01887 - 830 228
Fax Fax (44) 01887 - 830 765
Web www.scotland-golf.co.uk
Situation Situation Perth, 60 km
Aberfeldy (pop. 4 083), 9 km
Annual closure Fermeture annuelle no
club-house closed 11 → 03
Weekly closure Fermeture hebdomadaire no

Fees main season Tarifs haute saison	18 holes	
	Week days Semaine	**We/Bank holidays** We/Férié
Individual Individuel	£ 17	£ 21
Couple Couple	£ 34	£ 42

Caddie Caddie no **Electric Trolley** Chariot électrique no
Buggy Voiturette yes **Clubs** Clubs yes
Credit cards Cartes de crédit no

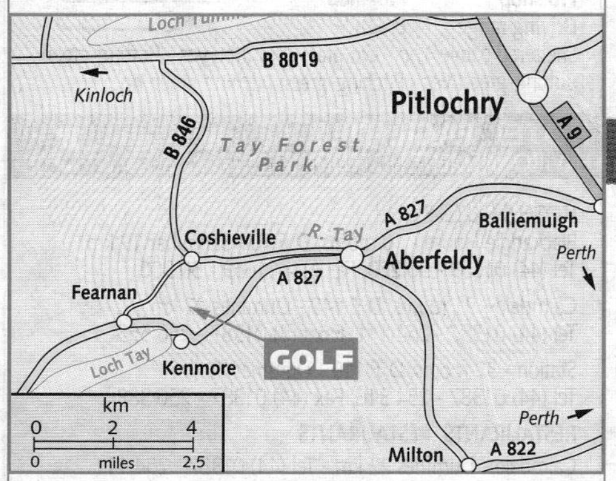

Access Accès : Perth, A9 North to Ballinluig, then A827 through Aberfeldy. Kenmore is approx. 9 km farther on the same road.
Map 1 on page 471 Carte 1 Page 471

GOLF COURSE
PARCOURS **13**/20

Site Site
Maintenance Entretien
Architect Architecte James Braid
Type Type parkland
Relief Relief
Water in play Eau en jeu
Exp. to wind Exposé au vent
Trees in play Arbres en jeu

Scorecard Carte de score	**Chp.** Chp.	**Mens** Mess.	**Ladies** Da.
Length Long.	5520	5220	4598
Par	69	69	72
Slope system	—	—	

Advised golfing ability 0 12 24 36
Niveau de jeu recommandé
Hcp required Handicap exigé no

CLUB HOUSE & AMENITIES
CLUB HOUSE ET ANNEXES **4**/10

Pro shop Pro-shop
Driving range Practice
Sheltered couvert no - On grass sur herbe no - Putting-green putting-green yes - Pitching-green pitching green no

HOTEL FACILITIES
ENVIRONNEMENT HOTELIER **6**/10

HOTELS HÔTELS
Kenmore Hotel - 40 rooms, D £ 92 - Kenmore, close
Tel (44) 01887 - 830 205, Fax (44) 01887 - 830 262

Guinach House - Aberfeldy 7 km
6 rooms, D from £ 95
Tel (44) 01887 - 820 251, Fax (44) 01887 - 829 607

Farleyer House - 19 rooms, D £ 150 - Aberfeldy 5 km
Tel (44) 01887 - 820 332, Fax (44) 01887 - 829 430

RESTAURANTS RESTAURANTS
Guinach House - Aberfeldy 5 km - Tel (44) 01887 - 820 251
Kenmore Hotel - Kenmore, close
Tel (44) 01887 - 830 205

Thornhill

15 | 6 | 5

After the city, seaside and sometimes upland courses, here we are out in the country with some pretty views over the surrounding Southern Uplands. Created by Willie Fernie and then restyled in 1979, this is a very short but rather technical layout designed more for families or friendly rounds but also completed with remarkable concern for quality. You need to be accurate because the greens are small and often treacherous and multi-tiered. This is an easy walk, but it is still very much a rural park and its difficulties shouldn't be taken lightly. Judging by the success of the club's prodigal son Andrew Coltart, this is a good course to learn on. The club-house of this "village course" is unpretentious but warm. Close by, art enthusiasts will visit Drumlanrig Castle which houses a fine collection of paintings and mementoes of Bonnie Prince Charlie.

Après les golfs des villes, du bord de mer, des montagnes parfois aussi, nous voici à la campagne, avec de jolies vues sur les Southern Uplands alentour. Créé par Willie Fernie, remanié en 1979, c'est un tracé très court, assez technique, résolument orienté vers le jeu en famille ou entre amis, mais avec un souci de qualité à remarquer. Il faut être précis, car les greens sont petits, souvent assez traîtres, parfois à plateaux. Peu accidenté, il conserve néanmoins un caractère de parc rural, et il ne faut pas prendre à la légère ses difficultés. Si l'on en juge par la réussite de l'enfant du club, Andrew Coltart, c'est un parcours formateur. Le club-house de ce "golf de village" est modeste, mais chaleureux. A proximité, les amateurs d'art visiteront le Drumlanrig Castle, avec une riche collection de peinture et des souvenirs du Bonnie Prince Charlie.

Thornhill Golf Club — 1893

Blacknest
SCO - THORNHILL, Dumfries-shire DG3 5DW

Office	Secrétariat	(44) 01848 - 331 779
Pro shop	Pro-shop	no Pro Shop
Fax	Fax	—
E-mail		thornhillgc@fsmail.net
Situation	Situation	Dumfries, 22 km
Annual closure	Fermeture annuelle	no
Weekly closure	Fermeture hebdomadaire	no

Fees main season Tarifs haute saison		Full day
	Week days Semaine	**We/Bank holidays** We/Férié
Individual Individuel	£ 30	£ 35
Couple Couple	£ 60	£ 70

Caddie Caddie no — **Electric Trolley** Chariot électrique no
Buggy Voiturette yes — **Clubs** Clubs no
Credit cards Cartes de crédit no

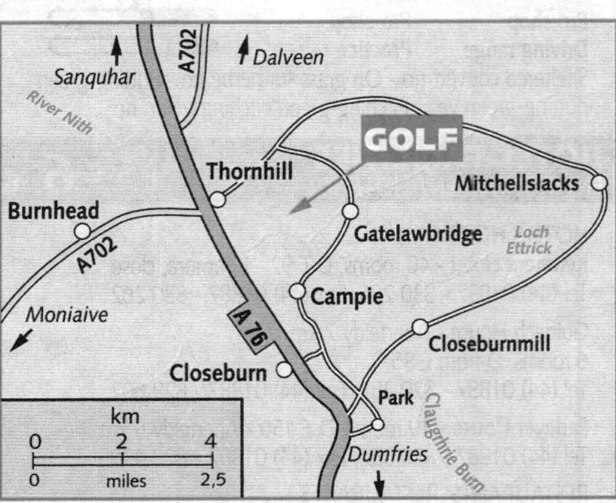

Access Accès : Glasgow, M74 - Edinburgh A702.
In Abington, A74, then A702 to Thornhill.
Golf on A76 (turn East in middle of village).
Map 2 on page 473 Carte 2 Page 473

GOLF COURSE — PARCOURS — 15/20

Site	Site	
Maintenance	Entretien	
Architect	Architecte	Willie Fernie
Type	Type	heathland, parkland
Relief	Relief	
Water in play	Eau en jeu	
Exp. to wind	Exposé au vent	
Trees in play	Arbres en jeu	

Scorecard Carte de score	**Chp.** Chp.	**Mens** Mess.	**Ladies** Da.
Length Long.	5562	5562	4925
Par	71	71	74
Slope system	—	—	—

Advised golfing ability Niveau de jeu recommandé: 0 12 24 36
Hcp required Handicap exigé: 28 Men, 36 Ladies

CLUB HOUSE & AMENITIES — CLUB HOUSE ET ANNEXES — 6/10

Pro shop Pro-shop
Driving range Practice
Sheltered couvert no - On grass sur herbe yes - Putting-green putting-green yes - Pitching-green pitching green no

HOTEL FACILITIES — ENVIRONNEMENT HOTELIER — 5/10

HOTELS HÔTELS

Blackaddie House - 10 rooms, D £ 70 - Sanquhar 19 km
Tel (44) 01659 - 50 270, Fax (44) 01659 - 50 900

Cairndale - 91 rooms, D £ 149 - Dumfries 22 km
Tel (44) 01387 - 254 111, Fax (44) 01387 - 250 555

Station - 32 rooms, D £ 110 - Dumfries 22 km
Tel (44) 01387 - 254 316, Fax (44) 01387 - 250 388

RESTAURANTS RESTAURANTS

Cairndale - Dumfries 22 km - Tel (44) 01387 - 254 111
Station - Dumfries 22 km - Tel (44) 01387 - 254 316

Turnberry *Ailsa Course*

19 | **9** | **7**

Regularly playing host to the British Open has forged this course's reputation as one of the world's greatest championship venues. The course is located at the southernmost end of a majestic series of links in Ayrshire and offers a splendid view over the Isle of Arran, the dark and mysterious Mull of Kintyre and the rock of Ailsa. Try and play here in fine weather (it happens more often than you might imagine) as the wind can make this a hellish course to handle. After an almost innocent first few holes, you soon find the sea down the left for the 8 most spectacular holes with the famous lighthouse, but the finish is no less gripping. Brought back to life after the war thanks to the work of MacKenzie Ross, the Ailsa course is challenging, untamed and beguiling. It simply has to be experienced at least once in a lifetime, at any price (and here it is not just any price). A course to savour from end to end, without worrying too much about your card.

La venue régulière du British Open a fait sa réputation parmi les plus grands parcours de championnat au monde. Situé dans la partie la plus au sud d'une série majestueuse de links de l'Ayrshire, il offre un spectacle splendide sur l'île d'Arran, le sombre et mystérieux Mull of Kintyre et le rocher d'Ailsa. A savourer par beau temps (plus fréquent qu'on ne le croit !), car le vent peut transformer le parcours en enfer du jeu. Après un départ presque innocent, on trouve vite la mer à main gauche, pour les huit trous les plus spectaculaires, avec le célèbre phare, mais la conclusion n'est pas moins prenante. Ressuscité après la guerre grâce au travail de Mackenzie Ross, l'Ailsa est exigeant, sauvage, enchanteur, il constitue une expérience à connaître au moins une fois dans sa vie, à n'importe quel prix (c'est effectivement le cas). Un parcours à savourer de bout en bout, sans trop penser au score.

The Westin Turnberry Resort Golf Courses — 1906

SCO - TURNBERRY, Ayrshire, KA26 9LT

Office	Secrétariat	(44) 01655 - 331 000
Pro shop	Pro-shop	(44) 01655 - 334 032
Fax	Fax	(44) 01655 - 331 069
Web	www.westin.com/turnberry	
Situation	Situation	Ayr, 24 km
Annual closure	Fermeture annuelle	no
Weekly closure	Fermeture hebdomadaire	no

Fees main season Tarifs haute saison — 18 holes

	Week days / Semaine	We/Bank holidays / We/Férié
Individual Individuel	£ 130	£ 175
Couple Couple	£ 260	£ 350

Hotel residents: £ 105

Caddie Caddie yes **Electric Trolley** Chariot électrique yes

Buggy Voiturette no **Clubs** Clubs yes

Credit cards Cartes de crédit

VISA - Eurocard - MasterCard - AMEX - DC

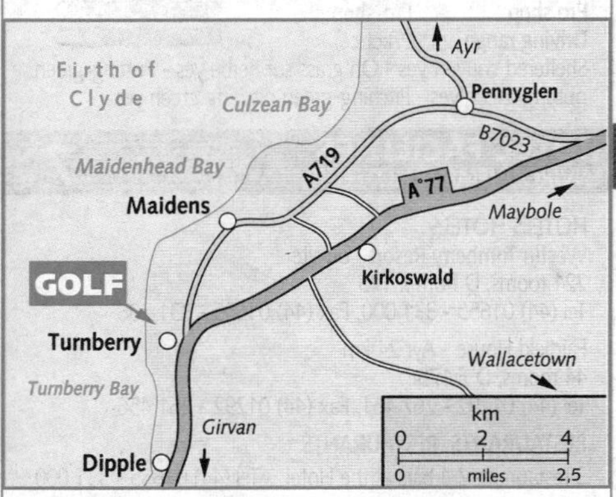

Access Accès : Glasgow, A77 to Turnberry

Map 3 on page 474 Carte 3 Page 474

GOLF COURSE — PARCOURS 19/20

Site	Site	
Maintenance	Entretien	
Architect	Architecte	Mackenzie Ross
Type	Type	links
Relief	Relief	
Water in play	Eau en jeu	
Exp. to wind	Exposé au vent	
Trees in play	Arbres en jeu	

Scorecard / Carte de score	Chp. / Chp.	Mens / Mess.	Ladies / Da.
Length Long.	6279	5800	5182
Par	70	69	75
Slope system	—	—	—

Advised golfing ability Niveau de jeu recommandé — 0 12 24 36

Hcp required Handicap exigé — no

CLUB HOUSE & AMENITIES — CLUB HOUSE ET ANNEXES 9/10

Pro shop Pro-shop

Driving range Practice

Sheltered couvert yes - On grass sur herbe yes - Putting-green putting-green yes - Pitching-green pitching green yes

HOTEL FACILITIES — ENVIRONNEMENT HOTELIER 7/10

HOTELS HÔTELS

Westin Turnberry Resort - on site
221 rooms, D from £ 175
Tel (44) 01655 - 331 000, Fax (44) 01655 - 331 706

Fairfield House - Ayr 24 km
44 rooms, D £ 175
Tel (44) 01292 - 267 461, Fax (44) 01292 - 261 456

RESTAURANTS RESTAURANTS

3 restaurants / 4 bars at the Hotel - Tel (44) 01655 - 331 000

The Ivy House - Alloway 20 km - Tel (44) 01655 - 442 336

Brig O'Doon House - Alloway 20 km
Tel (44) 01292 - 442 466

771

Turnberry *Kintyre Course*

16	9	7

The Kintyre Course was opened to great acclaim in the summer of 2001 and provides a perfect complement to its more illustrious sister. Building on the challenge laid down by the famous old Arran Course - a course of very considerable merit - the Kintyre is links golf at its exhilarating best. Created in 1909, the Arran was rebuilt on two previous occasions before architect Donald Steel was brought in to undertake a complete redesign in 1999. The alterations were so comprehensive that a change of name was warranted, with Kintyre maintaining a geographic link to the famous Mull of Kintyre across the water in Turnberry. The unveiling of the new course has introduced a new dimension complete with spectacular views and a magical setting. Kintyre will no more be considered as a second fiddle, or only as a warm-up round before playing the Ailsa course. Okay, you have to dig into your savings to play and stay in the impressive grand hotel, but if there are places in this world where pecuniary considerations come last, this has to be one of them.

Le Kintyre Course a été inauguré en été 2001, et s'est placé comme le complément de son voisin, le Ailsa Course. Remplaçant le fameux "Arran Course", le Kintyre représente un grand exemple d'architecture de links, plus encore que son prédécesseur. Créé en 1909, l'Arran a été remodelé en deux occasions, avant que l'architecte Donald Steel entreprenne un travail fondamental en 1999. Les changements ont été si importants qu'un changement de nom était nécessaire, celui de Kintyre assurant le lien évident avec le Mull of Kintyre, au large de Turnberry. C'est une nouvelle dimension que l'on trouve ici, avec des vues spectaculaires, une mise en scène remarquable et un challenge renouvelé. Kintyre ne saurait être considéré comme un parcours de second ordre, où l'on vient s'échauffer avant de jouer le "Ailsa Course". Plus que jamais, il faut casser sa tirelire pour séjourner dans le magnifique hôtel et jouer, mais Turnberry fait peut-être partie des endroits sans prix.

The Westin Turnberry Resort Golf Courses — 1909/2001

SCO - TURNBERRY, Ayrshire, KA26 9LT

Office	Secrétariat	(44) 01655 - 331 000
Pro shop	Pro-shop	(44) 01655 - 334 032
Fax	Fax	(44) 01655 - 331 069
Web	www.westin.com/turnberry	
Situation	Situation	Ayr, 24 km
Annual closure	Fermeture annuelle	no
Weekly closure	Fermeture hebdomadaire	no

Fees main season Tarifs haute saison — 18 holes

	Week days / Semaine	We/Bank holidays / We/Férié
Individual Individuel	£ 105	£ 105
Couple Couple	£ 210	£ 210

Hotel residents: £ 90

Caddie Caddie yes — **Electric Trolley** Chariot électrique yes

Buggy Voiturette no — **Clubs** Clubs yes

Credit cards Cartes de crédit
VISA - Eurocard - MasterCard - AMEX - DC

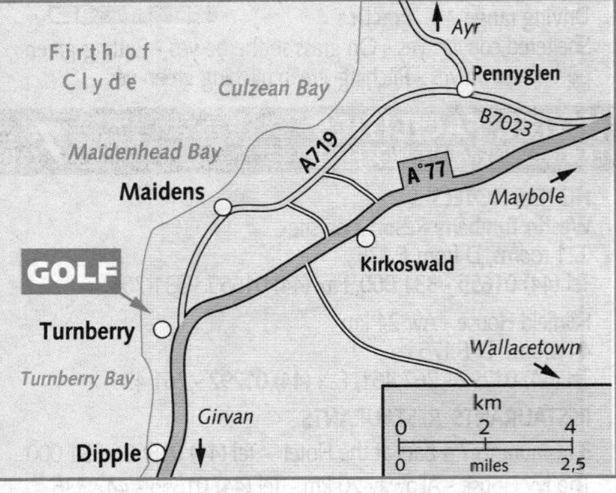

Access Accès : Glasgow, A77 to Turnberry
Map 3 on page 474 Carte 3 Page 474

GOLF COURSE — PARCOURS — 16/20

Site	Site	
Maintenance	Entretien	
Architect	Architecte	Mackenzie Ross (1945), Donald Steel (2001)
Type	Type	links
Relief	Relief	
Water in play	Eau en jeu	
Exp. to wind	Exposé au vent	
Trees in play	Arbres en jeu	

Scorecard Carte de score	Chp. Chp.	Mens Mess.	Ladies Da.
Length Long.	6274	5830	5109
Par	72	71	73
Slope system	—	—	—

Advised golfing ability Niveau de jeu recommandé — 0 12 24 36

Hcp required Handicap exigé — no

CLUB HOUSE & AMENITIES — CLUB HOUSE ET ANNEXES — 9/10

Pro shop Pro-shop
Driving range Practice
Sheltered couvert yes - On grass sur herbe yes - Putting-green putting-green yes - Pitching-green pitching green yes

HOTEL FACILITIES — ENVIRONNEMENT HOTELIER — 7/10

HOTELS HÔTELS
Westin Turnberry Resort - on site
221 rooms, D from £ 175
Tel (44) 01655 - 331 000, Fax (44) 01655 - 331 706

Fairfield House - Ayr 24 km
44 rooms, D £ 175
Tel (44) 01292 - 267 461, Fax (44) 01292 - 261 456

RESTAURANTS RESTAURANTS
3 restaurants / 4 bars at the Hotel - Tel (44) 01655 - 331 000
The Ivy House - Alloway 20 km - Tel (44) 01655 - 442 336
Brig O'Doon House - Alloway 20 km
Tel (44) 01292 - 442 466

West Kilbride

16 | 7 | 6

A very pretty course on the Ayrshire coast, without the claim to fame of its prestigious neighbours but always very welcoming on week days. The site is as magnificent as it is peaceful, with superb views over the Isle of Arran, Ailsa Craig and the north-west hills. But this 18-hole course is worth much more than its scenery. A combination of three par 3s, two par 5s and thirteen par 4s, plus very reasonable yardage overall makes this interesting prey for good golfers and the best players will find more than one opportunity to shine. The spread of difficulties makes for a well-balanced round of golf with only a single burn to interrupt the links landscape: bunkers that look to have been here since time began, thick bushes and the few trees that the wind has left standing. And of course the sea, whose incursions often tend to complicate the job of club officials, who are otherwise always kept busy protecting the course's reputation for magnificent green-keeping.

Un très joli parcours de la côte de l'Ayrshire, sans prétendre aux grands titres de gloire de ses prestigieux voisins, mais toujours accueillant en semaine. Le site est aussi magnifique et très tranquille, avec des vues superbes sur l'Ile d'Arran, Ailsa Craig et les collines du nord-ouest. Mais ce 18 trous vaut mieux que son panorama. Son association de trois pars 3, deux pars 5 et treize pars 4 et sa longueur très raisonnable en font une proie intéressante pour les golfeurs de niveau honorable, et les meilleurs y trouveront plus d'une occasion de s'y casser les dents. Le répartition des difficultés offre un bon rythme de jeu, un "burn" venant seul rompre leur nature propre aux links : des bunkers qui paraissent là depuis l'éternité, des buissons bien épais, quelques arbres ayant résisté au vent. Et à la mer, dont l'action vient parfois compliquer la tâche des responsables du Club, autrement toujours attentifs à conserver au lieu sa réputation d'entretien magnifique.

The West Kilbride Golf Club — 1893

33-35 Fullerton Drive, Seamill
SCO - WEST KILBRIDE, Ayrshire KA23 9HT

Office	Secrétariat	(44) 01294 - 823 911
Pro shop	Pro-shop	(44) 01294 - 823 042
Fax	Fax	(44) 01294 - 829 573
Web	www.westkilbridegolfclub.com	
Situation	Situation	Glasgow, 56 km
Annual closure	Fermeture annuelle	no
Weekly closure	Fermeture hebdomadaire	no

Fees main season Tarifs haute saison — 18 holes

	Week days Semaine	We/Bank holidays We/Férié
Individual Individuel	£ 35	*
Couple Couple	£ 70	*

Full week day: £ 45 / * No visitors at week-ends

Caddie Caddie no — **Electric Trolley** Chariot électrique yes

Buggy Voiturette no — **Clubs** Clubs yes

Credit cards Cartes de crédit
VISA - Eurocard - MasterCard - AMEX - DC - JCB

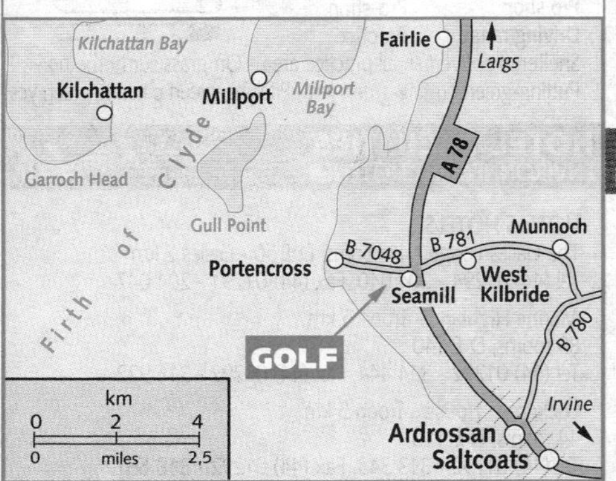

Access Accès : Glasgow, A80 → Airport. At Jct 29, A737 through Paisley, Beith. After Dalry turn right on B781. In West Kilbride, turn right towards the sea.
Map 3 on page 474 Carte 3 Page 474

GOLF COURSE — PARCOURS — 16/20

Site	Site	
Maintenance	Entretien	
Architect	Architecte	Tom Morris, James Braid
Type	Type	links
Relief	Relief	
Water in play	Eau en jeu	
Exp. to wind	Exposé au vent	
Trees in play	Arbres en jeu	

Scorecard Carte de score	**Chp.** Chp.	**Mens** Mess.	**Ladies** Da.
Length Long.	5898	5898	5292
Par	71	71	72
Slope system	—	—	—

Advised golfing ability Niveau de jeu recommandé — 0 12 24 36

Hcp required Handicap exigé — certificate

CLUB HOUSE & AMENITIES — CLUB HOUSE ET ANNEXES — 7/10

Pro shop Pro-shop
Driving range Practice
Sheltered couvert no - On grass sur herbe no - Putting-green putting-green yes - Pitching-green pitching green yes

HOTEL FACILITIES — ENVIRONNEMENT HOTELIER — 6/10

HOTELS HÔTELS

Thistle - 128 rooms, D £ 145 - Irvine 6 km
Tel (44) 01294 - 274 272, Fax (44) 01294 - 277 287

Brisbane House - Largs 7 km
23 rooms, D £ 95
Tel (44) 01475 - 687 200, Fax (44) 01475 - 676 295

Priory House - Largs 7 km
21 rooms, D £ 90
Tel (44) 01475 - 686 460, Fax (44) 01475 - 689 070

RESTAURANTS RESTAURANTS

Braidwoods - Dalry 6 km - Tel (44) 01294 - 833 544
Lagoon (Thistle) - Irvine 6 km - Tel (44) 01294 - 274 272

Western Gailes

17 | 5 | 7

Between the seaside dunes and the railway lines, Western Gailes is one of the best links down the whole coast of Scotland and its international reputation is fully warranted. Totally exposed to the prevailing south-west wind, it subtly changes its nature even if the wind varies just a few degrees. There are only three par 3s, every one more difficult than it looks. Rather strangely for a course that is hardly much wider than two fairways wedged between the sea and railway track, the club-house is almost in the middle. This means you play one half of the front 9 and one half of the back 9 with the wind behind you, and holes 5 to 13 with the wind in your face. This calls for some careful thinking over the line of play and attack, a requirement noticed very early on by Gene Sarazen, the inventor of the sand-wedge. This private club welcomes visitors, even of the female variety, although there are no real ladies tees. We'll just say that for them, this is an excellent par 74.

Entre les dunes de bord de mer et la voie ferrée, Western Gailes est un des meilleurs links de toute cette côte de l'Ecosse et sa réputation internationale est pleinement justifiée. Totalement exposé aux vents dominants de sud-ouest, il change subtilement de caractère selon que l'orientation se modifie de quelques degrés seulement. Il n'y a que trois par 3 ici, mais tous plus difficiles qu'ils ne paraissent. Assez curieusement pour un parcours guère plus large que deux fairways entre la mer et la voie ferrée, le club-house est presqu'au milieu : on joue ainsi la moitié de l'aller et la moitié du retour vent avec, et toute la partie du 5 au 13 vent contre, ce qui exige pas mal de réflexion sur la ligne de jeu... et la façon de négocier. Cette exigence fut très tôt remarquée par Gene Sarazen, l'inventeur du sand wedge. Ce club privé est accueillant aux visiteurs, même féminins, bien qu'elles n'aient pas vraiment de départs spécifiques : disons que c'est pour elles un excellent par 74.

Western Gailes Golf Club — 1898

Gailes
SCO - IRVINE, Ayrshire KA11 5AE

Office	Secrétariat	(44) 01294 - 311 649
Pro shop	Pro-shop	(44) 01294 - 311 649
Fax	Fax	(44) 01294 - 312 312
Web	www.westerngailes.com	
Situation	Situation	Troon, 5 km
Annual closure	Fermeture annuelle	no

Restaurant closed 10 → 04 inclusive

Weekly closure	Fermeture hebdomadaire	no
Fees main season	Tarifs haute saison	18 holes

	Week days / Semaine	We/Bank holidays / We/Férié
Individual Individuel	£ 95	£ 100
Couple Couple	£ 190	£ 200

Visitors: Monday, Wednesday, Friday & Sunday
Full day: £ 145

Caddie Caddie on request **Electric Trolley** Chariot électrique no
Buggy Voiturette no **Clubs** Clubs no
Credit cards Cartes de crédit VISA - Mastercard

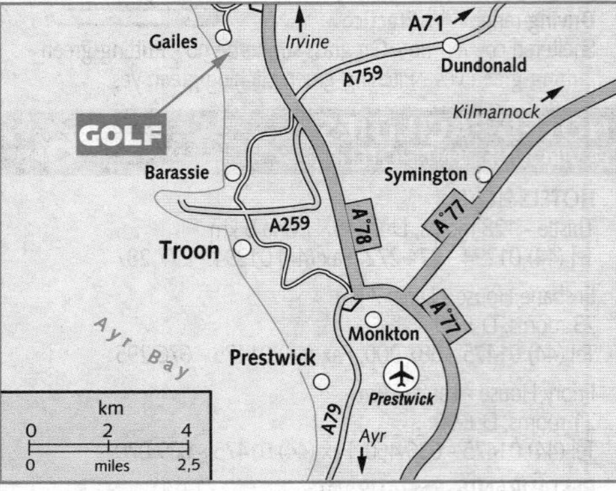

Access Accès : On A78, 3 km S of junction with A 71.
Map 3 on page 474 Carte 3 Page 474

GOLF COURSE — PARCOURS — 17/20

Site	Site	
Maintenance	Entretien	
Architect	Architecte	unknown
Type	Type	links
Relief	Relief	
Water in play	Eau en jeu	
Exp. to wind	Exposé au vent	
Trees in play	Arbres en jeu	

Scorecard / Carte de score	Chp. / Chp.	Mens / Mess.	Ladies / Da.
Length Long.	6308	5583	4975
Par	75	71	71
Slope system	—	—	—

Advised golfing ability / Niveau de jeu recommandé: 0 12 24 36
Hcp required / Handicap exigé: 24

CLUB HOUSE & AMENITIES — CLUB HOUSE ET ANNEXES — 5/10

Pro shop Pro-shop
Driving range Practice
Sheltered couvert small practice area - On grass sur herbe no - Putting-green putting-green yes - Pitching-green pitching green yes

HOTEL FACILITIES — ENVIRONNEMENT HOTELIER — 7/10

HOTELS HÔTELS
The Gailes Lodge - 41 rooms, D £ 50 - Gailes 2 km
Tel (44) 01294 - 204 040, Fax (44) 01294 - 204 047

Marine Highland - Troon 5 km
89 rooms, D £ 140
Tel (44) 01292 - 314 444, Fax (44) 01292 - 316 922

Lochgreen House - Troon 5 km
44 rooms, D £ 110
Tel (44) 01292 - 313 343, Fax (44) 01292 - 318 661

RESTAURANTS RESTAURANTS
Highgrove House - Troon 3 km - Tel (44) 01292 - 312 511
Apple Inn - Troon 5 km - Tel (44) 01292 - 318 819

Whitekirk

15 | 6 | 6

In a region where there are many high quality layouts, it is difficult for a course to make a name for itself and the Whitekirk promoters scored a significant victory over those who thought there wouldn't be enough space for another golfing venue. This course is a fine example of what can still be done with a restricted budget but with the determination to offer visitors excellent value for money. Practice facilities are of a standard seldom found in the UK, the greens are excellent (up to modern-day USGA standards), the layout very varied and the views (free of charge) over the Firth of Forth, East Lothian and the Fife and Bass Rock are magnificent. Naturally this layout cannot really match the genuine links courses found in the vicinity here, but it is a very serious design which cleverly uses the natural stretches of water. Strategy is immediately obvious without any hidden traps, an essential feature for a "pay-as-you-play" course.

Dans une région présentant des parcours d'une telle qualité, il est difficile de se faire un nom et les promoteurs de Whitekirk ont remporté une belle victoire sur ceux qui estimaient qu'il n'y avait plus de place disponible. Ce parcours est un bon exemple de ce que l'on peut encore faire avec un budget limité, mais avec la détermination d'offrir un bon rapport qualité-prix aux visiteurs de passage. Ils y trouveront des installations d'entraînement d'une rare qualité en Grande-Bretagne, des greens excellents (aux normes modernes de l'USGA), un tracé très varié et (gratuitement) de très belles vues sur le Firth of Forth, l'East Lothian, le Fife et Bass Rock. Certes, ce parcours ne peut tout à fait lutter avec les véritables links que l'on peut trouver alentour, mais son dessin a été sérieusement réalisé en utilisant les cours d'eau naturels, la stratégie est immédiatement évidente, sans pièges dissimulés, ce qui est essentiel pour un parcours "pay-as-you-play".

Whitekirk Golf Course — 1995

Whitekirk
SCO - Nr NORTH BERWICK, E. Lothian EH39 5PR

Office Secrétariat (44) 01620 - 870 300
Pro shop Pro-shop (44) 01620 - 870 300
Fax Fax (44) 01620 - 870 330
Web www.whitekirk.com
Situation Situation North Berwick, 5 km
Annual closure Fermeture annuelle no
Weekly closure Fermeture hebdomadaire no

Fees main season Tarifs haute saison	18 holes	
	Week days Semaine	**We/Bank holidays** We/Férié
Individual Individuel	£ 25	£ 35
Couple Couple	£ 50	£ 70

Full Day: £30 / £50 (We)

Caddie Caddie on request **Electric Trolley** Chariot électrique yes

Buggy Voiturette yes **Clubs** Clubs yes

Credit cards Cartes de crédit
VISA - Eurocard - MasterCard

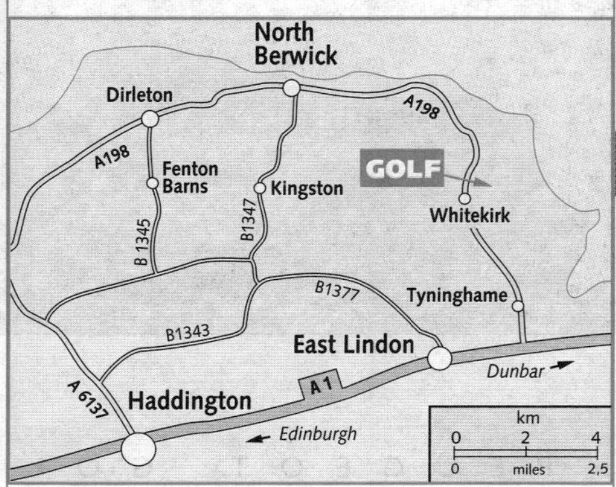

Access Accès : Edinburgh A1 → Berwick-upon-Tweed.
After East Linton, A198 on the left.
Golf on left side after Whitekirk village.
Map 3 on page 475 Carte 3 Page 475

GOLF COURSE — PARCOURS 15/20

Site Site
Maintenance Entretien
Architect Architecte Cameron Sinclair
Type Type heathland
Relief Relief
Water in play Eau en jeu
Exp. to wind Exposé au vent
Trees in play Arbres en jeu

Scorecard Carte de score	**Chp.** Chp.	**Mens** Mess.	**Ladies** Da.
Length Long.	5842	5645	4835
Par	72	72	72
Slope system	—	—	—

Advised golfing ability Niveau de jeu recommandé 0 12 24 36
Hcp required Handicap exigé no

CLUB HOUSE & AMENITIES — CLUB HOUSE ET ANNEXES 6/10

Pro shop Pro-shop
Driving range Practice
Sheltered couvert no - On grass sur herbe yes - Putting-green putting-green yes - Pitching-green pitching green yes

HOTEL FACILITIES — ENVIRONNEMENT HOTELIER 6/10

HOTELS HÔTELS
Marine Hotel - 83 rooms, D £ 140 - North Berwick 5 km
Tel (44) 0870 - 400 8129, Fax (44) 01620 - 894 480

Bayswell - Dunbar 12 km
13 rooms, D £ 80
Tel (44) 01368 - 862 225, Fax (44) 01368 - 862 225

Nether Abbey - North Berwick 5 km
14 rooms, D £ 90
Tel (44) 01620 - 892 802, Fax (44) 01620 - 895 298

RESTAURANTS RESTAURANTS
Marine - North Berwick 5 km - Tel (44) 01620 - 892 406
Whitekirk Restaurant - on site - Tel (44) 01620 - 870 300

PAYS DE GALLES

WALES

Celtic Manor - Roman Road

WALES

In the British Isles, Wales is not the best known country for golf, at least not to players on the continent, who are often only familiar with those courses seen on the television during the British Open or other top tournaments on the European Tour. Yet Wales has one of the highest concentrations of great courses when comparing with total numbers (161 nine- and eighteen-hole courses) but they are sometimes a little far away from major cities. Of course you won't find the sunny climes of Spain here, but it is not the North Pole either. The Gulf Stream brings a lot of mild weather and a few spots of rain are always good for the skin. This means that there are very few tourists, which can only be good news for golf-trotters who often have hundreds of acres of forest, miles of rugged coastline or sandy beaches and splendid landscapes all to themselves. And these are courses where you will have more than one opportunity to find playing partners from amongst the country's 71,000 registered players and to get to know the Welsh people, who are the very picture of their country: sometimes a little rough on the edges, discreet, always proud and profoundly hospitable. All they need do is tell the rest of the world that their golf courses are first-rate and they are indeed starting to get involved in big publicity and promotion campaigns. For example, the hosting of the Ryder Cup in 2010 will be an excellent opportunity to show the world what golf in Wales is like, even though it might have been a better option to prefer one of the country's great links course.

PAYS DE GALLES

Dans les Iles Britanniques, le Pays de Galles n'est pas le pays le plus connu pour le golf, en tout cas par les continentaux, qui ne connaissent souvent que les parcours vus à la télévision au moment de championnats comme le British Open ou autres épreuves des circuits européens. Pourtant, le Pays de Galles réunit une forte concentration de grands parcours par rapport au nombre total (161 de 9 et 18 trous), mais parfois très à l'écart des grandes métropoles. Certes, on ne trouve pas ici la chaleur de l'Espagne, mais ce n'est vraiment pas le Pôle Nord... le Gulf Stream adoucit le climat, et les quelques gouttes de pluie attendrissent la peau. S'il y a peu de touristes, tant mieux : on a souvent pour soi tout seul des centaines d'hectares de forêt, des kilomètres de côtes sauvages ou de plages, des paysages splendides. Et des parcours de golf où vous aurez l'occasion de trouver des compagnons de jeu parmi les 71.000 joueurs licenciés du pays, à l'image de leur pays, rudes parfois, discrets, chaleureux et fiers. Il leur reste à faire savoir que leurs parcours sont de première grandeur, mais ils commencent à se lancer dans de grandes campagnes de promotion. Par exemple, la réception de la Ryder Cup en 2010 est l'occasion de se faire connaître, même si on aurait aimé qu'elle se déroule sur l'un des grands links du pays.

Aberdovey

17	7	7

You can get here by train, a throw-back to the times when courses were often laid out close to railway tracks. Here the line does, in fact, run alongside the course but the trains are so infrequent that they don't make a nuisance of themselves. That's good news because this course – a typical links of nine holes out and nine in – benefits enormously from the flair of designers Fowler, Colt and Braid to be recognised as one of the most attractive in Wales. Situated in the Dovey estuary in the shadow of some impressive hills, the course is also within walking distance of the pretty resort of Aberdovey, which is probably why it lures an abundance of visitors in summer. One of the most intriguing challenges – just as it is at St Andrews – is that it certainly plays as two distinct nines. It can be into the teeth of the wind one way, and downwind the other but there is plenty of variety because of the capricious terrain and sand dunes. It can also throw up the odd surprise, too, like at the par three third hole where the green is hidden behind a cavernous bunker carved out of a dune.

On peut venir ici en train, ce qui rappelle le temps où les golfs étaient près du chemin de fer. Certes, il longe tout le parcours, mais les trains ne sont plus assez fréquents pour être vraiment gênants. Heureusement, car sur ce tracé – un links typique avec un vrai aller et un vrai retour – des gloires comme Fowler, Colt et Braid ont laissé leur "patte" pour en faire l'un des meilleurs du pays. Dans l'embouchure de la Dovey, au pied de hautes collines, ce parcours assez plat est à proximité immédiate de la jolie station balnéaire d'Aberdovey, d'où une forte fréquentation en été. A l'instar du Old Course de St Andrews, on joue pratiquement deux parcours de 9 trous différents, ce qui facilite le jeu quand il y a du vent avec, mais le complique inversement. Ici, les caprices du terrain et les dunes apportent de la variété, parfois même de la surprise comme au 3, un par 3 où le green est totalement dissimulé derrière un bunker très profond creusé dans une dune.

Aberdovey Golf Club — 1892

WAL - ABERDOVEY, Gwynedd LL35 0RT

Office	Secrétariat	(44) 01654 - 767 493
Pro shop	Pro-shop	(44) 01654 - 767 602
Fax	Fax	(44) 01654 - 767 027
Web	www.aberdoveygolf.co.uk	
Situation	Situation	Cardiff, 140 km

Aberdovey (Aberdyfi), 5 km

Annual closure Fermeture annuelle — no

Weekly closure Fermeture hebdomadaire — no

Fees main season Tarifs haute saison — 18 holes

	Week days / Semaine	We/Bank holidays / We/Férié
Individual Individuel	£ 38	£ 42
Couple Couple	£ 76	£ 84

* Full day: £ 50 / £ 55

Caddie Caddie no — **Electric Trolley** Chariot électrique no

Buggy Voiturette yes — **Clubs** Clubs no

Credit cards Cartes de crédit

VISA - MasterCard (Green fees & goods, only at Pro shop)

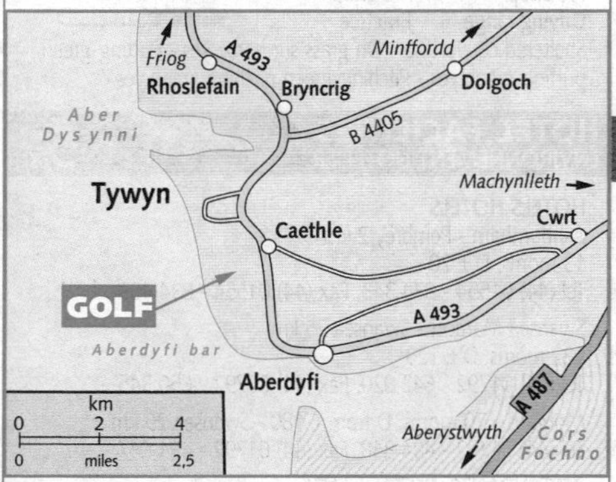

Access Accès : Cardiff A470 to Glantwymyn, then A489 to Machynlleth, A493 through Aberdyfi.
Golf course NW near Railway Station.
Map 5 on page 478 Carte 5 Page 478

GOLF COURSE — PARCOURS — 17/20

Site	Site	
Maintenance	Entretien	
Architect	Architecte	James Braid, H. Fowler, H.S. Colt
Type	Type	seaside course, links
Relief	Relief	
Water in play	Eau en jeu	
Exp. to wind	Exposé au vent	
Trees in play	Arbres en jeu	

Scorecard / Carte de score	Chp. / Chp.	Mens / Mess.	Ladies / Da.
Length Long.	5865	5551	5314
Par	71	71	74
Slope system	—	—	—

Advised golfing ability / Niveau de jeu recommandé — 0 12 24 36

Hcp required Handicap exigé — certificate

CLUB HOUSE & AMENITIES — CLUB HOUSE ET ANNEXES — 7/10

Pro shop Pro-shop
Driving range Practice
Sheltered couvert no - On grass sur herbe yes - Putting-green putting-green yes - Pitching-green pitching green yes

HOTEL FACILITIES — ENVIRONNEMENT HOTELIER — 7/10

HOTELS HÔTELS

Trefeddian - Aberdovey 3 km
59 rooms, D from £ 132
Tel (44) 01654 - 767 213, Fax (44) 01654 - 767 777

Penhelig Arms - Aberdovey 5 km
14 rooms, D £ 92
Tel (44) 01654 - 767 215, Fax (44) 01654 - 767 690

Ynishir Hall - Machynlleth 15 km
9 rooms, D £ 180
Tel (44) 01654 - 781 209, Fax (44) 01654 - 781 366

RESTAURANTS RESTAURANTS

Trefeddian - Aberdovey 3 km - Tel (44) 01654 - 767 213
Ynyshir Hall - Machynlleth 15 km - Tel (44) 01654 - 781 209

Ashburnham

16 | 6 | 5

Located to the west of Llanelli and not so far from Swansea, this is one of the oldest courses in Wales, overlooking Camarthen Bay. The fairways are very busy in Summer, so be warned. The first and last two holes have a rather marked inland character, but for the rest of the course you have the prevailing south-westerlies to contend with. Holes 3 to 8 run parallel to the sea with a head-wind, holes 9 to 15 are played with the wind behind you. With tight fairways, dangerous rough and other unwelcome but easily identifiable hazards, you play here with your clubs and your brains. The greens are on the large side and equally difficult to read, which would explain why the course record here is only 70. Even though players of all levels can measure up to this test, the less accomplished golfer should not hold out too much hope when the wind roars (but at least he or she might learn how to tackle it).

Situé à l'ouest de Llanelli, et pas si loin de Swansea, ce parcours très fréquenté en été et l'un des plus anciens du Pays de Galles, domine la baie de Carmarthen. Les deux premiers et deux derniers trous ont un caractère inland assez marqué. Ensuite, il faut jouer avec le vent dominant, car les trous du 3 au 8 sont joués parallèlement à la mer et vent contre, les trous 9 à 15 se jouent vent avec... Avec les fairways étroits, un rough et des obstacles bien dangereux, mais aussi bien identifiables, il faut jouer avec ses clubs, mais aussi sa tête. Ajoutons quelques coups aveugles, des bunkers où l'on a plus de mal à entrer qu'à y envoyer sa balle, et l'on obtient un links solide. Les greens sont assez grands, mais aussi très difficiles à lire, ce qui explique que le record ne soit ici que de 70. Et même si les joueurs de tous niveaux trouveront le test à leur mesure, les moins expérimentés ne doivent pas trop se faire d'illusions quand le vent souffle. Au moins, ils apprendront...

Ashburnham Golf Club — 1894

Cliff Terrace
WAL - BURRY PORT, Dyfed SA16 0HN

Office Secrétariat (44) 01554 - 832 269
Pro shop Pro-shop (44) 01554 - 833 846
Fax Fax (44) 01554 - 832 269
Web www.ashburnhamgolfclub.co.uk
Situation Situation Llanelli, 8 km
Swansea (pop. 181 906), 25 km
Annual closure Fermeture annuelle no
Weekly closure Fermeture hebdomadaire no

Fees main season Tarifs haute saison 18 holes

	Week days / Semaine	We/Bank holidays / We/Férié
Individual Individuel	£ 32,50	£ 42,50*
Couple Couple	£ 65	£ 85*

Full day: £ 37.50 and £ 42.50 (We)
* We: ask before coming

Caddie Caddie no — **Electric Trolley** Chariot électrique yes
Buggy Voiturette yes — **Clubs** Clubs yes
Credit cards Cartes de crédit
VISA - MasterCard (Pro Shop goods only)

Carmarthen
Kidwelly
R. Gwendraeth
Trimsaran
A 484
B 4317
B 4308
Swansea
Burry-port
Pembrey
Dwll
A 484
Llanelli
Burry Inlet
GOLF
0 2 4 km
0 2,5 miles

Access Accès : Cardiff M4. Jct 48, A4138 to Llanelli, then A484 to Burry Port.
Map 6 on page 480 Carte 6 Page 480

GOLF COURSE — PARCOURS 16/20

Site Site
Maintenance Entretien
Architect Architecte unknown
Type Type links
Relief Relief
Water in play Eau en jeu
Exp. to wind Exposé au vent
Trees in play Arbres en jeu

Scorecard / Carte de score	Chp. / Chp.	Mens / Mess.	Ladies / Da.
Length Long.	6312	5652	5007
Par	72	72	75
Slope system	—	—	—

Advised golfing ability 0 12 24 36
Niveau de jeu recommandé
Hcp required Handicap exigé certificate

CLUB HOUSE & AMENITIES — CLUB HOUSE ET ANNEXES 6/10

Pro shop Pro-shop
Driving range Practice
Sheltered couvert no - On grass sur herbe yes - Putting-green putting-green yes - Pitching-green pitching green yes

HOTEL FACILITIES — ENVIRONNEMENT HOTELIER 5/10

HOTELS HÔTELS
Ashburnham - Pembrey 2 km
13 rooms, D £ 70
Tel (44) 01554 - 834 343, Fax (44) 01554 - 834 483

Swansea Marriott - Swansea 25 km
122 rooms, D £ 120
Tel (44) 01792 - 642 020, Fax (44) 01792 - 650 345

Morgans - 20 rooms, D from £ 180 - Swansea 25 km
Tel (44) 01792 - 484 848, Fax (44) 01792 - 484 847

RESTAURANTS RESTAURANTS
Didier & Stephanie - Swansea 20 km
Tel (44) 01792 - 655 603
Hanson's - Swansea 25 km - Tel (44) 01792 - 466 200

Cardiff

14 | 6 | 8

This course is virtually in the middle of town, which largely explains why it is practically impossible to play here without being accompanied by a member. Quite simply, this is an excellent course, even considered by some to be one of the three best inland courses in Wales, despite the relatively short yardage. This very well maintained course is a classic example of parkland golfing, where the growing trees have gradually become a crucial factor. A few water hazards and particularly the very cleverly arranged green-side bunkers make the golfer's job a whole lot more difficult. What's more, the greens are medium-sized only, thus calling for even greater accuracy. In this respect it is interesting to note that modern courses seldom require any more virtuosity than their elders, just a little more power. From the back tees here, there are some short and some long par 4s, but virtually nothing in between. A great and appealing challenge, and a nice club-house.

Ce parcours est pratiquement situé en pleine ville. Mais s'il est impossible d'y jouer en week-end autrement qu'avec un membre, c'est aussi parce qu'il s'agit aussi d'un excellent parcours. Certains le considèrent même comme l'un des trois meilleurs "inland" du Pays de Galles, bien qu'il soit plutôt côté "court" que côté "long". Très bien entretenu, c'est un exemple classique de "parkland", dans lequel la croissance des arbres en a fait progressivement un facteur de jeu crucial. Quelques obstacles d'eau et surtout des bunkers de green disposés de manière intelligente rendent la tâche plus complexe. De plus, ces greens sont de taille plutôt moyenne, ce qui oblige à être précis. Il est d'ailleurs intéressant de constater que les parcours modernes ne réclament guère plus de virtuosité que les anciens, juste un peu plus de puissance. On remarquera d'ailleurs que, des départs arrière, il y a ici des par 4 courts et longs mais pratiquement pas de longueur moyenne. Le récent club-house a complété de manière imposante ce bon et beau "challenge".

Cardiff Golf Club — 1921

Sherborne Avenue
WAL - CYNCOED, CARDIFF CF2 6SJ

Office Secrétariat (44) 02920 - 753 320
Pro shop Pro-shop (44) 02920 - 754 772
Fax Fax (44) 02920 - 680 011
Web www.cardiffgolf.com
Situation Situation Cardiff, 3 km
Annual closure Fermeture annuelle no
Weekly closure Fermeture hebdomadaire Monday, Restaurant only

Fees main season Tarifs haute saison	Full day	
	Week days Semaine	**We/Bank holidays** We/Férié
Individual Individuel	£ 45	£ 45*
Couple Couple	£ 90	£ 90*

* We: only with a member

Caddie Caddie no — **Electric Trolley** Chariot électrique no
Buggy Voiturette no — **Clubs** Clubs yes
Credit cards Cartes de crédit (Pro Shop goods & Green fees)
VISA - Eurocard - Mastercard - Switch - Delta

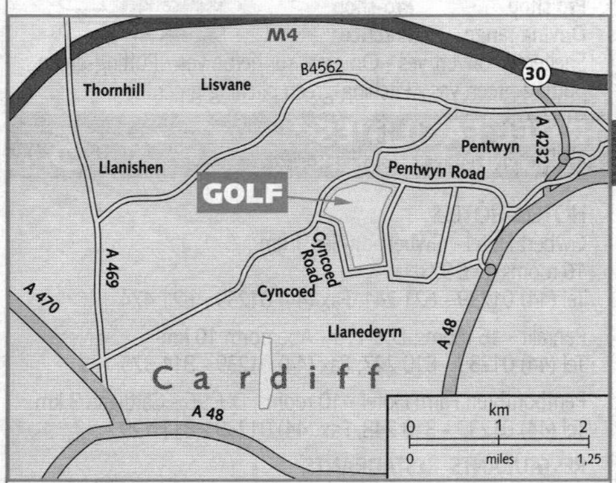

Access Accès : M4, A48, A48M
Map 6 on page 481 Carte 6 Page 481

GOLF COURSE — PARCOURS 14/20

Site Site
Maintenance Entretien
Architect Architecte Robert Walker
Type Type parkland
Relief Relief
Water in play Eau en jeu
Exp. to wind Exposé au vent
Trees in play Arbres en jeu

Scorecard Carte de score	**Chp.** Chp.	**Mens** Mess.	**Ladies** Da.
Length Long.	5412	5180	4750
Par	70	70	73
Slope system	—	—	—

Advised golfing ability Niveau de jeu recommandé 0 12 24 36
Hcp required Handicap exigé certificate

CLUB HOUSE & AMENITIES — CLUB HOUSE ET ANNEXES 6/10

Pro shop Pro-shop
Driving range Practice
Sheltered couvert practice area - On grass sur herbe yes - Putting-green putting-green yes - Pitching-green pitching green yes

HOTEL FACILITIES — ENVIRONNEMENT HOTELIER 8/10

HOTELS HÔTELS
St. David's Hotel & Spa - Cardiff 6 km
132 rooms, D from £ 230
Tel (44) 02920 - 454 045, Fax (44) 02920 - 313 075

Novotel Cardiff City Center - Cardiff 5 km
153 rooms, D £ 140
Tel (44) 02920 - 475 000, Fax (44) 02920 - 481 491

Townhouse - 8 rooms, D from £ 60 - Cardiff 4 km
Tel (44) 02920 - 239 399, Fax (44) 02920 - 223 214

RESTAURANTS RESTAURANTS
De Courcey's - Pentyrch 4 km - Tel (44) 02920 - 892 232
Woods Brasserie - Cardiff 6 km - Tel (44) 02920 - 492 400
Le Gallois - Cardiff 5 km - Tel (44) 02920 - 341 264

Cardigan

14	6	5

This is not the best known Welsh course, but it does bear comparison with Tenby or Glamorganshire. The club-house buildings, although not the smartest in the world, are at least functional, while the view over the sea, particularly from the 16th, costs nothing even for the "never-break-a-hundred" hacker. The club dates back to 1895, but the course has been restyled several times, the last effort being conducted by Hawtree and Sons without altering the feel of the original. A high standard course, with a special mention going to the visual and technical excellence of the last three holes. Yardage is in line with modern-day requirements, while the gorse and fern form the most obvious hazards for mis-hits; your ball somehow always seem to end up there whenever the wind confronts a poorly executed shot. In fact, this is a subtle blend of a links course, cliffs and pasture-land on a rather hilly setting, but the greens can generally be reached with low shots, at least if you work your way between the bunkers.

Ce n'est certes pas le plus connu des parcours gallois, mais il peut soutenir la comparaison avec Tenby ou Glamorganshire. Certes, les bâtiments du club-house ne sont pas les plus stylés du monde, mais il sont au moins fonctionnels. Quant à la vue somptueuse sur l'Océan, en particulier au départ du 16, elle est offerte, même aux mauvais joueurs. Le club date de 1895, mais le parcours a été plusieurs fois remanié, la dernière fois par le cabinet Hawtree & Sons sans en modifier l'esprit. Dans ce parcours de bon niveau, on soulignera la qualité visuelle et technique des trois derniers trous. Sa longueur répond à présent aux critères modernes. Les ajoncs et les fougères constituent l'une des menaces les plus flagrantes pour les balles, et si le vent les détourne, c'est toujours vers les obstacles. En fait, c'est un mélange assez subtil de links, de parcours de falaise, de pâturages, le tout assez accidenté, mais les greens acceptent en général les approches roulées, du moins si les bunkers les laissent passer.

Cardigan Golf Club — 1895/1928

Gwbert on Sea
WAL - CARDIGAN SA43 1PR

Office Secrétariat (44) 01239 - 621 775
Pro shop Pro-shop (44) 01239 - 615 359
Fax Fax (44) 01239 - 621 775
Web www.cardigangolf.co.uk
Situation Situation Cardigan (pop. 4 409), 3 km
Annual closure Fermeture annuelle no
Weekly closure Fermeture hebdomadaire no

Fees main season Tarifs haute saison	Week days Semaine	We/Bank holidays We/Férié
		Full day
Individual Individuel	£ 22,5	£ 27,5
Couple Couple	£ 45	£ 55

Caddie Caddie no — **Electric Trolley** Chariot électrique no
Buggy Voiturette yes — **Clubs** Clubs yes

Credit cards Cartes de crédit
VISA - Eurocard - MasterCard (Pro Shop goods only)

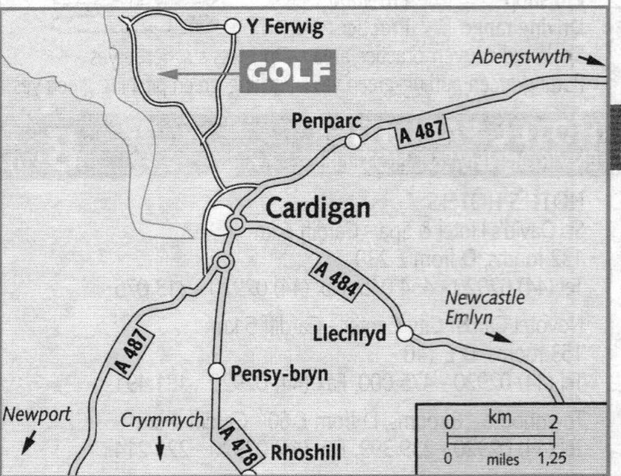

Access Accès : A 487 Cardigan to Aberystwyth Road. Fork left at War Memorial, 2 km.
Map 6 on page 480 Carte 6 Page 480

GOLF COURSE — PARCOURS 14/20

Site	Site	
Maintenance	Entretien	
Architect	Architecte	I.E. Grant, Hawtree & Sons
Type	Type	links, meadowland
Relief	Relief	
Water in play	Eau en jeu	
Exp. to wind	Exposé au vent	
Trees in play	Arbres en jeu	

Scorecard Carte de score	Chp. Chp.	Mens Mess.	Ladies Da.
Length Long.	6019	5784	5022
Par	72	72	74
Slope system	—	—	—

Advised golfing ability Niveau de jeu recommandé 0 12 24 36
Hcp required Handicap exigé no

CLUB HOUSE & AMENITIES — CLUB HOUSE ET ANNEXES 6/10

Pro shop Pro-shop
Driving range Practice
Sheltered couvert yes - **On grass** sur herbe yes - **Putting-green** putting-green yes - **Pitching-green** pitching green no

HOTEL FACILITIES — ENVIRONNEMENT HOTELIER 5/10

HOTELS HÔTELS
Gwbert Hotel - Gwbert-on-Sea 1 km
16 rooms, D £ 97
Tel (44) 01239 - 621 241, Fax (44) 01239 - 621 474

Penrallt - 16 rooms, D £ 110 - Aberporth 10 km
Tel (44) 01239 - 810 227, Fax (44) 01239 - 811 375

Pentbontbren Farm Hotel - 10 rooms, D £ 95 - Cardigan 3 km
Tel (44) 01239 - 810 248, Fax (44) 01239 - 811 129

RESTAURANTS RESTAURANTS
Penbontbren Farm Hotel - Cardigan 3 km
Tel (44) 01239 - 810 248
Gwbert Hotel - Gwbert-on-Sea 1 km
Tel (44) 01239 - 621 241

Carmarthen

14 | 7 | 4

Don't be fooled by the yardage, which is relatively short except for the first hole, an intimidating long and tough par 4. And watch out for the 17th, where the two-tiered green is treacherous enough to ruin any card. With this said, if you can move the ball both ways, have a certain instinct for the game and a fair degree of humility, approach this course with a serious but modest intent. There are no gimmicks or artificial-looking hazards here: it is quite simply a great test of golf, pleasant to walk despite the rolling terrain and a peaceful site out in the countryside. It gets pretty wet here in winter so try to make it in spring or summer. If you have the time, have a drink or (even better) take lunch after your round in the clubhouse and savour some splendid views of the Welsh coast. This should offer some consolation for shooting over your handicap on a course that J.H. Taylor obviously had great fun building.

La longueur réduite de ce parcours ne doit pas faire illusion. D'ailleurs, il commence par un long et difficile par 4 pour vous intimider, et le 17 se termine par un green à double plateau, assez traître pour vous casser la carte. Mais si vous avez quelque talent du maniement de balle, l'instinct du jeu, et une certaine humilité, prenez ce parcours avec sérieux et modestie. Pas de "gimmicks" ici, pas de décoration artificielle, pas de grands mouvements de terrain, c'est tout simplement un très bon test de golf, agréable à marcher en dépit de ses ondulations, un lieu de calme aussi en pleine campagne. Il peut être humide en hiver, venez plutôt aux beaux jours. Et comme vous serez bien reçu, prenez le temps de prendre un verre ou (encore mieux) de déjeuner après votre parcours devant l'un des plus beaux panoramas que l'on puisse trouver sur la côte galloise. Cela vous consolera de ne pas avoir cassé le par sur un parcours que J.H. Taylor a dû prendre beaucoup de plaisir à dessiner.

Carmarthen Golf Club — 1928

Rhydymarchog, Blaen-y-Coed Road
WAL - CARMARTHEN SA33 6EH

Office	Secrétariat	(44) 01267 - 281 588
Pro shop	Pro-shop	(44) 01267 - 281 493
Fax	Fax	(44) 01267 - 281 493
Web	www.carmarthengolfclub.com	
Situation	Situation	Carmarthen, 6 km
Annual closure	Fermeture annuelle	no
Weekly closure	Fermeture hebdomadaire	Wednesday, Restaurant only

Fees main season Tarifs haute saison — 18 holes

	Week days Semaine	We/Bank holidays We/Férié
Individual Individuel	£ 20	£ 25
Couple Couple	£ 40	£ 50

Half price when playing with a member

Caddie Caddie no — **Electric Trolley** Chariot électrique yes
Buggy Voiturette yes — **Clubs** Clubs yes
Credit cards Cartes de crédit
VISA - MasterCard (Pro shop only)

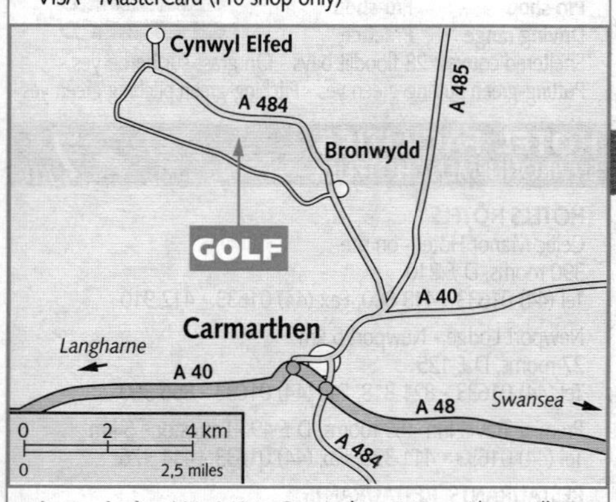

Access Accès : M4, A48 to Carmarthen, A40 → Abergwilli, then A484 North, left on Blaen-y-Coed road.
Map 6 on page 480 Carte 6 Page 480

GOLF COURSE — PARCOURS — 14/20

Site	Site	
Maintenance	Entretien	
Architect	Architecte	J.H. Taylor
Type	Type	parkland
Relief	Relief	
Water in play	Eau en jeu	
Exp. to wind	Exposé au vent	
Trees in play	Arbres en jeu	

Scorecard Carte de score	Chp. Chp.	Mens Mess.	Ladies Da.
Length Long.	5621	5433	4815
Par	71	71	72
Slope system	—	—	—

Advised golfing ability Niveau de jeu recommandé — 0 12 24 36
Hcp required Handicap exigé — certificate

CLUB HOUSE & AMENITIES — CLUB HOUSE ET ANNEXES — 7/10

Pro shop	Pro-shop	
Driving range	Practice	

Sheltered couvert large practice area - On grass sur herbe yes - Putting-green putting-green yes - Pitching-green pitching green yes

HOTEL FACILITIES — ENVIRONNEMENT HOTELIER — 4/10

HOTELS HÔTELS

Falcon - Carmarthen 7 km
18 rooms, D £ 66
Tel (44) 01267 - 234 959, Fax (44) 01267 - 221 277

Hurst House - Laugharne 19 km
7 rooms, D £ 150
Tel (44) 01994 - 427 417, Fax (44) 01994 - 427 730

RESTAURANTS RESTAURANTS

Ty Mawr Country House - Brechfa 15 km
Tel (44) 01267 - 202 332

Hurst House - Laugharne 19 km
Tel (44) 01994 - 427 417

Celtic Manor *Roman Road*

17	9	7

The Roman Road course was the first to be constructed at what has been developed as one of the most exciting complexes in Wales. It was designed by Robert Trent Jones Jr. (of Welsh stock), who was also the architect for the Wentwood Hills course, which is to host the 2010 Ryder Cup. Constructed around a valley near to the River Usk, Wentwood Hills is a monster at around 6,700 metres providing a challenge for the more accomplished golfer. However, millions of pounds have been poured into making Celtic Manor a hugely successful venture and the Roman Road course is a much more gentle challenge for the average golfer. As the name suggests, you come across the remains of a Roman road and even an ancient school for gladiators, although the battles fought here nowadays are of a more peaceful nature with a little white ball. A buggy is advisable for some, as the American style course winds its way through or across lakes, ravines, trees, streams and huge bunkers before you finally get the ball onto some vast and finely contoured greens.

Le Roman Course a été le premier construit dans ce qui est devenu l'un de splus énormes complexes du pays. Il a été dessiné par Robert Trent Jones Jr. (d'origine galloise), également l'architecte de Wentwood Hills qui recevra la Ryder Cup 2010. Construit autour d'une vallée près de la rivière Usk, c'est un véritable monstre (très physique) de près de 6700 mètres à usage de joueurs les plus accomplis. Des millions de Livres ont été dépensées pour faire de Celtic Manor un succès, mais le présent parcours est bien plus amusant pour le commun des golfeurs. Comme son nom l'indique, on y trouve les restes d'une voie romaine et même d'une école de gladiateurs, mais on aura ici à batailler de manière plus pacifique. La voiturette est conseillée pour les moins en forme, car sur ce parcours, très américain de style, on se promène au gré des lacs, des ravins, des bois, des cours d'eau et des immenses bunkers, avant de parvenir à poser sa balle sur de vastes greens très travaillés.

Celtic Manor — 1995

Coldra Woods
WAL - NEWPORT NP6 2YA

Office	Secrétariat	(44) 01633 - 413 000
Pro shop	Pro-shop	(44) 01633 - 410 312
Fax	Fax	(44) 01633 - 410 309
Web	www.celtic-manor.com	
Situation	Situation	Cardiff, 25 km

Newport (pop. 133 318), 5 km

Annual closure	Fermeture annuelle	no
Weekly closure	Fermeture hebdomadaire	no

Fees main season Tarifs haute saison — 18 holes

	Week days / Semaine	We/Bank holidays / We/Férié
Individual Individuel	£ 60	£ 60
Couple Couple	£ 120	£ 120

* Full week day: £ 74

Caddie Caddie no — **Electric Trolley** Chariot électrique no

Buggy Voiturette yes — **Clubs** Clubs yes

Credit cards Cartes de crédit
VISA - MasterCard - AMEX - Switch

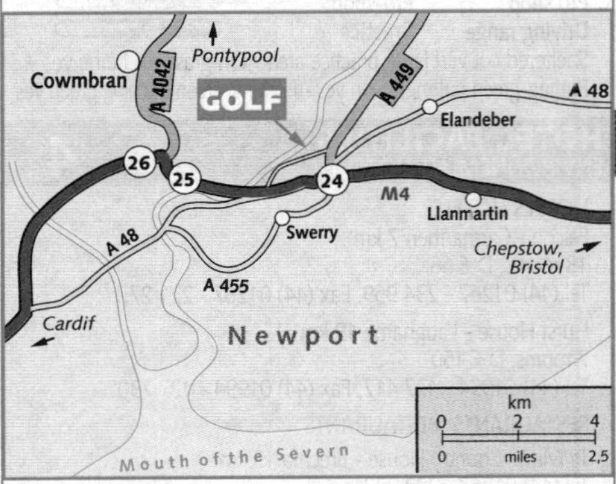

Access Accès : M4 Jct 24, then A48 → Newport
First right at Royal Oak Public House.
Turn right at top of the hill. Golf on right hand side.
Map 6 on page 481 Carte 6 Page 481

GOLF COURSE — PARCOURS — 17/20

Site	Site	
Maintenance	Entretien	
Architect	Architecte	R. Trent Jones Jr.
Type	Type	parkland
Relief	Relief	
Water in play	Eau en jeu	
Exp. to wind	Exposé au vent	
Trees in play	Arbres en jeu	

Scorecard Carte de score	Chp. / Chp.	Mens / Mess.	Ladies / Da.
Length Long.	6371	5998	4430
Par	70	70	70
Slope system	—	—	—

Advised golfing ability Niveau de jeu recommandé — 0 12 24 36

Hcp required Handicap exigé — certificate

CLUB HOUSE & AMENITIES — CLUB HOUSE ET ANNEXES — 9/10

Pro shop Pro-shop
Driving range Practice
Sheltered couvert 28 floodlit bays - On grass sur herbe yes - Putting-green putting-green yes - Pitching-green pitching green yes

HOTEL FACILITIES — ENVIRONNEMENT HOTELIER — 7/10

HOTELS HÔTELS

Celtic Manor Hotel - on site
390 rooms, D £ 210
Tel (44) 01633 - 413 000, Fax (44) 01633 - 412 910

Newport Lodge - Newport 5 km
27 rooms, D £ 125
Tel (44) 01633 - 821 818, Fax (44) 01633 - 856 360

Premier Travel Inn - 63 rooms, D £ 49 - Langstone 5 km
Tel (44) 01633 - 411 390, Fax (44) 01633 - 411 376

RESTAURANTS RESTAURANTS

Hedley's (Celtic Manor) - on site - Tel (44) 01633 - 413 000
Olive Tree (Celtic Manor) - on site - Tel (44) 01633 - 413 000
The Chandlery - Newport 5 km - Tel (44) 01633 - 256 622

Conwy

16 | 7 | 7

Sections of the artificial port created to prepare for the 1944 Normandy landings were built behind the green on the 2nd hole. This is only one page of history amongst many others, as the city has retained much of its ancient buildings and even held onto its medieval ramparts. The club has had five different club-houses in its time and the lastest opened in 1996. The course does not feature any dramatic changes in elevation, but there is never any question of tedium thanks to subtle shifts in landscape and the ubiquitous gorse. Naturally, you can add to this the course's own specific headaches, including prodigious length from the very back tees. Playing further forward is recommended. In every aspect this is a perfectly honest layout, where the penalty to pay matches the gravity of your mis-hit. Very natural and with obvious personality, Conwy deserves a prolonged and respectful visit.

Derrière le green du 2 ont été construites en 1943 des portions du port artificiel du débarquement de 1944. Ce n'est qu'une page d'histoire parmi d'autres, car la ville a conservé de nombreuses vieilles maisons et jusqu'à ses remparts médiévaux. Né de la passion pour le golf d'Ecossais puis de citoyens de Liverpool, le club a connu cinq club-houses différents, celui-ci datant de 1996. Le parcours a lui aussi évolué, notamment sa longueur, désormais respectable. Malgré le peu de relief, il échappe à la monotonie grâce à de subtils mouvements de terrain, et aussi à l'omniprésence de buissons d'ajoncs. Il faut encore y ajouter les difficultés propres du parcours, très long des départs les plus reculés, mais plus accessible des départs avancés. Sur tous les plans, il est d'une parfaite franchise, les punitions étant à la hauteur de la gravité des fautes commises. Très naturel, avec son évidente personnalité, et un accueil très chaleureux, Conwy mérite une visite aussi prolongée que respectueuse.

Conwy (Caernarvonshire) Golf Club — 1890

Morfa
WAL - CONWY, Gwynedd LL32 8 ER

Office	Secrétariat	(44) 01492 - 592 423
Pro shop	Pro-shop	(44) 01492 - 593 225
Fax	Fax	(44) 01492 - 593 363
Web	www.conwygolfclub.co.uk	
Situation	Situation	Colwyn Bay, 8 km

Llandudno (pop. 18 647), 4 km

Annual closure	Fermeture annuelle	no
Weekly closure	Fermeture hebdomadaire	no
Fees main season	Tarifs haute saison	18 holes

	Week days / Semaine	We/Bank holidays / We/Férié
Individual Individuel	£ 34	£ 39
Couple Couple	£ 68	£ 78

* Full day: £ 39 and £ 44 (We)

Caddie Caddie no — **Electric Trolley** Chariot électrique yes
Buggy Voiturette yes — **Clubs** Clubs no
Credit cards Cartes de crédit
VISA - MasterCard

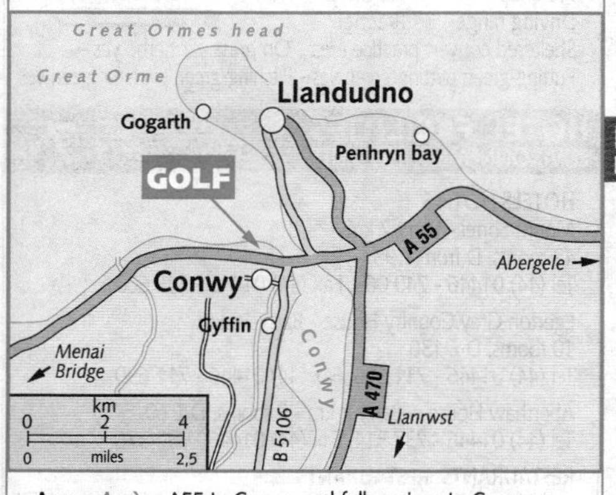

Access Accès : A55 to Conwy and follow signs to Conwy Marina.
Map 5 on page 478 Carte 5 Page 478

GOLF COURSE — PARCOURS — 16/20

Site	Site	
Maintenance	Entretien	
Architect	Architecte	unknown
Type	Type	links
Relief	Relief	
Water in play	Eau en jeu	
Exp. to wind	Exposé au vent	
Trees in play	Arbres en jeu	

Scorecard / Carte de score	Chp. / Chp.	Mens / Mess.	Ladies / Da.
Length Long.	6049	5819	5299
Par	72	72	74
Slope system	—	—	—

Advised golfing ability / Niveau de jeu recommandé: 0 12 24 36
Hcp required / Handicap exigé: certificate

CLUB HOUSE & AMENITIES — CLUB HOUSE ET ANNEXES — 7/10

Pro shop — Pro-shop
Driving range — Practice
Sheltered couvert no - On grass sur herbe yes - Putting-green putting-green yes - Pitching-green pitching green yes

HOTEL FACILITIES — ENVIRONNEMENT HOTELIER — 7/10

HOTELS HÔTELS
Bodysgallen Hall - 36 rooms, D from £ 175 - Llandudno 6 km
Tel (44) 01492 - 584 466, Fax (44) 01492 - 582 519

Berthlwyd Hall - 5 rooms, D from £ 70 - Conwy 3 km
Tel (44) 01492 - 592 409, Fax (44) 01492 - 572 290

Old Rectory - Llansanffraid Glan Conwy 6 km
6 rooms, D £ 130
Tel (44) 01492 - 580 611, Fax (44) 01492 - 584 555

RESTAURANTS RESTAURANTS
Lanterns - Llandudno 6 km - Tel (44) 01492 - 877 924
Paysanne - Deganwy 5 km - Tel (44) 01492 - 582 079
Old Rectory - Llansanffraid Glan Conwy 6 km
Tel (44) 01492 - 580 611

Glamorganshire

14	7	7

This is the fourth oldest club in Wales and the first inland course. Perched above the Bristol Channel, it provides some splendid views over Glamorgan and Monmouthshire, and over the English counties on the other side as well. The architect is unknown, but he sure knew his job. Aside from links courses, this is how our ancestors enjoyed their golfing; forget the acres of white sand, the shining blue lakes and manicured grass. Tee it up, hit the approach from whatever position you happen to be in and try and stop your ball on firm, slick greens. Notwithstanding its old fashioned virtues, the general condition of the course is excellent but here the emphasis is on playability and strategy rather than aesthetics. This is a totally forthright course where you can't lie about your game or hide any chinks in the armour: it is tradition in its finest and most vivid form, with some golfing history to boot. This is where Dr. Frank Stableford invented the scoring system that bears his name (or was it at Wallasey?).

C'est le quatrième plus ancien club du Pays de Galles et le premier "inland". Du haut de son perchoir au dessus du Bristol Channel, il offre des vues sur le Glamorgan et le Monmouthshire, mais aussi sur trois Comtés anglais. On ne connaît pas son architecte mais il connaissait son métier. Mis à part les links, c'est ainsi que nos ancêtres vivaient le golf : oubliez les hectares de sable blanc, les lacs aux eaux bleues, les brins de gazon au garde-à-vous. Tapez la balle sur le tee, puis jouez votre approche comme sa position vous l'impose, et tâchez d'arrêter votre balle sur un green ferme et roulant. L'état général du parcours est excellent, mais rien n'est fait pour faire "beau" au détriment de "bien". Il est parfaitement franc, et vous ne pourrez pas mentir, maquiller vos défauts, c'est la tradition dans ce qu'elle a de plus vivant. En plus, vous avez l'histoire : le Dr Frank Stableford aurait inventé ici la formule de jeu qui porte son nom, un fait revendiqué également par le club de Wallasey.

The Glamorganshire Golf Club — 1890

Lavernock Road
ENG - PENARTH CF64 5UP

Office	Secrétariat	(44) 02920 - 701 185
Pro shop	Pro-shop	(44) 02920 - 707 401
Fax	Fax	(44) 02920 - 701 185
Web	www.glamorganshiregolfclub.co.uk	
Situation	Situation	

Cardiff (pop. 279 055), 16 km

Annual closure	Fermeture annuelle	no
Weekly closure	Fermeture hebdomadaire	no
Fees main season	Tarifs haute saison	Full day

	Week days / Semaine	We/Bank holidays / We/Férié
Individual Individuel	£ 35	£ 40
Couple Couple	£ 70	£ 80

Caddie Caddie no — **Electric Trolley** Chariot électrique yes

Buggy Voiturette yes — **Clubs** Clubs yes

Credit cards Cartes de crédit
VISA - MasterCard (Pro Shop goods & Green fees only)

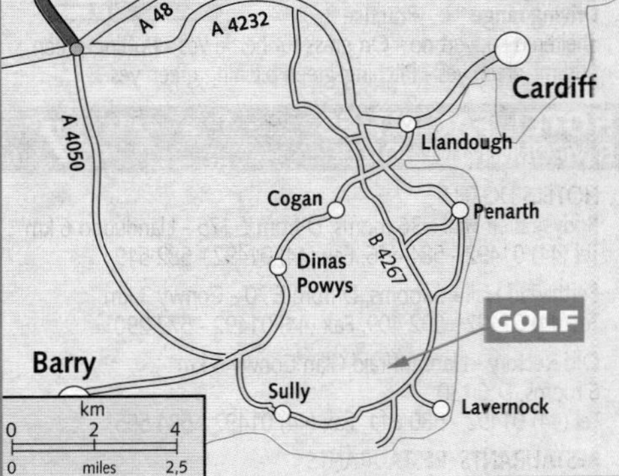

Access Accès : Cardiff South → Pennarth. B 4267 → Golf
Map 6 on page 481 Carte 6 Page 481

GOLF COURSE — PARCOURS — 14/20

Site	Site	
Maintenance	Entretien	
Architect	Architecte	unknown
Type	Type	parkland
Relief	Relief	
Water in play	Eau en jeu	
Exp. to wind	Exposé au vent	
Trees in play	Arbres en jeu	

Scorecard / Carte de score	Chp. / Chp.	Mens / Mess.	Ladies / Da.
Length Long.	5566	5345	5016
Par	70	70	72
Slope system	—	—	—

Advised golfing ability / Niveau de jeu recommandé: 0 12 24 36

Hcp required — Handicap exigé — certificate

CLUB HOUSE & AMENITIES — CLUB HOUSE ET ANNEXES — 7/10

Pro shop	Pro-shop
Driving range	Practice

Sheltered couvert practice area - On grass sur herbe yes - Putting-green putting-green yes - Pitching-green pitching green yes

HOTEL FACILITIES — ENVIRONNEMENT HOTELIER — 7/10

HOTELS HÔTELS

Mount Sorrel - Barry 7 km
42 rooms, D from £ 98
Tel (44) 01446 - 740 069, Fax (44) 01446 - 746 600

Egerton Grey Country House - Barry 10 km
10 rooms, D £ 130
Tel (44) 01446 - 711 666, Fax (44) 01446 - 711 690

Aberthaw House - Barry 8 km - 9 rooms, D £ 60
Tel (44) 01446 - 737 314, Fax (44) 01446 - 732 376

RESTAURANTS RESTAURANTS

Quayle's - Cardiff 16 km - Tel (44) 029 - 2034 1264
Armless Dragon - Cardiff 16 km - Tel (44) 029 - 2038 2357
Valentino's (Italian) - Cardiff 16 km - Tel (44) 029 - 2022 9697

Holyhead

16 | 7 | 5

The Menai Bridge effectively makes Anglesey a peninsula rather than an island, and it ensures that Trearddur Bay (as Holyhead is properly known) is one of Wales' most popular and best known golf courses. This course is difficult in the wind, but that is true for all links courses. It is short enough not to have staged very many prestigious tournaments, and rather hilly with tight, neatly contoured fairways. The natural rough is often dotted with thick heather, broom, gorse and even ferns, so it is an honest test for players of all levels (it was designed by James Braid, which says it all) with some of the best greens in the country. Exciting to play, intelligent and imaginative, Holyhead is well worth going out of your way for, especially as a new road across the island makes it even easier to get to, and in the summer is quite superb.

Le pont a fait d'Anglesey une presqu'île, et de "Trearddur Bay" (comme on appelle Holyhead) une oeuvre accessible et mieux connue. Les joueurs locaux vous raconteront quelques horribles histoires sur des golfeurs perdus et des scores terrifiants, mais le Pays de Galles est aussi celui des contes de fées. Ce parcours est difficile par grand vent, mais c'est le cas de tous les links. Assez court, ce qui explique qu'il n'ait pas reçu beaucoup de championnats très prestigieux, pas trop accidenté, il a des fairways étroits, bien modelés, des roughs naturels souvent parsemés d'une dense végétation de bruyère, de genêts, d'ajoncs et même de fougères. C'est un test d'une grande franchise pour tous les niveaux (il est signé James Braid, une référence), avec des greens parmi les meilleurs du pays. Superbe au printemps, excitant à jouer, intelligent et imaginatif, Holyhead mérite le détour, d'autant qu'il est maintenant beaucoup plus facile d'y accéder. En été, c'est une splendeur.

Holyhead (Caergybi) Golf Club 1912

Lon Carreg Fawr, Trearddur Bay
WAL - HOLYHEAD, Gwynedd LL65 2YG

Office Secrétariat (44) 01407 - 763 279
Pro shop Pro-shop (44) 01407 - 762 022
Fax Fax (44) 01407 - 763 279
Web www. holyheadgolfclub.co.uk
Situation Situation Holyhead (pop. 11 796), 3 km
Annual closure Fermeture annuelle no
Weekly closure Fermeture hebdomadaire no

Fees main season Tarifs haute saison Full day

	Week days Semaine	We/Bank holidays We/Férié
Individual Individuel	£ 25	£ 30
Couple Couple	£ 50	£ 60

Full day: £ 25/£29

Caddie Caddie no — **Electric Trolley** Chariot électrique no
Buggy Voiturette yes — **Clubs** Clubs yes
Credit cards Cartes de crédit
VISA - Mastercard (Pro shop only)

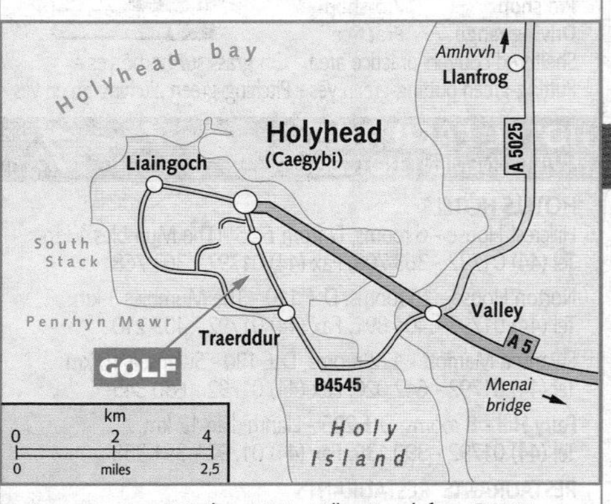

Access Accès : A55 then A5. In Valley, turn left on B4545.
Map 5 on page 478 Carte 5 Page 478

GOLF COURSE
PARCOURS — 16/20

Site	Site	
Maintenance	Entretien	
Architect	Architecte	James Braid
Type	Type	heathland
Relief	Relief	
Water in play	Eau en jeu	
Exp. to wind	Exposé au vent	
Trees in play	Arbres en jeu	

Scorecard Carte de score	Chp. Chp.	Mens Mess.	Ladies Da.
Length Long.	5922	5180	4825
Par	71	68	72
Slope system	—	—	—

Advised golfing ability 0 12 24 36
Niveau de jeu recommandé
Hcp required Handicap exigé certificate

CLUB HOUSE & AMENITIES
CLUB HOUSE ET ANNEXES — 7/10

Pro shop Pro-shop
Driving range Practice
Sheltered couvert no - On grass sur herbe no - Putting-green putting-green yes - Pitching-green pitching green yes

HOTEL FACILITIES
ENVIRONNEMENT HOTELIER — 5/10

HOTELS HÔTELS
Trearddur Bay Hotel - Holyhead 3 km
42 rooms, D £ 128
Tel (44) 01407 - 860 301, Fax (44) 01407 - 861 181

Yr Hendre - Holyhead 3 km
3 rooms, D £ 60
Tel (44) 01407 - 762 929, Fax (44) 01407 - 765 936

Dormy House - on site
7 rooms, D £ 140 (GF with dinner)
Tel (44) 01407 - 763 279, Fax (44) 01407 - 763 279

RESTAURANTS RESTAURANTS
Trearddur Bay Hotel - Holyhead 3 km
Tel (44) 01407 - 860 301

Langland Bay

14	7	7

This course is located in the Mumbles, a water sports centre at the entrance to the Gower peninsula, and a designated area of outstanding natural beauty. Although rather hilly in places, Langland Bay is perfectly walkable, offering views to fire any imagination. However the small greens, a fiendish collection of bunkers and threatening rough quickly bring you back to golfing reality. In fact, the hazards were clearly forged with the course and are dangerous without being downright treacherous. Everything is on an open table in front of you, so it is up to you to cross swords with the hazards in the great tradition of openness and challenge that remains the James Braid hallmark. Imaginative but totally natural, the course has unique charm, and although the yardage is short by today's standards, par (gross or net) is never a walk-over. A number of international players are members here, so they too must find this course to their liking and to their standard.

Ce parcours est situé dans les Mumbles, centre de sports nautiques, et à l'entrée de la péninsule de Gower, qui est un site classé de grande beauté. Le site est assez accidenté à certains endroits mais il est assez facile de jouer à pied. La vue splendide va vite vous occuper, mais de petits greens, une quantité de bunkers et un rough menaçant vous ramènent vite aux réalités du parcours. Les obstacles ont été bien fondus dans le parcours, ils sont dangereux sans être traîtres. Mais attention, les arrières de green sont souvent peu accueillants! Tout est exposé devant vous, à vous de combattre les périls, dans la grande tradition de franchise et d'exigence mesurée de James Braid. Imaginatif tout en restant naturel, c'est un parcours au charme unique, et bien qu'il manque de longueur selon nos critères du jour, il n'est guère facile d'attaquer le par (en brut ou en net) avec toutes les chances de succès. Le club compte nombre de joueurs internationaux parmi ses membres, ils doivent sans doute trouver ce parcours à leur goût et à leur niveau.

Langland Bay Golf Club — 1901

The Mumbles
WAL - SWANSEA SA3 4QR

Office Secrétariat (44) 01792 - 361 721
Pro shop Pro-shop (44) 01792 - 366 186
Fax Fax (44) 01792 - 361 082
Web www.langlandbaygolfclub.com
Situation Situation Swansea, 10 km
Annual closure Fermeture annuelle no
Weekly closure Fermeture hebdomadaire no

Fees main season Tarifs haute saison		Full day
	Week days Semaine	**We/Bank holidays** We/Férié
Individual Individuel	£ 40	£ 50
Couple Couple	£ 80	£ 100

Caddie Caddie no — **Electric Trolley** Chariot électrique no
Buggy Voiturette no — **Clubs** Clubs no
Credit cards Cartes de crédit
VISA - Eurocard - Mastercard (Pro Shop goods only)

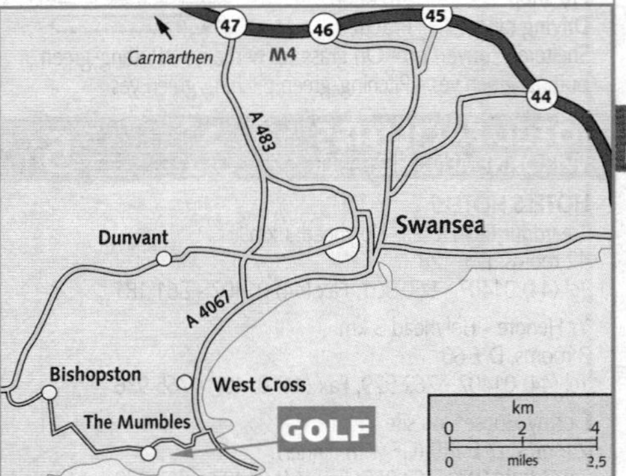

Access Accès : M4 exit 47 A4216 unto Swansea, then A4216 and to the end of A4067. Then → The Mumbles.
Map 6 on page 480 Carte 6 Page 480

GOLF COURSE — PARCOURS 14/20

Site Site
Maintenance Entretien
Architect Architecte — James Braid
Type Type — seaside course, parkland
Relief Relief
Water in play Eau en jeu
Exp. to wind Exposé au vent
Trees in play Arbres en jeu

Scorecard Carte de score	**Chp.** Chp.	**Mens** Mess.	**Ladies** Da.
Length Long.	5272	5146	4804
Par	70	70	73
Slope system	—	—	—

Advised golfing ability Niveau de jeu recommandé — 0 12 24 36
Hcp required Handicap exigé — certificate

CLUB HOUSE & AMENITIES — CLUB HOUSE ET ANNEXES 7/10

Pro shop Pro-shop
Driving range Practice
Sheltered couvert practice area - On grass sur herbe yes - Putting-green putting-green yes - Pitching-green pitching green yes

HOTEL FACILITIES — ENVIRONNEMENT HOTELIER 7/10

HOTELS HÔTELS

Hillcrest House - 6 rooms, D from £ 85 - The Mumbles 1 km
Tel (44) 01792 - 363 700, Fax (44) 01792 - 363 768

Norton House - 15 rooms, D £ 110 - The Mumbles 1 km
Tel (44) 01792 - 404 891, Fax (44) 01792 - 403 210

Swansea Marriott - 122 rooms, D £ 120 - Swansea 10 km
Tel (44) 01792 - 642 020, Fax (44) 01792 - 650 345

Fairy Hill - 8 rooms, D £ 225 - Llanrhidian 12 km
Tel (44) 01792 - 390 139, Fax (44) 01792 - 391 358

RESTAURANTS RESTAURANTS

Dermott's - Swansea 10 km - Tel (44) 01792 - 459 050
Claude's Restaurant - The Mumbles 1 km Tel (44) 01792 - 366 006
Frederick's - The Mumbles 1 km - Tel (44) 01792 - 368 900

Llandudno (Maesdu)

16	5	7

This seaside resort owes its existence and reputation to the railways. It has preserved a very Victorian feel and physiognomy, still resisting the flash modern age of cars, motorcycles and planes. Yet there is nothing stuffy about this corner of the world, the air along the huge pier and sheltered promenades is far too keen for that. The course was created in the early part of the 20th century, designed by one Tom Jones (whatever happened to him?) in a superb setting and beautiful parkland style with a few links features to add a little extra spice. This is yet another example of traditional architecture, built at a time when there were few resources to shift earth but a great deal of imagination in using existing terrain. Trees, bunkers and a few well-placed ponds provide the main ingredients of a pleasant challenge, where holiday-makers can have fun and good amateur golfers let rip. A particularly high mark should go to the excellence of the course's maintenance, especially the greens.

Cette station balnéaire a dû sa construction et sa notoriété au chemin de fer. Elle en gardé un esprit et une physionomie très victoriens, résistant au modernisme et au clinquant, à l'heure de l'automobile, de la moto et de l'avion. Rien pourtant ici ne sent la poussière, l'air est trop vif le long de l'immense jetée et des promenades abritées. Ce parcours est né au début du XXème siècle, sous le crayon d'un Tom Jones qui n'a guère laissé de traces indélébiles. Celui-ci bénéficie d'un environnement superbe, d'une esthétique de golf "parkland" avec quelques traits de links pour épicer le plat. C'est encore un bon exemple de l'architecture traditionnelle, disposant alors de peu de moyens pour remuer la terre, mais de pas mal d'imagination pour utiliser le terrain existant. Des arbres, des bunkers, et quelques mares bien placées fournissent les éléments d'un challenge agréable, où les vacanciers pourront s'amuser, et les bons amateurs se déchaîner. La qualité de l'entretien et en particulier des greens est à noter.

Llandudno (Maesdu) Golf Club — 1915

Hospital Road
WAL - LLANDUDNO LL30 1HU

Office	Secrétariat	(44) 01492 - 876 450
Pro shop	Pro-shop	(44) 01492 - 876 450
Fax	Fax	(44) 01492 - 876 450
Web	—	
Situation	Situation	Llandudno, 1,5 km
Annual closure	Fermeture annuelle	no
Weekly closure	Fermeture hebdomadaire	no
Fees main season	Tarifs haute saison	18 holes

	Week days / Semaine	We/Bank holidays / We/Férié
Individual Individuel	£ 25	£ 30
Couple Couple	£ 50	£ 60

Full day: £ 30 and £ 35 (We)

Caddie Caddie no — **Electric Trolley** Chariot électrique no

Buggy Voiturette yes — **Clubs** Clubs no

Credit cards Cartes de crédit
VISA - Eurocard - Mastercard - Switch (Pro Shop goods only)

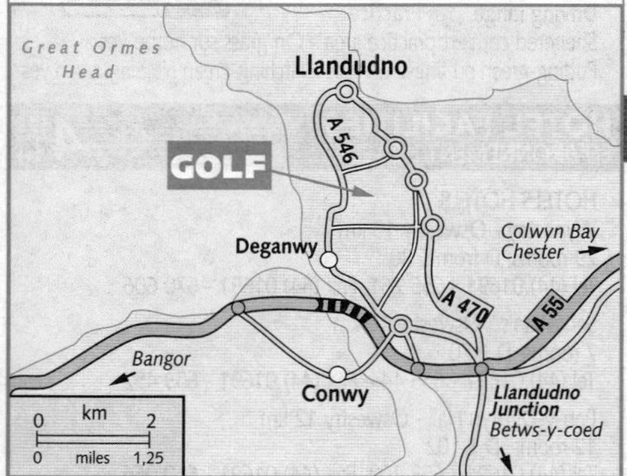

Access Accès : Manchester & Liverpool, A55, then A470 to Llandudno. Golf near the Hospital.
Map 5 on page 478 Carte 5 Page 478

GOLF COURSE — PARCOURS — 16/20

Site	Site	
Maintenance	Entretien	
Architect	Architecte	Tom Jones
Type	Type	parkland
Relief	Relief	
Water in play	Eau en jeu	
Exp. to wind	Exposé au vent	
Trees in play	Arbres en jeu	

Scorecard / Carte de score	Chp. / Chp.	Mens / Mess.	Ladies / Da.
Length Long.	5891	5630	5095
Par	72	72	75
Slope system	—	—	—

Advised golfing ability / Niveau de jeu recommandé: 0 12 24 36

Hcp required Handicap exigé: certificate

CLUB HOUSE & AMENITIES — CLUB HOUSE ET ANNEXES — 5/10

Pro shop Pro-shop
Driving range Practice
Sheltered couvert practice area - On grass sur herbe yes -
Putting-green putting-green yes - Pitching-green pitching green yes

HOTEL FACILITIES — ENVIRONNEMENT HOTELIER — 7/10

HOTELS HÔTELS
Bodysgallen Hall - Llandudno 4 km
36 rooms, D from £ 175
Tel (44) 01492 - 584 466, Fax (44) 01492 - 582 519

St. Tudno - 18 rooms, D £ 180 - Llandudno 1 km
Tel (44) 01492 - 874 411, Fax (44) 01492 - 860 407

Empire - 50 rooms, D £ 115 - Llandudno 1 km
Tel (44) 01492 - 860 555, Fax (44) 01492 - 860 791

The Wilton - 14 rooms, D £ 50 - Llandudno 1 km
Tel (44) 01492 - 878 343, Fax (44) 01492 - 876 086

RESTAURANTS RESTAURANTS
Mamma Rosa - Llandudno 1 km - Tel (44) 01492 - 870 070
Lanterns - Llandudno 1 km - Tel (44) 01492 - 877 924

Llanymynech

14	6	4

Apart from the fact that the name is well nigh impossible to pronounce to all but Welsh speakers, there is a great novelty factor about playing at Llanymynech. You stand on the tee of the dog-legged fourth hole in Wales and play your second shot to the green in England! Two holes later the situation is reversed as 15 holes are in the Principality and three in England. The course is also famous as the site of a battle with the Romans and as the place where the young Ian Woosnam learned the game. If that was not enough, it happens to be a good golf course, where the topology has been expertly utilized. A number of greens are elevated and a few ditches look safely out of range but, beware, it is an optical illusion as they wait for your ball. The perspectives here can be deceiving, therefore, even though the hilly terrain is not too taxing to walk. Varied and pleasing to the eye – the views from the 12th hole are stunning – there is no let up here if you want to card a good score. But it also presents the opportunity to have some fun with family on a course which is a short and interesting challenge.

A part le fait que son nom est impossible à prononcer, il y a ici quelque chose d'unique. Au départ du 4, vous êtes au Pays de Galles, en arrivant à votre balle pour jouer le green, vous êtes en Angleterre, et inversement deux trous plus tard, après trois trous "à l'étranger". Ce parcours est aussi fameux pour avoir été le site d'une bataille contre les Romains, et parce que Ian Woosnam y a exercé ses premiers talents. Cela dit, c'est aussi un bon parcours, où les accidents du terrain ont été utilisés intelligemment. Quelques greens sont ainsi surélevés, quelques fossés vous paraissent bien lointains, mais ils sont très proches pour les balles. Les perspectives offertes par les dénivellées sont parfois trompeuses, même si les reliefs ne sont pas un obstacle au jeu à pied. Varié, plaisant visuellement – la vue du 12 est magnifique – il ne permet guère de répit si l'on veut bien scorer. Mais on peut aussi s'y amuser entre amis ou en famille. Bref, un vrai bon golf, qui propose un bon défi à relever.

Llanymynech Golf Club — 1933

Pant
ENG - OSWESTRY SY10 8LB

Office	Secrétariat	(44) 01691 - 830 983
Pro shop	Pro-shop	(44) 01691 - 830 879
Fax	Fax	—
Web	www.llanymynechgolfclub.co.uk	
Situation	Situation	Oswestry, 10 km
Annual closure	Fermeture annuelle	no
Weekly closure	Fermeture hebdomadaire	no
Fees main season	Tarifs haute saison	18 holes

	Week days / Semaine	We/Bank holidays / We/Férié
Individual Individuel	£ 20	£ 25
Couple Couple	£ 40	£ 50

Full week day: £ 30. Reductions for Juniors.

Caddie Caddie no — **Electric Trolley** Chariot électrique no

Buggy Voiturette no — **Clubs** Clubs yes

Credit cards Cartes de crédit no

Access Accès : Manchester & Liverpool: M56, then M53, A55, A483 unto Ruabon, A5 unto Oswestry, then A483 again → Welshpool. Golf on right hand side (Pant).
Map 5 on page 478 Carte 5 Page 478

GOLF COURSE — PARCOURS — 14/20

Site	Site	
Maintenance	Entretien	
Architect	Architecte	unknown
Type	Type	open country, upland
Relief	Relief	
Water in play	Eau en jeu	
Exp. to wind	Exposé au vent	
Trees in play	Arbres en jeu	

Scorecard Carte de score	Chp. Chp.	Mens Mess.	Ladies Da.
Length Long.	5503	5310	4695
Par	70	70	71
Slope system	–	–	–

Advised golfing ability / Niveau de jeu recommandé: 0 12 24 36

Hcp required / Handicap exigé: certificate

CLUB HOUSE & AMENITIES — CLUB HOUSE ET ANNEXES — 6/10

Pro shop Pro-shop
Driving range Practice
Sheltered couvert practice area - On grass sur herbe yes
Putting-green putting-green yes - Pitching-green pitching green yes

HOTEL FACILITIES — ENVIRONNEMENT HOTELIER — 4/10

HOTELS HÔTELS

Wynnstay - Oswestry 10 km
29 rooms, D from £ 80
Tel (44) 01691 - 655 261, Fax (44) 01691 - 670 606

Sebastian's - Oswestry 10 km
7 rooms, D £ 70
Tel (44) 01691 - 655 444, Fax (44) 01691 - 653 452

Pen-y-Dyffryn Hall - Oswestry 12 km
12 rooms, D £ 102
Tel (44) 01691 - 653 700, Fax (44) 01691 - 650 066

RESTAURANTS RESTAURANTS

Sebastian's - Oswestry 10 km - Tel (44) 01691 - 655 444
Old Mill Inn - Llanforda 8 km - Tel (44) 01691 - 657 058

Marriott St Pierre *Old Course*

15	8	7

Managing this course allowed the Marriott group to rejuvenate and put the whole site centre-stage – so successfully that St Pierre was awarded the hosting of the Solheim Cup in 1996. With a hotel now set up in the little 14th century manor, the venue has become a leading resort which comprises two courses, the best known and most demanding of which is the "Old Course", a surprising name for a layout that was created as recently as 1961. Designed by C.K. Cotton, this has the style of a typical parkland course where the finishing holes bring a lot of water into play. It is certainly not the world's most subtle course, but this honesty has the advantage of letting the golfer feel immediately at home and of carding the score he or she really deserves. We would advise green-feers not to go for the back-tees, especially on the 18th, a huge par 3.

L'achat de ce golf par le groupe Marriott a permis un rajeunissement notable, ce qui lui a permis de recevoir la Solheim Cup en 1996. Avec son hôtel installé dans un petit manoir du XIVème siècle, c'est devenu un "resort" important, qui comprend deux parcours dont le plus connu et le plus exigeant est le "Old Course," dénommé ainsi bien qu'il ne date que de 1961. Dessiné par C.K. Cotton, c'est un parcours typique de l'esthétique de parcs avec quelques spécimens d'arbres magnifiques. Il commence par un interminable par 5, mais que l'on se rassure, la suite sera moins "inhumaine ", jusqu'au finale où l'eau est très en jeu, notamment au 18, un énorme par 3 de plus de 200 mètres. On conseillera donc aux visiteurs de ne pas choisir les départs arrière. Ce n'est sans doute pas le parcours le plus subtil du monde, mais cette franchise a l'avantage de permettre immédiatement de s'y sentir à l'aise, et de faire le score que l'on mérite vraiment. Et pour reprendre confiance, allez faire un tour sur le Mathern Course voisin.

Marriott St Pierre Hotel & Country Club 1961

St Pierre Park
WAL - CHEPSTOW, Gwent NP6 6YA

Office	Secrétariat	(44) 01291 - 625 261
Pro shop	Pro-shop	(44) 01291 - 635 205
Fax	Fax	(44) 01291 - 635 227
Web	www.marriott.com	
Situation	Situation	Newport, 20 km
Annual closure	Fermeture annuelle	no
Weekly closure	Fermeture hebdomadaire	no

Fees main season Tarifs haute saison		18 holes
	Week days Semaine	**We/Bank holidays** We/Férié
Individual Individuel	£ 60	£ 60
Couple Couple	£ 120	£ 120

We: booking essential / Hotel guests: £ 45

Caddie Caddie on request **Electric Trolley** Chariot électrique no

Buggy Voiturette yes **Clubs** Clubs yes

Credit cards Cartes de crédit
VISA - Mastercard - AMEX - DC

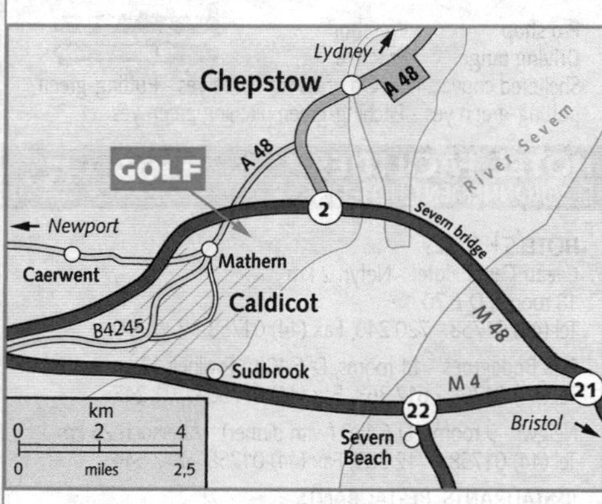

Access Accès : Newport A48 → Chepstow.
Golf 3 km (2 m. before Chepstow).
Map 6 on page 481 Carte 6 Page 481

GOLF COURSE
PARCOURS **15/20**

Site	Site	
Maintenance	Entretien	
Architect	Architecte	C.K. Cotton
Type	Type	parkland
Relief	Relief	
Water in play	Eau en jeu	
Exp. to wind	Exposé au vent	
Trees in play	Arbres en jeu	

Scorecard Carte de score	**Chp.** Chp.	**Mens** Mess.	**Ladies** Da.
Length Long.	6280	5920	5337
Par	71	71	75
Slope system	—	—	—

Advised golfing ability Niveau de jeu recommandé: 0 12 24 36

Hcp required Handicap exigé: no

CLUB HOUSE & AMENITIES
CLUB HOUSE ET ANNEXES **8/10**

Pro shop Pro-shop
Driving range Practice
Sheltered couvert 10 bays - On grass sur herbe yes - Putting-green putting-green yes - Pitching-green pitching green yes

HOTEL FACILITIES
ENVIRONNEMENT HOTELIER **7/10**

HOTELS HÔTELS
Marriott Hotel - on site
148 rooms, D from £ 156
Tel (44) 01291 - 625 261, Fax (44) 01291 - 629 975

George - Chepstow 3 km
14 rooms, D £ 86
Tel (44) 01291 - 625 363, Fax (44) 01291 - 627 418

Castle View - Chepstow 3 km
13 rooms, D £ 77
Tel (44) 01291 - 620 349, Fax (44) 01291 - 627 397

RESTAURANTS RESTAURANTS
Marriott Hotel - on site - Tel (44) 01291 - 625 261
Parva Farmhouse - Tintern 8 km - Tel (44) 01291 - 689 411

Nefyn & District

16	7	5

This course is hardly close to the major tourist routes, but the site at least deserves a visit. Spectaculaly perched atop cliffs, it is very similar to a links course although some holes are framed by heather rather than dunes. The course was founded in 1907, re-styled by J.H. Taylor and James Braid and completed in 1993. The site also houses a 9-holer between two sea inlets. The 18 hole course is no push-over but never too tough or unfair. You also have to play every shot in the book, compounded by the fact that you often have a choice between playing safe or "going for it". The latter option can turn out to be foolhardy indeed on certain blind-shots. Never mind, you can stop off at the pub close to the 12th hole to boost your sagging spirits before squaring up to a wonderful finish, of which for us the 15th is the crowning moment. Maintenance is excellent and the club-house extends a warm welcome.

Ce n'est pas exactement sur les autoroutes de touristes, mais le site au moins mérite une visite. Perché sur les falaises – on y voit la mer pratiquement de chaque départ – il est apparenté à un links, bien que certains trous soient plus définis par la bruyère que par les dunes. Ce golf a été fondé en 1907, remanié par J.H. Taylor et James Braid, et achevé en 1993. On y trouve aussi un 9 trous entre deux bras de mer. Le jeu n'est pas facile, mais n'est jamais trop sévère ni injuste. On doit d'autant plus y jouer toute la gamme des coups de golf que l'on a souvent le choix entre la sécurité et l'héroïsme, qui peut s'avérer folie sur certains coups aveugles. Mais on peut faire une halte pour reprendre ses esprits au pub non loin du green du 12, avant d'affronter un très beau finish, dont le 15 est pour nous le sommet. L'entretien est de très bonne qualité, même par temps hostile, et le club-house, refait à neuf, reste très chaleureux. Notre conseil ? Jouez les 27 trous !

Nefyn & District Golf Club — 1907

Morfa Nefyn
WAL - PWLLHELI, Gwynedd LL53 6DA

Office	Secrétariat	(44) 01758 - 720 966
Pro shop	Pro-shop	(44) 01758 - 720 102
Fax	Fax	(44) 01758 - 720 476
Web	www.nefyngolfclub.com	
Situation	Situation	Caernarfon, 32 km

Nefyn (pop. 2 548), 3 km

Annual closure	Fermeture annuelle	no
Weekly closure	Fermeture hebdomadaire	no

Fees main season Tarifs haute saison	18 holes	
	Week days Semaine	We/Bank holidays We/Férié
Individual Individuel	£ 31	£ 37*
Couple Couple	£ 62	£ 74*

Full day: £ 39 and £ 48 (We) / * We fee: Saturdays only

Caddie Caddie no — **Electric Trolley** Chariot électrique yes

Buggy Voiturette yes — **Clubs** Clubs yes

Credit cards Cartes de crédit
VISA - MasterCard (Pro shop only)

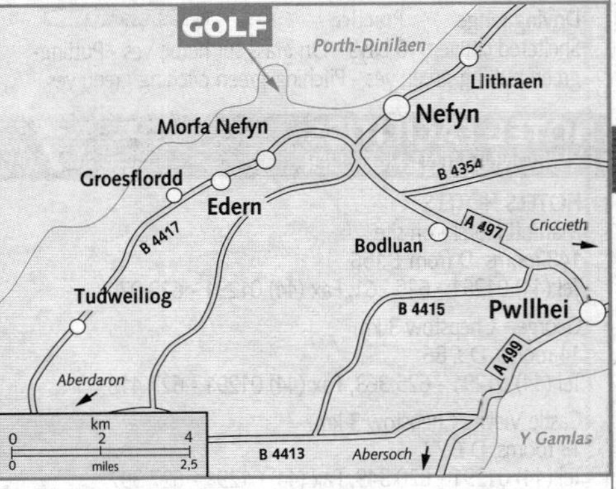

Access Accès : North coast Lleyn Peninsula, on B4417
Map 5 on page 478 Carte 5 Page 478

GOLF COURSE — PARCOURS — 16/20

Site	Site	
Maintenance	Entretien	
Architect	Architecte	James Braid J.H. Taylor
Type	Type	seaside course, links
Relief	Relief	
Water in play	Eau en jeu	
Exp. to wind	Exposé au vent	
Trees in play	Arbres en jeu	

Scorecard Carte de score	Chp. Chp.	Mens Mess.	Ladies Da.
Length Long.	5958	5750	5420
Par	71	71	75
Slope system	—	—	—

Advised golfing ability Niveau de jeu recommandé: 0 12 24 36

Hcp required Handicap exigé: no

CLUB HOUSE & AMENITIES — CLUB HOUSE ET ANNEXES — 7/10

Pro shop	Pro-shop
Driving range	Practice

Sheltered couvert no - On grass sur herbe yes - Putting-green putting-green yes - Pitching-green pitching green yes

HOTEL FACILITIES — ENVIRONNEMENT HOTELIER — 5/10

HOTELS HÔTELS

Caeau Capel Hotel - Nefyn 2 km
18 rooms, D £ 70
Tel (44) 01758 - 720 240, Fax (44) 01758 - 720 750

Plas Bodegroes - 11 rooms, D £ 100 - Pwllheli 12 km
Tel (44) 01758 - 612 363, Fax (44) 01758 - 701 247

Neigwl - 9 rooms, D £ 170 (with dinner) - Abersoch 25 km
Tel (44) 01758 - 712 363, Fax (44) 01758 - 712 544

RESTAURANTS RESTAURANTS

Plas Bodegroes - Pwllheli 12 km - Tel (44) 01758 - 612 363
Caeau Capel - Nefyn 2 km - Tel (44) 01758 - 720 240

Newport

15 | 6 | 7

A week's golfing in the Cardiff and Swansea region can comprise of playing a different course every day and of getting to know some superb and visually very contrasting layouts. Between St Pierre and Porthcawl, close to Celtic Manor, the Newport course is one of the best examples of a parkland golf course you could ever hope to find. What's more, green-keeping is excellent and the welcome from both the club-house and members is warm and friendly. They are rightly extremely proud of a varied layout with very reasonable yardage, spread over rolling landscape which is very pleasant to walk. You won't find any breathtaking designer ploys or excesses, just a sort of sobriety in a pretty country landscape. A quality course, quite simply.

Une semaine de golf dans la région de Cardiff et Swansea peut permettre de ne jamais jouer deux fois le même parcours, et d'en jouer de superbes, d'esthétiques très différentes, voire opposées, de jouer de grands resorts où l'argent n'a pas été compté ou des clubs d'ambitions plus simples, mais surtout pas moins sympathiques… Entre Marriott St Pierre et Porthcawl, près de l'immense Celtic Manor, le parcours de Newport est l'un des meilleurs exemples de golfs de parcs que l'on puisse trouver. Ce qui ne gâte rien, l'entretien y est toujours très soigné, et l'accueil, du club comme des membres, très amical et chaleureux. Ils sont fiers à juste raison d'un tracé très varié, et de longueur très raisonnable sur un terrain vallonné, mais où il est agréable de jouer à pied. On ne trouvera pas ici de trouvailles architecturales à couper le souffle, ni d'excès, mais une sorte de sobriété dans un joli paysage de campagne. La qualité, tout simplement.

Newport Golf Club — 1903

Great Oak, Rogerstone
WAL - NEWPORT, Gwent NP1 9FX

Office	Secrétariat	(44) 01633 - 892 643
Pro shop	Pro-shop	(44) 01633 - 893 271
Fax	Fax	(44) 01633 - 896 676
Web	—	
Situation	Situation	Newport, 6 km
Annual closure	Fermeture annuelle	no
Weekly closure	Fermeture hebdomadaire	no
Fees main season	Tarifs haute saison	18 holes

	Week days Semaine	We/Bank holidays We/Férié
Individual Individuel	£ 40	£ 45
Couple Couple	£ 80	£ 90

* Prior booking necessary / Full week day: £ 45

Caddie Caddie no — **Electric Trolley** Chariot électrique yes

Buggy Voiturette yes — **Clubs** Clubs yes

Credit cards Cartes de crédit
VISA - MasterCard

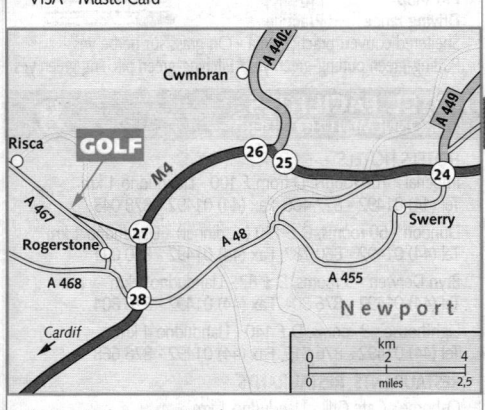

Access Accès : M4 Jct 27, then B4591.
Golf 1 km (1/2 m) W of exit.
Map 6 on page 481 Carte 6 Page 481

GOLF COURSE — PARCOURS — 15/20

Site	Site	
Maintenance	Entretien	
Architect	Architecte	unknown
Type	Type	parkland
Relief	Relief	
Water in play	Eau en jeu	
Exp. to wind	Exposé au vent	
Trees in play	Arbres en jeu	

Scorecard Carte de score	Chp. Chp.	Mens Mess.	Ladies Da.
Length Long.	5895	5632	5195
Par	72	72	74
Slope system	—	—	—

Advised golfing ability / Niveau de jeu recommandé: 0 12 24 36

Hcp required Handicap exigé: certificate

CLUB HOUSE & AMENITIES — CLUB HOUSE ET ANNEXES — 6/10

Pro shop Pro-shop
Driving range Practice
Sheltered couvert no - On grass sur herbe yes - Putting-green putting-green yes - Pitching-green pitching green yes

HOTEL FACILITIES — ENVIRONNEMENT HOTELIER — 7/10

HOTELS HÔTELS

Holiday Inn - 119 rooms, D from £ 70 - Newport 3 km
Tel (44) 01633 - 412 777, Fax (44) 01633 - 413 087

Newport Lodge - 27 rooms, D £ 125 - Newport 3 km
Tel (44) 01633 - 821 818, Fax (44) 01633 - 856 360

Parkway - 70 rooms, D £ 125 - Cwmbran 6 km
Tel (44) 01633 - 871 199, Fax (44) 01633 - 869 160

Celtic Manor Hotel - 432 rooms, D from £ 192- Newport 5 km
Tel (44) 01633 - 413 000, Fax (44) 01633 - 412 910

RESTAURANTS RESTAURANTS

Owens (Celtic Manor) - Newport 5 km
Tel (44) 01633 - 413 000

The Chandlery - Newport 5 km - Tel (44) 01633 - 256 622

North Wales (Llandudno)

16	6	8

Landudno is the seaside resort where Charles Dodgson (alias Lewis Carroll), treated his friends' children to readings of the stories that were to become Alice in Wonderland. It is also a resort where you can ride on one of the few cable-car tramways in the world to get to Great Orme's Head and see the Bronze Age copper mines. You will also find this rather little known links course, described by none other than Henry Cotton as a "gem". After a hesitant start, you are plunged into a landscape of dunes through which the course somehow winds it way. The front nine stretch alongside a railway line, the back nine return along the coastline, but the holes never run one behind the other; the direction they head in can cause a few surprises on your card. From one day to the next, a capricious wind can make life extremely complicated. There are good and bad things you will remember about this course, things like blind shots or weird ball positions. Not forgetting the gorse, heather and a few deep bunkers.

Llandudno, c'est la station balnéaire où Charles Dodgson (Lewis Carroll), racontait aux enfants de ses amis les futures histoires d'Alice au Pays des Merveilles. C'est aussi là que l'on peut prendre l'un des seuls tramways à câble du monde pour monter au Great Orme's Head, avec ses mines de cuivre de l'Age de Bronze. C'est enfin le site de ce links assez méconnu, décrit par Henry Cotton comme un "joyau". Après un départ hésitant, on plonge dans un paysage de dunes où se coule le parcours. Les neuf premiers trous longent une voie ferrée, les neuf derniers reviennent le long de la mer, mais les trous ne sont pas les uns derrière les autres, et leur orientation peut causer des surprises sur la carte. D'un jour à l'autre, les caprices du vent peuvent compliquer les choses. On se souviendra ici du bon et du mauvais caractère du parcours, qui peuvent vous réserver aussi bien des coups aveugles que des positions de balle bizarres. Ajoutons la bruyère, les ajoncs, et quelques profonds bunkers.

North Wales Golf Club — 1894

72 Brynian Road
WAL - WEST SHORE, LLANDUDNO LL30 2 DZ

Office	Secrétariat	(44) 01492 - 875 325
Pro shop	Pro-shop	(44) 01492 - 876 878
Fax	Fax	(44) 01492 - 873 355
Web		www.northwalesgolfclub.co.uk
Situation	Situation	Llandudno, 1 km
Annual closure	Fermeture annuelle	no
Weekly closure	Fermeture hebdomadaire	no
Fees main season	Tarifs haute saison	18 holes

	Week days / Semaine	We/Bank holidays / We/Férié
Individual Individuel	£ 30	£ 40
Couple Couple	£ 60	£ 80

Full day: £ 40/50 (We) / Monday: £ 20

Caddie Caddie no — **Electric Trolley** Chariot électrique no

Buggy Voiturette yes — **Clubs** Clubs yes

Credit cards Cartes de crédit
VISA - Eurocard - Mastercard (Pro shop goods only)

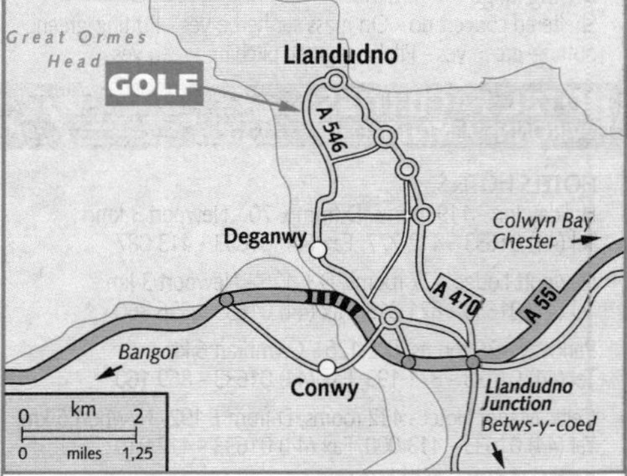

Access Accès : Manchester & Liverpool, A55, then A470 to Llandudno. Golf 1 km West of Llandudno on West Shore
Map 5 on page 478 Carte 5 Page 478

GOLF COURSE — PARCOURS — 16/20

Site	Site	
Maintenance	Entretien	
Architect	Architecte	unknown
Type	Type	links
Relief	Relief	
Water in play	Eau en jeu	
Exp. to wind	Exposé au vent	
Trees in play	Arbres en jeu	

Scorecard Carte de score	Chp. Chp.	Mens Mess.	Ladies Da.
Length Long.	5623	5331	5072
Par	71	71	73
Slope system	—	—	—

Advised golfing ability / Niveau de jeu recommandé: 0 12 24 36

Hcp required Handicap exigé: certificate

CLUB HOUSE & AMENITIES — CLUB HOUSE ET ANNEXES — 6/10

Pro shop Pro-shop
Driving range Practice
Sheltered couvert practice area - On grass sur herbe yes - Putting-green putting-green yes - Pitching-green pitching green yes

HOTEL FACILITIES — ENVIRONNEMENT HOTELIER — 8/10

HOTELS HÔTELS

Imperial - 100 rooms, D from £ 100 - Llandudno 1 km
Tel (44) 01492 - 877 466, Fax (44) 01492 - 378 043

Dunoon - 50 rooms, D £ 130 (w. dinner) - Llandudno 1 km
Tel (44) 01492 - 860 787, Fax (44) 01492 - 360 031

Bryn Derwen - 9 rooms, D £ 82 - Llandudno 1 km
Tel (44) 01492 - 876 804, Fax (44) 01492 - 376 804

Lighthouse - 3 rooms, D £ 140 - Llandudno 4 km
Tel (44) 01492 - 876 819, Fax (44) 01492 - 376 668

RESTAURANTS RESTAURANTS

Osborne's Cafe Grill - Llandudno 1 km
Tel (44) 01492 - 860 330

Garden Room - Llandudno 1 km - Tel (44) 01492 - 874 411

Terrace - Llandudno 1 km - Tel (44) 01492 - 874 411

Northop Country Park

15 | 9 | 6

The club-house is opulent and spacious, the adjacent hotel is luxurious, the nearby park is a beauty and golf course maintenance is virtually faultless. Northop County is one of Wales' newest courses but it has already hosted many high-level tournaments. It was designed by John Jacobs, one of the legendary names in modern golf instruction but not always as inspired as you might imagine when it comes to laying out a course. Here, though, he excelled himself for the whole course has been carefully designed in a rather classic British style and is becoming better as each passing year adds to its maturity. One decisive advantage here is that nothing is concealed from view and both reward and sanction are equal to the risk taken or mistake made. You can almost feel the teacher behind the architect. Amongst other excellent holes, the 8th is most memorable, a downhill par 5, together with the 16th, a slight dog-leg with trees and water on the right and in front of the green. An already high class course.

Le club-house est riche et grand, l'Hôtel adjacent est luxueux, le parc est beau, l'entretien presque sans fautes. Le parcours est récent, mais il a déjà reçu de nombreuses bonnes épreuves. Son auteur est John Jacobs, l'une des légendes de l'enseignement moderne de golf, mais pas toujours aussi inspiré comme architecte qu'on pourrait l'imaginer. Ici, il est à son meilleur. On en veut pour preuve cet ensemble très soigné, assez classiquement britannique, et chaque année qui passe lui ajoutant de la maturité, il se bonifie en vieillissant. Avantage décisif : rien n'est caché ici, et la récompense comme la punition sont à la hauteur du risque pris ou de la faute commise. On sent bien là l'enseignant derrière l'architecte ! Entre autres trous de qualité, on se souviendra du 8, un par 5 en descente, comme du 16, un léger dog-leg avec des arbres, de l'eau à droite comme devant le green. Un parcours de standard déjà élevé.

Northop Country Park — 1993

WAL - NORTHOP, Nr Chester, CH7 6WA

Office	Secrétariat	(44) 01352 - 840 440
Pro shop	Pro-shop	(44) 01352 - 840 440
Fax	Fax	(44) 01352 - 840 445
Web		—
Situation	Situation	Chester, 20 km
Annual closure	Fermeture annuelle	no
Weekly closure	Fermeture hebdomadaire	no

Fees main season Tarifs haute saison	Week days Semaine	We/Bank holidays We/Férié
	18 holes	
Individual Individuel	£ 40	£ 40
Couple Couple	£ 80	£ 80

Caddie Caddie no — Electric Trolley Chariot électrique no

Buggy Voiturette yes — Clubs Clubs yes

Credit cards Cartes de crédit
VISA - MasterCard

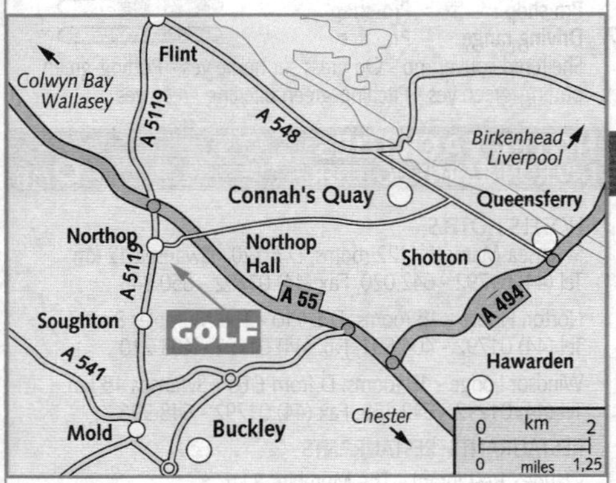

Access Accès : A55 (North Wales Coast Road).
Exit at Northop Connah's Quay.
Northop Country Park is on left side of exit road.
Map 5 on page 479 Carte 5 Page 479

GOLF COURSE — PARCOURS — 15/20

Site	Site	
Maintenance	Entretien	
Architect	Architecte	John Jacobs
Type	Type	parkland
Relief	Relief	
Water in play	Eau en jeu	
Exp. to wind	Exposé au vent	
Trees in play	Arbres en jeu	

Scorecard Carte de score	Chp. Chp.	Mens Mess.	Ladies Da.
Length Long.	6128	5765	4945
Par	72	72	72
Slope system	—	—	—

Advised golfing ability / Niveau de jeu recommandé: 0 12 24 36

Hcp required — Handicap exigé — yes

CLUB HOUSE & AMENITIES — CLUB HOUSE ET ANNEXES — 9/10

Pro shop — Pro-shop
Driving range — Practice
Sheltered couvert 6 bays - On grass sur herbe yes - Putting-green putting-green yes - Pitching-green pitching green yes

HOTEL FACILITIES — ENVIRONNEMENT HOTELIER — 6/10

HOTELS HÔTELS
St David's Park Hotel - Nr Chester 15 km
145 rooms, D £ 128
Tel (44) 01244 - 520 800, Fax (44) 01244 - 520 930

Kinsale Hall - Holywell 10 km
35 rooms, D £ 85
Tel (44) 01745 - 560 001, Fax (44) 01745 - 561 298

Crabwall Manor - 48 rooms, D £ 190 - Chester 15 km
Tel (44) 01244 - 851 666, Fax (44) 01244 - 851 400

RESTAURANTS RESTAURANTS
Crabwall Manor - Chester 15 km - Tel (44) 01244 - 851 666
Arkle - Chester 15 km - Tel (44) 01244 - 324 024

Pennard

17 | 6 | 6

Firstly there are the superb views over a rugged coastline, the sea, smugglers' beaches and dunes, then the countryside with remains of castles. In a highly romantic setting, don't ever let this course catch you napping. At first sight it can be intimidating with steep hills that make club selection a delicate business (there are a few blind shots to contend with) but the difficulties are not insurmountable even for a mid-handicapper, unless the wind begins to blow a little too hard. In calm weather, Pennard certainly could not claim to be a major championship course, but it is incredibly enjoyable both visually and technically. And when you do finally get to grips with it, you feel that you could be a good player. Course maintenance is of a very high standard, and the greens are slick and firm all year round (Winters are very mild here). Discovery strongly recommended.

D'abord il y a des vues exceptionnelles sur les côtes découpées, la mer, des plages de contrebandiers, les dunes, la campagne environnante, des châteaux en ruines. Dans un site hautement romantique, il faut éviter de rêver pour jouer ce parcours. Il peut intimider au premier abord avec ses reliefs qui compliquent notamment la sélection des clubs (quelques coups aveugles), mais ses difficultés ne sont pas insurmontables, même pour un joueur moyen, sauf si le vent se met à souffler un peu fort. Certes, par temps calme, Pennard ne saurait prétendre être un parcours de grands championnats car quelques trous sont un peu faibles par rapport à la qualité de certains autres, mais il procure un plaisir fou, visuellement et techniquement. Et quand vous parvenez à l'apprivoiser, vous avez l'impression d'être un grand joueur. L'entretien est ici très soigné, les greens rapides et fermes toute l'année (les hivers sont assez doux). Un endroit qui fait rêver qu'on ne bâtisse pas les villes à la campagne. A découvrir !

Pennard Golf Club 1896
2, Southgate Road, Southgate
WAL - SWANSEA SA3 2BT

Office	Secrétariat	(44) 01792 - 233 131
Pro shop	Pro-shop	(44) 01792 - 233 451
Fax	Fax	(44) 01792 - 234 797
Web		—
Situation	Situation	Swansea, 12 km
Annual closure	Fermeture annuelle	no
Weekly closure	Fermeture hebdomadaire	no

Fees main season / Tarifs haute saison	Week days / Semaine	We/Bank holidays / We/Férié
		Full day
Individual Individuel	£ 40	£ 50
Couple Couple	£ 80	£ 100

Caddie Caddie on request Electric Trolley Chariot électrique no

Buggy Voiturette no Clubs Clubs yes

Credit cards Cartes de crédit
VISA - Eurocard - Mastercard (Pro shop goods only)

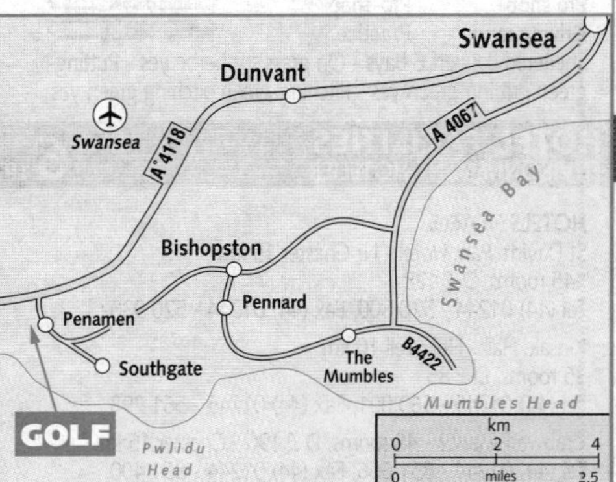

Access Accès : Cardiff, M4, A4067, B4436 to Pennard Church, → Golf
Map 6 on page 480 Carte 6 Page 480

GOLF COURSE
PARCOURS **17/20**

Site	Site	
Maintenance	Entretien	
Architect	Architecte	James Braid
Type	Type	links
Relief	Relief	
Water in play	Eau en jeu	
Exp. to wind	Exposé au vent	
Trees in play	Arbres en jeu	

Scorecard / Carte de score	Chp. / Chp.	Mens / Mess.	Ladies / Da.
Length Long.	5701	5508	4880
Par	71	71	73
Slope system	—	—	—

Advised golfing ability / Niveau de jeu recommandé: 0 12 24 36
Hcp required / Handicap exigé: certificate

CLUB HOUSE & AMENITIES
CLUB HOUSE ET ANNEXES **6/10**

Pro shop Pro-shop
Driving range Practice
Sheltered couvert no - On grass sur herbe yes - Putting-green putting-green yes - Pitching-green pitching green yes

HOTEL FACILITIES
ENVIRONNEMENT HOTELIER **6/10**

HOTELS HÔTELS

Swansea Marriott - 122 rooms, D £ 120 - Swansea 12 km
Tel (44) 01792 - 642 020, Fax (44) 01792 - 650 345

Norton House - 15 rooms, D £ 110 - The Mumbles 8 km
Tel (44) 01792 - 404 891, Fax (44) 01792 - 403 210

Windsor Lodge - 19 rooms, D from £ 65 - Swansea 15 km
Tel (44) 01792 - 642 158, Fax (44) 01792 - 648 996

RESTAURANTS RESTAURANTS

Claude's Restaurant - The Mumbles 8 km
Tel (44) 01792 - 366 006

La Braseria - Swansea 15 km - Tel (44) 01792 - 469 683

Annie's - Swansea 15 km - Tel (44) 01792 - 655 603

Pyle & Kenfig

16 | 7 | 5

There is not much missing at Pyle & Kenfig for this to rank amongst the very great courses. For once, a course of this type returns to the club-house at the 9th and in doing so emphasises the difference between the front and back nines, separated by a road. Although the outward half is not to be sniffed at, it doesn't have the dune landscape of the epic back nine, which has a single par 5 but some beefy par 3s and huge par 4s (from hole 16 to 18 with a head-wind to boot). The greatest difficulties are the rough, the positions you can get yourself into when straying off the fairway and the cleverly placed pot bunkers. The greens are on the flat side and generally reachable with bump and run shots, luckily for golfers because they are of course often very exposed to the wind. Not an easy course, but very forthright.

Il ne manque pas grand-chose à Pyle & Kenfig, qui jouxte quasiment Royal Porthcawl, pour être dans la cour des très grands parcours. Pour une fois, un parcours de ce type revient au club-house au 9, cela ne fait que souligner la différence entre l'aller et le retour, séparés par une route. Quelques modifications sont intervenues après la Seconde Guerre Mondiale mais bien que l'aller ne soit pas négligeable, il lui manque le caractère dunaire d'un retour héroïque, où l'on trouve un seul par 5, mais des par 3 très musclés et d'énormes par 4 (du 16 au 18, contre les vents dominants). Les plus grandes difficultés sont les roughs, les positions où l'on se trouve par rapport à la balle quand on s'égare hors des fairways – mais ceux-ci ont été élargis et les roughs un peu dégagés – et de profonds bunkers (trop) bien placés. Les greens sont assez plats, leur accès généralement possible en roulant, ce qui est fort heureux car l'exposition au vent est bien sûr importante. Un parcours pas facile, mais franc.

Pyle & Kenfig Golf Club — 1922

Waun-y-Mer
WAL - KENFIG, Mid Glamorgan CF33 4PU

Office Secrétariat (44) 01656 - 783 093
Pro shop Pro-shop (44) 01656 - 772 446
Fax Fax (44) 01656 - 772 822
Web www.pandkgolfclub.co.uk
Situation Situation Cardiff, 40 km
Port Talbot (pop. 51 023), 10 km
Annual closure Fermeture annuelle no
Weekly closure Fermeture hebdomadaire no

Fees main season Tarifs haute saison	18 holes	
	Week days Semaine	**We/Bank holidays** We/Férié
Individual Individuel	£ 45	£ 65*
Couple Couple	£ 90	£ 130*

* Visitors at week-ends: Sunday only

Caddie Caddie on request **Electric Trolley** Chariot électrique no
Buggy Voiturette no **Clubs** Clubs yes
Credit cards Cartes de crédit
VISA -Mastercard (Pro shop goods & Green fees only)

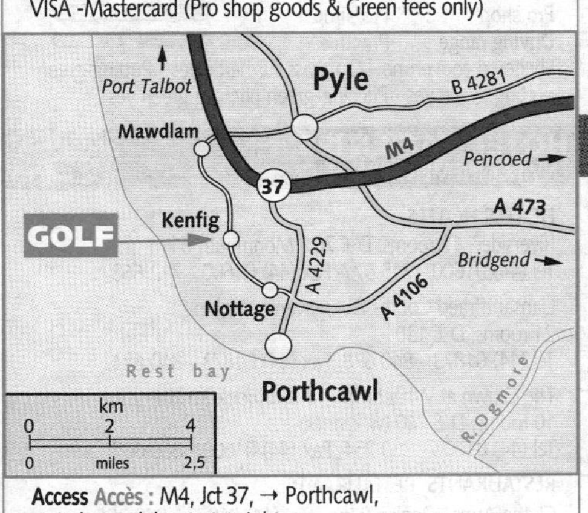

Access Accès : M4, Jct 37, → Porthcawl, at 3rd roundabout, 1st right
Map 6 on page 481 Carte 6 Page 481

GOLF COURSE — PARCOURS 16/20

Site Site
Maintenance Entretien
Architect Architecte Harry S. Colt
Type Type links, open country
Relief Relief
Water in play Eau en jeu
Exp. to wind Exposé au vent
Trees in play Arbres en jeu

Scorecard Carte de score	**Chp.** Chp.	**Mens** Mess.	**Ladies** Da.
Length Long.	6086	5571	4941
Par	71	71	74
Slope system	—	—	—

Advised golfing ability Niveau de jeu recommandé 0 12 24 36
Hcp required Handicap exigé certificate

CLUB HOUSE & AMENITIES — CLUB HOUSE ET ANNEXES 7/10

Pro shop Pro-shop
Driving range Practice
Sheltered couvert no - On grass sur herbe yes - Putting-green putting-green yes - Pitching-green pitching green yes

HOTEL FACILITIES — ENVIRONNEMENT HOTELIER 5/10

HOTELS HÔTELS
Atlantic - Porthcawl 2 km
18 rooms, D from £ 85
Tel (44) 01656 - 785 011, Fax (44) 01656 - 771 877

Seabank - 67 rooms, D £ 85 - Porthcawl 2 km
Tel (44) 01656 - 782 261, Fax (44) 01656 - 785 363

Rose and Crown - 8 rooms, D £ 45 - Porthcawl 2 km
Tel (44) 01656 - 784 850, Fax (44) 01656 - 772 345

Dormy House - 9 rooms, D £ 80 - Royal Porthcawl 2 km
Tel (44) 01656 - 782 251, Fax (44) 01656 - 771 687

RESTAURANTS RESTAURANTS
Seabank - Porthcawl 2 km - Tel (44) 01656 - 782 261
Atlantic - Porthcawl 2 km - Tel (44) 01656 - 785 011

Rolls of Monmouth (The)

16	6	5

You sometimes wonder why some good courses never reach the sort of stardom they might deserve. Here, despite the excellent road from Birmingham to Cardiff running close by, the reason might be the absence of any top tournament. From another angle, this tranquillity is a blessing for players who love to feel alone in the world. Although laid out over "rolling" landscape, the course's name comes from the Rolls family (as in Rolls Royce), whose estate overlooks the course. It is sited around a forest-covered hill in a park-land landscape lined with some superb trees. Walking can be a little hard on the legs but there are buggies to give you the time to admire the landscape and wild-life or to drive on and reconnoitre some of the blind shots that await you. As far as the course's very own personality is concerned, you'll remember best of all the magnificent par 3s.

On se demande pourquoi de bons parcours restent à l'écart de la célébrité. Dans le cas présent, l'excellente route de Birmingham à Cardiff passant pourtant à côté, il manque peut-être un grand tournoi pour faire un peu de promotion du lieu. D'un autre côté, cette tranquillité est une bénédiction pour les joueurs, qui adorent être seuls au monde, c'est bien connu. Certes le terrain est "rolling," mais le nom vient de la famille Rolls (comme Royce) dont la propriété domine le parcours, dessiné autour d'une grande colline boisée, dans un paysage de parc et de bois superbes. Marcher peut-être ici fatigant, mais il y a des voiturettes pour se donner le temps d'admirer le paysage et la vie sauvage, ou d'aller repérer les lieux sur les quelques coups aveugles. Pour ce qui est de la personnalité du parcours, on retiendra plus le retour que l'aller, on se souviendra de greens rapides et traîtres, des très beaux par 3, et d'un accueil très agréable

The Rolls of Monmouth — 1982

The Hendre
WAL - MONMOUTH, Gwent NP5 4HG

Office	Secrétariat	(44) 01600 - 715 353
Pro shop	Pro-shop	(44) 01600 - 715 353
Fax	Fax	(44) 01600 - 713 115
Web	www.therollsgolfclub.co.uk	
Situation	Situation	Cardiff, 58 km
Annual closure	Fermeture annuelle	no
Weekly closure	Fermeture hebdomadaire	no

Fees main season Tarifs haute saison	18 holes	
	Week days Semaine	**We/Bank holidays** We/Férié
Individual Individuel	£ 38	£ 42
Couple Couple	£ 76	£ 84

Monday offer: £ 35 with a 2 course lunch
Couples: £ 38 each every day

Caddie Caddie no — **Electric Trolley** Chariot électrique no
Buggy Voiturette yes — **Clubs** Clubs yes
Credit cards Cartes de crédit
VISA - Eurocard - Mastercard

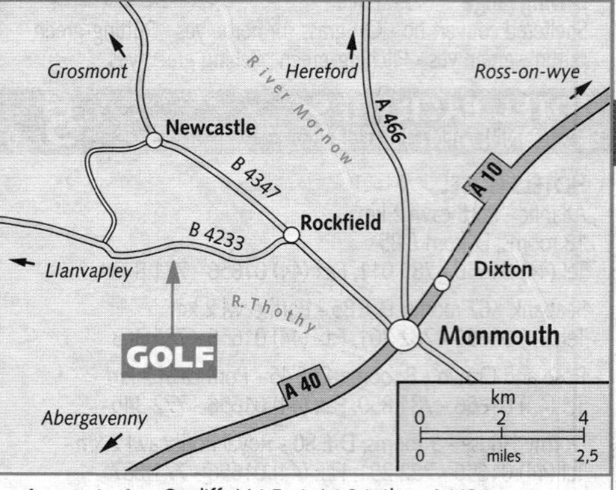

Access Accès : Cardiff, M4 East, Jct 24, then A449 to Monmouth. Golf on B4233 (Abergavenny Road), 5 km W of Monmouth.
Map 6 on page 481 Carte 6 Page 481

GOLF COURSE — PARCOURS — 16/20

Site	Site	
Maintenance	Entretien	
Architect	Architecte	Urbis Planning
Type	Type	parkland, hilly
Relief	Relief	
Water in play	Eau en jeu	
Exp. to wind	Exposé au vent	
Trees in play	Arbres en jeu	

Scorecard Carte de score	**Chp.** Chp.	**Mens** Mess.	**Ladies** Da.
Length Long.	6127	5718	5215
Par	72	72	75
Slope system	—	—	

Advised golfing ability Niveau de jeu recommandé: 0 12 24 36
Hcp required Handicap exigé: no

CLUB HOUSE & AMENITIES — CLUB HOUSE ET ANNEXES — 6/10

Pro shop Pro-shop
Driving range Practice
Sheltered couvert no - On grass sur herbe yes - Putting-green putting-green yes - Pitching-green pitching green yes

HOTEL FACILITIES — ENVIRONNEMENT HOTELIER — 5/10

HOTELS HÔTELS

Riverside - 17 rooms, D £ 70 - Monmouth 6 km
Tel (44) 01600 - 715 577, Fax (44) 01600 - 712 668

Llansantffraed Court - Abergavenny 10 km
21 rooms, D £ 130
Tel (44) 01873 - 840 678, Fax (44) 01873 - 840 674

The Crown at Whitebrook - Whitebrook 10 km
10 rooms, D £ 140 (w. dinner)
Tel (44) 01600 - 860 254, Fax (44) 01600 - 860 607

RESTAURANTS RESTAURANTS

Clytha Arms - Raglan 8 km - Tel (44) 01873 - 840 206

The Crown at Whitebrook - Whitebrook 10 km
Tel (44) 01600 - 860 254

Royal Porthcawl

19 | 7 | 6

The is the most famous course in Wales and does full honour to its reputation. Royal Porthcawl is an absolute must for great course "trophy-hunters". It is, of course, a links, although half a dozen very distinctive holes are more heathland in style and are played on a sort of high plateau overlooking the Bristol Channel. Contrary to many links, where holes are often laid out in line, the holes here shoot out in all directions and make club selection a real headache, depending on the wind. This is a part of what goes to make up the greatness and test value of this layout, where the slightest technical shortcoming will cost you dearly, and where the uninterrupted view over the sea might make you wish you had gone to the beach instead. A true masterpiece, beautifully maintained, which has staged some memorable Curtis Cup and Walker Cup matches and five British Amateur Championships.

C'est le plus fameux parcours du Pays de Galles, il honore dignement sa réputation, et doit figurer dans le "tableau" des chasseurs de grands golfs. C'est évidemment un parcours à caractère de links, qui descend doucement vers la mer, mais une demi-douzaine de trous de caractère un peu plus "terre de bruyère" trouvent place sur une sorte de haut plateau dominant le Canal de Bristol. Au contraire de nombreux links, dont les trous sont souvent alignés, ceux-ci tournent dans toutes les directions, à vous donner le vertige quant au choix de clubs suivant le vent. C'est une part de ce qui fait la grandeur et la valeur de test de ce parcours, où la moindre faiblesse technique se paie cher, où la vue constante de la mer peut vous faire regretter de ne pas avoir choisi d'aller à la plage. Un vrai chef-d'oeuvre merveilleusement entretenu, et le fait que ce soit un grand parcours de championnat est avéré par le fait que s'y sont déroulés de mémorables Curtis Cup et Walker Cup, des Championnats d'Europe par équipes ainsi que cinq British Amateur.

Royal Porthcawl Golf Club — 1891

WAL - PORTHCAWL, Mid Glamorgan CF36 3VW

Office	Secrétariat	(44) 01656 - 782 251
Pro shop	Pro-shop	(44) 01656 - 773 702
Fax	Fax	(44) 01656 - 771 687
Web	www.royalporthcawl.com	
Situation	Situation	Cardiff, 40 km

Port Talbot (pop. 51 023), 10 km

Annual closure Fermeture annuelle — no

Weekly closure Fermeture hebdomadaire — no

Fees main season Tarifs haute saison — 18 holes

	Week days / Semaine	We/Bank holidays / We/Férié
Individual Individuel	£ 80	£ 100
Couple Couple	£ 160	£ 200

* Full day: £ 120 and £ 150 (We)

Caddie Caddie on request **Electric Trolley** Chariot électrique yes

Buggy Voiturette no **Clubs** Clubs yes

Credit cards Cartes de crédit

VISA - MasterCard

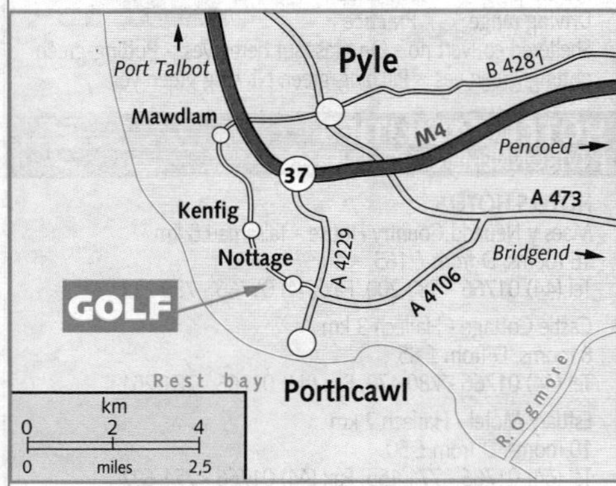

Access Accès : M4 Jct 37. At Porthcawl seafront, right → Locks Common, then left.

Map 6 on page 481 Carte 6 Page 481

GOLF COURSE — PARCOURS — 19/20

Site	Site	
Maintenance	Entretien	
Architect	Architecte	Charles Gibson
Type	Type	links
Relief	Relief	
Water in play	Eau en jeu	
Exp. to wind	Exposé au vent	
Trees in play	Arbres en jeu	

Scorecard Carte de score	Chp. Chp.	Mens Mess.	Ladies Da.
Length Long.	6083	5608	5231
Par	72	72	75
Slope system	—	—	—

Advised golfing ability Niveau de jeu recommandé — 0 12 24 36

Hcp required Handicap exigé — certificate

CLUB HOUSE & AMENITIES — CLUB HOUSE ET ANNEXES — 7/10

Pro shop Pro-shop

Driving range Practice

Sheltered couvert 2 bays - On grass sur herbe yes - Putting-green putting-green yes - Pitching-green pitching green yes

HOTEL FACILITIES — ENVIRONNEMENT HOTELIER — 6/10

HOTELS HÔTELS

Atlantic - 18 rooms, D from £ 85 - Porthcawl 1 km
Tel (44) 01656 - 785 011, Fax (44) 01656 - 771 877

Seabank - 67 rooms, D £ 85 - Porthcawl 3 km
Tel (44) 01656 - 782 261, Fax (44) 01656 - 785 363

Rose and Crown - 8 rooms, D £ 45 - Porthcawl 2 km
Tel (44) 01656 - 784 850, Fax (44) 01656 - 772 345

Dormy House - 9 rooms, D £ 80 - on site
Tel (44) 01656 - 782 251, Fax (44) 01656 - 771 687

RESTAURANTS RESTAURANTS

Seabank - Porthcawl 2 km - Tel (44) 01656 - 782 261

Atlantic - Porthcawl 1 km - Tel (44) 01656 - 785 011

Royal St David's

18	6	5

Overlooked by the extraordinary medieval Harlech castle with a fortified stairway running down to the sea, this course (named after the patron saint of Wales) is truly majestic. The pros say this is the toughest par 69 in the world, and certainly it is a severe test for any standard of golfer. The constant changes in hole direction are a further disruptive factor for golfers who already have to contend with the optical illusions created by the dune environment and the sensation of space. The shot you need to master here is of course the low ball anc you need a good measure of flair to place your bump 'n run shots close to the pin. High shots will more often than not end up in spots where your recovery can be "most amusing". A great course with an array of unforgettable holes.

Dominé par l'extraordinaire château médiéval d'Harlech, avec son escalier fortifié allant jusqu'à la mer, ce parcours (portant le nom du patron du Pays de Galles) acquiert une majesté supplémentaire. Les professionnels disent qu'il s'agit du par 69 le plus difficile du monde. Une chose est sûre, c'est un redoutable test pour le commun des mortels, quel que soit leur niveau. Les changements permanents d'orientation des trous perturbent les joueurs, déjà aux prises avec les illusions de distance que donne l'environnement de dunes, mais aussi la sensation d'espace. Le coup à maîtriser est bien sûr la balle basse, et il faut beaucoup de flair pour placer les obligatoires "bump'n run" à proximité du trou. Quant aux balles hautes, elles terminent leur course dans des endroits d'où il est amusant de s'extraire. Un grand parcours dont les auteurs semblent avoir été les amateurs fondateurs de "Harlech". Il a fêté son centenaire en 2004, et conservé sa jeunesse.

Royal St David's Golf Club — 1894

WAL - HARLECH, Gwynedd LL46 2UB

Office	Secrétariat	(44) 01766 - 780 361
Pro shop	Pro-shop	(44) 01766 - 780 857
Fax	Fax	(44) 01766 - 781 110
Web	www.royalstdavids.co.uk	
Situation	Situation	Harlech (pop. 1 880), 3 km
Annual closure	Fermeture annuelle	no
Weekly closure	Fermeture hebdomadaire	no

Fees main season Tarifs haute saison	18 holes	
	Week days Semaine	**We/Bank holidays** We/Férié
Individual Individuel	£ 42	£ 52*
Couple Couple	£ 84	£ 104*

Full day: £ 52 - £ 62 / * Booking essential at week-ends

Caddie Caddie no — **Electric Trolley** Chariot électrique no

Buggy Voiturette yes — **Clubs** Clubs yes

Credit cards Cartes de crédit
VISA - Mastercard

Access Accès : Manchester M56, A55 to Bangor, then A487 South to Porthmadog, A470 and A496 → Harlech. Golf on right side before Harlech.
Map 5 on page 478 Carte 5 Page 478

GOLF COURSE — PARCOURS — 18/20

Site	Site	
Maintenance	Entretien	
Architect	Architecte	unknown
Type	Type	links
Relief	Relief	
Water in play	Eau en jeu	
Exp. to wind	Exposé au vent	
Trees in play	Arbres en jeu	

Scorecard Carte de score	**Chp.** Chp.	**Mens** Mess.	**Ladies** Da.
Length Long.	5848	5713	5266
Par	69	69	74
Slope system	—	—	—

Advised golfing ability Niveau de jeu recommandé — 0 12 24 36

Hcp required Handicap exigé — certificate

CLUB HOUSE & AMENITIES — CLUB HOUSE ET ANNEXES — 6/10

Pro shop Pro-shop
Driving range Practice
Sheltered couvert no - On grass sur herbe yes - Putting-green putting-green yes - Pitching-green pitching green yes

HOTEL FACILITIES — ENVIRONNEMENT HOTELIER — 5/10

HOTELS HÔTELS

Maes y Neuadd Country House - Talsarnau 5 km
16 rooms, D from £ 165
Tel (44) 01766 - 780 200, Fax (44) 01766 - 780 211

Castle Cottage - Harlech 3 km
8 rooms, D from £ 85
Tel (44) 01766 - 780 479, Fax (44) 01766 - 781 251

Estuary Motel - Harlech 2 km
10 rooms, D from £ 50
Tel (44) 01766 - 771 155, Fax (44) 01766 - 771 697

RESTAURANTS RESTAURANTS

Maes y Neuadd - Harlech 5 km - Tel (44) 01766 - 780 200
Castle Cottage - Harlech 1 km - Tel (44) 01766 - 780 479

Southerndown

16 | 7 | 7

A good number of specialists lent a hand in laying out this course, including Fernie, Vardon, Braid, Fowler, Willie Park, H.S. Colt and, more recently Donald Steel. Perched high up overlooking Porthcawl, Southerndown has in fact resisted any attempts at serious human interference and stayed very natural in style. And it is true that the land was ideal for the building of a golf course. The fairways are cropped by sheep, who never go on strike and work most methodically. Very British in its sloping and hilly design but never over-tiring on the legs, this is not strictly a links course because the terrain is more clay-based than sandy (although well drained). Still, you are playing links-style golf here, hitting searing low shots under the wind and running the ball onto the greens. A tough test from the back tees, a little easier from the front and, all in all, well worth getting to know.

Bien des spécialistes se sont penchés sur ce parcours : Willie Fernie, puis les ténors de l'époque Vardon, Braid, Fowler, Willie Park, H.S. Colt et dernièrement Donald Steel, ce qui prouve l'intérêt de sa situation et du potentiel de son tracé original. Perché haut et dominant Porthcawl, Southerndown a pourtant réussi à se préserver des atteintes et rester très naturel: il est vrai que le terrain se prêtait idéalement à la construction d'un golf. Les fairways sont d'ailleurs tondus par les moutons, qui ne font jamais grève et travaillent avec méthode ! Très britannique dans son dessin typique des terrains en pente, mais sans fatigue excessive, ce n'est pas vraiment un links, parce que le terrain est plus argileux (bien drainé) que sablonneux, mais il faut utiliser le même type de jeu, avec des balles pénétrantes et basses. Difficile des départs arrière, il s'adoucit quand on avance un peu. A connaître.

Southerndown Golf Club — 1905

Ewenny
WAL - BRIDGEND, Mid. Glam. CF32 0QP

Office	Secrétariat	(44) 01656 - 880 476
Pro shop	Pro-shop	(44) 01656 - 881 112
Fax	Fax	(44) 01656 - 880 317
Web	www.southerndowngolf.co.uk	
Situation	Situation	Bridgend (pop. 14 311), 5 km
Annual closure	Fermeture annuelle	no
Weekly closure	Fermeture hebdomadaire	no

Fees main season / Tarifs haute saison — 18 holes

	Week days / Semaine	We/Bank holidays / We/Férié
Individual Individuel	£ 45	£ 65*
Couple Couple	£ 90	£ 130*

Full week day: £ 55 / * Week-ends: ask before coming

Caddie Caddie no — Electric Trolley Chariot électrique yes
Buggy Voiturette yes — Clubs Clubs yes
Credit cards Cartes de crédit
VISA - Eurocard - Mastercard

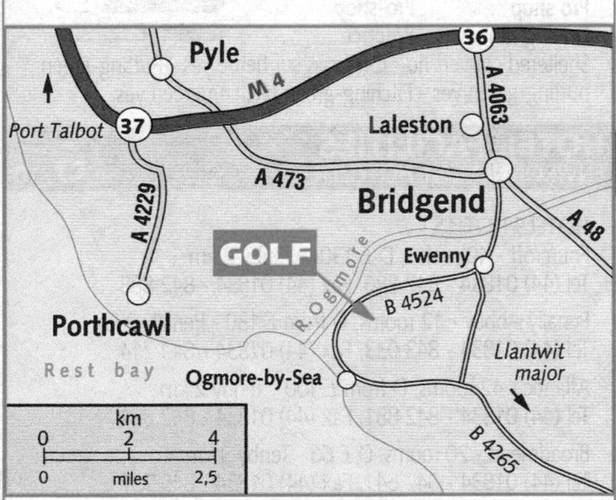

Access Accès : On the coast road Bridgend to Ogmore-by-Sea. Turn off at Pelican Inn (opp. Ogmore Castle)
Map 6 on page 481 Carte 6 Page 481

GOLF COURSE / PARCOURS — 16/20

Site	Site	
Maintenance	Entretien	
Architect	Architecte	Willie Fernie
Type	Type	downland
Relief	Relief	
Water in play	Eau en jeu	
Exp. to wind	Exposé au vent	
Trees in play	Arbres en jeu	

Scorecard / Carte de score	Chp. / Chp.	Mens / Mess.	Ladies / Da.
Length Long.	5840	5395	5049
Par	70	69	74
Slope system	—	—	—

Advised golfing ability / Niveau de jeu recommandé: 0 12 24 36
Hcp required / Handicap exigé: certificate

CLUB HOUSE & AMENITIES / CLUB HOUSE ET ANNEXES — 7/10

Pro shop — Pro-shop
Driving range — Practice
Sheltered couvert no - On grass sur herbe yes - Putting-green putting-green yes - Pitching-green pitching green yes

HOTEL FACILITIES / ENVIRONNEMENT HOTELIER — 7/10

HOTELS HÔTELS
Heronston - Bridgend 3 km
75 rooms, D £ 95
Tel (44) 01656 - 668 811, Fax (44) 01656 - 767 391

Coed-y-Mwstwrm - 28 rooms, D £ 150 - Coychurch 6 km
Tel (44) 01656 - 860 621, Fax (44) 01656 - 863 122

Great House - 19 rooms, D £ 140 - Laleston 7 km
Tel (44) 01656 - 657 644, Fax (44) 01656 - 668 892

RESTAURANTS RESTAURANTS
Frolics - Southerndown 3 km - Tel (44) 01656 - 880 127
Leicester's (Great House) - Laleston 7 km
Tel (44) 01656 - 657 644

Tenby

17	7	6

Firstly there is a landscape of wild dunes, looking as if they have been stirred by the wind for years on end. And then comes the course, fashioned by nature for centuries with the sporadic help of James Braid, as witnessed by the contours of some of the greens and the location of the many bunkers. There are very few continental golfers who have heard much about Welsh courses. This one is a must as you travel around the magnificent coastline of this very likeable country. Depending on the weather, the course can turn into a major championship test or a superb walk in the bracing sea-air. This is the time to test your creativity and invent special shots, because you will often end up in situations that are completely new to you. Tenby is a surprising, honest and charming course to play.

D'abord, il y a un paysage de dunes agitées comme par des années de bombardements, un parcours façonné par la nature pendant plus d'un siècle, avec l'aide sporadique de James Braid, visible par les contours de certains greens, et le placement de nombreux bunkers. Rares sont les golfeurs du continent qui ont entendu parler des parcours du Pays de Galles, mais les joueurs du cru ne s'en plaignent pas, qui sont restés à l'écart des groupes de touristes. Ce parcours est incontournable à ceux qui entreprennent un circuit des côtes magnifiques de ce pays attachant. Suivant le temps, il prendra des allures de grand test de championnat, ou de superbe promenade dans un air vivifiant. C'est alors le moment de tester votre créativité, d'inventer des coups de golf, parce que vous serez souvent dans des situations inconnues. Surprenant et franc, Tenby est aussi un parcours de charme, davantage que son club-house, de style incertain, mais avec un accueil gallois, ce qui est tout dire.

Tenby Golf Club — 1888

The Burrows
WAL - TENBY, Dyfed SA70 7NP

Office	Secrétariat	(44) 01834 - 842 978
Pro shop	Pro-shop	(44) 01834 - 844 447
Fax	Fax	(44) 01834 - 842 978
Web	www.tenbygolf.co.uk	
Situation	Situation	Swansea 60 km
Annual closure	Fermeture annuelle	no
Weekly closure	Fermeture hebdomadaire	no
Fees main season	Tarifs haute saison	18 holes

	Week days Semaine	We/Bank holidays We/Férié
Individual Individuel	£ 33,5	£ 39,5
Couple Couple	£ 67	£ 79

Full day: £ 49.50 - 58.50 (We)

Caddie Caddie on request **Electric Trolley** Chariot électrique yes

Buggy Voiturette no **Clubs** Clubs yes

Credit cards Cartes de crédit
VISA - Eurocard - Mastercard (Pro Shop goods only)

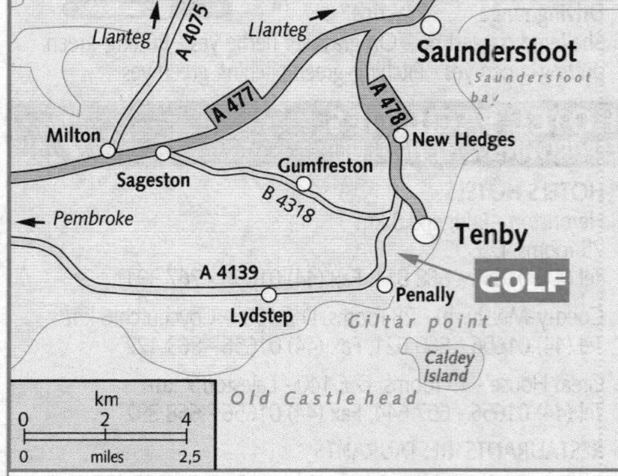

Access Accès : Cardiff, M4 West, A48, A477, A478 to Tenby. Golf near railway station.
Map 6 on page 480 Carte 6 Page 480

GOLF COURSE — PARCOURS — 17/20

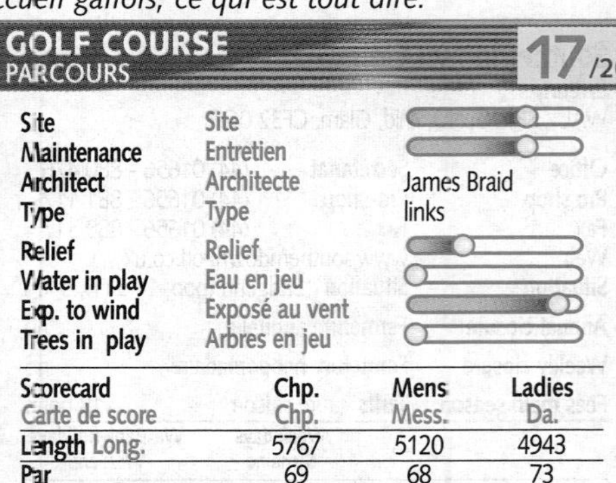

Site	Site	
Maintenance	Entretien	
Architect	Architecte	James Braid
Type	Type	links
Relief	Relief	
Water in play	Eau en jeu	
Exp. to wind	Exposé au vent	
Trees in play	Arbres en jeu	

Scorecard Carte de score	Chp. Chp.	Mens Mess.	Ladies Da.
Length Long.	5767	5120	4943
Par	69	68	73
Slope system	—	—	—

Advised golfing ability 0 12 24 36
Niveau de jeu recommandé
Hcp required Handicap exigé certificate

CLUB HOUSE & AMENITIES — CLUB HOUSE ET ANNEXES — 7/10

Pro shop Pro-shop
Driving range Practice
Sheltered couvert no - On grass sur herbe yes - Putting-green putting-green yes - Pitching-green pitching green yes

HOTEL FACILITIES — ENVIRONNEMENT HOTELIER — 6/10

HOTELS HÔTELS

Fourcroft - 40 rooms, D £ 130 - Tenby 2 km
Tel (44) 01834 - 842 886, Fax (44) 01834 - 842 888

Penally Abbey - 12 rooms, D from £ 130 - Penally 2 km
Tel (44) 01834 - 843 033, Fax (44) 01834 - 844 714

Atlantic - 42 rooms, D from £ 100 - Tenby 2 km
Tel (44) 01834 - 842 881, Fax (44) 01834 - 842 881

Broadmead - 20 rooms, D £ 66 - Tenby 3 km
Tel (44) 01834 - 842 641, Fax (44) 01834 - 845 757

RESTAURANTS RESTAURANTS

Fourcroft - Tenby 2 km - Tel (44) 01834 - 842 886
Broadmead - Tenby 3 km - Tel (44) 01834 - 842 641

Vale Hotel, Golf & Spa *The Lakes*

16	8	7

This resort, with hotel, fitness and health spa, indoor squash and tennis courts, gymnasiums and swimming pools, was built to compete with the resorts of St Pierre and Celtic Manor. Add to this a high-tech indoor training facility and suddenly you are light-years away from a traditional golf-club. Here the aim is to host big events. The resort boasts two courses : firstly "The Lakes", which features water on 9 holes, thus giving a slight American 'target-golf' flavour to what is otherwise a very British country setting. Luckily, the architect also remembered that a course needs players all year, which is why the front tees provide an intriguing challenge and one which remains within the bounds of human possibility. A second 18-hole layout has recently been opened : the "Welsh National" and it is one of the longest courses in the UK (at 7,500 yards). It has been designed to host major competitions.

Ce complexe avec hôtel, centre de mise en forme et de beauté, squash, tennis indoor, gymnases et autres piscines est destiné à lutter avec les complexes de St Pierre et Celtic Manor. Si l'on ajoute un centre d'entraînement high tech, nous voilà très loin du club traditionnel. Ici, on joue sur tous les tableaux. Cet ensemble propose deux 18 trous. D'abord "The Lakes" qui comporte 9 trous avec de l'eau en jeu, ce qui donne un caractère un peu américain à un paysage autrement très britannique, et impose un jeu de cible pratiquement sur tous les trous. Heureusement, l'architecte a aussi pensé qu'il faut des joueurs toute l'année, c'est pourquoi, même si la longueur générale est raisonnable, les départs avancés procurent un challenge intéressant, mais sans rien d'inhumain. Un second parcours vient de s'ajouter, le "Welsh National", l'un des parcours les plus longs de Grande-Bretagne (plus de 6700 m !!!), spécialement destiné aux grands tournois.

Vale Hotel Golf & Spa — **2003**
Hensol Park, Hensol, Nr Cardiff
WAL - VALE OF GLAMORGAN CF71 7TR

Office	Secrétariat	(44) 01443 - 667 800
Pro shop	Pro-shop	(44) 01443 - 665 899
Fax	Fax	(44) 01443 - 222 220
Web	www.vale-hotel.com	
Situation	Situation	Cardiff, 32 km
Annual closure	Fermeture annuelle	no
Weekly closure	Fermeture hebdomadaire	no

Fees main season Tarifs haute saison	18 holes	
	Week days Semaine	We/Bank holidays We/Férié
Individual Individuel	£ 40	£ 35*
Couple Couple	£ 80	£ 70*

* We: members' gyests only

Caddie Caddie no — **Electric Trolley** Chariot électrique no
Buggy Voiturette yes — **Clubs** Clubs yes
Credit cards Cartes de crédit
VISA - Eurocard - MasterCard - AMEX - DC

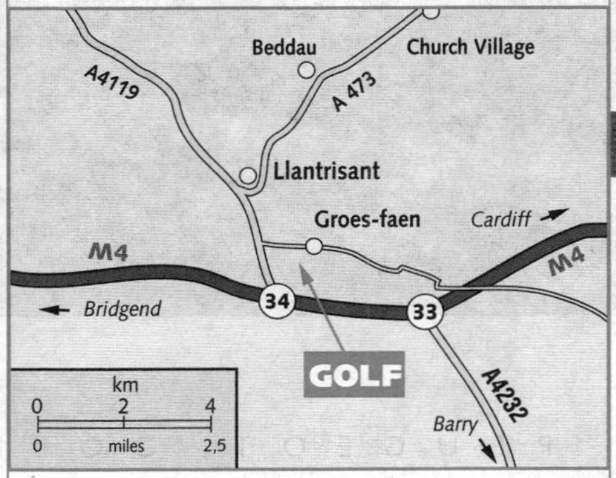

Access Accès : Just off Junction 34 of M4
Map 6 on page 481 Carte 6 Page 481

GOLF COURSE
PARCOURS — 16/20

Site	Site	
Maintenance	Entretien	
Architect	Architecte	Peter Johnson
Type	Type	parkland
Relief	Relief	
Water in play	Eau en jeu	
Exp. to wind	Exposé au vent	
Trees in play	Arbres en jeu	

Scorecard Carte de score	Chp. Chp.	Mens Mess.	Ladies Da.
Length Long.	6695	5905	5345
Par	73	73	74
Slope system	—	—	—

Advised golfing ability Niveau de jeu recommandé — 0 12 24 36
Hcp required Handicap exigé — certificate

CLUB HOUSE & AMENITIES
CLUB HOUSE ET ANNEXES — 8/10

Pro shop Pro-shop
Driving range Practice
Sheltered couvert 20 bays - On grass sur herbe no - Putting-green putting-green yes - Pitching-green pitching green yes

HOTEL FACILITIES
ENVIRONNEMENT HOTELIER — 7/10

HOTELS HÔTELS
Vale of Glamorgan Hotel - on site
143 rooms, D from £ 120
Tel (44) 01443 - 667 800, Fax (44) 01443 - 667 801

Greyhound Inn - 10 rooms, D £ 72 - Llantrisant 6 km
Tel (44) 01291 - 672 505, Fax (44) 01291 - 673 255

Coed-y-Mwstwr - 28 rooms, D £ 150 - Coychurch 12 km
Tel (44) 01656 - 860 621, Fax (44) 01656 - 863 122

Forte Travelodge - 40 rooms, D £ 47 - Pencoed 8 km
Tel (44) 01656 - 864 404, Fax (44) 01656 - 864 404

RESTAURANTS RESTAURANTS
Vale of Glamorgan Hotel - on site - Tel (44) 01443 - 667 800

IRLANDE
ULSTER

IRELAND
NORTHERN IRELAND

Waterville

GUIDE 2006/2007

IRELAND
NORTHERN IRLAND

Here, we have included in succession courses from the Republic of Ireland and Northern Ireland. There is no rush in this part of the world but to meet high demand, new courses are emerging faster than ever, with obvious concern for golfing excellence.

Amongst the most recent new-comers, we have included courses within the greater Dublin area such as Castleknock, Roganstown, Rathcore, the Irish PGA National, The Heritage, or again further south the second course at Powerscourt and Druids Heath. In the south-west, the "Lackabane" course at Killarney is included pending work on the club's "Killeen" course. For links fans, the second course at Rosapenna (Sandy Hill Links) also appears for the first time.

To select the top 100 Irish golf-courses, we have deliberately opted for the most representative layouts, and particularly seaside links courses that continental golfers can only rarely find at home. As you read through the list, you will see that certain great "classics" have moved with the times. For instance, the "Old" course at Ballyliffin, where Nick Faldo is currently doing some upgrading work, or again Waterville, where Tom Fazio has made some spectacular changes.

With more than 300 eighteen-hole and 100 nine-hole courses for 270,000 registered players, there is no shortage of space for visitors and Ireland is a golfing destination renowned the world over. You will always be made most welcome as the word hospitality here has true meaning, but don't expect to find any magnificent driving ranges (you often find just rough practice areas where you can hit your own balls) or sumptuous club-houses. Modern facilities and luxury come second to the excellence of the course and a warm welcome.

Having said that, today's trend is more in the "spectacular" mode, like for example high green-fees that may be considered as collateral damage sustained on account of a now very busy tourist trade. Whatever, remember to bring with you a letter of introduction from your club, and never forget to book tee-times in advance.

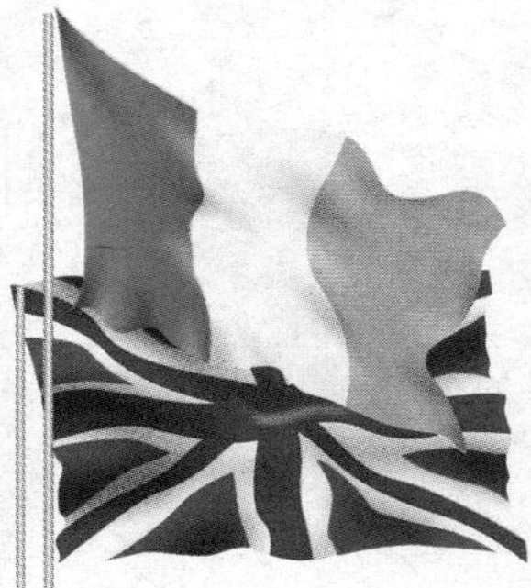

IRLANDE
IRLANDE DU NORD

Vous trouverez ici, successivement, les parcours de la République d'Irlande et d'Irlande du Nord. Dans ces pays, si rien ne sert de se presser, mais pour répondre à une forte demande, les nouveaux parcours sortent de terre plus vite qu'autrefois, avec un souci évident de grande qualité.

Ainsi, parmi les plus récents, nous avons inclus des parcours dans la zone d'influence de Dublin, comme Castleknock, Roganstown, Rathcore, l'Irish PGA National, The Heritage, ou encore, vers le sud, le second parcours de Powerscourt, ainsi que Druids Heath. Dans le sud-ouest, le parcours "Lackabane" de Killarney entre ici pendant les travaux effectués sur le parcours "Killeen" du club. Côté links, le second parcours de Rosapenna (Sandy Hill Links) fait aussi son apparition

Pour choisir les 100 meilleurs des golfs irlandais, nous avons volontairement conservé l'accent sur les plus représentatifs, en particulier les links, que les golfeurs continentaux ont rarement l'habitude de trouver chez eux. Au rythme de vos lectures, vous découvrirez aussi que certains "classiques" ont su évoluer, comme le "Old" de Ballyliffin où Nick Faldo intervient actuellement, ou encore Waterville, où Tom Fazio a effectué des transformations remarquées.

Avec plus de 300 parcours de 18 trous et 100 de 9 trous pour 270.000 joueurs licenciés, la place ne manque pas pour les visiteurs, et le territoire de l'Irlande reste une destination touristique connue du monde entier. Vous y serez toujours le bienvenu, car l'hospitalité n'est pas ici un vain mot, mais ne vous attendez pas à trouver des practices magnifiques (ce sont souvent de simples zones où l'on tape ses propres balles), ni toujours des club-houses somptueux. Ici, le modernisme et le luxe passent après la qualité du parcours et la chaleur de l'accueil, bien que la tendance actuelle aille plutôt dans le sens du spectaculaire... comme des tarifs élevés, un dommage collatéral d'une fréquentation touristique importante. Dans tous les cas, pensez à avoir une lettre d'introduction de votre club. Et surtout à réserver vos départs à l'avance !

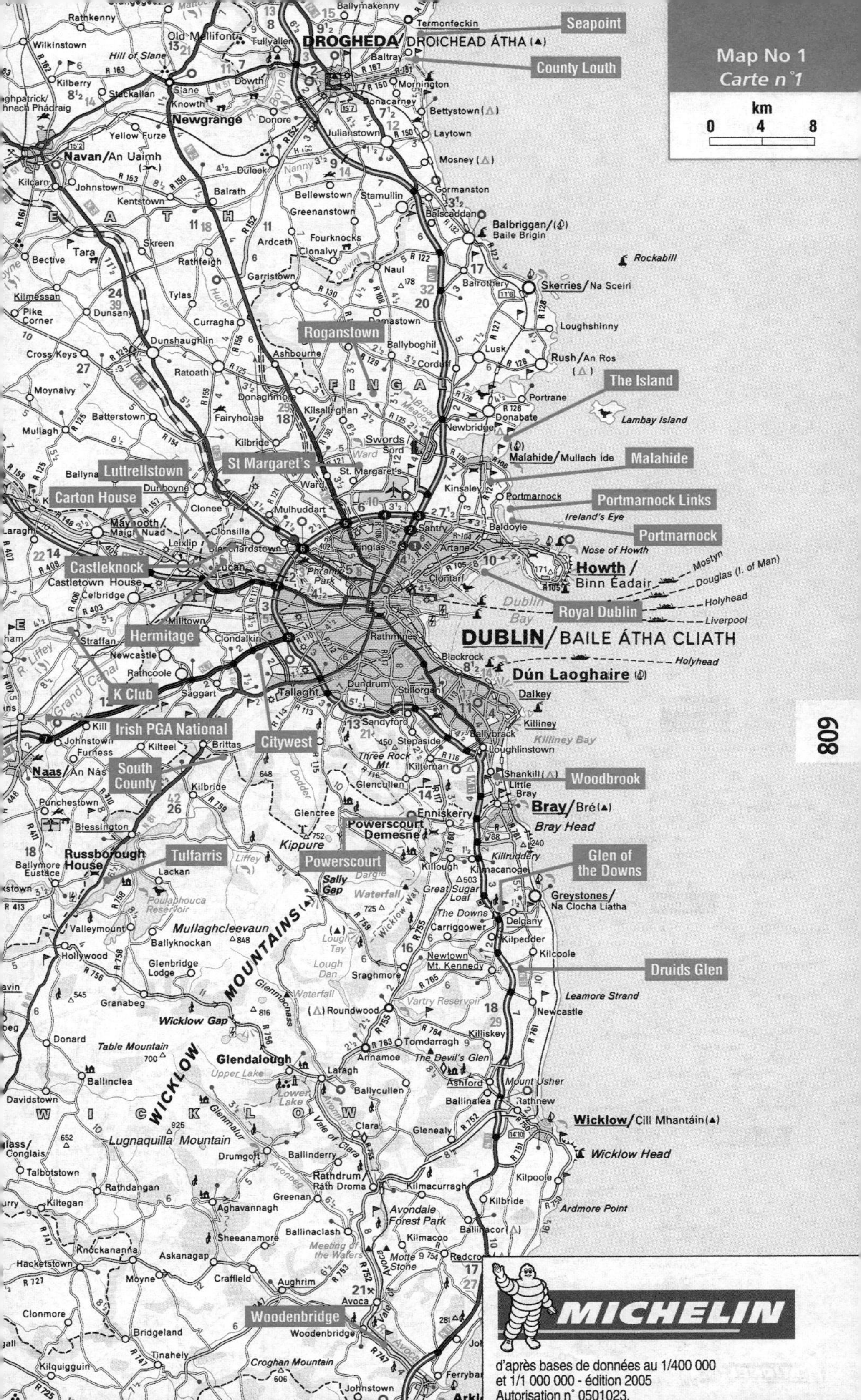

Map No 1
Carte n°1
km
0 4 8
Seapoint
County Louth
DROGHEDA/DROICHEAD ÁTHA
Roganstown
The Island
St Margaret's
Luttrellstown
Carton House
Malahide
Portmarnock Links
Portmarnock
Castleknock
Royal Dublin
DUBLIN/BAILE ÁTHA CLIATH
Hermitage
K Club
Irish PGA National
Citywest
South County
Woodbrook
Tulfarris
Powerscourt
Glen of the Downs
Druids Glen
Woodenbridge
Navan/An Uaimh
Newgrange
Balbriggan/Baile Brigin
Skerries/Na Sceirí
Rush/An Ros
Lambay Island
Malahide/Mullach Íde
Howth/Binn Éadair
Dún Laoghaire
Bray/Bré
Greystones/Na Clocha Liatha
Wicklow/Cill Mhantáin
Wicklow Head
WICKLOW MOUNTAINS
Lugnaquilla Mountain
Glendalough
Naas/An Nás
Russborough House
Mostyn
Douglas (I. of Man)
Holyhead
Liverpool
809
MICHELIN
d'après bases de données au 1/400 000
et 1/1 000 000 - édition 2005
Autorisation n° 0501023.

Map No 2
Carte n°2

km
0 10 20

Tory I.
Bloody Foreland Head
R 257
29
Crolly
Err
R 25
Aran Island
R 259
98
Dunglow
Derry
R 252
Gweebarre Bay
Finto
17
R 250
R 261
DON
Glenties
Glencolumbkille
Ardara
Rossan Point
672
R 262
R 263
20
15
Blue Stack
Killybegs
15
Donegal
Dún n
Donegal (Murvagh)
21
Donegal Bay
13
Ballyshannon
Bundoran
Bundoran / Bun Dobhrain
4
R. Erne
Inishmurray
A 47
Belleek
8-2006
Enniscrone
65 40
L. Melvin
23
County Sligo
Erris Head
Broad Haven
544
B 52
Belmullet
31
Ballycastle
16
R 280
Killala Bay
379
Easky
Rosses Point
15
Manorhamilton
R 314
R 314
Glenamoy
R 297
Sligo Bay
12
Strandhill
Sligo / Sligeach
Belmullet (Carn)
R 313
MAYO
R 282
Inishkea
17
Inishcrone
33
4
66 41
Bangor
R 316
12
The Ox Mountains
543
L. Gill
Blacksod Bay
20
Ballysadare
R 287
11
R 280
720
19
Crossmolina
7
Ballina / Béal an Átha
SLIGO
Dowra
810
Ballycroy
R 312
L. Corn
R 294
29
Keel
670
20
Nephin Beg Range
10
804
Nephin
R 310
20
47
Drumkeeran
R 280
Achill Island
17
698
18
Ballymote
R 294
Lough Allen
R 319
25
Foxford
Tobercurry
21
R 293
Arrow
R 207
521
Mulrany
R 315
Pontoon
R 312
25
Moy
7
20
19
Drumshanbo
Corraun
11
R 317
Castlebar / Caisleán an Bharraigh
R 310
Swinford
Charlestown
R 294
Boyle / Mainistir na Búille
Keadew
L. Key
26
R 209
Clare Island
Newport
11
16
39
Gorteen
Shannon
LE
Clew Bay
8
R 311
24
R 320
L. Gara
R 361
11
Carrick-on-Sh
Cora Droma R
Westport
11 18
93 58
Kiltamagh
R 322
Ballaghaderreen
Inishturk
Louisburgh
R 335
14
763
Westport / Cathair na Mart
R 324
20
15
R 201
Croagh Patrick
18
18
R 323
Frenchpark
50 80
R 368
17
23
R 369
Elphin
R 202
Inishbofin
20
Murrisk
19
41
Ballintober
18
R 293
28
Mweelrea Mts.
817
R 330
Partry Mountains
Ballyhaunis
ROSCOMMON
Killary Harbour
Claremorris
Castlerea
Rinvyle Pt.
R 335
681
Lough Mask
14
R 331
10
12
Tulsk
Strokestown
Letterfrack
6
22
Leenane
Ballinrobe
Ballymoe
R 371
13
22
Maumturk Mts
R 336
Kilmaine
60 97
19
22
R 360
R 364
Lanesborough
19
The Twelve Pins
728
701
9
R 345
Edgew
Meath
Clifden / An Clochán
Connemara
R 345
Clonbur
Cong
R 332
19
Dunmore
Roscommon / Ros Comáin
Glasson
19
R 334
Glennamaddy
Head
R 341
22
Lough Corrib
Tuam / Tuaim
IREL
Roundstone
5
Headford
R 328
Maam Cross
49
Clare
R 347
R 332
17
20
18
Connemara
Gortmore
31
Oughterard
Athlone
Lough Ree
27
13
R 340
27
12
23
Mount Bellew
Ballyforan
R 363
Carna
R 336
12
Kilkieran Bay
R 374
GALWAY
R 359
16
R 358
Athlone / Baile Átha Luain
Bearna
Galway / Gaillimh
9
R 347
Suck
Lettermullan
24
Spiddal
8
Athenry
21
Ballinasloe / Béal Átha na Sluaighe
Gorumna Island
R 336
Barna
6
Oranmore
R 348
14
River Shannon
Aran Islands
Galway Bay
R 357
Clonmacnoise
Inishmore
Craughwell
R 350
19
Black Head
17
20
90 55
Ferbane
Kilronan
Galway Bay
Ardrahan
Loughrea
R 355
Clonfert
30
Inishmaan
25
7
R 347
Kinvarra
15
20
R 356
Cloghan
R 477
Ballyvaughan
Banagher
Kilcormac
Inishe
Lahinch
18
R 480
Gort
28
Portumna
Lisdoonvarna
16
R 353
R 489
Kinnitty
Kilfenora
109 68
R 460
R 440
Birr
MICHELIN
Cliffs of Moher
R 478
R 481
R 476
23
20
52

Ballyliffin
Rosapenna
Portsalon
Machrie (GB)
Royal Portrush
Machrihanish (GB)
Portstewart
Castlerock
Cairndhu
Bangor
Clandeboye
Massereene
Royal Belfast
Malone
Knock
Castle Hume
Belvoir Park
Lisburn
Kirkistown Castle
Slieve Russell
Ardglass
Royal County Down
Warrenpoint
Dundalk
Headfort
Seapoint
County Louth
Mullingar
Rathcore
Esker Hills
The Island
K Club
Tulfarris
Londonderry
BELFAST
DUBLIN/BAILE ÁTHA CLIATH
NORTHERN IRELAND
MICHELIN

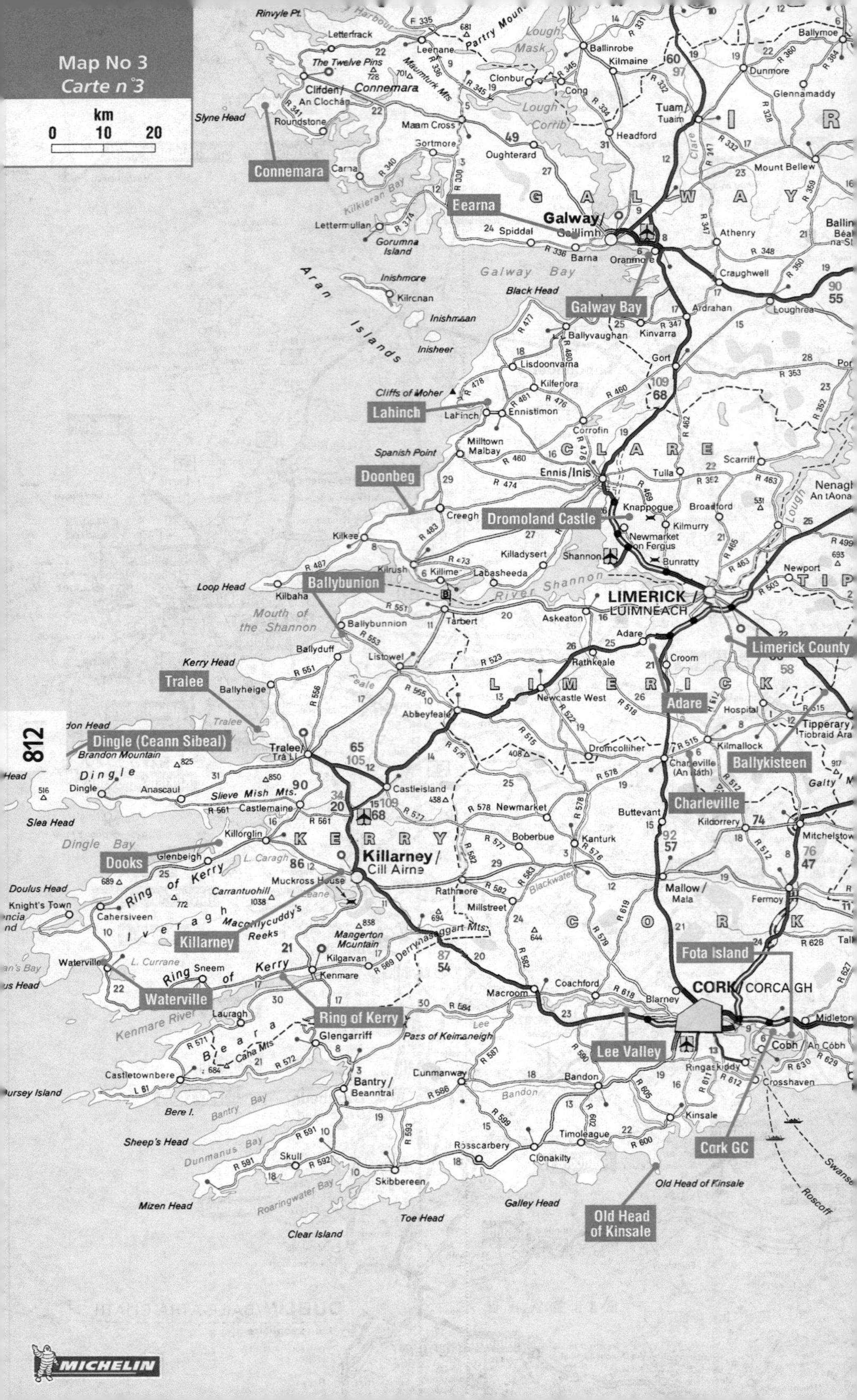

Map No 3
Carte n°3
km
0 10 20
Connemara
Bearna
Galway Bay
Lahinch
Doonbeg
Dromoland Castle
Ballybunion
Limerick County
Tralee
Dingle (Ceann Sibeal)
Adare
Tipperary
Ballykisteen
Charleville
Dooks
Killarney
Waterville
Ring of Kerry
Fota Island
Lee Valley
Cork GC
Old Head of Kinsale
Galway/ Gaillimh
LIMERICK / LUIMNEACH
Killarney / Cill Airne
CORK / CORCAIGH
Ennis/Inis
Tralee / Trá Lí
Tuam / Tuaim
Clifden / An Clochán
Aran Islands
Inishmore
Inishmaan
Inisheer
Cliffs of Moher
Mouth of the Shannon
River Shannon
Dingle Bay
Kenmare River
Bantry Bay
Dunmanus Bay
Roaringwater Bay
Galway Bay
Lough Mask
Lough Corrib
Macgillycuddy's Reeks
Slieve Mish Mts.
Loop Head
Kerry Head
Brandon Mountain
Slea Head
Mizen Head
Sheep's Head
Clear Island
Galley Head
Old Head of Kinsale
G A L W A Y
C L A R E
L I M E R I C K
K E R R Y
C O R K
812
MICHELIN

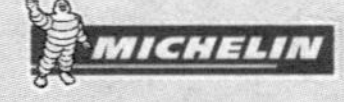

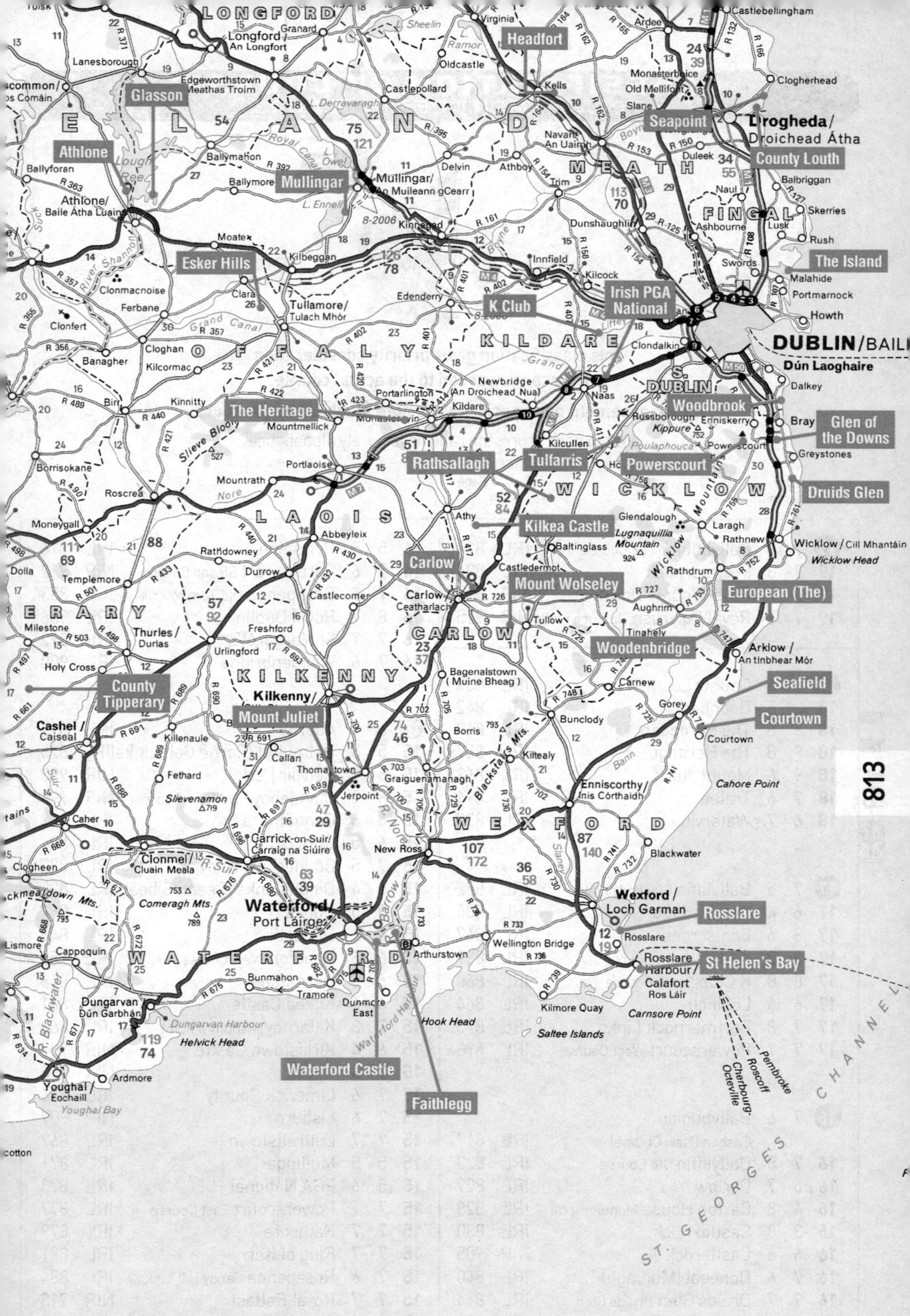
Headfort
Glasson
Athlone
Mullingar
Esker Hills
K Club
Irish PGA National
Seapoint
County Louth
The Island
Woodbrook
Glen of the Downs
Powerscourt
Druids Glen
The Heritage
Rathsallagh
Tulfarris
Kilkea Castle
Carlow
Mount Wolseley
European (The)
Woodenbridge
Seafield
Courtown
County Tipperary
Mount Juliet
Rosslare
St Helen's Bay
Waterford Castle
Faithlegg
LONGFORD
MEATH
FINGAL
KILDARE
S. DUBLIN
OFFALY
LAOIS
WICKLOW
CARLOW
KILKENNY
WEXFORD
WATERFORD
DUBLIN/BAILE
Dún Laoghaire
Drogheda/Droichead Átha
Longford/An Longfort
Athlone/Baile Átha Luain
Mullingar/An Muileann gCearr
Tullamore/Tulach Mhór
Naas
Kildare
Portlaoise
Carlow/Ceatharlach
Kilkenny
Thurles/Durlas
Cashel/Caiseal
Clonmel/Cluain Meala
Waterford/Port Láirge
Dungarvan/Dún Garbhán
Youghal/Eochaill
New Ross
Wexford/Loch Garman
Enniscorthy/Inis Córthaidh
Arklow/An tInbhear Mór
Wicklow/Cill Mhantáin
Rosslare Harbour/Calafort Ros Láir
Carnsore Point
Saltee Islands
Hook Head
Helvick Head
ST. GEORGE'S CHANNEL
813

CLASSIFICATION OF COURSES
CLASSEMENT DES PARCOURS

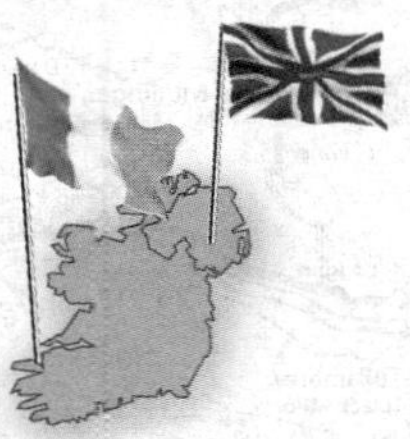

This classification gives priority consideration to the score awarded to the actual course.
Ce classement donne priorité à la note attribuée au parcours.
Within each score, the ranking is purely alphabetical

Course score / Note du parcours					Page
19	7	6	Ballybunion Old Course	IRL	820
19	7	8	Portmarnock	IRL	874
19	6	7	Royal County Down	NIR	914
19	7	7	Royal Portrush Dunluce Links	NIR	915
18	5	6	County Louth	IRL	835
18	3	5	Doonbeg	IRL	842
18	5	6	The European	IRL	849
18	9	8	The Heritage	IRL	857
18	9	6	Mount Juliet	IRL	869
18	7	6	Tralee	IRL	894
18	6	7	Waterville	IRL	897
17	7	5	Ballyliffin Glashedy Links	IRL	822
17	6	4	County Sligo	IRL	836
17	8	6	Enniscrone	IRL	847
17	8	8	K Club North Course	IRL	859
17	8	8	K Club South Course	IRL	860
17	6	6	Lahinch	IRL	864
17	7	8	Portmarnock Links	IRL	875
17	7	7	Powerscourt West Course	IRL	878
16	7	6	Ballybunion Cashen (New Course)	IRL	819
16	7	5	Ballyliffin Old Course	IRL	823
16	6	7	Carlow	IRL	827
16	4	8	Carton House Montgomerie	IRL	828
16	3	8	Castleknock	IRL	830
16	6	6	Castlerock	NIR	905
16	7	6	Donegal (Murvagh)	IRL	840
16	9	7	Druids Glen Druids Glen	IRL	844
16	8	6	Fota Island	IRL	851
16	7	7	Glasson	IRL	853
16	5	8	Grange	IRL	855
16	7	6	Old Head	IRL	872
16	5	5	Portsalon	IRL	876
16	7	6	Portstewart Strand Course	NIR	912
16	7	6	Rosapenna Old Tom Morris	IRL	883
16	8	7	Royal Dublin	IRL	886
16	7	7	St Margaret's	IRL	892
16	7	6	Woodenbridge	IRL	900
15	6	7	Adare	IRL	817
15	5	3	Belmullet (Carne Golf Links)	IRL	825
15	5	7	Belvoir Park	NIR	903
15	6	5	Clandeboye Dufferin Course	NIR	906
15	6	6	Connemara	IRL	833
15	6	5	Cork GC	IRL	834
15	7	5	County Tipperary	IRL	837
15	5	4	Dingle Links (Ceann Sibeal)	IRL	839
15	5	5	Dooks	IRL	841
15	6	6	Dundalk	IRL	846
15	6	6	Headfort New Course	IRL	856
15	6	8	Hermitage	IRL	858
15	6	6	Kilkea Castle	IRL	861
15	7	8	Killarney Mahony's Point	IRL	863
15	6	4	Kirkistown Castle	NIR	907
15	7	6	Knock	NIR	908
15	7	6	Limerick County	IRL	866
15	7	6	Lisburn	NIR	909
15	7	7	Luttrellstown	IRL	867
15	5	5	Mullingar	IRL	871
15	5	6	PGA National	IRL	873
15	7	7	Powerscourt East Course	IRL	877
15	7	7	Rathcore	IRL	879
15	7	7	Ring of Kerry	IRL	881
15	7	6	Rosapenna Sandy Hill Links	IRL	884
15	7	7	Royal Belfast	NIR	913
15	6	6	Seapoint	IRL	888
15	8	5	Slieve Russell	IRL	889
15	7	7	The Island	IRL	893
15	7	6	Tulfarris	IRL	895

CLASSIFICATION OF COURSES
CLASSEMENT DES PARCOURS

15	7	7	Westport	IRL	898
15	7	6	Woodbrook	IRL	899
14	6	4	Ardglass	NIR	901
14	7	6	Ballykisteen	IRL	821
14	6	5	Bangor	NIR	902
14	7	7	Bearna	IRL	824
14	4	8	Carton House The O'Meara	IRL	829
14	5	5	Courtown	IRL	838
14	7	8	Dromoland Castle	IRL	843
14	9	7	Druids Glen Druids Heath	IRL	845
14	6	6	Esker Hills	IRL	848
14	7	6	Galway Bay	IRL	852
14	7	8	Killarney Lackabane	IRL	862
14	7	8	Malahide Red + Blue + Yellow	IRL	868
14	5	6	Massereene	NIR	911
14	7	4	Rathsallagh	IRL	880
14	7	7	Roganstown	IRL	882
14	7	7	Seafield	IRL	887
14	7	8	South County	IRL	890
14	6	6	St Helen's Bay	IRL	891
14	5	6	Waterford Castle	IRL	896
13	6	6	Athlone	IRL	818
13	6	7	Bundoran	IRL	826
13	6	5	Cairndhu	NIR	904
13	4	6	Charleville	IRL	831
13	6	8	Citywest	IRL	832
13	7	7	Faithlegg	IRL	850
13	6	7	Glen of the Downs	IRL	854
13	7	6	Lee Valley	IRL	865
13	6	6	Malone	NIR	910
13	6	5	Mount Wolseley	IRL	870
13	5	6	Rosslare	IRL	885
13	7	7	Royal Portrush Valley	NIR	916
13	6	4	Warrenpoint	NIR	917

HOTEL FACILITIES
ENVIRONNEMENT HOTELIER

This classification gives priority consideration to the score awarded to the hotel facilities.

Ce classement donne priorité à la note attribuée à l'environnement hôtelier.

		Hotel facility score / Note de l'environnement hôtelier			Page
16	4	**8**	Carton House Montgomerie	IRL	828
14	4	**8**	Carton House O'Meara	IRL	829
16	3	**8**	Castleknock	IRL	830
13	6	**8**	Citywest	IRL	832
14	7	**8**	Dromoland Castle	IRL	843
16	5	**8**	Grange	IRL	855
18	9	**8**	The Heritage	IRL	857
15	6	**8**	Hermitage	IRL	858
17	8	**8**	K Club North Course	IRL	859
17	8	**8**	K Club South Course	IRL	860
14	7	**8**	Killarney Lackabane	IRL	862
15	7	**8**	Killarney Mahony's Point	IRL	863
14	7	**8**	Malahide Red + Blue + Yellow	IRL	868
19	7	**8**	Portmarnock	IRL	874
17	7	**8**	Portmarnock Links	IRL	875
14	7	**8**	South County	IRL	890
15	6	**7**	Adare	IRL	817
14	7	**7**	Bearna	IRL	824
15	5	**7**	Belvoir Park	NIR	903
13	6	**7**	Bundoran	IRL	826
16	6	**7**	Carlow	IRL	827
16	9	**7**	Druids Glen Druids Glen	IRL	844
14	9	**7**	Druids Glen Druids Heath	IRL	845
13	7	**7**	Faithlegg	IRL	850
16	7	**7**	Glasson	IRL	853
13	6	**7**	Glen of the Downs	IRL	854
15	7	**7**	Luttrellstown	IRL	867
15	7	**7**	Powerscourt East Course	IRL	877
17	7	**7**	Powerscourt West Course	IRL	878
15	7	**7**	Rathcore	IRL	879
15	7	**7**	Ring of Kerry	IRL	881
14	7	**7**	Roganstown	IRL	882
15	7	**7**	Royal Belfast	NIR	913
19	6	**7**	Royal County Down	NIR	914
16	8	**7**	Royal Dublin	IRL	886
19	7	**7**	Royal Portrush Dunluce Links	NIR	915
13	7	**7**	Royal Portrush Valley	NIR	916
14	7	**7**	Seafield	IRL	887
16	7	**7**	St Margaret's	IRL	892
15	7	**7**	The Island	IRL	893
18	6	**7**	Waterville	IRL	897

HOTEL FACILITIES
ENVIRONNEMENT HOTELIER

15	7	**7**	Westport	IRL	898
13	6	**6**	Athlone	IRL	818
16	7	**6**	Ballybunion Cashen (New Course)	IRL	819
19	7	**6**	Ballybunion Old Course	IRL	820
14	7	**6**	Ballykisteen	IRL	821
16	6	**6**	Castlerock	NIR	905
13	4	**6**	Charleville	IRL	831
15	6	**6**	Connemara	IRL	833
18	5	**6**	County Louth	IRL	835
16	7	**6**	Donegal (Murvagh)	IRL	840
15	6	**6**	Dundalk	IRL	846
17	8	**6**	Enniscrone	IRL	847
14	6	**6**	Esker Hills	IRL	848
18	5	**6**	The European	IRL	849
16	8	**6**	Fota Island	IRL	851
14	7	**6**	Galway Bay	IRL	852
15	6	**6**	Headfort New Course	IRL	856
15	6	**6**	Kilkea Castle	IRL	861
15	7	**6**	Knock	NIR	908
17	6	**6**	Lahinch	IRL	864
13	7	**6**	Lee Valley	IRL	865
15	7	**6**	Limerick County	IRL	866
15	7	**6**	Lisburn	NIR	909
13	6	**6**	Malone	NIR	910
14	5	**6**	Massereene	NIR	911
18	9	**6**	Mount Juliet	IRL	869
16	7	**6**	Old Head	IRL	872
15	5	**6**	PGA National	IRL	873
16	7	**6**	Portstewart Strand Course	NIR	912
16	7	**6**	Rosapenna Old Tom Morris	IRL	883
15	7	**6**	Rosapenna Sandy Hill Links	IRL	884
13	5	**6**	Rosslare	IRL	885
15	6	**6**	Seapoint	IRL	888
14	6	**6**	St Helen's Bay	IRL	891
18	7	**6**	Tralee	IRL	894
15	7	**6**	Tulfarris	IRL	895
14	5	**6**	Waterford Castle	IRL	896
15	7	**6**	Woodbrook	IRL	899
16	7	**6**	Woodenbridge	IRL	900
17	7	**5**	Ballyliffin Glashedy Links	IRL	822
16	7	**5**	Ballyliffin Old Course	IRL	823
14	6	**5**	Bangor	NIR	902
13	6	**5**	Cairndhu	NIR	904
15	6	**5**	Clandeboye Dufferin Course	NIR	906
15	6	**5**	Cork GC	IRL	834
15	7	**5**	County Tipperary	IRL	837
14	5	**5**	Courtown	IRL	838
15	5	**5**	Dooks	IRL	841
18	3	**5**	Doonbeg	IRL	842
13	6	**5**	Mount Wolseley	IRL	870
15	5	**5**	Mullingar	IRL	871
16	5	**5**	Portsalon	IRL	876
15	8	**5**	Slieve Russell	IRL	889
14	6	**4**	Ardglass	NIR	901
17	6	**4**	County Sligo	IRL	836
15	5	**4**	Dingle Links (Ceann Sibeal)	IRL	839
15	6	**4**	Kirkistown Castle	NIR	907
14	7	**4**	Rathsallagh	IRL	880
13	6	**4**	Warrenpoint	NIR	917
15	5	**3**	Belmullet (Carne Golf Links)	IRL	825

RECOMMENDED GOLFING STAY
SÉJOUR DE GOLF RECOMMANDÉ

Ballybunion Old Course	IRL	**19**	7	6	820
Ballyliffin Glashedy Links	IRL	**17**	7	5	822
Ballyliffin Old Course	IRL	**16**	7	5	823
Carton House Montgomerie	IRL	**16**	4	8	828
Carton House O'Meara	IRL	**14**	4	8	829
County Sligo	IRL	**17**	6	4	836
Druids Glen Druids Glen	IRL	**16**	9	7	844
Druids Glen Druids Heath	IRL	**14**	9	7	845
Headfort New Course	IRL	**15**	6	6	856
The Heritage	IRL	**18**	9	8	857
K Club North Course	IRL	**17**	8	8	859
Killarney Lackabane	IRL	**14**	7	8	862
Killarney Mahony's Point	IRL	**15**	7	8	863
Lahinch	IRL	**17**	6	6	864
Mount Juliet	IRL	**18**	9	6	869
Royal County Down	NIR	**19**	6	7	914
Portstewart East Course	NIR	**16**	7	6	912
Powerscourt West Course	IRL	**17**	7	7	878
Rosapenna Sandy Hill Links	IRL	**15**	7	6	884
Royal County Down	NIR	**19**	6	7	914
Royal Portrush Dunluce Links	NIR	**19**	7	7	915
Royal Portrush Valley	NIR	**13**	7	7	916

Adare

15	6	7

From time to time, being iconoclastic can make a pleasant change. There could be no doubting that Adare was designed by Robert Trent Jones, because this could just as easily be a course on the Costa del Sol. In other words, there is no real "feeling" with the Irish landscape, probably on account of the over-extensive earthworks and grading used to shape the course, the give-away bunker designs and the huge water hazard on the front 9, which cost a fortune to build. But this is still a great course once you forget its artificial side, which anyway is less apparent on the way in. Here, golfers have to cope with the river Maigue and indigenous trees such as oak, beech, pine and cedar. There is no hidden trap, which only emphasises the psychological fear factor. Long and challenging – and matured into one of the country's leading parkland courses – this course is almost certainly too tough for high-handicappers on account of the very many hazards. Even the better players will find it hard going.

De temps à autre, il n'est pas désagréable d'être iconoclaste: Adare a certes été dessiné par Robert Trent Jones, mais pourrait tout aussi bien se trouver sur la Costa del Sol. Autrement dit, on ne trouvera pas ici de véritable "sympathie" avec le paysage irlandais, en raison sans doute de mouvements de terrain trop importants, de dessin de bunkers trop révélateurs de leur auteur, de l'immense obstacle d'eau de l'aller, dont l'aménagement a coûté une fortune. Mais il reste un grand parcours de golf, dont on oubliera le côté parfois artificiel, d'ailleurs moins sensible au retour: il met essentiellement en jeu la rivière Maigue, et les arbres natifs du lieu : chênes, hêtres, pins ou cèdres. Aucun piège n'est caché, ce qui accentue le facteur psychologique de crainte. Long et exigeant, et devenu l'un des meilleurs "parkland" du pays, ce parcours reste sans doute très difficile pour les handicaps élevés, en raison de la multiplicité des obstacles, les autres n'y connaîtront guère de repos....

Adare Golf Club — 1995

Adare Manor
IRL - ADARE, Co Limerick

Office	Secrétariat	(353) 061 - 395 044
Pro shop	Pro-shop	(353) 061 - 395 044
Fax	Fax	(353) 061 - 396 987
Web		www.adaremanor.com
Situation	Situation	Limerick (pop. 52 039), 10 km
Annual closure	Fermeture annuelle	no
Weekly closure	Fermeture hebdomadaire	no

Fees main season Tarifs haute saison — 18 holes

	Week days / Semaine	We/Bank holidays / We/Férié
Individual Individuel	€ 125	€ 125
Couple Couple	€ 250	€ 250

€ 105 for hotel guests / € 65 after 15:00

Caddie Caddie yes — **Electric Trolley** Chariot électrique yes
Buggy Voiturette yes — **Clubs** Clubs yes

Credit cards Cartes de crédit
VISA - Eurocard - MasterCard - AMEX

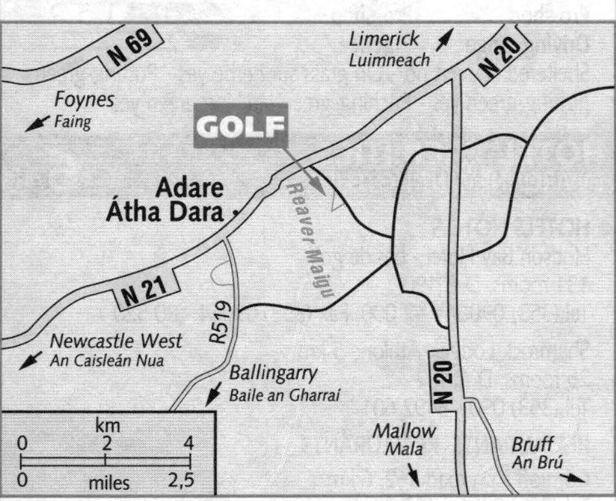

Access Accès : Limerick, N7 → Adare. Patrick's Well, straight through the fork in road, first left in village at gates, right to pro shop
Map 3 on page 812 Carte 3 Page 812

GOLF COURSE — PARCOURS — 15/20

Site	Site	
Maintenance	Entretien	
Architect	Architecte	Robert Trent Jones
Type	Type	inland, parkland
Relief	Relief	
Water in play	Eau en jeu	
Exp. to wind	Exposé au vent	
Trees in play	Arbres en jeu	

Scorecard Carte de score	Chp. Chp.	Mens Mess.	Ladies Da.
Length Long.	6489	5993	4925
Par	72	72	72
Slope system	—	—	—

Advised golfing ability Niveau de jeu recommandé — 0 12 24 36
Hcp required Handicap exigé — 28 Men, 36 Ladies

CLUB HOUSE & AMENITIES — CLUB HOUSE ET ANNEXES — 6/10

Pro shop Pro-shop
Driving range Practice
Sheltered couvert no - On grass sur herbe yes - Putting-green putting-green yes - Pitching-green pitching green yes

HOTEL FACILITIES — ENVIRONNEMENT HOTELIER — 7/10

HOTELS HÔTELS
Adare Manor Hotel - on site
113 rooms, D € 395
Tel (353) 061 - 396 566, Fax (353) 061 - 396 124

Woodlands Hotel - Adare 2 km
57 rooms, D from € 80
Tel (353) 061 - 605 100, Fax (353) 061 - 396 073

Dunraven Arms Hotel - Adare 0.5 km
86 rooms, D € 195
Tel (353) 061 - 396 633, Fax (353) 061 - 396 541

RESTAURANTS RESTAURANTS
Wild Geese - Adare 1 km - Tel (353) 061 - 396 451
Dunraven Arms - Adare 0.5 km - Tel (353) 061 - 396 633

Athlone

13 | 6 | 6

The gently rolling course of Athlone is magnificently sited on a peninsula overlocking Lough Ree. An old course that was remodelled in the late 1930s, the lack of yardage might lead to the better players under-estimating its difficulty and will invite them to play from the back-tees. It demands a wide variety of shots, especially when the wind blows from the lake, and skills in flighting the ball will help. The woods are on the outskirts of the course, as are most of the water hazards, although some isolated trees can come into play. Otherwise, you just avoid the bunkers, whose only criticism is the bland uniformity in design and shape. The greens are generally in good condition and moderately contoured. It's not the best season in Ireland anyway. Long-hitters will have fun on the three rather short par 5s, but accuracy is always important. Watch out for some tight fairways. Greens are currently being renovated and changes made to several holes as from the Autumn of 2005.

Doucement vallonné, le parcours d'Athlone dispose d'une situation magnifique sur une péninsule dominant le Lough Ree. Déjà ancien, bien que révisé à la fin des années 30, son manque de longueur ne doit pas le faire sous estimer par les joueurs de bon niveau, à qui on conseillera bien sûr les départs arrière. Il demande une grande variété de coups, surtout quand le vent vient du lac, il faut alors savoir travailler la balle. Les bois sont à la périphérie du parcours, de même que la plupart des obstacles d'eau, mais certains arbres isolés peuvent parfois venir en jeu. Autrement, pour bien scorer, il suffit d'éviter les bunkers, auxquels on peut simplement reprocher une certaine uniformité de dessin et de forme. Les greens sont généralement en bonne condition et de relief modéré. Les longs frappeurs s'amuseront sur trois par 5 assez courts, mais ne devront pas oublier la précision, les fairways peuvent être étroits. Une rénovation des greens est en cours, ainsi que la modification de plusieurs trous, à partir de l'automne 2005.

Athlone Golf Club — 1892

Hodson Bay
IRL - ATHLONE, Co. Westmeath

Office	Secrétariat	(353) 0906 - 492 073
Pro shop	Pro-shop	(353) 0906 - 446 008
Fax	Fax	(353) 0906 - 494 080
Web	—	
Situation	Situation	Dublin, 120 km

Athlone (pop. 7 691), 5 km

Annual closure	Fermeture annuelle	no
Weekly closure	Fermeture hebdomadaire	no

Fees main season Tarifs haute saison — 18 holes

	Week days Semaine	We/Bank holidays We/Férié
Individual Individuel	€ 30	€ 35
Couple Couple	€ 60	€ 70

Caddie Caddie on request **Electric Trolley** Chariot électrique no

Buggy Voiturette yes **Clubs** Clubs yes

Credit cards Cartes de crédit
VISA - MasterCard

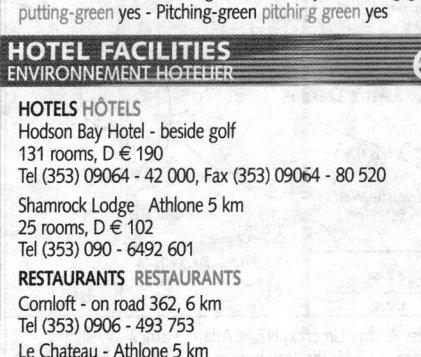

Access Accès : Athlone, N61 → Roscommon.
Golf beside Hodson Bay Hotel
Map 3 on page 813 Carte 3 Page 813

GOLF COURSE — PARCOURS 13/20

Site	Site	
Maintenance	Entretien	
Architect	Architecte	L McAllister Fred Hawtree
Type	Type	parkland
Relief	Relief	
Water in play	Eau en jeu	
Exp. to wind	Exposé au vent	
Trees in play	Arbres en jeu	

Scorecard Carte de score	Chp. Chp.	Mens Mess.	Ladies Da.
Length Long.	5922	5773	5104
Par	71	71	75
Slope system	—	—	—

Advised golfing ability Niveau de jeu recommandé — 0 12 24 36

Hcp required Handicap exigé — certificate

CLUB HOUSE & AMENITIES — CLUB HOUSE ET ANNEXES 6/10

Pro shop	Pro-shop
Driving range	Practice

Sheltered couvert no - On grass sur herbe yes - Putting-green putting-green yes - Pitching-green pitching green yes

HOTEL FACILITIES — ENVIRONNEMENT HOTELIER 6/10

HOTELS HÔTELS

Hodson Bay Hotel - beside golf
131 rooms, D € 190
Tel (353) 09064 - 42 000, Fax (353) 09064 - 80 520

Shamrock Lodge Athlone 5 km
25 rooms, D € 102
Tel (353) 090 - 6492 601

RESTAURANTS RESTAURANTS

Cornloft - on road 362, 6 km
Tel (353) 0906 - 493 753

Le Chateau - Athlone 5 km
Tel (353) 090 - 6494 517

Ballybunion *Cashen (New Course)*

16	7	6

Designing a new course in a mythical site such as this can be fatal to any course architect. But Robert Trent Jones has already designed enough great courses of his own to shrug off any mention of comparison, and his personality told him not to ape the old course, even though the dune-peppered landscape is similar (and sometimes even more impressive). The result here is a course that is slightly harder to decipher, where there is less room for intuition and more for knowledge of distance when choosing your clubs. A little American touch, even though approach shots can still be played "British" style. However, he has made maximum use of the terrain's natural contours and limited earthworks, while giving each hole its own individual character. The course's forceful personality (it is not everyone's cup of tea) would make this a must anywhere else, but here it lives in the shadow of the "Old Course".

Pour un architecte, signer un nouveau parcours dans un site aussi mythique peut être meurtrier. Robert Trent Jones avait déjà créé assez de grands parcours pour ne pas craindre la comparaison, et sa personnalité ne l'incitait pas à essayer de singer le "Old", bien que le paysage dunaire soit similaire (parfois plus impressionnant encore). De fait, il a créé un parcours plus complexe à déchiffrer, où la place de l'intuition est moins importante que la connaissance des distances pour choisir les clubs. Une petite touche américaine... même si les petites approches peuvent être souvent jouées "à la britannique". Cependant, il a su utiliser au maximum les contours naturels du terrain et limiter les terrassements, tout en donnant la touche de caractère individuel à chaque trou. La forte personnalité de ce parcours (qui ne fait pas toujours l'unanimité) en ferait n'importe où ailleurs un "must", mais le "Old" lui fait forcément ombrage.

Ballybunion Golf Club — 1971

Sandhill Road
IRL - BALLYBUNION, Co Kerry

Office	Secrétariat	(353) 068 - 27 146
Pro shop	Pro-shop	(353) 068 - 27 842
Fax	Fax	(353) 068 - 27 387
Web	www.ballybuniongolfclub.ie	
Situation	Situation	Ballybunion, 1 km
Annual closure	Fermeture annuelle	no
Weekly closure	Fermeture hebdomadaire	no

Fees main season Tarifs haute saison — 18 holes

	Week days Semaine	We/Bank holidays We/Férié
Individual Individuel	€ 95	*
Couple Couple	€ 190	*

* Members only. Buggies on Cashen course only

Caddie Caddie yes — **Electric Trolley** Chariot électrique no

Buggy Voiturette yes (Cashen course) **Clubs** Clubs yes

Credit cards Cartes de crédit
VISA - MasterCard - AMEX

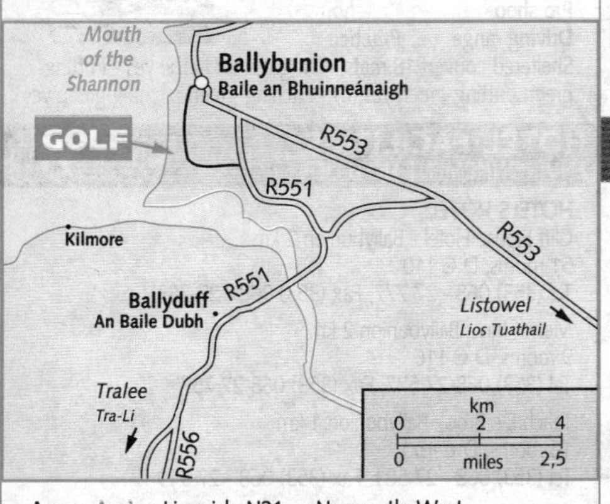

Access Accès : Limerick, N21 → Newcastle West, → Listowel, → Ballybunion
Map 3 on page 812 Carte 3 Page 812

GOLF COURSE — PARCOURS — 16/20

Site	Site	
Maintenance	Entretien	
Architect	Architecte	Robert Trent Jones
Type	Type	links
Relief	Relief	
Water in play	Eau en jeu	
Exp. to wind	Exposé au vent	
Trees in play	Arbres en jeu	

Scorecard Carte de score	Chp. Chp.	Mens Mess.	Ladies Da.
Length Long.	5830	5350	5160
Par	72	72	72
Slope system	—	—	

Advised golfing ability Niveau de jeu recommandé — 0 12 24 36

Hcp required Handicap exigé — 24 Men, 36 Ladies

CLUB HOUSE & AMENITIES — CLUB HOUSE ET ANNEXES — 7/10

Pro shop Pro-shop
Driving range Practice
Sheltered couvert 18 mats - On grass sur herbe yes - Putting-green putting-green yes (2) - Pitching-green pitching green yes

HOTEL FACILITIES — ENVIRONNEMENT HOTELIER — 6/10

HOTELS HÔTELS
Cliff House Hotel - Ballybunion 2 km
51 rooms, D € 110
Tel (353) 068 - 27 777, Fax (353) 068 - 27 783

Manor Inn - Ballybunion 2 km
9 rooms, D € 116
Tel (353) 068-27 577, Fax (353) 068-27 757

Teach De Broc - Ballybunion 1 km
16 rooms, D € 150
Tel (353) 068 - 27 581, Fax (353) 068 - 27 919

RESTAURANTS RESTAURANTS
Three Mermaids - Listowel 15 km - Tel (353) 068 - 22 443
Harty-Costello - Ballybunion 1 km - Tel (353) 068 - 27 129

Ballybunion *Old Course*

19	7	6

There are some courses you could write a book about, where anything less will fail to do them justice. The old course at Ballybunion is such a course. On a windless day (a rare occurrence), it's not easy playing here, while in a strong wind, it can be hell. But bowing the knee to a living masterpiece such as this is sheer bliss. The numbers on your card lose all their significance: there are no such things as par 3s, par 4s or par 5s - all that matters is survival. After a few almost ordinary holes (relatively speaking), the pulse starts to quicken on the 6th. On the remainder of an epic adventure, you will need ball control in every direction, skills with every club in the bag and technique for high and low shots alike. At the same time you'll admire the layout. Lost between huge sand dunes, the fairways look so narrow, the greens tiny and the bunkers absolutely ruthless. Tom Watson considers this ultimate test of technique and inspiration to be the greatest course in the world. Suffice it to say, every golfer will have to check it out for himself or herself, at least once in their career.

Faute de pouvoir écrire un livre sur certains grands parcours, il faudrait ne rien en dire. Le "Old Course" de Ballybunion est de ceux-là. Sans vent (c'est rare), il n'est pas facile. Il devient infernal par vent fort, mais quel bonheur de plier le genou devant un chef-d'oeuvre aussi vivant. Alors, les chiffres inscrits sur la carte ne signifient plus rien: plus de par 3, 4 ou 5, il s'agit de survivre. Après quelques trous presque anodins (c'est relatif !), le pouls s'accélère à partir du 6, la suite n'est plus qu'une longue épopée, où il faut travailler la balle dans tous les sens, jouer tous les clubs et tous les coups, maîtriser les balles hautes comme les balles au ras du sol. Et admirer le génie du dessin. Perdus dans d'immenses dunes, le fairway paraît bien étroit, les greens minuscules, les bunkers sans pitié. Tom Watson considère cet examen suprême de la technique et de l'inspiration comme le plus grand parcours du monde. Il reste au sommet du monde, et tout golfeur doit le vérifier un jour.

Ballybunion Golf Club — 1893

Sandhill Road
IRL - BALLYBUNION, Co Kerry

Office	Secrétariat	(353) 068 - 27 146
Pro shop	Pro-shop	(353) 068 - 27 842
Fax	Fax	(353) 068 - 27 387
Web	www.ballybuniongolfclub.ie	
Situation	Situation	Ballybunion, 1 km
Annual closure	Fermeture annuelle	no
Weekly closure	Fermeture hebdomadaire	no

Fees main season Tarifs haute saison — 18 holes

	Week days / Semaine	We/Bank holidays / We/Férie
Individual Individuel	€ 135	*
Couple Couple	€ 270	*

* Members only. Buggies on Cashen course only

Caddie Caddie yes — **Electric Trolley** Chariot électrique no

Buggy Voiturette yes (Cashen course) **Clubs** Clubs yes

Credit cards Cartes de crédit
VISA - MasterCard - AMEX

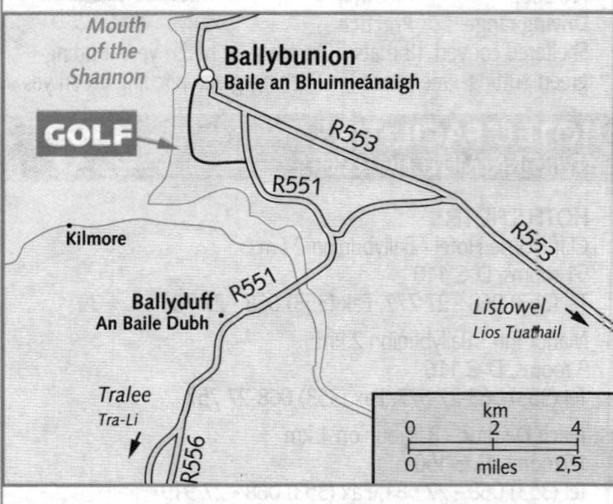

Access Accès : Limerick, N21 → Newcastle West, → Listowel, → Ballybunion

Map 3 on page 812 Carte 3 Page 812

GOLF COURSE — PARCOURS — 19/20

Site	Site	
Maintenance	Entretien	
Architect	Architecte	L. Hewson Tom Simpson
Type	Type	links
Relief	Relief	
Water in play	Eau en jeu	
Exp. to wind	Exposé au vent	
Trees in play	Arbres en jeu	

Scorecard / Carte de score	Chp. / Chp.	Mens / Mess.	Ladies / Da.
Length Long.	6241	6201	5004
Par	71	71	74
Slope system	—	—	—

Advised golfing ability Niveau de jeu recommandé — 0 12 24 36

Hcp required Handicap exigé — 24 Men, 36 Ladies

CLUB HOUSE & AMENITIES — CLUB HOUSE ET ANNEXES — 7/10

Pro shop Pro-shop
Driving range Practice
Sheltered couvert 18 mats - On grass sur herbe yes - Putting-green putting-green yes (2) - Pitching-green pitching green yes

HOTEL FACILITIES — ENVIRONNEMENT HOTELIER — 6/10

HOTELS HÔTELS

Cliff House Hotel - Ballybunion 2 km
51 rooms, D € 110
Tel (353) 068 - 27 777, Fax (353) 068 - 27 783

Manor Inn - Ballybunion 2 km
9 rooms, D € 116
Tel (353) 068-27 577, Fax (353) 068-27 757

Teach De Broc - Ballybunion 1 km
16 rooms, D € 150
Tel (353) 068 - 27 581, Fax (353) 068 - 27 919

RESTAURANTS RESTAURANTS

Three Mermaids - Listowel 15 km - Tel (353) 068 - 22 443
Harty-Costello - Ballybunion 1 km - Tel (353) 068 - 27 129

Ballykisteen

14 | 7 | 6

Laid out over a former horse farm and riding stables, Ballykisteen looks like a large park where trees and water form the main hazards. But the designers (Des Smyth and Declan Branigan) spared a thought for everyone. The further back you tee off, the narrower the fairways become, and the great number of tees means you can adapt each round to your ability. The course calls for every shot in the book: here a fade, there a draw. The greens are guarded to allow either the good old bump and run shots, or the new-style target shot approaches. Water is in play on ten holes, but with varying degrees of difficulty. It is at its worst on the 15th (with out-of-bounds to the left), one of Ireland's most demanding par 3s - the bogey should be gratefully accepted. Forthright and well-balanced, Ballykisteen still lacks in yardage, but who's really complaining?

Réalisé dans un ancien élevage de chevaux, Ballykisteen présente un caractère de grand parc, où les arbres et l'eau constituent les dangers. Mais les architectes (le champion irlandais Des Smyth et Declan Branigan) ont pensé à tout le monde. Plus on recule de départ, plus le parcours est étroit, et la multiplicité des départs permet de se faire un parcours "à sa main". Le dessin exige tous les coups de golf : certains trous demandent une balle en fade, un nombre égal réclame le draw. Et les défenses de green autorisent soit des balles roulées (bump and run), soit des balles levées (target golf). L'eau vient en jeu sur dix trous, mais avec différents niveaux de difficulté. Elle est au maximum sur le 15 (avec hors-limites à gauche), un des plus exigeants par 3 d'Irlande : le bogey y est très acceptable ! Honnête et bien équilibré, Ballykisteen manque toujours un peu de longueur, mais qui s'en plaindra ?

Ballykisteen Golf Club — 1995

IRL - MONARD, Co Tipperary

Office Secrétariat (353) 062 - 33 333
Pro shop Pro-shop (353) 062 - 33 333
Fax Fax (353) 062 - 33 668
Web www.ballykisteen.com
Situation Situation Limerick (pop. 52 039), 32 km
Tipperary, 5 km
Annual closure Fermeture annuelle no
Weekly closure Fermeture hebdomadaire no

Fees main season Tarifs haute saison	18 holes	
	Week days Semaine	We/Bank holidays We/Férié
Individual Individuel	€ 35	€ 85
Couple Couple	€ 70	€ 170

Caddie Caddie on request **Electric Trolley** Chariot électrique yes
Buggy Voiturette yes **Clubs** Clubs yes
Credit cards Cartes de crédit
VISA - MasterCard - DC

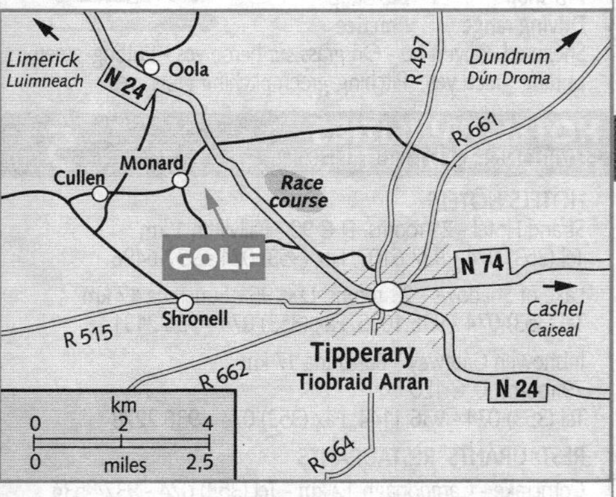

Access Accès : Tipperary N24 → Limerick. Golf 5 km, opposite Tipperary Racecourse
Map 3 on page 812 Carte 3 Page 812

GOLF COURSE — PARCOURS 14/20

Site Site
Maintenance Entretien
Architect Architecte Des Smyth, Declan Branigan
Type Type parkland
Relief Relief
Water in play Eau en jeu
Exp. to wind Exposé au vent
Trees in play Arbres en jeu

Scorecard Carte de score	Chp. Chp.	Mens Mess.	Ladies Da.
Length Long.	6089	5656	5005
Par	72	72	74
Slope system	—	—	—

Advised golfing ability Niveau de jeu recommandé 0 12 24 36
Hcp required Handicap exigé 28 Men, 36 Ladies

CLUB HOUSE & AMENITIES — CLUB HOUSE ET ANNEXES 7/10

Pro shop Pro-shop
Driving range Practice
Sheltered couvert 12 mats - On grass sur herbe yes - Putting-green putting-green yes - Pitching-green pitching green yes

HOTEL FACILITIES — ENVIRONNEMENT HOTELIER 6/10

HOTELS HÔTELS
Aherlow House - Glen of Aherlow 10 km
29 rooms, D € 135
Tel (353) 062 - 56 153, Fax (353) 062 - 56 212

Ballyglass Country House Hotel - Tipperary 4 km
10 rooms, D € 90
Tel (353) 062 - 52 104, Fax (353) 062 - 52 229

Ramada Hotel - 87 rooms - on site (end of 2005)
Tel 1-850-726232 (local)

RESTAURANTS RESTAURANTS
The Brown Trout - Tipperary 5 km - Tel (353) 062 - 51 912
Aherlow House - Glen of Aherlow 10 km
Tel (353) 062 - 56 153

821

Ballyliffin *Glashedy Links*

17	7	5

This recent course outstrips its neighbour in terms of technical play. The landscape is even more moon-like, with massive dunes, but a little grading work has resulted in levelling out a number of drive landing areas and in creating a collection of fairway and green-side bunkers that you are sure to encounter every now and then. This course grabs you by the throat from the word go and doesn't let you go. You need to hit low shots into the wind and with the wind, otherwise your ball will float upwards like a feather. You need to know how to fade and draw the ball to get around the dog-legs, you need brains and nerves to approach the greens, to stay on the putting surface and make the putt. You need a cool head to go fetch your ball instead of admiring the landscape (especially Glashedy Rock, off the coast). You need to play here and spend some time on the course to measure what you are capable of. One of the best courses in Ireland.

Ce parcours relativement récent dépasse son voisin en matière de technicité. Le paysage est encore plus lunaire, avec des dunes massives, où quelques terrassements ont permis d'adoucir certaines zones d'arrivée de drive, mais aussi de creuser une collection de bunkers de fairway et de green que l'on ne manquera pas d'expérimenter. Ce parcours vous prend à la gorge dès les premiers trous, et ne vous lâchera plus. Il faudra faire des balles basses, contre le vent, mais aussi avec, pour ne pas les voir voler comme des plumes. Il faudra maîtriser les effets de fade et de draw pour négocier les dog-legs, il faudra de la science et des nerfs pour attaquer les greens, pour y rester, et pour putter. Il faudra du sang-froid pour revenir à sa balle au lieu d'admirer le paysage (notamment sur le Glashedy Rock, au large). Il faudra jouer ici, y faire une sorte de retraite de golf pour mesurer vos capacités. Décidément, ce parcours fait partie des meilleurs du pays.

Ballyliffin Golf Club 1995

IRL - BALLYLIFFIN, Co Donegal

Office Secrétariat (353) 07493 - 76 119
Pro shop Pro-shop (353) 07493 - 78 100
Fax Fax (353) 07493 - 76 672
Web www.ballyliffingolfclub.com
Situation Situation Belfast, 160 km
Derry (pop. 72 334), 40 km
Annual closure Fermeture annuelle no
Weekly closure Fermeture hebdomadaire no

Fees main season Tarifs haute saison		18 holes
	Week days Semaine	**We/Bank holidays** We/Férié
Individual Individuel	€ 65	€ 75
Couple Couple	€ 130	€ 150

2 round special (one on each course): € 100

Caddie Caddie on request **Electric Trolley** Chariot électrique yes
Buggy Voiturette yes **Clubs** Clubs yes
Credit cards Cartes de crédit
VISA - MasterCard

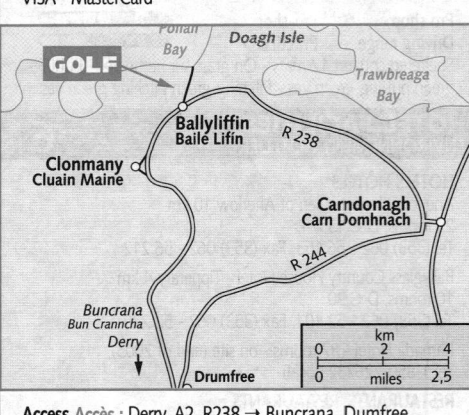

Access Accès : Derry, A2, R238 → Buncrana, Dumfree, Ballyliffin
Map 2 on page 811 Carte 2 Page 811

GOLF COURSE
PARCOURS **17/20**

Site — Site
Maintenance — Entretien
Architect Architecte Pat Ruddy
Tom Craddock
Type Type links, seaside course
Relief — Relief
Water in play — Eau en jeu
Exp. to wind — Exposé au vent
Trees in play — Arbres en jeu

Scorecard Carte de score	**Chp.** Chp.	**Mens** Mess.	**Ladies** Da.
Length Long.	6466	5820	5275
Par	72	73	72
Slope system	—	—	—

Advised golfing ability Niveau de jeu recommandé 0 12 24 36
Hcp required Handicap exigé 28 Men, 36 Ladies

CLUB HOUSE & AMENITIES
CLUB HOUSE ET ANNEXES **7/10**

Pro shop Pro-shop
Driving range Practice
Sheltered couvert no - On grass sur herbe yes - Putting-green putting-green yes - Pitching-green pitching green yes

HOTEL FACILITIES
ENVIRONNEMENT HOTELIER **5/10**

HOTELS HÔTELS
Strand Hotel - 21 rooms, D € 90 - Ballyliffin 1 km
Tel (353) 074 - 937 6107, Fax (353) 074 - 937 6486

Lake of Shadows - 23 rooms, D € 96 - Buncrana 17 km
Tel (353) 074 - 936 1005, Fax (353) 074 - 936 2131

Inishowen Gateway - Buncrana 17 km
79 rooms, D € 120
Tel (353) 074 - 936 1144, Fax (353) 074 - 936 2278

RESTAURANTS RESTAURANTS
Corncrake - Carndonagh 12 km - Tel (353) 074 - 9374 534
Ubiquitous Chip - Buncrana 16 km - Tel (353) 074 - 9362 530
St John's Country House - Fahan 18 km
Tel (353) 074 - 936 0289

Ballyliffin Old Course

16 | 7 | 5

The summer days are long enough in the north of Ireland to get a bellyful of golf, here with two 18-hole courses that really are worth the trip. Nick Faldo called the "Old Links" the "most natural golf course ever", which worked wonders for its renown. Here, you most definitely play the ball down on rolling fairways between stretches of rough where the limits between the two are often barely visible, and you rarely hit the ball on the flat. The landscape is on the beautiful side of austere, between the ocean waves, hills and endless stretches of sand-dunes, bushes and tall grass broken only by the odd white house in the distance. Everyone makes his own way across this peaceful expanse of land, as if he were the first ever to play here. As a fitting tribute, Nick Faldo was asked to oversee some refurbishing work, which includes new tee-boxes, the widening of some greens and re-bunkering of the whole course. Work will be completed by early 2006.

Les journées d'été sont assez longues au nord de l'Irlande pour se donner une... indigestion de golf avec deux 18 trous qui valent le voyage ! Le "Old Links" avait été qualifié par Nick Faldo de "golf le plus naturel qui soit", ce qui avait beaucoup fait pour la notoriété du lieu. Ici, on joue la balle où elle est, sur des fairways ondulant entre les roughs, parfois sans limite visible, et l'on tape rarement la balle à plat. Le paysage est d'une austère beauté, entre les flots de l'océan, les collines et des étendues infinies de dunes, de buissons, d'herbes hautes, ponctuées par de rares maisons blanches dans le lointain. Dans cet espace pacifique, chacun trace son chemin, comme s'il était le premier à jouer ici. Juste hommage, Nick Faldo a été chargé d'une rénovation qui comprend de nouveaux départs, l'élargissement de certains greens, et une complète refonte du bunkering. Elle sera achevée début 2006.

Ballyliffin Golf Club — 1947

IRL - BALLYLIFFIN, Co Donegal

Office Secrétariat (353) 07493 - 76 119
Pro shop Pro-shop (353) 07493 - 78 100
Fax Fax (353) 07493 - 76 672
Web www.ballyliffingolfclub.com
Situation Situation Belfast, 160 km
Derry (pop. 72 334), 40 km
Annual closure Fermeture annuelle no
Weekly closure Fermeture hebdomadaire no

Fees main season Tarifs haute saison — 18 holes

	Week days / Semaine	We/Bank holidays / We/Férié
Individual Individuel	€ 50	€ 55
Couple Couple	€ 100	€ 110

2 round special (one on each course): € 90 and € 110 (w-e)

Caddie Caddie on request **Electric Trolley** Chariot électrique yes
Buggy Voiturette yes **Clubs** Clubs yes
Credit cards Cartes de crédit
VISA - MasterCard

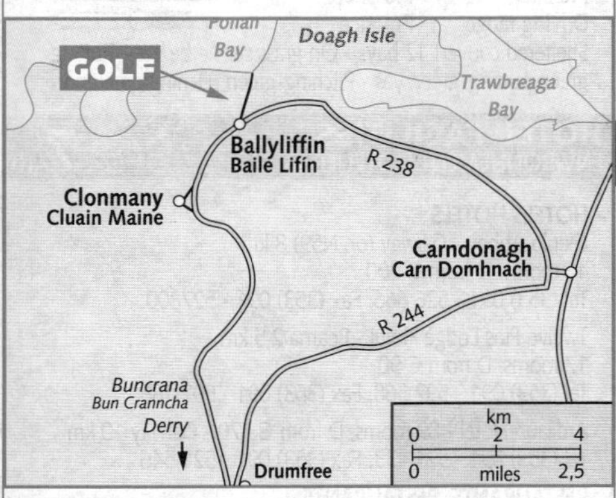

Access Accès : Derry, A2, R238 → Buncrana, Dumfree, Ballyliffin
Map 2 on page 811 Carte 2 Page 811

GOLF COURSE — PARCOURS 16/20

Site Site
Maintenance Entretien
Architect Architecte Lawrie, Pennink
Hackett, Hopkins, Nick Faldo (remod. 2005)
Type Type links
Relief Relief
Water in play Eau en jeu
Exp. to wind Exposé au vent
Trees in play Arbres en jeu

Scorecard Carte de score	Chp. Chp.	Mens Mess.	Ladies Da.
Length Long.	5951	5661	4859
Par	71	71	71
Slope system	—	—	—

Advised golfing ability Niveau de jeu recommandé 0 12 24 36
Hcp required Handicap exigé Men 28, Ladies 36

CLUB HOUSE & AMENITIES — CLUB HOUSE ET ANNEXES 7/10

Pro shop Pro-shop
Driving range Practice
Sheltered couvert no - On grass sur herbe yes - Putting-green putting-green yes - Pitching-green pitching green yes

HOTEL FACILITIES — ENVIRONNEMENT HOTELIER 5/10

HOTELS HÔTELS
Strand Hotel - 21 rooms, D € 90 - Ballyliffin 1 km
Tel (353) 074 - 937 6107, Fax (353) 074 - 937 6486

Lake of Shadows - 23 rooms, D € 96 - Buncrana 17 km
Tel (353) 074 - 936 1005, Fax (353) 074 - 936 2131

Inishowen Gateway - Buncrana 17 km
79 rooms, D € 120
Tel (353) 074 - 936 1144, Fax (353) 074 - 936 2278

RESTAURANTS RESTAURANTS
Corncrake - Carndonagh 12 km - Tel (353) 074 - 9374 534
Ubiquitous Chip - Buncrana 16 km - Tel (353) 074 - 9362 530
St John's Country House - Fahan 18 km
Tel (353) 074 - 936 0289

Bearna

14 | 7 | 7

This course was laid out over a marsh with granite subsoil (which protrudes here and there), but intensive draining was carried out before the course was built, which is one reason why it is in excellent condition. The relatively hilly site is magnificent, between Galway Bay and the hills of County Clare in the distance, countryside which was one of the major areas affected by the great famine of the 19th century. Although in the middle of the countryside with many water hazards to contend with, the style of this R.J. Browne layout has a strong links flavour, meaning that golfers who prefer seaside courses will feel the most comfortable over these 18 holes, where the difficulties gradually pile up as you progress. This is perhaps not the best course in the world but the peaceful setting, the keen air, the wild beauty of the nature all around and the sheer pleasure of playing here make it a rather unique layout, a good round of golf next to Galway before moving on up to Connemara.

Ce parcours a été construit sur un marécage avec un sous-sol de granit (qui affleure çà et là), mais un drainage intensif a précédé la construction du parcours, d'où sa très bonne condition. Le site relativement vallonné est magnifique, entre la baie de Galway, les collines du County Clare au loin, et la campagne, c'est un des sites historiques de la grande famine au XIXème siècle Bien qu'en pleine campagne, avec de nombreux obstacles d'eau, le style du parcours dessiné par R.J. Browne dégage un fort parfum de links. De fait, ce sont les amoureux des parcours en bord de mer qui se sentiront le plus à l'aise dans la montée en puissance de ces 18 trous, où les difficultés augmentent à mesure que l'on progresse. Ce n'est peut être pas le meilleur parcours du monde, mais la tranquillité du lieu, l'air vif, la sauvage beauté de la nature environnante, le plaisir de jouer ici rendent ce parcours assez unique, à jouer près de Galway, avant de continuer sa route jusqu'au Connemara.

Bearna Golf Club — 1996

Corboley
IRL - BARNA, Co. Galway

Office	Secrétariat	(353) 091 - 592 677
Pro shop	Pro-shop	(353) 091 - 592 677
Fax	Fax	(353) 091 - 592 674
Web	www.bearnagolfclub.com	
Situation	Situation	Galway (pop. 57 241), 11 km
Annual closure	Fermeture annuelle	no
Weekly closure	Fermeture hebdomadaire	no

Fees main season Tarifs haute saison	18 holes	
	Week days Semaine	We/Bank holidays We/Férié
Individual Individuel	€ 35	€ 45
Couple Couple	€ 70	€ 90

Special rates for husbands & wives

Caddie Caddie no — **Electric Trolley** Chariot électrique no
Buggy Voiturette yes — **Clubs** Clubs yes
Credit cards Cartes de crédit
VISA - Eurocard - MasterCard - AMEX - DC

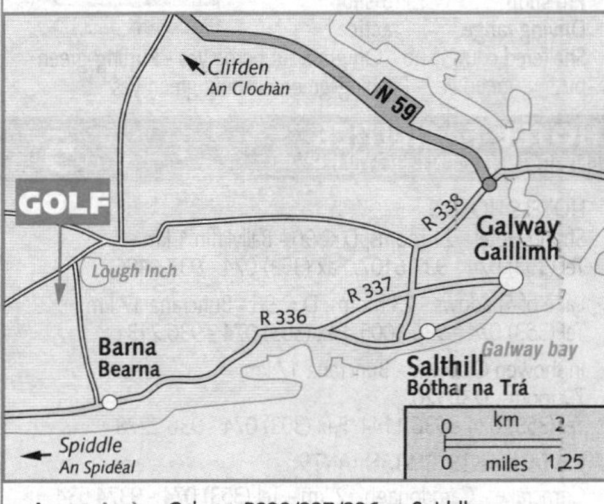

Access Accès : Galway, R338/337/336 → Spiddle.
At the end of Barna (Bearna), turn right → Golf
Map 2 on page 810 Carte 2 Page 810

GOLF COURSE — PARCOURS 14/20

Site	Site	
Maintenance	Entretien	
Architect	Architecte	R.J. Browne
Type	Type	open country
Relief	Relief	
Water in play	Eau en jeu	
Exp. to wind	Exposé au vent	
Trees in play	Arbres en jeu	

Scorecard Carte de score	Chp. Chp.	Mens Mess.	Ladies Da.
Length Long.	6174	5746	4684
Par	72	72	70
Slope system	—	—	—

Advised golfing ability Niveau de jeu recommandé: 0 12 24 36
Hcp required Handicap exigé: no

CLUB HOUSE & AMENITIES — CLUB HOUSE ET ANNEXES 7/10

Pro shop Pro-shop
Driving range Practice
Sheltered couvert 12 bays - On grass sur herbe yes - Putting-green putting-green yes - Pitching-green pitching green no

HOTEL FACILITIES — ENVIRONNEMENT HOTELIER 7/10

HOTELS HÔTELS

Glenlo Abbey - Galway (on N59) 8 km
46 rooms, D from € 200
Tel (353) 091 - 526 666, Fax (353) 091 - 527800

Twelve Pins Lodge Hotel - Bearna 2,5 km
17 rooms, D from € 90
Tel (353) 091 - 592 368, Fax (353) 091 - 592 185

Ardilaun Hotel - 89 rooms, D from € 170 - Galway 10 km
Tel (353) 091 - 521 433, Fax (353) 091 - 521 546

RESTAURANTS RESTAURANTS

O'Grady's on the Pier - Bearna 3 km - Tel (353) 091 - 592 223
Corboley's - on site - Tel (353) 091 - 592 866
Donnelly's - Bearna 3 km - Tel (353) 091 - 592 487

Belmullet (Carne Golf Links) | 15 | 5 | 3

Also known by the name of Carne, this is yet another world's end course, with impressive views over the rocky coast to the north of Mayo and Blacksod Bay. It is also one of the last designs by Eddie Hackett, who died in December 1996. The course is very hilly, so we would advise a buggy for all seniors if they want to keep a cool head. Everyone else would be well advised to study the course closely (without counting their score first time out), because a lot of shots and greens become blind if you are too far off the fairway, and the eight dog-legs are difficult to cope with if you don't get the right distance and angle for the green. Belmullet is an exciting prospect in match-play, because miracles are as frequent as disasters. However, this course is not to everyone's liking, especially to players who like parks with a pretty castle in the middle, but it is an essential experience in a site very exposed to the wind. But then, which links is not?

Egalement connu sous le nom de Carne, avec d'impressionnants panoramas sur la côte sauvage au nord du Mayo et Blacksod Bay, c'est encore un parcours au bout du monde, et l'un des tout derniers de Eddie Hackett, disparu en décembre 1996. Comme il est très accidenté, on conseillera aux seniors de prendre une voiturette, s'ils veulent garder la tête froide. Et à tout le monde de bien l'étudier (sans compter leur score la première fois) car beaucoup de coups et de greens seront aveugles s'ils s'écartent trop du fairway, et les huit doglegs seront difficiles à négocier si l'on évalue mal les distances pour avoir l'ouverture. En match-play, Belmullet est passionnant, car les miracles sont aussi fréquents que les désastres. Ce parcours toujours aussi excitant ne plaira pas à tout le monde, notamment à ceux qui aiment les parcs avec joli château, mais c'est une expérience à vivre, dans un site très exposé au vent, mais que serait un links sans vent ?

Belmullet Golf Club — 1993

IRL - BELMULLET, Co Mayo

Office — Secrétariat — (353) 097 - 82 292
Pro shop — Pro-shop — (353) 097 - 82 292
Fax — Fax — (353) 097 - 81477
Web — www.carnegolflinks.com
Situation — Situation — Ballina (pop. 6 852), 50 km
Belmullet, 1 km

Annual closure — Fermeture annuelle — no
Weekly closure — Fermeture hebdomadaire — no

Fees main season Tarifs haute saison	18 holes	
	Week days Semaine	We/Bank holidays We/Férié
Individual Individuel	€ 55	€ 55
Couple Couple	€ 110	€ 110

Caddie Caddie on request **Electric Trolley** Chariot électrique no

Buggy Voiturette yes — Clubs Clubs yes

Credit cards Cartes de crédit
VISA - Eurocard - MasterCard

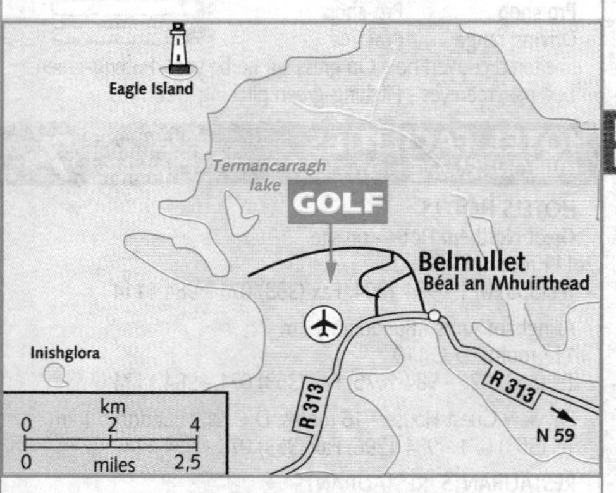

Access Accès : Ballina, N59 to Bangor. R313 to Belmullet.
→ Airport. Golf on the right
Map 2 on page 810 Carte 2 Page 810

GOLF COURSE — PARCOURS — 15/20

Site — Site
Maintenance — Entretien
Architect — Architecte — Eddie Hackett
Type — Type — links
Relief — Relief
Water in play — Eau en jeu
Exp. to wind — Exposé au vent
Trees in play — Arbres en jeu

Scorecard Carte de score	Chp. Chp.	Mens Mess.	Ladies Da.
Length Long.	6119	5819	4724
Par	72	72	73
Slope system	—	—	—

Advised golfing ability — Niveau de jeu recommandé — 0 12 24 36
Hcp required — Handicap exigé — no

CLUB HOUSE & AMENITIES — CLUB HOUSE ET ANNEXES — 5/10

Pro shop — Pro-shop
Driving range — Practice
Sheltered couvert no - On grass sur herbe yes - Putting-green putting-green yes - Pitching-green pitching green no

HOTEL FACILITIES — ENVIRONNEMENT HOTELIER — 3/10

HOTELS HÔTELS

Teach Torrais - Gaoth Saile 10 km
30 rooms, D from € 92
Tel (353) 097 - 86 888, Fax (353) 097 - 86 855

Downhill Inn - Ballina 50 km
45 rooms, D € 120
Tel (353) 096 - 73 444, Fax (353) 096 - 73 411

Ridgepool Hotel - Ballina 50 km
72 rooms, D € 140
Tel (353) 096 - 24 600, Fax (353) 096 - 24 602

RESTAURANTS RESTAURANTS

Club House Restaurant - on site - Tel (353) 097 - 82 292
Crockets on the Quay - Ballina 50 km - Tel (353) 096 - 75 936

Bundoran

13	6	7

The shortest courses are not always the easiest, often lacking par 5s to make those coveted birdies. Bundoran is one such number, and is also a part of history, being over 100 years old. Between the wars, the course was reshaped and toughened up by the grand champion Harry Vardon (the designer of Little Aston and the first designer of Woodhall Spa in England). Alternating parkland country with links holes, this is a good quality test that is ideal for a few rounds with friends or the family. Of course, with the wind, which can blow very hard indeed, things may get tough. Visitors enjoy a picturesque setting with several holes running alongside the ocean (you can even see people surfing) and some superb beaches. When exploring for golf in the north-west of Ireland - which is making itself a nice little international reputation - Bundoran is a highly recommendable stop-off, especially now that some extensive improvement work has started up.

Les parcours les plus courts ne sont pas toujours les plus faciles, car ils ont généralement peu de pars 5 pour faire des birdies! Bundoran en fait partie. Tout comme il appartient à l'histoire, car il a plus d'un siècle d'existence. Entre les deux guerres, il a été remodelé et durci par le grand champion Harry Vardon (l'auteur de Little Aston et le premier architecte de Woodhall Spa, en Angleterre). Alternant les paysages de parc et les vrais trous de links, c'est un test de bonne qualité, idéal pour quelques bonnes parties de golf entre amis ou en famille, mais qui (bien sûr) prend de la puissance avec le vent, parfois très fort ici. Il fait profiter ses visiteurs d'une situation pittoresque, avec plusieurs trous le long de l'océan (on y voit souvent des surfeurs) et de superbes plages. Dans une exploration golfique du Nord-Ouest de l'Irlande, qui commence à acquérir une réputation internationale, Bundoran est une halte très recommandable, d'autant que d'importants travaux d'amélioration sont en cours.

Bundoran Golf Club 1894

IRL - BUNDORAN, Co Donegal

Office — Secrétariat — (353) 01798 - 41 302
Pro shop — Pro-shop — (353) 01798 - 41 302
Fax — Fax — (353) 01798 - 42 014
Web — www.bundorangolfclub.com
Situation — Situation — Sligo (pop. 17 786), 40 km
Bundoran, 1 km

Annual closure — Fermeture annuelle — no
Weekly closure — Fermeture hebdomadaire — no

Fees main season — Tarifs haute saison	Week days — Semaine	We/Bank holidays — We/Férié
	18 holes	
Individual — Individuel	€ 40	€ 50
Couple — Couple	€ 80	€ 100

Caddie Caddie on request Electric Trolley Chariot électrique no

Buggy Voiturette yes Clubs Clubs yes

Credit cards Cartes de crédit
VISA (Pro shop goods & Green fees)

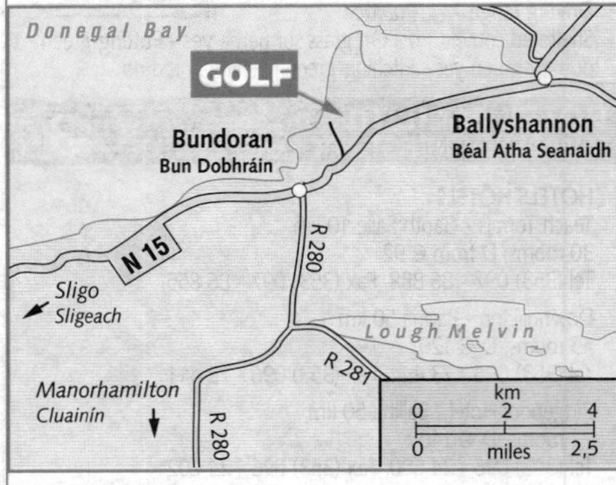

Access Accès : On N15 Sligo to Donegal
Map 2 on page 810 Carte 2 Page 810

GOLF COURSE — PARCOURS 13/20

Site — Site
Maintenance — Entretien
Architect — Architecte — Harry Vardon
Type — Type — links, links
Relief — Relief
Water in play — Eau en jeu
Exp. to wind — Exposé au vent
Trees in play — Arbres en jeu

Scorecard — Carte de score	Chp. — Chp.	Mens — Mess.	Ladies — Da.
Length Long.	5599	5234	5178
Par	69	69	75
Slope system	0	0	0

Advised golfing ability — Niveau de jeu recommandé — 0 12 24 36

Hcp required — Handicap exigé — no

CLUB HOUSE & AMENITIES — CLUB HOUSE ET ANNEXES 6/10

Pro shop — Pro-shop
Driving range — Practice

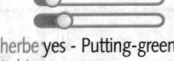

Sheltered couvert no - On grass sur herbe yes - Putting-green putting-green yes - Pitching-green pitching green yes

HOTEL FACILITIES — ENVIRONNEMENT HOTELIER 7/10

HOTELS HÔTELS

Great Northern Hotel - on site
111 rooms, D € 190
Tel (353) 071 - 984 1204, Fax (353) 071 - 984 1114

Allingham Arms - Bundoran 1 km
117 rooms, D € 110
Tel (353) 071 - 984 1075, Fax (353) 071 - 984 1171

Bayview Guest House - 16 rooms, D € 61 - Bundoran 1 km
Tel (353) 071 - 984 1296, Fax (353) 071 - 984 1147

RESTAURANTS RESTAURANTS

Le Chateaubrianne - Bundoran 2 km
Tel (353) 071 - 984 2160

Fitzgerald's Bistro - Bundoran 2 km - Tel (353) 071 - 984 1336

Carlow

16 | 6 | 7

There are some designers that always arouse our curiosity. Alongside Braid, Colt or Mackenzie, one such is Tom Simpson, whose philosophy has been taken up by numerous modern course architects, but not always so successfully. For Simpson, a course must be demanding for champions, less and less difficult the further forward the tee, and the most dangerous hazards should be designed to worry the very best players. This spirit abounds at Carlow, where virtually nothing has changed since the earliest days. It could be lengthened, that's for sure, but this par 70 stands up very well to every assault. All the difficulties are visible, but the strategic and aesthetic subtleties appear only gradually: the bunkering, the shaping of the fairways and the use of a little elevated land and rare water hazards reveal an in-depth knowledge of the game of golf. A engaging course, off the beaten track. Facilities have recently been extended to 27 holes with the construction of a third nine designed by Jeff Howes.

Certaines signatures éveillent la curiosité. A côté de Braid, Colt ou Mackenzie, Tom Simpson est de celles-là. Sa philosophie a été reprise par de nombreux architectes modernes, pas toujours avec un tel succès : un parcours doit être exigeant pour les champions, de moins en moins difficile à mesure que l'on avance de départ, et les obstacles les plus dangereux doivent menacer avant tout les meilleurs. On retrouve cet esprit à Carlow, où pratiquement rien n'a changé depuis les origines. Certes, on pourrait l'allonger un peu, mais ce par 70 résiste de toute façon aux assauts. Toutes les difficultés sont visibles, mais les subtilités stratégiques et esthétiques n'apparaissent que progressivement : le placement des bunkers, le travail de modelage des fairways, l'utilisation des quelques élévations de terrain et des rares obstacles d'eau révèlent une connaissance profonde du jeu. Un parcours attachant, hors des sentiers battus, avec un récent 9 trous signé par Jeff Howes pour agrémenter le lieu.

Carlow Golf Club — 1937

Deerpark, Dublin Road
IRL - CARLOW, Co Carlow

Office	Secrétariat	(353) 05991 - 31 695
Pro shop	Pro-shop	(353) 05991 - 41 745
Fax	Fax	(353) 05991 - 40 065
Web	www.carlowgolfclub.com	
Situation	Situation	Carlow (pop. 11 721), 5 km
Annual closure	Fermeture annuelle	no
Weekly closure	Fermeture hebdomadaire	no

Fees main season Tarifs haute saison — 18 holes

	Week days / Semaine	We/Bank holidays / We/Férié
Individual Individuel	€ 50	€ 60
Couple Couple	€ 100	€ 120

Caddie Caddie no — **Electric Trolley** Chariot électrique no
Buggy Voiturette yes — **Clubs** Clubs yes
Credit cards Cartes de crédit
VISA - MasterCard

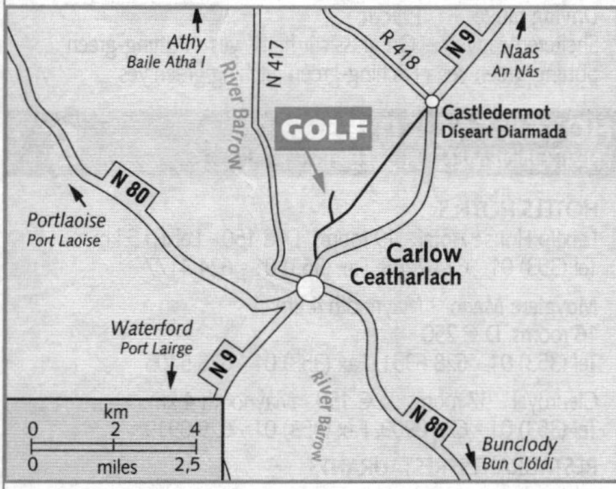

Access Accès : N9 Carlow → Dublin
Map 3 on page 813 Carte 3 Page 813

GOLF COURSE — PARCOURS — 16/20

Site	Site	
Maintenance	Entretien	
Architect	Architecte	Tom Simpson
Type	Type	parkland
Relief	Relief	
Water in play	Eau en jeu	
Exp. to wind	Exposé au vent	
Trees in play	Arbres en jeu	

Scorecard / Carte de score	Chp. / Chp.	Mens / Mess.	Ladies / Da.
Length Long.	5844	5731	5218
Par	70	70	75
Slope system	0	0	0

Advised golfing ability Niveau de jeu recommandé — 0 12 24 36
Hcp required Handicap exigé — no

CLUB HOUSE & AMENITIES — CLUB HOUSE ET ANNEXES — 6/10

Pro shop Pro-shop
Driving range Practice
Sheltered couvert no - On grass sur herbe yes - Putting-green putting-green yes - Pitching-green pitching green no

HOTEL FACILITIES — ENVIRONNEMENT HOTELIER — 7/10

HOTELS HÔTELS

Seven Oaks Hotel - Carlow 5 km
55 rooms, D from € 120
Tel (353) 059 - 9131 308, Fax (353) 059 - 9132 155

Dolmen Hotel - Carlow 5 km
80 rooms, D from € 140
Tel (353) 059 - 914 2002, Fax (353) 059 - 914 2375

Kilkea Castle - Castledermot 8 km
29 rooms, D € 216
Tel (353) 059 - 914 5156, Fax (353) 059 - 914 5187

RESTAURANTS RESTAURANTS

Teach Dolmain - Carlow 3 km - Tel (353) 05991 - 30 911
Tonlegee House - Athy 15 km - Tel (353) 059 - 863 1473

Carton House *The Montgomerie*

16 | 4 | 8

This course at Carton House, which will be home to the Irish Open for a second successive year in 2006, lies on the higher section of the estate dominated by Tyreconnell tower. The "O'Meara" is a real parkland but this one is to be found in much more open space. The promoters were obviously looking for a contrast in style between O'Meara and the thinking and preference of Scot Colin Montgomerie. After designing a course in Dubai with Desmond Muirhead, he showed definite talent for course architecture, particularly for the strategic aspects marked by very particular care taken over the bunkers, often very deep and punishing and accordingly recovering their real value as hazards. Water is hardly ever in play except on the 1st and 18th holes. The routing of this course is capricious in relation to the prevailing winds that are never far away. Good players of low shots will feel comfortable here and find their just reward. In a nutshell, the Montgomerie is a fine combination of tradition and modernity with excellent, well-designed and well protected greens that are often sharply contoured. Much too difficult for high handicappers.

Ce parcours de Carton House a trouvé place dans la partie supérieure de la propriété, dominée par la tour Tyreconnell, dans un espace beaucoup plus ouvert que le "O'Meara". Il y avait une volonté de contraste mais l'esthétique de links était dans la logique des goûts de l'Ecossais Colin Montgomerie. Après avoir créé un golf à Dubai avec Desmond Muirhead, il montre un talent certain pour l'architecture, en particulier pour les aspects stratégiques, avec un soin particulier pour les bunkers, souvent très profonds et punitifs, retrouvant ainsi leur valeur d'obstacles. L'eau n'est pratiquement pas en jeu, sauf au 1 au 18. L'itinéraire du parcours est capricieux par rapport aux vents dominants : les maîtres des balles basses seront à l'aise ici. En résumé, une bonne association de tradition et de modernité,qui bénéficie d'excellents greens bien dessinés et défendus, et souvent très animés.

Carton House Golf Club — 2003

IRL - MAYNOOTH, Co Kildare

Office	Secrétariat	(353) 01 - 628 6271
Pro shop	Pro-shop	(353) 01 - 628 6271
Fax	Fax	(353) 01 - 628 6555
Web	www.carton.ie	
Situation	Situation	Dublin, 22 km
Annual closure	Fermeture annuelle	no
Weekly closure	Fermeture hebdomadaire	no

Fees main season Tarifs haute saison	18 holes	
	Week days Semaine	We/Bank holidays We/Férié
Individual Individuel	€ 115	€ 135
Couple Couple	€ 230	€ 270

We: Friday → Sunday

Caddie Caddie on request **Electric Trolley** Chariot électrique yes

Buggy Voiturette yes **Clubs** Clubs yes

Credit cards Cartes de crédit
VISA - MasterCard - AMEX

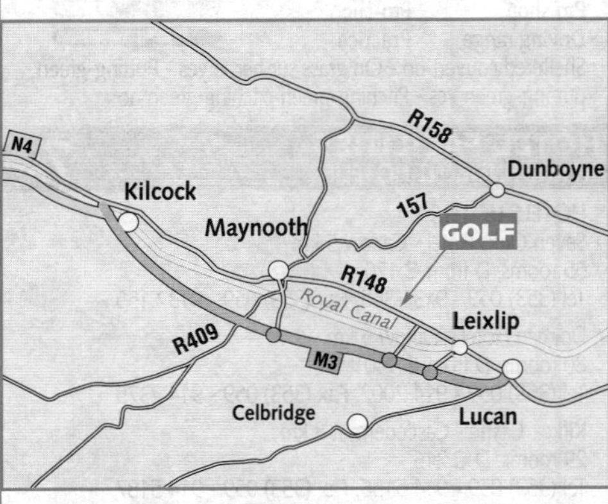

Access Accès : Dublin, M4 → Galway. Exit Lexlip West. On R148, → Maynooth. Golf on the right hand side.
Map 1 on page 809 Carte 1 Page 809

GOLF COURSE — PARCOURS 16/20

Site	Site	
Maintenance	Entretien	
Architect	Architecte	Colin Montgomerie
Type	Type	inland, links
Relief	Relief	
Water in play	Eau en jeu	
Exp. to wind	Exposé au vent	
Trees in play	Arbres en jeu	

Scorecard Carte de score	Chp. Chp.	Mens Mess.	Ladies Da.
Length Long.	6570	6138	5090
Par	72	72	72
Slope system	—	—	—

Advised golfing ability Niveau de jeu recommandé: 0 12 24 36

Hcp required Handicap exigé no

CLUB HOUSE & AMENITIES — CLUB HOUSE ET ANNEXES 4/10

Pro shop Pro-shop
Driving range Practice
Sheltered couvert - On grass sur herbe yes - Putting-green putting-green yes - Pitching-green pitching green yes

HOTEL FACILITIES — ENVIRONNEMENT HOTELIER 8/10

HOTELS HÔTELS
Leixlip House Hotel - 19 rooms, D € 150 - Leixlip 5 km
Tel (353) 01 - 624 2268, Fax (353) 01 - 624 4177

Moyglare Manor - Maynooth 4 km
16 rooms, D € 250
Tel (353) 01 - 628 6351, Fax (353) 01 - 628 5405

Glenroyal - 57 rooms, D € 150 - Maynooth 4 km
Tel (353) 01 - 629 0909, Fax (353) 01 - 629 0919

RESTAURANTS RESTAURANTS
Beckett's - Leixlip 5 km - Tel (353) 01 - 624 7040
The Bradaun - Leixlip 5 km - Tel (353) 01 - 624 2268
Glenroyal restaurants - Maynooth 4 km
Tel (353) 01 - 629 0909

Carton House *The O'Meara*

14	4	8

In this huge estate in County Kildare, Richard Castle (who designed Powescourt) built a wonderful castle back in the 18th century but it has not been used for the club-house here. This future resort houses two courses and facilities for fishing, shooting and horse-riding, a 160-bedroom hotel being due to open in 2006. The first course is a fair tribute by Mark O'Meara to his recent Irish ancestors. This quiet and modest man has designed a very likeable course in his own image in a park landscape, but without asking for anything too outlandish we did regret being a slight lack of daring and zip. You have to wait until the 13th, 14th and 15th holes and their water hazards to find rather more inspiration from the architect. But make no mistake about it, this is a very good course, well maintained and tastefully landscaped with considerable intelligence. The greens are excellent and well designed and would be the pride and joy of many other clubs. But there again, we do tend to expect rather a lot from such prestige names.

Dans cette immense propriété du Kildare, Richard Castle (l'architecte de Powescourt) construisit au XVIIIème siècle un superbe château. Mais il n'a pas été utilisé comme club-house du golf. Deux parcours ont trouvé place dans ce futur resort, où l'on peut aussi pratiquer la pêche, le tir et l'équitation, un hôtel de 160 chambres étant prévu pour l'été 2006. Le premier parcours est un juste hommage à ses récents ancêtres irlandais, par Mark O'Meara. Cet homme tranquille et modeste a conçu un parcours attachant à son image, dans un paysage de parc, mais l'on peut regretter que son dessin manque, sinon de folie, du moins d'audace et de souffle. Il faut attendre le passage du 13 au 15 et la mise en jeu de l'eau, pour trouver une inspiration plus affirmée. Que l'on ne s'y trompe pas, c'est un très bon parcours, bien entretenu, paysagé avec goût et intelligence, avec de très bons greens bien dessinés dont seraient fiers de nombreux clubs, mais on attend toujours plus de telles signatures.

Carton House Golf Club — 2002

IRL - MAYNOOTH, Co Kildare

Office	Secrétariat	(353) 01 - 628 6271
Pro shop	Pro-shop	(353) 01 - 628 6271
Fax	Fax	(353) 01 - 628 6555
Web	www.carton.ie	
Situation	Situation	Dublin, 22 km
Annual closure	Fermeture annuelle	no
Weekly closure	Fermeture hebdomadaire	no

Fees main season Tarifs haute saison	18 holes	
	Week days Semaine	**We/Bank holidays** We/Férié
Individual Individuel	€ 115	€ 135
Couple Couple	€ 230	€ 270

We: Friday → Sunday

Caddie Caddie on request **Electric Trolley** Chariot électrique yes

Buggy Voiturette yes **Clubs** Clubs yes

Credit cards Cartes de crédit
VISA - MasterCard - AMEX

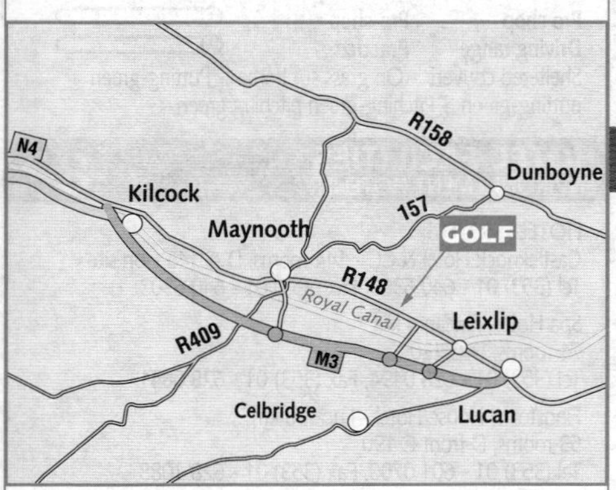

Access Accès : Dublin, M4 → Galway. Exit Lexlip West. On R148, → Maynooth. Golf on the right hand side.
Map 1 on page 809 Carte 1 Page 809

GOLF COURSE — PARCOURS — 14/20

Site	Site	
Maintenance	Entretien	
Architect	Architecte	Mark O'Meara
Type	Type	inland, parkland
Relief	Relief	
Water in play	Eau en jeu	
Exp. to wind	Exposé au vent	
Trees in play	Arbres en jeu	

Scorecard Carte de score	**Chp.** Chp.	**Mens** Mess.	**Ladies** Da.
Length Long.	6303	5950	4925
Par	72	72	72
Slope system	—	—	—

Advised golfing ability Niveau de jeu recommandé: 0 12 24 36

Hcp required Handicap exigé: no

CLUB HOUSE & AMENITIES — CLUB HOUSE ET ANNEXES — 4/10

Pro shop Pro-shop

Driving range Practice

Sheltered couvert - On grass sur herbe yes - Putting-green putting-green yes - Pitching-green pitching green yes

HOTEL FACILITIES — ENVIRONNEMENT HOTELIER — 8/10

HOTELS HÔTELS

Leixlip House Hotel - 19 rooms, D € 150 - Leixlip 5 km
Tel (353) 01 - 624 2268, Fax (353) 01 - 624 4177

Moyglare Manor - Maynooth 4 km
16 rooms, D € 250
Tel (353) 01 - 628 6351, Fax (353) 01 - 628 5405

Glenroyal - 57 rooms, D € 150 - Maynooth 4 km
Tel (353) 01 - 629 0909, Fax (353) 01 - 629 0919

RESTAURANTS RESTAURANTS

Beckett's - Leixlip 5 km - Tel (353) 01 - 624 7040

The Bradaun - Leixlip 5 km - Tel (353) 01 - 624 2268

Glenroyal restaurants - Maynooth 4 km
Tel (353) 01 - 629 0909

Castleknock

16	3	8

This is one of the more ambitious projects around Dublin. Just a few miles from the city centre, what looks to be a real oasis surrounded by trees is home to this 18-hole course, a 140-room hotel, two restaurants, a leisure and beauty centre and the inevitable conference rooms. Golf-wise, the objective was a members course with mandatory high-quality green-keeping all year round, and not necessarily a championship layout. Yardage is not excessive, hazards are more strategic than truly penalizing, topography very acceptable and the style of architect Jonathan Gaunt pleasing and rather discreet. He has taken very special care over the par 3s, well defended by water for the more gung-ho golfers while retaining more receptive areas for the fainter-hearted. Everything has been carefully thought through here with money well spent rather than saved.

C'est l'un des projets les plus ambitieux autour de Dublin. A quelques kilomètres du centre ville, une véritable oasis entourée de bois accueille ce parcours de 18 trous, un hôtel de plus de 140 chambres, deux restaurants, un centre de loisirs et de beauté, et les inévitables salles de conférence. Pour le parcours, l'objectif était un golf de membres avec un impératif de qualité d'entretien toute l'année, pas obligatoirement un parcours de championnat. La longueur n'est pas excessive, les obstacles sont plus stratégiques que vraiment pénalisants, le relief très acceptable, le style de l'architecte Jonathan Gaunt plaisant et assez discret. Mais il a particulièrement soigné les par 3, bien protégés par des obstacles d'eau pour les attaquants, mais qui préservent des zones plus accueillantes pour les golfeurs moins téméraires. Tout ici a été bien soigné, l'argent pas épargné, mais bien dépensé.

Castleknock Hotel & Country Club — 2005

Porterstown Road - Castleknock
IRL - DUBLIN 15

Office	Secrétariat	(353) 01 - 640 6300
Pro shop	Pro-shop	(353) 01 - 640 6300
Fax	Fax	(353) 01 - 640 6303
Web		www.castleknockhotel.com
Situation	Situation	Dublin, 9 km
Annual closure	Fermeture annuelle	no
Weekly closure	Fermeture hebdomadaire	no

Fees main season Tarifs haute saison	18 holes	
	Week days Semaine	**We/Bank holidays** We/Férié
Individual Individuel	€ 100	€ 100
Couple Couple	€ 200	€ 200

Caddie Caddie no — **Electric Trolley** Chariot électrique yes
Buggy Voiturette yes — **Clubs** Clubs yes

Credit cards Cartes de crédit
VISA - Eurocard - MasterCard - AMEX - DC

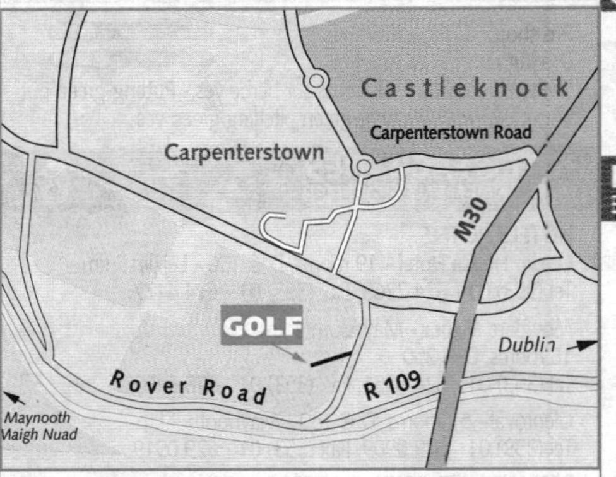

Access Accès : Proceed to Phoenix Park, → Blanchardstown Castleknock. In Caltleknock village, turn left at Myos Pub → Chapelizod. Turn right at next traffic lights, folow the road keeping to the left at second traffic lights. Golf on the left.
Map 1 on page 809 Carte 1 Page 809

GOLF COURSE — PARCOURS — 16/20

Site	Site	
Maintenance	Entretien	
Architect	Architecte	Jonathan Gaunt Steve Marnock
Type	Type	heathland
Relief	Relief	
Water in play	Eau en jeu	
Exp. to wind	Exposé au vent	
Trees in play	Arbres en jeu	

Scorecard Carte de score	**Chp.** Chp.	**Mens** Mess.	**Ladies** Da.
Length Long.	6033	n/a	n/a
Par	71	71	71
Slope system	—	—	—

Advised golfing ability Niveau de jeu recommandé: 0 12 24 36
Hcp required Handicap exigé: 36

CLUB HOUSE & AMENITIES — CLUB HOUSE ET ANNEXES — 3/10

Pro shop Pro-shop
Driving range Practice
Sheltered couvert - On grass sur herbe - Putting-green putting-green - Pitching-green pitching green

HOTEL FACILITIES — ENVIRONNEMENT HOTELIER — 8/10

HOTELS HÔTELS

Castleknock Hotel & CC - 144 rooms, D € 145 - on site
Tel (353) 01 - 640 6300, Fax (353) 01 - 640 6303

Spa Hotel - Lucan 4 km
71 rooms, D € 120
Tel (353) 01 - 628 0494, Fax (353) 01 - 628 0841

Finnstown House Hotel - Lucan 6 km
53 rooms, D from € 190
Tel (353) 01 - 601 0700, Fax (353) 01 - 628 1088

RESTAURANTS RESTAURANTS

Finnstown - Lucan 6 km - Tel (353) 01 - 601 0700

Ryans - Dublin 6 km - Tel (353) 01 - 671 9352

Charleville

13	4	6

One of the good courses to the north of Cork. The extra 9 holes make it even more pleasant to play. At the heart of the Golden Vale at the foot of the Ballyhoura Mountains, this is one of Ireland's best known farming regions and a good opportunity to note that the Irish are not just a people of sailors and fishermen. On this subject, the nearby Blackwater river is one of the finest sites in Ireland for tickling trout. This very busy course is in excellent condition (greens and fairways) but the bunkers are average only and rainy days are not ideal for playing here. The very many trees are often dangerous and clearly suggest a 3-wood rather than the driver. As the course is relatively short, this is not too much of a problem. It was designed more for club members than for over-demanding green-feers, but if you are in the region, you won't be disappointed.

L'un des bons parcours de 18 trous au nord de Cork, avec un 9 trous supplémentaire, qui en augmente encore l'agrément. Au coeur de la "Golden Vale", au pied des Ballyhoura Mountains, c'est l'une des régions agricoles les plus connues d'Irlande, une bonne occasion de vérifier que les Irlandais ne sont pas seulement un peuple de marins et de pêcheurs. A ce propos, la proche rivière Blackwater est l'un des meilleurs sites d'Irlande pour taquiner le poisson. Ce parcours très fréquenté est en excellente condition (greens et fairways), mais les bunkers sont simplement moyens, et les périodes pluvieuses ne sont pas idéales. Les arbres abondants sont souvent dangereux, ils incitent à laisser le driver dans le sac : comme le parcours n'est pas long, ce n'est pas un problème. Il a été conçu davantage pour les membres d'un club que pour des visiteurs trop exigeants. Si vous passez dans la région, vous ne serez pas déçu.

Charleville Golf Club — 1941

Smiths Road
IRL - CHARLEVILLE (RATH LUIRC), Co Cork

Office Secrétariat (353) 063 - 81 257
Pro shop Pro-shop (353) 063 - 81 274
Fax Fax (353) 063 - 81 274
Web www.charlevillegolf.com
Situation Situation Cork (pop. 127 187), 58 km
Limerick (pop. 52 039), 45 km

Annual closure Fermeture annuelle no

Weekly closure Fermeture hebdomadaire no

Fees main season Tarifs haute saison 18 holes

	Week days Semaine	We/Bank holidays We/Férié
Individual Individuel	€ 35	€ 40
Couple Couple	€ 70	€ 80

Students, IR£ 7

Caddie Caddie yes **Electric Trolley** Chariot électrique yes

Buggy Voiturette yes **Clubs** Clubs yes

Credit cards Cartes de crédit
VISA - MasterCard - AMEX

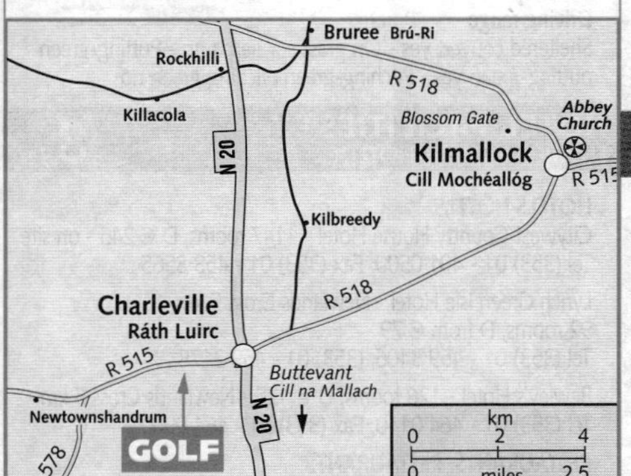

Access Accès : On main road Cork-Limerick
Map 3 on page 812 Carte 3 Page 812

GOLF COURSE PARCOURS — 13/20

Site Site
Maintenance Entretien
Architect Architecte E. Connaughton
Type Type inland, parkland
Relief Relief
Water in play Eau en jeu
Exp. to wind Exposé au vent
Trees in play Arbres en jeu

Scorecard Carte de score	Chp. Chp.	Mens Mess.	Ladies Da.
Length Long.	5845	5647	4781
Par	71	71	72
Slope system	—	—	—

Advised golfing ability Niveau de jeu recommandé 0 12 24 36

Hcp required Handicap exigé 28 Men, 36 Ladies

CLUB HOUSE & AMENITIES CLUB HOUSE ET ANNEXES — 4/10

Pro shop Pro-shop
Driving range Practice
Sheltered couvert 4 mats - On grass sur herbe yes - Putting-green putting-green yes - Pitching-green pitching green yes

HOTEL FACILITIES ENVIRONNEMENT HOTELIER — 6/10

HOTELS HÔTELS

Flemingstown House - Kilmallock 10 km
5 rooms, D € 100
Tel (353) 063 - 98 093, Fax (353) 063 - 98 546

Hibernian Hotel - 56 rooms, D € 120 - Mallow 40 km
Tel (353) 022 - 21 588, Fax (353) 022 - 22 632

Duhallow Hotel - 36 rooms, D € 100 - Kanturk 25 km
Tel (353) 029 - 56 042, Fax Fax (353) 029 - 56 1

Deerpark - 20 rooms, reopens in 2006 - Charleville 1.5 km
Tel (353) 063 - 81 581, Fax (353) 063 - 81 581

RESTAURANTS RESTAURANTS

Longueville - Mallow 24 km - Tel (353) 022 - 47 156
The Coffee Pot - Charleville adjacent - Tel (353) 063 - 81 203

831

Citywest

13	6	8

This is a green-fee course easily playable on week-ends and boasting good practice facilities (20 mats on the driving range are lit-up). It is a whole different picture from the recent, very fashionable private clubs in the region of Dublin. Christy O'Connor Jr. has cleverly made the most of limited space, where imposing trees provided a good working base and pleasant setting. Intelligent but not unduly stressful deployment of water, the use of some natural topography to lay a number of greens and careful bunkering have resulted in a varied, interesting and instructive course: here you have to play every shot in the book, but everyone can try their luck once in a while. Visually, some holes like the 8th and 9th definitely look a little artificial in this landscape, but time changes all that. A very useful addition at a time when fashion seems to be swinging a little too much in favour of upmarket courses. The facility has been enhanced recently by the addition of a delightful, par-68 Executive Course, which has also been designed by O'Connor.

Un parcours au green-fee, facilement accessible en week-end et pourvu de bonnes installations d'entraînement. Rien à voir avec les récents grands clubs privés de Dublin. Christy O'Connor Jr. a astucieusement tiré parti d'un espace limité, où l'implantation d'arbres déjà imposants a fourni une base de travail et un environnement plaisant. Une mise en place intelligente mais pas trop stressante d'obstacles d'eau, l'utilisation de quelques reliefs naturels pour implanter certains greens, un bunkering soigné ont contribué à en faire un parcours varié, intéressant et formateur : ici, on doit jouer tous les coups de golf, et tous pourront tenter leur chance. Visuellement, certains trous comme le 8 et le 9 paraissent certes un peu artificiels dans le paysage, mais le temps commence à effacer cela. Une réalisation fort utile, en un temps où l'on a un peu trop tendance à privilégier le "haut de gamme". Un délicieux parcours de par 68 également dessiné par O'Connor Jr. complète cet équipement.

Citywest Golf Club — 1994

IRL - SAGGART, Co Dublin

Office	Secrétariat	(353) 01 - 4010 878
Pro shop	Pro-shop	(353) 01 - 4010 878
Fax	Fax	(353) 01 - 4010 945
Web	www.citywesthotel.com	
Situation	Situation	Dublin, 16 km
Annual closure	Fermeture annuelle	no
Weekly closure	Fermeture hebdomadaire	no

Fees main season / Tarifs haute saison	18 holes	
	Week days / Semaine	We/Bank holidays / We/Férié
Individual Individuel	€ 50	€ 60
Couple Couple	€ 100	€ 120

Hotel guests: € 45 and € 50 (We) /Monday-Tuesday: € 40-45 (visitors)

Caddie Caddie no — Electric Trolley Chariot électrique yes

Buggy Voiturette yes — Clubs Clubs yes

Credit cards Cartes de crédit
VISA - MasterCard - AMEX

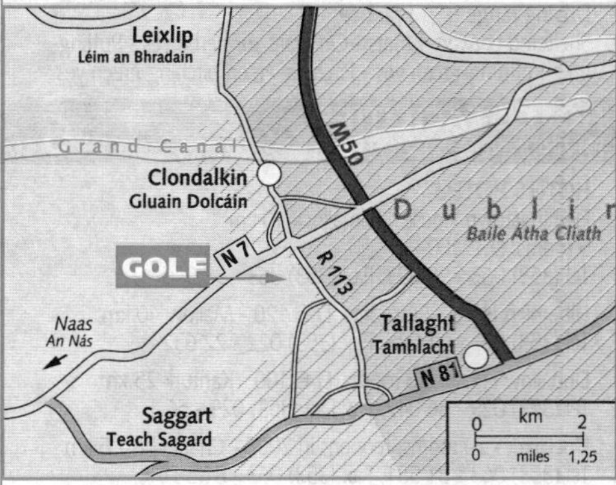

Access Accès : Dublin, N7 West. → Saggart. Golf 2 km

Map 1 on page 809 Carte 1 Page 809

GOLF COURSE — PARCOURS — 13/20

Site	Site	
Maintenance	Entretien	
Architect	Architecte	Christy O'Connor Jr.
Type	Type	parkland
Relief	Relief	
Water in play	Eau en jeu	
Exp. to wind	Exposé au vent	
Trees in play	Arbres en jeu	

Scorecard / Carte de score	Chp. / Chp.	Mens / Mess.	Ladies / Da.
Length Long.	6022	5683	4910
Par	69	69	70
Slope system	—	—	—

Advised golfing ability / Niveau de jeu recommandé: 0 12 24 36

Hcp required Handicap exigé no

CLUB HOUSE & AMENITIES — CLUB HOUSE ET ANNEXES — 6/10

Pro shop Pro-shop

Driving range Practice

Sheltered couvert yes - On grass sur herbe no - Putting-green putting-green yes - Pitching-green pitching green no

HOTEL FACILITIES — ENVIRONNEMENT HOTELIER — 8/10

HOTELS HÔTELS

Citywest Country House Hotel - 1147 rooms, D € 245 - on site
Tel (353) 01 - 401 0500, Fax (353) 01 - 458 8565

Lynch Green Isle Hotel - Newlands Cross 5 km
92 rooms, D from € 79
Tel (353) 01 - 459 3406, (353) 01 - 459 2178

Bewley's Hotel - 126 rooms, D € 125 - Newlands Cross 5 km
Tel (353) 01 - 464 0140, Fax (353) 01 - 464 0900

RESTAURANTS RESTAURANTS

Terrace Room - Saggart on site - Tel (353) 01 - 458 8566

The Winter Garden - Clondalkin 2 km - Tel (353) 01 - 459 3650

Bewley's Hotel - Newlands Cross 5 km
Tel (353) 01 - 464 0140

Connemara

15 | 6 | 6

An exceptional, terribly romantic and mind-soothing site set between the ocean and national park mountains. Here, you are transported hundreds of years back in history, and the actual course looks as if it has always been a part of the picture. For a long while we rued the total absence of any relief over the first few holes and the serious business only really starts at the 8th. Then come a number of gems (the 8th, 9th and 13th) and all the closing holes from the 15th onward. Nine additional and pretty spectacular holes can now replace the original front 9, although the best idea is to play all 27. Whichever holes you play, this layout effectively reminds you of the real state of your game and experience will come in handy if you want to card a good score. The fairway bunkers are more or less dangerous, depending on the wind, and the same goes for the rough and some formidable thickets (often around the greens) which are more or less in play.

Un site exceptionnel, terriblement romantique et apaisant, entre l'Océan et les montagnes du Parc National. On est transporté des milliers d'années en arrière, et le golf lui-même donne l'impression d'avoir toujours été là. On a longtemps pu regretter le manque total de relief et de spectacle dans les premiers trous où les choses sérieuses ne commençaient vraiment qu'à partir du 8. On trouvait ensuite quelques joyaux (8, 9, 13) et tout le finale à partir du 15. Neuf trous supplémentaires et assez spectaculaires peuvent maintenant remplacer l'aller, le mieux étant évidemment de jouer l'ensemble, malgré un léger manque d'unité. Quel que soit le tracé, le parcours vous rappelle à la réalité de votre golf, et il faut de l'expérience pour scorer. Selon le vent, la situation change du tout au tout, les bunkers de fairway, le rough et de redoutables buissons (souvent autour des greens) venant plus ou moins en jeu.

Connemara Golf Club — 1973

Ballyconneely
IRL - CLIFDEN, Co Galway

Office	Secrétariat	(353) 095 - 23 602
Pro shop	Pro-shop	(353) 095 - 23 502
Fax	Fax	(353) 095 - 23 662
Web	www.connemaragolflinks.com	
Situation	Situation	Clifden (pop. 920), 16 km
Annual closure	Fermeture annuelle	no
Weekly closure	Fermeture hebdomadaire	no

Fees main season Tarifs haute saison	Week days Semaine	We/Bank holidays We/Férié
	18 holes	
Individual Individuel	€ 60	€ 60
Couple Couple	€ 120	€ 120

Caddie Caddie on request **Electric Trolley** Chariot électrique no
Buggy Voiturette yes **Clubs** Clubs yes
Credit cards Cartes de crédit
VISA - Eurocard - MasterCard - AMEX

Access Accès : Galway N59 → Clifden. 16 km S of Clifden, golf in seaside village of Ballyconneely
Map 2 on page 810 Carte 2 Page 810

GOLF COURSE
PARCOURS — **15**/20

Site	Site	
Maintenance	Entretien	
Architect	Architecte	Eddie Hackett
Type	Type	links
Relief	Relief	
Water in play	Eau en jeu	
Exp. to wind	Exposé au vent	
Trees in play	Arbres en jeu	

Scorecard Carte de score	Chp. Chp.	Mens Mess.	Ladies Da.
Length Long.	6611	6263	5055
Par	72	72	72
Slope system	—	—	—

Advised golfing ability Niveau de jeu recommandé — 0 12 24 36
Hcp required Handicap exigé — 28 Men, 36 Ladies

CLUB HOUSE & AMENITIES
CLUB HOUSE ET ANNEXES — **6**/10

Pro shop Pro-shop
Driving range Practice
Sheltered couvert no - On grass sur herbe yes (own balls) - Putting-green putting-green yes - Pitching-green pitching green yes

HOTEL FACILITIES
ENVIRONNEMENT HOTELIER — **6**/10

HOTELS HÔTELS
Abbeyglen Castle Hotel - Clifden 16 km
49 rooms, D € 223 (w. dinner)
Tel (353) 095 - 21 201, Fax (353) 095 - 21 797

Rock Glen - 27 rooms, D € 186- Clifden 16 km
Tel (353) 095 - 21 035, Fax (353) 095 - 21 737

Erriseask Hotel - Ballyconneely 5 km
12 rooms, D € 120
Tel (353) 095 - 23 553, Fax (353) 095 - 23 639

RESTAURANTS RESTAURANTS
O'Grady's Seafood - Clifden 16 km
Tel (353) 095 - 21 450
High Moors - Clifden 16 km - Tel (353) 095 - 21 342

Cork GC

15 | 6 | 5

This course, which is more than 100 years old, was remodelled by Alister Mackenzie, one of the great names from the classical era (he was the joint designer of Augusta National, no less). Although well off the beaten golfer's track, Cork G.C. is well worth the visit. Located in a park on an island opposite the port of Cork, this is a marvellously technical course and you are constantly amazed at how easy it can be to drop so many strokes on such an honest and apparently benign course. But here, placing the drive is crucial, hazards are magnificently well placed and the putting surfaces are not easy to read. Water comes into play on only a few holes (ditches), but the rough can be as formidable as a huge lake. This very prettily landscaped and very well kept course has victoriously weathered the passing of time. Discover or return to Cork G.C. before setting out to explore the very many sights to see in this pretty region.

Ce parcours plus que centenaire a été remodelé par Alistair Mackenzie, l'un des grands architectes de l'ère classique (rappelons qu'il est co-auteur d'Augusta). Bien qu'il figure à l'écart des grands circuits golfiques, il mérite largement la visite. Dans un paysage de parc et situé dans une petite île face au port de Cork, c'est une petite merveille de technicité, et l'on s'étonne constamment de perdre autant de points sur un tracé aussi franc et apparemment aimable. Mais le placement des drives y est crucial, les obstacles sont magnifiquement placés, les surfaces de green sont peu faciles à lire. L'eau ne vient en jeu que sur quelques trous (fossés), mais le rough peut être tout aussi redoutable que l'immense lac. Ce parcours très joliment paysagé et très bien entretenu a victorieusement subi les atteintes du temps. A découvrir, ou redécouvrir, avant d'explorer les richesses touristiques de cette jolie région.

Cork Golf Club — 1888

IRL - LITTLE ISLAND, Co Cork

Office Secrétariat (353) 021 - 4353 451
Pro shop Pro-shop (353) 021 - 4353 421
Fax Fax (353) 021 - 4353 410
Web www.corkgolfclub.ie
Situation Situation Cork (pop. 127 187), 8 km
Cobh (pop. 6 468), 3 km
Annual closure Fermeture annuelle no
Weekly closure Fermeture hebdomadaire no

Fees main season Tarifs haute saison	Week days Semaine	We/Bank holidays We/Férié
	18 holes	
Individual Individuel	€ 80	€ 90
Couple Couple	€ 160	€ 180

Caddie Caddie on request **Electric Trolley** Chariot électrique yes
Buggy Voiturette yes **Clubs** Clubs yes
Credit cards Cartes de crédit
VISA - MasterCard - AMEX

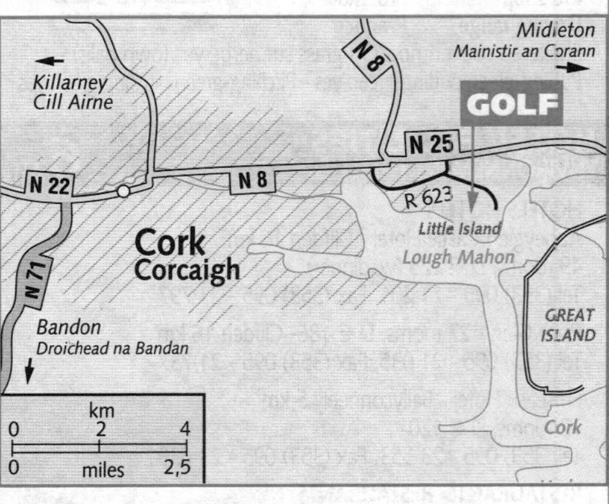

Access Accès : Cork East, N25, Golf 8 km
Map 3 on page 812 Carte 3 Page 812

GOLF COURSE — PARCOURS 15/20

Site Site
Maintenance Entretien
Architect Architecte Alister Mackenzie
Type Type parkland
Relief Relief
Water in play Eau en jeu
Exp. to wind Exposé au vent
Trees in play Arbres en jeu

Scorecard Carte de score	Chp. Chp.	Mens Mess.	Ladies Da.
Length Long.	6115	5910	5262
Par	72	72	74
Slope system	—	—	—

Advised golfing ability Niveau de jeu recommandé 0 12 24 36
Hcp required Handicap exigé certificate

CLUB HOUSE & AMENITIES — CLUB HOUSE ET ANNEXES 6/10

Pro shop Pro-shop
Driving range Practice
Sheltered couvert no - On grass sur herbe yes - Putting-green putting-green yes - Pitching-green pitching green yes

HOTEL FACILITIES — ENVIRONNEMENT HOTELIER 5/10

HOTELS HÔTELS
Silver Springs Hotel - 109 rooms, D € 135 - Cork 6 km
Tel (353) 021 - 450 7533, Fax (353) 021 - 450 7641

Jurys Cork Inn - Cork 8 km
133 rooms, D € 110
Tel (353) 021 - 494 3000, Fax (353) 021 - 427 6144

John Barleycorn Inn Hotel - Glanmire, Cork 4 km
16 rooms, D € 85
Tel (353) 021 - 482 1499, Fax (353) 021 - 482 1221

RESTAURANTS RESTAURANTS
Flemings - Cork 8 km - Tel (353) 021 - 482 1621
Jacobs on the Mall - Cork 8 km - Tel (353) 021 - 425 1530
Jacques - Cork 8 km - Tel (353) 021 - 427 7387

County Louth

18 | 5 | 6

How do you explain the fame of a golf course? County Louth (or Baltray) has not hosted many international tournaments, is not one of the star courses in the south-west of Ireland and is an hour's drive from Dublin, where there is no shortage of top courses. But recognition comes from being known by the connoisseurs. While some courses may be controversial, this one is acclaimed by all. The dunes may not be as Dantesque as elsewhere and all the difficulties are there to be seen, but this course needs a humble and clear-headed approach and close observation of each detail to appreciate the aristocratic grandeur of the whole layout. Designer Tom Simpson was perhaps the greatest strategist of all for the placing and design of bunkers, and here you recognise his cachet from hole 1 to 18. Whichever direction the wind blows, they are always in play. The fairways are comparatively wide but the rough and thickets are deadly. This sheer gem always deserves both respect and admiration and today is emerging from the shadows, which is good news all round.

A quoi tient la gloire d'un parcours ? County Louth (ou Baltray) n'a pas reçu beaucoup de grandes compétitions internationales, ne fait pas partie des vedettes du Sud-Ouest, il est à une heure de Dublin, où les grands parcours ne manquent pas. Mais on reconnaît un connaisseur s'il connaît celui-ci. S'il est des parcours controversés, County Louth fait l'unanimité. Certes, les dunes n'y sont pas aussi dantesques qu'ailleurs, on distingue toutes les difficultés, mais il faut l'aborder avec humilité et lucidité, en observer chaque détail pour apprécier la grandeur aristocratique de l'ensemble. L'architecte Tom Simpson était peut-être le plus grand stratège du placement et du dessin même des bunkers : on reconnaît sa signature du premier au dernier trou. Quelle que soit la direction du vent, il s'en trouve toujours en jeu. Les fairways sont relativement larges, mais les roughs et les buissons sont redoutables. Ce pur joyau mérite respect et admiration. Il sort de l'ombre, tant mieux.

County Louth Golf Club — 1892

Baltray
IRL - DROGHEDA, Co Louth

Office Secrétariat (353) 041 - 988 1530
Pro shop Pro-shop (353) 041 - 988 1536
Fax Fax (353) 041 - 988 1531
Web www.countylouthgolfclub.com
Situation Situation Drogheda (pop. 24 460), 5 km
Annual closure Fermeture annuelle no
Weekly closure Fermeture hebdomadaire no

Fees main season Tarifs haute saison 18 holes

	Week days Semaine	We/Bank holidays We/Férié
Individual Individuel	€ 110	€ 130
Couple Couple	€ 220	€ 260

Caddie Caddie on request **Electric Trolley** Chariot électrique no
Buggy Voiturette yes **Clubs** Clubs yes
Credit cards Cartes de crédit
VISA - MasterCard - AMEX

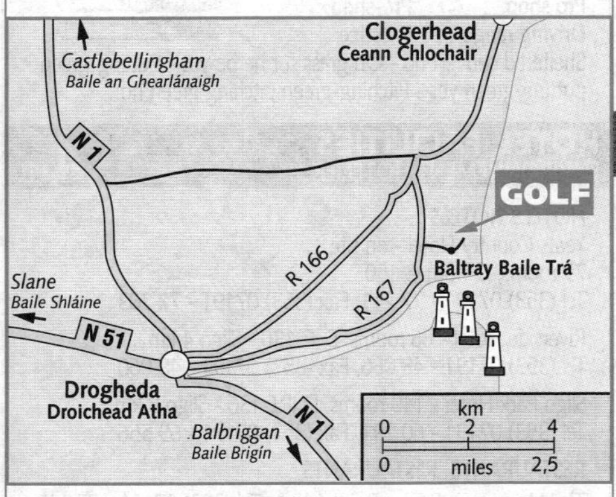

Access Accès : Dublin, M1 North → Drogheda.
7 km NE of Drogheda on R167
Map 1 on page 809 Carte 1 Page 809

GOLF COURSE — PARCOURS — 18/20

Site Site
Maintenance Entretien
Architect Architecte Tom Simpson
Type Type links
Relief Relief
Water in play Eau en jeu
Exp. to wind Exposé au vent
Trees in play Arbres en jeu

Scorecard Carte de score	Chp. Chp.	Mens Mess.	Ladies Da.
Length Long.	6245	6008	5286
Par	72	72	75
Slope system	—	—	—

Advised golfing ability Niveau de jeu recommandé 0 12 24 36
Hcp required Handicap exigé no

CLUB HOUSE & AMENITIES — CLUB HOUSE ET ANNEXES — 5/10

Pro shop Pro-shop
Driving range Practice
Sheltered couvert no - On grass sur herbe yes - Putting-green putting-green yes - Pitching-green pitching green yes

HOTEL FACILITIES — ENVIRONNEMENT HOTELIER — 6/10

HOTELS HÔTELS
Boyne Valley Hotel - Drogheda 5 km
72 rooms, D € 160
Tel (353) 041 - 983 7737, Fax (353) 041 - 983 9188

Neptune - Bettystown 10 km - 38 rooms, D € 160
Tel (353) 041 - 982 7107, Fax (353) 041 - 982 7412

Westcourt - Drogheda 5 km - 27 rooms, D € 150
Tel (353) 041 - 983 0965, Fax (353) 041 - 983 0970

RESTAURANTS RESTAURANTS
Triple House - Termonfeckin 3 km - Tel (353) 041 - 982 2616
Little Strand - Clogherhead 5 km - Tel (353) 041 - 988 1061
Bacchus at the Coastguard - Bettystown 10 km
Tel (353) 041 - 982 8251

County Sligo

17	6	4

From the fairways, magnificent views over the Atlantic, the bay of Drumcliff and Ben Bulben warrant a trip to Rosses Point. But this is also home to one of Ireland's greatest golf courses. As windless days are few and far between, the elements are an overriding factor: the fairways are wide enough, but balls too far left or right are snapped up by the bunkers and rough, both equally penalising. With this said, and if we exclude two or three blind shots, all the hazards are clearly visible and the player knows perfectly well what needs to be done to avoid them. It is simply a question of doing it! Golfers with little experience or even less nerve can choose their own tees, they are all well placed to vary the shape of the course. With 9 holes overlooking the site and the other half in a valley, you can look forward to a few climbs (nothing too exhausting) and elevated greens, but none are blind. A great links to savour, yard by yard. An additional nine holes with more of a parkland texture, were added on the wetlands known as Bomore, to the right of the sixth fairway.

Depuis le parcours, les vues magnifiques sur l'Atlantique, la baie de Drumcliff et le mont Ben Bulben justifieraient le voyage à Rosses Point. Mais c'est aussi l'un des plus grands parcours d'Irlande. Comme les jours sans vent sont rares, c'est un facteur dominant : les fairways sont assez larges, mais un petit écart amène vite la balle dans les roughs et les bunkers, tout aussi pénalisants. Cela dit, à l'exception de deux ou trois coups aveugles, tous les obstacles sont visibles, et l'on sait parfaitement ce qu'il faut éviter, à défaut de le faire ! Les golfeurs peu expérimentés ou pas trop courageux pourront choisir leurs tees de départ, ils sont tous très bien placés pour varier le parcours. Avec une moitié des trous dominant le site et l'autre moitié dans une vallée, on peut s'attendre à quelques montées (elles ne sont pas épuisantes), et à quelques greens surélevés, mais aucun n'est aveugle. Un grand links à savourer mètre par mètre. 9 autres trous de style parkland ont trouvé place à droite du fairway du 6.

County Sligo Golf Club — 1894

IRL - ROSSES POINT, Co Sligo

Office	Secrétariat	(353) 07191 - 77 134
Pro shop	Pro-shop	(353) 07191 - 77 171
Fax	Fax	(353) 07191 - 77 460
Web	www.countysligogolfclub.ie	
Situation	Situation	Sligo (pop. 17 786), 8 km
Annual closure	Fermeture annuelle	no
Weekly closure	Fermeture hebdomadaire	no

Fees main season Tarifs haute saison — 18 holes

	Week days / Semaine	We/Bank holidays / We/Férié
Individual Individuel	€ 68	€ 83
Couple Couple	€ 136	€ 166

We: Friday → Sunday

Caddie Caddie yes — **Electric Trolley** Chariot électrique yes

Buggy Voiturette yes — **Clubs** Clubs yes

Credit cards Cartes de crédit
VISA - Mastercard - Delta

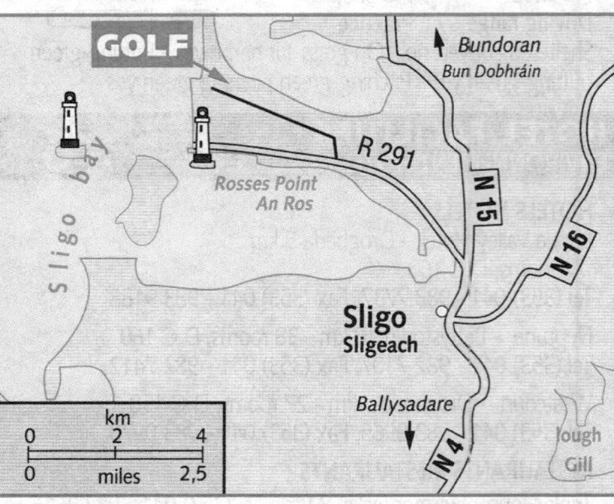

Access Accès : N15, 8 km NW of Sligo
Map 2 on page 810 Carte 2 Page 810

GOLF COURSE — PARCOURS — 17/20

Site	Site	
Maintenance	Entretien	
Architect	Architecte	Harry S. Colt, Charles Alison
Type	Type	links
Relief	Relief	
Water in play	Eau en jeu	
Exp. to wind	Exposé au vent	
Trees in play	Arbres en jeu	

Scorecard / Carte de score	Chp. / Chp.	Mens / Mess.	Ladies / Da.
Length Long.	6043	5840	5280
Par	71	71	75
Slope system	—	—	

Advised golfing ability / Niveau de jeu recommandé: 0 12 24 36

Hcp required Handicap exigé — 28 Men, 36 Ladies

CLUB HOUSE & AMENITIES — CLUB HOUSE ET ANNEXES — 6/10

Pro shop Pro-shop
Driving range Practice
Sheltered couvert no - On grass sur herbe yes - Putting-green putting-green yes - Pitching-green pitching green no

HOTEL FACILITIES — ENVIRONNEMENT HOTELIER — 4/10

HOTELS HÔTELS

Yeats Country Hotel - on site
79 rooms, D from € 150
Tel (353) 07191 - 77 211, Fax (353) 07191 - 77 203

Riverside Hotel - 66 rooms, D € 130 - Sligo 4 km
Tel (353) 07191 - 48 080, Fax (353) 07191 - 48 060

Sligo Park Hotel - 140 rooms, D IR£ 136 - Sligo 8 km
Tel (353) 07191 - 60 291, Fax (353) 07191 - 69 556

RESTAURANTS RESTAURANTS

The Moorings - Rosses Point 1 km - Tel (353) 07191 - 77 112

Waterfront Restaurant - Rosses Point 1 km
Tel (353) 07191 - 77 122

County Tipperary

15	7	5

A long way to Tipperary? Not from Shannon, Cork or Dublin at any rate, although this course is rather off the traditional golfing track and it's a pity, because professional golfer Philip Walton has also shown himself to be a good course architect. He has used the natural contours well, along with the lakes and the river that cross the course rather dangerously on the 4th, and there are visible signs of the so-called American influence, particularly around the greens. These have been carefully designed and call more for lofted approaches rather than the traditional British style run shots. Designed for all levels of play, this rather, but never excessively, long course (even from the back) was designed on rolling terrain (easily walkable) around an 18th century manor, now converted into a hotel. As a result, this is a very agreeable week-end destination in the peaceful Irish countryside.

De Shannon, de Cork ou de Dublin, ce n'est pas une longue route pour aller à Tipperary... Pourtant, ce parcours reste en dehors des circuits golfiques traditionnels, et c'est dommage, car l'excellent professionnel Philip Walton s'y révèle également bon architecte. Il a ainsi très bien utilisé les contours naturels, les lacs et la rivière qui traverse de manière dangereuse le 4, avec une influence de l'architecture dite américaine que l'on retrouve dans le dessin des greens, très travaillés, et qui appellent davantage un jeu de balles levées que des "bump 'n run" à la britannique. Conçu pour tous les niveaux de jeu, ce parcours assez long, mais sans excès (même du fond) a été construit sur un terrain assez ondulé (facile à marcher) autour d'un manoir du XVIIIème siècle transformé en hôtel, ce qui en fait une destination de week-end tout à fait acceptable, dans le calme de la campagne irlandaise.

County Tipperary Golf & Country Club 1993

Dundrum House Hotel
IRL - DUNDRUM, Co Tipperary

Office	Secrétariat	(353) 062 - 71 717
Pro shop	Pro-shop	(353) 062 - 71 717
Fax	Fax	(353) 062 - 71 718
Web		www.dundrumhousehotel.com
Situation	Situation	Tipperary, 8 km - Cashel, 9 km
Annual closure	Fermeture annuelle	no
Weekly closure	Fermeture hebdomadaire	no

Fees main season Tarifs haute saison	18 holes	
	Week days Semaine	**We/Bank holidays** We/Férié
Individual Individuel	€ 50	€ 60
Couple Couple	€ 100	€ 120

Hotel guests: € 38 / 42 (We)

Caddie Caddie no — **Electric Trolley** Chariot électrique yes
Buggy Voiturette yes — **Clubs** Clubs yes

Credit cards Cartes de crédit
VISA - MasterCard - AMEX

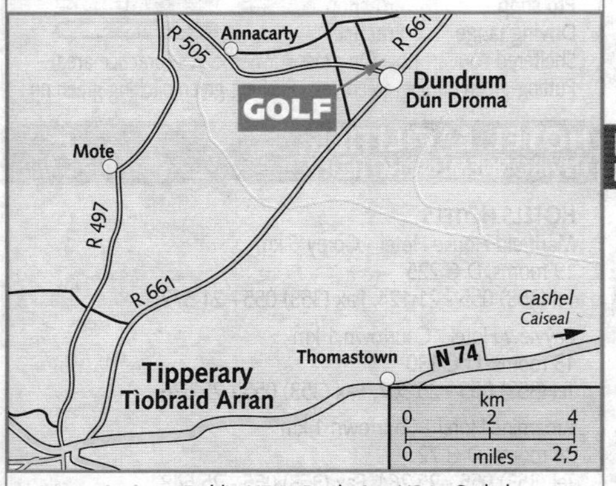

Access Accès : • Dublin N7 to Portlaoise. N8 to Cashel. R505 to Dundrum
• Cork N8 to Cashel. R505 to Dundrum
Map 3 on page 813 Carte 3 Page 813

GOLF COURSE
PARCOURS — 15/20

Site	Site	
Maintenance	Entretien	
Architect	Architecte	Philip Walton
Type	Type	parkland
Relief	Relief	
Water in play	Eau en jeu	
Exp. to wind	Exposé au vent	
Trees in play	Arbres en jeu	

Scorecard Carte de score	**Chp.** Chp.	**Mens** Mess.	**Ladies** Da.
Length Long.	6375	6162	4697
Par	72	72	72
Slope system	—	—	—

Advised golfing ability Niveau de jeu recommandé — 0 12 24 36
Hcp required Handicap exigé — no

CLUB HOUSE & AMENITIES
CLUB HOUSE ET ANNEXES — 7/10

Pro shop Pro-shop
Driving range Practice
Sheltered couvert no - On grass sur herbe yes (own balls) -
Putting-green putting-green yes - Pitching-green pitching green no

HOTEL FACILITIES
ENVIRONNEMENT HOTELIER — 5/10

HOTELS HÔTELS
Dundrum House Hotel - on site
86 rooms, D € 200 (w. dinner)
Tel (353) 062 - 71 116, Fax (353) 062 - 71 366

Cashel Palace - 23 rooms, D € 190 - Cashel 8 km
Tel (353) 062 - 62 707, Fax (353) 062 - 62 521

Aulber House - 12 rooms, D€ 100 - Cashel 8 km
Tel (353) 062 - 63 713, Fax (353) 062 - 63 715

RESTAURANTS RESTAURANTS
Rosemore (Dundrum House Hotel) - on site
Tel (353) 062 - 71 116

Venue Restaurant - on site - Tel (353) 062 - 71 717

Chez Hans - Cashel 10 km - Tel (353) 062 - 61 177

Courtown

14 | 5 | 5

Alongside the monster-length courses in this region like The European and Druid's Glen, albeit in different styles, the parkland landscape and unpretentiousness of the Courtown course is like a breath of fresh air. Although the course lies close to the sea, trees form natural shelter from the frequent wind, even though in return off-target big-hitters might find them a little too big for comfort. Add to this country scene the rolling contours of small hills and you get a course that is pleasant and varied: no two holes are the same. With a nice balance between holes presumed to be easy and others that are more demanding, Courtown is one of those good but somewhat old-fashioned courses - compared to today's modern designs – that everyone enjoys playing, even if you would never drive 200 miles out of your way to do so. After a cheerful welcome in the club-house, no-one will feel too intimidated on the first tee. The greens have been re-laid to USGA standards and several holes have been altered.

A côté des monstres de longueur que peuvent être, dans des styles différents, The European et Druids Glen, la longueur réduite, le paysage de parc et l'absence de prétention d'un Courtown constituent une sorte de respiration. Le parcours est très près de la mer mais les arbres constituent un abri naturel contre le vent, même si, en contrepartie, les frappeurs auront affaire à ces (grands) adversaires. Et si on ajoute à ce tableau champêtre les ondulations mesurées de petites collines, voici un ensemble agréable et varié : il n'y a pas deux trous identiques. Bien équilibré entre les trous présumés faciles et d'autres plus exigeants, Courtown fait partie de ces bons parcours un peu dépassés par rapport à une certaine modernité, et que chacun a plaisir à jouer même si l'on ne fait pas 500 km de route rien que pour le visiter. Après un accueil souriant au club, personne ne sera intimidé au départ du 1. Les greens ont été reconstruits aux normes USGA, et plusieurs trous modifiés.

Courtown Golf Club — 1936

IRL - COURTOWN, GOREY, Co. Wexford

Office Secrétariat (353) 055 - 25 166
Pro shop Pro-shop (353) 055 - 25 166
Fax Fax (353) 055 - 25 553
Web www.courtowngolfclub.com
Situation Situation Dublin, 95 km
Gorey (pop. 2 150), 6 km

Annual closure Fermeture annuelle no
Weekly closure Fermeture hebdomadaire no

Fees main season Tarifs haute saison	18 holes	
	Week days Semaine	**We/Bank holidays** We/Férié
Individual Individuel	€ 30	€ 35
Couple Couple	€ 60	€ 70

Caddie Caddie no — **Electric Trolley** Chariot électrique no
Buggy Voiturette yes — **Clubs** Clubs yes
Credit cards Cartes de crédit
Visa - MasterCard (not in the bar)

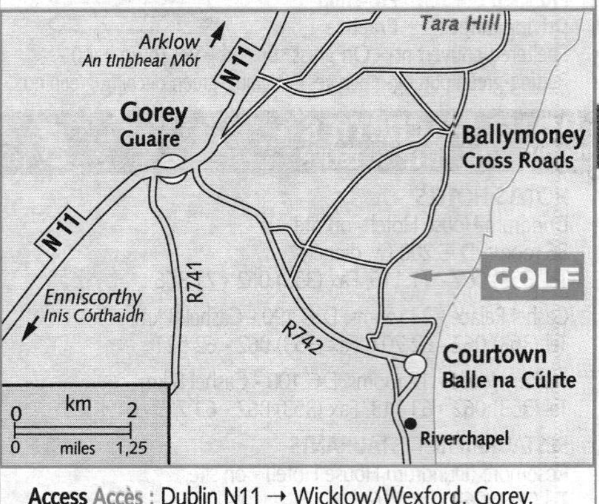

Access Accès : Dublin N11 → Wicklow/Wexford. Gorey, R742 → Courtown, Golf on the left.
Map 3 on page 813 Carte 3 Page 813

GOLF COURSE — PARCOURS — 14/20

Site Site
Maintenance Entretien
Architect Architecte — Harris & Associates
Type Type — parkland
Relief Relief
Water in play Eau en jeu
Exp. to wind Exposé au vent
Trees in play Arbres en jeu

Scorecard Carte de score	Chp. Chp.	Mens Mess.	Ladies Da.
Length Long.	5898	5725	4981
Par	71	71	73
Slope system	—	—	—

Advised golfing ability Niveau de jeu recommandé — 0 12 24 36
Hcp required Handicap exigé — no

CLUB HOUSE & AMENITIES — CLUB HOUSE ET ANNEXES — 5/10

Pro shop Pro-shop
Driving range Practice
Sheltered couvert no - On grass sur herbe yes (practice area) - Putting-green putting-green yes - Pitching-green pitching green no

HOTEL FACILITIES — ENVIRONNEMENT HOTELIER — 5/10

HOTELS HÔTELS

Marlfield House Hotel - Gorey 6 km
19 rooms, D € 225
Tel (353) 055 - 21 124, Fax (353) 055 - 21 572

Bayview Hotel - Courtown 1 km
13 rooms, D € 130
Tel (353) 055 - 25 307, Fax (353) 055 - 25 576

Ardamine Hotel - Courtown 1 km
24 rooms, D € 72
Tel (353) 055 - 25 264, Fax (353) 055 - 25 548

RESTAURANTS RESTAURANTS
Marlfield House - Gorey 6 km - Tel (353) 055 - 21 124
Rowan Tree - Gorey 6 km - Tel (353) 055 - 30 500

Dingle Links (Ceann Sibeal)

15	5	4

The first thing here is the magic of an outstanding site, overlooking Dingle Bay, the Blasket Islands and Mount Brandon, on a peninsula where you can find the vestiges of the stone age or the beginnings of Christianity. The many panels in Gaelic only add to the impression of a journey back in time. Designed by Eddie Hackett and Christy O'Connor Jr., this course looks as if it has always been here, and is a real pleasure to play on long summer days, even if the wind blows or if it rains a little (this may sometimes occur in Ireland). Without pretending to be in the same league as Ballybunion or Waterville, this is an interesting course for everyone, where emphasis should be laid on trying to play low shots. The main difficulty is making clean contact with the ball on sandy soil, escaping from bunkers and avoiding a meandering stream which comes into play on about ten holes. A delightful experience.

Ce que l'on voit d'abord, c'est la magie d'une situation exceptionnelle sur la baie de Dingle, les Blasket Islands et le Mount Brandon, dans une péninsule où l'on trouve aussi bien des vestiges de l'Age de pierre que des débuts du christianisme. La présence de nombreux panneaux en gaëlique accentue encore cette impression de voyage en remontant le temps. Créé par Eddie Hackett et Christy O'Connor Jr., Ceann Sibeal (Sybil Head) paraît avoir toujours été là, et c'est un plaisir d'y jouer pendant les longues journées d'été, même si le vent souffle, ou s'il pleut un peu (ce qui arrive parfois en Irlande). Sans prétendre appartenir à la même division que Ballybunion ou Waterville, c'est un parcours intéressant pour tous, où l'on jouera de préférence des balles basses, où la principale difficulté consiste à bien contacter la balle sur le sol sablonneux, à s'échapper des bunkers, et à éviter les méandres d'un cours d'eau, en jeu sur une dizaine de trous. Une expérience de charme.

Golf Chumann Cean Sibeal — 1972

Ballyoughteragh
IRL - BALLYFERRITER, Co Kerry

Office	Secrétariat	(353) 066 - 915 6255
Pro shop	Pro-shop	(353) 066 - 915 6255
Fax	Fax	(353) 066 - 915 6409
Web	www.dinglelinks.com	
Situation	Situation	Dingle, 16 km

Ballyferriter, 2 km

Annual closure	Fermeture annuelle	no
Weekly closure	Fermeture hebdomadaire	no

Fees main season Tarifs haute saison — 18 holes

	Week days Semaine	We/Bank holidays We/Férié
Individual Individuel	€ 65	€ 75
Couple Couple	€ 130	€ 150

Full day: € 85

Caddie Caddie on request **Electric Trolley** Chariot électrique no

Buggy Voiturette yes **Clubs** Clubs yes

Credit cards Cartes de crédit
VISA - MasterCard - AMEX

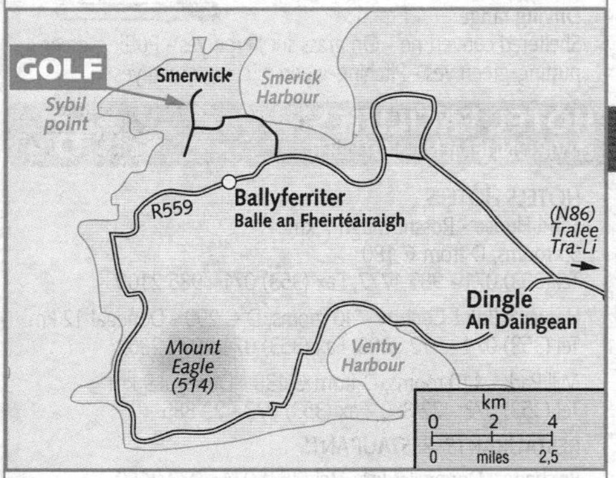

Access Accès : Tralee N86 → Derrymore, Camp, Anascaul, Dingle. R559 → Ballynana, Ballyferriter (Dingle Peninsula)
Map 3 on page 812 Carte 3 Page 812

GOLF COURSE — PARCOURS 15/20

Site	Site	
Maintenance	Entretien	
Architect	Architecte	Eddie Hackett Christy O'Connor Jr.
Type	Type	seaside course, links
Relief	Relief	
Water in play	Eau en jeu	
Exp. to wind	Exposé au vent	
Trees in play	Arbres en jeu	

Scorecard Carte de score	Chp. Chp.	Mens Mess.	Ladies Da.
Length Long.	6030	5870	4700
Par	72	72	73
Slope system	—	—	—

Advised golfing ability Niveau de jeu recommandé — 0 12 24 36

Hcp required Handicap exigé — certificate

CLUB HOUSE & AMENITIES — CLUB HOUSE ET ANNEXES 5/10

Pro shop Pro-shop
Driving range Practice
Sheltered couvert no - On grass sur herbe yes - Putting-green putting-green yes - Pitching-green pitching green no

HOTEL FACILITIES — ENVIRONNEMENT HOTELIER 4/10

HOTELS HÔTELS

Dingle Skellig Hotel - 112 rooms, D € 178 - Dingle 16 km
Tel (353) 066 - 915 0200, Fax (353) 066 - 915 1501

Benners Hotel - 52 rooms, D € 134 - Dingle 16 km
Tel (353) 066 - 915 1638, Fax (353) 066 - 915 1412

Smerwick Harbour - Ballyferriter 3 km
33 rooms, D from € 100
Tel (353) 066 - 915 6470, Fax (353) 066 - 915 6473

RESTAURANTS RESTAURANTS

Doyle's Seafood Bar - Dingle 16 km
Tel (353) 066 - 915 1174

Beginish - Dingle 16 km - Tel (353) 066 - 915 1588

The Chart House - Dingle 16 km - Tel (353) 066 - 915 2255

Donegal (Murvagh)

16	7	6

A word of advice: if your driving is not in tip-top condition, and unless you couldn't give the proverbial two hoots about playing 10 strokes over your handicap, avoid the back tees. The tiger tees are definitely no-go, except if you have the wind behind you all the way (and St Patrick to watch over you). You guessed it, this is one of the longest courses in all of Ireland. Some of the par 4s are real monsters, not to mention the 16th, a par 3, that is inaccessible to the common run of people. From the front tees, however, it is a little easier, and the effort of walking over hilly terrain will be rewarded by a great day's golfing. The greens are often open to bump and runs, and the short game experts can have a whale of a time. The surrounding dunes and general layout make this a very good, spectacular and exciting links course, but emphasis is more on the roughness of the course than on the finesse you find with the really great courses of this type. It has been upgraded by Pat Ruddy, who re-designed six holes.The club-house offers pretty views from the bar.

Un bon conseil : à moins d'avoir réglé votre driving à la perfection, de vous moquer éperdument de jouer dix coups au-dessus de votre handicap, évitez les départs arrière. A moins d'avoir vent avec sur tous les trous (il faut St Patrick pour veiller sur vous), évitez les départs de championnat, c'est le plus long parcours d'Irlande. Quelques par 4 sont de véritables monstres, sans même parler du 16, un par 3 inaccessible au commun des mortels. Cela dit, il s'adoucit un peu des départs avancés, et les efforts de la marche sur ce terrain accidenté seront récompensés par une belle journée de golf. Les greens sont souvent accessibles en roulant, et les virtuoses du petit jeu pourront s'y régaler. L'environnement de dunes, et le tracé général en font un très bon links, spectaculaire et excitant, mais l'accent a été mis davantage sur la rudesse que sur la finesse des plus grands parcours du genre. Ce parcours a été modernisé sur six trous par Pat Ruddy et le club-house offre de jolies vues depuis le bar.

Donegal Golf Club — 1960

IRL - LAGHY, Co Donegal

Office	Secrétariat	(353) 074 - 973 4054
Pro shop	Pro-shop	(353) 074 - 973 4054
Fax	Fax	(353) 074 - 973 4377
Web		www.donegalgolfclub.ie
Situation	Situation	Donegal (pop. 2 296), 7 km
Annual closure	Fermeture annuelle	no
Weekly closure	Fermeture hebdomadaire	no
Fees main season	Tarifs haute saison	18 holes

	Week days / Semaine	We/Bank holidays / We/Férié
Individual Individuel	€ 65	€ 65
Couple Couple	€ 130	€ 130

We: Friday → Sunday

Caddie Caddie on request **Electric Trolley** Chariot électrique yes

Buggy Voiturette yes **Clubs** Clubs yes

Credit cards Cartes de crédit no

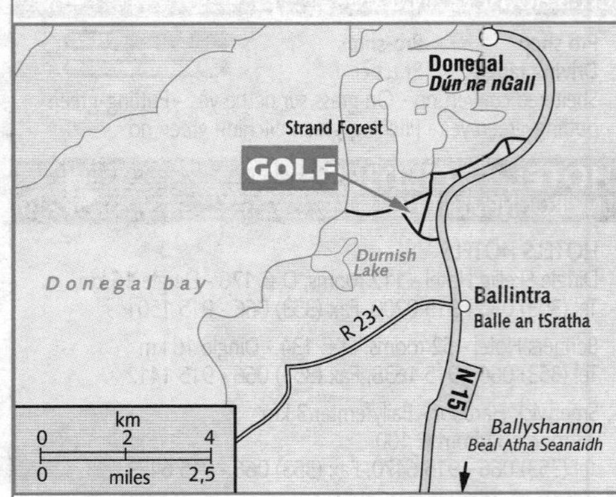

Access Accès : • Sligo, N15 → Donegal. 3 km before Donegal, turn left to Mullinasole/Murvagh peninsula
• Donegal N15 South → Ballyshannon. Laghy, turn right to Mullinasole/Murvagh peninsula

Map 2 on page 810 Carte 2 Page 810

GOLF COURSE — PARCOURS — 16/20

Site	Site	
Maintenance	Entretien	
Architect	Architecte	Eddie Hackett
Type	Type	links
Relief	Relief	
Water in play	Eau en jeu	
Exp. to wind	Exposé au vent	
Trees in play	Arbres en jeu	

Scorecard Carte de score	Chp. Chp.	Mens Mess.	Ladies Da.
Length Long.	6574	6249	5253
Par	73	73	75
Slope system	—	—	—

Advised golfing ability 0 12 24 36
Niveau de jeu recommandé

Hcp required Handicap exigé 28 Men, 36 Ladies

CLUB HOUSE & AMENITIES — CLUB HOUSE ET ANNEXES — 7/10

Pro shop Pro-shop
Driving range Practice
Sheltered couvert no - On grass sur herbe yes - Putting-green putting-green yes - Pitching-green pitching green yes

HOTEL FACILITIES — ENVIRONNEMENT HOTELIER — 6/10

HOTELS HÔTELS

Sand House - Rossnowlagh 7 km
55 rooms, D from € 180
Tel (353) 071 - 985 1777, Fax (353) 071 - 985 2100

Harvey's Point Country - 40 rooms, D € 290 - Donegal 12 km
Tel (353) 074 - 972 2208, Fax (353) 074 - 972 2352

Mill Park - 110 rooms, D from € 130 - Donegal 9 km
Tel (353) 073 - 22 880, Fax (353) 073 - 23 885

RESTAURANTS RESTAURANTS

Belshade - Donegal 7 km - Tel (353) 074 - 972 2660
Sand House - Rossnowlagh 7 km - Tel (353) 072 - 51 777
Harvey's Point Country - Donegal 12 km
Tel (353) 074 - 972 2208

Dooks

15	5	5

A very good links course, whose international fame has been eclipsed somewhat by its prestigious neighbours. While this course alone may not warrant a long journey, it would be a shame not to include Dooks in any golfing itinerary to south-west Ireland. It is an excellent practice outing before getting to grips with some even more difficult courses nearby. Opened in the 19th century, it was revised in 1973 by Eddie Hackett, with praiseworthy concern for preserving unity of style. There are no gigantic dunes here, just endless mounds and dales which add to the course's character (the new 4th hole over the Atlantic), and complicate the round just enough to keep everyone happy. Not very long but often narrow, Dooks gets tougher with the wind. The greens are not huge but are well-guarded, so accuracy and a sharp short game are the order of the day, with excellent scope for bump and run approach shots. The one or two blind shots merely add to the excitement. Last but not least, the club-house has been refurbished.

Un très bon parcours de links, dont la notoriété a été éclipsée par de prestigieux voisins. S'il ne justifie pas à lui seul un long voyage, il serait fort dommage de ne pas l'intégrer à un séjour golfique dans le Sud-Ouest de l'Irlande. C'est même un très bon galop d'entraînement avant d'affronter des adversaires encore plus difficiles. Créé au siècle dernier, il a été révisé en 1973 par Eddie Hackett, avec un louable souci de lui conserver son unité. On ne trouve pas ici de dunes gigantesques, mais les nombreuses buttes et dépressions ajoutent à son caractère (le nouveau 4 sur l'Atlantique), et compliquent assez le jeu pour plaire à tous. Pas très long, mais souvent étroit, il prend de la force avec le vent. Les greens ne sont pas immenses, et bien protégés, il convient alors d'être très exact, ou de sortir son meilleur petit jeu, en favorisant ces approches roulées qui sont un des plaisirs des links, avec quelques coups aveugles pour se donner des émotions. Signalons enfin la rénovation du club-house.

Dooks Golf Club — 1889

IRL - GLENBEIGH, Co Kerry

Office Secrétariat (353) 066 - 976 8205
Pro shop Pro-shop (353) 066 - 976 8205
Fax Fax (353) 066 - 976 8476
Web www.dooks.com
Situation Situation Killarney (pop. 8 809), 24 km
Killorglin (pop. 1 278), 8 km
Annual closure Fermeture annuelle no
Weekly closure Fermeture hebdomadaire no

Fees main season Tarifs haute saison — 18 holes

	Week days / Semaine	We/Bank holidays / We/Férié
Individual Individuel	€ 58	€ 58
Couple Couple	€ 116	€ 116

Caddie Caddie on request **Electric Trolley** Chariot électrique yes
Buggy Voiturette no **Clubs** Clubs no
Credit cards Cartes de crédit
VISA - Eurocard - MasterCard - AMEX

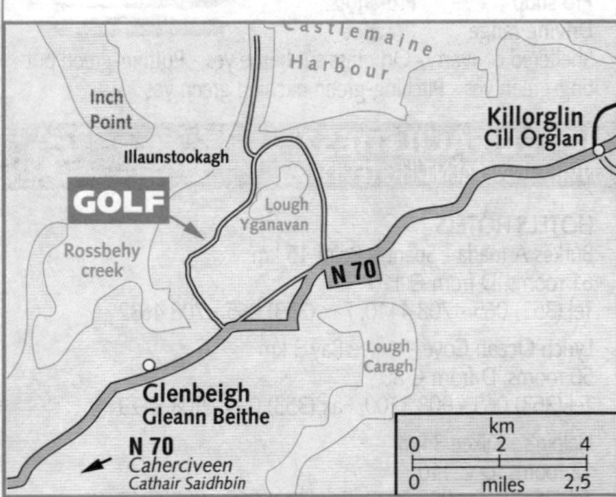

Access Accès : Killarney N72 → Killorglin. N70 → Glenbeigh (Ring of Kerry). Golf 3 km from Glenbeigh
Map 3 on page 812 Carte 3 Page 812

GOLF COURSE — PARCOURS — 15/20

Site Site
Maintenance Entretien
Architect Architecte Eddie Hackett
Type Type links, seaside course
Relief Relief
Water in play Eau en jeu
Exp. to wind Exposé au vent
Trees in play Arbres en jeu

Scorecard / Carte de score	Chp. / Chp.	Mens / Mess.	Ladies / Da.
Length Long.	5769	5409	4806
Par	71	71	72
Slope system	—	—	—

Advised golfing ability Niveau de jeu recommandé 0 12 24 36
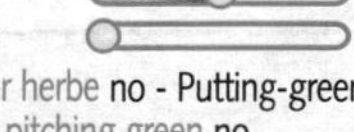
Hcp required Handicap exigé no

CLUB HOUSE & AMENITIES — CLUB HOUSE ET ANNEXES — 5/10

Pro shop Pro-shop
Driving range Practice
Sheltered couvert no - On grass sur herbe no - Putting-green putting-green yes - Pitching-green pitching green no

HOTEL FACILITIES — ENVIRONNEMENT HOTELIER — 5/10

HOTELS HÔTELS
Ard Na Sidhe - Caragh Lake, Killorglin 5 km
19 rooms, D from € 150
Tel (353) 066 - 976 9105, Fax (353) 066 - 976 9282

Towers Hotel - Glenbeigh 3 km
34 rooms, D € 112
Tel (353) 066 - 976 8212, Fax (353) 066 - 976 8260

Carrigh House - Carragh Lake 3 km
16 rooms, D from € 160
Tel (353) 066 - 976 9100, Fax (353) 066 - 976 9166

RESTAURANTS RESTAURANTS
Bianconi Inn - Killorglin 11 km - Tel (353) 066 - 976 1146
Nicks - Killorglin 11 km - Tel (353) 066 - 976 1219

Doonbeg

18	3	5

Finding a new links course is like stumbling upon some pirate's hidden treasure. The challenge facing Greg Norman was to weave a course through this exceptional site of dunes without spoiling it or upsetting the ecosystem. As a result most of the holes have been laid out with intelligence, sticking to the natural curves of the landscape and every now and then modelling sand-hills and bunkers, fairways and greens. Here you recover that "hand-made" feeling of past centuries with modern construction resources. One of the major difficulties is knowing how to gauge the exact influence of the wind in order to control ball flight and deal with approach shots to greens, some of which nestle spectacularly in sandy amphitheatres, while others are much more exposed. Their size and contours add more than a little fizz to your round. Add to this the omnipresent coast-line and you've guessed it: Doonbeg, which has undergone a gentle revision, looks to be another gem in the Irish crown of great links courses. This one comes at a price, especially since the course is still waiting for its club-house.

Un nouveau site de links, c'est comme la découverte du trésor des pirates. Le challenge de Greg Norman était d'insinuer un parcours dans ce lieu exceptionnel sans le détruire ni perturber l'écosytème. La plupart des trous ont ainsi été tracés en suivant les courbes naturelles du paysage, en sculptant çà et là buttes et bunkers, fairways et greens. C'est l'esprit des parcours "fait main" des siècles passés, avec les moyens de construction moderne. Il est difficile de mesurer l'influence du vent pour maîtriser ses trajectoires et négocier les approches vers les greens, car certains sont enserrés de manière spectaculaire dans des amphithéâtres de sable, d'autres beaucoup plus dégagés. Si l'on ajoute que l'océan est omniprésent, et qu'une petite révision en a déjà été faite, on aura compris que Doonbeg s'annonce comme l'un des joyaux d'une couronne de grands links irlandais. Mais il n'est pas donné... d'autant plus que l'on attend un club-house !

Doonbeg Golf Club — 2003

IRL - DOONBEG, Co. Clare

Office	Secrétariat	(353) 065 - 905 5600
Pro shop	Pro-shop	(353) 065 - 905 5600
Fax	Fax	(353) 065 - 965 5247
Web	www.doonbeggolfclub.com	
Situation	Situation	Ennis, 50 km
Annual closure	Fermeture annuelle	no
Weekly closure	Fermeture hebdomadaire	no

Fees main season Tarifs haute saison	18 holes	
	Week days Semaine	**We/Bank holidays** We/Férié
Individual Individuel	€ 185	€ 195
Couple Couple	€ 370	€ 390

Caddie Caddie yes — **Electric Trolley** Chariot électrique no

Buggy Voiturette yes — **Clubs** Clubs yes

Credit cards Cartes de crédit
VISA - MasterCard - AMEX - DC

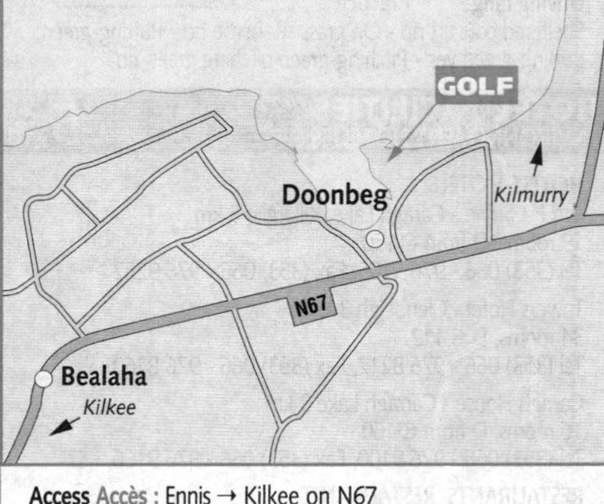

Access Accès : Ennis → Kilkee on N67
Map 3 on page 812 Carte 3 Page 812

GOLF COURSE — PARCOURS — 18/20

Site	Site	
Maintenance	Entretien	
Architect	Architecte	Greg Norman
Type	Type	links
Relief	Relief	
Water in play	Eau en jeu	
Exp. to wind	Exposé au vent	
Trees in play	Arbres en jeu	

Scorecard Carte de score	**Chp.** Chp.	**Mens** Mess.	**Ladies** Da.
Length Long.	6195	5770	4350
Par	72	72	72
Slope system	—	—	—

Advised golfing ability Niveau de jeu recommandé: 0 12 24 36

Hcp required Handicap exigé: 24 Men, 36 Ladies

CLUB HOUSE & AMENITIES — CLUB HOUSE ET ANNEXES — 3/10

Pro shop Pro-shop
Driving range Practice
Sheltered couvert - On grass sur herbe yes - Putting-green putting-green yes - Pitching-green pitching green yes

HOTEL FACILITIES — ENVIRONNEMENT HOTELIER — 5/10

HOTELS HÔTELS

Burkes Armada - Spanish Point 15 km
61 rooms, D from € 110
Tel (353) 065 - 708 4110, Fax (353) 065 - 708 4632

Lynch Ocean Cove - Kilkee Bay 3 km
50 rooms, D from € 80
Tel (353) 065 - 908 3100, Fax (353) 065 - 908 3123

Halpin's - Kilkee 3 km
12 rooms, D € 110
Tel (353) 065 - 905 6032, Fax (353) 065 - 905 6317

RESTAURANTS RESTAURANTS

Halpin's - Kilkee 3 km - Tel (353) 065 - 905 6032
Kilkee Bay - Kilkee 3 km - Tel (353) 065 - 906 0060

Dromoland Castle

14	7	8

Given that the existing course lacked the general excellence of the great inland and links courses of County Clare, the owners here decided on a major overhaul with a budget of 5 million. The work was assigned to J.B. Carr and Ron Kirby, the latter having worked with Jack Nicklaus at Mount Juliet and produced the finishing work at Old Head of Kinsale. They have given the lake that overlooks the site a much more strategic role and also built a fantastic few closing holes consisting of a par 4, the 16th, where the approach shot has to cross the Rine River, followed by a par 3 of 220 yards and the par 5 18th, where the drive has to cross a marsh before the hole turns sharply right. The course has been made longer and more varied with 18 new and cleverly contoured greens, befitting the upscale hotel facilities on site.

Compte-tenu du fait que le parcours existant manquait de la qualité globale et de la technicité des grands parcours inland ou des links du Comté de Clare, les responsables du lieu en ont entrepris une refonte majeure, avec un budget de 5 millions d'Euros, confiée à J.B. Carr et à Ron Kirby, collaborateur de Jack Nicklaus pour Mount Juliet et responsable de la finition d'Old Head of Kinsale. Ils ont donné au lac dominant le site une fonction beaucoup plus stratégique et aussi construit un finale magnifique, avec un par 4, le 16, où l'on doit jouer l'approche en survolant la Rine River, le 17, un par 3 de 200 mètres et le 18, un par 5 où le drive doit traverser un marais avant que le trou tourne à droite. Le parcours est devenu plus long, plus varié, avec 18 nouveaux greens bien modelés, il s'est hissé à la hauteur d'un équipement hôtelier haut de gamme.

Dromoland Castle Golf Club — 1985/2005

IRL - NEWMARKET-ON-FERGUS, Co Clare

Office	Secrétariat	(353) 061 - 368 444
Pro shop	Pro-shop	(353) 061 - 368 444
Fax	Fax	(353) 061 - 363 355
Web	www.dromoland.ie	
Situation	Situation	Limerick, 28 km
Ennis, 11 km		
Annual closure	Fermeture annuelle	no
Weekly closure	Fermeture hebdomadaire	no

Fees main season Tarifs haute saison — 18 holes

	Week days Semaine	We/Bank holidays We/Férié
Individual Individuel	€ 110	€ 110
Couple Couple	€ 220	€ 220

Monday → Thursday before 8:00 and after 16:00, € 60

Caddie Caddie yes — **Electric Trolley** Chariot électrique no

Buggy Voiturette yes — **Clubs** Clubs yes

Credit cards Cartes de crédit
VISA - Eurocard - MasterCard - AMEX - DC

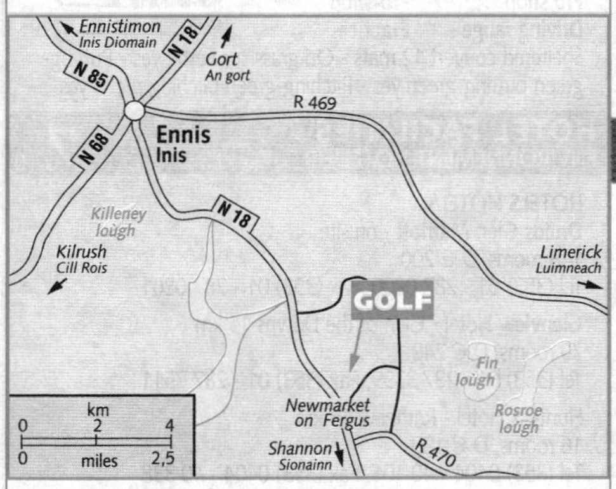

Access Accès : Limerick, N18 → Ennis. Outside Newmarket-on-Fergus, right → Dromoland Castle
Map 3 on page 812 Carte 3 Page 812

GOLF COURSE — PARCOURS — 14/20

Site	Site	
Maintenance	Entretien	
Architect	Architecte	Ron Kirby, J.B. Carr
Type	Type	parkland
Relief	Relief	
Water in play	Eau en jeu	
Exp. to wind	Exposé au vent	
Trees in play	Arbres en jeu	

Scorecard Carte de score	Chp. Chp.	Mens Mess.	Ladies Da.
Length Long.	6161	5669	4771
Par	72	72	72
Slope system	—	—	—

Advised golfing ability Niveau de jeu recommandé — 0 12 24 36

Hcp required Handicap exigé — no

CLUB HOUSE & AMENITIES — CLUB HOUSE ET ANNEXES — 7/10

Pro shop Pro-shop
Driving range Practice
Sheltered couvert new for 2006 - On grass sur herbe yes - Putting-green putting-green yes - Pitching-green pitching green yes

HOTEL FACILITIES — ENVIRONNEMENT HOTELIER — 8/10

HOTELS HÔTELS

Dromoland Castle Hotel - 100 rooms, D € 417 - on site
Tel (353) 061 - 368 144, Fax (353) 061 - 363 355

Lynch Clare Inn - Newmarket-on-Fergus 1,5 km
195 rooms, D € 135
Tel (353) 061 - 368 161, Fax (353) 061 - 368 622

Fitzpatrick Shannon Shamrock - Bunratty 12 km
115 rooms, D € 215
Tel (353) 061 - 361 177, Fax (353) 061 - 364 863

RESTAURANTS RESTAURANTS

Earl of Thomond - on site - Tel (353) 061 - 368 144

Weavers Inn - Newmarket-on-Fergus 1,5 km
Tel (353) 061 - 368 482

Druids Glen *Druids Glen*

16 | 9 | 7

You might easily imagine the club-house here in a chic suburb of London. It is certainly impressive for comfort, but it lacks Irish warmth. Likewise, you might find this course just about anywhere in the United States, and the very American style is compounded by the necessity to be practised in the art of target golf. These remarks come to mind only because of the course's stated cultural identity, as the problem for any foreign visitor is to decipher the signposts showing the way here - they are all written in Gaelic. With this said, we are talking about an excellent and often intimidating course, notably the 12th, 13th and 14th (another Amen corner), the only holes that are really hilly and often less challenging than they look, at least if you avoid playing the "tiger-tees" and stick more or less to the fairway. Very spectacular and always extremely well kept, this luxury course is well worth a close inspection. It became a 36-hole complex in the autumn of 2003 with the addition of a second 18, which was also designed by Pat Ruddy.

On imaginerait bien le club-house dans la banlieue chic de Londres. Son confort est impressionnant, mais il manque la chaleur irlandaise. De même, on pourrait trouver le parcours n'importe où aux USA, son style très américain étant accentué par la nécessité de jouer un "target golf". Ces remarques ne viennent à l'esprit qu'en raison de l'identité culturelle affichée : le problème pour un étranger est de déchiffrer les panneaux pour y parvenir, ceux-ci étant exclusivement rédigés en gaëlique. Cela dit, c'est un excellent parcours, souvent très intimidant, notamment aux 12, 13 et 14 (l'Amen Corner), seuls trous au relief vraiment accidenté, mais souvent moins exigeant qu'il n'y paraît, si l'on évite du moins les départs de championnat, et si l'on ne s'écarte pas trop de la piste. Très spectaculaire, et toujours aussi bien entretenu, cet ensemble de grand luxe mérite une visite attentive, d'autant qu'un 18 trous supplémentaire s'y est ouvert en automne 2003, également dessiné par Pat Ruddy.

Druids Glen Golf Club — 1995

IRL - NEWTOWN MOUNT KENNEDY, Co Wicklow

Office	Secrétariat	(353) 01 - 287 3600
Pro shop	Pro-shop	(353) 01 - 287 3600
Fax	Fax	(353) 01 - 287 3699
Web	www.druidsglen.ie	
Situation	Situation	Dublin, 35 km

Kilcoole, 2 km

Annual closure	Fermeture annuelle	no
Weekly closure	Fermeture hebdomadaire	no

Fees main season / Tarifs haute saison	18 holes	
	Week days / Semaine	We/Bank holidays / We/Férié
Individual Individuel	€ 160	€ 160
Couple Couple	€ 320	€ 320

Caddie Caddie on request Electric Trolley Chariot électrique no

Buggy Voiturette yes   Clubs Clubs yes

Credit cards Cartes de crédit
VISA - Eurocard - AMEX - DC

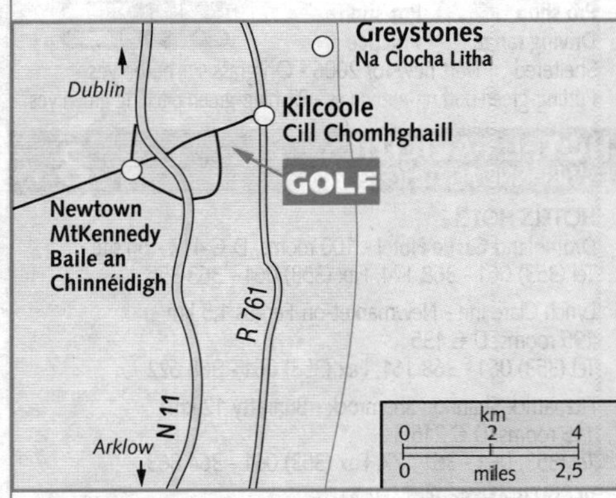

Access Accès : Dublin, N11 South. Turn left at Newtown Mt Kennedy (signpost). Golf 2 km

Map 1 on page 809 Carte 1 Page 809

GOLF COURSE — PARCOURS 16/20

Site	Site	
Maintenance	Entretien	
Architect	Architecte	Pat Ruddy, Tom Craddock
Type	Type	parkland
Relief	Relief	
Water in play	Eau en jeu	
Exp. to wind	Exposé au vent	
Trees in play	Arbres en jeu	

Scorecard / Carte de score	Chp. / Chp.	Mens / Mess.	Ladies / Da.
Length Long.	6416	5997	4773
Par	72	72	72
Slope system	—	—	—

Advised golfing ability / Niveau de jeu recommandé: 0 12 24 36

Hcp required / Handicap exigé: certificate

CLUB HOUSE & AMENITIES — CLUB HOUSE ET ANNEXES 9/10

Pro shop	Pro-shop
Driving range	Practice

Sheltered couvert 12 mats - On grass sur herbe yes - Putting-green putting-green yes - Pitching-green pitching green yes

HOTEL FACILITIES — ENVIRONNEMENT HOTELIER 7/10

HOTELS HÔTELS

Druids Glen Marriott - on site
148 rooms, D € 200
Tel (353) 01 - 287 0800, Fax (353) 01 - 287 0801

Glenview Hotel - Glen of the Downs 15 km
70 rooms, D € 240
Tel (353) 01 - 287 3399, Fax (353) 01 - 287 7511

Hunter's Hotel - Rathnew 15 km
16 rooms, D € 180
Tel (353) 0404 - 40 106, Fax (353) 0404 - 40 338

RESTAURANTS RESTAURANTS

Hungry Monk - Greystones 6 km - Tel (353) 01 - 287 5759
Cooper's - Greystones 6 km - Tel (353) 01 - 237 3914

Druids Glen *Druids Heath*

14 | 9 | 7

It was once again Pat Ruddy who was asked to lay out a second 18-hole course here. He took his time over it, and it shows. The beauty of the landscapes looking seaward and over to the Wicklow Mountains gives an impression of space enhanced by the rather understated rolling terrain created by the architect, bordered by a generous sprinkling of a hundred or so bunkers (including of the pot variety). Vegetation here is mainly broom and bushes, while trees – few and far between on this open land – are used for strategic purposes only, albeit very effectively. Water hazards are something of a rarity too, but the water you do find is very dangerous and the hazards here really are just that. In a word, this is not the easiest course around and some of the trickier aspects are disconcerting to say the least; it is a shame that the slopes on holes 12 and 13 only compound the natural tendency of most golfers to hit their ball towards the water. The quality of this design and the green-keeping call for the utmost respect, but some of you will prefer the original "Druids" course.

C'est de nouveau à Pat Ruddy que l'on a demandé de concevoir ici un second 18 trous. Il y a passé du temps et cela se sent. La beauté des paysages, vers la mer ou vers les Wicklow Mountains donne une impression d'espace renforcée par les ondulations sans exagération créées par l'architecte, délimitées par le généreux usage d'une centaine de bunkers (y compris des pot-bunkers). Quant à la végétation, elle est constituée de genêts et de buissons, les arbres – peu nombreux sur ce site très ouvert – étant utilisés de manière stratégique, et très efficace. Les obstacles d'eau ne sont pas si nombreux, mais ils sont dangereux, et les obstacles ici en sont vraiment. Bref, ce parcours n'est pas des plus faciles, certains aspects "tricky" peuvent déconcerter, et l'on peut regretter que les pentes du 12 et du 13 favorisent la tendance naturelle des golfeurs à envoyer leur balle dans l'eau. La qualité de la construction et de l'entretien imposent le respect, mais d'aucuns préfèrent le premier "Druids".

Druids Glen Golf Club — 2002

IRL - NEWTOWN MOUNT KENNEDY, Co Wicklow

Office	Secrétariat	(353) 01 - 287 3600
Pro shop	Pro-shop	(353) 01 - 287 3600
Fax	Fax	(353) 01 - 287 3699
Web	www.druidsglen.ie	
Situation	Situation	Dublin, 35 km

Kilcoole, 2 km

Annual closure	Fermeture annuelle	no
Weekly closure	Fermeture hebdomadaire	no

Fees main season Tarifs haute saison — 18 holes

	Week days / Semaine	We/Bank holidays / We/Férié
Individual Individuel	€ 120	€ 120
Couple Couple	€ 240	€ 240

Caddie Caddie on request **Electric Trolley** Chariot électrique no

Buggy Voiturette yes **Clubs** Clubs yes

Credit cards Cartes de crédit
VISA - Eurocard - AMEX - DC

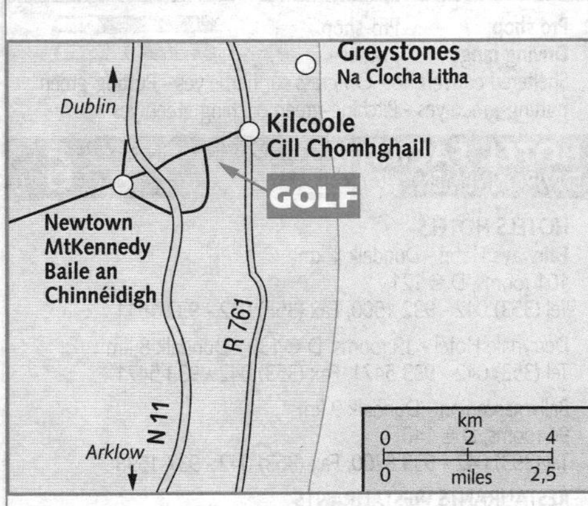

Access Accès : Dublin, N11 South. Turn left at Newtown Mt Kennedy (signpost). Golf 2 km
Map 1 on page 809 Carte 1 Page 809

GOLF COURSE — PARCOURS 14/20

Site	Site	
Maintenance	Entretien	
Architect	Architecte	Pat Ruddy
Type	Type	heathland
Relief	Relief	
Water in play	Eau en jeu	
Exp. to wind	Exposé au vent	
Trees in play	Arbres en jeu	

Scorecard / Carte de score	Chp. / Chp.	Mens / Mess.	Ladies / Da.
Length Long.	6691	6150	4976
Par	71	71	71
Slope system	—	—	—

Advised golfing ability / Niveau de jeu recommandé: 0 12 24 36

Hcp required Handicap exigé: certificate

CLUB HOUSE & AMENITIES — CLUB HOUSE ET ANNEXES 9/10

Pro shop Pro-shop
Driving range Practice
Sheltered couvert 12 mats - On grass sur herbe yes - Putting-green putting-green yes - Pitching-green pitching green yes

HOTEL FACILITIES — ENVIRONNEMENT HOTELIER 7/10

HOTELS HÔTELS

Druids Glen Marriott - on site
148 rooms, D € 200
Tel (353) 01 - 287 0800, Fax (353) 01 - 287 0801

Glenview Hotel - Glen of the Downs 15 km
70 rooms, D € 240
Tel (353) 01 - 287 3399, Fax (353) 01 - 287 7511

Hunter's Hotel - Rathnew 15 km
16 rooms, D € 180
Tel (353) 0404 - 40 106, Fax (353) 0404 - 40 338

RESTAURANTS RESTAURANTS

Hungry Monk - Greystones 6 km - Tel (353) 01 - 287 5759
Cooper's - Greystones 6 km - Tel (353) 01 - 287 3914

Dundalk

15	6	6

On a road linking some of the very greatest Irish courses, Dundalk is located between County Louth and Royal County Down. You certainly won't be wasting your time stopping off here, in the shadow of the Cooley Mountains and with the Mountains of Mourne in the background. Rejuvenated by Alliss and Thomas, this is still one of the country's most under-rated inland courses. Firstly, it is a course to test your driver, with a few long and very tough par 4s and strategically located fairway bunkers. The architects have also tightened the entrances to many of the greens, thus attaching greater importance to spot-on second shots, which are, nonetheless, made easier by the elimination of blind approaches. A generally very open course, you need to get into your stride right away, as many of the difficulties are concentrated over the first seven holes. With little difference between the white and yellow tees, there's every chance that inexperienced golfers will find this tough going score-wise.

Sur une route des très grands parcours d'Irlande, Dundalk se situe entre County Louth et Royal County Down, mais l'on ne perdra pas son temps en marquant une halte ici, à l'ombre des Cooley Mountains, avec au loin les Mountains of Mourne. Rajeuni par Peter Alliss et Dave Thomas, c'est toujours l'un des "inland " les plus sous-estimés du pays. C'est d'abord un parcours pour tester les drivers, avec quelques longs par 4 très difficiles, et des bunkers de fairway très stratégiques. Les architectes ont aussi rétréci les entrées de beaucoup de greens, ce qui accentue la nécessité de seconds coups précis, mais facilités par l'élimination des coups aveugles. Généralement très ouvert, il oblige à prendre vite le rythme, avec une forte concentration des difficultés sur les sept premiers trous. Il y a peu de différences entre les départs arrière et les départs hommes normaux : les golfeurs peu expérimentés auront du mal à y scorer...

Dundalk Golf Club — 1904

Blackrock
IRL - DUNDALK, Co Louth

Office Secrétariat (353) 042 - 932 1731
Pro shop Pro-shop (353) 042 - 932 1731
Fax Fax (353) 042 - 932 2022
Web www.dundalkgolfclub.ie
Situation Situation Dundalk (pop. 25 762), 5 km
Annual closure Fermeture annuelle no
Weekly closure Fermeture hebdomadaire no

Fees main season Tarifs haute saison — full day

	Week days / Semaine	We/Bank holidays / We/Férié
Individual Individuel	€ 55	€ 55
Couple Couple	€ 110	€ 110

Caddie Caddie no — **Electric Trolley** Chariot électrique yes
Buggy Voiturette yes — **Clubs** Clubs no
Credit cards Cartes de crédit
VISA - Eurocard - MasterCard (Pro Shop goods & Green fees)

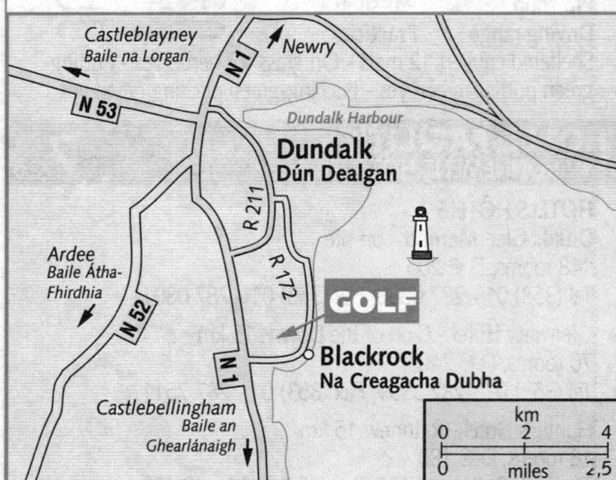

Access Accès : Dublin → Belfast, 1 km N. of Blackrock Village
Map 2 on page 811 Carte 2 Page 811

GOLF COURSE — PARCOURS 15/20

Site Site
Maintenance Entretien
Architect Architecte T. Shannon, Alliss & Thomas
Type Type inland, parkland
Relief Relief
Water in play Eau en jeu
Exp. to wind Exposé au vent
Trees in play Arbres en jeu

Scorecard / Carte de score	Chp. / Chp.	Mens / Mess.	Ladies / Da.
Length Long.	6160	6028	5134
Par	72	72	73
Slope system	—	—	—

Advised golfing ability Niveau de jeu recommandé — 0 12 24 36
Hcp required Handicap exigé 28 Men, 36 Ladies

CLUB HOUSE & AMENITIES — CLUB HOUSE ET ANNEXES 6/10

Pro shop Pro-shop
Driving range Practice
Sheltered couvert no - On grass sur herbe yes - Putting-green putting-green yes - Pitching-green pitching green yes

HOTEL FACILITIES — ENVIRONNEMENT HOTELIER 6/10

HOTELS HÔTELS

Fairways Hotel - Dundalk 1 km
101 rooms, D € 121
Tel (353) 042 - 932 1500, Fax (353) 042 - 932 1511

Derryhale Hotel - 19 rooms, D € 130 - Dundalk 8 km
Tel (353) 042 - 933 5471, Fax (353) 042 - 933 5471

Ballymascanion - Dundalk 9 km
96 rooms, D € 140
Tel (353) 042 - 935 8200, Fax (353) 042 - 937 1598

RESTAURANTS RESTAURANTS

Mashie + Spoon - on site - Tel (353) 042 - 932 2255
Jade Garden - Dundalk 5 km - Tel (353) 042 - 933 0378
Cube - Dundalk 5 km - Tel (353) 042 - 932 9898

Enniscrone

17	8	6

For many a year, Enniscrone was one of the least known links in Ireland. The rediscovery of this region has pulled it out of the shadows, as has the opening of nine new holes, a welcome addition in that the course sometimes lacked the subtle features associated with the greatest links courses. It is well worth the trip even though it can be a little tiring to walk. Some holes here have been redesigned (recently holes 17 and 18) and added to, while a whole series of holes have been laid out in the sand-dunes by Donald Steel, who has succeeded in preserving the feel of the original design by Eddie Hackett dating from 1974. Excursions into a lunar and quite spectacular landscape are much more adventurous, and your driving and ironwork here will need to be both daring and accurate. The wind off the sea can easily make Enniscrone doubly challenging and spoil the ambitions of many a hardy soul; in this case only experienced players can hope to make any impression. The others can say that they played a great course while the whole party sit down to admire the setting sun.

Enniscrone a longtemps été l'un des links méconnus d'Irlande. La redécouverte de cette région l'a placé au premier plan, ainsi que la création bienvenue de neuf nouveaux trous, car le parcours manquait parfois des subtilités des plus grands links. Il mérite le détour, même s'il reste parfois un peu fatigant à pied. Certains trous ont été revus et complétés (le 17 et le 18 récemment), et toute une série d'autres construits dans les dunes par Donald Steel, qui a su préserver l'esprit du dessin d'Eddie Hackett en 1974. Les voyages dans un paysage à la fois lunaire et spectaculaire sont bien plus aventureux, et le driving comme le jeu de fers devront être aussi audacieux que précis. Le vent venu de l'océan tout proche peut facilement doubler l'exigence d'Enniscrone et contrecarrer les ambitions des téméraires : seuls les joueurs expérimentés pourront alors espérer s'imposer. Les autres pourront se dire qu'ils ont joué un beau parcours, tout en contemplant avec leurs vainqueurs le coucher du soleil.

Enniscrone Golf Club — 1925/1974

IRL - ENNISCRONE, Co Sligo

Office	Secrétariat	(353) 096 - 36 297
Pro shop	Pro-shop	(353) 096 - 36 666
Fax	Fax	(353) 096 - 36 657
Web		www.enniscronegolf.com
Situation	Situation	Ballina (pop. 6 852), 13 km
Annual closure	Fermeture annuelle	no
Weekly closure	Fermeture hebdomadaire	no

Fees main season Tarifs haute saison — 18 holes

	Week days Semaine	We/Bank holidays We/Férié
Individual Individuel	€ 50	€ 65
Couple Couple	€ 100	€ 130

Caddie Caddie yes — **Electric Trolley** Chariot électrique no
Buggy Voiturette yes — **Clubs** Clubs yes
Credit cards Cartes de crédit
VISA - Eurocard - Mastercard - AMEX

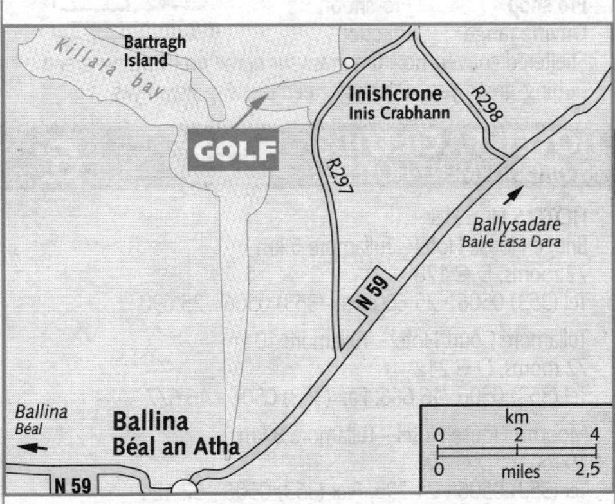

Access Accès : Killala Bay, 12 km North of Ballina
Map 2 on page 812 Carte 2 Page 812

GOLF COURSE — PARCOURS 17/20

Site	Site	
Maintenance	Entretien	
Architect	Architecte	Eddie Hackett Donald Steel
Type	Type	seaside course, links
Relief	Relief	
Water in play	Eau en jeu	
Exp. to wind	Exposé au vent	
Trees in play	Arbres en jeu	

Scorecard Carte de score	Chp. Chp.	Mens Mess.	Ladies Da.
Length Long.	6254	6133	5071
Par	73	73	73
Slope system	—	—	—

Advised golfing ability Niveau de jeu recommandé — 0 12 24 36
Hcp required Handicap exigé — 28 Men, 36 Ladies

CLUB HOUSE & AMENITIES — CLUB HOUSE ET ANNEXES 8/10

Pro shop Pro-shop
Driving range Practice
Sheltered couvert no - On grass sur herbe yes - Putting-green putting-green yes - Pitching-green pitching green no

HOTEL FACILITIES — ENVIRONNEMENT HOTELIER 6/10

HOTELS HÔTELS

Castle Arms - Enniscrone 1 km
27 rooms, D € 80
Tel (353) 096 - 36 156, Fax (353) 096 - 36 156

Downhill Inn - Ballina 13 km
45 rooms, D € 120
Tel (353) 096 - 73 444, Fax (353) 096 - 73 411

Ridgepool - Ballina 13 km
72 rooms, D € 152
Tel (353) 096 24 600, Fax (353) 096 24 602

RESTAURANTS RESTAURANTS

Clark's - Enniscrone a - Tel (353) 096 - 36 405
Downhill Inn - Ballina 13 km - Tel (353) 096 - 73 444

Esker Hills

14 | 6 | 6

Though hilly and physically demanding, the sand and gravel deposited by an ancient glacier made this terrain very suitable for golf-course construction. The drainage system is obviously excellent, running ground-water off to the natural lakes used abundantly by Christy O'Connor Jr., who has also made excellent use of the many trees. Winding their way through alternating hillocks and valleys, the course's very distinctive 18 holes have retained their pleasantly natural appearance. As usual with O'Connor, the fairways are wide open, bunkers are carefully shaped and placed, and the greens are on the large size without any excessive contouring so as to allow every kind of approach shot. As all hazards are generally in full view, you will enjoy playing here first time out and certainly leave you wanting to come back here to this central part of Ireland, the cradle of Irish civilisation. You will want to stop off at nearby Kilbeggan, home to a famous whiskey museum, a beverage which, so we were told, is as inseparable from life as golf itself.

Le terrain était très favorable à la construction d'un parcours, avec une large proportion de sable et de gravier déposés par un ancien glacier. Evidemment, le drainage y est excellent, vers des lacs naturels utilisés par Christy O'Connor Jr. avec gourmandise, tout comme pas mal d'arbres déjà sur place. De petites collines et vallées alternent, où s'insinuent 18 trous bien caractérisés, qui ont conservé un caractère plaisament naturel. Comme d'habitude avec l'architecte, les fairways sont généreux, les bunkers bien travaillés et positionnés ; les greens assez grands et sans ondulations excessives appellent tous les types d'approches. Et comme les obstacles sont généralement bien visibles, dès la première fois, on prendra plaisir à jouer, pour se donner le goût de revenir dans cette région du centre, berceau de la civilisation irlandaise. En s'arrêtant à Kilbeggan, où se trouve un fameux musée du whiskey, aussi inséparable de la vie que le golf, nous dit-on.

Esker Hills Golf Club — 1996

IRL - TULLAMORE, Co. Offaly

Office	Secrétariat	(353) 0506 - 55 999
Pro shop	Pro-shop	(353) 0506 - 55 999
Fax	Fax	(353) 0506 - 55 021
Web	www.eskerhillsgolf.com	
Situation	Situation	Tullamore (pop. 9 220), 5 km
Annual closure	Fermeture annuelle	no
Weekly closure	Fermeture hebdomadaire	

Fees main season Tarifs haute saison	Week days Semaine	We/Bank holidays We/Férié
		18 holes
Individual Individuel	€ 35	€ 45
Couple Couple	€ 70	€ 90

Caddie Caddie on request **Electric Trolley** Chariot électrique yes

Buggy Voiturette yes **Clubs** Clubs yes

Credit cards Cartes de crédit
VISA - MasterCard

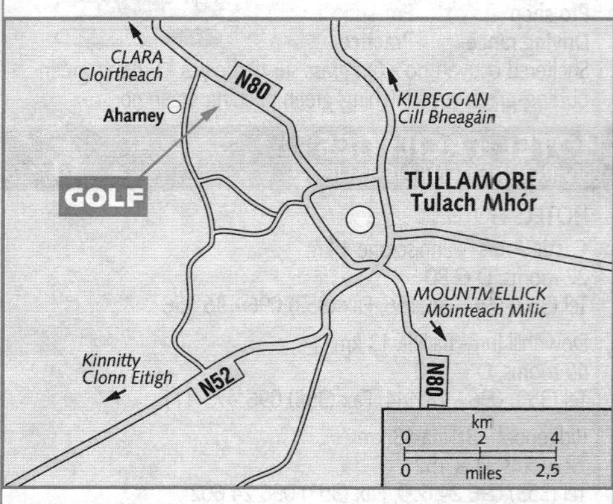

Access Accès : Dublin, N4 → Kinnegad. N6 → Kilbeggan. N52 → Tullamore then N80 North → Clara.
Map 3 on page 813 Carte 3 Page 813

GOLF COURSE — PARCOURS 14/20

Site	Site	
Maintenance	Entretien	
Architect	Architecte	Christy O'Connor Jr.
Type	Type	parkland, inland
Relief	Relief	
Water in play	Eau en jeu	
Exp. to wind	Exposé au vent	
Trees in play	Arbres en jeu	

Scorecard Carte de score	Chp. Chp.	Mens Mess.	Ladies Da.
Length Long.	6003	5563	4540
Par	71	71	72
Slope system	—	—	—

Advised golfing ability Niveau de jeu recommandé: 0 12 24 36

Hcp required Handicap exigé: no

CLUB HOUSE & AMENITIES — CLUB HOUSE ET ANNEXES 6/10

Pro shop Pro-shop
Driving range Practice
Sheltered couvert no - On grass sur herbe no - Putting-green putting-green yes - Pitching-green pitching green yes

HOTEL FACILITIES — ENVIRONNEMENT HOTELIER 6/10

HOTELS HÔTELS

Bridge House Hotel - Tullamore 5 km
72 rooms, D € 178
Tel (353) 0506 - 25 600, Fax (353) 0506 - 25 690

Tullamore Court Hotel - Tullamore 10 km
72 rooms, D € 212
Tel (353) 0506 -46 666, Fax (353) 0506 - 46 677

Moorhill House Hotel - Tullamore 8 km
10 rooms, D € 100
Tel (353) 0506 - 21 395, Fax (353) 0506 - 52 424

RESTAURANTS RESTAURANTS

Moorhill House - Tullamore 8 km - Tel (353) 0506 - 21 395
Tullamore Court - Tullamore 10 km - Tel (353) 0506-46 666

European (The)

18 | 5 | 6

The creation of "The European" was the work of Pat Ruddy, a professional enthusiast, journalist and course designer. This is his masterpiece, and looks almost hand-made. Between the dunes, the beach, the fairways, the greens and the bunkers bolstered by railway line sleepers, there was just enough room for a little marsh and a water hazard that is as worrying as it is unexpected. This course is a great trip to the land of golf where each round is so varied, so demanding and so exciting that no-one would care to mention the layout's one or two weaknesses. It takes time to appreciate the course's finer points, but the only thing on your mind when leaving is knowing when you can come back. The atmosphere of freshness and golfing tradition that reigns here is the icing on the cake, as opposed to clubs where personal wealth seems to be the only criterion for playing. The green-fee is now relatively high, as it is everywhere else... and there is the compensation of knowing that Tiger Woods set the course record of 67 during a visit in 2002.

La création de ce parcours a été l'œuvre de Pat Ruddy, enthousiaste professionnel, journaliste et architecte. C'est son chef-d'oeuvre, donnant l'impression d'avoir été fait à la main. Entre les dunes, la plage, les fairways, les greens et des bunkers renforcés de traverses de chemin de fer, il restait juste un peu de place pour un petit marais, et pour un obstacle d'eau aussi préoccupant qu'inattendu. Ce parcours est un grand voyage au pays du golf, où l'on n'a pas le courage de relever quelques faiblesses de dessin tant le jeu y est varié, exigeant, excitant. Il faut du temps pour en apprécier toutes les nuances, mais on a une seule idée en le quittant, c'est d'y revenir. L'atmosphère de fraîcheur et de purisme golfique qui règne ici est la cerise sur un gâteau, à l'opposé de clubs où la fortune paraît le seul critère pour jouer. Il est vrai aussi que le green-fee n'est plus donné... la seule consolation est de marcher dans les pas de Tiger Woods, auteur du record de 67 en 2002.

The European Club — 1989

IRL - BRITTAS BAY, Co Wicklow

Office Secrétariat (353) 0404 - 47 415
Pro shop Pro-shop (353) 0404 - 47 415
Fax Fax (353) 0404 - 47 449
Web www.theeuropeanclub.com
Situation Situation Arklow, 10 km
Wicklow (pop. 6 416), 12 km

Annual closure Fermeture annuelle — no
Weekly closure Fermeture hebdomadaire — no

Fees main season Tarifs haute saison — 18 holes

	Week days / Semaine	We/Bank holidays / We/Férié
Individual Individuel	€ 150	€ 150
Couple Couple	€ 300	€ 300

Caddie Caddie no — **Electric Trolley** Chariot électrique no
Buggy Voiturette no — **Clubs** Clubs yes
Credit cards Cartes de crédit
VISA - Eurocard - MasterCard

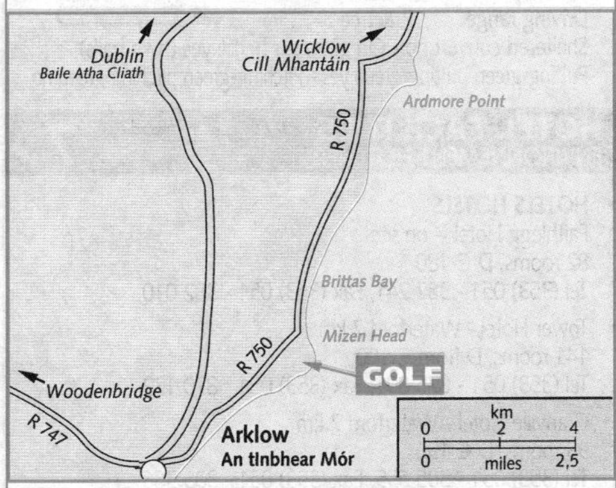

Access Accès : Dublin, N11. 56 km turn left at Jack White's Inn. Turn right at T Junction → Brittas Bay. 2 km
Map 1 on page 809 Carte 1 Page 809

GOLF COURSE — PARCOURS — 18/20

Site Site
Maintenance Entretien
Architect Architecte — Pat Ruddy
Type Type — links
Relief Relief
Water in play Eau en jeu
Exp. to wind Exposé au vent
Trees in play Arbres en jeu

Scorecard / Carte de score	Chp. / Chp.	Mens / Mess.	Ladies / Da.
Length Long.	6591	6039	5233
Par	71	71	69
Slope system	—	—	—

Advised golfing ability / Niveau de jeu recommandé — 0 12 24 36
Hcp required Handicap exigé — no

CLUB HOUSE & AMENITIES — CLUB HOUSE ET ANNEXES — 5/10

Pro shop Pro-shop
Driving range Practice
Sheltered couvert no - On grass sur herbe yes (own balls)
Putting-green putting-green yes - Pitching-green pitching green yes

HOTEL FACILITIES — ENVIRONNEMENT HOTELIER — 6/10

HOTELS HÔTELS
Grand Hotel - Wicklow 11 km - 32 rooms, D € 125
Tel (353) 0404 - 67 337, Fax (353) 0404 - 69 607

Tinakilly House Hotel - Rathnew 14 km
51 rooms, D from € 212
Tel (353) 0404 - 69 274, Fax (353) 0404 - 67 806

Hunter's Hotel - Rathnew 14 km
16 rooms, D € 180
Tel (353) 0404 - 40 106, Fax (353) 0404 - 40 338

RESTAURANTS RESTAURANTS
Kitty's (Restaurant & Pub) - Arklow 10 km
Tel (353) 0402 - 31 669
Tinakilly House - Rathnew 14 km - Tel (353) 0404 - 69 274

Faithlegg

13	7	7

The south-eastern coast is not the most popular with golf-trotters, and that's a good reason for discovering the region once you have visited the rest. Faithlegg was laid out over a former estate, as you can see with the old trees, which outline the fairways, the enclosure wall and the gardens. They add extra style and difficulties to the course as a whole. The architect has designed a very varied layout with no excessively steep hills, although some hazards are hardly visible and so complicate matters slightly in terms of strategy. With this said, they only await the really wayward shot. This is an averagely difficult and very competent course, the one criticism being the very ordinary bunkers with sand a little on the coarse side. However, you can get round the course quickly, as the rough is lenient and the undergrowth kept neatly trimmed. Faithlegg has hosted the Irish Ladies Open.

La côte Sud-Est de l'Irlande n'est pas vraiment la plus fréquentée par les touristes golfiques, c'est une bonne raison pour l'explorer quand vous aurez fini de parcourir les régions plus classiques. Faithlegg a été construit dans une ancienne propriété, comme on le remarque avec les arbres très adultes qui définissent les trous, le mur d'enceinte et les jardins : ils apportent une beauté supplémentaire et quelques difficultés au parcours. L'architecte a conçu un tracé très varié, sans reliefs excessifs, certains obstacles d'eau par exemple ne sont guère visibles, ce qui complique légèrement la stratégie, mais ils ne recueillent que les balles très écartées du bon chemin. De difficulté moyenne, c'est une réalisation sérieuse. On peut cependant estimer que la forme des bunkers ne sort pas de l'ordinaire, et que le sable pourrait être plus fin. En revanche, la vitesse de jeu est garantie par la clémence des roughs et le bon entretien des sous-bois. Ce parcours a reçu l'Irish Ladies Open.

Faithlegg Golf Club — 1992

IRL - FAITHLEGG, Co. Waterford

Office Secrétariat (353) 051 - 382 241
Pro shop Pro-shop (353) 051 - 380 587
Fax Fax (353) 051 - 382 010
Web www.faithlegg.com
Situation Situation Waterford, 7 km
Annual closure Fermeture annuelle no
Weekly closure Fermeture hebdomadaire no

Fees main season / Tarifs haute saison	Week days / Semaine	We/Bank holidays / We/Férié
18 holes		
Individual Individuel	€ 47	€ 59
Couple Couple	€ 94	€ 118

Caddie Caddie on request **Electric Trolley** Chariot électrique yes
Buggy Voiturette yes **Clubs** Clubs yes
Credit cards Cartes de crédit
VISA - MasterCard - AMEX

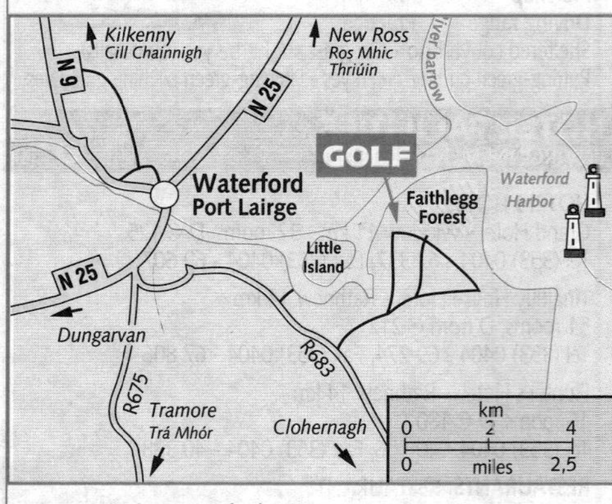

Access Accès : Waterford, R683
Map 3 on page 813 Carte 3 Page 813

GOLF COURSE — PARCOURS — 13/20

Site Site
Maintenance Entretien
Architect Architecte Patrick Merrigan
Type Type parkland
Relief Relief
Water in play Eau en jeu
Exp. to wind Exposé au vent
Trees in play Arbres en jeu

Scorecard / Carte de score	Chp. / Chp.	Mens / Mess.	Ladies / Da.
Length Long.	6057	5712	5160
Par	72	72	73
Slope system	—	—	—

Advised golfing ability / Niveau de jeu recommandé 0 12 24 36
Hcp required Handicap exigé no

CLUB HOUSE & AMENITIES — CLUB HOUSE ET ANNEXES — 7/10

Pro shop Pro-shop
Driving range Practice
Sheltered couvert no - On grass sur herbe yes (own balls) -
Putting-green putting-green yes - Pitching-green pitching green no

HOTEL FACILITIES — ENVIRONNEMENT HOTELIER — 7/10

HOTELS HÔTELS

Faithlegg Hotel - on site
82 rooms, D € 180
Tel (353) 051 - 382 241, Fax (353) 051 - 382 010

Tower Hotel - Waterford 7 km
141 rooms, D from € 100
Tel (353) 051 - 875 801, Fax (353) 051 - 870 129

Granville Hotel - Waterford 7 km
98 rooms, D € 190
Tel (353) 051 - 305 555, Fax (353) 051 - 305 566

RESTAURANTS RESTAURANTS

Dwyer's - Waterford 7 km - Tel (353) 051 - 877 478
O'Grady's - Waterford 7 km - Tel (353) 051 - 378 851

Fota Island

16	8	6

Since playing host to the Irish Open, when it drew much favourable comment from the competitors, this facility has since been sold by Dr Tim Mahony, owner of Mount Juliet to Fleming Group, which is building a hotel and a new 9-hole course. The present layout is not a links, but it makes no difference, and the original designers, Peter McEvoy and Christy O'Connor Jr., made a point of including some seaside features like pot bunkers and a double green, amongst the many other difficulties. Canadian architect Jeff Howes has remodeled all the greens and redesigned more or less 8 holes. You often see water (as far as the port of Cork) but it still only comes into play on half a dozen holes. The other hazards are primarily trees, green-side bunkers and a few stone walls here and there. This course is now more suitable for better players, who can make their choice between lofted and ground shots. Here, you hone your short game and play with your brains. You will also see a few ostriches, monkeys or llamas roaming in the adjacent natural park.

Ce parcours choisi pour l'Irish Open a depuis été vendu par Tim Mahony (propriétaire de Mount Juliet) au Fleming Group, qui construit un hôtel et un autre 9 trous. Que le 18 trous ne soit pas un links n'enlève rien à ses qualités, et les architectes McEvoy et O'Connor Jr. n'ont pas manqué d'en citer quelques traits, comme quelques pot-bunkers et un double-green, parmi d'autres difficultés. Le canadien Jeff Howes a remodelé tous les greens et plus ou moins huit trous. On voit souvent l'eau (jusqu'au port de Cork), elle ne vient réellement en jeu que sur une demi-douzaine de trous. Les autres obstacles sont de grands arbres, les bunkers de green et de petits murs de pierres çà et là. Ce parcours conviendra mieux encore maintenant aux joueurs de bon niveau, qui sauront faire le choix entre le target golf et les approches roulées. Ici, on travaille son petit jeu, on joue avec sa tête et on peut apercevoir quelques autruches, singes ou lamas du parc naturel adjacent.

Fota Island Golf Club — 1993

IRL - CARRIGTWOHILL, Co Cork

Office Secrétariat (353) 021 - 488 3710
Pro shop Pro-shop (353) 021 - 453 2032
Fax Fax (353) 021 - 488 2047
Web www.fotaisland.ie
Situation Situation Cork, 14 km
Cobh (pop. 6 468), 10 km

Annual closure Fermeture annuelle no
Weekly closure Fermeture hebdomadaire no

Fees main season Tarifs haute saison	18 holes	
	Week days Semaine	We/Bank holidays We/Férié
Individual Individuel	€ 83	€ 98
Couple Couple	€ 166	€ 196

€ 70 on Monday / We: Friday → Sunday

Caddie Caddie on request **Electric Trolley** Chariot électrique no
Buggy Voiturette yes **Clubs** Clubs yes
Credit cards Cartes de crédit
VISA - MasterCard - AMEX

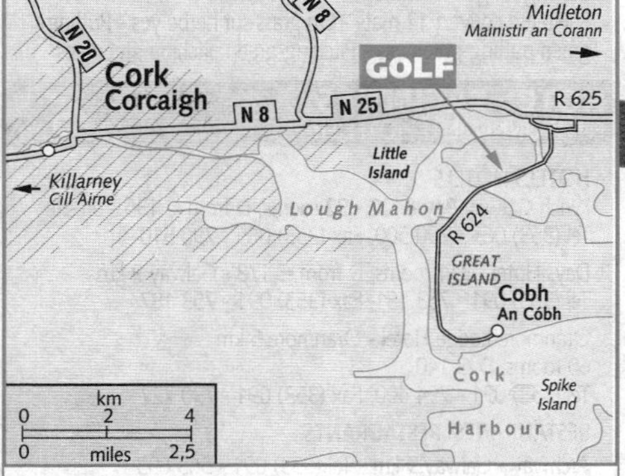

Access Accès : Cork N8 East → Cobh. R624 → Fota Island
Map 3 on page 812 Carte 3 Page 812

GOLF COURSE — PARCOURS — 16/20

Site Site
Maintenance Entretien
Architect Architecte Christy O'Connor Jr. P. McEvoy, J. Howes
Type Type parkland
Relief Relief
Water in play Eau en jeu
Exp. to wind Exposé au vent
Trees in play Arbres en jeu

Scorecard Carte de score	Chp. Chp.	Mens Mess.	Ladies Da.
Length Long.	6197	5788	4967
Par	72	72	72
Slope system	—	—	—

Advised golfing ability Niveau de jeu recommandé 0 12 24 36
Hcp required Handicap exigé 24 Men, 36 Ladies

CLUB HOUSE & AMENITIES — CLUB HOUSE ET ANNEXES — 8/10

Pro shop Pro-shop
Driving range Practice
Sheltered couvert no - On grass sur herbe yes - Putting-green putting-green yes - Pitching-green pitching green yes

HOTEL FACILITIES — ENVIRONNEMENT HOTELIER — 6/10

HOTELS HÔTELS

Midleton Park - Cork 7 km
40 rooms, D from € 135
Tel (353) 021 - 463 5100, Fax (353) 021 - 463 5101

Watersedge - Cobh 10 km
19 rooms, D from € 110
Tel (353) 021 481 5566, Fax (353) 021 481 2011

Silver Springs Hotel - Cork 12 km
109 rooms, D € 135
Tel (353) 021 - 450 7533, Fax (353) 021 - 450 7641

RESTAURANTS RESTAURANTS

Jacobs on the Mall - Cork 14 km - Tel (353) 021 - 425 1530
Trade Winds - Cobh 10 km - Tel (353) 021 - 481 3754

Galway Bay

14	7	6

Overlooking the Atlantic and the city of Galway, this recent course provides some outstanding viewpoints, but don't let them blur your judgment. The terrain given to Christy O'Connor Jr. was nothing more than ordinary, but he has made a great job of it and designed in a lot of appeal at the expense of some highly appropriate earthworks. As usual, the bunkers are very well placed and ready to collect any ball that doesn't quite manage to short-cut the dog-legs. There are also three lakes, but there are in play on three holes only. The many tee-off areas spread the range of difficulties, but only the back tees make this a severe test. The general difficulties are clearly visible and game strategy is obvious; this is important because the wind can turn nasty and make it even more essential to know how to play with it and against it. Welcome to a course designed with considerable talent, lacking only that intangible touch of greatness that separates the excellent from the exceptional.

Dominant l'océan et la ville de Galway, ce récent parcours offre des points de vue exceptionnels. Mais ils ne doivent pas influencer le jugement ! Le terrain mis à la disposition de Christy O'Connor Jr. était au départ assez ordinaire, il en a tiré un très bon parti, et l'a même rendu séduisant, au prix de travaux de terrassement très adéquats. Ses bunkers sont comme d'habitude très bien placés, et prêts à accueillir ceux qui ne parviennent pas à couper les dog-legs. De même, trois lacs sont mis en jeu, mais sur trois trous seulement. Les nombreux départs proposent un éventail de difficultés, seuls les départs arrière rendent ce parcours sévère. Les difficultés générales sont bien visibles, et la stratégie de jeu évidente : c'est important car le vent peut devenir méchant, et renforcer encore la nécessité de savoir jouer avec et contre lui. Un parcours réalisé avec talent, auquel ne manque que l'indéfinissable grandeur qui fait les exceptions.

Galway Bay Golf & Country Club — 1993

Renville
IRL - ORANMORE, Co Galway

Office Secrétariat (353) 091 - 790 711
Pro shop Pro-shop (353) 091 - 790 503
Fax Fax (353) 091 - 790 510
Web www.galwaybaygolfresort.com
Situation Situation Galway (pop. 57 241), 13 km
Oranmore (pop. 1 410), 5 km

Annual closure Fermeture annuelle: no
Weekly closure Fermeture hebdomadaire: no

Fees main season Tarifs haute saison — 18 holes

	Week days / Semaine	We/Bank holidays / We/Férié
Individual Individuel	€ 55	€ 70
Couple Couple	€ 110	€ 140

We: Friday → Sunday

Caddie Caddie no — **Electric Trolley** Chariot électrique no
Buggy Voiturette yes — **Clubs** Clubs yes
Credit cards Cartes de crédit
VISA - Eurocard - MasterCard - AMEX

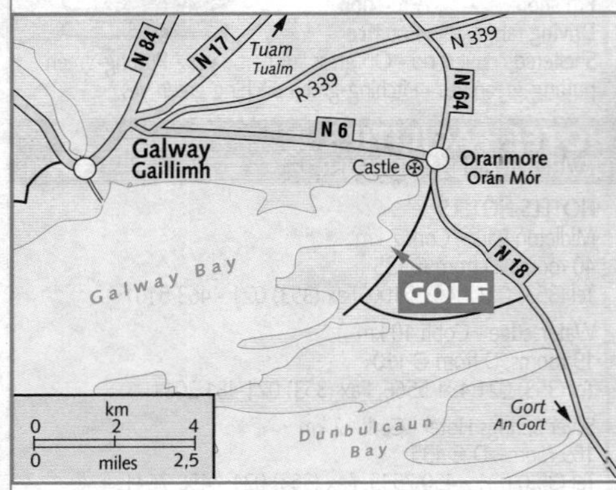

Access Accès : Galway N6 → Oranmore, → Renville
Map 2 on page 810 Carte 2 Page 810

GOLF COURSE — PARCOURS — 14/20

Site	Site	
Maintenance	Entretien	
Architect	Architecte	Christy O'Connor Jr.
Type	Type	seaside course
Relief	Relief	
Water in play	Eau en jeu	
Exp. to wind	Exposé au vent	
Trees in play	Arbres en jeu	

Scorecard / Carte de score	Chp. / Chp.	Mens / Mess.	Ladies / Da.
Length Long.	6533	6091	5205
Par	72	72	74
Slope system	—	—	—

Advised golfing ability Niveau de jeu recommandé: 0 12 24 36
Hcp required Handicap exigé: 28 Men, 36 Ladies

CLUB HOUSE & AMENITIES — CLUB HOUSE ET ANNEXES — 7/10

Pro shop Pro-shop
Driving range Practice
Sheltered couvert 12 mats - On grass sur herbe yes - Putting-green putting-green yes - Pitching-green pitching green yes

HOTEL FACILITIES — ENVIRONNEMENT HOTELIER — 6/10

HOTELS HÔTELS

Lynch Galway Bay & CC - 92 rooms, D from € 135 - on site
Tel (353) 065 - 790 500, Fax (353) 065 - 790 510

Days Hotel - 311 rooms, D from € 178 - Galway 9 km
Tel (353) 091 - 753 181, Fax (353) 091 - 753 187

Oranmore Lodge Hotel - Oranmore 5 km
60 rooms, D € 140
Tel (353) 091 - 794 400, Fax (353) 091 - 790 227

RESTAURANTS RESTAURANTS

Archway - Galway 9 km - Tel (353) 091 - 563 693
Galway Bay Golf Club - on site - Tel (353) 091 - 790 500
The Old Schoolhouse - Oranmore 2 km
Tel (353) 091 - 796 898

Glasson

16	7	7

Adapting a course to players of all abilities is something you would expect from a fine connoisseur of amateur and professional golf such as Christy O'Connor Jr. Given a remarkable site, long a favourite haunt of hikers and cyclists, he clearly rose to the occasion, and the views over Lough Ree are as magnificent as his deployment of the terrain on several holes. Other lakes add to both the course's scenic beauty and difficulty. And if we add to this a lot of very careful design on and around the greens, intelligently placed bunkers and the general balance of the layout, you will understand that this is one of the finest recent additions to the collection of Irish courses and one that will leave nobody indifferent. A little hilly but not excessively so, Glasson calls for a very precise game strategy and a cool head at all times. One further detail: you can reach the 18th tee by boat from Athlone.

On pouvait attendre d'un fin connaisseur du golf amateur et professionnel comme Christy O'Connor Jr. qu'il adapte un parcours de manière très sûre à tous les niveaux de jeu. Disposant d'un site remarquable, depuis longtemps connu des amateurs de randonnées cyclistes et pédestres, il en a visiblement été exalté, et les vues sur le Lough Ree sont aussi magnifiques que sa mise en jeu sur quelques trous. D'autres lacs contribuent aussi bien à la beauté scénique du parcours qu'à sa difficulté. Et si l'on ajoute le travail très soigné des greens, le placement intelligent des bunkers et l'équilibre général du tracé, on aura compris qu'il s'agit d'une des meilleures additions récentes à la collection des golfs irlandais, et qui ne peut laisser indifférent. Un peu accidenté, mais sans excès, Glasson demande une stratégie de jeu très précise et de garder la tête froide. Pour l'anecdote, on peut parvenir en bateau au départ du 18, depuis Athlone.

Glasson Golf Club — 1993

Glasson
IRL - ATHLONE, Co West Meath

Office	Secrétariat	(353) 09064 - 85 120
Pro shop	Pro-shop	(353) 09064 - 85 120
Fax	Fax	(353) 09064 - 85 444
Web	www.glassongolf.ie	
Situation	Situation	Athlone (pop. 7 691), 9 km
Annual closure	Fermeture annuelle	no
Weekly closure	Fermeture hebdomadaire	no

Fees main season Tarifs haute saison — 18 holes

	Week days / Semaine	We/Bank holidays / We/Férié
Individual Individuel	€ 60	€ 65
Couple Couple	€ 120	€ 130

We: Friday and Sunday / Saturday: € 75

Caddie Caddie on request **Electric Trolley** Chariot électrique yes

Buggy Voiturette yes **Clubs** Clubs yes

Credit cards Cartes de crédit
VISA - MasterCard

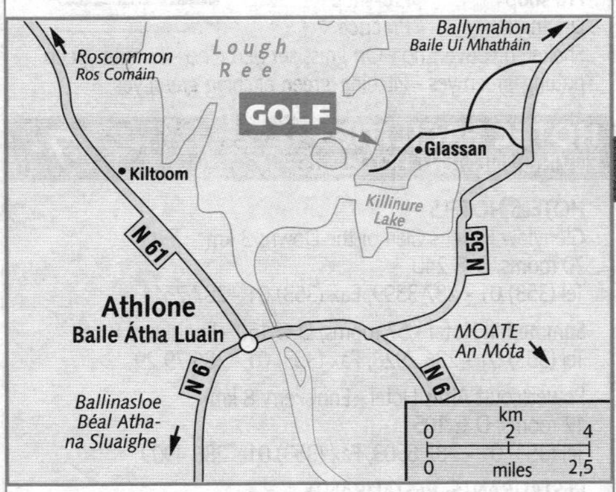

Access Accès : 10 km N.E. of Athlone on N55. Cavan road
Map 3 on page 813 Carte 3 Page 813

GOLF COURSE — PARCOURS — 16/20

Site	Site	
Maintenance	Entretien	
Architect	Architecte	Christy O'Connor Jr.
Type	Type	parkland
Relief	Relief	
Water in play	Eau en jeu	
Exp. to wind	Exposé au vent	
Trees in play	Arbres en jeu	

Scorecard Carte de score	Chp. Chp.	Mens Mess.	Ladies Da.
Length Long.	6510	6083	5100
Par	72	72	73
Slope system	—	—	—

Advised golfing ability Niveau de jeu recommandé — 0 12 24 36

Hcp required Handicap exigé — no

CLUB HOUSE & AMENITIES — CLUB HOUSE ET ANNEXES — 7/10

Pro shop Pro-shop
Driving range Practice
Sheltered couvert no - On grass sur herbe yes (+ 3 holes) - Putting-green putting-green yes (2) - Pitching-green pitching green yes

HOTEL FACILITIES — ENVIRONNEMENT HOTELIER — 7/10

HOTELS HÔTELS
Glasson Golf Hotel - on site
65 rooms, D from € 150
Tel (353) 09064 - 85 120, Fax (353) 09064 - 85 444

Hodson Bay Hotel - 131 rooms, D € 190 - Athlone 12 km
Tel (353) 09064 - 42 000, Fax (353) 09064 - 80 520

Shelmalier House - 7 rooms, D € 64 - Athlone 9 km
Tel (353) 09064 - 72 245, Fax (353) 09064 - 73 190

RESTAURANTS RESTAURANTS
Wineport - Glassan 3 km - Tel (353) 09064 - 85 466
Glasson Village - Glassan/Athlone 2 km
Tel (353) 09064 - 85 001

Glen of the Downs

13	6	7

This is only a recent addition to the generous variety of courses in County Wicklow, but its mature look already makes it appear much older. Laid out about 200 ft above sea level, it provides some splendid views over the Irish Sea and surrounding hills. The slopes are a feature of the course, which nonetheless is still definitely walkable. Architect Peter McEvoy, a remarkable golfer himself, has very carefully used the natural topology and the trees and ponds to produce a pretty layout. Likewise, the greens are sometimes elevated; if not, they are well guarded by bunkers. Straightforwardness is a valuable asset here on a course where golfing psychology is important: the hazards are often less dangerous than they seem. Although we could not rank Glen of the Downs in the top pack of courses in Ireland, it is still very pleasant and even more so with a new club-house.

Dans le County Wicklow, c'est une récente addition à un ensemble de parcours déjà fort important, mais son état est déjà celui d'un parcours bien plus ancien. Situé à une soixantaine de mètres au-dessus du niveau de la mer, il offre des vues splendides à la fois sur la Mer d'Irlande et sur les collines de la région. Ces reliefs sont d'ailleurs une marque du parcours, bien qu'il soit très jouable à pied. L'architecte (et très grand joueur) Peter McEvoy a très habilement utilisé ces accidents naturels, ainsi que les arbres et les petites mares pour poser joliment son tracé. De même, les greens sont parfois surélevés et bien défendus par des bunkers quand ils ne le sont pas. La franchise est de mise dans ce parcours, avec un aspect psychologique important : les obstacles sont souvent moins dangereux qu'on ne le croit. Bien qu'on ne puisse classer Glen of the Downs dans le peloton de tête des parcours d'Irlande, il n'en reste pas moins très agréable, avec un vaste club-house.

Glen of the Downs Golf Club — 1997

IRL - DELGANY, Co Wicklow

Office	Secrétariat	(353) 01 - 287 6240
Pro shop	Pro-shop	(353) 01 - 287 6240
Fax	Fax	(353) 01 - 287 0063
Web	www.glenofthedowns.com	
Situation	Situation	Dublin, 30 km
Annual closure	Fermeture annuelle	no
Weekly closure	Fermeture hebdomadaire	no

Fees main season Tarifs haute saison — 18 holes

	Week days Semaine	We/Bank holidays We/Férié
Individual Individuel	€ 65	€ 80
Couple Couple	€ 130	€ 160

Week days: € 50 before 10:00

Caddie Caddie no — **Electric Trolley** Chariot électrique no

Buggy Voiturette yes — **Clubs** Clubs yes

Credit cards Cartes de crédit

VISA - MasterCard - AMEX - DC

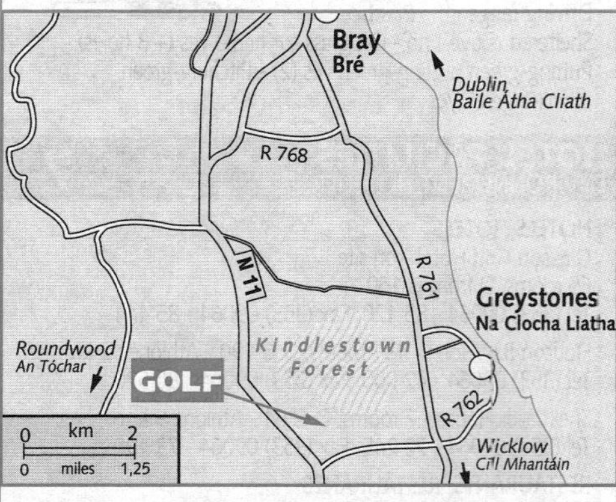

Access Accès : Dublin, N11 → Wicklow/Wexford. Kilmacanogue → Greystones. → Glen of the Downs.

Map 1 on page 809 Carte 1 Page 809

GOLF COURSE — PARCOURS — 13/20

Site	Site	
Maintenance	Entretien	
Architect	Architecte	Peter McEvoy
Type	Type	inland
Relief	Relief	
Water in play	Eau en jeu	
Exp. to wind	Exposé au vent	
Trees in play	Arbres en jeu	

Scorecard Carte de score	Chp. Chp.	Mens Mess.	Ladies Da.
Length Long.	5830	5410	4780
Par	71	71	71
Slope system	—	—	—

Advised golfing ability / Niveau de jeu recommandé: 0 12 24 36

Hcp required Handicap exigé: no

CLUB HOUSE & AMENITIES — CLUB HOUSE ET ANNEXES — 6/10

Pro shop	Pro-shop
Driving range	Practice

Sheltered couvert no - On grass sur herbe no - Putting-green putting-green yes - Pitching-green pitching green yes

HOTEL FACILITIES — ENVIRONNEMENT HOTELIER — 7/10

HOTELS HÔTELS

Glenview Hotel - Glen of the Downs 3 km
70 rooms, D € 240
Tel (353) 01 - 287 3399, Fax (353) 01 - 287 7511

Summerhill Hotel - 57 rooms, D € 150 - Enniskerry 8 km
Tel (353) 01 - 286 7928, Fax (353) 01 - 286 79 29

Powerscourt Arms Hotel - Enniskerry 8 km
12 rooms, D € 105
Tel (353) 01 - 282 8903, Fax (353) 01 - 286 4909

RESTAURANTS RESTAURANTS

Summerhill - Enniskerry 8 km - Tel (353) 01 - 286 7928
Tinakilly House - Rathnew 15 km - Tel (353) 0404 - 69 274
Cooper's - Greystones 5 km - Tel (353) 01 - 287 3914

Grange

16	5	8

The great James Braid created fewer courses in Ireland than in Scotland, but Grange is one of his most admirable designs. No wonder then that the club has a large number of members to make week-end green-fees a difficult proposition. A club-house was opened in 2003 to replace the wooden club-house built in the 1940s, but the design of the course, with its 6 par-threes, remains as close as possible to the original. You will appreciate the very subtle bunkering and the strategic use of water on the 18th. By and large, the course lo s to be tight and tough all the way, in fact only the first 6 holes really fit this category. But the impression of narrowness never leaves you: James Braid knew a thing a two about the psychology of your average golfer. But there again, the trees have doubtless grown a lot over the past one hundred years or so! Some of the greens are elevated (depending on terrain topology), all are well guarded and only a handful can really be reached by rolling the ball in. All in all, a classic course of which you will never grow weary.

Le grand James Braid n'a pas créé autant de parcours en Irlande qu'en Ecosse mais Grange figure parmi ses excellentes créations, avec un grand nombre de membres : il est très difficile de le jouer en week-end. On y cultive la tradition, et si le club-house en bois construit dans les années 40 a été remplacé par un nouveau en 2003, le dessin du parcours est resté aussi original que possible. On appréciera en particulier le bunkering très subtil, l'utilisation stratégique du cours d'eau au 18. En règle générale, le parcours paraît étroit et difficile, bien que seuls les six premiers trous le soient vraiment, mais l'impression d'étroitesse demeure : James Braid connaissait bien la psychologie de l'amateur. D'un autre côté, les arbres ont sans doute aussi beaucoup poussé depuis près de cent ans ! Côté greens, quelques-uns sont en élévation (suivant le terrain), la plupart sont bien défendus, seule une poignée étant vraiment accessibles en roulant. En résumé, un classique dont il est difficile de se lasser.

Grange Golf Club — 1910

IRL - RATHFARNHAM, DUBLIN 16

Office	Secrétariat	(353) 01 - 493 2889
Pro shop	Pro-shop	(353) 01 - 493 2299
Fax	Fax	(353) 01 - 493 2832
Web	www.grangegc.com	
Situation	Situation	Dublin, 10 km
Annual closure	Fermeture annuelle	no
Weekly closure	Fermeture hebdomadaire	no

Fees main season Tarifs haute saison	18 holes	
	Week days / Semaine	We/Bank holidays / We/Férié
Individual Individuel	€ 75	*
Couple Couple	€ 150	*

* We: members only

Caddie Caddie yes — **Electric Trolley** Chariot électrique no

Buggy Voiturette yes — **Clubs** Clubs yes

Credit cards Cartes de crédit
VISA - MasterCard - AMEX - DC

Access Accès : • Dublin, New Street, at Harold Cross, take left on Harold Cross Road. Left on Grange Road. • Or Western Parkway to the end, straight on Knocklyon, Scholars, Taylor Lane, Grange Road. **Map 1 on page 809** Carte 1 Page 809

GOLF COURSE — PARCOURS — 16/20

Site	Site	
Maintenance	Entretien	
Architect	Architecte	James Braid
Type	Type	parkland
Relief	Relief	
Water in play	Eau en jeu	
Exp. to wind	Exposé au vent	
Trees in play	Arbres en jeu	

Scorecard / Carte de score	Chp. / Chp.	Mens / Mess.	Ladies / Da.
Length Long.	5517	5420	5154
Par	68	68	73
Slope system	—	—	—

Advised golfing ability / Niveau de jeu recommandé: 0 12 24 36

Hcp required / Handicap exigé: certificate

CLUB HOUSE & AMENITIES — CLUB HOUSE ET ANNEXES — 5/10

Pro shop Pro-shop
Driving range Practice

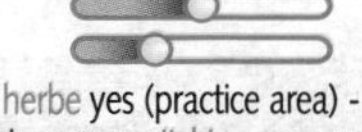

Sheltered couvert no - On grass sur herbe yes (practice area) - Putting-green putting-green yes - Pitching-green pitching green yes

HOTEL FACILITIES — ENVIRONNEMENT HOTELIER — 8/10

HOTELS HÔTELS

Mont Clare - 74 rooms, D € 205 - Dublin 5 km
Tel (353) 01 - 607 3800, Fax (353) 01 - 607 3800

Uppercross House - 50 rooms, D € 130 - Rathmines 12 km
Tel (353) 01 - 497 5486, Fax (353) 01 - 497 5361

Red Cow Morans Hotel - Clondalkin 7 km
123 rooms, D from € 190
Tel (353) 01 - 459 3650, Fax (353) 01 - 459 1588

RESTAURANTS RESTAURANTS

Johnnie Foxes - Glencullen 15 km - Tel (353) 01 - 295 5647

Killakee Restaurant - Rathfarnham 8 km
Tel (353) 01 - 493 8849

Yellow House - Rathfarnham 3 km - Tel (353) 01 - 493 8849

Headfort *New Course*

15 | 6 | 6

The nearby Kells monastery was where the enlightened "Book of Kells" manuscript was written, a famous document exhibited in Dublin. Although slightly less colourful, the two Headfort courses still give substantial food for thought and make for some excellent golfing. The "Old Course" was well known, but its traditional character never really made this a course to top your list. The course's intrinsic qualities have been put into perspective by the opening of a second, more original layout, designed by Christy O'Connor Jr. He has created a daring combination of British tradition and more American audacity with water hazards on twelve holes and the bringing into play of the Blackwater river. But being a man well schooled in golf at all levels, O'Connor has laid out neatly profiled bunkers designed not so much to over-penalise the average hacker, more to challenge the better golfer. The course is very long, with abundant trees, thus adding extra appeal to the site. Fifty kilometres of Dublin, this is a pretty destination with two very contrasting layouts.

C'est au monastère tout proche de Kells que fut élaboré le célèbre manuscrit enluminé "Book of Kells" exposé à Dublin. Moins colorés, les parcours d'Headfort n'en élèvent pas moins l'esprit par leur style. Le "Old Course," était bien connu, mais son côté traditionnel ne rendait pas vraiment urgent un long détour. Il voit ses qualités propres mises en valeur par un second 18 trous, d'architecture plus originale. On retrouvera le style de Christy O'Connor Jr. mélangeant avec goût la tradition britannique avec une audace plus américaine, avec la présence de l'eau sur une douzaine de trous, en particulier par la mise en valeur de la rivière Blackwater. Mais avec sa grande connaissance du jeu, O'Connor a disposé des bunkers bien profilés avec le souci de ne pas trop pénaliser les joueurs moyens, tout en opposant des défis aux meilleurs. Très long, ce parcours est bien arboré, ce qui ajoute à l'intérêt du lieu. A 50 kilomètres de Dublin, une jolie destination avec 36 trous très contrastés.

Headfort Golf Club — 2001

IRL - KELLS, Co Meath

Office	Secrétariat	(353) 046 - 924 0146
Pro shop	Pro-shop	(353) 046 - 924 0639
Fax	Fax	(353) 046 - 924 9282
Web	www.headfortgolfclub.ie	
Situation	Situation	Navan (pop. 3 447), 16 km
Annual closure	Fermeture annuelle	no
Weekly closure	Fermeture hebdomadaire	

Fees main season Tarifs haute saison	18 holes	
	Week days Semaine	We/Bank holidays We/Férié
Individual Individuel	€ 60	€ 65
Couple Couple	€ 120	€ 130

Caddie Caddie no — **Electric Trolley** Chariot électrique no

Buggy Voiturette yes — **Clubs** Clubs yes

Credit cards Cartes de crédit
VISA - MasterCard - AMEX

Access Accès : Dublin, N3 → Navan → Kells (Ceannánas)
Map 3 on page 813 Carte 3 Page 813

GOLF COURSE — PARCOURS — 15/20

Site	Site	
Maintenance	Entretien	
Architect	Architecte	Christy O'Connor Jr.
Type	Type	parkland, inland
Relief	Relief	
Water in play	Eau en jeu	
Exp. to wind	Exposé au vent	
Trees in play	Arbres en jeu	

Scorecard Carte de score	Chp. Chp.	Mens Mess.	Ladies Da.
Length Long.	6487	6117	5010
Par	72	72	72
Slope system	—	—	—

Advised golfing ability Niveau de jeu recommandé — 0 12 24 36

Hcp required Handicap exigé — no

CLUB HOUSE & AMENITIES — CLUB HOUSE ET ANNEXES — 6/10

Pro shop Pro-shop
Driving range Practice
Sheltered couvert no - **On grass** sur herbe yes (own balls) - **Putting-green** putting-green yes - **Pitching-green** pitching green yes

HOTEL FACILITIES — ENVIRONNEMENT HOTELIER — 6/10

HOTELS HÔTELS

Headfort Arms Hotel - 54 rooms, D € 150 - Kells 1,5 km
Tel (353) 046 - 924 0063, Fax (353) 046 - 924 0587

Ardboyne Hotel - 29 rooms, D € 135 - Navan 18 km
Tel (353) 046 - 902 3119, Fax (353) 046 - 902 2355

Newgrange Hotel - 62 rooms, D € 150 - Navan 18 km
Tel (353) 046 - 907 4100, Fax (353) 046 - 907 3977

Ma Dwyers Guest House - 9 rooms, D € 80 - Navan 18 km
Tel (353) 046 - 907 7992, Fax (353) 046 - 907 7995

RESTAURANTS RESTAURANTS

The Forge - Carnaross 15 km - Tel (353)046 - 924 5003
Headfort Arms Hotel - Kells 1,5 km - Tel (353) 046 - 924 0063

Heritage (The)

18	9	8

The name Seve Ballesteros has certainly added a definite cachet to this layout but his collaboration with Jeff Howes has also delivered the goods. This Canadian architect worked with Jack Nicklaus on the Mount Juliet course. The terrain here was almost made for golf and the outward stretch already looked parkland even before work got underway. Although there was much moving of earth, the course looks more natural than artificial, the latter tendency being so often the Achille's heel of modern layouts. Overall, this rather American-style course is a worthy host to top tournaments, given its already remarkable condition, the variety of holes and the shots you need to play. Sure, you need to be able to play a bit to appreciate the subtler sides to the course, but the average golfer will have fun too (playing from the front) despite some often intimidating second shots into the green with water to contend with on about ten holes. A very honest and fair challenge, carefully laid out in every respect with luxury hotel facilities to boot.

Certes, le nom de Ballesteros a apporté un cachet certain à cette collaboration fructueuse avec Jeff Howes. Cet architecte canadien avait travaillé avec Jack Nicklaus pour le parcours de Mount Juliet. Le terrain était ici favorable, le site de l'aller donnant déjà une allure de "parkland" avant même le début des travaux. Si ceux-ci ont été importants, le naturel l'emporte sur l'artificiel, si souvent le talon d'Achille des golfs modernes. Globalement, ce parcours – plutôt "américain" de style – est digne de recevoir de grandes compétitions, pour son état déjà remarquable, mais aussi par la diversité des trous, et des coups à jouer. Certes, il faut un bon niveau de golf pour apprécier les subtilités du dessin, mais l'amateur moyen y trouvera aussi son plaisir (des départs avancés), bien que certaines attaques de green soient très intimidantes, avec l'eau en jeu sur une dizaine de trous. Un challenge d'une grande franchise, soigné dans tous ses aspects, avec des équipements hôteliers de luxe.

The Heritage 2003
IRL - KILLENARD, Co Laois

Office Secrétariat (353) 0502 - 45 994
Pro shop Pro-shop (353) 0502 - 45 994
Fax Fax (353) 0502 - 42 392
Web www.theheritage.com
Situation Situation Kildare, 15 km
Dublin (pop. 481 854), 65 km
Annual closure Fermeture annuelle no
Weekly closure Fermeture hebdomadaire no

Fees main season Tarifs haute saison	Week days Semaine	We/Bank holidays We/Férié
		18 holes
Individual Individuel	€ 95	€ 110
Couple Couple	€ 190	€ 220

Reduced fees for hotel guests

Caddie Caddie yes **Electric Trolley** Chariot électrique yes
Buggy Voiturette yes **Clubs** Clubs yes
Credit cards Cartes de crédit
VISA - MasterCard - AMEX

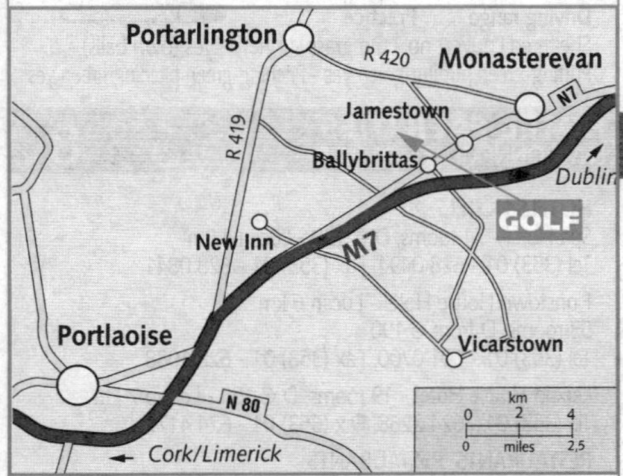

Access Accès : Dublin, M7/N7 → Cork. Exit Monasterevan. Pass through village and follow signs to the golf
Map 3 on page 813 Carte 3 Page 813

GOLF COURSE — PARCOURS 18/20

Site Site
Maintenance Entretien
Architect Architecte Seve Ballesteros, Jeff Howes
Type Type heatland, parkland
Relief Relief
Water in play Eau en jeu
Exp. to wind Exposé au vent
Trees in play Arbres en jeu

Scorecard Carte de score	Chp. Chp.	Mens Mess.	Ladies Da.
Length Long.	6588	6201	5173
Par	72	72	72
Slope system	—	—	—

Advised golfing ability Niveau de jeu recommandé 0 12 24 36
Hcp required Handicap exigé 36

CLUB HOUSE & AMENITIES — CLUB HOUSE ET ANNEXES 9/10

Pro shop Pro-shop
Driving range Practice
Sheltered couvert 10 bay floodlit - On grass sur herbe yes - Putting-green putting-green yes - Pitching-green pitching green yes

HOTEL FACILITIES — ENVIRONNEMENT HOTELIER 8/10

HOTELS HÔTELS
The Heritage Hotel - 98 rooms, D from € 275 - on site
Tel (353) 0502 - 45 500, Fax (353) 0502 - 42 393

Ivyleigh House - 6 rooms, D € 115 - Portlaoise 7 km
Tel (353) 0502 - 22 081, Fax (353) 0502 - 63 343

Killashee House - 142 rooms, D € 155 - Naas 42 km
Tel (353) 045 - 879 227, Fax (353) 045 - 879 266

The Heritage Portlaoise - Portlaoise 7 km
110 rooms, D from € 155
Tel (353) 0502 - 78 588, Fax (353) 0502 - 78 577

RESTAURANTS RESTAURANTS
The Thatch - on site - Tel (353) 0502 - 45 500
Arlington Room - on site - Tel (353) 0502 - 45 500

Hermitage

15 | 6 | 8

This course has led a quiet existence since staging the European Youths Championship in 1984 but it continues to figure regularly amongst the better Irish golf courses. There is nothing of the links about it, sure, but its park-landscape configuration (the trees are superb) on the banks of the Liffey, the moderately hilly relief (two or three steep climbs) and the closeness to Dublin make this a very interesting stop-off. It is not very long (especially from the normal tees) but it does require a lot of precision play and probably every club in your bag. A few blind shots and greens add a little uncertainty to it all, and the 10th (a par 3 towards the River Liffey) is an exciting prospect with the green way down below you. You shouldn't underestimate Hermitage which is capable of baring its teeth to anyone who is not permanently on his or her toes. This is a very fine example of an inland course and has hosted a number of top tournaments. It may not always stand up to the best player, but it has lost none of its charm.

Ce golf vit paisiblement depuis le début du siècle, et continue à figurer régulièrement parmi les bons parcours d'Irlande. Certes, il n'a rien d'un links, mais sa configuration de grand parc (les arbres sont superbes) en bordure de la Liffey, son relief modéré (deux ou trois fortes montées) et sa proximité de Dublin en font une étape fort intéressante. Il n'est pas très long (surtout des départs normaux), mais il demande pas mal de précision, et l'utilisation probable de tous les clubs du sac. Quelques coups et un green aveugles ajoutent un peu d'incertitude, et le 10 (un par 3 le long de la Liffey) amène quelque émotion, avec son green très en contrebas du départ. On ne doit pas sous-estimer Hermitage, il est capable de montrer les dents à ceux qui négligeraient de conserver en permanence leur concentration. Ce très bel exemple de parcours "inland" a reçu de grandes compétitions, il conserve son charme, sinon sa résistance aux meilleurs joueurs.

Hermitage Golf Club — 1902

Ballydowd
IRL - LUCAN, Co Dublin

Office Secrétariat (353) 01 - 626 8491
Pro shop Pro-shop (353) 01 - 626 8072
Fax Fax (353) 01 - 623 8881
Web www.hermitagegolf.ie
Situation Situation Dublin, 12 km
Maynooth (pop. 6 027), 4 km

Annual closure Fermeture annuelle — no
Weekly closure Fermeture hebdomadaire — no

Fees main season Tarifs haute saison	18 holes	
	Week days Semaine	**We/Bank holidays** We/Férié
Individual Individuel	€ 80	€ 85
Couple Couple	€ 160	€ 170

€ 45 before 9:00

Caddie Caddie no — **Electric Trolley** Chariot électrique yes
Buggy Voiturette yes — **Clubs** Clubs yes
Credit cards Cartes de crédit
VISA - MasterCard

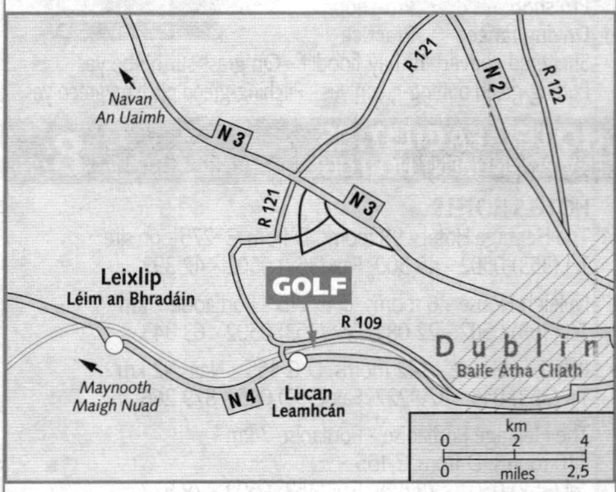

Access Accès : Dublin, N4 West
Map 1 on page 809 Carte 1 Page 809

GOLF COURSE — PARCOURS — 15/20

Site Site
Maintenance Entretien
Architect Architecte — M. McKenna
Type Type — parkland
Relief Relief
Water in play Eau en jeu
Exp. to wind Exposé au vent
Trees in play Arbres en jeu

Scorecard Carte de score	Chp. Chp.	Mens Mess.	Ladies Da.
Length Long.	6010	5800	5288
Par	71	70	73
Slope system	—	—	—

Advised golfing ability Niveau de jeu recommandé — 0 12 24 36
Hcp required Handicap exigé — 24 Men, 36 Ladies

CLUB HOUSE & AMENITIES — CLUB HOUSE ET ANNEXES — 6/10

Pro shop Pro-shop
Driving range Practice
Sheltered couvert no - On grass sur herbe yes (own balls) - Putting-green putting-green yes - Pitching-green pitching green yes

HOTEL FACILITIES — ENVIRONNEMENT HOTELIER — 8/10

HOTELS HÔTELS
Spa Hotel - 71 rooms, D € 120 - Lucan 4 km
Tel (353) 01 - 628 0494, Fax (353) 01 - 628 0841

Finnstown House Hotel - Lucan 6 km
53 rooms, D from € 190
Tel (353) 01 - 601 0700, Fax (353) 01 - 628 1088

Leixlip House Hotel - 19 rooms, D € 150 - Leixlip 7 km
Tel (353) 01 - 624 2268, Fax (353) 01 - 624 4177

RESTAURANTS RESTAURANTS
Finnstown - Lucan 6 km - Tel (353) 01 - 601 0700
Ryans - Dublin 6 km - Tel (353) 01 - 671 9352
Patrick Guilbaud - Dublin 12 km - Tel (353) 01 - 676 4192

K Club North Course

17	8	8

This ambitious development includes Straffan House which has been converted into a top, luxury hotel while the North Course will be the venue for the 2006 Ryder Cup. The brainchild of Dr Michael Smurfit, chairman of the Jefferson Smurfit Group, the venue has been expanded to 36 holes at a cost of 12 million Euros, through the addition of the South Course which was officially opened on July 1st 2003. Both layouts were designed by the Arnold Palmer company, which would explain why the North Course has resonances of Bay Hill in Florida, in length and difficulty. Only the most accomplished golfers can hope to cope without feeling too disillusioned about their game. Even from the forward tees, this is an uncompromising challenge, so don't waste time counting your strokes, or even your balls if you start flirting too boldly with the water, especially over the closing holes. What with the closeness of the River Liffey, we would suggest you play here in summer, despite the excellent drainage. After your game, be happy: a beer is cheaper than a green-fee...

Cet ambitieux complexe comprenait la transformation de la Straffan House en hôtel de grand luxe, puis ce parcours qui recevra la Ryder Cup 2006. Porté par Michael Smurfit, président du Jefferson Smurfit Group, le site a été porté à 36 trous avec le parcours Sud, pour un coût de 12 millions d'Euros. Les deux parcours sont dûs à l'Arnold Palmer Company, ce qui explique pourquoi le "North" présente une exigence digne de Bay Hill en Floride, pour la longueur et la difficulté technique. Seuls les golfeurs accomplis pourront prétendre le négocier sans trop perdre d'illusions sur leur golf. Même des départs avancés, il reste un challenge sans concessions, on évitera donc de compter ses coups, et parfois même ses balles, si l'on flirte trop audacieusement avec l'eau, notamment dans les derniers trous. En dépit d'importants drainages, la proximité de la rivière Liffey incite à le jouer surtout en été. Ensuite, prenez une bière au bar, elle est un peu moins chère que le green-fee.

The K Club — 1991

IRL - STRAFFAN, Co Kildare

Office	Secrétariat	(353) 01 - 601 7300
Pro shop	Pro-shop	(353) 01 - 601 7321
Fax	Fax	(353) 01 - 601 7399
Web	www.kclub.ie	
Situation	Situation	Dublin, 34 km
Annual closure	Fermeture annuelle	no
Weekly closure	Fermeture hebdomadaire	no

Fees main season Tarifs haute saison — 18 holes

	Week days Semaine	We/Bank holidays We/Férié
Individual Individuel	€ 250	€ 250
Couple Couple	€ 500	€ 500

Hotel guests: € 115

Caddie Caddie on request **Electric Trolley** Chariot électrique yes

Buggy Voiturette yes **Clubs** Clubs yes

Credit cards Cartes de crédit
VISA - Eurocard - MasterCard - AMEX - DC

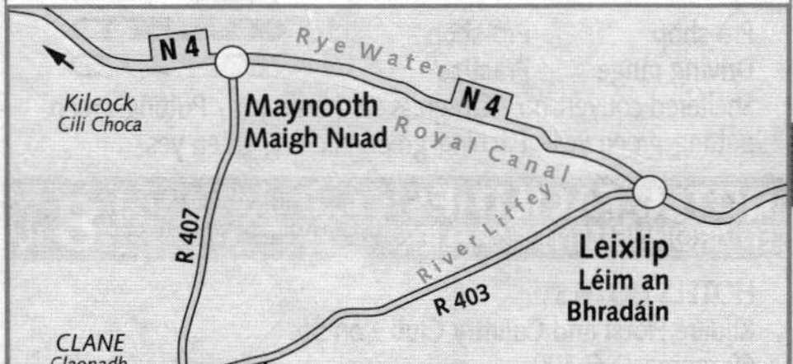

Kilcock
Cili Choca
N 4
Rye Water
N 4
Maynooth
Maigh Nuad
Royal Canal
River Liffey
Leixlip
Léim an Bhradáin
R 407
R 403
CLANE
Claonadh
Straffan
Grand Canal
GOLF
km 0 2 4
0 miles 2,5

Access Accès : N7 → Kill, → Straffan
Map 1 on page 809 Carte 1 Page 809

GOLF COURSE — PARCOURS — 17/20

Site	Site	
Maintenance	Entretien	
Architect	Architecte	Arnold Palmer
Type	Type	inland, parkland
Relief	Relief	
Water in play	Eau en jeu	
Exp. to wind	Exposé au vent	
Trees in play	Arbres en jeu	

Scorecard Carte de score	Chp. Chp.	Mens Mess.	Ladies Da.
Length Long.	6519	6063	4990
Par	72	72	73
Slope system	—	—	—

Advised golfing ability Niveau de jeu recommandé — 0 12 24 36

Hcp required Handicap exigé — 28 Men, 36 Ladies

CLUB HOUSE & AMENITIES — CLUB HOUSE ET ANNEXES — 8/10

Pro shop Pro-shop
Driving range Practice
Sheltered couvert no - On grass sur herbe yes - Putting-green putting-green yes - Pitching-green pitching green yes

HOTEL FACILITIES — ENVIRONNEMENT HOTELIER — 8/10

HOTELS HÔTELS

Kildare Hotel and Country Club - on site
69 rooms, D € 400
Tel (353) 01 - 601 7200, Fax (353) 01 - 601 7297

Leixlip House Hotel - Leixlip 10 km
19 rooms, D € 150
Tel (353) 01 - 624 2268, Fax (353) 01 - 624 4177

Beckett's - 10 rooms, D from € 130 - Leixlip 10 km
Tel (353) 01 - 624 7040, Fax (353) 01 - 624 7072

RESTAURANTS RESTAURANTS

The Legends - on site
Tel (353) 01 - 627 3111

The Burly Turk - on site - Tel (353) 01 - 627 3111

K Club *South Course*

17 | 8 | 8

Designed by Harrison Minchew from the Arnold Palmer company, it is in total contrast with the now famous and wonderfully tree-lined North Course. Even so, there is still water, water everywhere, particularly in a system of cascades and little waterfalls in a wall of fake rocks along the 7th hole. Sublime for some maybe, a tad kitsch for others. Here they have cultivated heather and the features of an inland course with a firm wish to bring the wind into play, all tempered by a certain degree of American immoderation. The fairways are manicured, the greens huge and contoured, the rough greedy and the bunkering spiteful. More than a million cubic metres of earth were shifted to bring to life what was peaceful pasture land. Money was no object here. Of course you have here a tough and exciting layout that many would have liked to see used for the match-play encounters in the 2006 Ryder Cup ahead of its neighbour. But there is no escaping the slight lack of elegant sobriety that is the hallmark of the great and authentic links courses. A sizeable achievement with green-fee to match.

Dessiné par Harrison Minchew du cabinet Arnold Palmer, le "South" contraste avec le North Course, fameux et magnifiquement arboré. Mais l'eau y est tout aussi présente… en particulier un jeu de cascades et de chutes d'eau dans une muraille de faux rochers le long du 7. Sublime ou complètement kitch ? Ici, la bruyère et les aspects d'un inland links ont été cultivés, avec la volonté de mettre le vent en jeu, mais avec un filtre américain. Les fairways sont modelés, les greens vastes et ondulés, le rough gourmand, et le bunkering méchant. Plus d'un million de mètres cube de terre ont dû être bougés pour animer ce qui n'était que pâturages. L'argent n'a pas été compté ici. Certes, voici un parcours difficile et excitant, et beaucoup auraient voulu le voir servir de cadre aux match-plays de la Ryder Cup 2006 plutôt que son voisin. On peut aussi trouver que manque ici la sobriété élégante des grands et vrais links. Un parcours aussi spécial que le montant des green-fees.

The K Club — 2003

IRL - STRAFFAN, Co Kildare

Office	Secrétariat	(353) 01 - 601 7300
Pro shop	Pro-shop	(353) 01 - 601 7321
Fax	Fax	(353) 01 - 601 7399
Web	www.kclub.ie	
Situation	Situation	Dublin, 34 km
Annual closure	Fermeture annuelle	no
Weekly closure	Fermeture hebdomadaire	no

Fees main season Tarifs haute saison — 18 holes

	Week days / Semaine	We/Bank holidays / We/Férié
Individual Individuel	€ 185	€ 185
Couple Couple	€ 370	€ 370

Hotel guests: € 115

Caddie Caddie on request **Electric Trolley** Chariot électrique yes

Buggy Voiturette yes **Clubs** Clubs yes

Credit cards Cartes de crédit

VISA - Eurocard - MasterCard - AMEX - DC

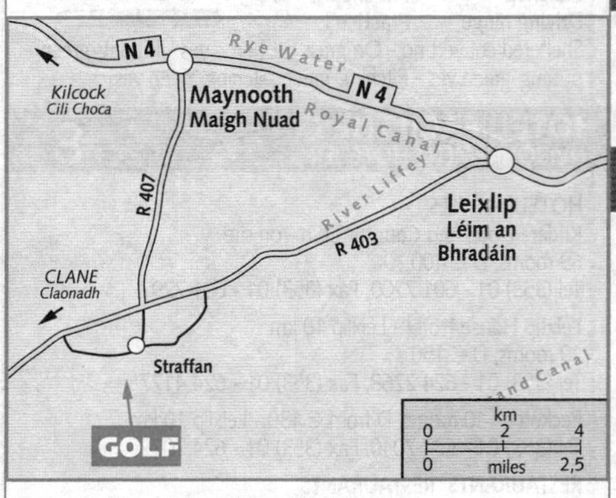

Access Accès : N7 → Kill, → Straffan

Map 1 on page 809 Carte 1 Page 809

GOLF COURSE — PARCOURS — 17/20

Site	Site	
Maintenance	Entretien	
Architect	Architecte	Arnold Palmer Design Company
Type	Type	links, heathland, open country
Relief	Relief	
Water in play	Eau en jeu	
Exp. to wind	Exposé au vent	
Trees in play	Arbres en jeu	

Scorecard Carte de score	Chp. Chp.	Mens Mess.	Ladies Da.
Length Long.	6550	6141	4965
Par	72	72	72
Slope system	—	—	—

Advised golfing ability Niveau de jeu recommandé — 0 12 24 36

Hcp required Handicap exigé — 24 Men, 36 Ladies

CLUB HOUSE & AMENITIES — CLUB HOUSE ET ANNEXES — 8/10

Pro shop Pro-shop

Driving range Practice

Sheltered couvert no - On grass sur herbe yes - Putting-green putting-green yes - Pitching-green pitching green yes

HOTEL FACILITIES — ENVIRONNEMENT HOTELIER — 8/10

HOTELS HÔTELS

Kildare Hotel and Country Club - on site
69 rooms, D € 400
Tel (353) 01 - 601 7200, Fax (353) 01 - 601 7297

Leixlip House Hotel - Leixlip 10 km
19 rooms, D € 150
Tel (353) 01 - 624 2268, Fax (353) 01 - 624 4177

Beckett's - Leixlip 10 km - 10 rooms, D from € 130
Tel (353) 01 - 624 7040, Fax (353) 01 - 624 7072

RESTAURANTS RESTAURANTS

The Legends - on site - Tel (353) 01 - 627 3111

The Burly Turk - on site - Tel (353) 01 - 627 3111

Kilkea Castle

15	6	6

At first sight, this is an impressive complex. Kilkea Castle is the oldest inhabited castle in Ireland and provides a splendid setting for this golf and hotel resort, where you can also try your hand at archery, clay-pigeon shooting and horse-riding, one of Ireland's national sports. Seen in comparison with the hotel's facilities, the green-fee is by no means prohibitive and in any case is in line with the very respectful quality of the course. The architects have used the natural terrain, streams and ponds to fine effect, especially in a strong finish. Existing trees are reasonably in play and new plantations should enhance the scenery and nature of hazards still further. They also tried to please everyone, so less experienced players always have the chance to stay away from trouble while others will face up to the challenge without too much trepidation. And while some US-style holes call for target shots, others welcome the good old bump 'n run as long as the clay soil is dry enough.

Au premier regard, l'ensemble est impressionnant. Kilkea Castle est le plus ancien château habité d'Irlande, il constitue un cadre splendide à cet ensemble golf et hôtel, où l'on peut également pratiquer le tir à l'arc, le tir au pigeon d'argile et l'équitation, un des sports nationaux de l'Irlande. En comparaison des équipements de l'hôtel, le green-fee n'est pas ici prohibitif, en tout cas par rapport à la très honorable qualité du parcours. Les architectes ont utilisé le terrain naturel, les cours d'eau et les mares avec beaucoup de sens de l'effet, en particulier dans le finale. Les arbres existants du domaine sont raisonnablement en jeu, et de nouvelles plantations devraient encore faire évoluer le décor et la nature des obstacles. On a aussi cherché ici à contenter tout le monde, tous les niveaux de jeu. Ainsi, les joueurs les moins aguerris ont toujours des possibilités de rester à l'écart des problèmes, les autres affronteront sans trop de peur les défis du lieu. De même, s'il faut parfois maîtriser les balles levées sur les trous "à l'américaine", d'autres trous permettent un jeu "bump' n' run", si le terrain argileux est du moins assez sec.

Kilkea Castle Golf Club — 1994

IRL - CASTLEDERMOT, Co. Kildare

Office	Secrétariat	(353) 0503 - 45 555
Pro shop	Pro-shop	(353) 0503 - 45 555
Fax	Fax	(353) 0503 - 45 505
Web	www.kilkeacastlehotelgolf.com	
Situation	Situation	Dublin, 65 km
Annual closure	Fermeture annuelle	no
Weekly closure	Fermeture hebdomadaire	no

Fees main season Tarifs haute saison	18 holes	
	Week days / Semaine	We/Bank holidays / We/Férié
Individual Individuel	€ 40	€ 45
Couple Couple	€ 80	€ 90

We: Friday → Sunday

Caddie Caddie on request **Electric Trolley** Chariot électrique no

Buggy Voiturette yes **Clubs** Clubs yes

Credit cards Cartes de crédit
VISA - Eurocard - MasterCard - AMEX

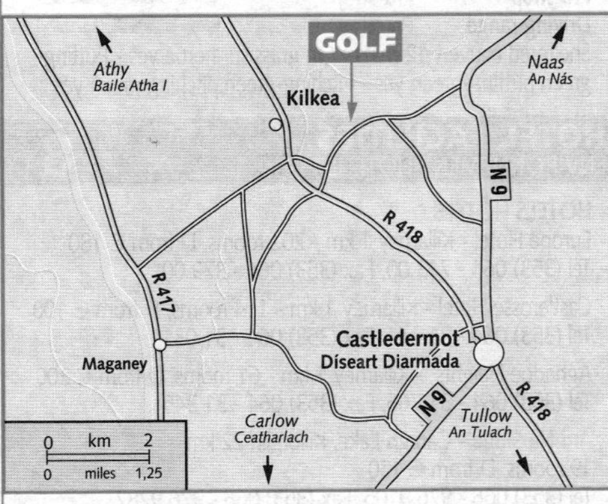

Access Accès : Dublin, N9 → Carlow. After Kilcullen, Ballymount, turn off at High Cross → Kilkea Castle.
Map 3 on page 813 Carte 3 Page 813

GOLF COURSE — PARCOURS 15/20

Site	Site	
Maintenance	Entretien	
Architect	Architecte	Andrew Gilbert, Jim Cassidy
Type	Type	parkland
Relief	Relief	
Water in play	Eau en jeu	
Exp. to wind	Exposé au vent	
Trees in play	Arbres en jeu	

Scorecard Carte de score	Chp. Chp.	Mens Mess.	Ladies Da.
Length Long.	6097	5891	5076
Par	70	70	72
Slope system	—	—	—

Advised golfing ability Niveau de jeu recommandé — 0 12 24 36

Hcp required Handicap exigé no

CLUB HOUSE & AMENITIES — CLUB HOUSE ET ANNEXES 6/10

Pro shop Pro-shop
Driving range Practice
Sheltered couvert no - On grass sur herbe yes (practice area) - Putting-green putting-green yes - Pitching-green pitching green yes

HOTEL FACILITIES — ENVIRONNEMENT HOTELIER 6/10

HOTELS HÔTELS

Kilkea Castle Hotel - on site
29 rooms, D € 215
Tel (353) 059 - 9145 156, Fax (353) 059 - 9145 187

Dolmen Hotel - Carlow 12 km
80 rooms, D from € 140
Tel (353) 059 - 914 2002, Fax (353) 059 - 914 2375

Seven Oaks Hotel - 55 rooms, D from € 120 - Carlow 12 km
Tel (353) 059 - 9131 308, Fax (353) 059 - 9132 155

RESTAURANTS RESTAURANTS

Kilkea Castle - Castledermot o - Tel (353) 059 - 9145 156
Tonlegee House - Athy 19 km - Tel (353) 059 - 863 1473
Rathsallagh House - Dunlavin 36 km - Tel (353) 045 - 403 112

Killarney *Lackabane*

14	7	8

Already boasting two excellent 18-hole courses, Killarney golf club opened this new Lackabane course in 2001, inaugurated by the Ladies European Tour. There is certainly water to contend with in the form of lakes and streams, but it is only really dangerous on fewer than half a dozen holes. In other words it was not designed for "normal" golfers, who in this superb region chop and change between this and "Mahony's Point" and "Killeen", at least when the latter will have re-opened its greens after renovation work (scheduled for Summer 2006). Here you will recognize the sober style of Donald Steel and his rather discreet shifting of earth. This pleasant course – intelligently laid out with very nicely designed greens (perhaps a little short of real venom) – doubtless lacks a little passion and real difficulty for the best golfers. Good serious golfing for players of all levels.

Déjà pourvu de deux 18 trous de bonne facture, le golf de Killarney a ouvert en 2001 ce nouveau parcours de Lackabane, inauguré par les joueuses du Ladies European Tour. Certes, l'eau y est en jeu sous forme de lacs et de cours d'eau, mais de manière dangereuse sur moins d'une demi-douzaine de trous. Autrement dit, il n'a pas été conçu pour les golfeurs "normaux", qui alterneront les plaisirs – dans cette superbe région – avec les parcours "Mahony's Point" et "Killeen", du moins quand celui-ci aura réouvert ses greens après rénovation (pour l'été 2006). On reconnaîtra ici le style sobre de Donald Steel, et ses mouvements de terrain assez doux. Intelligent dans son tracé, très convenable (peut-être un peu timide) dans le dessin des greens, ce parcours agréable manque sans doute un peu de passion et de vraies difficultés pour les meilleurs. Du bon travail sérieux, accessible à tous les niveaux.

Killarney Golf Club — 2001

O'Mahoney's Point
IRL - KILLARNEY, Co Kerry

Office	Secrétariat	(353) 064 - 31 034
Pro shop	Pro-shop	(353) 064 - 31 615
Fax	Fax	(353) 064 - 33 065
Web		www.killarney-golf.com
Situation	Situation	Killarney (pop. 8 809), 3 km
Annual closure	Fermeture annuelle	no
Weekly closure	Fermeture hebdomadaire	no

Fees main season Tarifs haute saison	18 holes	
	Week days Semaine	**We/Bank holidays** We/Férié
Individual Individuel	€ 90	€ 90
Couple Couple	€ 180	€ 180

Caddie Caddie yes — **Electric Trolley** Chariot électrique yes
Buggy Voiturette yes (Summer) **Clubs** Clubs yes
Credit cards Cartes de crédit
VISA - Eurocard - MasterCard - AMEX - DC

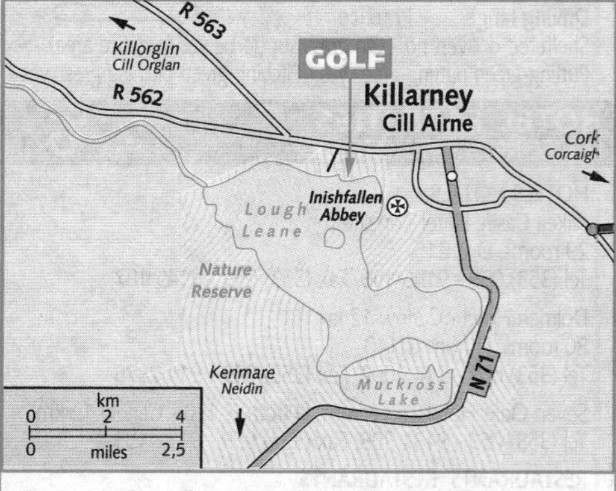

Access Accès : Killarney W, 3 km on R562 → Killorglin
Map 3 on page 812 Carte 3 Page 812

GOLF COURSE — PARCOURS — 14/20

Site	Site	
Maintenance	Entretien	
Architect	Architecte	Donald Steel
Type	Type	parkland
Relief	Relief	
Water in play	Eau en jeu	
Exp. to wind	Exposé au vent	
Trees in play	Arbres en jeu	

Scorecard Carte de score	**Chp.** Chp.	**Mens** Mess.	**Ladies** Da.
Length Long.	6410	6011	5117
Par	72	72	72
Slope system	—	—	—

Advised golfing ability Niveau de jeu recommandé: 0 12 24 36
Hcp required Handicap exigé: 36

CLUB HOUSE & AMENITIES — CLUB HOUSE ET ANNEXES — 7/10

Pro shop Pro-shop
Driving range Practice
Sheltered couvert 12 mats - On grass sur herbe yes - Putting-green putting-green yes - Pitching-green pitching green yes

HOTEL FACILITIES — ENVIRONNEMENT HOTELIER — 8/10

HOTELS HÔTELS
Europe Hotel - Killarney 1 km - 202 rooms, D from € 180
Tel (353) 064 - 713 00, Fax (353) 064 - 379 00

Castlerosse Hotel - Killarney 1 km - 114 rooms, D from € 100
Tel (353) 064 - 31 144, Fax (353) 064 - 31 031

Aghadoe Heights - Killarney 1 km - 61 rooms, D from € 200
Tel (353) 064 - 31 766, Fax (353) 064 - 31 345

Ard Na Sidhe - Caragh Lake, Killorglin 22 km
19 rooms, D from € 150
Tel (353) 066 - 976 9105, Fax (353) 066 - 976 9282

RESTAURANTS RESTAURANTS
Coopers - Killarney 4 km - Tel (353) 064 - 37 716
Chequers - Killarney 4 km - Tel (353) 064 - 35 333

Killarney *Mahony's Point*

15	7	8

A lively place to be at night, this charming town is a major tourist centre and an ideal holiday stop-off to explore the lakes in the National Park, the Kerry mountains... and the prestigious golf courses of south-west Ireland. The three 18-hole courses at Killarney are a part of these, and golfers often tend to show a slight sentimental preference for this one, especially the 3 closing holes, which include the 18th, a tough par 3 magnificently set alongside Lough Leane. Try and arrange to play here in the early evening to watch the sun set, when the surrounding forests blossom in the colours of autumn (play the newest, Lackabane layout in the morning). Though a rather short course, it requires a careful short game around very well-guarded greens and is famous for its par-three 18th, where the green juts into the lake. Generally, the beauty of the environment, the trees and the layout add to the pleasure of your day spent here, and the best players in your group will enjoy a good round without having to dig too deeply into their reserves.

Très animée le soir, cette charmante petite ville est un grand centre touristique, un lieu de séjour idéal pour explorer les lacs du National Park, les monts du Kerry... et les prestigieux parcours du Sud-Ouest. Les trois 18 trous de Killarney en font partie, et les joueurs ont souvent une petite préférence pour celui-ci, notamment pour les trois derniers trous, dont le magnifique 18, un par 3 difficile et magnifiquement situé le long du Lough Leane: il faut s'arranger pour le jouer au coucher du soleil, quand les forêts environnantes prennent leurs couleurs d'automne (jouer le nouveau Lackabane le matin), en terminant par le superbe 18, un par 3 le long du lac. Assez court, ce parcours est moins difficile à négocier qu'il n'y paraît à première vue, mais il réclame un petit jeu attentif, car les greens sont bien défendus. La beauté de l'environnement, des arbres et du dessin ajoute au plaisir de la journée, et les meilleurs joueurs du groupe auront plaisir à briller sans trop puiser dans leurs réserves.

Killarney Golf Club — 1891

O'Mahoney's Point
IRL - KILLARNEY, Co Kerry

Office	Secrétariat	(353) 064 - 31 034
Pro shop	Pro-shop	(353) 064 - 31 615
Fax	Fax	(353) 064 - 33 065
Web	www.killarney-golf.com	
Situation	Situation	Killarney (pop. 8 809), 3 km
Annual closure	Fermeture annuelle	no
Weekly closure	Fermeture hebdomadaire	no

Fees main season Tarifs haute saison — 18 holes

	Week days Semaine	We/Bank holidays We/Férié
Individual Individuel	€ 100	€ 100
Couple Couple	€ 200	€ 200

Caddie Caddie yes **Electric Trolley** Chariot électrique yes
Buggy Voiturette yes (Summer) **Clubs** Clubs yes
Credit cards Cartes de crédit
VISA - Eurocard - MasterCard - AMEX - DC

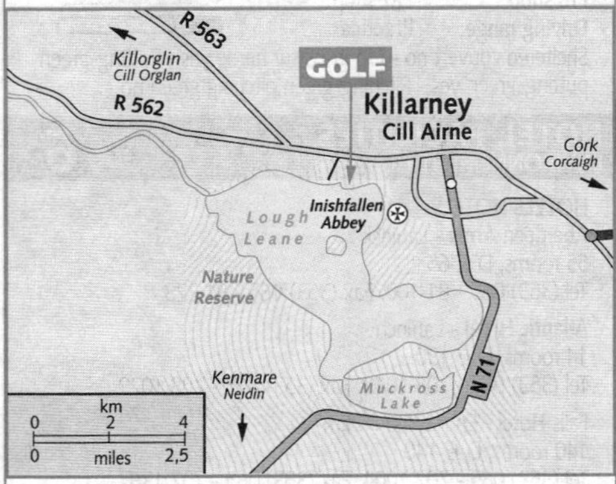

Killorglin Cill Orglan
R 563
R 562
GOLF
Killarney
Cill Airne
Cork Corcaigh
Inishfallen Abbey
Lough Leane
Nature Reserve
Kenmare Neidin
Muckross Lake
N 71
km 0 2 4
miles 0 2,5

Access Accès : Killarney W, 3 km on R562 → Killorglin
Map 3 on page 812 Carte 3 Page 812

GOLF COURSE — PARCOURS — 15/20

Site	Site	
Maintenance	Entretien	
Architect	Architecte	Sir Guy Campbell
Type	Type	parkland
Relief	Relief	
Water in play	Eau en jeu	
Exp. to wind	Exposé au vent	
Trees in play	Arbres en jeu	

Scorecard Carte de score	Chp. Chp.	Mens Mess.	Ladies Da.
Length Long.	6164	5826	4932
Par	72	72	74
Slope system	—	—	—

Advised golfing ability Niveau de jeu recommandé — 0 12 24 36
Hcp required Handicap exigé — 28 Men, 36 Ladies

CLUB HOUSE & AMENITIES — CLUB HOUSE ET ANNEXES — 7/10

Pro shop Pro-shop
Driving range Practice
Sheltered couvert 12 mats - On grass sur herbe yes - Putting-green putting-green yes - Pitching-green pitching green yes

HOTEL FACILITIES — ENVIRONNEMENT HOTELIER — 8/10

HOTELS HÔTELS

Europe Hotel - 202 rooms, D from € 180 - Killarney 1 km
Tel (353) 064 - 713 00, Fax (353) 064 - 379 00

Castlerosse Hotel - 114 rooms, D from € 100 - Killarney 1 km
Tel (353) 064 - 31 144, Fax (353) 064 - 31 031

Aghadoe Heights - 61 rooms, D from € 200 - Killarney 1 km
Tel (353) 064 - 31 766, Fax (353) 064 - 31 345

Ard Na Sidhe - Caragh Lake, Killorglin 22 km
19 rooms, D from € 150
Tel (353) 066 - 976 9105, Fax (353) 066 - 976 9282

RESTAURANTS RESTAURANTS

Dingle's - Killarney 4 km - Tel (353) 064 - 31 079
The Old Presbytery - Killarney 4 km - Tel (353) 064 - 30 555

Lahinch

17 | 6 | 6

Lahinch has long held pride of place in the collection of great courses in south-west Ireland. And its appeal has been enhanced by a major upgrading carried out by Martin Hawtree and completed in June 2003. As part of his re-design, Hawtree removed the old, short third which is replaced later in the round by a new, spectacular short eighth, which has been endorsed by Phil Mickelson. Meanwhile, the surrounding dunes invite visual comparison with Ballybunion. For instance, accurate approach play is rewarded, though players will also need the traditional bump and run shots in their armoury. Knowledge of the course is important in appreciating the effects of the wind and identifying where hazards are placed and the subtleties of sand-dune lies. Care is rewarded on this layout, where variety is the watchword and where flighters of the ball will have fun (beginners probably much less so). Look out for the extraordinary 4th and 5th holes (formerly the 5th and 6th), the first a par 5, where the second shot has to fly over a huge dune, the latter a par 3 with a blind green.

Parmi les grands parcours du sud-ouest, Lahinch tient depuis longtemps une belle place. Il a bénéficié d'un remodelage par Martin Hawtree, achevé en juin 2003. On notera en particulier le remplacement du 3 (par 3) par un nouveau 8 très spectaculaire. L'environnement de grandes dunes rapproche Lahinch de Ballybunion: si l'on parvient à rester droit, les approches des greens sont moins complexes, ceux-ci étant généralement accessibles avec des coups roulés. Il faut connaître ce parcours pour le négocier, apprécier les effets du vent, identifier la place des obstacles, composer avec les dunes, où la balle peut se trouver dans des situations "intéressantes". La prudence sera récompensée sur ce tracé spectaculaire et d'une très grande variété, où les virtuoses des effets de balle s'amuseront beaucoup. A signaler, les extraordinaires trous 4 et 5, un par 5 où le second coup doit survoler une énorme dune, et un par 3 avec un green aveugle. A connaître.

Lahinch Golf Club — 1892

IRL - LAHINCH, Co Clare

Office Secrétariat (353) 065 - 708 1003
Pro shop Pro-shop (353) 065 - 708 1003
Fax Fax (353) 065 - 708 1592
Web www.lahinchgolf.com
Situation Situation Lahinch (pop. 580), 0.5 km
Ennis (pop. 15 333), 32 km

Annual closure Fermeture annuelle — no
Weekly closure Fermeture hebdomadaire — no

Fees main season Tarifs haute saison	18 holes	
	Week days Semaine	**We/Bank holidays** We/Férié
Individual Individuel	€ 145	€ 145
Couple Couple	€ 290	€ 290

Caddie Caddie yes — **Electric Trolley** Chariot électrique no
Buggy Voiturette no — **Clubs** Clubs yes
Credit cards Cartes de crédit
VISA - Eurocard - MasterCard

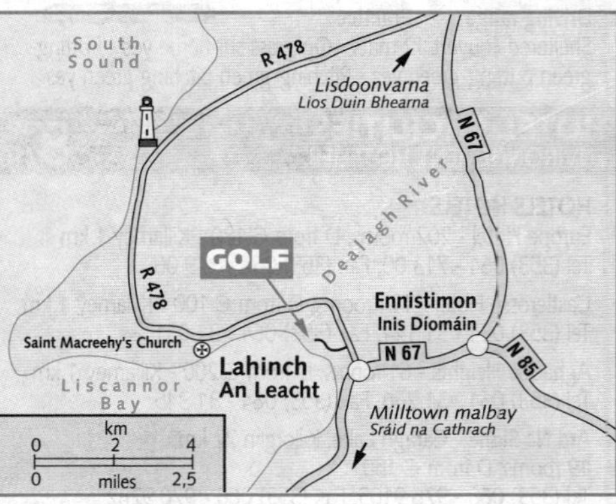

Access Accès : N18 Limerick → Ennis, N85 Ennis → Ennistymon, → Lahinch, 3 km
Map 3 on page 812 Carte 3 Page 812

GOLF COURSE — PARCOURS — 17/20

Site Site
Maintenance Entretien
Architect Architecte — Old Tom Morris, Alister Mackenzie
Type Type — links
Relief Relief
Water in play Eau en jeu
Exp. to wind Exposé au vent
Trees in play Arbres en jeu

Scorecard Carte de score	**Chp.** Chp.	**Mens** Mess.	**Ladies** Da.
Length Long.	6195	5905	4912
Par	71	72	74
Slope system	—	—	—

Advised golfing ability Niveau de jeu recommandé — 0 12 24 36
Hcp required Handicap exigé — 24 Men, 32 Ladies

CLUB HOUSE & AMENITIES — CLUB HOUSE ET ANNEXES — 6/10

Pro shop Pro-shop
Driving range Practice
Sheltered couvert no - On grass sur herbe yes - Putting-green putting-green yes - Pitching-green pitching green no

HOTEL FACILITIES — ENVIRONNEMENT HOTELIER — 6/10

HOTELS HÔTELS

Aberdeen Arms - Lahinch
55 rooms, D € 65
Tel (353) 065 - 81 100, Fax (353) 065 - 81 228

Atlantic Hotel - Lahinch
14 rooms, D € 130
Tel (353) 065 - 708 1049, Fax (353) 065 - 708 1029

Falls Hotel - Ennistymon 3 km
140 rooms, D € 140
Tel (353) 065 - 707 1004, Fax (353) 065 - 707 1367

RESTAURANTS RESTAURANTS

The Sea Farer - Lahinch - Tel (353) 065 - 708 1050
Dunes - Lahinch - Tel (353) 065 - 708 1100

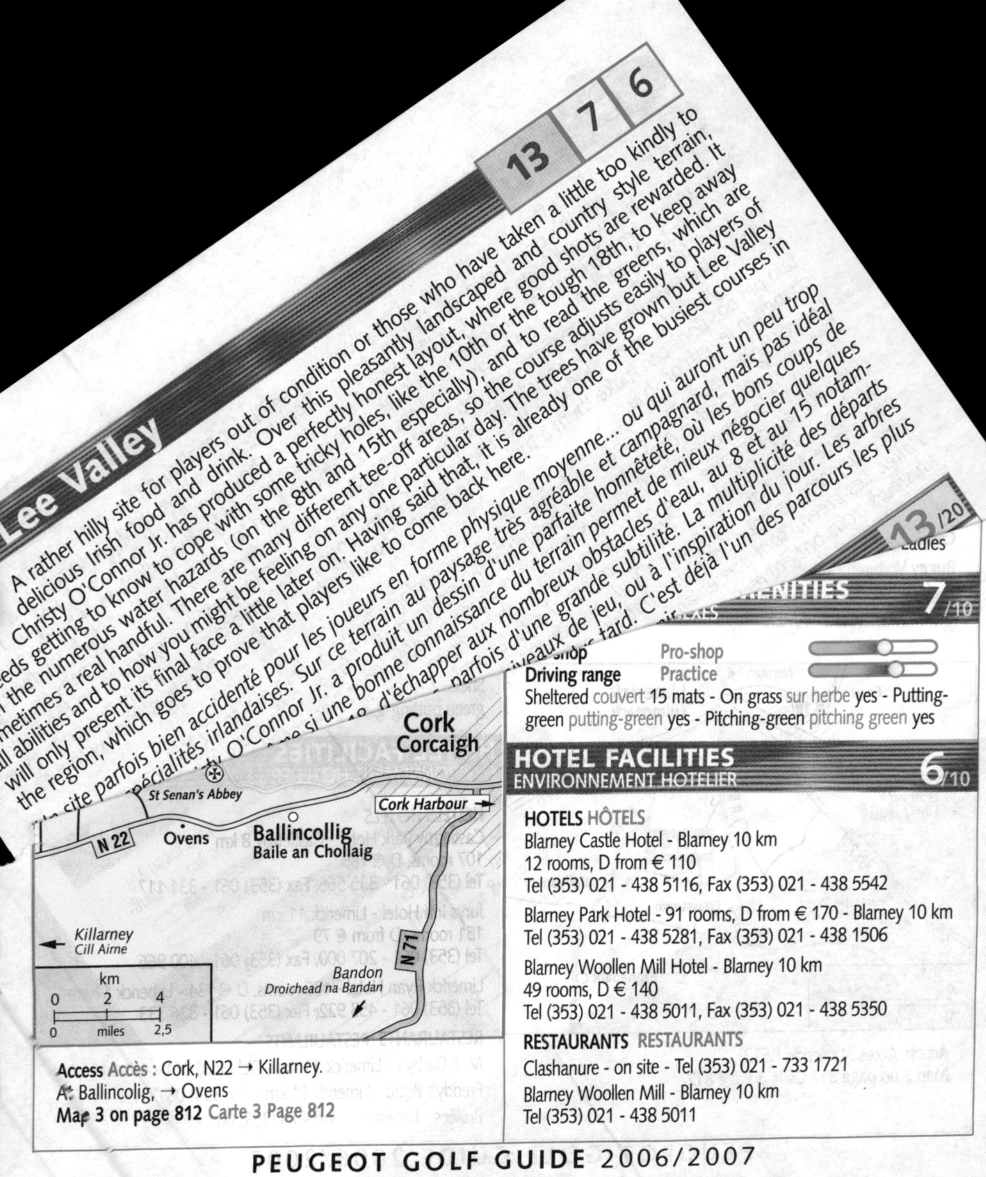

Lee Valley

13 | 7 | 6

A rather hilly site for players out of condition or those who have taken a little too kindly to delicious Irish food and drink. Over this pleasantly landscaped and country style terrain, Christy O'Connor Jr. has produced a perfectly honest layout, where good shots are rewarded. It needs getting to know to cope with some tricky holes, like the 10th or the tough 18th, to keep away from the numerous water hazards (on the 8th and 15th especially), and to read the greens, which are sometimes a real handful. There are many different tee-off areas, so the course adjusts easily to players of all abilities and to how you might be feeling on any one particular day. The trees have grown but Lee Valley will only present its final face a little later on. Having said that, it is already one of the busiest courses in the region, which goes to prove that players like to come back here.

Un site parfois bien accidenté pour les joueurs en forme physique moyenne... ou qui auront un peu trop ... spécialités irlandaises. Sur ce terrain au paysage très agréable et campagnard, mais pas idéal ... O'Connor Jr. a produit un dessin d'une parfaite honnêteté, où les bons coups de ... si une bonne connaissance du terrain permet de mieux négocier quelques ... 18, d'échapper aux nombreux obstacles d'eau, au 8 et au 15 notam- ... parfois d'une grande subtilité. La multiplicité des départs ... niveaux de jeu, ou à l'inspiration du jour. Les arbres ... tard. C'est déjà l'un des parcours les plus

13/20

Ladies

AMENITIES 7/10

Pro-shop	Pro-shop	
Driving range	Practice	

Sheltered couvert 15 mats - On grass sur herbe yes - Putting-green putting-green yes - Pitching-green pitching green yes

HOTEL FACILITIES 6/10
ENVIRONNEMENT HOTELIER

HOTELS HÔTELS

Blarney Castle Hotel - Blarney 10 km
12 rooms, D from € 110
Tel (353) 021 - 438 5116, Fax (353) 021 - 438 5542

Blarney Park Hotel - 91 rooms, D from € 170 - Blarney 10 km
Tel (353) 021 - 438 5281, Fax (353) 021 - 438 1506

Blarney Woollen Mill Hotel - Blarney 10 km
49 rooms, D € 140
Tel (353) 021 - 438 5011, Fax (353) 021 - 438 5350

RESTAURANTS RESTAURANTS

Clashanure - on site - Tel (353) 021 - 733 1721

Blarney Woollen Mill - Blarney 10 km
Tel (353) 021 - 438 5011

Access Accès : Cork, N22 → Killarney.
At Ballincolig, → Ovens
Map 3 on page 812 Carte 3 Page 812

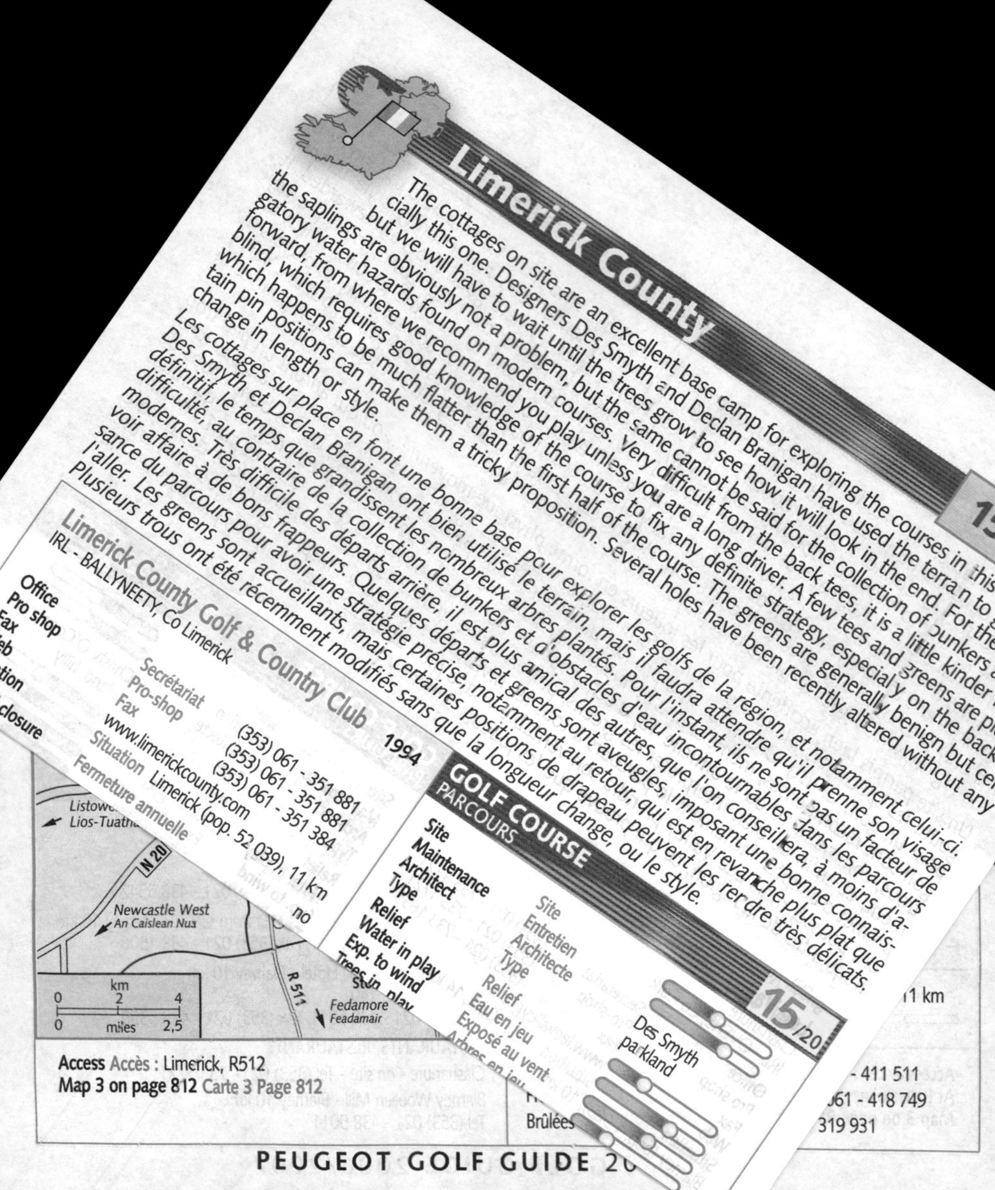

Limerick County

15

The cottages on site are an excellent base camp for exploring the courses in this re cially this one. Designers Des Smyth and Declan Branigan have used the terran to go but we will have to wait until the trees grow to see how it will look in the end. For the m the saplings are obviously not a problem, but the same cannot be said for the collection of bunkers an gatory water hazards found on modern courses. Very difficult from the back tees, it is a little kinder fu forward, from where we recommend you play unless you are a long driver. A few tees and greens are playe blind, which requires good knowledge of the course to fix any definite strategy, especially on the back 9, which happens to be much flatter than the first half of the course. The greens are generally benign but certain pin positions can make them a tricky proposition. Several holes have been recently altered without any change in length or style.

Les cottages sur place en font une bonne base pour explorer les golfs de la région, et notamment celui-ci. Des Smyth et Declan Branigan ont bien utilisé le terrain, mais il faudra attendre qu'il prenne son visage définitif, le temps que grandissent les nombreux arbres plantés. Pour l'instant, ils ne sont pas un facteur de difficulté, au contraire de la collection de bunkers et d'obstacles d'eau incontournables dans les parcours modernes. Très difficile des départs arrière, il est plus amical des autres, que l'on conseillera, à moins d'avoir affaire à de bons frappeurs. Quelques départs et greens sont aveugles, imposant une bonne connaissance du parcours pour avoir une stratégie précise, notamment au retour, qui est en revanche plus plat que l'aller. Les greens sont accueillants, mais certaines positions de drapeau peuvent les rendre très délicats. Plusieurs trous ont été récemment modifiés sans que la longueur change, ou le style.

Limerick County Golf & Country Club — 1994

IRL - BALLYNEETY, Co Limerick

Office	Secrétariat	(353) 061 - 351 881
Pro shop	Pro-shop	(353) 061 - 351 881
Fax	Fax	(353) 061 - 351 384
Web		www.limerickcounty.com
Situation	Situation	Limerick (pop. 52 039), 11 km
Annual closure	Fermeture annuelle	no

GOLF COURSE — PARCOURS — 15/20

Site	Site	
Maintenance	Entretien	
Architect	Architecte	Des Smyth
Type	Type	parkland
Relief	Relief	
Water in play	Eau en jeu	
Exp. to wind	Exposé au vent	
Trees in play	Arbres en jeu	

Access Accès : Limerick, R512
Map 3 on page 812 Carte 3 Page 812

Brûlées

11 km

- 411 511

061 - 418 749

319 931

Luttrellstown

15	7	7

In the grounds of a famous castle hotel, where Queen Victoria, Fred Astaire, Ronald Reagan and the Beckhams were distinguished guests in times gone by, this recent course was designed by Nicholas Bielenberg. It is laid out in a huge park, where age-old trees add beauty and majesty to a peerless atmosphere of tranquility. Trees and water used to be the main obvious difficulties, especially the many lakes and ponds on the estate. They will be even more in play now that Tom Mackenzie (from Donald Steel & C°) has been assigned with a complete overhaul of the course. He is mostly using the original layout, totally redesigning the bunkers and greens, has created some new holes (the 4th and 5th) and is building a new covered driving range. The current range is to be changed into a pitch and putt area. The course should be unveiled in June 2006.

Dans le domaine d'un célèbre Château-hôtel, qui a reçu des gloires telles que la Reine Victoria, Fred Astaire, Ronald Reagan ou le mariage de David Beckham, ce parcours a été dessiné par Nicholas Bielenberg, dans un immense parc avec des arbres centenaires, qui ajoutent leur beauté et leur majesté à une atmosphère incomparable de tranquillité. Les bois et l'eau constituaient jusqu'ici des difficultés évidentes, notamment les nombreux lacs et mares du domaine. Ils seront davantage encore en jeu dans une rénovation complète du parcours, confiée à Tom Mackenzie (de Donald Steel & Co). Il reprend largement le tracé original, repense totalement les bunkers et les greens et crée quelques trous (le 4 et le 5), et un driving-range avec de nouvelles installations d'entraînement couvertes, l'actuel driving range servant de zone de petit jeu. Le nouveau visage de ce golf devrait être révélé en juin 2006.

Luttrellstown Golf & Country Club — 1993

IRL - CLONSILLA, Co Dublin

Office	Secrétariat	(353) 01 - 808 9988
Pro shop	Pro-shop	(353) 01 - 808 9988
Fax	Fax	(353) 01 - 820 5218
Web	www.luttrellstown.ie	
Situation	Situation	Dublin, 10 km
Annual closure	Fermeture annuelle	no
Weekly closure	Fermeture hebdomadaire	no

Fees main season Tarifs haute saison	18 holes	
	Week days Semaine	**We/Bank holidays** We/Férié
Individual Individuel	€ 80	€ 95
Couple Couple	€ 160	€ 190

We: Friday and Saturday

Caddie Caddie on request **Electric Trolley** Chariot électrique no

Buggy Voiturette yes **Clubs** Clubs yes

Credit cards Cartes de crédit
VISA - MasterCard - AMEX - DC

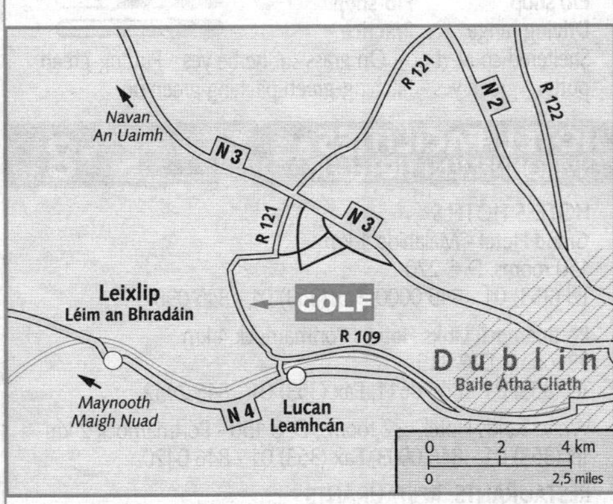

Access Accès : 10 km NW from Dublin on N3 → Clonsilla
Map 1 on page 809 Carte 1 Page 809

GOLF COURSE — PARCOURS 15/20

Site	Site	
Maintenance	Entretien	
Architect	Architecte	Nicholas Bielenberg Tom Mackenzie
Type	Type	parkland
Relief	Relief	
Water in play	Eau en jeu	
Exp. to wind	Exposé au vent	
Trees in play	Arbres en jeu	

Scorecard Carte de score	**Chp.** Chp.	**Mens** Mess.	**Ladies** Da.
Length Long.	6384	6032	5246
Par	72	72	72
Slope system	—	—	—

Advised golfing ability Niveau de jeu recommandé — 0 12 24 36

Hcp required Handicap exigé — 24 Men, 36 Ladies

CLUB HOUSE & AMENITIES — CLUB HOUSE ET ANNEXES 7/10

Pro shop Pro-shop
Driving range Practice
Sheltered couvert yes (new practice) - On grass sur herbe yes - Putting-green putting-green yes - Pitching-green pitching green yes

HOTEL FACILITIES — ENVIRONNEMENT HOTELIER 7/10

HOTELS HÔTELS

Jurys Christchurch Inn -182 rooms, D € 112 - Dublin 10 km
Tel (353) 01 - 454 0000, Fax (353) 01 - 454 0012

Bewley's Hotel - Newlands Cross 5 km
126 rooms, D € 125
Tel (353) 01 - 464 0140, Fax (353) 01 - 464 0900

West County Hotel - Lucan 5 km - 50 rooms, D € 120
Tel (353) 01 - 626 4011, Fax (353) 01 - 623 1378

RESTAURANTS RESTAURANTS

The Bradaun - Leixlip 5 km - Tel (353) 01 - 624 2268
Annadale - Lucan 4 km - Tel (353) 01 - 628 0622
Scott's - Castleknock 3 km - Tel (353) 01 - 821 3482

Malahide *Red + Blue + Yellow*

14	7	8

If you want to play every Eddie Hackett course in Ireland, you have a lot of golfing to do. With the experience of age, he was very kind here to the average week-enders, who return the compliment and come to play here in droves on 27 holes which offer a variety of challenges. In addition to the actual layout, the wind and wetness of the terrain can seriously dent any hopes of a good card. First time around, a number of blinds shots should require some reconnaissance work, but the course is by no means hilly. Bunkering is high quality, as is the use of water hazards, especially on the par 3s. Another side to the course's resistance is the elevation of certain greens, calling for some accurate iron-play. Once on the green, the surfaces are easy to read. A recent course, Malahide has matured admirably and is always good fun in amongst the region's great links courses. Note that work is now underway on the Yellow course further to the purchase of new land.

Si vous voulez jouer tous les parcours d'Eddie Hackett en Irlande, vous n'avez pas fini... Avec l'expérience de l'âge, il a été ici très amical avec les golfeurs moyens : ils le lui rendent bien et viennent nombreux sur les 27 trous, combinables à volonté. En dehors du tracé lui-même, le vent et l'humidité du terrain peuvent perturber les prétentions à bien scorer. La première fois, certains coups aveugles nécessitent une certaine reconnaissance, mais le parcours est facilement jouable à pied. Le "bunkering" est de grande qualité, de même que l'utilisation des obstacles d'eau, notamment sur les pars 3. Autre facteur de résistance du parcours, l'élévation de certains greens, qui oblige à des coups de fer très exacts, mais les surfaces de putting ne sont guère complexes à lire (pas assez ?). De construction récente, Malahide a pris de la maturité, c'est toujours une bonne récréation entre les grands links de la région. A signaler, les travaux entrepris sur le "Yellow" suite à l'acquisition de nouveaux terrains.

Malahide Golf Club — 1991

Beechwood, The Grange
IRL - MALAHIDE, Co Dublin

Office	Secrétariat	(353) 01 - 846 1611
Pro shop	Pro-shop	(353) 01 - 846 0002
Fax	Fax	(353) 01 - 846 1270
Web	www.malahidegolfclub.ie	
Situation	Situation	Dublin, 18 km
Annual closure	Fermeture annuelle	no
Weekly closure	Fermeture hebdomadaire	no
Fees main season	Tarifs haute saison	18 holes

	Week days / Semaine	We/Bank holidays / We/Férié
Individual Individuel	€ 55	*
Couple Couple	€ 110	*

* Members only

Caddie Caddie on request **Electric Trolley** Chariot électrique yes

Buggy Voiturette yes **Clubs** Clubs yes

Credit cards Cartes de crédit
VISA - Eurocard - MasterCard

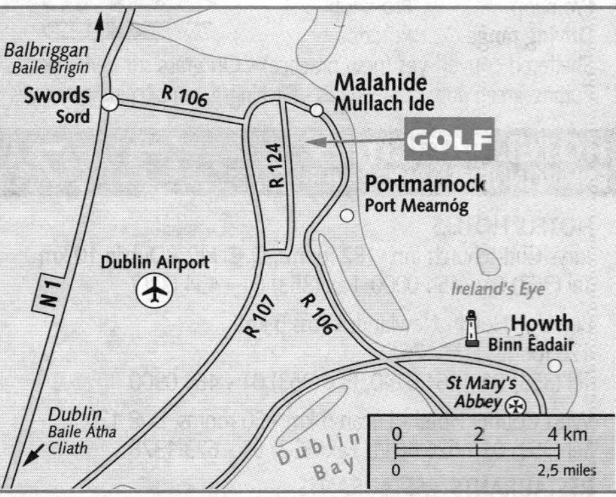

Access Accès : Dublin to Portmarnock Village. Left turn at traffic lights beside Church. Golf 3 km from there.
Map 1 on page 809 Carte 1 Page 809

GOLF COURSE — PARCOURS — 14/20

Site	Site	
Maintenance	Entretien	
Architect	Architecte	Eddie Hackett
Type	Type	parkland
Relief	Relief	
Water in play	Eau en jeu	
Exp. to wind	Exposé au vent	
Trees in play	Arbres en jeu	

Scorecard / Carte de score	Chp. / Chp.	Mens / Mess.	Ladies / Da.
Length Long.	6066	5742	5146
Par	71	70	74
Slope system	—	—	—

Advised golfing ability / Niveau de jeu recommandé: 0 12 24 36

Hcp required Handicap exigé: Men 28, Ladies 36

CLUB HOUSE & AMENITIES — CLUB HOUSE ET ANNEXES — 7/10

Pro shop Pro-shop
Driving range Practice
Sheltered couvert no - On grass sur herbe yes - Putting-green putting-green yes - Pitching-green pitching green no

HOTEL FACILITIES — ENVIRONNEMENT HOTELIER — 8/10

HOTELS HÔTELS

Grand Hotel - Malahide 1 km
150 rooms, D € 270
Tel (353) 01 - 845 0000, Fax (353) 01 - 845 0987

Portmarnock Links Hotel - Portmarnock 4 km
98 rooms, D € 315
Tel (353) 01 - 846 0611, Fax (353) 01 - 846 2442

White Sands Hotel - 32 rooms, D € 150 - Portmarnock 2 km
Tel (353) 01 - 846 0003, Fax (353) 01 - 846 0420

RESTAURANTS RESTAURANTS

Cruzzo - Malahide 1 km - Tel (353) 01 - 845 0599
Colonnade - Malahide 1 km - Tel (353) 01 - 845 0000
Bon Appetit - Malahide 1 km - Tel (353) 01 - 845 0314

Mount Juliet

18 | 9 | 6

There is hardly a country in the world where Jack Nicklaus has not left his mark as a course designer. If he claims to be the greatest course designer, our reply is that there are many "greatest designers" around the world. It all depends on what a designer can squeeze out of a given space. At Mount Juliet, Nicklaus was presented with a magnificent estate, profusely covered with oak, lime and beech trees. A lot of use has been found for water and very US-style bunkers, or sand-traps, as they say. The greens, vast and well-designed, only add to the difficulties of a course which demands a complete game from start to finish and, in particular an aptitude for target golf. The many different tee-off areas cater to players of differing abilities, but given the overall length, the back-tees should most definitely be reserved for single-figure handicappers. Spectacular and remarkably intelligent, this is an excellent Nicklaus vintage and was the venue for the American Express Championship in September 2002, when Tiger Woods triumphed and in October 2004 when Ernie Els won.

Il n'est guère de pays au monde où Jack Nicklaus n'ait laissé sa trace en tant qu'architecte. Et s'il annonce vouloir être le plus grand architecte, on répondra qu'il y a d'autres "meilleurs architectes au monde !" Tout dépend du parti qu'ils tirent d'un espace. A Mount Juliet, il a trouvé une magnifique propriété, généreusement occupée par les chênes, les tilleuls, les hêtres. Un généreux usage a été fait de l'eau (il y a même une cascade), et de bunkers au profil très américain. Et les greens eux-mêmes, vastes et bien travaillés, ajoutent aux difficultés : ce parcours exige un jeu complet, du départ au dernier trou, et singulièrement un jeu de "target golf". La diversité des départs permet de l'adapter aux possibilités des joueurs, mais sa longueur réserve les départs arrière aux handicaps à un chiffre. Spectaculaire et remarquablement intelligent, c'est un excellent Nicklaus. Il a accueilli le triomphe de Tiger Woods en 2002, et de Ernie Els en 2004 lors de l'American Express Championship.

Mount Juliet Golf Club — 1991

IRL - THOMASTOWN, Co Kilkenny

Office Secrétariat (353) 056 - 777 3000
Pro shop Pro-shop (353) 056 - 777 3071
Fax Fax (353) 056 - 777 3019
Web www.mountjuliet.com
Situation Situation Kilkenny (pop. 8 507), 16 km
Annual closure Fermeture annuelle no
Weekly closure Fermeture hebdomadaire no

Fees main season Tarifs haute saison 18 holes

	Week days / Semaine	We/Bank holidays / We/Férié
Individual Individuel	€ 130	€ 155
Couple Couple	€ 260	€ 310

We: Friday € 140 / Sunday → Tuesday € 110

Caddie Caddie on request **Electric Trolley** Chariot électrique yes
Buggy Voiturette no **Clubs** Clubs yes
Credit cards Cartes de crédit
VISA - MasterCard - AMEX - DC

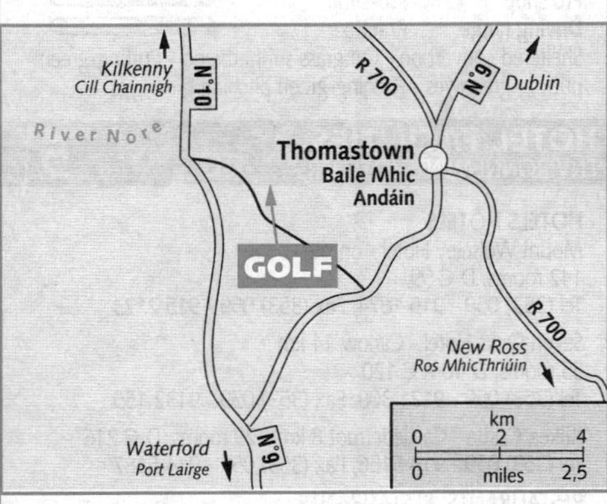

Access Accès : N10 South of Kilkenny
N9 South of Carlow
Map 3 on page 813 Carte 3 Page 813

GOLF COURSE — PARCOURS 18/20

Site	Site	
Maintenance	Entretien	
Architect	Architecte	Jack Nicklaus
Type	Type	parkland
Relief	Relief	
Water in play	Eau en jeu	
Exp. to wind	Exposé au vent	
Trees in play	Arbres en jeu	

Scorecard / Carte de score	Chp. / Chp.	Mens / Mess.	Ladies / Da.
Length Long.	6540	6230	4998
Par	72	72	73
Slope system	—	—	—

Advised golfing ability Niveau de jeu recommandé 0 12 24 36
Hcp required Handicap exigé 28 Men, 36 Ladies

CLUB HOUSE & AMENITIES — CLUB HOUSE ET ANNEXES 9/10

Pro shop Pro-shop
Driving range Practice
Sheltered couvert 5 bays - On grass sur herbe yes - Putting-green putting-green yes - Pitching-green pitching green yes

HOTEL FACILITIES — ENVIRONNEMENT HOTELIER 6/10

HOTELS HÔTELS
Mount Juliet House - 32 rooms, D € 494 - on site
Tel (353) 056 - 777 3000, Fax (353) 056 - 777 3019

Kilkenny Ormonde Hotel - Kilkenny 17 km
118 rooms, D € 159
Tel (353) 056 - 772 3900, Fax (353) 056 - 772 3977

Newpark Hotel - 130 rooms, D € 140 - Kilkenny 17 km
Tel (353) 056 - 776 0500, Fax (353) 056 - 776 0555

RESTAURANTS RESTAURANTS
Lacken House - Kilkenny 16 km - Tel (353) 056 - 776 1085
Langtons - Kilkenny 16 km - Tel (353) 056 - 776 5133
Zuni Restaurant - Kilkenny 16 km - Tel (353) 056 - 772 3999

Mount Wolseley

13 | 6 | 5

Set in the outskirts of Tullow, this was the ancestral home of the Wolseley family, who gave their name to the famous British car. More recently, it has become a typical Christy O'Connor Jr. golf course, with water hazards - into play on eleven holes - and fairway bunkers which some might feel often unfairly penalise good shots. High-level lady players will also feel frustrated as their tee-boxes are often too far forward (a frequent feature these days). Some men will find the back-tees too far backward (also a frequent feature these days!). However this very likeable course is most welcome in a lovely region and the overall honesty of the layout is conducive to attacking golf without the fear of too many unpleasant surprises. The variety of design and protection for the greens allow all sorts of approach shots. Outstanding par-fours are the 447-metre third, where the approach is played over water, and the 466-metre 15th where the distant church spire, offers the line off the tee. To accommodate a larger, 4-star hotel, the 9th and 10th holes have been altered.

Dans la propriété de famille des Wolseley, qui ont donné leur nom à de célèbres autos anglaises, ce récent parcours est typique du style architectural de Christy O'Connor Jr., avec ses obstacles d'eau (en jeu sur onze trous) et ses bunkers de fairway, mais on peut trouver que ces derniers pénalisent souvent les bons coups. Les femmes de bon niveau seront aussi frustrées, car leurs départs sont souvent trop avancés (c'est aujourd'hui fréquent). Quant aux hommes, ils pourront trouver en revanche leurs backtees trop éloignés (c'est aujourd'hui tout aussi fréquent!). Cela dit, cette sympathique réalisation est bienvenue dans une région très agréable, et la franchise générale du tracé permet de l'attaquer sans trop craindre les mauvaises surprises. La variété de dessin et de défense des greens permet toutes sortes d'approches. On notera de remarquables par 4 comme le 3 (447 m) ou le 15 (466 m), où il faut s'aligner sur un clocher lointain. Pour faire place à un hôtel 4 étoiles, les 9 et 10 ont été modifiés.

Mount Wolseley Golf Club — 1996

IRL - TULLOW, Co. Carlow

Office	Secrétariat	(353) 059 - 915 1674
Pro shop	Pro-shop	(353) 059 - 915 1674
Fax	Fax	(353) 059 - 915 2123
Web	www.mountwolseley.ie	
Situation	Situation	Dublin, 80 km

Carlow (pop. 11 721), 14 km

Annual closure Fermeture annuelle — no

Weekly closure Fermeture hebdomadaire

Fees main season Tarifs haute saison — 18 holes

	Week days / Semaine	We/Bank holidays / We/Férié
Individual Individuel	€ 50	€ 70
Couple Couple	€ 100	€ 140

We: Saturday only

Caddie Caddie on request **Electric Trolley** Chariot électrique yes

Buggy Voiturette yes **Clubs** Clubs yes

Credit cards Cartes de crédit
VISA - MasterCard - AMEX

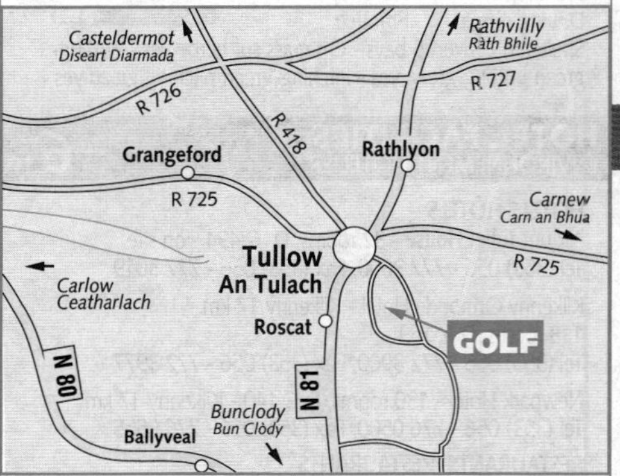

Access Accès : Dublin, N9 → Carlow. In Castledermot, R418 to Tullow
Map 3 on page 813 Carte 3 Page 813

GOLF COURSE — PARCOURS — 13/20

Site	Site	
Maintenance	Entretien	
Architect	Architecte	Christy O'Connor Jr.
Type	Type	parkland
Relief	Relief	
Water in play	Eau en jeu	
Exp. to wind	Exposé au vent	
Trees in play	Arbres en jeu	

Scorecard / Carte de score	Chp. / Chp.	Mens / Mess.	Ladies / Da.
Length Long.	6497	6140	4963
Par	72	72	74
Slope system	—	—	—

Advised golfing ability / Niveau de jeu recommandé — 0 12 24 36

Hcp required Handicap exigé — no

CLUB HOUSE & AMENITIES — CLUB HOUSE ET ANNEXES — 6/10

Pro shop Pro-shop

Driving range Practice

Sheltered couvert no - On grass sur herbe no - Putting-green putting-green yes - Pitching-green pitching green yes

HOTEL FACILITIES — ENVIRONNEMENT HOTELIER — 5/10

HOTELS HÔTELS

Mount Wolseley Hotel - on site
142 rooms, D € 99
Tel (353) 059 - 915 1674, Fax (353) 059 - 915 2123

Seven Oaks Hotel - Carlow 14 km
55 rooms, D from € 120
Tel (353) 059 - 9131 308, Fax (353) 059 - 9132 155

Kilkea Castle - Castledermot 8 km - 29 rooms, D € 216
Tel (353) 059 - 914 5156, Fax (353) 059 - 914 5187

RESTAURANTS RESTAURANTS

Mount Wolseley Hotel - on site - Tel (353) 059 - 915 1674
Kilkea Castle - Castledermot 8 km - Tel (353) 059 - 9145 156

Mullingar

15	5	5

James Braid, who designed this course in 1937, considered Mullingar to be among his best work. A little on the short side today (there was only limited space available at the time), this is still a very popular course with Irish players, although it has never gained an international reputation. It shouldn't leave foreigners feeling too lost, as you can find similar courses in the UK and on the continent, which only show how typical an inland design this is. The one slight difference would be the need to go for target golf, as the devilishly small greens are elevated and very well guarded up front. The hazards are dangerous and call for precision play (the par 3s are excellent). Skills in working the ball both ways, although not mandatory, do give an advantage here. A pleasant course for all levels (the ladies tees are nicely well forward) and one you won't be sorry to discover. It has been recently lengthened and re-bunkered while the 8th, 10th, 13th and 16th greens have been re-located.

James Braid, qui remodela ce parcours en 1937, le considérait comme un de ses meilleurs dessins. Aujourd'hui un peu court (l'espace disponible était réduit), c'est malgré tout un golf très populaire auprès des joueurs irlandais, mais sa réputation internationale reste à établir. Il ne devrait pas trop dépayser les étrangers, car on pourrait trouver aussi bien en Grande-Bretagne que sur le continent des parcours similaires, tant il est typique de l'esthétique et de l'architecture des "inland". Une seule nuance à cette appréciation: il vaut mieux jouer des balles de "target golf", car les greens sont bien défendus frontalement. Les obstacles sont dangereux, obligeant à un jeu précis (les pars 3 sont excellents), et si l'on sait travailler la balle, l'avantage sera sinon décisif, du moins important. Un parcours plaisant, pour tous niveaux (les départs dames sont gentiment avancés) et que l'on ne sera pas déçu de découvrir. Il a été récemment allongé, son bunkering revu et quatre trous ont été déplacés.

Mullingar Golf Club — 1894

Mullingar
IRL - BELVEDERE, Co West Meath

Office	Secrétariat	(353) 044 - 48 366
Pro shop	Pro-shop	(353) 044 - 40 088
Fax	Fax	(353) 044 - 41 499
Web	www.mullingargc.com	
Situation	Situation	Mullingar, 5 km
Annual closure	Fermeture annuelle	no
Weekly closure	Fermeture hebdomadaire	no

Fees main season Tarifs haute saison	18 holes	
	Week days Semaine	We/Bank holidays We/Férié
Individual Individuel	€ 40	€ 45
Couple Couple	€ 80	€ 90

Caddie Caddie yes — **Electric Trolley** Chariot électrique yes
Buggy Voiturette yes — **Clubs** Clubs yes

Credit cards Cartes de crédit
VISA - Mastercard

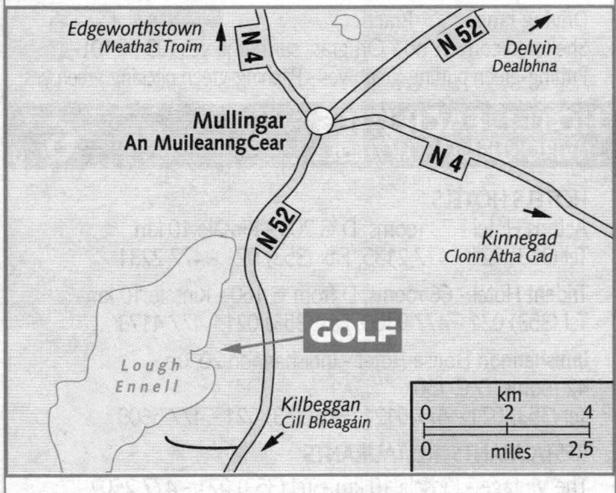

Edgeworthstown
Meathas Troim
N4
N52
Delvin
Dealbhna
Mullingar
An MuileanngCear
N4
N52
Kinnegad
Clonn Atha Gad
GOLF
Lough Ennell
Kilbeggan
Cill Bheagáin
km 0 2 4
0 miles 2,5

Access Accès : Dublin, M4 / N4 → Mullingar. In Mullingar, R52 to Belvedere
Map 3 on page 813 Carte 3 Page 813

GOLF COURSE — PARCOURS — 15/20

Site	Site	
Maintenance	Entretien	
Architect	Architecte	James Braid
Type	Type	parkland
Relief	Relief	
Water in play	Eau en jeu	
Exp. to wind	Exposé au vent	
Trees in play	Arbres en jeu	

Scorecard Carte de score	Chp. Chp.	Mens Mess.	Ladies Da.
Length Long.	5913	5450	4991
Par	72	72	74
Slope system	—	—	—

Advised golfing ability Niveau de jeu recommandé: 0 12 24 36
Hcp required Handicap exigé: no

CLUB HOUSE & AMENITIES — CLUB HOUSE ET ANNEXES — 5/10

Pro shop Pro-shop
Driving range Practice
Sheltered couvert no - On grass sur herbe yes (own balls) - Putting-green putting-green yes - Pitching-green pitching green yes

HOTEL FACILITIES — ENVIRONNEMENT HOTELIER — 5/10

HOTELS HÔTELS

Bloomfield House - Mullingar 5 km
65 rooms, D € 160
Tel (353) 044 - 40 894, Fax (353) 044 - 43 767

Greville Arms - Mullingar 5 km
39 rooms, D from € 120
Tel (353) 044 - 48 563, Fax (353) 044 - 48 052

RESTAURANTS RESTAURANTS

Oscars - Mullingar 5 km
Tel (353) 044 - 44 909

Belfry - Ballynagal 10 km
Tel (353) 044 - 42 488

Old Head

16	7	6

Like a boat leaving its harbour, this new course is exposed to all winds. It has a spectacular setting on a promontory in the Atlantic Ocean off the south coast of Ireland. So there was really little point in adding difficulties to those already inherent in an excellent and virtually sea-bound setting and the architects have not overtaxed the players' strength. Perched atop cliffs, 100 metres above Atlantic breakers, it is not a links course in the strict sense of the term, though this in no way reduces its impact as one of the world's most dramatic layouts. Tiger Woods, David Duval, Payne Stewart, Lee Janzen, Stuart Appleby and Mark O'Meara played a famous six-ball here in July 1999. For the more modest player, the number of tee-boxes helps adapt the course to its strengths and the forces of nature, but you are best advised to opt for match-play rather than aim to score to your handicap. The pretty town of Kinsale deserved a class course, and here it is, laid out by a succession of designers in Liam Higgins, Joe Carr, Patrick Merrigan and finally, Ron Kirby.

Comme un navire sortant du port, ce nouveau parcours est exposé à tous les vents, sur un spectaculaire promontoire avancé sur l'océan au sud de l'Irlande. On admirera la sagesse des architectes, car il n'était pas utile d'ajouter une profusion de difficultés à celles imposées par un site exceptionnel, pratiquement encerclé par la mer. Situé au sommet des falaises, à 100 mètres au-dessus des eaux, ce n'est pas un links à proprement parler, il n'en est pas moins l'un des parcours les plus excitants à jouer actuellement. Tiger Woods, David Duval, Payne Stewart, Lee Janzen, Stuart Appleby et Mark O'Meara y jouèrent un fameux 6-balles en 1999. Le nombre de tees permet d'adapter le parcours aux forces des plus modestes et celles de la nature, mais il vaudra mieux y jouer en match-play que de faire la course derrière son handicap. La jolie ville de Kinsale méritait un parcours de grande classe. Le voici, dessiné par une armée d'architectes : Liam Higgins, Joe Carr, Patrick Merrigan et enfin Ron Kirby.

Old Head Golf Links — 1997

IRL - KINSALE, Co. Cork

Office Secrétariat (353) 021 - 477 8444
Pro shop Pro-shop (353) 021 - 477 8444
Fax Fax (353) 021 - 477 8022
Web www.oldheadgolflinks.com
Situation Situation Cork, 48 km
Kinsale (pop. 2 007), 10 km

Annual closure Fermeture annuelle 1/11→15/4

Weekly closure Fermeture hebdomadaire

Fees main season Tarifs haute saison 18 holes

	Week days Semaine	We/Bank holidays We/Férié
Individual Individuel	€ 250	€ 250
Couple Couple	€ 500	€ 500

Caddie Caddie on request **Electric Trolley** Chariot électrique no

Buggy Voiturette yes **Clubs** Clubs yes

Credit cards Cartes de crédit
VISA - MasterCard - AMEX - DC

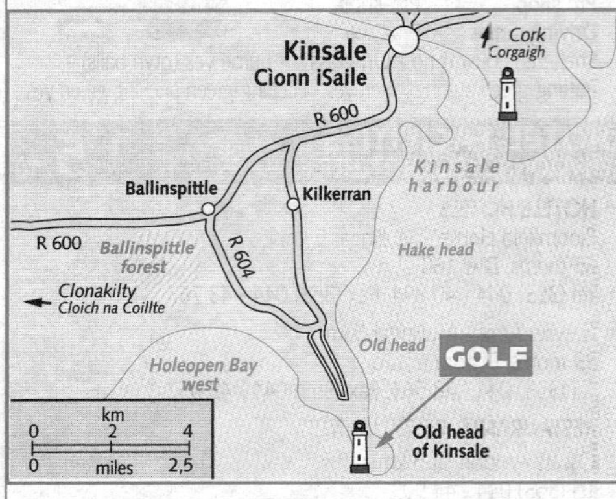

Access Accès : Cork → Kinsale, R 600 → Ballinspittle
Map 3 on page 812 Carte 3 Page 812

GOLF COURSE — PARCOURS 16/20

Site Site
Maintenance Entretien
Architect Architecte Ron Kirby, Joe Carr P. Merrigan...
Type Type seaside course
Relief Relief
Water in play Eau en jeu
Exp. to wind Exposé au vent
Trees in play Arbres en jeu

Scorecard Carte de score	Chp. Chp.	Mens Mess.	Ladies Da.
Length Long.	6080	5657	4827
Par	72	72	72
Slope system	—	—	—

Advised golfing ability Niveau de jeu recommandé 0 12 24 36
Hcp required Handicap exigé 24 Men, 36 Ladies

CLUB HOUSE & AMENITIES — CLUB HOUSE ET ANNEXES 7/10

Pro shop Pro-shop
Driving range Practice
Sheltered couvert no - On grass sur herbe yes (03 → 10) -
Putting-green putting-green yes - Pitching-green pitching green yes

HOTEL FACILITIES — ENVIRONNEMENT HOTELIER 6/10

HOTELS HÔTELS
Actons Hotel - 73 rooms, D € 200 - Kinsale 10 km
Tel (353) 021 - 477 2135, Fax (353) 021 - 477 2231

Trident Hotel - 66 rooms, D from € 160 - Kinsale 10 km
Tel (353) 021 - 477 9300, Fax (353) 021 - 477 4173

Innishannon House Hotel - Innishannon 20 km
42 rooms, D € 150
Tel (353) 021 - 477 5121, Fax (353) 021 - 477 5609

RESTAURANTS RESTAURANTS
The Vintage - Kinsale 10 km - Tel (353) 021 - 477 2502
Blue Haven Hotel - Kinsale 10 km - Tel (353) 021 - 477 2209
Restaurant d'Antibes - Kinsale 10 km
Tel (353) 021 - 477 2125

PGA National

15 | 5 | 6

This project was to be handled by the Nicklaus Organization, with Payne Stewart the designer. After his death, they asked Christy O'Connor Jr. to take over the job. Owing to the relative flatness of the terrain, he resorted to some typical earth-shifting and created more water hazards than is usually the case. Most of them do their job well on almost a dozen holes, the most effective being the stretch of water that runs along the whole length of the 16th hole. This abundance of wet stuff will not be to everyone's liking but they can always take refuge in the sand of the bunkers, which emphasize the design's rather American feel. Here you see the seriousness and care taken by O'Connor over his courses, although he, like many of his contemporaries, has insisted rather heavily on length to pose problems for golfers who cannot always hit their driver at least 220 yards. Palmerstown is the headquarters and the future training site for Irish PGA pros.

Ce projet devait être assumé par Nicklaus Organisation, avec Payne Stewart comme concepteur. A sa mort, on demanda à Christy O'Connor Jr. de reprendre cette réalisation. En raison de la relative platitude du terrain, il a eu recours aux fameux déblais/remblais et créé plus d'obstacles d'eau qu'à son habitude. La plupart d'entre eux remplissent bien leur rôle sur une bonne dizaine de trous, le plus efficace étant tout au long du 16. Cette abondance d'eau ne plaira pas à tous les joueurs, mais il pourront toujours se réfugier dans le sable des bunkers qui accentuent le côté américain du design. On retrouve ici le sérieux et l'aspect soigné des parcours de O'Connor, bien qu'il insiste sur la longueur – comme beaucoup de ses contemporains architectes – pour poser problème à ceux qui ne savent toujours pas driver à 200 mètres. Palmerstown est le quartier général et le futur site d'entraînement des pros de la PGA irlandaise...

PGA National Ireland — **2005**
Palmerstown House
IRL - KILL, Co Kildare

Office	Secrétariat	(353) 045 - 906 901
Pro shop	Pro-shop	(353) 045 - 906 901
Fax	Fax	(353) 045 - 871 377
Web	www.palmerstownhouse.com	
Situation	Situation	Dublin, 27 km
Annual closure	Fermeture annuelle	no
Weekly closure	Fermeture hebdomadaire	

Fees main season Tarifs haute saison	18 holes	
	Week days Semaine	We/Bank holidays We/Férié
Individual Individuel	€ 160	€ 175
Couple Couple	€ 320	€ 350

04 and 010: € 145/160 (We) - 11 → 03: € 100/115 (We)

Caddie Caddie no — **Electric Trolley** Chariot électrique yes

Buggy Voiturette yes — **Clubs** Clubs yes

Credit cards Cartes de crédit
VISA - Eurocard - MasterCard - AMEX

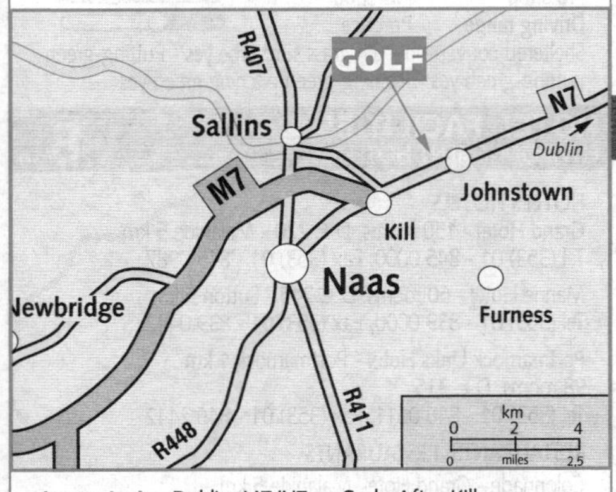

Access Accès : Dublin, M7/N7 → Cork. After Kill, at traffic lights, take a U-turn → Dublin. PGA National 450 m on left hand side.
Map 1 on page 809 Carte 1 Page 809

GOLF COURSE — PARCOURS 15/20

Site	Site	
Maintenance	Entretien	
Architect	Architecte	Christy O'Connor Jr.
Type	Type	parkland
Relief	Relief	
Water in play	Eau en jeu	
Exp. to wind	Exposé au vent	
Trees in play	Arbres en jeu	

Scorecard Carte de score	Chp. Chp.	Mens Mess.	Ladies Da.
Length Long.	6678	6261	5049
Par	72	72	72
Slope system	—	—	—

Advised golfing ability Niveau de jeu recommandé — 0 12 24 36

Hcp required Handicap exigé — no

CLUB HOUSE & AMENITIES — CLUB HOUSE ET ANNEXES 5/10

Pro shop Pro-shop
Driving range Practice
Sheltered couvert yes - On grass sur herbe yes - Putting-green putting-green yes - Pitching-green pitching green yes

HOTEL FACILITIES — ENVIRONNEMENT HOTELIER 6/10

HOTELS HÔTELS

Osprey - 104 rooms, D € 220 - Naas 3 km
Tel (353) 045 - 881 111, Fax (353) 045 - 881 112

Citywest Country House Hotel - Saggart 8 km
1147 rooms, D € 245
Tel (353) 01 - 401 0500, Fax (353) 01 - 458 8565

Tulfarris House & Golf - Blessington 10 km
157 rooms, opens in 2006
Tel (353) 045 - 867 600

Killashee House - 142 rooms, D € 155 - Naas 3 km
Tel (353) 045 - 879 227, Fax (353) 045 - 879 266

RESTAURANTS RESTAURANTS

Les Olives - Naas 3 km - Tel (353) 045 - 894 788

Portmarnock

19	7	8

This majestic links is straight to the point, honest, blunt and diabolical when the wind blows. While Ballybunion can sometimes appear a little baroque, Portmarnock posts an almost austere classicism. There is not one hazard too many, and not one too few to collect wayward shots, not to mention the rough, which is knee-high in places. The greens are huge, subtly contoured and formidably well-guarded. Every shot has to be perfect, from tee to final putt, otherwise stick your tail between your legs and accept that what you get is no more than what you give, with no chance of blaming a single hidden difficulty. If there is one course in this world to be admired for its power, visual amazement, intelligence and variety within unity of style, then it has to be Portmarnock. It is also a great lesson in sobriety for all the world's golf-course designers. You haven't lived if you haven't played Portmarnock at least once. There again, you could also spend your whole life playing here. Almost good value for (so much) money. A new club-house was opened recently at a cost of € 5 million.

Un chef-d'œuvre direct, franc, brutal, et diabolique quand le vent souffle. Si Ballybunion peut paraître parfois baroque, Portmarnock est d'un classicisme presque austère. Il n'y a pas un obstacle superflu, mais il n'en manque pas un pour recevoir les coups égarés, sans même parler d'un rough qui peut monter jusqu'aux genoux. Les greens sont vastes, leurs contours subtils, leurs défenses redoutables. Tous les coups doivent être parfaits, du départ au dernier putt, sinon, il faut accepter de ne recevoir que ce que vous donnez, sans pouvoir accuser une seule difficulté cachée. S'il est un parcours admirable par sa puissance, sa grandeur visuelle, son intelligence, sa diversité à l'intérieur même d'une unité de style, c'est Portmarnock. C'est une grande leçon de sobriété pour tous les architectes du monde. Il faut avoir joué ici une fois, on pourrait aussi y passer sa vie, avec entracte au nouveau club-house de 5 millions d'Euros. Ajoutons que le rapport qualité/green fee est presque bon !

Portmarnock Golf Club — 1894

IRL - PORTMARNOCK, Co. Dublin

Office	Secrétariat	(353) 01 - 846 2968
Pro shop	Pro-shop	(353) 01 - 846 2634
Fax	Fax	(353) 01 - 846 2601
Web	www.portmarnockgolfclub.ie	
Situation	Situation	Dublin, 16 km
Annual closure	Fermeture annuelle	no
Weekly closure	Fermeture hebdomadaire	Wednesday

Restaurant open all days

Fees main season Tarifs haute saison	18 holes	
	Week days Semaine	We/Bank holidays We/Férié
Individual Individuel	€ 165	€ 190
Couple Couple	€ 330	€ 380

Caddie Caddie on request **Electric Trolley** Chariot électrique yes

Buggy Voiturette medical reasons **Clubs** Clubs yes

Credit cards Cartes de crédit
VISA - Eurocard - MasterCard - AMEX

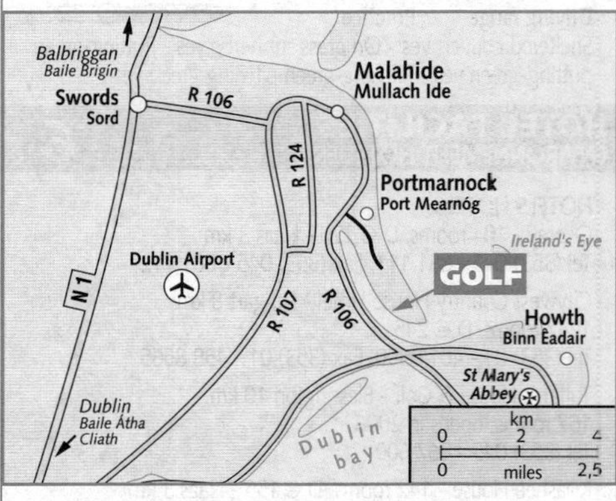

Access Accès : Baldoyle, Portmarnock Village. Golf Links bar, turn right. Golf 1,5 km
Map 1 on page 809 Carte 1 Page 809

GOLF COURSE — PARCOURS — 19/20

Site	Site	
Maintenance	Entretien	
Architect	Architecte	W.C. Pickeman George Ross
Type	Type	links
Relief	Relief	
Water in play	Eau en jeu	
Exp. to wind	Exposé au vent	
Trees in play	Arbres en jeu	

Scorecard Carte de score	Chp. Chp.	Mens Mess.	Ladies Da.
Length Long.	6656	6251	5304
Par	72	72	72
Slope system	—	—	—

Advised golfing ability 0 12 24 36
Niveau de jeu recommandé
Hcp required Handicap exigé 28 Men, 36 Ladies

CLUB HOUSE & AMENITIES — CLUB HOUSE ET ANNEXES — 7/10

Pro shop Pro-shop
Driving range Practice
Sheltered couvert no - On grass sur herbe yes - Putting-green putting-green yes - Pitching-green pitching green yes

HOTEL FACILITIES — ENVIRONNEMENT HOTELIER — 8/10

HOTELS HÔTELS

Grand Hotel - 150 rooms, D € 270 - Malahide 5 km
Tel (353) 01 - 845 0000, Fax (353) 01 - 845 0987

Marine Hotel - 50 rooms, D € 245 - Sutton 5 km
Tel (353) 01 - 839 0000, Fax (353) 01 - 839 0442

Portmarnock Links Hotel - Portmarnock 1 km
98 rooms, D € 315
Tel (353) 01 - 846 0611, Fax (353) 01 - 846 2442

RESTAURANTS RESTAURANTS

Colonnade - Grand Hotel, Malahide 5 km
Tel (353) 01 - 845 0000

Meridian Restaurant - Marine Hotel, Sutton 5 km
Tel (353) 01 - 839 0000

Portmarnock Links

17	7	8

Assuming such a prestigious name was a stiff task, but Bernhard Langer and Stan Eby accepted the challenge and came up with a great course. Only history will tell how great, but their initial achievement was to approach the site with a degree of modesty, and to learn from others – including its illustrious neighbour and other gems such as Carnoustie and Muirfield – without copying a single thing. There is nothing visually excessive and no signature hole, just a natural layout in unforgiving, changing landscape. While the first holes are visually unimpressive, their technical challenge is something else. From the 8th hole onward, the terrain becomes a little more lively and the choice of club a little tougher in a spectacular landscape of dunes. There is no water (to speak of) and no trees, either, nothing but bushes, dangerous rough, magnificently designed and located bunkers and greens that are really exciting to play. The result is more than anyone could ever have hoped for.

Il était difficile d'afficher un nom de golf aussi prestigieux, mais Bernhard Langer et Stan Eby ont relevé le défi, et réussi un grand parcours. L'histoire dira sa place exacte, mais la réussite première est d'avoir abordé modestement ce site, de n'avoir rien copié tout en retenant les leçons de l'illustre voisin, mais aussi de merveilles telles que Carnoustie ou Muirfield. Rien ici d'excessif visuellement, pas de trou-signature, rien que le déroulement naturel dans un paysage rude et changeant. Si les premiers trous ne sont pas visuellement impressionnants, quels challenges techniques ils présentent ! A partir du 8, le terrain devient plus animé, le choix de club plus difficile dans un paysage spectaculaire de dunes. Ici, pas d'eau (ou presque), pas d'arbres, rien que des buissons, un rough dangereux, des bunkers magnifiquement dessinés et placés, des greens passionnants à jouer. Le résultat dépasse les espérances, et en plus, ce parcours vieillit bien.

Portmarnock Hotel & Golf Links — 1995

IRL - PORTMARNOCK, Co Dublin

Office	Secrétariat	(353) 01 - 846 1800
Pro shop	Pro-shop	(353) 01 - 846 1800
Fax	Fax	(353) 01 - 846 1077
Web	www.portmarnock.com	
Situation	Situation	Dublin, 15 km
Annual closure	Fermeture annuelle	no
Weekly closure	Fermeture hebdomadaire	no

Fees main season / Tarifs haute saison — 18 holes	Week days / Semaine	We/Bank holidays / We/Férié
Individual Individuel	€ 125	€ 125
Couple Couple	€ 250	€ 250

€ 85 for hotel guests / Week days: special rates after 16:00

Caddie Caddie on request **Electric Trolley** Chariot électrique yes

Buggy Voiturette yes **Clubs** Clubs yes

Credit cards Cartes de crédit
VISA - MasterCard - AMEX

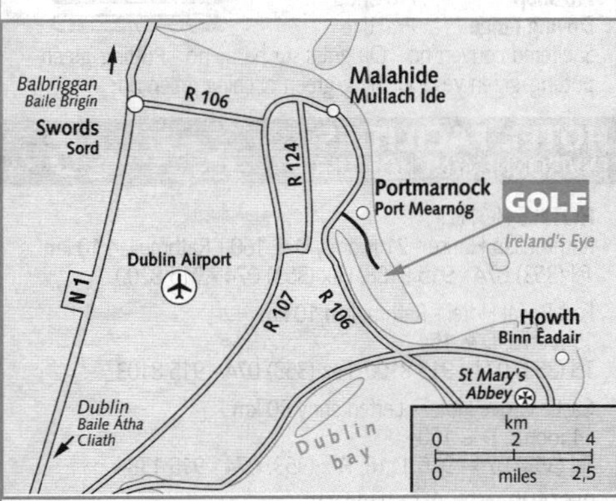

Access Accès : Dublin, Coast Road NE → Howth.
Map 1 on page 809 Carte 1 Page 809

GOLF COURSE — PARCOURS — 17/20

Site	Site	
Maintenance	Entretien	
Architect	Architecte	Bernhard Langer
Type	Type	links
Relief	Relief	
Water in play	Eau en jeu	
Exp. to wind	Exposé au vent	
Trees in play	Arbres en jeu	

Scorecard / Carte de score	Chp. / Chp.	Mens / Mess.	Ladies / Da.
Length Long.	6195	5909	4987
Par	71	71	71
Slope system	—	—	—

Advised golfing ability / Niveau de jeu recommandé: 0 12 24 36

Hcp required / Handicap exigé: 24 Men, 36 Ladies

CLUB HOUSE & AMENITIES — CLUB HOUSE ET ANNEXES — 7/10

Pro shop	Pro-shop
Driving range	Practice

Sheltered couvert no - On grass sur herbe only practice area
Putting-green putting-green yes - Pitching-green pitching green yes

HOTEL FACILITIES — ENVIRONNEMENT HOTELIER — 8/10

HOTELS HÔTELS

Portmarnock Links Hotel - 98 rooms, D € 315 - on site
Tel (353) 01 - 846 0611, Fax (353) 01 - 846 2442

Grand Hotel - Malahide 4 km
150 rooms, D € 270
Tel (353) 01 - 845 0000, Fax (353) 01 - 845 0987

White Sands Hotel - Portmarnock 1 km
32 rooms, D € 150
Tel (353) 01 - 846 0003, Fax (353) 01 - 846 0420

RESTAURANTS RESTAURANTS

Osborne (at Hotel) - on site - Tel (353) 01 - 846 0611
Old Street Wine Bar - Malahide 4 km - Tel (353) 01 - 845 1882
Bon Appetit - Malahide 4 km - Tel (353) 01 - 845 0314

Portsalon

16 | 5 | 5

Portsalon is an outstanding site, between the beach of Ballymostocker bay, one of the world's finest, and the Knockalla mountains. This age-old course is today run by locals, which means a friendly welcome guaranteed every time. After major re-modelling work by Pat Ruddy, who lengthened it to more than 7,000 yards and changed the par from 68 to 72. It has remained a very natural challenge, with unpredictable kicks that are all part of the fun of golf, when they bounce and rebound in the right direction. The rough is not too severe and the bunkers are sensibly and not excessively, in play. Though quirky, criss-cross holes have been eliminated, golfers new to the game will still enjoy the opportunity here to learn about the architecture of a links course, without undue suffering, especially continental Europeans, who have little contact with this style of golf. The wind is, of course, an element to be reckoned with, but it puts colour into your cheeks and gives you a hearty appetite for after the round.

Portsalon bénéficie d'une situation exceptionnelle, entre la plage de Ballymostocker Bay, l'une des plus belles du monde, et les Knockalla Mountains. Ce golf centenaire est aujourd'hui géré par des Irlandais locaux, c'est une garantie d'accueil amical. Le parcours a bénéficié d'un remodelage important par Pat Ruddy, qui l'a porté à plus de 6300 mètres, avec un par 72 au lieu de 68. Ce links est resté très naturel, avec les rebonds imprévisibles qui font le plaisir du jeu... quand ils sont favorables. Le rough n'est pas trop sévère, les bunkers bien en jeu, mais sans excès. Bien que les excentricités des origines et les trous se croisant aient été éliminés, les golfeurs peu expérimentés auront ici une belle occasion d'apprendre à aimer sans douleur l'architecture de links. notamment les Européeens du continent, peu familiarisés avec elle. Et la présence de l'eau, au 3 et au 16, ne devrait pas trop les gêner. Bien sûr, le vent est un élément important, mais il donne bonne mine et ouvre l'appétit.

Portsalon Golf Club — 1881

Portsalon
IRL - FANAD, Co Donegal

Office	Secrétariat	(353) 074 - 9159 459
Pro shop	Pro-shop	(353) 074 - 9159 459
Fax	Fax	(353) 074 - 9159 919
Web	—	
Situation	Situation	Derry (pop. 72 334), 50 km

Letterkenny (pop. 7 606), 32 km

Annual closure Fermeture annuelle — no

Weekly closure Fermeture hebdomadaire — no

Fees main season Tarifs haute saison — 18 holes

	Week days / Semaine	We/Bank holidays / We/Férié
Individual Individuel	€ 35	€ 40
Couple Couple	€ 70	€ 80

Caddie Caddie no — **Electric Trolley** Chariot électrique no

Buggy Voiturette yes — **Clubs** Clubs no

Credit cards Cartes de crédit
VISA - Eurocard - Mastercard - AMEX

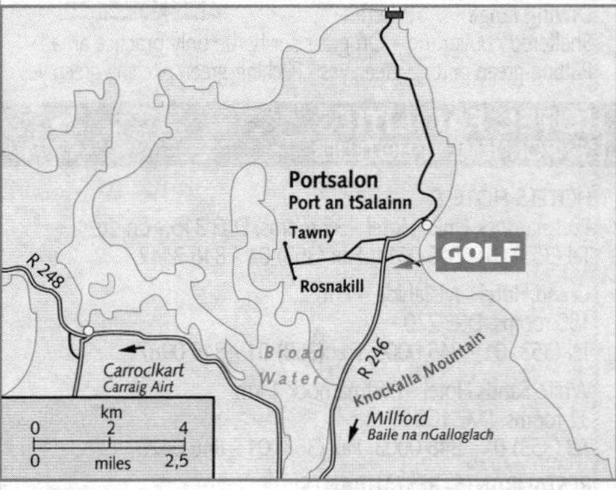

Access Accès : Derry, A2, N13 to Letterkenny. R245 to Rathmelton, Milford. R246 to Portsalon (Fanad Peninsula)
Map 2 on page 811 Carte 2 Page 811

GOLF COURSE — PARCOURS — 16/20

Site	Site	
Maintenance	Entretien	
Architect	Architecte	Mr Thompson
Type	Type	links
Relief	Relief	
Water in play	Eau en jeu	
Exp. to wind	Exposé au vent	
Trees in play	Arbres en jeu	

Scorecard / Carte de score	Chp. / Chp.	Mens / Mess.	Ladies / Da.
Length Long.	5354	5354	4499
Par	69	69	70
Slope system	—	—	—

Advised golfing ability / Niveau de jeu recommandé: 0 12 24 36

Hcp required Handicap exigé — no

CLUB HOUSE & AMENITIES — CLUB HOUSE ET ANNEXES — 5/10

Pro shop Pro-shop
Driving range Practice
Sheltered couvert no - On grass sur herbe no - Putting-green putting-green yes - Pitching-green pitching green no

HOTEL FACILITIES — ENVIRONNEMENT HOTELIER — 5/10

HOTELS HÔTELS

Rathmullan House - 21 rooms, D € 160 - Rathmullan 10 km
Tel (353) 074 - 915 8188, Fax (353) 074 - 915 8200

Fort Royal Hotel - Rathmullan 10 km
15 rooms, D € 154
Tel (353) 074 - 915 8100, Fax (353) 074 - 915 8103

Castle Grove Hotel - Letterkenny 30 km
14 rooms, D € 150
Tel (353) 074 - 915 1118, Fax (353) 074 - 915 1384

RESTAURANTS RESTAURANTS

Portsalon Store - Portsalon 1 km - Tel (353) 074 - 915 9107

Rosapenna Hotel - Downings 30 km
Tel (353) 074 - 915 5301

Powerscourt *East Course*

15	7	7

This is a magnificent site alongside the little town of Enniskerry, the gateway to the "Military Road" that crosses the wild landscape of the Wicklow Mountains in the immediate vicinity of Powerscourt Castle (hence the name of the course). The "East" course winds its way around a majestic estate over some sharp slopes that might make a buggy advisable for senior players. Former British Amateur champion Peter McEvoy has produced a championship course that is as honest as it is technically demanding, where water comes into play on only two holes (including the superb 16th hole, a par 3 and obvious tribute to the 12th at Augusta). The main hazards are the large trees and very strategically placed bunkers. Powerscourt is still a young course but the sand-based greens are already in excellent condition; for the moment, the fairways still need to gain a little firmness and the back-tees are best left alone... It played host to the AIB Irish Seniors Open in 2001.

C'est un site magnifique, à côté de la petite ville d'Enniskerry, porte d'entrée de la "Military Road" traversant les paysages sauvages des Wicklow Mountains, à proximité immédiate du Château de Powerscourt, dont le golf a emprunté le nom. Le parcours "East" a été insinué dans cet espace majestueux, au prix de quelques reliefs incitant à conseiller une voiturette aux seniors. Le grand champion amateur Peter McEvoy en a fait un parcours de championnat aussi franc qu'exigeant techniquement, où l'eau n'est en jeu que sur deux trous (dont le superbe 16, un par 3 en référence évidente au 12 d'Augusta). Les grands arbres constituent les principaux obstacles, avec des bunkers très stratégiques. Powerscourt est jeune encore, mais les greens en sable sont déjà en excellente condition, alors que les fairways ont toujours besoin d'acquérir un peu de fermeté : il vaut mieux ne pas jouer des départs arrière pour l'instant... Ce parcours a reçu l'Irish Seniors Open en 2001.

Powerscourt Golf Club — 1996

Powerscourt Estate
IRL - ENNISKERRY, Co Wicklow

Office	Secrétariat	(353) 01 - 204 6033
Pro shop	Pro-shop	(353) 01 - 204 6033
Fax	Fax	(353) 01 - 286 3561
Web	www.powerscourt.ie	
Situation	Situation	Dublin, 19 km

Enniskerry (pop. 1 275), 1 km

Annual closure	Fermeture annuelle	no
Weekly closure	Fermeture hebdomadaire	no
Fees main season	Tarifs haute saison	18 holes

	Week days / Semaine	We/Bank holidays / We/Férié
Individual Individuel	€ 130	€ 130
Couple Couple	€ 260	€ 260

Caddie Caddie on request **Electric Trolley** Chariot électrique no

Buggy Voiturette yes **Clubs** Clubs yes

Credit cards Cartes de crédit
VISA - MasterCard - AMEX - Laser

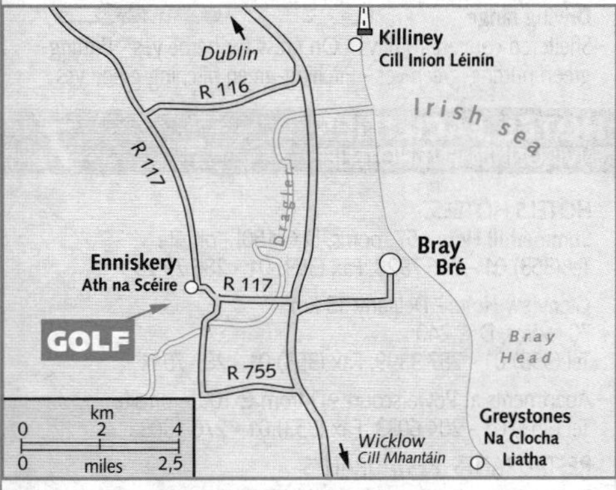

Access Accès : N11, South of Bray
Map 1 on page 809 Carte 1 Page 809

GOLF COURSE — PARCOURS — 15/20

Site	Site	
Maintenance	Entretien	
Architect	Architecte	Peter McEvoy
Type	Type	inland, parkland
Relief	Relief	
Water in play	Eau en jeu	
Exp. to wind	Exposé au vent	
Trees in play	Arbres en jeu	

Scorecard Carte de score	Chp. / Chp.	Mens / Mess.	Ladies / Da.
Length Long.	6410	5858	5322
Par	72	72	75
Slope system	—	—	—

Advised golfing ability Niveau de jeu recommandé: 0 12 24 36
Hcp required Handicap exigé: 36

CLUB HOUSE & AMENITIES — CLUB HOUSE ET ANNEXES — 7/10

Pro shop Pro-shop
Driving range Practice
Sheltered couvert 10 bays - On grass sur herbe yes - Putting-green putting-green yes - Pitching-green pitching green yes

HOTEL FACILITIES — ENVIRONNEMENT HOTELIER — 7/10

HOTELS HÔTELS

Summerhill Hotel - 57 rooms, D € 150 - on site
Tel (353) 01 - 286 7928, Fax (353) 01 - 286 79 29

Glenview Hotel - Delgany 13 km
70 rooms, D € 240
Tel (353) 01 - 287 3399, Fax (353) 01 - 287 7511

Apartments at Powerscourt - D from € 100 - on site
Tel (353) 01 - 204 6033, Fax (353) 01 - 276 1303

RESTAURANTS RESTAURANTS

Roly's Bistro - Dublin 15 km - Tel (353) 01 - 668 2611
Cooper's - Greystones 13 km - Tel (353) 01 - 287 3914
Hungry Monk - Greystones 13 km - Tel (353) 01 - 287 5759

Powerscourt *West Course*

17 | 7 | 7

This course could be your introduction to one of the up-and-coming stars of golf course architecture, David McLay Kidd, who designed the now famous Bandon Dunes (Oregon), Queenwood (near London) and the future new course at St Andrews. Having grown up at Gleneagles, he fully understands what undulating terrain is all about and the characteristics of heather soil, plus the need today to create greens that pose problems per se. The rather large putting surfaces reserve many a surprise for careless readers of greens. In other words, Kidd has intelligently played with the natural terrain, enhancing it rather than twisting it around. He has also been rather kind with the average hacker and avoided any undue stress with a layout that is neither too tight nor over-cluttered with hazards all the way to the green. Forthright and demanding, this course is certainly a more exciting prospect for the better players rather than beginners. At all events it adds even greater appeal to an already remarkable site.

Ce parcours permet de faire connaissance avec l'une des jeunes stars de l'architecture de golf, David McLay Kidd, auteur du fameux Bandon Dunes (Oregon), de Queenwood (près de Londres) et du futur nouveau parcours de St Andrews. Ayant grandi à Gleneagles, il comprend bien les sites un peu mouvementés et les caractéristiques des terres de bruyère, mais aussi la nécessité de créer aujourd'hui des greens posant des problèmes "en soi". Assez grands, ils réservent bien des surprises aux lecteurs inattentifs des surfaces de putting. Autrement, Kidd a joué intelligemment avec le terrain naturel, le mettant en valeur plus que le torturant, il a été assez gentil avec les joueurs moyens pour ne pas les contraindre, ni par un tracé trop étroit, ni par des obstacles trop nombreux sur la route des greens. Franc et exigeant, ce parcours passionnera sans doute plus les meilleurs joueurs que les débutants, il ajoute encore à la séduction d'un site remarquable.

Powerscourt Golf Club — 2003

Powerscourt Estate
IRL - ENNISKERRY, Co Wicklow

Office — Secrétariat — (353) 01 - 204 6033
Pro shop — Pro-shop — (353) 01 - 204 6033
Fax — Fax — (353) 01 - 286 3561
Web — www.powerscourt.ie
Situation — Situation — Dublin, 19 km
Enniskerry (pop. 1 275), 1 km

Annual closure — Fermeture annuelle — no
Weekly closure — Fermeture hebdomadaire — no

Fees main season / Tarifs haute saison	18 holes	
	Week days / Semaine	We/Bank holidays / We/Férié
Individual Individuel	€ 130	€ 130
Couple Couple	€ 260	€ 260

Caddie Caddie on request Electric Trolley Chariot électrique no

Buggy Voiturette yes Clubs Clubs yes

Credit cards Cartes de crédit
VISA - MasterCard - AMEX - Laser

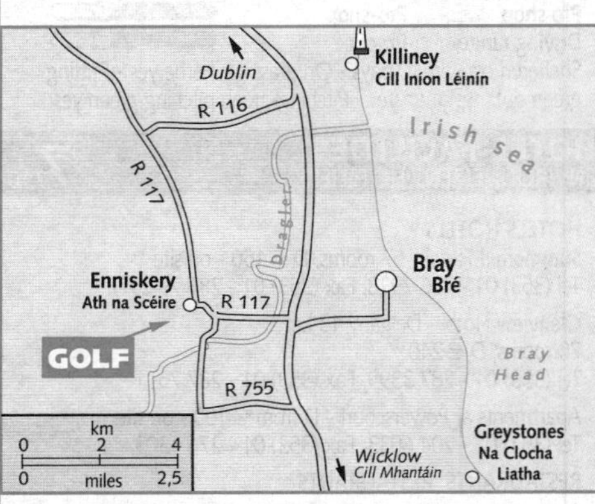

Access Accès : N11, South of Bray
Map 1 on page 809 Carte 1 Page 809

GOLF COURSE — PARCOURS 17/20

Site — Site
Maintenance — Entretien
Architect — Architecte — David McLay Kidd
Type — Type — inland, heathland
Relief — Relief
Water in play — Eau en jeu
Exp. to wind — Exposé au vent
Trees in play — Arbres en jeu

Scorecard / Carte de score	Chp. / Chp.	Mens / Mess.	Ladies / Da.
Length Long.	6191	5796	4678
Par	72	72	72
Slope system	—	—	—

Advised golfing ability / Niveau de jeu recommandé — 0 12 24 36

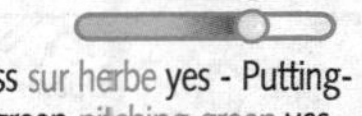

Hcp required — Handicap exigé — 36

CLUB HOUSE & AMENITIES — CLUB HOUSE ET ANNEXES 7/10

Pro shop — Pro-shop
Driving range — Practice
Sheltered couvert 10 bays - On grass sur herbe yes - Putting-green putting-green yes - Pitching-green pitching green yes

HOTEL FACILITIES — ENVIRONNEMENT HOTELIER 7/10

HOTELS HÔTELS

Summerhill Hote - 57 rooms, D € 150l - on site
Tel (353) 01 - 286 7928, Fax (353) 01 - 286 79 29

Glenview Hotel - Delgany 13 km
70 rooms, D € 240
Tel (353) 01 - 287 3399, Fax (353) 01 - 287 7511

Apartments at Powerscourt - D from € 100 - on site
Tel (353) 01 - 204 6033, Fax (353) 01 - 276 1303

RESTAURANTS RESTAURANTS

Roly's Bistro - Dublin 15 km - Tel (353) 01 - 668 2611
Cooper's - Greystones 13 km - Tel (353) 01 - 287 3914
Hungry Monk - Greystones 13 km - Tel (353) 01 - 287 5759

Rathcore

15	7	7

The primary strength of this course is the quality of the raw country site, which houses the ruins of two circular stone forts dating from sometime BC and still used in the early Middle Ages. The Rathcore (Dún Cúair) stone club-house has opted for the same round structure. Architect Mel Flanagan set out to build a "Celtic" style course and if the expression is original, it also rings true. The small stone walls which flank the greens and sometimes even the fairways, the natural springs that bring water into play on a dozen holes and the presence here and there of marshes, daffodils and wild flowers are all features of the Irish countryside. Despite all these hazards, the playing area is wide enough to perhaps please the average golfer more than the single-figure handicapper. Without wishing to go into too much detail, watch out for holes 11 and 16, two par 3s laid out in opposing directions and separated by wetlands. When all is said and done, a very becoming and most charming challenge for any golfer.

La première force de ce parcours tient à la qualité du site. En pleine campagne, il contient les ruines de deux forts circulaires en pierre datant d'avant J.C., et resta très actif au début du Moyen-Age. Le club-house en pierre de Rathcore (Dún Cúair) a repris cette forme ronde. L'architecte Mel Flanagan a voulu faire un parcours classique celtique, et si l'expression est originale, elle n'est pas si fausse. L'utilisation de murets en pierre pour flanquer les greens ou parfois même les fairways, les sources naturels qui mettent l'eau en jeu sur une douzaine de trous, la présence ici et là de marais, d'ajoncs, de fleurs sauvages témoigne d'éléments naturels au paysage irlandais. Malgré tous ces obstacles, les aires de jeu sont assez larges pour convenir aux golfeurs moyens plus encore qu'aux champions. Sans vouloir décrire ce parcours, on distinguera les 11 et 16, deux par 3 en directions opposées et séparés par des zones humides. Tous comptes faits, un challenge très attachant et plein de charme.

Rathcore Golf and Country Club — 2004

IRL - RATHCORE, Co Meath

Office	Secrétariat	(353) 046 - 954 1855
Pro shop	Pro-shop	(353) 046 - 954 1855
Fax	Fax	(353) 046 - 954 1855
Web	www.rathcoregolfandcountryclub.com	
Situation	Situation	Enfield, 5 km
Annual closure	Fermeture annuelle	no
Weekly closure	Fermeture hebdomadaire	no

Fees main season Tarifs haute saison	18 holes	
	Week days Semaine	**We/Bank holidays** We/Férié
Individual Individuel	€ 35	€ 45
Couple Couple	€ 70	€ 90

Friday: € 40

Caddie Caddie no — **Electric Trolley** Chariot électrique no

Buggy Voiturette yes — **Clubs** Clubs yes

Credit cards Cartes de crédit
VISA - MasterCard

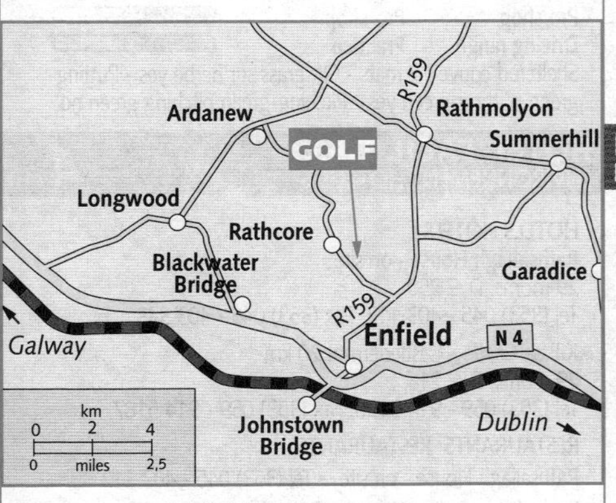

Access Accès : Dublin M4 → Galway.
Exit Enfield, then follow signs to the golf (5 km)
Map 3 on page 813 Carte 3 Page 813

GOLF COURSE — PARCOURS — 15/20

Site	Site	
Maintenance	Entretien	
Architect	Architecte	Mel Flanagan Irish Golf Design
Type	Type	parkland
Relief	Relief	
Water in play	Eau en jeu	
Exp. to wind	Exposé au vent	
Trees in play	Arbres en jeu	

Scorecard Carte de score	**Chp.** Chp.	**Mens** Mess.	**Ladies** Da.
Length Long.	5880	5400	4799
Par	72	72	72
Slope system	—	—	—

Advised golfing ability Niveau de jeu recommandé — 0 12 24 36

Hcp required Handicap exigé — no

CLUB HOUSE & AMENITIES — CLUB HOUSE ET ANNEXES — 7/10

Pro shop Pro-shop
Driving range Practice
Sheltered couvert no - On grass sur herbe no - Putting-green putting-green no - Pitching-green pitching green no

HOTEL FACILITIES — ENVIRONNEMENT HOTELIER — 7/10

HOTELS HÔTELS

Marriott Johnstown House - Enfield 5 km
126 rooms, D from € 210
Tel (353) 046 - 954 000, Fax (353) 046 - 954 001

Moyglare Manor - 16 rooms, D € 250 - Maynooth 15 km
Tel (353) 01 - 628 6351, Fax (353) 01 - 628 5405

Highfield House - 7 rooms, D € 55 - Trim 7 km
Tel (353) 046 - 943 6386, Fax (353) 046 - 943 8182

RESTAURANTS RESTAURANTS

Pavilion (Marriott) - Enfield 5 km
Tel (353) 046 - 954 000

Atrium Brasserie (Marriott) - Enfield 5 km
Tel (353) 046 - 954 000

Rathsallagh

14	7	4

Welcome to a huge park, where the age-old trees provide a sumptuous splash of colour come Autumn. Away from the madding crowd, the trees here are very much a factor in heightening the difficulty of the course. The slopes are sometimes steep and might hinder some senior players, but they also add to the problem of club selection. This is compounded by well-guarded and cleverly designed greens, where you can rarely get home without lofting the ball. A noticeable feature is the variety of the holes, with more than a few slight dog-legs that ideally call for some flighted shots (when the ground is damp the course plays very long). There is water on seven holes, and it is often threatening. Although generally honest and open, the course nonetheless harbours a few potential traps, including the 6th, a par 5 peppered with bunkers, ponds and ditches and a tricky hole to master. Other features are the difficulty of the closing holes and the very family atmosphere that reigns throughout the club.

Un immense parc avec des arbres centenaires, dont les couleurs automnales sont somptueuses. A l'écart des bruits du monde, leur présence est un facteur de difficulté effective dans le jeu. Les dénivellées sont parfois importantes, et peuvent poser des problèmes aux seniors, mais aussi pour bien choisir son club, et d'autant plus que les greens sont très défendus, très travaillés : on peut rarement y entrer en faisant rouler la balle. On remarquera aussi la variété des trous, avec pas mal de légers dog-legs obligeant à travailler ses effets (le parcours est très long quand le sol est humide). L'eau est présente sur sept trous, souvent de manière dangereuse. Généralement assez franc et ouvert, ce parcours recèle néanmoins quelques pièges, dont le 6, un par 5 truffé de bunkers, de mares et de fossés, et bien délicat à décrypter. A signaler aussi, la difficulté des derniers trous, et l'atmosphère très familiale qui règne dans ce club.

Rathsallagh Golf Club — 1995

IRL - DUNLAVIN, Co Wicklow

Office	Secrétariat	(353) 045 - 403 316
Pro shop	Pro-shop	(353) 045 - 403 316
Fax	Fax	(353) 045 - 403 295
Web	www.rathsallagh.com	
Situation	Situation	Dunlavin (pop. 693), 4 km
Annual closure	Fermeture annuelle	no
Weekly closure	Fermeture hebdomadaire	no

Fees main season Tarifs haute saison — 18 holes

	Week days Semaine	We/Bank holidays We/Férié
Individual Individuel	€ 60	€ 75
Couple Couple	€ 120	€ 150

We: Friday → Sunday / Hotel guests: € 50 and € 65 (We)

Caddie Caddie on request **Electric Trolley** Chariot électrique yes

Buggy Voiturette yes **Clubs** Clubs yes

Credit cards Cartes de crédit
VISA - MasterCard - AMEX

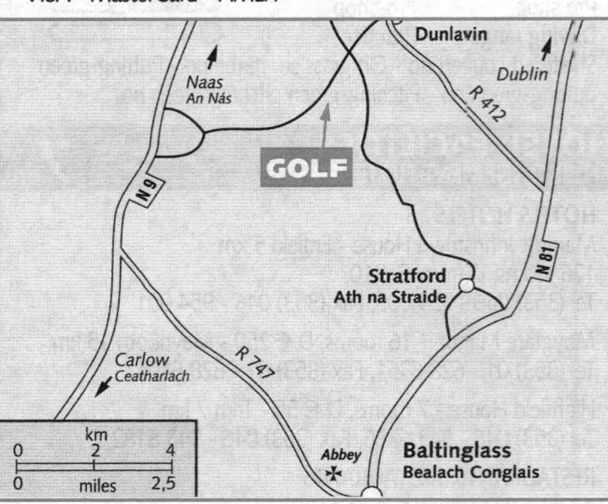

Access Accès : Dublin, N7 West. N9 → Waterford. → Dunlavin
Map 3 on page 813 Carte 3 Page 813

GOLF COURSE — 14/20
PARCOURS

Site	Site	
Maintenance	Entretien	
Architect	Architecte	Peter McEvoy Ch. O'Connor Jr.
Type	Type	inland, parkland
Relief	Relief	
Water in play	Eau en jeu	
Exp. to wind	Exposé au vent	
Trees in play	Arbres en jeu	

Scorecard Carte de score	**Chp.** Chp.	**Mens** Mess.	**Ladies** Da.
Length Long.	6321	5940	5033
Par	74	72	73
Slope system	—	—	—

Advised golfing ability 0 12 24 36
Niveau de jeu recommandé
Hcp required Handicap exigé 28 Men, 36 Ladies

CLUB HOUSE & AMENITIES — 7/10
CLUB HOUSE ET ANNEXES

Pro shop Pro-shop
Driving range Practice
Sheltered couvert 2 mats - On grass sur herbe yes - Putting-green putting-green yes - Pitching-green pitching green no

HOTEL FACILITIES — 4/10
ENVIRONNEMENT HOTELIER

HOTELS HÔTELS
Rathsallagh House - on site
29 rooms, D € 250
Tel (353) 045 - 403 112, Fax (353) 045 - 403 343

Kilkea Castle - Castledermot 20 km
29 rooms, D € 216
Tel (353) 059 - 914 5156, Fax (353) 059 - 914 5187

RESTAURANTS RESTAURANTS
Rathsallagh House - on site - Tel (353) 045 - 403 112
Priory Inn - Carlow-Kilkenny Road 4 km
Tel (353) 045 - 403 355

Ring of Kerry

15	7	7

A drive around Kerry is a must. One of the world's most picturesque roads from Killarney to Kenmare has been further enhanced from the golfer's point of view with a new course overlooking the bay and jagged cliffs of Kenmare and backed by the MacGillicuddy Reeks and the Caha Mountains. In this quite spectacular setting, Eddie Hackett has designed a very beautiful course with emphasis both on testing the better golfer and, at the same time, on showing respect for all golf-lovers, even the less skilled and the less ambitious. Here, the many different tee-boxes provide the flexibility needed to adapt a course to playing ability and strengths. Water has been intelligently brought into play without ever overdoing things, and the same goes for the vegetation. Players should, though, be wary of being lured into a false sense of security and pleasure by the wonderful scenery. You need to be on top of your game at all times to make any impression on a course which is easier once you get to know some of the more subtle aspects of the layout. A course to play.

Le tour du Kerry est incontournable. L'une des plus belles routes du monde, de Killarney à Kenmare, s'est enrichie pour les golfeurs d'une nouvelle halte, dominant la baie de Kenmare et ses dentellières, adossée aux MacGillicuddy Reeks et aux Caha Mountains. Dans ce site spectaculaire, Eddie Hackett a dessiné un très beau parcours, soucieux à la fois de tester les meilleurs, mais avec un grand respect de tous les amoureux du golf, même s'ils sont moins expérimentés ou ambitieux. Les nombreux départs autorisent ainsi cette souplesse d'adaptation nécessaire pour satisfaire les différents niveaux de jeu. L'eau a été mise en jeu avec intelligence, mais sans excès non plus, de même que la végétation. Que l'on se méfie quand même de l'impression de sécurité et de plaisir du paysage, il est nécessaire de rester vigilant pour réussir, et une connaissance un peu approfondie des subtilités du dessin ne sera pas inutile. A connaître.

Ring of Kerry Golf Club — 1998

IRL - TEMPLENOE, Kenmare, Co. Kerry

Office Secrétariat (353) 064 - 42 000
Pro shop Pro-shop (353) 064 - 42 000
Fax Fax (353) 064 - 42 533
Web www.ringofkerrygolf.com
Situation Situation Kenmare (pop. 1 420), 6 km
Annual closure Fermeture annuelle no
Weekly closure Fermeture hebdomadaire no

Fees main season Tarifs haute saison 18 holes

	Week days / Semaine	We/Bank holidays / We/Férié
Individual Individuel	€ 80	€ 80
Couple Couple	€ 160	€ 160

Caddie Caddie no — **Electric Trolley** Chariot électrique no
Buggy Voiturette yes — **Clubs** Clubs yes
Credit cards Cartes de crédit
VISA - MasterCard - AMEX - DC

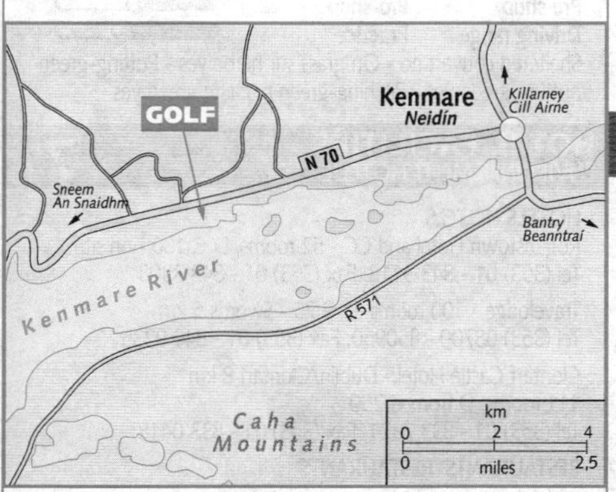

Access Accès : From Killarney, Ring of Kerry through Kenmare, then → Templenoe
Map 3 on page 812 Carte 3 Page 812

GOLF COURSE — PARCOURS 15/20

Site Site
Maintenance Entretien
Architect Architecte Eddie Hackett
Type Type seaside, parkland
Relief Relief
Water in play Eau en jeu
Exp. to wind Exposé au vent
Trees in play Arbres en jeu

Scorecard / Carte de score	Chp. / Chp.	Mens / Mess.	Ladies / Da.
Length Long.	6127	5742	4997
Par	72	72	72
Slope system	—	—	—

Advised golfing ability 0 12 24 36
Niveau de jeu recommandé
Hcp required Handicap exigé no

CLUB HOUSE & AMENITIES — CLUB HOUSE ET ANNEXES 7/10

Pro shop Pro-shop
Driving range Practice
Sheltered couvert 5 bays - On grass sur herbe yes - Putting-green putting-green yes - Pitching-green pitching green no

HOTEL FACILITIES — ENVIRONNEMENT HOTELIER 7/10

HOTELS HÔTELS
Sheen Falls Lodge - Kenmare 5 km
66 rooms, D € 425
Tel (353) 064 - 41 600, Fax (353) 064 - 41 386

Park Hotel - 46 rooms, D € 217 - Kenmare 5 km
Tel (353) 064 - 41 200, Fax (353) 064 - 41 402

The Lodge - 10 rooms, D from € 90 - Kenmare 7 km
Tel (353) 064 - 41 512, Fax (353) 064 - 42 724

RESTAURANTS RESTAURANTS
D'Arcy's - Kenmare 5 km - Tel (353) 064 - 41 589
The Lime Tree - Kenmare 5 km - Tel (353) 064 - 41 225
An Leath Phingin (Italian) - Kenmare 5 km
Tel (353) 064 - 41 559

Roganstown

14	7	7

Laid out over pleasantly rolling terrain, this course, close to Dublin, also features a 52-room hotel with spa and seminar facilities. The architecture was assigned to Christy O'Connor Jr., the guarantee of a serious layout and design. However, as the great man has already built about thirty other courses, comparisons are inevitable and you may find that his inspiration here is a little less potent and original than elsewhere. In his now well-established style, he has cleverly played with the meanders of the river Broadmeadow, which crosses the site, and the digging of several little extra lakes has brought water into play on two-thirds of the course. That's enough to deter the less experienced golfer, who should not think twice about playing from the front. Some of the more salient features are the par 3s, especially holes 9 and 13, and the excellence of the greens. The only suggestion of a downside is the distance between green and tee.

Créée dans un terrain agréablement ondulé, cette réalisation à quelques pas de Dublin comprend également un hôtel de 52 de chambres avec spa et équipements de séminaires. Le dessin du parcours a été confié à Christy O'Connor Jr. C'est une garantie de sérieux dans la conception comme dans la construction, mais comme il en a déjà produit près d'une trentaine, les comparaisons sont inévitables, et on peut avoir trouvé son inspiration plus puissante, ou plus originale ailleurs. Dans son style désormais bien établi, il a très bien joué avec les méandres de la rivière Broadmeadow qui parcourt le site, et la création de plusieurs petits lacs supplémentaires met l'eau en jeu sur les deux-tiers du parcours. De quoi effrayer les moins expérimentés, qui ne devront pas hésiter à utiliser les départs avancés. On retiendra particulièrement le dessin des par 3, notamment le 9 et le 17, ainsi que la qualité des greens. Un bémol, la distance entre les greens et les départs.

Roganstown Golf and Country Club — 2004

IRL - SWORDS, Co Dublin

Office	Secrétariat	(353) 01 - 843 3118
Pro shop	Pro-shop	(353) 01 - 843 3118
Fax	Fax	(353) 01 - 843 3303
Web	www.roganstown.com	
Situation	Situation	Dublin, 9 km
Annual closure	Fermeture annuelle	no
Weekly closure	Fermeture hebdomadaire	no

Fees main season Tarifs haute saison

	Week days Semaine	We/Bank holidays We/Férié
Individual Individuel	€ 85	€ 85
Couple Couple	€ 170	€ 170

Caddie Caddie on request **Electric Trolley** Chariot électrique yes

Buggy Voiturette yes **Clubs** Clubs yes

Credit cards Cartes de crédit
VISA - MasterCard - AMEX

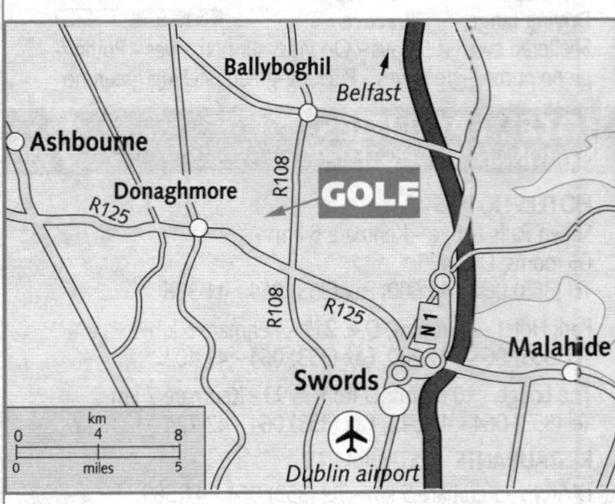

Access Accès : Dublin, N1 → Belfast to Swords, then R125 → Ashbourne. Golf signposted

Map 1 on page 809 Carte 1 Page 809

GOLF COURSE — PARCOURS — 14/20

Site	Site	
Maintenance	Entretien	
Architect	Architecte	Christy O'Connor Jr.
Type	Type	parkland
Relief	Relief	
Water in play	Eau en jeu	
Exp. to wind	Exposé au vent	
Trees in play	Arbres en jeu	

Scorecard Carte de score	Chp. Chp.	Mens Mess.	Ladies Da.
Length Long.	6300	5930	4871
Par	71	71	71
Slope system	—	—	—

Advised golfing ability Niveau de jeu recommandé — 0 12 24 36

Hcp required Handicap exigé — no

CLUB HOUSE & AMENITIES — CLUB HOUSE ET ANNEXES — 7/10

Pro shop	Pro-shop	
Driving range	Practice	

Sheltered couvert no - On grass sur herbe yes - Putting-green putting-green yes - Pitching-green pitching green yes

HOTEL FACILITIES — ENVIRONNEMENT HOTELIER — 7/10

HOTELS HÔTELS

Roganstown Hotel and CC - 52 rooms, D € 180 - on site
Tel (353) 01 - 843 3118, Fax (353) 01 - 843 3303

Travelodge - 100 rooms, D € 75 - Swords 5 km
Tel (353) 08700 - 850950, Fax (353) 01 - 840 9235

Clontarf Castle Hotel - Dublin/Clontarf 8 km
111 rooms, D from € 250
Tel (353) 01 - 833 2321, Fax (353) 01 - 833 0418

RESTAURANTS RESTAURANTS

Old Schoolhouse - Swords 6 km - Tel (353) 01 - 840 4160
La Stampa - Dublin 10 km - Tel (353) 01 - 677 8611
Shanahan's on the Green - Dublin 10 km
Tel (353) 01 - 407 0939

Rosapenna *Old Tom Morris*

16 | 7 | 6

Originally designed by Old Tom Morris in 1893, Rosapenna was reshaped by James Braid and Harry Vardon in 1906 and by Eddie Hackett in 1993, before Pat Ruddy added the latest update to what has become a 36-hole facility. Against such a background, the "Old Tom Morris" course should, on the face of it, be quite something, and it is. This is one of the obligatory stop-offs in the long trek of exploring golfing treasures in the north-west of Ireland, often unknown to foreign tourists but not so to the Irish themselves. Playing on a links is like going back to the origins of the game, when intuition and inspiration held the upper hand over pure technique, when the size of your score was merely relative because match-play was the formula that reigned supreme with amateur golfers. Exposure to the wind makes Rosapenna a tricky number to play, and even if the traps are seldom hidden, playing here several times makes it easier to choose tactics. Lack of experience could be a serious setback for high-handicappers. Great value for money.

Dessiné par Old Tom Morris en 1893, Rosapenna a bénéficié du travail de James Braid et Harry Vardon en 1906, puis de Eddie Hackett en 1993, avant que s'ajoute un second parcours à un ensemble de 36 trous ! Avec de tels signataires, ce parcours "Old Tom Morris" ne peut laisser indifférent, a priori. Il constitue l'une des étapes obligées dans une longue exploration de trésors golfiques souvent ignorés par les touristes étrangers, alors que les Irlandais en ont pris souvent le chemin. Jouer sur un links, c'est retrouver les origines du jeu, où l'intuition et l'inspiration prenaient le pas sur la technique pure, où l'importance du score était toute relative quand le match-play était la formule reine des amateurs. L'exposition au vent rend forcément Rosapenna délicat à jouer, et même si les pièges sont rarement dissimulés, jouer plusieurs fois améliore les choix tactiques. Le manque d'expérience pourra gêner les golfeurs très moyens. Le rapport qualité/prix est ici remarquable.

Rosapenna Hotel & Golf Links — 1893

IRL - DOWNINGS, Co Donegal

Office	Secrétariat	(353) 07491 - 55 301
Pro shop	Pro-shop	(353) 07491 - 55 301
Fax	Fax	(353) 07491 - 55 128
Web	www.rosapenna.ie	
Situation	Situation	Letterkenny, 40 km
Annual closure	Fermeture annuelle	no
Weekly closure	Fermeture hebdomadaire	no

Fees main season Tarifs haute saison	18 holes	
	Week days Semaine	**We/Bank holidays** We/Férié
Individual Individuel	€ 50	€ 50
Couple Couple	€ 100	€ 100

Caddie Caddie on request **Electric Trolley** Chariot électrique no

Buggy Voiturette yes **Clubs** Clubs yes

Credit cards Cartes de crédit
VISA - Eurocard - MasterCard - AMEX - DC

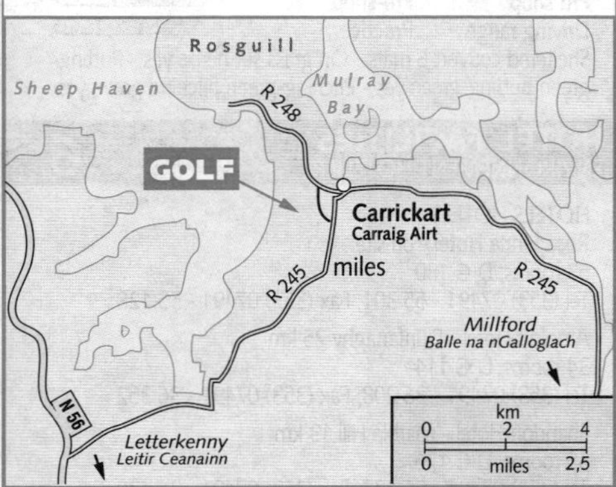

Access Accès : Letterkenny: R245 to Rathmelton, Millford, Cranford, Carrigart. Golf 2 km → Rosapenna

Map 2 on page 811 Carte 2 Page 811

GOLF COURSE — PARCOURS 16/20

Site	Site	
Maintenance	Entretien	
Architect	Architecte	Old Tom Morris Braid, Vardon
Type	Type	links
Relief	Relief	
Water in play	Eau en jeu	
Exp. to wind	Exposé au vent	
Trees in play	Arbres en jeu	

Scorecard Carte de score	**Chp.** Chp.	**Mens** Mess.	**Ladies** Da.
Length Long.	5950	5644	4555
Par	71	70	74
Slope system	—	—	—

Advised golfing ability Niveau de jeu recommandé — 0 12 24 36

Hcp required Handicap exigé — 36

CLUB HOUSE & AMENITIES — CLUB HOUSE ET ANNEXES 7/10

Pro shop Pro-shop

Driving range Practice

Sheltered couvert 6 mats - On grass sur herbe yes - Putting-green putting-green yes - Pitching-green pitching green yes

HOTEL FACILITIES — ENVIRONNEMENT HOTELIER 6/10

HOTELS HÔTELS

Rosapenna Hotel - on site
53 rooms, D € 180
Tel (353) 07491 - 55 301, Fax (353) 07491 - 55 128

Arnold's Hotel - Dunfanaghy 25 km
34 rooms, D € 114
Tel (353) 07491 - 36 208, Fax (353) 07491 - 36 352

Shandon Hotel - Marble Hill 13 km
55 rooms, D € 176
Tel (353) 07491 - 36 137, Fax (353) 07491 - 36 430

RESTAURANTS RESTAURANTS

Rosapenna Hotel - on site - Tel (353) 07491 - 55 301
The Cove - Dunfanaghy 25 km - Tel (353) 07491 - 36 300

883

Rosapenna *Sandy Hills Links*

15 | 7 | 6

Pat Ruddy was the man Rosapenna asked to design a new 18-hole course on a site of sand-dunes that was crying out for golf. The course literally winds its way between them, changing direction all the while; this makes it disconcertingly difficult to gauge the wind but provides for an exciting round of golf. Lovers of links courses will be delighted, so will people who can sometimes forget about their score and enjoy it even though their swing has long deserted them. Played from the tips, Sandy Hills can be a real mean monster, but the staggering of tee-boxes helps you to gently come to terms with it or, in any case, not to see too many par 5s, even though officially the card gives only 3 of them. With the usual few blind shots, here we are dealing with a totally classic, spectacular and inventive links course, excellent from start to finish, with two par 3s that really stand out, holes N° 7 and 11. This complex has become a must.

C'est à Pat Ruddy que Rosapenna a demandé le dessin d'un nouveau 18 trous dans un site de dunes qui n'attendait que cela. Le parcours serpente littéralement entre elles en changeant constamment de direction, ce qui certes peut rendre les trajectoires dans le vent déconcertantes mais aussi le jeu bien excitant. Les amoureux des links s'en réjouiront, eux qui savent oublier parfois le score et garder du plaisir quand bien même le swing se serait enfui. Joué du fond, Sandy Hills peut être un véritable monstre, mais l'étagement des départs permet de l'apprivoiser en douceur, en tout cas de ne pas voir trop de par 5, alors que la carte n'en donne officiellement que 3 ! Avec les quelques coups aveugles d'usage, nous avons affaire à un links tout à fait classique, spectaculaire et inventif, d'une qualité soutenue, où l'on distinguera deux par 3, le 7 et le 11. Cet ensemble de Rosapenna est devenu un must.

Rosapenna Hotel & Golf Links — 2003

IRL - DOWNINGS, Co Donegal

Office Secrétariat (353) 07491 - 55 301
Pro shop Pro-shop (353) 07491 - 55 301
Fax Fax (353) 07491 - 55 128
Web www.rosapenna.ie
Situation Situation Letterkenny, 40 km
Annual closure Fermeture annuelle no
Weekly closure Fermeture hebdomadaire no
Fees main season Tarifs haute saison 18 holes

	Week days Semaine	We/Bank holidays We/Férié
Individual Individuel	€ 75	€ 75
Couple Couple	€ 150	€ 150

Caddie Caddie on request **Electric Trolley** Chariot électrique no
Buggy Voiturette yes **Clubs** Clubs yes
Credit cards Cartes de crédit
VISA - Eurocard - MasterCard - AMEX - DC

Rosguill
Sheep Haven
Mulray Bay
R 248
GOLF
Carrickart
Carraig Airt
R 245
R 245
Millford
Balle na nGalloglach
N 56
Letterkenny
Leitir Ceanainn
0 2 4 km
0 2,5 miles

Access Accès : Letterkenny: R245 to Rathmelton, Millford, Cranford, Carrigart. Golf 2 km → Rosapenna
Map 2 on page 811 Carte 2 Page 811

GOLF COURSE — PARCOURS 15/20

Site Site
Maintenance Entretien
Architect Architecte Pat Ruddy
Type Type links
Relief Relief
Water in play Eau en jeu
Exp. to wind Exposé au vent
Trees in play Arbres en jeu

Scorecard Carte de score	Chp. Chp.	Mens Mess.	Ladies Da.
Length Long.	6440	5721	4382
Par	71	71	71
Slope system	—	—	—

Advised golfing ability Niveau de jeu recommandé 0 12 24 36
Hcp required Handicap exigé 36

CLUB HOUSE & AMENITIES — CLUB HOUSE ET ANNEXES 7/10

Pro shop Pro-shop
Driving range Practice
Sheltered couvert 6 mats - On grass sur herbe yes - Putting-green putting-green yes - Pitching-green pitching green yes

HOTEL FACILITIES — ENVIRONNEMENT HOTELIER 6/10

HOTELS HÔTELS
Rosapenna Hotel - on site
53 rooms, D € 180
Tel (353) 07491 - 55 301, Fax (353) 07491 - 55 128

Arnold's Hotel - Dunfanaghy 25 km
34 rooms, D € 114
Tel (353) 07491 - 36 208, Fax (353) 07491 - 36 352

Shandon Hotel - Marble Hill 13 km
55 rooms, D € 176
Tel (353) 07491 - 36 137, Fax (353) 07491 - 36 430

RESTAURANTS RESTAURANTS
Rosapenna Hotel - on site - Tel (353) 07491 - 55 301
The Cove - Dunfanaghy 25 km - Tel (353) 07491 - 36 300

Rosslare

13	5	6

This course is located on a peninsula, and what with there being no trees to protect it, is clearly exposed to the wind. This element makes any links course an exciting proposition and adds to the pleasure when you can keep control. It can, though, easily upset the more inexperienced player. This is the main difficulty at Rosslare, which has recently been upgraded to excellent effect. The bunkers are more strategic than really penalising and the well-watered greens will still hold slightly miscued shots, but before reaching them you need an accurate tee-shot to avoid the unforgiving rough. One particular feature here is the excellence of the par 3s and the closing holes along the sea, which are superb fun in match-play. Today, better suited to holiday golf than tournaments, Rosslare is a good course on which to become acclimatised with links golf. The club owns an additional nine holes, inland.

La situation de ce parcours sur une péninsule et l'absence d'arbres protecteurs impliquent une forte exposition au vent. Cet élément rend très excitants les parcours de links, et renforce le plaisir quand on réussit à en maîtriser les effets. Mais il tourne la tête des joueurs peu expérimentés ! C'est la principale difficulté de Rosslare, autrement un peu désuet au regard des joueurs du meilleur niveau, et qui a été bien remanié. Les bunkers sont plus stratégiques que vraiment pénalisants, l'arrosage des greens a facilité la réception des coups imparfaits, mais il faut encore de la précision au drive pour pouvoir les attaquer, car le rough peut être méchant. On distinguera particulièrement ici la qualité des pars 3, et celle des derniers trous le long de la mer, qui offrent un espace superbe en match-play. Aujourd'hui mieux adapté à un golf de vacances que de championnat, Rosslare est un bon parcours pour se familiariser avec l'architecture de links, après avoir joué les 9 trous "inland" peut-être.

Rosslare Golf Club — 1905

IRL - ROSSLARE STRAND, Co Wicklow

Office	Secrétariat	(353) 053 - 32 203
Pro shop	Pro-shop	(353) 053 - 32 032
Fax	Fax	(353) 053 - 32 262
Web	www.rosslaregolf.com	
Situation	Situation	Wexford (pop. 9 533), 18 km
Annual closure	Fermeture annuelle	no
Weekly closure	Fermeture hebdomadaire	no

Fees main season Tarifs haute saison	18 holes	
	Week days Semaine	**We/Bank holidays** We/Férié
Individual Individuel	€ 40	€ 60
Couple Couple	€ 80	€ 120

Caddie Caddie on request **Electric Trolley** Chariot électrique yes

Buggy Voiturette yes **Clubs** Clubs yes

Credit cards Cartes de crédit
VISA - Mastercard - AMEX

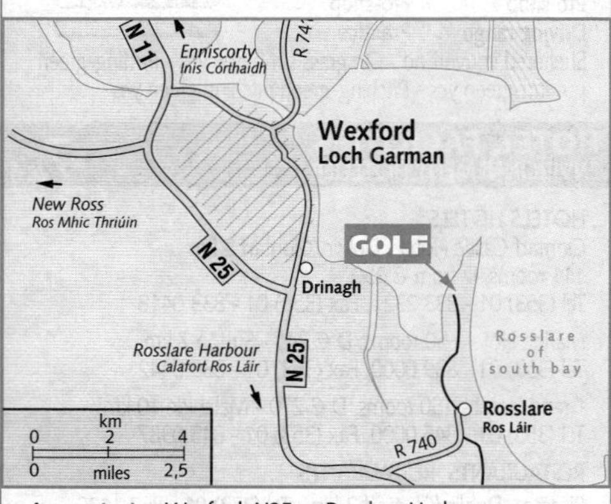

Access Accès : Wexford, N25 → Rosslare Harbour.
1 km after Killinick, left on R740 to Rosslare.
Golf → Rosslare Point/Burrow
Map 3 on page 813 Carte 3 Page 813

GOLF COURSE — PARCOURS — 13/20

Site	Site	
Maintenance	Entretien	
Architect	Architecte	Hawtree & Taylor
Type	Type	seaside course, links
Relief	Relief	
Water in play	Eau en jeu	
Exp. to wind	Exposé au vent	
Trees in play	Arbres en jeu	

Scorecard Carte de score	**Chp.** Chp.	**Mens** Mess.	**Ladies** Da.
Length Long.	5920	5650	5075
Par	72	72	73
Slope system	—	—	—

Advised golfing ability Niveau de jeu recommandé: 0 12 24 36
Hcp required Handicap exigé: no

CLUB HOUSE & AMENITIES — CLUB HOUSE ET ANNEXES — 5/10

Pro shop Pro-shop
Driving range Practice
Sheltered couvert no - On grass sur herbe yes (own balls) - Putting-green putting-green yes - Pitching-green pitching green yes

HOTEL FACILITIES — ENVIRONNEMENT HOTELIER — 6/10

HOTELS HÔTELS

Kelly's Resort - Rosslare Strand 1 km
118 rooms, D € 187
Tel (353) 053 - 32 114, Fax (353) 053 - 32 222

Cedars Hotel - 34 rooms, D € 150 - Rosslare Strand 1 km
Tel (353) 053 - 32 124, Fax (353) 053 - 32 243

Great Southern - Rosslare Harbour 4 km
100 rooms, D from € 130
Tel (353) 053 - 33 233, Fax (353) 053 - 33 543

RESTAURANTS RESTAURANTS

Ocean Bed Seafood Restaurant - Wexford 20 km
Tel (353) 053 - 23 935

Kelly's Resort - Rosslare Strand 1 km - Tel (353) 053 - 32 114

Royal Dublin

16 | 8 | 7

Royal Dublin is an excellent example of a classic links, peppered with deep fairway and green-side bunkers and a number of bushes, but these are often more decorative or useful for gauging distance than really dangerous. Refurbishment work by Martin Hawtree has changed the course dramatically, adding 400 yards to its length which is now 7,250 yards. There are new sixth, seventh and eighth holes while the 10th green has been re-located. Although the terrain is none too hilly, there are a couple of blind drives but nothing blind when approaching the greens. You could almost call this a kind course if the prevailing wind wasn't blowing in your face on the way in. This makes the back 9 an even trickier proposition, demanding certain skills in drawing the ball, a feat that many will find harder than others. A very natural looking course, generally busy, being so close to Dublin.

Bien qu'il n'appartienne pas au club très fermé des parcours exceptionnels, Royal Dublin est un excellent exemple de links classique, avec ses profonds bunkers de fairway et de greens (parfois très pénalisants), des buissons, mais souvent plus décoratifs ou utiles comme points de repère que vraiment dangereux. L'architecte Martin Hawtree a récemment porté sa longueur à 6525 mètres, en modifiant les 6, 7 et 8, et en déplaçant le green du 10. Bien que le terrain soit peu accidenté, on trouve ici quelques drives aveugles, mais aucun green de la sorte. On pourrait presque le qualifier d'aimable si le vent dominant n'était contraire au retour, ce qui rend cette partie du parcours encore plus délicate, exigeant notamment une bonne maîtrise des effets de draw, ce qui n'est pas donné à tout le monde ! Très naturel d'aspect, remanié par Harry S. Colt après la première Guerre Mondiale, il est très fréquenté étant donné sa proximité de Dublin.

Royal Dublin Golf Club — 1885

Bull Island
IRL - DUBLIN 3

Office	Secrétariat	(353) 01 - 833 6346
Pro shop	Pro-shop	(353) 01 - 833 6477
Fax	Fax	(353) 01 - 833 6504
Web	www.theroyaldublingolfclub.com	
Situation	Situation	Dublin, 7 km
Annual closure	Fermeture annuelle	no
Weekly closure	Fermeture hebdomadaire	no

Fees main season Tarifs haute saison	18 holes	
	Week days Semaine	**We/Bank holidays** We/Férié
Individual Individuel	€ 125	€ 125
Couple Couple	€ 250	€ 250

Saturday: only 16:00-17:00 / Other days: access limited

Caddie Caddie no — **Electric Trolley** Chariot électrique no
Buggy Voiturette yes — **Clubs** Clubs yes
Credit cards Cartes de crédit
VISA - MasterCard - AMEX

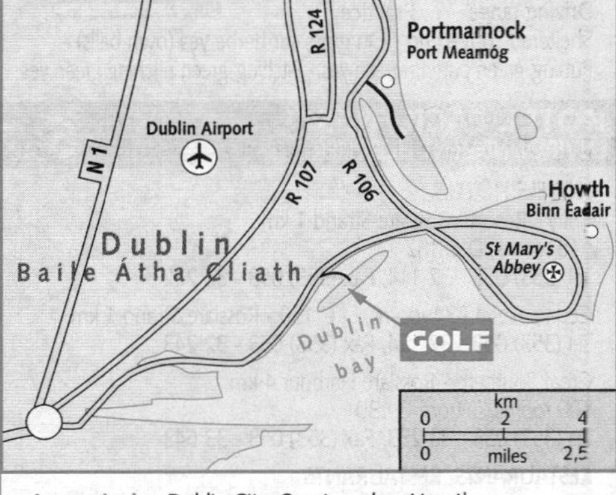

Access Accès : Dublin City, Coast road → Howth.
Bull Island Bridge, turn right
Map 1 on page 809 Carte 1 Page 809

GOLF COURSE — PARCOURS — 16/20

Site	Site	
Maintenance	Entretien	
Architect	Architecte	Harry S. Colt
Type	Type	links
Relief	Relief	
Water in play	Eau en jeu	
Exp. to wind	Exposé au vent	
Trees in play	Arbres en jeu	

Scorecard Carte de score	**Chp.** Chp.	**Mens** Mess.	**Ladies** Da.
Length Long.	6525	6030	5439
Par	72	72	74
Slope system	—	—	—

Advised golfing ability Niveau de jeu recommandé: 0 12 24 36
Hcp required Handicap exigé: 28 Men, 36 Ladies

CLUB HOUSE & AMENITIES — CLUB HOUSE ET ANNEXES — 8/10

Pro shop	Pro-shop
Driving range	Practice

Sheltered couvert no - On grass sur herbe yes - Putting-green putting-green yes - Pitching-green pitching green yes

HOTEL FACILITIES — ENVIRONNEMENT HOTELIER — 7/10

HOTELS HÔTELS

Clontarf Castle Hotel - Dublin/Clontarf 2 km
111 rooms, D from € 250
Tel (353) 01 - 833 2321, Fax (353) 01 - 833 0418

Marine Hotel - 50 rooms, D € 245 - Sutton 7 km
Tel (353) 01 - 839 0000, Fax (353) 01 - 839 0442

Grand Hotel - 150 rooms, D € 270 - Malahide 10 km
Tel (353) 01 - 845 0000, Fax (353) 01 - 845 0987

RESTAURANTS RESTAURANTS

Picasso - Dublin/Clontarf 2 km - Tel (353) 01 - 853 1120
Dollymount House - Dublin/Clontarf 8 km
Tel (353) 01 - 833 2492
Roly's Bistro - Dublin 13 km - Tel (353) 01 - 668 2611

Seafield

14 | 7 | 7

Just as you can get a taste of all four seasons in one Irish day, Seafield offers three distinct styles on a single course: the coastline (although this is not a real links course), heather and an attractive park, with the Tara Hills sitting nicely in the background. With such variety, Peter McEvoy has succeeded in designing a rather uniform layout, showcasing the contrasts but avoiding any visual clash. However, with the wind never far away, shifting from one section to the next can and does pose a few problems. McEvoy's imagination, golfing savvy and skill in moulding golf-course landscapes have produced a layout that is generally fair and honest without too many hidden difficulties. And he more or less had to, because water is a dominant factor on 15 holes and enough to scare off more than one inexperienced golfer. And if their putting is not up to it, they will suffer like everyone else on some typical McEvoy greens, i.e. pretty huge putting surfaces with some rather sharp breaks to boot. A welcome new-comer and one for which we will sit back and watch mature.

Tout comme on peut voir les quatre saisons en une journée irlandaise, Seafield propose trois parties distinctes en un seul parcours : le bord de mer, la bruyère et l'esthétique d'un parc, avec en toile de fond les Tara Hills. Dans cette diversité, Peter McEvoy a réussi à créer un parcours homogène, mettant en valeur les contrastes sans causer de chocs. Cependant, avec le vent souvent présent, le passage d'une zone à l'autre peut poser des problèmes. L'imagination de McEvoy, sa connaissance du jeu et son art d'aménager le paysage golfique ont donné ici un parcours généralement franc et direct, sans trop de difficultés cachées. Il le fallait car l'eau est un facteur dominant sur 15 trous, ce qui peut effrayer les amateurs peu expérimentés. Et s'ils ne sont pas à l'aise avec leur putter, ils souffriront comme tout le monde sur des greens caractéristiques de McEvoy, c'est-à-dire assez vastes, et avec des ondulations assez sévères. Une réalisation bienvenue, que l'on attendra de voir mûrir encore.

Seafield Golf & Country Club — 2002

IRL - BALLYMONEY, GOREY, Co Wexford

Office	Secrétariat	(353) 055 - 24 777
Pro shop	Pro-shop	(353) 055 - 24 777
Fax	Fax	(353) 055 - 24 837
Web	www.seafieldgolf.com	
Situation	Situation	Dublin, 85 km
Annual closure	Fermeture annuelle	no
Weekly closure	Fermeture hebdomadaire	no

Fees main season Tarifs haute saison — 18 holes

	Week days / Semaine	We/Bank holidays / We/Férié
Individual Individuel	€ 85	€ 95
Couple Couple	€ 170	€ 190

Caddie Caddie on request **Electric Trolley** Chariot électrique yes

Buggy Voiturette yes **Clubs** Clubs yes

Credit cards Cartes de crédit
VISA - MasterCard - AMEX

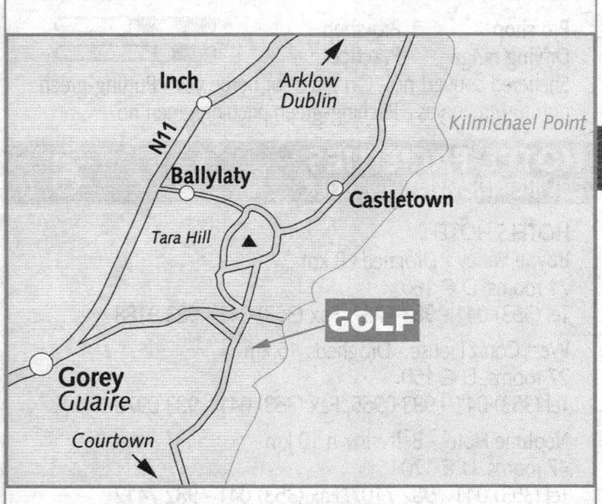

Access Accès : Dublin N11 South → Arklow, then → Gorey. Golf near the village of Ballymoney on left hand side, before Gorey.

Map 1 on page 809 Carte 1 Page 809

GOLF COURSE — PARCOURS — 14/20

Site	Site	
Maintenance	Entretien	
Architect	Architecte	Peter McEvoy
Type	Type	seaside, open country
Relief	Relief	
Water in play	Eau en jeu	
Exp. to wind	Exposé au vent	
Trees in play	Arbres en jeu	

Scorecard Carte de score	Chp. Chp.	Mens Mess.	Ladies Da.
Length Long.	5985	5905	4640
Par	71	71	71
Slope system	—	—	—

Advised golfing ability Niveau de jeu recommandé — 0 12 24 36

Hcp required Handicap exigé — no

CLUB HOUSE & AMENITIES — CLUB HOUSE ET ANNEXES — 7/10

Pro shop Pro-shop
Driving range Practice
Sheltered couvert - On grass sur herbe no - Putting-green putting-green yes - Pitching-green pitching green yes

HOTEL FACILITIES — ENVIRONNEMENT HOTELIER — 7/10

HOTELS HÔTELS

Ashdown Park - Gorey 4 km
79 rooms, D from € 150
Tel (353) 055 - 80 500, Fax (353) 055 - 80 777

Marlfield House Hotel - Gorey 4 km
19 rooms, D € 225
Tel (353) 055 - 21 124, Fax (353) 055 - 21 572

Woodenbridge Hotel - Arklow 10 km
63 rooms, D from € 90
Tel (353) 0402 - 35 146, Fax (353) 0402 - 35 573

RESTAURANTS RESTAURANTS

Marlfield House - Gorey 4 km - Tel (353) 055 - 21 124
Kitty's - Arklow 8 km - Tel (353) 0402 - 31 669

Seapoint

15 | 6 | 6

From the elevated 14th tee at County Louth, you can see much of the neighbouring course of Seapoint. Here, it is a return to similar moonscape scenery though early on, a large section of the course winds through heather and a more rural-looking landscape. This is rather an attractive contrast, and gives the impression of a course gradually building up speed through to the closing holes, all very spectacular and exciting when using the match-play format. The wind often has a word or two to say, and good ball control is required, especially with the tee shot, in order to avoid the fairway bunkers and get a good view of the greens to keep out of the often dangerous green-side traps. These greens are large and distinguished more by general slopes than by individual contouring. By and large, the difficulties are clearly visible (water comes into play on the 3rd, 4th and 9th holes), so at least you can start out here with a degree of confidence. Well worth knowing.

Depuis le départ reculé du 14 de County Louth, on aperçoit pratiquement tout le parcours voisin de Seapoint. On y retrouve au retour un paysage lunaire analogue, alors qu'une grande partie se déroule dans la bruyère et un paysage plus rural. Ce contraste est d'ailleurs assez séduisant, et donne une impression de montée en puissance progressive, jusqu'aux derniers trous, très spectaculaires et excitants en match-play. Le vent joue souvent un rôle et il faut un bon contrôle de balle, en particulier depuis les départs, pour éviter les bunkers de fairway et avoir une ouverture suffisante sur les greens pour échapper à leurs bunkers, souvent dangereux. Ces greens sont largement dimensionnés, et caractérisés davantage par des pentes générales que par des ondulations ponctuelles. En règle générale, les difficultés sont bien visibles (eau en jeu aux 3, 4 et 9), ce qui permet d'aborder Seapoint avec un minimum de confiance. A connaître.

Seapoint Golf Club — 1993

IRL - TERMONFECKIN, Co Louth

Office Secrétariat (353) 041 - 982 2333
Pro shop Pro-shop (353) 041 - 988 1066
Fax Fax (353) 041 - 982 2331
Web www.seapointgolfclub.com
Situation Situation Drogheda (pop. 24 460), 8 km
Annual closure Fermeture annuelle no
Weekly closure Fermeture hebdomadaire no
Fees main season Tarifs haute saison 18 holes

	Week days Semaine	We/Bank holidays We/Férié
Individual Individuel	€ 60	€ 75
Couple Couple	€ 120	€ 150

Friday: € 50

Caddie Caddie on request **Electric Trolley** Chariot électrique no
Buggy Voiturette yes **Clubs** Clubs yes
Credit cards Cartes de crédit
VISA - MasterCard - AMEX

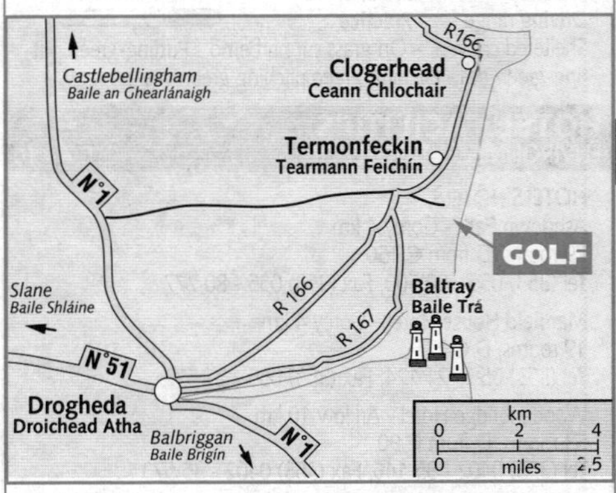

Access Accès : Drogheda, Termonfeckin Road
Map 1 on page 809 Carte 1 Page 809

GOLF COURSE — PARCOURS 15/20

Site Site
Maintenance Entretien
Architect Architecte Des Smyth, Declan Branigan
Type Type links
Relief Relief
Water in play Eau en jeu
Exp. to wind Exposé au vent
Trees in play Arbres en jeu

Scorecard Carte de score	Chp. Chp.	Mens Mess.	Ladies Da.
Length Long.	6463	6118	5162
Par	72	72	73
Slope system	—	—	—

Advised golfing ability Niveau de jeu recommandé 0 12 24 36
Hcp required Handicap exigé 28 Men, 36 Ladies

CLUB HOUSE & AMENITIES — CLUB HOUSE ET ANNEXES 6/10

Pro shop Pro-shop
Driving range Practice
Sheltered couvert no - On grass sur herbe yes - Putting-green putting-green yes - Pitching-green pitching green no

HOTEL FACILITIES — ENVIRONNEMENT HOTELIER 6/10

HOTELS HÔTELS

Boyne Valley - Drogheda 8 km
71 rooms, D € 160
Tel (353) 041 - 983 7737, Fax (353) 041 - 983 9188

West Court House - Drogheda 15 km
27 rooms, D € 150
Tel (353) 041 - 983 0965, Fax (353) 041 - 983 0970

Neptune Hotel - Bettystown 10 km
47 rooms, D € 170
Tel (353) 041 - 982 7107, Fax (353) 041 - 982 7412

RESTAURANTS RESTAURANTS

Triple House - Termonfeckin 1 km - Tel (353) 041 - 982 2616
Donegans - Monasterboice 5 km - Tel (353) 041 - 983 7383

Slieve Russell

15 | 8 | 5

The early 1990s saw the advent of a fine group of excellent new courses in Ireland, often tied in with hotels. Slieve Russell is one such project in a region that hitherto had earned a reputation as being a paradise for anglers, and whose isolation should appeal to golfers who want to get away from the world for a few days spent in the heart of nature. The landscape is parkland in style, but certain geographical features are reminiscent of a links course. Two large lakes come into play, joined by a stretch of water which lurks just as threateningly, and complete a full barrage of difficulties: sometimes very thick rough, thickets, fairway and green-side bunkers and greens with sometimes very pronounced contours. Of the more memorable holes, we noted the excellence of the par 3s (especially the 16th), the 2nd, where the water is already upon you, and the 13th, a magnificent par 5 alongside Lough Rud. This course has very quickly forged itself a pretty fine reputation, and understandably so.

Le début des années 90 a vu naître en Irlande un bon groupe d'excellents nouveaux parcours, souvent associés à des hôtels. Slieve Russell est de ceux-ci, dans une région jusqu'ici réputée comme un paradis des pêcheurs, et dont l'isolement devrait séduire les golfeurs qui veulent se retirer du monde, du moins en pleine nature et au moins quelques jours. Il se trouve dans un paysage de parc, mais certains reliefs font parfois penser aux links. Deux grands lacs viennent en jeu, réunis par un cours d'eau tout aussi menaçant, et complètent un arsenal de difficultés : rough parfois épais, buissons, bunkers de fairway et de greens, ceux-ci protégeant des greens au relief parfois prononcé. Parmi quelques trous mémorables, on soulignera la qualité des par 3 (notamment le 16), du 2, où l'eau est déjà présente, et du 13, un magnifique par 5 le long du Lough Rud. Ce parcours s'est vite fait une jolie réputation, on comprend pourquoi.

Slieve Russell Golf Club — 1992

IRL - BALLYCONNELL, Co Cavan

Office Secrétariat (353) 049 - 952 6458
Pro shop Pro-shop (353) 049 - 952 5090
Fax Fax (353) 049 - 952 6640
Web www.quinn-group.com
Situation Situation Cavan (pop. 3 509), 25 km
Belturbet (pop. 1 248), 11 km

Annual closure Fermeture annuelle no
Weekly closure Fermeture hebdomadaire no

Fees main season Tarifs haute saison 18 holes

	Week days / Semaine	We/Bank holidays / We/Férié
Individual Individuel	€ 65	€ 80
Couple Couple	€ 130	€ 160

We: Saturday only / Hotel guests : € 40

Caddie Caddie on request **Electric Trolley** Chariot électrique no
Buggy Voiturette yes **Clubs** Clubs yes
Credit cards Cartes de crédit
VISA - Eurocard - MasterCard - AMEX

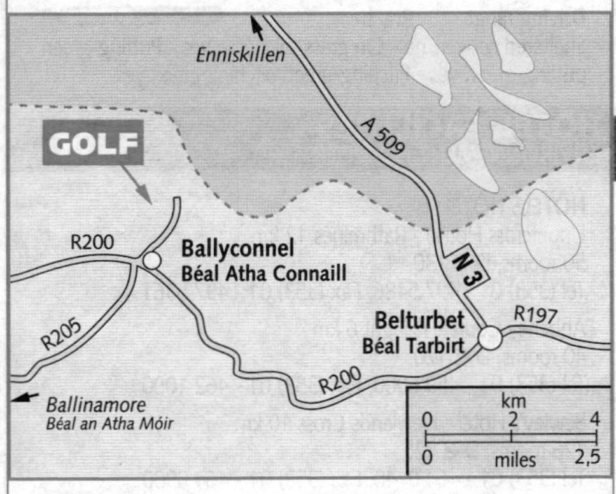

Access Accès : Dublin, N3 → Cavan. Belturbet, R200 → Ballyconnell
Map 2 on page 811 Carte 2 Page 811

GOLF COURSE — PARCOURS 15/20

Site Site
Maintenance Entretien
Architect Architecte Paddy Merrigan
Type Type parkland
Relief Relief
Water in play Eau en jeu
Exp. to wind Exposé au vent
Trees in play Arbres en jeu

Scorecard / Carte de score	Chp. / Chp.	Mens / Mess.	Ladies / Da.
Length Long.	6449	6018	4849
Par	72	72	72
Slope system	—	—	—

Advised golfing ability Niveau de jeu recommandé 0 12 24 36
Hcp required Handicap exigé certificate

CLUB HOUSE & AMENITIES — CLUB HOUSE ET ANNEXES 8/10

Pro shop Pro-shop
Driving range Practice
Sheltered couvert 5 bays - On grass sur herbe yes - Putting-green putting-green yes - Pitching-green pitching green yes

HOTEL FACILITIES — ENVIRONNEMENT HOTELIER 5/10

HOTELS HÔTELS
Slieve Russell Hotel - on site
219 rooms, D € 240
Tel (353) 049 - 952 6444, Fax (353) 049 - 952 6474

Hotel Kilmore - Cavan 12 km
39 rooms, D € 148
Tel (353) 049 - 433 2288, Fax (353) 049 - 433 2458

RESTAURANTS RESTAURANTS
Summit - on site
Tel (353) 049 - 26 444

Erne Bistro - Belturbet 11 km
Tel (353) 049 - 952 2443

South County

14	7	8

This course has the best of both worlds, being close to the Irish capital and in a remote country location. Nicholas Bielenberg had already designed the pleasant Luttrellstown course and here again has shown a lot of taste and concern for detail, like in the way he has shaped the terrain around the greens almost as if to reflect the surrounding Dublin Mountains. Inspired by the British style of open spaces, heather and parks which successively dominate the front and back nine, Bielenberg has kept the wraps on several secrets of strategy because you have to play the course several times to fully master some of the trickier aspects. There is also an urgent need to grasp the basic notions of target golf. South County is a members course and everyone will find something to keep them happy, even the average hacker, because despite a river and a couple of lakes, water is in play only on the back nine. With a neatly designed club-house built onto the side of a hill, this club seems destined to greater things and in any case is not quite as flashy as some other courses..

Ce parcours bénéficie de la proximité de Dublin et d'une situation campagnarde. Son architecte Nicholas Bielenberg a déjà conçu Luttrellstown et montre de nouveau ici beaucoup de goût et le souci du détail, comme dans les modelages autour des greens, qui reprennent le profil des Dublin Mountains environnantes. Inspiré par l'esthétique britannique des espaces de bruyère et des parcs, qui dominent successivement l'aller et le retour, Bielenberg a dissimulé quelques secrets de stratégie, car il faut jouer plusieurs fois ici pour bien comprendre ces aspects un peu "tricky", tout comme la nécessité de privilégier le "target golf". South County est un club de membres, et chacun d'eux pourra trouver son bonheur, même les moins expérimentés car, en dépit de la présence d'une rivière et de deux lacs, l'eau n'est vraiment en jeu qu'au retour. Avec un club-house bien conçu à flanc de colline, ce club paraît promis à un bon avenir, moins tapageur en tout cas que d'autres.

South County Golf Club — 1999

Lisheen Road
IRL - BRITTAS VILLAGE, Co Dublin

Office	Secrétariat	(353) 01 - 458 2965
Pro shop	Pro-shop	(353) 01 - 458 2965
Fax	Fax	(353) 01 - 458 2842
Web	www.southcountygolf.com	
Situation	Situation	Dublin, 15 km
Annual closure	Fermeture annuelle	no
Weekly closure	Fermeture hebdomadaire	no

Fees main season Tarifs haute saison — 18 holes

	Week days Semaine	We/Bank holidays We/Férié
Individual Individuel	€ 55	€ 55
Couple Couple	€ 110	€ 110

Week days before 10:00, € 30

Caddie Caddie no — **Electric Trolley** Chariot électrique no
Buggy Voiturette yes — **Clubs** Clubs yes
Credit cards Cartes de crédit
VISA - MasterCard

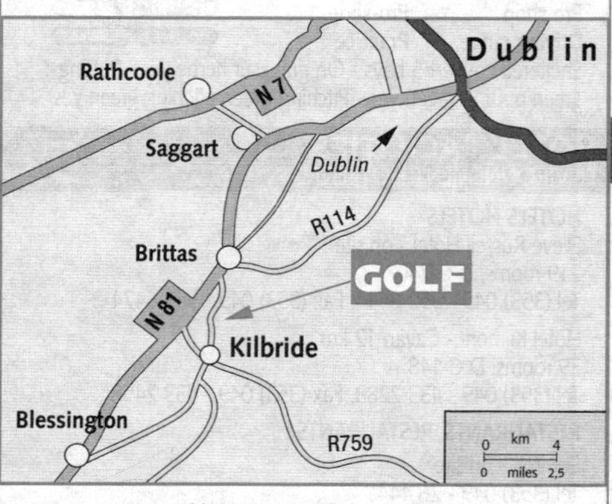

Access Accès : Dublin, N81. In Brittas → Kilbride
Map 1 on page 809 Carte 1 Page 809

GOLF COURSE — PARCOURS — 14/20

Site	Site	
Maintenance	Entretien	
Architect	Architecte	Nicholas Bielenberg
Type	Type	inland
Relief	Relief	
Water in play	Eau en jeu	
Exp. to wind	Exposé au vent	
Trees in play	Arbres en jeu	

Scorecard Carte de score	Chp. Chp.	Mens Mess.	Ladies Da.
Length Long.	6306	5978	4980
Par	72	72	72
Slope system	—	—	—

Advised golfing ability Niveau de jeu recommandé — 0 12 24 36
Hcp required Handicap exigé — no

CLUB HOUSE & AMENITIES — CLUB HOUSE ET ANNEXES — 7/10

Pro shop Pro-shop
Driving range Practice
Sheltered couvert no - On grass sur herbe yes - Putting-green putting-green yes - Pitching-green pitching green yes

HOTEL FACILITIES — ENVIRONNEMENT HOTELIER — 8/10

HOTELS HÔTELS

Uppercross House - Rathmines 12 km
50 rooms, D € 130
Tel (353) 01 - 497 5486, Fax (353) 01 - 497 5361

Abberley Court - Tallaght 6 km
40 rooms, D € 120
Tel (353) 01 - 459 6000, Fax (353) 01 - 462 1000

Bewley's Hotel - Newlands Cross 10 km
126 rooms, D € 125
Tel (353) 01 - 464 0140, Fax (353) 01 - 464 0900

RESTAURANTS RESTAURANTS

Thornton's - Dublin 15 km - Tel (353) 01 - 478 7008
Zen (Chinese) - Rathmines 12 km - Tel (353) 01 - 497 9428

St Helen's Bay

14	6	6

Some 6,000 trees have been planted at St Helen's Bay, and they of course underline the largely parkland nature of this course. Philip Walton, who made his golf-designer debut here, visibly had the amateur golfer in mind. Sure, there is water on six holes, but it is more psychologically scaring than terribly dangerous, the fairway bunkers are on the lenient side and the greens (moderately sized) are well defended but leave a way open for rolled approach shots, if preferred to lofted pitches. From the 14th hole onward, you head for links country, and the going gets tougher as you progress. The coup de grâce awaits you in the dunescape of the 17th and 18th holes, where your card can end in tatters... or maybe not, since you have had 16 holes to hone your swing. One of the major assets of this course is its versatility, and it gives a lot of pleasure to players of all levels. We should mention, in closing, that the "wall of famine", dating from 1846, comes into play on three holes.

6.000 arbres ont été plantés à St Helen's Bay, qui accentuent le paysage de parc d'une partie du parcours. Philip Walton, dont c'est le premier dessin, a visiblement pensé aux amateurs. Certes, l'eau vient en jeu sur six trous, mais de manière plus psychologique que terriblement dangereuse, les bunkers de fairway ne sont pas trop pénalisants, les greens (de dimension confortable) sont bien défendus, mais on peut en aborder la plupart en faisant rouler la balle, ou en la portant, au choix. A partir du 14, nous voici dans un paysage de links, dont la difficulté va croissant, pour culminer au 17 et au 18, deux trous pour détruire sa carte, ou pour la soigner : vous avez 16 trous pour vous y préparer ! La versatilité du parcours est l'un de ses arguments majeurs, il donne beaucoup de plaisir aux joueurs de tous niveaux. Pour l'anecdote, soulignons la mise en jeu sur trois trous du "mur de la famine", qui remonte à 1846.

St Helen's Bay Golf & Country Club — 1993

Kilrane
IRL - ROSSLARE HARBOUR, Co. Wexford

Office Secrétariat (353) 053 - 33 234
Pro shop Pro-shop (353) 053 - 33 234
Fax Fax (353) 053 - 33 803
Web www.sthelensbay.com
Situation Situation Wexford (pop. 15 393), 13 km
Rosslare Harbour, 2 km

Annual closure Fermeture annuelle — no
Weekly closure Fermeture hebdomadaire — no

Fees main season Tarifs haute saison	18 holes	
	Week days Semaine	**We/Bank holidays** We/Férié
Individual Individuel	€ 35	€ 42
Couple Couple	€ 70	€ 84

27 holes: € 40 and € 45 (We)

Caddie Caddie yes **Electric Trolley** Chariot électrique no
Buggy Voiturette yes **Clubs** Clubs yes
Credit cards Cartes de crédit
VISA - Eurocard - MasterCard - AMEX

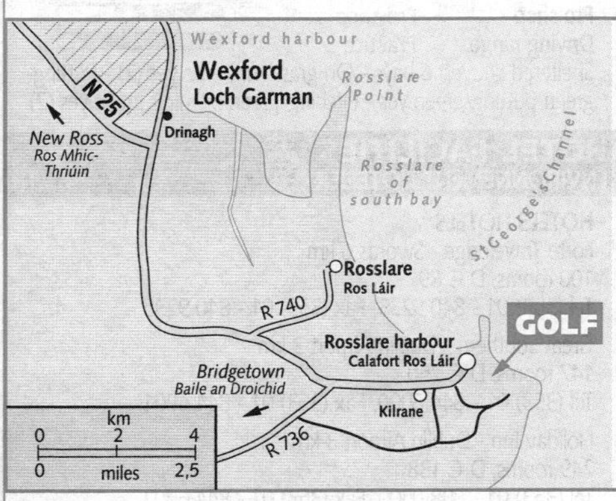

Access Accès : Dublin, N11 to Wexford. N25 to Rosslare Harbour
Map 3 on page 813 Carte 3 Page 813

GOLF COURSE — PARCOURS — 14/20

Site	Site	
Maintenance	Entretien	
Architect	Architecte	Philip Walton
Type	Type	links, parkland
Relief	Relief	
Water in play	Eau en jeu	
Exp. to wind	Exposé au vent	
Trees in play	Arbres en jeu	

Scorecard Carte de score	**Chp.** Chp.	**Mens** Mess.	**Ladies** Da.
Length Long.	6091	5813	4967
Par	72	72	72
Slope system	—	—	—

Advised golfing ability Niveau de jeu recommandé — 0 12 24 36
Hcp required Handicap exigé — no

CLUB HOUSE & AMENITIES — CLUB HOUSE ET ANNEXES — 6/10

Pro shop Pro-shop
Driving range Practice
Sheltered couvert 5 bays - On grass sur herbe yes - Putting-green putting-green yes - Pitching-green pitching green yes

HOTEL FACILITIES — ENVIRONNEMENT HOTELIER — 6/10

HOTELS HÔTELS
Kelly's Resort - Rosslare Strand 5 km
118 rooms, D € 187
Tel (353) 053 - 32 114, Fax (353) 053 - 32 222

Great Southern - Rosslare Harbour 4 km
100 rooms, D from € 130
Tel (353) 053 - 33 233, Fax (353) 053 - 33 543

Cedars Hotel - Rosslare Strand 5 km
34 rooms, D € 150
Tel (353) 053 - 32 124, Fax (353) 053 - 32 243

RESTAURANTS RESTAURANTS
Coopers - Killinick 6 km - Tel (353) 053 - 58 942
Lobster Pot - Carne 3 km - Tel (353) 053 - 31 110

St Margaret's

16	7	7

Before designing Druid's Glen, Pat Ruddy and Tom Craddock gave Dublin one of its best inland courses, at the expense of significant earthwork, as the former farming land was singularly lacking in geographical relief. They evidently had champion golfers in mind, but didn't forget the average amateur player either. Yet despite the many different tee-off areas, they haven't really managed to make it easy. Many of the greens are very well-guarded, and the style of golf is more American than British, meaning a lot of lofted iron shots, long and short. There are a few memorable holes, like the 8th or 12th, two real par 5s reachable only in three, and the 7th and 18th, two grand par 4s. These are all holes where water lurks dangerously. Elsewhere, the bunkers are comparatively flat and so don't set too many problems, even for players who have an aversion to sand. A course well worth getting to know.

Avant de produire Druids Glen, Pat Ruddy et Tom Craddock ont donné à Dublin l'un de ses meilleurs parcours intérieurs, au prix de terrassements importants, car ces anciens terrains agricoles manquaient singulièrement de relief. S'ils ont pensé aux champions, ils n'ont pas oublié les amateurs moyens, mais ils n'ont pas vraiment réussi, malgré le nombre de départs, à le rendre facile. Il faut dire que de nombreux greens sont très défendus, et que l'on joue plus un golf à l'américaine qu'à la "britannique", avec l'obligation de porter haut les coups de fer, y compris les petites approches. Quelques trous sont mémorables, comme le 8 et le 12, deux véritables par 5 à trois coups, le 7 et surtout le 18, deux par 4 de grand style. Ce sont tous des trous où l'eau est dangereuse. Ailleurs, les bunkers sont relativement plats, ce qui ne pose pas trop de problèmes, même à ceux qui n'adorent pas le sable. Un parcours à connaître.

St Margaret's Golf & Country Club 1992

IRL - ST MARGARET'S, Co Dublin

Office	Secrétariat	(353) 01 - 864 0400
Pro shop	Pro-shop	(353) 01 - 864 0400
Fax	Fax	(353) 01 - 864 0408
Web	www.stmargaretsgolf.com	
Situation	Situation	Dublin, 20 km Malahide (pop. 13 539), 10 km
Annual closure	Fermeture annuelle	no
Weekly closure	Fermeture hebdomadaire	no

Fees main season Tarifs haute saison	18 holes	
	Week days Semaine	**We/Bank holidays** We/Férié
Individual Individuel	€ 65	€ 75*
Couple Couple	€ 30	€ 150*

* We: Friday → Sunday

Caddie Caddie no — **Electric Trolley** Chariot électrique yes

Buggy Voiturette yes — **Clubs** Clubs yes

Credit cards Cartes de crédit
VISA - MasterCard - AMEX

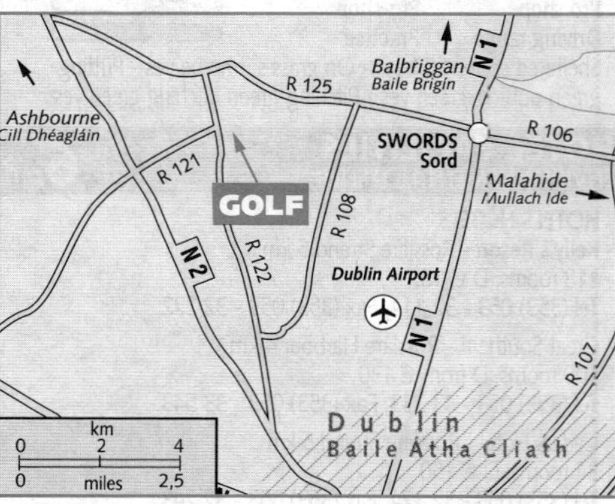

Access Accès : 6 km W. of Dublin Airport
Map 1 on page 809 Carte 1 Page 809

GOLF COURSE
PARCOURS — 16/20

Site	Site	
Maintenance	Entretien	
Architect	Architecte	Pat Ruddy Tom Craddock
Type	Type	parkland, inland
Relief	Relief	
Water in play	Eau en jeu	
Exp. to wind	Exposé au vent	
Trees in play	Arbres en jeu	

Scorecard Carte de score	**Chp.** Chp.	**Mens** Mess.	**Ladies** Da.
Length Long.	6226	5967	5195
Par	73	73	75
Slope system	—	—	—

Advised golfing ability 0 12 24 36
Niveau de jeu recommandé

Hcp required Handicap exigé 28 Men, 36 Ladies

CLUB HOUSE & AMENITIES
CLUB HOUSE ET ANNEXES — 7/10

Pro shop Pro-shop
Driving range Practice
Sheltered couvert 6 bays - On grass sur herbe yes (2) - Putting-green putting-green yes - Pitching-green pitching green yes (2)

HOTEL FACILITIES
ENVIRONNEMENT HOTELIER — 7/10

HOTELS HÔTELS
Forte Travelodge - Swords 6 km
100 rooms, D € 89
Tel (353) 01 - 840 9233, Fax (353) 01 - 840 9235

Great Southern - Dublin Airport 3 km
147 rooms, D € 250
Tel (353) 01 - 844 6000, Fax (353) 01 - 844 6001

Holiday Inn - Dublin Airport 3 km
249 rooms, D € 138
Tel (353) 01 - 808 0500, Fax (353) 01 - 844 6002

RESTAURANTS RESTAURANTS
Red Bank - Skerries 15 km - Tel (353) 01 - 849 1005
Old School House - Swords 8 km - Tel (353) 01 - 840 2846

The Island

15 | 7 | 7

A hundred years after it was first created, the original design here was drastically re-modelled by Fred Hawtree and Eddie Hackett and, most recently, by Jeff Howes. Though it is located on a peninsula, the course could be reached in the past only by boat, hence the name. Revisions have made it meaner but some of its beauty has been removed in the process. In contrast, there are no more blind greens, even though the terrain is hilly (but not too punishing). A kind course when there is little or no wind, The Island can turn nasty when the wind blows, especially on the holes close to the sea. This is when you need the deliberate low shot and, if that were not enough, the ability to stop the ball on the greens at the same time. Here you learn how to fashion every shot in the book, so much so that this club has schooled an impressive list of top men and lady players, which goes to show that power play on its own is not enough. The ideal venue for the region's golfing technicians.

Cent ans après sa naissance, Fred Hawtree et Eddie Hackett ont révisé de manière drastique le dessin original d'un parcours, qui a été encore revu récemment par Jeff Howes. Situé sur une péninsule, on ne pouvait autrefois y accéder qu'en barque, d'où son nom. Tous lui ont donné de la rudesse, mais retiré un peu de beauté. En revanche, il n'y a plus de greens aveugles, même si le terrain est un peu accidenté (pas de manière punitive). Assez aimable par vent faible ou nul, The Island peut devenir très méchant par vent fort, en particulier sur les trous proches de la mer, il faut alors maîtriser les balles basses, mais ce n'est pas suffisant, il faut en même temps arrêter la balle sur les greens. Ici, on apprend à fabriquer tous les coups de golf, et l'on comprend vite pourquoi ce club a formé une liste impressionnante de joueurs et surtout de bonnes joueuses, comme quoi la puissance ne suffit pas. The Island semble bien être l'un des grands rendez-vous des techniciens de la région.

The Island Golf Club — 1890

IRL - DONABATE, Co Dublin

Office	Secrétariat	(353) 01 - 843 6205
Pro shop	Pro-shop	(353) 01 - 843 5002
Fax	Fax	(353) 01 - 843 6860
Web	www.theislandgolfclub.com	
Situation	Situation	Dublin, 20 km
Annual closure	Fermeture annuelle	no
Weekly closure	Fermeture hebdomadaire	no

Fees main season Tarifs haute saison — 18 holes

	Week days / Semaine	We/Bank holidays / We/Férié
Individual Individuel	€ 110	€ 110*
Couple Couple	€ 220	€ 220*

* We: after 16:00 / Bank holidays: members only

Caddie Caddie on request **Electric Trolley** Chariot électrique yes

Buggy Voiturette yes **Clubs** Clubs yes

Credit cards Cartes de crédit
VISA - MasterCard - AMEX

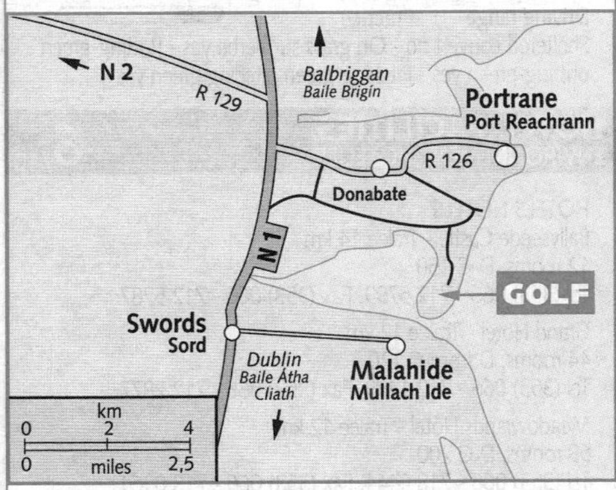

Access Accès : Dublin, N1 → Belfast. Turn right to Donabate. Side road to The Island signposted.

Map 1 on page 809 Carte 1 Page 809

GOLF COURSE — PARCOURS — 15/20

Site	Site	
Maintenance	Entretien	
Architect	Architecte	Fred Hawtree Eddie Hackett
Type	Type	links
Relief	Relief	
Water in play	Eau en jeu	
Exp. to wind	Exposé au vent	
Trees in play	Arbres en jeu	

Scorecard / Carte de score	Chp. / Chp.	Mens / Mess.	Ladies / Da.
Length Long.	6078	5791	5447
Par	71	71	70
Slope system	72	70	75

Advised golfing ability — Niveau de jeu recommandé: 0 12 24 36

Hcp required Handicap exigé — no

CLUB HOUSE & AMENITIES — CLUB HOUSE ET ANNEXES — 7/10

Pro shop Pro-shop

Driving range Practice

Sheltered couvert no - On grass sur herbe yes - Putting-green putting-green yes - Pitching-green pitching green yes

HOTEL FACILITIES — ENVIRONNEMENT HOTELIER — 7/10

HOTELS HÔTELS

Forte Travelodge - 100 rooms, D € 89 - Swords 8 km
Tel (353) 01 - 840 9233, Fax (353) 01 - 840 9235

Waterside Hotel - 18 rooms, D from € 120- Donabate 5 km
Tel (353) 01 - 843 6153, Fax (353) 01 - 843 6153

Redbank House - Skerries 10 km
18 rooms, D € 180 (w. dinner)
Tel (353) 01 - 849 0439, Fax (353) 01 - 849 1598

RESTAURANTS RESTAURANTS

Redbank House - Skerries 10 km - Tel (353) 01 - 849 0439

Giovanni's - Malahide 8 km - Tel (353) 01 - 845 1733

The Food Fare - Dublin Airport 8 km - Tel (353) 01 - 844 4085

Tralee

18 | 7 | 6

Give a great golfer terrain like this and he will give you a course to match his designer skills, imagination and audacity. Arnold Palmer had no shortage of the latter and he learnt the former; Tralee (with the complicity of mother nature) is one of his greatest courses. The front 9 unwind partly atop a cliff overhanging the ocean, which comes dangerously into play if direction and accuracy are wayward. The back 9 are even more impressive, amidst huge dunes in their natural state. Here, you often need to carry the ball a long way and you will be best advised to play from the front tees if your drive and long ironwork are not quite up to scratch. A heroic course, not always as refined in diabolical details as say Ballybunion, Portrush or County Down, but essential visiting for every true golfing enthusiast.

Donnez un terrain comme celui-ci à un grand golfeur à panache, il doit vous faire un parcours à la hauteur de ses connaissances d'architecte, de son imagination et de son audace. Le champion Arnold Palmer ne manquait pas de ces dernières qualités, il a appris les premières et Tralee (avec la complicité de la nature) est l'une de ses plus grandes réussites. L'aller se déroule partiellement au sommet d'une falaise longeant l'océan, qui vient dangereusement en jeu si l'on manque de direction et de précision. Le retour est plus impressionnant encore, au milieu d'énormes dunes à l'état sauvage. Là, il faut souvent porter loin la balle, et l'on aura intérêt à choisir les départs avancés si la qualité du drive et des longs fers n'est pas à la hauteur des défis. Un parcours héroïque, pas toujours aussi raffiné dans les détails diaboliques que Ballybunion, Portrush ou County Down, mais incontournable pour tout véritable amoureux du golf.

Tralee Golf Club — 1895

West Barron
IRL - ARDFERT, Co Kerry

Office	Secrétariat	(353) 066 - 713 6379
Pro shop	Pro-shop	(353) 066 - 713 6379
Fax	Fax	(353) 066 - 713 6008
Web	www.traleegolfclub.com	
Situation	Situation	Tralee (pop. 19 056), 12 km
Annual closure	Fermeture annuelle	nc
Weekly closure	Fermeture hebdomadaire	nc
Fees main season	Tarifs haute saison	18 holes

	Week days / Semaine	We/Bank holidays / We/Férié
Individual Individuel	€ 160	€ 160
Couple Couple	€ 320	€ 320

No visitors on Sundays & Bank holidays / Saturdays: 11:30 → 13:30

Caddie Caddie on request **Electric Trolley** Chariot électrique no

Buggy Voiturette no **Clubs** Clubs yes

Credit cards Cartes de crédit
VISA - MasterCard - AMEX

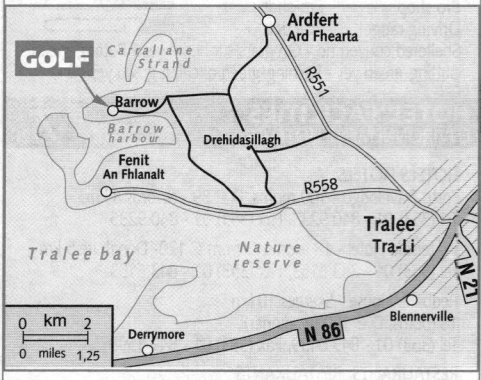

GOLF
Carrallane Strand
Ardfert
Ard Fhearta
R551
Barrow
Barrow harbour
Drehidasillagh
Fenit
An Fhlanalt
R558
Tralee
Tra-Li
Tralee bay
Nature reserve
N 21
Blennerville
N 86
Derrymore
0 km 2
0 miles 1,25

Access Accès : Fenit Road, 12 km NW of Tralee
Map 3 on page 812 Carte 3 Page 812

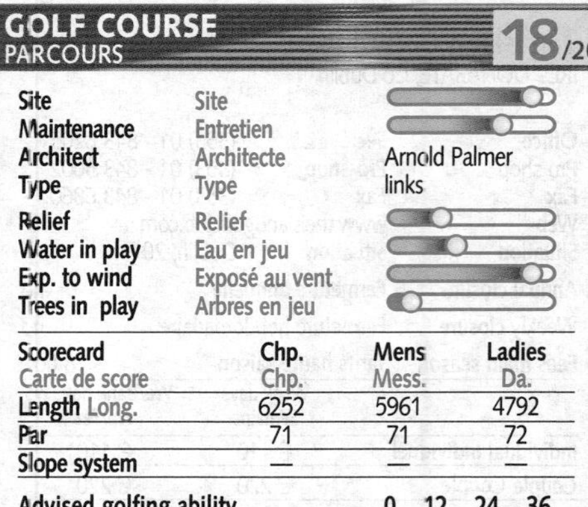

GOLF COURSE — PARCOURS — 18/20

Site	Site	
Maintenance	Entretien	
Architect	Architecte	Arnold Palmer
Type	Type	links
Relief	Relief	
Water in play	Eau en jeu	
Exp. to wind	Exposé au vent	
Trees in play	Arbres en jeu	

Scorecard Carte de score	Chp. Chp.	Mens Mess.	Ladies Da.
Length Long.	6252	5961	4792
Par	71	71	72
Slope system	—	—	—

Advised golfing ability Niveau de jeu recommandé — 0 12 24 36

Hcp required Handicap exigé — 24 Men, 36 Ladies

CLUB HOUSE & AMENITIES — CLUB HOUSE ET ANNEXES — 7/10

Pro shop Pro-shop
Driving range Practice
Sheltered couvert no - **On grass** sur herbe yes - **Putting-green** putting-green yes - **Pitching-green** pitching green yes

HOTEL FACILITIES — ENVIRONNEMENT HOTELIER — 6/10

HOTELS HÔTELS

Ballyseede Castle - Tralee 14 km
12 rooms, D € 150
Tel (353) 066 - 712 5799, Fax (353) 066 - 712 5287

Grand Hotel - Tralee 12 km
44 rooms, D from € 120
Tel (353) 066 - 712 1499, Fax (353) 066 - 712 2877

Meadowlands Hotel - Tralee 12 km
58 rooms, D € 200
Tel (353) 066 - 718 0444, Fax (353) 066 - 718 0964

RESTAURANTS RESTAURANTS

Tankard - Tralee 2 km - Tel (353) 066 - 713 6164
Oyster Tavern - Tralee 3 km - Tel (353) 066 - 713 6102

Tulfarris

15	7	6

With an hotel on site, this course is very attractively located on the shores of Lake Blessington and the layout, restyled and completed by Patrick Merrigan, is well suited to all levels of golfing ability. The fairways are wide, with bold routes to beckon the long-hitters and safer ways forward for the lesser players, and the use of trees, sand and water as hazards is cleverly balanced. In this respect, the fairway and green-side bunkers are particularly well located. The design successfully manages to retain a certain local colour despite the "foreign" architectural influences, because the natural landscape has been left unspoilt. High-handicappers will certainly find it something of a stiff challenge, but they will be glad to have had a go. Still a young course, it appears set for a brilliant future and we would not be at all surprised if it were to become one of Ireland's very best inland venues.

Avec un hôtel sur place, ce golf est des plus séduisants. Sa situation en bordure du lac de Blessington est très plaisante, le tracé remodelé et complété par Patrick Merrigan est bien adapté à tous les niveaux de jeu. Pour les frappeurs, des fairways larges et des chemins audacieux, et d'autres plus sûrs pour les joueurs plus modestes, une utilisation très équilibrée des arbres, de l'eau et du sable comme obstacles : les bunkers de fairways et de greens sont particulièrement bien placés. Le dessin réussit à conserver une certaine couleur "locale" en dépit d'influences architecturales "étrangères", parce que le paysage naturel n'a pas été bouleversé. Certes, les joueurs peu expérimentés trouveront le challenge un peu au-dessus de leur niveau, mais ils seront heureux de l'avoir affronté. Encore jeune, ce parcours d'avenir doit devenir l'un des meilleurs "inland" du pays.

Tulfarris Golf Club — 1987

Blessington Lakes
BLESSINGTON, Co Wicklow

Office Secrétariat (353) 045 - 867 555
Pro shop Pro-shop (353) 045 - 867 045
Fax Fax (353) 045 - 867 561
Web www.tulfarris.com
Situation Situation Dublin, 40 km
Annual closure Fermeture annuelle no
Weekly closure Fermeture hebdomadaire no

Fees main season Tarifs haute saison — 18 holes

	Week days Semaine	We/Bank holidays We/Férié
Individual Individuel	€ 60	€ 80
Couple Couple	€ 120	€ 160

Caddie Caddie on request **Electric Trolley** Chariot électrique yes
Buggy Voiturette yes **Clubs** Clubs yes
Credit cards Cartes de crédit
VISA - Eurocard - MasterCard - AMEX - DC

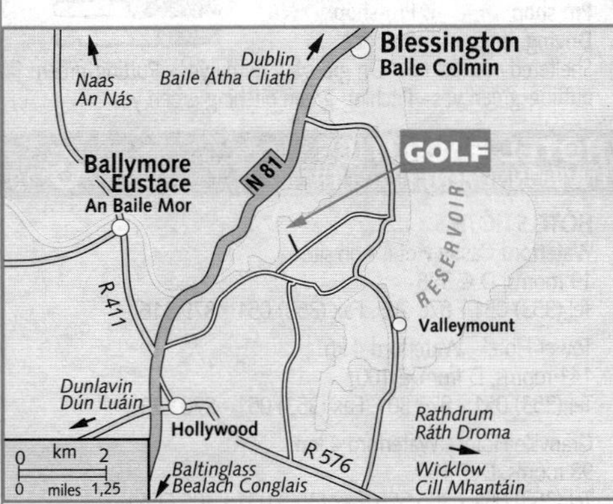

Access Accès : Dublin, R81 → Tallaght, Saggart, Tullow. Just after Blessington, turn left → Reservoir
Map 1 on page 809 Carte 1 Page 809

GOLF COURSE — PARCOURS 15/20

Site Site
Maintenance Entretien
Architect Architecte Paddy Merrigan
Type Type parkland
Relief Relief
Water in play Eau en jeu
Exp. to wind Exposé au vent
Trees in play Arbres en jeu

Scorecard Carte de score	Chp. Chp.	Mens Mess.	Ladies Da.
Length Long.	6410	5811	5135
Par	72	72	72
Slope system	—	—	—

Advised golfing ability Niveau de jeu recommandé 0 12 24 36
Hcp required Handicap exigé no

CLUB HOUSE & AMENITIES — CLUB HOUSE ET ANNEXES 7/10

Pro shop Pro-shop
Driving range Practice
Sheltered couvert yes - On grass sur herbe yes - Putting-green putting-green yes - Pitching-green pitching green yes

HOTEL FACILITIES — ENVIRONNEMENT HOTELIER 6/10

HOTELS HÔTELS
Tulfarris House - 157 rooms - on site (opens in 2006)
Tel (353) 045 - 867 600

Downshire House Hotel - Blessington 5 km
25 rooms, D € 121
Tel (353) 045 - 865 199, Fax (353) 045 - 865 335

Rathsallagh House - Dunlavin 17 km
29 rooms, D € 250
Tel (353) 045 - 403 112, Fax (353) 045 - 403 343

RESTAURANTS RESTAURANTS
Rathsallagh House - Dunlavin 17 km
Tel (353) 045 - 403 112

Waterford Castle

14 | 5 | 6

A few minutes on a ferry across the Suir river, and there you are in a sanctuary of peace and quiet where, if you break into your piggy bank, you can enjoy a dream stay at the on-site hotel, and admire some of the walls, which date back to the middle ages. This is perhaps not the course where you would spend the rest of your golfing days, but despite its young age it is in excellent condition and shouldn't be overlooked when in the region, especially now that it has been upgraded. Most of the work was concentrated on drainage, the elimination of redundant bunkers and a re-design of the long 13th hole. Meanwhile, the architects worked wonders with the physical relief (none too hilly) and the trees which neatly define the holes. This is not really a championship-standard course, but the hazards have been placed to test the very good players more than the average week-end golfer, who will, or should, have fun here. The large greens make it essential to choose the right club to get close to the pin. A number of water hazards add to the course's appeal.

Quelques minutes de ferry pour traverser la rivière Suir, et vous voilà dans une enclave de tranquillité où – si vous cassez un peu la tirelire – vous pourrez faire un séjour de rêve à l'hôtel sur place dont certains des murs datent du Moyen-Age. Le parcours n'est peut-être pas celui que l'on choisirait pour passer le reste de sa vie, mais il est en très bon état malgré sa jeunesse, et ne saurait être ignoré quand on visite la région. Une révision récente a permis d'améliorer le drainage, de supprimer quelques bunkers redondants et de redessiner le 13. Les architectes ont tiré un bon parti des reliefs du terrain, et des nombreux arbres pour définir les trous dans l'espace. Il ne s'agit pas vraiment d'un parcours de championnat, mais les obstacles ont été placés pour perturber plutôt les très bons joueurs que les joueurs moyens, qui s'y amuseront beaucoup. Les greens, de grande dimension, obligent à faire les bons choix de clubs pour se trouver près des drapeaux. Les obstacles d'eau ajoutent à l'intérêt de ce parcours.

Waterford Castle Golf Club — 1992

The Island
IRL - BALLYNAKILL, Co Waterford

Office Secrétariat (353) 051 - 871 633
Pro shop Pro-shop (353) 051 - 871 633
Fax Fax (353) 051 - 871 634
Web www.waterfordcastle.com
Situation Situation Waterford, 1.5 km
Annual closure Fermeture annuelle no
Weekly closure Fermeture hebdomadaire no

Fees main season Tarifs haute saison	18 holes	
	Week days Semaine	**We/Bank holidays** We/Férié
Individual Individuel	€ 50	€ 60
Couple Couple	€ 100	€ 120

We: Friday → Sunday

Caddie Caddie on request **Electric Trolley** Chariot électrique no
Buggy Voiturette yes **Clubs** Clubs yes
Credit cards Cartes de crédit
VISA - MasterCard - AMEX (Pro Shop & Bar)

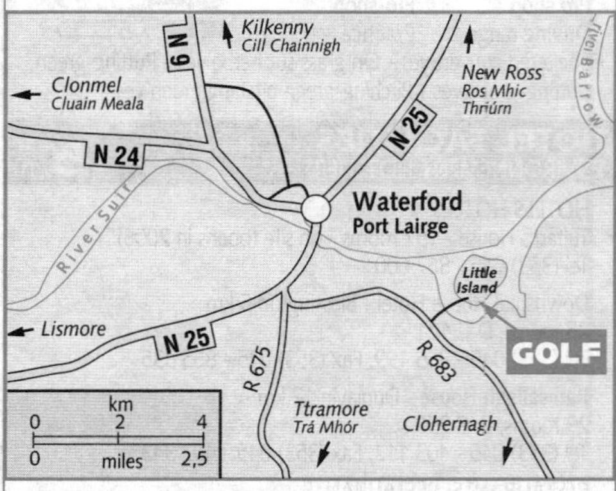

Access Accès : Waterford, R683. 4 km Ballinakill Road, private ferry to the Island
Map 3 on page 813 Carte 3 Page 813

GOLF COURSE — PARCOURS — 14/20

Site Site
Maintenance Entretien
Architect Architecte Des Smyth, Declan Branigan
Type Type parkland
Relief Relief
Water in play Eau en jeu
Exp. to wind Exposé au vent
Trees in play Arbres en jeu

Scorecard Carte de score	**Chp.** Chp.	**Mens** Mess.	**Ladies** Da.
Length Long.	6209	5810	5073
Par	72	72	72
Slope system	—	—	—

Advised golfing ability Niveau de jeu recommandé 0 12 24 36
Hcp required Handicap exigé no

CLUB HOUSE & AMENITIES — CLUB HOUSE ET ANNEXES — 5/10

Pro shop Pro-shop
Driving range Practice
Sheltered couvert no - On grass sur herbe yes - Putting-green putting-green yes - Pitching-green pitching green yes

HOTEL FACILITIES — ENVIRONNEMENT HOTELIER — 6/10

HOTELS HÔTELS
Waterford Castle Hotel - on site
19 rooms, D € 378
Tel (353) 051 - 878 203, Fax (353) 051 - 879 316

Tower Hotel - Waterford 4 km
141 rooms, D from € 100
Tel (353) 051 - 875 801, Fax (353) 051 - 870 129

Granville Hotel - Waterford 4 km
98 rooms, D € 190
Tel (353) 051 - 305 555, Fax (353) 051 - 305 566

RESTAURANTS RESTAURANTS
Dwyer's - Waterford 4 km - Tel (353) 051 - 877 478
Waterford Castle - on site - Tel (353) 051 - 878 203

Waterville

18 | 6 | 7

There has been a handsome reward for the bold decision to have the course extensively re-modelled by leading American architect Tom Fazio. While lengthening it to a formidable 7,309 yards off the back tees, he has radically re-shaped the front nine (rather featureless before) while delivering a greatly improved finishing stretch. Fazio worked wonders on the opening holes and the existing magic has been enhanced on the remainder, which snake impressively through sand dunes. All the while, the overall design retains an entirely natural look. There are no blind holes, virtually flat fairways and almost no dog-legs. But with sometimes blustery side-winds, you need to know how to flight the ball to keep it in play. If we add to this the fact that the putting surfaces are a little less puzzling than those at Ballybunion, for example, the overall problem here stems from its length (a "man's course", as they say), plus the technical side to the second shot once the drive has avoided the rough and a number of fairway bunkers. Waterville is a great course which should be played off the front tees.

La décision de repenser ce parcours a été couronnée de succès. Le grand architecte américain Tom Fazio l'a porté à plus de 6500 mètres, a radicalement modifié les trous de l'aller (autrefois sans relief) tout en améliorant encore le finale. Il a fait des merveilles sur les neuf premiers trous, beaucoup plus forts, mais la suite, insinuée dans les dunes, reste impressionnante. Malgré ce remodelage intensif, le tracé a conservé un aspect très naturel. Le travail architectural, pour naturel qu'il paraisse aujourd'hui, a été important : pas de trous aveugles, des fairways quasiment plats, quasiment aucun dog-leg. Mais il faudra savoir travailler la balle pour la garder en jeu, avec des vents latéraux souvent violents. Si l'on ajoute des surfaces de greens un peu moins énigmatiques qu'à Ballybunion par exemple, la difficulté de Waterville tient certes beaucoup à sa longueur, mais on peut aussi parler de la technicité des seconds coups, une fois que le drive a évité les roughs et certains bunkers de fairway.

Waterville Golf Links — 1889

IRL - WATERVILLE, Co Kerry

Office	Secrétariat	(353) 066 - 947 4102
Pro shop	Pro-shop	(353) 066 - 947 4102
Fax	Fax	(353) 066 - 947 4482
Web	www.watervillegolflinks.ie	
Situation	Situation	Waterville, 4 km
Annual closure	Fermeture annuelle	no
Weekly closure	Fermeture hebdomadaire	no

Fees main season Tarifs haute saison — 18 holes

	Week days Semaine	We/Bank holidays We/Férié
Individual Individuel	€ 150	€ 150
Couple Couple	€ 300	€ 300

Monday → Thursday before 8:00 and after 16:00, € 105

Caddie Caddie on request **Electric Trolley** Chariot électrique no

Buggy Voiturette yes **Clubs** Clubs yes

Credit cards Cartes de crédit

VISA - Eurocard - MasterCard - AMEX

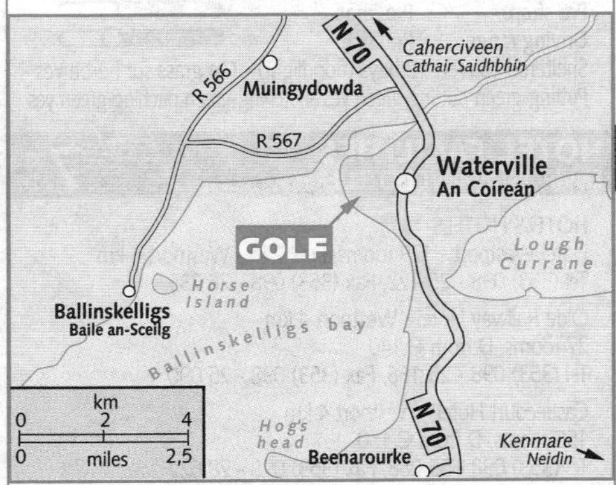

Access Accès : • Killarney N71 → Kenmate. N70 → Parknasilla, Waterville • Killarney → Killorglin. N70 → Glenbeigh, Cahirciveen, Waterville

Map 3 on page 812 Carte 3 Page 812

GOLF COURSE — PARCOURS — 18/20

Site	Site	
Maintenance	Entretien	
Architect	Architecte	E. Hackett, J.A. Mulcahy Tom Fazio (2004)
Type	Type	links
Relief	Relief	
Water in play	Eau en jeu	
Exp. to wind	Exposé au vent	
Trees in play	Arbres en jeu	

Scorecard Carte de score	Chp. Chp.	Mens Mess.	Ladies Da.
Length Long.	6579	6103	4749
Par	72	73	73
Slope system	0	0	0

Advised golfing ability Niveau de jeu recommandé — 0 12 24 36

Hcp required Handicap exigé — 28 Men, 36 Ladies

CLUB HOUSE & AMENITIES — CLUB HOUSE ET ANNEXES — 6/10

Pro shop Pro-shop

Driving range Practice

Sheltered couvert no - On grass sur herbe yes - Putting-green putting-green yes - Pitching-green pitching green yes

HOTEL FACILITIES — ENVIRONNEMENT HOTELIER — 7/10

HOTELS HÔTELS

Butler Arms - 48 rooms, D € 212 - Waterville 2 km
Tel (353) 066 - 947 4144, Fax (353) 066 - 947 4520

Bayview Hotel - 60 rooms, D € 96 - Waterville 2 km
Tel (353) 066 - 947 4122, Fax (353) 066 - 947 4680

Brookhaven House - 6 rooms, D € 102 - Waterville 2 km
Tel (353) 066 - 947 4431, Fax (353) 066 - 947 4724

RESTAURANTS RESTAURANTS

Sheilin Seafood - Waterville - Tel (353) 066 - 947 4231

Smugglers Inn - Waterville 500 m - Tel (353) 066 - 947 4330

The Point (Pub) - Renard Point (Caherciveen) 12 km
Tel (353) 066 - 947 2165

Westport

15 | 7 | 7

Although located on the edge of Clew Bay, this is a parkland course in texture. For many players, it will be the opportunity to catch their breath between Connemara and Carn or Enniscrone, and to find a little shelter when the wind is playing havoc elsewhere. The views here are just magnificent, between the bay and the blessed mountain of Croagh Patrick, where Ireland's patron saint spent 40 days of fasting and prayer. We wouldn't ask golfers to do the same, as they'll need all their strength to cope with this top-class course which was significantly upgraded in 2002. The only slight shortcoming remains the relative blandness of the first few holes, but the challenge grows stronger on the way in, with a special mention going to the very pretty 14th, a par 3, and especially the 15th, a splendid and very long par 5 along the bay. The hazards are visibly in play and clear enough to make strategy pretty obvious on your first visit.

Bien qu'il soit situé en bordure de la Clew Bay, ce parcours présente un caractère de parc. Ce sera pour beaucoup de joueurs l'occasion de reprendre leur souffle entre Connemara et Carne ou Enniscrone, et de trouver quelque abri, quand le vent joue un rôle important. Les vues sont ici magnifiques, entre la baie et la "montagne sacrée", le Croagh Patrick, où le saint patron de l'Irlande aurait passé 40 jours de jeûne et de prières. On n'en demandera pas autant aux golfeurs, qui ont besoin de toutes leurs forces sur ce parcours de qualité largement remanié en 2002. La seule nuance dans ce jugement, c'est la relative faiblesse des premiers trous, mais le challenge devient plus exigeant au retour, avec une mention particulière pour le 14, très joli par 3, et surtout le 15, un splendide par 5 très long en bordure de la baie. Les obstacles sont honnêtement en jeu, et assez visibles pour que la stratégie soit évidente dès la première visite.

Westport Golf Club — 1908

Carrowholly
IRL - WESTPORT, Co Mayo

Office	Secrétariat	(353) 098 - 28 262
Pro shop	Pro-shop	(353) 098 - 28 262
Fax	Fax	(353) 098 - 27 217
Web	www.golfwestport.com	
Situation	Situation	Galway (pop. 57 241), 50 km

Castlebar, 16 km

Annual closure	Fermeture annuelle	no
Weekly closure	Fermeture hebdomadaire	no

Fees main season Tarifs haute saison — 18 holes

	Week days Semaine	We/Bank holidays We/Férié
Individual Individuel	€ 42	€ 55
Couple Couple	€ 84	€ 110

Caddie Caddie on request **Electric Trolley** Chariot électrique no
Buggy Voiturette yes **Clubs** Clubs yes
Credit cards Cartes de crédit
VISA - Mastercard - AMEX

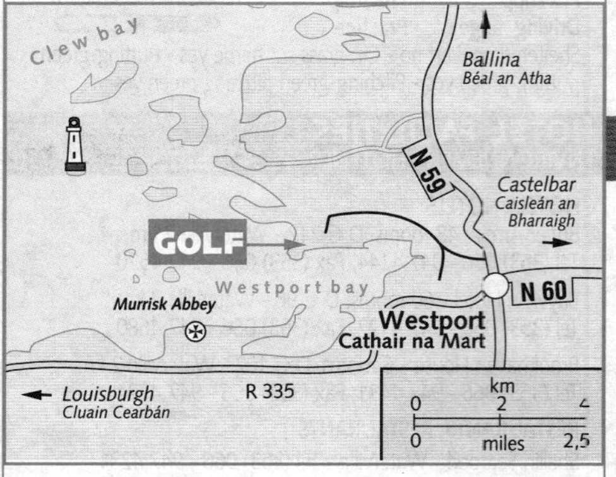

Access Accès : 4 km from Westport on Newport Road
Map 2 on page 810 Carte 2 Page 810

GOLF COURSE — PARCOURS — 15/20

Site	Site	
Maintenance	Entretien	
Architect	Architecte	Fred Hawtree
Type	Type	seaside course, parkland
Relief	Relief	
Water in play	Eau en jeu	
Exp. to wind	Exposé au vent	
Trees in play	Arbres en jeu	

Scorecard Carte de score	Chp. Chp.	Mens Mess.	Ladies Da.
Length Long.	6355	6095	5233
Par	73	73	74
Slope system	—	—	—

Advised golfing ability Niveau de jeu recommandé: 0 12 24 36
Hcp required Handicap exigé: certificate

CLUB HOUSE & AMENITIES — CLUB HOUSE ET ANNEXES — 7/10

Pro shop Pro-shop
Driving range Practice
Sheltered couvert 12 bays (floodlight) - On grass sur herbe yes - Putting-green putting-green yes - Pitching-green pitching green yes

HOTEL FACILITIES — ENVIRONNEMENT HOTELIER — 7/10

HOTELS HÔTELS

Hotel Westport - 129 rooms, D € 240 - Westport 4 km
Tel (353) 098 - 25 122, Fax (353) 098 - 26 739

Olde Railway Hotel - Westport 4 km
27 rooms, D from € 140
Tel (353) 098 - 25 166, Fax (353) 098 - 25 090

Castlecourt Hotel - Westport 4 km
155 rooms, D from € 150
Tel (353) 098 - 55 088, Fax (353) 098 - 28 622

RESTAURANTS RESTAURANTS

Ardmore House - Westport 4 km - Tel (353) 098 - 25 994
Linen Mill - Westport 4 km - Tel (353) 098 - 29 500

Woodbrook

15	7	6

This course was for many a year a star attraction to the south of Dublin, often playing host to the Carroll's International in the 1960s and the Irish Senior Open in 1998. Complete relaying of the tees and greens some years ago, under the supervision of Peter McEvoy, helped to restore the course's prestige and raise the challenge that awaits you. Clearly, the alternating inland and seaside holes provide a close examination of the talent of skilled players and the lesser player too, because the layout is reasonably playable by golfers of all abilities. This rather flat course overlooks the Irish sea, even though only holes 10 to 12 actually run along the coast. Although there are no huge difficulties, the wind can make life tricky, especially since the trees do little to break it. The only flaw is the Dublin to Wexford railway line, but this type of interference was commonplace in the past and together with the old-style club-house helps to create a site full of the charm of yesteryear.

Ce golf a longtemps été une vedette au sud de Dublin, recevant souvent le Carroll's International dans les années 60, et l'Irish Senior Open en 1998. Une réfection complète des départs et des greens il y a quelques années, sous l'autorité de Peter McEvoy, a contribué à lui rendre son prestige et à augmenter la qualité du défi. Il faut dire que l'alternance des trous inland et des trous de bord de mer permet un examen complet du talent des bons joueurs. Comme des moins bons d'ailleurs, car ce parcours est raisonnablement jouable à tous les niveaux. Assez plat, il domine du haut des falaises la mer d'Irlande, bien que seuls les trous du 10 au 12 longent effectivement la côte. Les difficultés ne sont pas immenses, mais le vent peut notamment compliquer les choses, d'autant que les arbres présents ne constituent pas vraiment des remparts. Seul défaut, le passage de la voie de chemin de fer Dublin-Wexford, mais ce genre d'interférence était autrefois fréquent, et contribue comme le "old style" du club-house à donner au lieu un certain charme d'antan.

Woodbrook Golf Club — 1926

Dublin Road
IRL - BRAY, Co. Wicklow

Office Secrétariat (353) 01 - 282 4799
Pro shop Pro-shop (353) 01 - 282 0205
Fax Fax (353) 01 - 282 1950
Web www.woodbrook.ie
Situation Situation Dublin, 20 km
Annual closure Fermeture annuelle no
Weekly closure Fermeture hebdomadaire no

Fees main season Tarifs haute saison 18 holes

	Week days Semaine	We/Bank holidays We/Férié
Individual Individuel	€ 95	€ 100
Couple Couple	€ 190	€ 200

Caddie Caddie on request **Electric Trolley** Chariot électrique no
Buggy Voiturette yes **Clubs** Clubs yes
Credit cards Cartes de crédit
VISA - MasterCard

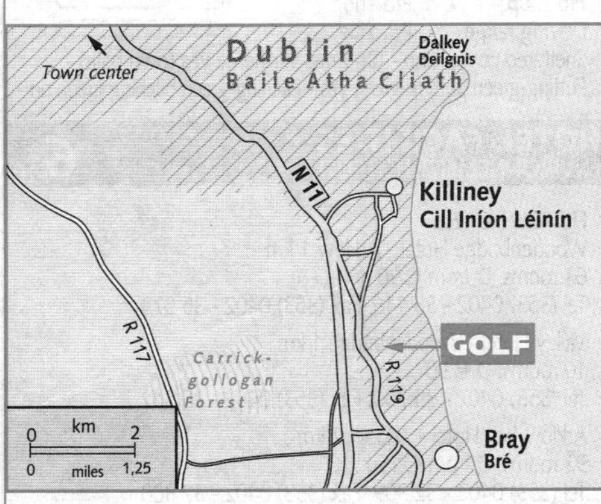

Access Accès : Dublin, N11. R761 → Bray. 1.5 km before Bray → Woodbrook Golf Club
Map 1 on page 809 Carte 1 Page 809

GOLF COURSE — PARCOURS 15/20

Site Site
Maintenance Entretien
Architect Architecte Peter McEvoy
Type Type inland
Relief Relief
Water in play Eau en jeu
Exp. to wind Exposé au vent
Trees in play Arbres en jeu

Scorecard Carte de score	Chp. Chp.	Mens Mess.	Ladies Da.
Length Long.	6362	6276	5609
Par	72	72	74
Slope system	—	—	—

Advised golfing ability Niveau de jeu recommandé 0 12 24 36
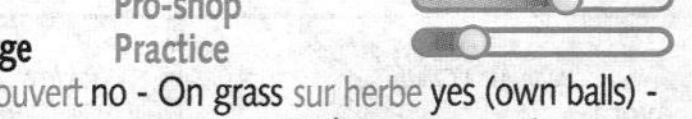
Hcp required Handicap exigé certificate

CLUB HOUSE & AMENITIES — CLUB HOUSE ET ANNEXES 7/10

Pro shop Pro-shop
Driving range Practice
Sheltered couvert no - On grass sur herbe yes (own balls) - Putting-green putting-green yes - Pitching-green pitching green yes

HOTEL FACILITIES — ENVIRONNEMENT HOTELIER 6/10

HOTELS HÔTELS
Woodland Court Hotel - 65 rooms, D € 140 - Bray 3 km
Tel (353) 01 - 276 0258, Fax (353) 01 - 276 0298

Summerhill Hotel - Enniskerry 10 km
57 rooms, D € 150
Tel (353) 01 - 286 7928, Fax (353) 01 - 286 79 29

Glenview Hotel - Glen of the Downs 12 km
70 rooms, D € 240
Tel (353) 01 - 287 3399, Fax (353) 01 - 287 7511

RESTAURANTS RESTAURANTS
Duzy's Cafe - Dun Laoghaire 12 km - Tel (353) 01 - 230 0210
Kish - Dalkey 10 km - Tel (353) 01 - 285 0377
Cavistons - Dun Laoghaire 12 km - Tel (353) 01 - 280 9245

Woodenbridge

16 | 7 | 6

Woodenbrige is located in the very pretty Vale of Avoca, famous for its tweeds, and essential visiting in the spring when the cherry trees are in full blossom. You will be following in the footsteps of the poet Thomas Moore. Created 100 years ago, this fine course became very popular when Patrick Merrigan upgraded it to 18 holes in 1993. The only vegetation is the few trees, here and there (woods outline the course's boundaries), which come very much into play from time to time, but the main hazards are the bunkers (none too penalising) and water, notably the river Avoca, which naturally dominated this region. There are no unpleasant surprises for visitors, as the difficulties are clearly visible from each tee and add to the course's overall honesty. There is no great need to flight your shots, and only the variety of approach shots (lofted or run) call for real talent.

Woodenbridge est situé dans la très jolie Vallée d'Avoca, célèbre pour ses tweeds, et qu'il faut absolument voir au printemps, quand les cerisiers sont en fleurs : si vous êtes sensible à la nature et la littérature, vous y suivrez les traces du poète Thomas Moore. Créé il y a cent ans, ce bon parcours est devenu très populaire quand Patrick Merrigan l'a porté à 18 trous en 1993. La seule végétation est ici constituée par des arbres çà et là (les bois marquant les limites du golf), ils sont parfois très en jeu, mais les obstacles principaux sont les bunkers (pas trop pénalisants quand on s'y retrouve) et des obstacles d'eau - notamment la rivière Avoca - naturellement abondants dans cette région. Les visiteurs ne risquent pas de mauvaises surprises, les difficultés sont bien visibles de chaque départ, ajoutant à la franchise générale du tracé. Il n'est pas utile de beaucoup travailler la balle, seule la variété des approches (balles levées ou balles roulées) exigeant un certain talent.

Woodenbridge Golf Club — 1897

Woodenbridge
IRL - ARKLOW, Co Wicklow

Office	Secrétariat	(353) 0402 - 35 202
Pro shop	Pro-shop	(353) 0402 - 35 202
Fax	Fax	(353) 0402 - 35 754
Web	www.woodenbridgegolfclub.com	
Situation	Situation	Dublin 74 km

Arklow, 7 km

Annual closure	Fermeture annuelle	no
Weekly closure	Fermeture hebdomadaire	no
Fees main season	Tarifs haute saison	18 holes

	Week days Semaine	We/Bank holidays We/Férié
Individual Individuel	€ 55	€ 65*
Couple Couple	€ 110	€ 130*

* Saturday: members only

Caddie Caddie on request **Electric Trolley** Chariot électrique no

Buggy Voiturette yes **Clubs** Clubs yes

Credit cards Cartes de crédit
VISA - Mastercard

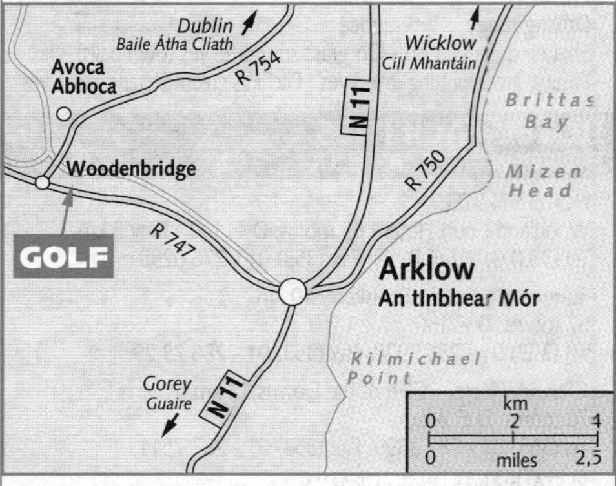

Access Accès : Dublin N11 South → Arklow.
7 km NW of Arklow on R747
Map 1 on page 809 Carte 1 Page 809

GOLF COURSE — PARCOURS — 16/20

Site	Site	
Maintenance	Entretien	
Architect	Architecte	Paddy Merrigan
Type	Type	forest, parkland
Relief	Relief	
Water in play	Eau en jeu	
Exp. to wind	Exposé au vent	
Trees in play	Arbres en jeu	

Scorecard Carte de score	Chp. Chp.	Mens Mess.	Ladies Da.
Length Long.	6350	6074	5490
Par	71	71	72
Slope system	—	—	—

Advised golfing ability Niveau de jeu recommandé: 0 12 24 36

Hcp required Handicap exigé: 24 Men, 36 Ladies

CLUB HOUSE & AMENITIES — CLUB HOUSE ET ANNEXES — 7/10

Pro shop	Pro-shop
Driving range	Practice

Sheltered couvert no - On grass sur herbe yes (own balls) - Putting-green putting-green yes - Pitching-green pitching green no

HOTEL FACILITIES — ENVIRONNEMENT HOTELIER — 6/10

HOTELS HÔTELS

Woodenbridge Hotel - Arklow 1 km
63 rooms, D from € 90
Tel (353) 0402 - 35 146, Fax (353) 0402 - 35 573

Valley Hotel - Woodenbridge 1 km
10 rooms, D € 90
Tel (353) 0402 - 35 200, Fax (353) 0402 - 35 542

Arklow Bay Hotel - Arklow 7 km
92 rooms, D from € 150
Tel (353) 0402 - 32 309, Fax (353) 0402 - 32 300

RESTAURANTS RESTAURANTS

Sheepwalk House - Avoca 4 km - Tel (353) 0402 - 35 189
Strawberry Tree - Aughrim 5 km - Tel (353) 0402 - 36 444

Ardglass

14	6	4

In this region, occupied by the Vikings, pirates and smugglers, you will also find the vestiges of a castle built by the Normans alongside the club-house. Other good news for non-golfers is the nearby Strangford Lough, a real sanctuary for birds. But back to golf. As the course runs impressively atop coastal cliffs, this is one of the country's finest sites, with a view as far as the Isle of Man (on a clear day). Worth seeing, and worth playing, too. An age-old course from an unknown architect, this is a good layout and links course with no steep relief and none of those enormous dunes that can have such an effect on easily influenced players. You need to play several rounds to grasp the subtleties of the course, because there are quite a few blind drives and so a high risk of ending up in the rough or bushes that do your card no good at all. And that's not to mention the exposure to the wind, which hardly helps matters. The bunkers are rather small, as are the greens. First time out, have fun with a match-play round.

Dans ce pays occupé par les Vikings, les pirates et les contrebandiers, on trouve aussi, à côté du club-house, les vestiges d'un château bâti par les Normands. A proximité, le Strangford Lough est un véritable sanctuaire d'oiseaux. Et comme la situation du parcours sur de hautes falaises est impressionnante, c'est un des grands sites du pays, avec une vue jusqu'à l'Ile de Man (quand il fait beau). A voir mais aussi à jouer. Centenaire, et d'architecte inconnu, c'est un bon tracé, un links au relief très modéré, mais sans les dunes énormes qui peuvent ailleurs effrayer les joueurs influençables. Il faut plusieurs visites pour en comprendre les subtilités, on trouve pas mal de départs aveugles, avec le risque de se retrouver dans un rough ou des buissons dangereux pour le score. Et l'exposition au vent n'arrange rien en ce domaine. Les bunkers sont assez petits, mais les greens aussi... La première fois, amusez-vous en match-play.

Ardglass Golf Club — 1896

Castle Place
NIR - ARDGLASS, Co Down BT30 7 TP

Office Secrétariat (44) 028 - 4484 1219
Pro shop Pro-shop (44) 028 - 4484 1022
Fax Fax (44) 028 - 4484 1841
Web www.ardglassgolfclub.com
Situation Situation Belfast (pop. 279 237), 48 km
Downpatrick, 11 km
Annual closure Fermeture annuelle no
Weekly closure Fermeture hebdomadaire Monday
Restaurant
Fees main season Tarifs haute saison 18 holes

	Week days / Semaine	We/Bank holidays / We/Férié
Individual Individuel	£ 32	£ 45
Couple Couple	£ 64	£ 90

Full day: £ 48 and £ 67 (We)

Caddie Caddie on request **Electric Trolley** Chariot électrique yes
Buggy Voiturette no **Clubs** Clubs yes
Credit cards Cartes de crédit
VISA - MasterCard - AMEX (Pro shop only)

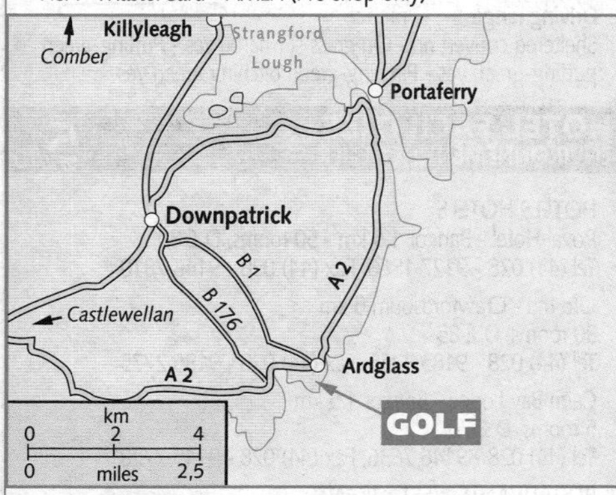

Access Accès : Belfast, A24, A7 to Downpatrick.
B1 to Ardglass. → Golf
Map 2 on page 811 Carte 2 Page 811

GOLF COURSE — PARCOURS 14/20

Site Site
Maintenance Entretien
Architect Architecte unknown
Type Type seaside course
Relief Relief
Water in play Eau en jeu
Exp. to wind Exposé au vent
Trees in play Arbres en jeu

Scorecard / Carte de score	Chp. / Chp.	Mens / Mess.	Ladies / Da.
Length Long.	5642	5238	4773
Par	70	70	70
Slope system	—	—	—

Advised golfing ability 0 12 24 36
Niveau de jeu recommandé
Hcp required Handicap exigé no

CLUB HOUSE & AMENITIES — CLUB HOUSE ET ANNEXES 6/10

Pro shop Pro-shop
Driving range Practice
Sheltered couvert no - On grass sur herbe yes - Putting-green putting-green yes - Pitching-green pitching green no

HOTEL FACILITIES — ENVIRONNEMENT HOTELIER 4/10

HOTELS HÔTELS
Abbey Lodge - 20 rooms, D £ 60 - Downpatrick 11 km
Tel (44) 028 - 4461 4511

The Mill at Ballydugan - Downpatrick 11 km
10 rooms, D £ 75
Tel (44) 028 - 4461 3654, Fax (44) 028 - 4483 9754

Burrendale Hotel - 68 rooms, D £ 110 - Newcastle 30 km
Tel (44) 028 - 4372 2599, Fax (44) 028 - 4372 2328

RESTAURANTS RESTAURANTS
Aldo's - Ardglass 1 km - Tel (44) 028 - 4384 1315
The Mill at Ballydugan - Downpatrick 11 km
Tel (44) 028 - 4461 3654

Bangor

14	6	5

The course is located virtually in the city of Bangor, David Feherty's home town, where, so they say, you'll see the finest landscapes in the whole of Northern Ireland. Bird-watching enthusiasts are just a few minutes away from the boat that takes them to the Copeland Islands, inhabited only by birds, and you are not far from the pretty town of Newtownards. Inveterate golfers, on the other hand, will enjoy playing on this course, rather off the beaten track, a little dated in terms of yardage but great fun to play all the same. James Braid laid out a few elevated greens, others being multi-tiered, plus a few fairway bunkers that are both strategic and punishing. Some of the dog-legs (the 5th, 13th, 14th and 15th holes) call for very accurate driving. In all, a course where you would probably not spend the rest of your life playing, but a good addition to the region's other courses.

Le golf est situé pratiquement dans la ville de Bangor, ville natale du champion David Feherty, où l'on trouve paraît-il les plus beaux paysages d'Irlande du Nord. Les amateurs d'ornithologie n'auront que quelques minutes à faire pour embarquer à destination des Copeland Islands, où ne vivent plus que des oiseaux, ou pour découvrir la jolie ville de Newtownards. Quant aux golfeurs invétérés, ils pourront s'exprimer sur ce parcours hors des sentiers battus, un peu daté en ce qui concerne la longueur, mais très amusant au demeurant. James Braid y a disposé quelques greens surélevés, d'autres à double plateau, et quelques bunkers de fairway à la fois stratégiques et punitifs. Certains dog-legs (5, 13, 14 et 15) demandent un driving très précis pour être maîtrisés. Au total, un parcours sur lequel on ne jouerait peut-être pas toute sa vie, mais un bon complément aux autres parcours de la région.

Bangor Golf Club 1903

Broadway
NIR - BANGOR, Co. Down BT20 4RH

Office Secrétariat (44) 028 - 9127 0922
Pro shop Pro-shop (44) 028 - 9146 2164
Fax Fax (44) 028 - 9145 3394
Web www.bangorgolfclubni.co.uk
Situation Situation Belfast, 20 km
Newtownards, 10 km

Annual closure Fermeture annuelle no
Weekly closure Fermeture hebdomadaire no

Fees main season Tarifs haute saison	Week days Semaine	We/Bank holidays We/Férié
	18 holes	
Individual Individuel	£ 29	£ 35*
Couple Couple	£ 58	£ 70*

* Saturday: members only

Caddie Caddie no — **Electric Trolley** Chariot électrique yes
Buggy Voiturette yes — **Clubs** Clubs yes
Credit cards Cartes de crédit
VISA - Access - MasterCard

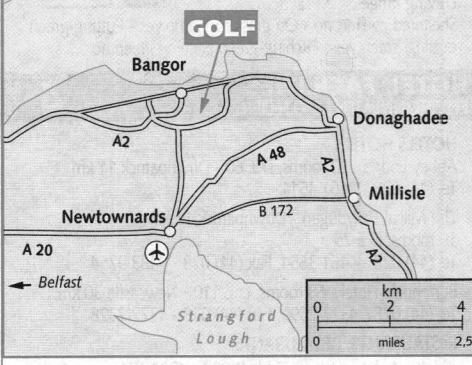

GOLF
Bangor
Donaghadee
A2
A 48
A2
Millisle
B 172
Newtownards
A 20
Belfast
A2
Strangford Lough
km 0 2 4
0 miles 2,5

Access Accès : Belfast, A2 → Bangor
Map 2 on page 811 Carte 2 Page 811

GOLF COURSE — PARCOURS 14/20

Site	Site	
Maintenance	Entretien	
Architect	Architecte	James Braid
Type	Type	inland
Relief	Relief	
Water in play	Eau en jeu	
Exp. to wind	Exposé au vent	
Trees in play	Arbres en jeu	

Scorecard Carte de score	Chp. Chp.	Mens Mess.	Ladies Da.
Length Long.	5781	5577	5113
Par	71	71	72
Slope system	—	—	—

Advised golfing ability Niveau de jeu recommandé 0 12 24 36
Hcp required Handicap exigé no

CLUB HOUSE & AMENITIES — CLUB HOUSE ET ANNEXES 6/10

Pro shop Pro-shop
Driving range Practice
Sheltered couvert no - On grass sur herbe yes - Putting-green putting-green yes - Pitching-green pitching green yes

HOTEL FACILITIES — ENVIRONNEMENT HOTELIER 5/10

HOTELS HÔTELS
Royal Hotel - Bangor 1.5 km - 50 rooms, D £ 80
Tel (44) 028 - 9127 1866, Fax (44) 028 - 9146 7810

Old Inn - Crawfordsburn 5 km
30 rooms, D £ 85
Tel (44) 028 - 9185 3255, Fax (44) 028 - 9185 2775

Cairn Bay Lodge - Bangor 1.5 km
5 rooms, D £ 70
Tel (44) 028 - 9146 7636, Fax (44) 028 - 9145 7728

RESTAURANTS RESTAURANTS
Shanks - Bangor 8 km - Tel (44) 028 - 9185 3313
Jenny Watts - Bangor 2.5 km - Tel (44) 028 - 9127 0401

Belvoir Park

15 | 5 | 7

The energetic rejuvenation of this course has turned it into one of the region's hidden gems in the region of Belfast, without ever affecting the intelligence of Harry Colt's original layout. Very reasonable in length, it is a real pleasure to play in this lush green park, well protected from the city noise by woods and thick curtains of trees, which also separate the fairways and call for unfailing accuracy. Despite everything, the fairways are of a fair width, and while there are fairway bunkers, their design rarely makes them dangerous. Ditches on the 10th and 12th are the only water hazards, but they play a key role. The course is generally not too hilly, except on the 3rd and 17th, the latter being a part of a very difficult finish, where many a card can fall apart. Fun to play and very prettily landscaped, Belvoir Park is rated amongst the country's finest inland courses and was the scene of Philip Walton's Smurfit Irish Professional Championship triumph in 1995.

Le rajeunissement énergique de ce parcours en a fait l'un des petits bijoux cachés de la région de Belfast, sans pour autant altérer l'intelligence du tracé original de Harry Colt, d'une longueur très raisonnable. C'est un plaisir d'évoluer dans ce grand parc en pleine verdure, bien protégé des bruits de la ville par de petits bois et d'épais rideaux d'arbres, séparant bien les fairways, tout en impliquant une certaine précision. Malgré tout, les fairways restent d'une largeur très acceptable, et si les bunkers y sont présents, leur dessin les rend rarement très dangereux. Les fossés au 10 et au 12 sont les seuls obstacles d'eau, mais ils y jouent un rôle fondamental. Le parcours est généralement de relief très modéré, sauf au 3 et au 17, ce dernier trou faisant partie d'un "finish" très difficile, où bien des cartes vont s'alourdir. Amusant à jouer, très joliment paysagé, Belvoir Park figure parmi les très bons parcours "inland" du pays.

Belvoir Park Golf Club — 1927

Church Road, Newtownbreda
NIR - BELFAST BT8 4AN

Office	Secrétariat	(44) 028 - 9049 1693
Pro shop	Pro-shop	(44) 028 - 9049 1693
Fax	Fax	(44) 028 - 9064 6113
Web	www.belvoirparkgolfclub.com	
Situation	Situation	Belfast, 5 km
Annual closure	Fermeture annuelle	no
Weekly closure	Fermeture hebdomadaire	no
Fees main season	Tarifs haute saison	full day

	Week days Semaine	We/Bank holidays We/Férié
Individual Individuel	£ 45	£ 55
Couple Couple	£ 90	£ 110

Caddie Caddie no — **Electric Trolley** Chariot électrique no
Buggy Voiturette yes — **Clubs** Clubs yes
Credit cards Cartes de crédit
VISA - Mastercard

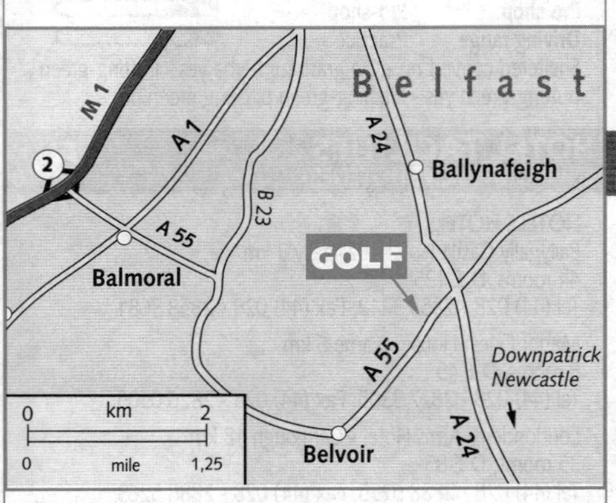

Access Accès : Belfast A24 → Saintfield. Turn off Ormeau Road (Newtownbreda)
Map 2 on page 811 Carte 2 Page 811

GOLF COURSE — PARCOURS — 15/20

Site	Site	
Maintenance	Entretien	
Architect	Architecte	Harry S. Colt
Type	Type	parkland
Relief	Relief	
Water in play	Eau en jeu	
Exp. to wind	Exposé au vent	
Trees in play	Arbres en jeu	

Scorecard Carte de score	Chp. Chp.	Mens Mess.	Ladies Da.
Length Long.	5958	5739	5152
Par	71	70	73
Slope system	—	—	—

Advised golfing ability Niveau de jeu recommandé — 0 12 24 36
Hcp required Handicap exigé — 24 Men, 36 Ladies

CLUB HOUSE & AMENITIES — CLUB HOUSE ET ANNEXES — 5/10

Pro shop Pro-shop
Driving range Practice
Sheltered couvert no - On grass sur herbe yes - Putting-green putting-green yes - Pitching-green pitching green no

HOTEL FACILITIES — ENVIRONNEMENT HOTELIER — 7/10

HOTELS HÔTELS
Holiday Inn Belfast - 170 rooms, D £ 155 - Belfast 6 km
Tel (44) 028 - 9032 8511, Fax (44) 028 - 9062 6546

La Mon House Hotel - 80 rooms, D £ 125 - Belfast 5 km
Tel (44) 028 - 9044 8631, Fax (44) 028 - 9044 8026

Stormont Hotel - Belfast 5 km - 109 rooms, D £ 148
Tel (44) 028 - 9065 1066, Fax (44) 028 - 9048 0240

RESTAURANTS RESTAURANTS
Restaurant Michael Deane - Belfast 5 km
Tel (44) 028 - 9033 1134
Aldens - Belfast 5 km - Tel (44) 028 - 9065 0079
Nick's Warehouse - Belfast 5 km - Tel (44) 028 - 9043 9690

Cairndhu

13 | 6 | 5

There are trees here, but if you hit your ball into the woods, you are almost certainly out of bounds. Cairndhu is a seaside course (not really a links) along the Antrim coast road. This is the road leading from Belfast to the great links courses in the north, and the views are often quite spectacular. Excellence of setting and environment are, though, virtually a constant factor throughout Ireland. Don't be too put off when setting eyes on the contours and relief of the first few holes, things calm down a little after the 4th hole and the terrain gently rolls, nothing more. The course demands some straight driving and accurate approach shots, especially when homing in on a number of small greens, although "average" hitters will basically be playing mid to short irons. Don't place too much faith in your own instinct for gauging distances, because here they can be misleading. The architect has made the most of the terrain and it would be a pity not to get to know a course like this.

Il y a des arbres, mais si vous envoyez votre balle dans les bois, elle est sans doute hors limites. Cairndhu est un parcours de bord de mer (pas vraiment un links), le long de l'Antrim Coast Road. C'est le chemin des écoliers pour aller de Belfast aux grands links du nord, et les vues y sont parfois spectaculaires, mais cette qualité d'environnement est quasiment une constante dans toute l'Irlande. A moins d'être cardiaque, ne vous affolez pas trop à la vue du relief des premiers trous, il s'adoucit après le 4 pour laisser place à de sobres ondulations. Ce parcours réclame de la précision au drive et aux approches, particulièrement pour attaquer certains greens de petite taille, mais les frappeurs "normaux" auront alors essentiellement à jouer des moyens et petits fers. Ne vous fiez pas trop à votre instinct pour les distances, il peut vous tromper. L'architecte a tiré un bon parti du terrain, il serait dommage de ne pas le connaître.

Cairndhu Golf Club **1928**
192 Coast Road, Ballygally
NIR - LARNE, Co Antrim

Office	Secrétariat	(44) 028 - 2858 3324
Pro shop	Pro-shop	(44) 028 - 2858 3954
Fax	Fax	(44) 028 - 2858 3324
E-mail	cairndhu@globalgolf.com	
Situation	Situation	Belfast, 30 km

Larne (pop. 17 575), 6 km

Annual closure	Fermeture annuelle	no
Weekly closure	Fermeture hebdomadaire	no
Fees main season	Tarifs haute saison	18 holes

	Week days Semaine	We/Bank holidays We/Férié
Individual Individuel	£ 20	£ 25*
Couple Couple	£ 40	£ 50*

* Visitors at We: Sunday only

Caddie Caddie no **Electric Trolley** Chariot électrique no

Buggy Voiturette no **Clubs** Clubs yes

Credit cards Cartes de crédit
VISA - Eurocard - MasterCard (Golf club only)

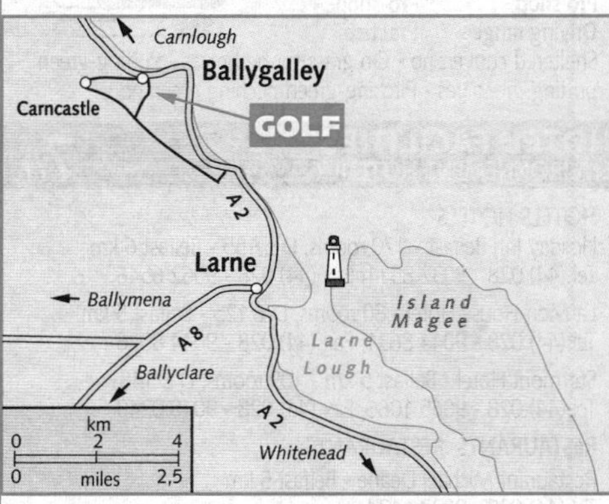

Access Accès : Belfast, M2 → Antrim. Exit 4. A8 to Larne. A2 to Ballygally
Map 2 on page 811 Carte 2 Page 811

GOLF COURSE
PARCOURS **13/20**

Site	Site	
Maintenance	Entretien	
Architect	Architecte	T. Morrison
Type	Type	seaside course parkland
Relief	Relief	
Water in play	Eau en jeu	
Exp. to wind	Exposé au vent	
Trees in play	Arbres en jeu	

Scorecard Carte de score	Chp. Chp.	Mens Mess.	Ladies Da.
Length Long.	5500	5436	4861
Par	70	70	73
Slope system	—	—	—

Advised golfing ability 0 12 24 36
Niveau de jeu recommandé
Hcp required Handicap exigé no

CLUB HOUSE & AMENITIES
CLUB HOUSE ET ANNEXES **6/10**

Pro shop Pro-shop
Driving range Practice
Sheltered couvert no - On grass sur herbe yes - Putting-green putting-green yes - Pitching-green pitching green no

HOTEL FACILITIES
ENVIRONNEMENT HOTELIER **5/10**

HOTELS HÔTELS
Ballygally Castle Hotel - Balligally 3 km
44 rooms, D £ 125
Tel (44) 028 - 2858 3212, Fax (44) 028 - 2858 3681

Manor Guest House - Larne 6 km
8 rooms, D £ 45
Tel (44) 028 - 2827 3305, Fax (44) 028 - 2826 0505

Londonderry Arms Hotel - Carnlough 18 km
35 rooms, D £ 85
Tel (44) 028 - 2888 5255, Fax (44) 028 - 2888 5263

RESTAURANTS RESTAURANTS
Lynden Heights - Ballygally 3 km - Tel (44) 028 - 2858 3560
Halfway House - Ballygally 2 km - Tel (44) 028- 2858 3265

Castlerock

16	6	6

Already at a venerable age, Castlerock is not one of the best known links courses, but it would be shame to overlook it. Designed by Ben Sayers, it certainly won't disappoint the better players and is also more within the reach of mid- to high-handicappers than its prestigious neighbours. This is a great introduction for people who have never played links golf; it has a very natural look to it, is in a beautifully wild setting and has the traditional difficulties found on this type of course. The bunkers, though, are appreciably less severe than elsewhere. To maintain the suspense, you will find a few blind drives, but the hazards everywhere are visible enough for you to forget, temporarily at least, that golf is a sport where there's no justice. Smallish greens call for great precision, and if you miss them you will have the opportunity to put your newly-honed short game to the test. Another important factor here is the warm welcome in the clubhouse. There is an additional nine-hole course down by the mouth of the River Bann.

Ayant atteint un âge vénérable, Castlerock ne figure sans doute pas parmi les links les plus connus, mais il serait bien regrettable de le négliger. Le long de l'embouchure de la Bann, ce parcours ne décevra en rien les meilleurs joueurs, mais il est aussi davantage à la portée du golfeur de handicap moyen ou élevé que ses voisins prestigieux. Pour ceux qui n'ont jamais joué un links, c'est une bonne initiation, par son aspect très naturel, la beauté sauvage de son environnement de dunes, et les difficultés traditionnelles de ce type de parcours : les bunkers sont notamment moins sévères qu'ailleurs. Pour maintenir le suspense, on trouve quelques drives aveugles, mais les obstacles sont partout assez visibles pour ne pas trop s'apercevoir que le golf est un sport sans justice. Des greens de surface assez réduite obligent à une certaine précision. Si on les manque, ce sera l'occasion de mettre en valeur sa virtuosité au petit jeu. La qualité de l'accueil est à souligner, ainsi que le 9 trous près de l'embouchure de la Bann.

Castlerock Golf Club — 1901

Circular Road
NIR - CASTLEROCK, Co Derry

Office Secrétariat (44) 028 - 7084 8314
Pro shop Pro-shop (44) 028 - 7084 9424
Fax Fax (44) 028 - 7084 9440
Web www.castlerockgc.co.uk
Situation Situation Belfast, 90 km
9 km from Coleraine (pop. 20 721), 9 km

Annual closure Fermeture annuelle — no
Weekly closure Fermeture hebdomadaire — no

Fees main season Tarifs haute saison	18 holes	
	Week days / Semaine	We/Bank holidays / We/Férié
Individual Individuel	£ 50	£ 70
Couple Couple	£ 100	£ 140

Caddie Caddie on request **Electric Trolley** Chariot électrique yes
Buggy Voiturette yes **Clubs** Clubs yes
Credit cards Cartes de crédit
VISA - MasterCard (Pro shop goods only)

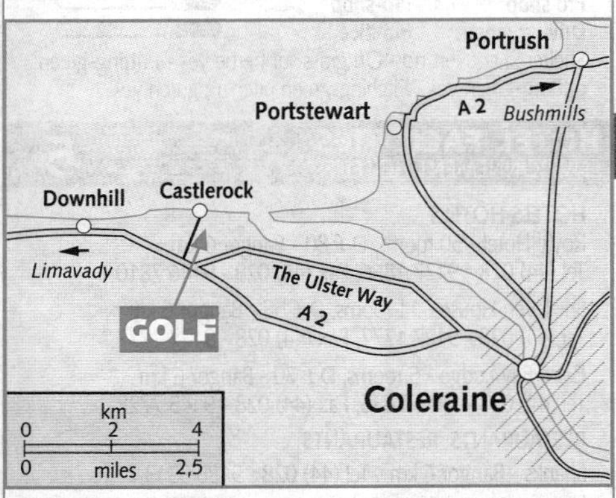

Access Accès : Belfast M2 North → Antrim. Turn right to A26 → Ballymena/Coleraine. Coleraine A2 → Castlerock
Map 2 on page 811 Carte 2 Page 811

GOLF COURSE — PARCOURS — 16/20

Site Site
Maintenance Entretien
Architect Architecte — Ben Sayers
Type Type — links, seaside course
Relief Relief
Water in play Eau en jeu
Exp. to wind Exposé au vent
Trees in play Arbres en jeu

Scorecard Carte de score	Chp. Chp.	Mens Mess.	Ladies Da.
Length Long.	6115	5850	5299
Par	73	73	75
Slope system	—	—	—

Advised golfing ability Niveau de jeu recommandé — 0 12 24 36
Hcp required Handicap exigé — 28 Men, 36 Ladies

CLUB HOUSE & AMENITIES — CLUB HOUSE ET ANNEXES — 6/10

Pro shop Pro-shop
Driving range Practice
Sheltered couvert no - On grass sur herbe yes (own balls) - Putting-green putting-green yes - Pitching-green pitching green no

HOTEL FACILITIES — ENVIRONNEMENT HOTELIER — 6/10

HOTELS HÔTELS
Brown Trout Golf & CC - Coleraine 6 km
15 rooms, D £ 100
Tel (44) 028- 7086 8209, Fax (44) 028- 7086 8878

Bohill Hotel & CC - Coleraine 8 km
37 rooms, D £ 80
Tel (44) 028- 7034 4406, Fax (44) 028- 7035 2424

Bushtown House Hotel - Coleraine 8 km
39 rooms, D £ 85
Tel (44) 028 - 7035 8367, Fax (44) 028 - 7032 0909

RESTAURANTS RESTAURANTS
Bushtown House - Coleraine 8 km - Tel (44) 028 - 7035 8367
The Lodge - Coleraine 8 km - Tel (44) 028 - 7034 4848

Clandeboye *Dufferin Course*

15	6	5

Standing alongside the short and amusing "Ava Course", Clandeboye is a layout of greater calibre in its variety and technical demands on players. Yardage is definitely no difficulty, especially for the long-hitters (they will enjoy the wide fairways), but players who are too short might have problems in carrying the ball. What's more, the uneven soil can also create some interesting lies. Game strategy is pretty obvious, as the difficulties are easily identifiable from the tee, albeit in a sometimes intimidating way. There is just the one blind green here, and the few elevated greens call for accurately and cleanly hit approach shots, especially since the putting surfaces are rather firm. Add to this the water, stream and ditches and you will realise that playing to your handicap here requires careful thought and attention.

A côté du "Ava Course", court et assez amusant, Clandeboye propose ici un parcours de plus grand calibre, par sa diversité et ses exigences techniques. Sa longueur n'est certes pas un facteur de difficultés importantes, en particulier pour les longs frappeurs (ils pourront se déchaîner sur des fairways larges), mais certains joueurs courts risquent d'avoir des problèmes quand il faut porter la balle. Par ailleurs, le sol irrégulier provoque quelques positions de balle intéressantes. La stratégie est assez évidente, les difficultés étant facilement identifiables de chaque départ, mais elles peuvent intimider. On trouve ici un seul green aveugle, quelques greens surélevés, les approches devront y être d'autant plus précises et les coups bien touchés que les surfaces de putting sont souvent assez fermes. Ajoutons la présence de cours d'eau et de fossés, et vous aurez compris que jouer son handicap demande de la réflexion et de l'attention.

Clandeboye Golf Club — 1933

Tower Road, Conlig
NIR - NEWTOWNARDS, Co Down BT23 3PN

Office	Secrétariat	(44) 028 - 9127 1767
Pro shop	Pro-shop	(44) 028 - 9127 1750
Fax	Fax	(44) 028 - 9147 3711
Web	www.cgc-ni.com	
Situation	Situation	Belfast, 15 km

Bangor, 4 km

Annual closure	Fermeture annuelle	no
Weekly closure	Fermeture hebdomadaire	no
Fees main season	Tarifs haute saison	18 holes

	Week days Semaine	We/Bank holidays We/Férié
Individual Individuel	£ 28	£ 33
Couple Couple	£ 56	£ 66

Caddie Caddie no — **Electric Trolley** Chariot électrique yes

Buggy Voiturette yes — **Clubs** Clubs yes

Credit cards Cartes de crédit
VISA - MasterCard - Access

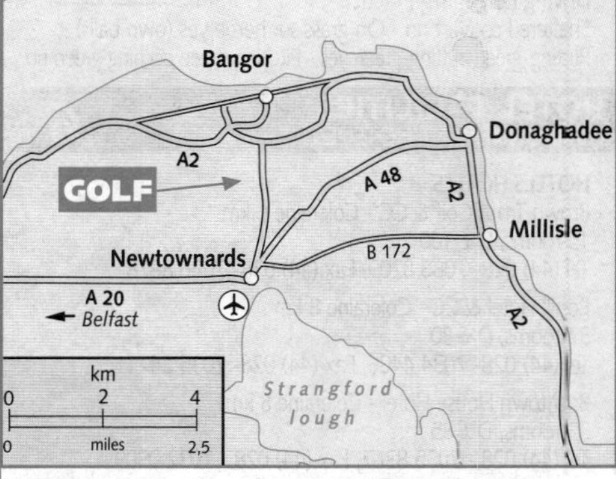

Access Accès : Belfast, A20 to Newtownards. A21 → Bangor.
Map 2 on page 811 Carte 2 Page 811

GOLF COURSE — PARCOURS 15/20

Site	Site	
Maintenance	Entretien	
Architect	Architecte	W.R. Robinson
Type	Type	inland, copse
Relief	Relief	
Water in play	Eau en jeu	
Exp. to wind	Exposé au vent	
Trees in play	Arbres en jeu	

Scorecard Carte de score	**Chp.** Chp.	**Mens** Mess.	**Ladies** Da.
Length Long.	5916	5700	5180
Par	71	71	73
Slope system	—	—	—

Advised golfing ability 0 12 24 36
Niveau de jeu recommandé
Hcp required Handicap exigé no

CLUB HOUSE & AMENITIES — CLUB HOUSE ET ANNEXES 6/10

Pro shop Pro-shop
Driving range Practice
Sheltered couvert no - On grass sur herbe yes - Putting-green putting-green yes - Pitching-green pitching green yes

HOTEL FACILITIES — ENVIRONNEMENT HOTELIER 5/10

HOTELS HÔTELS

Royal Hotel - 50 rooms, D £ 80 - Bangor 6 km
Tel (44) 028 - 9127 1866, Fax (44) 028 - 9146 7810

Shelleven House - 11 rooms, D £ 58 - Bangor 6 km
Tel (44) 028 - 9127 1777, Fax (44) 028 - 9127 1777

Cairn Bay Lodge - 5 rooms, D £ 70 - Bangor 6 km
Tel (44) 028 - 9146 7636, Fax (44) 028 - 9145 7728

RESTAURANTS RESTAURANTS

Shanks - Bangor 6 km - Tel (44) 028 - 9185 3313
Lodge - Bangor 6 km - Tel (44) 028 - 9185 2500
Pier 36 (Pub) - Donaghadee 9 km - Tel (44) 028 - 9188 4466
Grace Neill's (Pub) - Donaghadee 9 km
Tel (44) 028 - 9188 4595

Kirkistown Castle

15 | 6 | 4

With breath-taking views over the Irish Sea, gently contoured landscape and a sandy soil, you can understand why James Braid exclaimed "if only this spot were within 50 miles of London!" Not far from the sea, it is acknowledged as links terrain, so making it available for play even in the most hostile conditions. And the wind is most definitely a factor, magnifying every error and difficulty. The course's bunkering is particularly remarkable, but the green-side bunkers generally leave a way open for bump and run shots, which are just the job for firm greens like these. This pretty course is a high-class design, which is only to be expected from its architect, and offers a refreshing and quaintly old-fashioned alternative to modern layouts splattered with water hazards. Even with a par 69 and low yardage, this friendly course is well worth a visit.

Avec ses vues admirables et imprenables sur la mer d'Irlande, son relief très modéré et un sol sablonneux, on comprend que James Braid en ait dit : "Si seulement ce terrain se trouvait à moins de 50 miles de Londres !" Non loin de la mer, mais plus proche d'un parc que d'un véritable links, il en présente malgré tout certains aspects, sans parler du vent, qui souffle où il veut, mais qui amplifie toutes les erreurs et les difficultés. Le bunkering de ce parcours est particulièrement remarquable, mais les bunkers de greens laissent généralement une ouverture, ce qui permet de jouer les "bump and run" bien adaptés à des greens fermes. Ce joli parcours bénéficie d'un dessin de haut niveau, que l'on pouvait attendre de son architecte, et offre une alternative rafraîchissante et un peu surranée aux tracés modernes envahis d'obstacles d'eau. Même avec un par 69 et sa longueur réduite, ce parcours tout à fait amical mérite une visite.

Kirkistown Castle 1902

142, Main Road, Cloughey
NIR - NEWTOWNARDS, Co Down BT22 1JA

Office Secrétariat (44) 028 - 4277 1233
Pro shop Pro-shop (44) 028 - 4277 1004
Fax Fax (44) 028 - 4277 1699
Web www.linksgolfkirkistown.com
Situation Situation Bangor, 38 km
Newtownards, 30 km
Annual closure Fermeture annuelle no
Weekly closure Fermeture hebdomadaire no

Fees main season Tarifs haute saison	18 holes	
	Week days Semaine	**We/Bank holidays** We/Férié
Individual Individuel	£ 25	£ 30*
Couple Couple	£ 50	£ 60*

* Saturday: members only

Caddie Caddie no — **Electric Trolley** Chariot électrique no
Buggy Voiturette no — **Clubs** Clubs yes
Credit cards Cartes de crédit
VISA - MasterCard - Access (Green fees & Pro shop only)

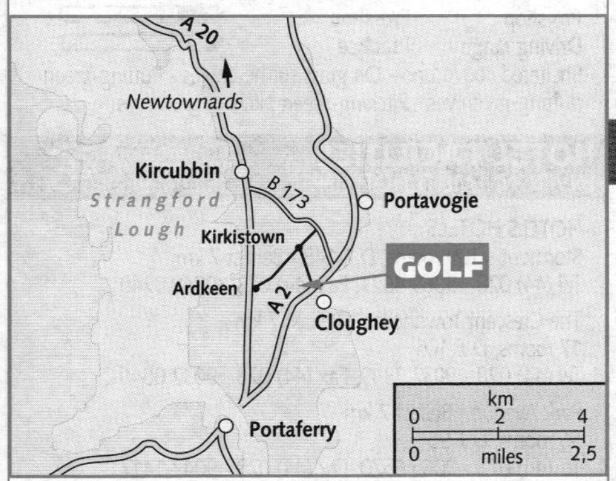

Access Accès : Belfast A20 to Newtownards. A20 to Kircubbin. B173 to Cloughey
Map 2 on page 811 Carte 2 Page 811

GOLF COURSE — PARCOURS 15/20

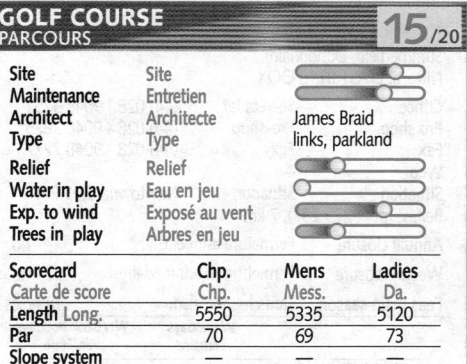

Site Site
Maintenance Entretien
Architect Architecte James Braid
Type Type links, parkland
Relief Relief
Water in play Eau en jeu
Exp. to wind Exposé au vent
Trees in play Arbres en jeu

Scorecard Carte de score	**Chp.** Chp.	**Mens** Mess.	**Ladies** Da.
Length Long.	5550	5335	5120
Par	70	69	73
Slope system	—	—	—

Advised golfing ability 0 12 24 36
Niveau de jeu recommandé
Hcp required Handicap exigé certificate

CLUB HOUSE & AMENITIES — CLUB HOUSE ET ANNEXES 6/10

Pro shop Pro-shop
Driving range Practice
Sheltered couvert no - On grass sur herbe yes - Putting-green putting-green yes - Pitching-green pitching green yes

HOTEL FACILITIES — ENVIRONNEMENT HOTELIER 4/10

HOTELS HÔTELS
Portaferry Hotel - Portaferry 7 km
14 rooms, D £ 110
Tel (44) 028 - 4272 8231, Fax (44) 028 - 4272 8999

The Narrows - Portaferry 6 km
13 rooms, D £ 95
Tel (44) 028- 4272 8148, Fax (44) 028- 4272 8105

RESTAURANTS RESTAURANTS
Portaferry Hotel - Portaferry 7 km
Tel (44) 028 - 4272 8231

The Restaurant (The Narrows) - Portaferry 6 km
Tel (44) 028- 4272 8148

Knock

15 | 7 | 6

This is a generally flat course with a hill in the middle, which you climb twice, although climb is hardly the word. As with all courses close to Belfast, Knock is very busy on week-ends and the week-days are quieter for green-fees. They will have a lot of fun here, unless their swing is off-colour or they start spraying their drives. If you do go into the woods, a little recovery shot back to the fairway is all you can hope for. Most of the holes are lined with trees, which make for a peaceful setting, but wayward hitters will suffer the consequences. The hazards are clearly visible and you feel confident from the very first visit; all you need do is avoid the two streams which meander throughout the course. Although not one of the country's most spectacular and original courses, Knock is at the very least extremely pleasant to play, perhaps more so for mid-handicappers than for the more proficient golfers.

C'est un parcours généralement plat, avec une colline en son centre, que l'on grimpe deux fois, mais il ne s'agit certes pas d'une escalade ! Comme tous les golfs à proximité de Belfast, Knock est très fréquenté en week-end, mais la semaine est plus calme pour les visiteurs. Il s'y amuseront beaucoup, sauf si leur swing est malade ce jour là et qu'ils "arrosent" au drive : il leur faudra bien souvent se contenter de se recentrer s'ils se sont un peu enfoncés dans les bois. La plupart des trous sont bordés d'arbres, ce qui garantit une tranquillité certaine, mais il faut en subir les conséquences si l'on s'écarte un peu. Les obstacles sont ici bien visibles, on se sent en confiance dès la première visite, il suffira d'éviter les méandres de deux cours d'eau qui vont et viennent sur le parcours. S'il ne figure pas parmi les golfs les plus spectaculaires et originaux du pays, Knock est du moins très agréable à jouer, peut-être davantage pour les joueurs moyens que pour les meilleurs.

Knock Golf Club — 1895

Summerfield, Dundonald
NIR - BELFAST BT16 OQX

Office	Secrétariat	(44) 028 - 9048 3251
Pro shop	Pro-shop	(44) 028 - 9048 3825
Fax	Fax	(44) 028 - 9048 7277
Web	—	
Situation	Situation	Newtownards, 9 km

Belfast (pop. 279 237), 7 km

Annual closure	Fermeture annuelle	no
Weekly closure	Fermeture hebdomadaire	no

Fees main season Tarifs haute saison — 18 holes

	Week days Semaine	We/Bank holidays We/Férié
Individual Individuel	£ 26	£ 41*
Couple Couple	£ 52	£ 82*

* Saturday: members only

Caddie Caddie no — **Electric Trolley** Chariot électrique no
Buggy Voiturette yes — **Clubs** Clubs yes
Credit cards Cartes de crédit
VISA - Eurocard - Mastercard

Access Accès : Belfast, A20 → Newtownards
Map 2 on page 811 Carte 2 Page 811

GOLF COURSE — PARCOURS — 15/20

Site	Site	
Maintenance	Entretien	
Architect	Architecte	H.S. Colt, Mackenzie Charles Alison
Type	Type	parkland
Relief	Relief	
Water in play	Eau en jeu	
Exp. to wind	Exposé au vent	
Trees in play	Arbres en jeu	

Scorecard Carte de score	Chp. Chp.	Mens Mess.	Ladies Da.
Length Long.	5800	5615	5205
Par	70	70	73
Slope system	—	—	

Advised golfing ability Niveau de jeu recommandé — 0 12 24 36
Hcp required Handicap exigé — certificate

CLUB HOUSE & AMENITIES — CLUB HOUSE ET ANNEXES — 7/10

Pro shop Pro-shop
Driving range Practice
Sheltered couvert no - On grass sur herbe yes - Putting-green putting-green yes - Pitching-green pitching green yes

HOTEL FACILITIES — ENVIRONNEMENT HOTELIER — 6/10

HOTELS HÔTELS
Stormont - 109 rooms, D £ 148 - Belfast 7 km
Tel (44) 028 - 9065 8621, Fax (44) 028 - 9048 0240

The Crescent Townhouse - Belfast 7 km
17 rooms, D £ 105
Tel (44) 028 - 9032 3349, Fax (44) 028 - 9032 0646

Park Avenue - Belfast 7 km
56 rooms, D £ 95
Tel (44) 028 - 9065 6520, Fax (44) 028 - 9047 1417

RESTAURANTS RESTAURANTS
Duke of York - Belfast 7 km - Tel (44) 028 - 9024 1062
Strand - Belfast 7 km - Tel (44) 028 - 9068 2266

Lisburn

15 | 7 | 6

A beautiful tree-lined drive leads to the Lisburn Golf Club, and sets the mood. Here, you are in the wide open space of park-land and meadows, with the feeling of tranquillity that prevails throughout the Irish countryside. But don't let such bucolic thoughts go to your head, as this course is far from easy, especially from the back tees. Having said that, the men's yellow and ladies tees are well forward so most golfers can breathe easily. Created in 1905, Lisburn was overhauled by Fred Hawtree, whose strategic positioning of fairway and green-side bunkers is clear to see, although the latter seldom block the front of the greens. The terrain is rather flat and only one hole could really be called blind, the 17th, a tricky hole before finishing on a spectacular downhill par 3, itself something of a rarity. This very pretty layout is well worth visiting if you are up Belfast way.

Une belle allée bordée d'arbres conduit au Golf de Lisburn, et donne l'ambiance. Nous allons nous trouver dans un espace de grand parc et de prairies, avec le sentiment de tranquillité associé à la campagne irlandaise. Mais il ne faudra pas se laisser endormir par des pensées bucoliques, ce parcours n'est pas des plus faciles, notamment du fond, mais les départs hommes et dames sont assez avancés pour que la majorité des golfeurs s'y trouve à l'aise. Créé en 1905, il a été révisé par Fred Hawtree, dont on peut remarquer le positionnement stratégique des bunkers de fairway et de greens, mais ces derniers masquent rarement l'entrée des greens. Le terrain est assez plat, et un seul green peut être considéré comme aveugle, au 17, un trou délicat, avant de finir par un par 3 spectaculaire en descente : une disposition très rare sur un parcours. Cette très jolie réalisation mérite le détour si vous passez à Belfast.

Lisburn Golf Club — 1905

68 Eglantine Road
NIR - LISBURN, Co Antrim

Office Secrétariat (44) 028 - 9267 7216
Pro shop Pro-shop (44) 028 - 9267 7217
Fax Fax (44) 028 - 9260 3608
Web www.lisburngolfclub.com
Situation Situation Belfast, 14 km
Lisburn, 4 km

Annual closure Fermeture annuelle no

Weekly closure Fermeture hebdomadaire no

Fees main season Tarifs haute saison 18 holes

	Week days / Semaine	We/Bank holidays / We/Férié
Individual Individuel	£ 30	£ 35
Couple Couple	£ 60	£ 70

Caddie Caddie no — **Electric Trolley** Chariot électrique no

Buggy Voiturette yes — **Clubs** Clubs no

Credit cards Cartes de crédit
VISA - MasterCard (Pro shop goods only)

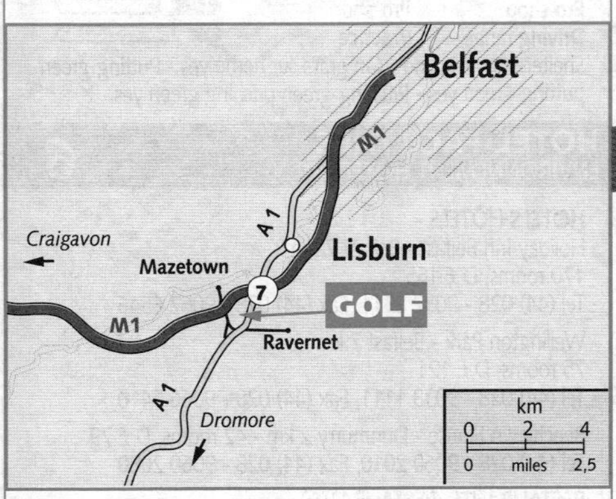

Access Accès : Belfast M1 → Lisburn. Turn left to A1 → Hillsborough. Golf 4 km S of Lisburn

Map 2 on page 811 Carte 2 Page 811

GOLF COURSE
PARCOURS — 15/20

Site Site
Maintenance Entretien
Architect Architecte Fred Hawtree
Type Type parkland
Relief Relief
Water in play Eau en jeu
Exp. to wind Exposé au vent
Trees in play Arbres en jeu

Scorecard / Carte de score	Chp. / Chp.	Mens / Mess.	Ladies / Da.
Length Long.	6075	5754	5049
Par	72	72	72
Slope system	—	—	—

Advised golfing ability Niveau de jeu recommandé 0 12 24 36

Hcp required Handicap exigé 24 Men, 36 Ladies

CLUB HOUSE & AMENITIES
CLUB HOUSE ET ANNEXES — 7/10

Pro shop Pro-shop
Driving range Practice
Sheltered couvert no - On grass sur herbe yes - Putting-green putting-green yes - Pitching-green pitching green yes

HOTEL FACILITIES
ENVIRONNEMENT HOTELIER — 6/10

HOTELS HÔTELS

Park Plaza - Belfast 12 km
106 rooms, D € 120
Tel (44) 028 - 9445 7000, Fax (44) 028 - 9442 3500

Holiday Inn Belfast - Belfast 4 km
170 rooms, D £ 155
Tel (44) 028 - 9032 8511, Fax (44) 028 - 9062 6546

The Old Rectory - Belfast 14 km
6 rooms, D € 60
Tel (44) 028 - 9066 7882, Fax (44) 028 - 9068 3759

RESTAURANTS RESTAURANTS

Tidy Doffer - Hillsborough 2 km - Tel (44) 028 - 9268 9188
Cayenne - Belfast 12 km - Tel (44) 028 - 9033 1532

Malone

13 | 6 | 6

A course with forty bunkers, both necessary and sufficient, as water hazards also play a significant role on certain holes: the 7th, 15th and 16th, a pretty and short par 3 where the tee-box and green bite into a large lake, and again on the 18th, a superb par 4 where slicers might spend a few nervous moments. Created in 1895, the Malone Golf Club, now with 27 holes, moved to this pleasantly rolling terrain in the early 1960s. It is a typical Fred Hawtree design with well-guarded greens of all different sizes, but with the front door left open for crisply hit rolled shots. The existing natural setting was hardly touched, the course being a frank and finely landscaped layout designed around the trees. Of course, visitors used to the British inland style will hardly notice any particular local character, but if you are in the region, you will find this a challenge of high standard. Indeed it was the scene of Tony Jacklin's first professional tournament win in 1966.

On trouve une quarantaine de bunkers ici, à la fois nécessaires et suffisants, car les obstacles d'eau jouent aussi un grand rôle, au 7, au 15, au 16, joli par 3 court où le départ et le green empiètent sur un lac de neuf hectares, et encore au 18, superbe par 4 où les slicers risquent d'éprouver des émotions fortes. Créé en 1895, le club de Malone – désormais pourvu de 27 trous – a émigré sur ce terrain agréablement vallonné au début des années 1960, avec un dessin assez typique de Fred Hawtree, des greens de dimensions variées, bien défendus, mais laissant souvent la porte ouverte aux approches roulées bien touchées. Il n'a guère modifié la nature existante, mais y a inscrit un tracé bien paysagé en fonction des arbres, et d'une parfaite franchise. Certes, les visiteurs habitués au style britannique "inland" ne trouveront pas ici de caractère local très fort, mais si vous vous trouvez dans la région, vous trouverez ici un challenge de très bonne qualité. C'est ici que Tony Jacklin signa sa première victoire chez les pros, en 1966.

Malone Golf Club — 1895

240, Upper Malone Road
NIR - DUNMURRY, Co Belfast BT17 9LB

Office Secrétariat (44) 028 - 9061 2758
Pro shop Pro-shop (44) 028 - 9061 4917
Fax Fax (44) 028 - 9043 1394
Web www.malonegolfclub.co.uk
Situation Situation Belfast, 8 km
Annual closure Fermeture annuelle no
Weekly closure Fermeture hebdomadaire no
Fees main season Tarifs haute saison 18 holes

	Week days / Semaine	We/Bank holidays / We/Férié
Individual Individuel	£ 55	£ 60
Couple Couple	£ 110	£ 120

Wednesday: visitors before 12:00 /Saturday: visitors after 15:30

Caddie Caddie no — **Electric Trolley** Chariot électrique no
Buggy Voiturette yes — **Clubs** Clubs yes
Credit cards Cartes de crédit
VISA - Eurocard - MasterCard
(Green-fees & Pro shop goods only)

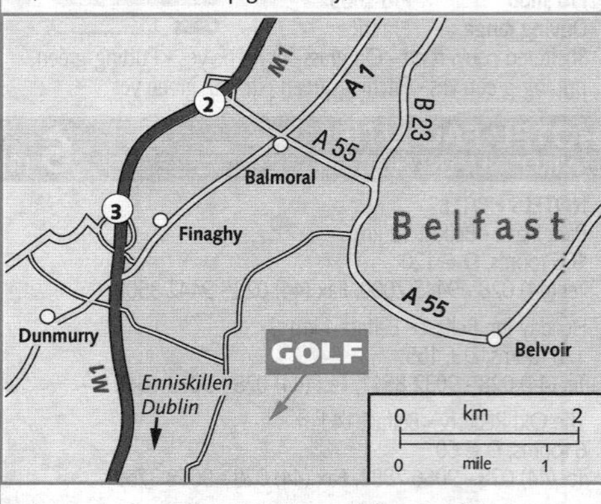

Access Accès : Belfast. B23 (Upper Malone Road)
Map 2 on page 811 Carte 2 Page 811

GOLF COURSE — PARCOURS 13/20

Site Site
Maintenance Entretien
Architect Architecte Fred Hawtree
Type Type inland, parkland
Relief Relief
Water in play Eau en jeu
Exp. to wind Exposé au vent
Trees in play Arbres en jeu

Scorecard / Carte de score	Chp. / Chp.	Mens / Mess.	Ladies / Da.
Length Long.	6036	5710	4123
Par	71	71	72
Slope system	—	—	—

Advised golfing ability Niveau de jeu recommandé 0 12 24 36
Hcp required Handicap exigé certificate

CLUB HOUSE & AMENITIES — CLUB HOUSE ET ANNEXES 6/10

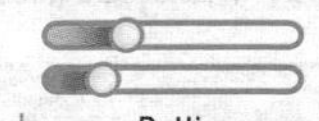

Pro shop Pro-shop
Driving range Practice
Sheltered couvert no - On grass sur herbe yes - Putting-green putting-green yes - Pitching-green pitching green yes

HOTEL FACILITIES — ENVIRONNEMENT HOTELIER 6/10

HOTELS HÔTELS
Holiday Inn Belfast - Belfast 7 km
170 rooms, D £ 155
Tel (44) 028 - 9032 8511, Fax (44) 028 - 9062 6546

Wellington Park - Belfast 7 km
75 rooms, D £ 121
Tel (44) 028 - 9038 1111, Fax (44) 028 - 9066 5410

Beechlawn House - Dunmurry 2 km - 42 rooms, D £ 79
Tel (44) 028 - 9060 2010, Fax (44) 028 - 9060 2080

RESTAURANTS RESTAURANTS
Cayenne - Belfast 6 km - Tel (44) 028 - 9033 1532
Nicks Warehouse - Belfast 7 km - Tel (44) 028 - 9043 9690
James Street South - Belfast 8 km - Tel (44) 028 - 9043 4310

Masserene

14	5	6

The course's location on the banks of Lough Neagh, the largest lake in the British Isles, is a convincing argument in its favour. There are others. Created in 1895, the course was tampered with on several occasions before Fred Hawtree came along in 1961 and brought some order and consistency to the layout. There are any number of trees here, many of which have been planted and are already of an age to come clearly into play (especially on the 17th). The front 9, on clay, can be heavy going in winter, but the back 9 are laid out over sandy soil which drains easily when it rains. There are a lot of hazards, basically bunkers (and water on the 16th), not always very deep but always well-placed and clearly visible. The variety in the size and shape of greens adds to the diversity of holes, and while beginners will unquestionably suffer, good players can test their driving accuracy. A course worth discovering.

Sa situation en bordure du Lough Neagh, le plus grand lac des Iles Britanniques, est un argument de taille (si l'on peut dire). Ce n'est pas le seul. Fondé en 1895, il a été modifié à de multiples reprises, avant que Fred Hawtree vienne mettre un peu d'ordre et de cohérence dans le tracé, en 1961. On trouve de nombreux arbres, dont beaucoup ont été plantés, mais ils ont assez atteint leur maturité pour venir nettement en jeu (spécialement au 17). L'aller, sur un sol argileux, peut être assez mou en hiver, mais le retour bénéficie d'un sol sablonneux, et bien drainant en cas de pluie. Les obstacles sont nombreux, essentiellement les bunkers (de l'eau au 16), mais pas très profonds, toujours bien placés et bien visibles. La variété de dimension et de forme des greens contribue à la diversité des trous, et si les débutants souffriront sans doute, les bons joueurs pourront y tester la précision de leurs drives. Un parcours à découvrir.

Massereene Golf Club — 1895

51 Lough Road
NIR - ANTRIM BT41 4OQ

Office Secrétariat (44) 028 - 9442 8096
Pro shop Pro-shop (44) 028 - 9446 4074
Fax Fax (44) 028 - 9448 7661
Web www.massereene.com
Situation Situation Belfast, 35 km
Antrim, 1.5 km
Annual closure Fermeture annuelle no
Weekly closure Fermeture hebdomadaire no

Fees main season Tarifs haute saison	18 holes	
	Week days Semaine	**We/Bank holidays** We/Férié
Individual Individuel	£ 22	£ 25*
Couple Couple	£ 44	£ 50*

* Saturday, after 16:00 only

Caddie Caddie on request **Electric Trolley** Chariot électrique yes
Buggy Voiturette no **Clubs** Clubs yes
Credit cards Cartes de crédit
VISA - MasterCard (Green-fees & Pro shop goods only)

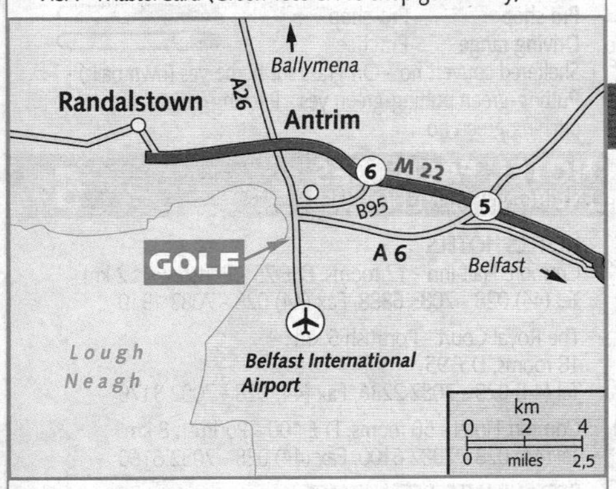

Access Accès : A26 S of Antrim. 1 km, right turn at leisure center. Golf 1.5 km along this road
Map 2 on page 811 Carte 2 Page 811

GOLF COURSE — PARCOURS 14/20

Site Site
Maintenance Entretien
Architect Architecte Fred Hawtree
Type Type inland, parkland
Relief Relief
Water in play Eau en jeu
Exp. to wind Exposé au vent
Trees in play Arbres en jeu

Scorecard Carte de score	**Chp.** Chp.	**Mens** Mess.	**Ladies** Da.
Length Long.	5980	5760	5048
Par	72	72	72
Slope system	—	—	—

Advised golfing ability 0 12 24 36
Niveau de jeu recommandé
Hcp required Handicap exigé no

CLUB HOUSE & AMENITIES — CLUB HOUSE ET ANNEXES 5/10

Pro shop Pro-shop
Driving range Practice
Sheltered couvert no - On grass sur herbe yes - Putting-green putting-green yes - Pitching-green pitching green yes

HOTEL FACILITIES — ENVIRONNEMENT HOTELIER 6/10

HOTELS HÔTELS
Dunadry Hotel & Country Club - Dunadry 6 km
83 rooms, D £ 135
Tel (44) 028 - 9443 4343, Fax (44) 028 - 9443 3767

Park Plaza - 106 rooms, D € 120 - Belfast 7 km
Tel (44) 028 - 9445 7000, Fax (44) 028 - 9442 3500

Galgorm Manor - 24 rooms, D £ 119 - Ballymena 18 km
Tel (44) 028 - 2588 1001, Fax (44) 028 - 2588 0080

RESTAURANTS RESTAURANTS
The Restaurant (Galgorm Manor) - Ballymena 18 km
Tel (44) 028 - 2588 1001
The Linen Mill (Dunadry Hotel) - Dunadry 6 km
Tel (44) 028 - 9443 4343
The Bistro (Dunadry Hotel) - 6 km - Tel (44) 028 - 9443 4343

Portstewart *Strand Course*

16	7	6

The seaside resorts of Portrush and Portstewart are very busy, but foreign tourists come here for the golf. Kept in the shadows of its illustrious neighbour for many a year, the Portstewart championship course (Strand) has been recently restyled and toughened up, and is now a very strong test of golf which unquestionably deserves a good visit. Seven new holes have been built over an area of what were virgin dunes, and the old holes were used as a base for an 18 holer (Riverside Course), which has completed a second 18 hole course (the "Old" course). From the back tees Portstewart is a very competent course with a dangerous collection of bunkers, but you can still play to your handicap... when the wind is just a breeze and the fairways roll well. The most intimidating hole is the first, a par 4, where you probably will have to make do with the bogey. The next holes are spectacular but not quite as fearsome as they look. Make a point of playing here. This 54-hole complex comprises the main Strand-Course, the Old Course (Par 64) and the Riverside Course (Par 68).

Les stations balnéaires de Portrush et Portstewart sont très fréquentées, mais les touristes étrangers viennent pour jouer au golf ! Longtemps à l'ombre de son illustre voisin, le principal parcours de Portstewart (Strand) a été récemment rajeuni et durci, c'est maintenant devenu un test fort respectable, qui mérite sans discussion le détour. Sept nouveaux trous ont été construits dans un espace de dunes autrefois vierge, et les anciens trous ont servi de base pour un dernier 18 trous, complétant un autre 18 trous (le "Old"). Des départs arrière, c'est devenu un très solide parcours, avec notamment une collection dangereuse de bunkers, mais il reste possible d'y jouer son handicap... quand le vent s'appelle brise, et quand les fairways roulent bien. Le trou le plus intimidant est le premier, un par 4 où il faut savoir se contenter d'un bogey. Les trous sont ensuite très spectaculaires, mais un peu moins terribles qu'ils ne paraissent. Ce complexe de 54 trous est à connaître sans faute.

Portstewart Golf Club — 1894

117, Strand Road
NIR - PORTSTEWART BT55 7PG

Office Secrétariat (44) 028 - 7083 2015
Pro shop Pro-shop (44) 028 - 7083 2601
Fax Fax (44) 028 - 7083 4097
Web www.portstewartgc.co.uk
Situation Situation Belfast, 75 km
Coleraine (pop. 20 721), 7 km

Annual closure Fermeture annuelle no
Weekly closure Fermeture hebdomadaire no

Fees main season Tarifs haute saison 18 holes

	Week days Semaine	We/Bank holidays We/Férié
Individual Individuel	£ 65	£ 85*
Couple Couple	£ 130	£ 170*

* Saturday, after 15:00 only

Caddie Caddie on request **Electric Trolley** Chariot électrique no
Buggy Voiturette yes **Clubs** Clubs yes
Credit cards Cartes de crédit
VISA - MasterCard

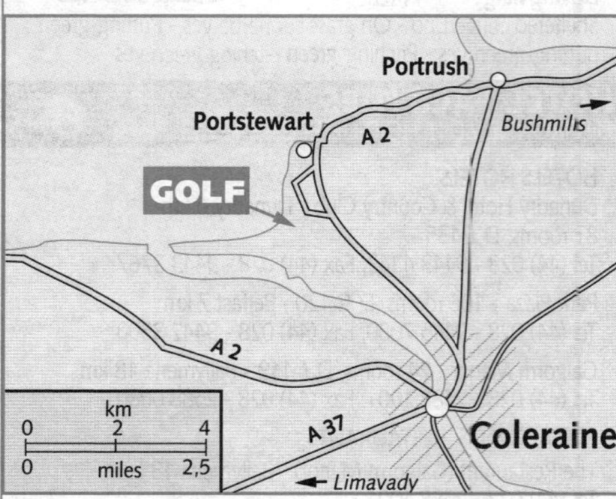

Access Accès : Belfast M2 North to Antrim. Turn right on A26 to Ballymena and Coleraine. Coleraine A2 → Portstewart
Map 2 on page 811 Carte 2 Page 811

GOLF COURSE — PARCOURS 16/20

Site Site
Maintenance Entretien
Architect Architecte Willie Park Jr. / Des Giffin
Type Type links
Relief Relief
Water in play Eau en jeu
Exp. to wind Exposé au vent
Trees in play Arbres en jeu

Scorecard / Carte de score	Chp. / Chp.	Mens / Mess.	Ladies / Da.
Length Long.	6167	5979	5301
Par	72	72	74
Slope system	—	—	—

Advised golfing ability Niveau de jeu recommandé 0 12 24 36
Hcp required Handicap exigé 28 Men, 36 Ladies

CLUB HOUSE & AMENITIES — CLUB HOUSE ET ANNEXES 7/10

Pro shop Pro-shop
Driving range Practice
Sheltered couvert no - On grass sur herbe yes (own balls) - Putting-green putting-green yes - Pitching-green pitching green no

HOTEL FACILITIES — ENVIRONNEMENT HOTELIER 6/10

HOTELS HÔTELS
Cromore Halt Inn - 12 rooms, D £ 75 - Portstewart 2 km
Tel (44) 028 - 7083 6888, Fax (44) 028 - 7083 1910

The Royal Court - Portrush 5 km
18 rooms, D £ 95
Tel (44) 028 - 7082 2236, Fax (44) 028 - 7082 3176

Comfort Hotel - 50 rooms, D £ 100 - Portrush 8 km
Tel (44) 028 - 7082 6100, Fax (44) 028 - 7082 6160

RESTAURANTS RESTAURANTS
Cromore Halt Inn - Portstewart 2 km
Tel (44) 028 - 7083 6888
Ramore Wine Bar - Portrush 4 km - Tel (44) 028 - 7082 4313

Royal Belfast

15 | 7 | 7

As you might expect from a course with a regal title in a major city, Royal Belfast is a rather exclusive club, but it is certainly not impossible to play here (especially during the week) if you book a tee-off time. Although you shouldn't expect the warm atmosphere of a vacation club in Florida, it would be a shame not to play the oldest established club in Ireland, not only for historical reasons but also because of the good course, modified slightly in the 1920s by Harry Colt. Although clearly visible, the hazards are genuinely dangerous (there is a total of 61 bunkers) and need extreme precision if they are to be avoided. So this is hardly what you would call a course for beginners. In addition, the greens are well-guarded and should be approached from exactly the right angle to keep your score down. Course maintenance is excellent.

Comme on peut l'attendre d'un golf avec un titre de noblesse et situé dans une capitale, Royal Belfast est un club assez exclusif, mais il n'est certes pas impossible d'y jouer (surtout en semaine) en réservant à l'avance. Bien sûr, il ne faut pas y attendre l'ambiance chaleureuse d'un club de vacances en Floride ! Il serait malgré tout dommage de ne pas visiter le plus ancien club établi en Irlande, non seulement pour raisons historiques, mais aussi parce qu'il dispose d'un bon parcours, auquel Harry Colt a apporté quelques modifications dans les années 1920. Bien que les obstacles soient visibles, ils sont effectivement dangereux (il y a 61 bunkers au total), et demandent une grande précision pour être évités. De fait, ce n'est pas exactement un parcours pour débutants ! De plus, les greens sont bien protégés, et il faut les aborder avec un angle d'attaque correct pour préserver un bon score. L'entretien est excellent.

Royal Belfast Golf Club — 1891

Station Road, Craigavad
NIR - HOLYWOOD, Co Down BT18 OBP

Office Secrétariat (44) 028 - 9042 8165
Pro shop Pro-shop (44) 028 - 9042 8586
Fax Fax (44) 028 - 9042 1404
Web www.royalbelfast.com
Situation Situation Belfast, 13 km
Bangor, 9 km
Annual closure Fermeture annuelle no
Weekly closure Fermeture hebdomadaire no

Fees main season Tarifs haute saison 18 holes

	Week days / Semaine	We/Bank holidays / We/Férié
Individual Individuel	£ 45	£ 55*
Couple Couple	£ 90	£ 110*

* Saturday, after 16:30 only

Caddie Caddie no — **Electric Trolley** Chariot électrique yes
Buggy Voiturette yes — **Clubs** Clubs yes
Credit cards Cartes de crédit
VISA - MasterCard (Green-fees & Pro shop only)

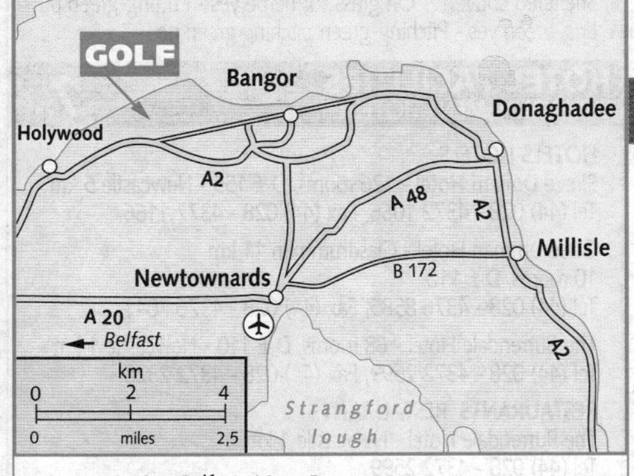

Access Accès : Belfast, A2 → Bangor.
Map 2 on page 811 Carte 2 Page 811

GOLF COURSE — PARCOURS 15/20

Site	Site	
Maintenance	Entretien	
Architect	Architecte	Harry S. Colt
Type	Type	parkland
Relief	Relief	
Water in play	Eau en jeu	
Exp. to wind	Exposé au vent	
Trees in play	Arbres en jeu	

Scorecard / Carte de score	Chp. / Chp.	Mens / Mess.	Ladies / Da.
Length Long.	5676	5575	5000
Par	71	70	72
Slope system	—	—	—

Advised golfing ability / Niveau de jeu recommandé: 0 12 24 36
Hcp required Handicap exigé 28 Men, 36 Ladies

CLUB HOUSE & AMENITIES — CLUB HOUSE ET ANNEXES 7/10

Pro shop Pro-shop
Driving range Practice
Sheltered couvert - On grass sur herbe yes - Putting-green putting-green yes - Pitching-green pitching green no

HOTEL FACILITIES — ENVIRONNEMENT HOTELIER 7/10

HOTELS HÔTELS
Corr's Corner Hotel - Belfast 7 km
30 rooms, D £ 110
Tel (44) 028 - 9084 9221, Fax (44) 028 - 9083 2118

Duke's Hotel - Belfast 8 km
12 rooms, D £ 70
Tel (44) 028 - 9023 6666, Fax (44) 028 - 9023 7177

Wellington Hotel - Belfast 8 km
75 rooms, D £ 121
Tel (44) 028 - 9038 1111, Fax (44) 028 - 9066 5410

RESTAURANTS RESTAURANTS
Sullivans - Holywood 6 km - Tel (44) 028 - 9042 1000
Shanks - Bangor 9 km - Tel (44) 028 - 9185 3313

Royal County Down

19 | 6 | 7

Choosing between Ballybunion, Royal Portrush, Portmarnock and Royal County Down is like trying to give an order of preference to four children. This is a masterly links, with enough blind shots and tricky greens to make a caddie well worthwhile on your first visit. Designed by Old Tom Morris, the course has undergone recent upgrading by Donald Steel, who has left an impressive stamp on the long 18th. Modernisation has not been at the cost of character or majesty and the hazards have not lost their strategic role: the rough, bushes, bunkers and huge dunes collect poor or over-ambitious shots. For a decent score, your game has to be up to the standard demanded by the course, and a degree of humility will also help you to come to terms with the hazards, without which the game of golf would be boring. If you can, tee off from the 10th; despite their excellence, the last 9 holes are a little less impressive than the front 9, which wind their way through sand dunes. This is, perhaps, the only hint of a blemish on an otherwise perfect masterpiece.

Choisir entre Ballybunion, Royal Portrush, Portmarnock et Royal County Down, c'est comme classer ses quatre enfants par ordre de préférence. Celui-ci est un links magistral, avec assez de coups aveugles et des greens assez délicats à lire pour inciter à prendre un caddie la première fois. Conçu par Old Tom Morris, ce parcours a été modernisé par Donald Steel, pour le meilleur au 18. Il n'a pas perdu son caractère et sa grandeur, et les obstacles ont conservé leur rôle stratégique : les roughs, les buissons, les bunkers, les immenses dunes recueillent tous les coups médiocres ou trop audacieux. Il faut un jeu à la hauteur du parcours pour y scorer décemment, mais aussi beaucoup d'humilité pour accepter les hasards sans lesquels le golf serait bien ennuyeux. Si l'on peut, on commencera par le retour : en dépit de leurs qualités golfiques, les derniers trous ne sont pas aussi impressionnants que les premiers, insinués dans les dunes. C'est peut-être la seule petite ombre à un tableau de maître.

Royal County Down — 1889

NIR - NEWCASTLE, Co Down

Office	Secrétariat	(44) 028 - 4372 3314
Pro shop	Pro-shop	(44) 028 - 4372 2419
Fax	Fax	(44) 028 - 4372 6281
Web	www.royalcountydown.org	
Situation	Situation	Belfast, 48 km

Newcastle (pop. 7 214), 1 km

Annual closure Fermeture annuelle — no

Weekly closure Fermeture hebdomadaire — no

Fees main season Tarifs haute saison — 18 holes

	Week days / Semaine	We/Bank holidays / We/Férié
Individual Individuel	£ 115	£ 130
Couple Couple	£ 230	£ 260

Wednesday and Saturday: members only
Week days after 14:00, £ 100 / Sundays

Caddie Caddie yes — **Electric Trolley** Chariot électrique yes

Buggy Voiturette no — **Clubs** Clubs yes

Credit cards Cartes de crédit
VISA - MasterCard - AMEX

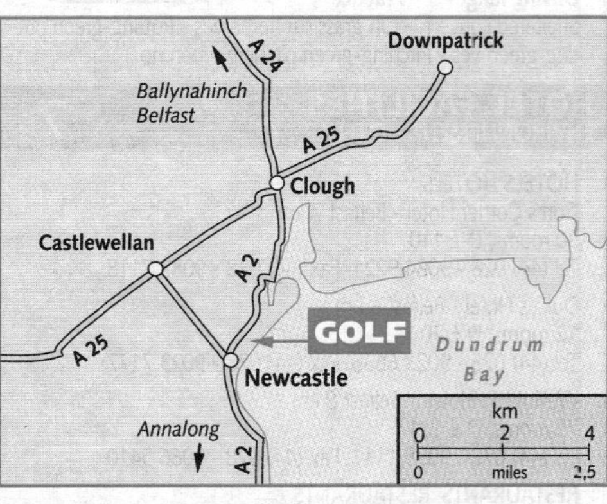

Access Accès : Belfast A24, 50 km through Newcastle on A2
Map 2 on page 811 Carte 2 Page 811

GOLF COURSE — PARCOURS — 19/20

Site	Site	
Maintenance	Entretien	
Architect	Architecte	Old Tom Morris
Type	Type	links
Relief	Relief	
Water in play	Eau en jeu	
Exp. to wind	Exposé au vent	
Trees in play	Arbres en jeu	

Scorecard Carte de score	Chp. Chp.	Mens Mess	Ladies Da.
Length Long.	6335	6084	5672
Par	71	71	76
Slope system	—	—	—

Advised golfing ability Niveau de jeu recommandé — 0 12 24 36

Hcp required Handicap exigé — 28 Men, 36 Ladies

CLUB HOUSE & AMENITIES — CLUB HOUSE ET ANNEXES — 6/10

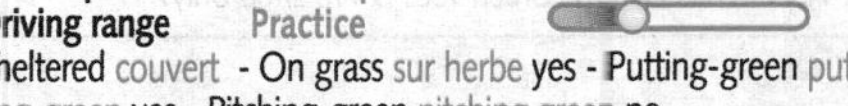

Pro shop Pro-shop
Driving range Practice

Sheltered couvert - On grass sur herbe yes - Putting-green putting-green yes - Pitching-green pitching green no

HOTEL FACILITIES — ENVIRONNEMENT HOTELIER — 7/10

HOTELS HÔTELS

Slieve Donard Hotel - 126 rooms, D £ 155 - Newcastle 5 km
Tel (44) 028 - 4372 1066, Fax (44) 028 - 4372 1166

Glasdrumman Hotel - Glasdrumman 11 km
10 rooms, D £ 110
Tel (44) 028 - 4376 8585, Fax (44) 028 - 4376 7041

The Burrendale Hotel - 68 rooms, D £ 110 - Newcastle 1 km
Tel (44) 028 - 4372 2599, Fax (44) 028 - 4372 2328

RESTAURANTS RESTAURANTS

The Burrendale Hotel - Newcastle 1 km
Tel (44) 028 - 4372 2599

Oak (Slieve Donard) - Newcastle 1 km
Tel (44) 028 - 4372 1066

Buck's Head (Pub) - Dundrum 6 km - Tel (44) 028 - 4375 1868

Royal Portrush *Dunluce Links*

19 | 7 | 7

Being so close to the Giant's Causeway effectively brings to mind how a course can dwarf your golf. The Dunluce, where the 1951 British Open was played, is rated as one of Ireland's greatest courses, a fact you can easily check for yourself. Over an area covered with enormous dunes, the course comes and goes in a perfectly nothing-to-hide manner. In fact, it never leaves you alone and not a single hole fails to impress, so woe betide the golfer who drops his guard. You need not only extreme skill with club and ball, but also nerves of steel so as not to shrink from the difficulties you are sure to encounter sooner or later. Even the greens, with some tantalising slopes, demand unfailing concentration. You need a certain level of golfing ability to appreciate the subtler sides to this devilish course, which really snarls when the wind blows. Harry Colt considered this to be his masterpiece. Which it is.

La proximité de la "Chaussée des Géants" fait penser que l'on peut facilement devenir un nain, golfiquement parlant du moins. Le "Dunluce" de Royal Portrush passe pour être l'un des plus grands parcours d'Irlande, vous le vérifierez aisément. Dans un espace occupé par d'énormes dunes, le parcours va et vient avec une franchise parfaite. Il n'est pas un trou pour vous laisser tranquille ou indifférent, pour vous permettre de baisser un seul instant la garde. Il faut non seulement une grande maîtrise de ses clubs et du maniement de la balle, mais aussi des nerfs d'acier pour ne pas fléchir devant les difficultés, à un moment ou à un autre. Même les greens exigent une concentration sans faille, avec leurs pentes déconcertantes. Il faut de l'amour pour les links, ou un certain niveau de jeu pour apprécier les beautés et les subtilités de ce parcours démoniaque, dont les dents sont encore plus acérées avec le vent. Harry Colt le considérait comme "son" chef-d'oeuvre. C'est un chef d'oeuvre, tout simplement.

Royal Portrush Golf Club — 1888

Bushmills Road
NIR - PORTRUSH, Co Antrim

Office Secrétariat (44) 028 - 7082 2311
Pro shop Pro-shop (44) 028 - 7082 3335
Fax Fax (44) 028 - 7082 3139
Web www.royalportrushgolfclub.com
Situation Situation Belfast, 90 km
Coleraine (pop. 20 721), 8 km
Annual closure Fermeture annuelle no
Weekly closure Fermeture hebdomadaire no

Fees main season Tarifs haute saison	18 holes	
	Week days Semaine	**We/Bank holidays** We/Férié
Individual Individuel	£ 95	£ 110
Couple Couple	£ 190	£ 220

Additional round: £ 50 (any day) / Access limited every day (ask before coming)

Caddie Caddie on request **Electric Trolley** Chariot électrique yes
Buggy Voiturette no **Clubs** Clubs yes
Credit cards Cartes de crédit
VISA - Eurocard - MasterCard - AMEX

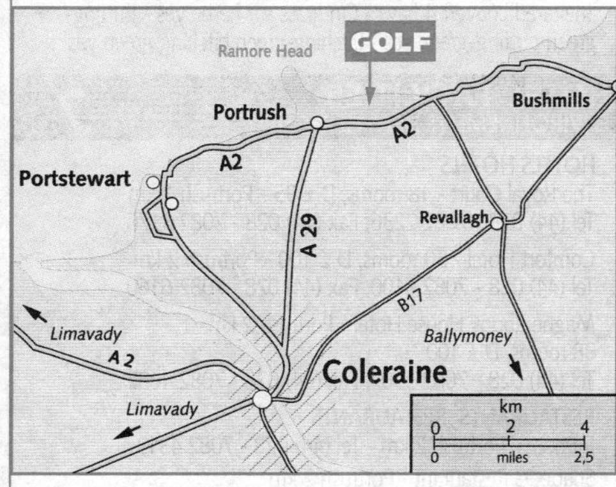

Access Accès : Belfast M2 North → Antrim. Turn right to A26 → Ballymena/Coleraine. Coleraine → Portrush
Map 2 on page 811 Carte 2 Page 811

GOLF COURSE — PARCOURS — 19/20

Site	Site	
Maintenance	Entretien	
Architect	Architecte	Harry S. Colt
Type	Type	links
Relief	Relief	
Water in play	Eau en jeu	
Exp. to wind	Exposé au vent	
Trees in play	Arbres en jeu	

Scorecard Carte de score	**Chp.** Chp.	**Mens** Mess.	**Ladies** Da.
Length Long.	6137	6000	5601
Par	72	72	75
Slope system	—	—	—

Advised golfing ability Niveau de jeu recommandé 0 12 24 36

Hcp required Handicap exigé 24 Men, 36 Ladies

CLUB HOUSE & AMENITIES — CLUB HOUSE ET ANNEXES — 7/10

Pro shop Pro-shop
Driving range Practice
Sheltered couvert 4 bays - On grass sur herbe yes - Putting-green putting-green yes - Pitching-green pitching green yes

HOTEL FACILITIES — ENVIRONNEMENT HOTELIER — 7/10

HOTELS HÔTELS
The Royal Court - 18 rooms, D £ 95 - Portrush 1 km
Tel (44) 028 - 7082 2236, Fax (44) 028 - 7082 3176

Comfort Hotel - 50 rooms, D £ 100 - Portrush 2 km
Tel (44) 028 - 7082 6100, Fax (44) 028 - 7082 6160

Magherabuoy House Hotel - Portrush 2 km
38 rooms, D £ 100
Tel (44) 028 - 7082 3507, Fax (44) 028 - 7082 4687

RESTAURANTS RESTAURANTS
Ramore - Portrush 2 km - Tel (44) 028 - 7082 4313

Snappers Restaurant - Portrush 2 km
Tel (44) 028 - 7082 4945

Bushmills Inn Restaurant - Bushmills 8 km
Tel (44) 028 - 2073 3000

Royal Portrush *Valley*

13	7	7

How can we assess the "second course" at Portrush? Would we rate it a good course if it went by any other name? The answer is yes, even though it is some way from the greatness and majesty of the Dunluce Links. Located, as its name suggests, in a valley between dunes, there are, strangely enough, no more than twenty bunkers, and the par 3s are particularly devoid of sand. Otherwise, the rolling terrain, rough, bushes and wind are trouble enough to upset most players, especially when the end-targets are as small as they generally are here. The nature of the terrain will also pose a few problems for players who are used to the immaculately prepared fairways of inland courses. As with all links courses, this is a test of ball-play and feeling, and the natural setting only adds to the appeal. Golfers who end up discovering this course by chance are generally surprised at the overall excellence of the layout. A very good practice course.

Comment juger le "second parcours" de Royal Portrush ? S'il portait un autre nom, serait-il considéré comme un très bon parcours ? A l'évidence oui, même s'il est loin de la grandeur et de la majesté du "Dunluce Links". Situé comme son nom l'indique dans une vallée entre les dunes, il ne compte curieusement qu'une vingtaine de bunkers, particulièrement rares sur les par 3. Autrement, les ondulations du terrain, les roughs, les buissons et le vent suffisent amplement à troubler les joueurs, surtout quand les cibles finales sont petites, ce qui est généralement le cas. Et la nature du terrain posera forcément des problèmes aux joueurs habitués aux fairways impeccablement garnis des parcours intérieurs. Comme tous les links, celui-ci est un test de toucher de balle, et son aspect naturel ajoute à la séduction. Ceux qui sont amenés à le découvrir par hasard sont généralement surpris de sa qualité générale. Un bon parcours d'entraînement.

Royal Portrush Golf Club — 1889

Bushmills Road
NIR - PORTRUSH, Co Antrim

Office Secrétariat (44) 028 - 7082 2311
Pro shop Pro-shop (44) 028 - 7082 3335
Fax Fax (44) 028 - 7082 3139
Web www.royalportrushgolfclub.com
Situation Situation Belfast, 90 km
Coleraine (pop. 20 721), 8 km

Annual closure Fermeture annuelle — no
Weekly closure Fermeture hebdomadaire — no

Fees main season Tarifs haute saison	18 holes	
	Week days Semaine	**We/Bank holidays** We/Férié
Individual Individuel	£ 37,5	£ 40
Couple Couple	£ 75	£ 80

Additional round: £ 15 / Access limited every day (ask before coming)

Caddie Caddie on request **Electric Trolley** Chariot électrique yes
Buggy Voiturette no **Clubs** Clubs yes
Credit cards Cartes de crédit
VISA - Eurocard - MasterCard - AMEX

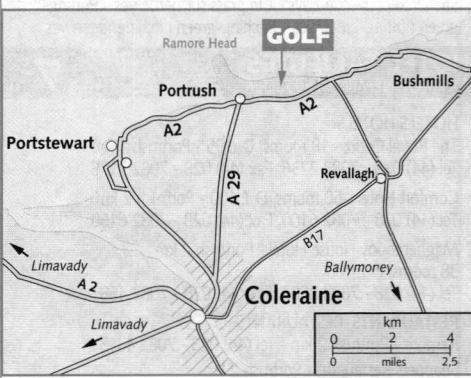

Access Accès : Belfast M2 North → Antrim. Turn right to A26 → Ballymena/Coleraine. Coleraine → Portrush
Map 2 on page 811 Carte 2 Page 811

GOLF COURSE — PARCOURS 13/20

Site Site
Maintenance Entretien
Architect Architecte unknown
Type Type links
Relief Relief
Water in play Eau en jeu
Exp. to wind Exposé au vent
Trees in play Arbres en jeu

Scorecard Carte de score	Chp. Chp.	Mens Mess.	Ladies Da.
Length Long.	5700	5450	4995
Par	70	68	72
Slope system	—	—	—

Advised golfing ability Niveau de jeu recommandé 0 12 24 36
Hcp required Handicap exigé no

CLUB HOUSE & AMENITIES — CLUB HOUSE ET ANNEXES 7/10

Pro shop Pro-shop
Driving range Practice
Sheltered couvert 4 bays - On grass sur herbe yes - Putting-green putting-green yes - Pitching-green pitching green yes

HOTEL FACILITIES — ENVIRONNEMENT HOTELIER 7/10

HOTELS HÔTELS
The Royal Court - 18 rooms, D £ 95 - Portrush 1 km
Tel (44) 028 - 7082 2236, Fax (44) 028 - 7082 3176

Comfort Hotel - 50 rooms, D £ 100 - Portrush 2 km
Tel (44) 028 - 7082 6100, Fax (44) 028 - 7082 6160

Magherabuoy House Hotel - Portrush 2 km
38 rooms, D £ 100
Tel (44) 028 - 7082 3507, Fax (44) 028 - 7082 4687

RESTAURANTS RESTAURANTS
Ramore - Portrush 2 km - Tel (44) 028 - 7082 4313

Snappers Restaurant - Portrush 2 km
Tel (44) 028 - 7082 4945

Bushmills Inn Restaurant - Bushmills 8 km
Tel (44) 028 - 2073 3000

Warrenpoint

13 | 6 | 4

The setting for the Warrenpoint course, between the Mountains of Mourne and Carlingford Lough, provides some breath-taking scenery and a marvellous sensation of space. To appreciate it fully, though, you will need to disregard the noise of the adjacent road, which is a shame. Once home to Ronan Rafferty, it is otherwise a very pleasant course, maybe more for mid- to high-handicappers than for the more skilled exponents, who might feel a little frustrated at its relatively modest challenge. But we need courses for every taste and anyway, there is no shortage of tough courses in Ireland. This layout requires no great length off the tee (which is a reserved privilege, anyway) but it does call for a sharp and subtle short game, as some approaches and bunkers around the greens are tricky. But these difficulties are generally on either side of the greens, so you can lay up short and stay out of trouble. A pleasant stop-off on "hard-working" holidays.

La situation du golf de Warrenpoint, entre les montagnes et la baie de Carlingford permet des points de vue majestueux, donnant une sensation merveilleuse d'espace, mais il faut, pour en profiter, faire abstraction du bruit de la route adjacente... C'est dommage, car ce parcours longtemps cher à Ronan Rafferty est autrement très agréable, peut-être davantage encore pour les handicaps moyens et élevés, alors que les meilleurs joueurs seront un peu frustrés s'ils attendent un adversaire à la mesure de leur talent. Mais il faut des golfs pour tous les goûts, et le pays ne manque pas de parcours difficiles. Celui-ci ne requiert pas une grande longueur (elle n'est pas donnée à tout le monde), mais plutôt de la finesse de petit jeu, car certains abords de greens sont délicats, de même que les bunkers. Mais ces difficultés sont plutôt de part et d'autre des greens, ce qui autorise à jouer court pour ne pas en souffrir. Une halte sympathique pour des vacances studieuses.

Warrenpoint Golf Club 1893
Lower Dromore Road
NIR - WARRENPOINT, Co Down BT34 3LN

Office	Secrétariat	(44) 028 - 4175 3695
Pro shop	Pro-shop	(44) 028 - 4175 2371
Fax	Fax	(44) 028 - 4175 2918
Web	www.warrenpointgolf.com	
Situation	Situation	Belfast, 50 km

Newry, 8 km

Annual closure	Fermeture annuelle	no
Weekly closure	Fermeture hebdomadaire	no
Fees main season	Tarifs haute saison	18 holes

	Week days Semaine	We/Bank holidays We/Férié
Individual Individuel	£ 26	£ 32*
Couple Couple	£ 52	£ 64**

* Saturday: members only (a few tee times may be available)

Caddie Caddie no — **Electric Trolley** Chariot électrique yes
Buggy Voiturette no — **lubs** Clubs yes
Credit cards Cartes de crédit
VISA - Eurocard - MasterCard (Pro shop only)

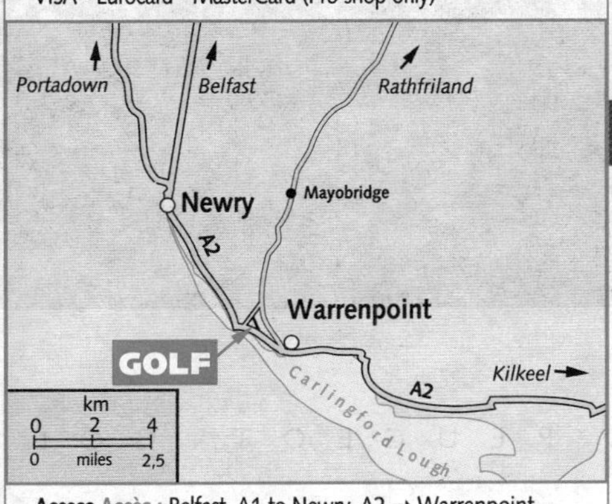

Access Accès : Belfast, A1 to Newry. A2 → Warrenpoint.
Map 2 on page 811 Carte 2 Page 811

GOLF COURSE — PARCOURS 13/20

Site	Site	
Maintenance	Entretien	
Architect	Architecte	unknown
Type	Type	parkland, hilly
Relief	Relief	
Water in play	Eau en jeu	
Exp. to wind	Exposé au vent	
Trees in play	Arbres en jeu	

Scorecard Carte de score	Chp. Chp.	Mens Mess.	Ladies Da.
Length Long.	6161	5778	5377
Par	71	71	72
Slope system	—	—	—

Advised golfing ability Niveau de jeu recommandé: 0 12 24 36
Hcp required Handicap exigé: no

CLUB HOUSE & AMENITIES — CLUB HOUSE ET ANNEXES 6/10

Pro shop Pro-shop
Driving range Practice
Sheltered couvert no - On grass sur herbe yes - Putting-green putting-green yes - Pitching-green pitching green no

HOTEL FACILITIES — ENVIRONNEMENT HOTELIER 4/10

HOTELS HÔTELS
Canal Court Hotel - Newry 12 km
110 rooms, D £ 130
Tel (44) 028 - 3025 1234, Fax (44) 028 - 3025 1177

Mourne Country - Newry 12 km
43 rooms, D £ 80
Tel (44) 028 - 3026 7922, Fax (44) 028 - 3026 0896

RESTAURANTS RESTAURANTS
Old Mill (Canal Court H.) - Newry 8 km
Tel (44) 028 - 3025 1234

Aylesfort House - Warrenpoint 1 km- Tel (44) 028 - 4177 2255

Annahaia - Newry 8 km - Tel (44) 028 - 3084 8084

ITALY

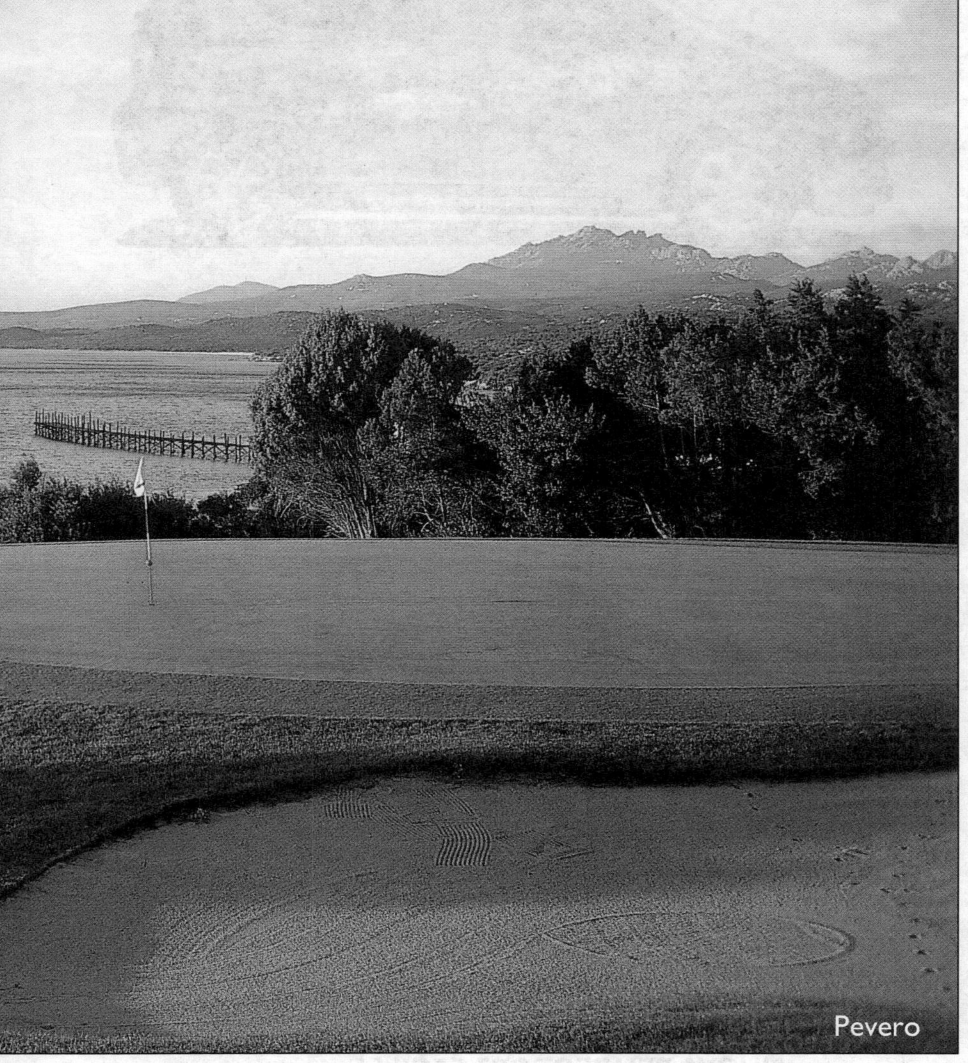
Pevero

ENTRARE NEL GREEN È FACILE.

www.peugeot.it 800 900 901 Pronto Peugeot

NUOVA PEUGEOT 1007. FACILE!

Con le porte elettriche scorrevoli Sésame, salire e scendere è semplicissimo. Peugeot 1007 è la prima Easy car del mercato che rende facile la vita, grazie anche ai kit Caméléo e al cambio 2Tronic.

PEUGEOT RACCOMANDA TOTAL

PEUGEOT. PERCHÉ L'AUTO SIA SEMPRE UN PIACERE.

Consumo carburante l/100 km: urbano da 5,3 a 8,6; extraurbano da 3,8 a 5,4; combinato da 4,4 a 6,6; emissioni CO_2 g/km: da 115 a 156.

ITALY

It is hard to imagine a more agreeable country and favourable climate than Italy, where history is all around you and closely integrated with very active modern-day life. Even though the winters can be rather cold in the north, excepting the lakes region, golf is an all-year sport. Yet, there are only about 150 18-hole courses (more than 220 overall) and not even 80,000 players. While Spain and Portugal have covered their coastlines with courses and touring golfers, Italy has neglected this side of the equation and has built courses mainly for local populations and particularly around major cities, mainly in the North of the country. It is such a pleasure playing golf here, though, with generally very elegant and well-equipped club-houses which make a point of cultivating social life and great food. They say that golf is an art of living; in Italy it certainly is. In this new edition, you will see that we have included a new and very pretty course close to Lake Garda, the Paradiso, plus two new courses in the south of Italy. Both are more than welcome because the potential for golf in this part of the country was largely untapped. Look out for San Domenico and Acaya.

ITALIA

E'difficile immaginare un paese più piacevole e con il clima migliore dell'Italia, nel quale la storia si trova ovunque intorno a te ma si integra perfettamente con la vita moderna superattiva. Anche se l'inverno può essere abbastanza freddo al nord, a parte nella regione dei laghi, il golf è uno sport che si pratica tutto l'anno. Per il momento ci sono solo poco più di 150 campi e neanche 80.000 giocatori. Mentre la Spagna e il Portogallo hanno riempito le loro coste di campi e turisti-golfisti, l'Italia ha trascurato questo aspetto ed ha costruito percorsi principalmente per la popolazione locale, in particolar modo intorno alle città più importanti e sopratutto nel nord del paese. E' veramente un piacere giocare a golf qui, oltretutto, di solito si trovano club-houses molto eleganti e ben attrezzate che sono il punto d'incontro della buona società e dove si mangia molto bene. Si dice che il golf sia un'arte di vivere: in Italia lo è certamente. In questa edizione è entrato Paradiso, un nuovissimo e piacevole campo vicino al lago di Garda e anche San Domenico e Acaya due graditi nuovi percorsi in Puglia che iniziano a rendere molto interessante questa regione finora sottovalutata sul piano golfistico.

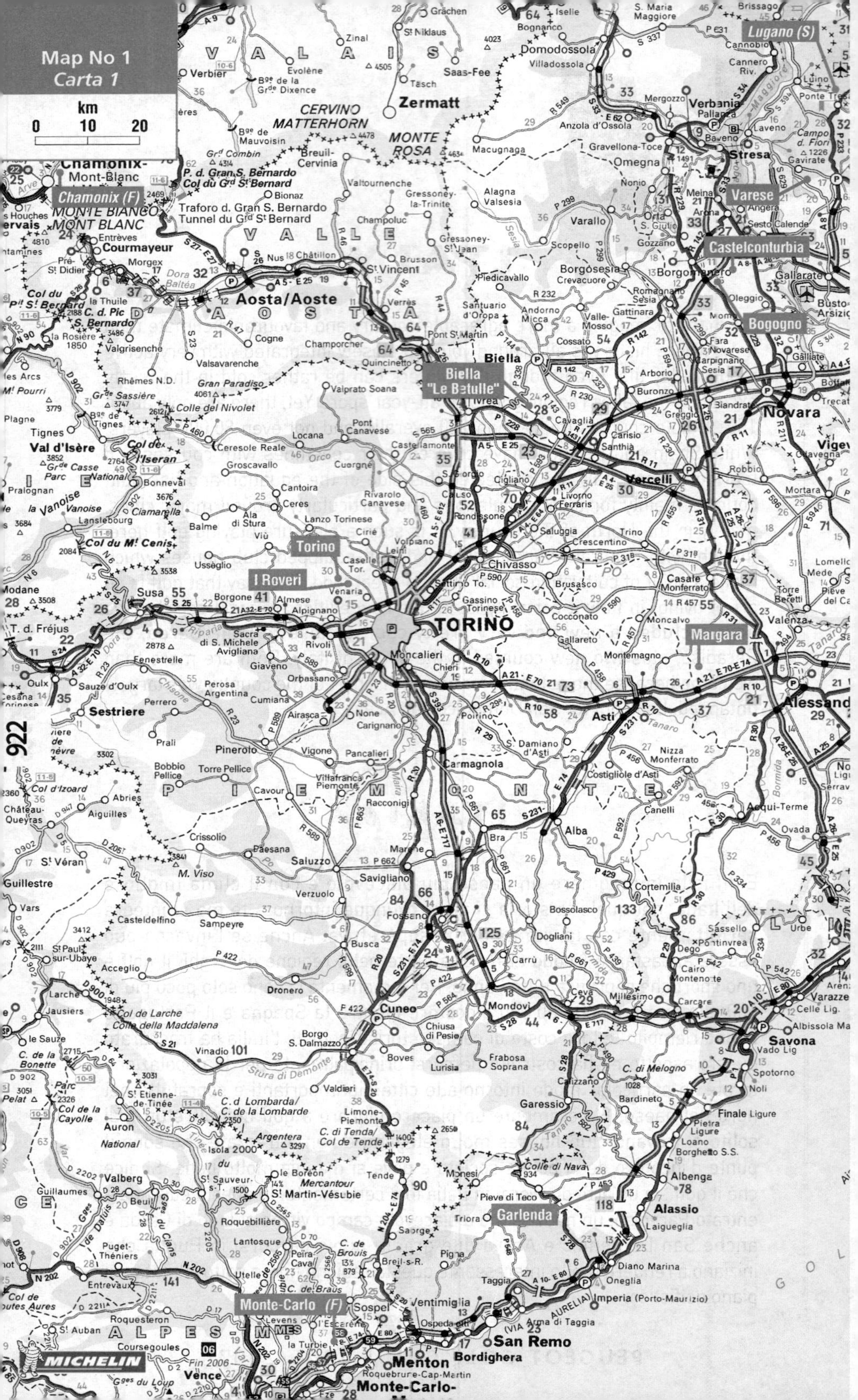

Map No 1
Carta 1
km
0 10 20
Lugano (S)
Chamonix (F)
Varese
Castelconturbia
Bogogno
Biella "Le Betulle"
Torino
I Roveri
Margara
Garlenda
Monte-Carlo (F)
Zermatt
CERVINO MATTERHORN
MONTE ROSA
Aosta/Aoste
Chamonix-Mont-Blanc
Courmayeur
Biella
Novara
Vercelli
TORINO
Asti
Alessandria
Cuneo
Savona
Alassio
San Remo
Bordighera
Menton
Monte-Carlo
Stresa
Verbania
Domodossola
Sestriere
Pinerolo
Alba
Mondovì
Ventimiglia
Imperia (Porto-Maurizio)
922
MICHELIN

Monticello
Villa d'Este
"L'Albenza" Bergamo
Barlassina
Milano
Le Robinie
Ambrosiano
Castello di Tolcinasco
Franciacorta
Palazzo Arzaga
Gardagolf
Paradiso
Verona
Rapallo
LUGANO
Como
Lecco
Bergamo
Monza
MILANO
BRESCIA
Pavia
Lodi
Cremona
Piacenza
Mantova
PARMA
Reggio nell' Emilia
GENOVA
S. Margherita Ligure
La Spezia
Carrara
Massa
Viareggio
Lucca
923
MICHELIN
d'après base de données au 1/1 000 000 - édition 2005.
Autorisation n°0501023.

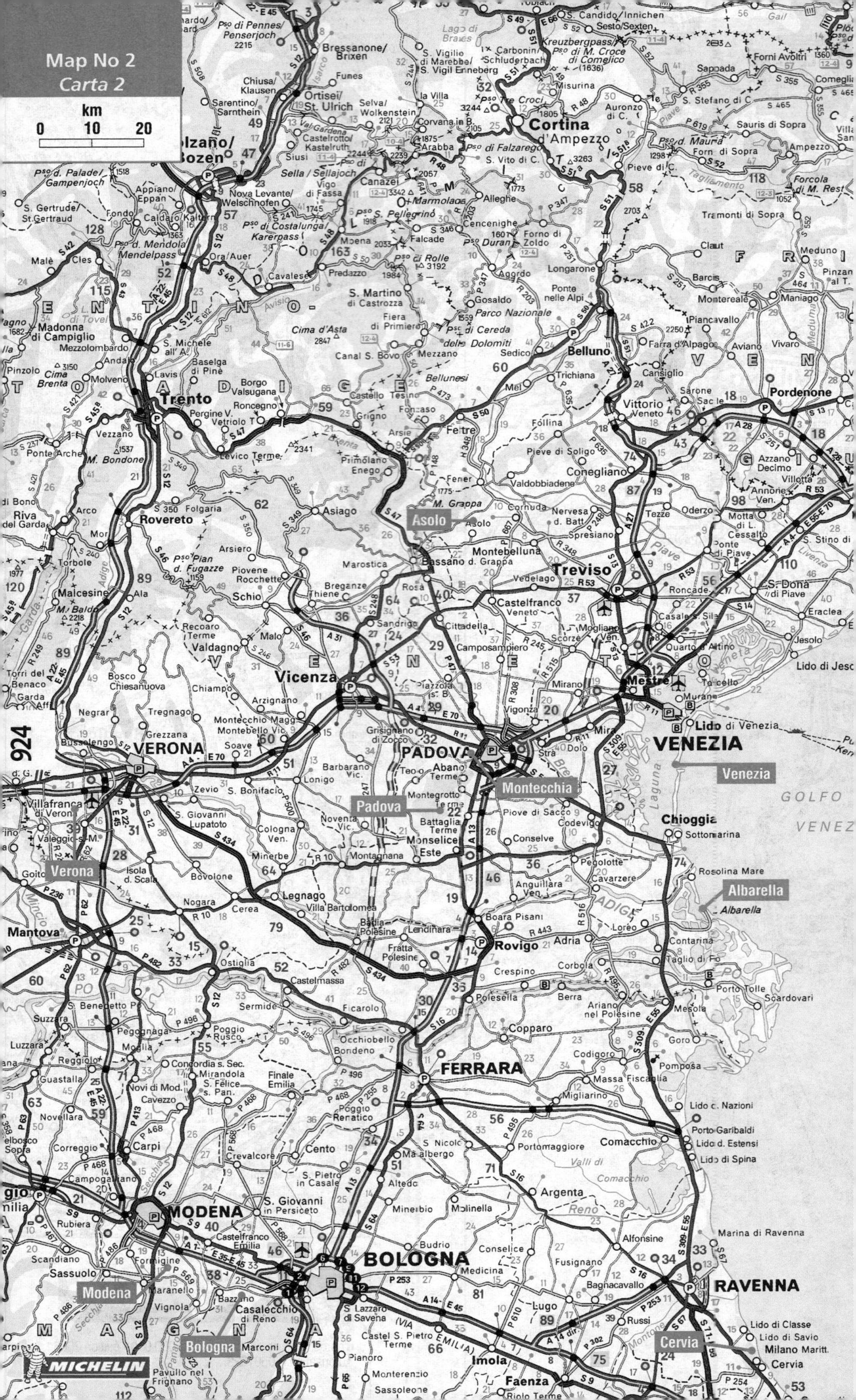

Map No 2
Carta 2
km
0 10 20
Bolzano/Bozen
Trento
Rovereto
Cortina d'Ampezzo
Belluno
Pordenone
Treviso
Asolo
Bassano d. Grappa
Vicenza
Verona
Padova
Montecchia
Venezia
Mestre
Chioggia
Albarella
Rovigo
Ferrara
Mantova
Modena
Bologna
Ravenna
Cervia
Imola
Faenza
Golfo di Venezia
Michelin

MICHELIN

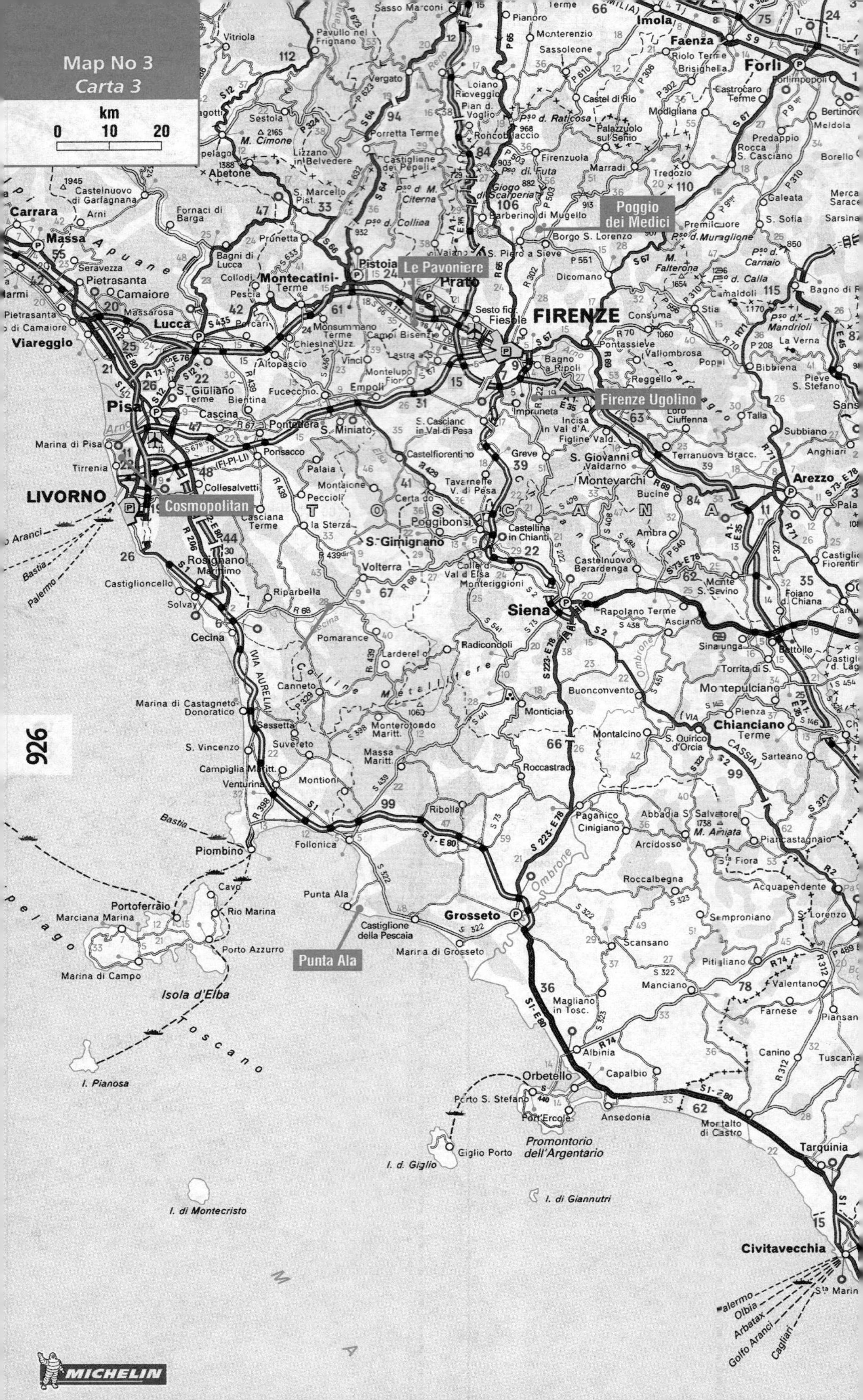
Map No 3
Carta 3
km
0 10 20
Poggio dei Medici
Le Pavoniere
Firenze Ugolino
Cosmopolitan
Punta Ala
FIRENZE
LIVORNO
Pisa
Lucca
Massa
Carrara
Viareggio
Pistoia
Prato
Siena
Arezzo
Grosseto
Civitavecchia
Imola
Faenza
Forlì
Montecatini-Terme
Empoli
S. Gimignano
Volterra
Piombino
Portoferraio
Isola d'Elba
I. Pianosa
I. di Montecristo
I. d. Giglio
I. di Giannutri
Promontorio dell'Argentario
Orbetello
Chianciano Terme
Montepulciano
MICHELIN

Cervia
Cesenatico
Bellaria
Viserba
Rimini
Miramare
Riccione
Cattolica
Gabicce Mare
Pesaro
Fano
Marotta
Senigallia
Falconara Maritt.
Ancona
Durrës
Mali Lošinj
Zadar
Šibenik
Split
Hvar
Kérkira
Igoumenitsa
Pátra
Savignano sul Rubicone
Santarcangelo di Rom.
Verucchio
Sogliano al Rubicone
S. Marino
Rimini
Gradara
Morciano di Rom.
Montecchio
Mercatino Conca
Macerata Feltria
Carpegna
Belforte all'Isauro
Sestino
Badia Tedalda
Mercatale
Urbino
Fossombrone
Urbania
Mondolfo
Mondavio
Corinaldo
Chiaravalle
Ostra
S. Marcello
Jesi
Montecarotto
Moie
S. Angelo in Vado
Piobbico
Acqualagna
Cagli
Pergola
Arcevia
Bocca Trabaria
S. Giustino
Apecchio
M. Catria
Cupramontana
Filottrano
Sassoferrato
Cingoli
Città di Castello
Pietralunga
Schéggia
Fabriano
Borgo Tufico
M A R C H E
Villa Potenza
Treia
Macerata
Osimo
Castelfidardo
Loreto
Recanati
Sirolo
Numana
Porto Recanati
Potenza Picena
Civitanova Marche
Porto S. Elpidio
S. Elpidio a Mare
Porto S. Giorgio
Fermo
Gubbio
Osteria di Gatto
Matelica
S. Severino Marche
Sforzacosta
Corridonia
Montegranaro
Tolentino
Castelraimondo
Campodonico
Gualdo Tadino
Mengara
Umbertide
Mercatale
Tuoro sul T.
Magione
Perugia
Lago Trasimeno
Valfabbrica
Bosco
Assisi
Nocera Umbra
Camerino
Muccia
Caldarola
S. Ginesio
Montegiorgio
Monterubbiano
Pedaso
Montefiore d. Aso
Servigliano
Ripatransone
Grottammare
S. Benedetto d. Tronto
Sarnano
Parco Nazionale dei Monti Sibillini
Fiastra
Colfiorito
Amandola
Comunanza
Montalto d. Marche
Offida
Ascoli Piceno
Spello
Sta Maria d. Angeli
Deruta
Foligno
Bevagna
Trevi
Visso
Montefalco
Marsciano
Città d. Pieve
Tavernelle
Montegallo
M. Vettore
Castelluccio
Triponzo
Norcia
Arquata d. T.
Acquasanta Terme
Civitella d. T.
Nereto
Campli
Valle Castellana
Teramo
U M B R I A
Massa Martana
Todi
Prato
Spoleto
Monteluco
Cascia
Amatrice
Ceppo
Montorio al Vomano
Villa Vomano
Orvieto
Acquasparta
Monteleone di Spoleto
Cittareale
Lago di Campotosto
Baschi
Castiglione in T.
San Gemini
Leonessa
Prati di Tivo
Isola d. Gr. Sasso d'It.
Bagnoregio
Lugnano in T.
Amelia
Terni
Posta
Borbona
Montereale
Gran Sasso d'Italia
Campo Imperatore
Valico b. Capannelle
Attigliano
Narni
Piediluco
M. Terminillo
Terminillo
Pizzoli
Assergi
Farindola
Montefiascone
Greccio
Rieti
Cittaducale
Antrodoco
L'Aquila
Castel d. Monte
Barisciano
Calignano
Torre de Passeri
Viterbo
Orte
Soriano nel Cimino
Vignanello
Contigliano
Velino
Navelli
Capestrano
Vetralla
L. di Vico
Borghetto
Magliano Sabina
Montenero S.
Rocca Sinibalda
Fiamignano
Rocca di Mezzo
Ovindoli
M. Velino
Ronciglione
Civita Castellana
Poggio Mirteto
Pescorocchiano
Borgorose
Magliano de Marsi
Celano
Castelvecchio Subequo
Forca Caruso
Sulmona
Sutri
Le Querce
Parco di Roma
Fiano R.
Orvinio
Carsoli
Tagliacozzo
Avezzano
Pescina
Trevignano R.
L. di Bracciano
Castelnuovo di Porto
L A Z I O
Palombara S.
Mandela
Capistrello
Trasacco
Manziana
Bracciano
Monterotondo
Mentana
Guidonia
Marco Simone
Tivoli
Castel Madama
Subiaco
Monti Simbruini
Civitella Roveto
Pso d. Diavolo
Parco
Scanno
Sasso
Cerveteri
Settebagni
Olgiata
Villa Adriana
Balsorano
Severa
Palidoro
ROMA
Roma Acquasanta
Palestrina
Forca d'Acero
Ladispoli
Fiuggi
Fregene
Frascati
Valmontone
Paliano
Anagni
Alatri
Sora
Castelgandolfo
Marino
Rocca di Papa
M. Cavo
Castel Gondolfo
Ostia Antica
Fiumicino
Artena
Colleferro
Ferentino
Isola del Liri
Abbazia di Casamari
MICHELIN

Map No 4
Carta 4
km
0 10 20
BARI
Mola di Bari
Polignano a Mare
Monopoli
San Domenico
Torre Canne
Fasano
Castellana Grotte
Conversano
Rutigliano
Capurso
Modugno
Bitetto
Sannicandro di Bari
Adelfia
Casamassima
Turi
Acquaviva d. Fonti
Sammichele
Putignano
Alberobello
Cassano d. Murge
Noci
Locorotondo
Cisternino
Ostuni
Carovigno
Brindisi
Kérkyra
Igoumenitsa
Pátra
Santeramo in Colle
Gioia d. Colle
Martina Franca
Ceglie Messapica
S. Vito d. Normanni
Tuturano
Mesagne
Latiano
Torchiarolo
S. Pietro Vernotico
Acaya
S. Cataldo
Squinzano
Trepuzzi
Surbo
Lecce
Campi Salentina
S. Donaci
S. Pancrazio Salentino
Oria
Francavilla Fontana
Grottaglie
Mottola
Massafra
Matera
Castellaneta
Laterza
Palagiano
Ginosa
Montescaglioso
TARANTO
S. Giorgio Ionico
Sava
Manduria
Avetrana
Lido Silvana
Porto Cesareo
Leverano
Monteroni di Lecce
Copertino
Melendugno
Martano
Nardò
Galatina
Galatone
Maglie
Gallipoli
Parabita
Casarano
Ugento
Marina di L
Capo di L
Riva dei Tessali
Bernalda
Pisticci
Lido di Metaponto
Scanzano
Policoro
Nova Siri Stazione
GOLFO DI TARANTO
Oriolo
Trebisacce
Sibari
Spezzano Albanese
Corigliano Calabro
Rossano
S. Demetrio Corone
Sta Sofia d'Epiro
Cariati
Campana
Longobucco
Acri
Cirò
Cirò Marina
Strongoli
Savelli
Camigliatello S.
M. Botte Donato 1928
Spezzano d. Sila
S. Giovanni in Fiore
Cosenza
Lorica
C. d'Ascione
Crotone
SILA
M. Gariglione
Petilia Policastro
Rogliano
Colosimi
Villaggio Mancuso
Mesoraca
Sersale
Cutro
Isola di Capo Rizzuto
MICHELIN

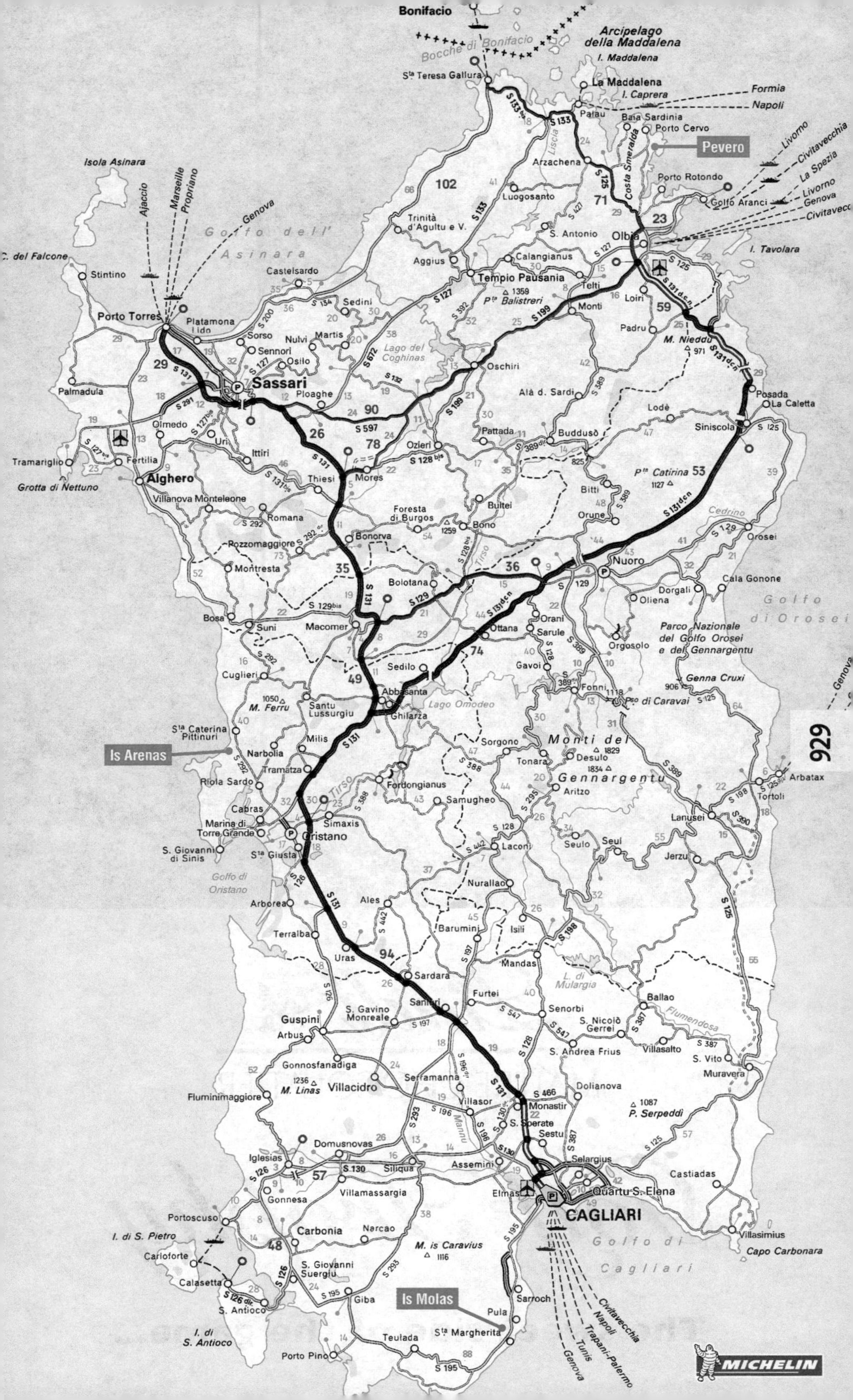
Is Arenas
Is Molas
Pevero
Sassari
Olbia
Nuoro
Oristano
Cagliari
929
MICHELIN

CLASSIFICATION OF GOLF COURSES
CLASSIFICA DEI PERCORSI

This classification gives priority consideration to the score awarded to the actual course.

Questa classifica è ordinata secondo il punteggio assegnato al perscorso.

Within each score, the ranking is purely alphabetical

Course score / Giudizio sul percorso				Page / Pagina
18	7	7	Biella - Le Betulle	941
18	8	8	Castelconturbia Giallo + Blu	945
17	8	7	Bogogno Bonora	942
17	8	7	Bogogno Del Conte	943
17	7	7	I Roveri	954
17	3	6	Is Arenas	955
17	7	8	Is Molas	956
17	8	7	Le Querce	958
17	8	8	Pevero	971
16	7	7	Bergamo - L'Albenza Blu + Giallo	940
16	9	8	Milano	963
16	8	6	Olgiata	967
16	8	9	Roma - Acquasanta	977
16	7	7	San Domenico	978
16	8	7	Torino - La Mandria Percorso Blu	979
16	7	9	Venezia	981
16	9	8	Villa d'Este	983
15	9	8	Arzaga	937
15	7	7	Castelgandolfo	946
15	8	8	Gardagolf Rosso + Bianco	952
15	8	8	Le Robinie	959
15	8	8	Marco Simone	961
15	8	7	Monticello Rosso	966
15	7	8	Paradiso del Garda	969
15	7	7	Poggio dei Medici	972
14	7	7	Acaya	934
14	8	8	Albarella	935
14	8	7	Barlassina	939
14	8	7	Castello di Tolcinasco Giallo + Blu	947
14	6	7	Cosmopolitan	949
14	7	8	Franciacorta	951
14	7	8	Garlenda	953
14	8	8	Le Pavoniere	957
14	7	7	Lignano	960
14	8	8	Padova Blue + Yellow	968
14	7	8	Parco di Roma	970
14	6	8	Punta Ala	973
14	8	7	Varese	980
13	7	7	Ambrosiano	936
13	7	7	Asolo Giallo + Verde	938
13	7	7	Bologna	944
13	6	9	Cervia	948
13	8	9	Firenze - Ugolino	950
13	7	7	Margara	962
13	7	7	Modena	964
13	8	8	Montecchia	965
13	8	8	Rapallo	974
13	6	8	Rimini	975
13	7	7	Riva dei Tessali	976
13	7	8	Verona	982

HOTEL FACILITIES
SERVIZI ALBERGHIERI

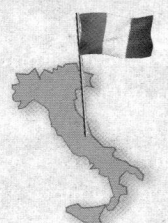

This classification gives priority consideration to the score awarded to the hotel facilities.

Questa classifica è ordinata secondo il punteggio assegnato ai servizi alberghieri.

		Hotel facility score / Giudizio sul offerta alberghiera		Page / Pagina
13	6	9	Cervia	948
13	8	9	Firenze - Ugolino	950

HOTEL FACILITIES
SERVIZI ALBERGHIERI

16	8	**9**	Roma - Acquasanta	977
16	7	**9**	Venezia	981
14	8	**8**	Albarella	935
15	9	**8**	Arzaga	937
18	8	**8**	Castelconturbia Giallo + Blu	945
14	7	**8**	Franciacorta	951
15	8	**8**	Gardagolf Rosso + Bianco	952
14	7	**8**	Garlenda	953
17	7	**8**	Is Molas	956
14	8	**8**	Le Pavoniere	957
15	8	**8**	Le Robinie	959
15	8	**8**	Marco Simone	961
16	9	**8**	Milano	963
13	8	**8**	Montecchia	965
14	8	**8**	Padova Blue + Yellow	968
15	7	**8**	Paradiso del Garda	969
14	7	**8**	Parco di Roma	970
17	8	**8**	Pevero	971
14	6	**8**	Punta Ala	973
13	8	**8**	Rapallo	974
13	6	**8**	Rimini	975
13	7	**8**	Verona	982
16	9	**8**	Villa d'Este	983
14	7	**7**	Acaya	934
13	7	**7**	Ambrosiano	936
13	7	**7**	Asolo Giallo + Verde	938
14	8	**7**	Barlassina	939
16	7	**7**	Bergamo - L'Albenza Blu + Giallo	940
18	7	**7**	Biella - Le Betulle	941
17	8	**7**	Bogogno Bonora	942
17	8	**7**	Bogogno Del Conte	943
13	7	**7**	Bologna	944
15	7	**7**	Castelgandolfo	946
14	8	**7**	Castello di Tolcinasco Giallo + Blu	947
14	6	**7**	Cosmopolitan	949
17	7	**7**	I Roveri	954
17	8	**7**	Le Querce	958
14	7	**7**	Lignano	960
13	7	**7**	Margara	962
13	7	**7**	Modena	964
15	8	**7**	Monticello Rosso	966
15	7	**7**	Poggio dei Medici	972
13	7	**7**	Riva dei Tessali	976
16	7	**7**	San Domenico	978
16	8	**7**	Torino - La Mandria Percorso Blu	979
14	8	**7**	Varese	980
17	3	**6**	Is Arenas	955
16	8	**6**	Olgiata	967

RECOMMENDED GOLFING STAY
SOGGIORNO GOLFISTICO RACCOMANDATO

Bogogno Bonora	**17**	8	7	942
Bogogno Del Conte	**17**	8	7	943
Castelconturbia Giallo + Blu	**18**	8	8	945
I Roveri	**17**	7	7	954
Riva dei Tessali	**13**	7	7	976
Torino - La Mandria Percorso Blu	**16**	8	7	979

RECOMMENDED HOLIDAYS
VACANZE RACCOMANDATA

Acaya	**14**	7	7	934
Albarella	**14**	8	8	935
Arzaga	**15**	9	8	937
Cervia	**13**	6	9	948
Cosmopolitan	**14**	6	7	949
Gardagolf Rosso + Bianco	**15**	8	8	952
Garlenda	**14**	7	8	953
Is Arenas	**17**	3	6	955
Is Molas	**17**	7	8	956
Lignano	**14**	7	7	960
Pevero	**17**	8	8	971
Punta Ala	**14**	6	8	973
Rapallo	**13**	8	8	974
Riva dei Tessali	**13**	7	7	976
Venezia	**16**	7	9	981
Villa d'Este	**16**	9	8	983

Acaya

14	7	7

Si viene in Puglia, nello sperone dello stivale italiano, soprattutto per godere delle sue belle spiagge e per ripercorrere la sua storia antichissima che porta i segni del commercio con la vicina Grecia e dell'occupazione dei Normanni che l'hanno salvata dalle invasioni. Fin da allora, Lecce è il suo capoluogo e tra il Rinascimento e l'età barocca si è arricchita di chiese e monumenti molto importanti. Ora si può venire qui anche per giocare a golf nei nuovi campi di San Domenico o di Acaya, un'opera di David Mezzacane ben realizzata in un centinaio di ettari non facili da sviluppare dove la vegetazione naturale è ancora molto rigogliosa tra una buca e l'altra. Sarà piacevole seguire l'evoluzione di questo percorso ancora molto giovane dove tutti si possono divertire a giocare e dove si può godere delle strutture di una bella club-house e di un ottimo hotel. Inoltre in ogni stagione il clima è davvero ottimo.

In the heel of the Italian boot, people came to Apulia for the sun-drenched beaches and to learn of the ancient period of trade with nearby Greece or the Norman occupation which saved the region from invasion. They made Lecce their capital, which a little later was enhanced with some superb Renaissance and Baroque landmarks. Today you might also come for some golfing, at San Domenico and Acaya, the latter being a pretty layout designed by David Mezzacane, carefully landscaped over almost 250 acres that were not so easy to develop and where the space between holes is gradually being reclaimed by natural vegetation. It will be a pleasure to monitor how this young course matures; it is very pleasant to play in every respect and offers both a fine club-house in a fortified farmhouse and an excellent hotel. To be played all year in a warm climate.

Acaya Golf Club — 2000

Strado Provinciale S. Cataldo, Frazione vernole
I - 73029 ACAYA (LE)

Office	Segreteria	(39) 0832 861 378
Pro shop	Pro shop	(39) 0832 861 378
Fax	Fax	(39) 0832 861 378
Web	www.acayagolfclub.it	
Situation	Località	Lecce, 15 km
Annual closure	Chiusura annuale	no
Weekly closure	Chiusura settimanale	no

Fees main season Tariffe alta stagione — 18 holes

	Week days / Settimana	We/Bank holidays / Feriale/Festivo
Individual Individuale	€ 60	€ 60
Couple Coppia	€ 120	€ 120

Caddie Caddie no **Electric Trolley** Carello elettrico no

Buggy Car yes **Clubs** Bastoni yes

Credit cards Carte di credito
VISA - Eurocard - MasterCard - AMEX - DC - JCB

Access Itinerario : Bari → Brindisi/Lecce, → San Cataldo. Motorway (Superstrada) Lecce-San Castaldo, exit → Otranto. 5 km, then follow signs.
Map 4 on page 928 Carta 4 Pagina 928

GOLF COURSE — PERCORSO — 14/20

Site	Paesaggio	
Maintenance	Manutenzione	
Architect	Architetto	David Mezzacane
Type	Tipologia	seaside course, open country
Relief	Relievo terreno	
Water in play	Acqua in gioco	
Exp. to wind	Esposto al vento	
Trees in play	Alberi in gioco	

Scorecard / Carta-score	Chp. / Camp.	Mens / Uomini	Ladies / Donne
Length Lunghezza	6206	5923	4997
Par	72	72	72
Slope system	125	125	121

Advised golfing ability Livello di gioco consigliato — 0 12 24 36
Hcp required Handicap richiesto 36

CLUB HOUSE & AMENITIES — CLUB HOUSE E SERVIZI — 7/10

Pro shop Pro shop
Driving range Campo pratica
Sheltered coperto - On grass in erba yes - Putting-green Putting-green yes - Pitching-green Green-pratica yes

HOTEL FACILITIES — ALBERGHI — 7/10

HOTELS ALBERGHI
Acaya Golf Hotel - 86 rooms, D € - on site
Tel (39) 0832 861 385, Fax (39) 0832 861 385

Patria Palace Hotel - Lecce 15 km
67 rooms, D € 225
Tel (39) 0832 245 111, Fax (39) 0832 245 002

Delle Palme - Lecce 15 km
96 rooms, D € 115
Tel (39) 0832 347 171, Fax (39) 0832 347 171

RESTAURANTS RISTORANTE
Locanda del Gallo - on site - Tel (39) 0832 861 102
Osteria degli Spiriti - Lecce 15 km - Tel (39) 0832 246 274

Albarella

14 | 8 | 8

Situato in una piccola isola nel delta del Po, vicino a Venezia e a Padova è un golf ben conosciuto in Italia, in particolare perchè ha ospitato numerosi tornei internazionali. E' stato costruito su un terreno molto aperto dove la vegetazione è poco significativa, molto vicino al mare ed alla spiaggia. Circondato da piccole dune di sabbia, il percorso può far pensare ad un links. Il gioco può cambiare radicalmente quando soffia forte il vento e capita abbastanza spesso, ma questa caratteristica tipicamente britannica qui ha i suoi limiti: l'Adriatico non è il Mare del Nord o l'Atlantico! Infatti questo è un piacevolissimo percorso di vacanza, ben tenuto e dove può facilmente giocare tutta la famiglia. Le difficoltà sono solitamente ben visibili e i rilievi praticamente inesistenti. I più critici possono dire che manca un pò di movimento, ma evidentemente Harris e Croze hanno pensato prima ai dilettanti quando hanno disegnato il percorso. Il record del campo è 63, ma anche i migliori giocatori dovranno essere al massimo della forma per riuscire a far meglio.

Albarella, located on a small peninsula in the estuary of the river Po, is one of Italy's best known courses, having hosted a considerable number of international tournaments. It is laid out on open terrain with little in the way of vegetation, close to the sea and beaches. Surrounded by small sand-dunes, some aspects of this layout are reminiscent of a typical links course. The way it plays changes drastically when the wind blows, a frequent occurrence here, but this British side to the course has its limits, as this is, after all, the Adriatic not the Atlantic. In actual fact this is a very good holiday course, which is well maintained and easy to play with all the family. Hazards are clearly visible and there is no relief to speak of. The more critically-minded might feel that the course could have been given more shape, but Harris and Croze obviously had amateur golfers in mind when designing the layout. Even though the course record is 63, the better players will find difficult to card low scores.

Circolo Golf Albarella — 1972

Isola di Albarella
I - 45010 ROSOLINA (RO)

Office Segreteria (39) 0426 - 330 124
Pro shop Pro shop (39) 0426 - 33 08
Fax Fax (39) 0426 - 330 830
Web www.isoladialbarella.it
Situation Località Venezia, 45 km
Chioggia (pop. 52 039) 24 km

Annual closure Chiusura annuale — no
Weekly closure Chiusura settimanale — tuesday

Fees main season Tariffe alta stagione	18 holes	
	Week days Settimana	We/Bank holidays Feriale/Festivo
Individual Individuale	€ 50	€ 60
Couple Coppia	€ 100	€ 120

Caddie Caddie no — **Electric Trolley** Carello elettrico no
Buggy Car yes — **Clubs** Bastoni yes
Credit cards Carte di credito
VISA - Eurocard - MasterCard

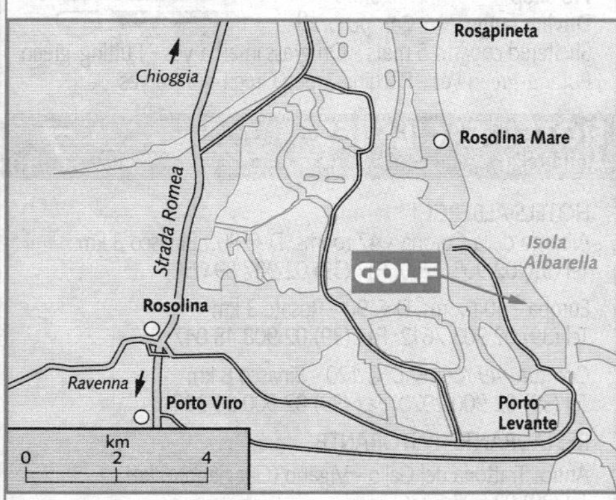

Access Itinerario : A4 Milano-Venezia. Exit (Uscita) Padova Est. S516 → Chioggia. In Chioggia, Strada Romea → Ravenna. After Rosolina, turn left to Isola Albarella. → Golf
Map 2 on page 924 Carta 2 Pagina 924

GOLF COURSE — PERCORSO — 14/20

Site Paesaggio
Maintenance Manutenzione
Architect Architetto — John Harris, Marco Croze
Type Tipologia — links, residential
Relief Relievo terreno
Water in play Acqua in gioco
Exp. to wind Esposto al vento
Trees in play Alberi in gioco

Scorecard Carta-score	Chp. Camp.	Mens Uomini	Ladies Donne
Length Lunghezza	6100	6100	5370
Par	72	72	72
Slope system	123	123	123

Advised golfing ability Livello di gioco consigliato — 0 12 24 36
Hcp required Handicap richiesto 34

CLUB HOUSE & AMENITIES — CLUB HOUSE E SERVIZI — 8/10

Pro shop Pro shop
Driving range Campo pratica
Sheltered coperto 4 mats - On grass in erba yes - Putting-green Putting-green yes - Pitching-green Green-pratica yes

HOTEL FACILITIES — ALBERGHI — 8/10

HOTELS ALBERGHI
Hotel Capo Nord - 42 rooms, D € 150 - Albarella 3 km
Tel (39) 0426 330 139, Fax (39) 0426 330 137

Club house - 22 rooms, D € 110 - on site
Tel (39) 0426 367 811, Fax (39) 0426 330 628

Grande Italia - 60 rooms, D € 165 - Chioggia 25 km
Tel (39) 041 400 515, Fax (39) 041 400 185

RESTAURANTS RISTORANTE
Al Centro di Marco e Melania - Cavanella d'Adige 15 km
Tel (39) 041 497 501
Molteni - Adria 15 km - Tel (39) 0426 42 520
Al Centro di Marco e Melania - Cavanella d'Adige 15 km
Tel (39) 041 497 501

Ambrosiano

13 | 7 | 7

Questo percorso di recente costruzione è molto vicino a Milano ma anche poco distante da Pavia, nella quale università hanno studiato nientemeno che il Petrarca e Leonardo da Vinci. La città è stata una roccaforte dei Visconti che stabilirono il loro mausoleo a nord della città, alla Certosa di Pavia, una straordinaria chiesa lombarda tra il gotico e il rinascimentale. A qualche chilometro di distanza c'è l'Ambrosiano e coloro che non amano più di tanto la storia e l'antichità potranno fare questo percorso anche due volte al giorno. Siccome è particolarmente piatto e con pochi alberi, non è facile capire subito la strategia di gioco e visualizzare i suoi tranelli. La disposizione intelligente dei numerosi ostacoli ne fa un percorso divertente e di qualità anche se il paesaggio non è eccezionale. E' decisamente più delicato dalle partenze di campionato.

Sure, this recent course is close to Milan, but it is also not far from Pavia, at whose university Petrarch and Leonardo da Vinci studied in days gone by. This was also one of the strongholds of the Visconti, who built their mausoleum to the north of the city at Certosa di Pavia (Charterhouse of Pavia), an extraordinary Lombardy-style church somewhere between the Gothic and Renaissance styles. It is also just a few miles from Ambrosiano. Golfers who have no time for history or old buildings can play this course twice in a day. Being virtually shorn of trees, it is hard to immediately appreciate game strategy and visualize the traps. The clever layout of the very many hazards makes this a very amusing and high quality course, even though the landscape is nothing to write home about. It is, however, a much trickier proposition when played from the back tees.

Golf Club Ambrosiano — 1994

Cascina Bertacca
I - 20080 BUBBIANO (MI)

Office	Segreteria	(39) 02 9084 0820
Pro shop	Pro shop	(39) 02 9084 0820
Fax	Fax	(39) 02 9084 9365
Web	www.golfclubambrosiano.com	
Situation	Località	Milano, 29 km

Pavia (pop. 74 065), 30 km

Annual closure	Chiusura annuale	no
Weekly closure	Chiusura settimanale	tuesday
Fees main season	Tariffe alta stagione	18 holes

	Week days Settimana	We/Bank holidays Feriale/Festivo
Individual Individuale	€ 37	€ 58
Couple Coppia	€ 74	€ 116

Caddie Caddie no **Electric Trolley** Carello elettrico no

Buggy Car yes **Clubs** Bastoni yes

Credit cards Carte di credito
VISA - Eurocard - MasterCard - CartaSi

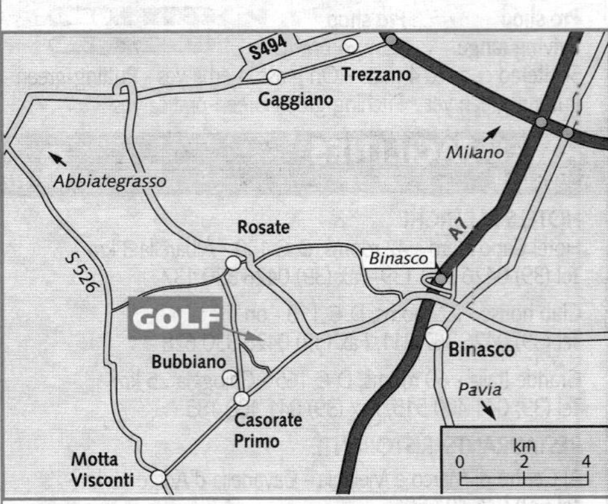

Access Itinerario : A7 Milano-Genova, Exit (Uscita) Binasco, right → Motta Visconti. 7 km, → Bubbiano. → Golf.
Map 1 on page 923 Carta 1 Pagina 923

GOLF COURSE — PERCORSO — 13/20

Site	Paesaggio	
Maintenance	Manutenzione	
Architect	Architetto	Cornish & Silva
Type	Tipologia	country
Relief	Relievo terreno	
Water in play	Acqua in gioco	
Exp. to wind	Esposto al vento	
Trees in play	Alberi in gioco	

Scorecard Carta-score	Chp. Camp.	Mens Uomini	Ladies Donne
Length Lunghezza	6281	6047	5316
Par	72	72	72
Slope system	133	131	128

Advised golfing ability 0 12 24 36
Livello di gioco consigliato

Hcp required Handicap richiesto no

CLUB HOUSE & AMENITIES — CLUB HOUSE E SERVIZI — 7/10

Pro shop Pro shop
Driving range Campo pratica
Sheltered coperto 5 mats - On grass in erba yes - Putting-green Putting-green yes - Pitching-green Green-pratica yes

HOTEL FACILITIES — ALBERGHI — 7/10

HOTELS ALBERGHI

Albergo della Corona - 47 rooms, D € 80 - Binasco 8 km
Tel (39) 02 905 2280, Fax (39) 02 907 89 051

Europa - 40 rooms, D € 90 - Rosate 3 km
Tel (39) 02 908 7612, Fax (39) 02 908 48 047

Comtur - 49 rooms, D € 120 - Binasco 8 km
Tel (39) 02 900 2020, Fax (39) 02 900 91 397

RESTAURANTS RISTORANTE

Antica Trattoria del Gallo - Vigano (Gaggiano) 6 km
Tel (39) 02 905 5276

Trattoria della Fratellanza - Gaggiano 9 km
Tel (39) 02 908 52 87

Rattattù - Gaggiano 9 km - Tel (39) 02 908 *598

Arzaga

15 | 9 | 8

Dopo i numerosi percorsi di assoluta qualità sorti nella regione dei laghi in Lombardia, abbiamo assistito alla nascita di una vera destinazione golfistica circondata da un magnifico paesaggio e a due passi da grandi città turistiche, commerciali e artistiche come Milano o ancora Brescia e Verona. Il golf di Palazzo Arzaga si trova tra queste due ultime città, appena sopra al lago di Garda. Il primo percorso di 18 buche opera di Jack Nicklaus II è stato inaugurato nel 1998 e ha dato vita ad un complesso importante con un hotel di lusso nell'antica villa della tenuta. E' un percorso in stile americano con pochi alberi in gioco, ma con molti ostacoli d'acqua e bunkers piazzati strategicamente sia in fairway che intorno ai greens. Questi ultimi con le loro pendenze contribuiscono a rendere difficile la riuscita di un buono score. Questo percorso, grazie ai numerosi tees di partenza, è divertente per tutti i giocatori e a questo se ne aggiunge un altro per ora di 9 buche soltanto disegnato dal Gary Player.

With so many top class courses in the region of the Lombardy lakes, we could be witnessing the birth of a real golfing destination, set in dream landscapes within the immediate vicinity of major tourist, business and cultural cities such as Milan or even Brescia and Verona. The Palazzo Arzaga course lies between these two cities just above lake Garda. This is an ambitious resort opened in 1998 with a sumptuous hotel in a patrician villa, tennis courts and a spa. Jack Nicklaus Junior has designed a blatantly American-styled layout with few trees coming into play but a lot of water hazards and strategically located bunkers. The greens are huge, sometimes tiered and elevated and contoured enough to compound the task of carding a good score here. Still, the course is playable by everyone with excellent green-keeping whatever the season. This very fine site also boasts a second, 9-hole course designed by Gary Player.

Arzaga Golf Club — 1998

Loc. Carzago
I - 25080 CAVALGESE DELLA RIVIERA

Office	Segreteria	(39) 030 680 6266
Pro shop	Pro shop	(39) 030 680 6171
Fax	Fax	(39) 030 680 6473
Web	www.palazzoarzaga.com	
Situation	Località	Verona (pop. 255 268), 45 km

Brescia (pop. 191 317), 28 km

Annual closure	Chiusura annuale	25/12→1/1
Weekly closure	Chiusura settimanale	no

Fees main season Tariffe alta stagione	18 holes	
	Week days Settimana	**We/Bank holidays** Feriale/Festivo
Individual Individuale	€ 61	€ 78
Couple Coppia	€ 122	€ 156

Caddie Caddie no — **Electric Trolley** Carello elettrico yes
Buggy Car yes — **Clubs** Bastoni yes
Credit cards Carte di credito
VISA - Eurocard - MasterCard - AMEX - DC - CartaSì

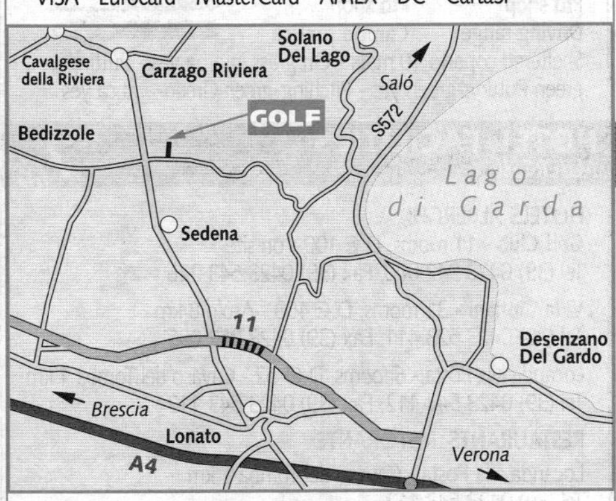

Access Itinerario : A4 Milano-Venezia. Exit (Uscita) Desenzano. Turn left, then left again → Brescia. → Sedena. 2 km turn right → Pedenghe. 400 m to the left.
Map 1 on page 923 Carta 1 Pagina 923

GOLF COURSE — PERCORSO — 15/20

Site	Paesaggio	
Maintenance	Manutenzione	
Architect	Architetto	Jack Nicklaus Jr
Type	Tipologia	country
Relief	Relievo terreno	
Water in play	Acqua in gioco	
Exp. to wind	Esposto al vento	
Trees in play	Alberi in gioco	

Scorecard Carta-score	**Chp.** Camp.	**Mens** Uomini	**Ladies** Donne
Length Lunghezza	6062	5885	5220
Par	72	72	72
Slope system	129	126	129

Advised golfing ability Livello di gioco consigliato: 0 12 24 36
Hcp required Handicap richiesto 34

CLUB HOUSE & AMENITIES — CLUB HOUSE E SERVIZI — 9/10

Pro shop Pro shop
Driving range Campo pratica
Sheltered coperto 10 mats - On grass in erba yes - Putting-green Putting-green yes - Pitching-green Green-pratica yes

HOTEL FACILITIES — ALBERGHI — 8/10

HOTELS ALBERGHI
Palazzo Arzaga Golf e Spa - on site
80 rooms, D from € 256
Tel (39) 030 680 600, Fax (39) 030 680 6270

Park Hotel - 66 rooms, D € 142- Desenzano del Garda 7,5 km
Tel (39) 030 914 3494, Fax (39) 030 914 2280

Grand Hotel Fasano - 75 rooms, D € 210 - Fasano 15 km
Tel (39) 0365 290 220, Fax (39) 0365 290 221

RESTAURANTS RISTORANTE
Al Mulino - Bedizzole 3 km - Tel (39) 030 674 317
La Lepre - Desenzano 7 km - Tel (39) 030 914 2313
Locanda Santa Giulia - Padenghe sul Garda 5 km
Tel (39) 030 99 950

Asolo *Giallo + Verde*

13 | 7 | 7

Con la sua ubicazione vicino a Vicenza, Treviso, Padova, Venezia ed anche all'Austria, Asolo è uno dei percorsi da conoscere quando si visita la superba regione del Veneto. A questa lista di famose cittadine ci sono da aggiungere Asolo con i suoi castelli e i suoi palazzi e Bassano del Grappa, conosciuta per le sue piccole case dipinte, le sue ceramiche e... la grappa! Questo circolo è immerso in un posto molto bello ed ampio e comprende tre percorsi di 9 buche combinabili tra loro in diversi percorsi di 18 buche. Stan Eby, della European Golf Design, ha concepito questo tracciato dove le difficoltà sono ben distribuite ed è quindi accessibile ai giocatori di ogni livello. Tutto qui è stato fatto con grande serietà e con una buona conoscenza sulle capacità diverse dei giocatori, ma gli amanti dei percorsi di carattere avrebbero preferito un po' più di audacia nel disegno. Asolo resta comunque un campo da visitare quando si è nella regione.

Being close to Vicenza, Treviso, Padova, Venice and even Austria, Asolo is a course to play when exploring this superb region of Veneto. We might add Asolo to this list of famous cities, with fortress and palaces, and Bassano del Grappa, famous for its little painted houses, porcelain and... Grappa liqueur! The golf course is spread over a very beautiful and uncluttered site and will shortly comprise three combinable 9 hole courses to form several different 18-hole layouts. Stan Eby from European Golf Design designed this course, which is well-balanced in the difficulties it presents, playable by golfers of all abilities but not always necessarily very exciting. Everything has been done very thoroughly here, with good insight into different levels of golfing skill, although golfers who like more personalized courses might have preferred a little more daring here and there. Nonetheless, Asolo is still a course that deserves a visit when in the region.

Asolo Golf Club — 1997

Via Ronche
I - 31034 CAVASO DEL TOMBA (TV)

Office Segreteria (39) 0423 942 000
Pro shop Pro shop (39) 0423 942 217
Fax Fax (39) 0423 543 226
Web www.asologolf.it
Situation Località Treviso (pop. 81.328), 35 km
Bassano del Grappa (pop. 39.625)

Annual closure Chiusura annuale 1/1→31/1
Weekly closure Chiusura settimanale tuesday
Fees main season Tariffe alta stagione 18 holes

	Week days Settimana	We/Bank holidays Feriale/Festivo
Individual Individuale	€ 45	€ 60
Couple Coppia	€ 90	€ 120

Caddie Caddie on request **Electric Trolley** Carello elettrico no
Buggy Car yes **Clubs** Bastoni yes
Credit cards Carte di credito
VISA - Eurocard - MasterCard - AMEX - DC - Cartasi

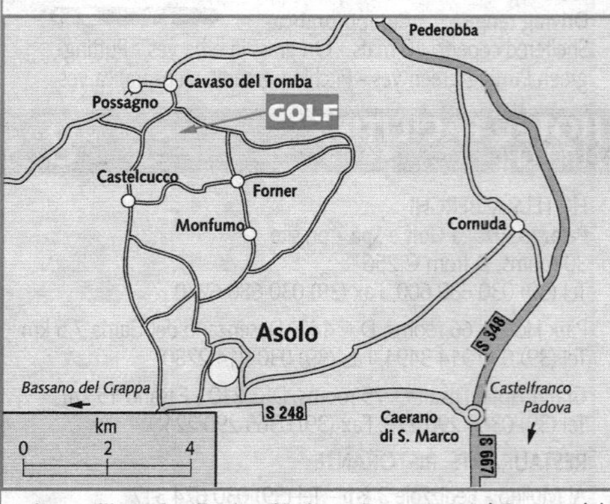

Access Itinerario : Treviso, S348, → Possagno and Cavaso del Tomba. Golf 2 km after Cavaso.
Map 2 on page 924 Carta 2 Pagina 924

GOLF COURSE — PERCORSO — 13/20

Site Paesaggio
Maintenance Manutenzione
Architect Architetto European Golf Design
Type Tipologia country
Relief Relievo terreno
Water in play Acqua in gioco
Exp. to wind Esposto al vento
Trees in play Alberi in gioco

Scorecard Carta-score	Chp. Camp.	Mens Uomini	Ladies Donne
Length Lunghezza	6242	5873	5161
Par	72	72	72
Slope system	137	131	132

Advised golfing ability Livello di gioco consigliato 0 12 24 36
Hcp required Handicap richiesto 34

CLUB HOUSE & AMENITIES — CLUB HOUSE E SERVIZI — 7/10

Pro shop Pro shop
Driving range Campo pratica
Sheltered coperto 10 mats - On grass in erba yes - Putting-green Putting-green yes - Pitching-green Green-pratica yes

HOTEL FACILITIES — ALBERGHI — 7/10

HOTELS ALBERGHI
Golf Club - 11 rooms, D € 100 - on site
Tel (39) 0423 942 000, Fax (39) 0423 543 226

Villa Cipriani - 31 rooms, D € 450 - Asolo 8 km
Tel (39) 0423 523 411, Fax (39) 0423 952 095

Locanda alla Posta - 6 rooms, D € 52 - Cavaso del Tomba 1 km
Tel (39) 0423 543 112, Fax (39) 0423 543 112

RESTAURANTS RISTORANTE
Locanda alla Posta - Cavaso del Tomba 1 km
Tel (39) 0423 543 112
A Due Archi - Asolo 8 km - Tel (39) 0423 952 201
Bistrot - Asolo 8 km - Tel (39) 0423 529 592
Belvedere - Bassano del Grappa 15 km - Tel (39) 0424 524 988

Barlassina

14	8	7

Aperto nel 1956 su disegno dell'architetto inglese John Morrison è stato modificato nel 1988, per quel che riguarda il tracciato di alcune buche e di molti greens. E' situato in una regione abbastanza ondulata ad una ventina di chilometri a nord di Milano poco distante dalle strade che portano verso il Lago di Como. La natura e' particolarmente piacevole e le buche ritagliate in mezzo agli alberi sono diventate decisamente più strette con il passare degli anni. In questo grande parco, scegliere di andare a piedi è sempre la cosa più piacevole e anche se per divertirsi non è necessario essere un grande campione, se giocherete dai tees di campionato dovrete sbagliare molto poco per fare un buono score. Tra i numerosi percorsi intorno a Milano, Barlassina merita una visita ma non durante il week-end dove il gioco è riservato ai soci.

Opened in 1956, this layout from British architect John Morrison was altered in 1988 with changes made to a number of holes and to the configuration of several greens. It is located over rolling countryside some twenty or so kilometres to the north of Milan, just off the road leading to Lake Como. The surroundings are pleasant indeed and the course full of trees, but still with rather wide fairways. Having said that, the once innocuous foliage is coming more and more into play as the years go by. In this large park, the walk is all the more enjoyable in that you don't have to be a top champion to play the course, or know how to hit the so-called technical shots. Having said that, if you play from the tips you have little room for error if you want to score well. Of the many courses around Milan, Barlassina is well worth a visit, except on week-ends when the course is reserved for members only.

Barlassina Country Club — 1956

Via Privata Golf 42
I - 20030 BIRAGO DI CAMNAGO (MI)

Office Segreteria (39) 0362 560 621
Pro shop Pro shop (39) 0362 560 621
Fax Fax (39) 0362 560 934
E-mail bccgolf@libero.it
Situation Località Milano, 26 km
Como (pop. 82 989), 25 km
Annual closure Chiusura annuale 25/12→1/1
Weekly closure Chiusura settimanale monday

Fees main season Tariffe alta stagione	18 holes	
	Week days Settimana	We/Bank holidays Feriale/Festivo
Individual Individuale	€ 60	€ 100*
Couple Coppia	€ 120	€ 200*

* We: members only (riservato ai soci)

Caddie Caddie yes — **Electric Trolley** Carello elettrico no
Buggy Car no — **Clubs** Bastoni yes
Credit cards Carte di credito no

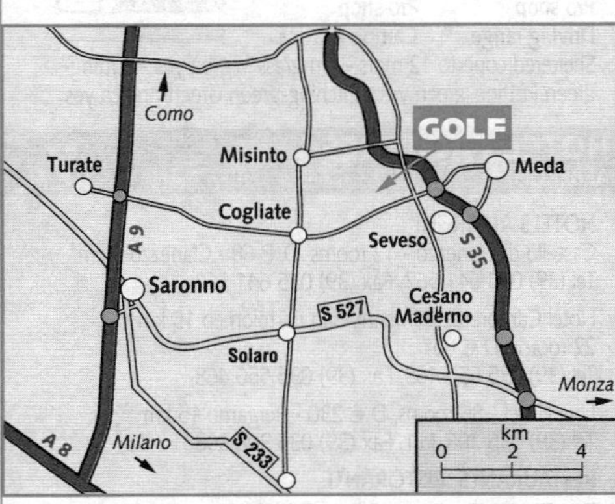

Access Itinerario : Milano North, take the S35 → Como. Exit (Uscita) Seveso/Barlassina.
Map 1 on page 923 Carta 1 Pagina 923

GOLF COURSE — PERCORSO — 14/20

Site Paesaggio
Maintenance Manutenzione
Architect Architetto John Morrison
Type Tipologia parkland
Relief Relievo terreno
Water in play Acqua in gioco
Exp. to wind Esposto al vento
Trees in play Alberi in gioco

Scorecard Carta-score	Chp. Camp.	Mens Uomini	Ladies Donne
Length Lunghezza	6197	6197	5418
Par	72	72	72
Slope system	135	135	126

Advised golfing ability Livello di gioco consigliato 0 12 24 36
Hcp required Handicap richiesto 34

CLUB HOUSE & AMENITIES — CLUB HOUSE E SERVIZI — 8/10

Pro shop Pro shop
Driving range Campo pratica
Sheltered coperto 8 mats - On grass in erba yes - Putting-green Putting-green yes - Pitching-green Green-pratica yes

HOTEL FACILITIES — ALBERGHI — 7/10

HOTELS ALBERGHI
Albergo della Rotonda - Saronno 12 km
92 rooms, D € 250
Tel (39) 02 967 032 32, Fax (39) 02 967 027 70

Castello di Carimate - Carimate 5 km
57 rooms, D from € 125
Tel (39) 031 - 791 770, Fax (39) 031 - 790 683

Hotel Arosio - 20 rooms, D € 90 - Arosio 4 km
Tel (39) 031 764 201, Fax (39) 031 764 109

RESTAURANTS RISTORANTE
Osteria del Pomiroeu - Seregno 7 km - Tel (39) 0362 237 973
Le Querce - Cantù 7 km - Tel (39) 031 731 336
La Rimessa - Mariano Comense 6 km - Tel (39) 031 749 668

Bergamo - L'Albenza *Blu + Giallo*

16	7	7

Se le 9 buche "blu" e le 9 buche "gialle" sono considerate il percorso di campionato, le 9 buche "rosse" costituiscono un'alternativa di qualità all'uno o all'altro e aggiungono un tocco in più ad un disegno che è già molto interessante con i suoi par 4 e suoi par 5 duri da raggiungere in due colpi. E' sicuramente la varietà una delle chiavi del successo dell'Albenza che alterna passaggi tra i boschi a spazi aperti, buche lunghe a buche corte, colpi di assoluta precisione e approcci a correre in perfetto stile "British". Bisogna saper "lavorare" la palla in entrambe le direzioni per avere dei colpi al green più facili e riflettere bene sulla scelta dei bastoni. Un percorso molto "educativo" se si giudica la carriera e il gioco molto completo di Costantino Rocca, che ha cominciato qui come caddie prima di diventare uno dei migliori giocatori del mondo.

If we consider the "blue" and "yellow" 9-hole courses to be the 18 hole championship course, the "red" course is an excellent alternative to both and adds a little more spice to a layout that is pretty hot as it is, in particular on account of the par 4s and the par 5s that are tough to reach in two. Talking of spice, variety is certainly one of the key assets of "L'Albenza", which winds its way now through the woods, now over open space, alternating short and long holes, or target golf and the more British bump and run approach. You often have to work the ball one way or the other for an easier shot at the greens and club choice requires careful thinking. This is a very "educational" course, judging by the career and very complete game of Costantino Rocca, who started off here as a caddie before becoming one of the world's best golfers..

Golf Club Bergamo - L'Albenza 1961

Via Longoni 12
I - 24030 ALMENNO SAN BARTOLOMEO (BG)

Office Segreteria (39) 035 640 028
Pro shop Pro shop (39) 035 643 288
Fax Fax (39) 035 643 066
Web www.golfbergamo.it
Situation Località Brescia (pop. 191 317), 50 km
Bergamo (pop. 117 837), 15 km
Annual closure Chiusura annuale 25/12→1/1
Weekly closure Chiusura settimanale monday
Fees main season Tariffe alta stagione 18 holes

	Week days Settimana	We/Bank holidays Feriale/Festivo
Individual Individuale	€ 50	€ 70
Couple Coppia	€ 100	€ 140

Caddie Caddie yes — **Electric Trolley** Carello elettrico yes
Buggy Car no — **Clubs** Bastoni yes
Credit cards Carte di credito
VISA - DC - CartaSi

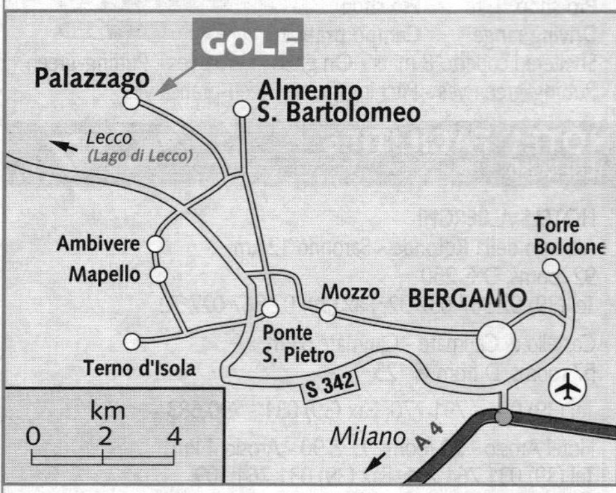

Access Itinerario : A4 Milano-Venezia, Exit (Uscita) Capriate. Turn right → Ponte San Pietro. At old house, turn left → Lecco. 2 km right → Almenno San Bartolomeo. Golf on left hand side.
Map 1 on page 923 Carta 1 Pagina 923

GOLF COURSE — PERCORSO 16/20

Site Paesaggio
Maintenance Manutenzione
Architect Architetto C.K. Cotton & Sutton
Type Tipologia forest
Relief Rilievo terreno
Water in play Acqua in gioco
Exp. to wind Esposto al vento
Trees in play Alberi in gioco

Scorecard Carta-score	Chp. Camp.	Mens Uomini	Ladies Donne
Length Lunghezza	6220	6100	5368
Par	72	72	72
Slope system	137	135	129

Advised golfing ability Livello di gioco consigliato 0 12 24 36
Hcp required Handicap richiesto 34

CLUB HOUSE & AMENITIES — CLUB HOUSE E SERVIZI 7/10

Pro shop Pro shop
Driving range Campo pratica
Sheltered coperto 12 mats - On grass in erba yes - Putting-green Putting-green yes - Pitching-green Green-pratica yes

HOTEL FACILITIES — ALBERGHI 7/10

HOTELS ALBERGHI
Castello di Clanezzo - 12 rooms, D € 68 - Clanezzo 3 km
Tel (39) 035 641 567, Fax (39) 035 641 567

Hotel Camoretti - Almenno San Bartolomeo 15 km
22 rooms, D € 65
Tel (39) 035 550 468, Fax (39) 035 550 468

Una Hotel - 86 rooms, D € 230 - Bergamo 15 km
Tel (39) 035 308 111, Fax (39) 035 308 308

RESTAURANTS RISTORANTE
Da Vittorio - Bergamo 15 km - Tel (39) 035 213 266
Palanca - Almenno San Salvatore 1 km - Tel (39) 035 640 800
Antica Osteria Giubi - Almenno S. Bartolomeo 2 km
Tel (39) 035 540 130

Biella - Le Betulle

18	7	7

Biella è il più grande centro italiano della lana e dei tessuti che hanno fatto la gloria della moda italiana ed è anche la sede di uno dei più discreti ma grandiosi golf della penisola. Qui il disegno del campo passa in secondo piano rispetto alla bellezza del paesaggio e di un terreno che sembrano essere fatti apposta per il golf, ma con la maestria di un architetto come John Morrison è stata raggiunta la perfezione. Il percorso è stato allungato nel corso degli anni per rispondere alle esigenze del gioco moderno, ma vi consigliamo di giocare dai tees normali a meno di non avere una tecnica da grande campione. In questo percorso si respira un'atmosfera assolutamente britannica, dove sono in gioco bunkers piazzati strategicamente, fossi diabolici e un'infinità di querce, castagni e betulle. A tutto questo si aggiunge una varietà notevole: qui infatti sobrietà, non vuol mai dire monotonia. E' sicuramente un eccellente banco di prova in un ambiente superbo, può essere un pò difficile per i giocatori inesperti.

Biella is one of Italy's production centres that have made such a name for Italian design and also the site of one of the greatest golf courses in Italy, where architectural design plays second fiddle to the beauty of the landscape and terrain that were just made for golf. Yet it still took the designer skills of John Morrison to perfect the chemistry. The course has since been lengthened to meet the demands of the modern game, but unless you have the technique of a champion, we would recommend the normal tees to avoid needless suffering. There is a British feel to this course, which brings strategically located bunkers into play, along with diabolic ditches and no end of oak, chestnut and birch trees. Add to all this a remarkable touch of variety and you'll realize that sobriety does not necessarily mean monotony. A great test of golf in superb surroundings, but maybe a little too tough for inexperienced players. Also, a layout that demands constantly high standards of green-keeping.

Golf Club Biella - Le Betulle — 1958

Località Valcarrozza
I - 13887 MAGNANO (BI)

Office	Segreteria	(39) 015 679 151
Pro shop	Pro shop	(39) 015 679 272
Fax	Fax	(39) 015 679 276
Web	www.golfclubbiella.it	
Situation	Località	Torino, 75 km

Biella (pop. 47 353), 18 km

Annual closure	Chiusura annuale	30/11→1/3
Weekly closure	Chiusura settimanale	no
Fees main season	Tariffe alta stagione	18 holes

	Week days Settimana	We/Bank holidays Feriale/Festivo
Individual Individuale	€ 60	€ 96
Couple Coppia	€ 120	€ 192

Caddie Caddie on request **Electric Trolley** Carello elettrico yes

Buggy Car yes **Clubs** Bastoni no

Credit cards Carte di credito
VISA - AMEX

Access Itinerario : A4 Milano-Torino, A5 → Aosta. Exit (Uscita) Albiano, → Biella. Cross the S228 and take S338 → Biella. Golf 12 km
Map 1 on page 922 Carta 1 Pagina 922

GOLF COURSE PERCORSO — 18/20

Site	Paesaggio	
Maintenance	Manutenzione	
Architect	Architetto	John Morrison
Type	Tipologia	forest
Relief	Relievo terreno	
Water in play	Acqua in gioco	
Exp. to wind	Esposto al vento	
Trees in play	Alberi in gioco	

Scorecard Carta-score	Chp. Camp.	Mens Uomini	Ladies Donne
Length Lunghezza	6497	6125	5390
Par	73	73	73
Slope system	144	141	131

Advised golfing ability Livello di gioco consigliato — 0 12 24 36
Hcp required Handicap richiesto 34

CLUB HOUSE & AMENITIES CLUB HOUSE E SERVIZI — 7/10

Pro shop Pro shop
Driving range Campo pratica
Sheltered coperto 10 mats - On grass in erba yes - Putting-green Putting-green yes - Pitching-green Green-pratica yes

HOTEL FACILITIES ALBERGHI — 7/10

HOTELS ALBERGHI

Golf Hotel Le Betulle - 20 rooms, D € 126 - on site
Tel (39) 015 679 357, Fax (39) 015 679 4921

Cascina Era - 29 rooms, D € 108 - Sandigliano 15 km
Tel (39) 015 249 3085, Fax (39) 015 249 3266

Agorà Palace - 60 rooms, D € 100 - Biella 18 km
Tel (39) 015 840 7324, Fax (39) 015 840 7423

RESTAURANTS RISTORANTE

La Bessa - Magnano 4 km - Tel (39) 015 679 186
Prinz Grill da Beppe e Teresio - Biella 18 km
Tel (39) 015 23 876
San Paolo - Biella 18 km - Tel (39) 015 8493 236
Golf Restaurant - on site - Tel (39) 015 679 151

Bogogno *Bonora*

17	8	7

Il grande successo delle prime 18 buche meritava un seguito che ha permesso di realizzare uno dei migliori complessi di 36 buche di tutta Europa e sicuramente di questa regione che pur non manca di grandi percorsi. Bonora è formato da nove buche del primo percorso aperto e nove nuove buche, che sono anche le più difficili, disegnate in uno spazio molto aperto con molti ostacoli d'acqua. Più delicato del suo vicino "del Conte" obbliga ad una grande, lunga e bella avventura perché non si torna in club-house fino alla 18a e ultima buca. Ma come sempre con il suo architetto Robert von Hagge, questo percorso sa essere divertente, non nasconde ostacoli ingiusti e sa ricompensare i buoni colpi anche se è molto impegnativo per i giocatori normali, quelli che non ambiscono ad una carriera da pro! Comunque... siccome le sensazioni sono il bello del golf, qui è molto divertente sperimentare le proprie capacità senza mettersi lo score in tasca.

The very successful outcome of the first 18-hole course called for a repeat performance, and the result has been to form one of the best 36-hole golf resorts to be found anywhere in Europe and more particularly in this region, where there is no shortage of excellent layouts. "Bonora" combines nine holes from the original course with nine new and more difficult holes laid out over wide open space with a whole lot of water hazards. Harder to play than its neighbour, it takes the golfer on a long and beautiful trek through golfing country because you only return to the club-house as you walk up the 18th hole. But as always with architect von Hagge, this is a consistently pleasant course to play, one that does not conceal unfair traps and but which does reward good shots, even though it is a tough proposition for the normal good player. Inexperienced golfers can gauge the progress they still need to make. In other words, because feelings always matter more than figures, you should firstly take time out to widen your range of shots before thinking about carding a good score.

Circolo Golf Bogogno — 2000

Via S. Isidoro 1
I - 28010 BOGOGNO (NO)

Office	Segreteria	(39) 0322 863 794
Pro shop	Pro shop	(39) 0322 863 339
Fax	Fax	(39) 0322 863 798
Web	www.circologolfbogogno.com	
Situation	Località	Milano, 66 km

Novara (pop. 102 037), 30 km

Annual closure	Chiusura annuale	no
Weekly closure	Chiusura settimanale	Monday
Fees main season	Tariffe alta stagione	18 holes

	Week days Settimana	We/Bank holidays Feriale/Festivo
Individual Individuale	€ 57	€ 70
Couple Coppia	€ 114	€ 140

Caddie Caddie no — **Electric Trolley** Carello elettrico yes
Buggy Car yes — **Clubs** Bastoni yes
Credit cards Carte di credito
VISA - DC - CartaSi

Access Itinerario : A4 Milano-Torino, Exit (Uscita) Novara. Then S229 → Borgomanero. About 29 km, turn right → Cressa. 800 m turn left to Bogogno.
Map 1 on page 922 Carta 1 Pagina 922

GOLF COURSE — PERCORSO — 17/20

Site	Paesaggio	
Maintenance	Manutenzione	
Architect	Architetto	Robert von Hagge
Type	Tipologia	inland
Relief	Relievo terreno	
Water in play	Acqua in gioco	
Exp. to wind	Esposto al vento	
Trees in play	Alberi in gioco	

Scorecard Carta-score	Chp. Camp.	Mens Uomini	Ladies Donne
Length Lunghezza	6284	5880	4907
Par	72	72	72
Slope system	136	136	130

Advised golfing ability Livello di gioco consigliato — 0 12 24 36
Hcp required Handicap richiesto 34

CLUB HOUSE & AMENITIES — CLUB HOUSE E SERVIZI — 8/10

Pro shop Pro shop
Driving range Campo pratica
Sheltered coperto 8 mats - On grass in erba yes - Putting-green Putting-green yes - Pitching-green Green-pratica yes

HOTEL FACILITIES — ALBERGHI — 7/10

HOTELS ALBERGHI

San Rocco - Orta San Giulio 20 km
82 rooms, D € 260
Tel (39) 0322 911 977, Fax (39) 0322 911 964

Residence Isotta - 16 rooms, D € 41 - Veruno 3 km
Tel (39) 0322 830 502, Fax (39) 0322 830 708

Relais Ca'Nova - 8 rooms, D € 140 - Bogogno 5 km
Tel (39) 0322 863 406, Fax (39) 0322 862 584

RESTAURANTS RISTORANTE

Pinocchio - Borgomanero 6 km - Tel (39) 0322 82 273

Osteria Tre Re - Agrate Conturbia 1 km
Tel (39) 0322 832 717

La Biscia - Sesto Calende 10 km - Tel (39) 0331 624 435

Bogogno *Del Conte*

17 | 8 | 7

Nato nel 1996, Bogogno si è subito imposto come uno dei campi più spettacolari d' Italia e d'altronde c'era da aspettarselo da un architetto come Robert von Hagge che non è certamente un "minimalista". Bisogna comunque dire che i suoi movimenti del terreno non sono mai inutili, sono fatti per variare le prospettive, rendere le buche più difficili e nello stesso tempo isolarle una dall'altra quando il terreno è particolarmente piatto. L'impatto visuale è un altro degli elementi molto importanti per von Hagge e qui a Bogogno rivela un aspetto quasi scozzese... Ma siamo in Italia, culla del teatro: lo sfondo delle Alpi e del Monte Rosa è stato valorizzato al massimo nel disegno del percorso. I giocatori avranno ampi spazi per muoversi ma dovranno stare attenti perchè non è sempre facile interpretarne le difficoltà. Bisogna avere i nervi saldi e un buon mestiere per tenere sulla distanza e preservare un buono score. Il "del Conte" unisce come l'altro percorso "Bonora" nove buche della prima realizzazione e nove buche più recenti.

Opened in 1996, Bogogno immediately became established as one of the most spectacular courses in Italy. This was only to be expected from course architect Robert von Hagge, who is hardly known for dabbling with "minimalism". It should be said, though, that the way he shapes a course is never gratuitous and that any shifting of earth is done to add variety, throw in a difficulty or two or isolate holes when the land is flat. The visual aspect is also very important and the topography this creates gives the course an almost Scottish flavour. But here we are in Italy, the land of theatre: the backdrop of the Alps and Monte Rosa is highlighted by the course's graphic beauty. The actors here will find wide open spaces which are fun to play on but not always easy to perform well with. You will need a strong nerve and good experience to last the course and keep your score down. Like its neighbour "Bonora", this "Conte" course combines nine holes from the original course with nine new holes.

Circolo Golf Bogogno — 1996

Via S. Isidoro 1
I - 28010 BOGOGNO (NO)

Office	Segreteria	(39) 0322 863 794
Pro shop	Pro shop	(39) 0322 863 339
Fax	Fax	(39) 0322 863 798
Web	www.circologolfbogogno.com	
Situation	Località	Milano, 66 km

Novara (pop. 102 037), 30 km

Annual closure	Chiusura annuale	no
Weekly closure	Chiusura settimanale	Monday
Fees main season	Tariffe alta stagione	18 holes

	Week days Settimana	We/Bank holidays Feriale/Festivo
Individual Individuale	€ 57	€ 70
Couple Coppia	€ 114	€ 140

Caddie Caddie no — **Electric Trolley** Carello elettrico yes
Buggy Car yes — **Clubs** Bastoni yes
Credit cards Carte di credito
VISA - DC - CartaSi

Access Itinerario : A4 Milano-Torino, Exit (Uscita) Novara. Then S229 → Borgomanero. About 29 km, turn right → Cressa. 800 m turn left to Bogogno.
Map 1 on page 922 Carta 1 Pagina 922

GOLF COURSE — PERCORSO 17/20

Site	Paesaggio	
Maintenance	Manutenzione	
Architect	Architetto	Robert von Hagge
Type	Tipologia	country, forest
Relief	Relievo terreno	
Water in play	Acqua in gioco	
Exp. to wind	Esposto al vento	
Trees in play	Alberi in gioco	

Scorecard Carta-score	Chp. Camp.	Mens Uomini	Ladies Donne
Length Lunghezza	6485	5755	4947
Par	72	72	72
Slope system	130	126	123

Advised golfing ability Livello di gioco consigliato — 0 12 24 36
Hcp required Handicap richiesto 34

CLUB HOUSE & AMENITIES — CLUB HOUSE E SERVIZI 8/10

Pro shop Pro shop
Driving range Campo pratica
Sheltered coperto 8 mats - On grass in erba yes - Putting-green Putting-green yes - Pitching-green Green-pratica yes

HOTEL FACILITIES — ALBERGHI 7/10

HOTELS ALBERGHI
San Rocco - Orta San Giulio 20 km
82 rooms, D € 260
Tel (39) 0322 911 977, Fax (39) 0322 911 964

Residence Isotta - 16 rooms, D € 41 - Veruno 3 km
Tel (39) 0322 830 502, Fax (39) 0322 830 708

Relais Ca'Nova - 8 rooms, D € 140 - Bogogno 5 km
Tel (39) 0322 863 406, Fax (39) 0322 862 584

RESTAURANTS RISTORANTE
Pinocchio - Borgomanero 6 km - Tel (39) 0322 82 273
Osteria Tre Re - Agrate Conturbia 1 km
Tel (39) 0322 832 717
La Biscia - Sesto Calende 10 km - Tel (39) 0331 624 435

Bologna

13	7	7

Bologna, da secoli punto di ritrovo per gli studenti di tutto il mondo, non è una delle città italiane di maggior attrazione turistica anche se non scarseggia di monumenti e musei importanti. E' anche uno dei centri più significativi per l'enogastronomia del paese e se si aggiunge la sua attività industriale e quella della vicina Modena c'è da chiedersi come mai questa regione non sia più ricca di percorsi di golf. Aperto da più di 40 anni, questo percorso è stato disegnato da C.K. Cotton e John Harris su di un terreno ondulato ai piedi degli Appennini. Il suo aspetto generale ricorda i percorsi britannici dell'interno con i greens ben difesi dai bunkers, ma senza un disegno particolarmente originale. Non si verrà qui per vedere paesaggi mozzafiato ma, il giusto grado di difficoltà rende il percorso piacevole per la grande maggioranza dei giocatori. Soltanto ai migliori mancherà il sapore della sfida più dura.

For centuries, Bologna has been one of the top cities for students and although not one of Italy's leading tourist destinations, there is no shortage of significant landmarks and museums. It is also one the country's top areas for food and drink. If we add to this the region's industrial activity and that of the neighbouring city of Modena, then the scarcity of golf courses might come as something of a surprise. Opened some forty years ago, this course was laid out by C.K. Cotton and John Harris over rolling terrain at the foot of the Apennines. Its overall shape is reminiscent of British inland courses, with greens well protected by bunkers and nothing particularly original about the layout as a whole. You certainly wouldn't come here just for thrills or striking visual beauty, but the moderation in the layout of hazards makes this a pleasant course for almost every player. Only the very best might rue the absence of a tougher challenge.

Golf Club Bologna — 1959

Via Sabbatini 69
I - 40050 MONTE SAN PIETRO (BO)

Office Segreteria (39) 051 969 100
Pro shop Pro shop (39) 051 969 505
Fax Fax (39) 051 6720 017
Web www.golfclubbologna.it
Situation Località Modena, 25 km
Bologna (pop. 381 161), 15 km
Annual closure Chiusura annuale no
Weekly closure Chiusura settimanale tuesday
Fees main season Tariffe alta stagione 18 holes

	Week days Settimana	We/Bank holidays Feriale/Festivo
Individual Individuale	€ 48	€ 60
Couple Coppia	€ 96	€ 120

Caddie Caddie no — **Electric Trolley** Carello elettrico no
Buggy Car yes — **Clubs** Bastoni yes
Credit cards Carte di credito no

Access Itinerario : A1 (Autostrada del Sole) Exit (Uscita) Casalecchio, S569 (Vigolese e di Bazzano) → Maranello, Vignola. After Ponte Ronca, turn left → Golf
Map 2 on page 924 Carta 2 Pagina 924

GOLF COURSE — PERCORSO 13/20

Site Paesaggio
Maintenance Manutenzione
Architect Architetto C.K. Cotton & Harris
Type Tipologia country, hilly
Relief Relievo terreno
Water in play Acqua in gioco
Exp. to wind Esposto al vento
Trees in play Alberi in gioco

Scorecard Carta-score	Chp. Camp.	Mens Uomini	Ladies Donne
Length Lunghezza	6098	5949	5226
Par	72	72	72
Slope system	126	127	125

Advised golfing ability 0 12 24 36
Livello di gioco consigliato
Hcp required Handicap richiesto 34

CLUB HOUSE & AMENITIES — CLUB HOUSE E SERVIZI 7/10

Pro shop Pro shop
Driving range Campo pratica
Sheltered coperto 5 mats - On grass in erba yes - Putting-green Putting-green yes - Pitching-green Green-pratica yes

HOTEL FACILITIES — ALBERGHI 7/10

HOTELS ALBERGHI
Alla Rocca - 55 rooms, D € 119 - Bazzano 5 km
Tel (39) 051 831 217, Fax (39) 051 830 690
Garden - 57 rooms, D € 216 - Anzola Emilia 4 km
Tel (39) 051 735 200, Fax (39) 051 735 673
Grand Hotel Baglioni - Bologna 15 km
124 rooms, D from € 350
Tel (39) 051 225 445, Fax (39) 051 234 840

RESTAURANTS RISTORANTE
Il Ristorante da Dino - Anzola Emilia 4 km - Tel (39) 051 732 364
Trebbi di Gianna e Perla - Monteveglio 5 km
Tel (39) 051 - 670 7929
Battibecco - Bologna 15 km - Tel (39) 051 223 298
Bitone - Bologna - Tel (39) 051 546 110

Castelconturbia *Giallo + Blu*

18 | 8 | 8

Anche se i tre percorsi di 9 buche sono intercambiabili tra loro per fare percorsi differenti, è il tracciato "blu e giallo" quello che è stato scelto per l'Open d'Italia dispuato qui nel 1991 e nel 1998. La firma di Robert Trent Jones si riconosce ovunque e non solo per i bunkers frastagliati. L'aspetto strategico qui è particolarmente importante e bisogna stare attenti alla larghezza ingannevole dei fairways, anche se, c'è sempre una parte ideale da dove attaccare meglio i greens che per la verità sono grandi ma con dislivelli e pendenze spesso diaboliche. Il gioco qui consiste sia nel cercare di evitare gli errori giocando in difesa che nell' attaccare con decisione. Castelconturbia richiede prima molta riflessione e dopo la capacità di metterla in atto: i giocatori inesperti hanno la vita difficile! Il percorso si snoda su un pendio senza rilievi particolari ma alcuni greens sopraelevati richiedono un'attenzione speciale. E' un complesso superbo impossibile da ignorare.

Although the three 9 hole courses can be combined to produce different layouts, the blue and yellow courses were the two chosen for the Italian Open in 1991 and 1998. The hallmark of Robert Trent Jones is omnipresent, and not only in the jagged sand traps. The strategic aspect is particularly important, and watch out for the deceiving width of fairways. Remember, too, that there is always the right side from which to attack greens in the best position, especially since the greens in question are pretty huge with diabolical slopes and breaks. Golf here consists in cutting out mistakes and in stopping short of all-out attack. Castelconturbia requires a lot of thought and the ability to turn thought into deed, so inexperienced players will find it hard going. The course is on the flat side, although some of the raised greens require special care. A superb resort, not to be missed.

Golf Club Castelconturbia — 1987

Via Suno 10
I - 28010 AGRATE CONTURBIA (NO)

Office	Segreteria	(39) 0322 832 093
Pro shop	Pro shop	(39) 0322 832 596
Fax	Fax	(39) 0322 832 428
E-mail	castelconturbia@tin.it	
Situation	Località	Novara, 33 km
Annual closure	Chiusura annuale	1/1→31/1
Weekly closure	Chiusura settimanale	tuesday
Fees main season	Tariffe alta stagione	18 holes

	Week days Settimana	We/Bank holidays Feriale/Festivo
Individual Individuale	€ 66	€ 102*
Couple Coppia	€ 132	€ 204*

*Members and guests only
(Ospiti solo durante i giorni feriali)

Caddie Caddie on request **Electric Trolley** Carello elettrico yes
Buggy Car yes **Clubs** Bastoni yes
Credit cards Carte di credito
VISA - Eurocard - MasterCard - AMEX - DC - CartaSì

Access Itinerario : A4 Milano-Torino, Exit (Uscita) Novara. Then S229 → Borgomanero. About 29 km, turn right → Cressa and Agrate Conturbia.
Map 1 on page 922 Carta 1 Pagina 922

GOLF COURSE — PERCORSO — 18/20

Site	Paesaggio	
Maintenance	Manutenzione	
Architect	Architetto	Robert Trent Jones
Type	Tipologia	forest, links
Relief	Relievo terreno	
Water in play	Acqua in gioco	
Exp. to wind	Esposto al vento	
Trees in play	Alberi in gioco	

Scorecard Carta-score	Chp. Camp.	Mens Uomini	Ladies Donne
Length Lunghezza	6230	5888	5145
Par	72	72	72
Slope system	145	142	132

Advised golfing ability 0 12 24 36
Livello di gioco consigliato
Hcp required Handicap richiesto 34

CLUB HOUSE & AMENITIES — CLUB HOUSE E SERVIZI — 8/10

Pro shop Pro shop
Driving range Campo pratica
Sheltered coperto 10 mats - On grass in erba yes - Putting-green Putting-green yes - Pitching-green Green-pratica yes

HOTEL FACILITIES — ALBERGHI — 8/10

HOTELS ALBERGHI

Concorde - 82 rooms, D € 134 - Arona 20 km
Tel (39) 0322 249 321, Fax (39) 0322 249 372

Golf Hotel - 19 rooms, D € 95 - on site
Tel (39) 0322 832 337, Fax (39) 0322 832 428

Tre Re - 31 rooms, D € 130 - Sesto Calende 14 km
Tel (39) 0331 924 229, Fax (39) 0331 913 023

RESTAURANTS RISTORANTE

San Pietro - Borgomanero 6 km - Tel (39) 0322 822 85
Taverna del Pittore - Arona 20 km - Tel (39) 0322 243 366
Osteria Tre Re - Agrate Conturbia 1 km
Tel (39) 0322 832 717
La Biscia - Sesto Calende 8 km - Tel (39) 0331 624 435

Castelgandolfo

15 | 7 | 7

Questo piccolo paese è famoso per essere la residenza estiva del Papa, in un'antica regione vulcanica, dove il clima è particolarmente mite. E' stata in passato una zona molto importante, conosciuta con il nome di Alba Longa, che la leggenda narra sia stata fondata da Enea e che si sia poi opposta a Roma nella guerra tra Orazi e Curiazi. Questo percorso è l'ideale per un match-play, perchè qui Robert Trent Jones non ha risparmiato le sue insidie, soprattutto quelle di un grande lago che entra in gioco pericolosamente in diverse buche. In più tra pini marittimi e clivi che addolciscono il rigore del paesaggio e quello del sole, ritroverete i soliti difficili bunkers e i greens a volte indecifrabili dell'architetto americano. Per rilassarsi la club-house è veramente molto piacevole in un'antica villa del XVII secolo, ben restaurata, che domina su tutto il percorso.

This little town is known for being the Pope's summer residence in a formerly volcanic region with a warm, balmy climate. It is importantly the site of Alba Longa which, according to legend was founded by Aeneas and then opposed Rome in the fighting with the Horatii and the Curiatii. So this layout is ideal for head-to-head match-play, as there is no shortage of traps spread around the course by Robert Trent Jones, especially a lake which comes into play most dangerously on several holes. Otherwise, you find the usual bunkers and often hard-to-read greens favoured by the American architect in a landscape of maritime pines and olive trees, which temper the course and the sunshine too. For relaxation after your round, the club-house is a real treat, a well-restored former 17th century patrician villa which overlooks the whole course.

Country Club Castelgandolfo — 1988

Via di Santo Spirito 13
I - 00040 CASTEL GANDOLFO (RM)

Office	Segreteria	(39) 06 931 2301
Pro shop	Pro shop	(39) 06 931 1065
Fax	Fax	(39) 06 931 2244
Web	www.countryclubcastelgandolfo.it	
Situation	Località	Roma, 26 km
Annual closure	Chiusura annuale	no
Weekly closure	Chiusura settimanale	monday
Fees main season	Tariffe alta stagione	18 holes

	Week days Settimana	We/Bank holidays Feriale/Festivo
Individual Individuale	€ 55	€ 65
Couple Coppia	€ 110	€ 130

Caddie Caddie on request — Electric Trolley Carello elettrico no
Buggy Car yes — Clubs Bastoni no
Credit cards Carte di credito
VISA - AMEX - CartaSi

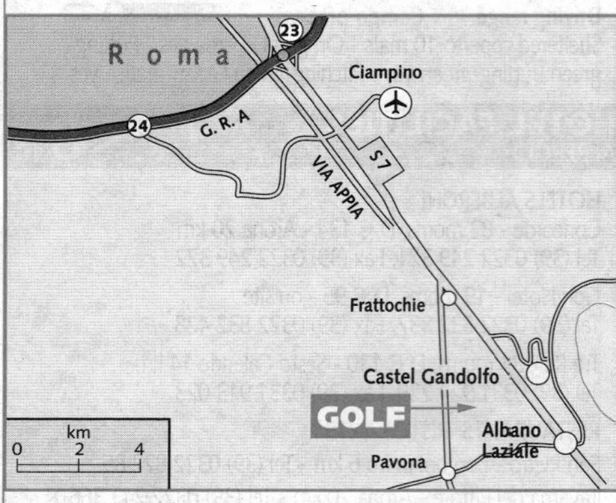

Access Itinerario : Roma, Via Appia Nuova. At Ciampino, go right to Via Nettunense. 2 km → Golf.
Map 3 on page 927 Carta 3 Pagina 927

GOLF COURSE PERCORSO — 15/20

Site	Paesaggio	
Maintenance	Manutenzione	
Architect	Architetto	Robert Trent Jones
Type	Tipologia	residential
Relief	Relievo terreno	
Water in play	Acqua in gioco	
Exp. to wind	Esposto al vento	
Trees in play	Alberi in gioco	

Scorecard Carta-score	Chp. Camp.	Mens Uomini	Ladies Donne
Length Lunghezza	6205	5855	5143
Par	72	72	72
Slope system	133	130	129

Advised golfing ability Livello di gioco consigliato: 0 12 24 36
Hcp required Handicap richiesto 34

CLUB HOUSE & AMENITIES CLUB HOUSE E SERVIZI — 7/10

Pro shop Pro shop
Driving range Campo pratica
Sheltered coperto 9 mats - On grass in erba yes - Putting-green Putting-green yes - Pitching-green Green-pratica yes

HOTEL FACILITIES ALBERGHI — 7/10

HOTELS ALBERGHI

Castelvecchio - 50 rooms, D € 150 - Castelgandolfo 3 km
Tel (39) 06 936 0308, Fax (39) 06 936 0579

Grand Hotel Helio Cabala - 40 rooms, D € 190 - Marino 3 km
Tel (39) 06 9366 1391, Fax (39) 06 9366 1125

Castelgandolfo Golf Resort - 24 rooms, D € 120 - on site
Tel (39) 06 9316 0911, Fax (39) 06 9316 0966

Hotel Miralago - 45 rooms, D € 90 - Albano Laziale 3 km
Tel (39) 06 932 2253, Fax (39) 06 932 2253

RESTAURANTS RISTORANTE

Antico Ristorante Pagnanelli - Castel Gandolfo 3 km
Tel (39) 06 936 0004

Da Mario - La Cavola d'Oro - Grottaferrata 8 km
Tel (39) 06 9431 5755

Castello di Tolcinasco *Giallo + Blu*

14	8	7

Per i grandi giocatori che si sono messi a disegnare campi da golf, la chiave del successo è sempre stata la qualità dei loro ingegneri ed architetti. Gary Player ha imparato la lezione da cattive esperienze e così Jack Nicklaus che non sempre ha firmato opere ben riuscite. Anche Arnold Palmer ha avuto dei periodi incerti ma il Castello di Tolcinasco fa parte delle sue opere di buona qualità pur non essendo eccezionale. Questo terreno particolarmente piatto si prestava decisamente per un tracciato all'americana che comprende 3 percorsi di 9 buche intercambiabili tra loro. Sede dell'Open d'Italia dal 2004 al 2006, il campo gode di un'ottima manutenzione e presenta le sue maggiori difficoltà nei molti bunkers, negli ostacoli d'acqua e nei folti rough che obbligano a scelte precise di strategia. Più impegnativo dai tees di campionato, questo percorso diventa nettamente più facile dalle partenze avanzate e consente ai dilettanti di divertirsi molto anche con lo score in tasca.

For the game's top players who have moved into course design, the key to success has always been the excellence of their engineers and architects. Gary Player learnt from experience, and so has Jack Nicklaus. Arnold Palmer has had a few patchy periods as well, but Castello di Tolcinasco is a layout of high, not to say outstanding quality. This rather open and flat terrain was just perfect for an American-style layout. It features three interchangeable 9-hole courses and has been selected to host the Italian Open from 2004 to 2006. The course is kept in excellent condition and presents a variety of hazards, from bunkers to water to some very dangerous rough which calls for very straight hitting. Tough from the back tees, this layout becomes a more human the further forward you move, which just goes to show that you can take account of all levels of playing ability yet still design a good tournament course. Whatever, average mid-handicappers will have a lot of fun here.

Castello di Tolcinasco G & CC — 1993

Loc. Tolcinasco
I - 20090 PIEVE EMANUELE (MI)

Office	Segreteria	(39) 02 904 280 35
Pro shop	Pro shop	(39) 02 907 227 40
Fax	Fax	(39) 02 907 890 51
Web	www.golftolcinasco.it	
Situation	Località	Milano, 8 km
Annual closure	Chiusura annuale	no
Weekly closure	Chiusura settimanale	monday(11 → 04)

Fees main season Tariffe alta stagione — 18 holes

	Week days Settimana	We/Bank holidays Feriale/Festivo
Individual Individuale	€ 45	€ 80
Couple Coppia	€ 90	€ 160

Caddie Caddie no — **Electric Trolley** Carello elettrico no
Buggy Car yes — **Clubs** Bastoni no
Credit cards Carte di credito
VISA - MasterCard - AMEX - DC - CartaSi

Access Itinerario : Milano Duomo, Via Torino, C° di Porto Ticinese, C° San Gottardo, straight in Via dei Missaglia. At traffic lights go left. 3 km, Castello di Tolcinasco.
Map 1 on page 923 Carta 1 Pagina 923

GOLF COURSE — PERCORSO 14/20

Site	Paesaggio	
Maintenance	Manutenzione	
Architect	Architetto	Arnold Palmer
Type	Tipologia	country, residential
Relief	Relievo terreno	
Water in play	Acqua in gioco	
Exp. to wind	Esposto al vento	
Trees in play	Alberi in gioco	

Scorecard Carta-score	Chp. Camp.	Mens Uomini	Ladies Donne
Length Lunghezza	6322	5788	4999
Par	72	72	72
Slope system	138	133	121

Advised golfing ability Livello di gioco consigliato — 0 12 24 36
Hcp required Handicap richiesto

CLUB HOUSE & AMENITIES — CLUB HOUSE E SERVIZI 8/10

Pro shop Pro shop
Driving range Campo pratica
Sheltered coperto 15 mats - On grass in erba no, 70 mats open air - Putting-green Putting-green yes - Pitching-green Green-pratica yes

HOTEL FACILITIES — ALBERGHI 7/10

HOTELS ALBERGHI

Albergho della Corona - 47 rooms, D € 80 - Binasco 6 km
Tel (39) 02 905 2280, Fax (39) 02 905 4353

Royal Garden Hotel - 154 rooms, D € 230 - Assago 11 km
Tel (39) 02 457 811, Fax (39) 02 457 02 901

Four Seasons - 104 rooms, D € 528 - Milano 12 km
Tel (39) 02 77 088, Fax (39) 02 77 085 000

RESTAURANTS RISTORANTE

Sadler - Milano 13 km - Tel (39) 02 581 044 51

Il Luogo di Aimo e Nadia - Milano 12 km - Tel (39) 02 416 886

Bacco e Arianna - Trezzano sul Naviglio 10 km
Tel (39) 02 4840 3895

947

Cervia

13 | 6 | 9

Questa parte della Costa Adriatica è una delle più affollate e più divertenti in assoluto. La fama di Cesenatico, Riccione e Milano Marittima ha varcato le frontiere e questo percorso è nato come ulteriore attrazione per coloro che amano le vacanze sportive. Non bisogna poi dimenticare la vicinanza con Ravenna, i suoi monumenti e i suoi famosi mosaici che figurano tra i tesori mondiali. Tracciato su un terreno piatto tra i pini e le dune sabbiose il percorso disegnato inizialmente da Marco Croze si presentava con 9 buche tipo links e le altre 9 di gusto decisamente più americano. Nel 2004 sono state inaugurate altre 9 buche ad opera di Baldovino Dassù e Alvise Rossi Fioravanti che si sono mescolate per una parte con le vecchie seconde nove dando vita ad un interessante percorso. Il vento, quasi sempre presente a Cervia, offre una bella sfida ai giocator ma il percorso è molto piacevole perché gli ostacoli pur essendo sempre in gioco non sono mai scoraggianti né insormontabili.

This section of the Adriatic coast is one of the most popular and entertaining along the whole Mediterranean basin. The reputation of Cesenatico, Riccione and especially Milano Marittima has spread abroad and this course should logically be an extra attraction for people who prefer the more sporting style of holiday. Let's not forget either nearby Ravenna, whose monuments and mosaics feature amongst the world's treasures. Spread over flat terrain amidst both pine trees and sandy dunes, this layout comprises 9 holes with the features of a real links course but then a slight American flavour over the other nine, all devoid of the the raw brutality of a Scottish links. In 2004, an additional 9 holes (designed by Baldovino Dassù and Alvise Rossi Fioravanti) brought with them an alternative to form a different full course. The wind can often stiffen the challenge but Cervia remains a very pleasant course to play, especially since all the hazards are in play but never dissuasive.

Adriatic Golf Club Cervia — 1985

Via Jelenia Gora 6
I - 48016 MILANO MARITTIMA (RA)

Office Segreteria (39) 0544 992 786
Pro shop Pro shop (39) 0544 995 137
Fax Fax (39) 0544 993 410
Web www.golfcervia.com
Situation Località Forlì (pop. 107 461), 28 km
Ravenna (pop. 137 721), 22 km

Annual closure Chiusura annuale — no
Weekly closure Chiusura settimanale — monday

Fees main season Tariffe alta stagione	18 holes	
	Week days / Settimana	We/Bank holidays / Feriale/Festivo
Individual Individuale	€ 52	€ 64
Couple Coppia	€ 104	€ 128

Caddie Caddie no — **Electric Trolley** Carello elettrico yes
Buggy Car yes — **Clubs** Bastoni yes
Credit cards Carte di credito
VISA - Eurocard - MasterCard - AMEX - DC - CartaSi

Access Itinerario : A14 Bologna-Rimini. Exit (Uscita) Cesena. → Cervia, → Pineta and Milano Marittima. → Golf
Map 2 on page 924 Carta 2 Pagina 924

GOLF COURSE — PERCORSO — 13/20

Site Paesaggio
Maintenance Manutenzione
Architect Architetto — Marco Croze
Type Tipologia — seaside course, parkland
Relief Rilievo terreno
Water in play Acqua in gioco
Exp. to wind Esposto al vento
Trees in play Alberi in gioco

Scorecard Carta-score	Chp. Camp.	Mens Uomini	Ladies Donne
Length Lunghezza	6296	6029	5185
Par	72	72	72
Slope system	126	124	120

Advised golfing ability Livello di gioco consigliato — 0 12 24 36
Hcp required Handicap richiesto 34

CLUB HOUSE & AMENITIES — CLUB HOUSE E SERVIZI — 6/10

Pro shop Pro shop
Driving range Campo pratica
Sheltered coperto 5 mats - On grass in erba yes - Putting-green Putting-green yes - Pitching-green Green-pratica yes

HOTEL FACILITIES — ALBERGHI — 9/10

HOTELS ALBERGHI

Mare e Pineta - Milano Marittima 500 m
168 rooms, D € 200
Tel (39) 0544 992 262, Fax (39) 0544 992 739

Deanna Golf Hotel - Milano Marittima 3
68 rooms, D € 98
Tel (39) 0544 991 365, Fax (39) 0544 994 251

Grand Hotel Cervia - 92 rooms, D € 260 - Cervia 2 km
Tel (39) 0544 970 500, Fax (39) 0544 972 086

RESTAURANTS RISTORANTE

Al Caminetto - Milano Marittima 5 - Tel (39) 0544 994 479
Nautilus da Franco - Cervia 2 km - Tel (39) 0544 976 486
Al Teatro - Cervia 2 km - Tel (39) 0544 716 39

Cosmopolitan

14	6	7

Un viaggio intelligente alla scoperta dell'Italia deve passare obbligatoriamente da Pisa per visitare la famosa Torre di marmo bianco ma anche i magnifici altri edifici della piazza del Duomo, con il Battistero, il Camposanto e ovviamente il Duomo, in stile puramente romanico. Scendendo verso Livorno, città portuale molto viva, si può fare una sosta al Cosmopolitan, un percorso aperto abbastanza di recente. E' stato disegnato da David Mezzacane su un terreno piatto e senza alberi e lo stile links era quindi sicuramente il migliore per dare carattere a questo percorso dove soltanto il posizionamento degli ostacoli d'acqua ha un leggero sapore americano. Nell'insieme il posto conserva un aspetto selvaggio del tutto inaspettato. E' abbastanza difficile giocarsi il proprio handicap soprattutto quando tira vento e ancor più se si gioca dalle partenze arretrate anche se la larghezza dei fairways e la buona dimensione dei greens perdonano gli errori dei giocatori inesperti.

A smart trip to discover the joys of Italy has to include a visit to Pisa to see the famous white marble bell-tower and the other fantastic buildings on the Piazza del Duomo, with the Battistero, Camposanto (closed cemetery), and of course the Duomo, all built primarily in pure Roman style. Driving down towards Livorno, a very lively harbour town, you can stop off at the recently opened Cosmopolitan course designed by David Mezzacane over flat and tree-less terrain. A links style was essential here to create some sort of lively addition to the open space, and only the introduction of a few water hazards gives this a slight American flavour. Despite everything, the whole course has retained an unexpected very natural appearance. Playing to your handicap here is a tall order, especially when the wind blows and even more so when playing from the back-tees. Yet the wide fairways and nicely-sized greens help forgive the shortcomings of inexperienced players.

Cosmopolitan Golf & Country Club — 1993

Via Pisorno 60
56018 TIRRENIA (PI)

Office Segreteria (39) 050 33 633
Pro shop Pro shop (39) 050 303 77
Fax Fax (39) 050 384 707
Web www.cosmopolitangolf.it
Situation Località Pisa (pop. 92 379), 18 km
Livorno (pop. 161 673), 11 km

Annual closure Chiusura annuale — no
Weekly closure Chiusura settimanale — monday(10 → 05)

Fees main season Tariffe alta stagione — 18 holes

	Week days Settimana	We/Bank holidays Feriale/Festivo
Individual Individuale	€ 50	€ 60
Couple Coppia	€ 100	€ 120

Caddie Caddie no — **Electric Trolley** Carello elettrico no
Buggy Car yes — **Clubs** Bastoni yes
Credit cards Carte di credito
VISA - Eurocard - MasterCard - AMEX - DC - CartaSì

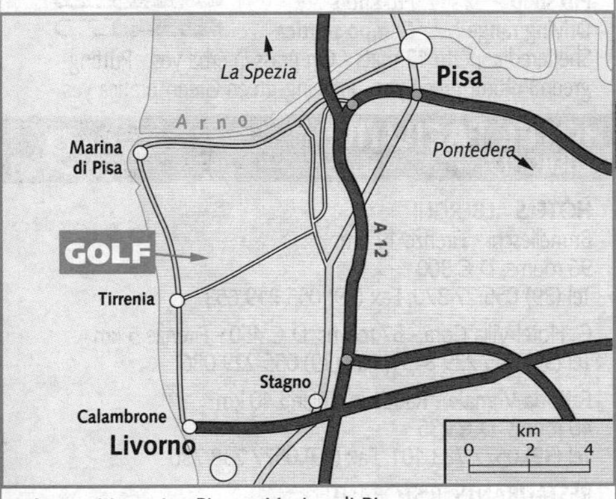

Access Itinerario : Pisa → Marina di Pisa. → Tirrenia and Livorno
Map 3 on page 926 Carta 3 Pagina 926

GOLF COURSE — PERCORSO — 14/20

Site Paesaggio
Maintenance Manutenzione
Architect Architetto — David Mezzacane
Type Tipologia — links
Relief Relievo terreno
Water in play Acqua in gioco
Exp. to wind Esposto al vento
Trees in play Alberi in gioco

Scorecard Carta-score	Chp. Camp.	Mens Uomini	Ladies Donne
Length Lunghezza	6291	5830	5125
Par	72	72	72
Slope system	130	129	126

Advised golfing ability Livello di gioco consigliato — 0 12 24 36
Hcp required Handicap richiesto 34

CLUB HOUSE & AMENITIES — CLUB HOUSE E SERVIZI — 6/10

Pro shop Pro shop
Driving range Campo pratica
Sheltered coperto no - On grass in erba yes - Putting-green Putting-green yes - Pitching-green Green-pratica yes

HOTEL FACILITIES — ALBERGHI — 7/10

HOTELS ALBERGHI
Green Park Resort - Calambrone (Tirrenia) 2 km
152 rooms, D € 250
Tel (39) 050 3135 711, Fax (39) 050 384 138

San Francesco - Tirrenia 1 km
25 rooms, D € 148
Tel (39) 050 33 572, Fax (39) 050 33 630

Royal Victoria Hotel - Pisa 18 km - 48 rooms, D € 130
Tel (39) 050 940 111, Fax (39) 050 940 180

RESTAURANTS RISTORANTE
Dante e Ivana - Tirrenia 1 km - Tel (39) 050 32 549
L'Arsella - Marina di Pisa 5 km - Tel (39) 050 366 15
A Casa Mia - Pisa 12 km - Tel (39) 050 879 265

Firenze - Ugolino

13 | 8 | 9

Il Circolo Golf Firenze aperto all'inizio del secolo si è Il Circolo Golf Firenze aperto all'inizio del secolo si è insediato in questo luogo soltanto nel 1933. Disegnato dallo studio Blandford & Gannon è stato modificato in seguito da Piero Mancinelli. Il posto è particolarmente piacevole e dunque è garantita una bella giornata di golf. Si consiglia l'uso del golf cart ai giocatori non in perfetta forma fisica, perchè il terreno è molto mosso. Per i professionisti di oggi, l'Ugolino manca un poco di lunghezza ma resta un buon percorso di gara per i dilettanti tra i quali la precisione conta ben più che la forza bruta. Ci sono dei par 3 abbastanza lunghi ma anche una lunga serie di corti par 4 dove è lecito pensare al birdie anche se non si riesce a farne molti perché i greens sono ben disegnati e ben difesi. L'Ugolino non è certamente un esempio di modernità, ma merita una visita anche se un viaggio a Firenze, una delle città più belle al mondo, lascia poco tempo per lo sport. Vale la pena di provarlo ... insieme ad un bicchiere di buon Chianti.

This club is the oldest in Italy but the present course opened here only in 1933. Designed by Blandford & Gannon, it was subsequently altered by Piero Mancinelli. This is a very pleasant site with a great day's golfing assured. We would simply advise a buggy for players whose physical condition is not what it was, as the course is rather hilly. For today's professionals, Ugolino is doubtless a little short but this is still an excellent course for amateur tournaments, where accuracy counts for much more than brute strength. The par 3s are rather long but there is also an impressive group of short par 4s where you might be tempted to think about birdies. Whether or not you make them remains in some doubt, as the greens are generally small, well contoured and well protected. Ugolino is by no means an example of modernity but it certainly deserves a visit, even if a trip to Florence leaves little time for sport. Certainly worth a try... together, of course, with a glass of local Chianti wine.

Golf Dell'Ugolino — 1933

Via Chiantigiana 3
I - 50015 GRASSINA (FI)

Office Segreteria (39) 055 2301 009
Pro shop Pro shop (39) 055 2301 278
Fax Fax (39) 055 2301 141
Web www.golfugolino.it
Situation Località Firenze (pop. 376 662), 12 km

Annual closure Chiusura annuale no

Weekly closure Chiusura settimanale monday(11 → 03)

Fees main season Tariffe alta stagione		18 holes
	Week days Settimana	**We/Bank holidays** Feriale/Festivo
Individual Individuale	€ 60	€ 80
Couple Coppia	€ 120	€ 160

Caddie Caddie no — **Electric Trolley** Carello elettrico yes
Buggy Car yes — **Clubs** Bastoni yes
Credit cards Carte di credito
VISA - AMEX - Cartasi

Access Itinerario : A1 Exit (Uscita) Firenze South (Sud). Turn right to Grassina then S222 (Chiantigiana). Golf 4 km on the left.
Map 3 on page 926 Carta 3 Pagina 926

GOLF COURSE — PERCORSO 13/20

Site Paesaggio
Maintenance Manutenzione
Architect Architetto Cecil R. Blandford, Peter Gannon
Type Tipologia hilly
Relief Relievo terreno
Water in play Acqua in gioco
Exp. to wind Esposto al vento
Trees in play Alberi in gioco

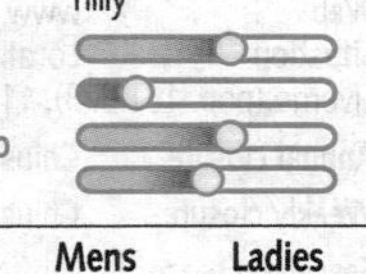

Scorecard Carta-score	**Chp.** Camp.	**Mens** Uomini	**Ladies** Donne
Length Lunghezza	5800	5676	4994
Par	72	72	72
Slope system	131	131	123

Advised golfing ability 0 12 24 36
Livello di gioco consigliato
Hcp required Handicap richiesto 34

CLUB HOUSE & AMENITIES — CLUB HOUSE E SERVIZI 8/10

Pro shop Pro shop
Driving range Campo pratica
Sheltered coperto 12 mats - On grass in erba yes - Putting-green Putting-green yes - Pitching-green Green-pratica yes

HOTEL FACILITIES — ALBERGHI 9/10

HOTELS ALBERGHI
Brunelleschi - Firenze 12 km
96 rooms, D € 300
Tel (39) 055 27 370, Fax (39) 055 219 653

G. Hotel Villa Cora - 57 rooms, D € 450 - Firenze 5 km
Tel (39) 055 229 8451, Fax (39) 055 229 086

Fattoria Vignale - Radda in Chianti 40 km
40 rooms, D € 235
Tel (39) 0577 783 101, Fax (39) 0577 738 730

RESTAURANTS RISTORANTE
Enoteca Pinchiorri - Firenze 12 km - Tel (39) 055 242 777
Il Caminetto del Chianti - Greve 5 km - Tel (39) 055 858 8909
Cibreo - Firenze 12 km - Tel (39) 055 234 1100

Franciacorta

14 | 7 | 8

Il golf di Franciacorta si trova vicino al lago d'Iseo che anche se non è il più celebre dei grandi laghi italiani, merita di essere conosciuto per il suo aspetto selvaggio, così come merita una visita il Monte Isola che si trova in mezzo al lago e dal quale si gode un panorama superbo delle Alpi. Con il "Domaine Imperial" in Svizzera, questo percorso è uno dei rari esempi in Europa dello stile spesso controverso ma sempre fedele allo spirito del golf di Pete Dye, che qui ha collaborato con Marco Croze, uno dei più prolifici architetti italiani. E' stato tracciato su un terreno mosso ma non troppo faticoso. Lo stile è decisamente americano con ostacoli d'acqua su circa la metà delle buche e con due greens in un'isola: ci si può scordare di arrivare a rotolo! Malgrado ciò i giocatori medi si potranno divertire molto perchè le difficoltà sono ben visibili e la strategia di gioco evidente.

The Golf de Franciacorta is situated close to Lake Iseo. This is not the most famous of the Italian "Great Lakes", but the wild scenery here is well worth seeing, as is the Monte Isola, located in the middle of the lake and offering superb views over the Alps. Along with the Domaine Impérial in Switzerland, this course is one of the rare examples in Europe of the often controversial style (but always true to the spirit of golf) of American designer Pete Dye, who here worked together with Marco Croze, one of the more prolific Italian course architects. The course is laid out on slightly hilly but never tiring terrain. The style is blatantly American, with water on almost half the holes and two island greens, so you can forget the bump and run shots. Despite this, average players can have a lot of fun, as all the difficulties are clear to see and game strategy is obvious.

Golf di Franciacorta — 1986

Loc. Castagnola
I - 25040 CORTE FRANCA (BS)

Office Segreteria (39) 030 984 167
Pro shop Pro shop (39) 030 982 8330
Fax Fax (39) 030 984 343
E-mail franciacortagolfclub@libero.it
Situation Località Bergamo, 32 km
Brescia (pop. 191 317), 28 km
Annual closure Chiusura annuale 25/12→1/1
Weekly closure Chiusura settimanale tuesday

Fees main season Tariffe alta stagione	18 holes	
	Week days Settimana	**We/Bank holidays** Feriale/Festivo
Individual Individuale	€ 40	€ 65
Couple Coppia	€ 80	€ 130

Caddie Caddie no — **Electric Trolley** Carello elettrico no
Buggy Car yes — **Clubs** Bastoni yes
Credit cards Carte di credito
VISA - Mastercard

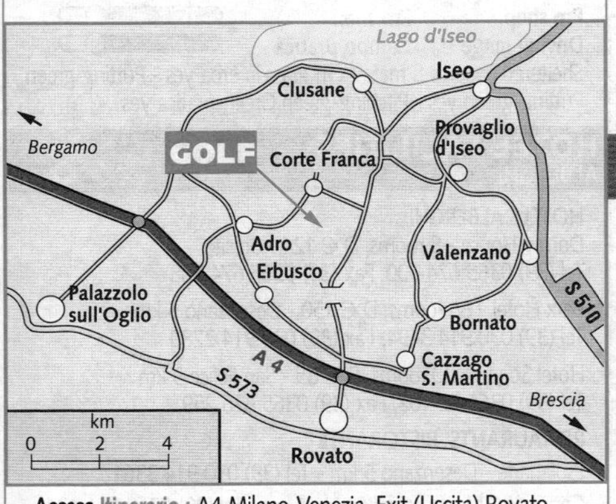

Access Itinerario : A4 Milano-Venezia. Exit (Uscita) Rovato, turn left then right → Iseo. 6 km → golf on left hand side.
Map 1 on page 923 Carta 1 Pagina 923

GOLF COURSE — PERCORSO — 14/20

Site Paesaggio
Maintenance Manutenzione
Architect Architetto — Pete Dye, Marco Croze
Type Tipologia — country
Relief Relievo terreno
Water in play Acqua in gioco
Exp. to wind Esposto al vento
Trees in play Alberi in gioco

Scorecard Carta-score	Chp. Camp.	Mens Uomini	Ladies Donne
Length Lunghezza	5924	5762	5095
Par	72	72	72
Slope system	131	130	128

Advised golfing ability Livello di gioco consigliato — 0 12 24 36
Hcp required Handicap richiesto 34

CLUB HOUSE & AMENITIES — CLUB HOUSE E SERVIZI — 7/10

Pro shop Pro shop
Driving range Campo pratica
Sheltered coperto 4 mats - On grass in erba yes - Putting-green Putting-green yes - Pitching-green Green-pratica yes

HOTEL FACILITIES — ALBERGHI — 8/10

HOTELS ALBERGHI
L'Albereta - 66 rooms, D from € 250 - Erbusco 9 km
Tel (39) 030 776 0550, Fax (39) 030 776 0573

Relais Franciacorta - 44 rooms, D € 175 - Corte Franca 3 km
Tel (39) 030 988 4234, Fax (39) 030 988 4224

Franciacorta Golf Hotel - 43 rooms, D € 173 - Paratico 8 km
Tel (39) 035 913 333, Fax (39) 035 913 600

RESTAURANTS RISTORANTE
Gualtiero Marchesi (Albereta) - Erbusco 9 km
Tel (39) 030 7760 562
Santa Giulia - Timoline 2 km - Tel (39) 030 9828 348
Il Volto - Iseo 5 km - Tel (39) 030 981 462

Gardagolf *Rosso + Bianco*

15	8	8

Grazie alla protezione delle Dolomiti che mitigano il vento, il lago di Garda vanta un clima formidabile, particolarmente dolce d'inverno. Per la sua ubicazione appena sopra al lago, la sua vista spettacolare e la sua vicinanza a Brescia, Bergamo e Milano, Gardagolf ha fatto in fretta ad ottenere un grande successo, tanto che può essere ora difficile riuscire a giocare nel week-end. Ma questa regione ha tante altre attrattive per trascorrerci più giorni se non addirittura settimane. Disegnato dallo Studio Cotton, Pennink and Steel, con 9 buche piatte e 9 buche in collina è considerato difficile dai tees di campionato (uomini e donne), ma nessuno vi obbligherà a partire da lì. L'acqua entra in gioco su circa un terzo delle buche e i bunkers sia del fairway che dei greens sono stati piazzati intelligentemente. Qui non bisogna fare colpi particolari e i giocatori lunghi ne trarranno beneficio, tanto più che i greens non richiedono studi particolari essendo generalmente piatti. Un buon percorso in una bellissima regione al quale si aggiungono 9 buche meno impegnative ma piacevoli.

Protected by the Dolomites, which cut out the wind, Lake Garda enjoys a wonderful climate which is surprisingly mild in winter. Located above the lake, spectacular in more ways than one and located close to Brescia, Bergamo and Milan, Gardagolf has rapidely become a popular venue and week-end green-fees can be hard to come by. Nonetheless, this region has appeal enough to spend several days or even weeks looking around. Designed by architects Cotton, Pennink and Steel with nine flat holes and nine hilly numbers, the course is considered to be hard from the back tees (men's and ladies) but there is no obligation to play from the tips. Water is in play on half a dozen holes and the green-side and fairway bunkers are cleverly located. There is no great need to work the ball in any direction, and straight-hitters should do well, especially as the greens have no hidden perils and are generally rather flat. A good course in a superb region and now with an additional 9-hole layout.

Gardagolf Country Club — 1986

Via A. Omodeo 2
I - 25080 SOIANO DEL LAGO (BS)

Office	Segreteria	(39) 0365 674 707
Pro shop	Pro shop	(39) 0365 679 014
Fax	Fax	(39) 0365 674 788
Web	www. gardagolf.it	
Situation	Località	Bergamo, 77 km

Brescia (pop. 191 317), 46 km

Annual closure	Chiusura annuale	1/11→15/3
Weekly closure (01/11 → 31/03)	Chiusura settimanale	monday

Fees main season Tariffe alta stagione	18 holes	
	Week days Settimana	**We/Bank holidays** Feriale/Festivo
Individual Individuale	€ 70	€ 80
Couple Coppia	€ 140	€ 160

Caddie Caddie no — **Electric Trolley** Carello elettrico no

Buggy Car yes — **Clubs** Bastoni yes

Credit cards Carte di credito
VISA - Eurocard - Mastercard - AMEX - DC- CartaSi

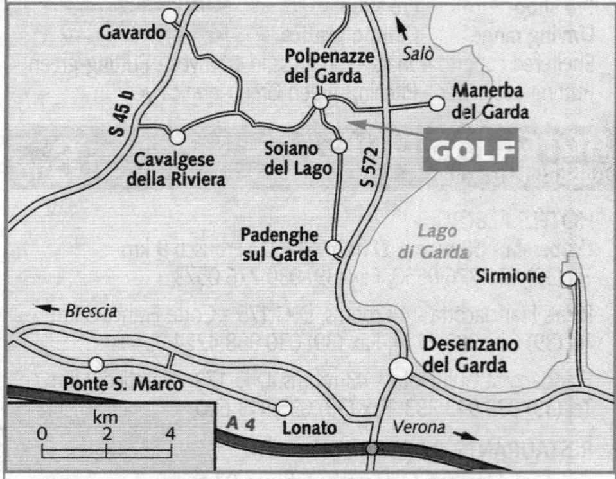

Access Itinerario : A4 Milano-Venezia. Exit (Uscita) Desenzano. → Salò. 5 km after Moniga cross, turn left at traffic lights. Golf 2 km
Map 1 on page 923 Carta 1 Pagina 923

GOLF COURSE — PERCORSO — 15/20

Site	Paesaggio	
Maintenance	Manutenzione	
Architect	Architetto	C.K. Cotton, Pennink Steel & Partners
Type	Tipologia	country
Relief	Relievo terreno	
Water in play	Acqua in gioco	
Exp. to wind	Esposto al vento	
Trees in play	Alberi in gioco	

Scorecard Carta-score	Chp. Camp.	Mens Uomini	Ladies Donne
Length Lunghezza	6505	6040	5353
Par	72	72	72
Slope system	139	141	133

Advised golfing ability Livello di gioco consigliato — 0 12 24 36
Hcp required Handicap richiesto 34

CLUB HOUSE & AMENITIES — CLUB HOUSE E SERVIZI — 8/10

Pro shop Pro shop
Driving range Campo pratica
Sheltered coperto 8 mats - On grass in erba yes - Putting-green Putting-green yes - Pitching-green Green-pratica yes

HOTEL FACILITIES — ALBERGHI — 8/10

HOTELS ALBERGHI
Dormy House - 8 rooms, D € 124 - on site
Tel (39) 0365 674 000, Fax (39) 0365 674 788

Park Hotel - 66 rooms, D € 150 - Desenzano 5 km
Tel (39) 030 914 3494, Fax (39) 030 914 2280

Hotel Sogno - 20 rooms, D € 85 - San Felice 3 km
Tel (39) 0365 62 102, Fax (39) 0365 626 259

RESTAURANTS RISTORANTE
Esplanade - Desenzano 5 km - Tel (39) 030 914 3361
Capriccio - Manerba del Garda 4 km - Tel (39) 0365 551 124
Al Porto - Moniga del Garda 5 km - Tel (39) 0365 502 069
Taverna Picedo - Picedo 3 km - Tel (39) 0365 674 103

Garlenda

14 | 7 | 8

Garlenda è stato costruito sulle colline che dominano le stazioni balneari di Alassio e Albenga ed è un percorso abbastanza corto che non spaventa i giocatori medi. John Harris lo ha disegnato con gusto rispettando il paesaggio, da una parte all'altra del fiume Lerrone che attraversa la 13, un lungo par 3. Da non molti anni ha subito un restyling di alcune buche ed è diventato par 72. Gli alberi sono di ostacolo in numerose buche e invitano i giocatori a compiere colpi ad effetto in numerose buche per avvicinarsi il più possibile ai greens, spesso di piccole dimensioni ma disegnati senza troppe difficoltà. Divertente per giocare con la famiglia e con gli amici anche di livello molto diverso, Garlenda non pretende di essere un grande percorso da campionato, ma offre una buona occasione per giocare in questa regione e trascorrere un piacevole soggiorno a "La Meridiana" (Relais-Châteaux) o nelle camere sopra il club house.

Garlenda was built in the hills overlooking the resorts of Albenga and Alassio, and is short enough to avoid scaring off the average golfer. John Harris designed the lay-out with taste and good landscaping sense on either side of the river Lerrone, which crosses the 13th hole, a long par 3. The original course has been altered somewhat and is now a par 72. Trees are a threat on many holes and sometimes invite the player to work the ball both ways in order to get as close as possible to the greens, which are often small but designed without too many difficulties. Fun to play with the family and friends, even of very different abilities, Garlenda does not claim to be a great championship course but offers a fine opportunity to play and even stay in this part of Italy, courtesy of the "La Meridiana" (Relais-Châteaux hotel) and rooms belonging to the club.

Golf Club Garlenda — 1965

Piazzetta Galleani - Via del Golf 7
I - 17033 GARLENDA (SV)

Office	Segreteria	(39) 0182 580 012
Pro shop	Pro shop	(39) 0182 582 573
Fax	Fax	(39) 0182 580 561
Web	www.garlendagolf.it	
Situation	Località	Genova, 75 km

Albenga (pop. 22 688), 8 km

Annual closure Chiusura annuale — no

Weekly closure Chiusura settimanale — wednesday
(01/09 → 30/06)

Fees main season Tariffe alta stagione — 18 holes

	Week days Settimana	We/Bank holidays Feriale/Festivo
Individual Individuale	€ 55	€ 75
Couple Coppia	€ 110	€ 150

Caddie Caddie yes — **Electric Trolley** Carello elettrico yes

Buggy Car yes — **Clubs** Bastoni yes

Credit cards Carte di credito
VISA - DC - CartaSì

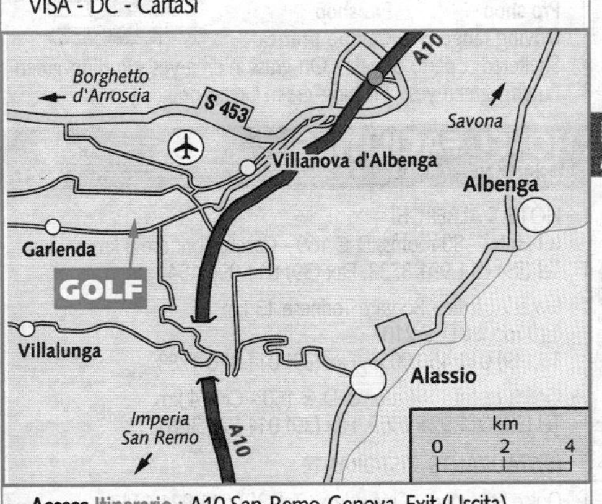

Access Itinerario : A10 San-Remo-Genova. Exit (Uscita) Albenga. Turn right → Albenga then right at turnabout under the motorway to Villanova d'Albenga and Garlenda.

Map 1 on page 922 Carta 1 Pagina 922

GOLF COURSE — PERCORSO — 14/20

Site	Paesaggio	
Maintenance	Manutenzione	
Architect	Architetto	John Harris
Type	Tipologia	country
Relief	Relievo terreno	
Water in play	Acqua in gioco	
Exp. to wind	Esposto al vento	
Trees in play	Alberi in gioco	

Scorecard Carta-score	Chp. Camp.	Mens Uomini	Ladies Donne
Length Lunghezza	6095	5960	5240
Par	72	72	72
Slope system	134	133	130

Advised golfing ability Livello di gioco consigliato — 0 12 24 36

Hcp required Handicap richiesto 34

CLUB HOUSE & AMENITIES — CLUB HOUSE E SERVIZI — 7/10

Pro shop Pro shop

Driving range Campo pratica

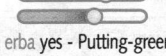

Sheltered coperto 8 mats - On grass in erba yes - Putting-green Putting-green yes - Pitching-green Green-pratica yes

HOTEL FACILITIES — ALBERGHI — 8/10

HOTELS ALBERGHI

La Meridiana - 28 rooms, D € 320 - Garlenda 5 km
Tel (39) 0182 580 271, Fax (39) 0182 580 150

Hermitage - 11 rooms, D € 125 - Garlenda 1 km
Tel (39) 0182 582 976, Fax (39) 0182 582 975

Grand Hotel Diana - 57 rooms, D € 220 - Alassio 10 km
Tel (39) 0182 642 701, Fax (39) 0182 640 304

Club House - 8 rooms, D € 108 - on site
Tel (39) 0182 583 813, Fax (39) 0182 585 789

RESTAURANTS RISTORANTE

Palma - Alassio 10 km - Tel (39) 0182 640 314
Il Rosmarino - Garlenda 5 km - Tel (39) 0182 580 271
Gin - Castelbianco 15 km - Tel (39) 0182 770 01

I Roveri

17 | 7 | 7

Questa antica riserva di caccia era il luogo ideale per la costruzione di un ambizioso complesso golfistico alle porte di Torino dove gli alberi maestosi sembravano fatti apposta per isolare le buche una dall'altra e creare una barriera naturale alle ambizioni dei giocatori poco precisi. Qui ci sono 27 buche ma il terzo percorso è decisamente sottotono rispetto alle 18 buche da campionato disegnate da Trent Jones e quindi sono utili soprattutto ai principianti. Nel percorso ufficiale, a parte la lunghezza , si noterà il piazzamento molto strategico degli ostacoli d'acqua, nonchè la posizione e il disegno molto elaborato dei bunkers. Qui bisogna saper giocare tutti i colpi ma soprattutto prendere i greens di volo perché è molto difficile raggiungerli facendo rotolare la palla. Una volta arrivati, le numerosissime pendenze possono dare notevoli problemi di putting. I Roveri è senza dubbio uno dei più bei percorsi d'Italia ed è sempre tenuto in condizioni eccellenti.

This former hunting estate was the ideal setting for building an ambitious golfing resort close to Turin. The age-old trees both demarcate and isolate the holes and form a natural barrier to the ambitions of wayward hitters. There are 27 holes here, although the par-3 course is a notch below the other two 9-hole layouts, probably to help the club's members who are just starting out. On the "championship" 18 hole course (designed by Trent Jones), yardage aside, you will notice the very strategic deployment of water and the very carefully plotted position and design of bunkers. You have to know how to hit it every way here, especially those US-style target golf shots, since you don't get much chance to roll the ball onto very well defended greens. Once there, the putting surfaces are nicely contoured and can pose a number of problems. I Roveri is definitely one of the very best courses in Italy and maintained in superb condition.

I Roveri Golf Club — 1971

Rotta Cerbiatta 24
I - 10070 FIANO TORINESE (TO)

Office Segreteria (39) 011 923 5719
Pro shop Pro shop (39) 011 924 1863
Fax Fax (39) 011 923 5669
Web www.iroveri.com
Situation Località Torino (pop. 903 705), 16 km
Annual closure Chiusura annuale no
Weekly closure Chiusura settimanale monday

Fees main season Tariffe alta stagione	Week days Settimana	We/Bank holidays Feriale/Festivo
	18 holes	
Individual Individuale	€ 65	€ 85
Couple Coppia	€ 130	€ 170

Caddie Caddie yes — **Electric Trolley** Carello elettrico yes
Buggy Car yes — **Clubs** Bastoni yes
Credit cards Carte di credito no

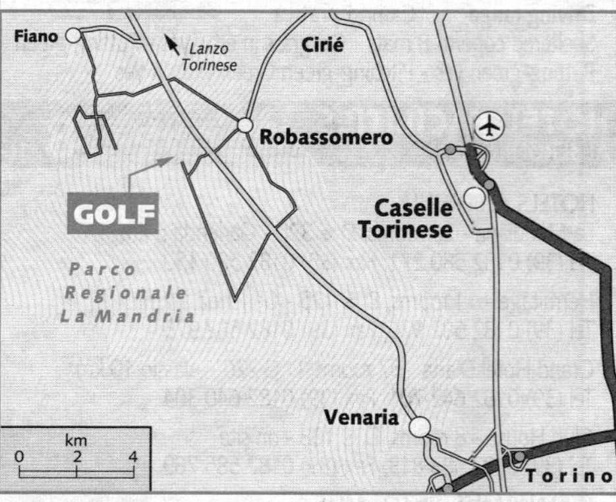

Access Itinerario : Milano to Torino, A4 - A45 Exit (Uscita) Venaria. → Lanzo. Golf to the left.
Map 1 on page 922 Carta 1 Pagina 922

GOLF COURSE — PERCORSO — 17/20

Site Paesaggio
Maintenance Manutenzione
Architect Architetto Robert Trent Jones
Type Tipologia forest, residential
Relief Relievo terreno
Water in play Acqua in gioco
Exp. to wind Esposto al vento
Trees in play Alberi in gioco

Scorecard Carta-score	Chp. Camp.	Mens Uomini	Ladies Donne
Length Lunghezza	6566	6218	5471
Par	72	72	72
Slope system	139	129	133

Advised golfing ability Livello di gioco consigliato 0 12 24 36
Hcp required Handicap richiesto 34

CLUB HOUSE & AMENITIES — CLUB HOUSE E SERVIZI — 7/10

Pro shop Pro shop
Driving range Campo pratica
Sheltered coperto 6 mats - On grass in erba yes - Putting-green Putting-green yes - Pitching-green Green-pratica yes

HOTEL FACILITIES — ALBERGHI — 7/10

HOTELS ALBERGHI
Jet Hotel - 80 rooms, D € 160 - Caselle Torinese 8 km
Tel (39) 011 991 3733, Fax (39) 011 996 1544

Hotel Atlantic - Borgaro Torinese 13 km
110 rooms, D € 210
Tel (39) 011 450 0055, Fax (39) 011 470 1783

Gotha Hotel - 44 rooms, D € 160 - Ciriè 4 km
Tel (39) 011 921 2059, Fax (39) 011 920 3661

RESTAURANTS RISTORANTE
Dolce Stil Novo - Ciriè 7 km - Tel (39) 011 921 1110
Club House restaurant - on site
Tel (39) 011 923 5494
Antica Zecca - Caselle Torinese 8 km - Tel (39) 011 996 1403

Is Arenas

17 | **3** | **6**

Anche se il club-house e le strutture sono ancora provvisori, il percorso merita sicuramente una visita, come anche tutto questo tratto di costa occidentale che conserva tracce dell'epoca preistorica. A parte Oristano, dalla quale il golf è molto vicino, si può dire che non sia veramente distante da nessuna delle altre grandi città, ma da queste parti, come in Corsica, le distanze si misurano con il tempo piuttosto che con la distanza! I promotori di Is Arenas hanno scelto un terreno non particolarmente mosso dove la costa si alterna tra dune sabbiose, pineta e macchia mediterranea. Gli ostacoli d'acqua sono parecchi e pericolosi ed oltre ad essere un elemento fondamentale del gioco offrono una gradevole sensazione di freschezza; l'intenso profumo e il miscuglio di colori della vegetazione sono una piacevolezza in più da aggiungere a quella del gioco. Questo percorso maestoso che porta la firma di von Hagge, Baril e Smelek esige intelligenza nella strategia di gioco, esperienza nel vento (e qui ce n'è sovente) e qualche finezza; in poche parole è richiesto di giocare veramente a golf!

The club-house and facilities are temporary but the course is well worth a visit, as is the whole of this west coast, which still bears the signs of invasions dating from prehistoric times. From nearby Oristano, you are never far from anywhere, but as in Corsica, a journey here is measured in hours not in miles. The promoters of Is Arenas have chosen a flattish location, whose seaside features are illustrated by a few sand-dunes alternating with forest and scrub-land. The many and dangerous water hazards are naturally a part of the course but also provide a refreshing touch, at least from a visual angle. Added to the scents and colours of the flowers and plant-life, they make your round of golf all the more enjoyable. This is a majestic and challenging layout cleverly designed by von Hagge. It requires some experience of playing in the wind, some down-to-earth course management with regards to the state of your own game and a touch of finesse. This course simply asks you to "play golf".

Is Arenas Golf & Country Club — 2000

Loc. Pineta Is Arenas
I - 09070 NARBOLIA (OR)

Office	Segreteria	(39) 0783 520 36
Pro shop	Pro shop	(39) 0783 520 36
Fax	Fax	(39) 0783 522 35
Web	www.isarenas.it	
Situation	Località Oristano (pop. 33 007), 18 km	
Annual closure	Chiusura annuale	no
Weekly closure	Chiusura settimanale	

Fees main season Tariffe alta stagione	18 holes	
	Week days Settimana	We/Bank holidays Feriale/Festivo
Individual Individuale	€ 70	€ 70
Couple Coppia	€ 140	€ 140

Lower GF in low season

Caddie Caddie no — **Electric Trolley** Carello elettrico no

Buggy Car yes — **Clubs** Bastoni yes

Credit cards Carte di credito
VISA - Eurocard - MasterCard - AMEX - DC - JCB

Access Itinerario : Cagliari ss 131 → Sassari. 104 km → Tramatza. San Vero Milis ss 292 → Cuglieri. Km 113,400 turn left on a small road → "Centro Operativo Is Arenas". Follow signs to golf.

Map 4 on page 929 Carta 4 Pagina 929

GOLF COURSE — PERCORSO — 17/20

Site	Paesaggio	
Maintenance	Manutenzione	
Architect	Architetto	Robert von Hagge
Type	Tipologia	seaside course
Relief	Relievo terreno	
Water in play	Acqua in gioco	
Exp. to wind	Esposto al vento	
Trees in play	Alberi in gioco	

Scorecard Carta-score	Chp. Camp.	Mens Uomini	Ladies Donne
Length Lunghezza	6327	5947	4889
Par	72	72	72
Slope system	140	136	132

Advised golfing ability Livello di gioco consigliato — 0 12 24 36

Hcp required Handicap richiesto 34

CLUB HOUSE & AMENITIES — CLUB HOUSE E SERVIZI — 3/10

Pro shop Pro shop
Driving range Campo pratica
Sheltered coperto 6 mats - On grass in erba yes - Putting-green Putting-green yes - Pitching-green Green-pratica yes

HOTEL FACILITIES — ALBERGHI — 6/10

HOTELS ALBERGHI

Mistral 2 - 132 rooms, D € 95 - Oristano 18 km
Tel (39) 0783 210 389, Fax (39) 0783 211 000

Sa Mola - 18 rooms, D € 70 - Bonárcado 18 km
Tel (39) 0783 56 58

Is Arenas Hotel - 8 rooms, ask for details - on site
Tel (39) 0783 520 36, Fax (39) 0783 522 35

RESTAURANTS RISTORANTE

Il Faro - Oristano 18 km - Tel (39) 0783 70 002
Leopardi - Cabras 15 km - Tel (39) 0783 290 807
Da Giovanni - Torre Grande 10 km - Tel (39) 0783 22 051
Cocco e Dessì - Oristano 18 km - Tel (39) 0783 300 720
Sa Funtà - Cabras 10 km - Tel (39) 0783 290 685

Is Molas

E' uno degli eccellenti percorsi che offre la Sardegna sede di quattro edizioni dell'Open d'Italia e si trova a soli 20 minuti di automobile da Cagliari capoluogo dell'isola. Anche se non si trova esattamente in riva al mare, ne subisce nettamente l'influenza: ancor più delle difficoltà del tracciato, il vento è il fattore decisivo del gioco. Il percorso è decisamente lungo, ma di solito è abbastanza duro e quindi la palla rotola molto ma rende più pericolosi gli ostacoli d'acqua. Disegnato dai britannici Cotton e Pennink, il percorso è stato costruito con la supervisione di Piero Mancinelli uno dei più grandi architetti italiani. Ben equilibrato nel tracciato, Is Molas si è ben integrato con l'aspetto originale del terreno ed ha conservato un aspetto naturale, tra il mare e le colline boschive. Spettacolare e originale, è un campo sia bello da vedere che appassionante per giocarci e per chi non gioca a golf c'è un mare incomparabile a due passi. A questo si aggiunge un nuovo percorso di 9 buche che diventeranno presto 18 e che renderanno questa destinazione sempre più attraente.

Although not exactly beside the sea, this course clearly comes under its influence and the wind is a key factor when playing here, just as much as the difficulties of the layout and the hazards. The course's very respectable length also has to be considered, even though the fairways often roll a lot and make the water hazards more dangerous in the process. Designed by British designers Cotton and Pennink, the course was actually built under the supervision of the late Piero Mancinelli, one of the great Italian course architects of our age. A well-balanced layout, Is Molas has successfully hugged the contours of the terrain and retained its very natural appearance between the sea and tree-covered hills. Spectacular and original, the course is at once pleasant to look at and exciting to play. For non-golfers, there is all the fun of the seaside just next door. Nine holes of a planned second course are now open, making this an even more attractive site for golfing.

Circolo Golf Is Molas — 1975

Loc. Is Molas
I - SANTA MARGHERITA DI PULA (CA)

Office	Segreteria	(39) 070 924 1013
Pro shop	Pro shop	(39) 070 924 1070
Fax	Fax	(39) 070 924 2121
Web		www.ismolas.it
Situation	Località	Cagliari (pop. 165 926), 35 km
Annual closure	Chiusura annuale	no
Weekly closure	Chiusura settimanale	no
Fees main season	Tariffe alta stagione	18 holes

	Week days / Settimana	We/Bank holidays / Feriale/Festivo
Individual Individuale	€ 75	€ 85
Couple Coppia	€ 150	€ 170

Caddie Caddie yes — **Electric Trolley** Carello elettrico no
Buggy Car yes — **Clubs** Bastoni yes
Credit cards Carte di credito
VISA - Eurocard - MasterCard - AMEX - DC - CartSi
Access Itinerario : Cagliari, S195 south to Pula.

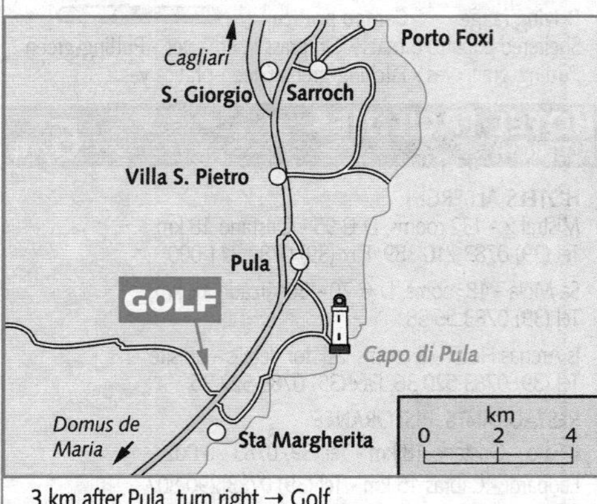

3 km after Pula, turn right → Golf
Map 4 on page 929 Carta 4 Pagina 929

GOLF COURSE — PERCORSO — 17/20

Site	Paesaggio	
Maintenance	Manutenzione	
Architect	Architetto	Cotton, Pennink Piero Mancinelli
Type	Tipologia	country
Relief	Relievo terreno	
Water in play	Acqua in gioco	
Exp. to wind	Esposto al vento	
Trees in play	Alberi in gioco	

Scorecard Carta-score	Chp. Camp.	Mens Uomini	Ladies Donne
Length Lunghezza	6383	6197	5395
Par	72	72	72
Slope system	133	130	131

Advised golfing ability 0 12 24 36
Livello di gioco consigliato
Hcp required Handicap richiesto 34

CLUB HOUSE & AMENITIES — CLUB HOUSE E SERVIZI — 7/10

Pro shop Pro shop
Driving range Campo pratica
Sheltered coperto 5 mats - On grass in erba yes - Putting-green Putting-green yes - Pitching-green Green-pratica yes

HOTEL FACILITIES — ALBERGHI — 8/10

HOTELS ALBERGHI
Is Molas Golf Hotel - 84 rooms, D € 230 (w. dinner) - on site
Tel (39) 070 924 1006, Fax (39) 070 924 1002

Baia di Nora - 121 rooms, D € 280 - Pula 4 km
Tel (39) 070 924 5551, Fax (39) 070 924 5600

Nora Club Hotel - 25 rooms, D € 155 - Pula 4 km
Tel (39) 070 924 421, Fax (39) 070 924 422 57

RESTAURANTS RISTORANTE
Su Gunventeddu - Nora-Pula 3 km - Tel (39) 070 920 9092
Urru - S. Margherita di Pula 5 km - Tel (39) 070 921 491
Sa Cardiga e Su Schironi - Capoterra 4 km
Tel (39) 070 71 652

Le Pavoniere

14 | 8 | 8

Dopo aver visitato bene Firenze è ora di girare verso ovest. Scoprire Montecatini Terme, una piacevole stazione termale ideale per rimettersi in forma dopo le abbuffate di bistecca alla fiorentina o di troppo Chianti e sopratutto Prato che ha sempre vissuto all'ombra di Firenze, ma alla quale non mancano certo le qualità. In particolare meritano una visita il Duomo, il Palazzo Pretorio o la stupefacente fortezza del Castello dell' Imperatore. E perchè no, ad una decina di chilometri, Le Pavoniere, aperto nel 1996 e disegnato da Arnold Palmer come il Castello di Tolcinasco in Lombardia. Si ritrova qui l'ispirazione sempre molto strategica del campione americano, dove gli ostacoli sono messi in gioco con grande intelligenza e con una buona conoscenza delle possibilità dei giocatori di ogni livello, anche se i più inesperti rischiano di soffrire un po'. Anche se piatto, questo percorso nasconde qualche sottigliezza che consente di non annoiarsi mai e i greens sono abbastanza grandi da offrire tante posizioni di bandiere diverse.

After a good look at Florence, it is time to head west of the city and discover Montecatini Terme, a pretty spa resort for treating people suffering from too much Bistecca alla Fiorentina or Chianti, and particularly Prato, for many a year overshadowed by Florence but nonetheless a town of many attractions. Visit the Duomo, the Palazzo Pretorio or the amazing fortress of Castello dell'Imperatore. Or again, a few miles further on, play Le Pavoniere, opened in 1986 and designed by Arnold Palmer, as was Castello di Tolcinasco in Lombardy. You can feel Arnie's highly strategic inspiration, where hazards are very cleverly brought into play and his excellent knowledge of players of differing abilities. All the same, the less experienced players might suffer a little here anyway. Although rather flat, the course is subtle enough to be played and enjoyed often, and the greens big enough to offer any number of different pin positions.

Golf Club Le Pavoniere — 1986

Via della Fattoria 6/29, Loc. Tavola
I - 50040 PRATO

Office	Segreteria	(39) 0574 620 855
Pro shop	Pro shop	(39) 0574 620 855
Fax	Fax	(39) 0574 624 558
Web	www.golfclublepavoniere.com	
Situation	Località	Firenze, 20 km
Annual closure	Chiusura annuale	no
Weekly closure	Chiusura settimanale	monday

01/10 → 31/03

Fees main season Tariffe alta stagione		18 holes
	Week days Settimana	**We/Bank holidays** Feriale/Festivo
Individual Individuale	€ 60	€ 80
Couple Coppia	€ 120	€ 160

Caddie Caddie no **Electric Trolley** Carello elettrico no

Buggy Car yes **Clubs** Bastoni yes

Credit cards Carte di credito
VISA - Eurocard - MasterCard - AMEX - DC - CartaSì

Access Itinerario : A11 Exit (Uscita) Prato Ovest. Take right → Poggio a Caiano. Right → Tavola. After four traffic lights, don't turn left, take the dead end way (senza uscita)

Map 3 on page 926 Carta 3 Pagina 926

GOLF COURSE — PERCORSO — 14/20

Site	Paesaggio	
Maintenance	Manutenzione	
Architect	Architetto	Arnold Palmer
Type	Tipologia	parkland, open country
Relief	Relievo terreno	
Water in play	Acqua in gioco	
Exp. to wind	Esposto al vento	
Trees in play	Alberi in gioco	

Scorecard Carta-score	**Chp.** Camp.	**Mens** Uomini	**Ladies** Donne
Length Lunghezza	6465	6137	5323
Par	72	72	72
Slope system	138	137	132

Advised golfing ability 0 12 24 36
Livello di gioco consigliato

Hcp required Handicap richiesto 34

CLUB HOUSE & AMENITIES — CLUB HOUSE E SERVIZI — 8/10

Pro shop Pro shop
Driving range Campo pratica

Sheltered coperto 12 mats - On grass in erba yes - Putting-green Putting-green yes - Pitching-green Green-pratica yes

HOTEL FACILITIES — ALBERGHI — 8/10

HOTELS ALBERGHI

Hermitage - 61 rooms, D € 104 - Poggio a Caiano 6 km
Tel (39) 055 877 040, Fax (39) 055 879 7057

Paggeria Medicea - 37 rooms, D € 150 - Artimino 10 km
Tel (39) 055 875 141, Fax (39) 055 875 1470

San Marco - 40 rooms, D € 95 - Prato 6 km
Tel (39) 0574 213 21, Fax (39) 0574 223 78

Giardino - 28 rooms, D € 134 - Prato 6 km
Tel (39) 0574 606 588, Fax (39) 0574 606 591

RESTAURANTS RISTORANTE

Il Piraña - Prato 6 km - Tel (39) 0574 25 746
Da Delfina - Artimino 7 km - Tel (39) 055 871 8074
Biagio Pignatta - Artimino 7 km - Tel (39) 055 875 1406

Le Querce

17 | 8 | 7

Il nome è una garanzia... gli alberi sul percorso sono quasi tutte bellissime querce! Inaugurato nel 1990 è composto dal Centro Tecnico Nazionale della Federazione Italiana Golf ma anche da un club privato. Le sue ottime qualità tecniche sono state messe in evidenza nell'edizione 1991 della World Cup, ma anche i giocatori meno esperti si potranno divertire a meno che non decidano di giocare dalle partenze arretrate! Perchè altrimenti è obbligatorio possedere sia potenza che precisione. Comunque è un campo molto onesto e la strategia di gioco in rapporto ai pericoli e agli ostacoli è ben evidente. Gli avvallamenti obbligano anche a pensare bene prima di scegliere un bastone, perchè i greens sono molto grandi, ben difesi e con parecchie pendenze: il putting non è mai facile se si è lontani dalla buca. Vi segnaliamo infine delle sequenze che possono decidere o meno la buona riuscita del vostro score, dalla 4 alla 6 e dalla 13 alla 15. Ben due "Amen Corner"... ma d'altronde siamo a due passi dalla Città Santa!

Le Querce is a course lined with oak-trees (querce, in Italian), which was opened in 1990 as a national golf centre for the Italian Golf Federation but also as a private club. The hosting of the World Cup here in 1991 highlighted the course's many qualities, but the not-so-good players can handle this okay as long as they keep well away from the back tees. Playing from the tips is a very demanding experience for both power and precision. This is a very open course, though, and game strategy with respect to the dangers and hazards is clear enough. The sloping terrain calls for thoughtful club selection, because while the greens are on the large side, they are well guarded and steeply contoured; putting here is never easy if you are too far from the hole. To finish, make a note of two stretches which can make or break your card: 4 through 6 and 13 through 15... two "Amen Corners" and a natural state of affairs being so close to the Holy City.

Golf Club Le Querce — 1990

Via Cassia Km 44,500
I - 01015 SUTRI (VT)

Office	Segreteria	(39) 0761 600 789
Pro shop	Pro shop	(39) 0761 600 789
Fax	Fax	(39) 0761 600 142
Web	www.golflequerce.it	
Situation	Località	Roma, 51 km

Viterbo (pop. 60 212), 31 km

Annual closure	Chiusura annuale	no
Weekly closure	Chiusura settimanale	Wednesday
Fees main season	Tariffe alta stagione	18 holes

	Week days Settimana	We/Bank holidays Feriale/Festivo
Individual Individuale	€ 50	€ 60
Couple Coppia	€ 100	€ 120

Caddie Caddie no — **Electric Trolley** Carello elettrico yes
Buggy Car yes — **Clubs** Bastoni yes
Credit cards Carte di credito
VISA - AMEX - CartaSi

Access Itinerario : Roma, Via Cassia. Before Monterosi, at the end of a long and straight road, take left → Golf.
Map 3 on page 927 Carta 3 Pagina 927

GOLF COURSE — PERCORSO — 17/20

Site	Paesaggio	
Maintenance	Manutenzione	
Architect	Architetto	Jim Fazio
Type	Tipologia	open country, hilly
Relief	Relievo terreno	
Water in play	Acqua in gioco	
Exp. to wind	Esposto al vento	
Trees in play	Alberi in gioco	

Scorecard Carta-score	Chp. Camp.	Mens Uomini	Ladies Donne
Length Lunghezza	6462	6052	5305
Par	72	72	72
Slope system	147	142	135

Advised golfing ability Livello di gioco consigliato — 0 12 24 36
Hcp required Handicap richiesto 34

CLUB HOUSE & AMENITIES — CLUB HOUSE E SERVIZI — 8/10

Pro shop Pro shop
Driving range Campo pratica
Sheltered coperto 10 mats - On grass in erba yes - Putting-green Putting-green yes - Pitching-green Green-pratica yes

HOTEL FACILITIES — ALBERGHI — 7/10

HOTELS ALBERGHI

Il Borgo di Sutri - 26 rooms, D € 130 - Sutri 2 km
Tel (39) 0761 608 690, Fax (39) 0761 608 308

Golf Club - 24 rooms, D € 65 - on site
Tel (39) 0761 608 979, Fax (39) 0761 600 142

Country Relais I Due Laghi - Anguillara Sabazia 20 km
36 rooms, D € 150
Tel (39) 0699 607 059, Fax (39) 0699 607 068

RESTAURANTS RISTORANTE

Il Borgo di Sutri - Sutri 4 km - Tel (39) 0761 608 690
Zi Zitta - Capranica 7 km - Tel (39) 0761 669 140
Golf restaurant - Le Querce 5 km - Tel (39) 0761 600 789
Casa Tuscia - Nepi 5 km - Tel (39) 0761 555 070

Le Robinie

15 | 8 | 8

A metà strada tra Milano, Varese e il Lago Maggiore, Le Robinie è un recente percorso che porta la firma di Jack Nicklaus. Esistono architetti di meno fascino e forse ancora più creativi ma l'Orso d'Oro continua ad essere un marchio di grande qualità anche se si può obiettare che tutti i suoi percorsi seguano un po' lo stesso modello secondo l'ingegnere che ha effettivamente seguito i lavori. Realizzato su un terreno molto piatto e senza vegetazione importante, è stata di grande importanza l'esperienza degli architetti americani e i lavori di movimentazione sono stati veramente di prim'ordine con numerosi ostacoli d'acqua creati per recuperare terra e riportarla in modo da ottenere tanti anfiteatri che dominano le buche. Molto lavoro è stato dedicato al disegno di bunkers e greens e il risultato grafico è assolutamente ottimo. Dalle partenze di campionato questo percorso è consigliato ai giocatori più esperti ma dai tees normali potrete trascorrere una piacevole giornata.

Mid-way between Milan, Varese and the unavoidable Lake Maggiore, Le Robinie is one of Italy's more recent courses and one of the most prestigious too, courtesy of its designer Jack Nicklaus. There are other, less fashionable and perhaps more creative architects, but the Golden Bear label is a quality guarantee even if all his courses do tend to follow more or less the same model, depending on the engineer. On terrain as flat as this, American experience is useful indeed and the excavation work made to contour the course was quite remarkable, including many water hazards in order to recover the earth which has been arranged to form amphitheatres around the holes. A lot of thought also went into the shapes of bunkers and greens, giving a very graphic look to the whole layout. From the back tees, this very open and forthright course is for experienced players only. Further forward and you are in for a great day's golfing.

Golf Club Le Robinie — 1992

Via per Busto Arsizio 9
I - 21058 SOLBIATE OLONA (VA)

Office Segreteria (39) 0331 329 260
Pro shop Pro shop (39) 0331 329 272
Fax Fax (39) 0331 329 266
Web www.lerobinie.com
Situation Località Milano, 35 km
Varese (pop. 83 798), 27 km

Annual closure Chiusura annuale — no
Weekly closure Chiusura settimanale — tuesday

Fees main season Tariffe alta stagione	18 holes	
	Week days Settimana	**We/Bank holidays** Feriale/Festivo
Individual Individuale	€ 46	€ 67
Couple Coppia	€ 92	€ 134

Caddie Caddie no **Electric Trolley** Carello elettrico no

Buggy Car yes **Clubs** Bastoni yes

Credit cards Carte di credito
VISA - Eurocard - MasterCard - AMEX - DC - CartaSì

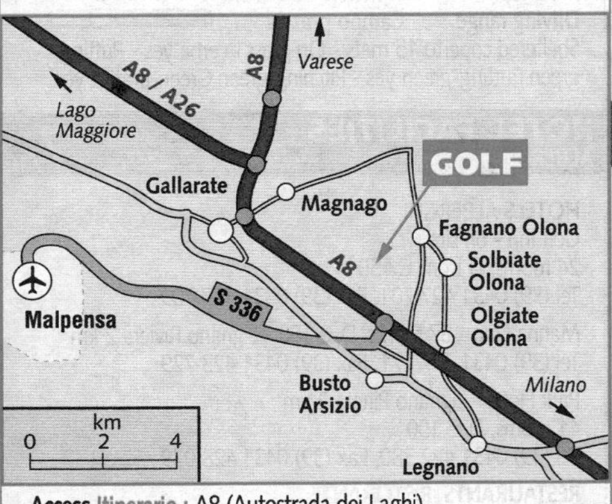

Access Itinerario : A8 (Autostrada dei Laghi).
Exit (Uscita) Busto Arsizio. Right then left, golf 2 km
Map 1 on page 923 Carta 1 Pagina 923

GOLF COURSE — PERCORSO — 15/20

Site Paesaggio
Maintenance Manutenzione
Architect Architetto — Jack Nicklaus
Type Tipologia — open country
Relief Relievo terreno
Water in play Acqua in gioco
Exp. to wind Esposto al vento
Trees in play Alberi in gioco

Scorecard Carta-score	**Chp.** Camp.	**Mens** Uomini	**Ladies** Donne
Length Lunghezza	6520	6168	5378
Par	72	72	72
Slope system	0	125	123

Advised golfing ability Livello di gioco consigliato — 0 12 24 36
Hcp required Handicap richiesto 34

CLUB HOUSE & AMENITIES — CLUB HOUSE E SERVIZI — 8/10

Pro shop Pro shop
Driving range Campo pratica
Sheltered coperto 19 mats - On grass in erba yes - Putting-green Putting-green yes - Pitching-green Green-pratica yes

HOTEL FACILITIES — ALBERGHI — 8/10

HOTELS ALBERGHI
Golf Hotel - 114 rooms, D from € 150 - on site
Tel (39) 0331 392 260, Fax (39) 0331 392 266

Pineta - 58 rooms, D € 150 - Busto Arsizio 4 km
Tel (39) 0331 381 220, Fax (39) 0331 381 220

Astoria - 51 rooms, D € 144 - Gallarate 5 km
Tel (39) 0331 791 043, Fax (39) 0331 772 671

RESTAURANTS RISTORANTE
Ma.Ri.Na - Olgiate Olona 2 km - Tel (39) 0331 640 463
Tradate - Tradate 8 km - Tel (39) 0331 841 401
Antica Osteria i 5 Campanili - Busto Arsizio 4 km
Tel (39) 0331 630 493
Piazzetta - Ferno 6 km - Tel (39) 0331 241 536

Lignano

14	7	7

Lignano è una stazione balneare di primaria importanza in Friuli, sulle rive dell'Adriatico ed è più o meno a metà strada tra Venezia e Trieste. La spiaggia lunga otto chilometri, è l'ideale per trascorrere piacevoli soggiorni con la famiglia nei paesi di Lignano Sabbiadoro o di Lignano Pineta. Il golfista potrà quindi dedicarsi al suo gioco preferito senza rimorsi quando i bambini sono al mare. Il percorso, disegnato da Marco Croze è particolarmente piatto, con pochi alberi ed è una combinazione tra lo stile "links" con un disegno ben studiato di fairways e bunkers e lo stile "Florida" con gli ostacoli d'acqua che entrano in gioco. Abbastanza difficile dalle partenze arretrate quando soffia vento, è più facile giocarsi l'handicap se si mette da parte il proprio orgoglio e ci si accontenta di partire davanti. Bisogna giocare due o tre volte per apprezzare le sottigliezze del percorso, ma non ci si annoierà restando qualche giorno.

Lignano is one of the topmost seaside resorts in Friuli on the shores of the Adriatic, about half-way between Venice and Trieste. The 5-mile long beach is perfect for very pleasant family holidays in the small towns of Lignano Sabbiadoro or Lignano Pineta. You guessed it, golfers can go about their favourite pastime with a clear conscience when the children are on the beach. This course, designed by Marco Croze, is virtually flat with few trees. It combines a sort of links style, where terrain has been cleverly contoured and given some large bunkers, with some very Floridian features when the water hazards come into play. A rather tough proposition from the back tees when the wind blows, it is easier to play to your handicap when swallowing your pride and not being too ambitious (i.e. opt for the front tees). You need two or three rounds to appreciate the finer points of this layout but you won't get bored playing here if you are around for several days.

Golf Club Lignano — 1991

Via della Bonifica
I - 33054 LIGNANO SABBIADORO (UD)

Office	Segreteria	(39) 0431 428 025
Pro shop	Pro shop	(39) 0431 423 274
Fax	Fax	(39) 0431 423 230
Web	www.golflignano.it	
Situation	Località	Venezia, 105 km

Portegruaro, 32 km

Annual closure	Chiusura annuale	no
Weekly closure	Chiusura settimanale	no

Fees main season Tariffe alta stagione — 18 holes

	Week days / Settimana	We/Bank holidays / Feriale/Festivo
Individual Individuale	€ 56	€ 66
Couple Coppia	€ 112	€ 132

Caddie Caddie no — **Electric Trolley** Carello elettrico no

Buggy Car yes — **Clubs** Bastoni yes

Credit cards Carte di credito
VISA - Eurocard - MasterCard - AMEX - DC - CartaSi

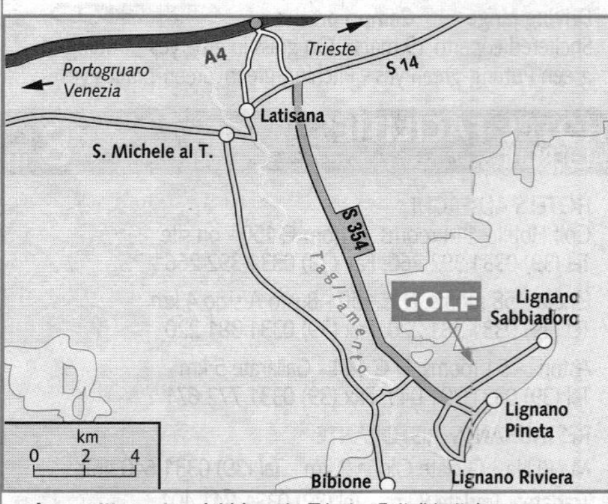

Access Itinerario : A4 Venezia-Trieste, Exit (Uscita) Latisana, → Lignano. 24 km, take right → Golf.

Map 2 on page 924 Carta 2 Pagina 924

GOLF COURSE — PERCORSO — 14/20

Site	Paesaggio	
Maintenance	Manutenzione	
Architect	Architetto	Marco Croze
Type	Tipologia	links
Relief	Relievo terreno	
Water in play	Acqua in gioco	
Exp. to wind	Esposto al vento	
Trees in play	Alberi in gioco	

Scorecard / Carta-score	Chp. / Camp.	Mens / Uomini	Ladies / Donne
Length Lunghezza	6301	6069	5328
Par	72	72	72
Slope system	133	129	131

Advised golfing ability 0 12 24 36
Livello di gioco consigliato
Hcp required Handicap richiesto 34

CLUB HOUSE & AMENITIES — CLUB HOUSE E SERVIZI — 7/10

Pro shop	Pro shop
Driving range	Campo pratica

Sheltered coperto 15 mats - On grass in erba yes - Putting-green Putting-green yes - Pitching-green Green-pratica yes

HOTEL FACILITIES — ALBERGHI — 7/10

HOTELS ALBERGHI
Golf Inn - on site
24 rooms, D from € 150
Tel (39) 0431 427 701, Fax (39) 0431 427 709

Marina Uno - 87 rooms, D € 180 - Lignano Riviera 2 km
Tel (39) 0431 427 171, Fax (39) 0431 423 729

Park Hotel - Lignano Pineta 2 km
41 rooms, D € 150
Tel (39) 0431 422 380, Fax (39) 0431 428 079

RESTAURANTS RISTORANTE
Newport - Lignano Riviera 2 km - Tel (39) 0431 427 171
Bidin - Lignano Sabbiadoro 2 km - Tel (39) 0431 719 88

Marco Simone

15	8	8

Si può scommettere che ben pochi turisti stranieri che vengono a visitare Roma hanno mai sentito parlare di Tivoli. Invece è uno dei posti più magici che si possano immaginare, soprattutto per i giardini e le fontane di Villa d'Este e per la ricchezza archeologica di Villa Adriana, antica dimora dell'imperatore Adriano. Le 27 buche del golf Marco Simone si trovano a meno di 10 chilometri in una campagna molto ondulata (è consigliato il golf cart). A ridosso di un antico castello di proprietà della stilista Laura Biagiotti, la club-house è immensa e con molti servizi. Il percorso disegnato con molta fantasia da Jim Fazio ha il merito di essere difficile dalle partenze di campionato ma è studiato intelligentemente per diventare più facile man mano che si accorciano le partenze.Gli ostacoli d'acqua così come le forme dei greens e dei bunkers gli confluiscono uno stile americano, mitigato dal paesaggio della campagna romana. Un gran bel percorso ormai maturo.

You can bet that very few foreign tourists coming to visit Rome have heard of Tivoli. Yet it is one of the most magic spots imaginable, particularly with the gardens and fountains of la Villa d'Este or the archaeological wealth of the Villa Adriana, the former mansion of Emperor Hadrian. The 27 holes that grace the Marco Simone golf course are less than 10 kilometres away, laid out over steeply rolling countryside (buggy recommended). Leaning against a former castle belonging to designer Laura Biagiotti, the club-house is huge and facilities luxurious, including tennis courts, swimming pool and health centre, but reserved for members only. The course, designed with much imagination by architect Jim Fazio, has the merit of being tough from the back tees but easier the further forward you go, which is only logical. Water hazards and the shaping of greens and bunkers create a very American feel, tempered only by the landscape of the Roman countryside. A very good course, already mature.

Golf Marco Simone — 1991

Via di Marco Simone 84/88
I - 00012 GUIDONIA MONTECELLO (RM)

Office	Segreteria	(39) 0774 366 469
Pro shop	Pro shop	(39) 0774 366 593
Fax	Fax	(39) 0774 366 476
Web	www.golfmarcosimone.com	
Situation	Località	Roma 37 km

Tivoli (pop. 52 809), 9 km

Annual closure	Chiusura annuale	25/12→1/1
Weekly closure	Chiusura settimanale	tuesday
Fees main season	Tariffe alta stagione	18 holes

	Week days Settimana	We/Bank holidays Feriale/Festivo
Individual Individuale	€ 45	€ 65
Couple Coppia	€ 90	€ 130

Caddie Caddie no — **Electric Trolley** Carello elettrico no

Buggy Car yes — **Clubs** Bastoni yes

Credit cards Carte di credito
VISA - Eurocard - MasterCard - AMEX - DC - CartaSi

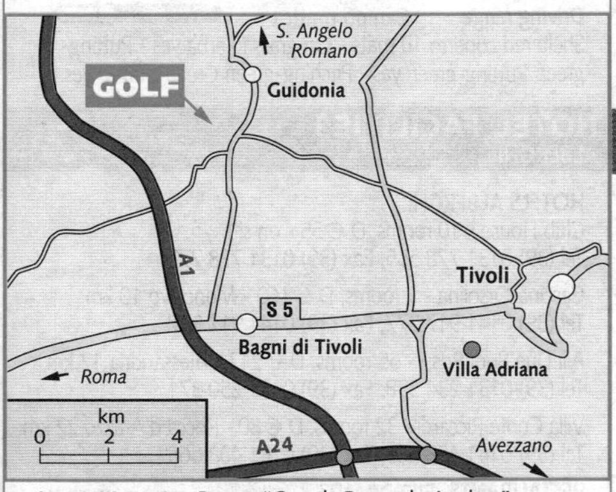

Access Itinerario : Roma, "Grande Raccordo Anulare" (Ring road), Exit (Uscita) 11, → Mentana. → Guidonia.
Map 3 on page 927 Carta 3 Pagina 927

GOLF COURSE — PERCORSO 15/20

Site	Paesaggio	
Maintenance	Manutenzione	
Architect	Architetto	Jim Fazio
Type	Tipologia	country, hilly
Relief	Relievo terreno	
Water in play	Acqua in gioco	
Exp. to wind	Esposto al vento	
Trees in play	Alberi in gioco	

Scorecard Carta-score	Chp. Camp.	Mens Uomini	Ladies Donne
Length Lunghezza	6343	6037	5320
Par	72	72	72
Slope system	140	137	134

Advised golfing ability Livello di gioco consigliato — 0 12 24 36

Hcp required Handicap richiesto 34

CLUB HOUSE & AMENITIES — CLUB HOUSE E SERVIZI 8/10

Pro shop Pro shop
Driving range Campo pratica
Sheltered coperto 10 mats - On grass in erba yes - Putting-green Putting-green yes - Pitching-green Green-pratica yes

HOTEL FACILITIES — ALBERGHI 8/10

HOTELS ALBERGHI

Grand Hotel Duca d'Este - Bagni di Tivoli 5 km
192 rooms, D € 160
Tel (39) 0774 3883, Fax (39) 0774 388 101

Torre Sant'Angelo - 35 rooms, D € 180 - Tivoli 9 km
Tel (39) 0774 332 533, Fax (39) 0774 332 533

Golf Club Marco Simone - on site
57 rooms, apartments & suites
Tel (39) 0774 366 469, Fax (39) 0774 366 476

RESTAURANTS RISTORANTE

Adriano - Villa Adriana 7 km - Tel (39) 0774 382 235
Granduca - Bagni di Tivoli 9 km - Tel (39) 0774 3883
5 Statue - Tivoli 7 km - Tel (39) 0774 335 366

Margara

13	7	7

Questo golf è situato fuori dalle rotte turistiche ma ci si può arrivare da Torino attraversando il Monferrato che merita una sosta nei suoi castelli per degustare i famosi vini piemontesi come il Barolo ed il Barbera. In questa occasione o durante un viaggio d'affari, una visita a Margara non è certo tempo perso. Si può anche soggiornare nell'immensa costruzione che ospita il club-house e dalla quale si gode la vista di tutto il percorso. Tre percorsi di 9 buche sono combinabili tra loro e sono stati disegnati dal professionista Agostino Reale e da Glauco Lolli Ghetti, proprietario della tenuta. Il percorso è abbastanza mosso e questo obbliga a scegliere attentamente i bastoni. Gli ostacoli sono quelli classici con molti bunkers e senza grandi movimenti e una curiosità alla buca 11, dove il green è interamente circondato da un fosso.

This course is located off the tourist trail, except during the period of Palio or the Wine Festival in Asti (September). But starting out from Turin, you can also take the Monferrato road with its castles and taste all the wines of Piedmont, including the famous Barolo and Barbera. On such an occasion or during a business trip a visit to Margara is time well spent. You can even stay here in the impressive club-house buildings, which overlook almost all the course. There are three combinable 9-hole courses, designed by the professional player Agostino Reale and Glauco Lolli Ghetti, son of the proprietor of this former farming estate. The course is a little hilly and so calls for careful club selection. Hazards are standard affairs with some slightly unimaginative bunkering and one curiosity at the 11th hole where the green is completely surrounded by a ditch.

Golf Club Margara — 1975

Via Tenuta Margara 25
I - 15043 FUBINE (AL)

Office Segreteria (39) 0131 778 555
Pro shop Pro shop (39) 0131 778 555
Fax Fax (39) 0131 778 772
Web www.golfmargara.it
Situation Località Asti, 29 km
Alessandria (pop. 90 289), 17 km
Annual closure Chiusura annuale 20/1→1/2
Weekly closure Chiusura settimanale monday
Fees main season Tariffe alta stagione 18 holes

	Week days Settimana	We/Bank holidays Feriale/Festivo
Individual Individuale	€ 40	€ 65
Couple Coppia	€ 80	€ 130

Caddie Caddie no — **Electric Trolley** Carello elettrico yes
Buggy Car yes — **Clubs** Bastoni yes
Credit cards Carte di credito
VISA - CartaSì

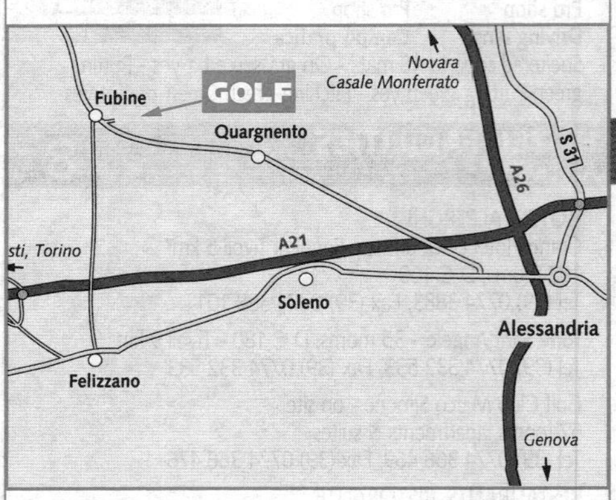

Access Itinerario : A21 Torino-Piacenza. Exit (Uscita) Felizzano. Turn left on S10. In Felizzano take left → Fubine. 3 km → golf
Map 1 on page 922 Carta 1 Pagina 922

GOLF COURSE — PERCORSO — 13/20

Site Paesaggio
Maintenance Manutenzione
Architect Architetto — Agostino Reale
Type Tipologia — open country
Relief Relievo terreno
Water in play Acqua in gioco
Exp. to wind Esposto al vento
Trees in play Alberi in gioco

Scorecard Carta-score	Chp. Camp.	Mens Uomini	Ladies Donne
Length Lunghezza	6308	6045	5319
Par	72	72	72
Slope system	–	130	128

Advised golfing ability Livello di gioco consigliato — 0 12 24 36
Hcp required Handicap richiesto 34

CLUB HOUSE & AMENITIES — CLUB HOUSE E SERVIZI — 7/10

Pro shop Pro shop
Driving range Campo pratica
Sheltered coperto 10 mats - On grass in erba yes - Putting-green Putting-green yes - Pitching-green Green-pratica yes

HOTEL FACILITIES — ALBERGHI — 7/10

HOTELS ALBERGHI
Club House - 10 rooms, D € 55 - on site
Tel (39) 0131 778 555, Fax (39) 0131 778 772

Cascina Orsolina - 9 rooms, D € 160 - Moncalvo 10 km
Tel (39) 0141 917 277, Fax (39) 0141 917 277

Alli Due Buoi Rossi - 55 rooms, D € 217 - Alessandria 17 km
Tel (39) 0131 234 598, Fax (39) 0131 250 371

Villa Conte Riccardi - 32 rooms, D € 80 - Rocca d'Arazzo 22 km
Tel (39) 0141 408 565, Fax (39) 0141 408 565

RESTAURANTS RISTORANTE
La Braja - Montemagno 10 km - Tel (39) 0141 653 925
La Fermata - Alessandria 17 km - Tel (39) 0131 251 350

Milano

16 | 9 | 8

Situato in prossimità del capoluogo lombardo nel cuore del Parco di Monza, è sicuramente uno dei circoli più prestigiosi che ama mantenere le tradizioni. Glannon e Blanford lo hanno disegnato su di un terreno piatto, dove gli alberi maestosi sono sia il mezzo per isolarsi completamente in una sorta di piacevole esclusività che un'impenetrabile barriera per evitare i principianti maldestri. I numerosi bunkers difendono molto bene i greens che sono di medie dimensioni, leggermente ondulati e solitamente ben tenuti. Giocando qui si ha la sensazione di muoversi in un parco immenso dove il silenzio viene meno soltanto nei giorni in cui si disputano le corse all'autodromo di Monza. Al suo percorso tradizionale si aggiunge un piacevole percorso di 9 buche indispensabile per soddisfare le esigenze dei numerosi soci. La club-house lussuosa con una splendida terrazza aggiungono fascino al golf Milano rendendolo una funzionale e solida struttura.

Located close to the capital of Lombardy in the Parco di Monza, this is obviously one of the most prestigious Italian clubs cultivating real golfing tradition. Gannon and Blanford laid the course out over flat terrain, where majestic trees create both a feeling of isolation and pleasant exclusivity, and a formidable line of defence for hitters who slug rather than think. The very many bunkers ably defend the average-sized greens that are slightly contoured and very well maintained. Here you get the feeling of playing in a huge park, where the silence is disturbed only on those days when the Monza race-track is in action. With good courses (27 holes in all) well suited to all standards of play, plus a huge, functional and luxurious club-house, which has replaced the former hunting lodge, the Golf Club Milano is a solid and practical golfing facility.

Golf Club Milano — 1928

Viale Mulini San Giorgio 7
I - 20052 PARCO DI MONZA (MI)

Office Segreteria (39) 039 303 081
Pro shop Pro shop (39) 039 304 561
Fax Fax (39) 039 304 427
Web www.golfclubmilano.it
Situation Località Milano, 25 km
Bergamo (pop. 117 837), 29 km
Annual closure Chiusura annuale 25/12→1/1
Weekly closure Chiusura settimanale monday

Fees main season Tariffe alta stagione		18 holes
	Week days Settimana	We/Bank holidays Feriale/Festivo
Individual Individuale	€ 60	€ 80
Couple Coppia	€ 120	€ 160

Caddie Caddie yes — **Electric Trolley** Carello elettrico no
Buggy Car yes — **Clubs** Bastoni yes
Credit cards Carte di credito
VISA - DC

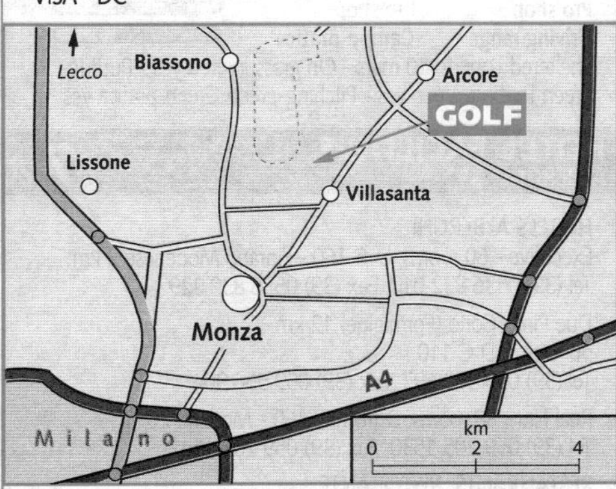

Access Itinerario : Milano A4, Tangenziale Est. Exit (Uscita) Vimercate. Take left → Villasanta. Cross road to Lecco, → Villasanta. First traffic lights, turn right → San Giorgio. → Parco di Monza, Golf
Map 1 on page 923 Carta 1 Pagina 923

GOLF COURSE — PERCORSO 16/20

Site Paesaggio
Maintenance Manutenzione
Architect Architetto Cecil R. Blandford, Peter Gannon
Type Tipologia parkland
Relief Relievo terreno
Water in play Acqua in gioco
Exp. to wind Esposto al vento
Trees in play Alberi in gioco

Scorecard Carta-score	Chp. Camp.	Mens Uomini	Ladies Donne
Length Lunghezza	6403	6239	5509
Par	72	72	72
Slope system	135	134	133

Advised golfing ability Livello di gioco consigliato 0 12 24 36
Hcp required Handicap richiesto 34

CLUB HOUSE & AMENITIES — CLUB HOUSE E SERVIZI 9/10

Pro shop Pro shop
Driving range Campo pratica
Sheltered coperto 8 mats - On grass in erba yes - Putting-green Putting-green yes - Pitching-green Green-pratica yes

HOTEL FACILITIES — ALBERGHI 8/10

HOTELS ALBERGHI
De La Ville - 62 rooms, D € 260 - Monza 2 km
Tel (39) 039 382 581, Fax (39) 039 367 647

Hotel Regency - 70 rooms, D € 160 - Lissone 2 km
Tel (39) 039 278 5329, Fax (39) 039 278 5365

Sant' Eustorgio - Arcore 4 km
45 rooms, D € 125
Tel (39) 039 601 3718, Fax (39) 039 617 531

RESTAURANTS RISTORANTE
Osteria del Pomiroeu - Seregno 6 km - Tel (39) 0362 237 973
Derby Grill - Monza 5 km - Tel (39) 039 382 581
Punt del Negar - Monza 5 km - Tel (39) 039 210 0600

Modena

13 | 7 | 7

Le scarpe, i treni e soprattutto le automobili (con la Ferrari a Maranello) hanno fatto la fama di Modena... così come il suo Duomo e la bella raccolta di quadri della Galleria Estense. Aperto nel 1987, il percorso del Modena Golf & Country Club è stato disegnato da Bernhard Langer, senza dubbio all'epoca della sua collaborazione con Buckley. Più tardi il campione tedesco si è molto evoluto perfezionandosi nel suo mestiere di architetto. Il suo disegno segue fedelmente gli aspetti del terreno poco movimentato dove gli alberi non sono un pericolo. La strategia di gioco è evidente da subito. Gli ostacoli sono costituiti maggiormente dai bunkers e dall'acqua molto presente e in particolare su due par 3 e alla 18 dove l'audacia può essere ricompensata o può distruggere un buono score. E' un percorso ideale per un circolo che ha soci di diverso livello, anche se i giocatori migliori resteranno un pò delusi e i cultori dei campi naturali lo troveranno un po' troppo artificiale. E' sicuramente destinato a migliorare nel tempo.

Footwear, rolling stock and particularly cars (Ferrari in Maranello) have forged the reputation of Modena... together with the Duomo and the fine collection of paintings at the Galleria Estense. Created in 1987, the Modena Golf & Country Club course was designed by Bernhard Langer, certainly during the period when he was working with Buckley. Since then, the German champion has covered a lot of ground and acquired maturity in his work as an architect. This design faithfully hugs the contours of rather flat terrain where trees are not a danger. Playing strategy is obvious as soon as you are on the course. Hazards are basically the bunkers and water hazards, especially on two of the par 3s and at the end, on the 18th, where daring may be rewarded or simply ruin your card. This is a real members' course where playing levels are necessarily very different and where the more skilled player might feel a little frustrated. Lovers of natural courses will find this layout a little artificial.

Modena Golf & Country Club 1987

Via Castelnuovo Rangone 4
I - 41050 COLOMBARO DI FORMIGINE (MO)

Office Segreteria (39) 059 553 482
Pro shop Pro shop (39) 059 470 029
Fax Fax (39) 059 3696
Web www.modenagolf.it
Situation Località Bologna, 40 km
Modena (pop. 176 022), 20 km

Annual closure Chiusura annuale no
Weekly closure Chiusura settimanale tuesday

Fees main season Tariffe alta stagione	18 holes
	Week days Settimana	**We/Bank holidays** Feriale/Festivo
Individual Individuale	€ 45	€ 60
Couple Coppia	€ 90	€ 120

Caddie Caddie no — **Electric Trolley** Carello elettrico yes
Buggy Car yes — **Clubs** Bastoni yes
Credit cards Carte di credito
VISA - Eurocard - MasterCard - AMEX - DC - CartaSi

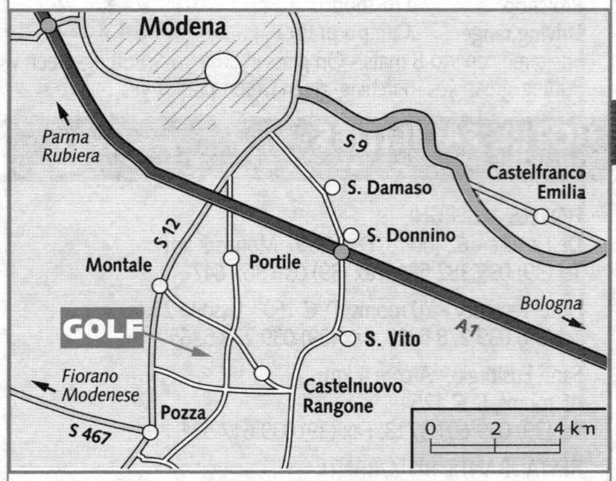

Access Itinerario : A1 (Autostrada del Sole), Exit (Uscita) Modena Sud. Go right → Modena for 5 km. A12 to the left. 12 km, Golf on the left hand side.
Map 2 on page 924 Carta 2 Pagina 924

GOLF COURSE — PERCORSO 13/20

Site Paesaggio
Maintenance Manutenzione
Architect Architetto Bernhard Langer
Type Tipologia open country
Relief Relievo terreno
Water in play Acqua in gioco
Exp. to wind Esposto al vento
Trees in play Alberi in gioco

Scorecard Carta-score	**Chp.** Camp.	**Mens** Uomini	**Ladies** Donne
Length Lunghezza	6423	6097	5350
Par	72	72	72
Slope system	131	128	127

Advised golfing ability 0 12 24 36
Livello di gioco consigliato
Hcp required Handicap richiesto 34

CLUB HOUSE & AMENITIES — CLUB HOUSE E SERVIZI 7/10

Pro shop Pro shop
Driving range Campo pratica
Sheltered coperto 10 mats - On grass in erba yes - Putting-green Putting-green yes - Pitching-green Green-pratica yes

HOTEL FACILITIES — ALBERGHI 7/10

HOTELS ALBERGHI
Executive - 60 rooms, D € 160 - Fiorano Modenese 3 km
Tel (39) 0536 832 010, Fax (39) 0536 830 229

Due Pini - Corlo (Formigine) 12 km
56 rooms, D € 110
Tel (39) 059 572 697, Fax (39) 059 556 904

Real Fini - 88 rooms, D from € 160 - Modena 20 km
Tel (39) 059 205 1530, Fax (39) 059 205 1542

RESTAURANTS RISTORANTE
Fini - Modena 20 km - Tel (39) 059 223 314
Arnaldo-Clinica Gastronomica - Rubiera 22 km
Tel (39) 059 626 124
Borso d'Este - Modena 20 km - Tel (39) 059 214 114

Montecchia

13	8	8

Questo percorso è stato aperto nel 1992 vicino alle stazioni termali di Abano Terme e Montegrotto e soprattutto a due passi dalla bella città di Padova, che per tanto tempo ha vissuto all'ombra della vicina Venezia. Gli affreschi di Mantegna e Giotto sono una visita da non mancare come la basilica di sant'Antonio dove i più religiosi potranno chiedere di non naufragare nei tanti ostacoli d'acqua disseminati sul percorso disegnato da Tom Macauley! Non ha avuto un compito facile su un terreno così piatto dove ha creato movimenti scavando e aggiungendo terra altrove. Le qualità tecniche rendono il percorso accessibile a giocatori di ogni livello anche se bisognerà giocare più volte perché resti impresso nella mente. Un altro percorso di 9 buche aggiunge maggior interesse a questo circolo molto piacevole.

This course was opened in 1992 close to the spa resorts of Abano Terme and Montegrotto Terme, and particularly within the vicinity of the fine city of Padua, which spent many a year in the shadows of neighbouring Venice. The frescoes of Mantegna and Giotto are exciting visiting. While in earlier times they used to pray to Saint Antonio de Padua for shipwrecked mariners, prayers can still be heard in Montecchia to avoid the water hazards that are very much in play on this Tom Macauley layout. Designing the course was no easy job on such flat land, but he succeeded in contouring the fairways by digging here to add over there. However, the technical qualities of the course, playable by golfers of all abilities, cannot conceal a slight problem of uniformity. This layout sticks in the mind only if you play it several times. A 9-hole layout has added to the appeal of what is a very pleasant site.

Golf della Montecchia — 1992

Via Montecchia 16
I - 35030 SELVAZZANO DENTRO (PD)

Office Segreteria (39) 049 805 5550
Pro shop Pro shop (39) 049 805 5965
Fax Fax (39) 049 805 5737
Web www.golfmontecchia.it
Situation Località Venezia, 42 km
Padova (pop. 211 391), 7 km
Annual closure Chiusura annuale 25/12→1/1
Weekly closure Chiusura settimanale
monday/tuesday, restaurant

Fees main season Tariffe alta stagione 18 holes

	Week days Settimana	We/Bank holidays Feriale/Festivo
Individual Individuale	€ 63	€ 68
Couple Coppia	€ 126	€ 136

Caddie Caddie no **Electric Trolley** Carello elettrico no
Buggy Car yes **Clubs** Bastoni yes
Credit cards Carte di credito
VISA - Eurocard - MasterCard - AMEX - DC - CartaSi

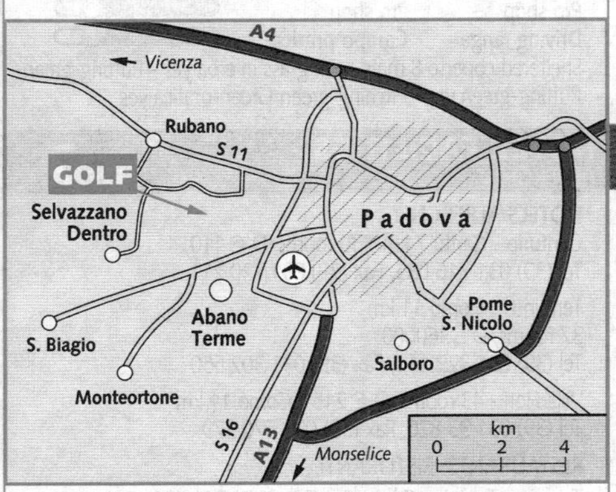

Access Itinerario : A4 Verona-Venezia. Exit (Uscita) Padova-Ovest. Take the Corso Australia, right to Tencarola, right again → Selvazzano Dentro. → Golf
Map 2 on page 924 Carta 2 Pagina 924

GOLF COURSE — PERCORSO 13/20

Site Paesaggio
Maintenance Manutenzione
Architect Architetto Tom MacAuley
Type Tipologia open country
Relief Relievo terreno
Water in play Acqua in gioco
Exp. to wind Esposto al vento
Trees in play Alberi in gioco

Scorecard Carta-score	Chp. Camp.	Mens Uomini	Ladies Donne
Length Lunghezza	6318	6078	5326
Par	72	72	72
Slope system	129	128	124

Advised golfing ability 0 12 24 36
Livello di gioco consigliato
Hcp required Handicap richiesto 34

CLUB HOUSE & AMENITIES — CLUB HOUSE E SERVIZI 8/10

Pro shop Pro shop
Driving range Campo pratica
Sheltered coperto 12 mats - On grass in erba yes - Putting-green Putting-green yes - Pitching-green Green-pratica yes

HOTEL FACILITIES — ALBERGHI 8/10

HOTELS ALBERGHI
La Piroga - 62 rooms, D € 115 - Selvazzano Dentro 3 km
Tel (39) 049 637 966, Fax (39) 049 637 460

Bristol Buja - 154 rooms, D € 148 - Abano Terme 6 km
Tel (39) 049 866 9390, Fax (39) 049 667 910

Harry's Terme - 66 rooms, D € 98 - Abano Terme 6 km
Tel (39) 049 667 011, Fax (39) 049 866 8500

RESTAURANTS RISTORANTE
Da Mario - Montegrotto Terme 6 km - Tel (39) 049 794 090

La Montecchia - Selvazzano Dentro 5 km
Tel (39) 049 805 5323

Ristorante La Montecchia - on site
Tel (39) 049 805 5323

Monticello *Rosso*

15 | 8 | 7

Ha da poco compiuto 30 anni, ma il grande complesso di Monticello è diventato famoso subito dopo la nascita per aver ospitato molte edizioni dell'Open d'Italia. Si trova a pochi chilometri dal bellissimo lago di Como e questo lo rende un posto perfetto per trascorrere una piacevole vacanza. Ha due percorsi di 18 buche ma quello di campionato è il percorso "rosso" e si snoda in una pianura ornata da varie specie di alberi e con le Alpi in sottofondo. Le difficoltà sono ben visibili e distribuite con saggezza per non infastidire troppo i giocatori medi e testare l'intelligenza e la tattica dei migliori. E' appena stato rimodernato dall'architetto Graham Cooke che ha reso molto più mossi i greens ed ha collegato quelli della 9 e della 18 con un lago di grande effetto che ha reso molto più difficile soprattutto l'ultima buca.

This is one of the great classic courses in Italy made famous by the Italian Open championships held here and by the very meticulous maintenance and green-keeping on both 18-hole courses. The wonderful lake Como a few miles down the road makes this a great spot for peaceful holidays. The "Rosso" course is laid out in a plain lined with little copses and with the Alps as a backdrop. The difficulties are clearly in view and judiciously spread in order to avoid overwhelming the average player. Instead, they test the intelligence and tactical sense of the better golfers. Monticello has assigned architect Graham Cooke with supervising renovation work on several greens. This is now complete and looks particularly spectacular between holes 9 and 18, where a lake has seriously upped the difficulty, especially on the closing hole.

Golf Club Monticello — 1974

Via Volta 4
I - 22070 CASSINA RIZZARDI (CO)

Office Segreteria (39) 031 928 055
Pro shop Pro shop (39) 031 928 003
Fax Fax (39) 031 880 207
Web www.golfmonticello.it
Situation Località Milano, 45 km
Como (pop. 82 989), 11 km

Annual closure Chiusura annuale 1/1→31/1
Weekly closure Chiusura settimanale monday
Fees main season Tariffe alta stagione 18 holes

	Week days Settimana	We/Bank holidays Feriale/Festivo
Individual Individuale	€ 55	€ 75
Couple Coppia	€ 110	€ 150

Seniors: € 41 / 56 (We)

Caddie Caddie no **Electric Trolley** Carello elettrico no
Buggy Car yes **Clubs** Bastoni yes
Credit cards Carte di credito
CB - Eurocard - Mastercard - AMEX - DC - CartaSi

Access Itinerario : Milano, A8 and A9 → Como. Exit (Uscita) Fino Mornasco. Turn left. Golf to the right.
Map 1 on page 923 Carta 1 Pagina 923

GOLF COURSE — PERCORSO — 15/20

Site Paesaggio
Maintenance Manutenzione
Architect Architetto — Biratti, Cavalsani, Fazio, Dassù, Cooke
Type Tipologia — country
Relief Relievo terreno
Water in play Acqua in gioco
Exp. to wind Esposto al vento
Trees in play Alberi in gioco

Scorecard Carta-score	**Chp.** Camp.	**Mens** Uomini	**Ladies** Donne
Length Lunghezza	6410	6023	5317
Par	72	72	72
Slope system	134	133	128

Advised golfing ability 0 12 24 36
Livello di gioco consigliato
Hcp required Handicap richiesto 36

CLUB HOUSE & AMENITIES — CLUB HOUSE E SERVIZI — 8/10

Pro shop Pro shop
Driving range Campo pratica
Sheltered coperto 8 mats - **On grass** in erba yes - **Putting-green** Putting-green yes - **Pitching-green** Green-pratica yes

HOTEL FACILITIES — ALBERGHI — 7/10

HOTELS ALBERGHI
Canturio - Cantù 7 km - 30 rooms, D € 110
Tel (39) 031 716 035, Fax (39) 031 720 211

Terminus - Como 11 km
37 rooms, D L 360000
Tel (39) 031 329 111, Fax (39) 031 302 550

Villa Flori - 43 rooms, D € 215 - Como 11 km
Tel (39) 031 33 820, Fax (39) 031 570 379

RESTAURANTS RISTORANTE
Tradate - Tradate 10 km - Tel (39) 0331 841 401
Tarantola - Appiano Gentile 3 km - Tel (39) 031 930 990
Al Ponte - Cantù 7 km - Tel (39) 031 712 561

Olgiata

16 | 8 | 6

Questo percorso è nato nella proprietà della famosa scuderia Dormello Olgiata che ha dato cavalli come Nearco e Ribot e comprende 27 buche disegnate da Charles Kenneth Cotton e realizzate da Piero Mancinelli. Il percorso principale di 18 buche ha ricevuto tutti gli elogi in occasione delle due edizioni della World Cup nel 1968 e nel 1984 e durante l'Open d'Italia nel 2002. E' un percorso classico dove l'acqua interviene raramente e i maggiori ostacoli sono costituiti dai numerosi alberi e dai bunkers che nei fairways diventano penalizzanti soprattutto per i giocatori migliori. Abbastanza piatto ha tuttavia qualche buca con il drive cieco, ma senza eccessi: generalmente questo percorso non nasconde le sue difficoltà. Ogni buca ha il suo carattere e questo vi aiuterà a ricordarle. Inoltre c'è sempre una piacevole sensazione di spazio e di isolamento tra un fairway e l'altro. Uno dei grandi percorsi italiani.

Built over a former horse-rearing estate which produced such horses as Nearco and Ribot, this great Roman club boasts 27 holes designed by Charles Kenneth Cotton and laid out by Piero Mancinelli. The main 18-hole course was much acclaimed during the 1968 and 1984 World Cups held here. This is a classic course, where water comes into play only on two holes and where the main hazards are the very many trees and bunkers. In the fairways, bunkers are most penalizing for the better players, which might reassure visitors. Rather flat, there are nonetheless a few holes where you are driving blind, but within reason: generally speaking, this course reveals what it has in store. Interestingly, each hole has its own character, so you remember them well. Each hole, too, gives a great sensation of space and isolation from one fairway to another. One of the great Italian courses.

Olgiata Golf Club — 1961

Largo Olgiata 15
I - 00123 ROMA

Office	Segreteria	(39) 06 3088 9141
Pro shop	Pro shop	(39) 06 3088 4344
Fax	Fax	(39) 06 3088 9968
Web	olgiatagolf	
Situation	Località	Roma, 19 km
Annual closure	Chiusura annuale	no
Weekly closure	Chiusura settimanale	monday
Fees main season	Tariffe alta stagione	18 holes

	Week days Settimana	We/Bank holidays Feriale/Festivo
Individual Individuale	€ 60	€ 90
Couple Coppia	€ 120	€ 180

Caddie Caddie no — **Electric Trolley** Carello elettrico no

Buggy Car yes — **Clubs** Bastoni yes

Credit cards Carte di credito
VISA - Eurocard - MasterCard - AMEX - DC - CartaSi

Vetralla
Olgiata
GOLF
Bracciano
Mad. di Bracciano
S 2
S 2 bis
La Storia
La Giustiniana
G. R. A
5
3
Tomba di Nerone
km 0 2 4
Ottavia
Roma

Access Itinerario : Roma, "Grande Raccordo Anulare" (Ring road), Exit (Uscita) Via Cassia. S493 to the left → Bracciano, → Golf on the right.

Map 3 on page 927 Carta 3 Pagina 927

GOLF COURSE — PERCORSO — 16/20

Site	Paesaggio	
Maintenance	Manutenzione	
Architect	Architetto	C.K. Cotton, Piero Mancinelli
Type	Tipologia	parkland, residential
Relief	Relievo terreno	
Water in play	Acqua in gioco	
Exp. to wind	Esposto al vento	
Trees in play	Alberi in gioco	

Scorecard Carta-score	Chp. Camp.	Mens Uomini	Ladies Donne
Length Lunghezza	6347	6054	5306
Par	72	72	72
Slope system	133	131	127

Advised golfing ability Livello di gioco consigliato — 0 12 24 36

Hcp required Handicap richiesto 34

CLUB HOUSE & AMENITIES — CLUB HOUSE E SERVIZI — 8/10

Pro shop Pro shop
Driving range Campo pratica
Sheltered coperto 8 mats - On grass in erba yes - Putting-green Putting-green yes - Pitching-green Green-pratica yes

HOTEL FACILITIES — ALBERGHI — 6/10

HOTELS ALBERGHI

Villa San Dominique - 62 rooms, D € 110 - Roma 8 km
Tel (39) 06 - 303 639 00, Fax (39) 06 - 303 105 10

Relais I Due Laghi - Le Cerque (Anguillara Sabazia) 12 km
35 rooms, D € 150
Tel (39) 06 9960 7059, Fax (39) 06 9960 7068

Lord Byron - Roma 12 km - 36 rooms, D € 420
Tel (39) 06 3220 404, Fax (39) 06 3220 405

RESTAURANTS RISTORANTE

Vino e Camino - Bracciano 8 km - Tel (39) 06 9980 3433

Chalet del Lago - Anguillara Sabazia 10 km
Tel (39) 06 9960 7053

Il Grottino da Norina - Anguillara Sabazia 10 km
Tel (39) 06 996 8181

Padova *Blue/Yellow (+ Red)*

14	8	8

E' il campo più antico della città, realizzato su un terreno praticamente piatto ai piedi dei Colli Euganei, colline di origine vulcanica colme di frutteti e vigneti da dove sgorgano calde sorgenti, conosciute fin dall'epoca dei Romani che hanno dato vita ad un gran numero di stazioni termali tra le quali Montegrotto e Abano. Il percorso disegnato da John Harris è di buona qualità e si adatta alla maggioranza dei giocatori. Qualche ostacolo d'acqua è stato scavato in modo da poter recuperare terra per effettuare movimenti in superficie e sono particolarmente pericolosi nelle buche tra la 5 e la 8. Il tracciato non esige virtuosismi particolari e i migliori giocatori qui potranno fare buoni risultati con una certa facilità. Dal 2003 il circolo dispone di un ulteriore percorso di 9 buche par 36 con caratteristiche tecniche molto valide che consentono una piacevole variante al percorso tradizionale. Il circolo dispone di una grande club-house ed è molto frequentato sia dai numerosi soci che dai golfisti stranieri attratti dal binomio terme e golf.

This course was built on virtually flat land at the foot of the Colli Euganei, volcanic hills dotted with orchards and vineyards and the source of hot springs already appreciated by the Romans. They spawned a number of spa resorts, including Abano Terme and others in the same region. This course is quality golfing and ideal for most players. A few water hazards have been dug out to collect some welcome earth with which to contour the course elsewhere, and are particularly dangerous from holes 5 to 8. The existing vegetation has been supplemented by many others trees and bushes, now coming more and more into play. The layout does not require any special skills and the best players might card a good score without being unduly tested. In 2003, a new 9-hole course (par 36) of a high technical standard was added to the layout and so helps to vary the fun of playing here. It is also a source of satisfaction for the many members and visitors who come to enjoy the spa and their golfing.

Golf Club Padova — 1964

Via Noiera 57
I - 35030 VALSANZIBIO DI GALZIGNANO TERME (PA)

Office	Segreteria	(39) 049 913 0078
Pro shop	Pro shop	(39) 049 913 1140
Fax	Fax	(39) 049 913 1193
Web	www.golfpadova.it	
Situation	Località	Venezia, 40 km

Padova (pop. 211 391), 17 km

Annual closure	Chiusura annuale	no
Weekly closure	Chiusura settimanale	monday

Fees main season Tariffe alta stagione		18 holes
	Week days Settimana	**We/Bank holidays** Feriale/Festivo
Individual Individuale	€ 60	€ 67*
Couple Coppia	€ 120	€ 134*

*Members & guests only (Ospiti solo durante i giorni feriali)

Caddie Caddie no — **Electric Trolley** Carello elettrico yes
Buggy Car yes — **Clubs** Bastoni yes
Credit cards Carte di credito VISA - CartaSì

Abano Terme
Padova
Montegrotto Terme
GOLF
Galzignano Terme
Cataio
A13
Valsanzibio
S16
Arquà Petrarca
Rovigo
km
0 2 4
Monselice

Access Itinerario : A13 Padova-Bologna. Exit (Uscita) Terme Euganee. In Battaglia Terme, turn right. 6 km, Galzignano. Turn left → Valsanzibio. Golf on the left
Map 2 on page 924 Carta 2 Pagina 924

GOLF COURSE — PERCORSO — 14/20

Site	Paesaggio	
Maintenance	Manutenzione	
Architect	Architetto	John Harris
Type	Tipologia	country
Relief	Relievo terreno	
Water in play	Acqua in gioco	
Exp. to wind	Esposto al vento	
Trees in play	Alberi in gioco	

Scorecard Carta-score	**Chp.** Camp.	**Mens** Uomini	**Ladies** Donne
Length Lunghezza	6067	5920	5328
Par	72	72	72
Slope system	130	126	126

Advised golfing ability Livello di gioco consigliato — 0 12 24 36
Hcp required Handicap richiesto 34

CLUB HOUSE & AMENITIES — CLUB HOUSE E SERVIZI — 8/10

Pro shop Pro shop
Driving range Campo pratica
Sheltered coperto 10 mats - On grass in erba yes - Putting-green Putting-green yes - Pitching-green Green-pratica yes

HOTEL FACILITIES — ALBERGHI — 8/10

HOTELS ALBERGHI

Majestic Hotel Terme - Galzignano Terme 1 km
117 rooms, D € 136 (with dinner)
Tel (39) 049 919 4000, Fax (39) 049 919 4250

Sporting Hotel Terme - Galzignano Terme 1 km
112 rooms, D € 195 (w. dinner)
Tel (39) 049 919 5000, Fax (39) 049 919 5250

Green Park Hotel Terme - Galzignano Terme 1 km
93 rooms, D € 144 (w. dinner)
Tel (39) 049 919 7000, Fax (39) 049 919 7250

RESTAURANTS RISTORANTE

Castellato da Taparo - Torreglia 5 km - Tel (39) 049 521 1717
Antico Brolo - Padova 17 km - Tel (39) 049 664 555
La Montanella - Arquà Petrarca 3 km - Tel (39) 0429 718 200

Paradiso del Garda

15 | 7 | 8

E' Jim Fazio l'architetto di questo percorso che si snoda su antichi vigneti della regione del Bardolino dove il terreno ondulato, la qualità del fondo e l'esposizione sono stati una condizione ottimale per la buona realizzazione. Il lago di Garda e il Monte Baldo fanno da scenario a questo campo molto ben modellato dove le caratteristiche naturali sono state preservate il più possibile. Qualche lago ed alcuni corsi d'acqua che interessano almeno una dozzina di buche rendono il gioco molto stimolante e qui certo non ci si può lasciar distrarre dalla piacevolezza dell'ambiente. Tra le buche particolari, la 17, un corto par 4 dove i più audaci tenteranno di raggiungere il green con il drive e la 18 anche lei tentatrice. Due birdies o un finale rovinoso possono essere il preludio della serata, ovviamente con davanti un buon bicchiere di Bardolino.

Jim Fazio designed this course over former vineyards in the region of Bardolino. The sloping terrain, together with the type of soil and lie of the land formed a great foundation for golf and no-one is complaining. Lake Garda and Mount Baldo form a theatrical setting for this carefully landscaped course whose natural features have been deliberately protected as far as possible. A few stretches of water and lakes add a little spice to almost a dozen holes, enough to stir you from the balmy insouciance inspired by the very Italian style elegance that abounds here. Two of the prettiest holes are the 17th, a short par 4 that the more gung-ho golfer will attempt to drive, and the 18th, equally tempting to attack. Two birdie holes or two impending disasters, but a great way to prepare your evening, over a glass or two of Bardolino, of course.

Paradiso del Garda Golf Club — 2004

Località Paradiso
I - 37019 PESCHIERA DEL GARDA (VR)

Office	Segreteria	(39) 045 640 5802
Pro shop	Pro shop	(39) 045 640 5802
Fax	Fax	(39) 045 640 5808
Web	www.golfclubparadiso.it	
Situation	Località	Brescia, 35 km

Verona, 14 km

Annual closure Chiusura annuale — no
Weekly closure Chiusura settimanale — no

Fees main season Tariffe alta stagione	18 holes	
	Week days Settimana	We/Bank holidays Feriale/Festivo
Individual Individuale	€ 57	€ 67
Couple Coppia	€ 114	€ 134

Caddie Caddie no — **Electric Trolley** Carello elettrico no
Buggy Car yes — **Clubs** Bastoni yes
Credit cards Carte di credito
VISA - Eurocard - MasterCard - AMEX - DC

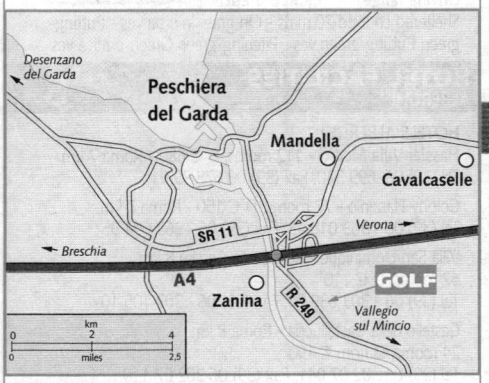

Desenzano del Garda
Peschiera del Garda
Mandella
Cavalcaselle
Verona
SR 11
Breschia
A4
Zanina
R 249
GOLF
Vallegio sul Mincio
km 0 2 4
miles 0 2,5

Access Itinerario : A4 Milano-Venice, Exit (Uscita) Peschiera del Garda, golf 1 km
Map 1 on page 923 Carta 1 Pagina 923

GOLF COURSE — PERCORSO — 15/20

Site	Paesaggio	
Maintenance	Manutenzione	
Architect	Architetto	Jim Fazio
Type	Tipologia	inland
Relief	Relievo terreno	
Water in play	Acqua in gioco	
Exp. to wind	Esposto al vento	
Trees in play	Alberi in gioco	

Scorecard Carta-score	Chp. Camp.	Mens Uomini	Ladies Donne
Length Lunghezza	5961	5496	4658
Par	71	71	71
Slope system	129	129	129

Advised golfing ability Livello di gioco consigliato — 0 12 24 36
Hcp required Handicap richiesto 36

CLUB HOUSE & AMENITIES — CLUB HOUSE E SERVIZI — 7/10

Pro shop Pro shop
Driving range Campo pratica
Sheltered coperto - On grass in erba no, 12 mats open air - Putting-green Putting-green yes - Pitching-green Green-pratica yes

HOTEL FACILITIES — ALBERGHI — 8/10

HOTELS ALBERGHI

Golf Hotel Paradiso - 63 rooms, ask for prices - on site
Tel (39) 045 640 5811

Puccini - 32 rooms, D € 110 - Peschiera 3 km
Tel (39) 045 640 1428, Fax (39) 045 640 1419

Bell'Arrivo - 27 rooms, D € 82 - Peschiera 3 km
Tel (39) 045 640 1322, Fax (39) 045 640 1311

RESTAURANTS RISTORANTE

El Pirlar - on site - Tel (39) 045 640 5811
Piccolo Mundo - Peschiera 3 km - Tel (39) 045 755 0025
Trattoria al Combattente - San Benedetto di Lugana 3 km
Tel (39) 045 755 0410

Parco di Roma

14	7	8

Quasi tutti i golfisti che abitano nelle grandi città sarebbero disposti a qualsiasi cosa pur di avere un golf così "in città". Parco di Roma è all'interno del Grande Raccordo Anulare ed è stato disegnato da P.B. Dye, figlio del famosissimo Pete, uno dei migliori artisti dell'architettura moderna del quale si riscontrano qui alcuni tratti tipici: greens grandissimi, difesi in modo aggressivo da bunkers o ostacoli d'acqua. Il terreno è molto ondulato e costituisce uno dei principali ostacoli insieme al rough. L'assenza quasi totale di alberi toglie uno degli elementi più divertenti e stimolanti del golf e comunque Parco di Roma si può definire un percorso difficile da tutti i tees di partenza e sicuramente complicato per i neofiti. Il terreno scosceso aumenta le difficoltà e impone il golf cart anche se dopo qualche giro gli ostacoli diventano più visivi che reali. Un'esperienza da provare...

Within the city limits of Rome, the Parco di Roma went for a leading architect in the person of P.B. Dye, a son of Pete Dye, one of the great artists of modern golf course architecture. Here we find any number of his personal hallmarks starting with huge and sharply contoured greens aggressively protected by astutely placed bunkers or water hazards. The terrain is wide open and sand, water and rough are effectively the main hazards. The absence of trees however removes one of the more amusing sides to golf, namely bending the ball around, above or under them. All the same, maybe inexperienced golfers should not risk playing this course without the company of better players because Parco di Roma is a difficult layout whichever tee-box you play from. Topography is very severe (buggy recommended) and players can very quickly find themselves in all sorts of trouble. Having said that, once you get used to the course you will find that the difficulties, often more visual than real, are a little less testing. A "different" and exciting experience.

Parco di Roma Golf Club — 2000

Via due Ponti, 110
I - 00191 ROMA

Office	Segreteria	(39) 06 - 336 533 96
Pro shop	Pro shop	(39) 06 - 336 533 96
Fax	Fax	(39) 06 - 336 609 31
Web	www.parcodiroma.it	
Situation	Località	in Roma
Annual closure	Chiusura annuale	no
Weekly closure	Chiusura settimanale	no

Fees main season Tariffe alta stagione	18 holes	
	Week days Settimana	**We/Bank holidays** Feriale/Festivo
Individual Individuale	€ 100	€ 100*
Couple Coppia	€ 200	€ 200*

Week-end: members' guests only
(Ospiti solo durante i giorni feriali)

Caddie Caddie no **Electric Trolley** Carello elettrico yes

Buggy Car yes **Clubs** Bastoni no

Credit cards Carte di credito
VISA - Eurocard - MasterCard - AMEX - DC

Access Itinerario : Roma Circolo / GRA Exit (Uscita) Flaminia → Roma, → Via due Ponti, golf 1 km
Map 3 on page 927 Carta 3 Pagina 927

GOLF COURSE — PERCORSO — 14/20

Site	Paesaggio	
Maintenance	Manutenzione	
Architect	Architetto	P.B. Dye
Type	Tipologia	open country, hilly
Relief	Relievo terreno	
Water in play	Acqua in gioco	
Exp. to wind	Esposto al vento	
Trees in play	Alberi in gioco	

Scorecard Carta-score	**Chp.** Camp.	**Mens** Uomini	**Ladies** Donne
Length Lunghezza	6500	6014	5307
Par	72	72	72
Slope system	139	138	133

Advised golfing ability Livello di gioco consigliato: 0 12 24 36

Hcp required Handicap richiesto 36

CLUB HOUSE & AMENITIES — CLUB HOUSE E SERVIZI — 7/10

Pro shop Pro shop
Driving range Campo pratica

Sheltered coperto 20 mats - On grass in erba yes - Putting-green Putting-green yes - Pitching-green Green-pratica yes

HOTEL FACILITIES — ALBERGHI — 8/10

HOTELS ALBERGHI

Hassler Villa Medici - 112 rooms, D € 680 - Roma 7 km
Tel (39) 06 699 340, Fax (39) 06 678 99 91

Colony Flaminio - 72 rooms, D € 150 - Roma 3 km
Tel (39) 06 - 363 018 43, Fax (39) 06 - 363 094 95

Villa San Dominique - Roma (Via Cassia) 8 km
62 rooms, D € 110
Tel (39) 06 - 303 639 00, Fax (39) 06 - 303 105 10

Castello della Castalluccia - Roma 8 km
24 rooms, D from € 190
Tel (39) 06 302 07 041, Fax (39) 06 302 07 ·10

RESTAURANTS RISTORANTE

La Pergola - Roma 6 km - Tel (39) 06 350 91
Il Convivio - Roma 8 km - Tel (39) 06 686 9432

Pevero

17	8	8

Questa regione chiamata Costa Smeralda è stata lanciata turisticamente nel 1961, sotto la spinta di un gruppo di investitori guidati da Karim Aga Khan. E' diventata una delle regioni favorite dal "jet-set" con alberghi da sogno, porti turistici, tennis-club e con il Golf del Pevero, fiore all'occhiello del luogo, all'esatto opposto del non meno famoso (e più recente) Golf di Sperone in Corsica. I due campi sono stati disegnati da Robert Trent Jones. Il Pevero è sontuoso, scavato in mezzo alle rocce coperte di vegetazione boscosa, interrotte da baie stupende e da un mare dai mille colori. Il disegno è molto tecnico ma soffre di essere un po' costretto tra le rocce e quindi bisogna essere veramente abili per fare un buono score. E' un percorso fantastico per un match-play soprattutto quando il vento soffia forte e... capita molto spesso. In questo caso contare i propri colpi (sicuramente molti più di quanti vi aspettiate) diventa inopportuno. E' comunque un luogo di vacanza da sogno.

This region, known as the Costa Smeralda, began to be exploited as tourist material in 1961, spurred on by Karim Aga Khan and a consortium of investors. It has become one of the jet-set's favourite playgrounds with its palace hotels, marinas, tennis clubs and the site's crowning glory, the Pevero golf course, lying almost directly opposite the no less famous (and more recent) Golf de Sperone in Corsica. Both were designed by Robert Trent Jones. The Pevero site is simply sumptuous, between tree-covered hills, a rocky coastline broken only by some splendid coves and a sea of ever changing colour. This layout is highly strategic, yardage is a matter of relative importance and a good score calls for the virtuosity of a fine technician, at least to avoid the rocks. This is a marvellous course for match-play golf, especially when the wind blows, as it does on occasions. In this case counting your strokes (certainly more than you bargained for) is meaningless. A dream holiday location.

Pevero Golf Club — 1971

Loc. Cala di Volpe
I - 07020 PORTO CERVO (SS)

Office	Segreteria	(39) 0789 958 000
Pro shop	Pro shop	(39) 0789 958 000
Fax	Fax	(39) 0789 965 72
Web		www.costasmeraldaresort.com
Situation	Località	Olbia (pop. 44 291), 30 km
Annual closure	Chiusura annuale	no
Weekly closure	Chiusura settimanale	tuesday

Fees main season Tariffe alta stagione	18 holes	
	Week days Settimana	We/Bank holidays Feriale/Festivo
Individual Individuale	€ 50	€ 100
Couple Coppia	€ 100	€ 200

GF with mandatory golf car (con obbligo del cart compreso nel prezzo) / Special GF in low season

Caddie Caddie no — **Electric Trolley** Carello elettrico yes

Buggy Car yes — **Clubs** Bastoni yes

Credit cards Carte di credito
VISA - Eurocard - MasterCard - AMEX - DC - CartaSì

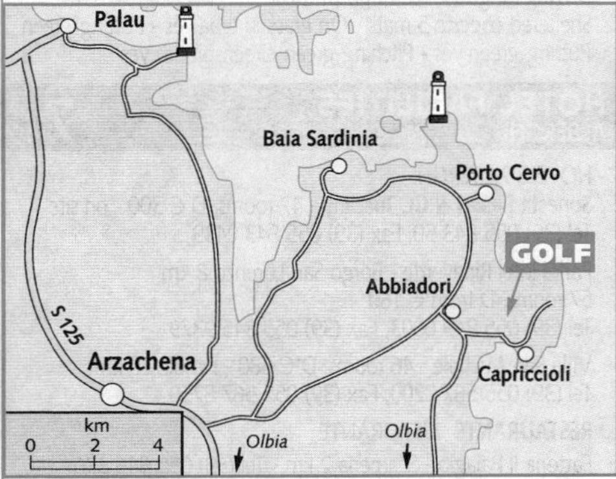

Access Itinerario : Olbia → Porto Cervo (Costa Smeralda). Golf on the right hand side.
Map 4 on page 929 Carta 4 Pagina 929

GOLF COURSE — PERCORSO 17/20

Site	Paesaggio	
Maintenance	Manutenzione	
Architect	Architetto	Robert Trent Jones
Type	Tipologia	seaside course
Relief	Relievo terreno	
Water in play	Acqua in gioco	
Exp. to wind	Esposto al vento	
Trees in play	Alberi in gioco	

Scorecard Carta-score	Chp. Camp.	Mens Uomini	Ladies Donne
Length Lunghezza	6150	5858	5135
Par	72	72	72
Slope system	136	133	129

Advised golfing ability Livello di gioco consigliato — 0 12 24 36

Hcp required Handicap richiesto 34

CLUB HOUSE & AMENITIES — CLUB HOUSE E SERVIZI 8/10

Pro shop Pro shop
Driving range Campo pratica
Sheltered coperto 5 mats - On grass in erba yes - Putting-green Putting-green yes - Pitching-green Green-pratica yes

HOTEL FACILITIES — ALBERGHI 8/10

HOTELS ALBERGHI

Cala di Volpe - 137 rooms, ask for prices - Cala di Volpe 1 km
Tel (39) 0789 976 111, Fax (39) 0789 976 617

Cervo & Conference Center - Porto Cervo 5 km
110 rooms, D from € 630
Tel (39) 0789 931 111, Fax (39) 0789 931 613

Le Ginestre - 80 rooms, D from € 350 - Porto Cervo 5 km
Tel (39) 0789 92 030, Fax (39) 0789 94 087

Romazzino - 94 rooms, D from € 1550 - Romazzino 3 km
Tel (39) 0789 977 111, Fax (39) 0789 977 614

RESTAURANTS RISTORANTE

Gianni Pedrinelli - Porto Cervo 3 km - Tel (39) 0789 92 436
Casablanca - Baia Sardinia 10 km - Tel (39) 0789 99 006
La Conchiglia - Baia Sardinia 6 km - Tel (39) 0789 99 241

Poggio dei Medici

15 | 7 | 7

Firenze possiede qualcosa in più oltre alla sua città: ha anche una campagna meravigliosa, dolce e affascinante dove ogni cosa è dotata di naturale armonia. Immersi in queste colline coperte di vigneti, olivi, pini e cipressi, in una regione dove si mangia molto bene e si producono vini stupendi, vi potrà capitare di pensare che il tempo si sia fermato. Il nome di questo golf (la collina dei Medici) riassume la storia e il paesaggio di Firenze. Bisognerà aspettare che gli alberi crescano ancora per vedere l'aspetto definitivo di questo percorso. E' stato inaugurato nel 1992 in una distesa molto vasta ed è stato disegnato dal campione italiano Baldovino Dassù e dall' architetto Alvise Rossi Fioravanti. Hanno dimostrato grande fantasia per come è stato utilizzato il terreno, come sono stati disegnati fairways e greens e per come sono stati fatti entrare in gioco gli ostacoli: rough, sabbia e acqua. Molto ondulato, esige una buona forma fisica e, a meno che non abbiate un handicap con una sola cifra, sarà meglio giocare dalle partenze normali.

Florence is a little more than just the city of Florence; there is also some wonderfully sweet and charming countryside where everything is visual and natural harmony. In the middle of hills covered with vines, olive, pine and cypress trees, in a land of sophisticated food and admirable wines, you could be forgiven for thinking that time has stood still. The name of this course ("The Hill of the Medici") sums up both the history and landscape of Florence. However, the trees here will need to grow a little before the course fully matures. It was designed over a very wide open space by Baldovino Dassù and Alvise Rossi Fioravanti. They have showed imagination in the way they used the terrain, contoured the fairways and greens and brought hazards into play, namely rough, sand and water. A very hilly course which is better played by the fitter golfer, and a difficult one, too, where the front tees are to be advised. If you only have time for the one round, match-play is the best solution for enjoyable golf.

Poggio dei Medici Golf Club — 1992

Via San Gavino 27
I - 50038 SCARPERIA (FI)

Office	Segreteria	(39) 055 843 0436
Pro shop	Pro shop	(39) 055 843 0436
Fax	Fax	(39) 055 843 0439
Web	www.poggiodeimedici.com	
Situation	Località	Firenze, 25 km
Annual closure	Chiusura annuale	no
Weekly closure	Chiusura settimanale	no

Fees main season Tariffe alta stagione — 18 holes

	Week days Settimana	We/Bank holidays Feriale/Festivo
Individual Individuale	€ 80	€ 80
Couple Coppia	€ 160	€ 160

Caddie Caddie yes — **Electric Trolley** Carello elettrico no
Buggy Car yes — **Clubs** Bastoni yes
Credit cards Carte di credito
VISA - Eurocard - MasterCard - AMEX - DC - CartaSi

Access Itinerario : Firenze, S65 → Bologna, → San Piero a Sieve, → Gabbiano.
Map 3 on page 926 Carta 3 Pagina 926

GOLF COURSE — PERCORSO — 15/20

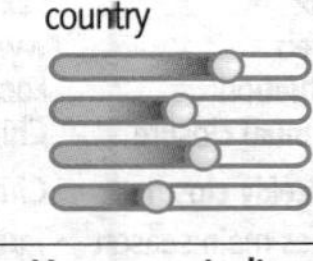

Site	Paesaggio	
Maintenance	Manutenzione	
Architect	Architetto	Baldovino Dassù A. Rossi Fioravanti
Type	Tipologia	country
Relief	Relievo terreno	
Water in play	Acqua in gioco	
Exp. to wind	Esposto al vento	
Trees in play	Alberi in gioco	

Scorecard Carta-score	Chp. Camp.	Mens Uomini	Ladies Donne
Length Lunghezza	6338	6082	5352
Par	73	73	73
Slope system	136	131	131

Advised golfing ability Livello di gioco consigliato — 0 12 24 36
Hcp required Handicap richiesto 34

CLUB HOUSE & AMENITIES — CLUB HOUSE E SERVIZI — 7/10

Pro shop Pro shop
Driving range Campo pratica
Sheltered coperto 5 mats - On grass in erba yes - Putting-green Putting-green yes - Pitching-green Green-pratica yes

HOTEL FACILITIES — ALBERGHI — 7/10

HOTELS ALBERGHI

Sonesta Resort & CC Tuscany - 47 rooms, D € 300 - on site
Tel (39) 055 843 50, Fax (39) 055 843 0439

Park Hotel Ripaverde - Borgo San Lorenzo 8 km
57 rooms, D from € 160
Tel (39) 055 849 6003, Fax (39) 055 845 9379

Villa San Michele - 46 rooms, D € 680 - Fiesole 20 km
Tel (39) 055 567 8200, Fax (39) 055 567 8250

RESTAURANTS RISTORANTE

Fattoria Il Palagio - Scarperia 2 km - Tel (39) 055 846 376
Degli Artisti - Borgo San Lorenzo 8 km - Tel (39) 055 845 7707
Cosimo de' Medici - Barberino di Mugello 3 km
Tel (39) 055 842 0370

Punta Ala

14	6	8

Non lontano dalla città storica di Siena (che merita una visita di qualche giorno), in faccia all'isola d'Elba e alla Corsica, Punta Ala è un luogo di vacanza di prim'ordine per tutta la famiglia. L'ottima qualità del suo golf permette quindi oltre al divertimento la possibilità di un'impegnativa giornata di golf. Disegnato da Giulio Cavalsani all'inizio degli anni '60 si snoda su un terreno molto ondulato (il golf-cart è consigliato). I molti dog-leg e la presenza interminabile di alberi impongono a coloro che vogliono fare un buono score molta concentrazione e buone capacità tecniche: diventa allora indispensabile saper fare ogni tipo di colpo per uscire dalla pineta quando si è finiti dentro. Abbastanza lungo dalle partenze arretrate, Punta Ala è decisamente più piacevole dalle partenze normali. Un campo divertente, in un posto molto tranquillo.

Not far from the historical city of Sienna (worth a visit of several days), opposite Elbe Island and Corsica and next to some top seaside resorts, Punta Ala is a first-rate holiday destination for all the family. The excellence of the golf course also means that golfers can both have fun and get down to some serious golfing. Designed by Giulio Cavalsani in the early 1960s, it is laid out over some very hilly terrain (buggy recommended) which calls for unwavering concentration. In addition, the unending presence of trees and many dog legs complicate matters still further if you are looking for a good score. You simply have to be able to work the ball in all directions to get that mis-hit ball safely out of the pine trees. Rather a long course from the back tees, Punta Ala is much kinder when you tee off further forward. A pretty course in a very calm setting..

Golf Club Punta Ala — 1964

Via del Golf 1
I - 58040 PUNTA ALA (GR)

Office Segreteria (39) 0564 922 121
Pro shop Pro shop (39) 0564 922 420
Fax Fax (39) 0564 920 182
Web www.puntaala.net
Situation Località Grosseto (pop. 72 662), 35 km
Annual closure Chiusura annuale no
Weekly closure Chiusura settimanale no

Fees main season Tariffe alta stagione	18 holes	
	Week days Settimana	**We/Bank holidays** Feriale/Festivo
Individual Individuale	€ 45	€ 65
Couple Coppia	€ 90	€ 130

Caddie Caddie no — **Trolley** Carello elettrico yes
Buggy Car yes — **Clubs** Bastoni yes
Credit cards Carte di credito
VISA - AMEX - DC - CartaSì

Livorno
S 1
Rondelli
Grosseto
Follonica
Ravi
Grilli
Pian d'Alma
GOLF
Macchiascandona
Punta Ala
A 24
Grosseto
km
0 2 4
Castiglione della Pescaia

Access Itinerario : Roma S322 (Via Aurelia).
In Grosseto, → Castiglione della Pescaia and Punta Ala
Map 3 on page 926 Carta 3 Pagina 926

GOLF COURSE — PERCORSO — 14/20

Site Paesaggio
Maintenance Manutenzione
Architect Architetto — Giulio Cavalsani
Type Tipologia — forest
Relief Relievo terreno
Water in play Acqua in gioco
Exp. to wind Esposto al vento
Trees in play Alberi in gioco

Scorecard Carta-score	**Chp.** Camp.	**Mens** Uomini	**Ladies** Donne
Length Lunghezza	6213	6036	5311
Par	72	72	72
Slope system	140	139	136

Advised golfing ability 0 12 24 36
Livello di gioco consigliato
Hcp required Handicap richiesto 34

CLUB HOUSE & AMENITIES — CLUB HOUSE E SERVIZI — 6/10

Pro shop Pro shop
Driving range Campo pratica
Sheltered coperto 8 mats - On grass in erba yes - Putting-green Putting-green yes - Pitching-green Green-pratica yes

HOTEL FACILITIES — ALBERGHI — 8/10

HOTELS ALBERGHI
Gallia Palace Hotel - Punta Ala 500 m
82 rooms, D from € 350
Tel (39) 0564 922 022, Fax (39) 0564 920 229

Piccolo Hotel - 24 rooms, D € 110 - Castiglione della P. 12 km
Tel (39) 0564 937 081, Fax (39) 0564 932 566

Hotel Alleluja - Punta Ala 1,5 km - 38 rooms, D from € 435
Tel (39) 0564 922 050, Fax (39) 0564 920 734

RESTAURANTS RISTORANTE
Da Bernardo - Punta Ala 1 km - Tel (39) 0564 920 269
Pierbacco - Castiglione della Pescaia 12 km
Tel (39) 0564 933 522
Lo Scalino - Punta Ala 1 km - Tel (39) 0564 922 168

Rapallo

13	8	8

Come molti golf europei, anche Rapallo è nato vicino ad un luogo di villeggiatura ed è situato nella parte orientale della Riviera, più mossa e selvaggia della parte occidentale, da Genova a Ventimiglia. Rapallo è una delle più eleganti stazioni balneari italiane e il percorso si snoda sulle colline che la circondano. Di lunghezza ridotta, ma rispettabile al momento della costruzione negli anni '30, il percorso non ha che due par 5 (la 2 e la 7) quattro par 3 e dodici par 4 tra i 255 e i 385 metri. L'architetto ha seguito armoniosamente i movimenti del terreno per disegnare il campo facendo entrare in gioco alberi e corsi d'acqua come ostacoli naturali. I greens di taglia piccola obbligano ad una precisione assoluta dato che sono anche molto ben difesi. Un golf piacevole per fare una partita tra amici che diventa molto più impegnativo dalle partenze di campionato.

Like many continental golf courses, Rapallo was designed near a holiday centre on the eastern side of the Riviera, a steeper and wilder section of coastline than further west, running from Genoa to Ventimiglia. Rapallo is one of Italy's most elegant seaside resorts and the golf course is laid out over the hills that overlook the town below. Today considered a short course (although this sort of yardage was quite respectable in the 1930s when it was first laid out), Rapallo has only two par 5s (the 2nd and 7th holes), four par 3s and twelve par 4s of between 255 and 385 metres. The architect used the terrain's natural contours to build a smoothly flowing layout, playing with trees and water as natural hazards. The small greens call for accurate approach shots, especially since they are well guarded. A pleasant course for a round with friends and relatively easy from the front tees. A good opportunity to shine without too much effort.

Cicolo Golf e Tennis Rapallo — 1930

Via Mameli 377
I - 16035 RAPALLO (GE)

Office	Segreteria	(39) 0185 261 777
Pro shop	Pro shop	(39) 0185 261 777
Fax	Fax	(39) 0185 261 779
Web	www.golftennisrapallo.it	
Situation	Località	Genova, 50 km

Rapallo (pop. 28 176), 2 km

Annual closure	Chiusura annuale	no
Weekly closure	Chiusura settimanale	tuesday
Fees main season	Tariffe alta stagione	18 holes

	Week days Settimana	We/Bank holidays Feriale/Festivo
Individual Individuale	€ 54	€ 87
Couple Coppia	€ 108	€ 174

Caddie Caddie on request — **Electric Trolley** Carello elettrico yes

Buggy Car yes — **Clubs** Bastoni yes

Credit cards Carte di credito
VISA - DC - CartSi

Access Itinerario : A12 Genova-Livorno. Exit (Uscita) Rapallo → Centro Cittadino. Golf 200 m on the right.

Map 1 on page 923 Carta 1 Pagina 923

GOLF COURSE — PERCORSO — 13/20

Site	Paesaggio	
Maintenance	Manutenzione	
Architect	Architetto	unknown
Type	Tipologia	country, hilly
Relief	Relievo terreno	
Water in play	Acqua in gioco	
Exp. to wind	Esposto al vento	
Trees in play	Alberi in gioco	

Scorecard Carta-score	Chp. Camp.	Mens Uomini	Ladies Donne
Length Lunghezza	5625	5625	4955
Par	70	70	70
Slope system	123	123	128

Advised golfing ability Livello di gioco consigliato: 0 12 24 36

Hcp required Handicap richiesto 34

CLUB HOUSE & AMENITIES — CLUB HOUSE E SERVIZI — 8/10

Pro shop	Pro shop
Driving range	Campo pratica

Sheltered coperto 15 mats - On grass in erba no - Putting-green Putting-green yes - Pitching-green Green-pratica yes

HOTEL FACILITIES — ALBERGHI — 8/10

HOTELS ALBERGHI

Excelsior Palace Hotel - Rapallo 2 km
135 rooms, D from € 475
Tel (39) 0185 230 666, Fax (39) 0185 230 214

Riviera - 20 rooms, D € 150 - Rapallo 2 km
Tel (39) 0185 50 248, Fax (39) 0185 65 668

Europa - 60 rooms, D € 185 - Rapallo 2 km
Tel (39) 0185 669 521, Fax (39) 0185 669 847

RESTAURANTS RISTORANTE

U Giancu - Rapallo 1 km - Tel (39) 0185 260 505

Luca - Rapallo 2,5 km - Tel (39) 0185 60 323

Hostaria Vecchia Rapallo - Rapallo 2 km
Tel (39) 0185 50 053

Rimini

13 | 6 | 8

In un luogo di villeggiatura, è stato concepito soprattutto con lo scopo di far divertire i giocatori senza appesantire troppo i loro scores! Il posto è il punto di partenza ideale sia per una puntata verso le famose spiagge dell'Adriatico che per andare alla scoperta delle ricchezze culturali di Ravenna e Ferrara. Rimini ha dei tesori propri ereditati in particolar modo dalla famiglia Malatesta che è stata esempio di rara raffinatezza ma anche di estrema crudeltà. Questo percorso si trova nell'entroterra, in una regione magnifica proprio ai piedi della Repubblica di San Marino nella valle della Marecchia. Il disegno di Brian Silva è abbastanza classico, facile da interpretare: sin dalla prima volta non sarà difficile decifrare i suoi segreti. Abbastanza piatto consente di andare a piedi senza stancarsi ma non deve essere sottovalutato; gli alberi e soprattutto gli ostacoli d'acqua sono sempre in gioco diventando a volte pericolosi. Ben disegnato, il golf di Rimini non ha una personalità spiccata ma la sua onestà e la bellezza del paesaggio piaceranno sicuramente.

In this holiday region the idea was to provide a layout that does not leave you dead and buried and which actually gives you the chance to card a good score. This site is also a good starting point for exploring not only the beaches of the Adriatic but also the cultural heritage of Ravenna and Ferrara. Rimini also has treasures of its own, inherited most notably from the Malatesta family, which unashamedly embraced both cruelty and refinement. The course is located just inland in a magnificent region along the edge of the Marecchia valley overlooked by the Republic of San Marino. Brian Silva's layout is in the classic style with no real surprises. It is rather flat and easy on the feet, but definitely not a course to be sniffed at. Woods, and mainly water hazards come into play and sometimes loom dangerously. A well-designed layout that hardly stands head and shoulders above the rest, but as a plain honest golf course you will enjoy it. Not to mention the site's outstanding beauty.

Rimini Golf Club — 1993

Via Tenuta 109
I - 47827 VILLA VERUCCHIO

Office	Segreteria	(39) 0541 678 122
Pro shop	Pro shop	(39) 0541 678 122
Fax	Fax	(39) 0541 670 572
Web	www.riminigolf.com	
Situation	Località	Rimini (pop. 131 062), 14 km
Annual closure	Chiusura annuale	no
Weekly closure	Chiusura settimanale	

Fees main season Tariffe alta stagione	18 holes	
	Week days Settimana	We/Bank holidays Feriale/Festivo
Individual Individuale	€ 50	€ 60
Couple Coppia	€ 110	€ 120

Caddie Caddie yes — **Electric Trolley** Carello elettrico yes

Buggy Car yes — **Clubs** Bastoni yes

Credit cards Carte di credito
VISA - Eurocard - MasterCard - AMEX - DC - JCB

Access Itinerario : A14 Bologna-Ancona. Exit (Uscita) Rimini Nord → Verucchio. At Santarcangelo, → Villa Verucchio. 10 km turn right.
Map 3 on page 927 Carta 3 Pagina 927

GOLF COURSE — PERCORSO 13/20

Site	Paesaggio	
Maintenance	Manutenzione	
Architect	Architetto	Brian Silva
Type	Tipologia	open country
Relief	Relievo terreno	
Water in play	Acqua in gioco	
Exp. to wind	Esposto al vento	
Trees in play	Alberi in gioco	

Scorecard Carta-score	Chp. Camp.	Mens Uomini	Ladies Donne
Length Lunghezza	6145	6145	5407
Par	72	72	72
Slope system	126	123	116

Advised golfing ability Livello di gioco consigliato — 0 12 24 36

Hcp required Handicap richiesto 34

CLUB HOUSE & AMENITIES — CLUB HOUSE E SERVIZI 6/10

Pro shop Pro shop
Driving range Campo pratica
Sheltered coperto 27 mats - On grass in erba yes - Putting-green Putting-green yes - Pitching-green Green-pratica yes

HOTEL FACILITIES — ALBERGHI 8/10

HOTELS ALBERGHI

Case Rosse - 7 rooms, D € 82 - on site
Tel (39) 0541 678 123, Fax (39) 0541 678 876

Hotel National - 86 rooms, D € 185 - Rimini 15 km
Tel (39) 0541 390 944, Fax (39) 0541 390 954

Villa Adriatica - Rimini 14 km
85 rooms, D € 100
Tel (39) 0541 545 99, Fax (39) 0541 269 62

RESTAURANTS RISTORANTE

Al Palazzo - Sant' Ermete 5 km - Tel (39) 0541 757 640

Acero Rosso - Rimini 15 km - Tel (39) 0541 535 77

Ro' e Buni - Villa Verucchio 1 - Tel (39) 0541 678 484

Riva dei Tessali

13 | 7 | 7

Questa parte della Puglia, dove la dominazione greca è stata particolarmente intensa, sta diventando un posto molto attraente per il turismo golfistico. Arte, spiagge bellissime e ora il vicino campo di Metaponto della stessa proprietà (6284 m, par 72) rendono molto interessante questa destinazione per una piacevole vacanza tutto l'anno. Il percorso di Riva dei Tessali è uno dei rari nel sud Italia dove i numerosissimi alberi assicurano l'ombra, molto spesso gradita e nello stesso tempo sono una delle principali difficoltà del percorso insieme agli ostacoli d'acqua. Disegnato da Marco Croze, non è molto lungo ma i greens di medie dimensioni sono ben difesi. Non è il percorso più spettacolare del mondo, ma ha il privilegio di essere alla portata di tutti.

The region of Apulia is hardly the part of Italy best known to foreign tourists, yet the Holy Week processions in Taranto (they give great insight into the depth of religious feeling in southern Italy) and a trip to the amazing town of Metera with its troglodyte dwellings further north are essential visiting. Taranto also boasts a Museo Archeologico Nazionale, which recalls the presence of the ancient Greeks in this part of Europe. Last but not least, the beach-lined seaboard, for example the Lido di Metaponto, makes this a remarkable holiday destination. Designed by Marco Croze, Riva dei Tessali is one of the rare golf courses to be found in the south of Italy, where the very many trees offer welcome shade and provide one of the course's main difficulties, together with water. The opening of the Metaponto course (6284 m, par 72) by the club has given this golfing destination extra special appeal.

Golf Club Riva dei Tessali — 1968

I - 74011 CASTELLANETA (TA)

Office	Segreteria	(39) 099 843 1844
Pro shop	Pro shop	(39) 099 843 9251
Fax	Fax	(39) 099 843 9001
Web	www.rivadeitessali.it	
Situation	Località	Taranto (pop. 208 214), 34 km

Lido di Metaponto, 12 km

Annual closure Chiusura annuale — no

Weekly closure Chiusura settimanale

Fees main season Tariffe alta stagione — 18 holes

	Week days Settimana	We/Bank holidays Feriale/Festivo
Individual Individuale	€ 47	€ 47
Couple Coppia	€ 94	€ 94

Caddie Caddie no — **Electric Trolley** Carello elettrico yes

Buggy Car yes — **Clubs** Bastoni yes

Credit cards Carte di credito

VISA - AMEX - CartaSi

Access Itinerario : Bari A14 → Taranto. At the end o f motorway, go to Palagiano. S106dir, turn right on S106. 18 km, → Riva dei Tessali

Map 4 on page 928 Carta 4 Pagina 928

GOLF COURSE — PERCORSO — 13/20

Site	Paesaggio	
Maintenance	Manutenzione	
Architect	Architetto	Marco Croze
Type	Tipologia	copse
Relief	Relievo terreno	
Water in play	Acqua in gioco	
Exp. to wind	Esposto al vento	
Trees in play	Alberi in gioco	

Scorecard Carta-score	Chp. Camp.	Mens Uomini	Ladies Donne
Length Lunghezza	5947	5709	5095
Par	72	72	72
Slope system	133	130	119

Advised golfing ability Livello di gioco consigliato — 0 12 24 36

Hcp required Handicap richiesto 34

CLUB HOUSE & AMENITIES — CLUB HOUSE E SERVIZI — 7/10

Pro shop Pro shop

Driving range Campo pratica

Sheltered coperto no - On grass in erba yes - Putting-green Putting-green yes - Pitching-green Green-pratica yes

HOTEL FACILITIES — ALBERGHI — 7/10

HOTELS ALBERGHI

Riva dei Tessali Golf Hotel - on site
120 rooms, D € 184
Tel (39) 099 843 9251, Fax (39) 099 843 9255

Europa - 46 rooms, D € 145 - Taranto 34 km
Tel (39) 099 452 5994, Fax (39) 099 452 5994

Residence Club Hotel - on site
20 rooms, D € 194
Tel (39) 099 843 9811, Fax (39) 099 843 8224

RESTAURANTS RISTORANTE

Da Fifina - Bernalda 10 km - Tel (39) 0835 543 134

Al Vecchio Frantoio - Bernalda 10 km - Tel (39) 0835 543 546

Roma - Acquasanta

16	8	9

In una campagna così calma e serafica, non si potrebbe mai immaginare di essere a un passo dal centro di Roma e a poche centinaia di metri da Cinecittà. Invece siamo sulla via Appia "nuova" a fianco di quella "antica" e la vista dell'Acquedotto che portava l'acqua alla capitale dell'Impero ci riporta alla mente la storia che comincia proprio in questa parte d'Italia. Il percorso dell'Acquasanta ne fa parte, perchè ha compiuto 100 anni nel 2003 ed è il più vecchio golf d'Italia, dove sono passate tutte le teste coronate e gli attori del cinema. E' un grande percorso stile britannico inserito in una vegetazione superba ma non soffocante. Dolcemente ondulato è attraversato da piccoli corsi d'acqua piazzati quasi sempre davanti ai greens. E' molto vario nel disegno e proprio per questo giocando qui non ci si annoia mai. Spettacolare e nello stesso tempo naturale il percorso si integra delicatamente nel paesaggio tipico della campagna romana. Quando il golf è Dolce Vita...

In countryside as lazy and as peaceful as this, it is hard to believe you are so close to the centre of Rome and a few hundred metres from Cinecittà. Maybe we are on the "new" Via Appia, alongside the old one. The view from the aqueduct that carried spring water to the capital of the Roman empire is a constant reminder of the history that surrounds this part of Italy. The Acquasanta course is all part of it, being the oldest club in Italy and one that has entertained kings, princes and movie stars. Above all, it is a great old-style course in a superb setting of plants and trees, although the latter are never too present. This is a pleasantly sloping course crossed by streams, often just in front of the greens. And thanks to the variety of the layout, you are never tired of playing here. Both spectacular and natural, the course blends delicately into the landscape of typical Roman countryside. A golf very much "dolce vita" style.

Circolo del Golf di Roma — 1903

Via Appia Nuova 716/A - Località Acquasanta
I - 00178 ROMA

Office	Segreteria	(39) 06 780 3407
Pro shop	Pro shop	(39) 06 783 951 68
Fax	Fax	(39) 06 783 462 19
Web	www.golfroma.it	
Situation	Località	Roma, 7 km
Annual closure	Chiusura annuale	no
Weekly closure	Chiusura settimanale	monday
Fees main season	Tariffe alta stagione	18 holes

	Week days Settimana	We/Bank holidays Feriale/Festivo
Individual Individuale	€ 64	€ 77*
Couple Coppia	€ 128	€ 154*

*Week-end: with members only (ospiti accettati con soci)

Caddie Caddie yes — **Electric Trolley** Carello elettrico yes
Buggy Car yes — **Clubs** Bastoni yes
Credit cards Carte di credito no

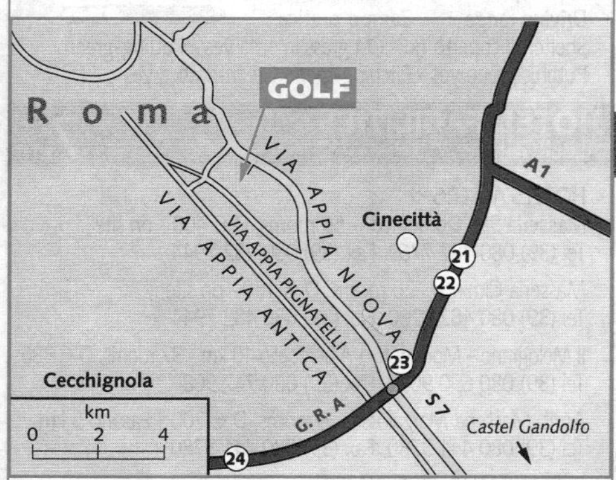

Access Itinerario : Roma, Via Appia Nuova.
At N° 716/A, small road with a stone → Golf
Map 3 on page 927 Carta 3 Pagina 927

GOLF COURSE — PERCORSO — 16/20

Site	Paesaggio	
Maintenance	Manutenzione	
Architect	Architetto	unknown
Type	Tipologia	open country, residential
Relief	Relievo terreno	
Water in play	Acqua in gioco	
Exp. to wind	Esposto al vento	
Trees in play	Alberi in gioco	

Scorecard Carta-score	Chp. Camp.	Mens Uomini	Ladies Donne
Length Lunghezza	6000	5854	5101
Par	71	71	71
Slope system	135	131	132

Advised golfing ability Livello di gioco consigliato — 0 12 24 36
Hcp required Handicap richiesto 34

CLUB HOUSE & AMENITIES — CLUB HOUSE E SERVIZI — 8/10

Pro shop Pro shop
Driving range Campo pratica
Sheltered coperto 7 mats - On grass in erba yes - Putting-green Putting-green yes - Pitching-green Green-pratica yes

HOTEL FACILITIES — ALBERGHI — 9/10

HOTELS ALBERGHI

Appia Park Hotel - 110 rooms, D € 165 - Roma 1 km
Tel (39) 06 716 741, Fax (39) 06 718 2457

Quirinale - 200 rooms, D € 325 - Roma 5 km
Tel (39) 06 4707, Fax (39) 06 482 0099

Victor Hotel - 30 rooms, D € 125 - Roma 1 km
Tel (39) 06 712 89 441, Fax (39) 06 712 89 441

RESTAURANTS RISTORANTE

Checchino dal 1887 - Roma 5 km
Tel (39) 06 574 3816

Paris - Roma 6 km - Tel (39) 06 581 5378

Agata e Romeo - Roma 6 km - Tel (39) 06 446 6115

La Pergola - Roma 6 km - Tel (39) 06 - 3509 21 52

San Domenico

16 | 7 | 7

Per tanto tempo ai margini dello sviluppo turistico del golf, ora il sud Italia sembra essersi svegliato con la realizzazione di strutture di ottimo livello. Un esempio eccellente è San Domenico che può contare anche sul suo lussuoso hotel realizzato in un'antica masseria vicino al villaggio di pescatori di Savelletri Il terreno tendenzialmente piatto è stato modellato ad arte da Andy Haggar e la European Golf Design per avere ovviamente un aspetto links. Gli ostacoli d'acqua e i grandi bunkers sono le maggiori difficoltà e gli ulivi molto suggestivi lasciano entrare il vento che mitiga il calore estivo.Sono stati inoltre creati dei "waste bunkers" con cespugli e arbusti tipici della regione. Con i suoi 6300 mt. San Domenico è un percorso solido, strategico e senza difficoltà nascoste dove i golfisti potranno godere in ogni momento di una magnifica vista sull'Adriatico.

Southern Italy, which for many a year has been uncharted territory for golf travel and tourism, seems to have emerged from the shadows with a few new excellent courses. One notable example is San Domenico, which boasts a very high standard hotel in an old farmhouse fortified to stave off invasion, found close to the fishing village of Savelletri. The generally flat terrain has been extensively contoured by Andy Haggar and European Golf Design with inescapable references to links-style courses. The only hazards are huge bunkers and water, while the rare olive trees do little to break the occasional breeze that blows and tempers the summer heat. "Waste bunkers" have been built and dotted with bushes and local plants. Stretching almost 7,000 yards, this is a serious and strategic test without hidden traps. It is also astutely landscaped and a course where golfers enjoy some magnificent views over the Adriatic, every step of the way.

San Domenico Golf — 2003

I - 72010 SAVELLETRI DI FASANO (BR)

Office	Segreteria	(39) 080 482 9200
Pro shop	Pro shop	(39) 080 482 9200
Fax	Fax	(39) 080 482 7944
Web	www.masseriasandomenico.com	
Situation	Località	Monopoli, 10 km

Fasano, 5 km

Annual closure	Chiusura annuale	no
Weekly closure	Chiusura settimanale	no

Fees main season Tariffe alta stagione		18 holes
	Week days Settimana	**We/Bank holidays** Feriale/Festivo
Individual Individuale	€ 90	€ 90
Couple Coppia	€ 180	€ 180

Low season: € 70

Caddie Caddie on request **Electric Trolley** Carello elettrico yes

Buggy Car yes **Clubs** Bastoni yes

Credit cards Carte di credito
VISA - Eurocard - MasterCard - AMEX - DC

Monopoli
Bari
Lamandia
GOLF
Savelletri
Torre Canne
Fasano
S 379
Taranto
km 0 2 4
0 miles 2,5

Access Itinerario : Bari, S16/E55 to Fasano.
In Fasano, turn left towards the sea → Savelletri di Fasano
Map 4 on page 928 Carta 4 Pagina 928

GOLF COURSE — PERCORSO — 16/20

Site	Paesaggio	
Maintenance	Manutenzione	
Architect	Architetto	Andy Haggar
Type	Tipologia	seaside course, links
Relief	Relievo terreno	
Water in play	Acqua in gioco	
Exp. to wind	Esposto al vento	
Trees in play	Alberi in gioco	

Scorecard Carta-score	**Chp.** Camp.	**Mens** Uomini	**Ladies** Donne
Length Lunghezza	6392	5993	5158
Par	72	72	72
Slope system	135	132	128

Advised golfing ability Livello di gioco consigliato — 0 12 24 36

Hcp required Handicap richiesto certificate

CLUB HOUSE & AMENITIES — CLUB HOUSE E SERVIZI — 7/10

Pro shop Pro shop
Driving range Campo pratica
Sheltered coperto no - On grass in erba yes - Putting-green Putting-green yes - Pitching-green Green-pratica yes

HOTEL FACILITIES — ALBERGHI — 7/10

HOTELS ALBERGHI

Masseria San Domenico - 55 rooms, D € 400 - on site
Tel (39) 080 482 7769, Fax (39) 080 482 7944

Masseria Cimino - 20 rooms, D € 150 - on site
Tel (39) 080 482 9200, Fax (39) 080 482 7944

I Melograno - Monopoli → Alberobello 10 km - 37 rooms, D € 380
Tel (39) 080 690 9030, Fax (39) 080 747 903

Agrit. Masseria Marzalossa - 8 rooms, D € 200 - Fasano 5 km
Tel (39) 080 441 3780, Fax (39) 080 441 3730

RESTAURANTS RISTORANTE

Masseria San Domenico - on site - Tel (39) 080 482 7769
La Mia Terra - Monopoli 10 km - Tel (39) 080 690 0969
Da Renzina - Savelletri 1 km - Tel (39) 080 432 9075

Torino - La Mandria *Percorso Blu*

16	8	7

E' il fratello maggiore e il vicino di casa de I Roveri, un complesso di 36 buche dove il percorso migliore è quello "Blu". Di lunghezza assolutamente rispettabile è stato disegnato da John Morrison prima di subire recentemente qualche modifica sotto la supervisione di Graham Cooke. Gli alberi secolari sono un pò ovunque, ma la larghezza dei fairways è sufficiente per non sentirsi soffocati. I bunkers difendono bene i greens di questo percorso dal deciso carattere britannico. Alcuni ostacoli d'acqua naturali sono stati fatti entrare in gioco con intelligenza, ma è comunque è sempre facile rimediare i propri errori. E' un percorso dove si cammina senza stancarsi, immerso in una natura particolarmente bella e inoltre è sufficientemente impegnativo per i giocatori bassi di handicap senza essere troppo difficile per i giocatori mediocri. Il percorso "giallo" è una valida alternativa al percorso tradizionale ed entrambi hanno il pregio di essere molto ben tenuti.

This is the elderly neighbour to "I Roveri", a 36 hole resort the most challenging section of which is the "Percorso Blu". With very respectable yardage, it was designed by John Morrison and underwent a number of more recent changes under the supervision of Graham Cooke. Age-old trees are almost everywhere but the fairways are wide enough to avoid any risk of claustrophobia. The greens are well defended by bunkers on a course that has classic British character. A few stretches of water have been cleverly brought into play, but here again it is always possible to make up for your mistakes. In all, this gives an easily walkable, very pleasant and well-landscaped course that is demanding enough for low-handicap golfers and not too tough for high-handicappers. The other course, the "Percorso giallo", is more or less the same sort of layout only with more water in play and presents an excellent additional layout on this very well maintained site.

Circolo Golf Torino — 1924

Via Grange 137
I - 10070 FIANO TORINESE

Office	Segreteria	(39) 011 923 5440
Pro shop	Pro shop	(39) 011 923 6028
Fax	Fax	(39) 011 923 5886
Web	www.circologolftorino.it	
Situation	Località	Torino, 16 km
Annual closure	Chiusura annuale	25/12→1/1
Weekly closure	Chiusura settimanale	monday
Fees main season	Tariffe alta stagione	18 holes

	Week days Settimana	We/Bank holidays Feriale/Festivo
Individual Individuale	€ 62	€ 93
Couple Coppia	€ 124	€ 186

Caddie Caddie yes — **Electric Trolley** Carello elettrico yes
Buggy Car yes — **Clubs** Bastoni yes
Credit cards Carte di credito no

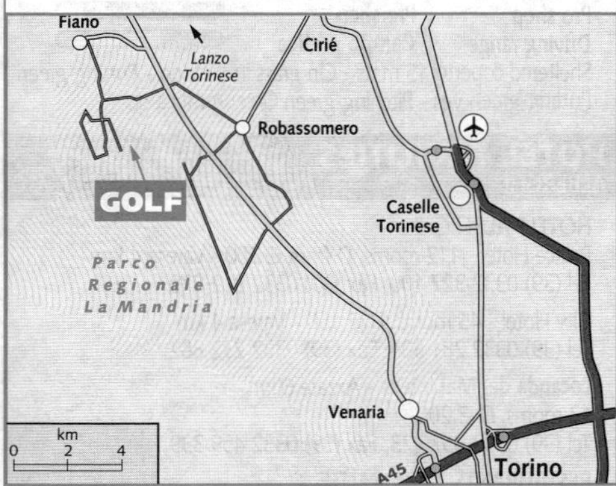

Access Itinerario : Milano to Torino, A4 - A45 Exit (Uscita) Venaria. → Lanzo. Golf to the left.
Map 1 on page 922 Carta 1 Pagina 922

GOLF COURSE — PERCORSO 16/20

Site	Paesaggio	
Maintenance	Manutenzione	
Architect	Architetto	John Morrison Cooke, Harris, Croze
Type	Tipologia	forest
Relief	Relievo terreno	
Water in play	Acqua in gioco	
Exp. to wind	Esposto al vento	
Trees in play	Alberi in gioco	

Scorecard Carta-score	Chp. Camp.	Mens Uomini	Ladies Donne
Length Lunghezza	6216	5943	5212
Par	72	72	72
Slope system	141	139	130

Advised golfing ability Livello di gioco consigliato — 0 12 24 36
Hcp required Handicap richiesto 34

CLUB HOUSE & AMENITIES — CLUB HOUSE E SERVIZI 8/10

Pro shop Pro shop
Driving range Campo pratica
Sheltered coperto 8 mats - On grass in erba yes - Putting-green Putting-green yes - Pitching-green Green-pratica yes

HOTEL FACILITIES — ALBERGHI 7/10

HOTELS ALBERGHI

Jet Hotel - 80 rooms, D € 160 - Caselle Torinese 8 km
Tel (39) 011 991 3733, Fax (39) 011 996 1544

Turin Palace Hotel - 120 rooms, D € 250 - Torino 16 km
Tel (39) 011 562 5511, Fax (39) 011 561 2187

Victoria - 106 rooms, D from € 138 - Torino 16 km
Tel (39) 011 561 1909, Fax (39) 011 561 1806

Gotha Hotel - 44 rooms, D € 160 - Cirié 5 km
Tel (39) 011 921 2059, Fax (39) 011 920 3661

RESTAURANTS RISTORANTE

Del Cambio - Torino 16 km - Tel (39) 011 543 760
Dolce Stil Novo - Cirié 5 km - Tel (39) 011 921 1110
Vintage 1997 - Torino 16 km - Tel (39) 011 535 948

Varese

14	8	7

Varese è una cittadina molto bella e raffinata situata tra Lugano e Milano. Il campo da golf è stato costruito appena sopra al lago di Varese, che è uno dei più piccoli laghi lombardi dove il clima è particolarmente mite e soleggiato. I golfisti più religiosi non potranno fare a meno di una visita al Sacro Monte, luogo di pellegrinaggio alla Vergine Maria da dove si può godere un fantastico panorama sui laghi e le montagne. Il percorso merita una visita per la sua particolarità. Non è molto lungo, ma il terreno molto mosso richiede una buona forma fisica e una buona padronanza dei colpi in situazioni delicate e nei pendii. La scelta del bastone non è mai facile perchè parecchi greens sono sopraelevati e siccome molti hanno anche due livelli, la precisione diventa un obbligo. Se il vostro giro non è andato molto bene, vi consolerete facilmente rilassandovi nella superba club-house (un antico monastero) e ammirando la bellezza del paesaggio.

Varese is a beautiful and refined city located between Lake Lugano and Milan. This course was built above Lake Varese, one of the smallest lakes in Lombardy, where the climate is particularly mild and sunny. The more religious-minded golfer won't want to miss visiting the Sacro Monte, the site of a great pilgrimage to the Virgin Mary plus the added bonus of wonderful views over lakes and mountains. This region is not only a tourist destination, it is also worth visiting for the originality of this course. It might not be very long but the hilly terrain requires a certain level of fitness and control when hitting the ball from tricky situations and sloping lies. Club selection is seldom straightforward, especially since a number of greens are elevated and many are two-tiered, making accuracy a must. If your round didn't go so well, the superb club-house (a former monastery) offers solace and consolation from where you can admire the beautiful landscape.

Golf Club Varese — 1934

Via Vitorio Veneto 32
I - 21020 LUVINATE (VA)

Office Segreteria (39) 0332 229 302
Pro shop Pro shop (39) 0332 821 043
Fax Fax (39) 0332 222 107
Web www.golfclubvarese.it
Situation Località Milano, 55 km
Varese (pop. 83 798), 5 km
Annual closure Chiusura annuale — no
Weekly closure Chiusura settimanale — monday

Fees main season Tariffe alta stagione	18 holes	
	Week days Settimana	**We/Bank holidays** Feriale/Festivo
Individual Individuale	€ 60	€ 85
Couple Coppia	€ 120	€ 170

Caddie Caddie on request **Electric Trolley** Carello elettrico no
Buggy Car yes **Clubs** Bastoni yes
Credit cards Carte di credito
VISA - CartaSì

Lago Maggiore
Gavirate
GOLF
Lugano
Induno Olona
Lago di Varese
Varese
Calcinàte del P.
Bizzozero
Vedano Olona
Azzate
A 8
Gallarate Milano
S 233
Milano
km 0 2 4

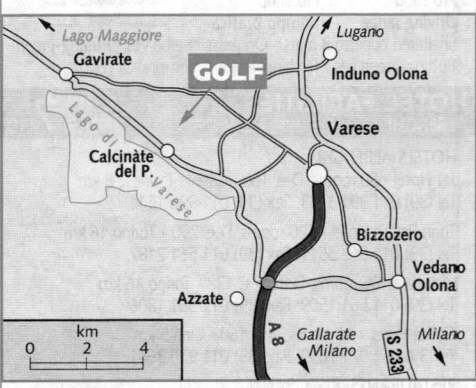

Access Itinerario : Varese, Via Manzoni, Via Sacco, Via S. Sanvito → Gavirate/Laveno. 5 km → Golf
Map 1 on page 922 Carta 1 Pagina 922

GOLF COURSE — PERCORSO — 14/20

Site Paesaggio
Maintenance Manutenzione
Architect Architetto — Cecil R. Blandford, Peter Gannon
Type Tipologia — parkland, hilly
Relief Relievo terreno
Water in play Acqua in gioco
Exp. to wind Esposto al vento
Trees in play Alberi in gioco

Scorecard Carta-score	**Chp.** Camp.	**Mens** Uomini	**Ladies** Donne
Length Lunghezza	6105	5942	5238
Par	72	72	72
Slope system	130	130	130

Advised golfing ability Livello di gioco consigliato — 0 12 24 36
Hcp required Handicap richiesto 34

CLUB HOUSE & AMENITIES — CLUB HOUSE E SERVIZI — 8/10

Pro shop Pro shop
Driving range Campo pratica
Sheltered coperto 15 mats - On grass in erba no - Putting-green Putting-green yes - Pitching-green Green-pratica no

HOTEL FACILITIES — ALBERGHI — 7/10

HOTELS ALBERGHI
Palace Hotel - 112 rooms, D from € 200 - Varese 4 km
Tel (39) 0332 327 100, Fax (39) 0332 312 870

City Hotel - 45 rooms, D € 150 - Varese 4 km
Tel (39) 0332 281 304, Fax (39) 0332 232 882

Locanda del Mai Intees - Azzate 6 km
13 rooms, D € 200
Tel (39) 0332 457 223, Fax (39) 0332 459 339

RESTAURANTS RISTORANTE
Al Vecchio Convento - Varese 5 km - Tel (39) 0332 261 005
Da Annetta - Capolago 5 km - Tel (39) 0332 490 020
Teatro - Varese 5 km - Tel (39) 0332 241 124

Venezia

16 | 7 | 9

Si dice che Venezia sia magica all'alba e a notte fonda, quindi rimane tutta la giornata per giocare a golf su questo percorso nell'estremità ovest del Lido, di fronte alla città dei Dogi, in una stazione balneare molto elegante dove c'è anche uno dei pochissimi casinò italiani. Disegnato da Cruikshank e rivisto da C.K. Cotton e Marco Croze, si snoda su terreno di dune sabbiose in mezzo a pioppi, pini ed olivi. La sua architettura tipicamente britannica si è perfettamente armonizzata negli anni e non costringe a porsi troppi problemi tattici quando non si è in forma. Bisogna comunque fare attenzione: in un ambiente così piacevole, gli errori si fanno facilmente e possono costare cari sullo score o in un match-play. Qualche ostacolo d'acqua e spesso il vento aggiungono il sapore della sfida a questo che rimane uno dei più bei campi italiani.

As Venice is sheer magic at dawn and nightfall, you have the whole day in between to play this course at the far western tip of the Lido, opposite the city of Doges, a very chic seaside resort which is also home to one of the rare casinos to be found in Italy. This course, however, is much more than just space in which you can try your luck at golf. Designed by Cruikshank and restyled by C.K. Cotton and Marco Croze, it stretches over dune land amidst poplar, pine and olive trees. The obvious British architecture here has aged well and you find yourself rather happy not to have to ask too many tactical questions when your game is off-colour. Caution is required nonetheless, as mistakes can occur so easily in such a pleasant setting and prove costly for your card or match-play score. A few water hazards and frequent wind add a little spice to this excellent feast of golf.

Circolo Golf Venezia — 1928

Via del Forte
I - 30011 ALBERONI (VE)

Office	Segreteria	(39) 041 731 333
Pro shop	Pro shop	(39) 041 276 0361
Fax	Fax	(39) 041 731 339
Web	www.circologolfvenezia.it	
Situation	Località	Venezia (pop. 277 305), 11 km
Annual closure	Chiusura annuale	25/12→31/1
Weekly closure	Chiusura settimanale	monday
Fees main season	Tariffe alta stagione	18 holes

	Week days Settimana	We/Bank holidays Feriale/Festivo
Individual Individuale	€ 55	€ 70
Couple Coppia	€ 110	€ 140

Caddie Caddie yes — **Electric Trolley** Carello elettrico yes
Buggy Car yes — **Clubs** Bastoni yes
Credit cards Carte di credito
VISA - AMEX - DC - CartaSì

Access Itinerario : Venezia to Lido with vaporetto
Map 2 on page 924 Carta 2 Pagina 924

GOLF COURSE — PERCORSO — 16/20

Site	Paesaggio	
Maintenance	Manutenzione	
Architect	Architetto	C.K. Cotton, Cruikshank, Croze
Type	Tipologia	seaside course
Relief	Relievo terreno	
Water in play	Acqua in gioco	
Exp. to wind	Esposto al vento	
Trees in play	Alberi in gioco	

Scorecard Carta-score	Chp. Camp.	Mens Uomini	Ladies Donne
Length Lunghezza	6199	6039	5353
Par	72	72	72
Slope system	139	138	133

Advised golfing ability Livello di gioco consigliato — 0 12 24 36
Hcp required Handicap richiesto 34

CLUB HOUSE & AMENITIES — CLUB HOUSE E SERVIZI — 7/10

Pro shop Pro shop
Driving range Campo pratica
Sheltered coperto 5 mats - On grass in erba yes - Putting-green Putting-green yes - Pitching-green Green-pratica yes

HOTEL FACILITIES — ALBERGHI — 9/10

HOTELS ALBERGHI

Danieli - 245 rooms, D from € 430 - Venezia 11 km
Tel (39) 041 522 6480, Fax (39) 041 520 0208

Excelsior - Venezia Lido 3 km
215 rooms, D from € 610
Tel (39) 041 526 0201, Fax (39) 041 526 7276

Cà del Borgo - Venezia Lido (Malamocco) 3 km
8 rooms, D € 200
Tel (39) 041 770 749, Fax (39) 041 770 744

RESTAURANTS RISTORANTE

Trattoria Favorita - Venezia Lido 3 km - Tel (39) 041 526 1626
Andri - Venezia Lido 12 km - Tel (39) 041 526 5482
Al Vecio Cantier - Venezia Lido 3 km - Tel (39) 041 526 8130

Verona

13	7	8

Se amate le storie d'amore struggenti, non c' è posto più adatto di Verona, teatro del tragico amore di Romeo e Giulietta. Autentiche o create per gli animi sensibili, la casa in via Cappello e la tomba di Giulietta meritano un giro dopo un'opera all'Arena o un caffè in Piazza delle Erbe. Da ogni parte la guardiate, Verona è una città bellissima resa ancor più attraente dalla sua vicinanza con il lago di Garda. Il golf club Verona è stato fondato nel 1963 e il percorso è stato realizzato in due tempi da John Harris nel suo stile assolutamente britannico. Molto mosso, obbliga i giocatori meno in forma ad usare il golf cart e a stare molto attenti ad attaccare i greens sopraelevati (ed anche un green cieco). Le prime nove buche sono abbastanza strette e "tricky" con qualche pericoloso fuori limite mentre le buche di ritorno sono più larghe e malgrado qualche ostacolo d'acqua consentono di non compromettere un buono score ottenuto sulle prime.

When you love tear-jerking tales of love and grief, you can hardly wish for a better setting than Verona, home to the tragic story of Romeo and Juliette. The house (Via Cappello) and tomb of Juliette are worth going out your way for, after an opera at the Arenas or a coffee on the Piazza delle Erbe. Whichever way you look at it, Verona is a superb city made even more attractive by the closeness of Lake Garda. The Verona Golf Club was founded in 1963 and the course laid out in two stages by John Harris, in a British parkland style consistent with the architect's own style. Very hilly, this course warrants a buggy for the more unfit golfer and a lot of concentration to hit some elevated greens (and one blind green as well). The first holes are rather narrow and tricky to negotiate - some dangerous out-of-bounds await the mis-hit shot - while the back 9 are wider with a few water hazards and shouldn't do too much damage to your card if you have scored well over the front nine.

Golf Club Verona — 1963

Loc. Ca' del Sale 15
I - 37066 SOMMACAMPAGNA (VR)

Office	Segreteria	(39) 045 510 060
Pro shop	Pro shop	(39) 045 510 317
Fax	Fax	(39) 045 510 242
Web		www.golfclubverona.com
Situation	Località	Verona (pop. 255 268), 13 km
Annual closure	Chiusura annuale	no
Weekly closure	Chiusura settimanale	tuesday
Fees main season	Tariffe alta stagione	18 holes

	Week days Settimana	We/Bank holidays Feriale/Festivo
Individual Individuale	€ 60	€ 70
Couple Coppia	€ 120	€ 140

Caddie Caddie no — **Electric Trolley** Carello elettrico yes
Buggy Car yes — **Clubs** Bastoni no
Credit cards Carte di credito
VISA - Mastercard
Access Itinerario : A4 Milano-Venezia, Exit (Uscita)

Sommacampagna. 1 km, take right then left → Golf.
Map 2 on page 924 Carta 2 Pagina 924

GOLF COURSE — PERCORSO — 13/20

Site	Paesaggio	
Maintenance	Manutenzione	
Architect	Architetto	John Harris
Type	Tipologia	country
Relief	Relievo terreno	
Water in play	Acqua in gioco	
Exp. to wind	Esposto al vento	
Trees in play	Alberi in gioco	

Scorecard Carta-score	Chp. Camp.	Mens Uomini	Ladies Donne
Length Lunghezza	6037	6037	5241
Par	72	72	72
Slope system	124	124	128

Advised golfing ability Livello di gioco consigliato — 0 12 24 36
Hcp required Handicap richiesto 34

CLUB HOUSE & AMENITIES — CLUB HOUSE E SERVIZI — 7/10

Pro shop Pro shop
Driving range Campo pratica
Sheltered coperto 12 mats - On grass in erba yes - Putting-green Putting-green yes - Pitching-green Green-pratica yes

HOTEL FACILITIES — ALBERGHI — 8/10

HOTELS ALBERGHI

Saccardi Quadrante Europe - Caselle di Sommacampagna 5 km
126 rooms, D € 165
Tel (39) 045 858 1400, Fax (39) 045 858 1402

Gabbia d'Oro - 27 rooms, D from € 370 - Verona 13 km
Tel (39) 045 800 3060, Fax (39) 045 590 293

Locanda Merica - 10 rooms, D € 80 - Sommacampagna 5 km
Tel (39) 045 515 160, Fax (39) 045 515 344

RESTAURANTS RISTORANTE

Il Desco - Verona 13 km - Tel (39) 045 595 358

Merica - Sommacampagna 2 km - Tel (39) 045 515 160

Osteria La Fontanina - Verona 13 km - Tel (39) 045 913 305

Villa d'Este

16 | 9 | 8

Disegnato nel 1926 da Peter Gannon, Villa d'Este è diventato rapidamente uno dei gioielli golfistici italiani. Merito è anche della sua posizione vicino al magnifico lago di Como, che si snoda in lunghezza e dove i piccoli porticcioli si succedono ai giardini esotici delle sue ville da sogno. La più bella è stata trasformata a Cernobbio in uno dei più affascinanti hotel, luogo di soggiorno da sogno. Villa d'Este è un percorso abbastanza mosso che si snoda ai bordi del piccolo lago di Montorfano in mezzo a pini, castani e querce ma dove si può facilmente giocare anche a piedi. Non è lungo, ma per fare un buono score bisogna mettere a punto una tecnica eccellente e saper fare colpi di prim'ordine soprattutto nei par 3. Ci sono solo due par 5 ma entrambi offrono buone possibilità per un birdie. Una club-house di gran classe aggiunge il tocco finale a questo posto tranquillo ed elegante.

Designed in 1926 by Peter Gannon, Villa d'Este has rapidly become one of the gems of Italian golf courses, much of which is due to a location close to the long Lake Como, where small harbours give way to exotic gardens around superb villas. The finest of these villas in Cernobbio has been transformed into one of the most charming hotels you could wish to find, the ideal site for a holiday... if not on too tight a budget. Villa d'Este, alongside the small lake of Montorfano, is a rather hilly course set amidst pine, chestnut and birch trees but is easily walkable all the same. Yardage is not too demanding but you need to develop good technique to play well here, bending the ball both ways especially on the six par 3s. There are only two par 5s but both offer a real chance of a birdie. A superb club-house adds the final touch to this tranquil and elegant site.

Circolo Golf Villa d'Este — 1926

Via Cantù 13
I - 22030 MONTORFANO (CO)

Office	Segreteria	(39) 031 200 200
Pro shop	Pro shop	(39) 031 200 898
Fax	Fax	(39) 031 200 786
Web	www.golfvilladeste.com	
Situation	Località	Varese, 30 km

Como (pop. 82 989), 9 km -

Annual closure	Chiusura annuale	1/12→1/3
Weekly closure	Chiusura settimanale	tuesday
Fees main season	Tariffe alta stagione	18 holes

	Week days Settimana	We/Bank holidays Feriale/Festivo
Individual Individuale	€ 80	€ 90*
Couple Coppia	€ 160	€ 180*

*We: with members only (ospiti accettati con soci)

Caddie Caddie yes — **Electric Trolley** Carello elettrico no

Buggy Car yes — **Clubs** Bastoni yes

Credit cards Carte di credito
VISA - AMEX - CartaSì

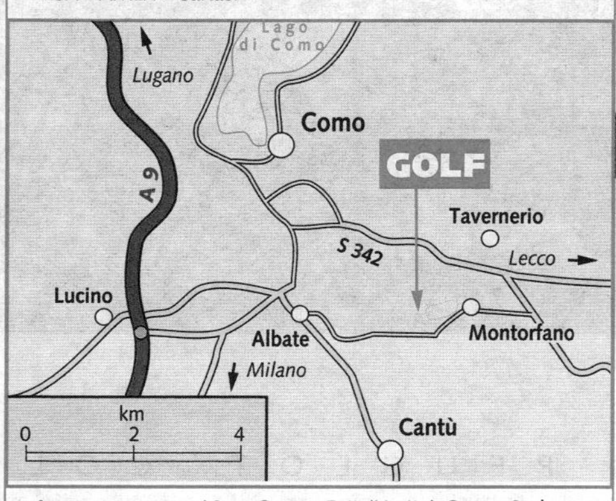

Access Itinerario : A9 → Como. Exit (Uscita) Como-Sud. Turn right → Cantù. 5 km → Montorfano. Golf on left hand side.
Map 1 on page 923 Carta 1 Pagina 923

GOLF COURSE — PERCORSO — 16/20

Site	Paesaggio	
Maintenance	Manutenzione	
Architect	Architetto	Peter Gannon
Type	Tipologia	forest
Relief	Relievo terreno	
Water in play	Acqua in gioco	
Exp. to wind	Esposto al vento	
Trees in play	Alberi in gioco	

Scorecard Carta-score	Chp. Camp.	Mens Uomini	Ladies Donne
Length Lunghezza	5727	5544	4869
Par	69	69	69
Slope system	130	129	123

Advised golfing ability Livello di gioco consigliato — 0 12 24 36

Hcp required Handicap richiesto 34

CLUB HOUSE & AMENITIES — CLUB HOUSE E SERVIZI — 9/10

Pro shop Pro shop
Driving range Campo pratica
Sheltered coperto 10 mats - On grass in erba no - Putting-green Putting-green yes - Pitching-green Green-pratica yes

HOTEL FACILITIES — ALBERGHI — 8/10

HOTELS ALBERGHI
Grand Hotel Villa d'Este - Cernobbio 13 km
174 rooms, D from € 590
Tel (39) 031 3481, Fax (39) 031 348 844

Villa Odescalchi - 57 rooms, D € 180 - Alzate Brianza 6 km
Tel (39) 031 630 822, Fax (39) 031 632 079

Santandrea Golf Hotel -12 rooms, D € 110 - Montorfano 3 km
Tel (39) 031 200 220, Fax (39) 031 200 786

RESTAURANTS RISTORANTE
Navedano - Como 8 km - Tel (39) 031 308 080
Il Cantuccio - Albavilla 8 km - Tel (39) 031 628 736
Crotto del Lupo - Como 9 km - Tel (39) 031 570 881
Al Ponte - Cantù 3 km - Tel (39) 031 712 561

NEDERLAND

THE NETHERLANDS

Kennemer

985

GUIDE 2006/2007

JE VOELT JE LEKKERDER IN EEN PEUGEOT.
PEUGEOT

THE NETHERLANDS

The Netherlands, with 251,000 golfers, is one of the countries in Europe where golf is developing fast. There are about 90 eighteen-hole courses, naturally spread around large cities, thus implying busy week-ends. But here, distances from one end of the country to the other are never too great, and the very dense road system makes for easy travelling round and about your holiday location. Alongside the great seaside courses, the country has a number of solid arguments to attract golf-trotters, with courses that, more often than not, blend in very tastefully with the natural landscape. This is still a little known destination, and one well worth discovering during the warmer months.

NEDERLAND

Met meer dan 251.000 spelers behoort Nederland tot de landen van Europa met een sterke groei. Er zijn meer dan 90 18-holes-banen, die logischerwijze vooral rond de grote steden liggen. Wat betekent dat het er vooral in de weekends druk kan zijn. Maar de afstanden van de ene naar de andere kant van dit land zijn nooit erg groot en het wegennet is vrij dicht, waardoor je een groot gebied rond de verblijfplaats kunt bereiken. Naast de 'grote' banen aan de kust heeft het land golftechnisch nog meer in zijn mars, met banen die vaak goed in het landschap zijn opgenomen. Het is een weinig bekende bestemming, die vooral in de zomer ontdekt moet worden.

Map No 1
Carte n°1
km
0 10 20
Amsterdam
Purmerend
Houtrak
Kennemer
Noordwijk
Hilversum
Lage Vuursche
Haagsche
De Pan
Hoge Kleij
Anderstein
Broekpolder
Batouwe
Cromstrijen
Efteling
Oosterhout
Goes
Wouwse Plantage
Toxandria
Royal Antwerp (B)
Royal Zoute (B)
Rinkven (B)
Gendersteyn
Eindhoven
Limburg (B)
Royal Latem (B)
AMSTERDAM
ROTTERDAM
DEN HAAG
('S-GRAVENHAGE)
UTRECHT
ANTWERPEN
(ANVERS)
BRUXELLES
IJsselmeer
988
MICHELIN

GRONINGEN
Drente
Sint Nicolaasga
Gelpenberg
Emmen
Assen
Zwolle
Nunspeet
Sybrook
Rheine/ Mesum (D)
Twente
Enschede
Hengelo
Deventer
Apeldoorn
Graafschap
ARNHEM
Rosendael
Wasserburg-Anholt (D)
Münster
Rijk van Nijmegen
DORTMUND
ESSEN
Essener Oefte (D)
Bergisch Land Wuppertal (D)
DUISBURG
Krefeld
Elfrather Mühle (D)
WUPPERTAL
Hubbelrath (D)
DÜSSELDORF
Krefelder (D)
Düsseldorfer (D)
Mönchengladbach
Schloss Myllendonk (D)
Herkenbosch
Gut Lärchenhof (D)
Spiegelven (B)
Zuid Limburgse
KÖLN
Maastricht
989
MICHELIN
d'après base de données au 1/1 000 000 édition - 2005.
Autorisation n°0501023.

CLASSIFICATION OF GOLF COURSES
RANKSCHIKKING VAN DE BANEN

This classification gives priority consideration to the score awarded to the actual course.

Deze rangschikking houdt vooral rekening met het cijfer, dat aan de baan werd toegekend.

Within each score, the ranking is purely alphabetical

Course score Cijfer van de banen				Page Pagina
18	8	7	Eindhoven	1000
18	7	8	Haagsche	1005
18	8	8	Kennemer	1010
18	7	8	Noordwijk	1012
17	7	7	Lage Vuursche	1011
16	8	5	Cromstrijen	996
16	8	7	De Pan	997
16	8	5	Efteling	999
16	7	6	Herkenbosch	1006
16	7	7	Hilversum	1007
16	8	8	Houtrak	1009
15	7	7	Amsterdam	992
15	7	4	Batouwe	994
15	7	6	Broekpolder	995
15	7	7	Gendersteyn	1002
15	7	6	Goes	1003
15	7	6	Graafschap	1004
15	6	7	Hoge Kleij	1008
15	7	7	Oosterhout	1014
15	7	7	Rosendael	1017
15	7	5	Sint Nicolaasga	1018
15	6	6	Sybrook	1019
15	7	6	Twente	1021
15	7	6	Wouwse Plantage	1022
14	7	6	Anderstein	993
14	8	5	Drente	998
14	5	5	Gelpenberg	1001
14	7	6	Nunspeet North + East	1013
14	8	7	Purmerend	1015
14	6	7	Rijk van Nijmegen Nijmeegse Baan	1016
14	7	6	Toxandria	1020
14	7	8	Zuid Limburg	1023

HOTEL FACILITIES
HOTELS IN OMGEVING

This classification gives priority consideration to the score awarded to the hotel facilities.

Deze classificatie is vooral gebaseerd op de score voor de hotel accommodatie.

Course score		Cijfer van hotels in omgeving		Page Pagina
18	7	**8**	Haagsche	1005
16	8	**8**	Houtrak	1009
18	8	**8**	Kennemer	1010
18	7	**8**	Noordwijk	1012
14	7	**8**	Zuid Limburg	1023
15	7	**7**	Amsterdam	992
16	8	**7**	De Pan	997
18	8	**7**	Eindhoven	1000
15	7	**7**	Gendersteyn	1002
16	7	**7**	Hilversum	1007
15	6	**7**	Hoge Kleij	1008
17	7	**7**	Lage Vuursche	1011
15	7	**7**	Oosterhout	1014
14	8	**7**	Purmerend	1015
14	6	**7**	Rijk van Nijmegen Nijmeegse Baan	1016
15	7	**7**	Rosendael	1017
14	7	**6**	Anderstein	993
15	7	**6**	Broekpolder	995
15	7	**6**	Goes	1003
15	7	**6**	Graafschap	1004
16	7	**6**	Herkenbosch	1006
14	7	**6**	Nunspeet North + East	1013
15	6	**6**	Sybrook	1019
14	7	**6**	Toxandria	1020
15	7	**6**	Twente	1021
15	7	**6**	Wouwse Plantage	1022
16	8	**5**	Cromstrijen	996
14	8	**5**	Drente	998
16	8	**5**	Efteling	999
14	5	**5**	Gelpenberg	1001
15	7	**5**	Sint Nicolaasga	1018
15	7	**4**	Batouwe	994

Amsterdam

15	7	7

Toen de oude Amsterdamse de helft van zijn holes aan de Spoorwegen verloor, vertrok de club naar een nieuw, open terrein aan de westkant van de stad (soms een beetje rumoerig door de overvliegende vliegtuigen). Aanvankelijk waren er problemen waardoor alle greens moesten worden gerenoveerd. Die ingreep en het verder groeien van de jonge aanplant, zullen de baan sterk verbeteren. De eerste zeven holes zijn niet om over naar huis te schrijven, met alleen de fairway bunkers en de wind als moeilijkheidsfactor. Dan wordt het spannender met twee par-4 holes en water. Water speelt ook een belangrijke rol op de tweede negen, vooral op de 14e (een par-5 dogleg met twee vijvers) en de 18e waar de green wordt afgeschermd door water. Een prachtige slothole. De baan is niet te druk.

When the old Amsterdam Golf Club lost half of its holes to the railways, the club moved out into a very open area to the west of the city (sometimes a little noisy because of the airport). Owing to a number of serious problems, the greens have all been re-laid and their maturity should do much to improve the terrain still further; the same goes for the newly planted trees and bushes. The seven first holes are not much to write home about, the only difficulties being the bunker fairways and wind. Then, it gets a little more exciting with two par 4s and water hazards. Water, in fact, is very much to the fore on the way in, especially on the 14th (a par 5 dog-leg with two ponds and two ditches) and the 18th, where the green is again guarded by water to make an excellent final hole. The course is not too crowded.

Amsterdamse Golfclub — 1990

Bauduinlaan 35
NL - 1047 HK AMSTERDAM

Office	Secretariaat	(31) 0651 291 414
Pro shop	Pro shop	(31) 020 497 5508
Fax	Fax	(31) 020 497 5966
Web	www.amsterdamsegolfclub.nl	
Situation	Locatie	Amsterdam, 15 km
Annual closure	Jaarlijkse sluiting	no
Weekly closure	Wekelijkse sluitingsdag	no

Fees main season Hoogseizoen tarieven	18 holes	
	Week days Weekdagen	**We/Bank holidays** We/Feestdagen
Individual Individueel	€ 55	*
Couple Paar	€ 110	*

* We: members only

Caddie Caddie no — **Electric Trolley** Electrische trolley no
Buggy Buggy yes — **Clubs** Clubs yes
Credit cards Creditcards
VISA - Mastercard - AMEX - Pin

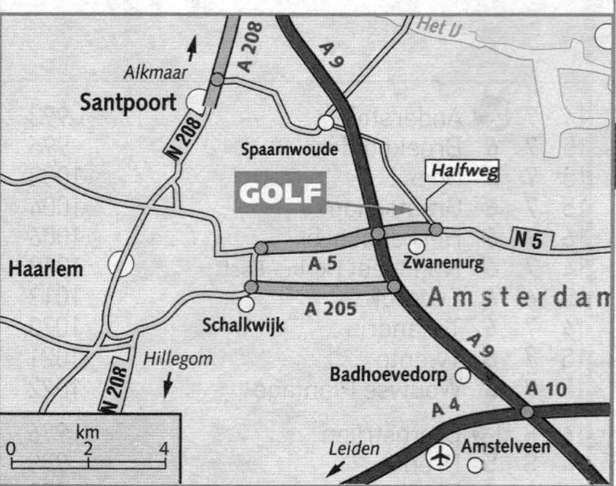

Access Toegang : Amsterdam N5/A5 → Haarlem. Exit Spaarnwoude. 1 km → Ruigoord/Houtrak
Map 1 on page 988 Auto kaart 1 Blz 988

GOLF COURSE — BAAN — 15/20

Site	Terrein	
Maintenance	Onderhoud	
Architect	Architect	Paul Rolin, Gérard Jol
Type	Type baan	inland, parkland
Relief	Reliëf	
Water in play	Waterhazards	
Exp. to wind	Windgevoelig	
Trees in play	Bomen	

Scorecard Scorekaart	**Chp.** Back tees	**Mens** Heren	**Ladies** Damen
Length Lengte	6108	5908	5064
Par	72	72	72
Slope system	134	132	128

Advised golfing ability Aanbevolen golfvaardigheid — 0 12 24 36
Hcp required Vereiste hcp — 36

CLUB HOUSE & AMENITIES — CLUB HOUSE EN ANNEXEN — 7/10

Pro shop Pro shop
Driving range Oefenbaan
Sheltered overdekt 8 mats - On grass op gras no - Putting-green putting-green yes - Pitching-green pitching-green yes

HOTEL FACILITIES — HOTELS IN OMGEVING — 7/10

HOTELS HOTELS

Radisson SAS - 243 rooms, D € 260 - Amsterdam 15 km
Tel (31) 020 - 623 1231, Fax (31) 020 - 520 8200

Canal House - 26 rooms, D € 190 - Amsterdam 15 km
Tel (31) 020 - 622 5182, Fax (31) 020 - 624 1317

Ambassade - 59 rooms, D € 180 - Amsterdam 15 km
Tel (31) 020 - 555 0222, Fax (31) 020 - 555 0277

RESTAURANTS RESTAURANTS

La Rive - Amsterdam 10 km - Tel (31) 020 - 520 3264
De Bokkedoorns - Overveen/Haarlem 15 km
Tel (31) 020 - 526 3600
De Jonge Dikkert - Amstelveen/Amsterdam 15 km
Tel (31) 020 - 643 3333

Anderstein

14 | 7 | 6

De spoorweg en de A12 op de achtergrond van een aantal holes zouden niet teveel de aandacht van de vele kwaliteiten van deze baan moeten afleiden. Het vroegere familiedomein is omgetoverd in een golfbaan met drie lussen van negen holes en het clubhuis in de vroegere boerenstal. De baan is in meerdere fasen tot stand gekomen. Veel van de oorspronkelijke holes zijn vrij smal omdat er in eerste aanleg niet veel ruimte was. De meeste 'nieuwe' holes liggen in open land. Door de geleidelijke groei is een grote variatie in holes ontstaan. Er zijn doglegs met brede fairways, holes met vijvers en slootjes, maar ook holes omzoomd door imposante bomen. En overall liggen strategisch geplaatste bunkers. Alles bij elkaar is het een zeer aantrekkelijke baan, zo ongeveer in het echte centrum van het land. Juist die grote variëteit maakt het wenselijk om meerdere keren te spelen als je de baan een beetje wilt gaan begrijpen. Doe dit vooral door de week, want in de weekenden zijn er veel leden op de been/baan.

The railway line and road that form a backdrop to some holes here should not conceal the many virtues of this course. The erstwhile family property was turned into a private course with three loops of nine holes each, where the old farmhouse serves as the club-house. The course was built in several phases. Some of the original holes are rather narrow as they were built within a restricted amount of space. Most of the new holes run through wide open land. The gradual construction has led to a large variety in holes. There are dog-legs with broad fairways, holes with massive water hazards, but also holes surrounded by impressive trees. And everywhere you will find strategically located bunkers. In all, this 'domain' has become a very attractive course. You definitely need to play here several times to understand your way around. If you do, make it a week day as there are a lot of members on week-ends.

Golfclub Anderstein — 1988

Woudenbergseweg 13 A
NL - 3953 ME MAARSBERGEN

Office Secretariaat (31) 0343 - 431 330
Pro shop Pro shop (31) 0343 - 431 560
Fax Fax (31) 0343 - 432 062
Web www.golfclubanderstein.nl
Situation Locatie Utrecht (pop. 234 106), 20 km
Amersfoort (pop. 131 221), 10 km

Annual closure Jaarlijkse sluiting — no
Weekly closure Wekelijkse sluitingsdag — no

Fees main season Hoogseizoen tarieven	18 holes	
	Week days Weekdagen	**We/Bank holidays** We/Feestdagen
Individual Individueel	€ 65	*
Couple Paar	€ 130	*

* We: members only

Caddie Caddie no — **Electric Trolley** Electrische trolley no
Buggy Buggy no — **Clubs** Clubs yes
Credit cards Creditcards no

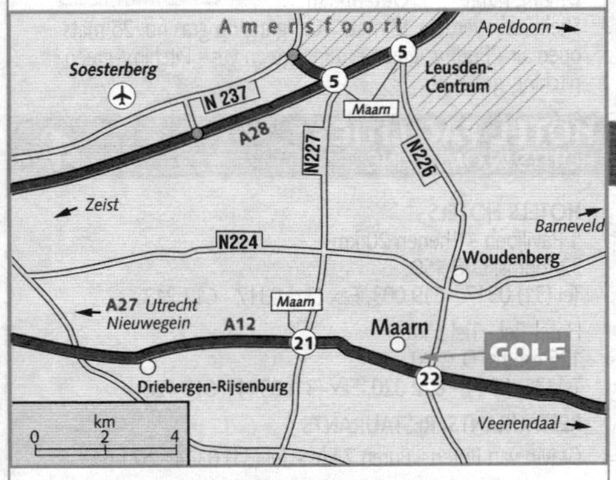

Access Toegang : A 12 Utrecht-Arnhem. Exit 22 → Maarsbergen, N226. 500 m turn left
Map 1 on page 988 Auto kaart 1 Blz 988

GOLF COURSE — BAAN — 14/20

Site Terrein
Maintenance Onderhoud
Architect Architect — Donald Steel, J.D. Van Heel, G. Jol
Type Type baan — parkland
Relief Reliëf
Water in play Waterhazards
Exp. to wind Windgevoelig
Trees in play Bomen

Scorecard Scorekaart	**Chp.** Back tees	**Mens** Heren	**Ladies** Damen
Length Lengte	6345	6004	5178
Par	72	72	72
Slope system	132	128	130

Advised golfing ability Aanbevolen golfvaardigheid — 0 12 24 36
Hcp required Vereiste hcp — no

CLUB HOUSE & AMENITIES — CLUB HOUSE EN ANNEXEN — 7/10

Pro shop Pro shop
Driving range Oefenbaan
Sheltered overdekt 3 mats - On grass op gras no - Putting-green putting-green yes (2) - Pitching-green pitching-green yes

HOTEL FACILITIES — HOTELS IN OMGEVING — 6/10

HOTELS HOTELS
De Witte Holevoet - 23 rooms, D € 110 - Scherpenzeel 7 km
Tel (31) 033 - 277 9111, Fax (31) 033 - 277 2613

De Hoefslag - 30 rooms, D € 230 - Bosch en Duin 15 km
Tel (31) 030 - 225 1051, Fax (31) 030 - 228 5821

Kasteel 't Kerckebosch - 30 rooms, D € 173 - Zeist 9 km
Tel (31) 030 - 692 6666, Fax (31) 030 - 692 6600

RESTAURANTS RESTAURANTS
De Hoefslag - Bosch en Duin 15 km - Tel (31) 030 - 225 1051
La Fine Bouche (Oud London) - Zeist 9 km
Tel (31) 0343 - 491 245
Hermitage - Zeist 9 km - Tel (31) 030 - 693 3159

Batouwe

15	7	4

Deze baan is oorspronkelijk aangelegd in open terrein, midden tussen de grote rivieren. De aanplant van honderden jonge bomen hebben het oorspronkelijke karakter van deze baan geleidelijk laten overgaan van een polder in een park. Bij de aanleg stonden er al een handjevol bomen en die zijn goed in het ontwerp ingepast. Ze staan langs de fairways of beschermen enkele greens, waardoor spelers twee keer moeten denken voordat ze een driver uit de tas halen. Er komen heel wat waterhazards in het spel, zoals op de 15e, een par-3 met een eilandgreen, of de 18e waar water de green beschermt tegen mislukte approaches. De andere holes hebben veel bunkers, vooral op de fairways. Hoewel de baan vrij kort is, zijn het vooral de elementen, zoals wind en water, die dwingen tot een nauwkeurige clubkeuze. Het ruime clubhuis ligt op een lichte verhoging, zodat het uitzicht biedt over een deel van de baan. De beste tijd om Batouwe te spelen is in het voorjaar, als de fruitbomen in de Betuwe in bloei staan.

This course has been laid out over wide open space between the main rivers at the centre of Holland. There were a handful of trees and these have been intelligently used by the architect, lining certain fairways, protecting a number of greens and forcing players to think twice before taking the driver out of the bag. A lot of water hazards come into play, like on the par 3 15th with an island green, or the 18th, where water protects the green from mis-hit approach shots. Most of the other holes just have lots of bunkers, especially of the fairway variety, numerous on two holes in particular. Hundreds of other trees have been planted but are no size as yet, so there is precious little protection from the wind. Even though the course itself is on the short side, the elements are a key factor here for choosing the right club. The best time to play De Batouwe is in the spring, when the region's fruit trees are in full blossom.

Betuws Golfcentrum de Batouwe — 1993

Oost Kanaalweg 1
NL - 4011 LA ZOELEN

Office	Secretariaat	(31) 0344 - 624 370
Pro shop	Pro shop	(31) 0344 - 624 370
Fax	Fax	(31) 0344 - 613 096
Web	www.debatouwe.nl	
Situation	Locatie	Tiel (pop. 33 571), 3 km
Annual closure	Jaarlijkse sluiting	no
Weekly closure	Wekelijkse sluitingsdag	no

Fees main season Hoogseizoen tarieven	18 holes	
	Week days Weekdagen	We/Bank holidays We/Feestdagen
Individual Individueel	€ 43	€ 53
Couple Paar	€ 86	€ 106

Caddie Caddie no — **Electric Trolley** Electrische trolley no
Buggy Buggy yes — **Clubs** Clubs yes
Credit cards Creditcards
VISA - MasterCard - Pin

Access Toegang : A15 Rotterdam-Arnhem/Nijmegen. Exit 33 → Maurik. 3.5 km → Echtfeld. Golf 1 km
Map 1 on page 988 Auto kaart 1 Blz 988

GOLF COURSE — BAAN — 15/20

Site	Terrein	
Maintenance	Onderhoud	
Architect	Architect	Alan Rijks
Type	Type baan	inland, parkland
Relief	Reliëf	
Water in play	Waterhazards	
Exp. to wind	Windgevoelig	
Trees in play	Bomen	

Scorecard Scorekaart	Chp. Back tees	Mens Heren	Ladies Damen
Length Lengte	5956	5689	5112
Par	72	72	72
Slope system	124	110	118

Advised golfing ability Aanbevolen golfvaardigheid: 0 12 24 36
Hcp required Vereiste hcp: no

CLUB HOUSE & AMENITIES — CLUB HOUSE EN ANNEXEN — 7/10

Pro shop Pro shop
Driving range Oefenbaan
Sheltered overdekt 10 mats - On grass op gras no, 25 mats open air - Putting-green putting-green yes - Pitching-green pitching-green yes

HOTEL FACILITIES — HOTELS IN OMGEVING — 4/10

HOTELS HOTELS
't Paviljoen - Rhenen 20 km
32 rooms, D € 150
Tel (31) 0317 - 619 003, Fax (31) 0317 - 617 213

Hotel Tiel - Tiel 5 km
125 rooms, D € 90
Tel (31) 0344 - 622 020, Fax (31) 0344 - 612 128

RESTAURANTS RESTAURANTS
Gravin van Buren - Buren 7 km - Tel (31) 0344 - 571 663
Brasserie Floris - Buren 7 km - Tel (31) 0344 - 572 770
't Kalkoentje - Rhenen 20 km - Tel (31) 0317 - 612 344

Broekpolder

15	7	6

Hier vindt u een voorbeeld van een baan waar de oorspronkelijk nogal kale ruimte geleidelijk aan voller en rijker is geworden. Na de aanleg in 1983 zijn bomen en struiken nu volgroeid hetgeen zowel bescherming tegen de wind biedt als een visuele verbetering is. Deze 'natuurlijke' ontwikkeling van de baan is nog versterkt door architectonische ingrepen die wat oorspronkelijke zwaktes hebben opgeheven. Waterhazards komen op vijf holes in het spel en vormen met de sloten de belangrijkste hindernissen. Ook bunkers spelen een rol in de verdediging van de grote greens. Sommige holes zijn behoorlijk aan de lange kant, maar toch is de baan geschikt voor spelers van alle niveaus. Broekpolder ligt maar een paar meter boven het zeeniveau, maar dat is voldoende om een paar mooie vergezichten over de omliggende polders op te leveren, met de haveninstallatie van Rotterdam op de achtergrond.

Here is an example of a course where original barren space is gradually becoming richer, visibly developing and maturing year in year out. Since 1983, the trees and bushes are now full grown, bringing greater protection from the wind and visual enhancement. The course's 'natural' evolution has been marked by architectural changes, which have put right some of the flaws in the course's original design. The water hazards come into play on four holes, and, with a number of ditches, form the main difficulties. The bunkers, too, provide a firm line of defence for the large greens. We might add that some of the holes are on the long side but overall the course can be played by golfers of all levels. Broekpolder is only a few metres above sea level, but that's enough to provide some pretty views over the surrounding lakes and fields, with the port of Rotterdam in the background.

Golfclub Broekpolder — 1982

Watersportweg 100
NL - 3138 HD VLAARDINGEN

Office Secretariaat (31) 010 - 249 5566
Pro shop Pro shop (31) 010 - 249 5566
Fax Fax (31) 010 - 249 5579
Web www.golfclubbroekpolder.nl
Situation Locatie Rotterdam, 12 km
Annual closure Jaarlijkse sluiting no
Weekly closure Wekelijkse sluitingsdag no
Fees main season Hoogseizoen tarieven 18 holes

	Week days Weekdagen	We/Bank holidays We/Feestdagen
Individual Individueel	€ 80	€ 110
Couple Paar	€ 160	€ 220

Caddie Caddie yes — **Electric Trolley** Electrische trolley no
Buggy Buggy no — **Clubs** Clubs yes
Credit cards Creditcards
VISA - MasterCard

Access Toegang : A20 Rotterdam → Vlaardingen.
Exit 8 → Broekpolderweg, Golf 3 km
Map 1 on page 988 Auto kaart 1 Blz 988

GOLF COURSE — BAAN 15/20

Site Terrein
Maintenance Onderhoud
Architect Architect — Frank Pennink, Gerard Jol (1991)
Type Type baan — parkland, inland
Relief Reliëf
Water in play Waterhazards
Exp. to wind Windgevoelig
Trees in play Bomen

Scorecard Scorekaart	Chp. Back tees	Mens Heren	Ladies Damen
Length Lengte	6408	6013	5229
Par	72	72	72
Slope system	131	128	128

Advised golfing ability Aanbevolen golfvaardigheid — 0 12 24 36
Hcp required Vereiste hcp 36

CLUB HOUSE & AMENITIES — CLUB HOUSE EN ANNEXEN 7/10

Pro shop Pro shop
Driving range Oefenbaan
Sheltered overdekt 18 mats - On grass op gras no - Putting-green putting-green yes - Pitching-green pitching-green yes

HOTEL FACILITIES — HOTELS IN OMGEVING 6/10

HOTELS HOTELS
Delta - 78 rooms, D from € 200 - Vlaardingen 5 km
Tel (31) 010 - 434 5477, Fax (31) 010 - 434 9525

New York - 72 rooms, D € 160 - Rotterdam 20 km
Tel (31) 010 - 439 0500, Fax (31) 010 - 484 2701

Parkhotel - 189 rooms, D € 220 - Rotterdam 15 km
Tel (31) 010 - 436 3611, Fax (31) 010 - 436 4212

RESTAURANTS RESTAURANTS
Parkheuvel - Rotterdam 15 km - Tel (31) 010 - 436 0766
Bistro Hosman Frères - Schiedam 10 km
Tel (31) 010 - 426 4096
La Vilette - Rotterdam 15 km - Tel (31) 010 - 414 8692

Cromstrijen

16	8	5

Deze baan ligt niet ver ten zuiden van Rotterdam in een wijd open gebied. Weliswaar vlakbij een autoweg, maar ook met fraaie vergezichten over de omliggende weidegebieden. De plaatselijke autoriteiten keurden de aanleg van een golfbaan goed op voorwaarde dat die open zou staan voor iedereen. Het resultaat daarvan is een openbare 9-holes baan naast een besloten 18-holes baan. Het meest opvallende natuurlijke element wordt gevormd door vier rijen met hoge bomen, een vroegere eendenkooi. De stukken water daartussen lopen door in een klein meertje, dat meerdere keren in het spel komt. Een andere moeilijkheidsfactor bestaat uit de 75 strategisch geplaatste bunkers en, natuurlijk, uit de wind. Er is veel aangeplant om de in oorsprong vrij vlakke baan wat extra contouren te geven. De greens zijn groot, met talloze glooiingen, goed ontworpen en sterk bewaakt. De baan is door Tom MacAuley ontworpen voor alle type golfers en wordt goed onderhouden. Naarmate de baan rijpt, zal het een van de meeste interessante banen van het land worden. Het clubhuis straalt de allure uit die bij die status past.

This course, situated not far south of Rotterdam, is laid out in wide open space, close to a motorway but with scenic views. The local authorities agreed to building the course as long as it was open to everyone. The result is a public 9-holer next to a private 18-hole course. The most striking natural elements are the four rows of trees, a former duck-decoy. Patches of water have been extended to form a real lake, which comes into play several times. The other hazards are the 75 strategically placed bunkers and, of course, the wind. A great many shrubs have been planted as well to give this flat course a little relief. The greens are huge, well-contoured, well-designed and very tightly- guarded. This very well maintained course, designed for all golfers, should become one of the most interesting in Holland. The club-house has the majestic allure to match this future ambition.

Golfclub Cromstrijen — 1991

Veerweg 26
NL - 3281 LX NUMANSDORP

Office	Secretariaat	(31) 0622 - 372 996
Pro shop	Pro shop	(31) 0186 - 654 630
Fax	Fax	(31) 0186 - 654 681
E-mail	g.c.cromstrijen@hetnet.nl	
Situation	Locatie	Rotterdam, 20 km

Dordrecht (pop. 113 394), 15 km

Annual closure	Jaarlijkse sluiting	no
Weekly closure	Wekelijkse sluitingsdag	no
Fees main season	Hoogseizoen tarieven	18 holes

	Week days Weekdagen	We/Bank holidays We/Feestdagen
Individual Individueel	€ 60	€ 75
Couple Paar	€ 120	€ 150

Caddie Caddie no — **Electric Trolley** Electrische trolley no
Buggy Buggy yes — **Clubs** Clubs yes
Credit cards Creditcards Pin

Access Toegang : Rotterdam A29. Exit 22 → Havens Numansdorp, → Veenhaven
Map 1 on page 988 Auto kaart 1 Blz 988

GOLF COURSE — BAAN 16/20

Site	Terrein	
Maintenance	Onderhoud	
Architect	Architect	Tom MacAuley
Type	Type baan	parkland
Relief	Reliëf	
Water in play	Waterhazards	
Exp. to wind	Windgevoelig	
Trees in play	Bomen	

Scorecard Scorekaart	Chp. Back tees	Mens Heren	Ladies Damen
Length Lengte	6107	5898	5006
Par	72	72	72
Slope system	121	120	117

Advised golfing ability Aanbevolen golfvaardigheid: 0 12 24 36
Hcp required Vereiste hcp 36

CLUB HOUSE & AMENITIES — CLUB HOUSE EN ANNEXEN 8/10

Pro shop Pro shop
Driving range Oefenbaan
Sheltered overdekt 10 mats - On grass op gras no, 18 mats open air - Putting-green putting-green yes - Pitching-green pitching-green yes

HOTEL FACILITIES — HOTELS IN OMGEVING 5/10

HOTELS HOTELS

Het Wapen van Willemstad - Willemstad 8 km
10 rooms, D € 80
Tel (31) 0168 - 473 450, Fax (31) 0168 - 473 705

Parkhotel - 189 rooms, D € 220 - Rotterdam 20 km
Tel (31) 010 - 436 3611, Fax (31) 010 - 436 4212

Dordrecht - 21 rooms, D € 140 - Dordrecht 17 km
Tel (31) 078 - 613 6011, Fax (31) 078 - 613 7470

RESTAURANTS RESTAURANTS

De 7 Bergsche Hoeve - Zevenbergen 15 km
Tel (31) 0168 - 324 166

Biggo - Rhoon 15 km - Tel (31) 010 - 501 8896

De Pan

16 | 8 | 7

Harry Colt heeft zijn stempel op meerdere banen in Nederland gezet en zijn ontwerpen zijn altijd een plezierige ervaring. Een korte bootreis was voor hem voldoende om hier naartoe te komen vanuit zijn geboorteland Engeland, waar hij ook een aantal meesterwerken afleverde. Hij was onder andere een van de eerste grote ontwerpers van banen in het binnenland. De Pan is een van die uitstekende voorbeelden van zijn vermogen net het juiste aantal hazards op te nemen om wat pikants aan het spel toe te voegen. Op heel natuurlijke wijze werkend met de omgeving en altijd een paar strategische verrassingen toevoegend, zoals een aantal fascinerende doglegs en veeleisende par-3 holes. De baan heeft meer glooiing dan je zou verwachten zo midden in Holland. De belangrijkste obstakels om te ontwijken zijn de bomen en een paar goed geplaatste bunkers. De fraai vorm gegeven greens worden goed bewaakt, maar sommigen zijn van elke verdediging ontbloot. Weggestopt in de bossen, ver van alle lawaai, is deze aantrekkelijke baan er een die u echt aan uw collectie moet toevoegen.

You often find the mark of Harry Colt in the Netherlands and it's always a pleasure. Coming here was a short boat trip from his native England, where he also produced a number of masterpieces. Among other things, he was one of the first great designers of inland courses. This is one excellent example of his skill in placing just the right number of hazards needed to add a little spice to the game, working very naturally with the surroundings and always adding a few strategic surprises, such as a number of compelling dog-legs and tough par 3s. The course undulates a little more than you might expect in this part of Holland, and the major hazards to be avoided are the trees and a few well-located bunkers. The nicely contoured greens are well-guarded, but some have no defence at all. Tucked away in the woods, this fine course is most definitely one to add to your collection.

Utrechtse Golf Club 'De Pan' — 1929

Amersfoortseweg 1
NL - 3735 LJ BOSCH EN DUIN

Office	Secretariaat	(31) 030 - 695 6427
Pro shop	Pro shop	(31) 030 - 695 6427
Fax	Fax	(31) 030 - 696 3769
Web		www.ugcdepan.nl
Situation	Locatie	Utrecht (pop. 234 106), 10 km
Annual closure	Jaarlijkse sluiting	no
Weekly closure	Wekelijkse sluitingsdag	no

Fees main season Hoogseizoen tarieven	Week days Weekdagen	We/Bank holidays We/Feestdagen
		18 holes
Individual Individueel	€ 85	*
Couple Paar	€ 170	*

* We: members only

Caddie Caddie no — **Electric Trolley** Electrische trolley no
Buggy Buggy yes — **Clubs** Clubs no
Credit cards Creditcards no

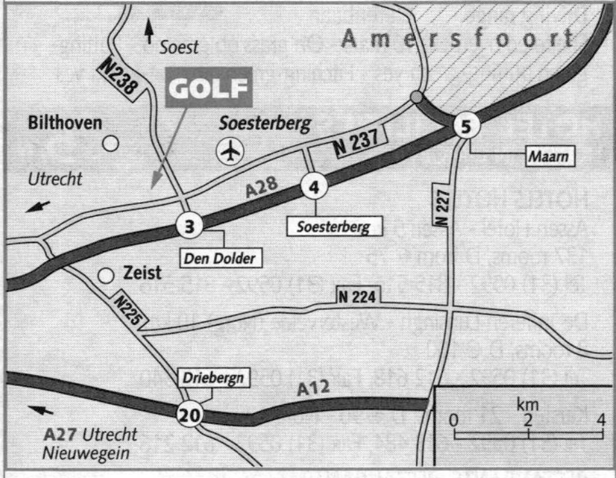

Access Toegang : Utrecht A28 → Amersfoort, Exit 3 → Den Dolder. 500 m left. 1.7 km parallel road
Map 1 on page 988 Auto kaart 1 Blz 988

GOLF COURSE — BAAN — 16/20

Site	Terrein	
Maintenance	Onderhoud	
Architect	Architect	Harry S. Colt
Type	Type baan	forest
Relief	Reliëf	
Water in play	Waterhazards	
Exp. to wind	Windgevoelig	
Trees in play	Bomen	

Scorecard Scorekaart	Chp. Back tees	Mens Heren	Ladies Damen
Length Lengte	6094	5701	4941
Par	72	72	72
Slope system	133	124	125

Advised golfing ability Aanbevolen golfvaardigheid — 0 12 24 36
Hcp required Vereiste hcp — 24

CLUB HOUSE & AMENITIES — CLUB HOUSE EN ANNEXEN — 8/10

Pro shop Pro shop
Driving range Oefenbaan
Sheltered overdekt 6 mats - On grass op gras no - Putting-green putting-green yes - Pitching-green pitching-green yes

HOTEL FACILITIES — HOTELS IN OMGEVING — 7/10

HOTELS HOTELS

De Hoefslag - Bosch en Duin 1 km
30 rooms, D € 230
Tel (31) 030 - 225 1051, Fax (31) 030 - 228 5821

Kasteel 't Kerckebosch - Zeist 5 km
30 rooms, D € 175
Tel (31) 030 - 692 6666, Fax (31) 030 - 692 6600

Grand Hotel Karel V - 91 rooms, D € 225 - Utrecht 10 km
Tel (31) 030 - 233 7555, Fax (31) 030 - 233 7500

RESTAURANTS RESTAURANTS

De Hoefslag - Bosch en Duin 1 km - Tel (31) 030 - 225 1051
Wilhelmina Park - Utrecht 10 km - Tel (31) 030 - 251 0693
Karel V - Utrecht 10 km - Tel (31) 030 - 233 7555

Drente

14	8	5

Het terrein waarop deze nieuwe golfbaan net ten zuiden van Groningen is aangelegd omvat maar liefst 220 hectare, waarvan 140 zijn gebruikt voor drie lussen van negen holes er een par-3 oefenbaan. Elke lus heeft zijn eigen karakteristiek. De Witte baan ligt in een volwassen bos. De bomen langs de fairways, die soms maar weinig ruimte ertussen over laten, vormen de belangrijkste obstakels. Zeker op de doglegs. Op vier holes komt ook nog water in het spel. Water is nog nadrukkelijker aanwezig op de Rode holes. Zoals op de tweede hole, waar een langgerekte vijver de fairway doorsnijdt. En de negende, een par-3 naar een green recht voor het clubhuis. De vier laatste holes omcirkelen een groot aaneengesloten bosperceel. De Gele baan heeft, naast opnieuw wat waterpartijen, een duidelijk open karakter. Op meerdere holes is heide aangeplant, maar nog niet tot wisdom gekomen. Het elegante clubhuis, met een deels rieten, deels koperen dak, biedt alle faciliteiten, waaronder een restaurant, een brasserie en een lounge-hoekje.

The grounds on which this new course, just south of Groningen, is located measures more than 220 hectares, of which 140 are used for three loops of nine holes each and par-3 compact course. Each loop has is own characteristics. The White course is laid out in mature woodlands, and the trees lining the fairways, sometimes leaving ample room between them, are the important obstacles, especially on doglegs. On four holes water comes into play, which is even more dominant on the Red holes. Like on the 2nd, where a stretched pond cuts the fairway in two parts and on the 9th hole, a par-3 with a green in front of the club-house. The four final holes encircle a large, untouched forest. The Yellow course has, apart from even more water hazards, a typical open character. On several holes heather has been planted, but not yet matured. The elegant club-house, with a partial straw, partial copper roof, offers all sorts of facilities, including a restaurant, a brasserie and a lounge-corner.

Drentsche Golf & Cou!ntry Club — 2003

Ten Oeverstraat 13
NL - 9489 TH ZEIJERVEEN

Office Secretariaat (31) 0592 - 379 680
Pro shop Pro shop (31) 0592 - 543 555
Fax Fax (31) 0592 - 379 689
Web www.dgcc.nl
Situation Locatie Groningen, 30 km
Assen, 5 km

Annual closure Jaarlijkse sluiting no
Weekly closure Wekelijkse sluitingsdag no

Fees main season Hoogseizoen tarieven		18 holes
	Week days Weekdagen	**We/Bank holidays** We/Feestdagen
Individual Individueel	€ 42,5	€ 52,5
Couple Paar	€ 85	€ 115

Caddie Caddie no — **Electric Trolley** Electrische trolley yes
Buggy Buggy yes — **Clubs** Clubs yes
Credit cards Creditcards Pin

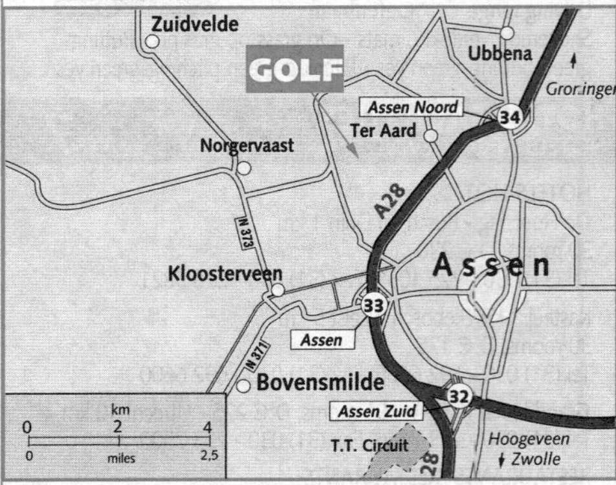

Access Toegang : Zwolle, A28 → Groningen. Exit 33, N371
Map 1 on page 989 Auto kaart 1 Blz 989

GOLF COURSE — BAAN — 14/20

Site Terrein
Maintenance Onderhoud
Architect Architect Gerard Jol
Type Type baan parkland
Relief Reliëf
Water in play Waterhazards
Exp. to wind Windgevoelig
Trees in play Bomen

Scorecard Scorekaart	**Chp.** Back tees	**Mens** Heren	**Ladies** Damen
Length Lengte	6436	6182	5182
Par	73	73	73
Slope system	137	133	130

Advised golfing ability Aanbevolen golfvaardigheid 0 12 24 36
Hcp required Vereiste hcp 36

CLUB HOUSE & AMENITIES — CLUB HOUSE EN ANNEXEN — 8/10

Pro shop Pro shop
Driving range Oefenbaan
Sheltered overdekt 10 mats - On grass op gras no - Putting-green putting-green yes - Pitching-green pitching-green yes

HOTEL FACILITIES — HOTELS IN OMGEVING — 5/10

HOTELS HOTELS
Assen Hotel - Assen 5 km
137 rooms, D from € 75
Tel (31) 0592 - 815 515, Fax (31) 0592 - 815 516

De Jufferen Lunsingh - Westervelde (Norg) 10 km
8 rooms, D € 100
Tel (31) 0592 - 612 618, Fax (31) 0592 - 612 340

Karsten - 21 rooms, D € 90 - Norg 12 km
Tel (31) 0592 - 613 484, Fax (31) 0592 - 612 216

RESTAURANTS RESTAURANTS
Villa Sasso - Haren 23 km - Tel (31) 050 - 309 1365
De Jufferen Lunsingh - Westervelde (Norg) 10 km
Tel (31) 0592 - 612 618

Efteling

16	8	5

DDeze baan is onderdeel van het bekende, gelijknamige attractiepark (ideaal voor de niet-golfers in de familie), waarvan sommige onderdelen vanaf de fairways te zien zijn. De baan ligt in een landelijke omgeving met aan weerszijden een natuurgebied. Veel open ruimtes waardoor de richting en kracht van de wind een grote rol spelen, omdat maar vier holes beschermd liggen. Bij gebrek aan bomen is water de belangrijkste hindernis, in de vorm van grote vijvers langs de baan of voor de green. Op de derde hole kronkelt een kreekje door de fairway, waardoor spelers voor de keuze worden gesteld rechts of links te houden. De greens zijn groot, goed gevormd en beschermd door handig geplaatste bunkers omgeven door heuveltjes en andere vormen van aarden wallen. Met smaak ontworpen door Donald Steel. Een prettige en boeiende baan geschikt voor spelers van alle niveaus. De baan is goed aangelegd en wordt goed onderhouden.

This recent course is part of the celebrated "De Efteling" theme park (ideal for non-golfers in the family), which you can actually see from the fairways. The whole piece is located in a rural spot surrounded by two nature reserves. There is a lot of very open space here, which gives great importance to the direction and strength of the wind, as only four holes are protected. For want of trees, water is the main hazard to cope with in the shape of large ponds lining the fairways or in front of the greens. At the 3rd, a stretch of water winds its way down the fairway forcing players to choose from which side of the fairway they want to play the hole. The greens are huge, well-contoured and protected by cleverly placed bunkers surrounded by mounds and other forms of earthwork. Tastefully designed by Donald Steel, this is a very pleasant and entertaining course for golfers of all abilities. Well built and well maintained.

Golfpark de Efteling — 1995

Veldstraat 6
NL - 5176 NB KAATSHEUVEL

Office Secretariaat (31) 0416 - 288 399
Pro shop Pro shop (31) 0416 - 288 399
Fax Fax (31) 0416 - 288 439
Web www.efteling.com
Situation Locatie Tilburg (pop. 163 383), 10 km
Annual closure Jaarlijkse sluiting no
Weekly closure Wekelijkse sluitingsdag no
Fees main season Hoogseizoen tarieven 18 holes

	Week days / Weekdagen	We/Bank holidays / We/Feestdagen
Individual Individueel	€ 47	€ 59,5
Couple Paar	€ 94	€ 119

Caddie Caddie no — **Electric Trolley** Electrische trolley yes
Buggy Buggy yes — **Clubs** Clubs yes
Credit cards Creditcards
VISA - MasterCard

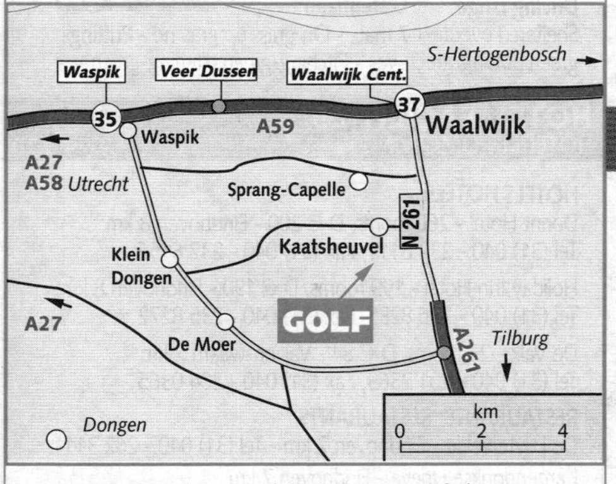

Access Toegang : Den Bosch A59, Exit 37 → Efteling → Golfpark
Map 1 on page 988 Auto kaart 1 Blz 988

GOLF COURSE — BAAN 16/20

Site Terrein
Maintenance Onderhoud
Architect Architect Donald Steel
Type Type baan open country
Relief Reliëf
Water in play Waterhazards
Exp. to wind Windgevoelig
Trees in play Bomen

Scorecard / Scorekaart	Chp. / Back tees	Mens / Heren	Ladies / Damen
Length Lengte	6408	5989	5053
Par	72	72	72
Slope system	131	119	121

Advised golfing ability Aanbevolen golfvaardigheid 0 12 24 36
Hcp required Vereiste hcp 36

CLUB HOUSE & AMENITIES — CLUB HOUSE EN ANNEXEN 8/10

Pro shop Pro shop
Driving range Oefenbaan
Sheltered overdekt 14 mats - On grass op gras no, 14 mats open air - Putting-green putting-green yes (3) - Pitching-green pitching-green yes

HOTEL FACILITIES — HOTELS IN OMGEVING 5/10

HOTELS HOTELS
De Efteling - Kaatsheuvel 1 km
120 rooms, D € 130
Tel (31) 0416 - 287 111, Fax (31) 0416 - 287 199

De Postelse Hoeve - Tilburg 10 km
35 rooms, D € 113
Tel (31) 013 - 463 6335, Fax (31) 013 - 463 9390

Queen Hotel - Waalwijk 5 km - 120 rooms, D € 92
Tel (31) 0416 - 674 684, Fax (31) 0416 - 674 680

RESTAURANTS RESTAURANTS
De Molen - Kaatsheuvel 1 km - Tel (31) 0416 - 530 230
Valentijn - Tilburg 10 km - Tel (31) 013 - 543 3386
Het Heerenhuys - Waalwijk 5 km - Tel (31) 0416 - 650 315

Eindhoven

18 | 8 | 7

Een van de beste banen in het binnenland met een niveau van onderhoud dat overeenkomt met de hoge kwaliteit van de geboden faciliteiten. De baan ligt midden in een prachtig bos met beekjes en vennetjes. Twee lussen van negen holes omcirkelen grote stukken bos, waardoor spelers een gevoel van afzondering en rust krijgen dat zeer bevorderlijk voor de concentratie is. Hoewel de fairways breed zijn - goed nieuws voor krachtpatsers - is het oppassen geblazen voor de doglegs, die vragen om met effect geslagen ballen, zowel naar links als naar rechts. Dit is een baan voor technisch ervaren spelers, met goed ontworpen greens, bewaakt door grote bunkers. Kenmerkend voor Harry Colt, duidelijk een van de grootste golf-architecten uit de eerste helft van deze eeuw. Zijn ontwerpen zijn veeleisend voor de goede, maar toch ook mild voor de stomme slagen van de gemiddelde speler. Een aardig element is het grote ven voor het clubhuis dat in de zomer als openlucht zwembad fungeert.

One of Holland's best inland courses with a standard of green-keeping to match the general excellence of facilities. The course is laid out in a magnificent forest with streams and ponds. The trees are right in the middle of the two parts of the course, out and in, and this gives players an impression of isolation and tranquillity that can be very useful for concentration. Although the fairways are wide - good news for big-hitters - still watch out for the dog-legs winding left and right and calling for a number of flighted shots in both directions. This is a course for skilled artists with well designed putting surfaces and greens firmly guarded by large bunkers, another distinctive feature of Harry Colt who was definitely one of the greatest course designers from the first half of the century. His layouts demand a great deal from good players but are somehow more lenient on duff shots from the average hacker. Another attractive feature is the large open-air swimming pool in front of the club-house.

Eindhovensche Golf — 1930

Eindhovenseweg 300
NL - 5553 VB VALKENSWAARD

Office	Secretariaat	(31) 040 - 201 4816
Pro shop	Pro shop	(31) 040 - 201 4816
Fax	Fax	(31) 040 - 207 6177
Web		—
Situation	Locatie	Eindhoven, 10 km
Annual closure	Jaarlijkse sluiting	no
Weekly closure	Wekelijkse sluitingsdag	no
Fees main season	Hoogseizoen tarieven	18 holes

	Week days / Weekdagen	We/Bank holidays / We/Feestdagen
Individual Individueel	€ 80	€ 80
Couple Paar	€ 160	€ 160

Caddie Caddie yes — **Electric Trolley** Electrische trolley no
Buggy Buggy no — **Clubs** Clubs yes
Credit cards Creditcards no

Access Toegang : Eindhoven A2 → Venlo. Exit 33. N69 → Valkenswaard. Golf 4 km
Map 1 on page 988 Auto kaart 1 Blz 988

GOLF COURSE — BAAN — 18/20

Site	Terrein	
Maintenance	Onderhoud	
Architect	Architect	Harry S. Colt
Type	Type baan	forest
Relief	Reliëf	
Water in play	Waterhazards	
Exp. to wind	Windgevoelig	
Trees in play	Bomen	

Scorecard Scorekaart	Chp. Back tees	Mens Heren	Ladies Damen
Length Lengte	6223	5923	5067
Par	72	72	72
Slope system	135	130	127

Advised golfing ability Aanbevolen golfvaardigheid: 0 12 24 36
Hcp required Vereiste hcp: 36, We 24

CLUB HOUSE & AMENITIES — CLUB HOUSE EN ANNEXEN — 8/10

Pro shop Pro shop
Driving range Oefenbaan
Sheltered overdekt 7 mats - On grass op gras no - Putting-green putting-green yes - Pitching-green pitching-green yes

HOTEL FACILITIES — HOTELS IN OMGEVING — 7/10

HOTELS HOTELS

Dorint Hotel - 260 rooms, D € 200 - Eindhoven 8 km
Tel (31) 040 - 232 6111, Fax (31) 040 - 232 6156

Holiday Inn Hotel - 199 rooms, D € 190 - Eindhoven 8 km
Tel (31) 040 - 235 8235, Fax (31) 040 - 235 8272

De Valk - 23 rooms, D € 84 - Valkenswaard 2 km
Tel (31) 040 - 201 2369, Fax (31) 040 - 204 0365

RESTAURANTS RESTAURANTS

De Luytervelde - Eindhoven 7 km - Tel (31) 040 - 262 3111

Karpendonkse Hoeve - Eindhoven 7 km
Tel (31) 040 - 281 3663

Avant Garde (Philips Stadion) - Eindhoven 7 km
Tel (31) 0416 - 250 5640

Gelpenberg

14	5	5

Zoals veel banen in Nederland is de Gelpenberg in twee fasen tot stand gekomen. En zoals vaker liggen negen holes in een bosgebied en de andere in vroeger agrarisch, meer open terrein. De oorspronkelijke negen holes zijn betrekkelijk smal, met bomen als voornaamste hindernis. Middenin het bos liggen flinke stukken hei, die op vier holes in het spel komen en voldoende problemen geven om het praktisch ontbreken van fairway-bunkers te verklaren. Omdat er zes doglegs bij zijn, zijn een goede strategie en effectvolle slagen (in de goede richting) een 'must'. De 'nieuwe' holes zijn veel breder, waardoor de wind er een grotere invloed op het spel krijgt. Een klein meertje komt op drie holes in het spel, net als een paar grote fairway bunkers, zoals op de 18e. De bunker die op deze slothole de fairway doorkruist moet een van de grootste van Europa zijn. Een baan die het waard is gespeeld te worden, door spelers van elk niveau.

Like several courses in the Netherlands, Gelpenberg was designed in two stages. Like the others, you find nine holes amidst an old forest and the others on former farming land which is much more open. The original nine holes are all pretty tight, with trees as the main hazards, so take care to keep out of trouble. In the middle of the forest, there is a huge area of heather which comes into play on four holes and causes enough difficulty to explain the virtual absence of fairway bunkers. And as there are six dog-legs to cope with, choosing the right strategy and bending the ball (in the right direction) are important. The nine holes added later are much wider but also much more exposed to the wind. A small lake comes into play on three holes as do some large fairway bunkers, notably on the 18th. The bunker splitting the fairway on this closing hole must be one of the largest in Europe. A course well worth getting to know, for players of all levels.

Drentse Golfclub De Gelpenberg — 1972

Gebbeveenweg 1
NL - 7854 TD AALDEN

Office Secretariaat (31) 0591 - 371 929
Pro shop Pro shop (31) 0591 - 372 174
Fax Fax (31) 0591 - 372 422
Web www.dgcdegelpenberg.nl
Situation Locatie Zwolle, 65 km
Emmen (pop. 93 476), 15 km
Annual closure Jaarlijkse sluiting no
Weekly closure Wekelijkse sluitingsdag no

Fees main season Hoogseizoen tarieven	18 holes	
	Week days Weekdagen	**We/Bank holidays** We/Feestdagen
Individual Individueel	€ 45	€ 55
Couple Paar	€ 90	€ 110

Caddie Caddie no — **Electric Trolley** Electrische trolley no
Buggy Buggy no — **Clubs** Clubs no
Credit cards Creditcards no

Meppel
Assen
N 376
N 381
Emmen
33
Aalden
GOLF
N 376
Erm
km
0 2 4
Coevorden
Emlichheim
N 34

Access Toegang : N37 Hoogeveen-Emmen, Exit Oosterhesselen → Zweeloo → Golf
Map 1 on page 989 Auto kaart 1 Blz 989

GOLF COURSE — BAAN 14/20

Site Terrein
Maintenance Onderhoud
Architect Architect — Frank Pennink, Donald Steel
Type Type baan — forest
Relief Reliëf
Water in play Waterhazards
Exp. to wind Windgevoelig
Trees in play Bomen

Scorecard Scorekaart	**Chp.** Back tees	**Mens** Heren	**Ladies** Damen
Length Lengte	6252	6031	5093
Par	71	71	71
Slope system	133	131	124

Advised golfing ability Aanbevolen golfvaardigheid — 0 12 24 36
Hcp required Vereiste hcp — 36

CLUB HOUSE & AMENITIES — CLUB HOUSE EN ANNEXEN 5/10

Pro shop Pro shop
Driving range Oefenbaan
Sheltered overdekt 2 mats - On grass op gras no, 11 mats open air - Putting-green putting-green yes - Pitching-green pitching-green yes

HOTEL FACILITIES — HOTELS IN OMGEVING 5/10

HOTELS HOTELS
Lubbelinkhof - Odoorn 12 km
32 rooms, D € 145
Tel (31) 0591 - 535 111, Fax (31) 0591 - 535 115

Golden Tulip - Westerbork 15 km
34 rooms, D € 105
Tel (31) 0593 - 331 444, Fax (31) 0593 - 332 888

RESTAURANTS RESTAURANTS
Idylle - Zweeloo 2 km - Tel (31) 0591 - 371 857
Adema - Aalden 2 km - Tel (31) 0591 - 371 454
Zuudbarge - Emmen 15 km - Tel (31) 0591 - 630 813

Gendersteyn

15	7	7

Deze baan is aangelegd in een landelijk gebied, tussen een autoweg en wat industrie. Gelukkig liggen een aantal holes verborgen in de bossen, waardoor een vredige atmosfeer wordt geschapen. Hoewel de baan nog betrekkelijk jong is, ogen de bomen zeer volwassen. Twee vijvers en een paar kleine vennetjes komen op verschillende manieren in het spel, zoals op de 6e, een par-3 waarvan de tee (niet de green) op een eiland ligt. De tweede negen strekken zich uit over een tot 20 meter verhoogd stuk land, zodat spelers worden geconfronteerd met blinde slagen en sterk hellende fairways. Het hoogste punt levert een fraai uitzicht over de omgeving op. Het vormt een welkome onderbreking van het vlakke deel van de baan. De greens kunnen lastig zijn, afhankelijk van de pin-positie en een aantal afslagen zijn veeleisend, maar er is altijd ruimte om een veilige weg te vinden. Geschikt voor alle type golfers.

This course is laid out in a rural zone between a motorway and an industrial estate, although several holes are tucked away in a woodland area and help give the site something of a more peaceful atmosphere. Although still very young, the trees create an air of maturity. Two lakes and several little ponds come into play in different ways, like on the 6th, a par 3 where the tee is an island (but not the green). The back 9 are built over a plot of fallow land some 20 metres high, where players are confronted with a few blind shots and any number of sloping lies. This altitude offers some pretty views over the region and breaks up the course's rather flat topograhy. The greens can be difficult, depending on the pin positions, and a number of drives can be tricky, but there is always room to play safe. For golfers of all levels.

Golfbaan Gendersteyn — 1994

Locht 140
NL - 5500 RP VELDHOVEN

Office	Secretariaat	(31) 040 - 253 4444
Pro shop	Pro shop	(31) 040 - 254 7101
Fax	Fax	(31) 040 - 254 9747
Web	www.gendersteijn.nl	
Situation	Locatie	Eindhoven, 10 km
Annual closure	Jaarlijkse sluiting	no
Weekly closure	Wekelijkse sluitingsdag	no

Fees main season Hoogseizoen tarieven		18 holes
	Week days Weekdagen	**We/Bank holidays** We/Feestdagen
Individual Individueel	€ 47,5	€ 57,5
Couple Paar	€ 95	€ 115

Caddie Caddie no — **Electric Trolley** Electrische trolley no
Buggy Buggy yes — **Clubs** Clubs yes
Credit cards Creditcards no

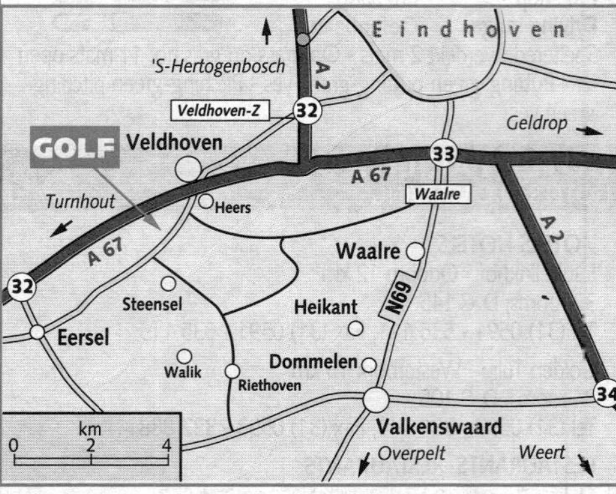

Access Toegang : Eindhoven A2 → Antwerpen. Exit 32 → Veldhoven → Eersel. Golf 2 km
Map 1 on page 988 Auto kaart 1 Blz 988

GOLF COURSE — BAAN — 15/20

Site	Terrein	
Maintenance	Onderhoud	
Architect	Architect	Alan Rijks
Type	Type baan	parkland
Relief	Reliëf	
Water in play	Waterhazards	
Exp. to wind	Windgevoelig	
Trees in play	Bomen	

Scorecard Scorekaart	**Chp.** Back tees	**Mens** Heren	**Ladies** Damen
Length Lengte	5965	5770	4869
Par	72	72	72
Slope system	127	128	126

Advised golfing ability Aanbevolen golfvaardigheid: 0 12 24 36
Hcp required Vereiste hcp: 36

CLUB HOUSE & AMENITIES — CLUB HOUSE EN ANNEXEN — 7/10

Pro shop Pro shop
Driving range Oefenbaan
Sheltered overdekt 10 mats - On grass op gras no, 16 mats open air - Putting-green putting-green yes - Pitching-green pitching-green yes

HOTEL FACILITIES — HOTELS IN OMGEVING — 7/10

HOTELS HOTELS

Dorint Hotel - 260 rooms, D € 200 - Eindhoven 8 km
Tel (31) 040 - 232 6111, Fax (31) 040 - 232 6156

Holiday Inn Hotel - Eindhoven 8 km
199 rooms, D € 190
Tel (31) 040 - 235 8235, Fax (31) 040 - 235 8272

Pierre - 60 rooms, D € 120 - Eindhoven 8 km
Tel (31) 040 - 212 1012, Fax (31) 040 - 212 1261

RESTAURANTS RESTAURANTS

De Luytervelde - Eindhoven 7 km - Tel (31) 040 - 262 3111
Avant-Garde - Eindhoven 7 km - Tel (31) 040 250 5640
The Old Valley - Eindhoven 7 km - Tel (31) 040 - 252 6575

Goes

15	7	6

Op het eerste gezicht lijkt deze baan misschien op een van de vele nieuwe 'polderbanen' die in Nederland zijn aangelegd. Banen die geleidelijk in karakter veranderen als de massaal geplante bomen en struiken van de vlakke open baan een vlakke parkbaan maken. Maar hier is meer aan de hand. Als je op de fairways loopt vallen direct de glooiingen en heuveltjes op, die elke slag een beetje moeilijker dan normaal kunnen maken. Deze heuveltjes zijn gemaakt met de grond die vrijkwam bij het graven van de waterpartijen die op dertien holes in het spel komen. Soms alleen langs de kant van de fairway, maar in veel gevallen vlak voor de green. Water is niet de enige hindernis om rekening mee te houden. Er ligt een flink aantal bunkers op strategische plaatsen. De greens zijn alle wat glooiend, maar zonder de overdreven contouren die je op veel nieuwe banen tegenkomt. Als afsluiting van het hele project is een ruim nieuw clubhuis gebouwd, dat een fraai uitzicht over de baan biedt. De baan maakt een bezoekje aan dit specifieke stukje Nederland nog meer de moeite waard.

At first view this course may look like one of the many courses recently developed in the flat Dutch "polderland". Courses that gradually change their character when the many planted trees and bushes turn a flat, open course into a flat parkland course. But at Goes there is more at stake. Walking its fairways you will notice the subtle undulations and hills that frequently make your next shot a little more awkward. These slopes result from the clever use of soil dug out to create the many water hazards that come into play, sometimes edging the fairway but on several occasions lurking in front of the greens. And water is not the only hazard to cope with, as a fair number of bunkers are strategically located on the fairways. The greens are rather distinctly contoured but don't have the excessive bumps often seen on today's new courses. The new club-house offers a view over the course and makes a visit to this particular part of Holland even more worthwhile.

Goese Golf — 1995

Krukweg 31
NL - 4465 BH GOES

Office	Secretariaat	(31) 0113 - 229 557
Pro shop	Pro shop	(31) 0113 - 229 557
Fax	Fax	(31) 0113 - 229 555
Web	www.goesegolf.nl	
Situation	Locatie	Goes (pop. 33 300), 3 km
Annual closure	Jaarlijkse sluiting	no
Weekly closure	Wekelijkse sluitingsdag	no

Fees main season Hoogseizoen tarieven	18 holes	
	Week days Weekdagen	**We/Bank holidays** We/Feestdagen
Individual Individueel	€ 55	€ 55
Couple Paar	€ 110	€ 110

Caddie Caddie no — **Electric Trolley** Electrische trolley yes
Buggy Buggy yes — **Clubs** Clubs yes
Credit cards Creditcards
VISA - MasterCard - AMEX - DC - Pin

Access Toegang : A58 → N256 → Goes Centrum → Goese Meer
Map 1 on page 988 Auto kaart 1 Blz 988

GOLF COURSE — BAAN — 15/20

Site	Terrein	
Maintenance	Onderhoud	
Architect	Architect	Donald Steel, H. Hertzberger
Type	Type baan	open country
Relief	Reliëf	
Water in play	Waterhazards	
Exp. to wind	Windgevoelig	
Trees in play	Bomen	

Scorecard Scorekaart	**Chp.** Back tees	**Mens** Heren	**Ladies** Damen
Length Lengte	6269	6110	5145
Par	72	72	72
Slope system	126	126	120

Advised golfing ability Aanbevolen golfvaardigheid — 0 12 24 36
Hcp required Vereiste hcp — 36

CLUB HOUSE & AMENITIES — CLUB HOUSE EN ANNEXEN — 7/10

Pro shop Pro shop
Driving range Oefenbaan
Sheltered overdekt 10 mats - On grass op gras no- Putting-green putting-green yes - Pitching-green pitching-green yes

HOTEL FACILITIES — HOTELS IN OMGEVING — 6/10

HOTELS HOTELS

Bolsjoi - 12 rooms, D € 79 - Goes 3 km
Tel (31) 0113 - 232 323, Fax (31) 0113 - 251 755

Le Manoir - 12 rooms, D € 195 - Kruiningen 15 km
Tel (31) 0113 - 381 753, Fax (31) 0113 - 381 763

Van Der Valk Hotel Goes - Goes 3 km
120 rooms, D € 95
Tel (31) 0113 - 315 800, Fax (31) 0113 - 315 805

RESTAURANTS RESTAURANTS

Inter Scaldes - Kruiningen 15 km - Tel (31) 0113 - 381 753
Nolet-Reymerswale - Yerseke 14 km - Tel (31) 0113 - 517 642
Het Binnenhof - Goes 3 km - Tel (31) 0113 - 227 405

Graafschap

15 | 7 | 6

Het specifieke karakter van deze goed ontworpen baan is de afwisseling tussen open en bebost terrein, een typische eigenschap van het hele gebied. Het uit zich hier in het feit dat bijna de helft van de holes begint in een open stuk en eindigt temidden van bomen. Of andersom. In tegenstelling tot veel nieuwe banen is hier weinig grond verzet, zelfs niet voor de waterhazards die klein en heel natuurlijk zijn. De meeste fairways zijn breed en mild voor afgedwaalde ballen, maar enkele losse bomen kunnen voor flinke problemen zorgen. In combinatie met de wind (in de open gedeelten) kunnen zij elke hoop op een goede score de nek omdraaien. Ondanks het ontbreken van reliëf valt er van prachtige vergezichten te genieten, vooral in de herfst. De greens zijn middelgroot, niet moeilijk te lezen en over het algemeen niet spectaculair. Wel afdoence bewaakt door bunkers.

The full character of this competently designed course lies with its alternating forest and open landscape, a frequent feature throughout the region. It is plain to see on almost half the holes, which start under the open sky and end up in the trees, or inversely. As opposed to many recent courses there has been little artificial moving of earth, even for the water hazards that are small and natural. Most of the fairways are wide and forgiving for wayward shots but several isolated trees can spell serious trouble. Combined with the wind (in the more exposed areas). they can dash any hope of playing to your handicap, a feat that otherwise is more than possible. Despite the lack of relief, there are some beautiful views to be had here, especially in the Autumn. The greens are mid-sized, pretty easy to read and generally, but none too imaginatively, well-guarded by a brace of bunkers.

Lochemse G&CC De Graafschap — 1992

Sluitdijk 4
NL - 7241 RR LOCHEM

Office	Secretariaat	(31) 0573 - 250 187
Pro shop	Pro shop	(31) 0573 - 250 187
Fax	Fax	(31) 0573 - 258 450
Web		www.lochemsegolfclub.nl
Situation	Locatie	Deventer, 25 km
Annual closure	Jaarlijkse sluiting	no
Weekly closure	Wekelijkse sluitingsdag	no

Fees main season Hoogseizoen tarieven	Week days Weekdagen	We/Bank holidays We/Feestdagen
	18 holes	
Individual Individueel	€ 45	€ 50
Couple Paar	€ 90	€ 100

Caddie Caddie no — **Electric Trolley** Electrische trolley no
Buggy Buggy no — **Clubs** Clubs yes
Credit cards Creditcards no

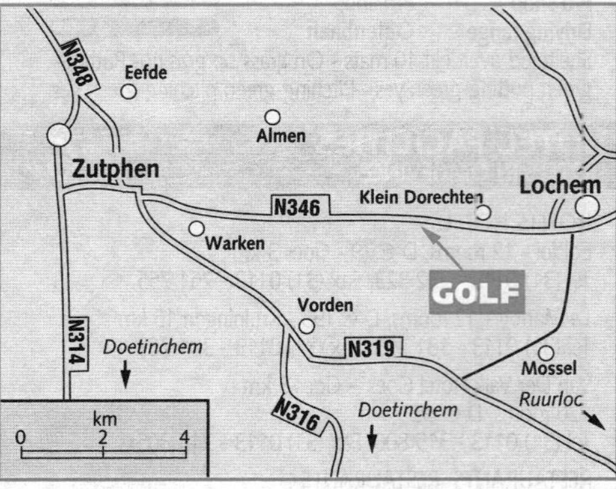

Access Toegang : A1 Amsterdam → Enschede. Exit 23. N348 → Zutphen. N346 → Lochem. Golf km 11.5
Map 1 on page 989 Auto kaart 1 Blz 989

GOLF COURSE — BAAN — 15/20

Site	Terrein	
Maintenance	Onderhoud	
Architect	Architect	Eschauzier & Thate
Type	Type baan	forest
Relief	Reliëf	
Water in play	Waterhazards	
Exp. to wind	Windgevoelig	
Trees in play	Bomen	

Scorecard Scorekaart	Chp. Back tees	Mens Heren	Ladies Damen
Length Lengte	6306	6057	5277
Par	72	72	72
Slope system	129	128	125

Advised golfing ability Aanbevolen golfvaardigheid: 0 12 24 36
Hcp required Vereiste hcp: 36

CLUB HOUSE & AMENITIES — CLUB HOUSE EN ANNEXEN — 7/10

Pro shop Pro shop
Driving range Oefenbaan
Sheltered overdekt 10 mats - On grass op gras no, 18 mats open air - Putting-green putting-green yes - Pitching-green pitching-green yes

HOTEL FACILITIES — HOTELS IN OMGEVING — 6/10

HOTELS HOTELS

De Scheperskamp - 50 rooms, D € 144 - Lochem 3 km
Tel (31) 0573 - 254 051, Fax (31) 0573 - 257 150

't Hof van Gelre - 38 rooms, D € 120 - Lochem 3 km
Tel (31) 0573 - 253 351, Fax (31) 0573 - 254 245

De Hoofdige Boer - 23 rooms, D € 110 - Almen 6 km
Tel (31) 0575 - 431 744, Fax (31) 0575 - 431 567

RESTAURANTS RESTAURANTS

Kawop - Lochem 3 km - Tel (31) 0573 - 253 342
Galantijn - Zutphen 8 km - Tel (31) 0575 - 517 286
De Stenen Tafel - Borculo 12 km - Tel (31) 0545 - 272 030
't Schulten Huis - Zutphen 8 km - Tel (31) 0575 - 510 005

Haagsche

18 | 7 | 8

De Hollandse kust leent zich uitstekend voor de aanleg van prachtige banen en deze is daar een goed voorbeeld van. Naar het ontwerp van de architecten Colt en Alison die borg stonden voor een uitdagend ontwerp. Het is maar goed dat de lengte niet overdreven is, want het komt vaak voor dat je slagen verliest in dichte struiken of in diepe bunkers. Maar als u door de wind met rust gelaten wordt en alle aandacht aan uw swing kunt besteden, dan hebt u een goede kans een mooi resultaat te scoren. Zoals je in de duinen kan verwachten zijn er maar weinig echt vlakke stukken op de fairways. Veel uphill of downhill slagen dus, plus interessante situaties rond de greens. De Haagsche heeft talloze internationale wedstrijden (waaronder het Dutch Open) mogen ontvangen. Het is de moeite waard hier een dag voor uit te trekken. Zowaar een linksbaan zonder het Kanaal te hoeven oversteken. Na een grote brand in 2003 is het statige clubhuis gelukkig weer in de oude glorie hersteld.

The Dutch coast is a marvellous site for building great courses and this is one of the finest. The cachet of designers Colt and Alison speaks volumes for the challenging style of this layout. Although not excessively long, there are more than enough opportunities to drop shots, in the thickets lining the fairways or in the pot bunkers. If the wind leaves you alone with just your problems of swing to cope with, you will have every chance of returning a good score. As you might expect among sand dunes, there are few really flat lies on the fairways, a lot of shots uphill and down, and some tantalising situations around the greens. Haagsche has hosted a number of international events (including the Dutch Open) and, with its counterparts along the coast, is well worth a special golfing holiday. Here is a great links to play without having to ferry across the Channel. After a fire in 2003 the prestigious club-house has recently been restored to its original, chic self.

Koninklijke Haagsche Golf & Countryclub

1938

Groot Haesebroekseweg 22
NL - 2243 EC WASSENAAR

Office	Secretariaat	(31) 070 - 517 9607
Pro shop	Pro shop	(31) 070 - 517 9607
Fax	Fax	(31) 070 - 514 0171
Web	www.khgcc.nl	
Situation	Locatie	Den Haag, 5 km
Annual closure	Jaarlijkse sluiting	no
Weekly closure	Wekelijkse sluitingsdag	no
Fees main season	Hoogseizoen tarieven	full day

	Week days / Weekdagen	We/Bank holidays / We/Feestdagen
Individual Individueel	€ 100	*
Couple Paar	€ 200	*

* We: members only

Caddie Caddie no — **Electric Trolley** Electrische trolley no
Buggy Buggy no — **Clubs** Clubs no
Credit cards Creditcards VISA - Mastercard

Access Toegang : A44 → Wassenaar
Map 1 on page 988 Auto kaart 1 Blz 988

GOLF COURSE — BAAN 18/20

Site	Terrein	
Maintenance	Onderhoud	
Architect	Architect	Harry S. Colt, Charles Alison
Type	Type baan	links
Relief	Reliëf	
Water in play	Waterhazards	
Exp. to wind	Windgevoelig	
Trees in play	Bomen	

Scorecard / Scorekaart	Chp. / Back tees	Mens / Heren	Ladies / Damen
Length Lengte	6142	5674	5006
Par	72	72	72
Slope system	131	129	126

Advised golfing ability / Aanbevolen golfvaardigheid — 0 12 24 36
Hcp required Vereiste hcp 24

CLUB HOUSE & AMENITIES — CLUB HOUSE EN ANNEXEN 7/10

Pro shop Pro shop
Driving range Oefenbaan
Sheltered overdekt 8 mats - On grass op gras no - Putting-green putting-green yes - Pitching-green pitching-green yes

HOTEL FACILITIES — HOTELS IN OMGEVING 8/10

HOTELS HOTELS
Le Méridien Hotel des Indes - Den Haag 5 km
92 rooms, D from € 300
Tel (31) 070 - 361 2345, Fax (31) 070 - 361 2350

Kurhaus - 255 rooms, D € 290 - Scheveningen 5 km
Tel (31) 070 - 416 2636, Fax (31) 070 - 416 2646

Auberge de Kieviet - 24 rooms, D € 190 - Wassenaar 1 km
Tel (31) 070 - 511 9232, Fax (31) 070 - 511 0969

RESTAURANTS RESTAURANTS
Auberge de Kievit - Wassenaar 1 km - Tel (31) 070 - 511 9232
Calla's - Den Haag 5 km - Tel (31) 070 - 345 5866
Savelberg - Voorburg 7 km - Tel (31) 070 - 387 2081

Herkenbosch

16	7	6

Het komt niet vaak voor dat de aanleg van een golfbaan in bestaande bossen wordt toegestaan. In het geval van Herkenbosch was het verkrijgen van een kapvergunning voor de fairways iets makkelijker, omdat er in die bossen voornamelijk mijnhout staat. En de vraag daarnaar is met de mijnen zelf verdwenen. Er zijn nog steeds heel veel van die smalle boompjes blijven staan en die vormen dan ook de belangrijkste hindernis. Vooral op de smallere holes en de vele doglegs. De begroeiing onder de bomen kan heel dicht zijn, hetgeen een extra afstraffing van onnauwkeurige slagen oplevert (neem wat extra ballen mee als u niet zo zuiver slaat). Dit is het enige zwakke punt in wat verder een knappe baan is, waarvan een deel over een heuvel is gedrapeerd, hetgeen resulteert in moeilijke uphill en downhill slagen. Er ligt daarentegen niet zoveel water. Al komt wat er ligt wel duidelijk in het spel, zoals op de fraaie 11e hole. De greens zijn tamelijk groot, goed ontworpen en goed bewaakt.

Only very rarely will the authorities allow a new golfcourse to be built in a fully wooded area. In the case of Herkenbosch permission to fell trees was granted because they were lean pines planted for the mining industry, for which demand has disappeared with the mines. There are still a lot of these trees left standing however and they now form the main hazards, especially on a number of tight holes and on the many doglegs. The undergrowth is thick to say the least and adds an extra and perhaps unwarranted difficulty, given that mis-hit shots are already punished enough (bring a stock of balls if you spray the ball off the tee). This is the only real flaw in what is an intelligent course, a part of which hugs a steepish hill to give some tricky holes uphill and down. By contrast there is little water to bother you, although what water there is is well in play, as on the very fine 11th hole. The greens are rather large, well-contoured and well-guarded.

Burggolf Herkenbosch — 1992

Stationsweg 100
NL - 6075 CD HERKENBOSCH

Office	Secretariaat	(31) 0475 - 529 529
Pro shop	Pro shop	(31) 0475 - 529 524
Fax	Fax	(31) 0475 - 533 580
Web		www.burggolf.nl
Situation	Locatie	Roermond (pop. 43 110), 5 km
Annual closure	Jaarlijkse sluiting	no
Weekly closure	Wekelijkse sluitingsdag	no

Fees main season Hoogseizoen tarieven	Week days Weekdagen	We/Bank holidays We/Feestdagen
		18 holes
Individual Individueel	€ 55	€ 65
Couple Paar	€ 110	€ 130

Caddie Caddie no — **Electric Trolley** Electrische trolley yes
Buggy Buggy yes — **Clubs** Clubs yes
Credit cards Creditcards

VISA - MasterCard - Pin
Access Toegang : Eindhoven A2 → Maastricht. Exit 40. N68, A68 → Roermond. N68, N281 → Herkenbosch → Golf
Map 1 on page 989 Auto kaart 1 Blz 989

GOLF COURSE — BAAN — 16/20

Site	Terrein	
Maintenance	Onderhoud	
Architect	Architect	Joan Dudok van Heel B. Steensels
Type	Type baan	forest
Relief	Reliëf	
Water in play	Waterhazards	
Exp. to wind	Windgevoelig	
Trees in play	Bomen	

Scorecard Scorekaart	Chp. Back tees	Mens Heren	Ladies Damen
Length Lengte	6141	5758	4981
Par	72	72	72
Slope system	137	136	129

Advised golfing ability Aanbevolen golfvaardigheid: 0 12 24 36
Hcp required Vereiste hcp: 36

CLUB HOUSE & AMENITIES — CLUB HOUSE EN ANNEXEN — 7/10

Pro shop Pro shop
Driving range Oefenbaan
Sheltered overdekt 8 mats - On grass op gras no - Putting-green putting-green yes - Pitching-green pitching-green yes

HOTEL FACILITIES — HOTELS IN OMGEVING — 6/10

HOTELS HOTELS
Kasteel Daelenbroeck - Herkenbosch 5 km
18 rooms, D € 120
Tel (31) 0475 - 532 465, Fax (31) 0475 - 536 030

Landhotel Cox - 53 rooms, D € 120 - Roermond 5 km
Tel (31) 0475 - 348 899, Fax (31) 0475 - 325 142

Kasteeltje Hattem - 7 rooms, D € 145 - Roermond 5 km
Tel (31) 0475 - 319 222, Fax (31) 0475 - 319 292

RESTAURANTS RESTAURANTS
Kasteel Daelenbroek - Herkenbosch 2 km
Tel (31) 0475 - 532 465
Onder de Boompjes (K. Hattem) - Roermond 5 km
Tel (31) 0475 - 319 222

Hilversum

16 | 7 | 7

Sinds deze baan aan het begin van de 20e eeuw is aangelegd zijn er een aantal ingrijpende wijzigingen in aangebracht. Hoewel sommige van die aanpassingen twijfelachtig zijn, blijft Hilversum wat het altijd is geweest: een verbluffend voorbeeld van een goed ontwerp voor een baan in het binnenland. Door de vele oude bomen zijn de meeste fairways behoorlijk smal, waardoor ze precisie en effectvolle slagen vereisen. De zanderige heuvels, die vaak tot slagen van glooiende hellingen dwingen, verhogen het technisch aspect van het spel. De spaarzame fairway-bunkers zijn goed geplaatst en moeilijk, de in omvang bescheiden greens worden goed bewaakt en de heidevelden voegen extra moeilijkheden aan de baan toe. De baan is heel rustig (de enige verstoring kan komen van fietsers of ruiters) en heeft het onderhoudsnivo de laatste tijd sterk verbeterd. Dat zou te maken kunnen hebben met het feit dat het Dutch Open hier vanaf 1994 bijna onafgebroken wordt gespeeld.

Since it was created at the turn of the 20th century, this course has undergone a number of significant changes. Although some of these are questionable, the course is still the strikingly good example of excellent inland design it always has been. Owing to the very many old trees, some fairways are very tight and require precision and flighted shots. The sandy slopes, which often call for shots hit from sloping lies, augment the technical aspect of playing here. The few fairway bunkers you come across are still well-placed and tough, the mid-sized greens are well-guarded and the heather adds an extra difficulty to the course. Very quiet (the only disturbance here might come from cyclists or horse-riders), Hilversum has significantly improved standards of green-keeping, as testified by the Dutch Open being played here since 1994.

Hilversumsche Golf Club — 1910

Soestdijkerstraatweg 172
NL - 1213 XJ HILVERSUM

Office Secretariaat (31) 035 - 683 8859
Pro shop Pro shop (31) 035 - 685 7140
Fax Fax (31) 035 - 685 3813
Web www.hilversumschegolfclub.nl
Situation Locatie Hilversum (pop. 84 213), 2 km
Annual closure Jaarlijkse sluiting no
Weekly closure Wekelijkse sluitingsdag no

Fees main season Hoogseizoen tarieven	18 holes	
	Week days Weekdagen	**We/Bank holidays** We/Feestdagen
Individual Individueel	€ 75	€ 75
Couple Paar	€ 150	€ 150

Caddie Caddie no — **Electric Trolley** Electrische trolley no
Buggy Buggy no — **Clubs** Clubs yes
Credit cards Creditcards no

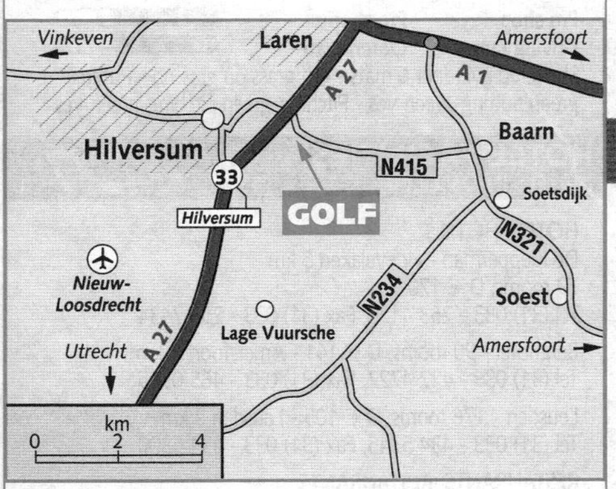

Access Toegang : Amsterdam A1 → Hilversum. A27 → Utrecht. Exit 33 → Hilversum. → Golf
Map 1 on page 988 Auto kaart 1 Blz 988

GOLF COURSE — BAAN — 16/20

Site Terrein
Maintenance Onderhoud
Architect Architect — Burrows, Del C. van Krimpen
Type Type baan — forest, inland
Relief Reliëf
Water in play Waterhazards
Exp. to wind Windgevoelig
Trees in play Bomen

Scorecard Scorekaart	**Chp.** Back tees	**Mens** Heren	**Ladies** Damen
Length Lengte	6098	5859	5102
Par	72	72	72
Slope system	137	135	131

Advised golfing ability Aanbevolen golfvaardigheid — 0 12 24 36
Hcp required Vereiste hcp — 24

CLUB HOUSE & AMENITIES — CLUB HOUSE EN ANNEXEN — 7/10

Pro shop Pro shop
Driving range Oefenbaan
Sheltered overdekt 6 mats - On grass op gras yes - Putting-green putting-green yes - Pitching-green pitching-green yes

HOTEL FACILITIES — HOTELS IN OMGEVING — 7/10

HOTELS HOTELS

Lapershoek - Hilversum 2 km
80 rooms, D € 175
Tel (31) 035 - 623 1341, Fax (31) 035 - 628 4360

De Hooge Vuursche - 25 rooms, D € 240 - Baarn 2 km
Tel (31) 035 - 541 2541, Fax (31) 035 - 542 3288

Ravel - 19 rooms, D € 130 - Hilversum 2 km
Tel (31) 035 - 621 0685, Fax (31) 035 - 624 3777

RESTAURANTS RESTAURANTS

Rust Wat - Blaricum 6 km - Tel (31) 035 - 538 3286
De Kastanjehof - Lage Vuursche 3 km
Tel (31) 035 - 666 8248
Spandershoeve - Hilversum 3 km - Tel (31) 035 - 621 1130

Hoge Kleij

15	6	7

Deze opvallende baan, in het midden van het land, was een van de eerste van een serie nieuwe privé banen die begin jaren '80 werden aangelegd. Een groot deel van de baan ligt temidden van bestaande bossen, de rest in meer open terrein. Door dat laatste biedt de Hoge Kleij een groter gevoel van ruimte dan de 'oudere' buren Hilversum en De Pan. Op enkele holes is goed gebruik gemaakt van de hoogteverschillen, terwijl de overige holes vrij vlak zijn. Dat maakt de baan toegankelijk voor elk niveau speler. Het mag dan geen spectaculaire baan zijn, er zitten een paar mooie holes tussen, met een grote variëteit in vormen, maten en moeilijkheden. Maar dat kun je verwachten van ontwerpers en kenners als Steel en Pennink, die zich nooit druk maken om al te subtiele details. De oefenfaciliteiten houden gelijke tred met de kwaliteit van de baan en hetzelfde kan worden gezegd van het clubhuis (met een goed restaurant).

This remarkable course in the middle of Holland was one of the first of a series of new private courses built in the first half of the 1980s. A large section was laid out in trees, the rest in wide open spaces, and this gives "Hoge Kleij" a much more definite impression of space than its elder neighbours at Hilversum and De Pan. The differences in level on several holes have been cleverly used, while the rest of the course is flat, making it easier for players of all levels and ages. This is hardly a spectacular course but there are some good holes here and a wide variety of shapes, sizes and difficulties. Again, this is only to be expected from designers and fine connoisseurs of golf such as Steel and Pennink, who never care unduly about excessively sophisticated details. Practice facilities are consistent with the standard of the course design and the same can be said for the club-house (with a good restaurant).

Golfclub De Hoge Kleij — 1986

Appelweg 4
NL - 3832 RK LEUSDEN

Office Secretariaat (31) 033 - 461 6944
Pro shop Pro shop (31) 033 - 461 6944
Fax Fax (31) 033 - 465 2921
Web www.hogekleij.nl
Situation Locatie Utrecht, 15 km
Amersfoort (pop. 110 117), 5 km
Annual closure Jaarlijkse sluiting no
Weekly closure Wekelijkse sluitingsdag no

Fees main season Hoogseizoen tarieven 18 holes

	Week days / Weekdagen	We/Bank holidays / We/Feestdagen
Individual Individueel	€ 62	€ 82
Couple Paar	€ 124	€ 164

Caddie Caddie no — **Electric Trolley** Electrische trolley no
Buggy Buggy no — **Clubs** Clubs yes
Credit cards Creditcards no

Zeldert
Hoogland
Soest
A1
A28
N321
Barneveld
Amersfoort
8
GOLF
Soesterberg
N 237
A28
5
6
Leusden-Z.
Maarn
4
Utrecht
Soesterberg
Doorn
N227
km
0 2 4

Access Toegang : A28 Utrecht-Amersfoort, Exit 5
Map 1 on page 988 Auto kaart 1 Blz 988

GOLF COURSE — BAAN — 15/20

Site Terrein
Maintenance Onderhoud
Architect Architect Donald Steel, Frank Pennink
Type Type baan forest
Relief Reliëf
Water in play Waterhazards
Exp. to wind Windgevoelig
Trees in play Bomen

Scorecard / Scorekaart	Chp. / Back tees	Mens / Heren	Ladies / Damen
Length Lengte	6231	6045	5242
Par	72	72	72
Slope system	132	128	128

Advised golfing ability Aanbevolen golfvaardigheid 0 12 24 36
Hcp required Vereiste hcp 36

CLUB HOUSE & AMENITIES — CLUB HOUSE EN ANNEXEN — 6/10

Pro shop Pro shop
Driving range Oefenbaan
Sheltered overdekt 6 mats - On grass op gras no - Putting-green putting-green yes - Pitching-green pitching-green yes

HOTEL FACILITIES — HOTELS IN OMGEVING — 7/10

HOTELS HOTELS
De Klepperman - Hoevelaken 5 km
79 rooms, D € 170
Tel (31) 033 - 253 4120, Fax (31) 033 - 253 7434

Berghotel - 90 rooms, D € 141 - Amersfoort 3 km
Tel (31) 033 - 422 4222, Fax (31) 033 - 465 0505

Leusden - 176 rooms, D € 105 - Leusden 2 km
Tel (31) 033 - 434 5345, Fax (31) 033 - 434 5300

RESTAURANTS RESTAURANTS
't Bloemendaeltje - Amersfoort 2 km - Tel (31) 033 - 475 0001
Tollius - Amersfoort 2 km - Tel (31) 033 - 465 1793
Dorloté - Amersfoort 2 km - Tel (31) 033 - 472 0444

Houtrak

16 | 8 | 8

Deze aantrekkelijke baan is, net als de naastgelegen baan van de Amsterdamse Golfclub, aangelegd in de eerste drooglegging van het IJ, het grote binnenwater dat onder meer de haven van Amsterdam omvat. De baan heeft, zolang de aangebrachte beplanting nog bescheiden is, het karakter van een polderbaan. Maar geleidelijk zal dat veel gevarieerder worden. Bij de aanleg is optimaal gebruik gemaakt van de enige oude bomen die op een hoek van het terrein staan. De architect, Gerad Jol, heeft er een volledige par-3 in kunnen verschuilen. Er zijn twaalfhonderd vrachtwagens met verse grond aangevoerd, waarmee licht glooiende contouren zijn geschapen. Verder zijn er heel wat waterpartijen, die vooral aan de buitenkant van het terrein zorgen voor een natuurlijke overgang naar de weilanden. Vanuit het iets hoger gelegen clubhuis, dat onlangs na een verwoestende brand is herbouwd, is er een prachtig zicht op zes holes die van of naar dit centrale punt lopen.

This attractive course was built in the first land-recovery of the IJ-estuary (just like the adjacent course at the Amsterdamse Golfclub). So as long as the newly planted trees and bushes are still small it will be ranked as a "polderbaan". But the nature of the course will gradually change, if only because of the clever use that has been made of some remaining trees in a corner of the terrain now hiding a full par-3 hole. In addition, more than 1200 truckloads of new soil were brought in and used to create slight undulations and there are a number of ponds serving as water hazards. On the outskirts of the course they provide a natural transition to the surrounding meadowland. From the somewhat elevated club-house you enjoy a magnificent view over six holes running to and fro'. Unfortunately it was gutted by fire early this year so for the time being a temporary facility has been set up.

Golfclub Houtrak — 1997

Machineweg 1b
NL - 1165 NB HALFWEG

Office	Secretariaat	(31) 023 - 513 2939
Pro shop	Pro shop	(31) 023 - 513 2939
Fax	Fax	(31) 023 - 513 2935
Web	www.houtrak.nl	
Situation	Locatie	Amsterdam, 15 km
Annual closure	Jaarlijkse sluiting	no
Weekly closure	Wekelijkse sluitingsdag	no

Fees main season Hoogseizoen tarieven	Week days Weekdagen	We/Bank holidays We/Feestdagen
		18 holes
Individual Individueel	€ 70	*
Couple Paar	€ 140	*

* We: members only

Caddie Caddie no — **Electric Trolley** Electrische trolley no
Buggy Buggy yes — **Clubs** Clubs yes
Credit cards Creditcards
VISA - MasterCard

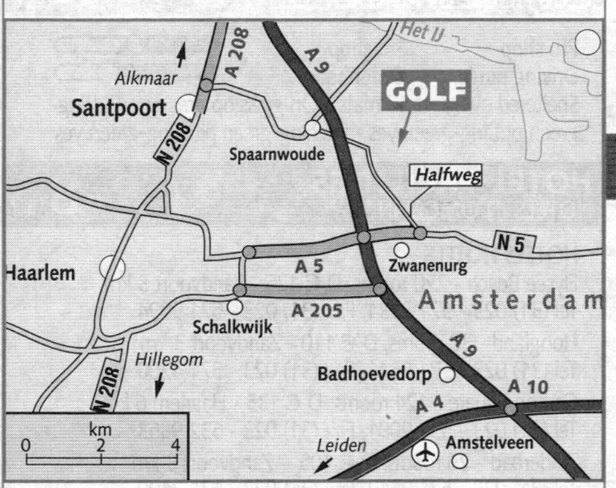

Access Toegang : Amsterdam, N5/A5 → Haarlem. Exit Spaarnwoude. 200 m turn left.
Map 1 on page 988 Auto kaart 1 Blz 988

GOLF COURSE — BAAN 16/20

Site	Terrein	
Maintenance	Onderhoud	
Architect	Architect	Gerard Jol
Type	Type baan	polder, open country
Relief	Reliëf	
Water in play	Waterhazards	
Exp. to wind	Windgevoelig	
Trees in play	Bomen	

Scorecard Scorekaart	Chp. Back tees	Mens Heren	Ladies Damen
Length Lengte	6395	6170	5199
Par	72	72	72
Slope system	136	132	128

Advised golfing ability Aanbevolen golfvaardigheid: 0 12 24 36
Hcp required Vereiste hcp: 36

CLUB HOUSE & AMENITIES — CLUB HOUSE EN ANNEXEN 8/10

Pro shop Pro shop
Driving range Oefenbaan
Sheltered overdekt 10 mats - On grass op gras no, 25 mats open air - Putting-green putting-green yes - Pitching-green pitching-green yes

HOTEL FACILITIES — HOTELS IN OMGEVING 8/10

HOTELS HOTELS

Radisson SAS - Amsterdam 10 km
243 rooms, D € 260
Tel (31) 020 - 623 1231, Fax (31) 020 - 520 8200

Canal House - 26 rooms, D € 190 - Amsterdam 10 km
Tel (31) 020 - 622 5182, Fax (31) 020 - 624 1317

Ambassade - 59 rooms, D € 180 - Amsterdam 10 km
Tel (31) 020 - 555 0222, Fax (31) 020 - 555 0277

RESTAURANTS RESTAURANTS

La Rive - Amsterdam 10 km - Tel (31) 020 - 520 3264
De Bokkedoorns - Overveen 15 km - Tel (31) 023 - 526 3600
d'Vijff Vlieghen - Amsterdam 10 km - Tel (31) 020 - 530 4060

Kennemer

18	8	8

Als Holland een vlak land is, dan liggen hier haar bergen. Duintoppen, wind en sobere vegetatie zijn de kenmerken van een echte linksbaan. De Kennemer is een van de mooiste voorbeeld daarvan in Europa. Je kunt de zee dan wel niet zien van hieruit, het stijlvolle, zeer traditionele clubhuis zal u zeker bekoren. De baan, ontworpen door Harry Colt in 1920, is in 1985 met negen holes uitgebreid, maar het gedeelte waar dit gebeurde had minder natuurlijke aanleg daarvoor. De verschillen in hoogte zijn beperkt (met hier en daar wat blinde slagen), al zal menige bal uiteindelijk na wat stuiteren en rollen op een interessante plaats tot rust komen. Laat de afwezigheid van water en de schaarste aan bomen (enkele vliegdennen) u niet overmoedig maken. De bunkers zijn talrijk en goed geplaatst, de struiken ontbreken niet. Als u ze weet te ontlopen, kunt u een goede score neerzetten. Op voorwaarde dat de wind niet te hard waait, maar dit spreekt vanzelf op dit type baan.

If Holland is a flat country then here are her mountains. High dunes, wind and scant vegetation are the unmistakable features of a links course, of which Kennemer is one of the finest examples in Europe. You don't really see the sea but you will appreciate the stylish and very traditional club-house. Designed by Harry Colt in 1920, the original course was supplemented with an additional 9 holes in 1985 but the natural terrain has not quite worked as well for the newer layout. The course is moderately hilly (with a few blind shots), enough for slightly wayward shots to kick, roll and end up in some pretty hairy positions. Don't feel too confident about the absence of water and the scarcity of trees; there are loads of bunkers, all well placed, and there is no shortage of prickly gorse, either. Keep out of them and you might hope to sign for a good score, providing the wind doesn't blow you and your card away. On this type of course, that goes without saying. An absolute must.

Kennemer Golf & Country Club 1927
Kennemerweg 78
NL - 2042 XT ZANDVOORT

Office	Secretariaat	(31) 023 - 571 8456
Pro shop	Pro shop	(31) 023 - 571 4974
Fax	Fax	(31) 023 - 571 9520
Web	www.kennemergolf.nl	
Situation	Locatie	Amsterdam, 25 km

Haarlem (pop. 150 213), 6 km

Annual closure	Jaarlijkse sluiting	no
Weekly closure	Wekelijkse sluitingsdag	no
Fees main season	Hoogseizoen tarieven	18 holes

	Week days Weekdagen	We/Bank holidays We/Feestdagen
Individual Individueel	€ 110	€ 110
Couple Paar	€ 220	€ 220

Caddie Caddie no — **Electric Trolley** Electrische trolley yes
Buggy Buggy yes — **Clubs** Clubs no
Credit cards Creditcards
VISA - MasterCard

GOLF COURSE
BAAN — **18**/20

Site	Terrein	
Maintenance	Onderhoud	
Architect	Architect	Harry S. Colt Frank Pennink van Hengel
Type	Type baan	links
Relief	Reliëf	
Water in play	Waterhazards	
Exp. to wind	Windgevoelig	
Trees in play	Bomen	

Scorecard Scorekaart	Chp. Back tees	Mens Heren	Ladies Damen
Length Lengte	6247	5778	5020
Par	72	72	72
Slope system	138	138	135

Advised golfing ability Aanbevolen golfvaardigheid — 0 12 24 36
Hcp required Vereiste hcp — 36

CLUB HOUSE & AMENITIES
CLUB HOUSE EN ANNEXEN — **8**/10

Pro shop Pro shop
Driving range Oefenbaan
Sheltered overdekt 10 mats - On grass op gras no - Putting-green putting-green yes - Pitching-green pitching-green yes

HOTEL FACILITIES
HOTELS IN OMGEVING — **8**/10

HOTELS HOTELS
Elysée Beach - 220 rooms, D € 125 - Zandvoort 3 km
Tel (31) 023 - 571 3234, Fax (31) 023 - 571 9094
Hoogland - 30 rooms, D € 110 - Zandvoort 3 km
Tel (31) 023 - 571 5541, Fax (31) 023 - 571 4200
Carlton Square - 124 rooms, D € 135 - Haarlem 6 km
Tel (31) 023 - 531 9091, Fax (31) 023 - 532 9853
Zuiderbad - 26 rooms, D € 105 - Zandvoort 3 km
Tel (31) 023 - 571 2613, Fax (31) 023 - 571 3190

RESTAURANTS RESTAURANTS
Kraantje Lek - Overveen 10 km - Tel (31) 023 - 524 12 66
Cheval Blanc - Heemstede 3 km - Tel (31) 023 - 529 3173

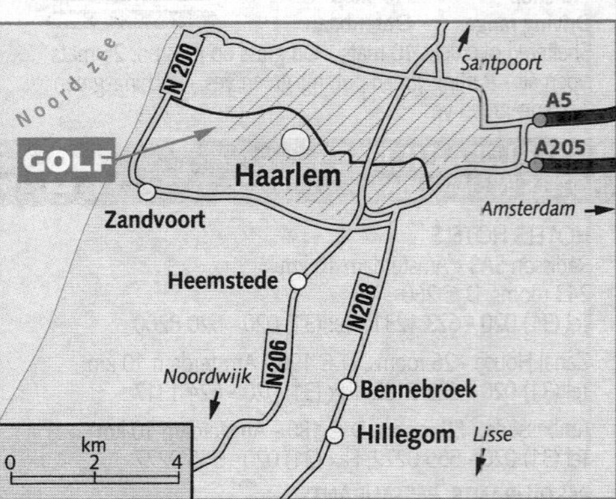

Access Toegang : Haarlem, Aerdenhout → Zandvoort
Map 1 on page 988 Auto kaart 1 Blz 988

Lage Vuursche

17 | 7 | 7

Van het begin af aan was het duidelijk dat deze baan, die op initiatief van enkele vermogende golfers tot stand is gekomen, een bijzondere toevoeging aan de Nederlandse golfcollectie moest worden. En dat is gelukt ook. De onmiskenbare Amerikaanse hand van de beide architecten is zichtbaar in de ruime opzet, de grote greens, de brede waterpartijen en de afwisseling in problemen waar de speler mee geconfronteerd wordt. De aandacht mag geen moment verslappen, want als je er in slaagt de meest opvallende hindernissen te ontwijken, dan zijn er altijd nog wel wat sluwe heuveltjes of geniepige bunkertjes die de score kunnen bederven. Als straks de beplanting in dit opvallend open terrein volgroeid is, zal de uitdaging nog groter zijn. Gelukkig wacht aan het eind van elke ronde een clubhuis dat qua allure en faciliteiten past bij een dergelijk mega-project.

Right from the beginning it was clear that this project, an initiative from several well-to-do very private course locals, was meant to be a special feature amongst the collection of Dutch courses. And so it is. Design work was assigned to Robert Trent Jones Jr. and one of the up-and-coming stars of golf course architecture, Kyle Phillips, who already has the highly acclaimed Kingsbarns, south of St Andrews, to his name. In Lage Vuursche, the unmistakable American identity of both architects is visible in the spacious lay-out, the large greens, the extensive water hazards and the variety of problems players are faced with. Concentration should never waver, as some cunningly placed hillocks and treacherous bunkers can easily ruin your card. Later on, when the trees and bushes in this remarkably open terrain have matured, the challenge will be even tougher. Luckily there is a well-equipped club-house waiting to console you.

Golfsociëteit de Lage Vuursche — 2000

Dolderseweg 262
NL - 3734 BS DEN DOLDER

Office	Secretariaat	(31) 030 - 229 2594
Pro shop	Pro shop	(31) 030 - 229 2594
Fax	Fax	(31) 030 - 225 9515
E-mail	secretariaat@golflagevuursche.nl	
Situation	Locatie	Utrecht, 12 km
Annual closure	Jaarlijkse sluiting	no
Weekly closure	Wekelijkse sluitingsdag	no

Fees main season Hoogseizoen tarieven	18 holes	
	Week days Weekdagen	**We/Bank holidays** We/Feestdagen
Individual Individueel	€ 110	*
Couple Paar	€ 220	*

* We: members only

Caddie Caddie no — **Electric Trolley** Electrische trolley no
Buggy Buggy yes — **Clubs** Clubs no
Credit cards Creditcards
VISA - Eurocard - MasterCard - AMEX

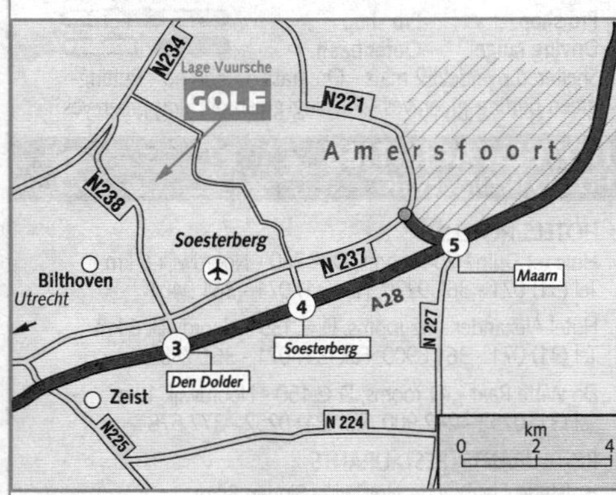

Access Toegang : • Utrecht, A27 → Hilversum. Exit 32. Right on N234 → Soest. Right on N238. Golf on left side.
• Utrecht A28 → Amersfoort. Exit 3. Left on N238. Golf on right side. **Map 1 on page 988** Auto kaart 1 Blz 988

GOLF COURSE — BAAN — 17/20

Site	Terrein	
Maintenance	Onderhoud	
Architect	Architect	Kyle Phillips, Robert Trent Jones Jr.
Type	Type baan	open country
Relief	Reliëf	
Water in play	Waterhazards	
Exp. to wind	Windgevoelig	
Trees in play	Bomen	

Scorecard Scorekaart	**Chp.** Back tees	**Mens** Heren	**Ladies** Damen
Length Lengte	6287	6038	4983
Par	71	71	71
Slope system	141	137	129

Advised golfing ability Aanbevolen golfvaardigheid — 0 12 24 36
Hcp required Vereiste hcp — 24

CLUB HOUSE & AMENITIES — CLUB HOUSE EN ANNEXEN — 7/10

Pro shop Pro shop
Driving range Oefenbaan
Sheltered overdekt 8 mats - On grass op gras yes - Putting-green putting-green yes - Pitching-green pitching-green yes

HOTEL FACILITIES — HOTELS IN OMGEVING — 7/10

HOTELS HOTELS

De Hoefslag - Bosch en Duin 2 km
30 rooms, D € 230
Tel (31) 030 - 225 1051, Fax (31) 030 - 228 5821

Kasteel 't Kerckebosch - Zeist 8 km
30 rooms, D € 175
Tel (31) 030 - 692 6666, Fax (31) 030 - 692 6600

Grand Hotel Karel V - 91 rooms, D € 225 - Utrecht 12 km
Tel (31) 030 - 233 7555, Fax (31) 030 - 233 7500

RESTAURANTS RESTAURANTS

De Hoefslag - Bosch en Duin 2 km - Tel (31) 030 - 225 1051
Wilhelmina Park - Utrecht 12 km - Tel (31) 030 - 251 0693
Karel V - Utrecht 12 km - Tel (31) 030 - 233 7555

Noordwijk

18	7	8

De derde parel in de trilogie van Nederlandse linksbanen. Met magnifiek uitzicht over de duinen en de bollenvelden in het binnenland. Een klassieke lay-out, waarbij alleen natuurlijke elementen in het spel komen. Met alle moeilijkheden van het golfspel in de duinen, zoals potbunkers, blinde slagen en de wind. Slechts vijf holes liggen in bebost terrein. Ook hier kennen de fairways maar weinig vlakke stukken, dus is een goede techniek nodig voor elke slag. En om de bal laag te houden als het waait. De meeste greens worden omringd door rough of heuveltjes, zonder al te veel bunkers, maar denk niet dat scoren gemakkelijk is. Andere interessante elementen zijn de dichte struiken in de rough, een enkel poeltje en het clubhuis dat vanaf een duintop uitzicht biedt over de wijde omgeving . Een uitdagende baan, die tot de beste van Europa gerekend kan worden (bij voorkeur spelen op een werkdag).

The third absolute gem in the magnificent trilogy of Dutch links, one that offers some magnificent views over the dunes and inland, covered with fields of flowers in the Spring. The layout is a classic, bringing into play only natural elements and the difficulties of golfing amidst sand dunes, including pot bunkers, blind shots and exposure to the wind. Only five holes are laid out over woody terrain. Again, there are few flat lies, so good technique is needed to shape the shot and to hit low balls when the wind blows. As most of the greens are surrounded by rough or rolling mounds, there aren't too many bunkers but don't ever think scoring is easy. Other interesting features are the thick bushes in the middle of the rough, a single water hazard and the welcome renovation of the club-house. A challenging layout that has to be rated amongst the front-running courses in Europe (choose a week-day to play here).

Noordwijkse Golfclub 1972
Randweg 25
NL - 2200 AB NOORDWIJK

Office	Secretariaat	(31) 0252 - 373 763
Pro shop	Pro shop	(31) 0252 - 373 763
Fax	Fax	(31) 0252 - 370 044
Web	www.noordwijksegolfclub.nl	
Situation	Locatie	Leiden (pop. 114 892), 15 km
Annual closure	Jaarlijkse sluiting	no
Weekly closure	Wekelijkse sluitingsdag	no

Fees main season Hoogseizoen tarieven	18 holes	
	Week days Weekdagen	**We/Bank holidays** We/Feestdagen
Individual Individueel	€ 95	*
Couple Paar	€ 190	*

* We: members only

Caddie Caddie no — **Electric Trolley** Electrische trolley no
Buggy Buggy yes — **Clubs** Clubs no

Credit cards Creditcards
VISA - Mastercard - Pin

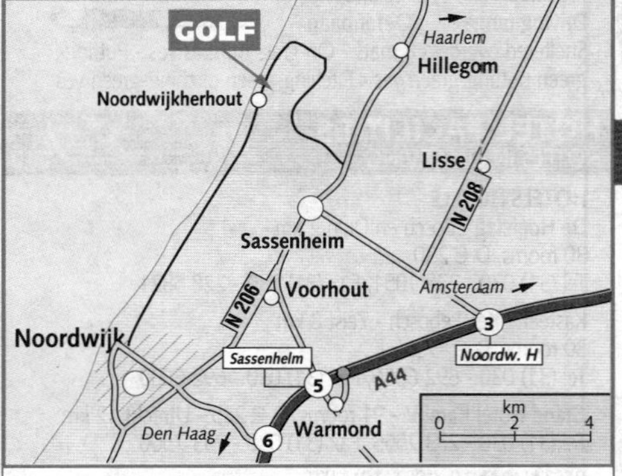

Access Toegang : Amsterdam, A4, A44 → Leiden. Exit 3 → Noordwijk aan Zee. 6 km → Nordwijkerhout. 1 km → Zee
Map 1 on page 988 Auto kaart 1 Blz 988

GOLF COURSE
BAAN — **18**/20

Site	Terrein	
Maintenance	Onderhoud	
Architect	Architect	Frank Pennink P. de Jong
Type	Type baan	links
Relief	Reliëf	
Water in play	Waterhazards	
Exp. to wind	Windgevoelig	
Trees in play	Bomen	

Scorecard Scorekaart	**Chp.** Back tees	**Mens** Heren	**Ladies** Damen
Length Lengte	6257	5810	4967
Par	72	72	72
Slope system	135	134	126

Advised golfing ability Aanbevolen golfvaardigheid — 0 12 24 36
Hcp required Vereiste hcp — 28

CLUB HOUSE & AMENITIES
CLUB HOUSE EN ANNEXEN — **7**/10

Pro shop Pro shop
Driving range Oefenbaan
Sheltered overdekt 2 mats - **On grass** op gras no - **Putting-green** putting-green yes - **Pitching-green** pitching-green yes

HOTEL FACILITIES
HOTELS IN OMGEVING — **8**/10

HOTELS HOTELS
Huis ter Duin - 254 rooms, D € 260 - Noordwijk 6 km
Tel (31) 071 - 361 9220, Fax (31) 071 - 361 9401

Hotel Alexander - 62 rooms, D € 135 - Noordwijk 6 km
Tel (31) 071 - 361 8900, Fax (31) 071 - 361 7882

De Witte Raaf - 41 rooms, D € 150 - Noordwijk 1 km
Tel (31) 0252 - 242 900, Fax (31) 0252 - 377 578

RESTAURANTS RESTAURANTS
Hofstede Cleyburch - Nordwijk- Binnen 8 km
Tel (31) 071 - 364 8448
De Palmentuin - Noordwijk 6 km - Tel (31) 071 - 367 6869
Latour ((Huis ter Duin) - Noordwijk 6 km - Tel (31) 071 - 365 1230

Nunspeet *North/East*

14	7	6

Temidden van oude bospercelen zijn drie lussen van elk negen holes aangelegd. Het levert een aantrekkelijke, maar ook vrij smalle golfbaan op. Misschien is het terrein net iets te klein voor 27 holes. Aan de andere kant, als je geen probleem hebt met het feit dat een paar holes wat kunstmatig aandoen, blijft er een 'spannende' baan over. Vooral de 'North'-baan, waar op de zesde hole een zandverstuiving voor een soort superbunker zorgt. Uiteraard zijn de bomen langs de baan de belangrijkste factor om rekening mee te houden, vooral op de doglegs, die ruim voorhanden zijn. En zo nu en dan komt er ook water in het spel, soms op letterlijk indringende wijze. Aardig is dat de 'North' en 'East' baan beide op een grote dubbelgreen eindigen, vlakbij het grote clubhuis dat, net als de oefenfaciliteiten, groot genoeg is om meerdere groepen te huisvesten.

Three loops of nine holes have been cut out of the existing woodland, making a pretty but somewhat narrow layout. Maybe the total area was just a tad too small for 27 holes. On the other hand, if you accept that some holes are a little artificial, what is left is an attractive layout. Especially the North course, where the 6th hole features a huge natural sandtrap in the form of a drifting dune. Trees are obviously the most significant hazard to cope with, especially on the doglegs that come thick and fast. Water also comes into play on some holes. One nice feature is that both the North and East courses finish on a large double-green close to the roomy club-house, which is large enough to cater to several groups at the same time.

Nunspeetse Golf & Country Club 1988
Plesmanlaan 30
NL - 8072 PT NUNSPEET

Office	Secretariaat	(31) 0341 - 255 255
Pro shop	Pro shop	(31) 0341 - 255 255
Fax	Fax	(31) 0341 - 255 285
Web	www.nunspeetsegolf.nl	
Situation	Locatie	Amersfoort, 40 km

Zwolle (pop. 99 139), 25 km

Annual closure	Jaarlijkse sluiting	no
Weekly closure	Wekelijkse sluitingsdag	no
Fees main season	Hoogseizoen tarieven	18 holes

	Week days Weekdagen	We/Bank holidays We/Feestdagen
Individual Individueel	€ 50	€ 55
Couple Paar	€ 100	€ 110

Caddie Caddie no — **Electric Trolley** Electrische trolley no
Buggy Buggy yes — **Clubs** Clubs yes
Credit cards Creditcards
VISA - MasterCard - AMEX - DC

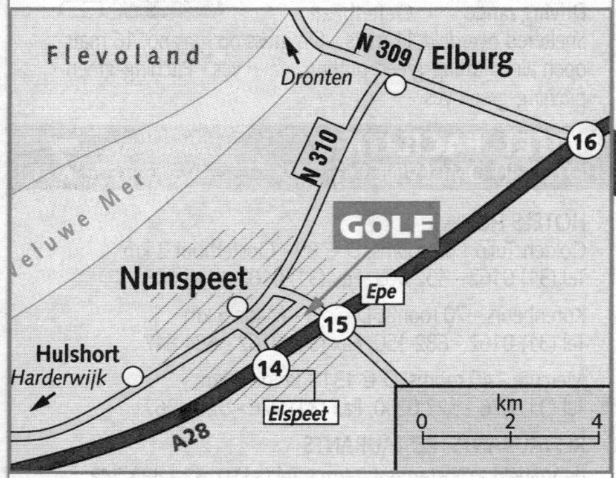

Access Toegang : A28 Exit 14 (Zwolle-Amersfoort)
→ Nunspeet. Golf 2 km
Map 1 on page 989 Auto kaart 1 Blz 989

GOLF COURSE — BAAN 14/20

Site	Terrein	
Maintenance	Onderhoud	
Architect	Architect	Paul Rolin
Type	Type baan	forest
Relief	Reliëf	
Water in play	Waterhazards	
Exp. to wind	Windgevoelig	
Trees in play	Bomen	

Scorecard Scorekaart	Chp. Back tees	Mens Heren	Ladies Damen
Length Lengte	6012	5853	5105
Par	72	72	72
Slope system	133	133	125

Advised golfing ability Aanbevolen golfvaardigheid — 0 12 24 36
Hcp required Vereiste hcp — no

CLUB HOUSE & AMENITIES — CLUB HOUSE EN ANNEXEN 7/10

Pro shop Pro shop
Driving range Oefenbaan
Sheltered overdekt 8 mats - On grass op gras no, 16 mats open air - Putting-green putting-green yes (2) - Pitching-green pitching-green yes

HOTEL FACILITIES — HOTELS IN OMGEVING 6/10

HOTELS HOTELS
De Mallejan - 38 rooms, D € 110 - Vierhouten 5 km
Tel (31) 0577 - 411 241, Fax (31) 0577 - 411 629

Keizerskroon - Apeldoorn 30 km
94 rooms, D € 160
Tel (31) 055 - 521 7744, Fax (31) 055 - 521 4737

Dennenheuvel - 34 rooms, D € 103 - Epe 10 km
Tel (31) 0578 - 612 326, Fax (31) 0578 - 677 699

RESTAURANTS RESTAURANTS
De Leest - Vaassen 14 km - Tel (31) 0578 - 571 382
Auberge Navet - Apeldoorn 30 km - Tel (31) 055 - 541 8664
't Soerel - Epe 10 km - Tel (31) 0578 - 688 276

Oosterhout

15	7	7

Het is jammer dat een deel van het aangrenzende industrieterrein vanaf de baan zichtbaar is en de langslopende autoweg continu hoorbaar is. Voor het overige waant u zich hier temidden van het buitenleven (weilanden, graanvelden, koeien) op een baan die veel aandacht voor ecologie heeft. Zo wordt de rough lang gehouden om de knaagdieren te huisvesten, die op hun beurt roofvogels aantrekken. Ondanks de relatief jonge leeftijd oogt de baan vrij volwassen. Een paar losse bomen en struiken zijn in het ontwerp opgenomen en vormen zo hindernissen, net als waterpartijen, talloze bunkers en de wind, die altijd aanwezig lijkt. Vier vijvertjes komen in het spel op acht holes, waarbij ze op de 5e en 15e recht voor de green liggen. Twee fraaie par-3 holes, die vooral onervaren spelers ontzag zullen inboezemen. Behalve een paar blinde bunkers heeft de baan een eerlijk karakter. Uitgezonderd misschien de 16e hole, een controversiële dogleg.

Unfortunately, a number of buildings from the nearby industrial estate can still be seen and the noise from the road is never-ending. Otherwise, you are in the country here (meadows, fields of wheat and cows) and the club pays very special attention to the environment. Hence rough that is left to grow rather tall, attracting rodents, falcons and eagles. Despite its tender age the course is remarkably mature. A few isolated trees or copses are fully integrated into the course and form one of the difficulties, along with the water hazards, numerous bunkers and the wind, which is always a frequent feature. Four small lakes come into play on eight holes, forming frontal hazards on the 5th and 15th holes, two fine par 3s which could be a real handful for inexperienced players. Despite a few hidden hazards, the course is fair and open in style, excepting the 16th, a still very controversial dog-leg.

Oosterhoutse Golf Club — 1989

Dukaatstraat 21
NL - 4903 RN OOSTERHOUT

Office	Secretariaat	(31) 0162 - 421 210
Pro shop	Pro shop	(31) 0162 - 436 397
Fax	Fax	(31) 0162 - 433 285
Web	www.ogcgolf.nl	
Situation	Locatie	Breda (pop. 129 125), 5 km
Annual closure	Jaarlijkse sluiting	no
Weekly closure	Wekelijkse sluitingsdag	no

Fees main season Hoogseizoen tarieven	18 holes	
	Week days Weekdagen	**We/Bank holidays** We/Feestdagen
Individual Individueel	€ 60	*
Couple Paar	€ 120	*

* We: members only

Caddie Caddie no — **Electric Trolley** Electrische trolley no
Buggy Buggy yes — **Clubs** Clubs no
Credit cards Creditcards no

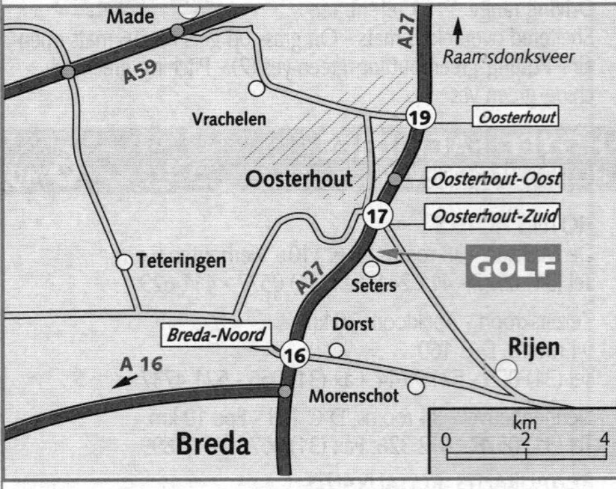

Access Toegang : A27, Exit 17 → Rijen. 200 m, turn right. → Golf
Map 1 on page 988 Auto kaart 1 Blz 988

GOLF COURSE — BAAN 15/20

Site	Terrein	
Maintenance	Onderhoud	
Architect	Architect	Joan Dudok van Heel
Type	Type baan	open country, parkland
Relief	Reliëf	
Water in play	Waterhazards	
Exp. to wind	Windgevoelig	
Trees in play	Bomen	

Scorecard Scorekaart	**Chp.** Back tees	**Mens** Heren	**Ladies** Damen
Length Lengte	6116	5908	5113
Par	72	72	72
Slope system	127	126	120

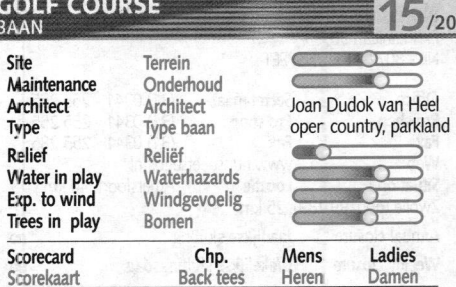

Advised golfing ability Aanbevolen golfvaardigheid — 0 12 24 36
Hcp required Vereiste hcp — 36

CLUB HOUSE & AMENITIES — CLUB HOUSE EN ANNEXEN 7/10

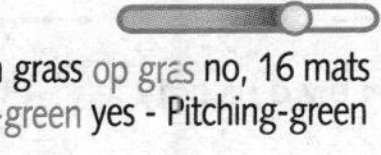

Pro shop Pro shop
Driving range Oefenbaan
Sheltered overdekt 11 mats - On grass op gras no, 16 mats open air - Putting-green putting-green yes - Pitching-green pitching-green yes

HOTEL FACILITIES — HOTELS IN OMGEVING 7/10

HOTELS HOTELS

Golden Tulip - 52 rooms, D € 89 - Oosterhout 2 km
Tel (31) 0162 - 452 003, Fax (31) 0162 - 435 003

Korenbeurs - 70 rooms, D € 78 - Made 5 km
Tel (31) 0162 - 682 150, Fax (31) 0162 - 684 647

Mercure - 40 rooms, D € 131 - Breda 5 km
Tel (31) 076 - 522 0200, Fax (31) 076 - 521 4967

RESTAURANTS RESTAURANTS

de Vrijheld - Oosterhout 2 km - Tel (31) 0162 - 433 243
Boschlust - Breda 5 km - Tel (31) 076 - 571 3383
De Stadstuin - Breda 2 km - Tel (31) 076 - 530 9636
Wolfslaar - Breda 5 km - Tel (31) 076 - 560 8008

Purmerend

14 | 8 | 7

Het heeft meer dan twee jaar geduurd, maar nu de complete ombouw van het complex is voltooid blijkt dat meer dan de moeite waard geweest. Het resultaat is twee volwaardige 18-holesbanen en een 9-holes oefenbaan. Op de nieuwe holes is nu nog veel open ruimte, maar dat zal, net als op de 'oude' holes is gebeurd, geleidelijk verdwijnen. De vele aangeplante bomen en struiken zullen het karakter van de baan veranderen in een parkbaan, waar de vele waterpartijen, in combinatie met een fors aantal bunkers, de belangrijkste hindernis vormen. Als compensatie is de baan echt ruim opgezet, waardoor op veel holes een minder nauwkeurig teeshot niet direct wordt afgestraft. Maar daarna is er nog voldoende 'ruimte' om de score toch te verprutsen. Het clubhuis, de oefenfaciliteiten en het aangrenzende hotel zijn in lijn met wat je van het op een na grootste commerciële golfcentrum in Nederland mag verwachten: ruim opgezet en een gastvrije ontvangst.

It took more than two years, but the extensive reconstruction of this resort has produced exceptional results and Purmerend was back in this Guide. There are now two 18-hole courses and a 9-hole practice course. The new holes still provide a lot of open space, but as seen with the "old" holes, that will not last long. The many trees and bushes planted will change the character of the course. Extensive water combined with an impressive number of bunkers form the majority of hazards. As if to compensate, the generous width of several fairways easily tolerates off-line tee-shots. But beware, the remaining distance to the greens on these same holes provides ample opportunity to ruin your card. The club-house, the practice facilities and the adjacent hotel are consistent with what you might expect to find at the second largest commercial golf centre in the Netherlands: bags of room and a friendly reception.

BurgGolf Purmerend — 1990

Westerweg 60
NL - 1445 AD PURMEREND

Office	Secretariaat	(31) 0299 - 689 160
Pro shop	Pro shop	(31) 0299 - 689 160
Fax	Fax	(31) 0299 - 647 081
Web	www.burggolf.nl	
Situation	Locatie	Amsterdam, 15 km
Annual closure	Jaarlijkse sluiting	no
Weekly closure	Wekelijkse sluitingsdag	no

Fees main season Hoogseizoen tarieven	18 holes	
	Week days Weekdagen	We/Bank holidays We/Feestdagen
Individual Individueel	€ 47,5	€ 57,5
Couple Paar	€ 95	€ 115

Caddie Caddie no — **Electric Trolley** Electrische trolley no
Buggy Buggy yes — **Clubs** Clubs yes
Credit cards Creditcards
VISA - MasterCard - AMEX - DC - Pin

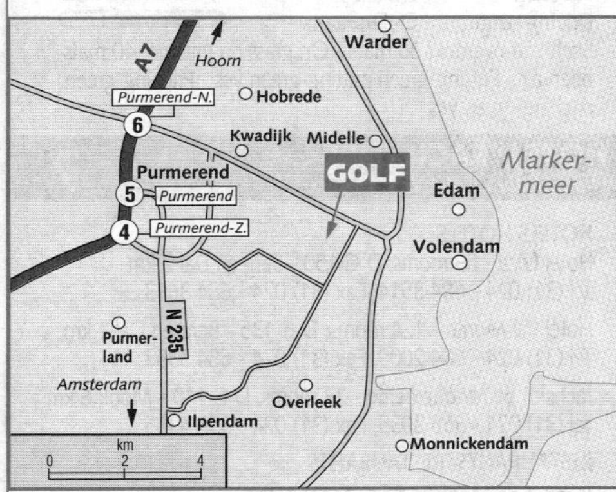

Access Toegang : Amsterdam A7 Exit 6 → Purmerend-Noord. Take right → Volendam
Map 1 on page 988 Auto kaart 1 Blz 988

GOLF COURSE — BAAN — 14/20

Site	Terrein	
Maintenance	Onderhoud	
Architect	Architect	Tom MacAuley, Bruno Steensels
Type	Type baan	polder, parkland
Relief	Reliëf	
Water in play	Waterhazards	
Exp. to wind	Windgevoelig	
Trees in play	Bomen	

Scorecard Scorekaart	Chp. Back tees	Mens Heren	Ladies Damen
Length Lengte	6087	5727	4971
Par	72	72	72
Slope system	128	124	122

Advised golfing ability Aanbevolen golfvaardigheid — 0 12 24 36
Hcp required Vereiste hcp — 36

CLUB HOUSE & AMENITIES — CLUB HOUSE EN ANNEXEN — 8/10

Pro shop Pro shop
Driving range Oefenbaan
Sheltered overdekt 14 mats - On grass op gras no - Putting-green putting-green yes (2) - Pitching-green pitching-green yes

HOTEL FACILITIES — HOTELS IN OMGEVING — 7/10

HOTELS HOTELS

Hampshire Waterland - 97 rooms, D € 100 - on site
Tel (31) 0299 - 689 160, Fax (31) 0299 - 644 691

De Fortuna - 25 rooms, D € 100 - Edam 3 km
Tel (31) 0299 - 371 671, Fax (31) 0299 - 371 469

Purmerend - 40 rooms, D € 75 - Purmerend 3 km
Tel (31) 0299 - 436 858, Fax (31) 0299 - 436 954

RESTAURANTS RESTAURANTS

Mario Uva - Neck 5 km - Tel (31) 0299 - 423 949
La Ciboulette- Zuidoostbeemster 4 km - Tel (31) 0299 - 683 585
Sichuan Food (Chinese) - Purmerend 2 km
Tel (31) 0299 - 426 450

Rijk van Nijmegen *Nijmeegse Baan*

14	6	7

Dit complex met 36 holes was een van de eerste commerciële golfbanen in Nederland. Het is een zeer succesvol project gebleken. De twee oorspronkelijke 9-holesbanen zijn in een latere fase samengevoegd en uitgebreid tot een volwaardige 18-holesbaan, de Groesbeekse Baan. Deze is wat korter, maar ook veel heuvelachtiger dan de andere, de Nijmeegse Baan. Hoewel de vele bosjes die tussen de holes zijn geplant wat bescherming bieden, is de wind een factor om terdege rekening mee te houden, vooral omdat de begroeiing om landschaptechnische redenen vrij laag wordt gehouden. Daardoor is wel een fraai uitzicht, tot diep in Duitsland, behouden gebleven. Er zijn veel bunkers die niet altijd van de tee zichtbaar zijn en meerdere holes met blinde slagen naar de green. Alles bij elkaar een prettige baan in een golvend landschap, dat in Nederland niet veel voorkomt.

This 36 holes complex was one of the early commercial golf projects in the Netherlands and a rather successful one, too. The two original short 9-holers were subsequently merged to form a second 18-hole course (Groesbeekse Baan). It is a little shorter but also much hillier than its senior counterpart, the Nijmeegse Baan. Although the many bushes planted between the holes seem to offer some protection from the wind, it is still a factor to consider. For planning reasons the bushes are kept low, which in turn provides wide views over the surrounding hills, even far into neighbouring Germany. There are lots of bunkers, some of which are not easily visible from the tees, and several holes with blind shots to the greens. Altogether, this is a pleasant course in rolling countryside not often seen in the Netherlands, with an excellent club-house and practice facilities.

Golfbaan Het Rijk van Nijmegen — 1987

Postweg 17
NL - 6561 KJ GROESBEEK

Office	Secretariaat	(31) 024 - 397 6644
Pro shop	Pro shop	(31) 024 - 397 6644
Fax	Fax	(31) 024 - 397 6942
Web	www.golfbaanhetrijkvannijmegen.nl	
Situation	Locatie	Nijmegen (pop. 147 000), 6 km
Annual closure	Jaarlijkse sluiting	no
Weekly closure	Wekelijkse sluitingsdag	no

Fees main season Hoogseizoen tarieven	18 holes	
	Week days Weekdagen	**We/Bank holidays** We/Feestdagen
Individual Individueel	€ 50	€ 55
Couple Paar	€ 100	€ 110

Caddie Caddie no — **Electric Trolley** Electrische trolley no
Buggy Buggy yes — **Clubs** Clubs yes
Credit cards Creditcards
VISA - MasterCard - AMEX - DC - Pin

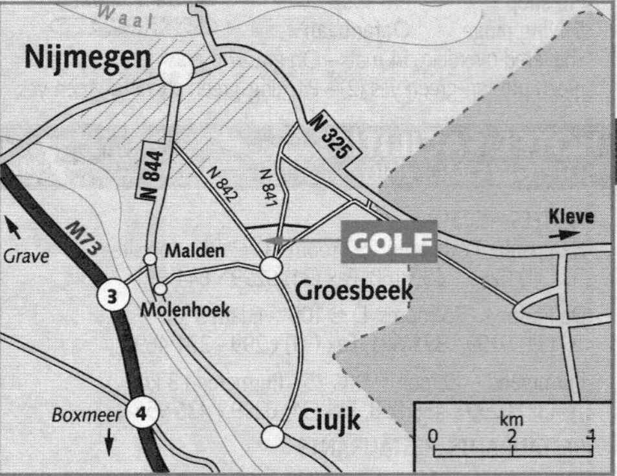

Access Toegang : Nijmegen: A73,Exit 3 → Groesbeek → Nijmegen
Map 1 on page 989 Auto kaart 1 Blz 989

GOLF COURSE — BAAN — 14/20

Site	Terrein	
Maintenance	Onderhoud	
Architect	Architect	Paul Rolin
Type	Type baan	parkland
Relief	Reliëf	
Water in play	Waterhazards	
Exp. to wind	Windgevoelig	
Trees in play	Bomen	

Scorecard Scorekaart	**Chp.** Back tees	**Mens** Heren	**Ladies** Damen
Length Lengte	6076	6010	5307
Par	72	72	72
Slope system	127	126	121

Advised golfing ability Aanbevolen golfvaardigheid — 0 12 24 36
Hcp required Vereiste hcp — 36

CLUB HOUSE & AMENITIES — CLUB HOUSE EN ANNEXEN — 6/10

Pro shop Pro shop
Driving range Oefenbaan
Sheltered overdekt 30 mats - On grass op gras no, 40 mats open air - Putting-green putting-green yes - Pitching-green pitching-green yes

HOTEL FACILITIES — HOTELS IN OMGEVING — 7/10

HOTELS HOTELS

Hotel Erica - 59 rooms, D € 150 - Berg en Dal 2 km
Tel (31) 024 - 684 3514, Fax (31) 024 - 684 3613

Hotel Val Monte - 124 rooms, D € 135 - Berg en Dal 2 km
Tel (31) 024 - 684 2000, Fax (31) 024 - 684 3353

Jachslot de Mookerheide - 23 rooms, D € 140 - Mook 6 km
Tel (31) 024 - 358 3035, Fax (31) 024 - 358 4355

RESTAURANTS RESTAURANTS

Jachslot de Mookerheide - Mook 6 km
Tel (31) 024 - 358 3035

Chalet Brakkestein - Nijmegen 5 km - Tel (31) 024 - 355 3949

Claudius - Nijmegen 5 km - Tel (31) 024 - 322 1456

Rosendael

15	7	7

De enige zwakke schakel hier is de rumoerige nabijheid van twee autowegen, die niet bestonden aan het eind van de vorige eeuw toen deze baan tussen bos, heide en doornenstruiken werd aangelegd. Dit zijn de oudste holes in Nederland en de eerste negen volgen nog het originele ontwerp. In de loop der tijden zijn ingrijpende veranderingen aangebracht, hoewel het oorspronkelijke plan van Del Court van Krimpen onaangetast is gebleven. We vermoeden dat Harry Colt iets met de latere wijzigingen te maken heeft gehad. Het zou niet verbazen, gegeven de positionering van de hazards en het natuurlijk karakter van de baan, die in licht heuvelachtig terrein ligt. De tweede negen holes zijn in 1977 gereedgekomen in een stijl die aansluit op de eerste negen. Let ook eens op de grappige holes, zoals de 13e, een korte dogleg met een hoger liggende tee en green. En alle par-3 holes, echte juweeltjes. Rosendael is zonder twijfel een van Neerlands beste banen.

The only weak point here is the noisy proximity of two motorways, which didn't exist at the turn of the century when this course was created through forest, heather and gorse. This was Holland's very first course and the front nine form the original layout. Significant changes have been made, although the original design of Del Court van Krimpen remains unspoiled. We suspect that Harry Colt had something to do with these changes, which wouldn't be surprising given the layout of hazards and the natural character of the course over slightly hilly terrain. The back nine were completed in 1977 in a style consistent with the rest of the course. Make a note of some amusing holes here, like the 13th, a short dog-leg with elevated tee and green, and all the par 3s, pure gems. Rosendael is unquestionably one of Holland's finest inland courses.

Rosendaelsche Golfclub — 1909

Apeldoornseweg 450
NL - 6816 SN ARNHEM

Office	Secretariaat	(31) 026 - 442 1438
Pro shop	Pro shop	(31) 026 - 443 7283
Fax	Fax	(31) 026 - 351 1196
Web	—	
Situation	Locatie	Arnhem (pop. 133 670), 2 km
Annual closure	Jaarlijkse sluiting	no
Weekly closure	Wekelijkse sluitingsdag	no

Fees main season Hoogseizoen tarieven	Week days Weekdagen	We/Bank holidays We/Feestdagen
	18 holes	
Individual Individueel	€ 70	*
Couple Paar	€ 140	*

* We: members only

Caddie Caddie no — Electric Trolley Electrische trolley no
Buggy Buggy no — Clubs Clubs no
Credit cards Creditcards no

Schaarsbergen, 21, Apeldoorn, National Park De Veluwezoom, Ede, Arnhem-N., 20, A50, A12, GOLF, Veenendaal, Arnhem-N., 26, Dieren, Velp, N 224, N 348, Arnhem, A348, Oosterbeerk, Doorwerth, Nijmegen, Rijn, A12, km 0 2 4, N 325, A325, Zevanaar, Westervoort

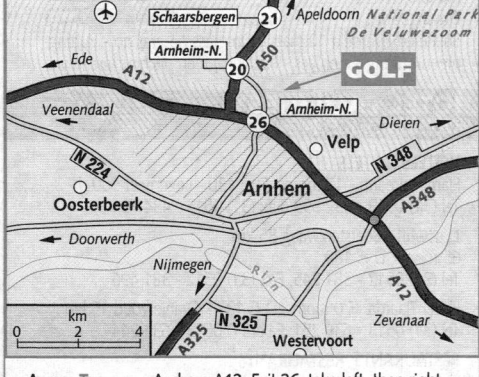

Access Toegang : Arnhem A12. Exit 26, take left, then right
Map 1 on page 989 Auto kaart 1 Blz 989

GOLF COURSE — BAAN — 15/20

Site	Terrein	
Maintenance	Onderhoud	
Architect	Architect	D.C. van Krimpen, Frank Pennink
Type	Type baan	forest
Relief	Reliëf	
Water in play	Waterhazards	
Exp. to wind	Windgevoelig	
Trees in play	Bomen	

Scorecard Scorekaart	Chp. Back tees	Mens Heren	Ladies Damen
Length Lengte	6326	6057	5159
Par	72	72	72
Slope system	134	132	126

Advised golfing ability / Aanbevolen golfvaardigheid: 0 12 24 36
Hcp required / Vereiste hcp: 36

CLUB HOUSE & AMENITIES — CLUB HOUSE EN ANNEXEN — 7/10

Pro shop — Pro shop
Driving range — Oefenbaan
Sheltered overdekt 2 mats - On grass op gras no - Putting-green putting-green yes - Pitching-green pitching-green yes

HOTEL FACILITIES — HOTELS IN OMGEVING — 7/10

HOTELS HOTELS
Rijnhotel - 68 rooms, D € 130 - Arnhem 4 km
Tel (31) 026 - 443 4642, Fax (31) 026 - 445 4847

Groot Warnsborn - 30 rooms, D € 180 - Arnhem 5 km
Tel (31) 026 - 445 5751, Fax (31) 026 - 443 1010

Velp Hotel - 74 rooms, D from € 140 - Velp 1 km
Tel (31) 026 - 364 9849, Fax (31) 026 - 364 2427

RESTAURANTS RESTAURANTS
De Steenen Tafel - Arnhem 1 km - Tel (31) 026 - 443 5313
Residence Roosendael - adjacent - Tel (31) 026 - 361 1597
La Rusticana (Italian) - Arnhem 5 km - Tel (31) 026 - 351 5607
Smaak - Arnhem 5 km - Tel (31) 026 - 442 6664

Sint Nicolaasga

15 | 7 | 5

Er is maar weinig reliëf in Friesland, de provincie van de wijde horizon en telkens wisselende luchten. In dit land van meren en weilanden vormen koeien en paarden een deel van het landschap. Er liggen maar weinig golfbanen, maar dit is een van de beste, heel fraai opgenomen in de omgeving. Een vlakke baan, niet erg lang, met brede fairways en weinig bomen, maar des te meer struiken om u dwars te zitten. Long-hitters kunnen zich laten gaan, maar moeten wel rekening houden met de wind, die het leven aardig zuur kan maken. Hetzelfde geldt voor de waterhazards (vijvertjes en sloten) die op zo'n twaalf holes in het spel komen. Deze baan is snel gerijpt en biedt veel variatie, zowel visueel (er is een hoop grond verplaatst) als golftechnisch. Een minpunt zijn de lange afstanden tussen de holes. Heel bijzonder is de klokkenstoel op het kerkhofje, aan drie zijden door de baan ingesloten.

There is little relief to speak of in the Frise, a region of endless horizons and changing skies. In this land of lakes, pastureland and crops, cows and horses are all part of the landscape. Golf courses are few and far between here but this is one of the best, blending in beautifully with the surrounding countryside. Very flat, not very long but with wide fairways, it has few trees to bother you but quite a few bushes. Long-hitters will let rip but will still have to watch out for the wind, which can make life very difficult. The same goes for the water hazards (ponds and ditches), in play on about a dozen holes. This course has quickly matured and has considerable variety both visually (a lot of earth was moved) and technically. The one minor flaw are the long walks between holes and the one peculiarity the little cemetery in front of the club-house, overlooked by a bell-tower and surrounded on three sides by the course.

BurgGolf Sint Nicolaasga — 1991

Legemeersterweg 16-18
NL - 8527 DS LEGEMEER

Office	Secretariaat	(31) 0513 - 499 466
Pro shop	Pro shop	(31) 0513 - 499 466
Fax	Fax	(31) 0513 - 499 777
Web	www.burggolf.nl	
Situation	Locatie	Heerenveen, 15 km
Annual closure	Jaarlijkse sluiting	no
Weekly closure	Wekelijkse sluitingsdag	no

Fees main season Hoogseizoen tarieven	18 holes	
	Week days Weekdagen	**We/Bank holidays** We/Feestdagen
Individual Individueel	€ 47,50	€ 57,50
Couple Paar	€ 95	€ 115

Caddie Caddie no — **Electric Trolley** Electrische trolley no
Buggy Buggy yes — **Clubs** Clubs yes
Credit cards Creditcards
VISA - MasterCard - AMEX - DC - Pin

Sneek
N 354
A7
Joure West
Joure
23
Lanweerder meer
Koevorder meer
Scharsterburg
Groningen
GOLF
Saint Nicolaasga
A6 (A50)
Emmelord
Amsterdam
Slotermeer
N 927
19
Tjeukemeer
km 0 2 4

Access Toegang : Amsterdam A6 → Groningen/Leeuwarden. Exit 19 → Woudsend. Golf 3.5 km
Map 1 on page 988 Auto kaart 1 Blz 988

GOLF COURSE — BAAN — 15/20

Site	Terrein	
Maintenance	Onderhoud	
Architect	Architect	Paul Rolin, Alan Rijks
Type	Type baan	polder, open country
Relief	Reliëf	
Water in play	Waterhazards	
Exp. to wind	Windgevoelig	
Trees in play	Bomen	

Scorecard Scorekaart	**Chp.** Back tees	**Mens** Heren	**Ladies** Damen
Length Lengte	6038	5756	4993
Par	72	72	72
Slope system	135	132	131

Advised golfing ability Aanbevolen golfvaardigheid — 0 12 24 36
Hcp required Vereiste hcp — 36

CLUB HOUSE & AMENITIES — CLUB HOUSE EN ANNEXEN — 7/10

Pro shop Pro shop
Driving range Oefenbaan
Sheltered overdekt 10 mats - On grass op gras no - Putting-green putting-green yes - Pitching-green pitching-green yes

HOTEL FACILITIES — HOTELS IN OMGEVING — 5/10

HOTELS HOTELS
Hampshire Inn - 17 rooms, D € 130 - Legemeer 500 m
Tel (31) 0513 - 432 999, Fax (31) 0513 - 434 794

Lauswolt - Beetsterzwaag 35 km
65 rooms, D € 180
Tel (31) 0512 - 381 245, Fax (31) 0512 - 381 496

Hotel Tjaarda - 70 rooms, D € 137 - Oranjewoud 15 km
Tel (31) 0513 - 636 251, Fax (31) 0513 - 631 244

RESTAURANTS RESTAURANTS
Hof van Sonoy - Blokzijl 20 km - Tel (31) 0527 - 291 708
Sir Sebastian - Heerenveen 15 km - Tel (31) 0513 - 650 408
't Jagertje - Langweer 4 km - Tel (31) 0513 - 499 297

Sybrook

15	6	6

Deze baan ligt buiten de traditionele toeristische routes, in het groene land van Twente, dichtbij Duitsland. Veel water, weilanden, dichte bossen en grote boerderijen, waarvan de architectuur kennelijk de inspiratie vormde toen het clubhuis met binnenplaats werd ontworpen. Sybrook is een van de weinige nieuwe banen die in bosgebied mochten worden aangelegd. Bossen waarin nog volop wild voorkomt. Die ziet u dan ook regelmatig in de vroege ochtend of avond. Er zijn wat waterhazards, maar niet overdreven veel. De aantrekkingskracht van deze baan zit in een aantal doorkijkjes en de bloeiende rhodondendrons. Het is geen ideale baan voor onstuimige spelers, want er wordt om voorzichtigheid en precisie gevraagd. Ondanks de jonge leeftijd, maakt de baan een volwassen indruk. De baan wordt eind 2005 uitgebreid naar 27 holes.

This is a course off the traditional tourist track in the very lush region of Twente, close to Germany. Water abounds, as do pasture-land, thick forest and large farms whose architecture obviously inspired that of the club-house built with an inner courtyard. Sybrook is one of the few new courses laid out in a forest, which is still home to all sorts of wild animals. You will see a lot of furry creatures at dawn or in the early evening. Several small water hazards come into play but never excessively so. The appeal of this course is all the greater for a number of views over the countryside and the flowering rhododendrons. Sybrook is not the ideal course for the reckless player, as it demands care, a little thought and considerable accuracy. Despite its infancy there is a clear impression of maturity. The course will be extended to 27 holes by the end of 2005.

Golf & Countryclub 't Sybrook — 1994

Veendijk 100
NL - 7525 PZ ENSCHEDE

Office	Secretariaat	(31) 0541 - 530 331
Pro shop	Pro shop	(31) 0541 - 530 331
Fax	Fax	(31) 0541 - 531 690
Web		www.sybrook.nl
Situation	Locatie	Oldenzaal, 3 km

Enschede (pop. 147 624), 5 km

Annual closure	Jaarlijkse sluiting	no
Weekly closure	Wekelijkse sluitingsdag	no

Fees main season Hoogseizoen tarieven	18 holes	
	Week days Weekdagen	**We/Bank holidays** We/Feestdagen
Individual Individueel	€ 50	€ 50
Couple Paar	€ 100	€ 100

Week ends: members & guests

Caddie Caddie no — **Electric Trolley** Electrische trolley no

Buggy Buggy no — **Clubs** Clubs no

Credit cards Creditcards
MasterCard - AMEX - DC - Pin

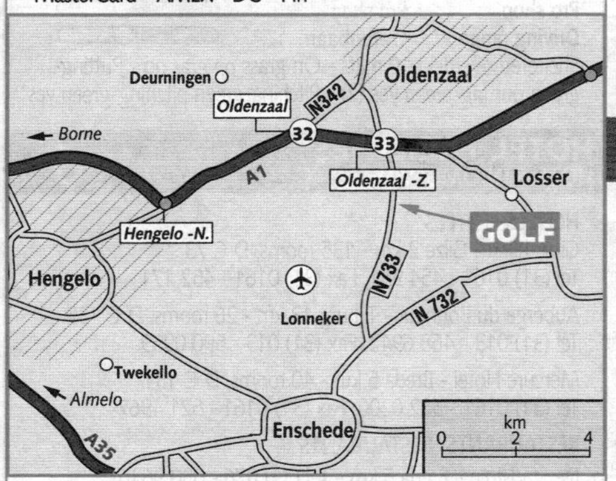

Access Toegang : Hengelo A1 → Germany.
Exit 33 → Enschede. 2,5 km, take left

Map 1 on page 989 Auto kaart 1 Blz 989

GOLF COURSE — BAAN — 15/20

Site	Terrein	
Maintenance	Onderhoud	
Architect	Architect	Alan Rijks Paul Rolin
Type	Type baan	forest
Relief	Reliëf	
Water in play	Waterhazards	
Exp. to wind	Windgevoelig	
Trees in play	Bomen	

Scorecard Scorekaart	**Chp.** Back tees	**Mens** Heren	**Ladies** Damen
Length Lengte	6242	5895	4994
Par	72	72	72
Slope system	133	129	123

Advised golfing ability Aanbevolen golfvaardigheid — 0 12 24 36

Hcp required Vereiste hcp — 36

CLUB HOUSE & AMENITIES — CLUB HOUSE EN ANNEXEN — 6/10

Pro shop Pro shop
Driving range Oefenbaan
Sheltered overdekt 10 mats - On grass op gras yes - Putting-green putting-green yes - Pitching-green pitching-green yes

HOTEL FACILITIES — HOTELS IN OMGEVING — 6/10

HOTELS HOTELS
De Broeierd - 61 rooms, D € 117 - Enschede 5 km
Tel (31) 053 - 850 6500, Fax (31) 053 - 850 6510
De Kroon - 20 rooms, D € 90 - Oldenzaal 3 km
Tel (31) 0541 - 512 402, Fax (31) 0541 - 520 630
't Lansink - 16 rooms, D € 100 - Hengelo 10 km
Tel (31) 074 - 291 0066, Fax (31) 074 - 243 5891

RESTAURANTS RESTAURANTS
Het Koesthuis Schuttersveld - Enschede 5 km
Tel (31) 053 - 432 2866
De Oude Raardskelder - Oldenzaal 3 km
Tel (31) 0541 - 532 553
La Petite Bouffe - Enschede 5 km - Tel (31) 053 - 430 3040

Toxandria

14	7	6

Een ontwerp van John S.F. Morrison, die werd geholpen door Harry Colt en Sir Guy Campbell. De baan is in de loop der tijd aangepast en met twee holes uitgebreid. Zo midden in een bos laat de baan een indruk van rust achter, als je het lawaai van de weg en de nabij gelegen vliegbasis even wegdenkt. In grote lijnen is het een echte Britse baan, zonder veel verrassingen, met natuurlijk de bomen als belangrijkste hindernis (er zijn veel doglegs). Vooral vanaf de backtees kan de baan soms erg nauw ogen. De ruwweg twintig natuurlijk aandoende fairway-bunkers spelen een belangrijke rol door hun strategische ligging. De greens zijn middelgroot, goed ontworpen, goed bewaakt en over het algemeen open genoeg om allerlei soorten approaches toe te staan. Aardigheidje: de 150-meter markers bestaan uit nestkastjes in de bomen.

Designed by John S.F. Morrison, who worked with Harry Colt and Sir Guy Campbell, this course has been altered and lengthened with two new holes. Laid out in a forest, it exudes an impression of tranquillity if you can forget the slight traffic noise and the planes from a nearby air base. The general style is rather British and offers no great surprises, while the main difficulties are, naturally, the trees (there are a lot of dog-legs), especially from the back-tees from where the fairways at times look despairingly narrow. The twenty or so very natural-looking fairway bunkers also play an important role through their strategic positioning. The greens are mid-size, slightly contoured, neatly designed, well-guarded and, by and large, open enough to allow all types of approach shots. Interestingly, the 150 yard-to-green markers are nests placed in the trees.

Noord-Brabantsche Golfclub Toxandria 1929

Veenstraat 89
NL - 5124 NC MOLENSCHOT

Office	Secretariaat	(31) 0161 - 411 200
Pro shop	Pro shop	(31) 0161 - 411 200
Fax	Fax	(31) 0161 - 411 715
Web	www.toxandria.nl	
Situation	Locatie	Breda (pop. 129 125), 10 km
Annual closure	Jaarlijkse sluiting	no
Weekly closure	Wekelijkse sluitingsdag	no

Fees main season Hoogseizoen tarieven	Week days / Weekdagen	We/Bank holidays / We/Feestdagen
		18 holes
Individual Individueel	€ 60	€ 75
Couple Paar	€ 120	€ 150

Caddie Caddie no — **Electric Trolley** Electrische trolley no
Buggy Buggy no — **Clubs** Clubs no
Credit cards Creditcards Pin

Oosterhout, 17, Oosterhout-Zuid, A27, Seters, N 285, Breda-Noord, 16, Dorst, Rijen, GOLF, A16, Breda, Molenschot, Breda, Bavel, A58, Tilburg, km 0 2 4, Ulvenhout

Access Toegang : A27 Utrecht-Breda Exit 16. N282 → Rijen. 4 km → Molenschot
Map 1 on page 988 Auto kaart 1 Blz 988

GOLF COURSE
BAAN — 14/20

Site	Terrein	
Maintenance	Onderhoud	
Architect	Architect	John Morrison Wim Thunissen
Type	Type baan	forest
Relief	Reliëf	
Water in play	Waterhazards	
Exp. to wind	Windgevoelig	
Trees in play	Bomen	

Scorecard Scorekaart	Chp. Back tees	Mens Heren	Ladies Damen
Length Lengte	6140	5834	5111
Par	72	72	72
Slope system	137	131	124

Advised golfing ability Aanbevolen golfvaardigheid — 0 12 24 36
Hcp required Vereiste hcp — 28

CLUB HOUSE & AMENITIES
CLUB HOUSE EN ANNEXEN — 7/10

Pro shop Pro shop
Driving range Oefenbaan
Sheltered overdekt 10 mats - On grass op gras no - Putting-green putting-green yes (2) - Pitching-green pitching-green yes

HOTEL FACILITIES
HOTELS IN OMGEVING — 6/10

HOTELS HOTELS
Gilze-Rijen - Gilze 2 km - 135 rooms, D € 73
Tel (31) 0161 - 454 951, Fax (31) 0161 - 452 171

Auberge du Bonheur - Tilburg 13 km - 26 rooms, D € 135
Tel (31) 013 - 468 6942, Fax (31) 013 - 590 0959

Mercure Hotel - Breda 5 km - 40 rooms, D € 131
Tel (31) 0161 - 522 0200, Fax (31) 0161 - 521 4967

RESTAURANTS RESTAURANTS
De Stadstuin - Breda 5 km - Tel (31) 076 - 530 9636
Boswachter Liesboch - Breda 5 km - Tel (31) 076 - 521 2736
Vanouds de Brouwers - Bavel (Road Breda-Gilze) 4 km
Tel (31) 0161 - 432 272

Twente

15	7	6

Tientallen jaren bracht de Twentsche Golfclub door op een kleine maar fijne 9-holesbaan, ingeklemd tussen Hengelo en Enschede. Die baan ligt er nog steeds, maar de club zelf is verhuisd naar een ruimere "outfit" in de bossen ten westen van de dubbelstad. Het decor van de baan wordt gevormd door oude bossen, met daartussen opvallend veel open ruimtes (van nature) en opvallend veel water (aangelegd) in de vorm van vijf vijvers. Soms hebben die alleen een decoratieve functie, maar op negen holes komt het water ook echt in het spel. Naast de bomen en het water is de lengte een factor om rekening mee te houden. Vooral op de tweede negen, met drie par-4 holes rond de 400 meter. Het ontwerp van de baan doet recht aan het typisch landschap van deze streek en dat geldt ook voor het clubhuis. Dat heeft door het hoge rode pannendak het karakter van een Twentsche boerderij.

For dozens of years the Twentsche Golfclub was based at a short but pretty 9-hole course, wedged in between Hengelo and Enschede. That original course is still open but the club moved to a larger outfit in the woods west of the Twin-cities. The stage there is set by old forests with a remarkable amount of open space (natural) and an equally remarkable amount of water (artificial) in the form of five ponds. Often the water only serves as decoration but on nine holes it actually comes into play. Apart from the water and the trees, length is a factor to reckon with, especially on the back-nine with three par-4 holes of around 440 yards. The design matches the typical landscape of this region very well, as does the club house looking like a traditional local farmhouse with a bright red tiled roof.

Twentsche Golf Club — 1997

Almelosestraat 17
NL - 7495 TG AMBT-DELDEN

Office	Secretariaat	(31) 074 - 384 1167
Pro shop	Pro shop	(31) 074 - 384 1054
Fax	Fax	(31) 074 - 384 1067
Web	www.twentschegolfclub.nl	
Situation	Locatie	Hengelo, 10 km
Annual closure	Jaarlijkse sluiting	no
Weekly closure	Wekelijkse sluitingsdag	no

Fees main season Hoogseizoen tarieven — 18 holes

	Week days Weekdagen	We/Bank holidays We/Feestdagen
Individual Individueel	€ 50	€ 60
Couple Paar	€ 100	€ 120

Caddie Caddie no — **Electric Trolley** Electrische trolley yes
Buggy Buggy yes — **Clubs** Clubs yes
Credit cards Creditcards Pin

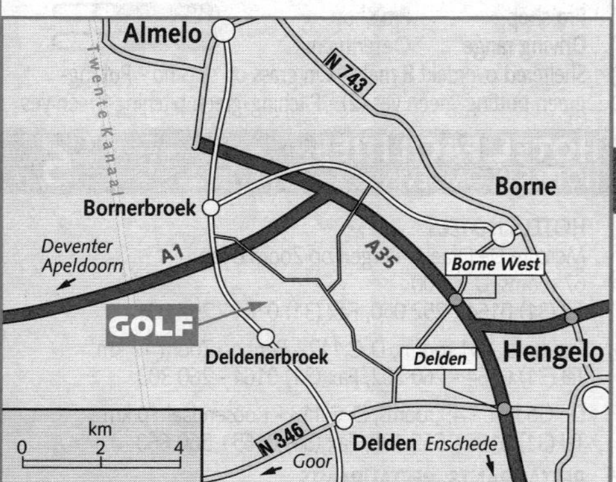

Access Toegang : Amsterdam, A1 → Hengelo, Exit 28, N347, then N346 → Delden, then → Bornebroek.
Map 1 on page 989 Auto kaart 1 Blz 989

GOLF COURSE — BAAN — 15/20

Site	Terrein	
Maintenance	Onderhoud	
Architect	Architect	Tom MacAuley
Type	Type baan	forest, parkland
Relief	Reliëf	
Water in play	Waterhazards	
Exp. to wind	Windgevoelig	
Trees in play	Bomen	

Scorecard Scorekaart	Chp. Back tees	Mens Heren	Ladies Damen
Length Lengte	6333	6178	5241
Par	72	72	72
Slope system	125	123	119

Advised golfing ability Aanbevolen golfvaardigheid — 0 12 24 36
Hcp required Vereiste hcp — 36

CLUB HOUSE & AMENITIES — CLUB HOUSE EN ANNEXEN — 7/10

Pro shop Pro shop
Driving range Oefenbaan
Sheltered overdekt 7 mats - On grass op gras no, 20 mats open air - Putting-green putting-green yes - Pitching-green pitching-green yes

HOTEL FACILITIES — HOTELS IN OMGEVING — 6/10

HOTELS HOTELS

Carelshaven - 20 rooms, D € 90 - Delden 4 km
Tel (31) 074 - 376 1305, Fax (31) 074 - 376 1291

't Lansing - 16 rooms, D € 95 - Hengelo 10 km
Tel (31) 074 - 291 0066, Fax (31) 074 - 243 5891

Hengelo - 203 rooms, D € 72 - Hengelo 10 km
Tel (31) 074 - 255 5055, Fax (31) 074 - 255 5010

RESTAURANTS RESTAURANTS

In de Kop'ren Smorre - Markelo 10 km
Tel (31) 0547 - 361 344

In den Weijenborg - Delden 3 km
Tel (31) 074 - 376 3079

1021

Wouwse Plantage

15	7	6

De oorspronkelijk aangelegde holes liggen in bebost terrein, waar bomen natuurlijk de belangrijkste hindernis vormen. Zeker op de vier dog-legs en de lange smalle 15e hole. Zo ook op de daaropvolgende schitterende par-3, waar de bomen voor de green weinig ruimte voor fouten laten. Later werden negen nieuwe holes aangelegd, op vroegere landbouwgrond, met vier kleine vijvertjes en een paar sloten, maar ook met bredere fairways. Oude en nieuwe holes zijn door elkaar gemengd, wat variatie in het spel, maar ook behoorlijke afstanden tussen de holes heeft opgeleverd. Een nadeel is dat je tegen de tijd dat je aan de 'oude' greens gewend bent, overstapt naar de nieuwe en omgekeerd. Dat maakt het spel niet eenvoudiger, maar misschien hebben alleen de wat betere spelers hier last van.

The front nine were laid out in woody terrain and trees naturally form the main difficulty, especially on the four dog-legs and the long, narrow 15th. Likewise, on the 16th, a beautiful par 3, the trees in front of the green leave little room for error. They then created nine new holes over much more open farming land with four small water hazards and a few ditches, but with much wider fairways. The old and new holes have been intermingled, thus varying the pleasure but sometimes leaving considerable distances between green and next tee. Another obvious drawback is that by the time you get accustomed to the grass and greens on the old holes, you are back to the new ones, and vice versa. This does not make scoring easy and it just might be that better players are more affected by this subtle difference than their less experienced counterparts.

Golf Wouwse Plantage — 1981

Zoomvlietweg 66
NL - 4624 RP BERGEN OP ZOOM

Office Secretariaat (31) 0165 - 377 106
Pro shop Pro shop (31) 0165 - 377 106
Fax Fax (31) 0165 - 377 101
Web www.golfwouwseplantage.nl
Situation Locatie Bergen op Zoom, 15 km
Roosendaal (pop. 62 784), 10 km
Annual closure Jaarlijkse sluiting no
Weekly closure Wekelijkse sluitingsdag no
Fees main season Hoogseizoen tarieven 18 holes

	Week days Weekdagen	We/Bank holidays We/Feestdagen
Individual Individueel	€ 70	€ 70
Couple Paar	€ 140	€ 140

Caddie Caddie no — **Electric Trolley** Electrische trolley no
Buggy Buggy yes — **Clubs** Clubs yes
Credit cards Creditcards no

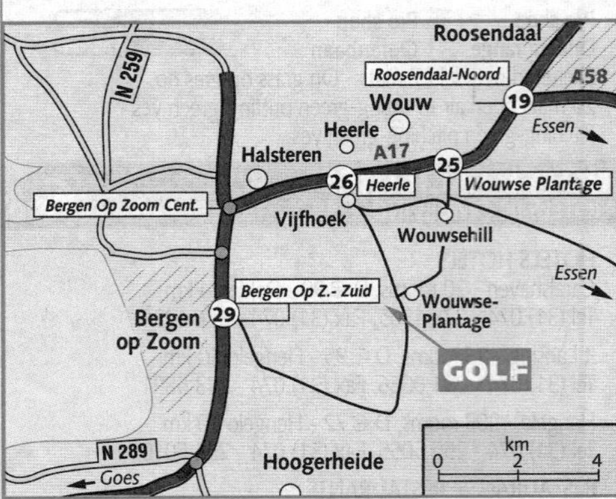

Access Toegang : A58 Breda → Bergen op Zoom.
Exit 26 → Wouwse Plantage. 100 m, turn right then left (Zoomvlietweg). Golf 3.5 km.
Map 1 on page 988 Auto kaart 1 Blz 988

GOLF COURSE — BAAN — 15/20

Site Terrein
Maintenance Onderhoud
Architect Architect Donald Steel, Paul Rolin
Type Type baan forest, parkland
Relief Reliëf
Water in play Waterhazards
Exp. to wind Windgevoelig
Trees in play Bomen

Scorecard Scorekaart	Chp. Back tees	Mens Heren	Ladies Damen
Length Lengte	6407	5859	5065
Par	72	72	72
Slope system	133	128	123

Advised golfing ability Aanbevolen golfvaardigheid 0 12 24 36
Hcp required Vereiste hcp 36

CLUB HOUSE & AMENITIES — CLUB HOUSE EN ANNEXEN — 7/10

Pro shop Pro shop
Driving range Oefenbaan
Sheltered overdekt 8 mats - On grass op gras no - Putting-green putting-green yes (2) - Pitching-green pitching-green yes

HOTEL FACILITIES — HOTELS IN OMGEVING — 6/10

HOTELS HOTELS
Mercure De Draak - Bergen op Zoom 8 km
57 rooms, D € 200
Tel (31) 0164 - 252 050, Fax (31) 0164 - 257 001

Parkhotel - 51 rooms, D € 112 - Berg op Zoom 12 km
Tel (31) 0164 - 260 202, Fax (31) 0164 - 260 303

De Goderië - 49 rooms, D € 113 - Roosendaal 10 km
Tel (31) 0165 - 555 400, Fax (31) 0165 - 560 660

RESTAURANTS RESTAURANTS
Mijn Keuken - Wouw 5 km - Tel (31) 0165 - 530 2208
Moerstede - Bergen op Zoom 8 km - Tel (31) 0164 - 258 800

Zuid Limburg

14	7	8

We zitten hier dicht bij Aken, een van de belangrijkste Duitse steden, waarvan de historische waarde, sinds de grootse plannen van Karel de Grote, nooit in twijfel is getrokken. Dit gebied is ook het hoogste van Nederland... iets onder de 300 meter (elk land heeft zijn bergen, Moeder Natuur bepaalt hoe hoog ze zijn!). De baan werd aangelegd als een 9-holes baan en werd uitgebreid tot 18 holes in 1990. De 'oude' holes lopen door een bos, terwijl acht van de 'nieuwe' holes in een open landschap liggen met sterke hoogteverschillen en prachtige vergezichten. Al met al is de baan goed te bespelen, voor iedereen. Om je handicap te spelen moet je wel de bomen op de eerste negen zien te ontlopen en op de twee negen vooral nauwkeurige teeshots afleveren. Afgedwaalde ballen komen snel op onplezierige plaatsen terecht, op sterk glooiende hellingen.

Here we are very close to Aachen, one of the great German cities whose historical importance since the grand European designs of Charlemagne has never been questioned. This lovely region is also the highest in the Netherlands...a little below 300 metres (each country has its natural mountains, mother nature decides how high!). The course here began as a 9-holer and was extended to 18 holes in 1980. The first holes wind their way through a forest while 8 of the last 9 are in open countryside with sharp differences in level and some beautiful views. All in all, the course is easily walkable and for everyone. Playing to your handicap involves keeping out of the trees on the way out and carefully placing your drive on the way in. Wayward shots can leave your ball in some very tricky positions with steeply sloping lies.

Zuid Limburgse Golf & Countryclub — 1956

Dalbissenweg 22
NL - 6281 NC MECHELEN

Office Secretariaat (31) 043 - 455 3958
Pro shop Pro shop (31) 043 - 455 3958
Fax Fax (31) 043 - 455 1576
Web —
Situation Locatie Aachen (Germany), 15 km
Maastricht (pop. 118 102), 25 km -

Annual closure Jaarlijkse sluiting — no
Weekly closure Wekelijkse sluitingsdag — no

Fees main season Hoogseizoen tarieven	18 holes	
	Week days Weekdagen	**We/Bank holidays** We/Feestdagen
Individual Individueel	€ 40	€ 50
Couple Paar	€ 80	€ 100

Caddie Caddie no — **Electric Trolley** Electrische trolley no
Buggy Buggy yes — **Clubs** Clubs no
Credit cards Creditcards Pin

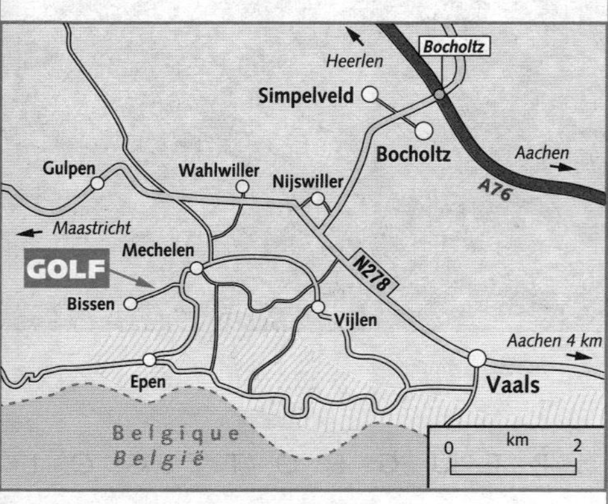

Access Toegang : N278 Maastricht → Aachen.
Gulpen → Landsrade.
Map 1 on page 989 Auto kaart 1 Blz 989

GOLF COURSE — BAAN — 14/20

Site	Terrein	
Maintenance	Onderhoud	
Architect	Architect	Fred Hawtree Rolin/Snelders
Type	Type baan	forest
Relief	Reliëf	
Water in play	Waterhazards	
Exp. to wind	Windgevoelig	
Trees in play	Bomen	

Scorecard Scorekaart	**Chp.** Back tees	**Mens** Heren	**Ladies** Damen
Length Lengte	5904	5494	5056
Par	71	71	71
Slope system	125	123	126

Advised golfing ability Aanbevolen golfvaardigheid — 0 12 24 36
Hcp required Vereiste hcp 36

CLUB HOUSE & AMENITIES — CLUB HOUSE EN ANNEXEN — 7/10

Pro shop Pro shop
Driving range Oefenbaan
Sheltered overdekt 10 mats - On grass op gras no, 10 mats open air - Putting-green putting-green yes - Pitching-green pitching-green yes

HOTEL FACILITIES — HOTELS IN OMGEVING — 8/10

HOTELS HOTELS
Landgoed Schoutenhof - 8 rooms, D € 114 - Epen 4 km
Tel (31) 043 - 455 2002, Fax (31) 043 - 455 2605

NH Zuid Limburg - 77 rooms, D € 140 - Epen 4 km
Tel (31) 043 - 455 1818, Fax (31) 043 - 455 2415

Brull - 26 rooms, D € 115 - Mechelen 1 km
Tel (31) 043 - 455 1263, Fax (31) 043 - 455 2300

RESTAURANTS RESTAURANTS
't Klauwes - Wahlwiller 4 km - Tel (31) 043 - 451 1548
Der Bloasbalg - Wahlwiller 5 km - Tel (31) 043 - 451 1364
't Hilleshagerhofke - Mechelen 1 km - Tel (31) 043 - 455 1950

NORGE

NORWAY

Evje

NORGE

They say that skiing is as important to the Norwegians as cycling is to the Danes, a logical assumption when snow covers the whole country for a good part of the year. Despite this, the west coast can be surprisingly mild thanks to the warming influence of the Gulf Stream. You can play golf between April and October from Bergen to Oslo, and for 125,000 Norwegians, golf clubs are the summer version of ski poles. As in all northern countries, golf here is a sporting activity like any other and golfing snobbery is never as blatant in Norway as it can be in other countries of Europe. Naturally, the 155 courses (50 eighteen-holers) are not all as well manicured as Augusta, but they are very quickly groomed into good condition once winter is over. Opening dates depend entirely on the thawing frost and snow.

NORWAY

Det hevdes at skigåing er like viktig for nordmenn som sykling er det for danskene. En logisk antagelse med tanke på at landet er dekket med snø en stor del av året. Til tross for dette kan det være overraskende mildt på vestkysten - takket været Golfstrømmens innflytelse. Fra Oslo til Bergen kan du spille golf i perioden april til oktober, og for 125.000 nordmenn er golfkøllene en slags sommerutgave av skistavene. Som i alle de nordiske landene er golf en sportsaktivitet på lik linje med de fleste andre idretter. Golf er heller ikke så snobbete som den kan oppleves i andre europeiske land. Naturligvis er ikke alle de 155 banene (50 av dem er 18 hulls) i så god stand og velstelt som Augusta, men så fort vinteren har tatt farvel fremstår banene i bra stand. Sesongåpning på den enkelte bane avhenger mye av våren og hvor raskt snø og frost slipper taket.

CLASSIFICATION OF GOLF COURSES
RANGERING AV BANENE

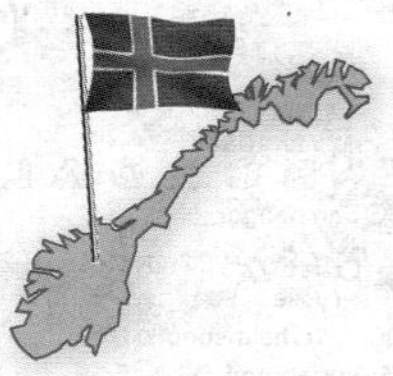

This classification gives priority consideration to the score awarded to the actual course.
Rangeringen er basert på poeng gitt til den aktuelle banen.

Within each score, the ranking is purely alphabetical

Course score / Rangering av banene				Page / Side
18	8	7	Miklagard	1035
17	8	5	Larvik	1032
17	7	6	Moss & Rygge	1036
16	7	5	Meland	1034
16	6	7	Stavanger	1039
15	7	5	Arendal	1030
15	6	5	Borre	1031
15	8	7	Losby	1033
15	7	9	Oslo	1037
15	6	3	Sorknes	1038

HOTEL FACILITIES
RANGERING AV HOTELLFASILITETENE

This classification gives priority consideration to the score awarded to the hotel facilities.
Rangeringen er basert på poeng gitt til hotellfasilitetene.

		Hotel facility score / Score hotellfasiliteter		Page / Side
15	7	**9**	Oslo	1037
15	8	**7**	Losby	1033
18	8	**7**	Miklagard	1035
16	6	**7**	Stavanger	1039
17	7	**6**	Moss & Rygge	1036
15	7	**5**	Arendal	1030
15	6	**5**	Borre	1031
17	8	**5**	Larvik	1032
16	7	**5**	Meland	1034
15	6	**3**	Sorknes	1038

Map No 1
Kort 1
km
0 10 20
Meland
Stavanger
1028
BERGEN
Haugesund
STAVANGER
Sandnes
Sola
Egersund
Flekkefjord
Kristiansand
HORDALAND
ROGALAND
AUST-AGDER
VEST-AGDER
Hardangervidda
Hardangerfjorden
Boknafjorden
Setesdalsheiene
Bykleheiene
Stølsheimen
Fresvikbreen
Hardanger-jøkulen
Haukelifjell
Hårteigen
Folgefonna
Ryfylke
Lysefjorden
Prekestolen
Suldalsvatn
Sirdalsvatn
Byglandsfj.
Setesdal
Jæren
Dalane
Listafjorden
Voss
Gudvangen
Aurland
Flåm
Undredal
Lærdalsøyri
Hopperstad
Leirvåg
Duesund
Lindås
Knarvik
Askøy
Kleppestø
Osterøya
Vaksdal
Dale
Stamnes
Tyssebotn
Samnanger
Tysse
Norheimsund
Øystese
Strandebarm
Ålvik
Kvanndal
Utne
Granvin
Ulvik
Bruravik
Eidfjord
Brimnes
Kinsarvik
Fossli
Vøringfossen
Lofthus
Tyssedal
Odda
Telavåg
Hjellestad
Klokkarvik
Steinsland
Krokeide
Osøyro
Hatvik
Vengjaneset
Eikelandsosen
Joncal
Tørvikbygd
Huftarøy
Halhjem
Storebø
Husavik
Sandvikvåg
Våge
Tysnesøy
Gjermundshavn
Ænes
Løfallstrand
Rosendal
Fitjar
Hodnanes
Jektevik
Stord
Rubbestadneset
Bømlo
Sagvåg
Sunde
Husnes
Leirvik
Utåker
Skånevik
Etne
Siggjarvåg
Mosterhamn
Langevåg
Utbjoa
Førde
Ølen
Buavåg
Sandeid
Vikedal
Sauda
Røldal
Haukeligrend
Edland
Rauland
Totak
Vinje
Åmot
Hovden
Bykle
Eidsborg
Dalen
Brunkeberg
Valle
Fyresdal
Haraldshaugen
Avaldsnes
Tysvær
Nedstrand
Sand
Jelsa
Vindsvik
Nesvik
Tøtlandsvik
Hjelmeland
Kopervik
Føresvik
Bokn
Åres
Skudeneshavn
Finnøy
Judaberg
Mortavika
Rennesøy
Vikevåg
Kvitsøy
Randaberg
Tau
Jørpeland
Hommersåk
Oanes
Forsand
Lauvvik
Oltedal
Dirdal
Svartevatn
Kleppe
Ålgård
Bryne
Nærbø
Varhaug
Vigrestad
Brusand
Sirevåg
Hellvik
Vikeså
Bjerkreim
Tonstad
Risnes
Åseral
Bygland
Byglandsfjord
Evje
Åmli
Dølemo
Iveland
Eiken
Moi
Sira
Hauge
Åna Sira
Kvinesdal
Hægebostad
Konsmo
Feda
Lyngdal
Apta
Vestbygda
Farsund
Alleen
Høllen
Vigeland
Nodeland
Søgne
Mosby
Vennesla
Birkeland
Lillesand
Hamre
Blakstad
Rykene
Lindesnes
MICHELIN

Sorknes
Lillehammer
Hamar
Gjøvik
Hønefoss
OSLO
Oslo
Myklagard
Lillestrøm
AKERSHUS
Losby
BUSKERUD
Drammen
Kongsberg
Notodden
Holmestrand
Horten
Borre
MOSS
Moss & Rygge
VESTFOLD
ØSTFOLD
SKIEN
Porsgrunn
Sandefjord
Tønsberg
Larvik
Fredrikstad
Sarpsborg
Halden
Arendal
MICHELIN
d'après base de données au 1/1 500 000 - édition 2005.
Autorisation n°0501023.

Arendal

15 | **7** | **5**

Arendal blir ofte kalt Nordens Venezia på grunn av de mange kanalene som rant gjennom byen. De fleste av disse har forsvunnet i dag, men stort antall trebygninger og hus bekrefter fremdeles hvor betydningsfullt disse kanalene var for Arendal. Denne golfbanen er ytterligere et argument som tjener byens livskraft, bygd i 1991 uten hjelp fra noen golfbanearkitekter. For en gang skyld har denne form for vågestykke blitt en suksess. Den er mye bakker (du bør være i god fysisk form) og enkelte vanskeligheter ser man ikke før de dukker opp. Får man imidlertid kontroll på vanskelighetene viser banen seg å være en meget god utfordring. Det er ikke en lang bane, men den er utmerket balansert og greenene er vel designet på måte som kan gjøre det vanskelig å spille til sitt handicap. Mens de første ni hullene er heller åpne, så medfører trær og vannhindre at det må utvises forsiktighet på hjemturens ni siste hull. Det er en stor fordel å ha spilt banen tidligere, og det gjelder å merke seg at klubbhuset er åpent rundt på grunn av skisesongen.

Arendal used to be called the Venice of the North on account of the very many canals that ran through the town. Most of these have disappeared today, but a good number of wooden buildings and houses still testify to the former importance of Arendal. This golf course is further argument in favour of the town's vitality, built in 1991 without the services of a golf architect. For once, this sort of venture has been successful. It is rather hilly (you need to be in good shape physically) and some of the difficulties are hidden from view, but once under control, it proves to be a very good challenge. This is not a long course but it is nicely balanced and the greens are designed well enough to make playing to your handicap a sometimes awkward proposition. In addition, while the front 9 are rather open, the trees and water hazards on the way home call for extreme caution. Well worth getting to know, and note that the club-house stays open all year for the skiing season.

Arendal og Omegn Golfklubb — 1991

Nes Verk
N - 4900 TVEDESTRAND

Office	Kontor	(47) 371 990 30
Pro shop	Pro shop	(47) 371 990 35
Fax	Fax	(47) 371 602 11
Web	www.arendalgk.no	
Situation	Beliggenhet	Arendal, 20 km
Annual closure	Årlig stenging	1/11→30/4
Weekly closure	Ukentlig stenging	no

Fees main season Tariffer i høysesongen	18 holes	
	Week days Ukedager	**We/Bank holidays** Week-end/Frydag
Individual Individuell	NKr 350	NKr 400
Couple Par	NKr 700	NKr 800

Juniors: – 50%

Caddie Caddie no **Electric Trolley** Elektrisk vogn yes

Buggy Golfbil yes **Clubs** Køller yes

Credit cards Kredittkort
VISA - Eurocard - MasterCard - DC - AMEX

Access Adkomst : Arendal, E18 → Tvedestrand Exit "Fjanesvingen". Golf 2 km from E18 on 112
Map 1 on page 1029 Kort 1 på side: 1029

GOLF COURSE — GOLFBANEN — 15/20

Site	Område	
Maintenance	Vedlikehold	
Architect	Arkitekt	unknown
Type	Type	inland
Relief	Relief	
Water in play	Vann-hinder	
Exp. to wind	Utsatt for vind	
Trees in play	Tre-hinder	

Scorecard Scorecard	**Chp.** Champ.-tee	**Mens** Herre-tees	**Ladies** Dame-tees
Length Lengde	5785	5528	4683
Par	72	72	72
Slope system	132	138	132

Advised golfing ability Anbefalt golfnivå — 0 12 24 36

Hcp required Obligatorisk Hcp 36

CLUB HOUSE & AMENITIES — KLUBHUS OG OMGIVELSER — 7/10

Pro shop Pro shop
Driving range Treningsbane
Sheltered ly yes - On grass på gress yes (Summer) - Putting-green putting-green yes - Pitching-green pitching-green yes

HOTEL FACILITIES — HOTELL FASILITETERNE — 5/10

HOTELS HOTEL FASILITETER
Tvedestrand Fjordhotel - Tvedestrand 10 km
18 rooms, D NKr 1090,-
Tel (47) 371 626 55, Fax (47) 371 626 18

Scandic Hotel Arendal - Arendal 20 km -
80 rooms, D NKr 1345,-
Tel (47) 370 521 50, Fax (47) 370 267 07

RESTAURANTS RESTAURANT
Vertshuset - Tvedestrand 10 km
Tel (47) 371 612 61

Borre

15	6	5

Folk som assosierer Norge med fjorder vil bli overrasket over de mange små buktene med fiskelandsbyer som ligger sørvest for Oslo. Før du tar dem i nærmere øyesyn er det verdt å gjøre et stopp ved Borre, like ved Horten. Banen ble anlagt rundt den noble herregården Semb. Deler av banen ligger på et tidligere jordbruksområde mens de øvrige hullene snor seg igjennom et skoglandskap. Tommy Nordström har gjort denne banen til en av de beste i landet. En bane som gir utfordringer for de gode spillerne, men som samtidig tar vare på de med høyt handicap. Den er vakkert bygd, men man likevel klart å gi den et naturlig utseende. Den avslører mange slags vanskeligheter og utfordringer, og du vil snarlig beklage din manglende evne til å slå ballene kontrollert i de forskjellige retningene. Banen er ikke spesielt preget av bakker og den er lett å gå rundt. Banen preges av ypperlige greener og med et meget hyggelig miljø. På Borre opplever man en golfrunde som helst ikke vil ta slutt. Så derfor, hvorfor ikke komme tilbake ved en senere anledning?

People who associate Norway with fjords will be surprised by the little coves and fishing villages lying to the south-west of Oslo. Before you see them for yourselves, stop off and play a round at Borre, close to Horten. The course was laid out around the noble mansion of Semb, partly over an old farm and partly over more woodland landscape. Tommy Nordström has made this into one of the country's best courses, one that is both challenging for the better golfer and well suited to higher-handicappers. Well landscaped but still with a crisp natural look, it clearly reveals difficulties of every kind and soon has you regretting your inability to bend the ball deliberately in either direction. The course is not too hilly and easily walkable, and with well-guarded, excellent greens and a very pleasant environment, this is one round of golf you will be sorry to finish. But there again, who is to stop you from coming back for more?

Borre Golfklubb — 1991

Semb Hovedgård
N - 3186 HORTEN

Office	Kontor	(47) 330 715 15
Pro shop	Pro shop	(47) 330 715 15
Fax	Fax	(47) 330 715 16
Web	www.borregb.no	
Situation	Beliggenhet	Horten, 2,5 km
Annual closure	Årlig stenging	1/11→31/3
Weekly closure	Ukentlig stenging	no

Fees main season Tariffer i høysesongen	Week days Ukedager	We/Bank holidays Week-end/Frydag
		Full day
Individual Individuell	NKr 400	NKr 450
Couple Par	NKr 800	NKr 900

Juniors: – 50%
2 players in each group may not have registered handicaps

Caddie Caddie no — **Electric Trolley** Elektrisk vogn no

Buggy Golfbil yes **Clubs** Køller yes

Credit cards Kredittkort
VISA - Eurocard - MasterCard - AMEX - DC - JCB

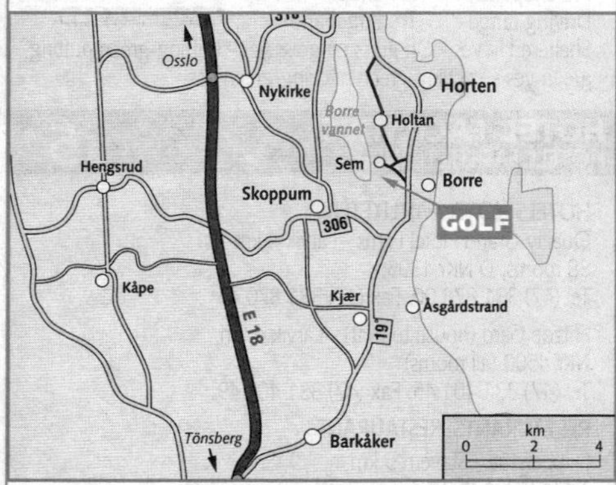

Access Adkomst : 2,5 km S of Horten city centre
Map 1 on page 1029 Kort 1 på side: 1029

GOLF COURSE — GOLFBANEN — 15/20

Site	Område	
Maintenance	Vedlikehold	
Architect	Arkitekt	Tommy Nordström
Type	Type	open country
Relief	Relief	
Water in play	Vann-hinder	
Exp. to wind	Utsatt for vind	
Trees in play	Tre-hinder	

Scorecard Scorecard	Chp. Champ.-tee	Mens Herre-tees	Ladies Dame-tees
Length Lengde	6265	5784	4810
Par	72	72	72
Slope system	137	135	131

Advised golfing ability Anbefalt golfnivå — 0 12 24 36

Hcp required Obligatorisk Hcp 36

CLUB HOUSE & AMENITIES — KLUBHUS OG OMGIVELSER — 6/10

Pro shop Pro shop
Driving range Treningsbane
Sheltered ly no - On grass på gress no, 57 mats open air - Putting-green putting-green yes - Pitching-green pitching-green yes

HOTEL FACILITIES — HOTELL FASILITETERNE — 5/10

HOTELS HOTEL FASILITETER

Rica Klubben Hotel - Tønsberg 4 km
145 rooms, D NKr 960,-
Tel (47) 333 597 00, Fax (47) 333 597 97

Norrlandia Grand Hotel Ocean - Horten 2,5 km
100 rooms, D NKr 970,-
Tel (47) 330 417 22, Fax (47) 330 445 07

RESTAURANTS RESTAURANT

Fishland - Horten 2,5 km
Tel (47) 330 488 10

Fregatten - Tønsberg 5 km
Tel (47) 333 147 76

Larvik

17 | 8 | 5

Du vil for alltid huske denne banen som en stor vakker park med til dels en fantastisk utsikt over sjøen. Banen ligger like ved Fritzøe Gårc med noen minneverdige arkitektoniske innslag som erindrer deg om å være på en linksbane. Her gjelder det å holde seg unna roughen. Den er både lang og saftig, og kan gi deg traumatiske opplevelser i forsøk på å komme ut på fairway igjen - hvis du i det hele tatt finner ballen. Dette til tross, både fairwayene og den korte roughen er brede nok for de fleste spillerne. Problemet er kanskje størst for de som virkelig vil slå langt og kan komme ut av kurs. Det er visselig ikke arkitekt Jan Sederholms stil å straffe for hardt de som hører hjemme blant middels- og høyhandicapere. Det eneste skjønnhetsfeilen ved banen er at den er for flat og hullene for i de fleste tilfeller den samme utforming. Heldigvis har vanskelighetene på banen en forskjellig og særegen karakter. Larvik er udiskutabelt en av de beste banene i Norge, og det vil være synd om man ikke får spilt banen hvis man en sjelden gang er i landet.

You may well remember this as a big, beautiful park with some great views over the sea, and as a course close to Fritzøe Gård with some memorable architectural features reminiscent of a links course. So first off, be careful to avoid the tall rough, from where escape can be traumatic, if ever you find your ball. However, the fairways and short rough are still wide enough for most players, except the really big hitters who might stray a little too much off-course. It is certainly not the usual style of architect Jan Sederholm to punish too severely the slightly wayward shots from mid- to high-handicappers. The only slight blemish is the overall flatness of the course, creating a certain sameness on most holes. Fortunately the difficulties are more distinctive. Larvik is unquestionably one of the country's finest courses and it would be a pity not to play it if you come to Norway only on rare occasions.

Larvik Golfklubb — 1994

Fritzsøe Gård
N - 3267 LARVIK

Office	Kontor	(47) 331 401 40
Pro shop	Pro shop	(47) 331 405 80
Fax	Fax	(47) 331 401 49
Web	www.larvikgolf.no	
Situation	Beliggenhet	Larvik, 3 km
Annual closure	Årlig stenging	1/12→31/3
Weekly closure	Ukentlig stenging	nc

Fees main season Tariffer i høysesongen — 18 holes

	Week days / Ukedager	We/Bank holidays / Week-end/Frydag
Individual Individuell	NKr 400	NKr 450
Couple Par	NKr 800	NKr 900

Juniors: – 50%
2 players in each group may not have registered handicaps

Caddie Caddie no — **Electric Trolley** Elektrisk vogn no
Buggy Golfbil yes — **Clubs** Køller yes
Credit cards Kreditkort
VISA - Eurocard - MasterCard - AMEX

Access Adkomst : Oslo, E18 → Skien/Kristiansand. Rv.301 to Stavern. 3km, right → Fritzsøe Gård.
Map 1 on page 1029 Kort 1 på side: 1029

GOLF COURSE — 17/20
GOLFBANEN

Site	Område	
Maintenance	Vedlikehold	
Architect	Arkitekt	Jan Sederholm
Type	Type	links, open country
Relief	Relief	
Water in play	Vann-hinder	
Exp. to wind	Utsatt for vind	
Trees in play	Tre-hinder	

Scorecard Scorecard	Chp. Champ.-tee	Mens Herre-tees	Ladies Dame-tees
Length Lengde	6235	5848	5093
Par	72	72	72
Slope system	130	130	122

Advised golfing ability Anbefalt golfnivå — 0 12 24 36
Hcp required Obligatorisk Hcp 36

CLUB HOUSE & AMENITIES — 8/10
KLUBHUS OG OMGIVELSER

Pro shop Pro shop
Driving range Treningsbane
Sheltered ly yes - On grass på gress yes - Putting-green putting-green yes - Pitching-green pitching-green yes

HOTEL FACILITIES — 5/10
HOTELL FASILITETERNE

HOTELS HOTEL FASILITETER
Quality Grand Hotel Farris - Larvik 4 km
88 rooms, D NKr 1395,-
Tel (47) 331 878 00, Fax (47) 331 870 45

Fritzøe Gård (house to rent) - Larvik 4 km
NKr 4500 (all rooms)
Tel (47) 331 401 45, Fax (47) 331 401 49

RESTAURANTS RESTAURANT
Skipperstua - Stavern 5 km
Tel (47) 331 992 15

Losby

15	8	7

Med vakker beliggenhet, og hotell allerede på plass, virker det som at alt er tilrettelagt for en lysende fremtid for Losby. Banen er plassert i et åpent landskap, hvor Peter Nordwall har lagt ut flere vannhindere, som ofte kommer inn i spillet. Greenene er godt beskyttet, og krever ferdigheter i presisjonsgolf. Innspillene må stemme både i retning og lengde. Da banen kan være litt vanskelig, anbefaler vi spillere med 24 eller höyere i handikap å heller spille matchgolf enn slaggolf. Banen er lang, velplanert og lett å gå. Den oppleves som en bane for fremtidige turneringer.

On a very pleasant site close to Oslo, Losby seems to be all the more destined for a bright future in that it already boasts an on-site hotel. The course has been laid out over very open land with pleasant trees, where Peter Nordwall has produced a number of water hazards that often come into play. In particular, the greens are very well guarded and call for some serious skills in target golf, starting with accurate approach shots in terms of both distance and direction. As the course is rather difficult for players with a handicap of 24 or higher, our advice to the lesser player would be to opt for the rather less depressing match-play formula. Being rather long, well landscaped and easy to walk, Losby is equally remarkable for some rather disconcerting greens, which help promise a fine future of championship golf for the course as a whole.

Losby GK — 2000

Losbyveien 270
N - 1475 FINSTADJORDET

Office	Kontor	(47) 679 233 43
Pro shop	Pro shop	(47) 679 233 40
Fax	Fax	(47) 679 233 45
Web	www.losby.no	
Situation	Beliggenhet	Lillestrøm 10 km
Annual closure	Årlig stenging	no
Weekly closure	Ukentlig stenging	no
Fees main season	Tariffer i høysesongen	18 holes

	Week days Ukedager	We/Bank holidays Week-end/Frydag
Individual Individuell	NKr 570	NKr 680
Couple Par	NKr 1140	NKr 1360

Juniors: – 50%

Caddie Caddie no — Electric Trolley Elektrisk vogn no

Buggy Golfbil no — Clubs Køller yes

Credit cards Kredittkort
VISA - Eurocard - MasterCard - DC - AMEX

Lillestrom
Lörenskog
Losby
Oslo
GOLF
Öyeren
120
E18
E6
Flateby
Kolbotn
Moss
Yttre Enebakk
Siggerud

Access Adkomst :
Map 1 on page 1029 Kort 1 på side: 1029

GOLF COURSE — GOLFBANEN — 15/20

Site	Område	
Maintenance	Vedlikehold	
Architect	Arkitekt	Peter Nordwall
Type	Type	open country
Relief	Relief	
Water in play	Vann-hinder	
Exp. to wind	Utsatt for vind	
Trees in play	Tre-hinder	

Scorecard Scorecard	Chp. Champ.-tee	Mens Herre-tees	Ladies Dame-tees
Length Lengde	6299	5823	4873
Par	72	72	72
Slope system	131	125	123

Advised golfing ability / Anbefalt golfnivå — 0 12 24 36

Hcp required Obligatorisk Hcp — 28 Men, 36 Ladies (We)

CLUB HOUSE & AMENITIES — KLUBHUS OG OMGIVELSER — 8/10

Pro shop — Pro shop
Driving range — Treningsbane

Sheltered ly 18 mats - On grass på gress no, 54 mats open air
Putting-green putting-green yes - Pitching-green pitching-green yes

HOTEL FACILITIES — HOTELL FASILITETERNE — 7/10

HOTELS HOTEL FASILITETER

Losby Gods - 70 rooms, D NKr 1265 - on site
Tel (47) 679 233 00, Fax (47) 679 233 01

Hotel Bristol - Oslo 15 km
252 rooms, D NKr 1800,-
Tel (47) 228 260 00, Fax (47) 228 260 01

Hotel Continental - Oslo 15 km
154 rooms, D NKr 2330,-
Tel (47) 228 240 00, Fax (47) 224 296 89

RESTAURANTS RESTAURANT

Stortovets Gjæstgiveri - Oslo 15 km - Tel (47) 233 563 60
Statholdergaarden - Oslo 15 km - Tel (47) 224 188 00
Losby Gods - on site - Tel (47) 679 233 00

Meland

16	7	5

På dette stedet får man inntrykk av å være i paradisets siste hjørne. Hadde det ikke vært for at banen er såpass god, kunne man fort ha glemt selve spillet, for istedet å beundre utsikten over det skiftende fjordlandskepet. Banen, som ligger vakkert mellom skog og steinrøys, reflekterer en utmerket forståelse for spillet golf. Her er det nok den mere erfarene golferen som vil trives best, da evnen til å skifte mellom presisjonsgolf og engelsk linksgolf er helt nødvendig. Det finnes vanskeligheter som ikke er synlige ved første øyekast, Så det kan väre en god ide å gå en treningsrunde. Dette er en ung bane, og den trenger litt tid til å sette seg. Men den er, med sine store velplanerte greener, allerede blandt de beste i Norge. Legg til den gode dreneringen, som kommer av at jorden består av sand og torv, og dette er absolutt en bane verdt å spille.

This is not the world's end, simply a site where the impression is of being in one of the last corners of paradise on earth. From most tees, the ever-changing views over the fjord might almost keep you from playing, if the course was not so good. The layout of the greens and fairways, which wind their way through forest dotted with flush rocks and today's obligatory water hazards, reflects an excellent knowledge of the game of golf. The more experienced players will enjoy this course the most, having to mix target golf with a number of British style bump 'n run shots. Not all the difficulties are clearly visible, though, so a practice round or a little reconnoitring might be a good idea. From the back tees, Meland is championship golf. It is a young course that needs to mature, but the often large and well-designed greens already figure amongst the best in Norway. Add to that drainage made easier by soil of sand and peat, then this is clearly and most definitely a course to play.

Meland GK 1999

N - 5918 FREKHAUG

Office	Kontor	(47) 561 746 00
Pro shop	Pro shop	(47) 561 746 20
Fax	Fax	(47) 561 777 22
Web		www.melandgolf.no
Situation	Beliggenhet	Bergen, 25 km
Annual closure	Årlig stenging	1/11→31/3
Weekly closure	Ukentlig stenging	no

Fees main season / Tariffer i høysesongen	Week days / Ukedager	We/Bank holidays / Week-end/Frydag
	18 holes	
Individual Individuell	NKr 350	NKr 450
Couple Par	NKr 700	NKr 900

Juniors: – 50%

Caddie Caddie no — Electric Trolley Elektrisk vogn no

Buggy Golfbil no — Clubs Køller yes

Credit cards Kredittkort
VISA - Eurocard - MasterCard - DC - AMEX

Meland
Knarvik
E39
Flatøy
Osterfjorden
Fløksand
564
Osterøy
GOLF
Herdlafjorden
Frekhaug
E39
Vågsbotn
Askøy
Oslo
Bergen

Access Adkomst : Bergen, E39 North, RV 564 → Rossland, 10 km until Floksand, → Golf

Map 1 on page 1028 Kort 1 på side: 1028

GOLF COURSE — GOLFBANEN 16/20

Site	Område	
Maintenance	Vedlikehold	
Architect	Arkitekt	Bob Hunt PGA Management
Type	Type	forest
Relief	Relief	
Water in play	Vann-hinder	
Exp. to wind	Utsatt for vind	
Trees in play	Tre-hinder	

Scorecard / Scorecard	Chp. / Champ.-tee	Mens / Herre-tees	Ladies / Dame-tees
Length Lengde	6203	5979	5257
Par	73	73	73
Slope system	133	131	128

Advised golfing ability / Anbefalt golfnivå: 0 12 24 36

Hcp required Obligatorisk Hcp 36

CLUB HOUSE & AMENITIES — KLUBHUS OG OMGIVELSER 7/10

Pro shop — Pro shop

Driving range — Treningsbane

Sheltered ly yes - On grass på gress no, 27 mats open air - Putting-green putting-green yes - Pitching-green pitching-green yes

HOTEL FACILITIES — HOTELL FASILITETERNE 5/10

HOTELS HOTEL FASILITETER

Alver Hotel - 88 rooms, D NKr 1040, - Alversund 18 km
Tel (47) 563 438 00, Fax (47) 563 438 90

Augustin Hotel - Bergen 25 km
109 rooms, D NKr 1550,-
Tel (47) 553 040 40, Fax (47) 553 040 10

Victoria Hotel - Bergen 25 km
43 rooms, D NKr 1490,-
Tel (47) 552 123 00, Fax (47) 552 123 50

RESTAURANTS RESTAURANT

Mount Floien - Bergen 25 km - Tel (47) 553 218 75
Holberg-Stuen - Bergen 25 km - Tel (47) 553 180 15
To Kokker - Bergen 25 km - Tel (47) 553 228 16

Miklagard

18	8	7

Når man kommer hit midt i det tradisjonelle landskapet man finner nord for Oslo, så er det som å komme inn i en annen verden, en verden som ser ut som en amerikansk golf og country club. Designen på banen er amerikansk, hvor målgolf er viktig for å nå de opphøyde greenene som er omringet av bunkere. Likevel har Trent Jones Jr. med suksess og skikkelighet blandet den amerikanske stilen med landskapet og vegetasjonen, som ikke har mistet noe av sin sjarm. Den naturlige topografien er noen ganger fremhevet og det krever at man kan slå slag fra ulike posisjoner og helninger, noe som ofte byr på større problemer for den uerfarne spilleren. I tillegg blir ofte spilleren konfrontert med strategiske muligheter hvor det er nødvendig med en viss grad av erfaring, men for de spillerne som satser og som har kontroll over spillet sitt burde mulighet for å komme seg rundt uskadd være tilstede. En majestetisk bane hvor ingen detalj er overlatt til tilfeldighetene. Selv om banen fortsatt har behov for tid til å modnes, så er alt her designet for å være fra øverste skuff. Miklagard er udiskutabelt en av de beste banene i Skandinavia.

Amidst the traditional landscape seen north of Oslo the design of the course is american, where target golf is in order to reach elevated greens guarded by deep bunkers. However, Trent Jones Jr. has skilfully blended this style with the landscape and vegetation which have lost none of their charm. The natural topography sometimes requires the ability to hit shots from all sorts of lies and slopes, something that might well bother the less experienced golfer. In addition, players are often confronted with strategic options that call for a certain degree of experience and reason, but the more adventurous souls on top of their game should manage to get round unscathed. A majestic course where careful attention has been paid to detail. And although Miklagard still needs to mature, everything here was designed to be top drawer. One of the finest courses in the whole of Scandinavia.

Miklagard Golf — 2002

Miklagard Golf, pb 87
N - 2041 KLØFTA

Office	Kontor	(47) 639 431 00
Pro shop	Pro shop	(47) 639 431 05
Fax	Fax	(47) 639 431 01
Web	www.miklagardgolf.no	
Situation	Beliggenhet	Oslo, 25 km
Annual closure	Årlig stenging	no
Weekly closure	Ukentlig stenging	no

Fees main season Tariffer i høysesongen	18 holes	
	Week days Ukedager	**We/Bank holidays** Week-end/Frydag
Individual Individuell	NKr 900	NKr 900
Couple Par	NKr 1800	NKr 1800

Week days: before 14:00 /
We: after 14:00 or before 9:00

Caddie Caddie no — **Electric Trolley** Elektrisk vogn yes
Buggy Golfbil yes — **Clubs** Køller yes

Credit cards Kredittkort
VISA - Eurocard - MasterCard - AMEX - DC

Holum
Borgen
Jessheim
Gardermoen
Gjerdrum
Ullensaker
Klöfta
Skarnes
2
GOLF
Sörum
E6
0
2 km
Oslo

Access Adkomst : Oslo E6 north, then riksvei (highway) 2 → Kongsvinger. Golf on right hand side after 200 m.
Map 1 on page 1029 Kort 1 på side: 1029

GOLF COURSE — GOLFBANEN — 18/20

Site	Område	
Maintenance	Vedlikehold	
Architect	Arkitekt	R. Trent Jones Jr.
Type	Type	parkland, open and forest
Relief	Relief	
Water in play	Vann-hinder	
Exp. to wind	Utsatt for vind	
Trees in play	Tre-hinder	

Scorecard Scorecard	**Chp.** Champ.-tee	**Mens** Herre-tees	**Ladies** Dame-tees
Length Lengde	6272	5915	4930
Par	72	72	72
Slope system	131	128	127

Advised golfing ability Anbefalt golfnivå — 0 12 24 36
Hcp required Obligatorisk Hcp — 36

CLUB HOUSE & AMENITIES — KLUBHUS OG OMGIVELSER — 8/10

Pro shop Pro shop
Driving range Treningsbane
Sheltered ly no - On grass på gress yes - Putting-green putting-green yes - Pitching-green pitching-green yes

HOTEL FACILITIES — HOTELL FASILITETERNE — 7/10

HOTELS HOTEL FASILITETER

First Hotel Millenium - Oslo 25 km
112 rooms, D NKr 1510,-
Tel (47) 210 228 00, Fax (47) 210 228 30

Radisson SAS Scandinavia Hotel - Oslo 25 km
488 rooms, D NKr 2100,-
Tel (47) 232 930 00, Fax (47) 232 930 01

Norlandia Karl Johan - Oslo 25 km
111 rooms, D NKr 1570,-
Tel (47) 231 617 00, Fax (47) 224 205 19

RESTAURANTS RESTAURANT

Oro (book before) - Oslo 25 km - Tel (47) 232 102 40
3 Brodre - Oslo 25 km - Tel (47) 231 006 70

Moss & Rygge

17	7	6

Denne helt nye banen befinner seg på gammelt jordbruksland nær Oslofjorden, og klatret umiddelbart oppover rankingen og ble en av Norges aller beste. Designet av engelskmannen Jeremy Turner, som bor og arbeider i Sverige, Moss & Rygge gjør ingen hemmelighet av sine bånd til britisk golf. Noe som blant annet vises på de første ni med linksinspirert arkitektur på noen hull. Som på linksbaner kan du på de fleste hullene rulle ballen inn på greenen; absolutt en fordel siden vinden ofte spiller en betydelig rolle her. Ett hull med blindt utslag (hull 3) og et halvt dusin delvis blinde greener kompletterer det som på mange måter er blitt et klassisk layout. De fleste problemer og hindringer er synlige, og du vil fort oppdage at det er en fordel å kunne skru ballen begge veier. Er du skjev fra tee, vil du oppdage at roughen kan straffe hardt, men majoriteten av spillere bør klare å treffe de brede fairwayene. Det er en høykvalitetsbane, veldesignet og innbyr til å bli spilt om og om igjen. Til tross for noe leire i grunnen, drenerer den bra og vedlikeholdet er eksellent.

This brand new course found room for itself on the land of an old farm close to Oslofjord and immediately scaled the ranks to become one of Norway's very best. Laid out by the English architect Jeremy Turner, Moss & Rygge makes no secret of its ties with British golf and on the outward nine there are even shades of links-style architecture. Likewise, most of the greens can be approached with run-on or chipped shops, making for easier play in the wind which can be a significant feature here. One blind drive (hole N°3) and half a dozen half-hidden greens complete what is a rather classic layout. All the difficulties and hazards are pretty much visible, though, and you will soon find out that bending the ball both ways is a great help. Wild hitters off the tee may have problems with the very many OB stakes, but the majority of players should be able to safely steer clear. An excellent quality course, well-landscaped and one you can play over and over. Despite the clay sub-soil, green-keeping beyond reproach.

Moss & Rygge Golfklubb — 2003

Evjetangen 15
N - 1570 DITTING

Office	Kontor	(47) 692 627 00
Pro shop	Pro shop	(47) 692 627 00
Fax	Fax	(47) 692 699 50
Web	www.evjegolf.no	
Situation	Beliggenhet	Moss, 8 km
Annual closure	Årlig stenging	1/12→31/3
Weekly closure	Ukentlig stenging	no

Fees main season Tariffer i høysesongen	18 holes	
	Week days Ukedager	We/Bank holidays Week-end/Frydag
Individual Individuell	NKr 400	NKr 450
Couple Par	NKr 800	NKr 900

Juniors: – 50%

Caddie Caddie no — **Electric Trolley** Elektrisk vogn no
Buggy Golfbil yes — **Clubs** Køller yes
Credit cards Kredittkort
VISA - Eurocard - MasterCard - AMEX - DC

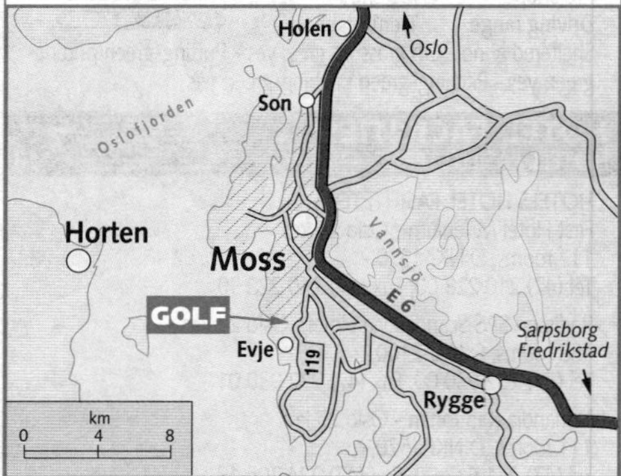

Access Adkomst : Along the road from Moss to Larkollen (R 119)
Map 1 on page 1029 Kort 1 på side: 1029

GOLF COURSE — GOLFBANEN — 17/20

Site	Område	
Maintenance	Vedlikehold	
Architect	Arkitekt	Jeremy Turner
Type	Type	forest, parkland
Relief	Relief	
Water in play	Vann-hinder	
Exp. to wind	Utsatt for vind	
Trees in play	Tre-hinder	

Scorecard / Scorecard	Chp. / Champ.-tee	Mens / Herre-tees	Ladies / Dame-tees
Length Lengde	6437	6071	4942
Par	72	72	72
Slope system	132	132	121

Advised golfing ability Anbefalt golfnivå — 0 12 24 36
Hcp required Obligatorisk Hcp — no

CLUB HOUSE & AMENITIES — KLUBHUS OG OMGIVELSER — 7/10

Pro shop — Pro shop
Driving range — Treningsbane
Sheltered ly yes - On grass på gress yes - Putting-green putting-green yes - Pitching-green pitching-green yes

HOTEL FACILITIES — HOTELL FASILITETERNE — 6/10

HOTELS HOTEL FASILITETER

Støtvig Hotell - Larkollen 5 km
54 rooms, D NKr 895
Tel (47) 692 361 00, Fax (47) 692 361 01

Hotell Refsnes Gods - Moss 15 km
61 rooms, D NKr 1490
Tel (47) 692 783 00, Fax (47) 692 783 01

Oslo

15 | 7 | 9

I denne meget hyggelige by gjelder det å ta turen om Ibsen museet, Nasjonalgalleriet og Edvard Munch museet for deretter å besøke Bygdøy og Vikingmuseet. Ditt neste stopp blir 18-hullsbanen på Bogstad, bare fire kilometer fra sentrum av landets hovedstad. Banen ble anlagt i 1925 og har opp gjennom årene gjennom en stadig utvikling. Den er lokalisert ved Bogstadvannet som ligger i et typisk norsk skoglandskap med fin utsikt til Holmenkollen og den berømte hoppbakken. Banen er omgitt av mye trær, men de er der mest som dekorasjon og utgjør sjelden noe fare for selve spillet unntatt for å skape noen få dog-leg hull. Vannet er ute av spill med unntak av hull 16, et meget vakkert par 3 hull over Bogstadvannet. Ellers er problemene godt spredt rundt om på banen og hullene kan oppfattes som meget forskjellige, alt fra de mest stressede til de mest avslappende. Greenene er store og til dels ondulerte. Derfor vil majoriteten av de som spiller her komme trygt rundt de 18 hullene uten altfor store problemer.

In this very pleasant city, make it along to the Ibsen Museum, the National Gallery (Nasjonalgalleriet) and the Edvard Munch museum, then visit the Bigdøy peninsula to see the Viking Boat Museum. Your next stop will be the 18-hole Oslo golf course, opened in 1925 but recently restyled. It is located on the edge of Lake Bogstad in a typically Norwegian forest setting with some fine views over the hills of Holmenkollen. There are a lot of trees on the course, but more for decoration than to provide any real danger, or to create a few dog-leg holes. Water keeps nicely out of the way except on the 16th, a pretty par 3 over a lake. Otherwise, the trouble is well spread around the course with some very different holes alternating stress and relaxation. The greens are on the large side and sometimes elevated and well-guarded, but the majority of players shouldn't have too much trouble getting home safely. This is the one big Oslo golf club, so you are best advised to play here during the week.

Oslo Golfklubb — 1924

Bogstad, Ankerveien 127
N - 0757 OSLO

Office	Kontor	(47) 225 105 60
Pro shop	Pro shop	(47) 225 054 92
Fax	Fax	(47) 225 105 61
Web	www.oslogk.no	
Situation	Beliggenhet	Oslo, 8 km
Annual closure	Årlig stenging	1/11→30/4
Weekly closure	Ukentlig stenging	no

Fees main season Tariffer i høysesongen	18 holes	
	Week days Ukedager	**We/Bank holidays** Week-end/Frydag
Individual Individuell	NKr 500	NKr 500
Couple Par	NKr 1000	NKr 1000

Juniors: –50%/Week days: before 14:00/We: after 14:00

Caddie Caddie no — **Electric Trolley** Elektrisk vogn no

Buggy Golfbil no — **Clubs** Køller yes

Credit cards Kredittkort
VISA - Eurocard - MasterCard - DC - AMEX

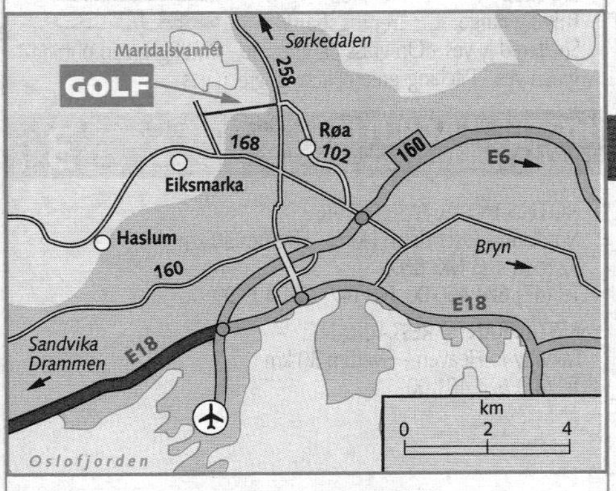

Access Adkomst : Follow signs → Bogstad Camping.
10 mn drive from centre of town
Map 1 on page 1029 Kort 1 på side: 1029

GOLF COURSE — GOLFBANEN — 15/20

Site	Område	
Maintenance	Vedlikehold	
Architect	Arkitekt	unknown
Type	Type	parkland
Relief	Relief	
Water in play	Vann-hinder	
Exp. to wind	Utsatt for vind	
Trees in play	Tre-hinder	

Scorecard Scorecard	**Chp.** Champ.-tee	**Mens** Herre-tees	**Ladies** Dame-tees
Length Lengde	6144	5789	4994
Par	72	72	72
Slope system	130	127	120

Advised golfing ability Anbefalt golfnivå — 0 12 24 36

Hcp required Obligatorisk Hcp — 20 Men/28 Ladies

CLUB HOUSE & AMENITIES — KLUBHUS OG OMGIVELSER — 7/10

Pro shop Pro shop
Driving range Treningsbane
Sheltered ly yes - On grass på gress no - Putting-green putting-green yes - Pitching-green pitching-green yes

HOTEL FACILITIES — HOTELL FASILITETERNE — 9/10

HOTELS HOTEL FASILITETER

Holmenkollen Park Hotel - Oslo 3 km
221 rooms, D NKr 1695,-
Tel (47) 229 220 00, Fax (47) 221 461 92

Clarion Royal Christiania - Oslo 7 km
378 rooms, D NKr 2095,-
Tel (47) 231 080 00, Fax (47) 231 080 80

Gyldenløve - Oslo 6 km - 168 rooms, D NKr 900,-
Tel (47) 226 010 90, Fax (47) 226 033 90

RESTAURANTS RESTAURANT

Frogneseteren - Oslo 5 km - Tel (47) 221 408 90
Le Canard - Oslo 7 km - Tel (47) 225 434 00
Restaurant Julius Fritzner - Oslo 7 km - Tel (47) 232 120 00

Sorknes

15	6	3

Når villgjessene flyr er ikke Lillehammer så langt unna, men det tar minst en time med bil for å komme til den nærmest byen Hamar. Storstedet Rena blir delt av Norges lengste elv Glomma. En av sideelvene heter Skynna som renner tvers gjennom golfbanen og utgjør en av de store hindringene. Den andre store hindringen er furuskogen. Banen ble lagt ut av J. Søgaard tidlig på 1990-tallet. På slutten av runden vil du huske greenen på hull 18 som er formet som et hjerte. Imidlertid handler banen om mer enn bare den fancy trimmingen av nevnte green. For det første, til tross for plasseringen utenfor allfarvei i bunn på en avsidesliggende dal så er det totalt sett en bra bane. For det andre, vedlikeholdet er bra og det er i seg selv en prestasjon når man tar klimaet i betraktning. Og til slutt, den generelle balansen i layout er fantastisk med en blanding av vanskelige og lette hull. Du vil huske banen for de mange forskjellige slagene som trengs for å komme rundt og det gjelder spesielt tre tøffe hull, inkludert det 17 (par 3 med vann).

As the wild-goose flies, Lillehammer is not so far away, but it takes at least an hour by car to reach the first large town of Hamar... Rena is crossed by the longest river in Norway, the Glomma, into which flows the Skynna, which also crosses this course and forms one of the hazards with the pine forest through which the course was laid out in the early 1990s. Over the closing stages you will remember the 18th green, a heart-shaped affair, but Sorknes has more to be said for it than that sort of fancy trimming. Firstly, despite its out-of-the-way location at the bottom of a remote valley, it is a good course. Secondly, maintenance is good, no mean feat in a climate that is anything but tropical, and finally the general balance of the layout is excellent. The variety of shots you will need to play makes this a course to remember with three tough holes, including the 17th, a par 3 with water. Well worth knowing, even if getting here is no easy matter.

Sorknes Golfklubb — 1992

Sorknes Golf, pb 70
N - 2451 RENA

Office	Kontor	(47) 624 418 70
Pro shop	Pro shop	(47) 624 418 70
Fax	Fax	(47) 624 400 27
Web	www.sorknesgolf.no	
Situation	Beliggenhet	Rena, 3 km
Annual closure	Årlig stenging	1/11→30/4
Weekly closure	Ukentlig stenging	no
Fees main season	Tariffer i høysesongen	18 holes

	Week days Ukedager	We/Bank holidays Week-end/Frydag
Individual Individuell	NKr 300	NKr 380
Couple Par	NKr 600	NKr 760

Week days: same fee for full day

Caddie Caddie no — **Electric Trolley** Elektrisk vogn no

Buggy Golfbil no — **Clubs** Køller yes

Credit cards Kredittkort
VISA - Eurocard - MasterCard - AMEX - DC

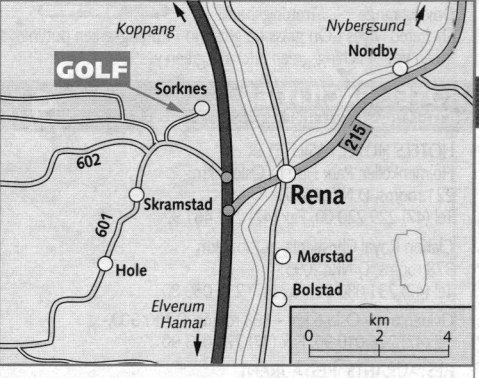

Access Adkomst : Oslo, E6, Rv.3 → Rena.
Golf 3 km from Rena city centre.
Map 1 on page 1029 Kort 1 på side: 1029

GOLF COURSE — 15/20
GOLFBANEN

Site	Område	
Maintenance	Vedlikehold	
Architect	Arkitekt	Juul Søgaard
Type	Type	forest
Relief	Relief	
Water in play	Vann-hinder	
Exp. to wind	Utsatt for vind	
Trees in play	Tre-hinder	

Scorecard Scorecard	Chp. Champ.-tee	Mens Herre-tees	Ladies Dame-tees
Length Lengde	6105	5695	4750
Par	72	72	72
Slope system	130	126	126

Advised golfing ability Anbefalt golfnivå — 0 12 24 36

Hcp required Obligatorisk Hcp — 35

CLUB HOUSE & AMENITIES — 6/10
KLUBHUS OG OMGIVELSER

Pro shop Pro shop
Driving range Treningsbane
Sheltered ly yes - On grass på gress no - Putting-green putting-green yes - Pitching-green pitching-green yes

HOTEL FACILITIES — 3/10
HOTELL FASILITETERNE

HOTELS HOTEL FASILITETER
Nordlandia Østerdalen Hotel - Elverum 30 km
82 rooms, D NKr 860,-
Tel (47) 624 450 00, Fax (47) 624 409 99

RESTAURANTS RESTAURANT
Fairway to Heaven - Elverum 30 km
Tel (47) 624 401 00

Stavanger

16	6	7

Den tidligere havnen for sardinfiske er nå senter for oljeproduksjonen i Nordsjøen, men byen er fremdeles like sjarmerende som tidligere år. Stavanger er også byen hvor man kan innlede reisen langs den vakre Vestlandskysten. Norge slik du ser det postkortene. Golfbanen, som ligger ved bredden Stokkavannet, ble anlagt midt i blant et kupert, men ikke urimelig bakkete landskap med fjell, trær, busker og myrer. Baneskaperne har klart å skape en naturskjønn og attraktivt ramme på og rundt banen som inneholder vanskeligheter av alle slag. Den har fått et meget godt rykte på seg fra de beste norske golfspillerne til tross for at lengden er forholdsvis kort. Banen er først og fremst for gode tekniske spillere. Du være nøyaktig og du må hele tiden skifte taktikk avhengig av tidligere slag. Derfor det gjelder det hele tide å gjøre riktig køllevalg. Hvis du vil ha en god score, prøv å utforske banen liten på forhånd. Hull 1, for eksempel, har et blind utslag med driven og et blindt innspill på greenen. Sagt på en annen måte, hvis du bruker 95 slag oftere enn du vanligvis gjør så må du begynne å spille taktisk for å komme rundt banen og ha glede av det.

This former sardine fishing port is now the North Sea oil production centre but is still as charming as ever. It is also the starting point for visiting the wonderful Fjord coast, the Norway you see on postcards. The present course, on the shores of Lake Stokka, was laid out amidst rolling but not unduly hilly countryside of rocks, trees, bushes and marshes, creating a picturesque and attractive setting, and difficulties of all sorts. It has acquired an excellent reputation with top Norwegian players, despite relatively short yardage, as this is a course for the golfing technician. You have to be accurate, be able to change tactics depending on the previous shot and be spot-on when choosing the right club to play. If you are set on carding a good score, try a little reconnoitring beforehand. Hole number one, for example, has a blind drive and a blind green to boot. With this said, if you break 95 more often than not, in theory you have what it takes to get around the course and enjoy it.

Stavanger Golfklubb — 1956

Longebakke 45
N - 4042 HAFRSFJORD

Office	Kontor	(47) 515 570 25
Pro shop	Pro shop	(47) 515 554 31
Fax	Fax	(47) 515 573 11
Web	www.sgk.no	
Situation	Beliggenhet	Stavanger, 5 km
Annual closure	Årlig stenging	1/12→31/3
Weekly closure	Ukentlig stenging	no

Fees main season / Tariffer i høysesongen	18 holes	
	Week days / Ukedager	We/Bank holidays / Week-end/Frydag
Individual Individuell	NKr 350	NKr 350
Couple Par	NKr 700	NKr 700

Caddie Caddie no — Electric Trolley Elektrisk vogn no

Buggy Golfbil no — Clubs Køller yes

Credit cards Kredittkort
VISA - Eurocard - MasterCard - AMEX - DC - JCB

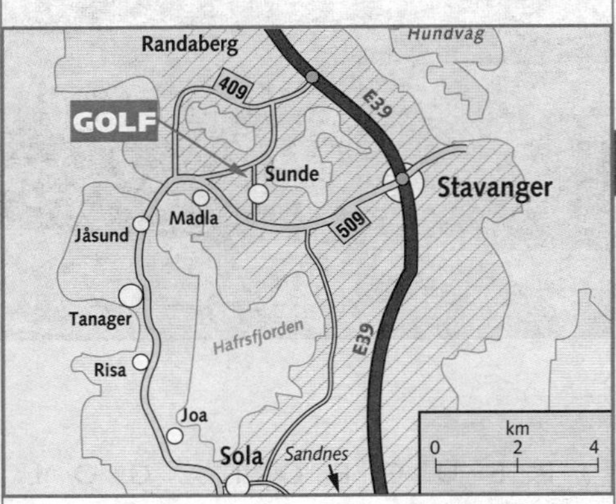

Access Adkomst : Stavanger Rv 510 to Madla. 300 m Rv 509
Map 1 on page 1028 Kort 1 på side: 1028

GOLF COURSE — GOLFBANEN 16/20

Site	Område	
Maintenance	Vedlikehold	
Architect	Arkitekt	Fred Smith
Type	Type	parkland
Relief	Relief	
Water in play	Vann-hinder	
Exp. to wind	Utsatt for vind	
Trees in play	Tre-hinder	

Scorecard / Scorecard	Chp. / Champ.-tee	Mens / Herre-tees	Ladies / Dame-tees
Length Lengde	5710	5494	4863
Par	71	71	71
Slope system	128	128	128

Advised golfing ability / Anbefalt golfnivå: 0 12 24 36
Hcp required — Obligatorisk Hcp — 36 (We 28/36)

CLUB HOUSE & AMENITIES — KLUBHUS OG OMGIVELSER 6/10

Pro shop — Pro shop
Driving range — Treningsbane
Sheltered ly no - On grass på gress no - Putting-green putting-green yes - Pitching-green pitching-green yes

HOTEL FACILITIES — HOTELL FASILITETERNE 7/10

HOTELS HOTEL FASILITETER

Radisson SAS Atlantic Hotel - Stavanger 5 km
352 rooms, D NOK 750,-/1495,-
Tel (47) 517 600 05, Fax (47) 517 600 01

Rica Park Hotel - Stavanger 5 km
59 rooms, D NOK 895,-/1325,-
Tel (47) 517 005 00, Fax (47) 517 004 00

Clarion Hotel - Stavanger 5 km - 249 rooms, D NKr 1990,-
Tel (47) 515 025 00, Fax (47) 515 025 01

RESTAURANTS RESTAURANT

Bevaremegvel - Stavanger 5 km - Tel (47) 518 438 60
Bistrohuset - Stavanger 5 km - Tel (47) 515 395 70

PORTUGAL

Vilamoura - Victoria

GUIDE 2006/2007

PORTUGAL

Today Portugal is one of the most popular of all European destinations. This is explained by a favourable climate, which extends a privileged refuge to frost-bound tourists from northern Europe, and also by firm commitment to development, particularly after the years of isolation and the revolution. Today a fully-committed European partner, Portugal has fully grasped the appeal of golf as an asset for tourism. Domestically the Portuguese continue to prefer soccer as their national sport and golf remains a pastime reserved for a certain elite – this happens to be the case in many other Latin countries. There are only 18,000 golfers in Portugal but 67 eighteen-hole courses. Do not be surprised to find a certain number of these around Lisbon (sometimes crowded with club members), in the direction of Cascais to the west and Setúbal to the south of the city. You then have to drive a few hundred kilometres to reach the new golfing Mecca of the Algarve. In the mid-1960s, Henry Cotton showed the way by designing Penina. Then it was Vilamoura which became a sort of model for golf resorts and has since entered the annals of successful golfing. Quinta do Lago and São Lourenço (San Lorenzo) then demonstrated the standard of quality of the country's courses. Today, three new courses have been included in the Peugeot Golf Guide: Vilamoura Victoria and two new courses at Ribagolfe, east of Lisbon. Elsewhere, Estela makes a welcome return to state the case for golf in the north of the country.

PORTUGAL

Portugal é um dos mais populares de todos os destinos Europeus. Isto explica-se por um clima favorável que oferece um refúgio privilegiado a turistas congelados do Norte da Europa e também por um firme cometimento ao desenvolvimento, principalmente depois de anos de isolamento e de revolução. Hoje, Portugal, um parceiro Europeu empenhado, assimilou completamente o interesse do Golfe como um activo para o turismo. Domesticamente os portugueses continuam a eleger o Futebol como seu desporto Nacional e o Golfe continua a ser um passatempo reservado para uma certa elite. – Isto acontece aliás em muitas países latinos. Há só 18.000 praticantes em Portugal, mas ma conta com 67 campos de 18 buracos. Não se admire de encontrar um certo numero deles nos arredores de Lisboa (às vezes cheios de sócios), na direcção de Cascais para Leste ou de Setúbal para Sul da Cidade. Terá então de conduzir algumas centenas de quilómetros para alcançar a nova Meca do Golfe no Algarve. Em meados dos anos 60, Henry Cotton mostrou o caminho ao desenhar a Penina. A seguir foi Vilamoura que se tornou uma espécie de modelo para os empreendimentos de Golfe entrando assim nos anais do Golfe com sucesso. A Quinta do Lago e São Lourenço demonstraram a seguir o nível de qualidade dos campos do país. Actualmente o "Peugeot Guide" incluiu mais três campos: O Vilamoura Victoria e os dois novos campos Ribagolfe a Leste de Lisboa. Noutras paragens, a Estela faz um bem-vindo regresso para assinalar o Golfe no Norte do país.

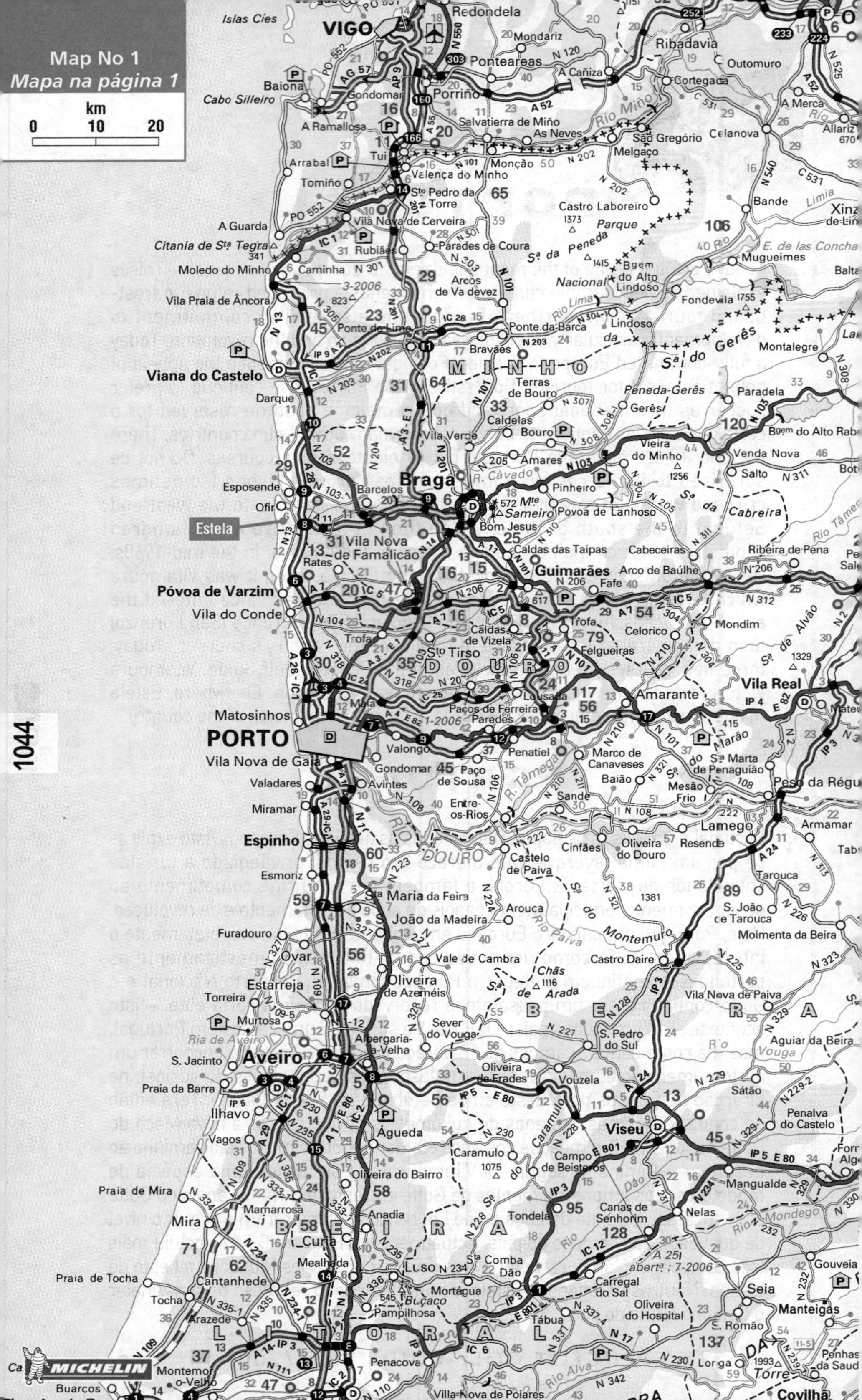

Map No 1
Mapa na página 1
km
0
10
20
Islas Cíes
VIGO
Redondela
Mondariz
Ponteareas
Ribadavia
Outomuro
A Cañiza
Cortegaça
Baiona
Cabo Silleiro
Gondomar
Porriño
A Ramallosa
Salvatierra de Miño
As Neves
São Gregório
Celanova
Melgaço
Tui
Arrabal
Valença do Minho
Monção
Tomiño
Sto Pedro da Torre
Castro Laboreiro
Bande
A Guarda
Vila Nova de Cerveira
Parque Nacional
Sa da Peneda
Citania de Sta Tegra
Rubiães
Parades de Coura
Moledo do Minho
Caminha
Mugueimes
Vila Praia de Âncora
Arcos de Va devez
Bgem do Alto Lindoso
Rio Lima
Lindoso
Fondevila
Ponte de Lima
Ponte da Barca
Sa do Gerês
Montalegre
Viana do Castelo
Bravães
MINHO
Darque
Terras de Bouro
Peneda-Gerês
Paradela
Gerês
Caldelas
Bouro
Vila Verde
Bgem do Alto Rabagão
Vieira do Minho
Venda Nova
Amares
Salto
Esposende
Barcelos
Braga
Pinheiro
Ofir
Estela
Mte Sameiro
Povoa de Lanhoso
Sa da Cabreira
Bom Jesus
Vila Nova de Famalicão
Caldas das Taipas
Cabeceiras
Ribeira de Pena
Rates
Guimarães
Arco de Baúlhe
Póvoa de Varzim
Fafe
Vila do Conde
Mondim
Trofa
Celorico
Caldas de Vizela
Felgueiras
Sto Tirso
DOURO
Amarante
Vila Real
Lousada
Paços de Ferreira
Paredes
Matosinhos
PORTO
Valongo
Penatiel
Marco de Canaveses
Sa do Marão
Sa Marta de Penaguião
Vila Nova de Gaia
Gondomar
Baião
Peso da Régua
Valadares
Avintes
Paço de Sousa
Mesão Frio
Miramar
Entre-os-Rios
Sande
Lamego
Armamar
Espinho
Cinfães
Oliveira do Douro
Resende
Castelo de Paiva
Esmoriz
Tarouca
Sta Maria da Feira
Arouca
S. João de Tarouca
S. João da Madeira
Sa de Montemuro
Moimenta da Beira
Furadouro
Ovar
Vale de Cambra
Castro Daire
Estarreja
Oliveira de Azeméis
Chãs Sa de Arada
Torreira
Vila Nova de Paiva
Murtosa
Sever do Vouga
BEIRA
Ria de Aveiro
Albergaria-a-Velha
S. Pedro do Sul
Aguiar da Beira
S. Jacinto
Aveiro
Oliveira de Frades
Praia da Barra
Vouzela
Sátão
Ilhavo
Penalva do Castelo
Águeda
Viseu
Vagos
Caramulo
Campo de Beisteros
Mangualde
Oliveira do Bairro
Praia de Mira
Mamarrosa
Anadia
Tondela
Canas de Senhorim
Nelas
Mira
Curia
Sta Comba Dão
Gouveia
Mealhada
Luso
Praia de Tocha
Cantanhede
Mortágua
Carregal do Sal
Seia
Tocha
Buçaco
Pampilhosa
Oliveira do Hospital
Manteigas
Arazede
Tábua
S. Romão
LITORAL
Penacova
Lorga
Torre
Penhas da Saúde
MICHELIN
Montemor-o-Velho
Buarcos
Vila Nova de Poiares
Covilhã
Rio Alva

Ourense
Castro Caldelas
O Barco
Puente de Domingo Flórez
Montes
Sta Colomba de Somoza
Astorga
Alto del Couso
A Rúa
Freixido
Alto del Rodicio
A Pobra de Trives
Casoio
Maceda
O Bolo
Riego
Baños de Molgas
Manzaneda
Manzaneda
E. de Prada
Teleno
Xunqueira de Ambía
Seixo
A Veiga
Peña Trevinca
Encinedo
Embalse de Bao
Alto de Covelo
Vilar de Barrio
Viana do Bolo
Truchas
Embalse de Las Portas
E. de S. Sebastián
S. Martín de Castañeda
Sierra de la Cabrera
Castrocontrigo
Laza
Ribadelago
Lago de Sanabria
Peña Nofre
A Gudiña
Pillo de la Canda
Galende
Puebla de Sanabria
Justel
Espadañedo
Cualedro
Alto de Fumaces
Alto do Cañizo
Padornelo
Palacios de Sanabria
Alto de Estivadas
A Mezquita
Pedralba
Ungilde
Mombuey
Santibáñez de Vidriales
Verín
Moimenta
E. de Cernadilla
E. de Valparaíso
Corraes
Calabor
Portelo
Feces
Parque Natural de Montesinho
Sa de la Culebra
Peña Mira
Villardeciervos
Ferreras de Abajo
Vila Verde da Raia
Vinhais
Figueruela de Arriba
Pto de Sazadón
Chaves
Bragança
Milhão
S. Vicente de la Cabeza
Rio Tuela
S. Vitero
Rebordelo
Penhas Juntas
Quintanilha
Trabazos
Vidago
Torre de D. Chama
Sa de Nogueira
Rio Sabor
Alcañices
TRÁS-OS-MONTES
Sta Comba de Rossas
Valpaços
Sta Luz
Carrazedo de Montenegro
Sa da Padrela
Vimioso
Fonfría
Carbajales de Alba
Vila Pouca de Aguiar
Macedo de Cavaleiros
Izeda
Mirandela
Morais
Murça
Bornes
Miranda do Douro
Ricobayo
Trindade
Sa de Bornes
Rio Duero
Embalse de Ricobayo
Rio Tua
Mogadouro
Sa do Mogadouro
Sendim
Bgem de Picote
Sabrosa
Alijó
Vila Flor
Bermillo de Sayago
Alfândega da Fé
Fermoselle
Carrazeda de Ansiães
Bgem da Bemposta
Pinhão
Fonte Longa
Embalse de Almendra
Villarino
S. João da Pesqueira
Torre de Moncorvo
Lagoaça
Masueco
Almeida
Trabanca
Carviçais
Embalse de Aldeadávila
Vila Nova de Foz Côa
Freixo de Espada à Cinta
Villaseco de los Reyes
Barruecopardo
Penedono
Embalse de Saucelle
Barca de Alva
Lede
Mêda
La Fregeneda
Vitigudino
Villar de Peralonso
Hinojosa de Duero
Sernancelhe
Lumbrales
Sando
BEIRA ALTA
Figueira de Castelo Rodrigo
El Cubo de Don Sancho
Marofa
Rio Huebra
Villavieja de Yeltes
Berzosa
S. Felices de los Gallegos
Trancoso
Vila Franca das Naves
Pinhel
La Fuente de S. Esteban
Almeida
Martín de Yeltes
Freixedas
Celorico da Beira
Castillejo de Martín Viejo
Sancti Spíritus
Cabrillas
Vecinos
Vilar Formoso
Rio Yeltes
Tamames
Arrifana
Guarda
Serra da Estrela
Fuentes de Oñoro
Ciudad Rodrigo
Cerdeira
Vale de Estrela
El Bodón
Pega
Valhelhas
Rio Côa
Aldeia da Ponte
Fuenteguinaldo
Belmonte
Teixoso
La Alberguería de Argañán
Sabugal
Caria
Sto Estêvão
MICHELIN
d' après base de données au 1/1 000 000 - édition 2005
Autorisation n°0501023.
1045

Map No 2
Mapa na página 2
km
0
10
20
1046
Praia d'El Rey
Quinta do Brinçal
Penha Longa
Belas
Oitavos
Ribagolfe
Quinta da Marinha
Aroeira
Quinta do Peru
Troia
MICHELIN
Praia de Mira
Mira
Mamarrosa
Oliveira do Bairro
Anadia
Curia
Mealhada
Luso
Buçaco
Pampilhosa
Praia de Tocha
Tocha
Cantanhede
Arazede
Cabo Mondego
Buarcos
Figueira da Foz
Montemor-o-Velho
Penacova
COIMBRA
Rio Mondego
Condeixa-a-Nova
Miranda do Corvo
Lousã
Soure
Louriçal
Degracias
Penela
Pedrógão
Praia da Vieira
Vieira
Monte Redondo
Pombal
Sicó
Pontão
Monte Real
Ansião
Figueiró dos Vinhos
S. Pedro de Moel
Pinhal de Leiria
Marinha Grande
Barqueiro
Alvaiázere
Cernache de Bonjardim
Martingança
Leiria
Batalha
Ourém
Nazaré
Cruz da Légua
Porto de Mós
Fátima
Ferreira do Zêzere
S. Martinho do Porto
Alcobaça
Mira de Aire
Tomar
Alfeizerão
Castelo de Bode
Foz del Arelho
Caldas da Rainha
Serra de Aire
Torres Novas
Sardoal
Ilha Berlenga
Cabo Carvoeiro
Baleal
Peniche
Óbidos
Alcanena
Constância
Atouguia da Baleia
Alcanede
Entroncamento
Abrantes
Rio Maior
Golegã
Vila Nova da Barquinha
Tramagal
Rossio
Bombarral
Lourinhã
Chamusca
Cadaval
Alcanhões
Bemposta
Cercal
Alpiarça
Praia de Sta Cruz
Santarém
Chouto
Sa de Montejunto
Almeirim
Torres Vedras
Aldeia Gavinha
Cartaxo
Aveiras de Cima
Azambuja
Alenquer
Muge
Sobral de Mte Agraço
Rio Tejo
Ericeira
Sapataria
Carregado
Salvaterra de Magos
São José da Lamarosa
Mafra
Arruda dos V.
Benavente
Montargil
Malveira
Vila Franca de Xira
Bucelas
Coruche
Rio Sorraia
Cabo da Roca
Alverca do Ribatejo
Colares
Sintra
Loures
Porto Alto
Couço
Amadora
Sto Estêvão
Sacavém
Mora
Cabo Raso
LISBOA
Queluz
Alcochete
Pavia
Cascais
Estoril
Oeiras
Montijo
Brotas
Canha
Almada
Barreiro
Lavre
Taipadas
Moita
Seixal
Cruzamento de Pegões
Arraiolos
Coina
Pinhal Novo
Vendas Novas
Palmela
Marateca
Montemor-o-Novo
Vila Nogueira de Azeitão
Setúbal
Santana
Sa da Arrábida
Santiago do Escoural
Portinho
Sesimbra
Península de Tróia
S. Cristóvão

Tondela
Canas de Senhorim
Nelas
Mangualde
Celorico da Beira
Castillejo de Martín Viejo
Vilar Formoso
Arrifana
Guarda
Fuentes de Oñoro
Comba Dão
Carregal do Sal
Gouveia
ESTRELA
Vale de Estrela
Seia
Manteigas
Cerdeira
Pega
El Bodón
Tábua
Oliveira do Hospital
S. Romão
Valhelhas
Aldeia da Ponte
Fuenteguinaldo
Loriga
Torre
Penhas da Saude
Teixoso
Belmonte
La Alberguería de Argañán
Sabugal
Arganil
SERRA
Covilhã
Caria
Sto Estêvão
S. Pedro de Açor
Unhais da Serra
Tortosendo
Navasfrías
Góis
Paúl
Meimoa
Sa de Mezas
Sa de Malcata
Valverde del Fresno
Pto de Perales
Gata
Fundão
Silvares
Penamacor
Acebo
Pampilhosa da Serra
Vale de Prazeres
Alpedrinha
Hoyos
Perales del Puerto
Sa da Gardunha
Orvalho
Cambas
Medelim
Cilleros
S. Vicente da Beira
Foz Giraldo
Monsanto
Moraleja
BEIRA
BAIXA
Oleiros
Termas de Monfortinho
Escalos de Cima
Alcains
Idanha a Nova
Alcafozes
Casillas
Sa de Alvelos
Salgueiro do Campo
Sobreira Formosa
Sarzedas
Zarza la Mayor
Castelo Branco
Ladoeiro
Zebreira
Segura
Proença-a-Nova
Ceclavín
Acehuche
Piedras Albas
Portezuelo
Rosmaninhal
Bgem de Cedillo
Vila Velha de Ródão
Malpica do T.
Embalse de Alcántara
Alcántara
Fratel
Cedillo
Herrera de Alcántara
Garrovillas
Montalvão
Santiago de Alcántara
RÍO TAJO
RIO TEJO
Brozas
Gavião
Nisa
Arez
Bgem da Póvoa
Membrío
Casar de Cáceres
Tolosa
Alpalhão
Castelo de Vide
Marvão
Valencia de Alcántara
Salorino
Herreruela
Arroyo de la Luz
Mte da Pedra
Flor da Rosa
Torrico de S. Pedro
Aliseda
Malpartida de Cáceres
Ponte de Sor
Crato
S. Vicente de Alcántara
Parque Natural de São Mamede
Portalegre
Sa de S. Mamede
Sa de S. Pedro
Alter do Chão
Galveias
PORTUGAL
La Codosera
Alburquerque
Puebla de Obando
Pto del Clavín
Avis
Cabeço de Vide
Arronches
Pto de los Conejeros
Villar del Rey
Pto del Zángano
Fronteira
Monforte
La Roca de la Sierra
Cordobilla de Lácara
Bgem do Caia
Casa Branca
Sousel
Sta Eulália
Campo Maior
La Nava de Santiago
Veiros
Vila Fernando
Vimieiro
Estremoz
Badajoz
Montijo
Elvas
Talavera la Real
Puebla de la Calzada
Évoramonte
Vila Boim
Borba
Sa de Ossa
Vila Viçosa
Bgem do Divor
Azaruja
Juromenha
Lobón
Arroyo de S. Serván
Alandroal
Corte de Peleas
S. Miguel de Machede
Redondo
Olivenza
La Albuera
Valverde de Leganés
Solana de Barros
Évora
Terena
GUADIANA
MICHELIN
1047

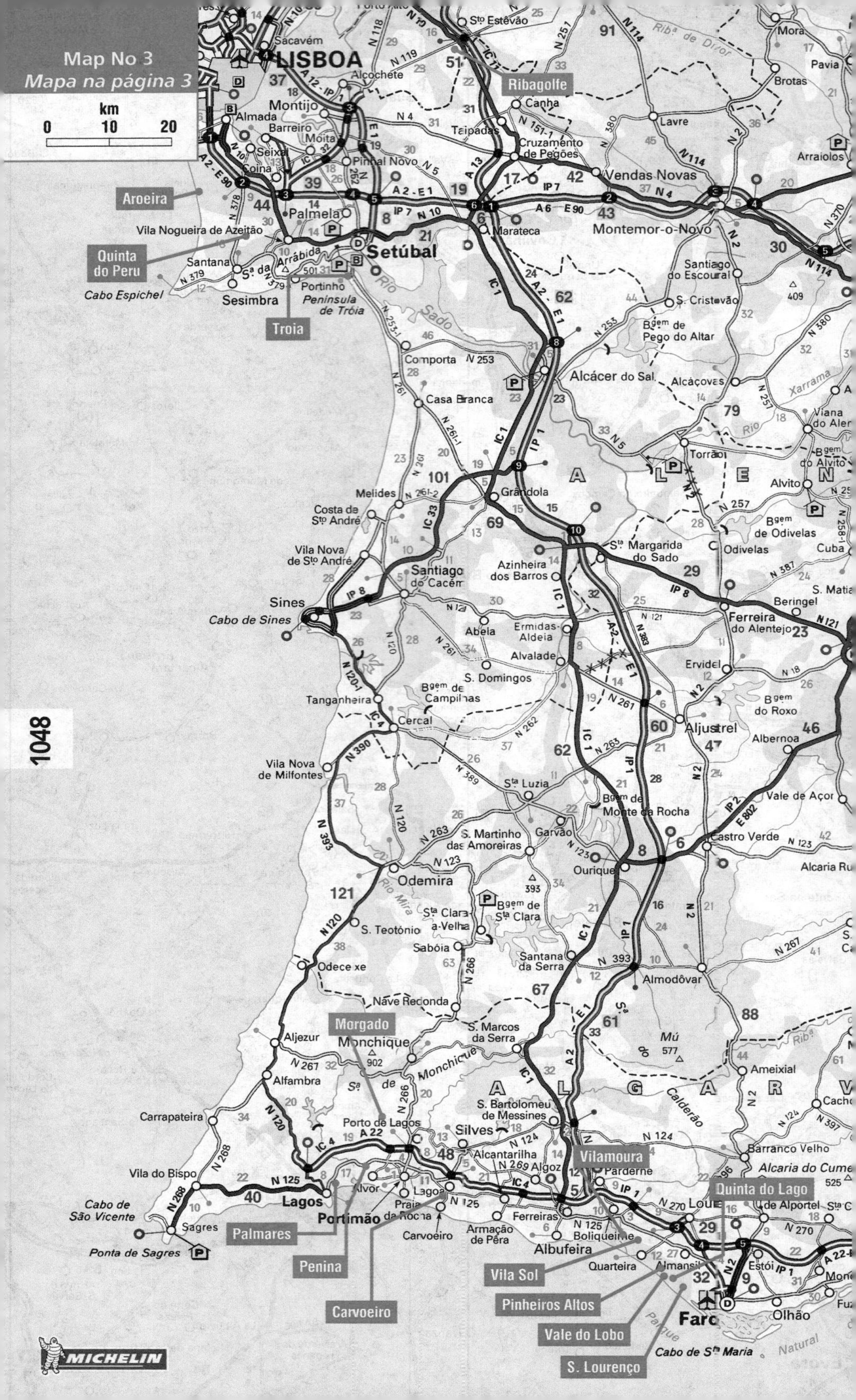
Map No 3
Mapa na página 3
km
0 10 20
Aroeira
Quinta do Peru
Troia
Ribagolfe
Morgado
Palmares
Penina
Carvoeiro
Vila Sol
Vilamoura
Pinheiros Altos
Vale do Lobo
S. Lourenço
Quinta do Lago
LISBOA
Setúbal
Sines
Odemira
Lagos
Portimão
Albufeira
Faro
Montemor-o-Novo
Alcácer do Sal
Grândola
Santiago do Cacém
Monchique
Silves
Olhão
Cabo Espichel
Cabo de Sines
Cabo de São Vicente
Ponta de Sagres
Cabo de Sta Maria
MICHELIN

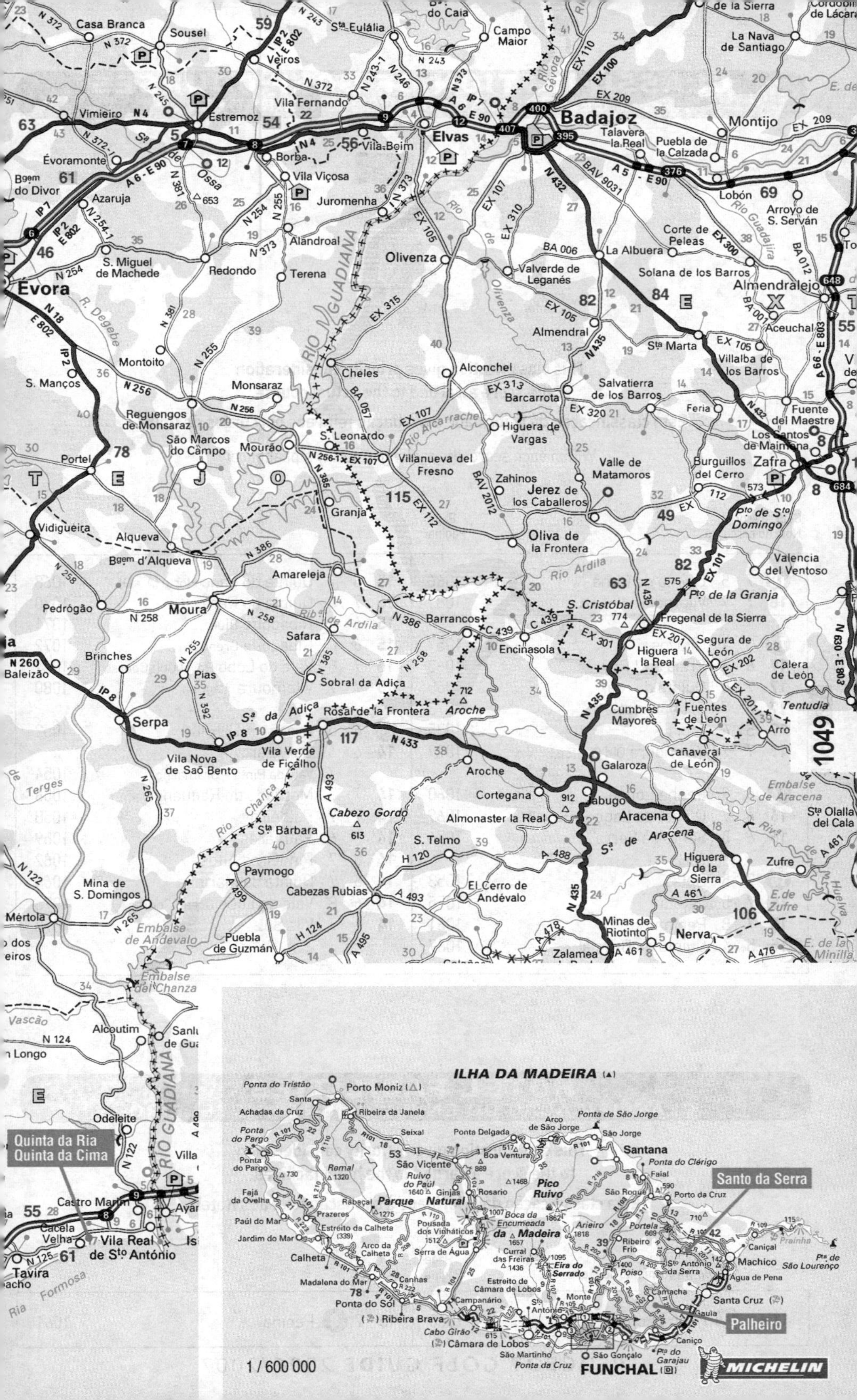
Casa Branca
Sousel
Sta Eulália
do Caia
Campo Maior
de la Sierra
Cordobil de Lácara
La Nava de Santiago
Veiros
Vila Fernando
Vimieiro
Estremoz
Elvas
Badajoz
Montijo
Talavera la Real
Puebla de la Calzada
Évoramonte
Borba
Vila Boim
Bgem do Divor
Vila Viçosa
Azaruja
Juromenha
Lobón
Arroyo de S. Serván
Alandroal
Corte de Peleas
Évora
S. Miguel de Machede
Redondo
Terena
Olivenza
Valverde de Leganés
La Albuera
Solana de los Barros
Almendralejo
Almendral
Aceuchal
Sta Marta
Villalba de los Barros
Montoito
Cheles
Alconchel
S. Manços
Monsaraz
Barcarrota
Salvatierra de los Barros
Reguengos de Monsaraz
Feria
Fuente del Maestre
S. Leonardo
Higuera de Vargas
Los Santos de Maimona
São Marcos do Campo
Mourão
Portel
Villanueva del Fresno
Valle de Matamoros
Burguillos del Cerro
Zafra
Zahinos
Jerez de los Caballeros
Granja
Pto de Sto Domingo
Vidigueira
Alqueva
Oliva de la Frontera
Bgem d'Alqueva
Amareleja
Valencia del Ventoso
Pto de la Granja
Pedrógão
Moura
S. Cristóbal
Barrancos
Fregenal de la Sierra
Safara
Encinasola
Segura de León
Higuera la Real
Calera de León
Brinches
Baleizão
Pias
Sobral da Adiça
Cumbres Mayores
Fuentes de León
Tentudía
Serpa
Sa da Adiça
Rosal de la Frontera
Aroche
Arro
Vila Nova de Saõ Bento
Vila Verde de Ficalho
Cañaveral de León
Galaroza
Cortegana
Jabugo
Aracena
Embalse de Aracena
Sta Olalla del Cala
Almonaster la Real
Cabezo Gordo
Sta Bárbara
S. Telmo
Sa de Aracena
Paymogo
Higuera de la Sierra
Zufre
Mina de S. Domingos
Cabezas Rubias
El Cerro de Andévalo
Mértola
Embalse de Andevalo
Puebla de Guzmán
Minas de Riotinto
Nerva
Zalamea
E. de la Minilla
Embalse del Chanza
Alcoutim
Odeleite
Quinta da Ria
Quinta da Cima
Castro Marim
Cacela Velha
Vila Real de Sto António
Tavira
Ria Formosa
RIO GUADIANA
1049
ILHA DA MADEIRA
Ponta do Tristão
Porto Moniz
Santa
Achadas da Cruz
Ribeira da Janela
Ponta do Pargo
Seixal
Ponta Delgada
Arco de São Jorge
Ponta de São Jorge
São Jorge
Santana
Ponta do Clérigo
São Vicente
Boa Ventura
Ruivo do Paúl
Pico Ruivo
Santo da Serra
Faial
Porto da Cruz
Fajã da Ovelha
Rabaçal
Parque Natural
Paúl do Mar
Prazeres
Pousada dos Vinháticos
Boca da Encumeada
da Madeira
Arieiro
Ribeiro Frio
Jardim do Mar
Estreito da Calheta
Arco da Calheta
Calheta
Serra de Água
Curral das Freiras
Eira do Serrado
Poiso
Sto António da Serra
Machico
Pta de São Lourenço
Caniçal
Madalena do Mar
Canhas
Estreito de Câmara de Lobos
Camacha
Santa Cruz
Ponta do Sol
Campanário
Ribeira Brava
Cabo Girão
Palheiro
Câmara de Lobos
São Martinho
Ponta da Cruz
São Gonçalo
Pta do Garajau
Caniço
FUNCHAL
1 / 600 000
MICHELIN

CLASSIFICATION OF GOLF COURSES
CLASSIFICAÇÃO DOS PERCURSOS

This classification gives priority consideration to the score awarded to the actual course.

Esta classificação dá prioridade à avaliação feita aos percursos de Golfe.

Within each score, the ranking is purely alphabetical

Course score / Nota do percurso				Page / Página
18	7	5	Quinta de Cima	1066
18	7	7	Vilamoura Victoria	1081
17	8	7	Oitavos	1057
17	6	6	Praia d'El Rey	1063
17	7	5	Quinta da Ria	1065
17	5	7	S. Lourenço	1073
17	5	4	Troia	1075
17	7	7	Vilamoura Old Course	1079
16	6	9	Penha Longa	1060
16	6	7	Quinta do Lago Sul (B + C)	1069
16	6	5	Santo da Serra	1074
15	7	5	Belas	1053
15	7	5	Estela	1055
15	7	8	Penina	1061
15	5	4	Quinta do Brinçal	1067
15	6	7	Quinta do Lago Norte (A + D)	1068
15	7	5	Quinta do Peru	1070
15	6	4	Ribagolfe Blue	1071
15	6	4	Ribagolfe Green	1072
15	7	8	Vale do Lobo Royal Golf Course	1077
15	7	7	Vilamoura Laguna	1080
14	6	5	Aroeira Aroeira II	1052
14	6	6	Carvoeiro Vale da Pinta + Gramacho	1054
14	7	7	Morgado do Reguengo	1056
14	7	7	Palheiro	1058
14	5	6	Palmares	1059
14	8	7	Pinheiros Altos	1062
14	6	7	Quinta da Marinha	1064
14	6	8	Vale do Lobo Ocean Course	1076
14	6	7	Vila Sol	1078

HOTEL FACILITIES
CLASSIFICAÇÃO DO ENVOLVIMENTO HOTELEIRO

This classification gives priority consideration to the score awarded to the hotel facilities.

Esta classificação dá prioridade à avaliação feita aos Hoteis.

		Hotel facility score / Nota do envolvimento hoteleiro		Page / Página
16	6	9	Penha Longa	1060
15	7	8	Penina	1061

HOTEL FACILITIES
CLASSIFICAÇÃO DO ENVOLVIMENTO HOTELEIRO

14	6	**8**	Vale do Lobo Ocean Course	1076
15	7	**8**	Vale do Lobo Royal Golf Course	1077
14	7	**7**	Morgado do Reguengo	1056
17	8	**7**	Oitavos	1057
14	7	**7**	Palheiro	1058
14	8	**7**	Pinheiros Altos	1062
14	6	**7**	Quinta da Marinha	1064
15	6	**7**	Quinta do Lago Norte (A + D)	1068
16	6	**7**	Quinta do Lago Sul (B + C)	1069
17	5	**7**	S. Lourenço	1073
14	6	**7**	Vila Sol	1078
17	7	**7**	Vilamoura Old Course	1079
15	7	**7**	Vilamoura Laguna	1080
18	7	**7**	Vilamoura Victoria	1081
14	6	**6**	Carvoeiro Vale da Pinta + Gramacho	1054
14	5	**6**	Palmares	1059
17	6	**6**	Praia d'El Rey	1063
14	6	**5**	Aroeira Aroeira II	1052
15	7	**5**	Belas	1053
15	7	**5**	Estela	1055
17	7	**5**	Quinta da Ria	1065
18	7	**5**	Quinta de Cima	1066
15	7	**5**	Quinta do Peru	1070
16	6	**5**	Santo da Serra	1074
15	5	**4**	Quinta do Brinçal	1067
15	6	**4**	Ribagolfe Green	1071
15	6	**4**	Ribagolfe Blue	1072
17	5	**4**	Troia	1075

RECOMMENDED GOLFING STAY
ESTADIA DE GOLFE RECOMENDADA

Aroeira Aroeira II	**14**	6	5	1052
Oitavos	**17**	8	7	1057
Penha Longa	**16**	6	9	1060
Quinta da Marinha	**14**	6	7	1064
Quinta da Ria	**17**	7	5	1065
Quinta de Cima	**18**	7	5	1066
Quinta do Lago Norte (A + D)	**15**	6	7	1068
Quinta do Lago Sul (B + C)	**16**	6	7	1069
Ribagolfe Blue	**15**	6	4	1071
Ribagolfe Green	**15**	6	4	1072
S. Lourenço	**17**	5	7	1073
Vale do Lobo Ocean Course	**14**	6	8	1076
Vale do Lobo Royal Golf Course	**15**	7	8	1077
Vilamoura Old Course	**17**	7	7	1079
Vilamoura Laguna	**15**	7	7	1080
Vilamoura Victoria	**18**	8	8	1081

RECOMMENDED HOLIDAYS
FÉRIAS RECOMENDADAS

Carvoeiro Vale da Pinta + Gramacho	**14**	6	6	1054
Palheiro	**14**	7	7	1058
Palmares	**14**	5	6	1059
Penina	**15**	7	8	1061
Pinheiros Altos	**14**	8	7	1062
Praia d'El Rey	**17**	6	6	1063
Quinta da Marinha	**14**	6	7	1064
Quinta do Lago Norte (A + D)	**15**	6	7	1068
Quinta do Lago Sul (B + C)	**16**	6	7	1069
S. Lourenço	**17**	5	7	1073
Santo da Serra	**16**	6	5	1074
Vale do Lobo Ocean Course	**14**	6	8	1076
Vale do Lobo Royal Golf Course	**15**	7	8	1077
Vila Sol	**14**	6	7	1078
Vilamoura Old Course	**17**	7	7	1079
Vilamoura Laguna	**15**	7	7	1080
Vilamoura Victoria	**18**	8	8	1081

Aroeira *Aroeira II*

14 | 6 | 5

A primeira impressão é a de um ambiente muito agradável entre pinheiros e flores silvestres, habitat natural de diversos tipos de aves. Sem interferir com esse quadro o arquitecto Frank Pennink realizou há 30 anos um percurso de uma grande franqueza, e com um traçado muito simples. Muito mais tarde seguiu-se-lhe Donald Steel que realizou 18 buracos muito mais americanizados, nomeadamente pela inclusão de alguns obstáculos de água. Tanto num percurso como no outro os jogadores médios e os principiantes sentem-se à vontade, caminha facilmente e os "rough" não são muito penalizantes. Os melhores jogadores, no entanto, podem achá-los um pouco monótonos para jogar muitas vezes, uma vez que lhes faltam verdadeiros desafios, com a excepção do 11, redesenhado por Robert Trent Jones no Aroeira I e do longuíssimo 17 no Aroeira II. Em contrapartida a Aroeira é um local ideal para se jogar uma partida em família ou para uma partida entre amigos.

The first impression is one of a very pleasant setting of pine-trees and wild flowers and the natural habitat for numerous birds. Without spoiling the scenery, architect Frank Pennink laid out a clear and candid course of rather simple design some 30 years ago. Much later Donald Steel stepped in with a much more Americanised flavour and the introduction of water hazards which give the layout a slightly artificial feel. Hazards as a whole are seldom too dangerous. High-handicappers and beginners will feel immediately at home on this friendly and easily walkable course, where the rough and undergrowth are never penalising. The better players might possibly find it boring to play regularly, given the absence of real challenge. Only the 11th hole, redesigned by Robert Trent Jones at Aroeira I and the extra long 17th at Aroeira II stand out from a pretty colourless picture. By contrast, Aroeira is a spot to play with all the family and for giving less experienced players welcome practice.

Clube Golfe Aroeira — 2000

Herdade da Aroeira
P - 2815-207 CHARNECA DA CAPARICA

Office Secretariado (351) 21 - 297 9110
Pro shop Pro-shop (351) 21 - 297 9110
Fax Fax (351) 21 - 297 1238
Web www.aroeira.com
Situation Localização Lisboa, 11 km
Setubal (pop. 89 106), 48 km
Annual closure Fecho anual no
Weekly closure Fecho semanal no
Fees main season Tarifas de época alta 18 holes

	Week days Semana	We/Bank holidays Fim de sem./Feriad
Individual Individual	€ 48	€ 75
Couple Casal	€ 96	€ 150

Juniors: € 16 and € 30 (We)
Caddie Caddie on request **Electric Trolley** Trolley eléctrico no
Buggy Buggy yes **Clubs** Tacos yes
Credit cards Cartão de crédito VISA

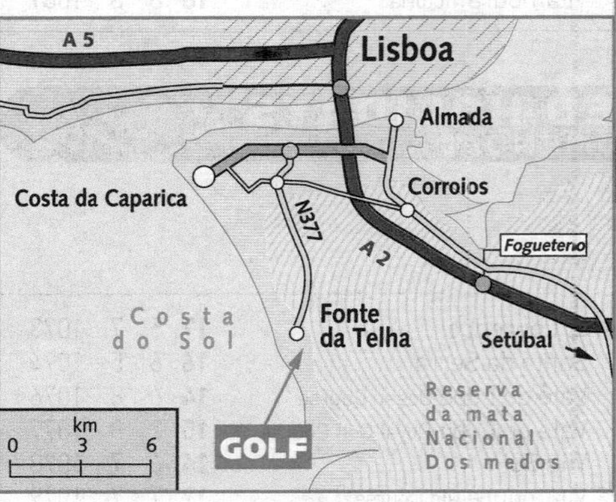

Access Acesso : A2 Lisboa → Setubal, N377 → Caparica, Golf
Map 2 on page 1046 Mapa 2 Página 1046

GOLF COURSE — PERCURSO — 14/20

Site Sitio
Maintenance Conversa
Architect Arquitecto Donald Steel
Type Tipo forest
Relief Relevo
Water in play Lago
Exp. to wind Exposto ao vento
Trees in play Arvores

Scorecard Cartão de resultados	Chp. Camp.	Mens Homens	Ladies Senhoras
Length Compriment	6367	5903	4805
Par	72	72	72
Slope system	130	125	117

Advised golfing ability Nivel de jogo recomendado 0 12 24 36
Hcp required Handicap exigido 36

CLUB HOUSE & AMENITIES — CLUB HOUSE E ANEXOS — 6/10

Pro shop Pro-shop
Driving range Campo de prática
Sheltered coberto 4 mats - On grass om relva yes - Putting-green putting-green yes - Pitching-green pitching-green yes

HOTEL FACILITIES — INFRAESTRUCTURAS HOTELEIRAS — 5/10

HOTELS HOTELS
Costa da Caparica - Caparica 3 km
340 rooms, D € 150
Tel (351) 21 - 291 8900, Fax (351) 21 - 291 0687

Praia do Sol - Caparica 3 km - 54 rooms, D € 70
Tel (351) 21 - 290 0012, Fax (351) 21 - 290 2541

RESTAURANTS RESTAURANTES
Centyonze - São João da Caparica 4 km
Tel (351) 21 - 290 3968
Maniés - Caparica 3 km - Tel (351) 21 - 290 3398

Belas

15	7	5

Belas está próxima de Lisboa, mas também do Palácio de Queluz, uma espécie de pequeno Versailles, com laivos de «rococo», alternando os quartos íntimos com as salas de aparato, tudo rodeado de magníficos jardins... Não se encontrará em Belas um gosto tão ostensivo na decoração. A essência de um percurso de golf não reside verdadeiramente no luxo nem na simetria dos jardins â francesa. O Arquitecto Rocky Roquemore moldou o seu traçado num terreno bastante aberto e muito acidentado onde temos o direito de preferir jogar com um "buggy" (pode dizer que é por causa do Sol). Devido a certos aspectos visuais e técnicos, pelo tipo de jogo que é necessário desenvolver, Belas pode lembrar Pevero ou Is Molas. Em todo o caso é pêlos seus desafios que representa um bom futuro percurso de campeonato, ao ponto que os "handicaps" mais elevados terão sem duvida alguma dificuldade em retirar um enorme prazer em jogá-lo. Trata-se sobretudo de um bom conjunto de buracos mas com deficiências ao nível da sequência.

Belas is close to the Castle of Queluz, a sort of smaller style Versailles with a touch of rococo and alternating small chambers and huge state rooms, all surrounded by superb gardens. You won't find such an ostentatious taste for decoration at Belas, as the essence of a golf course is neither sheer luxury nor the symmetry of French style gardens. The architect has laid out this course over rather open, rolling terrain where you have every right to prefer playing with a buggy (say it is because of the sun). Through certain visual and technical aspects and the type of game you need to produce, Belas is reminiscent of Pevero or Is Molas. Whatever, given the challenges here this has to be a future excellent championship course, even if that means it not always being too much fun for high-handicappers. The course unwinds agreeably with a nice balance of all kinds of hazard. This is undoubtedly a good course even though certain sequences of holes leave a little to be desired.

Clube de Golfe de Belas — 1997

Alameda do Aqueduto – Belas Clube de Campo
P - 2605-199 BELAS

Office	Secretariado	(351) 21 - 962 6640
Pro shop	Pro-shop	(351) 21 - 962 6640
Fax	Fax	(351) 21 - 962 6641
Web	www.belasgolf.com	
Situation	Localização	Lisboa, 18 km
Annual closure	Fecho anual	no
Weekly closure	Fecho semanal	no

Fees main season Tarifas de época alta	Week days Semana	We/Bank holidays Fim de sem./Feriad
18 holes		
Individual Individual	€ 75	€ 86
Couple Casal	€ 150	€ 172

Caddie Caddie no — **Electric Trolley** Trolley eléctrico no
Buggy Buggy yes — **Clubs** Tacos yes
Credit cards Cartão de crédito
VISA - Mastercard - DC

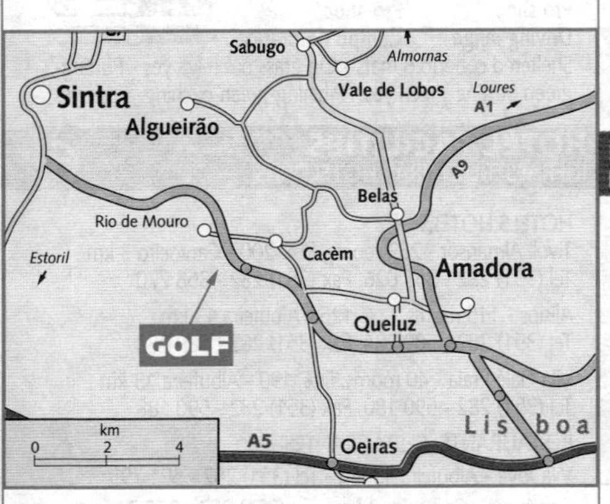

Access Acesso : Lisboa, N 117 → Sintra/Queluz and Belas. Follow signs to Golf.
Map 2 on page 1046 Mapa 2 Página 1046

GOLF COURSE — PERCURSO 15/20

Site	Sitio	
Maintenance	Conversa	
Architect	Arquitecto	Rocky Roquemore
Type	Tipo	open country, hilly
Relief	Relevo	
Water in play	Lago	
Exp. to wind	Exposto ao vento	
Trees in play	Arvores	

Scorecard Cartão de resultados	Chp. Camp.	Mens Homens	Ladies Senhoras
Length Compriment	6380	6065	4995
Par	72	72	72
Slope system	123	119	116

Advised golfing ability Nivel de jogo recomendado — 0 12 24 36
Hcp required Handicap exigido — 28 Men/36 Ladies

CLUB HOUSE & AMENITIES — CLUB HOUSE E ANEXOS 7/10

Pro shop Pro-shop
Driving range Campo de prática
Sheltered coberto no - On grass om relva yes - Putting-green putting-green yes - Pitching-green pitching-green yes

HOTEL FACILITIES — INFRAESTRUCTURAS HOTELEIRAS 5/10

HOTELS HOTELS
Pousada D. Maria I. - 26 rooms, D € 182 - Queluz 8 km
Tel (351) 21 - 435 6158, Fax (351) 21 - 435 6189

Palacio de Seteais - 30 rooms, D € 310 - Sintra 12 km
Tel (351) 21 - 923 3200, Fax (351) 21 - 923 4277

Tivoli Sintra - 76 rooms, D € 140 - Sintra 12 km
Tel (351) 21 923 7200, Fax (351) 21 923 7245

RESTAURANTS RESTAURANTES
Cozinha Velha - Queluz 8 km - Tel (351) 21 - 435 6158
Tacho Real - Sintra 12 km - Tel (351) 219 - 235 277
Cantinho de São Pedro - Sintra 12 km
Tel (351) 21 - 923 0267

Carvoeiro *Vale da Pinta + Gramacho*

14	6	6

Muito ondulados, mas não deixam de ser fáceis para jogar a pé. Estes percursos foram desenhado pelo Americano Ronald Fream. Os que conhecem o seu estilo poderão julgar que ele aqui não foi tão exigente para os golfistas como em outros locais. Visivelmente manteve o espirito de que são sobretudo turistas de nível de jogo médio que visitam a região. Para mais, quis preservar a natureza do terreno e portanto não abusou dos obstáculos de água. Os "greens" são bastante profundos e requerem jogadas de boa precisão nos "approaches." Estão razoavelmente defendidos, o que acentua e realça a relação "amigável" que se obtém em contacto com o percurso. As saídas múltiplas permitem adaptá-los a todos os níveis de jogo e a serem divertidos sem se ter a sensação de serem um percursos demasiado fáceis. Os melhores jogadores ficarão talvez "aguados" por mais dificuldades. A propósito, durante o passeio e poder-se-ão admirar belas oliveiras, algumas com mais de 700 anos; existe um exemplar que se calcula que tenha 1200 anos ; se pudesse contar-nos a sua vida....

This slightly hilly but nonetheless easily walkable course was designed by Ronald Fream. Those of you who know his style might consider that he has been less demanding here than elsewhere, and visibly he bore in mind the fact that primarily mid-to-high handicappers visit the region on holiday. He also set out to preserve the natural look of the terrain and did not overdo the water hazards. The greens are rather deep and call for accurate approach shots, but they are reasonably defended, a fact that underlines the friendly feeling you get with this course. The many different tee-areas suit the course to all players, who can enjoy themselves without feeling that this is just a walk-over, but the best might want more than this. In passing, a word of admiration for the beautiful olive-trees, some of which are over 700 years old. One is even 1200 years old and its life-story would make interesting reading.

Carvoeiro Golfe — 1992

Apartado 1011
P - 8401-908 CARVOEIRO

Office	Secretariado	(351) 282 - 340 900
Pro shop	Pro-shop	(351) 282 - 340 900
Fax	Fax	(351) 282 - 340 901
Web	www.pestanagolf.com	
Situation	Localização	Carvoeiro, 13 km

Faro (pop. 33 664), 42 km

Annual closure	Fecho anual	no
Weekly closure	Fecho semanal	no
Fees main season	Tarifas de época alta	18 holes

	Week days Semana	We/Bank holidays Fim de sem./Feriad
Individual Individual	€ 90	€ 90
Couple Casal	€ 180	€ 180

Juniors: – 50%

Caddie Caddie no — **Electric Trolley** Trolley eléctrico no

Buggy Buggy yes — **Clubs** Tacos yes

Credit cards Cartão de crédito
VISA - AMEX - DC

Access Acesso : N125 Lagos-Faro. Lagoa → Carvoeiro
Map 3 on page 1048 Mapa 3 Página 1048

GOLF COURSE — PERCURSO — 14/20

Site	Sitio	
Maintenance	Conversa	
Architect	Arquitecto	Ronald Fream
Type	Tipo	inland, residential
Relief	Relevo	
Water in play	Lago	
Exp. to wind	Exposto ao vento	
Trees in play	Arvores	

Scorecard Cartão de resultados	Chp. Camp.	Mens Homens	Ladies Senhoras
Length Compriment	6115	5662	4860
Par	71	71	71
Slope system	123	119	118

Advised golfing ability Nivel de jogo recomendado — 0 12 24 36

Hcp required Handicap exigido — 28 Men, 36 Ladies

CLUB HOUSE & AMENITIES — CLUB HOUSE E ANEXOS — 6/10

Pro shop	Pro-shop
Driving range	Campo de prática

Sheltered coberto 6 mats - On grass om relva yes - Putting-green putting-green yes - Pitching-green pitching-green yes

HOTEL FACILITIES — INFRAESTRUCTURAS HOTELEIRAS — 6/10

HOTELS HOTELS

Tivoli Almansor - 289 rooms, D € 200 - Carvoeiro 3 km
Tel (351) 282 - 358 026, Fax (351) 282 - 358 770

Alisios - 115 rooms, D € 125 - Albufeira 13 km
Tel (351) 282 - 589 284, Fax (351) 282 - 589 288

Vila Galé Praia - 40 rooms, D € 190 - Albufeira 13 km
Tel (351) 282 - 590 180, Fax (351) 282 - 590 188

RESTAURANTS RESTAURANTES

Vila Joya - Albufeira 13 km - Tel (351) 282 - 591 795
Centianes - Carvoeiro 3 km - Tel (351) 282 - 358 724
O Cabaz do Praia - Albufeira 13 km - Tel (351) 289 - 512 137

Estela

15 | 7 | 5

Estamos na Costa Verde, um local ideal para Duarte Sottomayor ter podido homenagear os "Links" britânicos. Essa ilusão reforça-se no Inverno quando o vento e a chuva nos gelam os ossos e mesmo no verão quando o sol e a calma tornam o percurso muito mais agradável. As grandes diferenças estão no tipo de relva, "Bermuda" que não oferece as mesmas características das "festucas" escocesas e na ausência de pancadas cegas. As dificuldades porem aqui não faltam (com dois lagos) tem de jogar-se o percurso diversas vezes para entender certos buracos. Não é difícil que isso aconteça uma vez que é o único grande percurso nesta região do país. A estratégia é simples, importa principalmente manter a bola nos "fairways" pois as dunas reservam algumas situações delicadas e o ataque aos "greens", de dimensões médias, pode apresentar-se difícil mesmo sem eles estarem muito defendidos. Como nota menos positiva, salientam-se a qualidade dos bunkers e uma certa falta de largueza o que sem duvida limitou as possibilidades do arquitecto.

Duarte Sottomayor paid his own tribute to British links golfing. The illusion can appear even more real in winter, when the cold and wind freeze you to the bone, and even in summer, when the sun and calm conditions make the course a friendlier proposition. The major difference lies with the grass which golf-wise has nothing in common with Scottish fescue grass, and with the absence of blind shots. There is no shortage of difficulties, though, and you will need to play several rounds in order to appreciate some of the holes. That won't be too much to ask as this is the only top course in this part of Portugal. Strategy is simple, the most important thing being to stay in the fairway, as the dunes can land you in some very sticky situations and the second shot into the medium-sized but not unduly protected greens can pose a problem or two. On the downside, we noted the only very average quality of bunkering and a certain lack of space, which limited the potential left open to the architect.

Estela Golf Club — 1988

Lugar Rio Alto - Estela
P - 4490 PÓVOA DO VARZIM

Office	Secretariado	(351) 252 - 601 567
Pro shop	Pro-shop	(351) 252 - 601 567
Fax	Fax	(351) 252 - 612 701
Web	www.estelagolf.pt	
Situation	Localização	Porto, 46 km

Póvoa do Varzim, 10 km

Annual closure	Fecho anual	no
Weekly closure	Fecho semanal	no
Fees main season	Tarifas de época alta	18 holes

	Week days / Semana	We/Bank holidays / Fim de sem./Feriad
Individual Individual	€ 50	€ 75
Couple Casal	€ 100	€ 150

Caddie Caddie no — **Electric Trolley** Trolley eléctrico no
Buggy Buggy yes — **Clubs** Tacos yes
Credit cards Cartão de crédito
VISA - Mastercard - AMEX

Access Acesso : IC1 Porto, EN13 → Esposende, → Praia da Apúlia
Map 1 on page 1044 Mapa 1 Página 1044

GOLF COURSE — PERCURSO 15/20

Site	Sitio	
Maintenance	Conversa	
Architect	Arquitecto	Duarte Sottomayor
Type	Tipo	seaside course, links
Relief	Relevo	
Water in play	Lago	
Exp. to wind	Exposto ao vento	
Trees in play	Arvores	

Scorecard Cartão de resultados	Chp. Camp.	Mens Homens	Ladies Senhoras
Length Compriment	6155	5878	5268
Par	72	72	72
Slope system	131	128	134

Advised golfing ability Nivel de jogo recomendado — 0 12 24 36
Hcp required Handicap exigido — certificate

CLUB HOUSE & AMENITIES — CLUB HOUSE E ANEXOS 7/10

Pro shop Pro-shop
Driving range Campo de prática
Sheltered coberto no - On grass om relva yes - Putting-green putting-green yes - Pitching-green pitching-green yes

HOTEL FACILITIES — INFRAESTRUCTURAS HOTELEIRAS 5/10

HOTELS HOTELS

Estalagem Estela Sol - 35 rooms, D € 60 - Estela 3 km
Tel (351) 252 600 050, Fax (351) 252 600 051

Novotel Vermar - 208 rooms, D € 100 - Póvoa do Varzim 8 km
Tel (351) 252 298 900, Fax (351) 252 298 901

Mercure Póvoa do Varzim - Póvoa do Varzim 8 km
86 rooms, D€ 65
Tel (351) 252 290 400, Fax (351) 252 290 401

RESTAURANTS RESTAURANTES

A Lareira - Fão 16 km - Tel (351) 253 981 588

O Marinheiro - Povoa de Varzim 8 km
Tel (351) 252 - 682 151

Assador Mirandes - Póvoa do Varzim 8 km
Tel (351) 252 615 922

Morgado do Reguengo

14	7	7

O Campo de Golfe do Morgado do Reguengo, o ultimo a ser construído no Algarve. Está localizado numa das mais belas propriedades da região, acerca de 6 km da Praia da Rocha, entre Portimão e Lagos. Está rodeado de terrenos agrícolas que incluem vinhas, figueiras e outras espécies típicas do Algarve. O local prestar-se-ia para realizar um magnífico trabalho, no entanto apesar das condições naturais, o campo não é tão interessante como podia, uma vez que apesar de se encontrar numa das maiores propriedades do Algarve foi construído com algum aperto. Tratando-se de um campo recente é natural que com a maturação venha a melhorar bastante. O club-house é muito agradável e de traça simples e moderna. As facilidades de prática também são de óptima qualidade. O campo destina-se principalmente a jogadores de todos os níveis, mas os jogadores compridos terão aqui uma vantagem devido a ser bastante comprido dos "tees" de trás e para alem disso requerer saídas bem colocadas. O ambiente é magnífico e muito tranquilo, podendo ter-se vistas muito agradáveis da Serra de Monchique.

Morgado do Reguengo is the latest course to be built in the Algarve. The site is one of the finest in the region located 6km from Praia da Rocha, between Portimão and Lagos. It is surrounded by farm land which includes vineyards, fig trees and other typically indigenous species. The site deserved a wonderful course but despite the natural conditions the course is not as interesting as it could have been. Although located on one of the larger properties in the Algarve, it was squeezed into a narrow stretch of land. But this is a young course and will probably improve when it matures. The club-house is very pleasant, natural and modern. The practice facilities are also excellent. The course can be played by players of all levels but long hitters will hold the advantage because from the back tees you need to hit straight and a long way.

Morgado do Reguengo Golfe — 2003

Apartado 293
P - 8501-912 PORTIMÃO

Office	Secretariado	(351) 282 - 402 150
Pro shop	Pro-shop	(351) 282 - 402 152
Fax	Fax	(351) 282 - 402 153
E-mail	playgolf@golfedomorgado.com	
Situation	Localização	Lagos, 23 km
Annual closure	Fecho anual	no
Weekly closure	Fecho semanal	no

Fees main season Tarifas de época alta	18 holes	
	Week days Semana	**We/Bank holidays** Fim de sem./Feriad
Individual Individual	€ 80	€ 80
Couple Casal	€ 160	€ 160

Caddie Caddie no — **Electric Trolley** Trolley eléctrico yes
Buggy Buggy yes — **Clubs** Tacos yes
Credit cards Cartão de crédito
VISA - MasterCard - AMEX

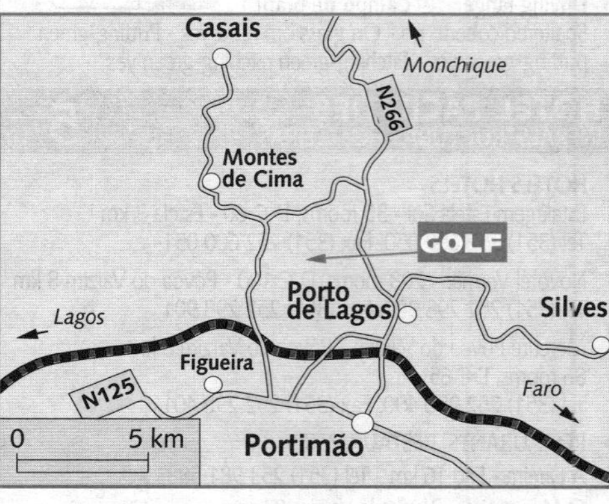

Access Acesso : Faro, Via do Infante to Portimão. Turn right on N124 → Manchique. Golf 2 km on left hand side.
Map 3 on page 1048 Mapa 3 Página 1048

GOLF COURSE — PERCURSO — 14/20

Site	Sitio	
Maintenance	Conversa	
Architect	Arquitecto	Russell Talley European Golf Design
Type	Tipo	inland
Relief	Relevo	
Water in play	Lago	
Exp. to wind	Exposto ao vento	
Trees in play	Arvores	

Scorecard Cartão de resultados	**Chp.** Camp.	**Mens** Homens	**Ladies** Senhoras
Length Compriment	6399	5857	4824
Par	73	73	73
Slope system	—	—	—

Advised golfing ability Nivel de jogo recomendado — 0 12 24 36
Hcp required Handicap exigido yes

CLUB HOUSE & AMENITIES — CLUB HOUSE E ANEXOS — 7/10

Pro shop Pro-shop
Driving range Campo de prática
Sheltered coberto - On grass om relva no, 25 mats open air - Putting-green putting-green yes - Pitching-green pitching-green yes

HOTEL FACILITIES — INFRAESTRUCTURAS HOTELEIRAS — 7/10

HOTELS HOTELS
Bela Vista - 14 rooms, D € 115 - Praia da Rocha 7 km
Tel (351) 282 - 450 480, Fax (351) 282 - 415 369

Casabela Hotel - Vale de Areia (P. da Rocha) 7 km
63 rooms, D € 165
Tel (351) 282 - 461 580, Fax (351) 282 - 461 581

Pestana Don João II Village - Alvor (Altenfeld) 10 km
352 rooms, D € 200
Tel (351) 282 - 400 700, Fax (351) 282 - 400 799

RESTAURANTS RESTAURANTES
O Bicho - Portimão 5 km - Tel (351) 282 - 422 977
Por do Sol - Portimão 5 km - Tel (351) 282 - 459 505
Titanic - Portimão 5 km - Tel (351) 282 - 422 371

Oitavos

17	8	7

Trata-se de um bom percurso, localizado junto à costa perto de Cascais na antiga Quinta da Marinha, vizinho de outro já existente, propriedade de outra empresa. Depois de haver na zona um Trent Jones é Arthur Hills que foi encarregue do desenho deste percurso. A localização é muito interessante, muito próxima do Mar com belas vistas da Serra. Está bastante exposto ao vento o que vai complicar a tarefa dos jogadores. Porem, havendo bastante paralelismo no desenho, todo o vento contra passa a ser a favor sem que haja muita diferença. O solo arenoso e as ondulações próprias desse tipo de terrenos bem como a sobriedade do desenho de Hills conferem ao local um carácter menos americano do que se poderia imaginar. Só algumas depressões fazem figura de obstáculos de água. Os jogadores pouco experimentados ou mesmo médios terão certamente dificuldade em fazerem aqui bons resultados, ou mesmo em ultrapassar as subtilezas do desenho. Aconselha-se que joguem preferencialmente em "Match Play" o que será menos mortal para os seus "Ego".

This good course located at Quinta da Marinha is a neighbour to the other well-known layout that belongs to another company. Here too, they went for an American architect. After Robert Trent Jones, Arthur Hills was assigned with the architecture and this was his first course in Europe. It is an interesting site, very close to the sea but with some pleasant views over the mountains behind. It has also been very well maintained. The course is rather exposed to the wind but as the holes often run up and down, any headwind will always become a tailwind with very few subtle changes of direction. The sandy soil, measured slopes and general sobriety of Hills' design give the course a slightly less American character than one might have imagined, with only a few ditches serving as water hazards. Inexperienced or average players will almost certainly find this tough going, so match play should be the order of the day to avoid too many bruised egos.

Oitavos Golfe 2001

Casa da Quinta, 25 - Qta da Marinha
P - 2750-715 CASCAIS

Office Secretariado (351) 214 - 860 600
Pro shop Pro-shop (351) 214 - 860 000
Fax Fax (351) 214 - 860 906
Web www.quintadamarinha-oitavosgolfe.pt
Situation Localização Lisboa , 26 km
Cascais (pop. 29 882), 6 km

Annual closure Fecho anual no

Weekly closure Fecho semanal no

Fees main season Tarifas de época alta	18 holes	
	Week days Semana	**We/Bank holidays** Fim de sem./Feriad
Individual Individual	€ 90	€ 150
Couple Casal	€ 180	€ 300

Special fees for juniors

Caddie Caddie on request **Electric Trolley** Trolley eléctrico yes
Buggy Buggy yes **Clubs** Tacos yes

Credit cards Cartão de crédito
VISA - AMEX

Access Acesso : Lisboa A5 → Cascais, N 247 → Praia do Guincho, Golf just after Quinta da Marinha.
Map 2 on page 1046 Mapa 2 Página 1046

GOLF COURSE
PERCURSO — **17**/20

Site Sitio
Maintenance Conversa
Architect Arquitecto — Arthur Hills
Type Tipo — seaside course, open country

Relief Relevo
Water in play Lago
Exp. to wind Exposto ao vento
Trees in play Arvores

Scorecard Cartão de resultados	**Chp.** Camp.	**Mens** Homens	**Ladies** Senhoras
Length Compriment	6379	5947	4573
Par	71	71	71
Slope system	134	128	121

Advised golfing ability Nivel de jogo recomendado — 0 12 24 36
Hcp required Handicap exigido 36

CLUB HOUSE & AMENITIES
CLUB HOUSE E ANEXOS — **8**/10

Pro shop Pro-shop
Driving range Campo de prática
Sheltered coberto no - On grass om relva yes - Putting-green putting-green yes - Pitching-green pitching-green yes

HOTEL FACILITIES
INFRAESTRUCTURAS HOTELEIRAS — **7**/10

HOTELS HOTELS
Fortaleza do Guincho - Praia do Guincho 3 km
27 rooms, D € 265
Tel (351) 214 - 870 491, Fax (351) 214 - 870 431

Casa da Pergola - 10 rooms, D € 100 - Cascais 4 km
Tel (351) 214 - 820 040, Fax (351) 214 - 834 791

Estalagem Senhora da Guia - 43 rooms, D € 250 - Cascais 3 km
Tel (351) 214 869 239, Fax (351) 214 - 869 227

RESTAURANTS RESTAURANTES
Casa Velha - Cascais 4 km - Tel (351) 214 - 832 586
Verbasco - Cascais 4 km - Tel (351) 214 - 860 606
Porto de Santa Maria - Praia do Guincho 3 km
Tel (351) 214 - 870 240

Palheiro

14 | 7 | 7

Este percurso está localizado muito perto da Quinta do Palheiro Ferreiro, vasta mansão rodeada de um parque à inglesa com milhares de flores raras e de árvores exóticas. Do golf tem-se magnificas vistas sobre o Funchal e a costa sul da Madeira, 800 metros mais abaixo. Esta situação de um golf de montanha, tem a vantagem de ser dominante e exótica, tem o inconveniente de apresentar desníveis dificeis de aguentar a pé durante 18 buracos. A tarefa do arquitecto Cabell Robinson não era das mais fáceis. Não foi capaz de evitar por isso algumas pancadas cegas. Para alem disso encontram-se aqui alguns buracos sem grande interesse, sem duvida devido a falta de espaço, mas tambêm alguns buracos esplendidos. São tanto "tricky" como espectaculares, acessivel a todos os niveis, este percurso não deixará ninguém indiferente e criará lembranças tanto gloriosas como visuais... sobretudo quando os carrinhos evitam o cansaço fisico.

This course is located close to "la Quinta do Palheiro Ferreiro", a huge house surrounded by English-style gardens with thousands of rare flowers and exotic trees. From the course you get some superb vistas over Funchal and the southern coast of Madeira, 800 metres further down. This sort of mountainous golf course location has the advantage of being dominant; the downside is the steep sloping terrain which for 18 holes of golf is tough going on foot. The job of Cabell Robinson was anything but easy, and not surprisingly he was unable to avoid a few blind shots. In fact, there are a few holes here that offer no real appeal probably because of the lack of space. There are, however, some splendid holes to make up for it. Tricky and spectacular and playable by all, this course won't leave you indifferent but will give some great memories both visually and for the golf you played, especially when taking a buggy to avoid what is a very tiring walk.

Palheiro Golfe — 1994

Sitio do Balançal - S. Gonçalo
P - 9050-296 FUNCHAL - MADEIRA

Office	Secretariado	(351) 291 - 790 120
Pro shop	Pro-shop	(351) 291 - 792 116
Fax	Fax	(351) 291 - 792 116
Web	www.palheirogolf.com	
Situation	Localização	Funchal, 8 km
Annual closure	Fecho anual	no
Weekly closure	Fecho semanal	no
Fees main season	Tarifas de época alta	18 holes

	Week days Semana	We/Bank holidays Fim de sem./Feriad
Individual Individual	€ 77	€ 77
Couple Casal	€ 154	€ 154

Caddie Caddie no — **Electric Trolley** Trolley eléctrico no
Buggy Buggy yes — **Clubs** Tacos yes
Credit cards Cartão de crédito
VISA - MasterCard

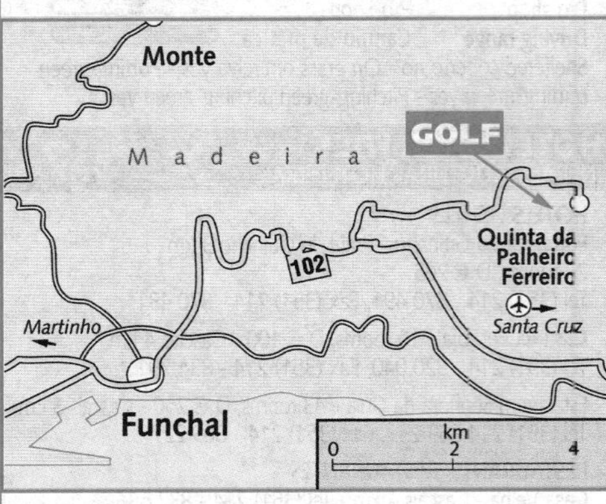

Access Acesso : Funchal, → Airport.
Leave at Camacha, follow the signs.
Map 3 on page 1049 Mapa 3 Página 1049

GOLF COURSE — PERCURSO — 14/20

Site	Sitio	
Maintenance	Conversa	
Architect	Arquitecto	Cabell B. Robinson
Type	Tipo	mountain
Relief	Relevo	
Water in play	Lago	
Exp. to wind	Exposto ao vento	
Trees in play	Arvores	

Scorecard Cartão de resultados	Chp. Camp.	Mens Homens	Ladies Senhoras
Length Compriment	6022	5847	4921
Par	71	71	71
Slope system	—	—	—

Advised golfing ability Nivel de jogo recomendado — 0 12 24 36
Hcp required Handicap exigido 36

CLUB HOUSE & AMENITIES — CLUB HOUSE E ANEXOS — 7/10

Pro shop Pro-shop
Driving range Campo de prática
Sheltered coberto no - On grass om relva no - Putting-green putting-green yes - Pitching-green pitching-green yes

HOTEL FACILITIES — INFRAESTRUCTURAS HOTELEIRAS — 7/10

HOTELS HOTELS
Reids - 164 rooms, D € 520 - Funchal 8 km
Tel (351) 291 - 717 171, Fax (351) 291 - 717 177

Estal. Casa Velha do Palheiro
37 rooms, D € 180 - Funchal (Estrada de Camacha) 8 km
Tel (351) 291 - 790 350, Fax (351) 291 - 794 925

Estalag. Quintina de São João - Funchal 8 km
43 rooms, D € 135
Tel (351) 291 - 740 920, Fax (351) 291 - 740 928

RESTAURANTS RESTAURANTES
Casa Velha - Funchal 8 km - Tel (351) 291 - 205 600
Quinta Palmeira - Funchal 8 km - Tel (351) 291 - 221 814
A Morgadinha (Es. Quintina) - Funchal - Tel (351) 291 - 740 920

Palmares

14	5	6

Como alguns dos percursos portugueses mais antigos foi desenhado por Frank Pennink. Desenvolve-se a partir de dois espaços diferentes: cinco buracos são à beira mar, com uma arquitectura que faz lembrar um "links", os outros estão construídos entre pinheiros em zonas muito mais acidentados e com magníficas vistas sobre o Atlântico. Os buracos de borda de água constituem o encanto e o interesse principal deste percurso que para alem disso tem um desenho demasiado simples. Alguns "drives" podem causar problemas mas os golfistas de diversos níveis não encontrarão muitas dificuldades para além das criadas pelo seu próprio jogo. Os "greens" são muito rudimentares, bastante pequenos e pouco defendidos. Nesta bela paisagem seria de mau gosto estragar o prazer! Se este percurso não dá para maravilhar pela sua qualidade, não deixa de ser muito agradável para se passar uma tarde em família ou com um grupo de amigos ainda que de níveis de golf diferentes, sobretudo pela magnificas vistas que se conseguem de diversos locais.

Like many courses in Portugal, Palmares was designed by Frank Pennink using two different sorts of space: five holes run along the seashore in true links style, the others are laid out amidst a much hillier pine forest with some magnificent views over the Atlantic. The seaboard holes give the course its basic charm and appeal, as otherwise the design is fairly simple. Some tee-shots can cause problems, but apart from those arising from the state of your game there are no real difficulties here, however good or bad the player. The greens are very simple, smallish and wide open. In such pretty countryside it would have been in very poor taste to make life too difficult. This course might not be over-exciting, but it is great fun to play with the family or friends, whatever their ability, mainly on account of the magnificent views from different parts of the course.

Palmares Golf — **1976**

Apartado 74 - Meia Praia
P - 8601-901 LAGOS

Office	Secretariado	0 5008 959
Pro shop	Pro-shop	(351) 282 - 790 500
Fax	Fax	(351) 282 - 790 509
Web	www.palmaresgolf.com	
Situation	Localização	Lagos, 6 km

Portimão (pop. 21 196), 15 km

Annual closure	Fecho anual	no
Weekly closure	Fecho semanal	no
Fees main season	Tarifas de época alta	18 holes

	Week days Semana	We/Bank holidays Fim de sem./Feriad
Individual Individual	€ 83	€ 83
Couple Casal	€ 166	€ 166

Caddie Caddie no — **Electric Trolley** Trolley eléctrico yes
Buggy Buggy yes — **Clubs** Tacos yes
Credit cards Cartão de crédito
VISA - AMEX

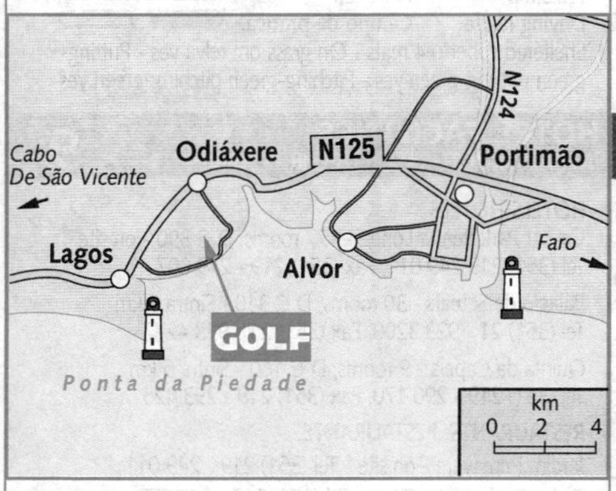

Access Acesso : N125 Portimão → Sagres, → Meia Praia
Map 3 on page 1048 Mapa 3 Página 1048

GOLF COURSE
PERCURSO — 14/20

Site	Sitio	
Maintenance	Conversa	
Architect	Arquitecto	Frank Pennink
Type	Tipo	seaside course, inland
Relief	Relevo	
Water in play	Lago	
Exp. to wind	Exposto ao vento	
Trees in play	Arvores	

Scorecard Cartão de resultados	**Chp.** Camp.	**Mens** Homens	**Ladies** Senhoras
Length Compriment	5961	5614	5020
Par	71	71	71
Slope system	117	113	116

Advised golfing ability Nivel de jogo recomendado — 0 12 24 36
Hcp required Handicap exigido — 28 Men, 36 Ladies

CLUB HOUSE & AMENITIES
CLUB HOUSE E ANEXOS — 5/10

Pro shop Pro-shop
Driving range Campo de prática
Sheltered coberto no - On grass om relva yes - Putting-green putting-green yes - Pitching-green pitching-green no

HOTEL FACILITIES
INFRAESTRUCTURAS HOTELEIRAS — 6/10

HOTELS HOTELS
Tivoli Lagos - 324 rooms, D € 120 - Lagos 5 km
Tel (351) 282 - 790 000, Fax (351) 282 - 790 345

Pestana Alvor Praia - Praia dos Tres Imãos 7 km
195 rooms, D € 300
Tel (351) 282 - 400 900, Fax (351) 282 - 400 999

Marina Rio - 36 rooms, D € 95- Lagos 14 km
Tel (351) 282 - 769 859, Fax (351) 282 - 769 960

RESTAURANTS RESTAURANTES
Dom Sebastião - Lagos 5 km - Tel (351) 282 - 762 795
O Galeão - Lagos 5 km - Tel (351) 282 - 763 909

Penha Longa

16	6	9

Implantado num belo local histórico, recheado com vestígios do passado, é um dos bons percursos que se construíram na região. O desenho de Robert Trent Jones Júnior é muito imaginativo e seduzirá principalmente os bons jogadores que deverão saber ultrapassar com habilidade os numerosos obstáculos que se lhes deparam. Para alem do terreno acidentado que oferece belas vistas do mar e da serra, o comprimento do percurso, o vento que por vezes se faz sentir e a sua variedade exigem um jogo muito complete desde as pancadas de saída, e até se atingir os "greens". Estes são de boa dimensão e bem modelados. Os jogadores menos habilitados poderão escolher jogar dos "tees" mais avançadas para poderem retirar do jogo um máximo de prazer. É certo que as dificuldades subsistem, mas se não derem demasiada importância ao seu "score" terão muitas ocasiões de exercer a sua destreza, ou mesmo de progredir num percurso exigente, sobretudo depois de terem feito a "mão" nalgum dos percursos mais fáceis existentes na região.

In a beautiful historical site dotted with vestiges from the past, this is one of the better courses that have been opened in the region. The very imaginative design of Robert Trent Jones Jr. will primarily appeal to very good players, who will need all their skills to negotiate the numerous hazards and the steep hills that provide some beautiful views over the sea and mountain. The length – often compounded by a strong wind – and the variety of the course demand a good, all-round game from tee to green, most of the latter being large and well contoured. Lesser players will play from the front tees to really enjoy themselves. The difficulties are still there, of course, but if they don't pay too much attention to dropped strokes, average golfers will have opportunities enough to exercise their skills and even make progress on a demanding course. This is a good test after getting warmed up on some of the easier courses in the region. Maintenance is generally good. A number of top tournaments have been played here.

Penha Longa Hotel & Golf Resort — 1994

Estrada da Lagoa Azul - Linhó
P - 2714-511 SINTRA

Office	Secretariado	(351) 219 - 249 031
Pro shop	Pro-shop	(351) 219 - 249 011
Fax	Fax	(351) 219 - 249 024
Web	www.penhalonga.com	
Situation	Localização	Lisboa, 25 km

Sintra (pop. 33 664), 2 km

Annual closure	Fecho anual	no
Weekly closure	Fecho semanal	no

Fees main season Tarifas de época alta	**Week days** Semana	**We/Bank holidays** Fim de sem./Feriac
		18 holes
Individual Individual	€ 89	€ 110
Couple Casal	€ 178	€ 220

Special fees for Hotel guests

Caddie Caddie no — **Electric Trolley** Trolley eléctrico yes
Buggy Buggy yes — **Clubs** Tacos yes

Credit cards Cartão de crédito
VISA - Mastercard - AMEX

Serra de Sintra
Sintra
GOLF
N 249
Alcabideche
Estoril
10
9
A 5
Lisboa
N6
Cascais
Oeiras
Costa do Estoril
km
0 2 4

Access Acesso : N9 Estoril → Sintra, → Lagon Azul

Map 2 on page 1046 Mapa 2 Página 1046

GOLF COURSE — PERCURSO — 16/20

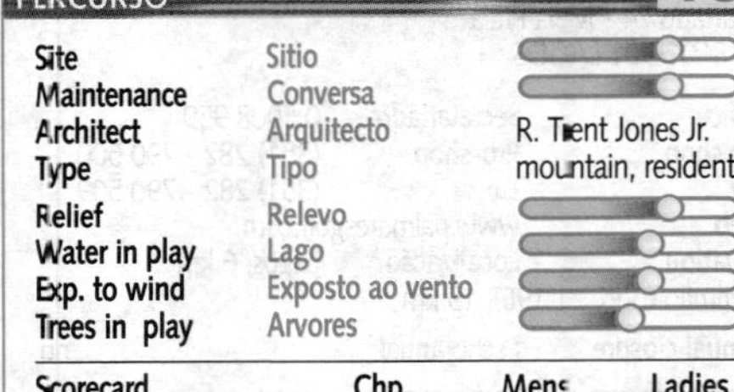

Site	Sitio	
Maintenance	Conversa	
Architect	Arquitecto	R. Trent Jones Jr.
Type	Tipo	mountain, residential
Relief	Relevo	
Water in play	Lago	
Exp. to wind	Exposto ao vento	
Trees in play	Arvores	

Scorecard Cartão de resultados	**Chp.** Camp.	**Mens** Homens	**Ladies** Senhoras
Length Compriment	6313	5944	5092
Par	72	72	72
Slope system	119	115	123

Advised golfing ability Nivel de jogo recomendado — 0 12 24 36

Hcp required Handicap exigido — yes

CLUB HOUSE & AMENITIES — CLUB HOUSE E ANEXOS — 6/10

Pro shop Pro-shop
Driving range Campo de prática
Sheltered coberto 4 mats - On grass om relva yes - Putting-green putting-green yes - Pitching-green pitching-green yes

HOTEL FACILITIES — INFRAESTRUCTURAS HOTELEIRAS — 9/10

HOTELS HOTELS

Caesar Park Penha Longa - 177 rooms, D € 390 - on site
Tel (351) 219 249 011, Fax (351) 219 - 249 007

Palacio de Seteais - 30 rooms, D € 310 - Sintra 5 km
Tel (351) 21 - 923 3200, Fax (351) 21 - 923 4277

Quinta da Capela - 9 rooms, D € 160 - Sintra 5 km
Tel (351) 219 - 290 170, Fax (351) 219 - 293 425

RESTAURANTS RESTAURANTES

Jardim Primavera - on site - Tel (351) 219 - 249 011
Tacho Real - Sintra 5 km - Tel (351) 219 - 235 277
Lawrence's - Sintra 5 km - Tel (351) 219 - 105 500

Penina

15	7	8

Trata-se do primeiro Campo de Golfe do Algarve. No decorrer do tempo, sofreu alguns melhoramentos mas sem grandes modificações. Continua a ser um percurso longo e difícil jogado dos "Tees" de campeonato. Torna-se, porém mais acessível dos "Tees" normais. É um percurso bastante plano, tendo algumas árvores que agora já são de grande porte, a dificultar as pancadas que não chegam no entanto a ser "perigosas". O seu traçado salienta-se por número razoável de "bunkers" com bom desenho mas sem características especiais parassinalar. A sua colocação sugere um estilo britânico que se torna evidente se nos lembrarmos que o percurso foi desenhado por Henry Cotton. A Penina pode por vezes ter reminiscências de "Carnoustie" sem no entanto se poder considerar um verdadeiro "links" o que aumentaria ainda a sua dificuldade. Se conseguirmos bater as bolas compridas e direitas elas estarão sempre em boa posição. Os "greens" bastante grandes e razoavelmente planos não causam problemas - embora haja necessidade de lá chegar...

This was the Algarve's very first course which in recent years has been given a fresh look but with no notable changes made. It is still long and tough from the back tees, but mellows the further forward you go. The course is very flat and covered with a variety of sometimes very large trees which although in play are none too dangerous. The layout is marked by a huge number of bunkers that are neatly designed but without any real personality. Their positioning testifies to an obvious British style in the knowledge that Henry Cotton in fact designed the course. In some ways Penina is a little reminiscent of Carnoustie but without the links features, which would only increase the difficulty here. If you can drive long and straight you will always find your ball in a good position. The large and generally flat greens pose no real problem, the trouble is reaching them. A noticeable feature is the four par 5s on the back nine. The course's setting and the Penina Hotel make this an excellent destination.

Penina Golf & Resort Hotel — 1966

P.O. Box 146
P - 8501-952 PORTIMÃO

Office	Secretariado	(351) 282 - 420 200
Pro shop	Pro-shop	(351) 282 - 420 223
Fax	Fax	(351) 282 - 420 300
Web	www.lemeridien-penina.com	
Situation	Localização	Portimão, 4 km
Annual closure	Fecho anual	no
Weekly closure	Fecho semanal	no
Fees main season	Tarifas de época alta	18 holes

	Week days Semana	We/Bank holidays Fim de sem./Feriad
Individual Individual	€ 100	€ 100
Couple Casal	€ 200	€ 200

Special fees for Penina Hotel guests

Caddie Caddie no — **Electric Trolley** Trolley eléctrico yes

Buggy Buggy yes — **Clubs** Tacos yes

Credit cards Cartão de crédito
VISA - Eurocard - MasterCard - AMEX - DC

Access Acesso : Portimão-Lagos
Map 3 on page 1048 Mapa 3 Página 1048

GOLF COURSE — PERCURSO 15/20

Site	Sitio	
Maintenance	Conversa	
Architect	Arquitecto	Henry Cotton
Type	Tipo	open country
Relief	Relevo	
Water in play	Lago	
Exp. to wind	Exposto ao vento	
Trees in play	Arvores	

Scorecard Cartão de resultados	Chp. Camp.	Mens Homens	Ladies Senhoras
Length Compriment	6439	6054	5322
Par	73	73	73
Slope system	131	126	124

Advised golfing ability Nivel de jogo recomendado — 0 12 24 36

Hcp required Handicap exigido — no

CLUB HOUSE & AMENITIES — CLUB HOUSE E ANEXOS 7/10

Pro shop Pro-shop
Driving range Campo de prática
Sheltered coberto 4 mats - On grass om relva yes - Putting-green putting-green yes - Pitching-green pitching-green yes

HOTEL FACILITIES — INFRAESTRUCTURAS HOTELEIRAS 8/10

HOTELS HOTELS

Le Méridien Penina - 196 rooms, D € 325 - on site
Tel (351) 282 - 420 200, Fax (351) 282 - 420 300

Pestana Alvor Praia - Praia dos Tres Imãos 8 km
195 rooms, D € 300
Tel (351) 282 - 400 900, Fax (351) 282 - 400 999

Algarve - 209 rooms, D € 240 - Praia da Rocha 7 km
Tel (351) 282 - 402 000, Fax (351) 282 - 402 099

RESTAURANTS RESTAURANTES

Titanic - Praia da Rocha 7 km - Tel (351) 282 - 422 371

Das Amendoeiras - Praia da Rocha 7 km
Tel (351) 282 - 402 000

O Búzio - Praia dos Tres Imãos 8 km - Tel (351) 282 - 458 772

Pinheiros Altos

14 | 8 | 7

As duas voltas de 9 buracos são muito diferentes uma da outra. Os primeiros são muito acidentados e cansativos; desenvolvem-se entre pinheiros, sempre em jogo. Os segundos são planos, com agua praticamente em todos os buracos. Esta falta de unidade pode explicar-se pela intervenção de McEvoy a Howard Swan sobre o desenho original de Ronald Fream. O ritmo de jogo pode ser prejudicado para os jogadores que se deixem perturbar pelo ambiente circundante. A qualidade e o desenho dos "greens", alguns difíceis de "ler" é um dos seus pontos positivos; para mais estão bem defendidos, o que torna os "aproaches" muito interessantes. Não é um percurso para se jogar todos os dias, mas merece algumas vistas muito atentas, desde que se utilizem as saídas de trás e se esteja em boa forma física. Muito próximo do parque natural da Ria Formosa este "golf" dispõe de um otimo "club-house" e de muito boas instalações de treino, nomeadamente para o jogo curto.

The two 9-hole courses are very different. The front nine, hilly and tiring, are laid out in a pine forest where trees come very much into play. The back nine are flatter with water on virtually every hole. This lack of unity might be explained by the work made by McEvoy and Howard Swan on Ronald Fream's original design and this might upset players who are over-attentive to surroundings. Otherwise, the excellence and design of the greens, some of which are tricky to read, are very positive factors, all the more so in that their defence makes for some very interesting approach shots. This is not a course you would play every day, but it does deserve some careful visiting, providing you and your game are fit enough for the back-tees. Close to the Ria Formosa Nature Park, the course boasts a very good club-house and excellent practice facilities, particularly for your short game.

Pinheiros Campo de Golfe — 1989

P.O. Box 146 – Penina
P - 8501-952 PORTIMÃO

Office	Secretariado	(351) 289 - 359 910
Pro shop	Pro-shop	(351) 289 - 359 910
Fax	Fax	(351) 289 - 394 392
Web	www.pinheirosaltos.pt	
Situation	Localização	Faro, 15 km
Annual closure	Fecho anual	no
Weekly closure	Fecho semanal	no

Fees main season Tarifas de época alta	18 holes	
	Week days Semana	**We/Bank holidays** Fim de sem./Feriad
Individual Individual	€ 120	€ 120
Couple Casal	€ 240	€ 240

Buggies included

Caddie Caddie no — **Electric Trolley** Trolley eléctrico no

Buggy Buggy yes — **Clubs** Tacos yes

Credit cards Cartão de crédito
VISA - MasterCard - AMEX - DC

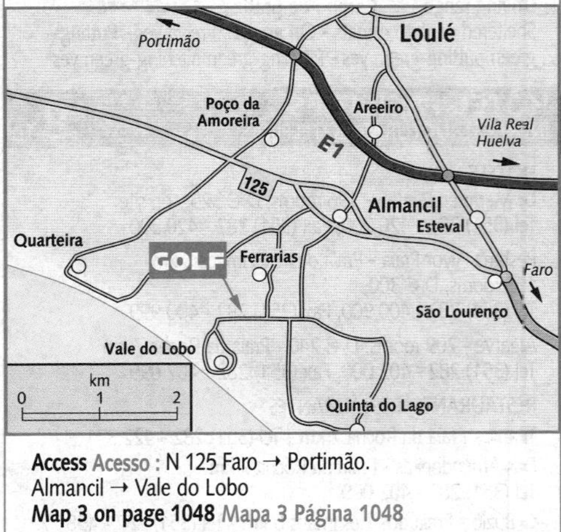

Access Acesso : N 125 Faro → Portimão. Almancil → Vale do Lobo
Map 3 on page 1048 Mapa 3 Página 1048

GOLF COURSE — PERCURSO — 14/20

Site	Sitio	
Maintenance	Conversa	
Architect	Arquitecto	Ronald Fream
Type	Tipo	forest, open country
Relief	Relevo	
Water in play	Lago	
Exp. to wind	Exposto ao vento	
Trees in play	Arvores	

Scorecard Cartão de resultados	**Chp.** Camp.	**Mens** Homens	**Ladies** Senhoras
Length Compriment	6236	5766	4914
Par	72	72	72
Slope system	125	120	120

Advised golfing ability Nivel de jogo recomendado: 0 12 24 36

Hcp required Handicap exigido: 28 Men, 36 Ladies

CLUB HOUSE & AMENITIES — CLUB HOUSE E ANEXOS — 8/10

Pro shop Pro-shop
Driving range Campo de prática
Sheltered coberto no - On grass om relva yes - Putting-green putting-green yes - Pitching-green pitching-green yes

HOTEL FACILITIES — INFRAESTRUCTURAS HOTELEIRAS — 7/10

HOTELS HOTELS

Quinta do Lago - Quinta do Lago 3 km
141 rooms, D € 520
Tel (351) 289 - 350 350, Fax (351) 289 - 396 393

Dona Filipa - 147 rooms, D € 400 - Vale do Lobo 3 km
Tel (351) 289 - 357 200, Fax (351) 289 - 357 201

Ria Park - 175 rooms, D € 230 - Vale do Garrão 3 km
Tel (351) 289 - 359 800, Fax (351) 289 - 359 888

RESTAURANTS RESTAURANTES

Casa Velha - Quinta do Lago 2 km - Tel (351) 289 - 394 983
Pequeno Mundo - Almancil 5 km - Tel (351) 289 - 399 866
Enrique Leis - Vale Formoso 6 km - Tel (351) 289 - 393 438

Praia d'El Rey

17 | 6 | 6

Cabell Robinson foi durante muito tempo o braço direito de Robert Trent Jones. Impôs-se como um arquitecto imaginativo e muito conhecedor a todos os níveis do golf. Praia D'El Rey é disso a demonstração. Com uma boa localização à beira mar rodeado de pinheiros, por vezes com vistas espectaculares, este percurso tem muitos aspectos em que se assemelha a um Links tradicional, obrigando a bem trabalhar a bola. Quando o vento sopra, raramente tão violentamente como na Escócia ou Irlanda, isso acrescenta um condimento especial a um "prato" de boa qualidade. Praia d'El Rey prometia vir a ser um dos grandes percursos da península Ibérica, no entanto está já muito prejudicada pelo nível excessivo de construção que lá realizaram, sobretudo junto a buracos fundamentais. Tem a vantagem de permitir tanto partidas de golf de alto nível como jornadas agradáveis em família.

For many years Robert Trent Jones' right-hand man, Cabell Robinson has won recognition as an imaginative designer and excellent connoisseur of golf played at all levels. Praia d'El Rey is further demonstration of his expertise. Set on a very beautiful and often spectacular seaside site enhanced with pine-trees on a number of holes, the course is in many ways reminiscent of a traditional links, with the need to steer the ball in every direction. And while the wind is more benign than in Scotland or Ireland, it can often add a little spice to what is already a savoury dish. Praia d'El Rey was a highly promising course emerging as one of the great layouts on the Iberian Peninsula. This status is now however under threat due to excess real estate development primarily near some of the signature holes. It still provides the advantage of great rounds of golf for highly skilled players and enjoyable days out golfing with the family.

Praia d'El Rey Golf & CC — 1997

Vale Janela, Apartado 2
P - 2514-999 OBIDOS

Office Secretariado (351) 262 - 905 005
Pro shop Pro-shop (351) 262 - 905 005
Fax Fax (351) 262 - 905 009
Web www.praia-del-rey.com
Situation Localização Peniche, 5 km
Annual closure Fecho anual no
Weekly closure Fecho semanal no

Fees main season Tarifas de época alta	18 holes	
	Week days Semana	**We/Bank holidays** Fim de sem./Feriad
Individual Individual	€ 75	€ 95
Couple Casal	€ 150	€ 190

Special fees for Juniors

Caddie Caddie no — **Electric Trolley** Trolley eléctrico yes
Buggy Buggy yes — **Clubs** Tacos yes
Credit cards Cartão de crédito
VISA - Mastercard - AMEX

Access Acesso : Lisboa, A8-IC1 → Obidos, N114 → Peniche.
Map 2 on page 1046 Mapa 2 Página 1046

GOLF COURSE — PERCURSO 17/20

Site Sitio
Maintenance Conversa
Architect Arquitecto — Cabell B. Robinson
Type Tipo — seaside course, links
Relief Relevo
Water in play Lago
Exp. to wind Exposto ao vento
Trees in play Arvores

Scorecard Cartão de resultados	**Chp.** Camp.	**Mens** Homens	**Ladies** Senhoras
Length Compriment	6501	6104	4744
Par	72	72	72
Slope system	118	114	115

Advised golfing ability Nivel de jogo recomendado — 0 12 24 36
Hcp required Handicap exigido 28

CLUB HOUSE & AMENITIES — CLUB HOUSE E ANEXOS 6/10

Pro shop Pro-shop
Driving range Campo de prática
Sheltered coberto 6 mats - On grass om relva yes - Putting-green putting-green yes - Pitching-green pitching-green yes

HOTEL FACILITIES — INFRAESTRUCTURAS HOTELEIRAS 6/10

HOTELS HOTELS
Marriott Praia del Rey - 178 rooms, D € 290 - on site
Tel (351) 262 905 100, (351) 262 905 101

Estal. do Convento - 31rooms , D € 90 - Obidos 12 km
Tel (351) 262 - 959 216, (351) 262 - 959 159

Pousada do Castelo - 9 rooms, D € 238 - Obidos 12 km
Tel (351) 262 - 959 105, (351) 262 - 959 148

Dona Leonor - Caldas de Rainha 15 km - 30 rooms , D € 45
Tel (351) 262 - 842 171, (351) 262 - 842 172

RESTAURANTS RESTAURANTES
Pousada do Castelo - Obidos 12 km - (351) 262 - 955 080
A Ilustre Casa de Ramiro - Obidos 12 km - (351) 262 - 959 194

Quinta da Marinha

14	6	7

Embora situado numa imensa zona de pinhal, este percurso merecia que lhe tivessem concedido um pouco mais de espaço para permitir a Robert Trent Jones dar a verdadeira medida do seu talento. O desenho de alguns buracos é de muito boa qualidade, mas para conseguir um par 71, tiveram de se criar 5 pares 5 para contrabalançar os 6 pares 3 (entre os quais os belos 5 e 14) o que provoca um ritmo de jogo pouco habitual. Aqueles que conhecem o estilo do arquitecto não ficam surpreendidos mas terão a impressão que já jogaram aqueles buracos noutro lugar qualquer. Isto não retira o prazer ao jogo e apreciação do local, donde se podem apreciar algumas belas vistas do mar, nomeadamente do buraco n° 14 que é de certo modo o buraco modelo do percurso. As dificuldades são numerosas, equilibradas e bem visíveis, permitindo jogar o percurso desde a primeira vez sem temer armadilhas escondidas. Em contrapartida não fica muito por descobrir se o percurso for jogado frequentemente. Com mais alguns hectares de terreno tinha-se conseguido um êxito total.

Although sited in a huge pine estate, this course probably deserved more space to enable Trent Jones to fully express his many talents. This is certainly an excellent layout, but to achieve a par 71 he had to create five par 5s to offset the six par 3s (including the pretty 5th and 14th holes). As a result this is rather an unusual course that lacks balance. Those of you who know the designer's style will not be surprised, but you will get the impression of having already played some of these holes before. But don't let that detract you from the pleasure of golfing on a site that offers some beautiful views over the sea, notably from the 14th, the course's signature hole. Difficulties are manifold but visible, so newcomers need have no fear of hidden hazards. By contrast you will soon get to the bottom of everything the course has to offer if you play here often. This looks very much like a missed opportunity to create a great golf course. If only more land were available.

Clube Golfe Quinta da Marinha

Quinta da Marinha, Casa 36
P - 2750 CASCAIS

Office	Secretariado	(351) 21 - 486 0180
Pro shop	Pro-shop	(351) 21 - 486 0180
Fax	Fax	(351) 21 - 486 9032
Web	www.quinta-da-marinha.pt	
Situation	Localização	Cascais, 6 km
Annual closure	Fecho anual	no
Weekly closure	Fecho semanal	no

Fees main season Tarifas de época alta	18 holes	
	Week days Semana	**We/Bank holidays** Fim de sem./Feriad
Individual Individual	€ 70	€ 80
Couple Casal	€ 140	€ 160

Juniors: – 25%

Caddie Caddie no — **Electric Trolley** Trolley eléctrico yes

Buggy Buggy yes — **Clubs** Tacos yes

Credit cards Cartão de crédito
VISA - AMEX

Access Acesso : Lisboa A5, → Cascais, N 247 → Praia do Guincho
Map 2 on page 1046 Mapa 2 Página 1046

GOLF COURSE — PERCURSO 14/20

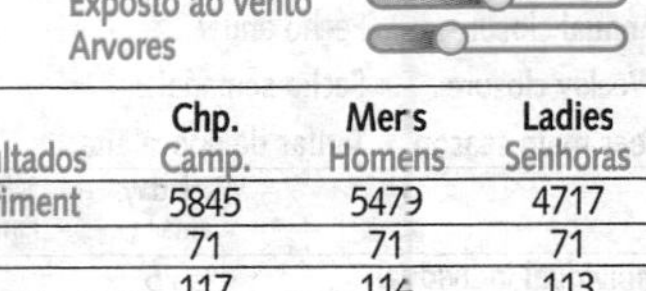

Site	Sitio	
Maintenance	Conversa	
Architect	Arquitecto	Robert Trent Jones
Type	Tipo	forest, residential
Relief	Relevo	
Water in play	Lago	
Exp. to wind	Exposto ao vento	
Trees in play	Arvores	

Scorecard Cartão de resultados	**Chp.** Camp.	**Mens** Homens	**Ladies** Senhoras
Length Compriment	5845	5479	4717
Par	71	71	71
Slope system	117	114	113

Advised golfing ability Nivel de jogo recomendado — 0 12 24 36

Hcp required Handicap exigido no

CLUB HOUSE & AMENITIES — CLUB HOUSE E ANEXOS 6/10

Pro shop Pro-shop
Driving range Campo de prática
Sheltered coberto no - On grass om relva yes - Putting-green putting-green yes - Pitching-green pitching-green no

HOTEL FACILITIES — INFRAESTRUCTURAS HOTELEIRAS 7/10

HOTELS HOTELS

Estalagem Villa Albatroz - 11 rooms, D € 320 - Cascais 4 km
Tel (351) 214 - 863 410, Fax (351) 214 - 844 680

Atlantic Gardens - 149 rooms, D € 140 - Cascais 4 km
Tel (351) 214 - 825 900, Fax (351) 214 - 825 977

Estalagem Sra. da Guia - 43 rooms, D € 250 - Cascais 4 km
Tel (351) 214 - 869 239, Fax (351) 214 - 869 227

Quinta da Marinha - 200 rooms, D € 195 - Cascais 5 km
Tel (351) 214 - 860 100, Fax (351) 214 - 869 488

RESTAURANTS RESTAURANTES

Four Seasons - Estoril 4 km - Tel (351) 214 - 648 000

Porto de Santa Maria - Praia do Guincho 3 km
Tel (351) 214 - 870 240

Quinta da Ria

17	7	5

É uma das mais recentes realizações no que se refere a campos de "Golf" do Algarve. Trata-se de um bonito percurso, implantado à beira mar, sobre uma falésia que domina o mais belo braço de mar ligado à Ria Formosa. Rocky Roquemore teve de se esmerar para realizar um percurso equilibrado num pedaço de terreno limitado. A ausência de construções e o cuidado da manutenção compensam uma certa falta de espaço. Para alem disso o percurso não é comprido mas tem "greens" bem defendidos e alguns buracos bem desenhados. Trata-se de um óptimo percurso para descontrair e jogar entre amigos, com algumas vistas deslumbrantes. Embora bastante exposto, não sofre de grandes ventos, uma vez que está implantado num dos melhores locais, quanto ao clima, do pais.

This is one of the more recent golf course productions in the Algarve. It is a lovely course located by the sea on a cliff over the most beautiful inlet of the Ria Formosa. Rocky Roquemore was hard pushed to design a smoothly balanced golf course over a limited stretch of land. The absence of building sites and excellent green-keeping largely offset the lack of space. The course is not long but has well defended greens and some holes are particularly well designed. A wonderful course to play with friends and to enjoy some spectacular views. Although somewhat exposed, wind is not a real problem since the course is laid out in an area which climate-wise is second to none in Portugal.

Quinta da Ria 2002
P - 8900-057 VILA NOVA DE CACELA

Office	Secretariado	(351) 281 - 950 580
Pro shop	Pro-shop	(351) 281 - 700 335
Fax	Fax	(351) 281 - 950 589
Web	www.quintadariagolf.com	
Situation	Localização	Tavira, 12 km
Annual closure	Fecho anual	no
Weekly closure	Fecho semanal	no

Fees main season Tarifas de época alta	18 holes	
	Week days Semana	**We/Bank holidays** Fim de sem./Feriad
Individual Individual	€ 90	€ 90
Couple Casal	€ 180	€ 180

Juniors: € 40

Caddie Caddie no — **Electric Trolley** Trolley eléctrico yes
Buggy Buggy yes — **Clubs** Tacos yes
Credit cards Cartão de crédito
VISA - MasterCard - AMEX

Access Acesso : EN 125 Faro → Tavira → Monte Gordo. 5 km after Conceião (Km 142), turn right on municipal road.
Map 3 on page 1049 Mapa 3 Página 1049

GOLF COURSE 17/20
PERCURSO

Site	Sitio	
Maintenance	Conversa	
Architect	Arquitecto	Rocky Roquemore
Type	Tipo	seaside course, open country
Relief	Relevo	
Water in play	Lago	
Exp. to wind	Exposto ao vento	
Trees in play	Arvores	

Scorecard Cartão de resultados	**Chp.** Camp.	**Mens** Homens	**Ladies** Senhoras
Length Compriment	6016	5872	4980
Par	72	72	72
Slope system	120	118	122

Advised golfing ability 0 12 24 36
Nivel de jogo recomendado
Hcp required Handicap exigido yes

CLUB HOUSE & AMENITIES 7/10
CLUB HOUSE E ANEXOS

Pro shop Pro-shop
Driving range Campo de prática
Sheltered coberto - On grass om relva yes - Putting-green putting-green yes - Pitching-green pitching-green yes

HOTEL FACILITIES 5/10
INFRAESTRUCTURAS HOTELEIRAS

HOTELS HOTELS
Convento de Santo António - Tavira 10 km
7 rooms, D € 150
Tel (351) 281 - 321 573, Fax (351) 281 - 325 632

Vila Galé Tavira - 268 rooms, D € 137 - Tavira 10 km
Tel (351) 281 - 329 900, Fax (351) 281 - 329 950

Casablanca - 42 rooms, D € 90 - Monte Gordo 10 km
Tel (351) 281 - 511 444, Fax (351) 281 - 511 999

RESTAURANTS RESTAURANTES
Vila Galé Tavira - Tavira 10 km - Tel (351) 281 - 329 900
Portas do Mar - Quatro Aguas 10 km
Tel (351) 281 - 321 255

Quinta de Cima

18 | 7 | 5

Ao lado do seu irmão, "Quinta da Ria" apresenta-se fazendo figura do percurso de campeonato. Não se trata só do seu comprimento, mas também de ritmo de jogo e da dificuldade dos buracos. Desde o início é indispensável pensar na estratégia, na escolha dos tacos e das trajectórias. Os obstáculos vão estar decisivamente em jogo desde os primeiros buracos; quer se trate de "bunkers" bem colocados e desenhados ou obstáculos de água sob a forma de lagos ou de riachos ou de valas. Aqui o estilo de jogo a desenvolver é francamente o estilo Americano. Felizmente o vento raramente sopra com força e não virá a perturbar as bolas altas e bem batidas. Porem, não é fácil de cumprir o seu "handicap" e embora todos os jogadores dos diferentes níveis se podem divertir, só os de melhor nível poderão impor-se. Resumindo, um bonito desenho, um belo ambiente, algumas reminiscências de " Las Brisas" – menos acidentado – aqui está uma realização já em bom nível, apesar da sua juventude.

Next to its sister course, the Quinta da Ria, Quinta de Cima looks and plays even more like a top tournament course. This is not only a matter of length but also of balance and the difficulty of holes. From the very first tee you need to carefully consider game strategy, choice of club and ball trajectory. Hazards are definitely very much in play on all holes, whether for the well-designed, cleverly located bunkers or the water hazards which here come in the shape of lakes, streams and ditches. The course definitely calls for American style golf but fortunately there is never too much wind in these parts to blow high approach shots off-course. Playing to your handicap is not easy, let it be said, and while players of all levels can have fun, only the best will prosper. In a nutshell, a pretty design, a beautiful setting and a few reminders of Las Brisas but with fewer slopes. A great course already playing well despite its tender age.

Quinta da Cima — 2002

P - 8900-057 VILA NOVA DE CACELA

Office	Secretariado	(351) 281 - 950 580
Pro shop	Pro-shop	(351) 918 - 700 335
Fax	Fax	(351) 281 - 950 589
Web	www.quintadariagolf.com	
Situation	Localização	Tavira, 12 km
Annual closure	Fecho anual	no
Weekly closure	Fecho semanal	no

Fees main season Tarifas de época alta	18 holes	
	Week days Semana	We/Bank holidays Fim de sem./Feriad
Individual Individual	€ 90	€ 90
Couple Casal	€ 180	€ 180

Juniors (up to 18): € 40

Caddie Caddie no — **Electric Trolley** Trolley eléctrico yes

Buggy Buggy yes — **Clubs** Tacos yes

Credit cards Cartão de crédito
VISA - MasterCard - AMEX

Access Acesso : EN 125 Faro → Tavira → Monte Gordo. 5 km after Conceião (Km 142), turn right on municipal road.
Map 3 on page 1049 Mapa 3 Página 1049

GOLF COURSE — PERCURSO — 18/20

Site	Sitio	
Maintenance	Conversa	
Architect	Arquitecto	Rocky Roquemore
Type	Tipo	parkland, open country
Relief	Relevo	
Water in play	Lago	
Exp. to wind	Exposto ao vento	
Trees in play	Arvores	

Scorecard Cartão de resultados	Chp. Camp.	Mens Homens	Ladies Senhoras
Length Compriment	6256	6045	4971
Par	72	72	72
Slope system	129	127	119

Advised golfing ability Nivel de jogo recomendado — 0 12 24 36

Hcp required Handicap exigido — yes

CLUB HOUSE & AMENITIES — CLUB HOUSE E ANEXOS — 7/10

Pro shop Pro-shop

Driving range Campo de prática

Sheltered coberto - On grass om relva yes - Putting-green putting-green yes - Pitching-green pitching-green yes

HOTEL FACILITIES — INFRAESTRUCTURAS HOTELEIRAS — 5/10

HOTELS HOTELS

Vila Galé Albacora - 161 rooms, D € 162 - Quatro Aguas 10 km
Tel (351) 281 - 380 800, Fax (351) 281 - 380 850

Pousada de São Brás - São Brás Alportel 31 km
32 rooms, D € 132
Tel (351) 289 - 842 305, Fax (351) 289 - 841 276

Golf Colina Verde Aparthotel - Maragota 20 km
31 rooms, D € 115
Tel (351) 289 - 790 110, Fax (351) 289 - 791 245

RESTAURANTS RESTAURANTES

A Chaminé - Altura 4 km - Tel (351) 281 - 950 100
Fernando - Altura 4 km - Tel (351) 281 - 956 455

Quinta do Brinçal

15	5	4

Este percurso é uma das melhores senão a melhor realização de Rocky Roquemore ao nível do "lay out". Numa bonita paisagem campestre com uma ondulação agradável, Rocky Roquemore apresentou um bom "test" de golf, muito franco, com alguns "greens" muito bem protegidos, mas com as dificuldades sempre visíveis e sem golpes cegos apesar do ligeiro relevo. O seu comprimento é muito respeitável mas as saídas da frente encurtam-no em 450 metros, o que encantará aqueles que regressam sempre enfadados com a sua procura de distância. Para alem disso oferece uma boa ocasião para se ir visitar o Castelo de Óbidos. Trata-se de uma linda cidade medieval e renascentista, dominada pôr um castelo onde está instalada a Pousada. Não é mesmo ao lado do golf, mas julgamos que um jogador não tem dificuldade de fazer meia hora de automóvel pois não? Com o dever cultural cumprido e com a consciência tranquila ela poderá consagrar-se a este excelente test de golf se e quando está em boas condições de manutenção.

This course is one of Rocky Roquemore's best layouts in Portugal. In pretty country landscape with pleasant rolling valleys, Roquemore has produced a good and very candid test of golf with some very well protected greens, visible difficulties and no blind shots despite ground topography. Yardage is very respectable but the front tees shorten the course by 450 metres, a joy and relief for golfers who strive for distance but actually get very little. It is also a good opportunity to go and see the Castle of Obidos, a very pretty medieval renaissance town overlooked by a castle, which houses the Pousada, a hotel and restaurant comparable to the Spanish Paradors. This is not quite alongside the golf course, but a half-hour ride for a golfer is nothing, surely. With a clear conscience after your shot of culture, it's time to think about golfing... when the course is in good condition.

Quinta do Brinçal — 1994

Apartado 219
P - 2040-998 RIO MAIOR

Office	Secretariado	(351) 243 - 908 148
Pro shop	Pro-shop	(351) 243 - 908 148
Fax	Fax	(351) 243 - 908 149
E-mail	quintadobrincal@camin.pt	
Situation	Localização	Lisboa, 59 km
Annual closure	Fecho anual	no
Weekly closure	Fecho semanal	no

Fees main season Tarifas de época alta	18 holes	
	Week days Semana	We/Bank holidays Fim de sem./Feriad
Individual Individual	€ 40	€ 60
Couple Casal	€ 80	€ 120

Caddie Caddie no — **Electric Trolley** Trolley eléctrico no
Buggy Buggy yes — **Clubs** Tacos no

Credit cards Cartão de crédito
VISA

Access Acesso : Lisboa, A1. Km 46 in Avéiras, → Rio Maior. Quebradas, → Golf.
Map 2 on page 1046 Mapa 2 Página 1046

GOLF COURSE — PERCURSO — 15/20

Site	Sitio	
Maintenance	Conversa	
Architect	Arquitecto	Rocky Roquemore
Type	Tipo	inland, forest
Relief	Relevo	
Water in play	Lago	
Exp. to wind	Exposto ao vento	
Trees in play	Arvores	

Scorecard Cartão de resultados	Chp. Camp.	Mens Homens	Ladies Senhoras
Length Compriment	6612	5550	4863
Par	72	72	72
Slope system	126	121	117

Advised golfing ability Nivel de jogo recomendado — 0 12 24 36
Hcp required Handicap exigido — 28 Men/36 Ladies

CLUB HOUSE & AMENITIES — CLUB HOUSE E ANEXOS — 5/10

Pro shop Pro-shop
Driving range Campo de prática
Sheltered coberto 20 mats - On grass om relva yes - Putting-green putting-green yes - Pitching-green pitching-green yes

HOTEL FACILITIES — INFRAESTRUCTURAS HOTELEIRAS — 4/10

HOTELS HOTELS

Quinta da Ferraria - Ribeira de São João 12 km
14 rooms, D € 99
Tel (351) 243 - 945 001, Fax (351) 243 - 945 696

Quinta da Cortiçada - 9 rooms, D € 113 - Rio Maior 4 km
Tel (351) 243 - 470 000, Fax (351) 243 - 470 009

Casa do Foral - 8 rooms, D € 65 - Rio Maior 5 km
Tel (351) 258 - 992 610, Fax (351) 258 - 992 611

RESTAURANTS RESTAURANTES

Adega da Raposa - Rio Maior 5 km - Tel (351) 243 - 995 166
Cantinho da Serra - Alto da Serra / Rio Maior 5 km
Tel (351) 243 - 991 367

Quinta do Lago *Norte (A + D)*

15 | 6 | 7

Sob o nome de Norte (Ex "Ria Formosa") reuniram-se os percursos A e D da Quinta do Lago. Tendo sido cada 9 buracos desenhados por dois arquitectos diferentes: William Mitchell e Rocky Roquemore, resultou num certo desequilíbrio visual e golfístico, uma vez que as personalidades dos dois signatários é forçosamente diferente. Este "defeito" contribui, porem, para dar muita variedade aos 18 buracos que são, pelo menos, idênticos do ponto de vista da vegetação e da dimensão. A estratégia é bastante simples, os "greens" são desenhados com gosto, o desenho geral é bastante imaginativo com uma estética muito americana, sobretudo pela integração de vários lagos. Em relação ao outro percurso do complexo é ainda mais adequado a todos os níveis de jogo, quer se trate de jogar para o seu próprio resultado ou numa competição. Se juntarmos a este vasto complexo o belo e mítico percurso do São Lourenço confirma-se a necessidade de uma visita.

The North Course (A + D) of Quinta do Lago, formerly Ria Formosa, was designed by two different architects (9 holes each), namely William Mitchell and Rocky Roquemore. The result is a slight impression, both visually and in golfing terms, of this being a slightly disjointed course created by two necessarily different personalities and styles. In reality, this "flaw" adds considerable variety to the 18-hole layout, where the vegetation at least is the same. Game strategy is simple to see, the greens have been tastefully designed and the general layout is rather imaginative and mainly American in style with the presence of several lakes. Compared to the other course on the same site, the A + D combination is even better suited to all levels, whichever way you play. If you combine this huge golfing resort with the fabulous neighbouring course of San Lorenzo, then you are in for a long visit.

Quinta do Lago Golf Club — 1977

P - 8135-024 ALMANCIL

Office	Secretariado	(351) 289 - 390 705
Pro shop	Pro-shop	(351) 289 - 390 700
Fax	Fax	(351) 289 - 394 013
Web	www.quintadolagogolf.com	
Situation	Localização	Faro, 12 km
Annual closure	Fecho anual	no
Weekly closure	Fecho semanal	no

Fees main season Tarifas de época alta	18 holes	
	Week days Semana	**We/Bank holidays** Fim de sem./Feriad
Individual Individual	€ 150	€ 150
Couple Casal	€ 300	€ 300

Caddie Caddie no — **Electric Trolley** Trolley eléctrico yes
Buggy Buggy yes — **Clubs** Tacos yes
Credit cards Cartão de crédito
VISA - AMEX

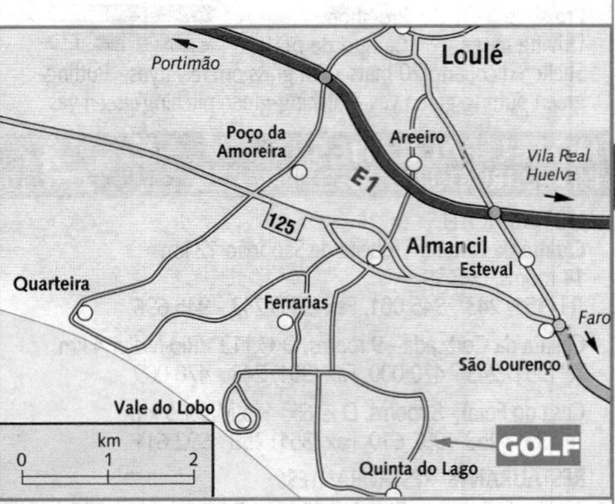

Access Acesso : N 125 Faro → Portimão, Almancil → Quinta do Lago
Map 3 on page 1048 Mapa 3 Página 1048

GOLF COURSE — PERCURSO — 15/20

Site	Sitio	
Maintenance	Conversa	
Architect	Arquitecto	William Mitchell, Rocky Roquemore
Type	Tipo	forest, residential
Relief	Relevo	
Water in play	Lago	
Exp. to wind	Exposto ao vento	
Trees in play	Arvores	

Scorecard Cartão de resultados	**Chp.** Camp.	**Mens** Homens	**Ladies** Senhoras
Length Compriment	6205	5804	5031
Par	72	72	72
Slope system	131	126	122

Advised golfing ability Nivel de jogo recomendado — 0 12 24 36
Hcp required Handicap exigido — 28 Men, 36 Ladies

CLUB HOUSE & AMENITIES — CLUB HOUSE E ANEXOS — 6/10

Pro shop Pro-shop
Driving range Campo de prática
Sheltered coberto no - On grass om relva no (25 mats)
Putting-green putting-green yes - Pitching-green pitching-green yes

HOTEL FACILITIES — INFRAESTRUCTURAS HOTELEIRAS — 7/10

HOTELS HOTELS
Quinta do Lago - Quinta do Lago 3 km
141 rooms, D € 520
Tel (351) 289 - 350 350, Fax (351) 289 - 396 393

Dona Filipa - 147 rooms, D € 400 - Vale do Lobo 6 km
Tel (351) 289 - 357 200, Fax (351) 289 - 357 201

RESTAURANTS RESTAURANTES
Casa Velha - Quinta do Lago 3 km - Tel (351) 289 - 394 983
São Gabriel - Almancil 5 km - Tel (351) 265 - 394 521
Henrique Leis - Vale Formoso (Loulé) 10 km
Tel (351) 289 - 393 438
Casa dos Pinheiros - Almancil 5 km - Tel (351) 289 - 394 832

Quinta do Lago *Sul (B + C)*

16	6	7

A despeito da qualidade dos outros grupos de 9 buracos, a combinação dos percursos (B e C) é a que foi mais utilizada nas grandes competições. O seu comprimento não deve assustar. E razoável a partir das saídas normais. Desenhado por William Mitchel é um campo de estilo americano. A largura dos "fairways" e o equilíbrio do comprimento dos buracos, torna o percurso acessível a todos os jogadores com alguma experiência. Para mais, a natureza arenosa do terreno permite não só andar com prazer, mas também fazer rolar muito a bola. Os obstáculos de agua entram em jogo em alguns buracos mas a principal dificuldade são os pinheiros que sobressaem de outros tipos de vegetação. Pelo seu equilíbrio e largueza este percurso permite um jogo confortável sem criar problemas inúteis aos golfistas em férias ao mesmo tempo que é um bom "test" para jogadores de baixo "handicap" e profissionais. A Quinta do Lago conquistou uma bela reputação e tem estado a ser mantida em muito boa qualidade apesar do elevado numero de jogadores que a visitam anualmente.

Despite the excellence of the other two 9-hole courses, the B + C combination is the most gratifying and the most frequently used for top tournaments. The yardage is nothing to be afraid of and is reasonable from the normal tees. Designed by the late William Mitchell, it is a typical American course where wide fairways and nicely balanced length of holes make for a course that is playable by any golfer with some experience. What's more, the sandy subsoil makes it a pleasure to walk and gives balls a lot of extra roll. Water hazards are in play only on a few holes and the main difficulties are the pine-trees looming over the heather and the broom. A nicely balanced course for a relaxing round of golf and one that doesn't create needless problems for golfers on holiday. It is also a good test for low handicappers and pros. Quinta do Lago has acquired a great reputation and is usually pretty well maintained considering the huge numbers of players who come and play it every year.

Quinta do Lago Golf Club — 1974

P - 8135-024 ALMANCIL

Office	Secretariado	(351) 289 - 390 705
Pro shop	Pro-shop	(351) 289 - 390 700
Fax	Fax	(351) 289 - 394 013
Web	www.quintadolagogolf.com	
Situation	Localização	Faro, 12 km
Annual closure	Fecho anual	no
Weekly closure	Fecho semanal	no

Fees main season Tarifas de época alta	18 holes	
	Week days Semana	**We/Bank holidays** Fim de sem./Feriad
Individual Individual	€ 150	€ 150
Couple Casal	€ 300	€ 300

Caddie Caddie no — **Electric Trolley** Trolley eléctrico yes

Buggy Buggy yes — **Clubs** Tacos yes

Credit cards Cartão de crédito
VISA - AMEX

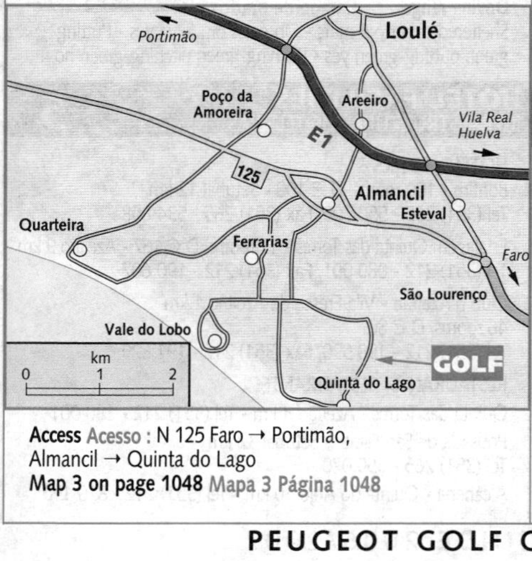

Access Acesso : N 125 Faro → Portimão, Almancil → Quinta do Lago

Map 3 on page 1048 Mapa 3 Página 1048

GOLF COURSE — PERCURSO — 16/20

Site	Sitio	
Maintenance	Conversa	
Architect	Arquitecto	William Mitchell
Type	Tipo	forest, residential
Relief	Relevo	
Water in play	Lago	
Exp. to wind	Exposto ao vento	
Trees in play	Arvores	

Scorecard Cartão de resultados	**Chp.** Camp.	**Mens** Homens	**Ladies** Senhoras
Length Compriment	6488	5870	5192
Par	72	72	72
Slope system	127	118	120

Advised golfing ability Nivel de jogo recomendado: 0 12 24 36

Hcp required Handicap exigido: 28 Men, 36 Ladies

CLUB HOUSE & AMENITIES — CLUB HOUSE E ANEXOS — 6/10

Pro shop Pro-shop

Driving range Campo de prática

Sheltered coberto no - On grass om relva no (25 mats) - Putting-green putting-green yes - Pitching-green pitching-green yes

HOTEL FACILITIES — INFRAESTRUCTURAS HOTELEIRAS — 7/10

HOTELS HOTELS

Quinta do Lago - Quinta do Lago 3 km
141 rooms, D € 520
Tel (351) 289 - 350 350, Fax (351) 289 - 396 393

Dona Filipa - 147 rooms, D € 400 - Vale do Lobo 6 km
Tel (351) 289 - 357 200, Fax (351) 289 - 357 201

RESTAURANTS RESTAURANTES

Casa Velha - Quinta do Lago 3 km - Tel (351) 289 - 394 983

São Gabriel - Almancil 5 km - Tel (351) 265 - 394 521

Henrique Leis - Vale Formoso (Loulé) 10 km
Tel (351) 289 - 393 438

Casa dos Pinheiros - Almancil 5 km - Tel (351) 289 - 394 832

Quinta do Peru

15 | 7 | 5

A visão de algum excesso imobiliárias é em parte compensada pelos belas paisagens. Esta agradável impressão é confirmada pela qualidade do percurso geralmente em razoável condição. Com aos excepções de 2 pares 3, compr dos e bem protegidos por lagos, este desenho de Rocky Roquemore adapta-se muito bem a todo o tipo de jogadores se estes não escolherem as saídas mais longas. O sentimento dominante é o de um percurso bem equilibrado e de uma grande franqueza e com os obstáculos bem visíveis. As dificuldades são bastante numerosas para evitar o aborrecimento sem no entanto se tornar opressivo, tendo "greens" bem desenhados. Construído no meio de um agradável pinhal, com um relevo moderado está evidentemente destinado ser apreciado por todos os tipos de jogador. Os melhores jogadores tirarão dele melhor partido a partir das saídas de trás. A qualidade das instalações de treino e do club-house permitem que se passe uma jornada agradável.

The sight of some excessive property development is compensated by a number of beautiful landscapes and this pleasant impression is confirmed by the excellence of a course that is usually in good condition. With the exception of two pars 3, both long and tightly defended by water, this Rocky Roquemore design is well suited to players of all abilities if they avoid the back-tees. The overall feeling is one of a nicely balanced and fair course, where hazards are clearly there to be seen. Although evenly spaced to give golfers room to breathe, there are enough difficulties to keep you on your toes and the greens are interesting. Laid out in a flattish and pleasant pine forest, this course is obviously designed for fun and the better players will be better off playing from the back. The standard of practice facilities and the club-house makes this a good day's golfing.

Club Quinta do Peru 1994

Alameda da Serra, 2
P - 2975-666 QUINTA DO CONDE

Office Secretariado (351) 21 - 213 4320
Pro shop Pro-shop (351) 21 - 213 4320
Fax Fax (351) 21 - 213 4321
Web www.golfquintadoperu.com
Situation Localização Lisboa, 46 km
Setubal (pop. 89 106), 12 km

Annual closure Fecho anual no
Weekly closure Fecho semanal no

Fees main season Tarifas de época alta	18 holes	
	Week days Semana	**We/Bank holidays** Fim de sem./Feriad
Individual Individual	€ 58	€ 88
Couple Casal	€ 116	€ 176

Juniors: € 24

Caddie Caddie no **Electric Trolley** Trolley eléctrico yes
Buggy Buggy yes **Clubs** Tacos yes
Credit cards Cartão de crédito
VISA - AMEX

Almada
Lisboa
A2
Setúbal
Reserva da Mata Nacional dos Medos
N10
Vila Fresca do Azeitão
Azeitão
GOLF
km 0 3 6
Sesimbra

Access Acesso : A2 Lisboa → Setubal, N10 → Azeitão, Golf
Map 2 on page 1046 Mapa 2 Página 1046

GOLF COURSE 15/20
PERCURSO

Site Sitio
Maintenance Conversa
Architect Arquitecto Rocky Roquemore
Type Tipo forest, residential
Relief Relevo
Water in play Lago
Exp. to wind Exposto ao vento
Trees in play Arvores

Scorecard Cartão de resultados	**Chp.** Camp.	**Mens** Homens	**Ladies** Senhoras
Length Compriment	6074	5617	4486
Par	72	72	72
Slope system	137	132	127

Advised golfing ability 0 12 24 36
Nivel de jogo recomendado
Hcp required Handicap exigido 28 Men, 36 Ladies

CLUB HOUSE & AMENITIES 7/10
CLUB HOUSE E ANEXOS

Pro shop Pro-shop
Driving range Campo de prática
Sheltered coberto 5 mats - On grass om relva yes - Putting-green putting-green yes - Pitching-green pitching-green no

HOTEL FACILITIES 5/10
INFRAESTRUCTURAS HOTELEIRAS

HOTELS HOTELS
Bonfim - 100 rooms, D € 100 - Setubal 12 km
Tel (351) 265 - 550 700, Fax (351) 265 - 534 858

Estalagem Quinta das Torres - 12 rooms, D € 167 - Azeitão 9 km
Tel (351) 212 - 080 001, Fax (351) 212 - 190 607

Club d'Azeitão - Vila Fresca de Azeitão 1 km
46 rooms, D € 80
Tel (351) 212 - 198 590, Fax (351) 212 - 191 629

RESTAURANTS RESTAURANTES
Quinta das Torres - Azeitão 3 km - Tel (351) 212 - 180 001
Pousada de São Filipe - Setubal 12 km
Tel (351) 265 - 550 070
Alcanena - Quinta do Anjo 10 km - Tel (351) 212 - 870 150

Ribagolfe *Blue*

15 | 6 | 4

É um dos dois percursos situados a 45 minutos de Lisboa numa bonita mata de sobreiros com a European Golf Design, Peter Townsend concebeu-o claramente para ser um Golfe de Campeonato, quanto mais não fosse pelo seu comprimento. Com os seus 6700 metros não se torna muito cansativo para andar apesar de certas ondulações e pequenos vales e graças à beleza dos sobreiros. O reverso da medalha é um certo número de buracos muito semelhantes: temos uma certa dificuldade em os memorizar e tornam – se desinteressantes. Dito isto, graças ao número de "tees" a maioria dos jogadores podem circular aqui sem grandes problemas e mesmo entregar resultados bastante agradáveis pois os "greens" são vastos mas pouco ondulados. È mais difícil para os jogadores compridos pois terão tendência para se deixarem embalar.Tem de tomar atenção pois os "fairways" não são muito largos. Os bunkers grandes e alguns obstáculos de água, como o do 14 onde é necessário conhecer bem a sua distância para poder cortar pelo caminho mais curto.

This is one of the two courses that go to make up this sprawling resort lying in a pretty forest some 45 minutes outside of Lisbon. With E.G.D., Peter Townsend designed this clearly as a championship course, if only for its yardage. Total length is 7,370 yards but at least it is an easy course to walk despite the beautifully sloping terrain and dales lined with magnificent cork oak-trees. The downside is that a certain number of holes are rather similar; they hardly stick in the mind and the appeal tends to wear off after a while. Having said that, the large number of tee-boxes make this a course where most golfers might card a flattering score because the greens are huge with only a few contours. It can be tougher for the long-hitters, because while they can let rip at leisure they will need to be careful with narrow fairways, some rather large bunkers and a few water hazards that threaten the shot: on the 14th, you will need to know just how far you can hit it to make that short-cut.

Ribagolfe — 2004

Vargem Fresca, EN 10, km 93, Infantado
P - 2135-407 SAMORA CORREIA

Office Secretariado (351) 263 930 040
Pro shop Pro-shop (351) 263 930 040
Fax Fax (351) 263 930 049
Web www.ribagolfe.pt
Situation Localização Lisboa, 59 km
Coruche, 29 km
Annual closure Fecho anual no
Weekly closure Fecho semanal no

Fees main season Tarifas de época alta	18 holes	
	Week days Semana	**We/Bank holidays** Fim de sem./Feriad
Individual Individual	€ 45	€ 60
Couple Casal	€ 90	€ 120

Juniors under 18: – 50%

Caddie Caddie no — **Electric Trolley** Trolley eléctrico no
Buggy Buggy yes — **Clubs** Tacos yes
Credit cards Cartão de crédito
VISA - MasterCard - AMEX

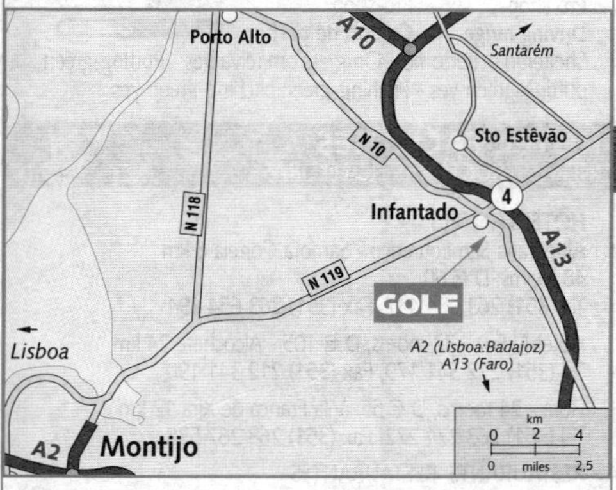

Access Acesso : Lisboa, IC3 → Alcochete, En119 → Coruche, Infantado
Map 2 on page 1046 Mapa 2 Página 1046

GOLF COURSE — PERCURSO — 15/20

Site Sitio
Maintenance Conversa
Architect Arquitecto Peter Townsend, European Golf Design
Type Tipo forest, links
Relief Relevo
Water in play Lago
Exp. to wind Exposto ao vento
Trees in play Arvores

Scorecard Cartão de resultados	**Chp.** Camp.	**Mens** Homens	**Ladies** Senhoras
Length Compriment	6707	6000	5200
Par	72	72	72
Slope system	130	125	124

Advised golfing ability Nivel de jogo recomendado — 0 12 24 36
Hcp required Handicap exigido

CLUB HOUSE & AMENITIES — CLUB HOUSE E ANEXOS — 6/10

Pro shop Pro-shop
Driving range Campo de prática
Sheltered coberto no - On grass om relva yes - Putting-green putting-green yes - Pitching-green pitching-green yes

HOTEL FACILITIES — INFRAESTRUCTURAS HOTELEIRAS — 4/10

HOTELS HOTELS
Albergaria San Lourenço - Samora Correia 6 km
48 rooms, D € 60
Tel (351) 263 654 447, Fax (351) 263 654 694

Hôtel Al Foz - 32 rooms, D € 105 - Alcochete 24 km
Tel (351) 212 341 179, Fax (351) 212 341 190

Flora - 24 rooms, D € 55- Vila Franca de Xira 12 km
Tel (351) 263 271 272, Fax (351) 263 267 538

RESTAURANTS RESTAURANTES
O Forno - Vila Franca de Xira 12 km
Tel (351) 263 282 106

Ribagolfe *Green*

16 | 6 | 4

Foi a um antigo jogador do circuito Europeu, Michael King que o desenho foi confiado, sempre sob a direcção da European Golf Design. Trata-se do mesmo enquadramento com muitos sobreiros e se o estilo é mais britânico do que americano (como o Percurso Azul) não escapa a uma certa uniformidade, possivelmente devido ao tipo de vegetação. Este percurso foi imaginado para ser utilizado sobretudo por jogadores de Clube pelo que o seu comprimento é muito mais razoável bem como a sua largura. Os "greens" são bastante grandes e moderadamente ondulados, mas as suas defesas não são suficientemente espectaculares para conseguirem comover os jogadores precisos. Os obstáculos de água só entram em jogo em dois buracos o que vem acrescentar conforto a uma jornada de golfe tranquila entre amigos. Outros obstáculos são pequenos vales que ameaçam as saícas nos pares 3 o que trás alguma pimenta. Trata-se de uma realização séria com boa manutenção.

The design of this course was assigned to another former European Tour player, Michael King, again under the expert supervision of European Golf Design. This is again the same type of environment with a lot of cork oak-trees, and while the style is more British than American (like the Blue Course), there is still a certain feeling of uniformity, maybe due primarily to the type of vegetation. This course is intended more for members, which explains why the yardage and the the width of fairways are much more reasonable. The greens are pretty huge and moderately contoured, but their lines of defence are perhaps not spectacular enough to scare the more accurate players. Water hazards are in play only on two holes, which again adds to the cool comfort of a peaceful day spent golfing with friends. Other hazards like little dales threaten the tee shot on the par 3 holes and add a little spice. A serious piece of golf with excellent green-keeping to match.

Ribagolfe **2004**
Vargem Fresca, EN 10, km 93, Infantado
P - 2135-407 SAMORA CORREIA

Office	Secretariado	(351) 263 930 040
Pro shop	Pro-shop	(351) 263 930 040
Fax	Fax	(351) 263 930 049
Web	www.ribagolfe.pt	
Situation	Localização	Lisboa, 59 km

Coruche, 29 km

Annual closure	Fecho anual	no
Weekly closure	Fecho semanal	no

Fees main season Tarifas de época alta	18 holes	
	Week days Semana	**We/Bank holidays** Fim de sem./Feriad
Individual Individual	€ 45	€ 60
Couple Casal	€ 90	€ 120

Juniors under 18: – 50%

Caddie Caddie no — **Electric Trolley** Trolley eléctrico no

Buggy Buggy yes — **Clubs** Tacos yes

Credit cards Cartão de crédito
VISA - MasterCard - AMEX

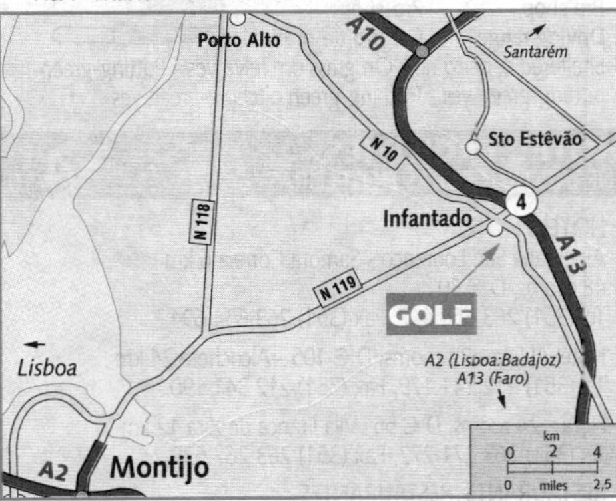

Access Acesso : Lisboa, IC3 → Alcochete, En119 → Coruche, Infantado

Map 2 on page 1046 Mapa 2 Página 1046

GOLF COURSE — PERCURSO 16/20

Site	Sitio	
Maintenance	Conversa	
Architect	Arquitecto	Michael King European Golf Design
Type	Tipo	forest
Relief	Relevo	
Water in play	Lago	
Exp. to wind	Exposto ao vento	
Trees in play	Arvores	

Scorecard Cartão de resultados	**Chp.** Camp.	**Mens** Homens	**Ladies** Senhoras
Length Compriment	6214	5750	4998
Par	72	72	72
Slope system	124	119	119

Advised golfing ability Nivel de jogo recomendado — 0 12 24 36

Hcp required Handicap exigido — certificate

CLUB HOUSE & AMENITIES — CLUB HOUSE E ANEXOS 6/10

Pro shop Pro-shop
Driving range Campo de prática
Sheltered coberto no - On grass om relva yes - Putting-green putting-green yes - Pitching-green pitching-green yes

HOTEL FACILITIES — INFRAESTRUCTURAS HOTELEIRAS 4/10

HOTELS HOTELS
Albergaria San Lourenço - Samora Correia 6 km
48 rooms, D € 60
Tel (351) 263 654 447, Fax (351) 263 654 694

Hôtel Al Foz - 32 rooms, D € 105 - Alcochete 24 km
Tel (351) 212 341 179, Fax (351) 212 341 190

Flora - 24 rooms, D € 55- Vila Franca de Xira 12 km
Tel (351) 263 271 272, Fax (351) 263 267 538

RESTAURANTS RESTAURANTES
O Forno - Vila Franca de Xira 12 km
Tel (351) 263 282 106

S. Lourenço

17 | 5 | 7

É incontestavelmente um dos melhores percursos de Portugal tanto pelo seu traçado como pelo seu ambiente. Apresenta-se no seu melhor quando está bem tratado, o que é bastante difícil devido ao grande numero de jogadores que o visitam. Num belo local rodeado de casas de grande qualidade, Jo Lee demonstrou uma grande imaginação e uma preocupação de espectáculo visual e golfístico. Aqui é necessário não só utilizar todos os ferros do saco, mas também utilizá-los de forma diferente tão importante se torna a colocação das pancadas para se conseguir um bom resultado. Há um encontro de todas as dificuldades: arvores, "bunkers", lagos e largos braços da Ria Formosa. A tranquilidade a beleza da paisagem e as belas vistas do mar, incitam a dar o melhor de si próprio e a responder aos desafios técnicos postos pelo arquitecto. É certo que os jogadores inexperientes terão dificuldades, mas para aqueles que tem um "handicap" razoável será o culminar de uma esplendida jornada de "golf".

This is unquestionably one of Portugal's top courses for its design and setting. It looks and plays its best when green-keeping stays top-notch, and that is not always easy when you consider the huge numbers of visitors. Given a very beautiful site dotted by some equally attractive villas, Joseph Lee employed heaps of imagination and considerable concern for golf as a visual spectacle. Here, you not only use every club in your bag, you also use clubs in different ways. That's how important positioning the ball can be for a good score. The course has every difficulty in the book: trees, fairway bunkers, lakes and a large arm of the Ria Formosa. The tranquillity and beauty of the landscape prompt the golfer to excel and meet the technical challenges laid down by the designer. Inexperienced players will have problems, sure, but with a decent handicap a day spent here can be the perfect climax to a golfing holiday. The better players will have fun trying to tame a course such as this one.

S. Lourenço Golf Club — 1988

Le Meridien D. Filipa, Vale do Lobo
P - 8135-901 ALMANCIL

Office	Secretariado	(351) 289 - 396 522
Pro shop	Pro-shop	(351) 289 - 396 522
Fax	Fax	(351) 289 - 357 201
Web	www.lemeridien-donafilipa.com	
Situation	Localização	Faro, 15 km
Annual closure	Fecho anual	no
Weekly closure	Fecho semanal	no

Fees main season Tarifas de época alta — 18 holes

	Week days / Semana	We/Bank holidays / Fim de sem./Feriad
Individual Individual	€ 150	€ 150
Couple Casal	€ 300	€ 300

Caddie Caddie on request **Electric Trolley** Trolley eléctrico yes

Buggy Buggy yes **Clubs** Tacos yes

Credit cards Cartão de crédito
VISA - AMEX

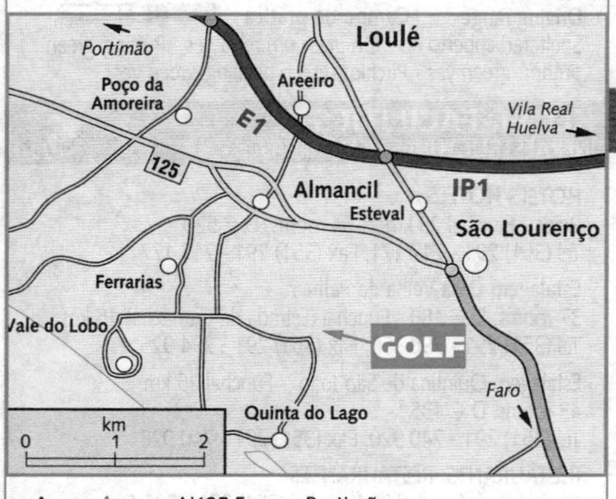

Access Acesso : N125 Faro → Portimão, Almancil → Quinta do Lago
Map 3 on page 1048 Mapa 3 Página 1048

GOLF COURSE — PERCURSO — 17/20

Site	Sitio	
Maintenance	Conversa	
Architect	Arquitecto	Joseph Lee
Type	Tipo	seaside course, forest
Relief	Relevo	
Water in play	Lago	
Exp. to wind	Exposto ao vento	
Trees in play	Arvores	

Scorecard Cartão de resultados	Chp. Camp.	Mens Homens	Ladies Senhoras
Length Compriment	6238	5837	5171
Par	72	72	72
Slope system	137	132	127

Advised golfing ability Nivel de jogo recomendado — 0 12 24 36

Hcp required Handicap exigido — 28 Men, 36 Ladies

CLUB HOUSE & AMENITIES — CLUB HOUSE E ANEXOS — 5/10

Pro shop Pro-shop
Driving range Campo de prática
Sheltered coberto no - On grass om relva yes - Putting-green putting-green yes - Pitching-green pitching-green no

HOTEL FACILITIES — INFRAESTRUCTURAS HOTELEIRAS — 7/10

HOTELS HOTELS

Quinta do Lago - Quinta do Lago 2 km
141 rooms, D € 520
Tel (351) 289 - 350 350, Fax (351) 289 - 396 393

Dona Filipa - Vale do Lobo 3 km
147 rooms, D € 400
Tel (351) 289 - 357 200, Fax (351) 289 - 357 201

RESTAURANTS RESTAURANTES

Casa Velha - Quinta do Lago 3 km - Tel (351) 289 - 394 983
Sáo Gabriel - Almancil 5 km - Tel (351) 265 - 394 521
Henrique Leis - Vale Formoso (Loulé) 5 km
Tel (351) 289 - 393 438
Casa dos Pinheiros - Almancil 4 km - Tel (351) 289 - 394 832

Santo da Serra

16	6	5

A várias centenas de metros de altitude, é um dos percursos mais extraordinários da Europa. O inconveniente da sua situação, em média montanha, é a de que se torna bastante cansativo par jogar a pé e por vezes tem bastante nevoeiro devido às nuvens baixas. A beleza do espectáculo, nomeadamente nos buracos 12 e 13, valem alguns esforços. O Arquitecto Robert Trent Jones jogou com delícia e imaginação sobre um terreno extraordinário e propõe aos jogadores de todos os níveis desafios empolgantes; estes terão que estudar bem a estratégia a seguir em cada buraco sem se distraírem demasiado com a paisagem. As dificuldades são múltiplas mas sempre bem visíveis, com uma vegetação muito rica, "roughs" bastante densos, "bunkers" muito em jogo, "greens" bem trabalhados. Tem só um obstáculo de água, mas em contrapartida o seu comprimento mantém-se razoável... se não houver vento. Aconselha-se jogar na modalidade de "match play". É um percurso muito divertido a que foi acrescentado um 3° percurso de 9 buracos.

At several hundred metres above sea level, this course primarily offers a breath-takingly beautiful panorama over the island of Madeira and the Atlantic Ocean. The drawback of being halfway up a mountain is the toll it takes on your feet and legs. But the beauty of the site, especially on the 12th and 13th holes, is well worth the effort. Designer Robert Trent Jones used a lot of fun and imagination over this remarkable terrain and offers some exciting challenges to players of all abilities, who will need to consider carefully their strategy on each hole without being distracted by the scenery. The difficulties are many and varied but always clearly in view: lush vegetation, pretty thick rough, omnipresent bunkers, well-designed greens but just the one water hazard. By contrast, yardage is reasonable... as long as the wind doesn't blow. Try it in match play, it's great fun. A third equally excellent 9 hole course has been added. It is rather shorter and less hilly.

Clube de Golf Santo da Serra — 1991

Casais Próximos - Santo António da Serra
P - 9200-152 MACHICO (MADEIRA)

Office Secretariado (351) 291 - 550 100
Pro shop Pro-shop (351) 291 - 552 356
Fax Fax (351) 291 - 550 105
Web www.santodaserragolf.com
Situation Localização Funchal, 26 km
Machico (pop. 2 142), 6 km

Annual closure Fecho anual — no
Weekly closure Fecho semanal — no

Fees main season Tarifas de época alta	18 holes	
	Week days Semana	**We/Bank holidays** Fim de sem./Feriad
Individual Individual	€ 85	€ 85
Couple Casal	€ 170	€ 170

Caddie Caddie no — **Electric Trolley** Trolley eléctrico no
Buggy Buggy yes — **Clubs** Tacos yes
Credit cards Cartão de crédito
VISA - AMEX - DC

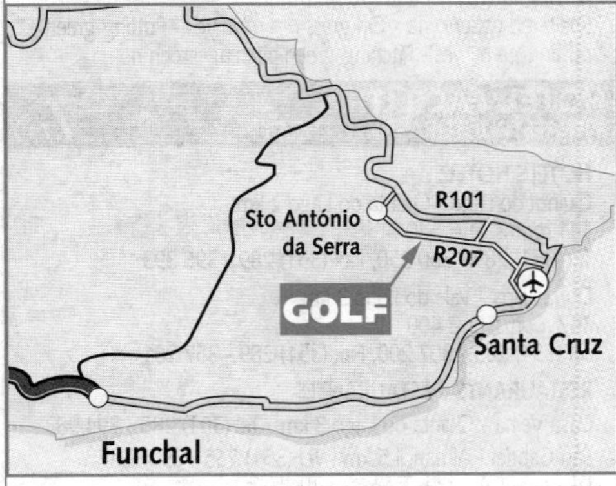

Access Acesso : E 101 Funchal → Machico.
N 675 → Sto da Serra
Map 3 on page 1049 Mapa 3 Página 1049

GOLF COURSE — PERCURSO — 16/20

Site Sitio
Maintenance Conversa
Architect Arquitecto — Robert Trent Jones
Type Tipo — mountain, hilly
Relief Relevo
Water in play Lago
Exp. to wind Exposto ao vento
Trees in play Arvores

Scorecard Cartão de resultados	Chp. Camp.	Mens Homens	Ladies Senhoras
Length Compriment	6092	5624	4624
Par	72	72	72
Slope system	141	136	125

Advised golfing ability Nivel de jogo recomendado — 0 12 24 36
Hcp required Handicap exigido 36

CLUB HOUSE & AMENITIES — CLUB HOUSE E ANEXOS — 6/10

Pro shop Pro-shop
Driving range Campo de prática
Sheltered coberto no - On grass om relva yes - Putting-green putting-green yes - Pitching-green pitching-green yes

HOTEL FACILITIES — INFRAESTRUCTURAS HOTELEIRAS — 5/10

HOTELS HOTELS
Reids - Funchal 25 km - 164 rooms, D € 520
Tel (351) 291 - 717 171, Fax (351) 291 - 717 177

Estalagem Casa Velha do Palheiro -
37 rooms, D € 180 - Funchal (Estrada de Camacha) 15 km
Tel (351) 291 - 790 350, Fax (351) 291 - 794 925

Estalagem Quintina de São João - Funchal 25 km
43 rooms, D € 135
Tel (351) 291 - 740 920, Fax (351) 291 - 740 928

RESTAURANTS RESTAURANTES
Casa Velha - Funchal 25 km - Tel (351) 291 - 205 600
Quinta Palmeira - Funchal 25 km - Tel (351) 291 - 221 814
A Morgadinha (Es. Quintina) - Funchal - Tel (351) 291 - 740 920

Troia

17 | 5 | 4

Foi e é um dos melhores percursos de Portugal e mesmo da Península Ibérica. Infelizmente e embora tenha sido recentemente melhorado a sua manutenção foi sempre irregular devido sobretudo a uma deficiente rede de rega. É pena, porque a inteligência estratégica de Robert Trent Jones foi magistral. Localizado numa península à beira mar, ele interpretou a tradição dos "links" com a presença constante da areia bem como um envolvimento de pinheiros e plantas silvestres especificas da região. O percurso parece por vezes mais estreito do que é na realidade mas os obstáculos são bem visíveis e estão bem colocados, come por exemplo alguns "bunkers" profundos que defendem vigorosamente "greens" geralmente bastante pequenos e bem modelados. Troia é um grande desafio para os bons jogadores mas é também um teste empolgante para os outros; é sempre muito instrutivo jogar num grande percurso de golf, num quadro tão atraente e natural como este.

It was and still is one of the best Courses in Portugal and even in the whole of the Iberian Peninsula. Nevertheless, and despite improvement work, inadequate and inconsistent green-keeping due mainly to a poor irrigation system still dulls its prestige. This is a pity, because the strategic intelligence deployed by designer Robert Trent Jones is brilliant. Over a seaboard peninsula he has given his own interpretation of the links tradition with ubiquitous sand and a setting of maritime pines and wild plants, both typical of this region. The course often looks tighter than it actually is, but the hazards are clear to see and well located, particularly several deep bunkers. They provide stern defence for greens that are generally rather small and well contoured. Troia is a great challenge for the better player and an exciting test for the rest. There is always something to learn from playing a great golf course in such a natural and attractive setting.

Troia Golf — 1981

Complexo Turistico de Troia
P - 7570 CARVALHAL, GDL

Office Secretariado (351) 265 - 494 112
Pro shop Pro-shop (351) 265 - 494 112
Fax Fax (351) 265 - 494 315
Web www.troiahotels.com
Situation Localização Lisboa, 42 km
Setúbal (pop. 89 106 h), 2 km

Annual closure Fecho anual — no
Weekly closure Fecho semanal — no

Fees main season / Tarifas de época alta	Week days / Semana	We/Bank holidays / Fim de sem./Feriad
18 holes		
Individual Individual	€ 59	€ 71
Couple Casal	€ 118	€ 142

Caddie Caddie no — **Electric Trolley** Trolley eléctrico no
Buggy Buggy yes — **Clubs** Tacos yes
Credit cards Cartão de crédito
VISA - Eurocard - MasterCard - AMEX - DC

Lisboa
A 2
Setúbal
N 10
Azeitão
Tróia
Reserva natural do estuario do Sado
GOLF
Baia de Setúbal
km 0 2 4
Costa da Galé

Access Acesso : Lisboa → Setúbal. Ferry-boat.
N 253-1 → Melides
Map 2 on page 1046 Mapa 2 Página 1046

GOLF COURSE — PERCURSO — 17/20

Site Sitio
Maintenance Conversa
Architect Arquitecto — Robert Trent Jones
Type Tipo — seaside course, links
Relief Relevo
Water in play Lago
Exp. to wind Exposto ao vento
Trees in play Arvores

Scorecard / Cartão de resultados	Chp. / Camp.	Mens / Homens	Ladies / Senhoras
Length Compriment	6320	5831	4872
Par	72	72	72
Slope system	124	119	117

Advised golfing ability 0 12 24 36
Nivel de jogo recomendado
Hcp required Handicap exigido 36

CLUB HOUSE & AMENITIES — CLUB HOUSE E ANEXOS — 5/10

Pro shop Pro-shop
Driving range Campo de prática
Sheltered coberto no - On grass om relva yes - Putting-green putting-green yes - Pitching-green pitching-green yes

HOTEL FACILITIES — INFRAESTRUCTURAS HOTELEIRAS — 4/10

HOTELS HOTELS
Pousada de São Felipe - Castelo de São Felipe 6 km - 16 rooms, D € 185
Tel (351) 265 - 550 070, Fax (351) 265 - 539 240

Bonfim - 100 rooms, D € 100 - Setúbal5 km
Tel (351) 265 - 550 700, Fax (351) 265 - 534 858

Estalagem do Sado - 66 rooms, D € 90 - Setúbal 6 km
Tel (351) 265 - 542 800, Fax (351) 265 - 542 828

RESTAURANTS RESTAURANTES
Soltroia Beach Club - Troia 2 km
Mira Ponte - Troia 2 km
El Toro - Setúbal 6 km - Tel (351) 265 - 524 995

Vale do Lobo *Ocean Course*

14	6	8

O Ocean surge do reerranjo do antigo percurso de Vale de Lobo, da autoria de Henry Cotton, por Rocky Roquemore. Não se pode dizer que neste caso tenha sido uma melhoria. Permitiu a criação de um novo percurso, o Royal, que sob o ponto de vista comercial melhorou a oferta naquela região já bem servida de campos de "golf". Não se trata de um percurso muito comprido e por isso pode ser jogado pelos mais variados tipos de jogadores. Se não fosse o excesso de construção junto ao campo seria uma proposta ainda mais agradável. Como principais atractivos salienta-se a proximidade do mar e das belas vistas que se desfrutam de vários buracos.

The Ocean is the result of a rearranged layout produced by Rocky Roquemore using the original Henry Cotton design, but whether or not he has achieved any real improvement is a moot point. The main point of the exercise was to create a new course, the Royal, which has enhanced the already huge commercial supply of golf courses in the region. The course is not long and so can be played by players of all abilities. If there wasn't so much construction work going on so close to the course it would be an even more attractive proposition. The course's overriding appeal lies with the closeness of the Atlantic and the beautiful views from various points on the course.

Vale do Lobo Golf Club — 1968

P - 8135-864 VALE DO LOBO

Office	Secretariado	(351) 289 - 353 535
Pro shop	Pro-shop	(351) 289 - 353 535
Fax	Fax	(351) 289 - 353 003
Web	www.valedolobo.com	
Situation	Localização	Faro, 21 km
Annual closure	Fecho anual	no
Weekly closure	Fecho semanal	no

Fees main season Tarifas de época alta	18 holes	
	Week days Semana	**We/Bank holidays** Fim de sem./Feriad
Individual Individual	€ 150	€ 150
Couple Casal	€ 300	€ 300

Special fees for families

Caddie Caddie no — **Electric Trolley** Trolley eléctrico no

Buggy Buggy yes — **Clubs** Tacos yes

Credit cards Cartão de crédito
VISA - Eurocard - AMEX - DC

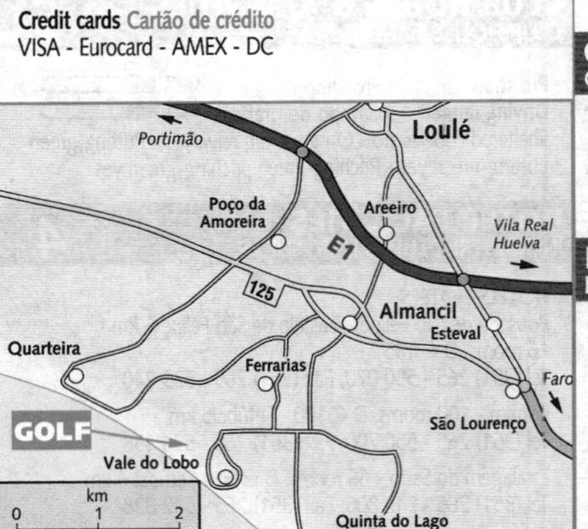

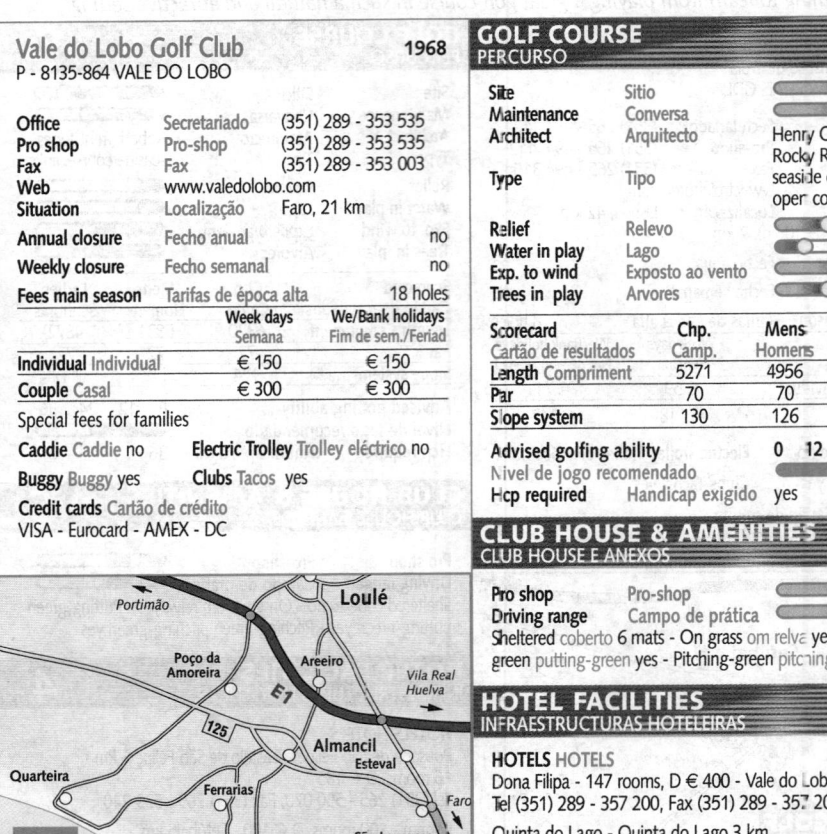

Access Acesso : Faro, Road 125 → Albufeira. Turn in Amancil and follow signs to Vale do Lobo.

Map 3 on page 1048 Mapa 3 Página 1048

GOLF COURSE — PERCURSO — 14/20

Site	Sitio	
Maintenance	Conversa	
Architect	Arquitecto	Henry Cotton, Rocky Roquemore
Type	Tipo	seaside course, open country
Relief	Relevo	
Water in play	Lago	
Exp. to wind	Exposto ao vento	
Trees in play	Arvores	

Scorecard Cartão de resultados	**Chp.** Camp.	**Mens** Homens	**Ladies** Senhoras
Length Compriment	5271	4956	4378
Par	70	70	70
Slope system	130	126	124

Advised golfing ability Nivel de jogo recomendado — 0 12 24 36

Hcp required Handicap exigido — yes

CLUB HOUSE & AMENITIES — CLUB HOUSE E ANEXOS — 6/10

Pro shop Pro-shop

Driving range Campo de prática

Sheltered coberto 6 mats - On grass om relva yes - Putting-green putting-green yes - Pitching-green pitching-green yes

HOTEL FACILITIES — INFRAESTRUCTURAS HOTELEIRAS — 8/10

HOTELS HOTELS

Dona Filipa - 147 rooms, D € 400 - Vale do Lobo 1 km
Tel (351) 289 - 357 200, Fax (351) 289 - 357 201

Quinta do Lago - Quinta do Lago 3 km
141 rooms, D € 520
Tel (351) 289 - 350 350, Fax (351) 289 - 396 393

RESTAURANTS RESTAURANTES

Sáo Gabriel - Almancil 3 km - Tel (351) 265 - 394 521

Aux Bons Enfants - Almancil 6 km - Tel (351) 289 - 396 840

Casa do Lago - Quinta do Lago 4 km
Tel (351) 289 - 394 911

Vale do Lobo *Royal Golf Course*

15 | 7 | 8

Vale do Lobo, era um dos mais famosos percursos de Portugal, sobretudo devido a um dos seus buracos (agora é o 16 do Royal) que se joga por cima de uma serie de três falésias. Os restantes 26 não estavam à mesma altura. Acrescentando-lhe 9 buracos novos e alguns melhoramentos, eis que surge o percurso "Royal", fruto do trabalho realizado com um intervalo de 30 anos entre Henry Cotton e Rocky Roquemore. Aos restantes 18 buracos passaram a chamar-se "Ocean Course". No "Royal" nota-se que os estilos dos dois arquitectos se fundem harmoniosamente, numa espécie de casamento entre a estética e os estilos de jogo americano e britânico. Há que felicitar Roquemore por ter evitado com inteligência as rupturas visuais brutais, embora cada buraco tenha a personalidade suficiente para ser memorizado. Vale do Lobo oferece agora excelentes testes de "golf", acrescido do facto de serem uns belos percursos, arborizado por milhares de pinheiros, oliveiras, figueiras e laranjeiras que invadem frequentemente com o jogo.

This used to be one of Portugal's most famous courses, especially for one of the holes here (now the 16th of the "Royal") played over three rows of cliffs. The other 26 holes unfortunately were not always up to scratch. Today, with nine new holes and a little rejuvenation, here is the "Royal Course", the work of Henry Cotton and Rocky Roquemore with a 30-year interval in between. The other 18 holes are now the "Ocean Course". On the "Royal", the styles of the two architects blend together perfectly, sort of dovetailing the visual appeal and styles of American and British courses. Roquemore must be congratulated for having cleverly avoided any clashes in overall visual harmony, even though each hole has enough personality to stick in the mind. Vale do Lobo now provides an excellent test of golf in addition to being a very pretty course lined with thousands of pine, olive, fig and orange trees which frequently come into play.

Vale do Lobo Golf Club — 1968

P - 8135-864 VALE DO LOBO

Office	Secretariado	(351) 289 - 353 535
Pro shop	Pro-shop	(351) 289 - 353 535
Fax	Fax	(351) 289 - 353 003
Web	www.valedolobo.com	
Situation	Localização	Faro, 21 km
Annual closure	Fecho anual	no
Weekly closure	Fecho semanal	no

Fees main season Tarifas de época alta	Week days Semana	We/Bank holidays Fim de sem./Feriad
		18 holes
Individual Individual	€ 135	€ 135
Couple Casal	€ 270	€ 270

Special fees for families

Caddie Caddie no — **Electric Trolley** Trolley eléctrico no

Buggy Buggy yes — **Clubs** Tacos yes

Credit cards Cartão de crédito
VISA - Eurocard - AMEX - DC

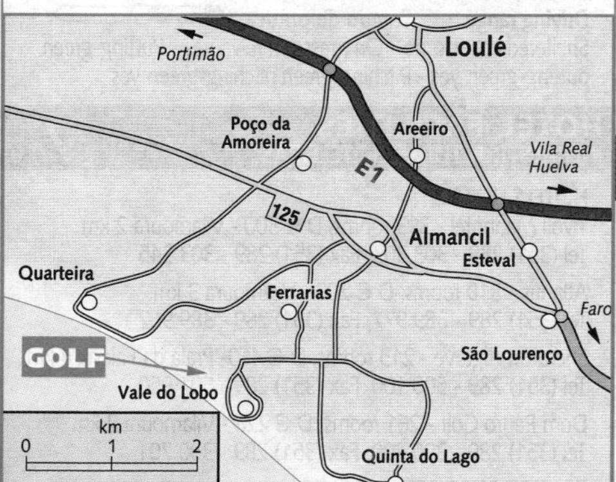

Access Acesso : Faro, Road 125 → Albufeira. Turn in Amancil and follow signs to Vale do Lobo.

Map 3 on page 1048 Mapa 3 Página 1048

GOLF COURSE — PERCURSO — 15/20

Site	Sitio	
Maintenance	Conversa	
Architect	Arquitecto	Henry Cotton, Rocky Roquemore
Type	Tipo	seaside course, forest
Relief	Relevo	
Water in play	Lago	
Exp. to wind	Exposto ao vento	
Trees in play	Arvores	

Scorecard Cartão de resultados	Chp. Camp.	Mens Homens	Ladies Senhoras
Length Compriment	6050	5650	4925
Par	72	72	72
Slope system	—	—	—

Advised golfing ability Nivel de jogo recomendado: 0 12 24 36

Hcp required Handicap exigido: 27 Men/35 Ladies

CLUB HOUSE & AMENITIES — CLUB HOUSE E ANEXOS — 7/10

Pro shop	Pro-shop
Driving range	Campo de prática

Sheltered coberto 6 mats - On grass om relva yes - Putting-green putting-green yes - Pitching-green pitching-green yes

HOTEL FACILITIES — INFRAESTRUCTURAS HOTELEIRAS — 8/10

HOTELS HOTELS

Dona Filipa - 147 rooms, D € 400 - Vale do Lobo 1 km
Tel (351) 289 - 357 200, Fax (351) 289 - 357 201

Quinta do Lago - Quinta do Lago 3 km
141 rooms, D € 520
Tel (351) 289 - 350 350, Fax (351) 289 - 396 393

RESTAURANTS RESTAURANTES

Sáo Gabriel - Almancil 3 km - Tel (351) 265 - 394 521
Aux Bons Enfants - Almancil 6 km - Tel (351) 289 - 396 840
Casa do Lago - Quinta do Lago 4 km
Tel (351) 289 - 394 911

Vila Sol

14 | 6 | 7

Criado em 1991 numa zona de pinhal com alguns sobreiros bem como algumas figueiras a amendoeiras. Vila Sol foi desenhada por Donald Steel que não procurou renegar o seu estilo britânico. Renunciou a quaisquer movimentos de terra espectaculares, conservando o lado natural do terreno. Pode lamentar-se que não tenha um traçado mais original, mas não deixa de ser um percurso que se adapta bem a uma grande variedade de categorias de jogadores, embora os primeiros buracos sejam um pouco difíceis para amadores. Podem porem tranquilizar-se; o seguimento é mas tranquilo. Bastante estreito, o percurso pode causar problemas aos jogadores imprecisos. Deverão jogar com cuidado para evitar as árvores e salvar o seu par. Com excepção do "green" do 11, os outros são bastante visíveis, pouco protegidos, planos a de dimensão média. Geralmente com boa manutenção, este percurso não é uma obra prima, mas merece o desvio.

Created in 1991 over an estate of pine, cork oak, fig and almond trees, Vila Sol was laid out by Donald Steel working in a distinctly British style. Preferring to keep the terrain's natural look, there was no spectacular earth moving. This is a moot point as we would have liked a more personal layout. As it is, the course is very fair and playable by all golfers, even though the first holes are a tough test for the average hacker. They can relax, though, because the course tends to lighten up later on. Having said that, this is a rather tight layout which will cause problems for wayward hitters. Getting out of the trees to save par requires some well-flighted recovery shots. With the exception of the 11th hole, all the greens are visible, relatively undefended, rather flat and medium-sized. A well maintained course, hardly a masterpiece but well worth the trip.

Golf de Vila Sol — 1991

Morgadinhos, Alto do Semino, Est. Nacional 396, km 24,8
P - 8125-307 VILAMOURA

Office	Secretariado	(351) 289 - 300 500
Pro shop	Pro-shop	(351) 289 - 300 522
Fax	Fax	(351) 289 - 316 499
Web	www.vilasol.pt	
Situation	Localização	Faro, 18 km

Quarteira (pop.8 905), 3 km

Annual closure	Fecho anual	no
Weekly closure	Fecho semanal	no
Fees main season	Tarifas de época alta	18 holes

	Week days / Semana	We/Bank holidays / Fim de sem./Feriad
Individual Individual	€ 100	€ 100
Couple Casal	€ 200	€ 200

Special fees for juniors

Caddie Caddie no — **Electric Trolley** Trolley eléctrico yes

Buggy Buggy yes — **Clubs** Tacos yes

Credit cards Cartão de crédito
VISA - AMEX

Access Acesso : N1, N125 → Faro, N 396 → Quarteira
Map 3 on page 1048 Mapa 3 Página 1048

GOLF COURSE — PERCURSO — 14/20

Site	Sitio	
Maintenance	Conversa	
Architect	Arquitecto	Donald Steel
Type	Tipo	forest, residential
Relief	Relevo	
Water in play	Lago	
Exp. to wind	Exposto ao vento	
Trees in play	Arvores	

Scorecard Cartão de resultados	Chp. Camp.	Mens Homens	Ladies Senhoras
Length Compriment	6335	5975	5406
Par	72	72	72
Slope system	133	129	131

Advised golfing ability Nivel de jogo recomendado — 0 12 24 36

Hcp required Handicap exigido — 28 Men, 36 Ladies

CLUB HOUSE & AMENITIES — CLUB HOUSE E ANEXOS — 6/10

Pro shop Pro-shop

Driving range Campo de prática

Sheltered coberto no - **On grass** om relva yes - **Putting-green** putting-green yes - **Pitching-green** pitching-green yes

HOTEL FACILITIES — INFRAESTRUCTURAS HOTELEIRAS — 7/10

HOTELS HOTELS

Tivoli Marinotel - 393 rooms, D € 300 - Vilamoura 2 km
Tel (351) 289 - 303 303, Fax (351) 289 - 303 345

Atlantis - 310 rooms, D € 200 - Vilamoura 3 km
Tel (351) 289 - 389 977, Fax (351) 289 - 389 962

Sheraton Algarve - 215 rooms, D € 460- Praia da Falésia 4 km
Tel (351) 289 - 500 100, Fax (351) 289 - 501 950

Dom Pedro Golf - 261 rooms, D € 228 - Vilamoura 2 km
Tel (351) 289 - 300 700, Fax (351) 289 - 300 701

RESTAURANTS RESTAURANTES

Willie's - Vilamoura 4 km - Tel (351) 289 - 380 849
Gril Sirius - Vilamoura 3 km - Tel (351) 289 - 303 303
Pier One - Vilamoura 3 km - Tel (351) 289 - 322 734

Vilamoura *Old Course*

17	7	7

Construído entre 1973 e 2005, o complexo de Vilamoura foi-se pouco a pouco modernizando. O primeiro, Vilamoura I, embora com a infeliz denominação actual de "Old Course", continua a ser o mais interessante e a sua renovação, em particular a de alguns "greens", acrescenta ao prazer da sua reabertura. O arquitecto Frank Pennink soube preservar a naturalidade de uma paisagem magnífica, servida de uma bela vegetação. O seu percurso lembra muitas vezes a arquitectura dos golfes britânicos de interior, aqui com a vantagem do clima. Embora tenha um par 73, é suficientemente longo para perturbar os jogadores imprecisos, pois as arvores estão muito em jogo. Os pares 3 também não são fáceis. É um percurso para bons controladores, expertos na arte de trabalhar a bola. Os seus cinco pares 5 podem no entanto, salvar os resultados que de outro modo estariam ameaçados. Um excelente "test" bem rejuvenescido e geralmente com excelente manutenção.

Built between 1973 and 2005, the Vilamoura resort has gradually been modernised. The oldest, Vilamoura (renamed Old Course) is still the most interesting and its restyling, especially the greens, has made its re-opening all the more enjoyable. Designer Frank Pennink has successfully preserved the natural look of magnificent landscape and vegetation. The layout is often reminiscent of some of the great British parkland courses, with the climate as an added benefit. Although a par 73, it is long enough to upset wayward hitters as the trees are very much in play. The par 3s are no walkover, either, making this a course for the technically minded golfer who excels in flighting the ball. But rest assured, the 5 par 5s can save a card that the other holes might have condemned to the litterbin. An excellent test of golf now looking wonderfully younger and well maintained.

Vilamoura Golf Club — 1969

P - 8125-507 VILAMOURA

Office	Secretariado	(351) 289 - 310 341
Pro shop	Pro-shop	(351) 289 - 301 166
Fax	Fax	(351) 289 - 310 321
Web	www.vilamoura.net	
Situation	Localização	Faro, 20 km

Quarteira (pop. 8 905), 3 km

Annual closure	Fecho anual	no
Weekly closure	Fecho semanal	no
Fees main season	Tarifas de época alta	18 holes

	Week days / Semana	We/Bank holidays / Fim de sem./Feriad
Individual Individual	€ 120	€ 120
Couple Casal	€ 240	€ 240

Juniors under 18: € 62,50

Caddie Caddie on request **Electric Trolley** Trolley eléctrico yes

Buggy Buggy yes **Clubs** Tacos yes

Credit cards Cartão de crédito
VISA - AMEX

Access Acesso : N125 Lagos-Faro. → Vilamoura
Map 3 on page 1048 Mapa 3 Página 1048

GOLF COURSE — PERCURSO — 17/20

Site	Sitio	
Maintenance	Conversa	
Architect	Arquitecto	Frank Pennink
Type	Tipo	forest
Relief	Relevo	
Water in play	Lago	
Exp. to wind	Exposto ao vento	
Trees in play	Arvores	

Scorecard Cartão de resultados	Chp. Camp.	Mens Homens	Ladies Senhoras
Length Compriment	6254	5913	5086
Par	73	73	73
Slope system	126	124	127

Advised golfing ability Nivel de jogo recomendado: 0 12 24 36

Hcp required Handicap exigido: 24 Men, 28 Ladies

CLUB HOUSE & AMENITIES — CLUB HOUSE E ANEXOS — 7/10

Pro shop Pro-shop

Driving range Campo de prática

Sheltered coberto yes - On grass om relva yes - Putting-green putting-green yes - Pitching-green pitching-green yes

HOTEL FACILITIES — INFRAESTRUCTURAS HOTELEIRAS — 7/10

HOTELS HOTELS

Tivoli Marinotel - 393 rooms, D € 300 - Vilamoura 3 km
Tel (351) 289 - 303 303, Fax (351) 289 - 303 345

Atlantis - 310 rooms, D € 200 - Vilamoura 4 km
Tel (351) 289 - 389 977, Fax (351) 289 - 389 962

Sheraton Algarve - 215 rooms, D € 460 - Praia da Falésia 4 km
Tel (351) 289 - 500 100, Fax (351) 289 - 501 950

Dom Pedro Golf - 261 rooms, D € 228- Vilamoura 3 km
Tel (351) 289 - 300 700, Fax (351) 289 - 300 701

RESTAURANTS RESTAURANTES

Willie's - Vilamoura 4 km - Tel (351) 289 - 380 849
Gril Sirius - Vilamoura 3 km - Tel (351) 289 - 303 303
Pier One - Vilamoura 2 km - Tel (351) 289 - 322 734

Vilamoura *Laguna*

15 | 7 | 7

Apresentando diferenças substanciais dos outros campos do complexo, este percurso tem uma estética e uma paisagem muito diferentes. De facto, é constituído por uma interessante combinação de buracos que se desenvolvem até próximo do mar. O desenho é do arquitecto Rocky Roquemore com a colaboração de Joseph Lee que foi um dos grandes representantes da "Escola da Florida", come se verifica, sobretudo nos segundos 9 buracos que são, alias, os mais interessantes. Como o seu nome indica a água está presente em cerca de metade dos buracos, mas o aspecto natural do terreno foi mantido. Os jogadores com distância podem exprimir-se ai melhor do que nos outros percursos do complexo, visto terem "fairways" mais largos e o arvoredo ser menos ameaçador, mesmo que visualmente seja mais intimidante do que o é na realidade. É, apesar de tudo, muito difícil fazer aqui bons resultados e deverá ser mais divertido para jogar na modalidade de "match-play". Os greens têm um desenho interessante mas há que cuidar da sua manutenção, o que aliás se justifica como num complexo que é uma verdadeira fábrica de golfe.

In a different style and landscape to the other courses in the resort, this layout consists of an interesting combination of holes set close to the Atlantic. It was designed by the late Joseph Lee (and Rocky Roquemore), one of the great representatives of the Florida school, and this becomes apparent primarily on the homeward 9. As its name suggests, water is in great supply on about half the holes but the terrain's natural look has been preserved. Big-hitters can hit more freely than on the resort's other courses as the fairways are wider and the trees less threatening. Even though it looks more intimidating than it plays, making a good score can be hard going so match-play is often more fun. The greens are interestingly designed, but maintenance needs watching on a site where golf is non-stop business.

Vilamoura Golf Club — 1990

P - 8125-507 VILAMOURA

Office	Secretariado	(351) 289 - 310 341
Pro shop	Pro-shop	(351) 289 - 301 166
Fax	Fax	(351) 289 - 310 321
Web	www.vilamoura.net	
Situation	Localização	Faro, 20 km

Quarteira (pop. 8 905), 3 km

Annual closure Fecho anual — no

Weekly closure Fecho semanal — no

Fees main season Tarifas de época alta	18 holes	
	Week days Semana	**We/Bank holidays** Fim de sem./Feriad
Individual Individual	€ 70	€ 70
Couple Casal	€ 140	€ 140

Juniors under 18: € 37,50

Caddie Caddie on request **Electric Trolley** Trolley eléctrico yes

Buggy Buggy yes **Clubs** Tacos yes

Credit cards Cartão de crédito
VISA - AMEX

Access Acesso : N125 Lagos-Faro. → Vilamoura
Map 3 on page 1048 Mapa 3 Página 1048

GOLF COURSE — PERCURSO — 15/20

Site	Sitio	
Maintenance	Conversa	
Architect	Arquitecto	Joseph Lee Rocky Roquemore
Type	Tipo	open country
Relief	Relevo	
Water in play	Lago	
Exp. to wind	Exposto ao vento	
Trees in play	Arvores	

Scorecard Cartão de resultados	**Chp.** Camp.	**Mens** Homens	**Ladies** Senhoras
Length Compriment	6111	5757	4900
Par	72	72	72
Slope system	129	126	121

Advised golfing ability Nivel de jogo recomendado — 0 12 24 36

Hcp required Handicap exigido — 28 Men, 36 Ladies

CLUB HOUSE & AMENITIES — CLUB HOUSE E ANEXOS — 7/10

Pro shop Pro-shop

Driving range Campo de prática

Sheltered coberto yes - On grass om relva yes - Putting-green putting-green yes - Pitching-green pitching-green yes

HOTEL FACILITIES — INFRAESTRUCTURAS HOTELEIRAS — 7/10

HOTELS HOTELS

Tivoli Marinotel - 393 rooms, D € 300 - Vilamoura 3 km
Tel (351) 289 - 303 303, Fax (351) 289 - 303 345

Atlantis - 310 rooms, D € 200 - Vilamoura 4 km
Tel (351) 289 - 389 977, Fax (351) 289 - 389 962

Sheraton Algarve - 215 rooms, D € 460 - Praia da Falésia 4 km
Tel (351) 289 - 500 100, Fax (351) 289 - 501 950

Dom Pedro Golf - 261 rooms, D € 228- Vilamoura 3 km
Tel (351) 289 - 300 700, Fax (351) 289 - 300 701

RESTAURANTS RESTAURANTES

Willie's - Vilamoura 4 km - Tel (351) 289 - 380 849
Gril Sirius - Vilamoura 3 km - Tel (351) 289 - 303 303
Pier One - Vilamoura 2 km - Tel (351) 289 - 322 734

Vilamoura *Victória*

18	8	8

Um novo percurso para a coroa do "resort" de Vilamoura que se coloca em conjunto com o "Old Course" e o Laguna entre os melhores. È, no entanto, o mais moderno e o mais comprido, foi utilizado para a "World Cup" em 2005. Por enquanto está um pouco desprovido de árvores em jogo, mas apesar da sua exposição o vento é raramente tão violento como sobre os "Links" britânicos. O desenho da equipa de Arnold Palmer é tipicamente,"resort", muito profissional com boa modulação, partindo de um terreno plano e com uma colocação dos obstáculos muito séria. Dito isto, são todos bem visíveis dos "tees" de saída sendo a estratégia de jogo, portanto, evidente; Trata-se de evitar os "bunkers" e os obstáculos de água, muito em jogo em sete buracos. Embora o jogo de Alvo ("target") esteja aqui valorizado existem várias possibilidades de jogar "bump n'run". Trata-se de um percurso novo mas é imaginativo e bem integrado, não muito artificial e deverá ter um bom envelhecimento.

A new course of the Vilamoura resort, ranked right up there with the Old course and the Laguna as one of the best around. For the moment it is more or less devoid of any trees in play but despite its lack of shelter the wind is seldom as brutal as what you might find on a typical British links course. The architecture by the Arnold Palmer design team is typically "resort" in style and highly professional; there has been some fine contouring of what was originally flat terrain and hazards have been cleverly brought into play. Having said that, they are all visible from the tee-box so strategy is obvious. You simply avoid the bunkers and the water hazards that are very much in play on seven holes. And while target golf is the preferred option here, you will have a number of opportunities to try the good old bump 'n run shot. This is a brand new course, for sure, but it is imaginative, well-landscaped and not too artificial, so it should age well.

Vilamoura Golf Club — 2005

P - 8125-507 VILAMOURA

Office	Secretariado	(351) 289 - 310 341
Pro shop	Pro-shop	(351) 289 - 301 166
Fax	Fax	(351) 289 - 310 321
Web	www.vilamoura.net	
Situation	Localização	Faro, 20 km

Quarteira (pop. 8 905), 3 km

Annual closure	Fecho anual	no
Weekly closure	Fecho semanal	no
Fees main season	Tarifas de época alta	18 holes

	Week days Semana	We/Bank holidays Fim de sem./Feriad
Individual Individual	€ 150	€ 150
Couple Casal	€ 300	€ 300

Caddie Caddie on request **Electric Trolley** Trolley eléctrico yes

Buggy Buggy yes **Clubs** Tacos yes

Credit cards Cartão de crédito
VISA - AMEX

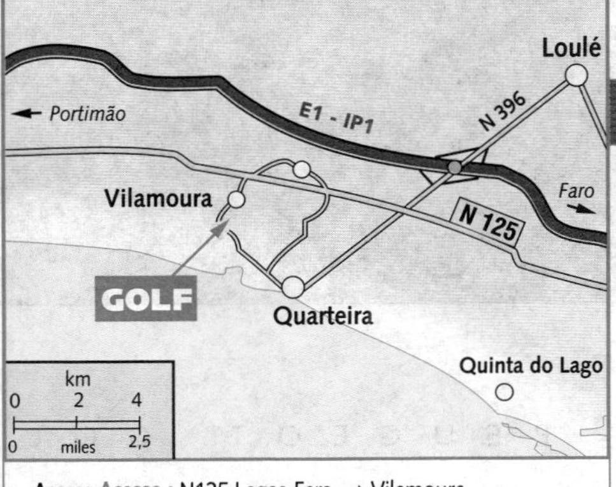

Access Acesso : N125 Lagos-Faro. → Vilamoura
Map 3 on page 1048 Mapa 3 Página 1048

GOLF COURSE PERCURSO — 18/20

Site	Sitio	
Maintenance	Conversa	
Architect	Arquitecto	Arnold Palmer
Type	Tipo	seaside, open country
Relief	Relevo	
Water in play	Lago	
Exp. to wind	Exposto ao vento	
Trees in play	Arvores	

Scorecard Cartão de resultados	Chp. Camp.	Mens Homens	Ladies Senhoras
Length Compriment	6560	5628	4762
Par	72	72	72
Slope system	124	120	117

Advised golfing ability Nivel de jogo recomendado — 0 12 24 36

Hcp required Handicap exigido certificate

CLUB HOUSE & AMENITIES CLUB HOUSE E ANEXOS — 7/10

Pro shop Pro-shop
Driving range Campo de prática
Sheltered coberto yes - On grass om relva yes - Putting-green putting-green yes - Pitching-green pitching-green yes

HOTEL FACILITIES INFRAESTRUCTURAS HOTELEIRAS — 7/10

HOTELS HOTELS

Tivoli Marinotel - Vilamoura 3 km - 393 rooms, D € 300
Tel (351) 289 - 303 303, Fax (351) 289 - 303 345

Atlantis - Vilamoura 4 km - 310 rooms, D € 200
Tel (351) 289 - 389 977, Fax (351) 289 - 389 962

Sheraton Algarve - Praia da Falésia 4 km - 215 rooms, D € 460
Tel (351) 289 - 500 100, Fax (351) 289 - 501 950

Dom Pedro Golf - Vilamoura 3 km - 261 rooms, D € 228
Tel (351) 289 - 300 700, Fax (351) 289 - 300 701

RESTAURANTS RESTAURANTES

Willie's - Vilamoura 4 km - Tel (351) 289 - 380 849
Gril Sirius - Vilamoura 3 km - Tel (351) 289 - 303 303
Pier One - Vilamoura 2 km - Tel (351) 289 - 322 734

ESPAÑA

SPAIN

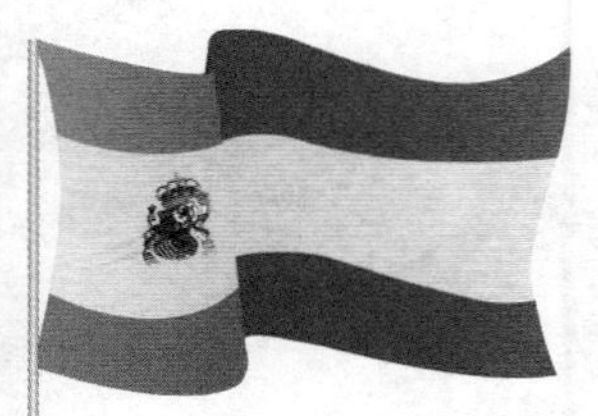

ESPAGNE

Golf in Spain is now growing very fast indeed. Over the past five years, the number of registered players has doubled and should top 280,000 by early 2006. This translates to twelve percent growth per year for the past ten years. And it has all gone hand in hand with a substantial increase in the number of courses.

Spain today boasts 300 golf courses (including 75 nine-holers and 81 compact par-3 courses). At the time of going to press, many other layouts were under development and should be up and running by the end of 2006. Courses today are being built not only in popular tourist areas like the Canary Islands, the Balearic Islands, the Costa del Sol, Costa Brava and the coastline from Valencia to Alicante, but also in places like Castile, Murcia, Galicea, Asturias, Barcelona or Madrid. In Barcelona, you might recall that the El Prat course, designed by Javier Arana, had to bow to expansion plans for the city's airport. The club has now moved and asked Greg Norman to design two new courses, both of which are included in this edition. There are also several new courses in the south, the El Puerto and Sherry Golf courses in the region of Jerez, and also the excellent La Reserva and the "New Course" at San Roque, which complement the excellent golfing facilities to be found in the region of Sotogrande. Another new course is a Trent Jones Jr. layout at Majorque, Alcanada.

Spain continues to confirm its status as one of Europe's top golfing destinations, benefiting as it does from a pleasant climate and excellent standards for courses and services. The golfing tradition here dates back over a hundred years and has helped hatch some of the world's leading professional and amateur golfers. But as golf is still not a very popular sport in Spain (in the true sense of the word), the country is only now beginning to produce public courses to rank with the top private clubs that are generally located around major cities. Most of them admit visitors, sometimes with certain restrictions in order to favour their members, but as they can also sometimes offer special conditions, it is worthwhile making enquiries about this when booking your tee-off time.

ESPAÑA

El golf está creciendo en España a velocidad de Fórmula 1. En los últimos cinco años se ha doblado el número de jugadores federados -en la franja de 280.000 al entrar en 2006, con un crecimiento del 12 por ciento en los últimos diez años- lo cual ha llevado a una ampliación muy notable de las instalaciones.

Cuenta España con cerca de 300 campos de golf (75 de ellos de 9 hoyos), 81 instalaciones entre canchas, campos cortos y pitch & putt; y otros varios están en construcción para ponerse en juego antes de que finalice el año 2006. No solamente se construye en las conocidas zonas turísticas como son Canarias, Baleares, la Costa del Sol, la Costa Brava y las costas de Valencia y Alicante, sino también en Castilla, Murcia, Galicia, Vizcaya, el Pirineo, Asturias, Barcelona y Madrid. En Barcelona, ya sabíamos que El Prat diseñado por Javier Arana había tenido que ceder sus instalaciones para la ampliación del aeropuerto; el club ha emigrado encargando a Greg Norman dos nuevos recorridos que se presentan en esta edición. Asimismo se incorporan otros varios recorridos abiertos recientemente en el sur, como El Puerto y Sherry Golf en la región de Jerez, el excelente campo de La Reserva y el "New Course" de San Roque que amplían la oferta en la zona de Sotrogrande, y el espectacular Alcanada de Trent Jones Jr. en el norte de Mallorca.

España sigue siendo uno de los principales destinos del turismo de golf en Europa, atraído por la bonanza del clima y también por la calidad de las instalaciones y servicios de este país. España también tiene una tradición centenaria en el deporte del golf que ha producido y produce extraordinarios campeones profesionales así como una élite de jugadores amateur que triunfan en las competiciones europeas. Y como el golf todavía no es un deporte popular hay una clara tendencia a construir y equipar campos municipales y públicos como alternativa a los clubs privados históricos que se encuentran, generalmente, junto a las grandes ciudades. Pero la mayoría de los campos admiten visitantes, a veces con ciertas limitaciones y muy frecuentemente ofrecen precios especiales en los green-fees y servicios, por lo que es conveniente consultar las condiciones en el momento de reservar las horas de salida.

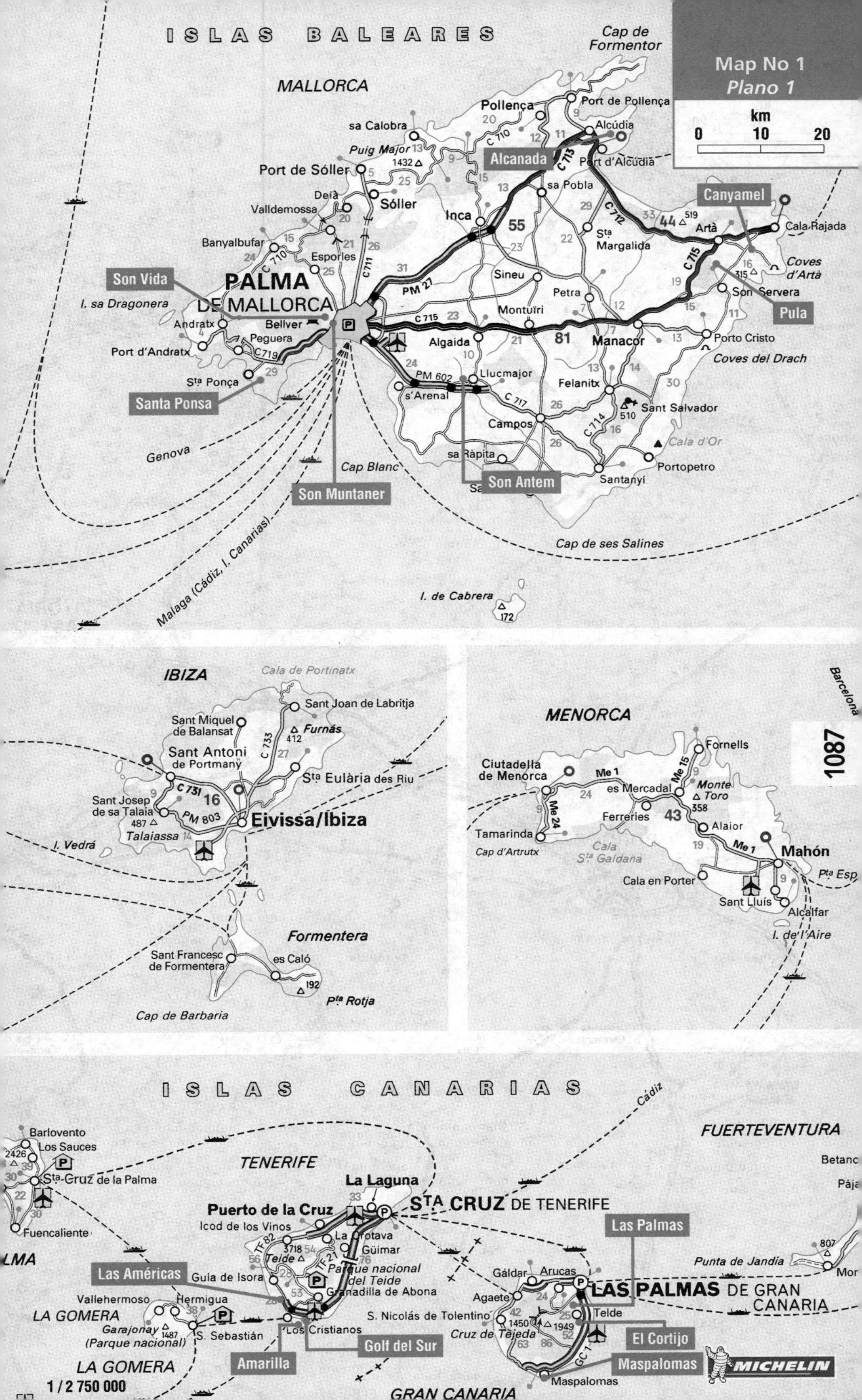
ISLAS BALEARES
Map No 1
Plano 1
km
0
10
20
MALLORCA
Cap de Formentor
Pollença
Port de Pollença
Alcúdia
Alcanada
Port d'Alcúdia
sa Calobra
Puig Major
Port de Sóller
Sóller
Deià
Valldemossa
Banyalbufar
Esporles
Inca
sa Pobla
Sta Margalida
Artà
Canyamel
Cala Rajada
Coves d'Artà
Son Servera
Pula
Son Vida
PALMA DE MALLORCA
I. sa Dragonera
Andratx
Bellver
Peguera
Port d'Andratx
Sta Ponça
Santa Ponsa
Sineu
Petra
Montuïri
Algaida
Manacor
Porto Cristo
Coves del Drach
Llucmajor
s'Arenal
Felanitx
Sant Salvador
Campos
Cala d'Or
sa Ràpita
Portopetro
Santanyí
Son Antem
Son Muntaner
Cap Blanc
Genova
Malaga (Cádiz, I. Canarias)
Cap de ses Salines
I. de Cabrera
IBIZA
Cala de Portinatx
Sant Joan de Labritja
Furnás
Sant Miquel de Balansat
Sant Antoni de Portmany
Sta Eulària des Riu
Sant Josep de sa Talaia
Talaiassa
Eivissa/Ibiza
I. Vedrá
Formentera
Sant Francesc de Formentera
es Caló
Pta Rotja
Cap de Barbaria
MENORCA
Barcelona
Fornells
Ciutadella de Menorca
es Mercadal
Monte Toro
Ferreries
Alaior
Tamarinda
Cap d'Artrutx
Cala Sta Galdana
Mahón
Cala en Porter
Sant Lluís
Alcalfar
I. de l'Aire
ISLAS CANARIAS
Cádiz
FUERTEVENTURA
Barlovento
Los Sauces
Sta Cruz de la Palma
Fuencaliente
TENERIFE
La Laguna
STA CRUZ DE TENERIFE
Puerto de la Cruz
Icod de los Vinos
La Orotava
Güimar
Teide
Parque nacional del Teide
Granadilla de Abona
Guía de Isora
Las Américas
Los Cristianos
Golf del Sur
Amarilla
Las Palmas
Gáldar
Arucas
Agaete
LAS PALMAS DE GRAN CANARIA
Telde
S. Nicolás de Tolentino
Cruz de Tejeda
El Cortijo
Maspalomas
GRAN CANARIA
Punta de Jandía
Vallehermoso
Hermigua
LA GOMERA
Garajonay (Parque nacional)
S. Sebastián
MICHELIN
1 / 2 750 000

1087

Map No 2
Plano 2
km
0 10 20
Pedreña
Neguri
Lerma
MICHELIN
Cantabria
C. de Ajo
Isla
Noja
Ajo
Santoña
Escalante
Laredo
Castro-Urdiales
Cabo Matxitxako
Machichaco
Costa
Bakio
Bermeo
Plentzia
Getxo
Areeta
Mungia
Santurtzi
Portugalete
Barakaldo
BILBAO
Gernika
Torrelavega
El Astillero
Solares
Colindres
Ampuero
Liérganes
Sarón
Puente Viesgo
Vargas
Las Caldas de Besaya
Los Corrales de Buelna
Cueva de Altamira
Corvera
Ontaneda
Villacarriedo
Alceda
Arenas de Iguña
Arredondo
Ramales de la Victoria
El Puente
Pto de Braguia
Pto de la Sía
Carranza
Balmaseda
Zalla
Güeñes
Sodupe
Arrigorroaga
Galdakao
Amorebieta
Durango
Pto de Urkiola
Artea
Llodio
Artziniega
Amurrio
Orduña
Pto de Orduña
Murguía
Legutiano
Gorbeia
Pto de Barazar
Pto del Escudo
Pto de las Estacas de Trueba
Espinosa de los Monteros
Villasana de Mena
Villasante
Corconte
Arija
Reinosa
Cervatos
Embalse del Ebro
Puerto Pozazal
Cilleruelo de Bezana
Soncillo
Río Nela
Villarcayo
Medina de Pomar
Quincoces de Yuso
Berberana
PAÍS
VITORIA-GASTEIZ
Subijana
Valdenoceda
Pto de la Mazorra
Escalada
Trespaderne
Quintana Martín Galíndez
Basconcillos del Tozo
Tubilla del Agua
Sedano
Oña
Frías
Río Ebro
E. de Sobrón
Amaya
Humada
Altotero
Poza de la Sal
Busto de Bureba
Pancorbo
Miranda de Ebro
Treviño
Zambrana
Labastida
Pto de Herrera
Haro
La Nuez de Arriba
Pto de Páramo de Masa
Villadiego
Briviesca
Monasterio de Rodilla
Pto de la Brújula
Cerezo de Riotirón
Casalarreina
Sotopalacio
BURGOS
Las Huelgas Reales
Rubena
Belorado
Sto Domingo de la Calzada
Nájera
Cenicero
Navarrete
Villanueva de Argaño
Castrojeriz
Miraflores
Arlanzón
Villafranca-Montes de Oca
Montes de Oca
Arcos
Sarracín
Pampliega
E. de Uzquiza
Pradoluengo
Ezcaray
S. Millán de la Cogolla
Torrecilla en Cameros
Anguiano
Pineda de la S.
San Millán
Valdezcaray
S. Lorenzo
Sierra de la Demanda
Sta María del Campo
Cuevas de S. Clemente
Riocavado de la Sierra
Canales de la Sierra
E. de Mansilla
Villanueva de Cameros
Villahoz
S. Millán de Lara
Covarrubias
Río Arlanza
Barbadillo del Mercado
Salas de los Infantes
Neila
Montenegro de Cameros
Pto de Sta Inés
Puerto de Piqueras
Espinosa de C.
Sto Domingo de Silos
Castrillo de la Reina
Laguna Negra de Urbión
Villafruela
Valdosa
Quintanar de la Sierra
Sierra de Urbión
Cebollera
LEÓN
Palacios de la Sierra
Duruelo de la Sierra
Peñas de Cervera
Tórtoles de E.
Hontoria del Pinar
Vinuesa
El Royo
Huerta del Rey
E. de la Cuerda del Pozo
Gumiel de Hizán
Caleruega
Olmedillo de Roa
Navaleno
S. Leonardo de Yagüe
La Horra
Pto de Mojón Pardo
Abejar
Cidones
Roa de Duero
Alcubilla de Avellaneda
Aranda de Duero
Peñaranda de Duero
Calatañazor
Hinodejo
Langa de Duero
El Burgo
Quintana Redonda

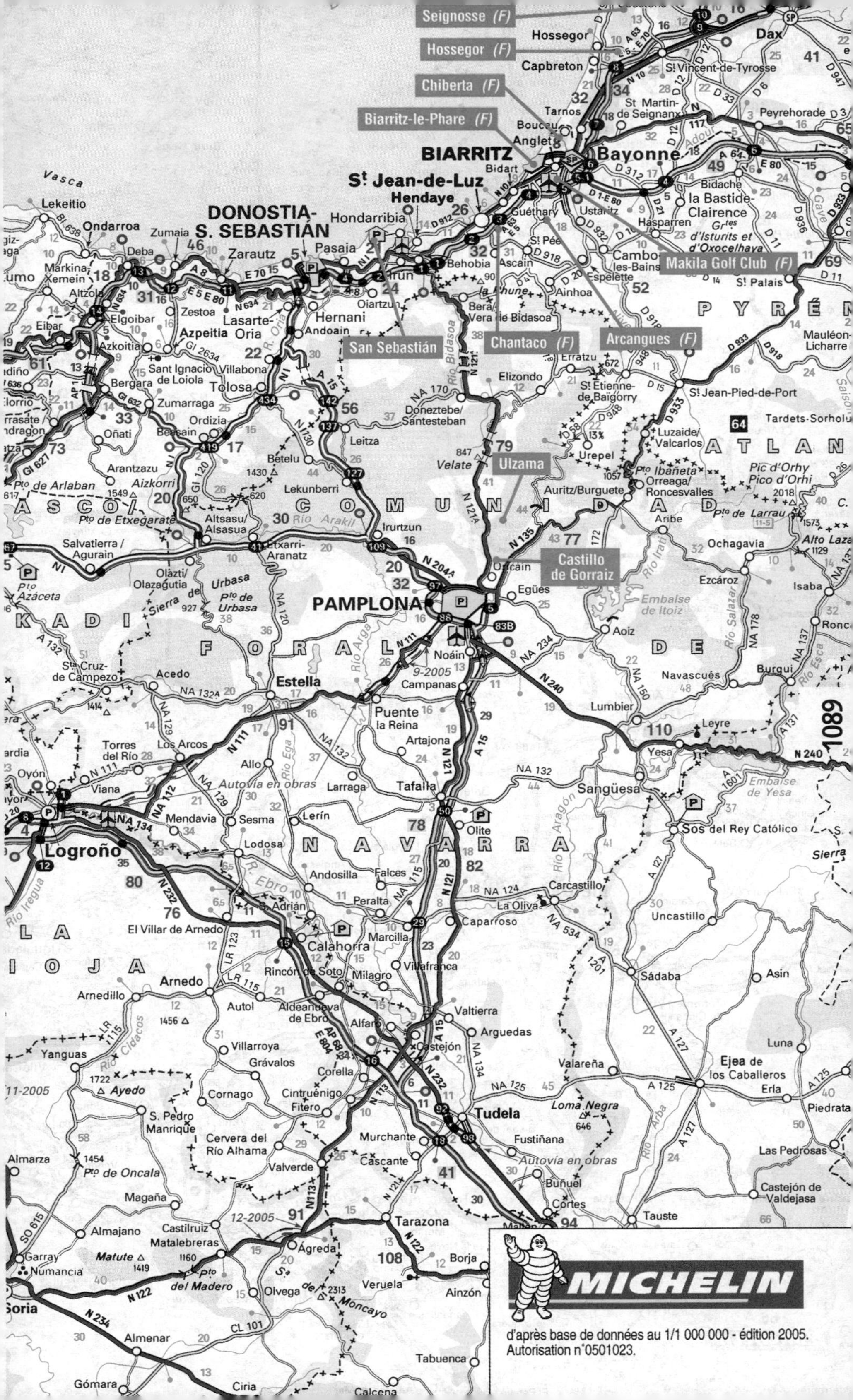

Seignosse (F)
Hossegor (F)
Chiberta (F)
Biarritz-le-Phare (F)
Makila Golf Club (F)
San Sebastián
Chantaco (F)
Arcangues (F)
Ulzama
Castillo de Gorraiz
BIARRITZ
Bayonne
Dax
Hossegor
Capbreton
St Vincent-de-Tyrosse
Anglet
Bidart
St Jean-de-Luz
Hendaye
Hondarribia
DONOSTIA-S. SEBASTIÁN
Pasaia
Irun
Zarautz
Zumaia
Deba
Ondarroa
Lekeitio
Tolosa
Hernani
Andoain
Azpeitia
Bergara
Oñati
Beasain
Ordizia
Altsasu/Alsasua
Irurtzun
Elizondo
St Jean-Pied-de-Port
Orreaga/Roncesvalles
Auritz/Burguete
PAMPLONA
Estella
Puente la Reina
Tafalla
Olite
Sangüesa
Lumbier
Aoiz
Logroño
Calahorra
Tudela
Tarazona
Ágreda
Soria
Ejea de los Caballeros
Sos del Rey Católico
Uncastillo
Sádaba
Borja
N A V A R R A
C O M U N I D A D F O R A L D E
P Y R É N
A T L A N
1089
MICHELIN
d'après base de données au 1/1 000 000 - édition 2005.
Autorisation n°0501023.

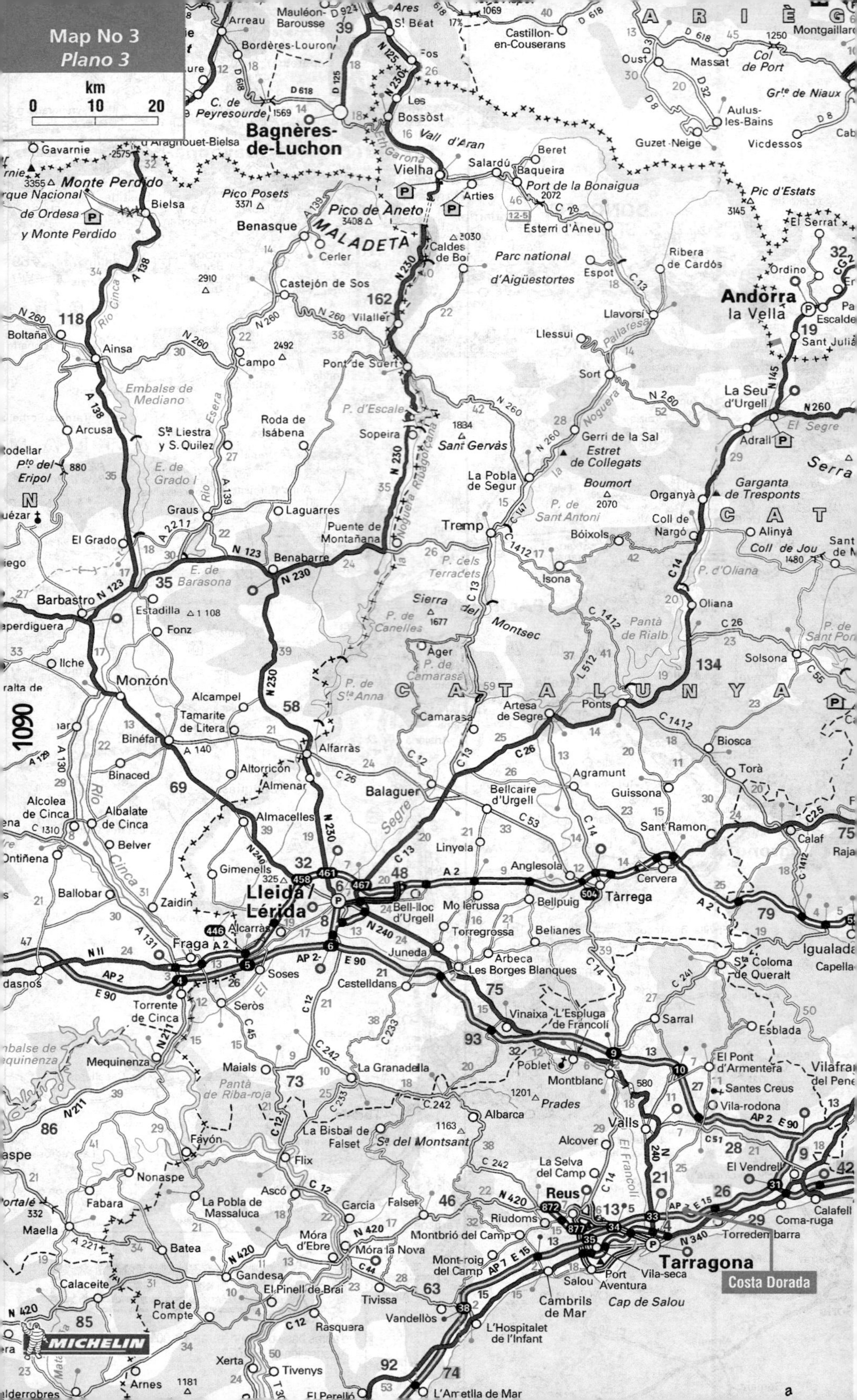
Map No 3
Plano 3
km
0 10 20
Bagnères-de-Luchon
Arreau
Mauléon-Barousse
Ares
St Béat
Fos
Les Bossòst
Bordères-Louron
C. de Peyresourde
Castillon-en-Couserans
Massat
Oust
Col de Port
Montgaillard
Grte de Niaux
Aulus-les-Bains
Guzet-Neige
Vicdessos
Gavarnie
Aragnouet-Bielsa
Monte Perdido
Parque Nacional de Ordesa y Monte Perdido
Bielsa
Pico Posets
Benasque
Pico de Aneto
Maladeta
Cerler
Vall d'Aran
Vielha
Salardú
Beret
Baqueira
Port de la Bonaigua
Arties
Esterri d'Àneu
Caldes de Boí
Parc national d'Aigüestortes
Espot
Ribera de Cardós
Pic d'Estats
El Serrat
Ordino
Andorra la Vella
Escaldes
Sant Julià
Llavorsí
Llessui
Sort
Castejón de Sos
Vilaller
Boltaña
Ainsa
Campo
Pont de Suert
Embalse de Mediano
Arcusa
Sta Liestra y S. Quilez
Roda de Isábena
Sopeira
P. d'Escales
Sant Gervàs
Gerri de la Sal
Estret de Collegats
La Seu d'Urgell
Adrall
El Segre
Serra
Garganta de Tresponts
Organyà
Coll de Nargó
Alinyà
Coll de Jou
Boumort
La Pobla de Segur
Tremp
P. de Sant Antoni
Bóixols
Isona
Pto del Eripol
Graus
Laguarres
Puente de Montañana
E. de Grado I
El Grado
Benabarre
E. de Barasona
Barbastro
Estadilla
Fonz
P. de Canelles
Sierra del Montsec
Àger
P. de Camarasa
P. de Sta Anna
Pantà de Rialb
Oliana
P. d'Oliana
Solsona
Ilche
Monzón
Alcampel
Tamarite de Litera
Binéfar
Binaced
Alfarràs
Altorricón
Almenar
Camarasa
Artesa de Segre
Ponts
CATALUNYA
Biosca
Torà
Agramunt
Guissona
Balaguer
Bellcaire d'Urgell
Sant Ramon
Calaf
Alcolea de Cinca
Albalate de Cinca
Belver
Almacelles
Linyola
Anglesola
Cervera
Tàrrega
Bellpuig
Mollerussa
Bell-lloc d'Urgell
Gimenells
Lleida/Lérida
Ballobar
Zaidín
Alcarràs
Fraga
Torregrossa
Belianes
Juneda
Arbeca
Les Borges Blanques
Igualada
Capella
Sta Coloma de Queralt
Soses
Torrente de Cinca
Seròs
Castelldans
Vinaixa
L'Espluga de Francolí
Sarral
Esblada
Poblet
Montblanc
El Pont d'Armentera
Santes Creus
Vila-rodona
Vilafranca del Penedès
Mequinenza
Maials
La Granadella
Pantà de Riba-roja
Prades
Albarca
Valls
Alcover
La Selva del Camp
La Bisbal de Falset
Sa del Montsant
Fayón
Flix
Nonaspe
Ascó
La Pobla de Massaluca
Garcia
Falset
Móra d'Ebre
Móra la Nova
Riudoms
Montbrió del Camp
Reus
Mont-roig del Camp
Batea
Gandesa
El Pinell de Brai
Tivissa
Vandellòs
Salou
Port Aventura
Vila-seca
Tarragona
Torredembarra
Coma-ruga
Calafell
El Vendrell
Cambrils de Mar
Cap de Salou
Costa Dorada
L'Hospitalet de l'Infant
Rasquera
Xerta
Tivenys
El Perelló
L'Ametlla de Mar
Arnes
Calaceite
Prat de Compte
Fabara
Maella
Mequinenza
MICHELIN

1091
Foix
Chalabre
Mouthoumet
Couiza
Rennes-les-Bs
Lavelanet
Tarascon
Ussat
Quillan
Tuchan
Salses-le-Chau
Port-Leucate
Port-Barcarès
Belcaire
St Paul-de-Fenouillet
Axat
Rivesaltes
St Laurent-de-la Salanque
Col de Chioula
Latour-de-France
Estagel
Sournia
PERPIGNAN
Ax-les-Thermes
Quérigut
C. de Jau
Millas
Canet-Plage
Ille-s-Têt
Molitg-les-Bains
St Cyprien-Plage
Tunel d'Envalira
Pic Carlit
Prades
Vinça
Thuir
Elne
Argelès
C. de Puymorens
Col de la Quillane
Olette
Collioure
Font-Romeu
Vernet-les-Bs
Port-Vendres
PYRÉNÉES-ORIENTALES
St Martin
Pic du Canigou
Céret
le Boulou
Banyuls
Tunnel
Mont-Louis
Amélie-les-Bs-Palalda
Arles
le Perthus
Cerbère
Llivia
Saillagouse
Roc de France
Portbou
Puigcerdà
Bourg-Madame
la Preste
La Jonquera
Fontanals
Cerdaña
Peralada
Bellver de Cerdanya
Prats-de-Mollo
Roc de Frausa
Capmany
Núria
Setcases
El Port de Llançà
El Port de la Selva
Puigmal
Col d'Ares
Llançà
Martinet
Collada de Toses
Queralbs
Coll. d'Ares
P. de Boadella
Super-Molina
La Molina
Ribes de Freser
Camprodon
Torremirona
12-2005
S. Pere de Rodes
Cadaq
del Cadi
La Pobla de Lillet
Gombrèn
Sant Joan de les Abadesses
Sant Pau de Seguries
Castellfollit de la Roca
Figueres
Roses
Bagà
Castelló d'Empúries
CATALUÑA
Ripoll
Collado de Coubet
Olot
Besalú
Golf de Roses
Les Llosses
Bàscara
Pals
Empúries
Llorenc
P. de La Baells
Vilada
Puigsacalm
Sta Pau
Banyoles
L'Escala
Berga
Viladamat
Sant Agustí de Lluçanes
Sant Quirze de Besora
Bas
Empordà
L'Espunyola
Sant Boi de Lluçanes
Amer
Torroella de Montgrí
Manlleu
P. de Susqueda
Girona/Gerona
Gironella
Prats de Lluçanes
Sant Hipòlit de Voltregà
P. de Sau
Parlavà
Autovía en obras
Osona Montanya
La Bisbal d'Empordà
Begur
Puig-reig
Olost
Anglès
Vilanova de Sau
Cassà de la Selva
Palafrugell
Navàs
Vic
PGA de Catalunya
Calonge
Balsareny
Sant Hilari Sacalm
Caldes de Malavella
Palamós
Súria
Artés
Tona
Viladrau
Sta Coloma de Farners
Llagostera
Sant Antoni de C.
Sallent
Moià
Sa de Montseny
Arbúcies
Sils
Platja d'Aro
Centelles
S' Agaró
Castellterçol
Montseny
Breda
Hostalric
Vidreres
S. Feliu de Guíxols
Manresa
Sant Quirze Safaja
Figaro
Sant Celoni
Tordera
Tossa de Mar
Golf d'Aro (Mas Nou)
La Garriga
Lloret de Mar
Monistrol
Caldes de Montbui
Cardedeu
Sta Susanna
Blanes
El Prat
Castellar del Vallès
Granollers
Malgrat de Mar
Pineda de Mar
Masia Bach
Terrassa/Tarrasa
Sabadell
S. Andreu de Llavaneres
Calella
Costa Brava
Castellolí
Sant Pol de Mar
Esparreguera
Canet de Mar
Olesa
La Roca
Argentona
Arenys de Mar
Martorell
Rubí
S. Cugat
Mataró
Premià de Mar
Sant Sadurní d'Anoia
El Masnou
Badalona
San Cugat
Molins de Rei
BARCELONA
Begues
Gavà
El Prat de Llobregat
Genova
Sta Margarida i Els Monjos
Garraf
Castelldefels
Sitges
Vilanova i la Geltrú
Costa Dorada
MICHELIN

Map No 4
Plano 4
km
0 10 20
Lerma
RSHE Club de Campo
Jarama R.A.C.E.
La Moraleja
La Herreria
Club de Campo
La Dehesa
Puerta de Hierro
MICHELIN
VALLADOLID
MADRID
Segovia
El Escorial
Ávila
Aranda de Duero
Aranjuez
Palencia
Covarrubias
Lerma
Sto Domingo de Silos
Magaz
Baltanás
Espinosa de C.
Baños de Cerrato
Dueñas
Cevico de la Torre
Villafruela
Valdosa
Peñas de Cerv
Valoria la Buena
Tórtoles de E.
Esguevillas de E.
Fombellida
Gumiel de Hizán
Caleruega
Villanubla
Cabezón
Villafuerte
Olmedillo de Roa
La Horra
Zaratán
Roa de Duero
Simancas
Laguna de Duero
Tudela de Duero
Quintanilla de Onésimo
Peñafiel
Fuentecén
Peñaranda de Duero
Tordesillas
Boecillo
Montemayor de Pililla
Cogeces del Monte
Valdestillas
Portillo
Campaspero
Sacramenia
Honrubia de la Cuesta
Serrada
Mojados
La Seca
S. Miguel del Arroyo
Olombrada
Fuentidueña
Maderuelo
Rubio
Iscar
Cuéllar
Pedrajas de S. Esteban
Hontalbilla
Olmedo
Samboal
Boceguillas
Cantalejo
Sepúlveda
Riaza
Ataquines
Coca
Navas de Oro
Navalmanzano
Aguilafuente
Cerezo de Abajo
La Pinilla
Lobo
S. Cristóbal de la Vega
Nava de la Asunción
Turégano
Prádena
Carbonero el Mayor
Pedraza
Puerto de Somosierra
Arévalo
Montuenga
Sta María la Real de Nieva
La Salceda
Pto de Navafria
GUADARRAMA
Buitrago del Lozoya
E. de El Villar
Tiñosillos
Adanero
Sangarcía
Torrecaballeros
San Ildefonso-La Granja
Rascafría
Lozoyuela
Sanchidrián
Abades
Madrona
Peñalara
La Roca
La Cabrera
E. de El Atazar
Labajos
Velayos
Pto de la Morcuera
Miraflores de la Sierra
Torrelaguna
Puebla de
Mingorria
Villacastín
Pto de Navacerrada
COMUNIDAD DE MADRID
Cercedilla
Navacerrada
Viñuelas
El Molar
El Casar
Valdihuela
El Espinar
S. Rafael
E. de Serones
Pto de Guadarrama
Guadarrama
Manzanares el Real
Colmenar Viejo
Las Navas del Marqués
Valle de los Caídos
Collado Villalba
Marchamalo
Pto de Paramera
Navalperal de P.
Galapagar
Torrelodones
Alcobendas
Cobeña
Azuqueca de Henares
El Hoyo de Pinares
Barraco
SIERRA
Robledo de Chavela
Las Rozas de M.
El Pardo
Cebreros
Valdemorillo
Barajas
Burgohondo
Pozuelo de Alarcón
Alcalá de Henares
El Tiemblo
E. de S. Juan
Navaluenga
E. del Burguillo
Brunete
Torrejón de Ardoz
GREDOS
Coslada
Piedralaves
S. Martín de Valdeiglesias
Chapinería
Villaviciosa de Odón
Loeches
Casavieja
La Adrada
Aldea del Fresno
Leganés
Sotillo de la Adrada
Cadalso de los Vidrios
Villa del Prado
Móstoles
Getafe
Arganda del Rey
Navalcarnero
Fuenlabrada
Orusco de T.
Méntrida
Almorox
Pinto
Navamorcuende
Valmojado
Griñón
Parla
S. Martín de la Vega
Morata de Tajuña
Perales de T.
El Real de S. Vicente
Escalona
Torrejón de la Calzada
Sta Cruz del Retamar
Ciempozuelos
Valdemoro
Camarena
Illescas
Seseña
Río Alberche
Maqueda
Yuncos
Esquivias
Chinchón
Colmenar de Oreja
Sta Olalla
Fuensalida
Torrijos
Añover de Tajo
Noblejas
Villarrubia de Santiago
Río Duero
Río Pisuerga
Río Esgueva
Río Cega
Río Duratón
Río Eresma
Río Arlanza
Río Guadarrama
Jarama
Tiétar
Canal de Castilla
E. de Linares del Arroyo
CASTILLA Y LEÓN
ESPAÑA

1092

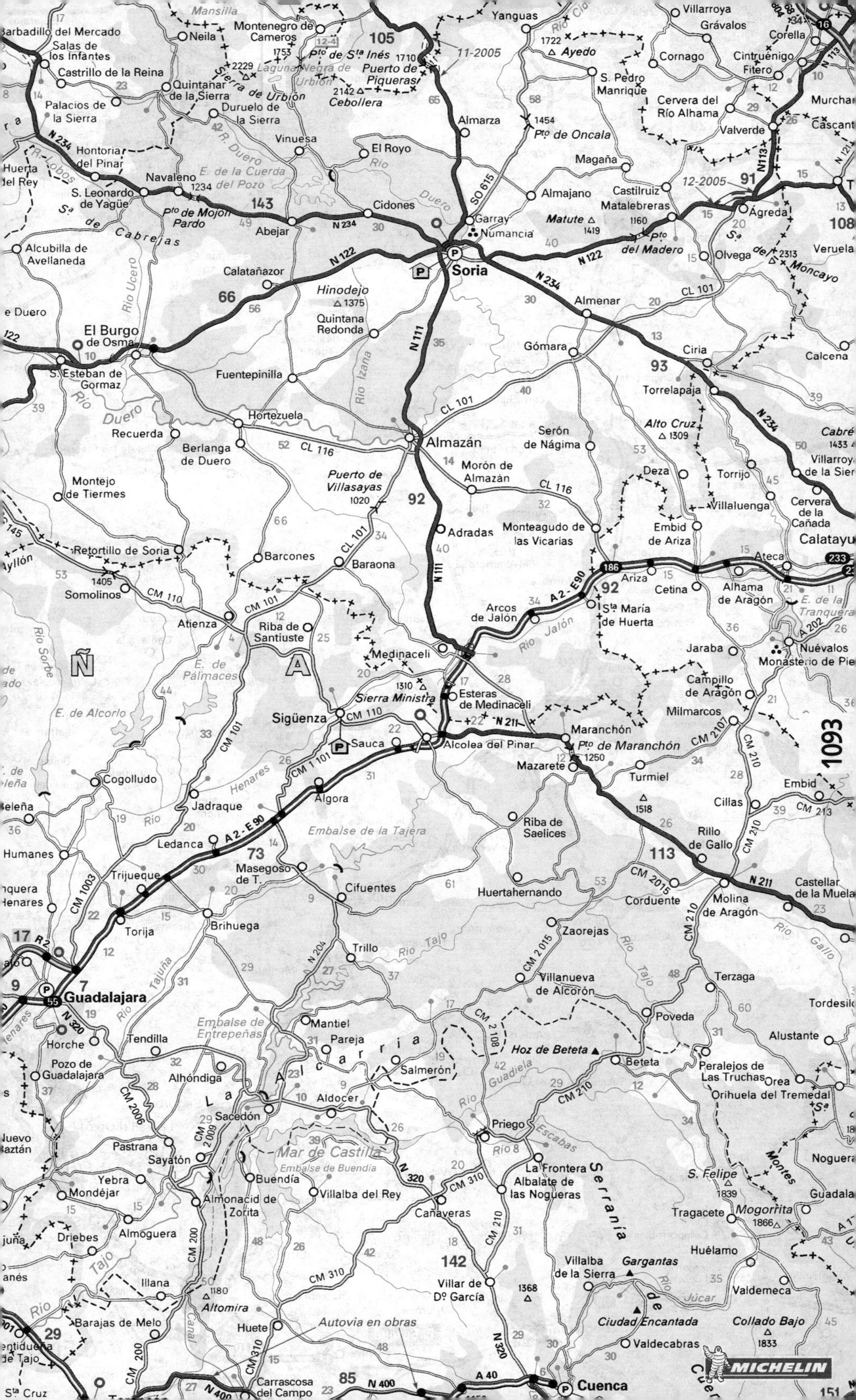
Mansilla
Barbadillo del Mercado
Neila
Montenegro de Cameros
105
Yanguas
Villarroya
Grávalos
Corella
Salas de los Infantes
Castrillo de la Reina
Quintanar de la Sierra
Sierra de Urbión
Laguna Negra de Urbión
Pto de Sta Inés
Puerto de Piqueras
11-2005
1722
Ayedo
Cornago
Cintruénigo
Fitero
Palacios de la Sierra
Duruelo de la Sierra
2142
Cebollera
S. Pedro Manrique
Cervera del Río Alhama
Valverde
Murchante
Cascante
Almarza
1454
Pto de Oncala
Hontoria del Pinar
N 234
Vinuesa
El Royo
Magaña
Huerta del Rey
Navaleno
E. de la Cuerda del Pozo
R. Duero
SO 615
Almajano
Castilruiz
12-2005
91
S. Leonardo de Yagüe
1234
143
Pto de Mojón Pardo
Cidones
Matalebreras
1160
Garray
Numancia
Matute
1419
Ágreda
108
Sa de Cabrejas
Abejar
Pto del Madero
Alcubilla de Avellaneda
N 122
Soria
Olvega
Veruela
Sa del Moncayo
2313
Calatañazor
Hinodejo
1375
N 234
CL 101
66
Almenar
Duero
Quintana Redonda
El Burgo de Osma
N 111
Gómara
Ciria
Calcena
S. Esteban de Gormaz
Fuentepinilla
93
Torrelapaja
Río Izana
Duero
CL 101
Alto Cruz
1309
Cabré
1433
Hortezuela
Recuerda
Berlanga de Duero
Almazán
CL 116
Serón de Nágima
Villarroya de la Sierra
Montejo de Tiermes
Morón de Almazán
Deza
Torrijo
Puerto de Villasayas
1020
92
CL 116
Cervera de la Cañada
Villaluenga
Embid de Ariza
Adradas
Monteagudo de las Vicarías
Calatayud
Retortillo de Soria
Barcones
Baraona
CL 101
Ayllón
1405
Somolinos
CM 110
186
Ariza
Cetina
Ateca
Alhama de Aragón
233
CM 101
A 2 - E 90
92
Sta María de Huerta
E. de la Tranquera
Arcos de Jalón
Atienza
Riba de Santiuste
Río Jalón
Río Sorbe
Ñ
A
Medinaceli
Jaraba
Nuévalos
Monasterio de Piedra
A 202
E. de Pálmaces
1310
Sierra Ministra
Esteras de Medinaceli
Campillo de Aragón
E. de Alcorlo
Sigüenza
CM 110
N 211
Milmarcos
Sauca
Alcolea del Pinar
Maranchón
Pto de Maranchón
1250
Mazarete
CM 2107
Turmiel
Cogolludo
CM 101
CM 1 101
Henares
Algora
Embid
Cillas
CM 210
CM 213
Beleña
Jadraque
1518
Riba de Saelices
Rillo de Gallo
Embalse de la Tajera
Humanes
Ledanca
A 2 - E 90
73
113
Masegoso de T.
Trijueque
CM 1003
Cifuentes
Huertahernando
CM 2015
Corduente
Molina de Aragón
N 211
Castellar de la Muela
Torija
Brihuega
Zaorejas
Río Gallo
17
R 2
Guadalajara
N 204
Trillo
Río Tajo
CM 2015
Villanueva de Alcorón
Terzaga
Río Tajuña
Tordesilos
Horche
N 320
Embalse de Entrepeñas
Mantiel
CM 2108
Poveda
Alustante
Tendilla
Pareja
La Alcarria
Hoz de Beteta
Beteta
Pozo de Guadalajara
Alhóndiga
Salmerón
Río Guadiela
Peralejos de Las Truchas
Orea
Orihuela del Tremedal
CM 2006
Sacedón
Aldocer
CM 210
Nuevo Baztán
CM 2009
Mar de Castilla
Priego
Escabas
Pastrana
Sayatón
Embalse de Buendía
N 320
La Frontera
Serranía
Nogueras
Yebra
Buendía
Villalba del Rey
CM 310
Albalate de las Nogueras
S. Felipe
1839
Mondéjar
Almonacid de Zorita
Cañaveras
Guadalaviar
Tragacete
Mogorrita
1866
Tajuña
Driebes
Almoguera
CM 210
Huélamo
Río Tajo
CM 200
142
Villalba de la Sierra
Gargantas
Illana
CM 310
1180
Altomira
Villar de Do García
1368
Júcar
Valdemeca
Barajas de Melo
Ciudad Encantada
Collado Bajo
1833
Huete
Autovía en obras
N 320
Valdecabras
29
Fuentidueña de Tajo
Canal
CM 310
MICHELIN
Sta Cruz
N 400
Carrascosa del Campo
85
N 400
A 40
Cuenca
151

Map No 5
Plano 5
km
0 10 20
Morata de Jalón
Doña Godina
Muel
Fuentes de Ebro
Pina
Bujaraloz
Almonacid de la Sierra
Longares
Villanueva del Huerva
Alto de las Borderas
Quinto
Gelsa
Cariñena
Fuendetodos
Belchite
Sástago
Codos
Pto de Paniza
Azuara
Azaila
Escatrón
Nuévalos
Miedes
Mainar
Herrera
Lécera
La Puebla de Hijar
Samper de Calanda
Daroca
Badules
Moyuela
Híjar
Cubel
Sta Cruz
Ferreruela de Huerva
Albalate del Arzobispo
Embid
Burbáguena
Laguna de Gallocanta
Fonfría
Muniesa
Ariño
Retuerta
Sa de Cucalón
Oliete
Cortes de Aragón
E. de Cueva Foradada
Alloza
Andorra
Castels
Bello
Calamocha
Segura de los Baños
Barrachina
Obón
Calanda
Castellar de la Muela
Caminreal
Bañón
Vivel del Río Martín
Alcorisa
Monreal del Campo
Pto Mínguez
Montalbán
Portalrubio
Utrillas
Mas de las Matas
El Pobo de Dueñas
Molinos
Castellote
Ejulve
Sa de S. Just
Ojos Negros
Rillo
Argente
Mezquita de Jarque
Tordesilos
Torre la Carcel
Perales del Alfambra
Aliaga
Forcall
Ródenas
Olocau de Rey
Palomera
Camarillas
Sta Eulalia
Aguilar del Alfambra
Cañada de Benatanduz
Pozondón
Alfambra
Escorihuela
Cinctorres
Bronchales
Villarquemado
Villarroya de los Pinares
Cantavieja
Sa Alta
Albarracín
Pto de Villarroya
Pto de Las Cabrillas
Noguera
Cella
Allepuz
Tarayuela
La Iglesuela del Cid
Cedrillas
Sa de Gúdar
Guadalaviar
Valdelinares
Vilafranca
Frías de Albarracín
E. del Arquillo de S. Blas
Alcalá de la Selva
Peñarroya
Teruel
Universales
Terriente
Bezas
Mosqueruela
Benassal
Pto de Escandón
Linares de Mora
Vistabella del Maestrat
Javalón
Villel
Mora de Rubielos
El Cañigral
La Puebla de Valverde
Penyagolosa
Rubielos de Mora
Atzeneta del Maestrat
Port del Remolcador
Sarrión
Javalambre
Luchena
Torrebaja
Salvacañete
Ademuz
E. de Arenós
Zucaina
Huérguina
Manzanera
Ludiente
El Cubillo
L'Alcora
Torrijas
Montanejos
E. de María Cristina
Sa de Javalambre
Fuentes de Ayódar
Sta Cruz de Moya
Cuerda
Aras de los Olmos
Caudiel
E. de Sitjar
Landete
Abejuela
Onda
La Yesa
Titaguas
Cerro
Jérica
Vila-real
Autovía apert.: 12-2005
Talayuelas
Espadà
Garaballa
Segorbe
Altura
Cardenete
La Vall d'Uixó
E. del Generalísimo
Alcublas
Mira
Chelva
Algar de Palància
Almenara
Aliaguilla
Sinarcas
Villar del Arzobispo
E. de Contreras
Casinos
Serra
Sagunt/Sagunto
E. de Loriguilla
Escorpion
Camporrobles
COMUNIDAD
La Pobla de Vallbona
El Port de Sagunt
Pedralba
Llíria
Benaguasil
Bétera
Puçol
Minglanilla
Villargordo del Cabriel
Utiel
Chera
Massamagrell
Vilamarxant
Hierbas
Requena
El Bosque
Cheste
Manises
Burjassot
Chiva
VALÈNCIA
MICHELIN
El Grau de V.

1094

Torrente de Cinca
Seròs
Embalse de Mequinenza
Mequinenza
Maials
Pantà de Riba-roja
La Granadella
Fayón
La Bisbal de Falset
Sª del Montsant
Caspe
Nonaspe
Flix
Fabara
La Pobla de Massaluca
Ascó
Alto del Portalé
Maella
Batea
Móra d'Ebre
Móra la Nova
Garcia
Falset
Alcañiz
Calaceite
Gandesa
El Pinell de Brai
Tivissa
Prat de Compte
Valjunquera
Rasquera
Vandellòs
Xerta
Tivenys
Arnes
L'Espina
Valderrobres
El Perelló
Tortosa
Beceite
Mas de Barberans
Torre Miró
La Pobla de Benifassà
Sta Bàrbara
La Sénia
Bel
Rossell
Ulldecona
Morella
Riu Cérvol
Maestrat
Xert
Traiguera
La Jana
Sant Mateu
Càlig
Tírig
Vinaròs
Alcanar
Benicarló
Albocàsser
Peníscola
Les Coves de Vinromà
Alcalà de Xivert
Sta Magdalena de Polpis
La Torre en Besora
Vilanova d'Alcolea
Alcossebre
Torreblanca
Cabanes
La Pobla Tornesa
Orpesa
Benicàssim/ Benicasim
Castelló de la Plana / Castellón de la Plana
El Grau de C.
Almassora
Borriana
Vinaixa
L'Espluga de Francolí
Sarral
Poblet
Montblanc
El Pont d'Armentera
Santes Creus
Vila-rodona
Prades
Albarca
Valls
Alcover
La Selva del Camp
El Francolí
El Vendrell
Reus
Riudoms
Montbrió del Camp
Mont-roig del Camp
Torredembarra
Tarragona
Vila-seca
Port Aventura
Salou
Cambrils de Mar
Cap de Salou
L'Hospitalet de l'Infant
L'Ametlla de Mar
Golf de Sant Jordi
L'Ampolla
L'Aldea
Amposta
Deltebre
Ríumar
Cap de Tortosa
I. de Buda
S. Carles de la Ràpita
els Columbrets
Costa Dorada
Bonmont (Terres Noves)
Panoramica
Mediterraneo
Costa del Azahar
Cost
GOLF
MICHELIN

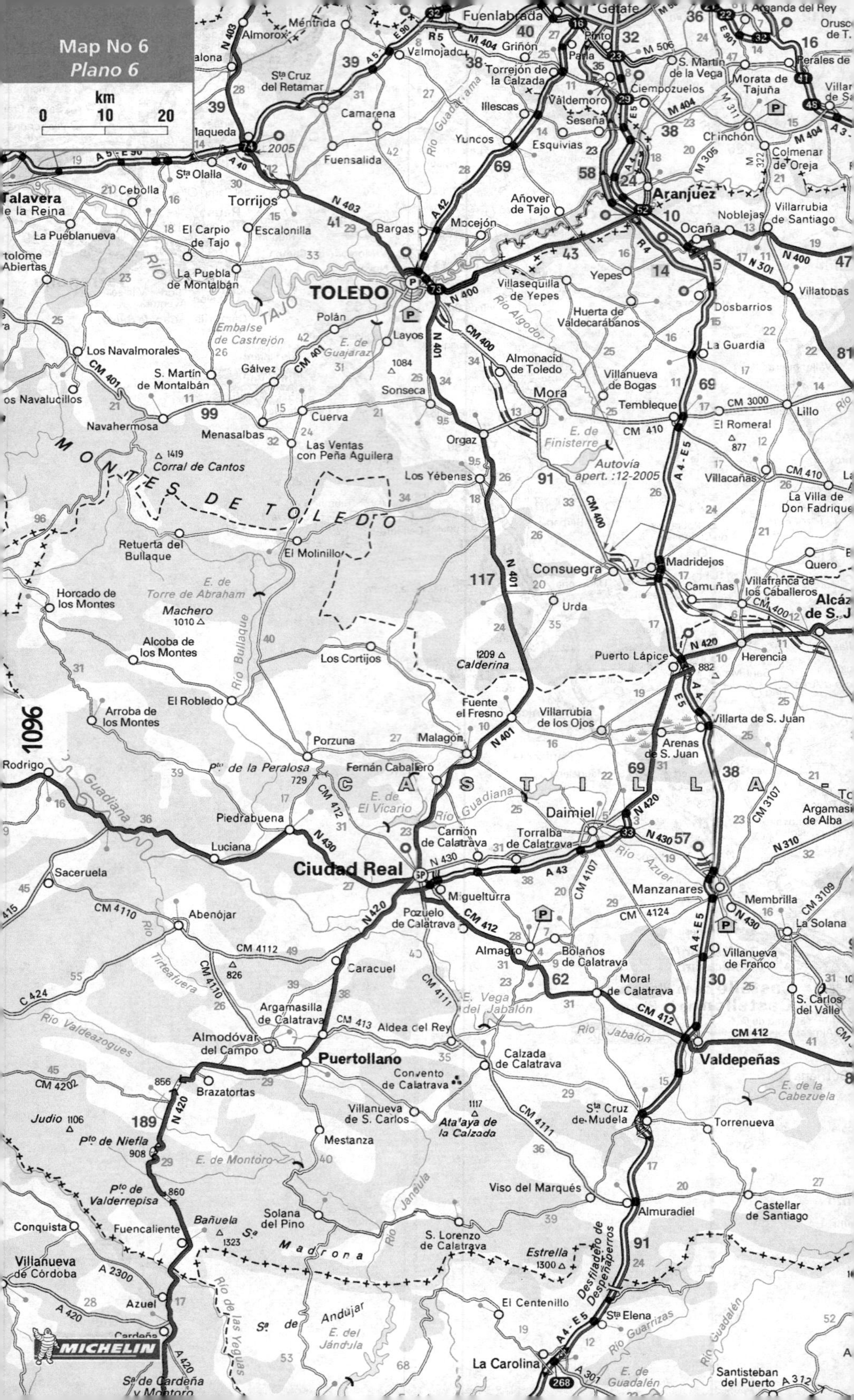
Map No 6
Plano 6
km
0 10 20
Almorox
Méntrida
Fuenlabrada
Getafe
Arganda del Rey
Valmojado
Griñón
Torrejón de la Calzada
Pinto
Parla
S. Martín de la Vega
Morata de Tajuña
Perales de Tajuña
Sta Cruz del Retamar
Ciempozuelos
Valdemoro
Camarena
Illescas
Seseña
Chinchón
Colmenar de Oreja
Maqueda
Fuensalida
Yuncos
Esquivias
Sta Olalla
Cebolla
Talavera de la Reina
Torrijos
Aranjuez
Añover de Tajo
Villarrubia de Santiago
Noblejas
Ocaña
La Pueblanueva
El Carpio de Tajo
Escalonilla
Bargas
Mocejón
La Puebla de Montalbán
Villasequilla de Yepes
Yepes
Villatobas
TOLEDO
Río Tajo
Embalse de Castrejón
Polán
Layos
E. de Guajaraz
Huerta de Valdecarábanos
Dosbarrios
Río Algodor
La Guardia
Los Navalmorales
Gálvez
Almonacid de Toledo
Villanueva de Bogas
S. Martín de Montalbán
Sonseca
Mora
Los Navalucillos
Tembleque
Lillo
Navahermosa
Cuerva
Menasalbas
El Romeral
Las Ventas con Peña Aguilera
Orgaz
E. de Finisterre
Autovía apert.: 12-2005
Corral de Cantos
Los Yébenes
Villacañas
La Villa de Don Fadrique
MONTES DE TOLEDO
Retuerta del Bullaque
El Molinillo
Consuegra
Madridejos
Quero
Camuñas
Villafranca de los Caballeros
E. de Torre de Abraham
Horcado de los Montes
Machero
Urda
Alcázar de S. Juan
Alcoba de los Montes
Los Cortijos
Calderina
Puerto Lápice
Herencia
Río Bullaque
El Robledo
Fuente el Fresno
Villarrubia de los Ojos
Villarta de S. Juan
Arroba de los Montes
Arenas de S. Juan
Porzuna
Malagón
Rodrigo
Pto de la Peralosa
Fernán Caballero
CASTILLA
Río Guadiana
E. de El Vicario
Argamasilla de Alba
Piedrabuena
Carrión de Calatrava
Torralba de Calatrava
Daimiel
Luciana
Ciudad Real
Río Azuer
Saceruela
Miguelturra
Manzanares
Membrilla
Abenójar
Pozuelo de Calatrava
La Solana
Almagro
Bolaños de Calatrava
Caracuel
Villanueva de Franco
Río Tirteafuera
Moral de Calatrava
S. Carlos del Valle
Argamasilla de Calatrava
E. Vega del Jabalón
Río Valdeazogues
Almodóvar del Campo
Aldea del Rey
Río Jabalón
Valdepeñas
Puertollano
Calzada de Calatrava
Brazatortas
Convento de Calatrava
E. de la Cabezuela
Villanueva de S. Carlos
Atalaya de la Calzada
Sta Cruz de Mudela
Judío
Torrenueva
Pto de Niefla
Mestanza
E. de Montoro
Río Jándula
Viso del Marqués
Pto de Valderrepisa
Almuradiel
Castellar de Santiago
Conquista
Fuencaliente
Bañuela
Solana del Pino
Sa Madrona
S. Lorenzo de Calatrava
Estrella
Villanueva de Córdoba
Desfiladero de Despeñaperros
Azuel
El Centenillo
Sa de Andujar
Sta Elena
Río Guarrizas
Río Guadalén
Cardeña
Río de las Yeguas
E. del Jándula
La Carolina
Santisteban del Puerto
E. de Guadalén
Sa de Cardeña y Montoro
MICHELIN

Embalse de Buendía
Yebra
Mondéjar
Buendía
Villalba del Rey
La Frontera
Albalate de las Nogueras
Serranía
S. Felipe
Tragacete
Mogorrita
Almonacid de Zorita
Cañaveras
Driebes
Almoguera
Tajo
Huélamo
142
Villalba de la Sierra
Gargantas
Illana
Villar de Dº García
Valdemeca
Altomira
Barajas de Melo
Huete
Autovia en obras
Ciudad Encantada
Collado Bajo
Valdecabras
Canal
Cuenca
85
Carrascosa del Campo
A 40
Tarancón
Puerto de Cabrejas
Sta Cruz de la Zarza
Torrejoncillo del Rey
Cañete
Uclés
Fuente de Pedro Naharro
Villarrubio
Saelices
Palomares del Campo
Montalbo
Entredichos
Horcajo de Santiago
Casas de Luján
Cigüela
73
Villares del Saz
N 420
S. Lorenzo de la Parrilla
61
Carboneras de Guadazaón
Puebla de Almenara
Villarejo de Fuentes
Valeria
Corral de Almaguer
Cruz
Villamayor de Santiago
A 3 - E 901
Villar de Cañas
Olivares
Valverde de Júcar
N 320
72
Cardenete
Almodóvar del Pinar
Tresjuncos
Villalgordo del Marquesado
Osa de la Vega
Villanueva de Alcardete
La Almarcha
Buenache de Alarcón
Guadazaón
Quintanar de la Orden
N 301
54
Los Hinojosos
Enguídanos
Honrubia
Villaescusa de Haro
Campillo de Altobuey
Embalse de Alarcón
Belmonte
Sta María del Campo Rus
N III
Motilla del Palancar
El Toboso
Mota del Cuervo
El Pedernoso
La Alberca de Záncara
Alarcón
58
Minglanilla
Las Pedroñeras
El Picazo
Iniesta
Campo de Criptana
Pedro Muñoz
40
Las Mesas
S. Clemente
N 310
Sisante
65
Villanueva de la Jara
Villalpardo
El Provencio
Záncara
Casasimarro
Casas de Fernando Alonso
Ledaña
Autovía apert. :12-2005
Quintanar del Rey
Villagarcía del Llano
Socuéllamos
71
Villarrobledo
Minaya
A 31
N 301
Tarazona de la Mancha
Mahora
N 322
L A M A N C H A
92
La Roda
Júcar
Córcoles
CM 3106
La Gineta
Valdeganga
06-2005
E. de Peñarroya
Munera
60
Barrax
Ruidera
Sotuélamos
N 430
Ossa de Montiel
153
El Bonillo
Los Barreros
Lezuza
Albacete
Chinchilla de Monte Aragón
Alhambra
Bolos
Trasvase
Sta Ana
Balazote
El Salobral
86
Pozo Cañada
Villahermosa
Viveros
S. Pedro
Pozuelo
Pétrola
Villanueva de los Infantes
Robledo
Villanueva de la Fuente
Roble
Montiel
Peñas de S. Pedro
Pozohondo
Albaladejo
Alcaraz
Peñascosa
Segura
Fuente
Alcadozo
E. del Bayco
Torre de Juan Abad
Guadalmena
de Alcaraz
Villamanrique
Almenaras
Bogarra
Tobarra
Albatana
Ayna
Mundo
Liétor
Fábricas de Riópar
Hellín
Molinicos
105
Elche de la Sierra
E. de Talave
E. de Guadalmena
Puente de Génave
Siles
Yeste
E. del Cenajo
La Puerta de Segura
Orcera
Letur
E. de la Fuensanta
Arguellite
121
MICHELIN

1097

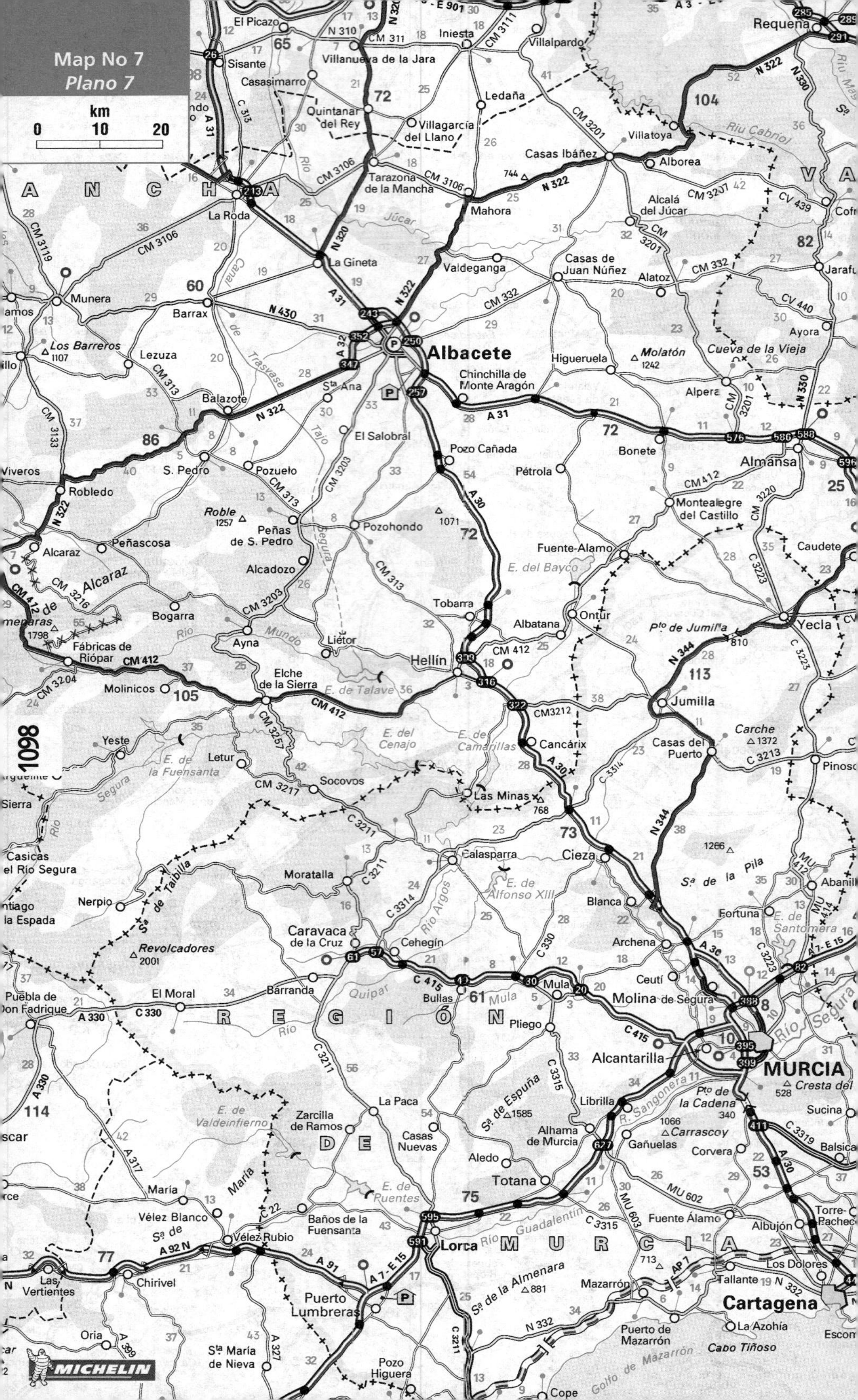

Map No 7
Plano 7
km
0 10 20
El Picazo
Sisante
Casasimarro
Villanueva de la Jara
Iniesta
Villalpardo
Requena
Quintanar del Rey
Villagarcía del Llano
Ledaña
Villatoya
Riu Cabriol
Casas Ibáñez
Alborea
Tarazona de la Mancha
Mahora
Alcalá del Júcar
La Roda
La Gineta
Júcar
Valdeganga
Casas de Juan Núñez
Alatoz
Jarafuel
Munera
Barrax
Albacete
Ayora
Los Barreros
Lezuza
Sta Ana
Chinchilla de Monte Aragón
Higueruela
Molatón
Cueva de la Vieja
Alpera
Balazote
El Salobral
Pozo Cañada
Bonete
Almansa
Viveros
S. Pedro
Pozuelo
Pétrola
Robledo
Roble
Montealegre del Castillo
Peñas de S. Pedro
Pozohondo
Alcaraz
Peñascosa
Alcadozo
Fuente-Alamo
E. del Bayco
Caudete
Tobarra
Bogarra
Ontur
Albatana
Ayna
Liétor
Mundo
Fábricas de Riópar
Hellín
Pto de Jumilla
Yecla
Molinicos
Elche de la Sierra
E. de Talave
Jumilla
Yeste
E. del Cenajo
E. de Camarillas
Cancárix
Carche
Casas del Puerto
Letur
E. de la Fuensanta
Pinoso
Socovos
Las Minas
Segura
Casicas del Río Segura
Calasparra
Cieza
Moratalla
Sa de la Pila
Nerpio
Sa de Taibilla
E. de Alfonso XIII
Blanca
Abanilla
Fortuna
E. de Santomera
Caravaca de la Cruz
Cehegín
Archena
Revolcadores
Quipar
Bullas
Mula
Ceutí
Molina de Segura
Puebla de Don Fadrique
El Moral
Barranda
Pliego
R E G I Ó N
Alcantarilla
MURCIA
Cresta del
Pto de la Cadena
E. de Valdeinfierno
La Paca
Sa de Espuña
Librilla
Carrascoy
Sucina
Zarcilla de Ramos
Casas Nuevas
Alhama de Murcia
Gañuelas
Corvera
Balsicas
D E
Aledo
Totana
María
E. de Puentes
Vélez Blanco
Baños de la Fuensanta
Fuente Álamo
Albujón
Torre-Pacheco
Vélez Rubio
Lorca
Río Guadalentín
M U R C I A
Las Vertientes
Chirivel
Sa de la Almenara
Los Dolores
Tallante
Mazarrón
Cartagena
Puerto Lumbreras
Puerto de Mazarrón
La Azohía
Oria
Sta María de Nieva
Cabo Tiñoso
Golfo de Mazarrón
Pozo Higuera
Cope
MICHELIN

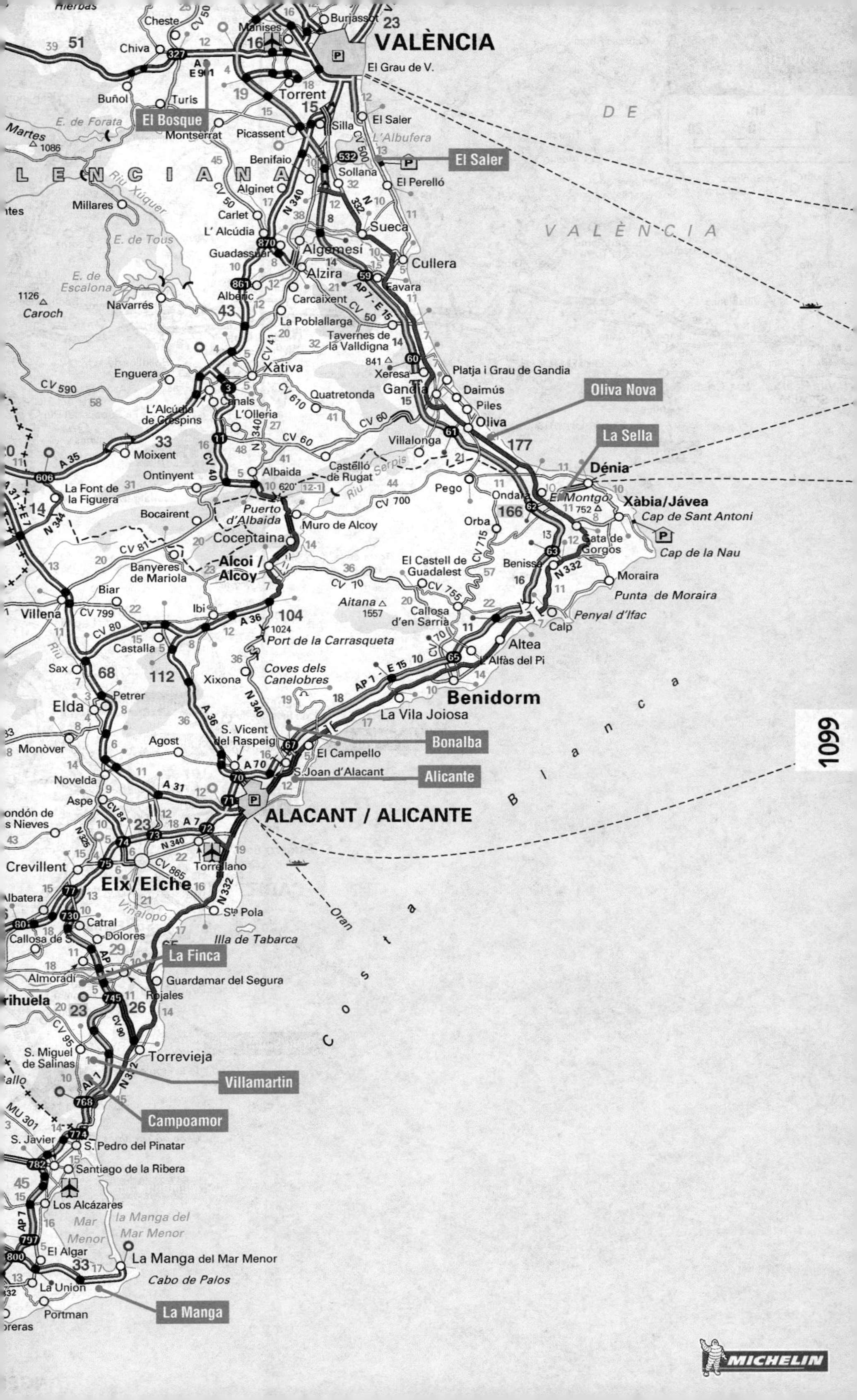

Cheste
Manises
Burjassot
VALÈNCIA
Chiva
El Grau de V.
Buñol
Turís
Torrent
El Bosque
E. de Forata
Montserrat
Picassent
Silla
El Saler
L'Albufera
DE
Martes
1086
Benifaio
El Saler
Sollana
El Perelló
LENCIANA
Riu Xúquer
Alginet
Millares
Carlet
Sueca
L' Alcúdia
E. de Tous
Guadassuar
Algemesí
Cullera
VALÈNCIA
Alzira
E. de Escalona
Favara
1126
Caroch
Navarrés
Alberic
Carcaixent
La Pobla Llarga
Tavernes de la Valldigna
841
Enguera
Xàtiva
Xeresa
Platja i Grau de Gandia
Quatretonda
Gandia
Daimús
Oliva Nova
L'Alcúdia de Crespins
Canals
L'Olleria
Piles
Oliva
Villalonga
La Sella
Moixent
Ontinyent
Albaida
Castelló de Rugat
Riu Serpis
Dénia
La Font de la Figuera
Pego
Ondara
El Montgó
752
Xàbia/Jávea
Puerto d'Albaida
Bocairent
Muro de Alcoy
Orba
Cap de Sant Antoni
Cocentaina
Gata de Gorgos
Cap de la Nau
Alcoi / Alcoy
Banyeres de Mariola
El Castell de Guadalest
Benissa
Moraira
Biar
Aitana 1557
Punta de Moraira
Villena
Ibi
Callosa d'en Sarrià
Penyal d'Ifac
Calp
1024
Port de la Carrasqueta
Castalla
Altea
L'Alfàs del Pi
Sax
Coves dels Canelobres
Xixona
Benidorm
Petrer
Elda
La Vila Joiosa
S. Vicent del Raspeig
Bonalba
Agost
Monòver
El Campello
S. Joan d'Alacant
Alicante
Novelda
Aspe
ALACANT / ALICANTE
Hondón de las Nieves
Torrellano
Crevillent
Elx/Elche
Albatera
Vinalopó
Sta Pola
Oran
Catral
Callosa de S.
Dolores
Illa de Tabarca
Costa Blanca
La Finca
Almoradí
Guardamar del Segura
Rojales
Orihuela
S. Miguel de Salinas
Torrevieja
Villamartin
Campoamor
S. Javier
S. Pedro del Pinatar
Santiago de la Ribera
Los Alcázares
Mar Menor
la Manga del Mar Menor
El Algar
La Manga del Mar Menor
Cabo de Palos
La Union
La Manga
Portman

1099

MICHELIN

Map No 8
Plano 8
km
0 10 20
1100
Cabezas Rubias
El Cerro de Andévalo
Higuera de la Sierra
Zufre
Minas de Riotinto
Nerva
Zalamea la Real
Calañas
Tharsis
Alosno
El Madroño
El Castillo de las Guardas
Valverde del Camino
Las Pajanosas
Alcoutim
Sanlúcar de Guadiana
Villanueva de los Castillejos
E. de Sancho
S. Silvestre de Guzmán
S. Bartolomé de la Torre
E. del Piedras
Aznalcóllar
Gerena
Odeleite
Beas
Gibraleón
Trigueros
La Palma del Condado
Castilleja del Campo
Sanlúcar la Mayor
Santiponce
Camas
Villablanca
Niebla
Cartaya
Lepe
Ayamonte
Vila Real de Sto António
Isla Cristina
La Antilla
El Rompido
Punta Umbría
Huelva
S. Juan del Puerto
Moguer
Palos de la Frontera
La Rábida
Bonares
Rociana del Condado
Bollullos Par del Condado
Almonte
Pilas
Bollullos de la M.
Aznalcázar
Coria del Río
La Puebla del Río
Villamanrique de la Condesa
Colinas
Mazagón
El Rocío
Villafranco del Guadalquivir
Islantilla
Zaudin
GOLFO DE CÁDIZ
Torre de la Higuera
Matalascañas
Parque nacional de Doñana
Isla Mayor
RÍO GUADALQUIVIR
RÍO GUADIANA
Lebrija
Trebujena
El Cuervo
Montecastillo
Sanlúcar de Barrameda
Chipiona
Costa Ballena
Sherry Jerez
Jerez de la Frontera
El Puerto
Rota
El Puerto de Sta María
Bahía de Cádiz
CÁDIZ
El Portal
Puerto Real
San Fernando
Islas Canarias
Costa de la Luz
Sancti Petri
Chiclana de la Frontera
Naveros
Novo Sancti Petri
Autovía en obras
Conil de la Frontera
Vejer de la Frontera
Cabo de Trafalgar
Barbate
Montenmedio
MICHELIN

Sevilla
Pineda
Guadalhorce
La Quinta
Lauro Golf
Los Arqueros
Alhaurin
Los Naranjos
Las Brisas
Monte Mayor
La Reserva
Aloha
Guadalmina
Torrequebrada
Mijas
La Cala
Málaga
Marbella
San Roque
Sotogrande
Valderrama
Almenara
Alcaidesa
CÓRDOBA
SEVILLA
Carmona
Écija
Osuna
Antequera
Ronda
Marbella
Estepona
Fuengirola
Algeciras
Gibraltar
La Línea de la Concepción
Tarifa
Ceuta
RÍO GUADALQUIVIR
MICHELIN

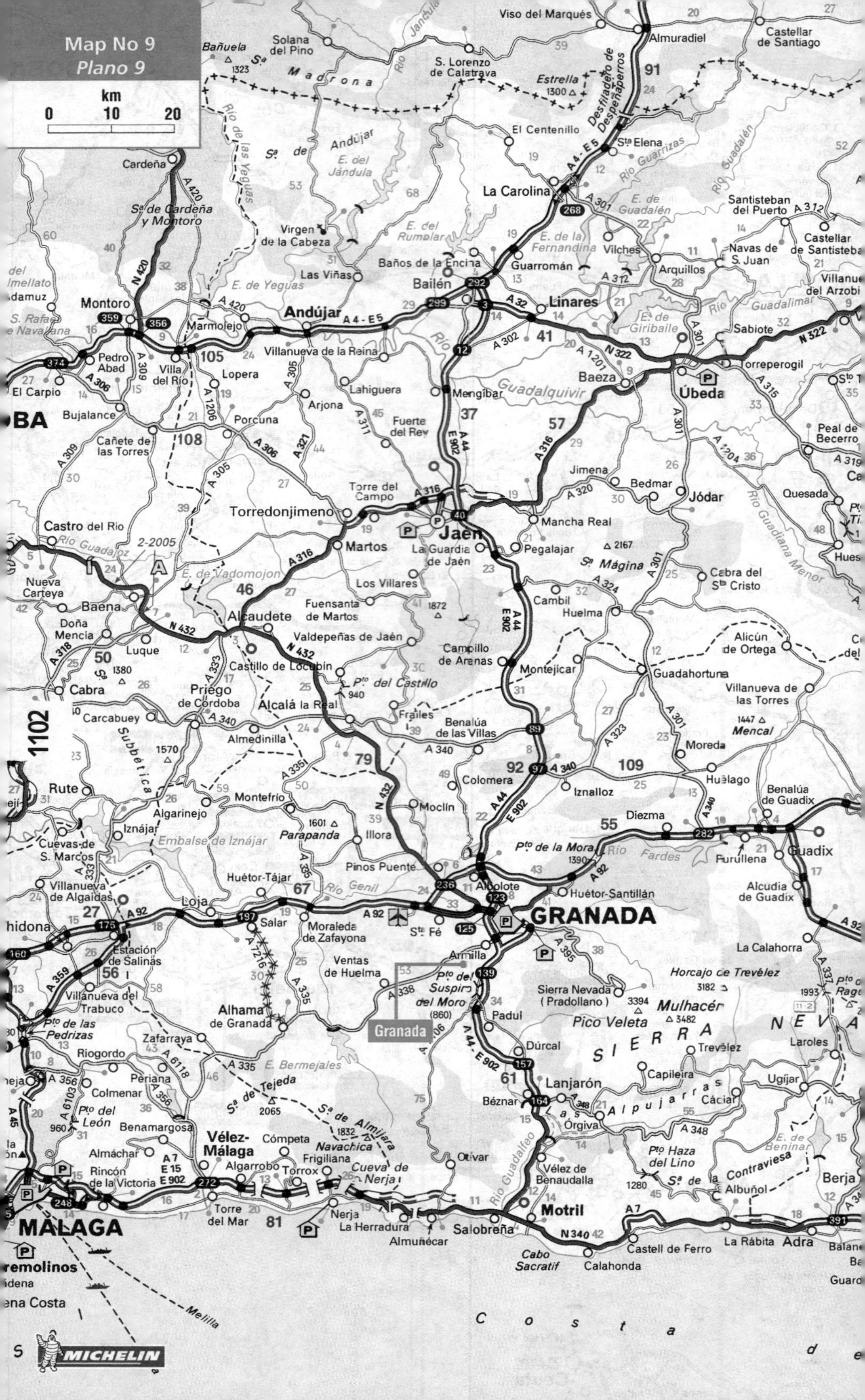

Map No 9
Plano 9
km
0
10
20
Viso del Marqués
Almuradiel
Castellar de Santiago
Bañuela
Solana del Pino
S. Lorenzo de Calatrava
Sª Madrona
Estrella
Desfiladero de Despeñaperros
Río Jándula
Río de las Yeguas
Sª de Andújar
E. del Jándula
El Centenillo
Sta Elena
Río Guarrizas
Río Guadalén
Cardeña
Sª de Cardeña y Montoro
La Carolina
E. de Guadalén
Santisteban del Puerto
Castellar de Santisteban
Virgen de la Cabeza
E. del Rumblar
E. de la Fernandina
Vilches
Navas de S. Juan
Arquillos
Baños de la Encina
Guarromán
Las Viñas
Bailén
Linares
Villanueva del Arzobispo
Montoro
E. de Yeguas
Andújar
E. de Giribaile
Sabiote
Marmolejo
Villanueva de la Reina
Pedro Abad
Villa del Río
Lopera
Baeza
Torreperogil
El Carpio
Lahiguera
Mengíbar
Río Guadalquivir
Úbeda
Bujalance
Arjona
Porcuna
Fuerte del Rey
Peal de Becerro
Cañete de las Torres
Jimena
Bedmar
Jódar
Quesada
Torre del Campo
Torredonjimeno
Jaén
Mancha Real
Castro del Río
Río Guadajoz
Martos
La Guardia de Jaén
Pegalajar
Sª Mágina
E. de Vadomojon
Cabra del Sto Cristo
Río Guadiana Menor
Nueva Carteya
Los Villares
Cambil
Huelma
Baena
Fuensanta de Martos
Doña Mencía
Alcaudete
Valdepeñas de Jaén
Luque
Campillo de Arenas
Alicún de Ortega
Castillo de Locubín
Montejícar
Guadahortuna
Cabra
Pto del Castillo
Villanueva de las Torres
Priego de Córdoba
Alcalá la Real
Frailes
Carcabuey
Benalúa de las Villas
Mencal
Subbética
Almedinilla
Moreda
Colomera
Rute
Iznalloz
Huélago
Montefrío
Benalúa de Guadix
Algarinejo
Moclín
Diezma
Iznájar
Parapanda
Embalse de Iznájar
Illora
Pto de la Mora
Río Fardes
Purullena
Guadix
Cuevas de S. Marcos
Pinos Puente
Villanueva de Algaidas
Huétor-Tájar
Río Genil
Albolote
Huétor-Santillán
Alcudia de Guadix
Loja
Salar
Moraleda de Zafayona
Sta Fé
GRANADA
Estación de Salinas
Ventas de Huelma
Armilla
La Calahorra
Horcajo de Trevélez
Villanueva del Trabuco
Pto del Suspiro del Moro
Sierra Nevada (Pradollano)
Mulhacén
Alhama de Granada
Padul
Pico Veleta
Pto de las Pedrizas
Granada
Zafarraya
SIERRA NEVADA
Riogordo
Dúrcal
Trevélez
Laroles
E. Bermejales
Periana
Lanjarón
Capileira
Ugíjar
Colmenar
Sª de Tejeda
Béznar
Cáciar
Pto del León
Sª de Almijara
Las Alpujarras
Órgiva
Benamargosa
Vélez-Málaga
Cómpeta
Navachica
Pto Haza del Lino
E. de Benínar
Almáchar
Frigiliana
Vélez de Benaudalla
Rincón de la Victoria
Algarrobo
Torrox
Cueva de Nerja
Río Guadalfeo
Órvar
Sª de la Contraviesa
Berja
Albuñol
Torre del Mar
Nerja
Motril
MÁLAGA
La Herradura
Salobreña
Castell de Ferro
La Rábita
Adra
Almuñécar
Cabo Sacratif
Calahonda
Torremolinos
Melilla
Costa de
MICHELIN

Torre de Juan Abad
Villamanrique
Alcaraz
CM 3216
CM 412
Almenaras
1798
Fábricas de Riópar
Molinicos
105
Bogarra
Alcadozo
CM 3203
CM 313
Ayna
Liétor
Tobarra
Albatana
E. del Bayco
Hellín
CM 412
Elche de la Sierra
E. de Talave
CM 3212
N 322
CM 3204
Puente de Génave
A 310
Siles
Yeste
E. de Camarillas
E. del Cenajo
Cancár
La Puerta de Segura
Orcera
Arguellite
E. de la Fuensanta
Letur
CM 3257
CM 3217
Socovos
Las Minas
768
121
Segura de la Sierra
A 314
A 317
Beas de Segura
Cortijos Nuevos
1809
Yelmo
Garganta
Hornos
Casicas del Río Segura
Moratalla
C 3211
Calasparra
E. de Alfonso XIII
Guadalquivir
Río Blanquilla
Cazorla
1830
A 319
Segura
Pontones
Santiago de la Espada
Nerpio
Sa de Taibilla
C 3314
Río Argos
Caravaca de la Cruz
Cehegín
E. del Tranco
1964
Revolcadores
2001
A 317
C 415
Bullas
Mula
Pto de las Palomas
1290
Puebla de Don Fadrique
El Moral
Barranda
A 330
C 330
Quípar
Pliego
R E G I Ó N
La Losa
Sa de la Sagra
2381
Sa de Castril
E. de S. Clemente
Cabañas
2028
E. de la Bolera
A 326
114
C 3211
C 3315
La Paca
Sa de Espuña
1585
E. de Valdeinfierno
Zarcilla de Ramos
Casas Nuevas
Alhama de Murcia
Castril
Huéscar
A 317
D E
Aledo
Totana
Pozo Alcón
Castilléjar
A 7301
Galera
Orce
María
E. de Puentes
75
E. del Negratín
Cortes de Baza
Vélez Blanco
Baños de la Fuensanta
Lorca
Benamaurel
Vélez Rubio
A 92 N
A 91
Cúllar Baza
Las Vertientes
77
Chirivel
Sa de la Almenara
A 7 - E 15
Puerto Lumbreras
1103
A 315
Zújar
Baza
Oria
A 399
Sta María de Nieva
A 327
59
Caniles
Lúcar
1722
A 334
Pozo Higuera
C 3211
Sta Bárbara
2271
Albox
Pulpí
Águilas
Cope
Cabo
Sierra de Baza
Tíjola
Olula del Río
Cantoria
A 334
Huércal-Overa
AP 7
Serón
Purchena
Macael
A 8200
Cuevas del Almanzora
S. Juan de los Terreros
Río Almanzora
Tetica
2080
A 349
Albánchez
A 8202
A 332
Los Lobos
Sierra de los Filabres
2168
Antas
Vera
Villaricos
Desert Springs
Fiñana
Escúllar
Calar Alto
Tahal
108
Uleila del Campo
Lubrín
Los Gallardos
Garrucha
Abrucena
Doña María Ocaña
Gérgal
A 349
A 8200
Sorbas
Turre
Mojácar
Valle del Este
N 340A
126
ALP 118
Ohanes
Laujar de Andarax
Canjáyar
Alboloduy
N 324
A 92
Tabernas
Lucainena de las Torres
Río Andarax
Illar
Alhamilla
1387
Carboneras
Gádor
A 348
Alhama de Almería
Benahadux
Níjar
A 7 - E 15
N 341
Morrón
2236
Sierra de Gádor
A 391
La Mesa Roldán
125
ALMERÍA
S. Isidro
Parque natural
A 358
A 7 - E 15
Las Negras
Dalías
de Cabo de Gata - Níjar
Pta de la Polacra
129
El Alquián
125
El Ejido
Aguadulce
Punta del Río
Cabo de Gata
Roquetas de Mar
S. José
Almerimar
Golfo de Almería
Cabo de Gata
Melilla
Almerimar
MICHELIN

CLASSIFICATION OF GOLF COURSES
CLASIFICACION DE LOS RECORRIDOS

This classification gives priority consideration to the score awarded to the actual course.

Esta clasificacíon da prioridad a la nota atribuida al recorrido.

Within each score, the ranking is purely alphabetical

Course score / Nota del recorrido				Page / Página
19	8	8	Valderrama	1202
18	6	8	El Saler	1131
18	8	8	Las Brisas	1156
18	7	7	PGA de Catalunya	1181
18	8	9	Puerta de Hierro Abajo	1183
18	7	7	Real Sociedad Club de Campo Norte	1186
18	8	8	San Roque New Course	1188
18	8	8	Sotogrande	1198
17	8	8	Alcanada	1108
17	7	8	Aloha	1113
17	7	6	Emporda	1132
17	7	7	Fontanals	1134
17	7	8	La Cala Norte	1142
17	7	6	Lerma	1159
17	8	8	Montecastillo	1171
17	7	7	Neguri	1173
17	7	7	Real Sociedad Club de Campo Sur	1187
17	8	8	San Roque Old Course	1189
17	7	8	Sevilla	1193
16	8	7	Bonmont	1116
16	7	7	Castillo de Gorraiz	1119
16	8	8	Club de Campo Negro	1121
16	8	7	Costa Ballena	1122
16	6	5	El Bosque	1126
16	5	8	El Cortijo	1127
16	8	8	El Prat Amarillo	1128
16	8	8	El Prat Rosa	1129
16	7	8	Golf del Sur	1136
16	8	8	Islantilla Verde/Azul	1140
16	7	8	La Cala Sur	1143
16	8	8	La Moraleja La Moraleja 2	1150
16	8	8	La Reserva	1152
16	7	8	Las Américas	1155
16	7	7	Los Naranjos	1161
16	7	7	Masia Bach	1164
16	7	8	Maspalomas	1165
16	7	6	Mediterraneo	1166
16	6	7	Mijas Los Lagos	1167
16	8	7	Montenmedio	1172
16	7	7	Novo Sancti Petri	1174
16	6	7	Pals (Platja de Pals)	1177
16	6	6	Pedreña	1179
16	8	9	Puerta de Hierro Arriba	1184
16	8	8	Son Antem Oeste	1195
16	8	9	Son Muntaner	1196
16	6	6	Ulzama	1201
16	5	6	Valle del Este	1203
16	7	6	Villamartin	1204
16	7	6	Zaudín	1205
15	8	8	Alicante	1110
15	8	8	Almenara	1111
15	7	7	Amarilla	1114
15	6	6	Canyamel	1118
15	6	6	Desert Springs	1125
15	4	8	El Puerto	1130
15	6	7	Golf d'Aro (Mas Nou)	1135
15	7	7	Guadalmina Sur	1139
15	7	7	La Finca	1145
15	6	7	La Herreria	1146
15	5	7	La Manga Norte	1147
15	5	7	La Manga Sur	1148
15	8	8	La Moraleja La Moraleja 1	1149
15	6	5	La Sella	1153
15	7	8	Marbella	1163
15	7	7	Peralada	1180
15	7	9	Pineda	1182

CLASSIFICATION OF GOLF COURSES
CLASIFICACION DE LOS RECORRIDOS

14	6	7	Alcaidesa	1107
14	7	6	Alhaurín	1109
14	7	7	Almerimar	1112
14	7	6	Bonalba	1115
14	7	6	Campoamor	1117
14	5	7	Cerdaña	1120
14	7	7	Costa Brava	1123
14	6	7	Granada	1137
14	7	6	Guadalhorce	1138
14	7	6	La Dehesa	1144
14	8	8	La Quinta	1151
14	8	8	Las Palmas	1157
14	7	7	Lauro	1158
14	6	7	Los Arqueros	1160
14	7	4	Montanya	1169
14	6	7	Oliva Nova	1175
14	6	4	Panoramica	1178
14	6	6	San Sebastián	1190
14	6	7	Santa Ponsa Santa Ponsa I	1192
14	7	7	Sherry Golf	1194
14	6	9	Son Vida	1197
14	7	7	Torrequebrada	1200
13	6	6	Costa Dorada	1124
13	8	7	Escorpion Azul	1133
13	7	6	Jarama R.A.C.E.	1141
13	4	6	Málaga	1162
13	6	7	Mijas Los Olivos	1168
13	5	5	Monte Mayor	1170
13	6	5	Pula	1185
13	6	5	Sant Cugat	1191
13	7	7	Torremirona	1199

HOTEL FACILITIES
HOTELES CERCANOS

This classification gives priority consideration to the score awarded to the hotel facilities.

Esta clasificacíon da prioridad a la nota atribuida a los hoteles cercanos.

		Hotel facility score / Nota de los hoteles cercanos		Page / Página
15	7	**9**	Pineda	1182
18	8	**9**	Puerta de Hierro Abajo	1183
16	8	**9**	Puerta de Hierro Arriba	1184
16	8	**9**	Son Muntaner	1196
14	6	**9**	Son Vida	1197
17	8	**8**	Alcanada	1108
15	8	**8**	Alicante	1110
15	8	**8**	Almenara	1111
17	7	**8**	Aloha	1113
16	8	**8**	Club de Campo Negro	1121
16	5	**8**	El Cortijo	1127
16	8	**8**	El Prat Amarillo	1128
16	8	**8**	El Prat Rosa	1129
15	4	**8**	El Puerto	1130
18	6	**8**	El Saler	1131
16	7	**8**	Golf del Sur	1136
16	8	**8**	Islantilla Verde/Azul	1140
17	7	**8**	La Cala Norte	1142
16	7	**8**	La Cala Sur	1143
15	8	**8**	La Moraleja La Moraleja 1	1149
16	8	**8**	La Moraleja La Moraleja 2	1150
14	8	**8**	La Quinta	1151
16	8	**8**	La Reserva	1152
16	7	**8**	Las Américas	1155
18	8	**8**	Las Brisas	1156
14	8	**8**	Las Palmas	1157
15	7	**8**	Marbella	1163
16	7	**8**	Maspalomas	1165
17	8	**8**	Montecastillo	1171
18	8	**8**	San Roque New Course	1188
17	8	**8**	San Roque Old Course	1189
17	7	**8**	Sevilla	1193
16	8	**8**	Son Antem Oeste	1195
18	8	**8**	Sotogrande	1198
19	8	**8**	Valderrama	1202
14	6	**7**	Alcaidesa	1107
14	7	**7**	Almerimar	1112
15	7	**7**	Amarilla	1114

HOTEL FACILITIES
HOTELES CERCANOS

16	8	**7**	Bonmont	1116
16	7	**7**	Castillo de Gorraiz	1119
14	5	**7**	Cerdaña	1120
16	8	**7**	Costa Ballena	1122
14	7	**7**	Costa Brava	1123
13	8	**7**	Escorpion Azul	1133
17	7	**7**	Fontanals	1134
15	6	**7**	Golf d'Aro (Mas Nou)	1135
14	6	**7**	Granada	1137
15	7	**7**	Guadalmina Sur	1139
15	7	**7**	La Finca	1145
15	6	**7**	La Herreria	1146
15	5	**7**	La Manga Norte	1147
15	5	**7**	La Manga Sur	1148
14	7	**7**	Lauro	1158
14	6	**7**	Los Arqueros	1160
16	7	**7**	Los Naranjos	1161
16	7	**7**	Masia Bach	1164
16	6	**7**	Mijas Los Lagos	1167
13	6	**7**	Mijas Los Olivos	1168
16	8	**7**	Monteenmedio	1172
17	7	**7**	Neguri	1173
16	7	**7**	Novo Sancti Petri	1174
14	6	**7**	Oliva Nova	1175
16	6	**7**	Pals (Platja de Pals)	1177
15	7	**7**	Peralada	1180
18	7	**7**	PGA de Catalunya	1181
18	7	**7**	Real Sociedad Club de Campo Norte	1186
17	7	**7**	Real Sociedad Club de Campo Sur	1187
14	6	**7**	Santa Ponsa Santa Ponsa I	1192
14	7	**7**	Sherry Golf	1194
13	7	**7**	Torremirona	1199
14	7	**7**	Torrequebrada	1200
14	7	**6**	Alhaurín	1109
14	7	**6**	Bonalba	1115
14	7	**6**	Campoamor	1117
15	6	**6**	Canyamel	1118
13	6	**6**	Costa Dorada	1124
15	6	**6**	Desert Springs	1125
17	7	**6**	Emporda	1132
14	7	**6**	Guadalhorce	1138
13	7	**6**	Jarama R.A.C.E.	1141
14	7	**6**	La Dehesa	1144
17	7	**6**	Lerma	1159
13	4	**6**	Málaga	1162
16	7	**6**	Mediterraneo	1166
15	6	**6**	Pedreña	1179
14	6	**6**	San Sebastián	1190
16	6	**6**	Ulzama	1201
16	5	**6**	Valle del Este	1203
16	7	**6**	Villamartin	1204
16	7	**6**	Zaudín	1205
16	6	**5**	El Bosque	1126
15	6	**5**	La Sella	1153
13	5	**5**	Monte Mayor	1170
13	6	**5**	Pula	1185
13	6	**5**	Sant Cugat	1191
14	7	**4**	Montanya	1169
14	6	**4**	Panoramica	1178

RECOMMENDED GOLFING STAY
ESTANCIA DE GOLF RECOMENDADA

Almenara	**15**	8	8	1111
El Prat Amarillo	**16**	8	8	1128
El Prat Rosa	**16**	8	8	1129
Emporda	**17**	7	6	1132
Islantilla Verde/Azul	**16**	8	8	1140
La Cala Norte	**17**	7	8	1142
La Cala Sur	**16**	7	8	1143
La Manga Norte	**15**	5	7	1147
La Manga Sur	**15**	5	7	1148
La Reserva	**16**	8	8	1152
Mijas Los Lagos	**16**	6	7	1167
Mijas Los Olivos	**13**	6	7	1168
Montecastillo	**17**	8	8	1171
San Roque New Course	**18**	8	8	1188
San Roque Old Course	**17**	8	8	1189
Son Antem Oeste	**16**	8	8	1195
Son Muntaner	**16**	8	9	1196
Son Vida	**14**	6	9	1197

Alcaidesa

14	6	7

Alcaidesa es un buen ejemplo del fuerte desarrollo del golf en el extremo sur de España donde se concentran diez recorridos de 18 hoyos (contando el que Alcaidesa abrirá dentro de unos meses). Con impresionantes vistas sobre el Mediterráneo y la enorme Roca de Gibraltar que domina gran parte del recorrido, el campo se autodenomina links porque está junto al mar y hay que saber jugar con viento, pero la naturaleza del suelo, el diseño y la preparación de las zonas de caída de la bola son benignos y cómodos para que jugadores de cualquier edad y handicap puedan disfrutar de un buen día de golf, sin prescindir del reto de saber dirigir la bola. Los greenes no son inmensos ni excesivamente complicados pero para hacer una buena tarjeta o ganar un partido hay que afinar en el juego corto y pegar recto. La brisa marina casi constante en la zona tiene poder para alargar muy seriamente el campo y cambiarlo radicalmente según la dirección del viento.

Alcaidesa has become a symbol of the development of the sport in the extreme south of Spain. The present course is even more in keeping with the spectacular vista over the Mediterranean sea and the massive rock of Gibraltar, which dominates a large part of the course. Alcaidesa has been called a links because it is situated along the coastline and because you need to know how to handle the wind. However, the type of soil, layout and breadth of the landing areas are well suited to players of all ages and abilities who are looking for a good day's golfing without having to bend the ball one way or the other. The greens are neither oversized nor too complicated, but to card a good score or win your bet, you will need to hit it straight and have a sharp short game. The virtually permanent sea breeze can seriously stiffen the challenge and the course plays very differently according to how the wind blows.

Alcaidesa Links Golf Course — 1991

Ctra. Nacional, Km 124,6
E - 11315 LA LÍNEA (Cádiz)

Office Secretaría (34) 956 - 791 040
Pro shop Pro-shop (34) 956 - 791 040
Fax Fax (34) 956 - 791 041
Web www.alcaidesa.com
Situation Situación Gibraltar, 10 km
Algeciras (pop. 101 556), 15 km

Annual closure Cierre anual no
Weekly closure Cierre semanal no

Fees main season Precios tempor. alta	18 holes	
	Week days Semana	**We/Bank holidays** Fin de sem./fiestas
Individual Individual	€ 75	€ 75
Couple Pareja	€ 150	€ 150

Caddie Caddie on request **Electric Trolley** Carro eléctrico no
Buggy Coche yes **Clubs** Palos yes
Credit cards Tarjetas de crédito
VISA - MasterCard - AMEX - DC

Access Acceso : Marbella → Estepona, Sotogrande → Cádiz, Golf on the left (km 124,6)
Map 8 on page 1101 Plano 8 Página 1101

GOLF COURSE RECORRIDO — 14/20

Site Emplazamiento
Maintenance Mantenimiento
Architect Arquitecto Peter Alliss, Clive Clark
Type Tipo seaside course
Relief Relieve
Water in play Agua
Exp. to wind Exp. al viento
Trees in play Arboles

Scorecard Tarjeta	Chp. Campeonato	Mens Caballeros	Ladies Damas
Length Longitud	5766	5435	4579
Par	72	72	72
Slope system	123	119	107

Advised golfing ability Nivel de juego aconsejado 0 12 24 36
Hcp required Handicap exigido 28 Men., 36 Ladies

CLUB HOUSE & AMENITIES CLUB HOUSE Y DEPENDENCIAS — 6/10

Pro shop Pro-shop
Driving range Campo de prácticas
Sheltered cubierto no - On grass sobre hierba yes - Putting-green putting-green yes - Pitching-green pitching-green yes

HOTEL FACILITIES HOTELES CERCANOS — 7/10

HOTELS HOTELES
NH Almenara - 160 rooms, D € 223 - Sotogrande 5 km
Tel (34) 956 - 582 000, Fax (34) 956 - 582 001

Hotel Quercus La Línea - 9 rooms, D € 160 - La Línea
Tel (34) 956 - 792 159, Fax (34) 956 - 797 144

Royal Golf - 70 rooms, D € 150 - Sotogrande 4 km
Tel (34) 956 - 796 263, Fax (34) 956 - 785 159

San Roque Suites - 50 rooms, D € 216 - San Roque 10 km
Tel (34) 956 - 613 030, Fax (34) 956 - 613 012

RESTAURANTS RESTAURANTES
Los Remos - San Roque 5 km - Tel (34) 956 - 698 412
Pedro - San Roque 5 km - Tel (34) 956 - 698 453
Vicente - Sotogrande 7 km - Tel (34) 956 790 212

Alcanada

17	8	8

El último campo nacido en la privilegiada isla de Mallorca está situado en la bahía de Alcúdia, al norte de la isla, frente al faro que da nombre e imagen al club. Esta descripción del entorno se disfruta en su plenitud en el alto tee del 7 que domina un panorama de ensueño. El campo es largo, con pares 4 por encima de los 415 metros y pares 5 por encima de los 550, y la brisa local puede complicarlo; las calles son generosamente anchas pero hay regatos de agua y rough denso a sus bordes. Los greenes son muy escurridizos tanto para sujetar la bola en ellos como para patear, lo cual convierte esta parte del juego en un desafío total. El recorrido es movido y variado, con alguna subida fuerte, por lo cual hay que sacar de la bolsa golpes imaginativos y técnicos tanto para acceder a ciertos greenes como para librar las situaciones comprometidas que sin duda se presentarán. En definitiva, el buen jugador tendrá el placer de jugar un golf muy completo y el jugador o jugadora menos expertos disfrutarán la experiencia de jugar un campo bueno y bonito. Y si hace calor, no dejen de tomar un cochecito para reservar fuerzas para el juego.

The latest course to open in Majorca lies in the bay of Alcúdia, to the north of the island opposite the lighthouse of the same name. The full picture is apparent from the 7th tee, which overlooks a dream landscape. Par 4s in excess of 450 yards and par 5s of over 600 yards make this a long course where a sea breeze only tends to make matters worse. The fairways are wide enough for most but are flanked by streams and rather thick rough. And the greens not only fail to hold the ball but also make for hard reading. The course is a little hilly with a few steep slopes where you will need all your creative flair to reach the greens and escape from a number of tricky situations. In short, experienced golfers will have fun playing a course of such variety, while the lesser mortal will discover what a good and beautiful golf course is all about. Take a buggy in hot weather.

Club de Golf Alcanada — 2003

Carretera del Faro s/n
E- 07400 PORT D'ALCÚDIA (Mallorca - Islas Baleares)

Office Secretaría (34) 971 - 549 560
Pro shop Pro-shop (34) 971 - 549 560
Fax Fax (34) 971 - 897 578
Web www.golf-alcanada.com
Situation Situación Alcúdia (pop. 13.000), 4 km
Palma de Mallorca (pop. 350 000), 60 Km
Annual closure Cierre anual no
Weekly closure Cierre semanal no

Fees main season Precios tempor. alta	18 holes	
	Week days Semana	**We/Bank holidays** Fin de sem./fiestas
Individual Individual	€ 75	€ 75
Couple Pareja	€ 150	€ 150

Caddie Caddie no — **Electric Trolley** Carro eléctrico yes
Buggy Coche yes — **Clubs** Palos yes
Credit cards Tarjetas de crédito
VISA - MasterCard - AMEX - DC

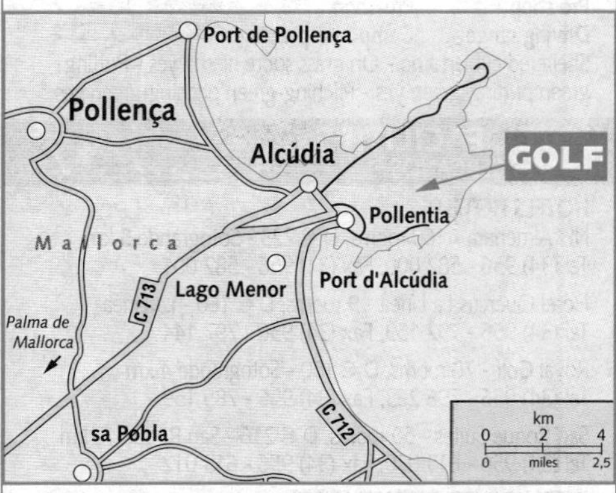

Access Acceso : Palma, PM-27 → Inca, → Puerto de Alcudia. Golf signposted
Map 1 on page 1087 Plano 1 Página 1087

GOLF COURSE — RECORRIDO — 17/20

Site Emplazamiento
Maintenance Mantenimiento
Architect Arquitecto R. Trent Jones Jr
Type Tipo seaside course
Relief Relieve
Water in play Agua
Exp. to wind Exp. al viento
Trees in play Arboles

Scorecard Tarjeta	**Chp.** Campeonato	**Mens** Caballeros	**Ladies** Damas
Length Longitud	6499	6152	5241
Par	72	72	72
Slope system	129	128	123

Advised golfing ability Nivel de juego aconsejado 0 12 24 36
Hcp required Handicap exigido 33 Men, 35 Ladies

CLUB HOUSE & AMENITIES — CLUB HOUSE Y DEPENDENCIAS — 8/10

Pro shop Pro-shop
Driving range Campo de prácticas
Sheltered cubierto no - On grass sobre hierba yes - Putting-green putting-green yes - Pitching-green pitching-green yes

HOTEL FACILITIES — HOTELES CERCANOS — 8/10

HOTELS HOTELES
Alcudiamar - Port d'Alcúdia 2 km
106 rooms, D € 200
Tel (34) 971 - 897 215, Fax (34) 971 - 897 226

Son Ciurana - 12 rooms, D € 154 - Alcúdia 6 km
Tel (34) 971 - 549 662, Fax (34) 971 - 549 788

Son Brull - 23 rooms, D € 200 - Pollença 20 km
Tel (34) 971 - 535 353, Fax (34) 971 - 531 068

RESTAURANTS RESTAURANTES
La Terraza - Port de Alcúdia 2 km - Tel (34) 971 - 545 611
Mesón Dulcinea - Port d'Alcúdia 2 km
Tel (34) 971 - 548 825
Es Convent - Alcúdia 6 km - Tel (34) 971 - 548 716

Alhaurín

14	7	6

Al lado de Mijas, este ambicioso proyecto es prometedor, sobre todo teniendo en cuenta que la firma de Ballesteros es una excelente publicidad. En un magnífico entorno, con vistas espectaculares hacia la montaña, ha diseñado un recorrido bastante accidentado (a veces demasiado), que exige un juego preciso, aunque sólo sea para evitar algunos barrancos, e incluso el rough, a menudo en la línea de juego y muy salvaje. Favorece a quienes juegan con "fade", por lo que los jugadores con tendencia al "slice" no se sentirán muy agobiados. Un buen número de tees de salida permite adaptar el recorrido a todos los niveles de juego, pero los jugadores con poca experiencia tendrán problemas. Los obstáculos de agua dan a veces un aspecto americano a este diseño que a pesar de todo está en armonía con el paisaje. Hay que tener muy en cuenta el recorrido anejo de 9 hoyos reservado a los "junior",... y a los padres si los chicos les invitan!

Next door to Mijas, this ambitious resort promises a great deal, all the more so in that the label of Ballesteros is a commercial argument of the highest order. In a magnificent setting with spectacular views over mountains, Seve has designed a very, and sometimes too, hilly course, which demands precision golf if only to avoid a number of precipices or even the rough, a frequent hazard and now growing wild. It is a course for players who fade the ball, allowing the amateur's slice more leeway than usual. The many different tees make this a course for all levels but inexperienced players will definitely have problems. Water hazards sometimes give the layout a very American style, although the general character blends in harmoniously with the setting. Worthy of note is the adjoining 18-hole course reserved for juniors, and their parents if invited by the kids!

Alhaurín Golf Hotel & Resort — 1992

Apartado de Correos 235
E - 29120 ALHAURÍN EL GRANDE

Office	Secretaria	(34) 952 - 595 970
Pro shop	Pro-shop	(34) 952 - 595 800
Fax	Fax	(34) 952 - 594 586
Web	www.alhauringolf.com	
Situation	Situación	Alhaurín, 3 km

Fuengirola (pop. 43 048), 15 km

Annual closure	Cierre anual	no
Weekly closure	Cierre semanal	no
Fees main season	Precios tempor. alta	18 holes

	Week days Semana	We/Bank holidays Fin de sem./fiestas
Individual Individual	€ 57	€ 57
Couple Pareja	€ 114	€ 114

Caddie Caddie no — **Electric Trolley** Carro eléctrico no
Buggy Coche yes — **Clubs** Palos no yes
Credit cards Tarjetas de crédito
VISA - AMEX

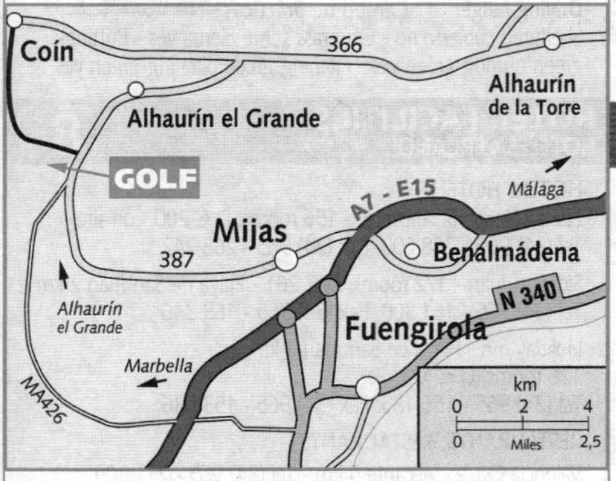

Access Acceso : Málaga → Marbella. Exit (Salida) "Churiana", → Mijas → Alhaurín El Grande
Map 8 on page 1101 Plano 8 Página 1101

GOLF COURSE — RECORRIDO — 14/20

Site	Emplazamiento	
Maintenance	Mantenimiento	
Architect	Arquitecto	Seve Ballesteros
Type	Tipo	mountain
Relief	Relieve	
Water in play	Agua	
Exp. to wind	Exp. al viento	
Trees in play	Arboles	

Scorecard Tarjeta	**Chp.** Campeonato	**Mens** Caballeros	**Ladies** Damas
Length Longitud	6221	5857	4941
Par	72	72	72
Slope system	142	140	118

Advised golfing ability Nivel de juego aconsejado — 0 12 24 36
Hcp required Handicap exigido — no

CLUB HOUSE & AMENITIES — CLUB HOUSE Y DEPENDENCIAS — 7/10

Pro shop Pro-shop
Driving range Campo de prácticas
Sheltered cubierto - On grass sobre hierba yes - Putting-green putting-green yes - Pitching-green pitching-green no

HOTEL FACILITIES — HOTELES CERCANOS — 6/10

HOTELS HOTELES
Hotel Alhaurin Golf - 38 rooms, D € 130 - Alhaurín
Tel (34) 952 - 595 800, Fax (34) 952 - 594 195

Byblos - 144 rooms, D € 358 - Fuengirola 12 km
Tel (34) 952 - 473 050, Fax (34) 952 - 476 783

Mijas - 202 rooms, D € 125 - Mijas 6 km
Tel (34) 952 - 485 800, Fax (34) 952 - 485 825

RESTAURANTS RESTAURANTES
Fonda El Postillón - Alhaurín - Tel (34) 952 - 594 487
Valparaiso - Cta de Fuengirola 8 km - Tel (34) 952 - 485 996

Alicante

15 | 8 | 8

Alicante golf nació en una zona de actividad turística muy intensa con el doble objetivo de atender a una población de residentes y a la alta demanda que se produce en períodos de vacaciones. En este contexto, este campo se distingue por una esmerada puesta a punto del concepto deportivo y del de servicios. Aquí Severiano Ballesteros lleva a la práctica su ideal de campo equilibrado, con seis pares 3, seis pares 4 y seis pares 5. El campo está muy bien acabado, incluso desde el punto de vista estético, a pesar de que varios de los últimos hoyos (existe el proyecto de ampliar el campo hacia otra zona no tan urbanizada) son inmensas avenidas verdes entre bloques de apartamentos, que se compensan con calles generosamente amplias. Esta sensación de amplitud permite atacar los hoyos largos con un buen margen de confianza, especialmente necesaria para jugar unos greenes muy interesantes. Nótese el terreno en reparación permanente 50 metros delante del 14 (par 5): las ruinas de una casa romana del siglo II.

The golf course of Alicante has made room for itself in a very busy tourist area with the twin objective of satisfying local golfers and of meeting extra demand during the holiday periods. In this setting, the course stands out for its excellence both as a polished sports resort and for the services on offer. Seve Ballesteros has developed here his conception of a well-balanced course with six par 3s, six par 4s and six par 5s. It certainly is very well designed, particularly in terms of visual appeal and the diversity of the finishing holes. And there are plans to extend the course in a less built-up area, which is good news since some of the wide-open fairways here are lined with condos. This impression of space means you can go for the wider holes with added confidence, a considerable asset for hitting some interestingly contoured and well-protected greens. For the record, the ground under repair on the 15th hole houses the ruins of an ancient Roman villa dating from the 2nd century.

Alicante Golf — 1998

Avda. Locutor Vicente Hipólito, 37 – La Condomina
E - 03540 PLAYA DE SAN JUAN (Alicante)

Office	Secretaría	(34) 965 - 153 794
Pro shop	Pro-shop	(34) 965 - 152 043
Fax	Fax	(34) 965- 163 707
Web	www.alicantegolf.com	
Situation	Situación	Alicante (pop. 275.000), 5 km
Annual closure	Cierre anual	no
Weekly closure	Cierre semanal	no

Fees main season Precios tempor. alta	Week days Semana	We/Bank holidays Fin de sem./fiestas
18 holes		
Individual Individual	€ 69	€ 69
Couple Pareja	€ 138	€ 138

Buggy included in green-fee

Caddie Caddie no — **Electric Trolley** Carro eléctrico yes

Buggy Coche yes — **Clubs** Palos yes

Credit cards Tarjetas de crédito
VISA - MasterCard

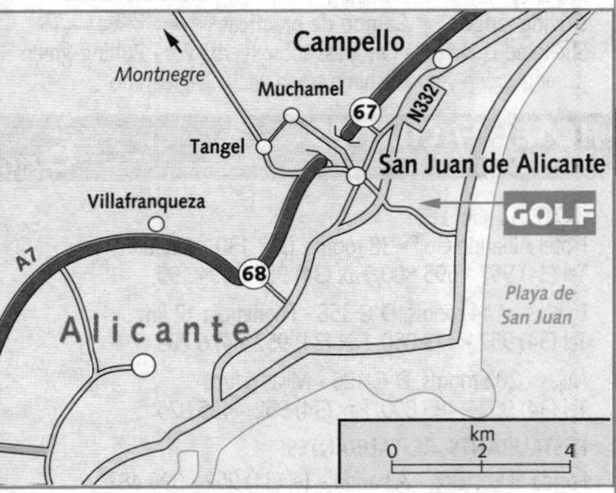

Access Acceso : Alicante, Motorway (Autopista) A-7, Exit (Salida) 68 → "Playas"

Map 7 on page 1099 Plano 7 Página 1099

GOLF COURSE — RECORRIDO — 15/20

Site	Emplazamiento	
Maintenance	Mantenimiento	
Architect	Arquitecto	Seve Ballesteros
Type	Tipo	parkland
Relief	Relieve	
Water in play	Agua	
Exp. to wind	Exp. al viento	
Trees in play	Arboles	

Scorecard Tarjeta	Chp. Campeonato	Mens Caballeros	Ladies Damas
Length Longitud	6236	6057	5254
Par	72	72	72
Slope system	132	131	129

Advised golfing ability Nivel de juego aconsejado — 0 12 24 36

Hcp required Handicap exigido — 28 Men, 36 Ladies

CLUB HOUSE & AMENITIES — CLUB HOUSE Y DEPENDENCIAS — 8/10

Pro shop Pro-shop

Driving range Campo de prácticas

Sheltered cubierto no - On grass sobre hierba yes - Putting-green putting-green yes - Pitching-green pitching-green yes

HOTEL FACILITIES — HOTELES CERCANOS — 8/10

HOTELS HOTELES

Hansa Hesperia Alicante - 156 rooms, D € 200 - on site
Tel (34) 965 - 268 600, Fax (34) 965 - 268 242

Sidi San Juan - 172 rooms, D € 261 - Playa de San Juan 2 km
Tel (34) 965 - 161 300, Fax (34) 965 - 163 346

Holiday Inn - Playa de San Juan 2 km
126 rooms, D € 123
Tel (34) 965 - 156 185, Fax (34) 965 - 153 936

RESTAURANTS RESTAURANTES

Valencia Once - Alicante 5 km - Tel (34) 965 - 211 309
Dársena - Alicante 5 km - Tel (34) 965 - 207 589
Nou Manolin - Alicante 5 km - Tel (34) 965 - 200 368
La Cantera - Alicante 5 km - Tel (34) 965 - 263 606

Almenara

15	8	8

Este campo, en Sotogrande Alto, entre Valderrama y The San Roque Club, está construido en un terreno de fuerte desnivel y el diseño de Dave Thomas le añade dificultad, con calles estrechas que limitan alcornoques y pinos silvestres, un gran lago natural y sus típicos bunkers de calle de altos taludes que castigan todas las bolas que no estén perfectamente dirigidas. No es un campo largo y por causa de los peligros que flanquean y cruzan las calles es recomendable dejar el driver en la bolsa en muchos hoyos del recorrido. Es un campo que pide colocar las salidas en el lugar adecuado de la calle para poder encarar unos tiros a green muy sugestivos con la mayor capacidad de maniobra posible. La construcción es buena, el mantenimiento está muy cuidado y los greenes, no especialmente grandes pero con interesantes movimientos, son excelentes. No es obligatorio jugar en coche, pero pocas piernas resistirán hacerlo a pie.

On the heights of Sotogrande between Valderrama and San Roque, the Almenara course has been built over very hilly terrain and the Dave Thomas layout adds even more difficulties with narrow fairways outlined by Sylvester pines and cork oak trees, a large natural lake and typical, high-lipped fairway bunkers which catch anything hit off-target. This is not a wide course and what with the danger lurking alongside or across the fairways you are often better off leaving the driver in the bag. This is indeed a layout that calls for an accurate tee-shot put just in the right spot so as to approach the greens more easily. A well built course where maintenance is good and the greens - never very large but interestingly contoured - are excellent. You don't have to play with a buggy, but if you walk you will need sturdy legs. Definitely a course to add to your collection, along with the neighbouring La Reserva. It has now 27 holes.

Almenara Golf Hotel — 1999

Avenida Almenara s/n
E - 11310 SOTOGRANDE (Cádiz)

Office	Secretaria	(34) 956 - 582 000
Pro shop	Pro-shop	(34) 902 - 181 836
Fax	Fax	(34) 956 - 582 024
Web	www.sotogrande.com	
Situation	Situación	Estepona, 30 km

Algeciras (pop. 101 556), 30 km

Annual closure	Cierre anual	no
Weekly closure	Cierre semanal	no

Fees main season Precios tempor. alta	Week days Semana	We/Bank holidays Fin de sem./fiestas
18 holes		
Individual Individual	€ 85	€ 85
Couple Pareja	€ 170	€ 170

Green-fees € 70 low season

Caddie Caddie on request **Electric Trolley** Carro eléctrico yes

Buggy Coche yes **Clubs** Palos yes

Credit cards Tarjetas de crédito
VISA - Eurocard - MasterCard - AMEX

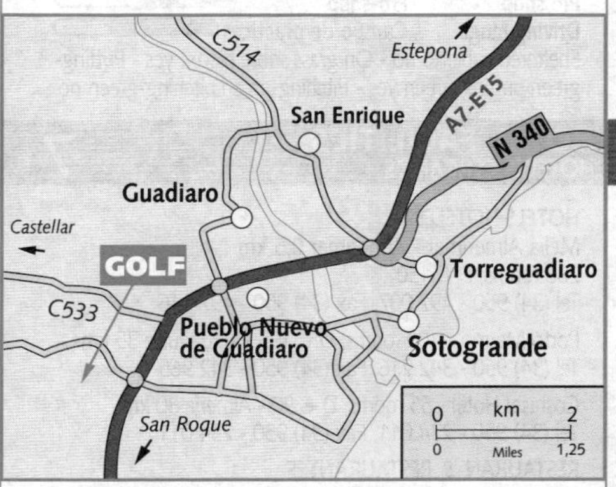

Access Acceso : Marbella N-340 → Algeciras. Exit (salida 127). → Valderrama, Sotogrande Alto.

Map 8 on page 1101 Plano 8 Página 1101

GOLF COURSE — RECORRIDO — 15/20

Site	Emplazamiento	
Maintenance	Mantenimiento	
Architect	Arquitecto	Dave Thomas
Type	Tipo	inland, forest
Relief	Relieve	
Water in play	Agua	
Exp. to wind	Exp. al viento	
Trees in play	Arboles	

Scorecard Tarjeta	Chp. Campeonato	Mens Caballeros	Ladies Damas
Length Longitud	6221	5795	4798
Par	72	72	72
Slope system	137	135	127

Advised golfing ability / Nivel de juego aconsejado: 0 12 24 36

Hcp required Handicap exigido 28 Men/36 Ladies

CLUB HOUSE & AMENITIES — CLUB HOUSE Y DEPENDENCIAS — 8/10

Pro shop	Pro-shop
Driving range	Campo de prácticas

Sheltered cubierto no - On grass sobre hierba yes - Putting-green putting-green yes - Pitching-green pitching-green yes

HOTEL FACILITIES — HOTELES CERCANOS — 8/10

HOTELS HOTELES

NH Almenara - 160 rooms, D € 223 - on site
Tel (34) 956 - 582 000, Fax (34) 956 - 582 001

Royal Golf - 70 rooms, D € 150 - Sotogrande 4 km
Tel (34) 956 - 796 263, Fax (34) 956 - 785 159

NH Sotogrande - 106 rooms, D € 270 - Sotogrande 5 km
Tel (34) 956 - 695 444, Fax (34) 956 - 695 445

RESTAURANTS RESTAURANTES

El Relinque - Pueblo Nuevo Guadiaro 1,5 km
Tel (34) 956 - 695 168

Bar Pepe - Torreguadiaro 2 km - Tel (34) 956 - 615 353

Almerimar

14	7	7

Situado en un zona urbanizada con toda clase de distracciones, colaboraron en su diseño Ron Kirby y Gary Player. Tiene una vegetación rica que, en contraste con el fondo de montañas áridas, da la impresión de un oasis. La propiedad japonesa se propone situar este complejo como uno de los grandes centros turísticos del sur de Europa. Sus calles anchas, sus bunkers grandes y sus amplios obstáculos de agua en la línea de juego en una media docena de hoyos, dan a este recorrido un incontestable estilo de inspiración americana. Su longitud puede parecer importante desde cualquiera de los tees de salida, pero las bolas por lo general ruedan bastante. El punto álgido del recorrido se encuentra en el hoyo 12, un par 3, más bien largo, con el green en medio de una isla y que intimidará a muchos jugadores.

Located in a built-up area where there are all sorts of leisure facilities, this course was designed at a period when Ron Kirby and Gary Player were working together. Lush vegetation affords a pleasant, oasis-style contrast with the arid mountains in the background. The course has been taken over by a Japanese group, which is keen to transform the complex into one of the biggest tourist resorts in southern Europe. With wide fairways, large bunkers and huge water hazards in play on half a dozen holes, the course is unquestionably American in style. It may seem a little long, whichever tee you use, but the ball generally rolls a long way here. The signature hole here is the 12th hole, a rather long par 3 with an island green. A daunting prospect for many a player.

Golf Almerimar S.L. 1976
Urbanización Almerimar
E - 04700 EL EJIDO (Almería)

Office Secretaria (34) 950 - 497 007
Pro shop Pro-shop (34) 950 - 497 007
Fax Fax (34) 950 - 497 146
Web www.almerimargolfapartments.com
Situation Situación Almería (pop. 159 587), 32 km
El Ejido (pop. 41 700), 10 km
Annual closure Cierre anual no
Weekly closure Cierre semanal no

Fees main season Precios tempor. alta	18 holes	
	Week days Semana	We/Bank holidays Fin de sem./fiestas
Individual Individual	€ 80	€ 80
Couple Pareja	€ 160	€ 160

Caddie Caddie on request **Electric Trolley** Carro eléctrico yes
Buggy Coche yes **Clubs** Palos yes
Credit cards Tarjetas de crédito
VISA - MasterCard - AMEX

1112

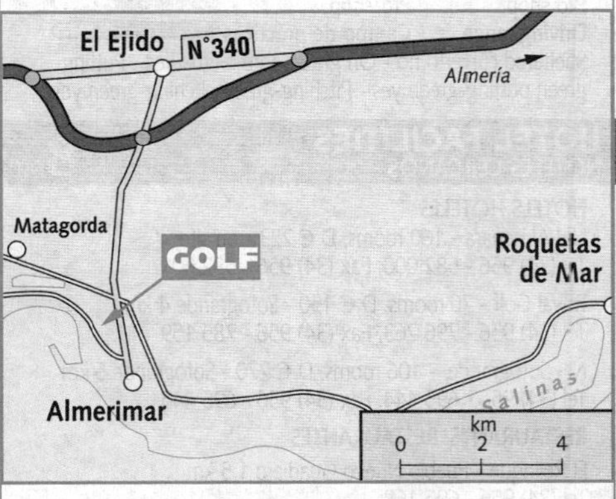

Access Acceso : Almería N340 → El Ejido, Almerimar
Map 9 on page 1103 Plano 9 Página 1103

GOLF COURSE
RECORRIDO — **14**/20

Site Emplazamiento
Maintenance Mantenimiento
Architect Arquitecto Gary Player, Ron Kirby
Type Tipo seaside course
Relief Relieve
Water in play Agua
Exp. to wind Exp. al viento
Trees in play Arboles

Scorecard Tarjeta	**Chp.** Campeonato	**Mens** Caballeros	**Ladies** Damas
Length Longitud	5981	5892	5101
Par	72	72	72
Slope system	122	122	119

Advised golfing ability 0 12 24 36
Nivel de juego aconsejado
Hcp required Handicap exigido 28 Men, 36 Ladies

CLUB HOUSE & AMENITIES
CLUB HOUSE Y DEPENDENCIAS — **7**/10

Pro shop Pro-shop
Driving range Campo de prácticas
Sheltered cubierto no - On grass sobre hierba yes - Putting-green putting-green yes - Pitching-green pitching-green no

HOTEL FACILITIES
HOTELES CERCANOS — **7**/10

HOTELS HOTELES
Meliá Almerimar - Almerimar 0,5 km
286 rooms, D € 150
Tel (34) 950 - 497 007, Fax (34) 950 - 497 146

Porto Magno - 400 rooms, D € 193 - Aguadulce 35 km
Tel (34) 950 - 342 216, Fax (34) 950 - 342 965

Costasol Hotel - 55 rooms, D € 90 - Almería 30 km
Tel (34) 950 - 234 011, Fax (34) 950 - 234 011

RESTAURANTS RESTAURANTES
El Segoviano - Almerimar 10 km - Tel (34) 950 - 480 084
El Bello Rincón - Ctra de Almería 25 km
Tel (34) 950 - 238 427

Aloha

17	7	8

Ya desde su apertura sedujo este recorrido diseñado por Javier Arana y las recientes obras efectuadas lo han mejorado aún más. Aquí es primordial la precisión de los golpes, sobre todo los de salida: Aloha no es un recorrido muy largo, pero sí a veces estrecho y accidentado. Los árboles son a menudo peligrosos, ciertos greenes son ciegos, otros en alto, pero que ruedan siempre bien. Por tanto hay que permanecer constantemente atento, sobre todo para pegar a la bola con efecto en cualquier dirección. Con su original diseño, este recorrido deja una impresión de gran armonía e inteligente utilización golfística del terreno, sobre todo en tres hoyos de gran calidad: el 1, el 12 y el 18. Algunas inclinaciones naturales del campo pueden ser peligrosas, al igual que muchos obstáculos de agua, sobre todo en la segunda vuelta. Agradable y bien decorado, Aloha es un excelente test de golf y un lugar donde no se cansa uno de jugar. Puede incluso esperar su turno de salida jugando el recorrido de 9 pares 3.

This course, designed by Javier Arana, was an attractive proposition from the first day it opened and recent work has helped to improve the overall layout. It is important here to place your shots carefully, especially off the tee. Aloha is not a very long course but it is sometimes tight and hilly; the trees are often dangerous and a number of greens are blind, multi-tiered and very fast. You have to keep your wits about you all the time, especially when trying to work the ball in all directions. Although an original layout, Aloha leaves an impression of harmony and intelligent use of terrain from a golfing point of view, especially on holes 1, 12 and 18, all three excellent. A number of natural banks can cause problems, as can several water hazards, particularly on the back nine. Pleasant to play and well laid out, Aloha is an excellent test of golf which is always a pleasure to play after first of all trying your hand on the par-3 nine-hole course.

Club de Golf Aloha — 1975

Urbanización Aloha Golf
E - 29660 NUEVA ANDALUCIA (Málaga – Costa del Sol)

Office Secretaria (34) 952 - 812 388
Pro shop Pro-shop (34) 952 - 907 085
Fax Fax (34) 952 - 812 389
Web www.clubdegolfaloha.com
Situation Situación Marbella (pop. 84 410), 7 km
San Pedro de Alcantara, 3 km
Annual closure Cierre anual no
Weekly closure Cierre semanal no

Fees main season Precios tempor. alta	18 holes	
	Week days / Semana	We/Bank holidays / Fin de sem./fiestas
Individual Individual	€ 140	€ 140
Couple Pareja	€ 280	€ 280

Ask before coming (Visitantes consultar condiciones)
Caddie Caddie on request **Electric Trolley** Carro eléctrico yes
Buggy Coche yes **Clubs** Palos yes
Credit cards Tarjetas de crédito
VISA - Eurocard - MasterCard - AMEX - JCB

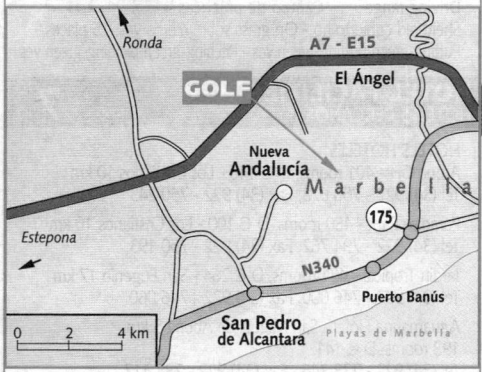

Access Acceso : Marbella → Cádiz. Nueva Andalucia km 180, turn right → Golf
Map 8 on page 1101 Plano 8 Página 1101

GOLF COURSE
RECORRIDO — 17/20

Site Emplazamiento
Maintenance Mantenimiento
Architect Arquitecto Javier Arana
Type Tipo residential, parkland
Relief Relieve
Water in play Agua
Exp. to wind Exp. al viento
Trees in play Arboles

Scorecard Tarjeta	**Chp.** Campeonato	**Mens** Caballeros	**Ladies** Damas
Length Longitud	6293	5997	5236
Par	72	72	72
Slope system	135	131	121

Advised golfing ability 0 12 24 36
Nivel de juego aconsejado
Hcp required Handicap exigido 28 Men, 36 Ladies

CLUB HOUSE & AMENITIES
CLUB HOUSE Y DEPENDENCIAS — 7/10

Pro shop Pro-shop
Driving range Campo de prácticas
Sheltered cubierto no - On grass sobre hierba yes - Putting-green putting-green yes - Pitching-green pitching-green no

HOTEL FACILITIES
HOTELES CERCANOS — 8/10

HOTELS HOTELES
Andalucia Plaza - Nueva Andalucia 4 km
415 rooms, D € 218
Tel (34) 952 - 812 000, Fax (34) 952 - 814 792

Puente Romano - Marbella, Cta de Cádiz 2 km
274 rooms, D € 487
Tel (34) 952 - 820 900, Fax (34) 952 - 775 766

RESTAURANTS RESTAURANTES
Cypriano - Puerto Banús 5 km - Tel (34) 952 - 811 077
Taberna del Alabardero - Puerto Banús 5 km
Tel (34) 952 - 812 794
Le Biarritz - Puerto Banús 5 km - Tel (34) 952 811 248

Amarilla

15 | 7 | 7

Este es un buen campo de vacaciones. Está en un plano descendente hacia el mar por lo cual algunos hoyos disfrutan de unas vistas espléndidas dominando el Atlántico y otros hoyos lo sortean audazmente. El 5 es un par 3 de 115 metros que se conoce como Pebble Beach porque hay que tirar sobre un acantilado. El 6, en cambio, es un par 4 de 331 metros, en subida, de espaldas al mar, que preside el Teide, el volcán dormido y nevado en invierno que domina el panorama desde el centro de la isla. No es un campo difícil ni especialmente largo, suele soplar una brisa marina que refresca y motiva al buen jugador a desplegar los recursos de su juego con viento. Campo de alta ocupación en una zona de fuerte turismo invernal, se esmera el mantenimiento y la mejora del recorrido. El pitch & putt es recomendable por su esmerado cuidado y decoración.

Here is an excellent holiday course. It is located on a slope stretching down to the sea and offers some holes with splendid views over the Atlantic and others a little less spectacular but just as interesting and daring. Hole No 5 for example is a par 3 of 126 yards, reminiscent of Pebble Beach because you have to hit the tee-shot over a cliff. By contrast, the 6th is an uphill 364-yard par 4, turning away from the sea, overlooked by the Teide, a dormant volcano whose winter snows enhance the panorama in the middle of the island. Amarilla is not an impossible course nor is it particularly long, and there is often a stiff sea breeze which refreshes and encourages golfers who know how to cope with wind. As the course is very busy in winter, it calls for constantly high-quality green-keeping, and gets it. The pitch'n putt layout is highly recommended for its manicured appearance and decoration.

Amarilla Golf & Country Club — 1989

Urbanización Amarilla Golf
E - 38639 SAN MIGUEL DE ABONA (Tenerife - Islas Canarias)

Office	Secretaria	(34) 922 - 730 319
Pro shop	Pro-shop	(34) 922 - 785 124
Fax	Fax	(34) 922 - 785 557
Web		www.amarillagolf.es
Situation	Situación	Playa de Las Américas, 15 km

Santa Cruz de Tenerife (pop. 203 000), 60 km

Annual closure	Cierre anual	no
Weekly closure	Cierre semanal	no

Fees main season — Precios tempor. alta — 18 holes

	Week days / Semana	We/Bank holidays / Fin de sem./fiestas
Individual Individual	€ 75	€ 75
Couple Pareja	€ 150	€ 150

Caddie Caddie no — Electric Trolley Carro eléctrico no
Buggy Coche yes — Clubs Palos yes
Credit cards Tarjetas de crédito
VISA - Eurocard - MasterCard - AMEX

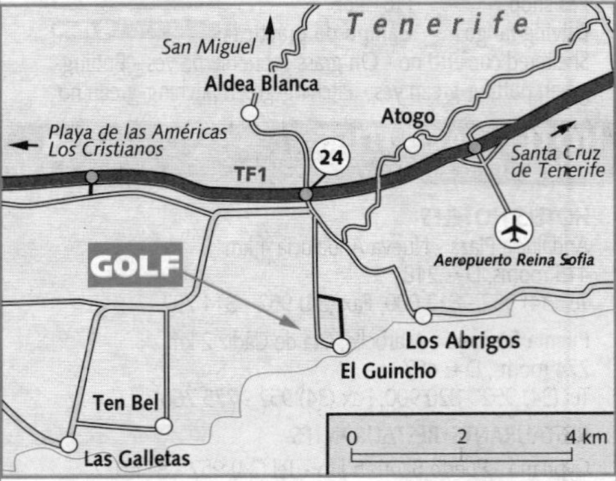

Access Acceso : Motorway TF1 / Autovía del Sur - Tenerife Sur. Exit (Salida) San Miguel de Abona-Los Abrigos. Go towards the sea, → Las Galletas
Map 1 on page 1087 Plano 1 Página 1087

GOLF COURSE / RECORRIDO — 15/20

Site	Emplazamiento	
Maintenance	Mantenimiento	
Architect	Arquitecto	Donald Steel
Type	Tipo	parkland
Relief	Relieve	
Water in play	Agua	
Exp. to wind	Exp. al viento	
Trees in play	Arboles	

Scorecard / Tarjeta	Chp. / Campeonato	Mens / Caballeros	Ladies / Damas
Length Longitud	6077	5782	4967
Par	72	72	72
Slope system	129	125	124

Advised golfing ability — Nivel de juego aconsejado: 0 12 24 36
Hcp required — Handicap exigido: 28 Men, 36 Ladies

CLUB HOUSE & AMENITIES / CLUB HOUSE Y DEPENDENCIAS — 7/10

Pro shop — Pro-shop
Driving range — Campo de prácticas
Sheltered cubierto no - On grass sobre hierba yes, 15 places - Putting-green putting-green yes - Pitching-green pitching-green yes

HOTEL FACILITIES / HOTELES CERCANOS — 7/10

HOTELS HOTELES

Arona GH - 401 rooms, D € 146 - Los Cristianos 10 km
Tel (34) 922 - 750 678, Fax (34) 922 - 750 243

Paradise Park - 480 rooms, D € 100 - Los Cristianos 10 km
Tel (34) 922 - 794 762, Fax (34) 922 - 750 193

Jardin Tropical - 421 rooms, D € 264 - San Eugenio 17 km
Tel (34) 922 - 746 000, Fax (34) 922 - 746 060

Aguamarina Hotel - San Miguel de Abona 5 km
198 rooms, D € 141
Tel (34) 922 - 738 345 , Fax (34) 922 - 738 417

RESTAURANTS RESTAURANTES

Perlas del Mar - Los Abrigos 3 km - Tel (34) 922 - 170 014
Avencio - El Médano 2 km - Tel (34) 922 - 176 079

Bonalba

14	7	6

Confirma la clase de Ramón Espinosa. Bonalba es un recorrido que hay que conocer. La diversidad de los hoyos y la variedad de golpes que hay que jugar constituye un desafío para los más técnicos que, después de los primeros hoyos sin grandes problemas, tendrán que jugar sobre varios pequeños lagos. Pero no hay que dejarse impresionar por esas dificultades: desde los tees de salida adelantados, resultará divertido para cualquier jugador. Sólo los buenos pegadores escogerán las salidas de atrás, donde la longitud y colocación de los obstáculos dan al recorrido su verdadera fisonomía. El campo es llano en su mayor parte aunque al final tiene cuatro hoyos de cuestas pronunciadas. La vegetación está creciendo –se plantaron 3.000 árboles, muchos de ellos palmeras- y en unos años afectará mucho más a la amplitud de las calles. Pero ya desde ahora es un recorrido que merece la pena conocer.

This is definitely a Ramón Espinosa layout which, despite its tender years is a course worth knowing. The variety between holes and shots makes it a good challenge for artists who, like the rest, have to negotiate a number of small lakes, in play on half the holes, especially at the beginning. Thereafter the going gets a little easier. But don't be put off by the water; if they play from the front tees, players of all abilities can get along together here. Only the big-hitters will prefer the tips where the length of the layout and position of hazards give the course its true physiognomy. The course is generally flat although some of the slopes are rather more pronounced on the closing four holes. Vegetation has grown and the 3,000 newly planted trees (including a number of palm-trees) will increasingly come into play. This is already a layout well worth knowing about.

Golf & Spa Bonalba — 1995

Partida de Bonalba s/n
E - 03110 MUTXAMIEL (Alicante)

Office Secretaria (34) 965 - 955 955
Pro shop Pro-shop (34) 965 - 955 955
Fax Fax (34) 965 - 955 078
Web www.golfbonalba.com
Situation Situación Alicante (pop. 275 111), 15 km
Annual closure Cierre anual — no
Weekly closure Cierre semanal — no

Fees main season / Precios tempor. alta	Week days / Semana	We/Bank holidays / Fin de sem./fiestas
18 holes		
Individual Individual	€ 60	€ 60
Couple Pareja	€ 120	€ 120

Caddie Caddie no — **Electric Trolley** Carro eléctrico yes
Buggy Coche yes — **Clubs** Palos yes
Credit cards Tarjetas de crédito
VISA - MasterCard - AMEX

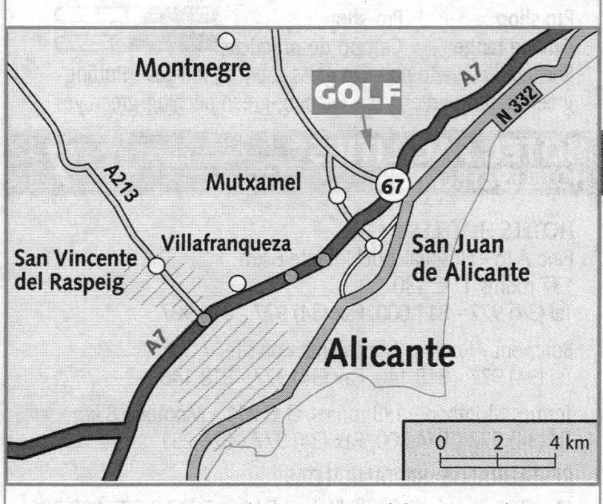

Access Acceso : A7 → Alicante, Exit (Salida) 67 → Alcoy → Busot → Golf
Map 7 on page 1099 Plano 7 Página 1099

GOLF COURSE — RECORRIDO — 14/20

Site Emplazamiento
Maintenance Mantenimiento
Architect Arquitecto — Ramón Espinosa
Type Tipo — country, hilly
Relief Relieve
Water in play Agua
Exp. to wind Exp. al viento
Trees in play Arboles

Scorecard / Tarjeta	Chp. / Campeonato	Mens / Caballeros	Ladies / Damas
Length Longitud	6367	6096	5329
Par	72	72	72
Slope system	133	131	128

Advised golfing ability Nivel de juego aconsejado — 0 12 24 36
Hcp required Handicap exigido — 28 Men, 36 Ladies

CLUB HOUSE & AMENITIES — CLUB HOUSE Y DEPENDENCIAS — 7/10

Pro shop Pro-shop
Driving range Campo de prácticas
Sheltered cubierto no - On grass sobre hierba no (24 mats) - Putting-green putting-green yes - Pitching-green pitching-green yes

HOTEL FACILITIES — HOTELES CERCANOS — 6/10

HOTELS HOTELES
Bonalba Golf & Resort - on site
100 rooms, D € 92
Tel (34) 965 - 959 506, Fax (34) 965 - 959 516

Hansa Hesperia Alicante - 156 rooms, D € 200 - on site
Tel (34) 965 - 268 600, Fax (34) 965 - 268 242

Sidi San Juan - 172 rooms, D € 261 - Playa de San Juan 2 km
Tel (34) 965 - 161 300, Fax (34) 965 - 163 346

RESTAURANTS RESTAURANTES
El Patio de San Juan - San Juan de Alicante 3 km
Tel (34) 965 - 656 800

La Maestra - San Juan de Alicante 3 km
Tel (34) 965 - 658 560

Bonmont

16	8	7

Robert Trent Jones Jr, siguiendo la tradición de su padre, ha creado un diseño muy estratégico en el que constantemente hay que calcular los riesgos antes de jugar. Lo ha construido con un refinamiento estético muy personal, removiendo grandes cantidades de tierra, tarea indispensable para poder jugar en un terreno tan rocoso. El terreno es muy accidentado: tiene profundos barrancos, riachuelos y lagos, bunkers grandes magistralmente colocados, como es norma de la casa Trent Jones, y greenes muy interesantes y provocadores. Con estos elementos y distancias razonables parece evidente que estamos hablando de algo excepcional, y lo es, aunque el problema de Bonmont es el fuerte viento dominante que distorsiona las distancias y el diseño. Ojalá el visitante acierte un día de relativa calma para disfrutar un campo que provoca excelentes golpes por sus retos y por el buen cuidado del terreno.

In the family tradition, Robert Trent Jones Jnr. has designed a highly strategic layout where risks constantly need calculating before each shot. He has modelled space in his very own tasteful and stylish way, but also with impressive contouring of the land. And it was necessary for this rocky terrain to be at all playable. The terrain is uneven and hilly: watch out for some deep ravines, ditches and lakes, strategically well-located bunkering and (as usual with Trent Jones) a number of very tricky and deceptive greens. When you consider the above plus the course's very respectable yardage, it is obvious that this is no ordinary layout. The greatest problem playing Bonmont is the prevailing wind, which is often very gusty and completely changes all notion of distance and evaluation. First time out, try and play in calm weather or in no worse than a light breeze.

Club de Golf Bonmont Terres Noves 1990

Urbanización Terres Noves, parcela 84
E - 43300 MONT-ROIG DEL CAMP (Tarragona)

Office Secretaria (34) 977 - 818 140
Pro shop Pro-shop (34) 977 - 818 140
Fax Fax (34) 977 - 818 146
Web www.bonmont.com
Situation Situación Cambrils, 15 km
Hospitalet del Infante (pop. 2 690), 6 km

Annual closure Cierre anual no
Weekly closure Cierre semanal no

Fees main season Precios tempor. alta	18 holes	
	Week days Semana	We/Bank holidays Fin de sem./fiestas
Individual Individual	€ 50	€ 50
Couple Pareja	€ 70	€ 70

Caddie Caddie no — **Electric Trolley** Carro eléctrico no
Buggy Coche yes — **Clubs** Palos yes
Credit cards Tarjetas de crédito
VISA - Eurocard - MasterCard - AMEX - DC

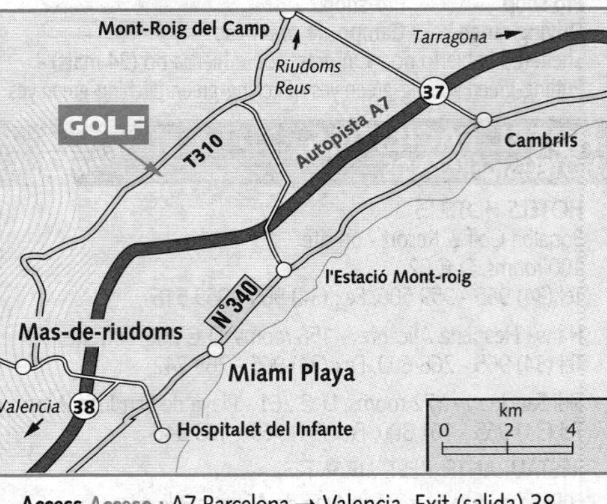

Access Acceso : A7 Barcelona → Valencia, Exit (salida) 38. Hospitalet del Infante → Mora, 2 km → Mont Roig, Golf 4 km
Map 5 on page 1095 Plano 5 Página 1095

GOLF COURSE
RECORRIDO — 16/20

Site Emplazamiento
Maintenance Mantenimiento
Architect Arquitecto R. Trent Jones Jr
Type Tipo residential, open country
Relief Relieve
Water in play Agua
Exp. to wind Exp. al viento
Trees in play Arboles

Scorecard Tarjeta	**Chp.** Campeonato	**Mens** Caballeros	**Ladies** Damas
Length Longitud	6371	6050	5141
Par	72	72	72
Slope system	136	132	126

Advised golfing ability Nivel de juego aconsejado 0 12 24 36
Hcp required Handicap exigido 27 Men, 36 Ladies

CLUB HOUSE & AMENITIES
CLUB HOUSE Y DEPENDENCIAS — 8/10

Pro shop Pro-shop
Driving range Campo de prácticas
Sheltered cubierto no - On grass sobre hierba yes - Putting-green putting-green yes - Pitching-green pitching-green yes

HOTEL FACILITIES
HOTELES CERCANOS — 7/10

HOTELS HOTELES
Pino Alto - Hospitalet del Infante 6 km
137 rooms, D € 130
Tel (34) 977 - 811 000, Fax (34) 977 - 810 907

Bonmont - Rooms, Apartments - on site
Tel (34) 977 - 818 140, Fax (34) 977 - 818 146

Termes Montbrio - 133 rooms, D € 211 - Montbrio 8 km
Tel (34) 977 - 814 000, Fax (34) 977 - 826 251

RESTAURANTS RESTAURANTES
Mar Brava - Hospitalet de l'Infant 5 km - Tel (34) 977 820 206
Panorámico Bonmont - on site - Tel (34) 977 818 129

Campoamor

14 | 7 | 6

La belleza del lugar anuncia una agradable jornada en medio de un paisaje con poco arbolado en el que predomina la vegetación de monte. Es un recorrido no muy accidentado, con calles inclinadas y bunkers hondos y hundidos y con una longitud que gustará a los pegadores que podrán intentar llegar a green en dos pares 4 muy cortos (el 11 y el 13) y ganar golpes en los pares 5. El diseño de Sanz y García no denota una gran imaginación ya que lo que han intentado ante todo es agradar a todos los jugadores, logrando un recorrido muy funcional. Con greens correctos y poco protegidos se pueden obtener buenos resultados para salir satisfechos del campo. Bien es verdad que se pueden encontrar en la región recorridos más difíciles, pero Campoamor es un buen test para afinar su juego sin demasiadas dificultades. Un auténtico recorrido de vacaciones.

A very pretty site heralds a pleasant day's golfing in rather open countryside, where the garrigue shrub is the main and most attractive form of vegetation. The course is not hilly but certain fairways slope considerably with deep bunkers and the length will appeal to big-hitters, who can try and reach two very short par 4s (the 11th and 13th) from the tee and pick up strokes on the par 5s. The Sanz and García layout has nothing exceptionally imaginative about it, but their aim was to appeal to players, so the course's functional side is a positive point. The greens are good but have few bunkers and the opportunities are there to card a good score, always a welcome treat for the wounded ego. You can certainly find more challenging courses than this in the region but Campoamor is a great place to sharpen up your game without too many mishaps. A real holiday course.

Real Club de Golf Campoamor — 1989

C/. Valencia 1, 1°
E - 03300 ORIHUELA (Alicante)

Office Secretaria (34) 965 - 320 410
Pro shop Pro-shop (34) 965 - 320 506
Fax Fax (34) 965 - 322 454
Web www.lomasdecampoamor.es
Situation Situación Alicante, 57 km
Torrevieja (pop. 25 891), 8 km

Annual closure Cierre anual — no
Weekly closure Cierre semanal — no
Fees main season Precios tempor. alta — 18 holes

	Week days / Semana	We/Bank holidays / Fin de sem./fiestas
Individual Individual	€ 52	€ 52
Couple Pareja	€ 104	€ 104

Caddie Caddie no — **Electric Trolley** Carro eléctrico no
Buggy Coche yes — **Clubs** Palos yes
Credit cards Tarjetas de crédito no

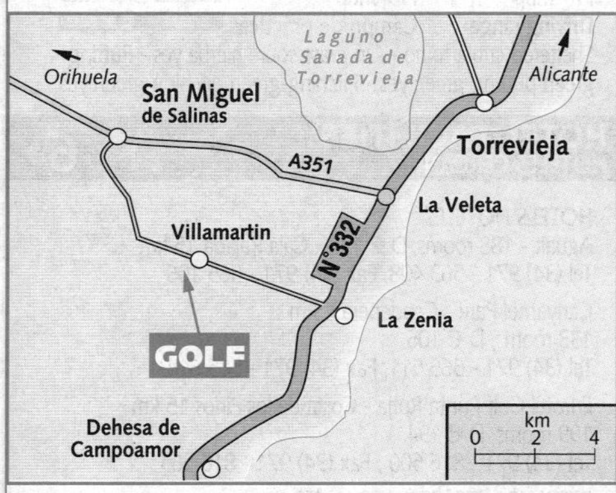

Access Acceso : N332 Torrevieja → Dehesa de Campoamor, Cabo Roig, Km 48 → Golf
Map 7 on page 1099 Plano 7 Página 1099

GOLF COURSE — RECORRIDO — 14/20

Site Emplazamiento
Maintenance Mantenimiento
Architect Arquitecto — Gregorio Sanz, Carmelo García
Type Tipo — hilly, residential
Relief Relieve
Water in play Agua
Exp. to wind Exp. al viento
Trees in play Arboles

Scorecard / Tarjeta	Chp. / Campeonato	Mens / Caballeros	Ladies / Damas
Length Longitud	6203	6056	5094
Par	72	72	72
Slope system	140	134	130

Advised golfing ability Nivel de juego aconsejado — 0 12 24 36
Hcp required Handicap exigido — 28 Men, 36 Ladies

CLUB HOUSE & AMENITIES — CLUB HOUSE Y DEPENDENCIAS — 7/10

Pro shop Pro-shop
Driving range Campo de prácticas
Sheltered cubierto no - On grass sobre hierba yes - Putting-green putting-green yes - Pitching-green pitching-green yes

HOTEL FACILITIES — HOTELES CERCANOS — 6/10

HOTELS HOTELES
Golf Campoamor - Dehesa de Campoamor on site
66 rooms, D € 133
Tel (34) 965 - 320 410, Fax (34) 965 - 320 506

Montepiedra - Dehesa de Campoamor 8 km
64 rooms, D € 118
Tel (34) 965 - 320 300, Fax (34) 965 - 320 634

Torrejoven - 105 rooms, D € 95 - Torrevieja 20 km
Tel (34) 965 - 707 145, Fax (34) 965 - 715 315

RESTAURANTS RESTAURANTES
Cabo Roig - Torrevieja 8 km - Tel (34) 966 - 760 290
Morales - Los Montesinos - Tel (34) 966 - 721 293

Canyamel

15 | 6 | 6

Emplazado dentro de un paisaje típico del interior mallorquín, es un éxito de José Gancedo el haber conseguido realizar algunos hoyos espectaculares en la parte más accidentada (los nueve primeros hoyos). Se ha preservado la naturaleza, así como algunos muros de cultivo e incluso una antigua granja que delimita el ángulo del dog-leg del hoyo 9. Al igual que en otros campos de la isla hay que reflexionar antes de atacar, logrando muchas veces mejores resultados si se juega por la seguridad y se saben evitar los problemas. Mejor es reservar fuerzas para atacar unos greenes a menudo en alto, con escalones y bien protegidos. Su longitud es razonable (aunque las señoras juegan dos pares 4 largos) y se agradece un mantenimiento pulcro y un cuidado estético en el ajardinamiento para pasar un día de golf satisfactorio. Un campo que merece plenamente perder medio día de mar y playa.

In a typical setting of Majorcan countryside, Canyamel is a pretty little number designed by José Gancedo. The hillier part of the course (the front 9) includes some quite spectacular holes. The land's natural beauty has been preserved, together with some low walls and even an old farmhouse marking the corner of the dog-leg on the 9th. As with many other courses on the island this is not a layout you want to attack without thinking first. Playing safe often gives better results. If you keep out of trouble, the going is easier and you can save your strength (important here) to negotiate some tricky approach shots to elevated, multi-tiered and well-defended greens. Very human in length, Canyamel is a course you want to play several times, not to understand it (it has little to hide) but to enjoy getting your score down, even though the par 4s are a little long for the ladies. Good fun all the way before spending the rest of the day on the beach.

Canyamel Golf — 1987

Av. D'es Cap Vermell s/n
E - 07589 CANYAMEL CAPDEPERA (Mallorca)

Office	Secretaria	(34) 971 - 841 313
Pro shop	Pro-shop	(34) 971 - 841 313
Fax	Fax	(34) 971 - 841 384
Web		www.canyamel.com
Situation	Situación	Palma (pop. 308 616), 76 km
Annual closure	Cierre anual	no
Weekly closure	Cierre semanal	no

1118

Fees main season Precios tempor. alta	18 holes	
	Week days Semana	**We/Bank holidays** Fin de sem./fiestas
Individual Individual	€ 73	€ 73
Couple Pareja	€ 146	€ 146

Caddie Caddie no — **Electric Trolley** Carro eléctrico no
Buggy Coche yes — **Clubs** Palos yes
Credit cards Tarjetas de crédito
VISA - MasterCard

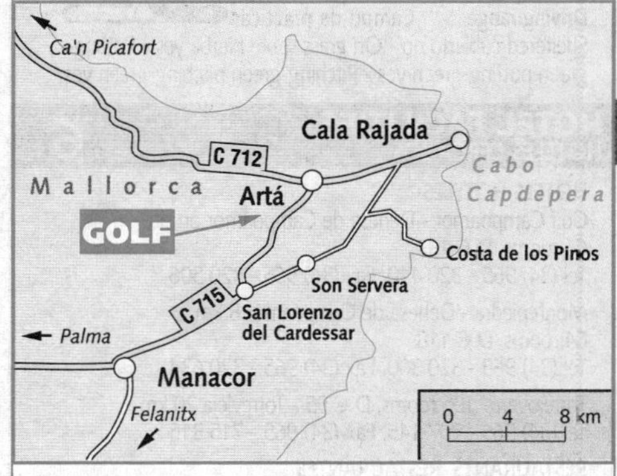

Access Acceso : C715 Palma → Manacor → Artá → Canyamel
Map 1 on page 1087 Plano 1 Página 1087

GOLF COURSE — RECORRIDO — 15/20

Site	Emplazamiento	
Maintenance	Mantenimiento	
Architect	Arquitecto	José Gancedo
Type	Tipo	country, mountain
Relief	Relieve	
Water in play	Agua	
Exp. to wind	Exp. al viento	
Trees in play	Arboles	

Scorecard Tarjeta	**Chp.** Campeonato	**Mens** Caballeros	**Ladies** Damas
Length Longitud	6550	6040	5335
Par	73	73	73
Slope system	—	128	125

Advised golfing ability Nivel de juego aconsejado — 0 12 24 36
Hcp required Handicap exigido — 27 Men, 35 Ladies

CLUB HOUSE & AMENITIES — CLUB HOUSE Y DEPENDENCIAS — 6/10

Pro shop Pro-shop
Driving range Campo de prácticas
Sheltered cubierto no - On grass sobre hierba yes - Putting-green putting-green yes - Pitching-green pitching-green yes

HOTEL FACILITIES — HOTELES CERCANOS — 6/10

HOTELS HOTELES

Aguait - 188 rooms, D € 132 - Cala Rajada 15 km
Tel (34) 971 - 563 408, Fax (34) 971 - 565 106

Canyamel Park - Capdepera 1 km
133 rooms, D € 106
Tel (34) 971 - 565 511, Fax (34) 971 - 565 614

Eurotel Golf Punta Rotja - Costa de los Pinos 15 km
199 rooms, D € 194
Tel (34) 971 - 816 500 , Fax (34) 971 - 816 565

RESTAURANTS RESTAURANTES

Ses Rotjes - Cala Rajada 15 km - Tel (34) 971 - 563 108
Los Pablos - Capdepera 5 km - Tel (34) 971 - 565 543

Castillo de Gorraiz

16	7	7

El tiempo está confirmando que este complejo deportivo no solamente atiende a la activa afición golfística navarra sino que la potencia con su recorrido entretenido y bien dispuesto. Las instalaciones son muy completas con un amplísimo campo de prácticas, tenis y piscina. Su creador es Cabell Robinson, autor también de La Cala en la Costa del Sol y de soberbios recorridos en Marruecos (él del Rey en Agadir y él impresionante Amelkis de Marrakech). Ha sabido aprovechar el terreno reservando una parte a residencias entre las que serpentean las calles anchas y muy abiertas. Los tees de salida son elevados dominando los hoyos. No siempre es necesario utilizar el drive ya que al peligro de roughs densos recomienda la prudencia si no se tiene mucha precisión. Tres grandes obstáculos de agua se encuentran en la línea de juego, lo que obliga a bien calcular tanto la distancia como la precisión de los golpes. Un recorrido bien logrado.

Time has shown that the Castillo de Gorraiz resort is more than good enough to satisfy the locals' appetite for golf. Facilities are excellent, with a huge driving range, tennis courts and a pool. The course is the work of Cabell Robinson, who designed La Cala on the Costa del Sol and some superb courses in Morocco (including the King's Course in Agadir and the majestic Amelkis in Marrakech). Here he has worked wonders with the terrain, a part of which is reserved for villas through which the wide and very open fairways wind their way around the course. The tee-boxes are elevated so you are looking down on the holes, and you don't always have to use the driver; danger from the thick rough calls for care if accuracy is not your forte. At the other end of the fairway, the huge, roundly-contoured greens give you the opportunity to show off your putting skills. Three large water hazards are also in play, so length as well as accuracy is at a premium. A very fine course.

Club de Golf Castillo de Gorraiz — 1995

Urbanización de Gorraiz, s/n
E - 31620 VALLE DE EGÜES (Navarra)

Office	Secretaria	(34) 948 - 337 073
Pro shop	Pro-shop	(34) 948 - 337 073
Fax	Fax	(34) 948 - 337 315
Web	www.golfgorraiz.com	
Situation	Situación	Pamplona, 5 km
Annual closure	Cierre anual	no
Weekly closure	Cierre semanal	no
Fees main season	Precios tempor. alta	18 holes

	Week days Semana	We/Bank holidays Fin de sem./fiestas
Individual Individual	€ 30	€ 50*
Couple Pareja	€ 60	€ 100

* We: Friday after 14:00 → Sunday

Caddie Caddie no **Electric Trolley** Carro eléctrico no

Buggy Coche yes **Clubs** Palos yes

Credit cards Tarjetas de crédito VISA

Puerto de Velate
Auritz/ Burguete
Vitoria San Sebastián
Río Ultzama
N 121
N 135
N 240
Sorauren
Ezcabarte
5
Villava
GOLF
Huarte
Agoítz
NA 150
N 111
Irunea/Pamplona
A 15
Zaragoza
4
0 km 2

Access Acceso : A-15 Exit (Salida) Pamplona → Francia. Turn at Olaz-Huarte
Map 2 on page 1089 Plano 2 Página 1089

GOLF COURSE — RECORRIDO — 16/20

Site	Emplazamiento	
Maintenance	Mantenimiento	
Architect	Arquitecto	Cabell B. Robinson
Type	Tipo	parkland, residential
Relief	Relieve	
Water in play	Agua	
Exp. to wind	Exp. al viento	
Trees in play	Arboles	

Scorecard Tarjeta	Chp. Campeonato	Mens Caballeros	Ladies Damas
Length Longitud	6365	6036	5131
Par	72	72	72
Slope system	129	124	119

Advised golfing ability / Nivel de juego aconsejado: 0 12 24 36

Hcp required Handicap exigido no

CLUB HOUSE & AMENITIES — CLUB HOUSE Y DEPENDENCIAS — 7/10

Pro shop Pro-shop
Driving range Campo de prácticas
Sheltered cubierto 12 mats - On grass sobre hierba no, 21 mats open air - Putting-green putting-green yes - Pitching-green pitching-green yes

HOTEL FACILITIES — HOTELES CERCANOS — 7/10

HOTELS HOTELES

Iruña Park - 225 rooms, D € 138 - Pamplona 7 km
Tel (34) 948 - 197 119, Fax (34) 948 - 172 387

Hotel Iriguibel - 37 rooms, D € 80 - Huarte 5 km
Tel (34) 948 - 361 190, Fax (34) 948 - 332 232

AC Ciudad de Pamplona - Pamplona 5 km
117 rooms, D € 138
Tel (34) 948 - 266 011, Fax (34) 948 - 173 626

RESTAURANTS RESTAURANTES

Hartza - Pamplona 5 km - Tel (34) 948 - 224 568
Palacio Castillo de Gorraiz - Huarte 5 km
Tel (34) 948 - 337 330
Rodero - Pamplona 5 km - Tel (34) 948 - 228 035

Cerdaña

14	5	7

Situado en el centro del valle más amplio de los Pirineos, este es un recorrido para disfrutar del golf natural y genuino en plena naturaleza. Ese fue el objetivo bien logrado de Javier Arana, cuyos diseños dejan siempre de lado lo que es trivial y son testimonio de un gran conocimiento del golf. Ha sabido adaptarse a un terreno en el que las desnivelaciones ya eran suficientes para no añadir más dificultades. Las calles son claras, sin trampas, lo esencial del juego se desarrolla en las llegadas a green, donde es necesario evitar árboles y algunos bunkers peligrosos. No muy largo, a veces estrecho, de greenes pequeños, este recorrido exige precisión, favorece el placer del golf entre jugadores de diferente nivel o en familia. Es un campo frecuentado generalmente por residentes y su casa club está reducida a caddie-master y vestuarios, mientras el hotel Chalet del Golf atiende los restantes servicios. El campo tiene otros nueve hoyos, interesantes, que a veces se ponen al juego mezclados con la obra de Arana.

Located in a large valley in the Pyrenees, this course is more than just a pleasant walk. And this is only to be expected from Javier Arana, whose layouts are always out of the ordinary and reveal considerable golfing intelligence. He has done a lot of tinkering with the terrain and the marked differences in relief in order not to add too many hazards. With the fairways free of traps, the key to playing the course is around the small greens, avoiding the trees and the few dangerous bunkers. Not particularly long and sometimes tight, this course places emphasis on accuracy and provides shared golfing pleasure among players of different levels or with the family. Without having relinquished any of its tough, natural appearance, the course is in good condition even though the bunkers don't take too kindly to water. There are a lot of members playing here and the Chalet du Golf hotel provides the majority of facilities. In addition, 9 interesting and cleverly landscaped new holes.

Real Club de Golf de Cerdaña — 1929

Apartat de correus 63
E - 17520 PUIGCERDA (Girona)

Office	Secretaria	(34) 972 - 141 408
Pro shop	Pro-shop	(34) 972 - 141 040
Fax	Fax	(34) 972 - 881 338
Web	www.rcgcerdanya.com	
Situation	Situación	Barcelona, 150 km

Puigcerdà (pop. 6 414), 1 km

Annual closure	Cierre anual	no
Weekly closure	Cierre semanal	no
Fees main season	Precios tempor. alta	18 holes

	Week days / Semana	We/Bank holidays / Fin de sem./fiestas
Individual Individual	€ 100	€ 100
Couple Pareja	€ 200	€ 200

Caddie Caddie no — **Electric Trolley** Carro eléctrico yes
Buggy Coche yes — **Clubs** Palos yes
Credit cards Tarjetas de crédito
VISA - Eurocard - MasterCard - AMEX

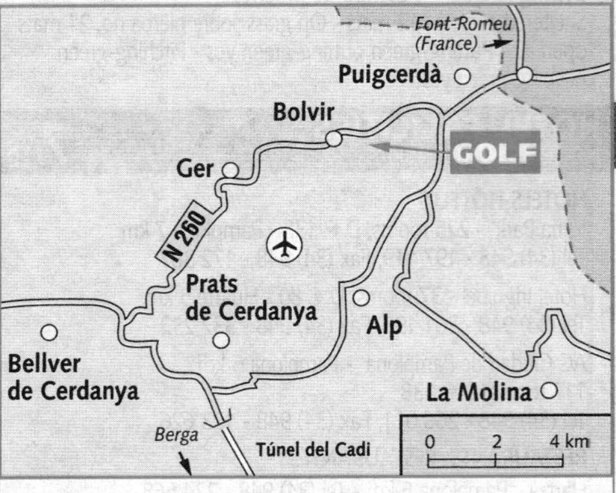

Access Acceso : Barcelona A18 → Manresa → "Tunel del Cadi y Puigcerdà"
Map 3 on page 1091 Plano 3 Página 1091

GOLF COURSE — RECORRIDO — 14/20

Site	Emplazamiento	
Maintenance	Mantenimiento	
Architect	Arquitecto	Javier Arana
Type	Tipo	mountain, parkland
Relief	Relieve	
Water in play	Agua	
Exp. to wind	Exp. al viento	
Trees in play	Arboles	

Scorecard / Tarjeta	Chp. / Campeonato	Mens / Caballeros	Ladies / Damas
Length Longitud	5886	5726	5015
Par	71	71	71
Slope system	129	127	121

Advised golfing ability / Nivel de juego aconsejado: 0 12 24 36
Hcp required Handicap exigido: 27 Men, 36 Ladies

CLUB HOUSE & AMENITIES — CLUB HOUSE Y DEPENDENCIAS — 5/10

Pro shop	Pro-shop	
Driving range	Campo de prácticas	

Sheltered cubierto 7 mats - On grass sobre hierba yes - Putting-green putting-green yes - Pitching-green pitching-green yes

HOTEL FACILITIES — HOTELES CERCANOS — 7/10

HOTELS HOTELES
Torre del Remei - Bolvir 1 km
22 rooms, D € 220
Tel (34) 972 - 140 182, Fax (34) 972 - 140 449

RESTAURANTS RESTAURANTES
Torre del Remei - Bolvir de Cerdanya 1 km
Tel (34) 972 - 140 182

La Tieta - Puigcerdà 2 km
Tel (34) 972 - 880 156

Chalet del Golf - Puigcerdà
Tel (34) 972 - 884 320

Club de Campo *Negro*

16	8	8

Una vez más, Javier Arana demuestra aquí estar entre los mejores arquitectos del siglo. A la vez exigente por su longitud así como por la precisión que requiere, este campo nos proporciona un placer siempre renovado. De mediano relieve, no se deja descubrir tan fácilmente y hace falta jugar varias veces para llegar a entender todas sus sutilezas. Los árboles, las cuestas y los bunkers de las calles constituyen sus principales dificultades, y le damos las gracias a Arana de no haber creado demasiados problemas en los accesos a los greenes. Con la remodelación de Manolo Piñero de los nueve primeros en 1998 y las otras obras que acabaron en 2002 (el complejo de golf tiene ahora 36 hoyos) este recorrido llamado ahora Negro es par 71 (el 12 ha pasado a ser par 4) y presenta nuevos desafíos en unos greenes a veces muy escalonados. Este club municipal gestionado por el Ayuntamiento de Madrid tiene diversas secciones deportivas y una ocupación altísima en todas ellas, por lo que un buen consejo para el visitante es que procure evitar los fines de semana y los días de fiesta.

Here again, Javier Arana gives a further demonstration of why he will go down as one of the century's greatest architects. What a shame his great talent is not on show outside his home country. Demanding both in length and accuracy, this course, located just outside of Madrid, is a real joy to play every time. Averagely hilly (but easy to walk), the course is not easy to discover and needs several rounds to grasp the subtler points. The trees, the slopes and fairway bunkers are the main difficulties, and we should be grateful to Arana for not having created too many difficulties when approaching the greens. Manuel Piñero's restyling of the outward 9 holes and other work completed in 2002 (the resort boasts 36 holes) have given this "Negro" course new challenges presented by multi-tiered greens. The club is run by the City of Madrid and has invested in a number of different sporting activities. Weekends are very busy.

Club de Campo Villa de Madrid — 1932

Carretera de Castilla km 2
E - 28040 MADRID

Office	Secretaria	(34) 915 - 502 010
Pro shop	Pro-shop	(34) 915 - 502 010
Fax	Fax	(34) 915 - 502 023
Web	www.clubvillademadrid.com	
Situation	Situación	Madrid, 1 km
Annual closure	Cierre anual	no
Weekly closure	Cierre semanal	no

Fees main season Precios tempor. alta	18 holes	
	Week days Semana	**We/Bank holidays** Fin de sem./fiestas
Individual Individual	€ 46,50	€ 87,50
Couple Pareja	€ 93	€ 175

Access to the club (Acceso al Club):
€ 13 (weekdays), € 26,50 (We)

Caddie Caddie no — **Electric Trolley** Carro eléctrico yes
Buggy Coche yes — **Clubs** Palos yes
Credit cards Tarjetas de crédito no

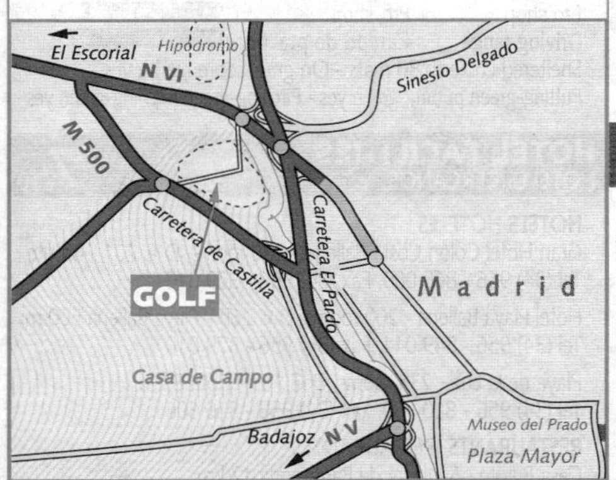

Access Acceso : Madrid, Carretera de Castilla → Segovia
Map 4 on page 1092 Plano 4 Página 1092

GOLF COURSE
RECORRIDO — 16/20

Site	Emplazamiento	
Maintenance	Mantenimiento	
Architect	Arquitecto	Javier Arana
Type	Tipo	forest
Relief	Relieve	
Water in play	Agua	
Exp. to wind	Exp. al viento	
Trees in play	Arboles	

Scorecard Tarjeta	**Chp.** Campeonato	**Mens** Caballeros	**Ladies** Damas
Length Longitud	6374	6045	5111
Par	72	72	72
Slope system	133	129	118

Advised golfing ability Nivel de juego aconsejado — 0 12 24 36
Hcp required Handicap exigido — 28 Men, 36 Ladies

CLUB HOUSE & AMENITIES
CLUB HOUSE Y DEPENDENCIAS — 8/10

Pro shop Pro-shop
Driving range Campo de prácticas
Sheltered cubierto 112 mats - On grass sobre hierba yes - Putting-green putting-green yes - Pitching-green pitching-green yes

HOTEL FACILITIES
HOTELES CERCANOS — 8/10

HOTELS HOTELES
Majadahonda - Majadahonda 3 km
41 rooms, D € 164
Tel (34) 916 - 382 122 , Fax (34) 916 - 382 157

La Moraleja - 37 rooms, D € 217 - Alcobendas 3 km
Tel (34) 916 - 618 055, Fax (34) 916 - 612 188

Villamagna - 182 rooms, D € 417 - Madrid 4 km
Tel (34) 915 - 871 234, Fax (34) 915 - 751 358

RESTAURANTS RESTAURANTES
El Caserón de Araceli - San Augustin de Guadalix 6 km
Tel (34) 918 - 418 531
Zalacain - Madrid 5 km - Tel (34) 915 - 614 840
La Trainera - Madrid 5 km - Tel (34) 915 - 760 575

Costa Ballena

16	8	7

Olazábal ha hecho en Costa Ballena, campo típicamente comercial y núcleo de una enorme promoción inmobiliaria, un recorrido amplio, donde el jugador se siente invitado a pegar sólidamente el driver, sembrado de obstáculos (bunkers y agua) estratégicos con greenes muy amplios, rápidos y ondulados y también técnicamente protegidos, de manera el jugador experto tiene siempre la opción evaluar sus posibilidades y recursos. Situado junto a la playa, es frecuente el viento intenso. Con 27 hoyos, sus dos recorridos principales son Olivos y Palmeras (el tercero, Ficus, es un par 34 de 2.500 metros) y además tiene 9 hoyos pares 3 entre 100 y 180 metros. Es notable su mantenimiento y su zona de entrenamiento, con un campo de prácticas capaz para 120 jugadores, e instalaciones de análisis de swing y preparación física que lo han convertido ya en un centro de alto rendimiento para profesionales y amateurs. El terreno es llano, fácil de andar, y el clima de la zona es suave en invierno y en verano.

At Costa Ballena, Olazábal has designed a typical business-venture course at the centre of a huge property development programme. This is a course of wide open spaces where players feel the urge to take out the driver despite the strategic hazards (water and sand) and huge greens that are slick, trickily contoured and well protected in such a way that the better player can weigh up his capacity for attack and recovery. And being close to the beach the course is also exposed to the wind. There are 27 holes here, the main course being the Olivos and Palmeras layouts (the 3rd course is a par 34 with 9 par-three holes (110 to 198 yards). We were impressed by the excellence of green-keeping and the practice facilities with a huge driving range, swing analysis equipment and material for physical preparation which together form a top-class facility for professionals and amateurs. The terrain is flat, easy to walk and the climate mild in winter and summer alike.

Costa Ballena Club de Golf — 1996

Ctra Chipiona – El Puerto de Santa María Km 5
E - 11521 ROTA (Cádiz)

Office Secretaria (34) 956 - 847 070
Pro shop Pro-shop (34) 956 - 847 070
Fax Fax (34) 956 - 847 050
Web www.ballenagolf.com
Situation Situación Rota (pop. 30.000), 8 km
Jerez de la Frontera (pop. 195.000), 25 km

Annual closure Cierre anual no
Weekly closure Cierre semanal no

Fees main season Precios tempor. alta	18 holes	
	Week days Semana	**We/Bank holidays** Fin de sem./fiestas
Individual Individual	€ 59	€ 59
Couple Pareja	€ 118	€ 118

Caddie Caddie yes — **Electric Trolley** Carro eléctrico no
Buggy Coche yes — **Clubs** Palos yes
Credit cards Tarjetas de crédito
VISA - MasterCard - AMEX - 4B

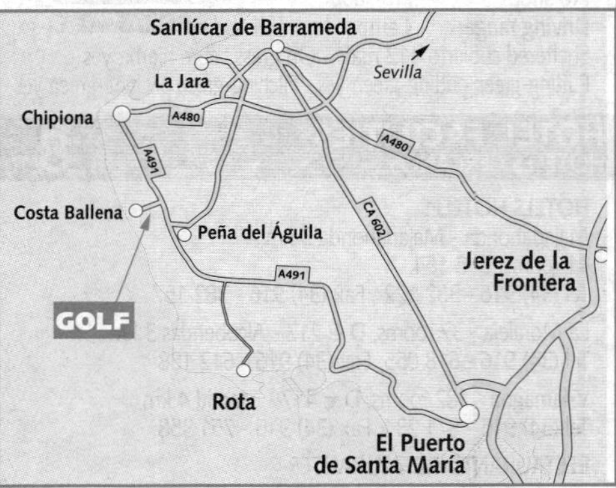

Access Acceso : Sevilla A4 → Jerez then → El Puerto de Sta María, A491 → Chipiona. Golf between Rota and Chipiona.
Map 8 on page 1100 Plano 8 Página 1100

GOLF COURSE — RECORRIDO — 16/20

Site Emplazamiento
Maintenance Mantenimiento
Architect Arquitecto — José Maria Olazábal, Integral Golf Design
Type Tipo — seaside
Relief Relieve
Water in play Agua
Exp. to wind Exp. al viento
Trees in play Arboles

Scorecard Tarjeta	**Chp.** Campeonato	**Mens** Caballeros	**Ladies** Damas
Length Longitud	6302	6036	5155
Par	72	72	72
Slope system	131	128	122

Advised golfing ability Nivel de juego aconsejado — 0 12 24 36
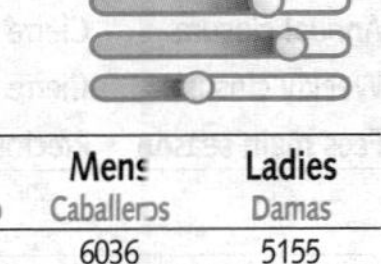
Hcp required Handicap exigido — 28 Men, 36 Ladies

CLUB HOUSE & AMENITIES — CLUB HOUSE Y DEPENDENCIAS — 8/10

Pro shop Pro-shop
Driving range Campo de prácticas
Sheltered cubierto 30 mats - On grass sobre hierba yes - Putting-green putting-green yes - Pitching-green pitching-green yes

HOTEL FACILITIES — HOTELES CERCANOS — 7/10

HOTELS HOTELES

Gran Hotel Colón Costa Ballena - 200 rooms, D € 201 - on site
Tel (34) 956 - 865 000, Fax (34) 956 - 379 010

Hotel Playa Ballena - 200 rooms, D € 265 - Playa Ballena 500 m
Tel (34) 956 - 849 044, Fax (34) 956 - 379 010

Playa de la Luz - 235 rooms, D € 163 - Rota 8 km
Tel (34) 956 - 810 500, Fax (34) 956 - 810 606

RESTAURANTS RESTAURANTES

Casa Bigote - Sanlúcar de Barrameda 12 km
Tel (34) 956 - 870 952

El Quinto Pino - Chipiona 2 km - Tel (34) 956 - 371 757

La Española - Chipiona 4 km - Tel (34) 956 - 373 771

Costa Brava

14	7	7

El gabinete del arquitecto Hamilton Stutt no es de los más conocidos, pero aquí ha construido un recorrido simpático, sin dificultades infranqueables permitiendo que jugadores de todos los niveles y edades pasen un día agradable. El relieve es mesurado, las pendientes suaves, alternan hoyos anchos y estrechos, limitados las más de las veces por alcornoques y pinos que incluso invaden la calle del 2, lo que obliga a jugar bolas altas, bajas o con efecto, para rodearlos. Los greenes están bien protegidos, correctamente diseñados y la mayor parte de las veces se puede aprochar rodando la bola. La remodelación de cinco greenes de la primera vuelta, las mejoras en la estética del campo y el buen mantenimiento del terreno de juego expresan la filosofía de este club para abrazar familiarmente a socios españoles y extranjeros y a visitantes de todas las procedencias durante los períodos de vacaciones.

Hamilton Stutt is not the most famous name in golf course design, but here they have produced a pleasant course without insuperable difficulties on which players of all levels and all ages can spend an enjoyable day. The ground relief is moderate with a few gentle slopes and alternating wide and tight fairways edged by pine and oak trees that are often very much in play, particularly hole N° 2. The player often has to work the ball to get around them, hit the ball over the top... or keep low below the branches. The greens are well defended and correctly designed, but most of them can be approached with chip shots. The restyling of five of the first nine holes plus improvements to the visual beauty of the site and standards of green-keeping reflect the thinking of a club that is keen to appeal to both members and holiday visitors.

Club de Golf Costa Brava — 1968

Urbanitzacio Golf Costa Brava
E - 17246 SANTA CRISTINA D'ARO (GIRONA)

Office Secretaria (34) 972 - 837 150
Pro shop Pro-shop (34) 972 - 837 055
Fax Fax (34) 972 - 837 272
Web www.golfcostabrava.com
Situation Situación Girona (pop. 70 409), 30 km
San Feliu de Guixols (pop. 16 088), 7 km
Annual closure Cierre anual no
Weekly closure Cierre semanal no
Fees main season Precios tempor. alta 18 holes

	Week days Semana	We/Bank holidays Fin de sem./fiestas
Individual Individual	€ 80	€ 80
Couple Pareja	€ 160	€ 160

Juniors: - 50%

Caddie Caddie no — **Electric Trolley** Carro eléctrico no
Buggy Coche yes — **Clubs** Palos yes
Credit cards Tarjetas de crédito VISA

Access Acceso : C250 Sant Feliu → Girona, Santa Cristina d'Aro → Golf
Map 3 on page 1091 Plano 3 Página 1091

GOLF COURSE — RECORRIDO 14/20

Site Emplazamiento
Maintenance Mantenimiento
Architect Arquitecto Hamilton Stutt & Co
Type Tipo residential, hilly
Relief Relieve
Water in play Agua
Exp. to wind Exp. al viento
Trees in play Arboles

Scorecard Tarjeta	Chp. Campeonato	Mens Caballeros	Ladies Damas
Length Longitud	5629	5495	4710
Par	70	70	70
Slope system	130	130	125

Advised golfing ability Nivel de juego aconsejado 0 12 24 36
Hcp required Handicap exigido 27 Men, 36 Ladies

CLUB HOUSE & AMENITIES — CLUB HOUSE Y DEPENDENCIAS 7/10

Pro shop Pro-shop
Driving range Campo de prácticas
Sheltered cubierto 4 mats - On grass sobre hierba yes - Putting-green putting-green yes - Pitching-green pitching-green yes

HOTEL FACILITIES — HOTELES CERCANOS 7/10

HOTELS HOTELES
Golf Costa Brava - 91 rooms, D € 144 - Santa Cristina 500 m
Tel (34) 972 - 835 151, Fax (34) 972 - 837 588

Hostal de la Gavina - 74 rooms, D € 329 - S'Agaró 7 km
Tel (34) 972 - 321 100, Fax (34) 972 - 321 573

Park Hotel Sant Jorge - 104 rooms, D € 211 - Platja d'Aro 12 km
Tel (34) 972 - 652 311, Fax (34) 972 - 652 576

Mas Tapiolas - 39 rooms, D € 211 - Solius 3 km
Tel (34) 972 - 837 017 , Fax (34) 972 - 837 134

RESTAURANTS RESTAURANTES
Els Tinars - Llagostera 6 km - Tel (34) 972 - 830 626
Les Panolles - Santa Cristina 1 km - Tel (34) 972 - 837 011
El Moli d'en Tarrés - Santa Cristina d'Aro 3 km
Tel (34) 972 - 837 394

Costa Dorada

13	6	6

El lugar es agradable y tranquilo. A pesar de que el recorrido se sitúa muy a menudo en la falda de la ladera y es ondulado, no se necesita alquilar un coche. Las calles con hierba bien tupida sostienen bien la bola, los greens la aguantan bien, sólo algunos olivos aislados o agrupados pueden perturbar la trayectoria de juego: no es un recorrido de gran dificultad y gustará a la mayoría de los jugadores. El recorrido no ofrece emociones fuertes, aunque la segunda vuelta, a partir del 12, es más técnica que la primera, especialmente en los dos pares 5 (el largo 13 y el empinado 16). Si Gancedo se concentró aquí en hacer un campo para una afición emergente, sin excesivos problemas ni complicaciones, es cierto que lo ha conseguido por el éxito de ocupación del campo. En la familia de campos gratos y agradables para todos los niveles de juego, Costa Dorada ocupa un buen lugar.

The site is pleasant and relaxing after reaching the course set in a little palm grove. Although much of Costa Dorada is laid out on the side of a hill with rolling fairways, it is easily walkable. The lushly-grassed fairways carry the ball well and the greens pitch well, too. Only a few isolated or bunches of olive trees can get in the way of your ball, so this is not too complicated a course to get around. Most players will like its open style but they shouldn't expect too much in the way of excitement, even though from the 12th hole onwards the course becomes more technical, especially the two par 5s (holes 13 and 16). If Gancedo was especially more concerned with creating a course likely to appeal to beginners by restricting potential problems, he has certainly succeeded in terms of popularity. In the family of golf-courses for everyone, Costa Dorada is right up there with the best.

Club de Golf Costa Dorada Tarragona 1982

Apdo 600
E - 43080 TARRAGONA

Office	Secretaria	(34) 977 - 653 361
Pro shop	Pro-shop	(34) 977 - 653 361
Fax	Fax	(34) 977 - 653 028
Web	www.golfcostadoradatarragona.com	
Situation	Situación	Tarragona, 5 km
Annual closure	Cierre anual	no
Weekly closure	Cierre semanal	no
Fees main season	Precios tempor. alta	18 holes

	Week days Semana	We/Bank holidays Fin de sem./fiestas
Individual Individual	€ 52	€ 83
Couple Pareja	€ 104	€ 166

Juniors: - 50%

Caddie Caddie no — **Electric Trolley** Carro eléctrico yes
Buggy Coche yes — **Clubs** Palos yes
Credit cards Tarjetas de crédito
VISA - MasterCard

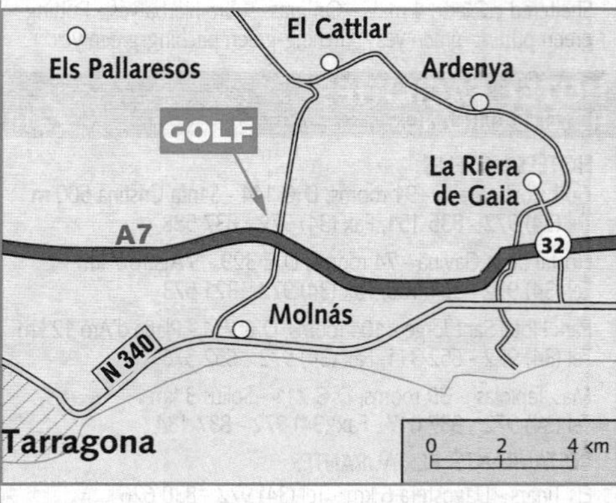

Access Acceso : A7 Barcelona → Valencia, Exit (Salida) 32, RN340 → Tarragona, Ctra El Catllar, Golf 2,7 km.
Map 5 on page 1095 Plano 5 Página 1095

GOLF COURSE
RECORRIDO — 13/20

Site	Emplazamiento	
Maintenance	Mantenimiento	
Architect	Arquitecto	José Gancedo
Type	Tipo	hilly
Relief	Relieve	
Water in play	Agua	
Exp. to wind	Exp. al viento	
Trees in play	Arboles	

Scorecard Tarjeta	**Chp.** Campeonato	**Mens** Caballeros	**Ladies** Damas
Length Longitud	6223	5978	5136
Par	72	72	72
Slope system	132	133	126

Advised golfing ability Nivel de juego aconsejado: 0 12 24 36
Hcp required Handicap exigido: no

CLUB HOUSE & AMENITIES
CLUB HOUSE Y DEPENDENCIAS — 6/10

Pro shop Pro-shop
Driving range Campo de prácticas
Sheltered cubierto 6 mats - **On grass** sobre hierba yes - **Putting-green** putting-green yes - **Pitching-green** pitching-green no

HOTEL FACILITIES
HOTELES CERCANOS — 6/10

HOTELS HOTELES

Imperial Tarraco - Tarragona 6 km
155 rooms, D € 122
Tel (34) 977 - 233 040, Fax (34) 977 - 216 566

Lauria - 72 rooms, D € 81 - Tarragona 6 km
Tel (34) 977 - 236 712, Fax (34) 977 - 236 700

Ciutat de Tarragona - 168 rooms, D € 123 - Tarragona 6 km
Tel (34) 977 - 250 222, Fax (34) 977 - 250 699

RESTAURANTS RESTAURANTES

Sol Ric - Tarragona 6 km
Tel (34) 977 - 232 032

Can Sala (Les Fonts) - N 240, 2 km, Tarragona 4 km
Tel (34) 977 - 228 575

Desert Springs

15	6	6

Sin duda es el campo más original de Europa, diseñado por el campeón amateur inglés Peter McEvoy imitando los campos desérticos de Arizona. Estamos en el norte de la provincia de Almería, tierra árida quemada por el sol, muy cerca de los platós naturales donde se han rodado muchas películas del oeste y escenas de películas tan famosas. El proyecto comprende otro campo de 18 hoyos, una urbanización de 1.800 viviendas y un hotel de cinco estrellas, todo ello en fase de construcción. Cactus, rocas, cauces secos, riachuelos y lagos, además de una típica decoración del salvaje oeste, serpentean entre las calles verdes, amplias y despejadas, por lo que la precisión de los golpes, sin ser exagerada, es de todo punto obligada. Especial mención merecen unos greenes pequeños y de formidable movimiento, varios de ellos presentados como un oasis, en los cuales cada pat, por corto que sea, es un tremendo desafío de temple y técnica. La densa urbanización del complejo afecta al 1 y al 18, donde el jugador se siente examinado desde terrazas y balcones.

The most original course in Europe laid out by Peter McEvoy, visibly inspired here by the deserts of Arizona. This is the north of the province of Almería, an arid sun-scorched region very close to the natural plateaus where a number of movies have been filmed on location, beginning with Lawrence of Arabia. The project includes another 18-hole course, a large residential estate and a 5-star hotel, all of which are still under construction. The course's green fairways wind their through cacti, rocks, dried up canals, streams and lakes, in other words your typical décor from the American wild west. All these hazards mean that accuracy is at a premium and that is no exaggeration. A special mention should go to the small and interestingly contoured greens, some of which form a sort of oasis and where each putt is a challenge to the coolest golfer's self-control. The building development scheme affects holes N° 1 and 18, where players will necessarily feel closely watched.

Desert Springs Golf Club — 2001

Cuevas de Almanzora
E - 04618 VILLARICOS (Almería – Andalucía)

Office Secretaria (34) 950 - 467 411
Pro shop Pro-shop (34) 950 - 467 411
Fax Fax (34) 950 - 467 428
Web www.almanzora.com
Situation Situación Almería, 100 km
Vera (pop. 6.000), 4 km

Annual closure Cierre anual no
Weekly closure Cierre semanal no
Fees main season Precios tempor. alta 18 holes

	Week days Semana	We/Bank holidays Fin de sem./fiestas
Individual Individual	€ 80	€ 80
Couple Pareja	€ 160	€ 160

Caddie Caddie no — **Electric Trolley** Carro eléctrico yes
Buggy Coche yes — **Clubs** Palos yes
Credit cards Tarjetas de crédito
VISA - MasterCard - AMEX - 4D

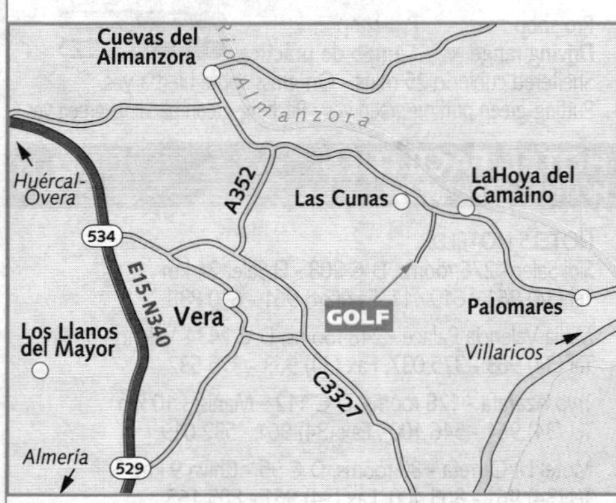

Access Acceso : E15/N340 Alicante → Almería. Exit (Salida) 537, then A332 → Cuevas de Almanzora, then turn right → Palomares.
Map 9 on page 1103 Plano 9 Página 1103

GOLF COURSE — RECORRIDO — 15/20

Site Emplazamiento
Maintenance Mantenimiento
Architect Arquitecto — Peter McEvoy
Type Tipo — desert, open country
Relief Relieve
Water in play Agua
Exp. to wind Exp. al viento
Trees in play Arboles

Scorecard Tarjeta	Chp. Campeonato	Mens Caballeros	Ladies Damas
Length Longitud	6173	5742	5149
Par	72	72	72
Slope system	125	124	122

Advised golfing ability Nivel de juego aconsejado — 0 12 24 36
Hcp required Handicap exigido — 28 Men, 36 Ladies

CLUB HOUSE & AMENITIES — CLUB HOUSE Y DEPENDENCIAS — 6/10

Pro shop Pro-shop
Driving range Campo de prácticas
Sheltered cubierto no - On grass sobre hierba yes - Putting-green putting-green yes - Pitching-green pitching-green yes

HOTEL FACILITIES — HOTELES CERCANOS — 6/10

HOTELS HOTELES
Parador de los Reyes Católicos - Mojácar 8 km
98 rooms, D € 141
Tel (34) 950 - 478 250, Fax (34) 950 - 478 183

Oasis Tropical - Mojácar 8 km
398 rooms, D € 144
Tel (34) 950 - 397 000, Fax (34) 950 - 397 070

Marina Mar - 389 rooms, D € 144 - Mojácar 8 km
Tel (34) 902 - 333 412, Fax (34) 902 - 397 046

RESTAURANTS RESTAURANTES
Terraza Carmona - Vera 5 km - Tel (34) 950 - 390 180
El Almejero - Garrucha 5 km - Tel (34) 950 - 460 405

El Bosque

16 | 6 | 5

La buena calidad del conjunto inmobiliario no sólo no molesta a los jugadores sino que se adapta muy bien al estilo americano del recorrido. Si añadimos que más vale alquilar un coche, uno podría creerse en Estados Unidos. El Bosque figura entre los buenos éxitos de Robert Trent Jones en España. La ondulación del terreno es importante, se juega a menudo con los pies desnivelados y felizmente la estrategia de juego es clara ya que si los obstáculos son bien visibles, no dejan de ser peligrosos. La primera vez uno se siente acosado (para obtener un buen resultado) por una serie de greenes ciegos que requieren trayectorias altas. No hay que dudar tirar a bandera puesto que los greenes aguantan bien la bola. Los hoyos están bien integrados en el paisaje cuyo diseño y dificultades son variados, sobre todo cuatro excelentes dog-legs. Hay que hacer mención especial de los pares 3.

The surrounding real estate is a stylish programme and won't bother the players, especially since the properties blend in very well with what is a very American-style course. Add to that the definite advantage of playing with a buggy and you might think you actually were on American soil. El Bosque is one of the great success-stories of Robert Trent Jones in Spain. It is hilly, you are often faced with a sloping lie, but game strategy is pretty clear. And that's lucky, because although the hazards are visible they are patently very dangerous. First time out, players looking for a good score will have trouble only with a series of blind greens which demand high approach shots. Go for the pin, too, because these greens pitch well. The holes blend in well with the landscape, and the design and difficulties vary considerably. In particular there are four beautiful dog-legs. A special mention should go to the excellence of the par 3s.

El Bosque Hotel & Country Club — 1975

Carretera de Godelleta, km 4,1
E - 46370 CHIVA (Valencia)

Office	Secretaría	(34) 961 - 808 009
Pro shop	Pro-shop	(34) 961 - 808 000
Fax	Fax	(34) 961 - 808 064
Web	www.elbosquegolf.com	
Situation	Situación	Chiva (pop. 7 562), 5 km

Valencia (pop. 751 734), 20 km

Annual closure	Cierre anual	no
Weekly closure	Cierre semanal	no
Fees main season	Precios tempor. alta	18 holes

	Week days Semana	We/Bank holidays Fin de sem./fiestas
Individual Individual	€ 70	*
Couple Pareja	€ 140	*

* Members'guests only (sólo invitados de socios)

Caddie Caddie no — **Electric Trolley** Carro eléctrico yes
Buggy Coche yes — **Clubs** Palos yes
Credit cards Tarjetas de crédito — VISA - AMEX

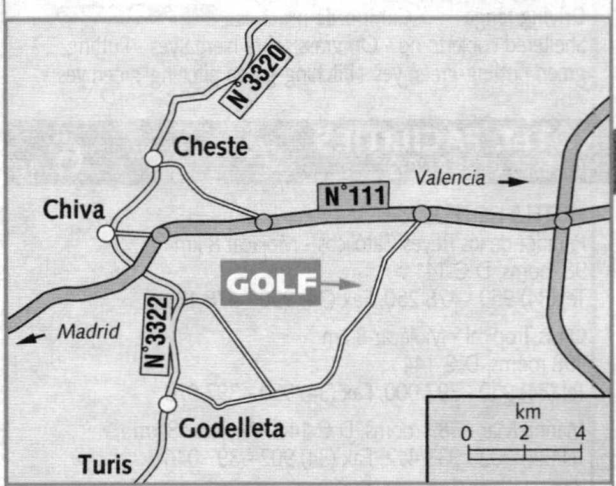

Access Acceso : N111 Valencia → Madrid, Exit (Salida) Godelleta. Km. 324, → Godelleta, Golf km. 4,1
Map 5 on page 1095 Plano 5 Página 1095

GOLF COURSE — RECORRIDO — 16/20

Site	Emplazamiento	
Maintenance	Mantenimiento	
Architect	Arquitecto	Robert Trent Jones
Type	Tipo	country, hilly, residential
Relief	Relieve	
Water in play	Agua	
Exp. to wind	Exp. al viento	
Trees in play	Arboles	

Scorecard Tarjeta	Chp. Campeonato	Mens Caballeros	Ladies Damas
Length Longitud	6249	5913	5087
Par	72	72	72
Slope system	141	129	125

Advised golfing ability Nivel de juego aconsejado — 0 12 24 36
Hcp required Handicap exigido — 28 Men, 36 Ladies

CLUB HOUSE & AMENITIES — CLUB HOUSE Y DEPENDENCIAS — 6/10

Pro shop Pro-shop
Driving range Campo de prácticas
Sheltered cubierto 25 mats - On grass sobre hierba yes
Putting-green putting-green yes - Pitching-green pitching-green yes

HOTEL FACILITIES — HOTELES CERCANOS — 5/10

HOTELS HOTELES
Sidi Saler - 276 rooms, D € 208 - El Saler 24 km
Tel (34) 961 - 610 411, Fax (34) 961 - 610 833

Melia Valencia Palace - 248 rooms, D € 243 - Valencia 30 km
Tel (34) 963 - 375 037, Fax (34) 963 - 375 532

Tryp Azafata - 128 rooms, D € 112 - Manises 10 km
Tel (34) 961 - 546 100 , Fax (34) 961 - 532 079

Motel La Carreta - 80 rooms, D € 95 - Chiva 9 km
Tel (34) 961 - 805 400, Fax (34) 961 - 805 165

RESTAURANTS RESTAURANTES
Azafata - Manises 10 km - Tel (34) 961 - 546 100
Albacar - Valencia 30 km - Tel (34) 963 - 951 005

El Cortijo

16 | 5 | 8

Blake Stirling, que fue jefe del equipo de Pete Dye, ha construido con Marco Martin un gran campo (en España decimos "campazo") en una finca que había sido una platanera. Los primeros nueve recuerdan algo a un links, con todas las salvedades del mundo porque estamos rodeados de palmeras y lagos paradisíacos que entrarán ¿fatalmente? en juego en la otra parte del campo. Largas distancias, cambiantes casi siempre por los vientos atlánticos, y greenes rápidos que piden mucho estudio en el pat además de un inteligente sentido estratégico porque su diseño permite varias opciones de ataque. El club, que tiene un amplio complejo deportivo, ha sido un éxito y actualmente tiene una ocupación tan alta que no admite visitantes los fines de semana y festivos. Un consejo de buen amigo es ir con tiempo suficiente para jugar los excelentes nueve hoyos cortos que hay en el campo (pitch & putt) anejo.

Blake Sterling, formerly project manager with Pete Dye, teamed up with Marco Martin to design this great and highly ambitious course spread over an old banana plantation. The front nine have very much the feel of a links course, with all the sand in the world piled up and surrounded by palm trees and paradisiacal lakes that you will always find in play over the back nine. The holes are on the long side and never quite the same, depending on the wind blowing in from the Atlantic. The slick greens call for some very careful putting and intelligent strategy as their layout means you can approach them in different ways. This club, which owns a huge sports resort, is a great success right now and so busy that visitors are turned away at week-ends. During the week, don't forget to also play the little 9-hole course, short but fun.

El Cortijo Club de Campo — 1999

El Cortijo de San Ignacio s/n
E - 35218 TELDE (Gran Canaria - Islas Canarias)

Office	Secretaria	(34) 928 - 711 111
Pro shop	Pro-shop	(34) 928 - 711 111
Fax	Fax	(34) 928 - 714 905
Web	www.elcortijo.es	
Situation	Situación	Las Palmas, 6,5 km
Annual closure	Cierre anual	no
Weekly closure	Cierre semanal	no

Fees main season Precios tempor. alta	18 holes	
	Week days Semana	We/Bank holidays Fin de sem./fiestas
Individual Individual	€ 75	*
Couple Pareja	€ 150	*

* Week ends: members only (Sólo socios)

Caddie Caddie no — **Electric Trolley** Carro eléctrico no
Buggy Coche yes — **Clubs** Palos yes
Credit cards Tarjetas de crédito
VISA - MasterCard

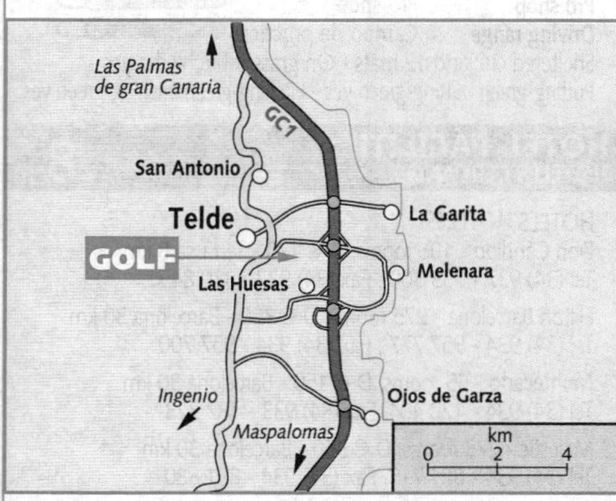

Access Acceso : Palma, Motorway (Autopista) GC 1.
Km 6,4 → Golf
Map 1 on page 1087 Plano 1 Página 1087

GOLF COURSE — RECORRIDO 16/20

Site	Emplazamiento	
Maintenance	Mantenimiento	
Architect	Arquitecto	Blake Sterling Marco Martin
Type	Tipo	parkland
Relief	Relieve	
Water in play	Agua	
Exp. to wind	Exp. al viento	
Trees in play	Arboles	

Scorecard Tarjeta	Chp. Campeonato	Mens Caballeros	Ladies Damas
Length Longitud	6308	5833	4635
Par	72	72	72
Slope system	132	130	120

Advised golfing ability Nivel de juego aconsejado — 0 12 24 36
Hcp required Handicap exigido — 28 Men, 36 Ladies

CLUB HOUSE & AMENITIES — CLUB HOUSE Y DEPENDENCIAS 5/10

Pro shop Pro-shop
Driving range Campo de prácticas
Sheltered cubierto yno - On grass sobre hierba yes - Putting-green putting-green yes - Pitching-green pitching-green yes

HOTEL FACILITIES — HOTELES CERCANOS 8/10

HOTELS HOTELES
Hotel Santa Catalina - Las Palmas 5 km
187 rooms, D € 238
Tel (34) 928 - 243 040, Fax (34) 928 - 242 764

Hotel Rural El Cortijo - 18 rooms, D € 103 - on site
Tel (34) 928 - 712 427, Fax (34) 928 - 715 029

Tenesoya - 42 rooms, D € 68 - Las Palmas 5 km
Tel (34) 928 - 469 608, Fax (34) 928 - 460 279

RESTAURANTS RESTAURANTES
5 Jotas - on site - Tel (34) 928 - 682 943
Casa Carmelo - Las Palmas 5 km - Tel (34) 928 - 469 056
Amaiur - Las Palmas 5 km - Tel (34) 928 - 370 717

El Prat *Amarillo*

16	8	8

A pesar del alto precio del green-fee, como suele suceder en los campos muy exclusivos, el nuevo Prat merece ciertamente una visita con calma y concentración. Sobre una finca de gran extensión, que rodean pinos muy altos que apenas entran en juego, Greg Norman ha hecho un campo muy técnico, no especialmente largo de tee a green, de extrema dificultad tanto para poner el drive en la calle como para sujetar la bola en los greenes. Calles estrechas vigiladas por bunkers enormes y profundos que castigan definitivamente para el par del hoyo las salidas imperfectas; bunkers que defienden los greenes con la doble amenaza de que el golpe de recuperación puede ser más que complicado; greenes en alto con pliegues hacia el exterior que obligan a aprochar siempre con una altísima propiedad de toque y distancia. Los greenes, muy grandes, muy rápidos y extraordinariamente movidos, harán las delicias de los pateadores sobresalientes. Es un campo difícil, demasiado exigente para la inmensa mayoría de los jugadores, pero hay que verlo como exponente del golf moderno que se basa en la estrategia, la precisión y la calidad.

Despite the stiff green-fees now charged by the majority of exclusive golf clubs, the new course at El Prat is most definitely worth a visit, with a cool head and all the concentration you can muster. Over a large estate surrounded by tall but seldom obtrusive pine-trees, Greg Norman has laid out a very technical course, not so long but one where it can be so difficult to hit both the greens and fairways. The latter are tight and flanked with bunkers that are so deep that you can forget all about making par should your ball end up there. And the green-side traps are just as threatening. The multi-tiered greens call for cool-headed putting skills, but good putters will enjoy plying their trade on these huge, slick and very fast surfaces. It is a difficult course, perhaps too challenging for most amateurs, but a good example of modern golfing where you need strategy, accuracy and good basic skills.

Real Club de Golf El Prat — 2003

Plans de Bonvilar 17
E – 08227 TERRASSA (Barcelona)

Office	Secretaria	(34) 937 - 281 000
Pro shop	Pro-shop	(34) 937 - 281 000
Fax	Fax	(34) 937 - 281 010
Web	www.rcgep.com	
Situation	Situación	Barcelona, 30 km
Annual closure	Cierre anual	no
Weekly closure	Cierre semanal	no

Fees main season Precios tempor. alta	18 holes	
	Week days Semana	**We/Bank holidays** Fin de sem./fiestas
Individual Individual	€ 105	€ 210
Couple Pareja	€ 210	€ 420

Caddie Caddie no — **Electric Trolley** Carro eléctrico yes
Buggy Coche yes — **Clubs** Palos yes

Credit cards Tarjetas de crédito
VISA - Eurocard - MasterCard - AMEX

Access Acceso : Barcelona C-58 → Sabadell, Terrassa, Manresa. Exit (salida) 16 Sabadell Norte. In Sabadell, N-150 → Terrassa, turn 2nd roundabout → Mercavallés. Golf signposted on right hand side.
Map 3 on page 1091 Plano 3 Página 1091

GOLF COURSE RECORRIDO — 16/20

Site	Emplazamiento	
Maintenance	Mantenimiento	
Architect	Arquitecto	Greg Norman
Type	Tipo	open country
Relief	Relieve	
Water in play	Agua	
Exp. to wind	Exp. al viento	
Trees in play	Arboles	

Scorecard Tarjeta	**Chp.** Campeonato	**Mens** Caballeros	**Ladies** Damas
Length Longitud	6344	6012	5131
Par	72	72	72
Slope system	131	126	128

Advised golfing ability Nivel de juego aconsejado — 0 12 24 36
Hcp required Handicap exigido — 28 Men, 36 Ladies

CLUB HOUSE & AMENITIES CLUB HOUSE Y DEPENDENCIAS — 8/10

Pro shop Pro-shop
Driving range Campo de prácticas
Sheltered cubierto 12 mats - On grass sobre hierba yes - Putting-green putting-green yes - Pitching-green pitching-green yes

HOTEL FACILITIES HOTELES CERCANOS — 8/10

HOTELS HOTELES
Don Cándido - 106 rooms, D € 120 - Terrassa 8 km
Tel (34) 937 - 333 300 , Fax (34) 937 - 330 849

Hilton Barcelona - 275 rooms, D € 350 - Barcelona 30 km
Tel (34) 934 - 957 777 , Fax (34) 934 - 957 700

Montecarlo - 55 rooms, D € 150 - Barcelona 30 km
Tel (34) 934 - 120 404, Fax (34) 933 - 187 323

Majestic - 273 rooms, D € 350 - Barcelona 30 km
Tel (34) 934 - 881 717, Fax (34) 934 - 881 830

RESTAURANTS RESTAURANTES
La Viña - Terrassa 4 km - Tel (34) 937 - 850 850
Can Font - Terrassa 4 km - Tel (34) 937 - 142 355
Via Veneto - Barcelona 30 km - Tel (34) 932 - 007 244

El Prat *Rosa*

16	8	8

Es una pena que en la espléndida finca que tuvo a su disposición para hacer 45 hoyos, Greg Norman haya repetido su fórmula una y otra vez. Este campo Rosa tiene el aliciente de que los nueve primeros, estéticamente espléndidos, se juegan por el bosque y los nueve segundos en terreno escarpado al pie de la montaña que lo domina. Es probable que en este campo el jugador de experiencia reconozca uno de los mejores hoyos que ha jugado en su vida (quizás el 2, el 11) y también, acaso, algunos de los más incomprensibles (el 8 ó el 10). En el hoyo 16 se encontrará el único obstáculo de agua del campo porque tanto el diseñador como razones medioambientales han sustituido aquí el agua por inmensos campos de cebada cuyas espigas mece el viento a mediados de mayo. Aviso al visitante: de green a tee las distancias son largas y la circulación del campo está pensada para ir en coche. Rosa y Amarillo están llamados a ser una referencia para la competición de alto voltaje; aunque todavía tienen que madurar en diversos aspectos de la calidad del terreno, de la hierba y de la arena que tienen que ver, naturalmente, con su extremada juventud.

It is a pity that over the whole of this estate made available to Greg Norman you find the same level of difficulty whatever course you play. This Rosa course is a very motley affair with the outward nine played in a magnificent forest and the last nine lying at the foot of a mountain over very broken terrain. The more experienced players will perhaps find here the toughest holes of their lives (2 and 11) and maybe also the two most unintelligible (8 or 10). The only water hazard is on the 16th, such was the architect's desire to adapt to surroundings and replace water by barley fields, whose ears are blown away by the wind in May. Be warned: the long distances between holes and the whole layout here call for buggies. The El Prat courses were designed to be championship venues but they need to develop and mature, a normal state of affairs for courses as young as these.

Real Club de Golf El Prat — 2003

Plans de Bonvilar 17
E – 08227 TERRASSA (Barcelona)

Office	Secretaria	(34) 937 - 281 000
Pro shop	Pro-shop	(34) 937 - 281 000
Fax	Fax	(34) 937 - 281 010
Web	www.rcgep.com	
Situation	Situación	Barcelona, 30 km
Annual closure	Cierre anual	no
Weekly closure	Cierre semanal	no
Fees main season	Precios tempor. alta	18 holes

	Week days Semana	We/Bank holidays Fin de sem./fiestas
Individual Individual	€ 105	€ 210
Couple Pareja	€ 210	€ 420

Caddie Caddie no — **Electric Trolley** Carro eléctrico yes
Buggy Coche yes — **Clubs** Palos yes
Credit cards Tarjetas de crédito
VISA - Eurocard - MasterCard - AMEX

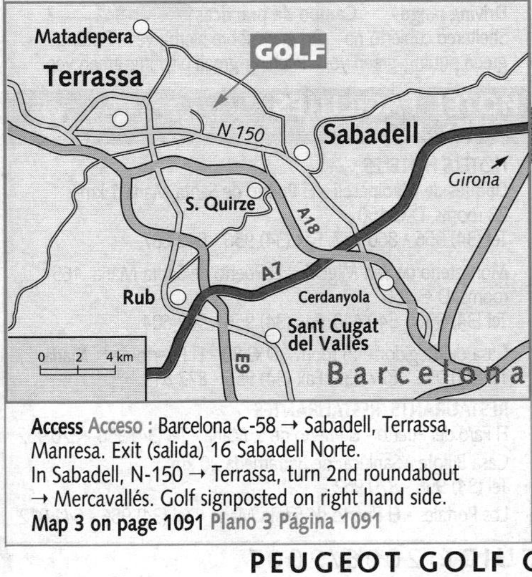

Matadepera
GOLF
Terrassa
N 150
Sabadell
Girona
S. Quirze
A18
A7
Rub
Cerdanyola
Sant Cugat del Vallès
E9
0 2 4 km
Barcelona

Access Acceso : Barcelona C-58 → Sabadell, Terrassa, Manresa. Exit (salida) 16 Sabadell Norte.
In Sabadell, N-150 → Terrassa, turn 2nd roundabout → Mercavallés. Golf signposted on right hand side.
Map 3 on page 1091 Plano 3 Página 1091

GOLF COURSE — RECORRIDO — 16/20

Site	Emplazamiento	
Maintenance	Mantenimiento	
Architect	Arquitecto	Greg Norman
Type	Tipo	open country
Relief	Relieve	
Water in play	Agua	
Exp. to wind	Exp. al viento	
Trees in play	Arboles	

Scorecard Tarjeta	**Chp.** Campeonato	**Mens** Caballeros	**Ladies** Damas
Length Longitud	6215	5941	5035
Par	72	72	72
Slope system	136	131	126

Advised golfing ability — Nivel de juego aconsejado — 0 12 24 36
Hcp required — Handicap exigido — 28 Men, 36 Ladies

CLUB HOUSE & AMENITIES — CLUB HOUSE Y DEPENDENCIAS — 8/10

Pro shop Pro-shop
Driving range Campo de prácticas
Sheltered cubierto 12 mats - On grass sobre hierba yes - Putting-green putting-green yes - Pitching-green pitching-green yes

HOTEL FACILITIES — HOTELES CERCANOS — 8/10

HOTELS HOTELES
Don Cándido - 106 rooms, D € 120 - Terrassa 8 km
Tel (34) 937 - 333 300 , Fax (34) 937 - 330 849

Hilton Barcelona - 275 rooms, D € 350 - Barcelona 30 km
Tel (34) 934 - 957 777 , Fax (34) 934 - 957 700

Montecarlo - 55 rooms, D € 150 - Barcelona 30 km
Tel (34) 934 - 120 404, Fax (34) 933 - 187 323

Majestic - 273 rooms, D € 350 - Barcelona 30 km
Tel (34) 934 - 881 717, Fax (34) 934 - 881 880

RESTAURANTS RESTAURANTES
Neichel - Barcelona 30 km - Tel (34) 932 - 038 408
Estrella de Plata (tapas) - Tel (34) 933 - 196 007 - Barcelona
El Xampanyet (tapas) - Tel (34) 933 - 197 003 - Barcelona

El Puerto

15 | 4 | 8

Un nuevo campo público construido para entretener y divertir a jugadores de muy diversas características. Para las señoras no es largo; los pegadores podrán disfrutar en unas calles generosamente anchas y los estilistas podrán presumir ante unos greenes que tienen zonas de bandera muy marcadas con plataformas y pliegues. Hay que calibrar bien la línea y la distancia a la bandera para no verse sorprendido por algunos bunkers integrados en el diseño del green. En varios pares 4 y 5 se agradece una posición de green alta y ofrecida al jugador como un anfiteatro, cosa que, curiosamente no sucede en los pares 3 donde cabría algo más de perspectiva. Hay que salvar obstáculos de agua en diez hoyos, algunos en forma de canal que no se ven a pie de calle. Los nueve primeros son llanos y del 11 al 17 hay cuestas que cambian la tónica del juego. Buen ajardinamiento y buen mantenimiento del campo colaboran a pasar un día agradable y, probablemente, en los días de mucho calor habrá una amable brisa atlántica. La nota baja de la casa-club responde a que es provisional.

This public course is located amidst brandy and sherry wine-cellars and at the heart of the very touristy Bay of Cadiz. It is not a long course, especially from the ladies tees, and big hitters will enjoy the wide fairways while players with good ball control will see off opponents on the multi-tiered greens. You need to putt intelligently as some of the slopes on the greens conceal bunkers lurking just behind. On some of the par 4s and par 5s, the greens are sited in a sort of amphitheatre, but strangely enough not on the par 3s. Water lurks on 10 holes in the form of barely visible streams. The outward nine cross a plain but then slopes appear and change the whole tempo of the round. The course's beautiful garden appearance with olive trees, pine and other indigenous plants, plus good overall green-keeping, make for a pleasant day spent golfing. When it really gets hot, there might even be an Atlantic breeze to cool you down. The club-house is still only temporary.

Golf El Puerto — 2003

Ctra. de Sanlúcar, km 1
E- 11500 EL PUERTO DE SANTA MARÍA (Cádiz)

Office Secretaria (34) 956 - 876 541
Pro shop Pro-shop (34) 956 - 876 541
Fax Fax (34) 956 - 854 866
Web www.golfelpuerto.com
Situation Situación Jerez de la Frontera, 15 km
El Puerto de Santa María , 1 km
Annual closure Cierre anual: no
Weekly closure Cierre semanal: no
Fees main season Precios tempor. alta: 18 holes

	Week days Semana	We/Bank holidays Fin de sem./fiestas
Individual Individual	€ 54	€ 54
Couple Pareja	€ 108	€ 108

Caddie Caddie no — **Electric Trolley** Carro eléctrico yes
Buggy Coche yes — **Clubs** Palos yes
Credit cards Tarjetas de crédito
VISA - Eurocard - MasterCard - AMEX

Access Acceso : Jerez N-IV → Puerto de Santa María to Sanlúcar de Barrameda, then CA-602.
Golf 1 km on right hand side
Map 8 on page 1100 Plano 8 Página 1100

GOLF COURSE — RECORRIDO 15/20

Site Emplazamiento
Maintenance Mantenimiento
Architect Arquitecto: Manuel Piñero
Type Tipo: open country
Relief Relieve
Water in play Agua
Exp. to wind Exp. al viento
Trees in play Arboles

Scorecard Tarjeta	Chp. Campeonato	Mens Caballeros	Ladies Damas
Length Longitud	6410	6011	4925
Par	72	72	72
Slope system	128	124	123

Advised golfing ability Nivel de juego aconsejado: 0 12 24 36
Hcp required Handicap exigido: 28 Men, 36 Ladies

CLUB HOUSE & AMENITIES — CLUB HOUSE Y DEPENDENCIAS 4/10

Pro shop Pro-shop
Driving range Campo de prácticas
Sheltered cubierto no - On grass sobre hierba yes - Putting-green putting-green yes - Pitching-green pitching-green yes

HOTEL FACILITIES — HOTELES CERCANOS 8/10

HOTELS HOTELES

Duques de Medinaceli - El Puerto de Santa María 1 km
28 rooms, D € 150
Tel (34) 956 - 860 777, Fax (34) 956 - 542 687

Monasterio de San Miguel - El Puerto de Santa María 165 rooms, D € 150
Tel (34) 956 - 540 440, Fax (34) 956 - 542 604

Casa del Regidor - 15 rooms, D € 80 - El Puerto de S. María
Tel (34) 956 - 877 333, Fax (34) 956 - 872 813

RESTAURANTS RESTAURANTES

El Faro del Puerto - El Puerto de S. María - Tel (34) 956 - 870 952
Casa Bigote - Sanlúcar de Barrameda 20 km
Tel (34) 956 - 870 952
Los Portales - El Puerto de Santa María - Tel (34) 956 - 541 812

El Saler

18	6	8

El placer de saborear uno de los mejores recorridos de Europa sólo puede verse alterado por un cuidado mediano. Los hoyos de links (del 5 al 9 y del 16 al 18) pueden compararse a los mejores recorridos del Reino Unido a los que el arquitecto Javier Arana ha rendido homenaje. Los demás hoyos presentan la misma estética y sólo el bosque les da un aspecto diferente. Hay varios greenes y obstáculos ciegos, lo que es característico en este tipo de recorridos que se amoldan a las dunas. Los greenes son inmensos con caídas y ondulaciones difíciles de apreciar y de jugar. En todos los aspectos del juego, por longitud, por el trazado de los hoyos y por el diseño de los greenes, este campo resiste perfectamente el asalto de las nuevas distancias que consigue el material moderno. Por supuesto, cumplir aquí el handicap es problemático porque hay que dominar todos los golpes de golf, sobre todo con viento, pero es casi una alegría perder ante tal soberbio recorrido. Incluso le será muy difícil conseguir un neto igual al 62 de Langer en el Open de España de 1984.

Only rather average standards of maintenance might spoil the joys of savouring one of Europe's best courses. The links holes (5 to 9 and 16 to 18) bear comparison with the best courses in the UK, to which architect Javier Arana has paid tribute here. The other holes are equally attractive but run through a forest. There are a lot of blind greens and hazards here, but that is typical of this kind of course which hugs the dunes. The greens are often huge and the slopes hard to read. This is a course that staunchly resists the inroads made by modern equipment in every aspect of the game, whether for length, hole layout or configuration of the greens. Naturally, playing to your handicap on a course of this standard can pose problems, as it requires every shot in the book, especially when the wind blows. But losing to a course like this is almost a pleasure. Even with a net score, you will be hard put to equal the achievement of Bernhard Langer, who carded a 62 here in the 1984 Spanish Open...

Campo de Golf El Saler — 1968

Av. Pinares, 151
E - 46012 VALENCIA

Office	Secretaria	(34) 961 - 610 384
Pro shop	Pro-shop	(34) 961 - 610 384
Fax	Fax	(34) 961 - 627 366
Web	www.parador.es	
Situation	Situación	Valencia, 8 km
Annual closure	Cierre anual	no
Weekly closure	Cierre semanal	no
Fees main season	Precios tempor. alta	18 holes

	Week days / Semana	We/Bank holidays / Fin de sem./fiestas
Individual Individual	€ 88	€ 88
Couple Pareja	€ 176	€ 176

Caddie Caddie no — **Electric Trolley** Carro eléctrico yes
Buggy Coche yes — **Clubs** Palos yes
Credit cards Tarjetas de crédito
VISA - Eurocard - AMEX

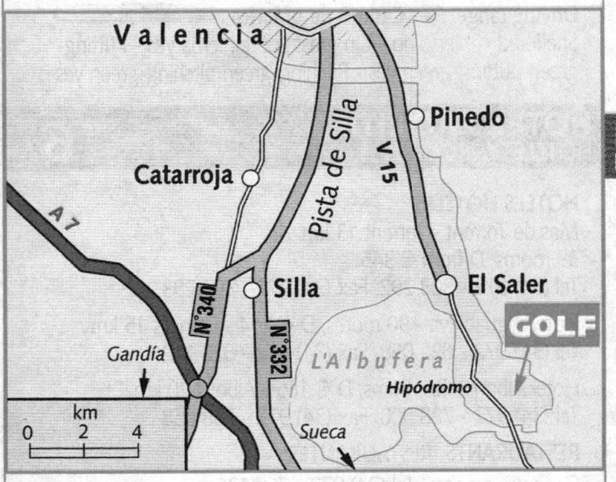

Access Acceso : V15 Valencia → El Saler, Golf 8 km
Map 7 on page 1099 Plano 7 Página 1099

GOLF COURSE — RECORRIDO — 18/20

Site	Emplazamiento	
Maintenance	Mantenimiento	
Architect	Arquitecto	Javier Arana
Type	Tipo	links
Relief	Relieve	
Water in play	Agua	
Exp. to wind	Exp. al viento	
Trees in play	Arboles	

Scorecard Tarjeta	**Chp.** Campeonato	**Mens** Caballeros	**Ladies** Damas
Length Longitud	6355	6042	5178
Par	72	72	72
Slope system	131	127	128

Advised golfing ability Nivel de juego aconsejado: 0 12 24 36
Hcp required Handicap exigido: 27 Men, 35 Ladies

CLUB HOUSE & AMENITIES — CLUB HOUSE Y DEPENDENCIAS — 6/10

Pro shop Pro-shop
Driving range Campo de prácticas
Sheltered cubierto no - On grass sobre hierba yes - Putting-green putting-green yes - Pitching-green pitching-green yes

HOTEL FACILITIES — HOTELES CERCANOS — 8/10

HOTELS HOTELES
Parador "Luis Vivés" - El Saler
58 rooms, D € 135
Tel (34) 961 - 611 186, Fax (34) 961 - 627 016

Melia Valencia Palace - Valencia 10 km
248 rooms, D € 243
Tel (34) 963 - 375 037, Fax (34) 963 - 375 532

Casa Quiquet - El Saler 5 km - 34 rooms, D € 70
Tel (34) 961 - 200 750, Fax (34) 961 - 212 677

RESTAURANTS RESTAURANTES
Oscar Torrijos - Valencia 10 km - Tel (34) 963 - 732 949
Sidi Saler - El Saler 5 km - Tel (34) 961 - 610 411
Rias Gallegas - Valencia 10 km - Tel (34) 963 - 572 007

Empordà *Links*

17 | 7 | 6

Este campo tiene cuatro recorridos de 9 hoyos, dos transcurren en medio de un frondoso bosque de pinos –recorrido Forest- y otros dos, que componen el recorrido Links, son despejados, expuestos a los vientos dominantes en la zona. Von Hagge despliega aquí su característico diseño de calles contorneadas de montículos que asemejan dunas, para calvario de las bolas que se salen de las calles. Sobre todo porque los tiros a unos greenes muy grandes, bien en alto, bien con zonas muy marcadas y siempre muy defendidos, requieren una precisión considerable de línea y distancia. Los greenes son de excelente calidad, bien diseñados y a menudo muy largos, lo que complica la elección del palo en función de la colocación de las banderas. El agua entra en juego en 9 de los 18 hoyos, a veces de manera dramática y el jugador se enfrentará más de una vez a golpes impresionantes, esos golpes que cuando salen justifican todo un día de golf. Espectacular y muy bien concebido, jugar aquí es apasionante.

This club offers four 9-hole loops forming two full 18-hole courses: the "Forest", which as its name suggests winds its way through a lush pine forest, and this, the "Links", a wide-open course exposed to the prevailing wind. Von Hagge has again employed his very own sand-dune style which punishes any ball off the straight and narrow. By and large the greens are neatly contoured, very well-defended and very large, whence the importance of good club selection, depending on pin positions, and of accurate ironwork. Water comes into play on 9 of the 18 holes, sometimes spectacularly so, and golfers here can be faced with some very impressive shots to make; but hitting just one of them sweetly will make the whole day spent here more than worthwhile. Spectacular and so well designed, this course really is an exciting place to play golf, and you could do worse than play the neighbouring "Forest" course while you are at it.

Empordà Golf Club — 1991

Ctra. Palafrugell a Torroella de Montgrí
E - 17257 GUALTA (Girona)

Office	Secretaría	(34) 972 - 760 450
Pro shop	Pro-shop	(34) 972 - 760 450
Fax	Fax	(34) 972 - 757 100
Web	www.empordagolf.com	
Situation	Situación	Palafrugell, 12 km

Girona (pop. 70 409), 30 km

Annual closure Cierre anual — no

Weekly closure Cierre semanal — no

1132

Fees main season Precios tempor. alta	18 holes	
	Week days Semana	**We/Bank holidays** Fin de sem./fiestas
Individual Individual	€ 70	€ 70
Couple Pareja	€ 140	€ 140

Caddie Caddie no — **Electric Trolley** Carro eléctrico yes

Buggy Coche yes — **Clubs** Palos yes

Credit cards Tarjetas de crédito
VISA - Eurocard - MasterCard - AMEX

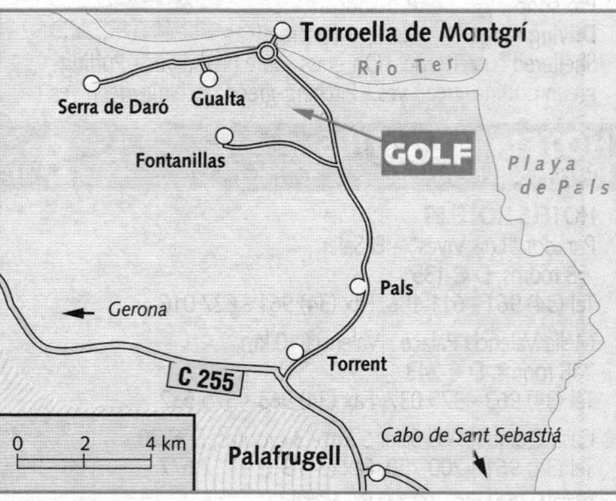

Access Acceso : A7 Exit (Salida) 6 → Girona and GI650 E643, between Pals and Torroella de Montgrí

Map 3 on page 1091 Plano 3 Página 1091

GOLF COURSE — RECORRIDO — 17/20

Site	Emplazamiento	
Maintenance	Mantenimiento	
Architect	Arquitecto	Robert von Hagge
Type	Tipo	forest, open country
Relief	Relieve	
Water in play	Agua	
Exp. to wind	Exp. al viento	
Trees in play	Arboles	

Scorecard Tarjeta	**Chp.** Campeonato	**Mens** Caballeros	**Ladies** Damas
Length Longitud	6304	5971	5060
Par	71	71	71
Slope system	131	131	127

Advised golfing ability Nivel de juego aconsejado — 0 12 24 36

Hcp required Handicap exigido — 28 Men, 36 Ladies

CLUB HOUSE & AMENITIES — CLUB HOUSE Y DEPENDENCIAS — 7/10

Pro shop Pro-shop
Driving range Campo de prácticas
Sheltered cubierto no - On grass sobre hierba yes - Putting-green putting-green yes - Pitching-green pitching-green yes

HOTEL FACILITIES — HOTELES CERCANOS — 6/10

HOTELS HOTELES
Mas de Torrent - Torrent 13 km
39 rooms, D from € 345
Tel (34) 972 - 303 292, Fax (34) 972 - 303 293

Hotel Aiguablava - 90 rooms, D € 214 - Fornells 15 km
Tel (34) 972 - 622 058, Fax (34) 972 - 622 112

Hotel Albons - 32 rooms, D € 165 - Albons 20 km
Tel (34) 972 - 788 500, Fax (34) 972 - 788 658

RESTAURANTS RESTAURANTES
Ciureny - on site - Tel (34) 972 - 760 136
Sa Punta - Pals 17 km - Tel (34) 972 - 667 376
Mas Pou - Palau-Sator 6 km - Tel (34) 972 - 634 125

Escorpión *Azul*

13	8	7

En 2002 Escorpión, que es el club social más amplio del golf valenciano, abrió nueve nuevos hoyos realizados por Alfonso Vidaor, lo que ha supuesto una reordenación del campo, ahora dividido en tres grupos de nueve hoyos, y ha supuesto también cambios en los últimos hoyos del campo que construyó Kirby. Construido en un antiguo naranjal, Escorpión Azul ofrece una vegetación compuesta de naranjos y también de palmeras y algarrobos. Sus excelentes cuidados realzan el interés de un diseño sencillo y no excepcional. Si bien hay que deplorar la semejanza repetitiva de los pares 4 (en dog-leg), debe resaltarse al menos la calidad técnica de los pares 5 y de los pares 3. No obstante, no se puede decir que este recorrido sea muy difícil por lo que se puede jugar fácilmente en familia o entre amigos de diferentes niveles de juego. Los greenes son buenos, bien diseñados, y los antegreenes, se pueden atacar rodando la bola. Hay agua en la línea de juego de ocho hoyos, sin que esto pueda asustar al jugador con cierta precisión. Finalmente, hay que resaltar la calidad y belleza del conjunto que alberga la casa club, muy bien restaurada.

In 2002, this club commissioned Alfonso Vidaor to lay out nine new holes and today you find three combinable nine-hole courses which have slightly altered the closing stretch of the original course designed by Ron Kirby. Built in a former orange orchard, Escorpion naturally has a lot of orange trees, together with palms and carobs. It is easily walkable and excellent maintenance work enhances the appeal of what is an honest but never exceptional layout. The repetitive style of the par 4s (all dog-legs) is a pity, but the par 3s and 5s are high standard, technical holes. Having said that, no-one would consider this to be a tough course and it is fun to play with the family or friends. The greens are grassy and well-designed and the few frontal and green-side hazards mean you can often roll the ball onto the putting surface. Water is in play on eight of the holes but should not unduly scare the more accurate players. One last item is the club house, whose splendid buildings have been beautifully renovated.

Club de Golf Escorpión — 1975

Apartado de Correos No 1
E - 46117 - BETERA (Valencia)

Office Secretaria (34) 961 - 601 211
Pro shop Pro-shop (34) 961 - 602 687
Fax Fax (34) 961 - 690 187
Web www.clubescorpion.com
Situation Situación Valencia, 20 km

Annual closure Cierre anual no
Weekly closure Cierre semanal no

Fees main season Precios tempor. alta 18 holes

	Week days Semana	We/Bank holidays Fin de sem./fiestas
Individual Individual	€ 80	*
Couple Pareja	€ 160	*

* Week-ends: members only (sólo socios)

Caddie Caddie no — **Electric Trolley** Carro eléctrico no
Buggy Coche yes — **Clubs** Palos yes
Credit cards Tarjetas de crédito no

Access Acceso : A7 → Ademús, Exit (Salida) 11, → Betera (3,5 km)
Map 5 on page 1095 Plano 5 Página 1095

GOLF COURSE — RECORRIDO — 13/20

Site Emplazamiento
Maintenance Mantenimiento
Architect Arquitecto Ron Kirby
Type Tipo country
Relief Relieve
Water in play Agua
Exp. to wind Exp. al viento
Trees in play Arboles

Scorecard Tarjeta	Chp. Campeonato	Mens Caballeros	Ladies Damas
Length Longitud	6081	5765	4951
Par	71	71	71
Slope system	129	124	124

Advised golfing ability Nivel de juego aconsejado 0 12 24 36
Hcp required Handicap exigido 28 Men, 36 Ladies

CLUB HOUSE & AMENITIES — CLUB HOUSE Y DEPENDENCIAS — 8/10

Pro shop Pro-shop
Driving range Campo de prácticas
Sheltered cubierto 5 mats - On grass sobre hierba yes - Putting-green putting-green yes - Pitching-green pitching-green yes

HOTEL FACILITIES — HOTELES CERCANOS — 7/10

HOTELS HOTELES
Valencia Golf Hotel - 31 rooms, D € 90 - on site
Tel (34) 961 - 698 046, Fax (34) 961 - 698 183

Adhoc Parque - 41 rooms, D € 85 - on site
Tel (34) 961 - 698 393, Fax (34) 961 - 698 191

La Calderona - 42 rooms, D € 246 - Bétera 3 km
Tel (34) 961 - 699 400, Fax (34) 961 - 699 417

RESTAURANTS RESTAURANTES
La Masía Romaní - Bétera 18 km - Tel (34) 961 - 690 773
Casa Gijón - Quart de Poblet 18 km
Tel (34) 961 545 011
Torrijos - Valencia 20 km - Tel (34) 963 - 732 949

Fontanals

17	7	7

Fontanals madura, los árboles crecen y entran en juego y junto con el agua que, a veces escondida, reta al jugador en doce hoyos del campo, lo llevan a ser un buen campo de competición y de match-play. Rodeado de montañas, aunque llano, con algunas ondulaciones, es un test de primer orden con multitud de obstáculos, encontrándose los más peligrosos en los hoyos cortos. Numerosos bunkers de calle y de green, con contornos muy elaborados (un poco al estilo de Trent Jones) ponen a prueba el sentido táctico y el virtuosismo del jugador sin que la suerte intervenga para nada en un buen resultado. Se ha cuidado mucho la estética con muretes o guijarros delimitando los obstáculos de agua. Por momentos impresionante y siempre espectacular, este recorrido de Ramón Espinosa es largo, propicio para los buenos pegadores y en general para jugadores con experiencia y con un buen juego corto. Difícilmente se le encontrarán defectos a este campo espléndido.

As the course has matured, trees have increasingly come into play on this fine championship layout. Surrounded by mountains but flat with only a few rolling fairways, the Fontanals course is a test of golf of the highest order with a multitude of hazards, the most dangerous of which are reserved for the short holes. Countless fairway and green-side bunkers, all carefully shaped (a little in the style of Trent Jones), are a great test for the tactical mind and virtuosity of any player, and luck plays no role in a good score. Very special care has been given to the visual aspect with the water hazards neatly lined with low walls or pebbles. Often impressive and sometimes quite spectacular, this course by Ramón Espinosa is long and can be recommended to long-hitters and in general to experienced players with a sharp short game. They will be hard pushed to detect any flaws at all in this superb test of golf.

Golf Fontanals de Cerdanya — 1994

E - 17538 SORIGUEROLA,
(Girona – La Cerdanya)

Office Secretaria (34) 972 - 144 374
Pro shop Pro-shop (34) 972 - 144 374
Fax Fax (34) 972 - 890 856
Web www.fontanalsgolf.com
Situation Situación Puigcerdá (pop. 6 414), 7 km
Annual closure Cierre anual — no
Weekly closure Cierre semanal — no
restaurant closed on tuesdays

Fees main season Precios tempor. alta	18 holes	
	Week days Semana	**We/Bank holidays** Fin de sem./fiestas
Individual Individual	€ 50	€ 120
Couple Pareja	€ 100	€ 240

Caddie Caddie no **Electric Trolley** Carro eléctrico yes
Buggy Coche yes **Clubs** Palos yes
Credit cards Tarjetas de crédito
VISA - Eurocard - MasterCard

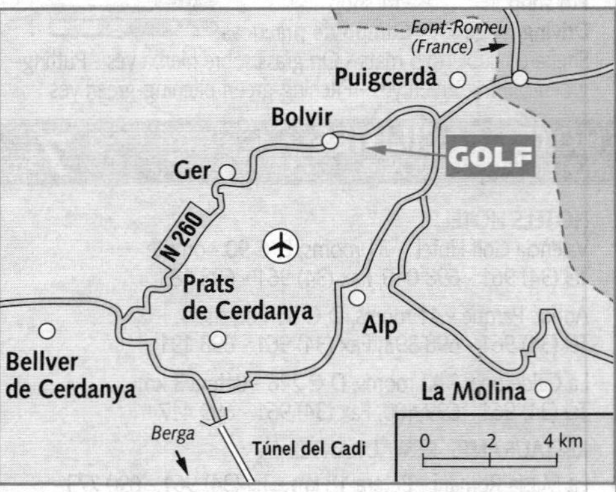

Access Acceso : Barcelona A18 → Manresa / Puigcerdà.
Manresa E9 → Puigcerdà, Alp → Golf on left hand side
Map 3 on page 1091 Plano 3 Página 1091

GOLF COURSE — RECORRIDO — 17/20

Site Emplazamiento
Maintenance Mantenimiento
Architect Arquitecto — Ramón Espinosa
Type Tipo — open country
Relief Relieve
Water in play Agua
Exp. to wind Exp. al viento
Trees in play Arboles

Scorecard Tarjeta	**Chp.** Campeonato	**Mens** Caballeros	**Ladies** Damas
Length Longitud	6454	6159	5256
Par	72	72	72
Slope system	136	131	132

Advised golfing ability Nivel de juego aconsejado — 0 12 24 36
Hcp required Handicap exigido — 28 Men, 36 Ladies

CLUB HOUSE & AMENITIES — CLUB HOUSE Y DEPENDENCIAS — 7/10

Pro shop Pro-shop
Driving range Campo de prácticas
Sheltered cubierto 14 mats - **On grass** sobre hierba yes -
Putting-green putting-green yes - **Pitching-green** pitching-green yes

HOTEL FACILITIES — HOTELES CERCANOS — 7/10

HOTELS HOTELES
Hotel Golf Fontanals - on site
60 rooms, D € 190
Tel (34) 972 - 891 818, Fax (34) 972 - 891 740

Hotel del Lago - Puigcerdà 2 km
30 rooms, D € 88
Tel (34) 972 - 881 000, Fax (34) 972 - 141 511

Torre del Remei - 22 rooms, D € 220 - Bellver de Cerdanya 7 km
Tel (34) 972 - 140 182, Fax (34) 972 - 140 449

RESTAURANTS RESTAURANTES
Torre del Remei - Bellver de Cerdanya 10 km
Tel (34) 972 - 140 182
La Vila - Puigcerdà 7 km - Tel (34) 972 - 140 804

Golf d'Aro (Mas Nou)

15	6	7

Encaramado en la cima de un monte que domina las playas, como un mirador dominando la geografía espectacular de la Costa Brava -mar y pinos-, es un campo impresionante en la mayoría de sus hoyos. Ramón Espinosa pensó más en los buenos jugadores que los handicaps altos, los cuales tienen que asustarse ante los profundos barrancos que flanquean una docena de hoyos (una regla local los considera igual que obstáculos de agua porque es imposible recuperar las bolas que caen en ellos). Más vale no relajar la concentración y es mejor la precisión que la distancia. Es preferible evitar los días de viento. Antes de pensar en el resultado más vale reconocer el terreno una o dos veces, aunque sólo sea para identificar los sitios peligrosos, calcular las distancias y... cuántas bolas conviene llevar en la bolsa. Nada fácil pero interesante, en un escenario realmente espectacular. Tras atravesar una temporada de problemas, el campo tiene un nuevo propietario que lo ha devuelto al buen estado que merece su diseño, incluyendo la rehabilitación de la casa-club.

Perched on the summit of a little mountain overlooking the beaches, like a watchtower dominating the spectacular scenery of the Costa Brava - all sea and pines -, this is an impressively spacious course, at least for most of the holes. Ramón Espinosa obviously had the good golfer in mind more than the high-handicapper, who might not be too impressed by some fearsomely deep ravines filled with dense bushes lining about a dozen holes. Luckily, a local rule considers these to be water hazards as it is impossible to recover your ball. Focus is the key word here, with accuracy taking priority over distance. When the wind really blows, you might be best advised to stay in the club-house. You would also be wise to reconnoitre the course a few times before thinking about a good score, locating the danger spots and taking account of distance. Nothing is easy but everything is interesting in this truly spectacular setting. After a period of uncertainty, this club has preserved the standards of green-keeping it deserves and the refurbishing of the clubhouse was most welcome.

Club Golf d'Aro — 1990

Url. Mas Nou s/n - Aparttado Correo 429
E - 17250 PLATJA D'ARO (Girona - Costa Brava)

Office Secretaria (34) 972 - 826 900
Pro shop Pro-shop (34) 972 - 816 727
Fax Fax (34) 972 - 826 906
Web www.golfdaro.com
Situation Situación Platja d'Aro, 4 km
Sant Feliu de Guixols , 10 km
Annual closure Cierre anual no
Weekly closure Cierre semanal no

Fees main season Precios tempor. alta	18 holes	
	Week days Semana	We/Bank holidays Fin de sem./fiestas
Individual Individual	€ 72	€ 72
Couple Pareja	€ 144	€ 144

Caddie Caddie no — **Electric Trolley** Carro eléctrico yes
Buggy Coche yes — **Clubs** Palos yes
Credit cards Tarjetas de crédito
VISA - Eurocard - MasterCard

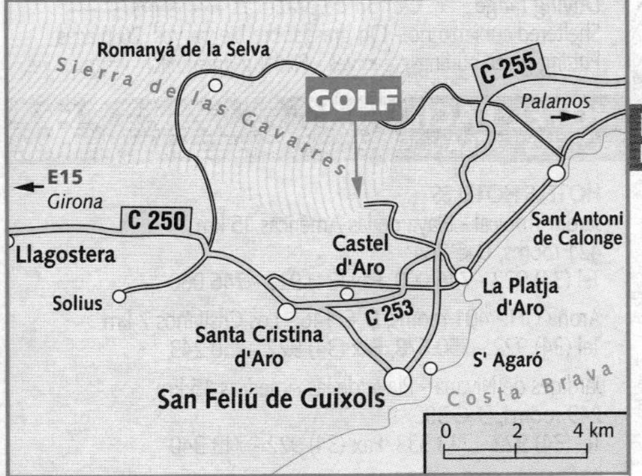

Access Acceso : Barcelona, A2. Exit (Salida) 9. Platja d'Aro, turn right → Urban. Mas Nou
Map 3 on page 1091 Plano 3 Página 1091

GOLF COURSE — RECORRIDO — 15/20

Site Emplazamiento
Maintenance Mantenimiento
Architect Arquitecto — Ramón Espinosa
Type Tipo — mountain, parkland
Relief Relieve
Water in play Agua
Exp. to wind Exp. al viento
Trees in play Arboles

Scorecard Tarjeta	Chp. Campeonato	Mens Caballeros	Ladies Damas
Length Longitud	6218	6004	5031
Par	72	72	72
Slope system	131	127	123

Advised golfing ability Nivel de juego aconsejado — 0 12 24 36
Hcp required Handicap exigido — 36

CLUB HOUSE & AMENITIES — CLUB HOUSE Y DEPENDENCIAS — 6/10

Pro shop Pro-shop
Driving range Campo de prácticas
Sheltered cubierto 10 mats - On grass sobre hierba yes -
Putting-green putting-green yes - Pitching-green pitching-green yes

HOTEL FACILITIES — HOTELES CERCANOS — 7/10

HOTELS HOTELES
Park Hotel Sant Jorge - Platja d'Aro 4 km - 104 rooms, D € 211
Tel (34) 972 - 652 311, Fax (34) 972 - 652 576

Golf Costa Brava - Santa Cristina 10 km - 91 rooms, D € 144
Tel (34) 972 - 835 151, Fax (34) 972 - 837 588

Platjapark - Platja d'Aro 4 km - 200 rooms, D € 164
Tel (34) 972 - 816 805, Fax (34) 972 - 816 803

RESTAURANTS RESTAURANTES
Las Panolles - Platja d'Aro 8 km - Tel (34) 972 - 837 011
Carles Camos-Big Rock - Platja d'Aro 3 km
Tel (34) 972 - 818 012
Arabi - Platja d'Aro 5 km - Tel (34) 972 - 816 376

Golf del Sur *Norte/Sur*

16	7	8

Este es un campo con tres recorridos de 9 hoyos que se pueden combinar entre sí. El recorrido principal consiste en jugar los campos Sur y Norte. Recientes obras de acondicionamiento han mejorado mucho el estado del campo. Sus hoyos más famosos son el 2 del Sur, un par 3 de 193 metros cuyo green es una isla verde rodeada de la arena negra propia de la zona. y el hoyo 4 del recorrido Norte, un par 4 de 289 metros impresionante porque sube de espaldas al mar junto a un formidable barranco. Es un recorrido muy variado en el que José Gancedo hace sus peculiares guiños al jugador, bien poniéndole ante un golpe original, bien reclamándole un approach de buen tacto. Las referencias y la decoración del campo se fundamentan en la flora autóctona que, además de alegrar los ojos, enmarca al jugador en el hoyo. Los amantes de dominar la fuerza del viento para llevar la bola a su destino disfrutarán mucho en este campo con espléndidas vistas al Atlántico.

This course comprises 3 nine-holers but the reference course is certainly the South and North played together. Recent development work has done much to improve the general condition of the course, where perhaps the most remarkable hole is N°2 on the South layout, a par 3 of 212 yards, where the green is a sort of green island amidst bunkers full of the region's black sand. Almost as impressive is hole N°4 on the North course, a great par 4 of just 318 yards, where the terraced steps up the fairway towards the sea present a tremendous barrier. This is a very varied layout where José Gancedo had players very much in mind, asking them to carefully place their shots before thinking about doing anything too original, and calling for a sharp short game. The decoration is the island's natural flora, which not only is a sight to behold but also comes into play. Golfers who like to challenge a swirling wind will love this course, which also offers some splendid views.

Golf del Sur — 1989

Urbanizacion Golf del Sur
E - 38639 SAN MIGUEL DE ABONA (Tenerife – Islas Canarias)

Office	Secretaria	(34) 922 - 738 170
Pro shop	Pro-shop	(34) 922 - 738 170
Fax	Fax	(34) 922 - 738 272
Web	www.golfdelsur.net	
Situation	Situación	Playa de Las Américas, 11 km

Santa Cruz de Tenerife (pop. 203 000), 62 km

Annual closure	Cierre anual	no
Weekly closure	Cierre semanal	no
Fees main season	Precios tempor. alta	18 holes

	Week days / Semana	We/Bank holidays / Fin de sem./fiestas
Individual Individual	€ 80	€ 80
Couple Pareja	€ 160	€ 160

Caddie Caddie no — **Electric Trolley** Carro eléctrico yes

Buggy Coche yes — **Clubs** Palos yes

Credit cards Tarjetas de crédito
VISA - MasterCard - AMEX

Access Acceso : Motorway TF1 / Autovia del Sur, Exit (Salida) 24 (Km 62.5), → Los Abrigos.
First right to Urbanización Golf del Sur
Map 1 on page 1087 Plano 1 Página 1087

GOLF COURSE — 16/20
RECORRIDO

Site	Emplazamiento	
Maintenance	Mantenimiento	
Architect	Arquitecto	José Gancedo
Type	Tipo	parkland
Relief	Relieve	
Water in play	Agua	
Exp. to wind	Exp. al viento	
Trees in play	Arboles	

Scorecard Tarjeta	Chp. Campeonato	Mens Caballeros	Ladies Damas
Length Longitud	5870	5578	4829
Par	72	72	72
Slope system	120	118	118

Advised golfing ability Nivel de juego aconsejado — 0 12 24 36

Hcp required Handicap exigido — 28 Men, 36 Ladies

CLUB HOUSE & AMENITIES — 7/10
CLUB HOUSE Y DEPENDENCIAS

Pro shop Pro-shop
Driving range Campo de prácticas
Sheltered cubierto no - On grass sobre hierba yes, 20 places
Putting-green putting-green yes - Pitching-green pitching-green yes

HOTEL FACILITIES — 8/10
HOTELES CERCANOS

HOTELS HOTELES

Jardin Tropical - Playa de las Américas 15 km
421 rooms, D € 264
Tel (34) 922 - 746 000, Fax (34) 922 - 746 060

Arona GH - 401 rooms, D € 146 - Los Cristianos 7 km
Tel (34) 922 - 750 678, Fax (34) 922 - 750 243

Jardines de Nivaria - Playa de las Américas 15 km
249 rooms, D € 380
Tel (34) 922 - 713 333, Fax (34) 922 - 713 340

RESTAURANTS RESTAURANTES

El Rincón del Arroz - Los Cristianos 7 km - Tel (34) 922 - 797 370
El Jable - San Isidro 7 km - Tel (34) 922 - 390 698
Avencio - El Médano 2 km - Tel (34) 922 - 176 079

Granada

14	6	7

A noventa minutos de la costa, este recorrido no sólo ofrece una buena oportunidad de jugar al golf cuando se va a visitar la soberbia ciudad de Granada, sino que merece la pena por sí mismo. Está situado en altura frente a Sierra Nevada, pero sin demasiadas cuestas, su longitud es razonable, salvo en los pares 3 y en los demás hoyos (sobre todo en los 9 segundos) si se sale de atrás. Las dificultades están colocadas de manera estratégica y peligrosa si no se tiene mucha precisión, especialmente los temibles obstáculos de agua entre los hoyos 15 y 17. Los greens están bien diseñados, son bastante grandes, bien protegidos, con sutiles ondulaciones. En este tipo de recorrido con dificultades bien repartidas, no hay que dudar en atacar en cuanto la ocasión se presenta. Sería mejor jugar con golfistas de mismo nivel para apreciar más los desafíos tácticos, pero es un recorrido muy agradable para todo tipo de jugadores.

This course, 90 minutes inland, not only provides a great opportunity to play golf when visiting the superb city of Granada, it is also well worth playing. At altitude, it stands opposite the Sierra Nevada, although the layout is rather flat and length reasonable, except the par 3s and if you choose to play from the back tees (especially on the back nine). Hazards are strategically placed and often dangerous for wayward shots, especially the formidable water hazards between the 15th and 17th holes. The greens are well-designed, rather large and well defended with tricky slopes. This is a type of course where the difficulties are evenly spread, inviting players to attack whenever the opportunity arises. We recommend playing here with golfers of your own level in order to better appreciate the tactical challenges, but the course is a pleasant day's golfing for everyone.

Granada Club de Golf — 1986

Avda. de los Corsarios s/n
E - 18110 LAS GABIAS (Granada)

Office Secretaria (34) 958 - 584 060
Pro shop Pro-shop (34) 958 - 584 060
Fax Fax (34) 958 - 584 436
Web www.granadaclubdegolf.com
Situation Situación Granada (pop. 287 864), 8 km
Annual closure Cierre anual no
Weekly closure Cierre semanal no
Fees main season Precios tempor. alta 18 holes

	Week days / Semana	We/Bank holidays / Fin de sem./fiestas
Individual Individual	€ 52	€ 69*
Couple Pareja	€ 69	€ 93*

* Weekend: Friday → Sunday

Caddie Caddie no — **Electric Trolley** Carro eléctrico no
Buggy Coche yes — **Clubs** Palos yes
Credit cards Tarjetas de crédito
VISA - Eurocard - Mastercard - AMEX

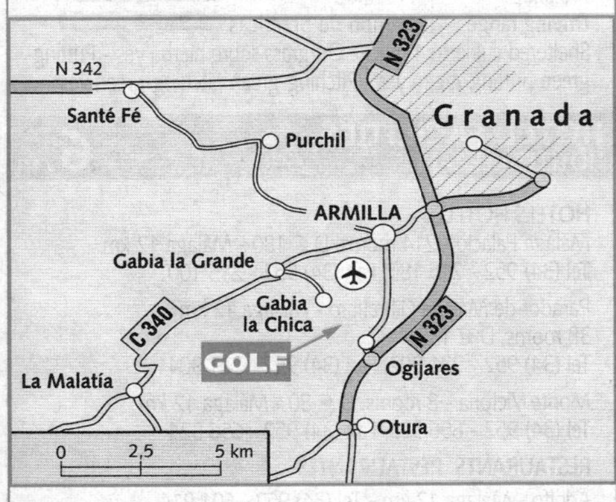

Access Acceso : Granada N323 → Mortril, Armilla → C340 → Gabia La Grande
Map 9 on page 1102 Plano 9 Página 1102

GOLF COURSE — RECORRIDO — 14/20

Site Emplazamiento
Maintenance Mantenimiento
Architect Arquitecto Ibergolf
Type Tipo open country
Relief Relieve
Water in play Agua
Exp. to wind Exp. al viento
Trees in play Arboles

Scorecard / Tarjeta	Chp. / Campeonato	Mens / Caballeros	Ladies / Damas
Length Longitud	6037	5623	5135
Par	71	71	71
Slope system	125	123	124

Advised golfing ability Nivel de juego aconsejado 0 12 24 36
Hcp required Handicap exigido no

CLUB HOUSE & AMENITIES — CLUB HOUSE Y DEPENDENCIAS — 6/10

Pro shop Pro-shop
Driving range Campo de prácticas
Sheltered cubierto no - On grass sobre hierba yes - Putting-green putting-green yes - Pitching-green pitching-green yes

HOTEL FACILITIES — HOTELES CERCANOS — 7/10

HOTELS HOTELES
Melia Granada - 191 rooms, D € 160 - Granada 8 km
Tel (34) 958 - 227 400, Fax (34) 958 - 227 403

Alhambra Palace - en La Alhambra 8 km
126 rooms, D € 170
Tel (34) 958 - 221 468, Fax (34) 958 - 226 404

Parador de Granada - en La Alhambra 8 km
36 rooms, D € 250
Tel (34) 958 - 221 440, Fax (34) 958 - 226 404

RESTAURANTS RESTAURANTES
Bogavante - Granada 8 km - Tel (34) 958 - 259 112
Tavares - Granada 8 km - Tel (34) 958 - 226 769
Taberna Tendido 1 (tapas) - Granada 8 km
Tel (34) 958 - 272 302

1137

Guadalhorce

14	7	6

En la campiña al oeste de Málaga, este recorrido diseñado por el finlandés Kosti Kuronen presenta dos caras: los nueve primeros hoyos son bastante clásicos, los nueve últimos más imaginativos con greenes en alto, calles y lagos bien cuidados. Los greenes son de excelente calidad, a veces dobles (6 y 8, 12 y 16), rápidos y bien protegidos, y aguantan bien la bola. Varios de ellos son tan largos que a veces hay que llegar a la bandera con tres palos más. El conjunto no es que sea excepcional, pero es muy agradable y divertido e jugar todas las fórmulas de golf, tanto con jugadores de mismo nivel como de niveles muy diferentes. Sobre todo reserva sus dificultades a los mejores, respondiendo exactamente a la definición de un buen campo de golf, y el hecho de que no sea necesario alquilar un coche hace que sea muy placentero el jugar en familia. Algunos bunkers estratégicos le dan un cierto encanto e incitan a jugarlo varias veces.

In the countryside to the west of Málaga, this course, designed by Finnish architect Kosti Kuronen, offers two different faces. The front nine are classical holes, while the back nine are more imaginative with elevated greens, lakes and well laid out fairways. The greens are excellent, sometimes double (6 and 8, 12 and 16), fast and well-defended, but they pitch well. Some of them are so huge that there is at least a 3-club difference from one end to the other. This is probably not an exceptional course but it is very pleasant and fun to play with players of your own standard or with anyone, for that matter. In fact, the difficulties of Guadalhorce, as with any good course, are reserved for the better players, and being easily playable on foot it is great fun to play with all the family. A few strategic traps add a little spice to the round and certainly make you want to come back for more.

Guadalhorce Club de Golf — 1990

Ctra Cartama Km 7 - Apdo. Correos 48
E - 29590 CAMPANILLAS (Málaga)

Office	Secretaría	(34) 952 - 179 378
Pro shop	Pro-shop	(34) 952 - 179 378
Fax	Fax	(34) 952 - 179 372
Web	www.guadalhorce.com	
Situation	Situación	Fuengirola, 15 km

Málaga (pop. 534 683), 6 km

Annual closure	Cierre anual	no
Weekly closure	Cierre semanal	no
Fees main season	Precios tempor. alta	18 holes

	Week days Semana	We/Bank holidays Fin de sem./fiestas
Individual Individual	€ 55	*
Couple Pareja	€ 110	*

* Weekends: members only (sólo socios)

Caddie Caddie no — **Electric Trolley** Carro eléctrico no
Buggy Coche yes — **Clubs** Palos yes
Credit cards Tarjetas de crédito
VISA - Mastercard - AMEX

Access Acceso : Málaga → Parque Tecnologico, Exit (Salida) "Campanillas", 2 km, Golf
Map 8 on page 1101 Plano 8 Página 1101

GOLF COURSE — RECORRIDO — 14/20

Site Emplazamiento
Maintenance Mantenimiento
Architect Arquitecto — Kosti Kuronen
Type Tipo — open country, hilly
Relief Relieve
Water in play Agua
Exp. to wind Exp. al viento
Trees in play Arboles

Scorecard Tarjeta	Chp. Campeonato	Mens Caballeros	Ladies Damas
Length Longitud	6194	5860	4992
Par	72	72	72
Slope system	116	116	112

Advised golfing ability Nivel de juego aconsejado — 0 12 24 36
Hcp required Handicap exigido — 27 Men, 35 Ladies

CLUB HOUSE & AMENITIES — CLUB HOUSE Y DEPENDENCIAS — 7/10

Pro shop Pro-shop
Driving range Campo de prácticas
Sheltered cubierto 4 mats - On grass sobre hierba yes - Putting-green putting-green yes - Pitching-green pitching-green yes

HOTEL FACILITIES — HOTELES CERCANOS — 6/10

HOTELS HOTELES
Málaga Palacio - 214 rooms, D € 180 - Málaga 12 km
Tel (34) 952 - 215 185, Fax (34) 952 - 215 100

Parador de Málaga Gibralfaro - Málaga 12 km
38 rooms, D € 135
Tel (34) 952 - 221 902, Fax (34) 952 - 221 904

Monte Victoria - 8 rooms, D € 80 - Málaga 12 km
Tel (34) 952 - 656 525, Fax (34) 952 - 656 524

RESTAURANTS RESTAURANTES
Adolfo - Málaga 12 km - Tel (34) 952 - 601 914
Cueva del Camborio - Málaga 12 km - Tel (34) 952 - 347 816
Doña Francisquita - on site - Tel (34) 952 179 370

Guadalmina *Sur*

15	7	7

Es el segundo recorrido creado en la Costa del Sol, diseñado por el legendario Javier Arana. Mucho más llano que el "Norte", sus calles son más anchas, con árboles a menudo en la línea de juego. Las últimas reformas lo devuelven a la categoría de campo interesante y exigente, según lo ideó su diseñador: se han ampliado varios greenes introduciendo desniveles y obstáculos de agua que obligan a afrontar los tiros a green con mayor estrategia y precisión y se ha mejorado el sistema de riego consiguiendo un mejor estado del campo. La primera vuelta tiene algunos hoyos bastante largos, mientras que en los 9 segundos hay algun par 4 corto con oportunidad de birdie para aliviar la tarjeta. El 6 es un par 5 de 555 metros que en 1965 parecía una distancia descomunal. Tiene pares 3 de buena calidad (sobre todo el 11). Pionero de la zona de Marbella, a principios de los 70 sus calles vieron a Michael Caine y Glenda Jackson rodando "A Touch of Class". Con otro recorrido de 18 hoyos, Guadalmina norte, y nueve hoyos cortos, es una cita obligada del golf costasoleño.

This is the second course opened on the Costa del Sol designed by the legendary Javier Arana. It has wide fairways and trees which often get in the way. The latest overhaul has made the course more demanding, the way Arana would have wished, as several greens have been enlarged with sharper contours and water hazards now compel players to attack the greens with greater strategy and precision. The front nine include some rather long holes, while the inward half has a number of shortish holes, notably the short part 4s. Note, too, that hole N° 6, a par 5 of some 610 yards was described as a monster back in 1965. How times change. The par 3s are excellent (especially the 11th). One of the pioneering layouts round about Marbella in the 1970s, the course served as the setting for the film "A Touch of Class" starring Michael Caine and Glenda Jackson. Now with a second 18-hole course, Guadalmina is one of the golfing "musts" along the southern coast.

Guadalmina Club de Golf — 1965

Urbanización Guadalmina Alta
E - 29678 SAN PEDRO DE ALCANTARA
(Málaga – Costa del Sol)

Office Secretaria (34) 952 - 883 375
Pro shop Pro-shop (34) 952 - 886 522
Fax Fax (34) 952 - 883 483
Web www.guadalmina.com
Situation Situación San Pedro de Alcantara, 1 km
Estepona (pop. 36 307), 14 km

Annual closure Cierre anual — no
Weekly closure Cierre semanal — no
Fees main season Precios tempor. alta — 18 holes

	Week days Semana	We/Bank holidays Fin de sem./fiestas
Individual Individual	€ 125	€ 125
Couple Pareja	€ 250	€ 250

Caddie Caddie no — **Electric Trolley** Carro eléctrico yes
Buggy Coche yes — **Clubs** Palos no
Credit cards Tarjetas de crédito
VISA - AMEX

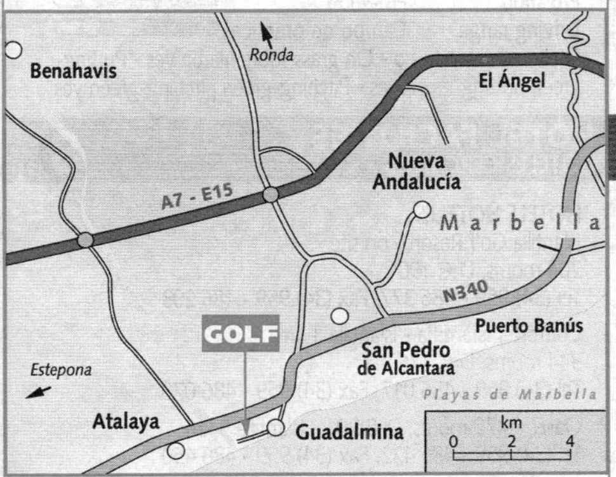

Access Acceso : N340 Marbella → San Pedro de Alcantara
Map 8 on page 1101 Plano 8 Página 1101

GOLF COURSE — RECORRIDO — 15/20

Site Emplazamiento
Maintenance Mantenimiento
Architect Arquitecto — Javier Arana
Type Tipo — seaside course, parkland
Relief Relieve
Water in play Agua
Exp. to wind Exp. al viento
Trees in play Arboles

Scorecard Tarjeta	Chp. Campeonato	Mens Caballeros	Ladies Damas
Length Longitud	6113	5799	5002
Par	71	71	71
Slope system	140	137	126

Advised golfing ability Nivel de juego aconsejado — 0 12 24 36
Hcp required Handicap exigido — 27 Men, 35 Ladies

CLUB HOUSE & AMENITIES — CLUB HOUSE Y DEPENDENCIAS — 7/10

Pro shop Pro-shop
Driving range Campo de prácticas
Sheltered cubierto no - On grass sobre hierba yes - Putting-green putting-green yes - Pitching-green pitching-green no

HOTEL FACILITIES — HOTELES CERCANOS — 7/10

HOTELS HOTELES
Guadalmina - 80 rooms, D € 265 - on site
Tel (34) 952 - 882 211, Fax (34) 952 - 882 291

Barceló Marbella Golf Hotel - 207 rooms, D € 218 - on site
Tel (34) 952 - 889 099, Fax (34) 952 - 888 564

Atalaya Park - 448 rooms, D € 284 - Estepona 2 km
Tel (34) 952 - 889 000, Fax (34) 952 - 889 002

El Paraiso - 182 rooms, D € 200 - Estepona 3 km
Tel (34) 952 - 883 000, Fax (34) 952 - 882 019

RESTAURANTS RESTAURANTES
Meridiana - Marbella 15 km - Tel (34) 952 - 776 190
Cipriano - Puerto Banús 9 km - Tel (34) 952 - 811 077

Islantilla *Verde/Azul*

16	8	8

Con 27 hoyos y una bonita casa club de estilo andaluz, el conjunto de este ambicioso proyecto de 300 has. domina el Atlántico desde un parque de frondosos pinos. El campo nació con tres recorridos de 9 hoyos con la expresa voluntad de combinarlos por sus diferentes características, aunque el Verde y el Azul se han ido imponiendo como la combinación más frecuente. El azul puede considerarse el más difícil, un desafío para los handicaps medios y bajos ya que hay que pegar largo y recto y los contornos de los greenes piden a gritos un juego corto sensible. El recorrido verde es el más largo de los tres, no es tan exigente en cuanto a la línea del golpe porque sus calles se pueden llamar anchas y abiertas, pero el diseño de los hoyos vuelve a invitar al jugador a pensar los golpes y la estrategia mejor para cubrir el a veces glorioso camino de tee a green. Además de los numerosos bunkers bien diseñados y de un cierto número de obstáculos de agua, greenes ondulados y a menudo en alto hacen muy técnico el recorrido. Si al gusto de jugar se añade el placer de las vistas sobre el Océano, Islantilla es una buena razón para acercarse al límite suroeste de España.

The 27 holes and attractive Andalusian style clubhouse of this ambitious complex overlook the Atlantic Ocean from a huge and very thick pine forest. The club started out with three 9-hole courses with the idea of combining them any way you like. Actually, the Verde and Azul form the best pairing. The Azul course is considered to be the most difficult, a real challenge for good players because you have to hit it long and straight and have a sharp short game. The Verde is the longest of the three but hardly the most challenging as the fairways are wide open. However, the design of holes calls for careful thought over the best strategy to reach the greens. Many well-designed bunkers, several water hazards and undulating greens make this a course for the artist. If you combine the pleasure of playing and the surrounding view (notably over the ocean on hole No 12), Islantilla is an excellent reason to drive on to the extreme limits of south-west Spain.

Islantilla Golf Club — 1991

Paseo Barranco del Moro s/n.
E - 21416 ISLANTILLA – ISLA CRISTINA (Huelva - Andalucía)

Office	Secretaria	(34) 959 - 486 039
Pro shop	Pro-shop	(34) 959 - 486 049
Fax	Fax	(34) 959 - 486 104
Web	www.islantillagolfresort.com	
Situation	Situación	Sevilla, 147 km

Huelva (pop. 144 579), 40 km

Annual closure	Cierre anual	no
Weekly closure	Cierre semanal	no

Fees main season Precios tempor. alta	18 holes	
	Week days Semana	**We/Bank holidays** Fin de sem./fiestas
Individual Individual	€ 63	€ 63
Couple Pareja	€ 126	€ 126

Caddie Caddie no — **Electric Trolley** Carro eléctrico yes
Buggy Coche yes — **Clubs** Palos yes
Credit cards Tarjetas de crédito
VISA - AMEX - DC

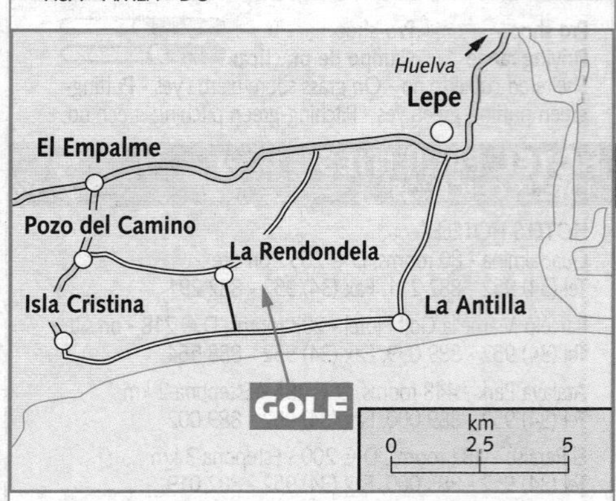

Access Acceso : A-49 (Sevilla-Huelva), Exit (salida) Ayamonte. At Lepe → La Antilla. In Urbanización Islantilla, at Isla Cristina.
Map 8 on page 1100 Plano 8 Página 1100

GOLF COURSE — RECORRIDO — 16/20

Site	Emplazamiento	
Maintenance	Mantenimiento	
Architect	Arquitecto	Enrique Canales, Luis Recasens
Type	Tipo	seas de course, forest
Relief	Relieve	
Water in play	Agua	
Exp. to wind	Exp. al viento	
Trees in play	Arboles	

Scorecard Tarjeta	**Chp.** Campeonato	**Mens** Caballeros	**Ladies** Damas
Length Longitud	6142	5697	4945
Par	72	72	72
Slope system	123	120	118

Advised golfing ability Nivel de juego aconsejado — 0 12 24 36
Hcp required Handicap exigido — 28 Men, 36 Ladies

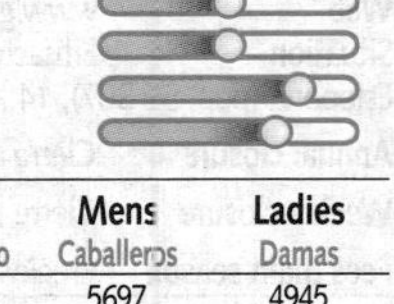

CLUB HOUSE & AMENITIES — CLUB HOUSE Y DEPENDENCIAS — 8/10

Pro shop Pro-shop
Driving range Campo de prácticas
Sheltered cubierto no - On grass sobre hierba yes - Putting-green putting-green yes - Pitching-green pitching-green yes

HOTEL FACILITIES — HOTELES CERCANOS — 8/10

HOTELS HOTELES
Islantilla Golf Resort - on site
204 rooms, D € 190
Tel (34) 959 - 486 377, Fax (34) 959 - 486 203

Confortel Islantilla - Islantilla 1 km
344 rooms, D € 176
Tel (34) 959 - 486 017, Fax (34) 959 - 486 070

Oasis - 475 rooms, D € 201 - Islantilla 5 km
Tel (34) 959 - 486 422, Fax (34) 959 - 486 450

RESTAURANTS RESTAURANTES
El Coral - La Antilla 2 km - Tel (34) 959 - 481 406
Meson La Isla - Isla Cristina 5 km - Tel (34) 959 - 343 018

Jarama R.A.C.E.

13	7	6

El plan de mejoras en el campo ha sido altamente eficaz devolviendo por un lado al campo la personalidad con que lo creó el diseño de Arana y por otro lado poniéndolo en condiciones de mantenimiento que colaboran con jugador. Bien situado, con magníficas vistas sobre la Sierra de Guadarrama, sería un sitio muy tranquilo para jugar si la proximidad del circuito automovilístico no trajese a veces problemas sonoros. Lo cual no desaconseja en absoluto la visita a este recorrido que requiere una cierta longitud de pegada (¡sobre todo desde atrás!), pero es lo suficientemente amplio para permitir ciertas escapadas de los drives. El trazado tiene en los árboles, que a veces se meten en las calles, y en los bunkers, obstáculos que Arana siempre puso en juego con nobleza e inteligencia, sus principales defensas, pero los jugadores imprecisos tendrán en definitiva mayores problemas cuando no consigan controlar sus tiros a green. La precisión, más que la longitud será la que nos permitirá aquí cumplir el handicap.

Recent revamping of the drainage systems has solved the problems that diminished the pleasure of playing here in damp conditions and failed to do justice to this very interesting layout by Javier Arana. Well located with some wonderful views, this would be a very quiet place to play if it weren't for the racing track close-by (going by the same name of Jarama), which can be noisy at times. It would, though, be a shame to turn down a visit here, because while the course demands length off the tee (especially from the back), it is wide enough to forgive the all too frequent sliced or hooked drive. The layout often brings trees into play – encroaching onto the fairways – together with bunkers which form hazards always laid out by Arana with daring and intelligence. They form the main defences against wayward hitters who fail to control their approach shots to the greens. Accuracy more than length is called for if you want to hope to play to your handicap.

Club Jarama R.A.C.E. — 1967

Carretera Madrid Burgos, Km 28,100
E - 28707 SAN SEBASTIAN DE LOS REYES (Madrid)

Office	Secretaria	(34) 916 - 570 011
Pro shop	Pro-shop	(34) 916 - 589 121
Fax	Fax	(34) 916 - 570 462
Web	www.race.es	
Situation	Situación	Madrid, 28 km
Annual closure	Cierre anual	no
Weekly closure	Cierre semanal	no
Fees main season	Precios tempor. alta	18 holes

	Week days Semana	We/Bank holidays Fin de sem./fiestas
Individual Individual	€ 67,30*	€ 113,90*
Couple Pareja	€ 134,60*	€ 227,80*

* Members' guests only
(Visitantes sólo si son invitados de socio)

Caddie Caddie no — **Electric Trolley** Carro eléctrico yes
Buggy Coche yes — **Clubs** Palos no
Credit cards Tarjetas de crédito no

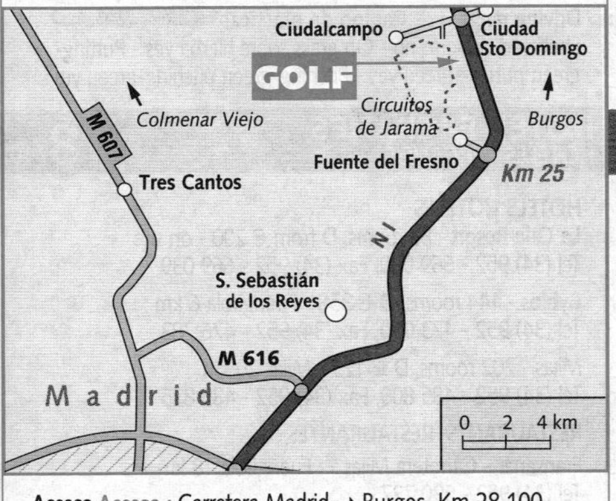

Access Acceso : Carretera Madrid → Burgos, Km 28,100
Map 4 on page 1092 Plano 4 Página 1092

GOLF COURSE — RECORRIDO — 13/20

Site	Emplazamiento	
Maintenance	Mantenimiento	
Architect	Arquitecto	Javier Arana
Type	Tipo	country
Relief	Relieve	
Water in play	Agua	
Exp. to wind	Exp. al viento	
Trees in play	Arboles	

Scorecard Tarjeta	**Chp.** Campeonato	**Mens** Caballeros	**Ladies** Damas
Length Longitud	6486	6069	5082
Par	72	72	72
Slope system	116	115	119

Advised golfing ability Nivel de juego aconsejado — 0 12 24 36
Hcp required Handicap exigido — 28 Men, 36 Ladies

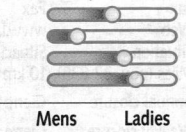

CLUB HOUSE & AMENITIES — CLUB HOUSE Y DEPENDENCIAS — 7/10

Pro shop Pro-shop
Driving range Campo de prácticas
Sheltered cubierto 60 mats - On grass sobre hierba yes - Putting-green putting-green yes - Pitching-green pitching-green yes

HOTEL FACILITIES — HOTELES CERCANOS — 6/10

HOTELS HOTELES

Chamartin - 318 rooms, D € 180 - Madrid 20 km
Tel (34) 913 - 344 900, Fax (34) 917 - 330 214

Majadahonda - 41 rooms, D € 164 - Majadahonda 20 km
Tel (34) 916 - 382 122 , Fax (34) 916 - 382 157

La Moraleja - 37 rooms, D € 217 - Alcobendas 15 km
Tel (34) 916 - 618 055, Fax (34) 916 - 612 188

RESTAURANTS RESTAURANTES

Mesón Tejas Verde - S.S. de Los Reyes 10 km
Tel (34) 916 - 527 307

Vicente - S.S. de Los Reyes 10 km - Tel (34) 916 - 513 171

Izamar - S.S. de Los Reyes 10 km - Tel (34) 916 - 543 893

La Cala *Norte*

17 | 7 | 8

Es un verdadero éxito el haber podido alojar dos recorridos en una región tan montañosa..., ¡pero se necesita estar en excelente condición física para prescindir de un coche! . El "Norte" ofrece buenas ocasiones de utilizar el driver, pero en general es tan importante colocar la bola y los roughs son tan peligrosos (matorrales), que la madera 3 es más que suficiente. Las ondulaciones del recorrido y las impresiones ópticas exigen reflexión tanto en cada golpe como en la elección del palo, por lo que los jugadores ya experimentados se desenvolverán mejor. Sólo después de haberlo jugado una o dos veces se puede intentar obtener un buen resultado, pero es un recorrido para jugar sobre todo match-play, apasionante por el diseño de las caídas de los greenes, generalmente protegidos por grandes y profundos bunkers. Pequeño consuelo en caso de decepción: sólo hay agua en dos hoyos y la vista panorámica sobre esta región agreste es magnífica.

Accommodating two courses (three now) into such a mountainous region was something of an exploit, but you need to be pretty fit to refuse a buggy. The "Norte" offers some fine opportunities to take the driver out of the bag, but as a general rule, positioning the ball is so important and the rough so dangerous (scrub) that the 3-wood (or long-iron) will suffice. The general relief of this course and the optical illusions call for careful consideration when choosing the club before every shot, which is why we recommend it for experienced players. After one or two reconnaissance rounds they might think about scoring, but this is a course made for match-play, an exciting format on these contoured greens which are generally well-defended by large, deep bunkers. A minor compensation in the event of wayward shot-making is the thought that water only comes into play on two holes and the vista over this wild region is magnificent.

La Cala Resort — 1990

Apartado de Correos 106
E - 29649 MIJAS COSTA (Málaga – Costa del Sol)

Office	Secretaría	(34) 952 - 669 033
Pro shop	Pro-shop	(34) 952 - 669 000
Fax	Fax	(34) 952 - 669 039
Web		www.lacala.com
Situation	Situación	Marbella, 20 km

Mijas (pop. 32 835), 10 km

Annual closure Cierre anual — no
Weekly closure Cierre semanal — no

Fees main season Precios tempor. alta	18 holes	
	Week days Semana	**We/Bank holidays** Fin de sem./fiestas
Individual Individual	€ 70	€ 70
Couple Pareja	€ 140	€ 140

Caddie Caddie no — **Electric Trolley** Carro eléctrico no
Buggy Coche yes — **Clubs** Palos yes
Credit cards Tarjetas de crédito
VISA - MasterCard - AMEX

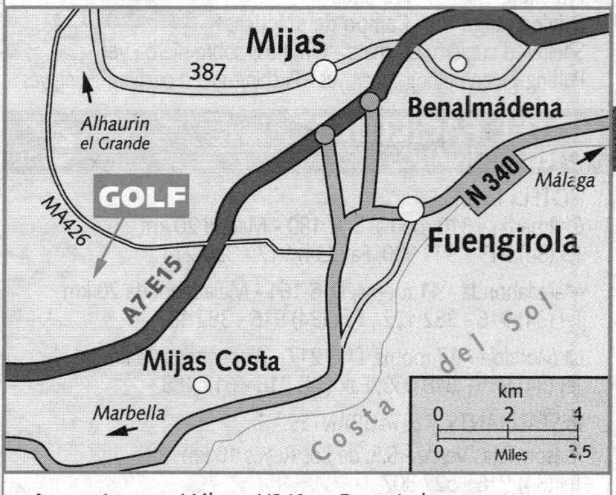

Access Acceso : Málaga, N340 → Fuengirola, Cala de Mijas → Golf
Map 8 on page 1101 Plano 8 Página 1101

GOLF COURSE — RECORRIDO — 17/20

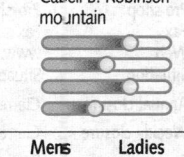

Site	Emplazamiento	
Maintenance	Mantenimiento	
Architect	Arquitecto	Cabell B. Robinson
Type	Tipo	mountain
Relief	Relieve	
Water in play	Agua	
Exp. to wind	Exp. al viento	
Trees in play	Arboles	

Scorecard Tarjeta	**Chp.** Campeonato	**Mens** Caballeros	**Ladies** Damas
Length Longitud	6187	5782	4759
Par	73	73	73
Slope system	138	132	119

Advised golfing ability Nivel de juego aconsejado — 0 12 24 36
Hcp required Handicap exigido — 28 Men, 36 Ladies

CLUB HOUSE & AMENITIES — CLUB HOUSE Y DEPENDENCIAS — 7/10

Pro shop Pro-shop
Driving range Campo de prácticas
Sheltered cubierto no - On grass sobre hierba yes - Putting-green putting-green yes - Pitching-green pitching-green yes

HOTEL FACILITIES — HOTELES CERCANOS — 8/10

HOTELS HOTELES

La Cala Resort - 83 rooms, D from € 200 - on site
Tel (34) 952 - 669 000, Fax (34) 952 - 669 039

Byblos - 144 rooms, D € 358 - Fuengirola 6 km
Tel (34) 952 - 473 050, Fax (34) 952 - 476 783

Mijas - 202 rooms, D € 125 - Mijas 20 km
Tel (34) 952 - 485 800, Fax (34) 952 - 485 825

RESTAURANTS RESTAURANTES

Fransanar - Carretera Mijas → Fuengirola 18 km
Tel (34) 952 - 590 727

El Tomate - Fuengirola 6 km - Tel (34) 952 - 473 599

La Terraza - on site - Tel (34) 952 - 669 000

La Cala *Sur*

16	7	8

Preferir uno u otro de los dos recorridos de La Cala es una cuestión de gusto. El "Sur" da la impresión de ser un poco más corto, o en todo caso que perdona más los errores. También aquí los desniveles son engañosos y no hay que fiarse de la longitud teórica de los hoyos. Los drives aterrizan a menudo en zonas en alto y una vegetación densa forma una buena parte de los rafs. Algunas pendientes pronunciadas alrededor de los greenes exigen un buen juego corto y mucha intuición. Al igual que en el "Norte", poco importa el resultado cuando se juega por primera vez y para mantener intacto el placer de jugar hay que aceptar las cosas como vienen y con un cierto sentido del humor. Si es mejor que los principiantes se abstengan y prefieran las excelentes instalaciones del campo de prácticas, los jugadores más aguerridos alquilarán un coche para saborear una jornada apasionante.

Preference for one or the other of La Cala courses is a matter of taste. The "Sur" gives the impression of being a little less long, or in any case of being more forgiving for mis-hit shots. Here, too, the terrain's physical contours are misleading and not too much faith should be put in the theoretical lengths of holes. The drive often lands on plateaus which players should not stray too far from, as a large part of rough here is dense vegetation. A number of steep slopes around the greens call for a sharp short game and loads of intuition. As with the "Norte", the score is of little consequence when playing the course for the first time. To really enjoy yourself, take things as they come and never lose your sense of humour. While beginners should refrain from playing the course and stick to the excellent practice facilities, the more proficient players can hop in a buggy and soak up an exciting day's golf. A third course (Europa) has just opened and we will be reporting on it in the next edition.

La Cala Resort — 1990

Apartado de Correos 106
E - 29649 MIJAS COSTA (Málaga – Costa del Sol)

Office	Secretaria	(34) 952 - 669 033
Pro shop	Pro-shop	(34) 952 - 669 000
Fax	Fax	(34) 952 - 669 039
Web	www.lacala.com	
Situation	Situación	Marbella, 20 km

Mijas (pop. 32 835), 10 km

Annual closure	Cierre anual	no
Weekly closure	Cierre semanal	no
Fees main season	Precios tempor. alta	18 holes
	Week days Semana	**We/Bank holidays** Fin de sem./fiestas
Individual Individual	€ 70	€ 70
Couple Pareja	€ 140	€ 140

Caddie Caddie no — **Electric Trolley** Carro eléctrico no
Buggy Coche yes — **Clubs** Palos yes
Credit cards Tarjetas de crédito
VISA - MasterCard - AMEX

Mijas
387
Alhaurin el Grande
Benalmádena
GOLF
MA426
N 340
Málaga
Fuengirola
A7-E15
Costa del Sol
Mijas Costa
Marbella
km 0 2 4
0 Miles 2,5

Access Acceso : Málaga, N340 → Fuengirola, Cala de Mijas → Golf
Map 8 on page 1101 Plano 8 Página 1101

GOLF COURSE 16/20
RECORRIDO

Site	Emplazamiento	
Maintenance	Mantenimiento	
Architect	Arquitecto	Cabell B. Robinson
Type	Tipo	mountain
Relief	Relieve	
Water in play	Agua	
Exp. to wind	Exp. al viento	
Trees in play	Arboles	

Scorecard Tarjeta	**Chp.** Campeonato	**Mens** Caballeros	**Ladies** Damas
Length Longitud	5925	5412	4467
Par	72	72	72
Slope system	135	128	117

Advised golfing ability Nivel de juego aconsejado — 0 12 24 36
Hcp required Handicap exigido — 28 Men, 36 Ladies

CLUB HOUSE & AMENITIES 7/10
CLUB HOUSE Y DEPENDENCIAS

Pro shop Pro-shop
Driving range Campo de prácticas
Sheltered cubierto no - On grass sobre hierba yes - Putting-green putting-green yes - Pitching-green pitching-green yes

HOTEL FACILITIES 8/10
HOTELES CERCANOS

HOTELS HOTELES
La Cala Resort - 83 rooms, D from € 200 - on site
Tel (34) 952 - 669 000, Fax (34) 952 - 669 039

Byblos - 144 rooms, D € 358 - Fuengirola 6 km
Tel (34) 952 - 473 050, Fax (34) 952 - 476 783

Mijas - 202 rooms, D € 125 - Mijas 20 km
Tel (34) 952 - 485 800, Fax (34) 952 - 485 825

RESTAURANTS RESTAURANTES
Fransanar - Carretera Mijas → Fuengirola 18 km
Tel (34) 952 - 590 727
El Tomate - Fuengirola 6 km - Tel (34) 952 - 473 599
La Terraza - on site - Tel (34) 952 - 669 000

La Dehesa

14 | 7 | 6

El recorrido de La Dehesa forma parte de un gran complejo concebido para el ocio familiar, siendo igual de agradable para el golfista como para el no golfista que tantas veces se siente relegado a mero acompañante durante unas vacaciones de golf. Las instalaciones de entrenamiento les permitirán incluso iniciarse en la práctica del golf. A la hora de diseñar el campo, Manuel Piñero pensó en todos los jugadores: es un campo competitivo, pero existen siempre soluciones para salirse de los peligros que encierra. Estos son numerosos durante los 18 hoyos, sobre todo en la primera vuelta, pero están los suficientemente a la vista para poder decidir rápidamente atacar o ser prudente. Los greenes son suficientemente amplios, bien defendidos, pero agradables de atacar y de jugar. Final espectacular, con un par 4 largo y retador y un par 3 desde un tee alto a un green rodeado de agua. Los espacios muy abiertos, el respeto del entorno existente y las magníficas vistas de la sierra madrileña dan al lugar una gran belleza.

This course is part of a large resort designed for family recreation, an equally pleasant spot for golfers and non-golfers alike. On a golfing day, the latter are often left having to accompany their playing partners, but not so here. What's more, the practice facilities might even entice them into having a swing themselves. In designing this course, Manuel Piñero spared a thought for everyone: it is a competitive layout, but there are always solutions for getting around the main difficulties. There is surely a lot of danger, well spread over the 18 holes but especially present on the outward 9, but hazards are visible enough for anyone to decide quickly whether to "go for it" or "lay up". The greens are huge, well-protected and pleasant to approach and play. The closing holes are spectacular with a long par-4 and challenging par-3 with island green. Wide open space, the respect for existing natural beauty and some magnificent views over the Madrid sierra make this a wonderful spot for golf.

Golf La Dehesa — 1992

Avda. Universidad 2
E - 28691 VILLANUEVA DE LA CAÑADA (Madrid)

Office	Secretaría	(34) 918 - 157 022
Pro shop	Pro-shop	(34) 902 - 157 022
Fax	Fax	(34) 918 - 155 468
E-mail	ketty73@terra.es	
Situation	Situación	Madrid, 28 km

Brunete (pop. 2 505), 5 km

Annual closure	Cierre anual	no
Weekly closure	Cierre semanal	no
Fees main season	Precios tempor. alta	18 holes

	Week days / Semana	We/Bank holidays / Fin de sem./fiestas
Individual Individual	€ 75	€ 160
Couple Pareja	€ 150	€ 320

Caddie Caddie no — **Electric Trolley** Carro eléctrico yes
Buggy Coche yes — **Clubs** Palos no
Credit cards Tarjetas de crédito no

Access Acceso : • N-VI (at La Coruña) and M-503, → Villlanueva de la Cañada, → Universidad
• N-V (at Extremadura) and M-501, → Brunete, → Villanueva de la Cañada, → Universidad
Map 4 on page 1092 Plano 4 Página 1092

GOLF COURSE — RECORRIDO — 14/20

Site	Emplazamiento	
Maintenance	Mantenimiento	
Architect	Arquitecto	Manuel Piñero
Type	Tipo	country
Relief	Relieve	
Water in play	Agua	
Exp. to wind	Exp. al viento	
Trees in play	Arboles	

Scorecard Tarjeta	Chp. Campeonato	Mens Caballeros	Ladies Damas
Length Longitud	6444	6037	5146
Par	72	72	72
Slope system	120	116	120

Advised golfing ability Nivel de juego aconsejado: 0 12 24 36
Hcp required Handicap exigido: 28 Men, 36 Ladies

CLUB HOUSE & AMENITIES — CLUB HOUSE Y DEPENDENCIAS — 7/10

Pro shop Pro-shop
Driving range Campo de prácticas
Sheltered cubierto 20 mats - On grass sobre hierba yes - Putting-green putting-green yes - Pitching-green pitching-green yes

HOTEL FACILITIES — HOTELES CERCANOS — 6/10

HOTELS HOTELES
Husa Princesa - 275 rooms, D € 241 - Madrid 30 km
Tel (34) 915 - 422 100 , Fax (34) 915 - 427 328

Majadahonda - Majadahonda 15 km
41 rooms, D € 164
Tel (34) 916 - 382 122 , Fax (34) 916 - 382 157

Victoria Palace - 90 rooms, D € 174 - El Escorial 1 km
Tel (34) 918 - 901 511, Fax (34) 918 - 901 248

RESTAURANTS RESTAURANTES
Zalacain - Madrid 28 km - Tel (34) 915 - 614 840
El Vivero - Brunete 5 km - Tel (34) 918 - 159 222
La Partida - Villanueva de la Cañada 1 km
Tel (34) 918 - 156 890

La Finca

15	7	7

Enclavado a cinco kilómetros del mar al sur de Alicante, en una zona de clima tan benigno que atrae a muchos residentes centroeuropeos, José Gancedo ha hecho un recorrido espectacular en un valle abierto, sin grandes desniveles, sembrado de olivos y limoneros. En su obra más reciente, el que fuera gran campeón amateur ha derrochado la originalidad que en él suele ser característica, por ejemplo el hoyo 6 tiene un green cuadrado y un bunker en L que lo defiende; y el green del 14 tiene forma de embudo. Los greenes son rápidos y complicados, muchos de ellos con diferentes plataformas que condicionan los tiros a green y, naturalmente, la técnica del putt. Es un campo para pegar largo y con espacios precisos para encarar el reto de las entradas en green, campo para disfrute de los más expertos que apreciarán las sutilezas del arquitecto para jugar una vuelta de golf interesante con toques de humor y de diversión. Un campo que no se olvida y que probablemente merecerá una nota más alta cuando haya alcanzado la mayoría de edad.

Lying 5 kilometres from the sea in a region where a very pleasant climate attracts tourists from northern Europe in their droves, José Gancedo has laid out a spectacular course in a very open and more or less flat valley lined with lemon trees and olive groves. With this very recent course, he has broken with tradition in a number of respects, for example the square green on the 6th with an L-shaped bunker, or again on the 14th with a funnel-shaped green. The putting surfaces are generally slick, complex and often multi-tiered, a factor which influences approach shots and, of course, the putting stroke. This is a course for long-hitters with very precise drive landing areas to be hit if you want an easier second shot. The better players should be able to cope with the difficulties deployed by the architect and the course is dotted with touches of humour and points of interest. A layout you will not forget in a hurry and one that should probably deserve a higher score as it matures.

La Finca Algorfa Golf — 2002

Ctra. Algorfa-Los Montesinos, km.3
E - 03169 ALGORFA (Alicante)

Office Secretaria (34) 966 – 729 010
Pro shop Pro-shop (34) 966 – 729 010
Fax Fax (34) 966 – 729 011
Web www.golflafinca.com
Situation Situación Alicante, 45 Km
Torrevieja (pop. 26.000), 12 Km

Annual closure Cierre anual — no
Weekly closure Cierre semanal — no
Fees main season Precios tempor. alta — 18 holes

	Week days / Semana	We/Bank holidays / Fin de sem./fiestas
Individual Individual	€ 75	€ 75
Couple Pareja	€ 150	€ 150

Caddie Caddie no — **Electric Trolley** Carro eléctrico no
Buggy Coche yes — **Clubs** Palos yes
Credit cards Tarjetas de crédito
VISA - MasterCard - AMEX - 4D

Access Acceso : A7/E15 Aliante-Murcia, Exit (salida) 77, then A-37 (→ Cartagena) exit 743 → Algorfa, take left on first traffic light in town on CV 935, Golf 3 Km
Map 7 on page 1099 Plano 7 Página 1099

GOLF COURSE — RECORRIDO — 15/20

Site Emplazamiento
Maintenance Mantenimiento
Architect Arquitecto — José Gancedo
Type Tipo — parkland
Relief Relieve
Water in play Agua
Exp. to wind Exp. al viento
Trees in play Arboles

Scorecard / Tarjeta	Chp. / Campeonato	Mens / Caballeros	Ladies / Damas
Length Longitud	6394	6032	5411
Par	72	72	72
Slope system	136	131	132

Advised golfing ability Nivel de juego aconsejado — 0 12 24 36
Hcp required Handicap exigido — 28 Men, 32 Ladies

CLUB HOUSE & AMENITIES — CLUB HOUSE Y DEPENDENCIAS — 7/10

Pro shop Pro-shop
Driving range Campo de prácticas
Sheltered cubierto no - On grass sobre hierba yes - Putting-green putting-green yes - Pitching-green pitching-green yes

HOTEL FACILITIES — HOTELES CERCANOS — 7/10

HOTELS HOTELES
Hotel La Laguna - Rojales 3 km
97 rooms, D € 171
Tel (34) 965 - 725 577, Fax (34) 965 - 725 855

Huerto del Cura - Elx/Elche 22 km
82 rooms, D € 115
Tel (34) 966 – 610 011, Fax (34) 965 – 421 910

SH Palacio de Tudemir - Orihuela 15 km
50 rooms, D € 132
Tel (34) 966 - 738 010, Fax (34) 966 - 738 070

RESTAURANTS RESTAURANTES
La Finca - on site - Tel (34) 965 - 967 050
El Cruce - Almoradí 3 km - Tel (34) 965 - 700 356

La Herrería

15	6	7

Es muy raro poder jugar a proximidad de monumentos históricos como el Monasterio de San Lorenzo del Escorial que domina el recorrido. La Herrería es tan espectacular como las vistas que proporciona. En el diseño del general Antonio Lucena Gómez los peligros para la tarjeta del jugador vienen del parque de robles, fresnos, encinas y enebros; de unos bunkers que defienden tanto la caída de los drives como los greenes, éstos generalmente llanos, a veces en alto, bien moldeados. Estas dificultades no son nunca infranqueables sea cual sea el nivel del jugador ya que son muy visibles para permitir adoptar una estrategia que nos permita eludir las malas sorpresas. Si el 2 es un par 4 muy complicado, las vistas panorámicas de los hoyos 12, 13 y 14 permiten reposar el espíritu antes de abordar el hoyo 18, uno de los mejores pares 4 de España... La reciente remodelación de los nueve primeros es el signo del buen mantenimiento que se merece un buen campo a los pies de un gran monumento.

It is rare indeed to be able to swing a club so close to historical landmarks such as the magnificent Monasterio de San Lorenzo de El Escorial, which overlooks this course. La Herreria is also one of the truly public courses in the Madrid area. The site is as spectacular as the vistas from the course, designed by Antonio Lucena Gomez. The main hazards are the trees (oak, ash and juniper) and bunkers, guarding both the drive landing zone and the greens, the latter being flat, rather elevated and well shaped. These difficulties are never impossible to negotiate, whatever your level of proficiency, and are visible enough to adopt a strategy to avoid unpleasant surprises. While the second hole is a rather complicated par 4, the scenic views from the 12th, 13th and 14th holes are enough to calm frayed nerves before attacking the 18th, one of the best par 4s in Spain. The recent reshaping of the front nine has underlined a concern to protect the excellence of this course

La Herrería Club de Golf — 1968

Carretera de Robledo de Chavela s/n
E - 28200 SAN LORENZO DE EL ESCORIAL (Madrid)

Office Secretaria (34) 918 - 907 040
Pro shop Pro-shop (34) 918 - 907 040
Fax Fax (34) 918 - 902 613
Web www.golflaherreria.com
Situation Situación Madrid, 57 km
Monasterio San Lorenzo de El Escorial, 800 m

Annual closure Cierre anual no
Weekly closure Cierre semanal no

Fees main season Precios tempor. alta		18 holes
	Week days Semana	**We/Bank holidays** Fin de sem./fiestas
Individual Individual	€ 60	€ 104*
Couple Pareja	€ 120	€ 208*

Week-ends: Friday after 12:00, Saturday, Sunday

Caddie Caddie no — **Electric Trolley** Carro eléctrico yes
Buggy Coche yes — **Clubs** Palos yes
Credit cards Tarjetas de crédito no

Access Acceso : Madrid A6 → Segovia.
Exit (Salida) El Escorial, M600 → San Lorenzo de El Escorial.
→ Robledo de Chavela, Golf on the left
Map 4 on page 1092 Plano 4 Página 1092

GOLF COURSE — RECORRIDO — 15/20

Site Emplazamiento
Maintenance Mantenimiento
Architect Arquitecto — Antonio Lucena Gómez
Type Tipo — forest, hilly
Relief Relieve
Water in play Agua
Exp. to wind Exp. al viento
Trees in play Arboles

Scorecard Tarjeta	Chp. Campeonato	Mens Caballeros	Ladies Damas
Length Longitud	6091	5979	5118
Par	72	72	72
Slope system	123	121	119

Advised golfing ability Nivel de juego aconsejado — 0 12 24 36

Hcp required Handicap exigido — 28 Men, 36 Ladies

CLUB HOUSE & AMENITIES — CLUB HOUSE Y DEPENDENCIAS — 6/10

Pro shop Pro-shop
Driving range Campo de prácticas
Sheltered cubierto no - On grass sobre hierba yes - Putting-green putting-green yes - Pitching-green pitching-green no

HOTEL FACILITIES — HOTELES CERCANOS — 7/10

HOTELS HOTELES
Victoria Palace - San Lorenzo 2 km
90 rooms, D € 174
Tel (34) 918 - 901 511, Fax (34) 918 - 901 248

Botánico - San Lorenzo de El Escorial 500 m
20 rooms, D € 120
Tel (34) 918 - 907 879, Fax (34) 918 - 908 158

Miranda Suizo - 52 rooms, D € 90 - San Lorenzo 2 km
Tel (34) 918 - 904 711, Fax (34) 918 - 904 352

RESTAURANTS RESTAURANTES
Charolés - San Lorenzo 2 km - Tel (34) 918 - 905 975
Parilla Principe - San Lorenzo 2 km - Tel (34) 918 - 901 611

La Manga *Norte*

15 | 5 | 7

El recorrido Norte de La Manga, vecino inmediato del "Sur" en un espectacular parque de palmeras, es algo más corto que su "hermano" famoso. Mucha gente lo prefiere porque es más técnico y pide al jugador salidas más precisas y tiros a green con intención. Los greenes no son muy grandes, no son muy largos. Pero las calles son estrechas, limitadas por barrancos y otros roughs de mala recuperación, o sea que puede ser muy divertido (siempre que el resultado acompañe, naturalmente) para una amplia gama de jugadores que logren jugar una vuelta ordenada. No sería adecuado marcar preferencias entre uno u otro, que presentan muy buen mantenimimento, sino que los dos, con el recorrido "Oeste" y con los otros 18 hoyos cortos par 57, componen un variado abanico de posibilidades para jugar al golf según los ánimos y estado de forma de cada uno. Tanto en el propio hotel del campo como en los alrededores hay múltiples ofertas de otras actividades deportivas. Estamos en una reconocida zona de vacaciones de playa y sol.

This much shorter course and immediate neighbour to the "South" layout stretches over a large park planted with palm trees. Many players prefer this North course which is more technical and calls for greater accuracy both for driving and iron shots. The greens are neither huge nor too deep and fairways are lined with ravines and thick rough. Having said that, the course can be fun overall when on top of your game and for a wide range of golfers who approach playing it in a sensible way. It would be unfair to state any preference for one or the other as they are equally well maintained, as is the "Oeste" course and the 18-hole compact course (par 57), which offers a wide range of possibilities according to ambition and proficiency. In addition to the four courses you will find any number of sporting activities in this holiday region of beaches and sunshine where it is perhaps a little too hot to play in the middle of summer.

Hyatt La Manga Club de Golf — 1970

Los Belones
E - 30385 CARTAGENA - MURCIA

Office	Secretaria	(34) 968 - 175 000
Pro shop	Pro-shop	(34) 968 - 175 000
Fax	Fax	(34) 968 - 175 058
Web	www.lamangaclub.es	
Situation	Situación	Murcia, 75 km

Cartagena (pop. 173 061), 30 km

Annual closure	Cierre anual	no
Weekly closure	Cierre semanal	no

Fees main season Precios tempor. alta	18 holes	
	Week days Semana	**We/Bank holidays** Fin de sem./fiestas
Individual Individual	€ 176	€ 176
Couple Pareja	€ 352	€ 352

Hotel guests: € 76 / Under 16: – 40%

Caddie Caddie on request **Electric Trolley** Carro eléctrico yes

Buggy Coche yes **Clubs** Palos yes

Credit cards Tarjetas de crédito
VISA - MasterCard - AMEX - DC

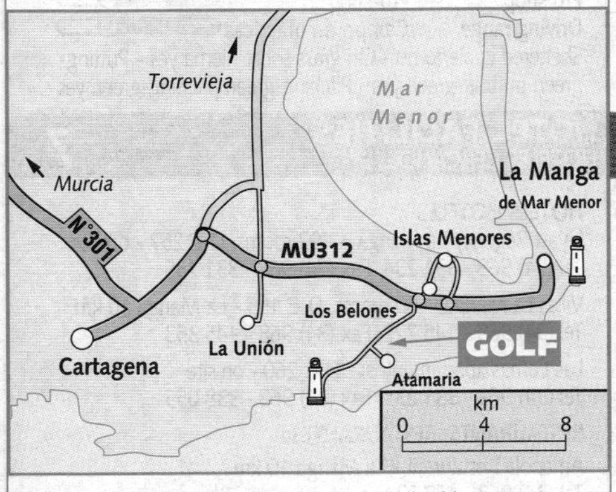

Access Acceso : Murcia → Cartagena, → La Manga
Map 7 on page 1099 Plano 7 Página 1099

GOLF COURSE — RECORRIDO — 15/20

Site	Emplazamiento	
Maintenance	Mantenimiento	
Architect	Arquitecto	Robert Dean Puttman Arnold Palmer
Type	Tipo	residential, hilly
Relief	Relieve	
Water in play	Agua	
Exp. to wind	Exp. al viento	
Trees in play	Arboles	

Scorecard Tarjeta	**Chp.** Campeonato	**Mens** Caballeros	**Ladies** Damas
Length Longitud	5753	5429	4964
Par	71	71	71
Slope system	126	121	127

Advised golfing ability Nivel de juego aconsejado — 0 12 24 36

Hcp required Handicap exigido no

CLUB HOUSE & AMENITIES — CLUB HOUSE Y DEPENDENCIAS — 5/10

Pro shop Pro-shop
Driving range Campo de prácticas
Sheltered cubierto no - On grass sobre hierba yes - Putting-green putting-green yes - Pitching-green pitching-green yes

HOTEL FACILITIES — HOTELES CERCANOS — 7/10

HOTELS HOTELES

Hyatt Regency La Manga - 192 rooms, D € 257 - on site
Tel (34) 968 - 331 234, Fax (34) 968 - 331 235

Villas La Manga - 60 rooms, D € 155 - La Manga 10 km
Tel (34) 968 - 145 222, Fax (34) 968 - 145 353

Las Lomas apartamentos - D € 260 - on site
Tel (34) 968 - 331 234, Fax (34) 968 - 338 055

RESTAURANTS RESTAURANTES

Amapola Restaurant - La Manga 10 km
Tel (34) 968 - 137 234

Borsalino - La Manga 10 km - Tel (34) 968 - 563 130

San Remo - La Manga 10 km - Tel (34) 968 - 140 813

La Manga *Sur*

15	5	7

El complejo de La Manga es desde hace mucho tiempo uno de los más famosos de España con construcciones inmobiliarias que no todos apreciarán. El recorrido "Sur", que siempre ha sido el más largo y famoso porque ha acogido torneos profesionales y de todas las categorías amateur, se convierte ahora en un par 73, un monstruo de seis mil quinientos metros desde las salidas más largas, dentro de un plan de renovación de los tres campos del complejo. Esta nueva configuración del campo para que sea altamente competitivo tanto en las distancias como en la estrategia de juego ha realizado el propio departamento técnico de La Manga Club, teniendo en cuenta, sin embargo, la obra original de Puttman y las reformas del taller de Arnold Palmer de 1992. Obstáculos de agua, bunkers y configuración de los greenes son los principales elementos que se han utilizado para actualizar el reto de este campo.

La Manga has long been one of Spain's most famous resorts and a site for real estate property development that is not to everyone's taste. The "South" course, which has always been the longest and best known for top level tournaments, has been transformed into a par 73 stretching nigh on 7,500 yards from the back tees. This is all part of an overall renewal scheme for the resort as a whole. To be fully competitive in terms of distance and strategy, the new layout was managed by the technical department of La Manga Club, which gave full consideration to the original layout and to the alterations made by the Arnold Palmer team in 1992. Further to the renewal of the first nine holes on the "South" course, modernization work for the rest of the layout has involved water hazards, bunkering and the configuration of greens.

Hyatt La Manga Club de Golf — 1970

Los Belones
E - 30385 CARTAGENA - MURCIA

Office	Secretaría	(34) 968 - 175 000
Pro shop	Pro-shop	(34) 968 - 175 000
Fax	Fax	(34) 968 - 175 058
Web	www.lamangaclub.es	
Situation	Situación	Murcia, 75 km

Cartagena (pop. 173 061), 30 km

Annual closure	Cierre anual	no
Weekly closure	Cierre semanal	no
Fees main season	Precios tempor. alta	18 holes

	Week days Semana	We/Bank holidays Fin de sem./fiestas
Individual Individual	€ 176	€ 176
Couple Pareja	€ 352	€ 352

Hotel guests: € 76 / Under 16: – 40%

Caddie Caddie on request **Electric Trolley** Carro eléctrico yes

Buggy Coche yes **Clubs** Palos yes

Credit cards Tarjetas de crédito
VISA - MasterCard - AMEX - DC

Torrevieja
Mar Menor
Murcia
La Manga de Mar Menor
N°301
MU312
Islas Menores
Los Belones
La Unión
GOLF
Cartagena
Atamaria
km 0 4 8

Access Acceso : Murcia → Cartagena, → La Manga
Map 7 on page 1099 Plano 7 Página 1099

GOLF COURSE — RECORRIDO 15/20

Site	Emplazamiento	
Maintenance	Mantenimiento	
Architect	Arquitecto	Thomas/Puttman Arnold Palmer
Type	Tipo	residential, country
Relief	Relieve	
Water in play	Agua	
Exp. to wind	Exp. al viento	
Trees in play	Arboles	

Scorecard Tarjeta	Chp. Campeonato	Mens Caballeros	Ladies Damas
Length Longitud	6499	6127	5139
Par	73	73	73
Slope system	138	134	129

Advised golfing ability Nivel de juego aconsejado — 0 12 24 36

Hcp required Handicap exigido — 28 Men, 36 Ladies

CLUB HOUSE & AMENITIES — CLUB HOUSE Y DEPENDENCIAS 5/10

Pro shop Pro-shop
Driving range Campo de prácticas
Sheltered cubierto no - On grass sobre hierba yes - Putting-green putting-green yes - Pitching-green pitching-green yes

HOTEL FACILITIES — HOTELES CERCANOS 7/10

HOTELS HOTELES

Hyatt Regency La Manga - 192 rooms, D € 257 - on site
Tel (34) 968 - 331 234, Fax (34) 968 - 331 235

Villas La Manga - 60 rooms, D € 155 - La Manga 10 km
Tel (34) 968 - 145 222, Fax (34) 968 - 145 353

Las Lomas apartamentos - D € 260 - on site
Tel (34) 968 - 331 234, Fax (34) 968 - 338 055

RESTAURANTS RESTAURANTES

Amapola Restaurant - La Manga 10 km
Tel (34) 968 - 137 234

Borsalino - La Manga 10 km - Tel (34) 968 - 563 130

San Remo - La Manga 10 km - Tel (34) 968 - 140 813

La Moraleja *La Moraleja 1*

15	8	8

En la época de la construcción de este campo (como de Muirfield Village en los Estados Unidos), Jack Nicklaus trabajada con Desmond Muirhead, uno de los arquitectos más originales de la época y uno de los que menos creen en la soberanía de la distancia. En efecto, La Moraleja 1 es un campo relativamente corto pero exige la máxima precisión si se quiere conseguir un buen resultado, sobre todo porque los greenes son bastante pequeños, muy ondulados, rápidos y muy bien defendidos. Es fundamental, por tanto, colocar las salidas con un buen ángulo de entrada en green, lo cual resulta ser el quid del campo: ser preciso por un lado, elegir bien los palos y llevar la bola a posiciones seguras y útiles para el golpe siguiente. Los pegadores impenitentes tendrán la opción de tirar a green en algun par 4, meterse de dos en los pares 5... eso sí, con un riesgo alto porque los peligros son constantes. Un campo muy divertido sin ser por ello una obra maestra inolvidable.

When building this course (the same goes for Muirfield Village in the United States), Jack Nicklaus was working with the late Desmond Muirhead, one of the most original course designers of our day, and one who doesn't go for length at any price. While La Moraleja 1 is on the short side, it demands extreme accuracy for a good card, especially since the greens are only average in size, steeply contoured, quick and very well guarded. To be in the right position to make your approach, the drive has to be exactly in the right place, a feat that is not always so easy and one that demands clear-headed club selection. On the four very short par 4s, for example, you are best advised to use a long iron. Incorrigible big-hitters can attempt to get as close as possible to the green and also reach the par 5s in two, but as trouble is never far away they will find it a risky business. A very amusing course rather than an unforgettable masterpiece.

Golf La Moraleja — 1976

Paseo Marquesa Viuda de Aldana, 50
E - 28109 LA MORALEJA-MADRID

Office	Secretaria	(34) 916 - 500 700
Pro shop	Pro-shop	(34) 916 - 507 018
Fax	Fax	(34) 916 - 504 331
Web	www.golflamoraleja.com	
Situation	Situación	Madrid, 12 km
Annual closure	Cierre anual	no
Weekly closure	Cierre semanal	no

Fees main season Precios tempor. alta	18 holes	
	Week days Semana	We/Bank holidays Fin de sem./fiestas
Individual Individual	€ 80	€ 160
Couple Pareja	€ 160	€ 320

Members' guests only (solamente acompañados de socios)

Caddie Caddie no — **Electric Trolley** Carro eléctrico yes
Buggy Coche yes — **Clubs** Palos yes
Credit cards Tarjetas de crédito no

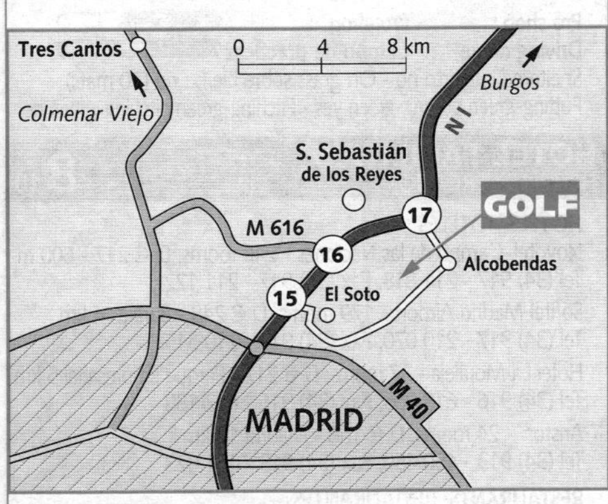

Access Acceso : Madrid → Burgos
Map 4 on page 1092 Plano 4 Página 1092

GOLF COURSE — RECORRIDO — 15/20

Site	Emplazamiento	
Maintenance	Mantenimiento	
Architect	Arquitecto	Jack Nicklaus Desmond Muirhead
Type	Tipo	country
Relief	Relieve	
Water in play	Agua	
Exp. to wind	Exp. al viento	
Trees in play	Arboles	

Scorecard Tarjeta	**Chp.** Campeonato	**Mens** Caballeros	**Ladies** Damas
Length Longitud	5958	5775	4923
Par	72	72	72
Slope system	127	124	122

Advised golfing ability Nivel de juego aconsejado — 0 12 24 36
Hcp required Handicap exigido

CLUB HOUSE & AMENITIES — CLUB HOUSE Y DEPENDENCIAS — 8/10

Pro shop Pro-shop
Driving range Campo de prácticas
Sheltered cubierto no - On grass sobre hierba no (30 mats) - Putting-green putting-green yes - Pitching-green pitching-green no

HOTEL FACILITIES — HOTELES CERCANOS — 8/10

HOTELS HOTELES
Novotel-Campo de las Naciones - 246 rooms, D € 217 - 600 m
Tel (34) 917 - 211 818, Fax (34) 917 - 211 122
Sofitel Madrid Airport - 179 rooms, D € 248 - Barajas 4 km
Tel (34) 917 - 210 070, Fax (34) 917 - 210 515
Hotel La Moraleja - 37 rooms, D € 217 - Parque Empresarial 5 km
Tel (34) 916 - 618 055, Fax (34) 916 - 612 188
Aristos - 24 rooms, D € 166 - Madrid 12 km
Tel (34) 913 - 450 450, Fax (34) 913 - 451 023

RESTAURANTS RESTAURANTES
La Broche - Madrid 10 km - Tel (34) 913 - 993 437
Principe de Viana - Madrid 10 km - Tel (34) 914 - 571 549
La Bola - Madrid 10 km - Tel (34) 915 476 930

La Moraleja *La Moraleja 2*

16	8	8

Este segundo recorrido del gran club de La Moraleja ha sido diseñado por los arquitectos asociados a Jack Nicklaus. La Moraleja 2 no lleva la firma del gran Nicklaus, pero su influencia sobre sus colaboradores se deja sentir de manera muy evidente. Los greenes son de gran tamaño y la rapidez y ondulaciones de la superficie, exigen por un lado muy buen toque de pat y mucha vista para entender las caídas y, por otro lado, entrar en green por la zona de la bandera para no meterse en territorio de tres pats. Están bien protegidos por obstáculos de agua, por algunos árboles, por unos bunkers muy dibujados, sobre todo los que defienden el green doble del 9 y el 18. Es un campo largo y se juega varias veces en subida, presenta un mantenimiento excelente y se presta por tanto a grandes y espectaculares golpes pero sobre todo es un campo inteligente que pide estrategia y una buena dosificación del esfuerzo y de los recursos propios. Es un campo que hay que jugar, y es más cómodo hacerlo entre semana.

This second golf course on the Club La Moraleja was designed by architects associated with Jack Nicklaus, and although not carrying his signature the great man evidently had some influence on his partners. The greens are huge and three-putts not an uncommon occurrence, especially if you are nowhere near the pin, as the numerous slopes and speed of the putting surfaces call for careful reading and a delicate touch. They are often well-guarded by water, sometimes by trees and by well-designed bunkers, especially on the 9th and 18th holes, which share a double green. This is a long course which sometimes climbs steeply and green-keeping works in favour of long spectacular shots. Stay on your toes the whole time, because he difficulties here crop up when you least expect them. As a result, game strategy, depending on the shape of your game, plays a significant role. Well worth knowing, but avoid week-ends.

Golf La Moraleja — 1992

Paseo Marquesa Viuda de Aldana, 50
E - 28109 LA MORALEJA-MADRID

Office Secretaria (34) 916 - 500 700
Pro shop Pro-shop (34) 916 - 507 018
Fax Fax (34) 916 - 504 331
Web www.golflamoraleja.com
Situation Situación Madrid, 12 km

Annual closure Cierre anual no
Weekly closure Cierre semanal no

Fees main season Precios tempor. alta	18 holes	
	Week days Semana	**We/Bank holidays** Fin de sem./fiestas
Individual Individual	€ 80	€ 160
Couple Pareja	€ 160	€ 320

Members' guests only (solamente acompañados de socios)

Caddie Caddie no — **Electric Trolley** Carro eléctrico yes
Buggy Coche yes — **Clubs** Palos yes
Credit cards Tarjetas de crédito no

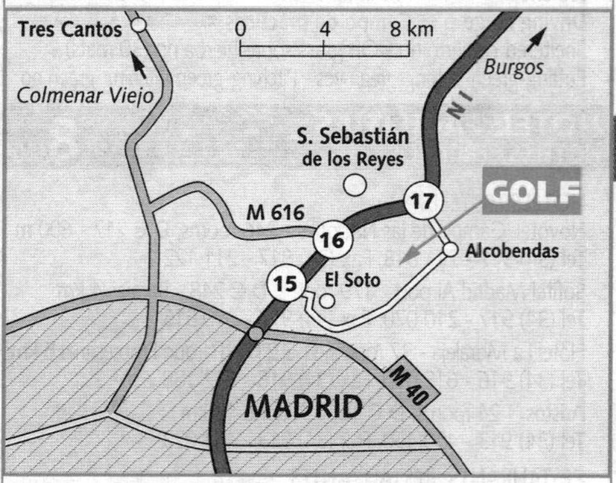

Access Acceso : Madrid → Burgos
Map 4 on page 1092 Plano 4 Página 1092

GOLF COURSE — RECORRIDO — 16/20

Site Emplazamiento
Maintenance Mantenimiento
Architect Arquitecto — Golden Bear Design Associates
Type Tipo — country
Relief Relieve
Water in play Agua
Exp. to wind Exp. al viento
Trees in play Arboles

Scorecard Tarjeta	**Chp.** Campeonato	**Mens** Caballeros	**Ladies** Damas
Length Longitud	6451	5888	5014
Par	72	72	72
Slope system	121	119	109

Advised golfing ability Nivel de juego aconsejado — 0 12 24 36
Hcp required Handicap exigido — no

CLUB HOUSE & AMENITIES — CLUB HOUSE Y DEPENDENCIAS — 8/10

Pro shop Pro-shop
Driving range Campo de prácticas
Sheltered cubierto no - On grass sobre hierba no (30 mats) - Putting-green putting-green yes - Pitching-green pitching-green no

HOTEL FACILITIES — HOTELES CERCANOS — 8/10

HOTELS HOTELES

Novotel-Campo de las Naciones - 246 rooms, D € 217 - 600 m
Tel (34) 917 - 211 818, Fax (34) 917 - 211 122

Sofitel Madrid Airport - 179 rooms, D € 248 - Barajas 4 km
Tel (34) 917 - 210 070, Fax (34) 917 - 210 515

Hotel La Moraleja - 37 rooms, D € 217 - Parque Empresarial 5 km
Tel (34) 916 - 618 055, Fax (34) 916 - 612 188

Aristos - 24 rooms, D € 166 - Madrid 12 km
Tel (34) 913 - 450 450, Fax (34) 913 - 451 023

RESTAURANTS RESTAURANTES

La Broche - Madrid 10 km - Tel (34) 913 - 993 437
Principe de Viana - Madrid 10 km - Tel (34) 914 - 571 549
La Bola - Madrid 10 km - Tel (34) 915 476 930

La Quinta

14	8	8

El gran campeón Manuel Piñero y Antonio García Garrido han diseñado uno de los recorridos más técnicos de la región. Sus 27 hoyos tienen tres combinaciones de 9: San Pedro (A), Ronda (B) y Guadaiza (C) –par 36 de 3.055 metros-, siendo las dos primeras las que componen los 18 hoyos abiertos en 1989. Como las distancias no son excesivas, los jugadores precisos se encontrarán más a gusto que los pegadores a pesar de que las zonas de caída del drive sean anchas y los tees de salida a menudo en alto. Hay dificultades de todas clases: árboles, bunkers de green, canales y lagos no siempre a la vista. El relieve es bastante accidentado, sin que sea exagerado, lo que complica la apreciación de los aproches: conviene tirar a bandera para evitar los pats largos ya que las caídas de green son difíciles de apreciar. El entorno inmobiliario (cosa inevitable en la región) está parcialmente escondido por la vegetación de este gran jardín y resort de gran lujo.

Manuel Piñero and Antonio Garrido designed this, one of the region's most technical golf courses comprising 27 holes composed of three 9-holers: San Pedro (A), Ronda (B) and Guadaiza (a par 36 of 3,360 yards). The first two form the original 18-hole course opened in 1989. Not being over-long, accurate players will probably feel more at home than the big hitters, even though the landing areas for drives are pretty wide and the tees often elevated. There are all kinds of hazards here, from trees to green-side bunkers to rivers and lakes, and they are not always very visible. This is pretty hilly terrain, a factor which complicates the approach shot. It is also important to go for the pin to avoid over-long putts, as the greens are tricky to read. The property development surroundings are not to everyone's liking but are unavoidable in this part of the world and are partly concealed by the trees and vegetation worthy of large gardens. A top luxury resort.

La Quinta Golf & Country Club — 1989

Urbanización La Quinta Golf
E - 29660 NUEVA ANDALUCÍA - MARBELLA
(Málaga – Costa del Sol)

Office Secretaria (34) 952 - 762 376
Pro shop Pro-shop (34) 952 - 762 376
Fax Fax (34) 952 - 762 399
Web www.laquintagolf.com
Situation Situación Marbella, 16 km
San Pedro de Alcantara, 3 km

Annual closure Cierre anual no
Weekly closure Cierre semanal no

Fees main season Precios tempor. alta	18 holes	
	Week days / Semana	We/Bank holidays / Fin de sem./fiestas
Individual Individual	€ 82	€ 82
Couple Pareja	€ 164	€ 164

Caddie Caddie on request **Electric Trolley** Carro eléctrico yes
Buggy Coche yes **Clubs** Palos yes
Credit cards Tarjetas de crédito
VISA - MasterCard - AMEX

Ronda
Benahavis
El Ángel
GOLF
Nueva Andalucía
A7 - E15
Marbella
N340
Puerto Banús
San Pedro de Alcantara
Estepona
Playas de Marbella
Atalaya
Guadalmina
km 0 2 4

Access Acceso : Marbella N340 → San Pedro de Alcantara, → Ronda, Golf 3 km
Map 8 on page 1101 Plano 8 Página 1101

GOLF COURSE — RECORRIDO 14/20

Site Emplazamiento
Maintenance Mantenimiento
Architect Arquitecto Manuel Piñero, Antonio Garrido
Type Tipo residential, hilly
Relief Relieve
Water in play Agua
Exp. to wind Exp. al viento
Trees in play Arboles

Scorecard Tarjeta	Chp. Campeonato	Mens Caballeros	Ladies Damas
Length Longitud	5915	5667	4991
Par	71	71	71
Slope system	128	125	126

Advised golfing ability Nivel de juego aconsejado 0 12 24 36
Hcp required Handicap exigido 28 Men, 36 Ladies

CLUB HOUSE & AMENITIES — CLUB HOUSE Y DEPENDENCIAS 8/10

Pro shop Pro-shop
Driving range Campo de prácticas
Sheltered cubierto 10 mats - On grass sobre hierba yes - Putting-green putting-green yes - Pitching-green pitching-green yes

HOTEL FACILITIES — HOTELES CERCANOS 8/10

HOTELS HOTELES
The Westin La Quinta Golf Resort - on site
172 rooms, D € 318
Tel (34) 952 - 762 000, Fax (34) 952 - 762 020

Puente Romano - Marbella, Cta de Cádiz 3 km
274 rooms, D € 487
Tel (34) 952 - 820 900, Fax (34) 952 - 775 766

Pyr Hotel - 319 rooms, D € 171 - Puerto Banús 2 km
Tel (34) 952 - 817 353, Fax (34) 952 - 817 907

RESTAURANTS RESTAURANTES
Albatros - Golf - Tel (34) 952 - 762 333
Cipriano - Puerto Banús 5 km - Tel (34) 952 - 811 077

La Reserva

16 | 8 | 8

Estéticamente este nuevo activo de Sotogrande es espectacular por los grandes espacios, el ajardinamiento de los fondos de los greenes, la distribución de los elementos –agua, arena blanca, pinos y el verde intenso de greenes y calles- y el panorama desde varios tees elevados, especialmente el del 15. Es un campo largo –desde los tees negros, para profesionales, mide 6.448 metros- no solamente por las distancias sino también por la configuración de defensa de los greenes. De buena factura y mantenimiento, las cuestas y la configuración de las calles harán las delicias de los jugadores experimentados por la variedad de golpes que tendrán que poner en juego. Los greenes son grandes y frecuentemente escalonados, de manera que hay que llegar por el lado bueno y calibrar bien el tipo de putting requerido en cada momento.

After Almenara, this new development from Sotogrande Golf is spectacular for the wide open spaces used, the visual variety of the colours around the course – blue water, white sand, pines and the deep greens of fairways and putting surfaces – enhanced by some scenic views from a number of tees, particularly from the 15th. A long course from the tips (more than 7,000 yards), the greens are very well defended and don't even think about rolling your ball up to the pin. The craftsman golfer will do well here because you need a fair share of nous on these undulating – albeit wide – fairways. Likewise, on the large and often multi-tiered greens take time to carefully study the slopes and speed to avoid any unpleasant surprises. Greenkeeping is very satisfactory and the whole layout is most pleasant for holiday golfing and playing with friends, but also for the better player. A very intelligent course in an area where there is no shortage of great places to play golf.

La Reserva Club de Golf — 2004

Avda. de la Reserva s/n.
E-11310 SOTOGRANDE (Cádiz)

Office Secretaria (34) 956 – 785 252
Pro shop Pro-shop (34) 956 – 785 252
Fax Fax (34) 956 – 785 272
Web www.sotogrande.com
Situation Situación Marbella, 60 km
Algeciras (pop 101.556), 30 Km
Annual closure Cierre anual no
Weekly closure Cierre semanal no
Fees main season Precios tempor. alta 18 holes

	Week days Semana	We./Bank holidays Fin de sem./fiestas
Individual Individual	€ 140	€ 140
Couple Pareja	€ 280	€ 280

Caddie Caddie no — **Electric Trolley** Carro eléctrico yes
Buggy Coche yes — **Clubs** Palos yes
Credit cards Tarjetas de crédito
VISA - MasterCard - AMEX

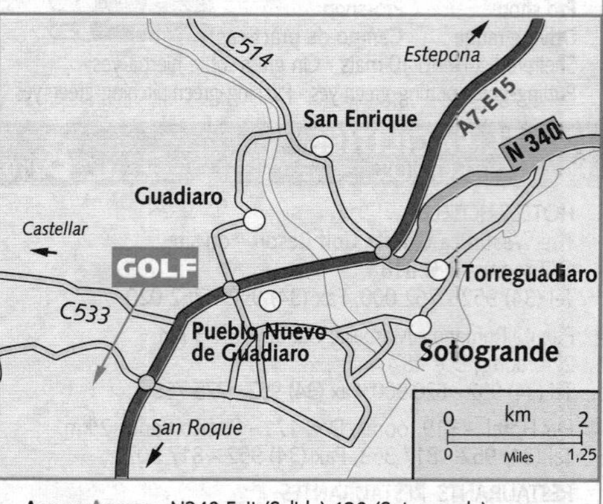

Access Acceso : N340 Exit (Salida) 130 (Sotogrande), → Castellar
Map 8 on page 1101 Plano 8 Página 1101

GOLF COURSE — RECORRIDO — 16/20

Site Emplazamiento
Maintenance Mantenimiento
Architect Arquitecto — Cabell B. Robinson
Type Tipo — open country
Relief Relieve
Water in play Agua
Exp. to wind Exp. al viento
Trees in play Arboles

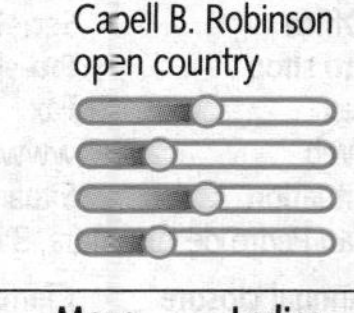

Scorecard Tarjeta	Chp. Campeonato	Mens Caballeros	Ladies Damas
Length Longitud	6448	6043	5104
Par	72	72	72
Slope system	133	133	126

Advised golfing ability Nivel de juego aconsejado — 0 12 24 36
Hcp required Handicap exigido — 28 Men, 36 Ladies

CLUB HOUSE & AMENITIES — CLUB HOUSE Y DEPENDENCIAS — 8/10

Pro shop Pro-shop
Driving range Campo de prácticas
Sheltered cubierto - On grass sobre hierba yes - Putting-green putting-green yes - Pitching-green pitching-green yes

HOTEL FACILITIES — HOTELES CERCANOS — 8/10

HOTELS HOTELES
NH Almenara - 160 rooms, D € 223 - Sotogrande
Tel (34) 956 - 582 000, Fax (34) 956 - 582 001

Guadacorte Park - 109 rooms, D € 130 - Los Barrios 20 km
Tel (34) 956 - 677 500 , Fax (34) 956 - 678 600

NH Sotogrande - 106 rooms, D € 270 - Sotogrande
Tel (34) 956 - 695 444, Fax (34) 956 - 695 445

RESTAURANTS RESTAURANTES
Barbesula - Pueblo Nuevo Guadiaro 4 km
Tel (34) 956 - 695 600
Bar Pepe - Torreguadiaro - Tel (34) 956 - 615 353

La Sella

15 | 6 | 5

Situado a la falda de una montaña no es un recorrido excesivamente cansado, pero en pleno verano es mejor alquilar un coche. De longitud moderada, si se dominan con maestría todos los palos se puede lograr un buen resultado. Con barrancos y quebradas, hay que colocar la bola de salida para evitar los accidentes del terreno. Pinos, naranjos, olivos y almendros le dan un cierto colorido y suponen muchos problemas para jugadores sin precisión. Los greenes son pequeños y hay varios aflanados. Con una arquitectura bastante personal, La Sella demuestra que sus creadores conocían muy bien toda la gama de jugadores, adaptando las dificultades a los diferentes tees de salida. Efectivamente, Juan de la Cuadra lo diseñó con la experta ayuda de José María Olazábal. Si se falla la entrada en green habrá que emplear todo el virtuosismo del campeón español para salvar el par.

Although laid out on the side of a mountain, the course can be walked, although a buggy is advisable in mid-summer to get a bit of air. La Sella is not too long, but if all your clubs are in good working order, a good score should not be beyond you. When the ravines and hilly landscape threaten, try and place your drive safely to avoid trouble. The pine, orange, olive and almond trees bring a touch of colour and relief, and sometimes a number of problems for wayward hitters who will be hard put to hit some rather small greens. A very personal design, La Sella shows how much the architects knew about players of all ability, as difficulties are geared to the different tees. Not surprisingly, the course was laid out by Juan de la Cuadra, expertly assisted by José-Maria Olazábal. If you miss the greens, you will need some of the Spanish champion's virtuosity to save par. La Sella is a good address in the region.

La Sella Golf **1991**
Ctra La Xara - Jesús Pobre
E - 03749 JESUS POBRE (Alicante)

Office	Secretaria	(34) 966 - 454 252
Pro shop	Pro-shop	(34) 966 - 454 110
Fax	Fax	(34) 966 - 454 201
E-mail	info@lasellagolf.com	
Situation	Situación	Jávea (pop. 16 603), 8 km

Denia (pop. 25 157), 8 km

Annual closure	Cierre anual	no
Weekly closure	Cierre semanal	no
Fees main season	Precios tempor. alta	18 holes

	Week days Semana	We/Bank holidays Fin de sem./fiestas
Individual Individual	€ 70	€ 70
Couple Pareja	€ 140	€ 140

Caddie Caddie no — **Electric Trolley** Carro eléctrico no
Buggy Coche yes — **Clubs** Palos yes
Credit cards Tarjetas de crédito
VISA - MasterCard - AMEX

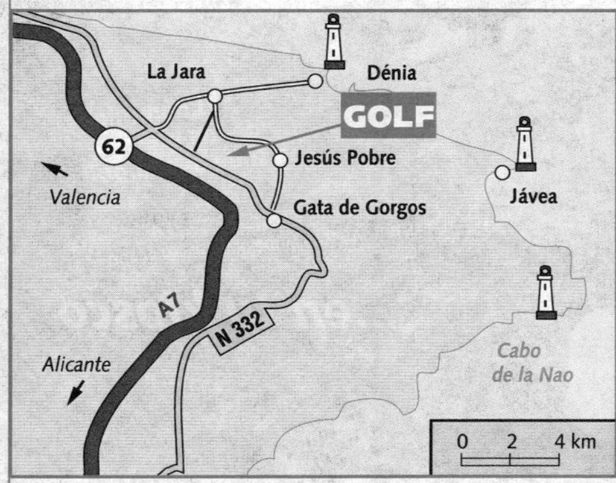

Access Acceso : A7 Valencia - Alicante,
Exit (Salida) 62 → Denia → Jara → Golf
Map 7 on page 1099 Plano 7 Página 1099

GOLF COURSE — RECORRIDO **15/20**

Site	Emplazamiento	
Maintenance	Mantenimiento	
Architect	Arquitecto	Juan de la Cuadra J.M. Olazábal
Type	Tipo	country, hilly
Relief	Relieve	
Water in play	Agua	
Exp. to wind	Exp. al viento	
Trees in play	Arboles	

Scorecard Tarjeta	**Chp.** Campeonato	**Mens** Caballeros	**Ladies** Damas
Length Longitud	6289	6113	5250
Par	72	72	72
Slope system	—	136	131

Advised golfing ability Nivel de juego aconsejado — 0 12 24 36
Hcp required Handicap exigido — 28 Men, 36 Ladies

CLUB HOUSE & AMENITIES — CLUB HOUSE Y DEPENDENCIAS **6/10**

Pro shop Pro-shop
Driving range Campo de prácticas
Sheltered cubierto 2 mats - On grass sobre hierba yes - Putting-green putting-green yes - Pitching-green pitching-green yes

HOTEL FACILITIES — HOTELES CERCANOS **5/10**

HOTELS HOTELES
Denia Marriott La Sella - 186 rooms, D € 179 - on site
Tel (34) 966 - 454 054, Fax (34) 965 - 757 880
Parador de Jávea - 70 rooms, D € 221 - Jávea 10 km
Tel (34) 965 - 790 200, Fax (34) 965 - 790 308
Villa Mediterránea - 12 rooms, D € 223 - Jávea 8 km
Tel (34) 965 - 795 233, Fax (34) 965 - 794 581
Los Angeles - Denia 6 km - 61 rooms, D € 133
Tel (34) 965 - 780 458, Fax (34) 966 - 420 906

RESTAURANTS RESTAURANTES
Romano - Denia 6 km - Tel (34) 966 - 421 789
El Poblet - Denia 6 km - Tel (34) 965 - 784 179
La Casa del Arroz - Denia 6 km - Tel (34) 965 - 781 047

Las Américas

16 | 7 | 8

Es el más "urbano" de los campos del sur de Tenerife, en un oasis verde del formidable complejo hotelero y residencial Playa de Las Américas. Pero el ladrillo de los alrededores guarda prudente distancia y a ello colabora un diseño abierto con múltiples referencias - palmeras y agua, sobre todo- que ocupan la atención del jugador. No es un campo largo -en el 4 y en el 14 los pegadores tirarán a green- pero hay que tener cuidado con los fuera límites, el agua, los bunkers bien colocados y los greenes, muy francos, que son grandes, rápidos y movidos y, por lo tanto, hay que jugarlos con respeto. Habitualmente sopla una brisa que refresca la temperatura y altera un poco el vuelo de la bola. El mantenimiento del campo merece un aplauso especial.

This is the most residential of all the courses on the south coast of Tenerife, lying in the lush oasis of the huge hotel and residential resort of la Playa de las Américas. Turn your eyes away from the bricks and last few cranes that surround the course and take a close look at a layout that has much to be said for it, especially the palm trees and water hazards that should keep you busy for some time. This is not a very long course (the longer-hitters can try and drive the green on holes 4 and 14), but watch out for OB, the water and some well-placed bunkers close to the greens. The putting surfaces are true, large and slick, so treat them with respect. To cool the summer heat, there is often a refreshing little breeze blowing here, and it can easily have an influence on where your ball ends up, so again, care is called for. A special mention should go to the excellent standard of maintenance and green-keeping.

Golf Las Américas — 1998

Playa de Las Américas
E - 38660 ARONA (Tenerife – Islas Canarias)

Office Secretaria (34) 922 - 752 005
Pro shop Pro-shop (34) 922 - 752 005
Fax Fax (34) 922 - 705 250
Web www.golf-tenerife.com
Situation Situación Santa Cruz de Tenerife, 75 km
Annual closure Cierre anual no
Weekly closure Cierre semanal no
Fees main season Precios tempor. alta 18 holes

	Week days / Semana	We/Bank holidays / Fin de sem./fiestas
Individual Individual	€ 90	€ 90
Couple Pareja	€ 180	€ 180

Caddie Caddie no — **Electric Trolley** Carro eléctrico yes
Buggy Coche yes — **Clubs** Palos yes
Credit cards Tarjetas de crédito
VISA - Eurocard - MasterCard - AMEX

Access Acceso : Motorway TF1/ Autovia del Sur, km 72 Exit (Salida) 28
Map 1 on page 1087 Plano 1 Página 1087

GOLF COURSE — RECORRIDO — 16/20

Site Emplazamiento
Maintenance Mantenimiento
Architect Arquitecto John Jacobs & Golf Associates
Type Tipo parkland
Relief Relieve
Water in play Agua
Exp. to wind Exp. al viento
Trees in play Arboles

Scorecard Tarjeta	Chp. Campeonato	Mens Caballeros	Ladies Damas
Length Longitud	6039	5860	5026
Par	72	72	72
Slope system	123	121	120

Advised golfing ability Nivel de juego aconsejado 0 12 24 36
Hcp required Handicap exigido 28 Men, 36 Ladies

CLUB HOUSE & AMENITIES — CLUB HOUSE Y DEPENDENCIAS — 7/10

Pro shop Pro-shop
Driving range Campo de prácticas
Sheltered cubierto no - On grass sobre hierba yes, 20 places
Putting-green putting-green yes - Pitching-green pitching-green yes

HOTEL FACILITIES — HOTELES CERCANOS — 8/10

HOTELS HOTELES

Hotel Las Madrigueras - 57 rooms, D € 315 - on site
Tel (34) 922 - 777 818, Fax (34) 922 - 777 819

Jardin Tropical - Playa de las Américas 4 km
421 rooms, D € 264
Tel (34) 922 - 746 000, Fax (34) 922 - 746 060

Mediterránea Palace - Playa de Las Américas 2 km
535 rooms, D € 126
Tel (34) 922 - 794 400 , Fax (34) 922 - 757 515

RESTAURANTS RESTAURANTES

El Patio - Costa Adeje 5 km - Tel (34) 922 - 750 678
El Jable - San Isidro 5 km - Tel (34) 922 - 390 698
La Cava - Los Cristianos 5 km - Tel (34) 922 - 790 493

Las Brisas

18 | 8 | 8

Este que empezó llamándose Nueva Andalucía, donde se jugó la Copa Canadá de 1973 y la Copa del Mundo de 1989, es uno de los grandes recorridos de la Costa del Sol, aunque conservando una dimensión humana por el gran número de tees de salida que permiten que los jugadores de nivel medio puedan evolucionar sin miedo. Rodeado de bonitos chalés, el terreno es poco accidentado, y numerosos greenes en alto complican los aproches. Numerosos bunkers y obsáculos de agua (en la línea de juego en 12 hoyos) protegen los greens. Aquí es necesario poseer un juego preciso y muy completo (hoyos estrechos alternan con otros más anchos), se debe tirar a bandera y saber dar toda clase de golpes para obtener un buen resultado. Ya en el green queda todavía mucho por hacer ya que no es fácil calcular las caídas. Es apasionante jugar en este campo tanto en stroke-play como en match-play, es el más divertido de todos los "monumentos" de la región, aunque sólo sea por su seducción visual añadida a la calidad del desafío.

This course used to be known as Nueva Andalucía, where the World Cup was played in 1989. It is one of the really great courses on the Costa del Sol but one that has kept a very human dimension through the number of tees, allowing players of average standard to play the course without feeling terrorised. Surrounded by beautiful villas, the terrain is pretty even but the many elevated greens make approach shots a tricky business. The greens are well protected by the many bunkers and water hazards (affecting 12 holes in all). Las Brisas calls for accurate, comprehensive golf (tight holes alternate with wider fairways) and the ability to play most shots in order to card a good score. The emphasis here is on American-style target golf. Although once on the greens, you are still far from home and dry, because none of them are easy to read. An exciting course for stroke-play and match-play, this is the most amusing of the region's golfing landmarks.

Real Club de Golf Las Brisas — 1968

Apartado 147 - Nueva Andalucía
E - 29660 MARBELLA (Málaga – Costa del Sol)

Office Secretaria (34) 952 - 813 021
Pro shop Pro-shop (34) 952 - 813 021
Fax Fax (34) 952 - 815 518
Web www.lasbrisasgolf.com
Situation Situación Marbella, 15 km
San Pedro de Alcantara, 6 km
Annual closure Cierre anual no
Weekly closure Cierre semanal no

Fees main season Precios tempor. alta	18 holes	
	Week days Semana	We/Bank holidays Fin de sem./fiestas
Individual Individual	€ 150	€ 150
Couple Pareja	€ 300	€ 300

Main season: mostly members and guests,

Caddie Caddie yes — **Electric Trolley** Carro eléctrico yes
Buggy Coche yes — **Clubs** Palos yes
Credit cards Tarjetas de crédito
VISA - MasterCard

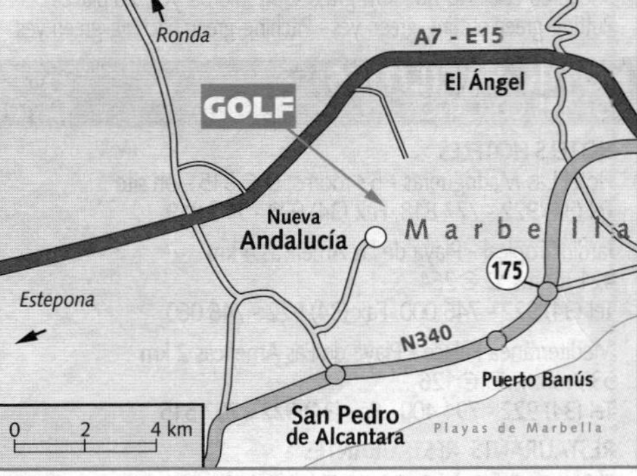

Access Acceso : Marbella N340 → San Pedro de Alcantara, Nueva Andalucía (km 174), turn right → Golf
Map 8 on page 1101 Plano 8 Página 1101

GOLF COURSE — RECORRIDO — 18/20

Site Emplazamiento
Maintenance Mantenimiento
Architect Arquitecto — Robert Trent Jones
Type Tipo — residential, parkland
Relief Relieve
Water in play Agua
Exp. to wind Exp. al viento
Trees in play Arboles

Scorecard Tarjeta	Chp. Campeonato	Mens Caballeros	Ladies Damas
Length Longitud	6130	5866	5069
Par	72	72	72
Slope system	128	125	126

Advised golfing ability Nivel de juego aconsejado — 0 12 24 36
Hcp required Handicap exigido — 24 Men, 32 Ladies

CLUB HOUSE & AMENITIES — CLUB HOUSE Y DEPENDENCIAS — 8/10

Pro shop Pro-shop
Driving range Campo de prácticas
Sheltered cubierto 4 mats - On grass sobre hierba yes - Putting-green putting-green yes - Pitching-green pitching-green yes

HOTEL FACILITIES — HOTELES CERCANOS — 8/10

HOTELS HOTELES
Puente Romano - Marbella 4 km
217 rooms, D € 487
Tel (34) 952 - 820 900, Fax (34) 952 - 775 766

Melia Don Pepe - Marbella 8 km
200 rooms, D € 469
Tel (34) 952 - 770 300, Fax (34) 952 - 779 954

Coral Beach - Marbella 13 km - 170 rooms, D € 311
Tel (34) 952 824 500, Fax (34) 952 826 257

RESTAURANTS RESTAURANTES
Cipriano - Puerto Banús 4 km - Tel (34) 952 - 811 077
Don Leone - Puerto Bañus 4 km - Tel (34) 952 - 811 716

Las Palmas

14	8	8

Es el club más antiguo de España, fundado en 1891 en las afueras de Las Palmas. La expansión de la ciudad obligó a trasladarlo en 1956 y se asienta ahora en un paraje natural, llamado los Llanos de Bandama, a 14 kilómetros de la capital de la isla de Gran Canaria. El ambiente del club y su diseño natural mantienen la tradición inglesa de sus fundadores. El terreno es muy escarpado y la casa-club de estilo clásico domina todo el recorrido y ofrece unas espléndidas vistas sobre las rocas volcánicas y barrancos que lo rodean. El campo no es de medidas largas, pero hay varios hoyos en subida que hay que tratar con el máximo respeto. Es preciso dominar el vuelo de la bola para mantener la bola en juego en un recorrido, que sin ser estrecho, incita al jugador a pensar cuál es el mejor sitio para colocar cada salida.

This is Spain's oldest golf club, whose course was originally laid out in the suburbs of Las Palmas de Gran Canaria. In 1956, as the city expanded, the club moved out into the country close to Llanos de Bandama, some 14 km from the capital of Grand Canary. The atmosphere in this club, just like the actual course, faithfully upholds the British tradition laid down by the club's founding members. The course is very hilly (but only a limited number of buggies are available) and the very classically styled club-house overlooks the whole course providing a magnificent scenic view of the surrounding volcanic rocks and ravines. The 18 holes (designed by Mackenzie Ross but restyled since) are not particularly wide and there are quite a few uphill holes that need to be negotiated very carefully. Accuracy is of the essence to keep the ball in play on a course where the tight fairways force the golfer to think long and hard about careful placing of the ball before each shot.

Real Club de Golf de Las Palmas — 1891

Lugar campo de golf nº 12
E - 35380 SANTA BRIGIDA (Gran Canaria - Islas Canarias)

Office	Secretaria	(34) 928 - 350 104
Pro shop	Pro-shop	(34) 928 - 350 104
Fax	Fax	(34) 928 - 350 110
Web	www.realclubdegolfdelaspalmas.com	
Situation	Situación	Las Palmas, 14 km
Annual closure	Cierre anual	no
Weekly closure	Cierre semanal	no

Fees main season Precios tempor. alta	Week days Semana	We/Bank holidays Fin de sem./fiestas
	18 holes	
Individual Individual	€ 76	*
Couple Pareja	€ 152	*

* Members' guests only (Sólo invitados de socios)

Caddie Caddie no — **Electric Trolley** Carro eléctrico no
Buggy Coche yes — **Clubs** Palos yes
Credit cards Tarjetas de crédito
VISA - Eurocard - MasterCard - AMEX - DC

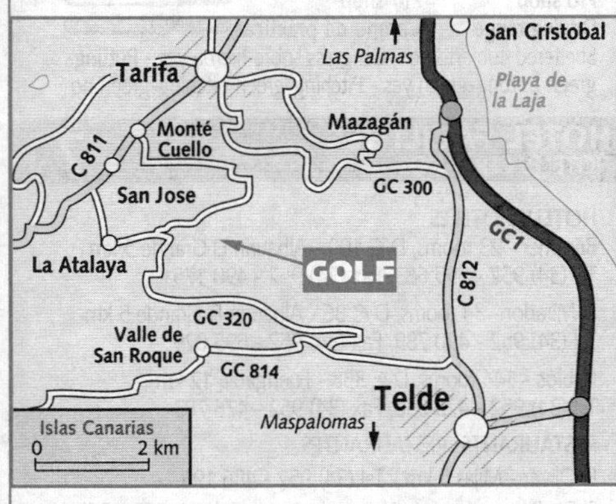

Access Acceso : Las Palmas C811 → Santa Brigida. On the left, → Golf
Map 1 on page 1087 Plano 1 Página 1087

GOLF COURSE — RECORRIDO — 14/20

Site	Emplazamiento	
Maintenance	Mantenimiento	
Architect	Arquitecto	Mackenzie Ross, Juan Dominguez
Type	Tipo	parkland
Relief	Relieve	
Water in play	Agua	
Exp. to wind	Exp. al viento	
Trees in play	Arboles	

Scorecard Tarjeta	Chp. Campeonato	Mens Caballeros	Ladies Damas
Length Longitud	5915	5666	5190
Par	71	71	71
Slope system	130	128	127

Advised golfing ability Nivel de juego aconsejado — 0 12 24 36
Hcp required Handicap exigido — 28 Men, 36 Ladies

CLUB HOUSE & AMENITIES — CLUB HOUSE Y DEPENDENCIAS — 8/10

Pro shop Pro-shop
Driving range Campo de prácticas
Sheltered cubierto 15 mats - On grass sobre hierba yes - Putting-green putting-green yes - Pitching-green pitching-green yes

HOTEL FACILITIES — HOTELES CERCANOS — 8/10

HOTELS HOTELES

Golf Bandama - 38 rooms, D € 160 - on site
Tel (34) 928 - 351 538, Fax (34) 928 - 350 873

Santa Catalina - 187 rooms, D € 238 - Las Palmas 14 km
Tel (34) 928 - 243 040, Fax (34) 928 - 242 764

Santa Brigida - 41 rooms, D € 90 - Santa Brigida 3 km
Tel (34) 928 - 355 511, Fax (34) 928 - 355 701

RESTAURANTS RESTAURANTES

Amaiur - Las Palmas 14 km - Tel (34) 928 - 370 717

Las Grutas de Artiles - Santa Brigida 7 km
Tel (34) 928 - 640 575

El Novillo Precoz - Las Palmas 14 km - Tel (34) 928 - 221 659

Lauro

14	7	7

Al final de una carretera de montaña está situado en un lugar muy tranquilo. Cada hoyo lleva el nombre de un célebre torero, pero no por eso se trata de un recorrido agresivo que exija dotes de combate. Al contrario, la belleza de los paisajes inspira calma y el recorrido en sí mismo es más bien acogedor, incluso para los jugadores con poca experiencia. Cantidad de olivos bordean la mayor parte de las calles y algunos obstáculos de agua están situados en plena línea de juego (hoyos 9,14,17 y 18) sin ser temibles. De razonable dificultad, prácticamente sin trampas escondidas (los obstáculos son perfectamente visibles), Lauro Golf es un recorrido muy noble y el sitio ideal para evaluar el nivel de su juego actual y las propias posibilidades frente a jugadores de nivel equivalente. El campo, que tiene tres grupos de 9 hoyos, ha mejorado en mantenimiento y estado y ha introducido modificaciones en los hoyos 5, 6 y 7 del recorrido principal.

This course is a quiet little place at the end of a mountain road. Each hole bears the name of a famous torero but the course itself is far from being aggressive and does not call for any real fighting virtues. On the contrary, the beautiful landscape inspires peace and quiet and the layout is a friendly one, even for inexperienced players. Numerous olive trees line most of the fairways and certain water hazards are very much to the fore (on the 9th, 14th, 17th and 18th holes) but never fearsome. Never too demanding with virtually no hidden traps (all hazards are clearly visible) and benign greens, Lauro Golf is a very fair layout and the ideal spot to assess your current game and potential and to measure up with players of similar ability. The better players can card flattering scores and do their ego a world of good. The course – formed from three 9-hole loops – has shown a great improvement, both through green-keeping and the changes made to holes 5, 6 and 7 on the "main" course.

Lauro Golf — 1992

Ctra de Málaga a Coín (A-366), km 77
E - 29130 ALHAURIN DE LA TORRE (Málaga – Costa del Sol)

Office	Secretaría	(34) 952 - 963 091
Pro shop	Pro-shop	(34) 952 - 963 091
Fax	Fax	(34) 952 - 414 757
Web	www.laurogolf.com	
Situation	Situación	Málaga, 15 km

Alhaurín de la Torre, 5 km

Annual closure	Cierre anual	no
Weekly closure	Cierre semanal	no
Fees main season	Precios tempor. alta	18 holes

	Week days / Semana	We/Bank holidays / Fin de sem./fiestas
Individual Individual	€ 50	€ 50
Couple Pareja	€ 100	€ 100

Caddie Caddie no **Electric Trolley** Carro eléctrico yes

Buggy Coche yes **Clubs** Palos yes

Credit cards Tarjetas de crédito
VISA - Eurocard - Mastercard - AMEX

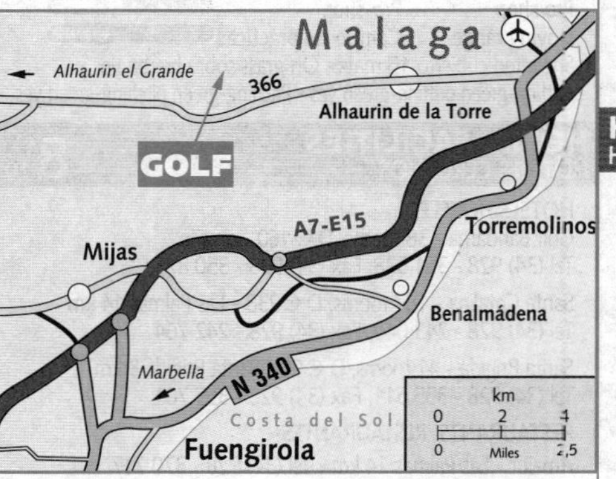

Access Acceso : Málaga, N340 → Torremolinos, Exit (Salida) "Churiana", C344, turn right to Alhaurín

Map 8 on page 1101 Plano 8 Página 1101

GOLF COURSE — RECORRIDO — 14/20

Site	Emplazamiento	
Maintenance	Mantenimiento	
Architect	Arquitecto	Folco Nardi
Type	Tipo	country
Relief	Relieve	
Water in play	Agua	
Exp. to wind	Exp. al viento	
Trees in play	Arboles	

Scorecard Tarjeta	**Chp.** Campeonato	**Mens** Caballeros	**Ladies** Damas
Length Longitud	6070	5689	4864
Par	72	72	72
Slope system	135	132	126

Advised golfing ability Nivel de juego aconsejado — 0 12 24 36

Hcp required Handicap exigido — 28 Men, 36 Ladies

CLUB HOUSE & AMENITIES — CLUB HOUSE Y DEPENDENCIAS — 7/10

Pro shop	Pro-shop
Driving range	Campo de prácticas

Sheltered cubierto no - On grass sobre hierba yes - Putting-green putting-green yes - Pitching-green pitching-green no

HOTEL FACILITIES — HOTELES CERCANOS — 7/10

HOTELS HOTELES

Brisamer - 23 rooms, D € 100 - Alhaurín El Grande 5 km
Tel (34) 952 - 595 683, Fax (34) 952 - 490 175

El Mirador - 34 rooms, D € 86 - Alhaurín El Grande 5 km
Tel (34) 952 - 490 789, Fax (34) 952 - 595 029

Byblos - 144 rooms, D € 358 - Fuengirola 12 km
Tel (34) 952 - 473 050, Fax (34) 952 - 476 783

RESTAURANTS RESTAURANTES

El Olivar - Mijas 5 km - Tel (34) 952 - 486 196

El Ermitaño - Alhaurín El Grande 5 km - Tel (34) 952 - 963 004

Fonda El Postillón - Alhaurín El Grande 5 km
Tel (34) 952 - 594 487

Lerma

17 | 7 | 6

Uno de los arquitectos más originales de esta época, José Gancedo, ha diseñado en un magnífico paraje castellano un campo a la vez espectacular y lleno de encanto. Si se le puede considerar como difícil para los buenos jugadores, sobre todo desde las barras de atrás, se adapta sin embargo perfectamente a los jugadores todos los niveles. Tendrán aún más placer ya que no es imposible cumplir su handicap, siempre y cuando sean conscientes de sus limitaciones. El trazado exige una excelente estrategia y un buen dominio de la bola. Suele recompensar más al jugador técnico que coloca la bola que al pegador que puede encontrar dificultades con los árboles o los obstáculos de agua. Sin embargo en el 18 los pegadores tendrán la oportunidad de jugar a green por encima del lago, sobre todo si juegan en match-play, la fórmula ideal para descubrir el campo. Bien equilibrado en su desarrollo, con un buen diseño, Lerma pertenece sin duda a la categoría de campos "inteligentes".

José Gancedo, one of the most original architects of our day and age, has designed a spectacular and truly charming layout over a beautiful Castellan landscape. While considered tough for the better players, especially from the back-tees, it is nonetheless largely suitable for players of all abilities. They will find it all the more pleasing in that playing to their handicap is not impossible as long as they know their limits. The course demands tight strategy and excellent ball control and generally will reward the accurate technician more than the long-hitters, who may have problems with the trees and water. But on the 18th, they can try and hit the green over the lake, especially in match-play, the ideal format when discovering this course. Well-balanced and nicely-landscaped, Lerma is undoubtedly one of the more "intelligent" courses to be found in Spain.

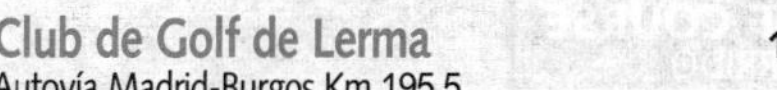

Club de Golf de Lerma — 1992

Autovía Madrid-Burgos Km 195,5
E - 09340 LERMA (Burgos – Castilla-León)

Office	Secretaria	(34) 947 - 171 214
Pro shop	Pro-shop	(34) 947 - 171 214
Fax	Fax	(34) 947 - 171 216
E-mail	administracion@golflerma.com	
Situation	Situación	Burgos (pop. 169 111), 45 km

Lerma (pop. 2 417), 8 km

Annual closure Cierre anual — no

Weekly closure Cierre semanal — monday (lunes): 1/10→31/3

Fees main season Precios tempor. alta — 18 holes

	Week days Semana	We/Bank holidays Fin de sem./fiestas
Individual Individual	€ 42	€ 55
Couple Pareja	€ 84	€ 110

Caddie Caddie no — **Electric Trolley** Carro eléctrico yes

Buggy Coche yes — **Clubs** Palos yes

Credit cards Tarjetas de crédito — VISA

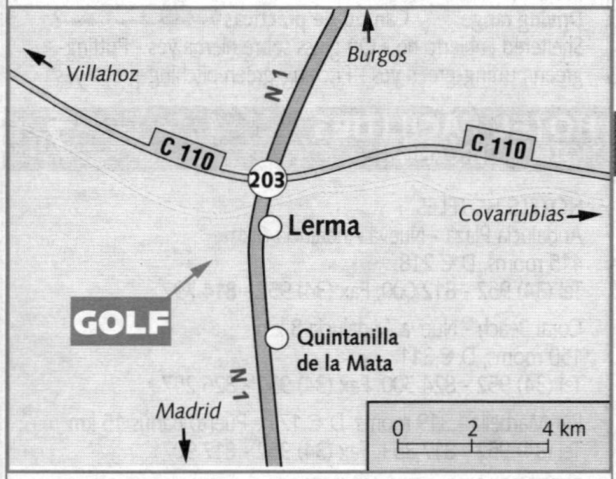

Access Acceso : Madrid → Burgos, Km 195
Map 4 on page 1092 Plano 4 Página 1092

GOLF COURSE — RECORRIDO — 17/20

Site	Emplazamiento	
Maintenance	Mantenimiento	
Architect	Arquitecto	José Gancedo
Type	Tipo	country
Relief	Relieve	
Water in play	Agua	
Exp. to wind	Exp. al viento	
Trees in play	Arboles	

Scorecard Tarjeta	**Chp.** Campeonato	**Mens** Caballeros	**Ladies** Damas
Length Longitud	6263	5905	5064
Par	72	72	72
Slope system	125	125	115

Advised golfing ability Nivel de juego aconsejado — 0 12 24 36

Hcp required Handicap exigido — 28 Men, 36 Ladies

CLUB HOUSE & AMENITIES — CLUB HOUSE Y DEPENDENCIAS — 7/10

Pro shop Pro-shop
Driving range Campo de prácticas

Sheltered cubierto 8 mats - On grass sobre hierba yes - Putting-green putting-green yes - Pitching-green pitching-green yes

HOTEL FACILITIES — HOTELES CERCANOS — 6/10

HOTELS HOTELES

Alisa - 36 rooms, D € 74 - Lerma 8 km
Tel (34) 947 - 170 250, Fax (34) 947 - 171 160

Parador de Lerma - 70 rooms, D € 188 - Lerma 4 km
Tel (34) 947 - 177 110, Fax (34) 947 - 170 685

Landa Palace - 39 rooms, D € 232 - Burgos 35 km
Tel (34) 947 - 257 777, Fax (34) 947 - 264 676

Rey Chindasvinto - 14 rooms, D € 60 - Covarrubias 22 km
Tel (34) 947 - 406 560, Fax (34) 947 - 406 543

RESTAURANTS RESTAURANTES

Lis 2 - Lerma 8 km - Tel (34) 947 - 170 126
Casa Ojeda - Burgos 35 km - Tel (34) 947 - 209 052

Los Arqueros

14	6	7

Desde los paisajes áridos de la carretera que sube a Ronda, da la impresión de ser un golf "extremado". En realidad no lo es, pero sus pronunciadas cuestas aconsejan utilizar un coche para jugar más fácilmente en este recorrido cuya construcción exigió enormes obras para nivelar el terreno. No es muy largo, estrecho en algunos sitios, los obstáculos son peligrosos y situados en la línea de juego, lo que incita a jugar con cierta prudencia. Teniendo en cuenta que el arquitecto es Seve Ballesteros, atraerá más bien a los jugadores de ataque que serán recompensados por sus golpes audaces, sobre todo los que juegan con "fade" o los especialistas en bolas altas cuyo objetivo son unos greenes no inmensos, sin grandes trampas, que aguantan bien la bola y su trayectoria a la hora de patear. De gran imaginación y espectacular, se recomienda conocerlo antes de seguir camino hacia la bella ciudad de Ronda.

From the road and arid landscape leading to Ronda, the impression is one of an extremely hilly golf course. This is not quite the case, but the steep slopes call for the use of a buggy to play a little more easily on a course whose construction demanded very considerable grading work. It is not very long but is sometimes tight and hazards are always in play and dangerously placed. The result can sometimes be an over-cautious approach when playing the course. Designed by Seve Ballesteros, Los Arqueros should appeal to attacking players and will reward bold strokes. This is particularly true for players who fade the ball or who are specialists of high shots aimed at the smallish greens, which have little in the way of traps, pitch well and putt true. Imaginative and sometimes quite spectacular, this course is to be recommended before getting back on the road and heading for the beautiful town of Ronda.

Los Arqueros Golf & Country Club — 1990

Apartado de Correos 110
E - 29670 SAN PEDRO DE ALCANTARA
(Málaga – Costa del Sol)

Office	Secretaria	(34) 952 - 784 600
Pro shop	Pro-shop	(34) 952 - 784 600
Fax	Fax	(34) 952 - 786 707
Web	www.taywoodspain.com	
Situation	Situación	Marbella, 10 km

San Pedro de Alcantara, 6 km

Annual closure	Cierre anual	no
Weekly closure	Cierre semanal	no

1160

Fees main season Precios tempor. alta	18 holes	
	Week days Semana	**We/Bank holidays** Fin de sem./fiestas
Individual Individual	€ 70	€ 70
Couple Pareja	€ 140	€ 140

Caddie Caddie no — **Electric Trolley** Carro eléctrico no
Buggy Coche yes — **Clubs** Palos yes
Credit cards Tarjetas de crédito
VISA - Eurocard - MasterCard - AMEX - DC - JCB

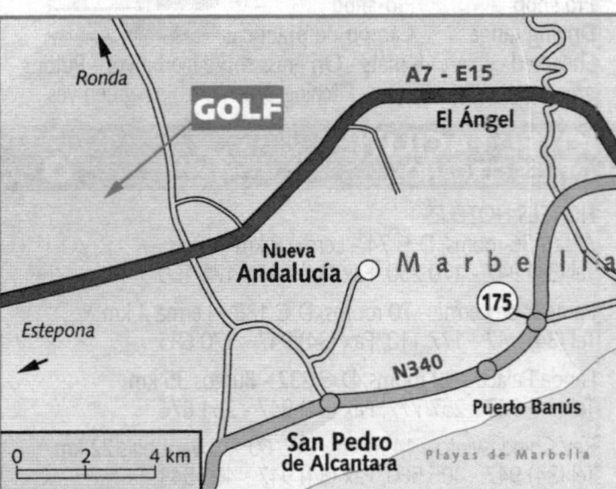

Access Acceso : Marbella N340 → Cadiz, San Pedro de Alcantara, C339 → Ronda, Golf 4 km on the left
Map 8 on page 1101 Plano 8 Página 1101

GOLF COURSE — RECORRIDO — 14/20

Site	Emplazamiento	
Maintenance	Mantenimiento	
Architect	Arquitecto	Seve Ballesteros
Type	Tipo	mountain, hilly
Relief	Relieve	
Water in play	Agua	
Exp. to wind	Exp. al viento	
Trees in play	Arboles	

Scorecard Tarjeta	**Chp.** Campeonato	**Mens** Caballeros	**Ladies** Damas
Length Longitud	5729	5306	4819
Par	71	71	71
Slope system	132	129	129

Advised golfing ability Nivel de juego aconsejado: 0 12 24 36
Hcp required Handicap exigido: 28 Men, 36 Ladies

CLUB HOUSE & AMENITIES — CLUB HOUSE Y DEPENDENCIAS — 6/10

Pro shop	Pro-shop
Driving range	Campo de prácticas

Sheltered cubierto no - On grass sobre hierba yes - Putting-green putting-green yes - Pitching-green pitching-green yes

HOTEL FACILITIES — HOTELES CERCANOS — 7/10

HOTELS HOTELES

Andalucia Plaza - Nueva Andalucía 6 km
415 rooms, D € 218
Tel (34) 952 - 812 000, Fax (34) 952 - 814 792

Coral Beach - Nueva Andalucía 8 km
150 rooms, D € 311
Tel (34) 952 - 824 500, Fax (34) 952 - 826 257

Pyr Marbella - 319 rooms, D € 171 - Puerto Banús 15 km
Tel (34) 952 - 817 353, Fax (34) 952 - 817 907

RESTAURANTS RESTAURANTES

El Rodeito - Nueva Andalucía 6 km - Tel (34) 952 - 815 699
Cipriano - Puerto Banús 10 km - Tel (34) 952 - 811 077

Los Naranjos

16 | 7 | 7

En el corazón del "Valle del golf" en Nueva Andalucía, Los Naranjos, sin ser un monstruo, es uno de los más famosos diseños de Robert Trent Jones. Las mejoras en el mantenimiento del recorrido y la construcción de una nueva casa club han contribuido a restaurar su gloria. Los nueve primeros hoyos, ligeramente accidentados, obligan a reflexionar tanto sobre la elección del palo como sobre la trayectoria de la bola. Los nueve segundos son prácticamente llanos, insinuándose entre naranjos, y más favorables a los pegadores que no dudarán en salir de atrás. Los jugadores más razonables encontrarán que este recorrido es ya bastante largo desde los tees de salida "normales". ¿Por qué sufrir si se puede evitar? En cada partido hallarán toda clase de situaciones diferentes de las que podrán gozar. Los greenes están bien protegidos, son muy grandes y se ven bien las caídas.

At the heart of "Golf Valley" in Nueva Andalucía, "Los Naranjos" (meaning Orange Trees) is one of Robert Trent Jones' most famous designs but it is no monster. Considerably improved maintenance and the building of a new club house have helped restore its former glory. The front nine over slightly broken terrain require careful thought as much for the choice of club as for the trajectory of the ball. The back nine are virtually flat holes winding their way between the orange trees. They will appeal to long hitters who in every case won't think twice about playing the course from the tips. More reasonable players will find the course long enough from the "normal" tees; after all, why suffer when you don't have to? All sorts of different situations arise every time you play here, so the course is sure-fire enjoyment every time. The greens are well-defended, often huge but never too difficult to read.

Los Naranjos Golf Club — 1977

Apartado de Correos, 64
E - 29660 NUEVA ANDALUCIA (Málaga – Costa del Sol)

Office Secretaria (34) 952 - 812 428
Pro shop Pro-shop (34) 952 - 812 428
Fax Fax (34) 952 - 811 428
Web www.losnaranjos.com
Situation Situación Marbella, 15 km
San Pedro de Alcantara, 6 km
Annual closure Cierre anual no
Weekly closure Cierre semanal no

Fees main season Precios tempor. alta	18 holes	
	Week days Semana	**We/Bank holidays** Fin de sem./fiestas
Individual Individual	€ 84	€ 84
Couple Pareja	€ 168	€ 168

Caddie Caddie no **Electric Trolley** Carro eléctrico yes
Buggy Coche yes **Clubs** Palos yes
Credit cards Tarjetas de crédito
VISA - Eurocard - MasterCard - AMEX

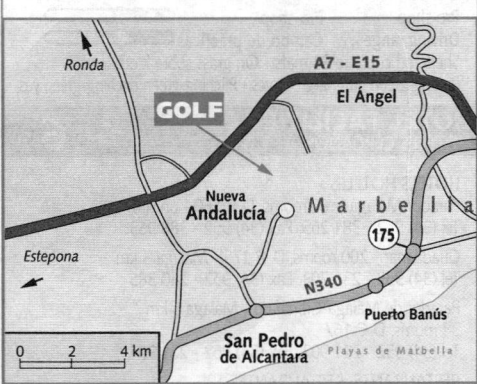

Access Acceso : Marbella N340 → Cádiz, Nueva Andalucía (km 180), turn right → Golf
Map 8 on page 1101 Plano 8 Página 1101

GOLF COURSE — RECORRIDO — 16/20

Site Emplazamiento
Maintenance Mantenimiento
Architect Arquitecto Robert Trent Jones
Type Tipo parkland, residential
Relief Relieve
Water in play Agua
Exp. to wind Exp. al viento
Trees in play Arboles

Scorecard Tarjeta	**Chp.** Campeonato	**Mens** Caballeros	**Ladies** Damas
Length Longitud	6457	6038	5143
Par	72	72	72
Slope system	130	129	124

Advised golfing ability Nivel de juego aconsejado 0 12 24 36
Hcp required Handicap exigido 28 Men, 36 Ladies

CLUB HOUSE & AMENITIES — CLUB HOUSE Y DEPENDENCIAS — 7/10

Pro shop Pro-shop
Driving range Campo de prácticas
Sheltered cubierto no - On grass sobre hierba yes - Putting-green putting-green yes - Pitching-green pitching-green yes

HOTEL FACILITIES — HOTELES CERCANOS — 7/10

HOTELS HOTELES

Puente Romano - 217 rooms, D € 487 - Marbella 5 km
Tel (34) 952 - 820 900, Fax (34) 952 - 775 766

Andalucia Plaza - Nueva Andalucía 1,5 km
415 rooms, D € 218
Tel (34) 952 - 812 000, Fax (34) 952 - 814 792

Pyr Marbella - 319 rooms, D € 171 - Puerto Banús 4 km
Tel (34) 952 - 817 353, Fax (34) 952 - 817 907

RESTAURANTS RESTAURANTES

Mesón El Coto - San Pedro → Ronda 7 km
Tel (34) 952 - 785 123

El Rodeito - Nueva Andalucía 6 km - Tel (34) 952 - 815 699

Los Naranjos - on site - Tel (34) 952 - 816 625

Málaga

13	4	6

Este es el primer campo golf de Málaga y el primer campo propiedad y dirigido por la empresa estatal Paradores, rama hostelera del Turismo estatal. Paradores ha puesto interés en tener el campo en buenas condiciones y prolongar hasta las puertas de Málaga el turismo de golf que tiene su epicentro alrededor de Marbella. El campo es un monumento histórico construído por H.S. Colt y supervisado por Tom Simpson, que alterna el diseño de parque natural, entre árboles frondosos, con los hoyos al borde de la playa a los que solamente faltan las dunas para que sea un auténtico links. El lugar tiene un gran encanto natural y los primeros nueve hoyos son especialmente interesantes, con bunkers muy bien situados y una distribución de espacios que anima a emplear todos los recursos del buen juego corto.

This was not only the very first course on the Costa del Sol, it is now also the first course to be controlled and managed by the state enterprise Paradores, the hotel branch of Spanish Tourism. Paradores set out to keep the course in sufficiently good condition in order to prolong Marbella-based golf tourism down as far as Málaga. The course is a sort of historical monument designed by H.S. Colt under the supervision of Tom Simpson. The result is an alternating string of natural parkland holes, very thick trees and seaside holes where only the dunes are lacking for this to look like a real links course. The natural site has a lot of charm about it, especially the particularly interesting front nine. Bunkers are well located and space has been cleverly used to add spice to the back nine, where a tight short game comes in very handy.

Real Club de Campo de Málaga — 1925

Apdo 324
E - 29080 MALAGA (Málaga – Costa del Sol)

Office	Secretaria	(34) 952 - 376 677
Pro shop	Pro-shop	(34) 951 - 011 120
Fax	Fax	(34) 952 - 376 612
Web	www.rccm-golf.com	
Situation	Situación	Málaga, 10 km

Torremolinos (pop. 35 309), 4 km

Annual closure	Cierre anual	no
Weekly closure	Cierre semanal	no
Fees main season	Precios tempor. alta	18 holes

	Week days / Semana	We/Bank holidays / Fin de sem./fiestas
Individual Individual	€ 69	€ 69
Couple Pareja	€ 138	€ 138

Caddie Caddie no — **Electric Trolley** Carro eléctrico no
Buggy Coche yes — **Clubs** Palos yes
Credit cards Tarjetas de crédito
VISA - Eurocard - MasterCard - AMEX

Access Acceso : Málaga → Torremolinos, on the left → Parador del Golf
Map 8 on page 1101 Plano 8 Página 1101

GOLF COURSE — RECORRIDO — 13/20

Site	Emplazamiento	
Maintenance	Mantenimiento	
Architect	Arquitecto	Harry S. Colt, Tom Simpson
Type	Tipo	seaside course
Relief	Relieve	
Water in play	Agua	
Exp. to wind	Exp. al viento	
Trees in play	Arboles	

Scorecard Tarjeta	Chp. Campeonato	Mens Caballeros	Ladies Damas
Length Longitud	6173	6045	5139
Par	72	72	72
Slope system	124	124	119

Advised golfing ability Nivel de juego aconsejado: 0 12 24 36
Hcp required Handicap exigido: 27 Men, 36 Ladies

CLUB HOUSE & AMENITIES — CLUB HOUSE Y DEPENDENCIAS — 4/10

Pro shop Pro-shop
Driving range Campo de prácticas
Sheltered cubierto 21 mats - On grass sobre hierba yes - Putting-green putting-green yes - Pitching-green pitching-green yes

HOTEL FACILITIES — HOTELES CERCANOS — 6/10

HOTELS HOTELES
Parador Málaga - 60 rooms, D € 160 - on site
Tel (34) 952 - 381 255, Fax (34) 952 - 388 963

Guadalmar - 200 rooms, D € 175 - Málaga 3 km
Tel (34) 952 - 231 703, Fax (34) 952 - 240 385

Parador de Málaga-Gibralfaro - Málaga 5 km
38 rooms, D € 167
Tel (34) 952 - 221 902, Fax (34) 952 - 221 904

RESTAURANTS RESTAURANTES
Casa Pedro - Málaga 3 km - Tel (34) 952 - 290 013
Calycanto - Málaga 3 km - Tel (34) 952 - 212 222
El Chinitas - Málaga - Tel (34) 952 - 210 972

Marbella

15 | 7 | 8

Es un campo difícil de andar porque tiene muchas cuestas y vale la pena alquilar un coche, con lo cual se podrán superar más descansadamente las complicaciones técnicas que presenta. La gran diversidad de hoyos y de golpes que hay que jugar es asombrosa, encontrando los famosos bunkers marca del arquitecto y algunos obstáculos de agua peligrosos que requieren un serio análisis de su buena forma de juego, antes de tomar una decisión entre el ataque o la prudencia. Teniendo en cuenta que los greenes tienen muchas caídas, hay que atacar resueltamente a bandera. No se trata ni mucho menos de un recorrido imposible, pero resultará muy complicado para los jugadores de handicap alto. Algunas hondonadas y sinuosidades del terreno son una seria amenaza para los drives en algunos hoyos. Bien es verdad que por momentos el maravilloso panorama sobre el mar puede servir de consuelo a ciertos desastres.

A very uphill and downhill course which is difficult to play on foot. Playing on wheels keeps your mind fresher to cope with the course's technical difficulties, as this demanding layout is very much back in the modern trend. The variety of holes and the shots they require are remarkable. There are, of course, the architect's hallmark bunkers and a number of dangerous water hazards, which call for serious analysis of current playing form before deciding whether to attack or lay up. All the more so in that the greens are well designed and definitely favour players who go for the pin. It is not an impossible course, far from it, but high-handicappers may suffer, especially with the few ravines and hollows that pose a serious threat to a number of tee-shots. The scenic views over the sea should more than compensate should disaster strike.

Marbella Golf & Country Club — 1988

Carretera Cádiz-Málaga, km.188
E - 29600 MARBELLA (Málaga – Costa del Sol)

Office Secretaria (34) 952 - 830 500
Pro shop Pro-shop (34) 952 - 830 500
Fax Fax (34) 952 - 834 353
Web www.marbellagolf.com
Situation Situación Marbella, 5 km
Fuengirola (pop. 43 048), 20 km

Annual closure Cierre anual — no
Weekly closure Cierre semanal — no

Fees main season Precios tempor. alta		18 holes
	Week days Semana	We/Bank holidays Fin de sem./fiestas
Individual Individual	€ 75	€ 75
Couple Pareja	€ 150	€ 150

Caddie Caddie no — **Electric Trolley** Carro eléctrico no
Buggy Coche yes — **Clubs** Palos yes
Credit cards Tarjetas de crédito
VISA - MasterCard - AMEX

Access Acceso : Marbella N340 → Fuengirola, Golf km 188
Map 8 on page 1101 Plano 8 Página 1101

GOLF COURSE — RECORRIDO — 15/20

Site Emplazamiento
Maintenance Mantenimiento
Architect Arquitecto — Robert Trent Jones
Type Tipo — hilly
Relief Relieve
Water in play Agua
Exp. to wind Exp. al viento
Trees in play Arboles

Scorecard Tarjeta	Chp. Campeonato	Mens Caballeros	Ladies Damas
Length Longitud	5953	5602	4777
Par	72	72	72
Slope system	129	127	118

Advised golfing ability Nivel de juego aconsejado — 0 12 24 36
Hcp required Handicap exigido — 26 Men, 34 Ladies

CLUB HOUSE & AMENITIES — CLUB HOUSE Y DEPENDENCIAS — 7/10

Pro shop Pro-shop
Driving range Campo de prácticas
Sheltered cubierto no - On grass sobre hierba yes - Putting-green putting-green yes - Pitching-green pitching-green yes

HOTEL FACILITIES — HOTELES CERCANOS — 8/10

HOTELS HOTELES
Los Monteros - 168 rooms, D € 310 - Marbella 1 km
Tel (34) 952 - 771 700, Fax (34) 952 - 825 846
Artola - 32 rooms, D € 121 - Artola 7 km
Tel (34) 952 - 831 390, Fax (34) 952 - 830 450
Hotel Don Carlos - Marbella
241 rooms, D € 302
Tel (34) 952 - 831 940, Fax (34) 952 - 833 429

RESTAURANTS RESTAURANTES
La Fonda - Marbella 3 km - Tel (34) 952 - 772 512
Santiago - Marbella 3 km - Tel (34) 952 - 774 339

Masia Bach

16 | 7 | 7

Construído en un terreno muy accidentado, con muy duras cuestas de andar, sobre todo de green a tee, hay que ponderar si el coche es necesario para que el cansancio no perjudique nuestro golf. José María Olazábal ha sabido sacar provecho de un terreno quebrado con serios peligros para todas las bolas que se desvían de la trayectoria requerida o no llegan a volar aguas y barrancos. El relieve impide a veces ver los greens desde los tees de salida de los pares 4 y 5, pero los bunkers de calle indican la línea de juego y recogen las bolas imprecisas. Los pares 3, generalmente con hondonadas en medio, parecen peligrosos pero son de longitud razonable. Los greenes tienen muchas caídas, son o muy largos o muy anchos y aguantan bien la bola, por lo que es esencial acertar la selección del palo y la estrategia más adecuada para atacar o protegerse de las diferentes posiciones de las banderas. El campo es largo y desafiante por metros y también por su estructura por lo que es un excelente test para calibrar la forma incluso de jugadores expertos.

A buggy can come in handy here to cross the broken terrain between holes, but much of the course itself is not too hilly. José María Olazábal has brought the best out of what, at first sight, looks to be much more rugged and dangerous terrain. Here, danger lurks for any ball that veers left or right. Indeed, the relief sometimes obscures any view of the greens from the tees on the par 4s and 5s, but the fairway bunkers show the line of play and often stop mis-hit balls in their tracks. Generally laid out with large hollows between tee and green, the par 3s look dangerous but their lengths are very reasonable. The greens are very undulating, sometimes very long or very wide: you will find that taking pin position into the equation before selecting which club to play is more important than usual. This course is a real challenge for its length, an excellent test to appreciate the state of your game, even for experienced players. One last word for the par-31 nine-hole course.

Club de Golf Masia Bach — 1990

Ctra de Martorell-Capellades - Km 19,5
E - 08635 SANT ESTEVE SESROVIRES (Barcelona)

Office Secretaria (34) 937 - 728 800
Pro shop Pro-shop (34) 937 - 728 800
Fax Fax (34) 937 - 728 810
Web www.golfmasiabach.com
Situation Situación Barcelona, 25 km
Martorell (pop. 16 793), 7 km

Annual closure Cierre anual — no
Weekly closure Cierre semanal — monday

Fees main season Precios tempor. alta	18 holes	
	Week days Semana	**We/Bank holidays** Fin de sem./fiestas
Individual Individual	€ 65	€ 150
Couple Pareja	€ 130	€ 300

Caddie Caddie no — **Electric Trolley** Carro eléctrico yes
Buggy Coche yes — **Clubs** Palos yes
Credit cards Tarjetas de crédito
VISA - Eurocard - MasterCard - AMEX

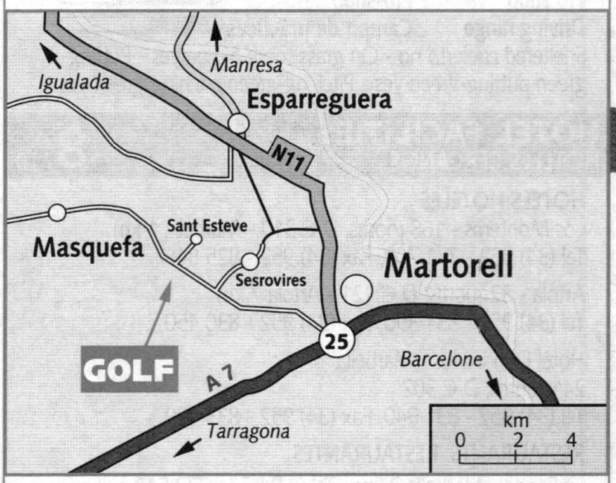

Access Acceso : Barcelona A2/A7 → Tarragona, Exit (Salida) 25 → Martorell, B224 → Capellades, Golf on right hand side
Map 2 on page 1089 Plano 2 Página 1089

GOLF COURSE — RECORRIDO — 16/20

Site Emplazamiento
Maintenance Mantenimiento
Architect Arquitecto — José María Olazábal
Type Tipo — mountain
Relief Relieve
Water in play Agua
Exp. to wind Exp. al viento
Trees in play Arboles

Scorecard Tarjeta	**Chp.** Campeonato	**Mens** Caballeros	**Ladies** Damas
Length Longitud	6271	6038	5173
Par	72	72	72
Slope system	136	133	131

Advised golfing ability Nivel de juego aconsejado — 0 12 24 36

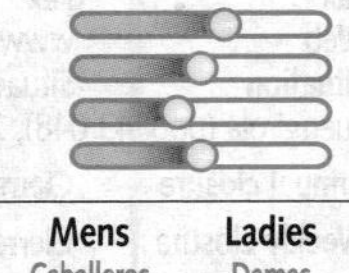

Hcp required Handicap exigido — 28 Men, 36 Ladies

CLUB HOUSE & AMENITIES — CLUB HOUSE Y DEPENDENCIAS — 7/10

Pro shop Pro-shop
Driving range Campo de prácticas
Sheltered cubierto 15 mats - On grass sobre hierba yes - Putting-green putting-green yes - Pitching-green pitching-green yes

HOTEL FACILITIES — HOTELES CERCANOS — 7/10

HOTELS HOTELES
Bristol - Sant Andreu de la Barca 9 km
57 rooms, D € 138
Tel (34) 936 - 821 177, Fax (34) 936 - 823 797

Hotel Barceló Barcelona Golf - on site
150 rooms, D € 107
Tel (34) 937 - 756 800, Fax (34) 937 - 756 805

AC Martorell - 92 rooms, D € 90 - Martorell 7 km
Tel (34) 937 - 745 160, Fax (34) 937 - 745 161

RESTAURANTS RESTAURANTES
Las Torres - Sant Esteve 5 km - Tel (34) 937 - 714 181
C.G. Masia Bach - on site - Tel (34) 937 - 728 800

Maspalomas

16 | 7 | 8

Prácticamente en el borde del mar y cerca de la ciudad, Maspalomas fue construido en un terreno muy llano cerca de las dunas, lo que le da un aspecto de links que uno no se espera encontrar en la Isla de Gran Canaria. La paternidad de Mackenzie Ross ofrece la garantía de autenticidad de estilo. Aunque es un recorrido de competición muy exigente, sin embargo es un buen campo para ir de vacaciones. Es un par 73 de longitud razonable, pero con dificuldades enormes, que invita a los jugadores a proceder sin complejos y según sus posibilidades. No hay que dormirse ni extraviarse en las dunas, donde el rough es muy peligroso. Grandes bunkers con una arena de agradable color amarillo esperan las bolas poco precisas. La flora subtropical compuesta de palmeras, pinos canarios y marítimos, ibiscos, buganvillas, etc., confiere un color muy particular a este diseño bastante británico. Es un campo de altísima ocupación, donde hay que jugar muy rápido pues los marshalls retiran del campo a los partidos que no cumplan su horario de paso por el 9.

Virtually by the sea and in town, Maspalomas was built on a very flat land. Its layout, close to sand-dunes, gives it a links style which you wouldn't expect to find on Grand Canary island, and the patronage of Mackenzie Ross provides a sure-fire guarantee of authenticity in terms of style. Although this is a rather challenging tournament course, it still makes for very good holiday golfing and so is a very "functional" golfing facility in this part of the world. This is a par 73 of reasonable length with no insurmountable difficulties, inviting players to "go for it" to the best of their ability. But they'll need to keep on their toes and not stray into the dunes where the rough can make a big dent in your card. Large bunkers filled with pretty yellow sand also await the mis-hit ball . The sub-tropical vegetation of palm-trees, Canary pines, hibiscus-trees and bougainvillaea add special colour to this very British-style layout where you will need to avoid slow play. Players who fall behind the clock are requested to leave the course after the 9th hole.

Club de Golf Maspalomas — 1968

Avda de Nackerman s/n
E - 35100 MASPALOMAS (Gran Canaria - Islas Canarias)

Office	Secretaria	(34) 928 - 762 581
Pro shop	Pro-shop	(34) 928 - 767 343
Fax	Fax	(34) 928 - 768 245
Web	www.maspalomasgolf.net	
Situation	Situación	Las Palmas, 30 km
Annual closure	Cierre anual	no
Weekly closure	Cierre semanal	no
Fees main season	Precios tempor. alta	18 holes

	Week days Semana	We/Bank holidays Fin de sem./fiestas
Individual Individual	€ 75	€ 75
Couple Pareja	€ 150	€ 150

Caddie Caddie no — **Electric Trolley** Carro eléctrico no
Buggy Coche yes — **Clubs** Palos yes

Credit cards Tarjetas de crédito
VISA - Eurocard - MasterCard

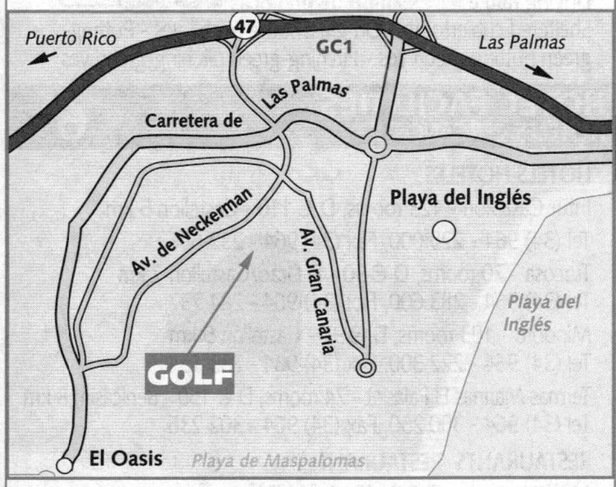

Access Acceso : Autopista Sur, → Maspalomas
Map 1 on page 1087 Plano 1 Página 1087

GOLF COURSE — RECORRIDO — 16/20

Site	Emplazamiento	
Maintenance	Mantenimiento	
Architect	Arquitecto	Mackenzie Ross
Type	Tipo	open country, seaside
Relief	Relieve	
Water in play	Agua	
Exp. to wind	Exp. al viento	
Trees in play	Arboles	

Scorecard Tarjeta	**Chp.** Campeonato	**Mens** Caballeros	**Ladies** Damas
Length Longitud	6189	6037	5210
Par	73	73	73
Slope system	—	122	126

Advised golfing ability Nivel de juego aconsejado — 0 12 24 36
Hcp required Handicap exigido — 30

CLUB HOUSE & AMENITIES — CLUB HOUSE Y DEPENDENCIAS — 7/10

Pro shop Pro-shop
Driving range Campo de prácticas
Sheltered cubierto 12 mats - On grass sobre hierba yes - Putting-green putting-green yes - Pitching-green pitching-green yes

HOTEL FACILITIES — HOTELES CERCANOS — 8/10

HOTELS HOTELES

Ifa-Faro - Maspalomas 3 km
183 rooms, D € 250
Tel (34) 928 - 142 214, Fax (34) 928 - 141 940

Palm Beach - 347 rooms, D € 305 - Maspalomas 3 km
Tel (34) 928 - 140 806, Fax (34) 928 - 141 808

Gran Hotel Costa Meloneras - San Bartolomé 2,5 km
1137 rooms, D € 157
Tel (34) 928 - 128 100, Fax (34) 928 - 128 122

RESTAURANTS RESTAURANTES

La Aquarela - Maspalomas 1 km - Tel (34) 928 - 140 178
Amaiur - Maspalomas 1 km - Tel (34) 928 - 761 414
Orangerie - Maspalomas 3 km - Tel (34) 928 - 140 806

Mediterraneo

16	7	6

Este recorrido ha contribuido a la fama creciente de su arquitecto Ramón Espinosa. Es una joya depositada en un amplio valle, sus sutiles dificultades lo hacen más delicado de lo que a primera vista parece, sin por ello desalentar a los jugadores de nivel medio. Los bunkers de calle y de green están inteligentemente situados y bien visibles e indican la táctica de juego que hay que adoptar. Algunos árboles aislados obligan a pegar la bola con efecto y hay obstáculos de agua –lagos y canales- en línea de juego en siete hoyos, completando una panoplia de dificultades muy variadas. Los greens, que están preparados para que rueden a la velocidad del Circuito Profesional Americano –recordemos que es el campo de origen de Sergio García- añaden un componente de alta calidad al juego pues son de lectura tan delicada como el toque con que hay que jugarlos. Inteligente y franco, es un recorrido para todo el mundo y se puede aconsejar tanto por su armonía como por su cuidadoso mantenimiento: se pasa una óptima jornada.

This layout has done much to enhance the growing reputation of architect Ramón Espinosa. It is a gem of a course located in a wide valley, and the subtly placed hazards make it tougher than you might think at first sight, although not to the point of scaring off the lesser players. The fairway and green-side bunkers are cleverly located and visible enough to help your game tactics. A few isolated trees call for elaborate shots, moving the ball both ways, and small ponds are in play on seven holes, thus completing a highly varied panoply of hazards. The greens, prepared at US Tour speeds (this is the home course of young Sergio García) are high-quality putting surfaces which are tough to read and require an excellent touch. An intelligent and honest course, this is a golfing arena for everyone. Being well-balanced and well-cared for, it is a course well worth recommending for spending a great day out.

Club de Campo Mediterraneo — 1978

Urbanización "La Coma" S/N
E - 12190 BORRIOL (Castellón)

Office	Secretaria	(34) 964 - 321 227
Pro shop	Pro-shop	(34) 964 - 321 653
Fax	Fax	(34) 964 - 321 653
Web	www.ccmediterraneo.com	
Situation	Situación	Castellón de la Plana, 5 km
Annual closure	Cierre anual	no
Weekly closure	Cierre semanal	no
Fees main season	Precios tempor. alta	18 holes

	Week days Semana	We/Bank holidays Fin de sem./fiestas
Individual Individual	€ 42	€ 48
Couple Pareja	€ 84	€ 96

Caddie Caddie no — **Electric Trolley** Carro eléctrico no

Buggy Coche yes — **Clubs** Palos yes

Credit cards Tarjetas de crédito
VISA - Mastercard

Access Acceso : A7 Barcelona-Valencia, Exit (Salida) 46
→ Castellón Norte. 700 m on the right
→ "Club de Campo". Golf 2,5 km
Map 5 on page 1095 Plano 5 Página 1095

GOLF COURSE — RECORRIDO — 16/20

Site	Emplazamiento	
Maintenance	Mantenimiento	
Architect	Arquitecto	Ramón Espinosa
Type	Tipo	country
Relief	Relieve	
Water in play	Agua	
Exp. to wind	Exp. al viento	
Trees in play	Arboles	

Scorecard Tarjeta	Chp. Campeonato	Mens Caballeros	Ladies Damas
Length Longitud	6384	6014	5230
Par	72	72	72
Slope system	133	129	124

Advised golfing ability / Nivel de juego aconsejado: 0 12 24 36

Hcp required / Handicap exigido: 28 Men, 36 Ladies

CLUB HOUSE & AMENITIES — CLUB HOUSE Y DEPENDENCIAS — 7/10

Pro shop Pro-shop
Driving range Campo de prácticas
Sheltered cubierto no - On grass sobre hierba yes - Putting-green putting-green yes - Pitching-green pitching-green yes

HOTEL FACILITIES — HOTELES CERCANOS — 6/10

HOTELS HOTELES

Intur Castellón - 123 rooms, D € 110 - Castellón 5 km
Tel (34) 964 - 225 000, Fax (34) 964 - 232 606

Turcosa - 70 rooms, D € 90 - El Grao/Castellón 7 km
Tel (34) 964 - 283 600, Fax (34) 964 - 284 737

Mindoro - 103 rooms, D € 97 - Castellón 5 km
Tel (34) 964 - 222 300, Fax (34) 964 - 233 154

Termas Marinas El Palasiet - 74 rooms, D € 150 - Benicasim 8 km
Tel (34) 964 - 300 250, Fax (34) 964 - 302 236

RESTAURANTS RESTAURANTES

Mare Nostrum - El Grao/Castellón 7 km
Tel (34) 964 - 282 929

Tasca del Puerto - El Grao/Castellón 7 km
Tel (34) 964 - 284 481

Mijas *Los Lagos*

16	6	7

De los dos recorridos de Mijas, éste es para los "pegadores" y el que da mayor sensación de espacio. Bien es verdad que hay ocho lagos en la línea de juego en una decena de hoyos, pero las calles son anchas. Y menos mal, porque Los Lagos es muy largo, sin muchas cuestas, lo que permite jugarlo sin recurrir a un coche. Algo característico de Trent Jones es la disposición de los bunkers, no sólo para defender los greens, sino para dificultar la tarea de quienes intentan cortar en los dog-legs. Además, presenta una cierta variedad visual en hoyos que son muy semejantes entre sí. Los greens son extensos, con bastantes caídas, en muy buen estado, y su rapidez no impide que aguanten bien la bola: cosa muy importante ya que a menudo hay que tirar a green con hierros largos. Que los jugadores medianos no se desanimen, pueden acortar el recorrido escogiendo tees de salida más adelantados.

Of the two courses at Mijas, this is the one for the big-hitters and for the greatest impression of open space. Sure, the eight lakes are very much to the fore on ten holes, but the fairways are wide. And so they should be, because "Los Lagos" is very long. But it is a pleasant course to play walking as the terrain is relatively flat. Typical of Trent Jones, the bunkers are there not only to defend the greens but also to trap players who try and cut corners on the dog-legs. They also add a little variety to holes that are often very similar in style. The greens are huge, undulating and in good condition, and although fast they pitch well. This is important because approach shots often call for a long iron. Average players should not lose heart though, as they can shorten the course considerably by playing off the front-tees.

Mijas Golf Club — 1976

Camino Viejo de Coín, Km 3,5
E – 29649 MIJAS-COSTA (Costa del Sol – Málaga)

Office	Secretaria	(34) 952 - 476 843
Pro shop	Pro-shop	(34) 952 - 476 843
Fax	Fax	(34) 952 - 467 943
Web	www.mijasgolf.org	
Situation	Situación	Málaga, 25 km
Annual closure	Cierre anual	no
Weekly closure	Cierre semanal	no

Fees main season Precios tempor. alta	18 holes	
	Week days Semana	**We/Bank holidays** Fin de sem./fiestas
Individual Individual	€ 70	€ 70
Couple Pareja	€ 140	€ 140

Caddie Caddie no — **Electric Trolley** Carro eléctrico yes

Buggy Coche yes — **Clubs** Palos yes

Credit cards Tarjetas de crédito
VISA - MasterCard

Access Acceso : Málaga N340 → Cádiz. Exit (Salida) "Cambio de Sentido", Fuengirola → Mijas, Golf 3 km

Map 8 on page 1101 Plano 8 Página 1101

GOLF COURSE — RECORRIDO — 16/20

Site	Emplazamiento	
Maintenance	Mantenimiento	
Architect	Arquitecto	Robert Trent Jones
Type	Tipo	country
Relief	Relieve	
Water in play	Agua	
Exp. to wind	Exp. al viento	
Trees in play	Arboles	

Scorecard Tarjeta	**Chp.** Campeonato	**Mens** Caballeros	**Ladies** Damas
Length Longitud	6367	6007	5148
Par	71	71	71
Slope system	110	111	110

Advised golfing ability Nivel de juego aconsejado: 0 12 24 36

Hcp required Handicap exigido: 28 Men, 36 Ladies

CLUB HOUSE & AMENITIES — CLUB HOUSE Y DEPENDENCIAS — 6/10

Pro shop Pro-shop

Driving range Campo de prácticas

Sheltered cubierto no - On grass sobre hierba yes - Putting-green putting-green yes - Pitching-green pitching-green no

HOTEL FACILITIES — HOTELES CERCANOS — 7/10

HOTELS HOTELES

Byblos - 144 rooms, D € 358 - Mijas 200 m
Tel (34) 952 - 473 050, Fax (34) 952 - 476 783

Tamisa Golf - 24 rooms, D € 190 - Mijas 500 m
Tel (34) 952 - 585 988, Fax (34) 952 - 663 893

Sunset Beach Club - 250 rooms, D € 117 - Mijas 500 m
Tel (34) 952 - 579 406

Confortel Fuengirola - 180 rooms, D € 207- Fuengirola 6 km
Tel (34) 952 - 921 000, Fax (34) 952 - 921 001

RESTAURANTS RESTAURANTES

Casa Roberto - Fuengirola 4 km - Tel (34) 952 - 465 809
El Golf Hoyo 5 - Mijas 400 m - Tel (34) 952 - 467 674

Mijas *Los Olivos*

13 | 6 | 7

De los dos recorridos de Mijas, Los Olivos conviene más a los jugadores de nivel medio. Por supuesto es estrecho, rodeado de numerosos olivos, algunos lagos pueden perturbar a los jugadores con poca técnica, su relieve es ligeramente más accidentado que el de "Los Lagos", pero encontrarán un trazado más a su medida y al alcance de sus posibilidades. Los greens son más pequeños, algunos ciegos, pero aguantan correctamente la bola y la progresión general del recorrido lo hace más divertido para jugar en familia cuando el resultado es menos importante que el placer. No es un recorrido para atacar y ciertamente no fue diseñado para ello. Da la impresión que Trent Jones quiso poner de relieve en Mijas dos facetas muy diferentes de su buen hacer. En todo caso, este conjunto permite que todos puedan escoger según su forma actual.

When choosing between the two courses at Mijas, average players are perhaps better off playing Los Olivos, restyled a few years ago. The course is certainly tight and bordered by numerous olive trees, there are a few lakes to scare players with limited technique and the relief is in part much more broken than its sister course, Los Lagos. But the layout is probably much more within their scope and ability. The greens are smaller and some are blind, but they pitch pretty well and the general layout makes this course fun for playing with the family when scores are less important than having a good time. It is not a course for attacking players and visibly was not designed to be so. You get the impression that Trent Jones wanted to demonstrate two very different facets of his architectural know-how at Mijas. In any case, this golfing resort allows everyone to choose according to the shape of their game.

Mijas Golf Club — 1976

Camino Viejo de Coín, Km 3,5
E – 29649 MIJAS-COSTA (Costa del Sol – Málaga)

Office	Secretaría	(34) 952 - 476 843
Pro shop	Pro-shop	(34) 952 - 476 843
Fax	Fax	(34) 952 - 467 943
Web	www.mijasgolf.org	
Situation	Situación	Málaga, 25 km
Annual closure	Cierre anual	no
Weekly closure	Cierre semanal	no
Fees main season	Precios tempor. alta	18 holes

	Week days / Semana	We/Bank holidays / Fin de sem./fiestas
Individual Individual	€ 70	€ 70
Couple Pareja	€ 140	€ 140

Caddie Caddie no — **Electric Trolley** Carro eléctrico yes
Buggy Coche yes — **Clubs** Palos yes

Credit cards Tarjetas de crédito
VISA - MasterCard

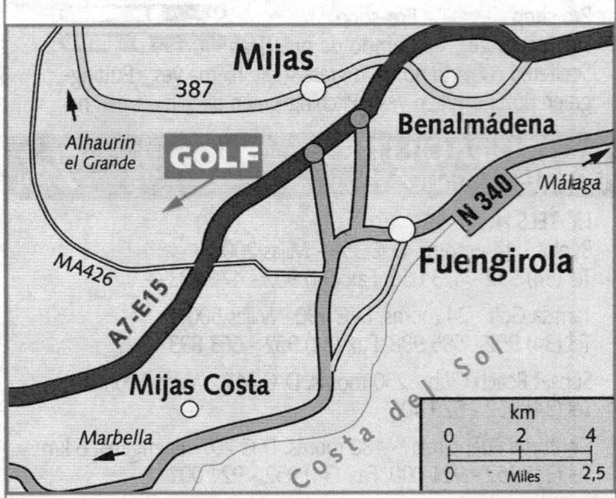

Access Acceso : Málaga N340 → Cádiz. Exit (Salida) "Cambio de Sentido", Fuengirola → Mijas, Golf 3 km
Map 8 on page 1101 Plano 8 Página 1101

GOLF COURSE — RECORRIDO — 13/20

Site	Emplazamiento	
Maintenance	Mantenimiento	
Architect	Arquitecto	Robert Trent Jones
Type	Tipo	country, hilly
Relief	Relieve	
Water in play	Agua	
Exp. to wind	Exp. al viento	
Trees in play	Arboles	

Scorecard Tarjeta	Chp. Campeonato	Mens Caballeros	Ladies Damas
Length Longitud	5840	5601	4877
Par	70	70	70
Slope system	115	113	114

Advised golfing ability Nivel de juego aconsejado: 0 12 24 36
Hcp required Handicap exigido: 28 Men, 36 Ladies

CLUB HOUSE & AMENITIES — CLUB HOUSE Y DEPENDENCIAS — 6/10

Pro shop Pro-shop
Driving range Campo de prácticas
Sheltered cubierto no - On grass sobre hierba yes - Putting-green putting-green yes - Pitching-green pitching-green no

HOTEL FACILITIES — HOTELES CERCANOS — 7/10

HOTELS HOTELES
Byblos - 144 rooms, D € 358 - Mijas 200 m
Tel (34) 952 - 473 050, Fax (34) 952 - 476 783

Tamisa Golf - 24 rooms, D € 190 - Mijas 500 m
Tel (34) 952 - 585 988, Fax (34) 952 - 663 893

Sunset Beach Club - 250 rooms, D € 117 - Mijas 500 m
Tel (34) 952 - 579 406

Confortel Fuengirola - 180 rooms, D € 207- Fuengirola 6 km
Tel (34) 952 - 921 000, Fax (34) 952 - 921 001

RESTAURANTS RESTAURANTES
Casa Roberto - Fuengirola 4 km - Tel (34) 952 - 465 809
El Golf Hoyo 5 - Mijas 400 m - Tel (34) 952 - 467 674

Montanyà

14 | 7 | 4

Dave Thomas no ha querido añadir demasiadas dificultades técnicas a un recorrido bastante físico por sus cuestas. Naturalmente, hay árboles en la línea de juego, también algunos obstáculos de agua y aunque los bunkers de green están bastante alejados son poco visibles (están como hundidos) al igual que los bunkers de calle. Los greenes tienen en general un declive bastante importante y son peligrosos cuando están rápidos, que es lo habitual salvo en los días más húmedos. Todo ello hace que la estrategia de juego sea delicada cuando no se conoce el recorrido. Una vez conocido se pueden cortar los dog-legs con un buen drive, ya sea volando los árboles o imprimiendo efecto a la bola. Agradable y variado merece la pena jugarlo varias veces, pero dada su situación en altura y en el interior, no se aconseja ir en invierno a no ser que se quiera contemplar el panorama de los Pirineos nevados desde la terraza de su confortable casa-club.

Dave Thomas did not want to add too many technical difficulties to an already hilly and physically quite demanding course. The trees are there, of course, together with a little water, but while the green-side bunkers are not too close to the greens, they are hard to see (being sunk into dips). The same goes for the fairway bunkers. There is quite a lot of slope on the greens, which can be difficult when playing fast, as they often do. All this makes for a tricky choice of game strategy when playing the course for the first time. When you know the course, long drivers can cut corners on the dog-legs either by hitting over the trees or by flighting the ball. Pleasant and varied, this pretty course is well worth a few visits but the high-altitude location inland is not to be recommended in winter, except perhaps to gaze over the panorama of the snow-covered Pyrenees from the terrace of the very comfortable club-house.

Club de Golf Montanyà — 1989

Masia l'Estanyol s/n.
E - 08553 EL BRULL (Barcelona)

Office	Secretaria	(34) 938 - 840 170
Pro shop	Pro-shop	(34) 938 - 840 170
Fax	Fax	(34) 938 - 840 407
Web	www.golfmontanya.com	
Situation	Situación	Barcelona, 60 km

Vic / Vich (pop. 30 060), 17 km

Annual closure	Cierre anual	no
Weekly closure	Cierre semanal	no

Fees main season Precios tempor. alta	18 holes	
	Week days Semana	**We/Bank holidays** Fin de sem./fiestas
Individual Individual	€ 65	€ 130
Couple Pareja	€ 130	€ 260

Caddie Caddie no — **Electric Trolley** Carro eléctrico yes
Buggy Coche yes — **Clubs** Palos yes
Credit cards Tarjetas de crédito
VISA - MasterCard

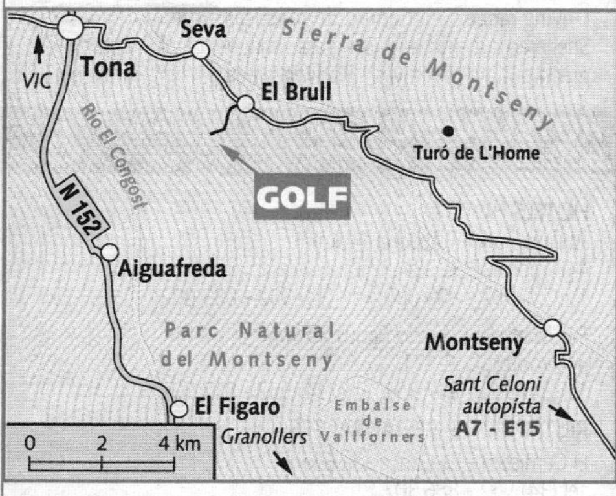

Access Acceso : Barcelona, N152 → Vic (Vich).
Tona → Seva, El Brull
Map 3 on page 1091 Plano 3 Página 1091

GOLF COURSE — RECORRIDO — 14/20

Site	Emplazamiento	
Maintenance	Mantenimiento	
Architect	Arquitecto	Dave Thomas
Type	Tipo	forest, hilly
Relief	Relieve	
Water in play	Agua	
Exp. to wind	Exp. al viento	
Trees in play	Arboles	

Scorecard Tarjeta	**Chp.** Campeonato	**Mens** Caballeros	**Ladies** Damas
Length Longitud	6197	6067	5177
Par	72	72	72
Slope system	128	126	123

Advised golfing ability Nivel de juego aconsejado — 0 12 24 36
Hcp required Handicap exigido — 28 Men, 36 Ladies

CLUB HOUSE & AMENITIES — CLUB HOUSE Y DEPENDENCIAS — 7/10

Pro shop Pro-shop
Driving range Campo de prácticas
Sheltered cubierto 25 mats - On grass sobre hierba yes
Putting-green putting-green yes - Pitching-green pitching-green no

HOTEL FACILITIES — HOTELES CERCANOS — 4/10

HOTELS HOTELES
El Montanyà - Montanyà 4 km
120 rooms, D € 179
Tel (34) 938 - 840 606, Fax (34) 938 - 840 558

Ciutat de Vic - Vic 20 km
36 rooms, D € 123
Tel (34) 938 - 892 551, Fax (34) 938 - 891 447

Hotel Seva - 23 rooms, D € 80 - Seva 4 km
Tel (34) 938 - 840 376, Fax (34) 938 - 840 460

RESTAURANTS RESTAURANTES
Estanyol - on site - Tel (34) 938 - 840 354
El Montanyà - Montanyà 4 km - Tel (34) 938 - 840 004
La Pedrera - Seva 4 km - Tel (34) 938 - 840 376

Monte Mayor

13	5	5

El golf más extravagante de toda la región y sin duda de España. Diseñado por José Gancedo, este recorrido o gusta o se cetesta. En plena montaña y muy expuesto al viento, reserva toda clase de sorpresas, hasta tal punto que algunos hoyos "normales" parecen insulsos. Sinuoso entre rocas, franqueando quebradas, bajando colinas, en medio de una vegetación salvaje y tupida, hay que conservar el dominio de sí mismo. Si se sale de calle, ¡oh desgracia!. Pero las reglas locales son indulgentes: toda bola perdida se considera que reposa en un obstáculo de agua lateral. Uno se encuentra solo ante su propio juego como si estuviese al otro lado del mundo. Que el emblema del recorrido sea un toro no es mera casualidad: hay que luchar contra él, aguantar sus embistes, esquivar sus ataques. Se acaba agotado pero encantado de los magníficos paisajes. Un recorrido barroco, de gran inteligencia e imposible de ignorar.

The most extravagant course in the whole region and certainly in the whole of Spain. Designed by José Gancedo, you either love it or hate it, with no middle ground. Right in the mountains and very exposed to the wind, it reserves every sort of surprise to the extent where certain "normal" holes look positively insipid. Winding its way through rocks, crossing gorges and running down hills amidst wild thick vegetation, the course calls for a cool head. Too bad if you miss the fairways. But the local rules are pretty lenient as any lost ball is considered to be in a side water hazard. Here you are at the world's end, alone with your game of golf. It is no accident to see that the course's emblem is a bull; you have to fight it, stave off its charges and sidestep its attacks. You leave the 18th green exhausted but delighted with the magnificent landscapes. A baroque course of great intelligence and one that is impossible to overlook.

Monte Mayor Golf Club — 1989

Avda. Montemayor
E - 29679 BENAHAVÍS (Málaga – Costa del Sol)

Office Secretaría (34) 952 - 937 111
Pro shop Pro-shop (34) 952 - 937 111
Fax Fax (34) 952 - 937 112
Web www.montemayorgolf.com
Situation Situación Marbella, 22 km
Estepona (pop. 36 307), 14 km
Annual closure Cierre anual no
Weekly closure Cierre semanal no
Fees main season Precios tempor. alta 18 holes

	Week days Semana	We/Bank holidays Fin de sem./fiestas
Individual Individual	€ 90	€ 90
Couple Pareja	€ 180	€ 180

Green fees include golf cars
Caddie Caddie no **Electric Trolley** Carro eléctrico no
Buggy Coche incl. with green-fee **Clubs** Palos no
Credit cards Tarjetas de crédito
VISA - Mastercard - AMEX

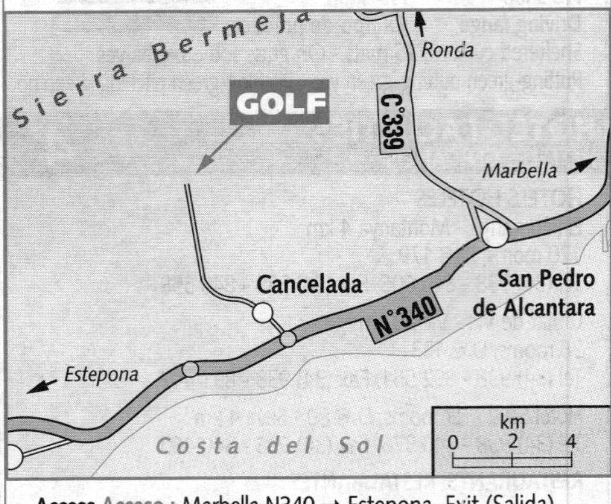

Access Acceso : Marbella N340 → Estepona. Exit (Salida) "La Cancelada". Km 163,6 on the right → Golf
Map 8 on page 1101 Plano 8 Página 1101

GOLF COURSE — RECORRIDO — 13/20

Site Emplazamiento
Maintenance Mantenimiento
Architect Arquitecto José Gancedo
Type Tipo mountain
Relief Relieve
Water in play Agua
Exp. to wind Exp. al viento
Trees in play Arboles

Scorecard Tarjeta	Chp. Campeonato	Mens Caballeros	Ladies Damas
Length Longitud	5652	5354	4800
Par	71	71	71
Slope system	136	132	124

Advised golfing ability Nivel de juego aconsejado 0 12 24 36
Hcp required Handicap exigido 28 Men, 36 Ladies

CLUB HOUSE & AMENITIES — CLUB HOUSE Y DEPENDENCIAS — 5/10

Pro shop Pro-shop
Driving range Campo de prácticas
Sheltered cubierto no - On grass sobre hierba no - Putting-green putting-green yes - Pitching-green pitching-green no

HOTEL FACILITIES — HOTELES CERCANOS — 5/10

HOTELS HOTELES
Atalaya Park - Estepona 14 km
448 rooms, D € 284
Tel (34) 952 - 889 000, Fax (34) 952 - 889 002

Pyr Marbella - Puerto Banús 25 km
319 rooms, D € 171
Tel (34) 952 - 817 353, Fax (34) 952 - 817 907

RESTAURANTS RESTAURANTES
El Carnicero - La Cancelada 6 km
Tel (34) 952 - 886 307
El Rocio - Estepona 14 km - Tel (34) 952 - 800 046

Montecastillo

17	8	8

Era de esperar encontrarse un día con la firma de Jack Nicklaus en el sur de España. Ha sacado buen partido de un terreno moderadamente accidentado, y si los greens están frecuentemente en alto, no hay hoyos ciegos ni hoyos en subida, lo que confirma su filosofía de que: "hay que ver lo que hay que hacer". Prueba de ello el 18 con el tee de salida allá en alto. En realidad es un recorrido franco y difícil de lidiar, pero su dificultad general no impide jugarlo en familia (salvo los principiantes), siempre y cuando cada uno se mantenga tranquilo y no se obsesione por el resultado. Todas las dificultades se concentran en la línea de juego (sobre todo los obstáculos de agua), y hay muchos fuera de límites. La variedad de situaciones incita a jugarlo varias veces para comprender mejor sus sutilezas. Espectacular y original (por la región), este recorrido no reniega el espíritu americano de su autor. Los que conocen sus otras realizaciones no quedarán defraudados.

It was only to be expected that one day Jack Nicklaus would leave his mark in southern Spain. He has extracted the best out of a moderately hilly terrain, and while the greens are frequently elevated, there are no blind or uphill holes thus illustrating the great man's philosophy of: "you have to see what you have to do". Witness hole N° 18 with a very elevated tee. As a result, this is a very open but very tricky course to get around, but the general difficulty does not prevent this from being a layout for all the family (but not beginners) as long as you keep cool and don't get obsessed with your score. All the hazards of situations will make you want to play Montecastillo several times to fully understand the more subtle sides to the course. Spectacular and original (for the region, that is), the course does not break with the American spirit of its designer. Players who know his other courses will not be surprised.

Montecastillo Resort — 1992

Carretera de Arcos, km. 9,6
E - 11406 JEREZ DE LA FRONTERA (Cádiz)

Office Secretaria (34) 956 - 151 200
Pro shop Pro-shop (34) 956 - 151 200
Fax Fax (34) 956 - 151 209
Web www.montecastillo.com
Situation Situación Sevilla, 78 km
Jerez (pop. 184 364), 6 km

Annual closure Cierre anual no
Weekly closure Cierre semanal no

Fees main season / Precios tempor. alta	Week days / Semana	We/Bank holidays / Fin de sem./fiestas
	18 holes	
Individual Individual	€ 100	€ 100
Couple Pareja	€ 200	€ 200

Caddie Caddie no — **Electric Trolley** Carro eléctrico no
Buggy Coche yes — **Clubs** Palos yes

Credit cards Tarjetas de crédito
VISA - Eurocard - MasterCard - AMEX - DC

Access Acceso : Jerez, N342 → Arcos de la Frontera, 9,8 km turn right, Golf 1,5 km
Map 8 on page 1100 Plano 8 Página 1100

GOLF COURSE — RECORRIDO 17/20

Site Emplazamiento
Maintenance Mantenimiento
Architect Arquitecto Jack Nicklaus
Type Tipo country
Relief Relieve
Water in play Agua
Exp. to wind Exp. al viento
Trees in play Arboles

Scorecard / Tarjeta	Chp. / Campeonato	Mens / Caballeros	Ladies / Damas
Length Longitud	6456	6043	5230
Par	72	72	72
Slope system	138	132	132

Advised golfing ability Nivel de juego aconsejado 0 12 24 36
Hcp required Handicap exigido 28 Men, 36 Ladies

CLUB HOUSE & AMENITIES — CLUB HOUSE Y DEPENDENCIAS 8/10

Pro shop Pro-shop
Driving range Campo de prácticas
Sheltered cubierto 18 mats - On grass sobre hierba yes - Putting-green putting-green yes - Pitching-green pitching-green yes

HOTEL FACILITIES — HOTELES CERCANOS 8/10

HOTELS HOTELES
Montecastillo - Montecastillo 100 m
120 rooms, D € 324
Tel (34) 956 - 151 200, Fax (34) 956 - 151 209

Hotel Jerez - Jerez 10 km
131 rooms, D € 172
Tel (34) 956 - 300 600, Fax (34) 956 - 305 001

Prestige Palmera Plaza - 55 rooms, D € 272 - Jerez 15 km
Tel (34) 956 - 031 500, Fax (34) 956 - 031 800

RESTAURANTS RESTAURANTES
El Bosque - Jerez 10 km - Tel (34) 956 - 303 333
Mesa Redonda - Jerez 10 km - Tel (34) 956 - 340 069

Montenmedio

16	8	7

La Dehesa de Montenmedio es un recorrido de buena calidad en general, salido del pincel de Alejandro Maldonado y que creemos es, hasta ahora, su realización más prestigiosa. La región está cada día mejor equipada de golfs, y es cada vez más difícil encontrar terrenos entre Málaga, Marbella y Gibraltar. Las novedades van hacia el oeste. En este recorrido, por el momento no se aceptan más de 60 jugadores al día, distribuidos en partidos a veinte minutos de intervalo, lo que garantiza una gran comodidad de juego. Las calles y greenes son anchos favoreciendo a los jugadores de tipo medio que son la mayor parte de los visitantes de la región. La mayor parte de las veces en los segundos golpes hacia los greenes se pueden utilizar hierros medianos. Los pares 3 exigen mucha precisión. No obstante hay que permanecer vigilantes y no atacar de cualquier manera, ya que la configuración natural del terreno ha sido preservada al igual que la vegetación, mientras que el agua es un elemento más bien decorativo que no dificulta el juego.

La Dehesa de Montenmedio is a course of generally excellent standard thanks to the design skills of Alejandro Maldonado, from whom this is the most prestigious achievement to date as far as we know. This region is being given more and more courses as land becomes increasingly scarce between Málaga, Marbella and Gibraltar. The west is where it is all happening. For the time being, the club admits only 60 players a day teeing off at 20 minute intervals, so you are in for a relaxed round. The fairways and greens are wide, which is good news for the average players who form the core of green-feers visiting the region. Most of their approach shots will be medium-irons, and the par 3s call for an accurate tee-shot. However, they will need to be careful and not go for the greens in any old way, because the designer has kept the terrain's natural contours and vegetation. There is water but it is more decorative than really in play.

Dehesa Montenmedio Golf & Country Club

1996

Carretera A-48 km 42,5
E - 11150 VEJER DE LA FRONTERA-BARBATE
(Cádiz - Andalucía)

Office	Secretaria	(34) 956 - 451 216
Pro shop	Pro-shop	(34) 956 - 455 004
Fax	Fax	(34) 956 - 451 295
Web	www.monteenmedio.com	
Situation	Situación	Cádiz (pop.157 355), 42 km
Annual closure	Cierre anual	no
Weekly closure	Cierre semanal	no

Fees main season Precios tempor. alta	Week days Semana	We/Bank holidays Fin de sem./fiestas
	18 holes	
Individual Individual	€ 75	€ 75
Couple Pareja	€ 150	€ 150

Caddie Caddie yes — **Electric Trolley** Carro eléctrico yes

Buggy Coche yes — **Clubs** Palos yes

Credit cards Tarjetas de crédito
VISA - MasterCard - AMEX - DC

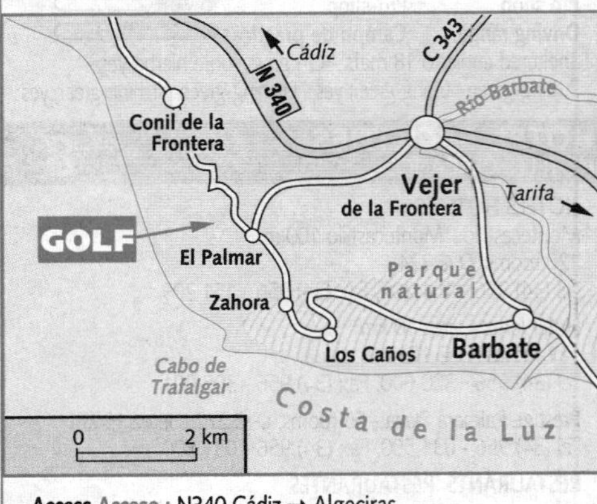

Access Acceso : N340 Cádiz → Algeciras.
Map 8 on page 1100 Plano 8 Página 1100

GOLF COURSE — RECORRIDO 16/20

Site	Emplazamiento	
Maintenance	Mantenimiento	
Architect	Arquitecto	Alejandro Maldonado
Type	Tipo	parkland
Relief	Relieve	
Water in play	Agua	
Exp. to wind	Exp. al viento	
Trees in play	Arboles	

Scorecard Tarjeta	Chp. Campeonato	Mens Caballeros	Ladies Damas
Length Longitud	5931	5782	5101
Par	72	72	72
Slope system	135	133	129

Advised golfing ability Nivel de juego aconsejado: 0 12 24 36

Hcp required Handicap exigido: 28 Men, 34 Ladies

CLUB HOUSE & AMENITIES — CLUB HOUSE Y DEPENDENCIAS 8/10

Pro shop Pro-shop
Driving range Campo de prácticas
Sheltered cubierto no - On grass sobre hierba yes - Putting-green putting-green yes - Pitching-green pitching-green yes

HOTEL FACILITIES — HOTELES CERCANOS 7/10

HOTELS HOTELES
Convento de San Francisco - Vejer 4 km
25 rooms, D € 77
Tel (34) 956 - 451 001, Fax (34) 956 - 451 004

Royal Andalus Golf - Chiclana de la Frontera 20 km
263 rooms, D € 235
Tel (34) 956 - 494 109, Fax (34) 956 - 494 490

Flamenco - 114 rooms, D € 165 - Conil 3 km
Tel (34) 956 - 440 711, Fax (34) 956 - 440 542

RESTAURANTS RESTAURANTES
Torres - Barbate 5 km - Tel (34) 956 - 430 985

Neguri

17 | 7 | 7

Junto a El Saler o el Club de Campo, Neguri es uno de los grandes ejemplos del estilo de Javier Arana, a la vez humilde (en su respeto a la tradición), y muy personal (en su interpretación). Campo para los entendidos, Neguri está en perfectos condiciones aunque la tierra éste demasiado cansada. A su trazado clásico y de una rara elegancia, pocos cambios han sido incorporados desde sus orígenes aunque numerosos pinos hayan sido plantados para sustituir las especies desaparecidas en primera línea de calle. Ha sido una saludable iniciativa ya que reconstruyen, con el conjunto de bunkers, las principales dificultades de juego. Muy difícil desde las barras de atrás, Neguri es un poco más asequible desde las otras salidas, pero sus sutilezas exigen un cierto nivel de juego para poder ser apreciadas plenamente. Los primeros hoyos discurren colgados del acantilado, con frecuencia barridos por el viento, mientras el bosque de pinos ocupa la segunda parte del recorrido por lo que conviene dominar distintas estrategias de juego.

With El Saler, Aloha or Club de Campo, Neguri is one of the great examples of the Javier Arana style, at once humble (in his respect of tradition) and very personal (in his interpretation). Considered to be a private club, Neguri opens its doors only to members' guests, although visitors can hardly be accused of invading the course given that Bilbao is not yet a major tourist destination. A course for connoisseurs, Neguri is in good condition, although the soil seems to be growing a little weary. A few changes have been made, including pine-trees planted to replace the trees that have disappeared from the front-line of the fairway limits. This is a welcome initiative, because along with bunkers trees form the course's main difficulties, basically on the back 9, naturally. Very tough from the back-tees, Neguri mellows slightly when playing further forward but the course's subtleties require a certain level of proficiency to be fully appreciated.

Real Sociedad de Golf de Neguri — **1911**
Campo "La Galea", Aptdo de Correos 9
E - 48990 ALGORTA-GETXO (Vizcaya – País Vasco)

Office Secretaria (34) 944 - 910 200
Pro shop Pro-shop (34) 944 - 910 200
Fax Fax (34) 944 - 605 611
E-mail rsgn@rsgolfneguri.com
Situation Situación Bilbao, 13 km
Algorta (pop. 79 517), 2 km
Annual closure Cierre anual — no
Weekly closure Cierre semanal — no
Fees main season Precios tempor. alta — 18 holes

	Week days Semana	We/Bank holidays Fin de sem./fiestas
Individual Individual	€ 145*	€ 145*
Couple Pareja	€ 290*	€ 290*

Member's guests only (Sólo invitados de socios)

Caddie Caddie no — **Electric Trolley** Carro eléctrico yes
Buggy Coche no — **Clubs** Palos no
Credit cards Tarjetas de crédito — VISA

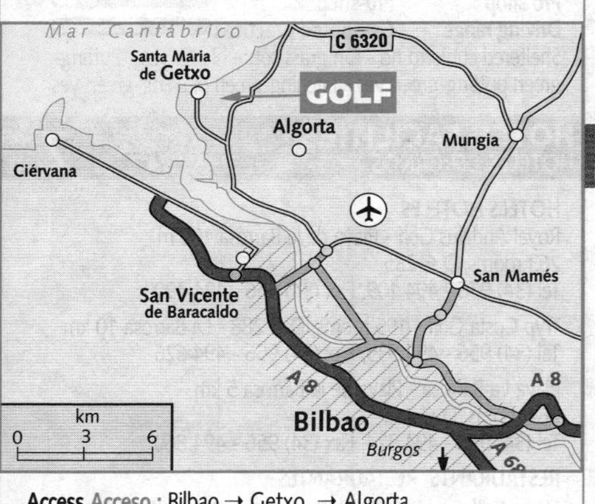

Access Acceso : Bilbao → Getxo, → Algorta
Map 2 on page 1088 Plano 2 Página 1088

GOLF COURSE
RECORRIDO — 17/20

Site Emplazamiento
Maintenance Mantenimiento
Architect Arquitecto — Javier Arana
Type Tipo — forest,, seaside
Relief Relieve
Water in play Agua
Exp. to wind Exp. al viento
Trees in play Arboles

Scorecard Tarjeta	Chp. Campeonato	Mens Caballeros	Ladies Damas
Length Longitud	6280	6054	5112
Par	72	72	72
Slope system	127	124	121

Advised golfing ability Nivel de juego aconsejado — 0 12 24 36
Hcp required Handicap exigido — 28 Men, 36 Ladies

CLUB HOUSE & AMENITIES
CLUB HOUSE Y DEPENDENCIAS — 7/10

Pro shop Pro-shop
Driving range Campo de prácticas
Sheltered cubierto 20 mats - On grass sobre hierba yes - Putting-green putting-green yes - Pitching-green pitching-green yes

HOTEL FACILITIES
HOTELES CERCANOS — 7/10

HOTELS HOTELES
Los Tamarises - 42 rooms, D € 98 - Algorta 4 km
Tel (34) 944 - 910 005, Fax (34) 944 - 911 310

Igeretxe Agustín - 21 rooms, D € 98 - Algorta 2 km
Tel (34) 944 - 910 009, Fax (34) 944 - 608 599

Lopez de Aro - Bilbao 13 km
53 rooms, D € 200
Tel (34) 944 - 235 500, Fax (34) 944 - 234 500

RESTAURANTS RESTAURANTES
Jolastoki - Neguri - Tel (34) 949 - 912 031
Cubita - Algorta 2 km - Tel (34) 944 - 911 700
Zortziko - Bilbao 13 km - Tel (34) 944 - 239 743

Novo Sancti Petri

16	7	7

Con 36 hoyos el campo responde a su alta ocupación. El diseño de Ballesteros es propio de un campo de vacaciones, sin excesivas complicaciones pero dispuesto a plantear diversas dificultades a jugadores de nivel medio, con obstáculos de agua en ciertas zonas, bunkers bien hechos aunque no intimidatorios y líneas de árboles que obligan a esmerarse en la precisión de los golpes de salida. Favorece a los jugadores que tienen facilidad para mover la bola de derecha a izquierda y los aproches hacia los amplios greenes han de hacerse por alto ya que están bien protegidos. El recorrido A es más variado, con hoyos muy abiertos, más expuesto a la brisa marina y con relieves moderados; mientras el recorrido B es más llano, generalmente entre pinos. Uno y otro, en definitiva, tienen que dejar al jugador con el dulce sabor de boca de haber sabido superar el test de un gran campeón.

With 36 holes, this layout is just what any holidaying golfer is looking for. This Ballesteros design is just what the proverbial doctor ordered without any excessive complications but just a few headaches for the average player: water hazards here and there and a light scattering of well-placed bunkers to make sure you keep it straight off the tee. It all works in favour of golfers who can flight the ball from right to left and hit high approach shots to attack nicely-sized but well protected greens. Course A offers the most variety with a number of very open holes exposed to the sea breeze and only moderate slopes to contend with. Course B is flatter and winds its way through a pine forest. All in all, both courses give players the pleasant impression of having successfully sat the examination prepared by the great golfer who designed them.

Club de Golf Novo Sancti Petri 1991

Playa de La Barrosa
E - 11139 CHICLANA DE LA FRONTERA (Cádiz)

Office	Secretaria	(34) 956 - 494 005
Pro shop	Pro-shop	(34) 956 - 494 847
Fax	Fax	(34) 956 - 494 350
Web	www.golf-novosancti.es	
Situation	Situación	Jerez, 50 km

Chiclana de la Frontera (pop. 46 610), 11 km

Annual closure	Cierre anual	no
Weekly closure	Cierre semanal	no

1174

Fees main season Precios tempor. alta		18 holes
	Week days Semana	**We/Bank holidays** Fin de sem./fiestas
Individual Individual	€ 61	€ 61
Couple Pareja	€ 122	€ 122

Caddie Caddie on request **Electric Trolley** Carro eléctrico yes

Buggy Coche yes **Clubs** Palos yes

Credit cards Tarjetas de crédito
VISA - Eurocard - MasterCard - AMEX - DC

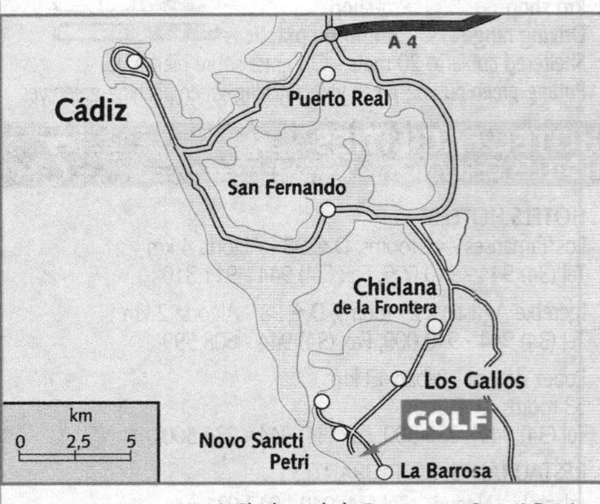

Access Acceso : N340 Chiclana de la Frontera → Sancti Petri
Map 8 on page 1100 Plano 8 Página 1100

GOLF COURSE
RECORRIDO — 16/20

Site	Emplazamiento	
Maintenance	Mantenimiento	
Architect	Arquitecto	Seve Ballesteros
Type	Tipo	seaside course
Relief	Relieve	
Water in play	Agua	
Exp. to wind	Exp. al viento	
Trees in play	Arboles	

Scorecard Tarjeta	**Chp.** Campeonato	**Mens** Caballeros	**Ladies** Damas
Length Longitud	6476	6097	5206
Par	72	72	72
Slope system	132	132	128

Advised golfing ability Nivel de juego aconsejado: 0 12 24 36

Hcp required Handicap exigido 28 Men, 36 Ladies

CLUB HOUSE & AMENITIES
CLUB HOUSE Y DEPENDENCIAS — 7/10

Pro shop	Pro-shop
Driving range	Campo de prácticas

Sheltered cubierto no - On grass sobre hierba yes - Putting-green putting-green yes - Pitching-green pitching-green yes

HOTEL FACILITIES
HOTELES CERCANOS — 7/10

HOTELS HOTELES

Royal Andalus Golf - Playa de la Barrosa 100 m
263 rooms, D € 235
Tel (34) 956 - 494 109, Fax (34) 956 - 494 490

Tryp Costa Golf - 195 rooms, D € 288 - La Barrosa 10 km
Tel (34) 956 - 494 535, Fax (34) 956 - 494 626

Playa La Barrosa - Playa de la Barrosa 5 km
264 rooms, D € 215
Tel (34) 956 - 494 824, Fax (34) 956 - 494 850

RESTAURANTS RESTAURANTES

Novo Golf Gachito - Chiclana de la Frontera 100 m
Tel (34) 956 - 495 249

El Faro - Cádiz 25 km - Tel (34) 956 - 211 068

Oliva Nova

14	6	7

Esta es una de las realizaciones de Severiano Ballesteros, en el extremo sur de la Costa Valenciana, lindando con la superturística y residencial costa de Alicante donde los campos de golf se multiplican para atender la demanda y preferencias de alemanes y centroeuropeos en general. Oliva Nova ofrece un campo completo por su cuidado mantenimiento y los diversos elementos del trazado que permiten jugar golpes muy variados. El agua es un elemento de riesgo que aparece constantemente, tanto señalando la referencia de dirección de los golpes de salida como enmarcando muchos greenes. Los greenes son delicados de atacar y de jugar, por sus caídas acusadas y porque varios de ellos están construídos en pendiente, en subida por la parte delantera y en bajada por el fondo. En un terreno llano próximo al mar, que disfruta por lo tanto de la refrescante brisa marina, el recorrido todavía necesita tiempo para que la vegetación plantada adquiera envergadura.

This is one of the designs by Severiano Ballesteros to the extreme south of the Costa Valenciana, where golf courses are mushrooming to attract customers from Northern Europe and especially Germany. Oliva Nova is a very complete and well-groomed course, where the layout calls for a whole variety of shots. Water is a risk element that is constantly around to attract shots hit slightly off the fairway or to guard any number of greens. The latter are difficult both to approach and to play, being sharply contoured and in many cases built on slopes, where the front part of the green slopes sideways and the rear section runs away. Close to the sea (the cooling sea-breeze is always much appreciated), this course calls for a little patience while we wait for the newly planted bushes and trees to really grow.

Club de Golf Oliva Nova — 1997

E - 46780 OLIVA (Valencia)

Office Secretaria (34) 962 - 857 975
Pro shop Pro-shop (34) 962 - 857 666
Fax Fax (34) 962 - 857 667
Web www.olivanovagolf.com
Situation Situación Valencia, 76 km
Gandía (pop. 52 000), 8 km

Annual closure Cierre anual no
Weekly closure Cierre semanal no

Fees main season Precios tempor. alta 18 holes

	Week days Semana	We/Bank holidays Fin de sem./fiestas
Individual Individual	€ 69	€ 69
Couple Pareja	€ 138	€ 138

Caddie Caddie no — **Electric Trolley** Carro eléctrico yes
Buggy Coche yes — **Clubs** Palos yes
Credit cards Tarjetas de crédito
VISA - Eurocard - MasterCard - AMEX

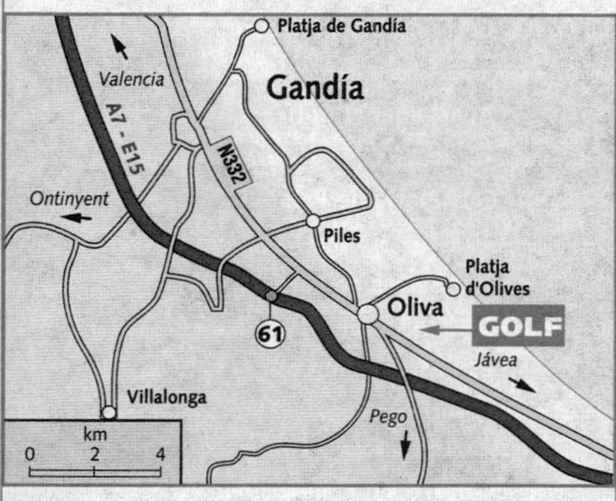

Access Acceso : Valencia, A7. Exit (Salida) 61. Go through Oliva → Gandía. Km 209 on N-332, turn left → Golf.
Map 7 on page 1099 Plano 7 Página 1099

GOLF COURSE — RECORRIDO — 14/20

Site Emplazamiento
Maintenance Mantenimiento
Architect Arquitecto — Seve Ballesteros
Type Tipo — parkland, inland
Relief Relieve
Water in play Agua
Exp. to wind Exp. al viento
Trees in play Arboles

Scorecard Tarjeta	Chp. Campeonato	Mens Caballeros	Ladies Damas
Length Longitud	6270	6037	5157
Par	72	72	72
Slope system	128	126	120

Advised golfing ability Nivel de juego aconsejado — 0 12 24 36
Hcp required Handicap exigido — 36

CLUB HOUSE & AMENITIES — CLUB HOUSE Y DEPENDENCIAS — 6/10

Pro shop Pro-shop
Driving range Campo de prácticas
Sheltered cubierto no - On grass sobre hierba yes - Putting-green putting-green yes - Pitching-green pitching-green yes

HOTEL FACILITIES — HOTELES CERCANOS — 7/10

HOTELS HOTELES
Oliva Nova Beach & Golf Hotel - Oliva 1 km
90 rooms, D € 214
Tel (34) 962 - 853 300, Fax (34) 962 - 855 108

Bayren I - Gandía 14 km - 161 rooms, D € 140
Tel (34) 962 - 840 300, Fax (34) 962 - 840 653

Don Ximo Club Hotel - Gandía 14 km - 68 rooms, D € 116
Tel (34) 962 - 845 393, Fax (34) 962 - 841 269

RESTAURANTS RESTAURANTES
Kiko Port - Oliva 6 km - Tel (34) 962 - 856 152
Soqueta - Oliva 6 km - Tel (34) 962 - 851 452
Gamba - Gandía 14 km - Tel (34) 962 - 841 310

La Costa
★ ★ ★ ★

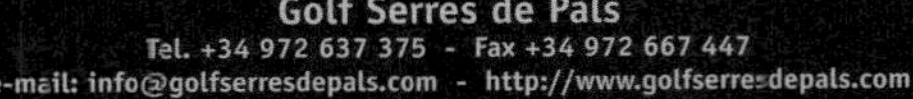

Pals (Platja de Pals)

16	6	7

Este campo que se llama Platja de Pals desde que ha dejado de ser un club de socios para convertirse en un campo comercial, tiene acreditada una reputación que realmente se merece. Su situación entre pinos, su tranquilidad, su moderado relieve (algunos greens elevados), la flexibilidad entre diferentes tees de salida, lo convierten en un recorrido atractivo para todos los niveles. Su terreno arenoso aguanta bien la lluvia y ofrece una confortable alfombra a los jugadores. Su diseño clásico pone esencialmente en línea de juego árboles y bunkers que protegen los greens. El bosque no sólo es denso, lo que obliga a pegar un buen drive para evitarlo y buenos golpes para salir de él, sino que además la envergadura de los pinos, en forma de sombrilla, estrecha las calles y alguna que otra vez la bola queda encaramada en las ramas. El arquitecto ha revalorizado este terreno ideal para construir un golf conservando su aspecto natural. Los greenes son fáciles de apreciar, generalmente pequeños en la primera vuelta y hasta inmensos en algunos hoyos de la segunda.

Pals is no longer just a members' club but a business venture course, although its reputation remains as rightfully deserved as ever. This is a very appealing course for all levels, laid out in the quiet of pine-trees with mainly smooth unbroken terrain (only a few elevated greens) and the flexibility afforded by several different tee-boxes. The sandy terrain also soaks up any rain very quickly and provides a very comfortable carpet for players to play on. The classic design basically brings bunkers into play to defend the greens, and uses trees. The forest is not only pretty thick – requiring good drives to keep out, and very good recovery shots to get out, of the woods – but the span of these parasol pines tends to make the fairways narrower, and the branches sometimes even keep the balls! The architect has successfully developed this ideal terrain for building a golf course while preserving its natural character. The greens are easy to read, not very large on the front nine but sometimes huge over the second half of the course.

Golf Platja de Pals — 1966

Arenales de Mar – Camí del Golf s/n.
E - 17256 PALS (Girona – Costa Brava)

Office Secretaría (34) 972 - 667 739
Pro shop Pro-shop (34) 972 - 667 739
Fax Fax (34) 972 - 636 799
Web www.golfplatjadepals.com
Situation Situación Palafrugell, 12 km - Pals (pop. 1 675), 4 km
Annual closure Cierre anual no
Weekly closure Cierre semanal no
Fees main season Precios tempor. alta 18 holes

	Week days Semana	We/Bank holidays Fin de sem./fiestas
Individual Individual	€ 75	€ 75
Couple Pareja	€ 150	€ 150

Caddie Caddie no — **Electric Trolley** Carro eléctrico yes
Buggy Coche yes — **Clubs** Palos yes
Credit cards Tarjetas de crédito
VISA - Eurocard - MasterCard - AMEX

Access Acceso : A7 Exit (Salida) 6 → Girona, C255 → Palafrugell, GE650 → Pals.
Map 3 on page 1091 Plano 3 Página 1091

GOLF COURSE — RECORRIDO 16/20

Site	Emplazamiento	
Maintenance	Mantenimiento	
Architect	Arquitecto	F.W. Hawtree
Type	Tipo	forest
Relief	Relieve	
Water in play	Agua	
Exp. to wind	Exp. al viento	
Trees in play	Arboles	

Scorecard Tarjeta	Chp. Campeonato	Mens Caballeros	Ladies Damas
Length Longitud	6222	5940	5089
Par	73	73	73
Slope system	127	122	120

Advised golfing ability Nivel de juego aconsejado 0 12 24 36
Hcp required Handicap exigido 35

CLUB HOUSE & AMENITIES — CLUB HOUSE Y DEPENDENCIAS 6/10

Pro shop Pro-shop
Driving range Campo de prácticas
Sheltered cubierto 12 mats - On grass sobre hierba yes - Putting-green putting-green yes - Pitching-green pitching-green yes

HOTEL FACILITIES — HOTELES CERCANOS 7/10

HOTELS HOTELES
Mas de Torrent - 39 rooms, D from € 345 - Torrent 6 km
Tel (34) 972 - 303 292, Fax (34) 972 - 303 293

Parador d'Aiguablava - 87 rooms, D € 210 - Aiguablava 12 km
Tel (34) 972 - 622 162, Fax (34) 972 - 622 166

La Costa - 120 rooms, D € 276 - Platja de Pals 200 m
Tel (34) 972 - 667 740, Fax (34) 972 - 667 736

RESTAURANTS RESTAURANTES
La Costa - on site - Tel (34) 972 - 667 740

Sa Punta - Platja de Pals 1 km - Tel (34) 972 - 667 376

Triton - Gualta 10 km - Tel (34) 972 - 757 038

Panorámica

14 | 6 | 4

Panorámica es un campo situado en un espacio relativamente llano, cómodo y agradable para el amateur medio. La primera vuelta tienes tres pares 3 y tres pares 5, sin demasiadas complicaciones, capaces de animar a muchos jugadores a realizar una buena vuelta. Hay varios tees de salida en alto que invitan a pegar drives fáciles y, desde las marcas medias, el campo no es excesivamente largo. También hay varios greenes en alto, sin visión para precisar el approach. El rough suele estar cortado corto y el estado general del mantenimiento del campo es excelente por lo que el jugador tiene muchas probabilidades de divertirse saliendo satisfecho de su vuelta. A ello se añade un cuidado entorno de olivos, algarrobos y almendros y su ubicación en una zona de rica gastronomía mediterránea. Viene siendo lugar de encuentro de jugadores centroeuropeos de vacaciones o de entrenamiento, pues su zona de prácticas es especialmente destacable.

Panorámica is a course built over a relatively flat setting, enjoyable and playable by the average golfer. The outward nine include three par 3s and three par 5s without too many difficulties and might let many of you card a good score. All the tee-boxes are elevated, which will tempt a lot of players to use the driver, and from the forward tees the course is not too long. Likewise, the greens are more or less elevated so you don't always get a clear view of the approach you should be playing. The rough is not too long and overall green-keeping is of an excellent standard so the players here are kept happy. Equally enjoyable are the landscapes of olive groves, carob and almond trees plus a site in a region rich in Mediterranean gastronomy. Panorámica has become one of those venues where golfers from northern and central Europe like to meet up on holiday or for some winter golfing practice. Facilities are immaculate.

Panoramica Golf & Country Club — 1995

Urbanización Panorámica s/n
E - 12320 SANT JORDI (Castellón)

Office	Secretaría	(34) 964 - 493 072
Pro shop	Pro-shop	(34) 964 - 493 072
Fax	Fax	(34) 964 - 493 063
Web	www.novapanoramica.com	

Situation Situación Peñíscola (pop. 3 077), 25 km
Vinaròs (pop. 19 202), 15 km

Annual closure Cierre anual — no
Weekly closure Cierre semanal — no
restaurant closed on mondays

Fees main season Precios tempor. alta — 18 holes

	Week days Semana	We/Bank holidays Fin de sem./fiestas
Individual Individual	€ 45	€ 60
Couple Pareja	€ 90	€ 120

Caddie Caddie no — **Electric Trolley** Carro eléctrico no
Buggy Coche yes — **Clubs** Palos yes
Credit cards Tarjetas de crédito
VISA - Eurocard - MasterCard

Alcanar
N 238
Traiguera
San Jorge
GOLF
Vinarós
Cálig
A 7 - E 15
N°340
Benicarló
km 0 2,5 5
43
Peniscola
42

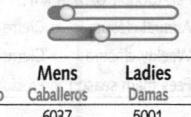

Access Acceso : A7 Barcelona-Valencia, Exit (Salida) 42 → Vinaròs. 1 km. → Sant Raphaël on the right. 6 km on the left, → Golf
Map 5 on page 1095 Plano 5 Página 1095

GOLF COURSE — RECORRIDO — 14/20

Site Emplazamiento
Maintenance Mantenimiento
Architect Arquitecto — Bernhard Langer
Type Tipo — country, forest, residential
Relief Relieve
Water in play Agua
Exp. to wind Exp. al viento
Trees in play Arboles

Scorecard Tarjeta	Chp. Campeonato	Mens Caballeros	Ladies Damas
Length Longitud	6429	6037	5001
Par	72	72	72
Slope system	128	124	123

Advised golfing ability — 0 12 24 36
Nivel de juego aconsejado
Hcp required Handicap exigido — 28 Men, 36 Ladies

CLUB HOUSE & AMENITIES — CLUB HOUSE Y DEPENDENCIAS — 6/10

Pro shop Pro-shop
Driving range Campo de prácticas
Sheltered cubierto no - On grass sobre hierba yes - Putting-green putting-green yes - Pitching-green pitching-green yes

HOTEL FACILITIES — HOTELES CERCANOS — 4/10

HOTELS HOTELES
Parador - 108 rooms, D € 151 - Benicarló 20 km
Tel (34) 964 - 470 100, Fax (34) 964 - 470 934

Hostería del Mar - 85 rooms, D € 145 - Peñíscola 29 km
Tel (34) 964 - 480 600, Fax (34) 964 - 481 363

Panorámica Golf Residence (Apartments) D € 160 - on site
Tel (34) 964 - 493 022 , Fax (34) 964 - 493 022

RESTAURANTS RESTAURANTES
El Langostino de Oro - Vinaròs 15 km - Tel (34) 964 - 451 204
El Faro - Vinaròs 15 km - Tel (34) 964 - 456 362
El Cortijo - Benicarló 20 km - Tel (34) 964 - 470 075

Pedreña

16 | 6 | 6

En este marco incomparable, con unas vistas magníficas, Severiano Ballesteros hizo su aprendizaje. Y cuando recorremos este trazado muy británico (con todas las astucias estratégicas de su diseñador Harry Colt), cuando debemos negociar con los árboles, entendemos que el campeón español haya acumulado todos los recursos para salirse de las situaciones más difíciles. Aquí hace falta pegar recto (lo que no es precisamente su fuerte). Bastante accidentado, con roughs a menudo muy densos, el campo tiene algunos greenes ciegos lo que complica todavía más sus aspectos técnicos que compensan ampliamente su falta de longitud. Sin embargo el jugador medio que sepa jugar recto se las arreglará muy bien, sobre todo en match-play, ya que es un campo perfecto para asumir riesgos. En cuanto a los mejores, deberán aplacar sus ansias y adaptar su técnica a la situación. Pedreña es un gran test de sabiduría para el jugador experto que pueda dibujar el recorrido y sepa negociar los movimientos de sus greenes.

This impressive site with some magnificent views is where Severiano Ballesteros learnt his trade. When you play this classical layout (with all the strategic tricks of architect Harry Colt) and as you cope with all the trees and sometimes struggle to find your way out of them, you realise that the Spanish champion learnt his amazing art of recovery in very tough conditions indeed. Here, you have to drive straight (that was never Seve's forte). Rather hilly, with some often thick rough, this highly-reputed course includes undulated greens (a few are blind), which complicate a still further the technical aspects of playing here and easily make up for the lack of yardage. Having said that, average and straight players should get by just fine, especially in match-play, because this is the ideal terrain for taking risks. As for the wunderkinds, they'll just have to keep a check on their adrenaline flow and adjust their technique to matters at hand.

Real Golf de Pedreña — 1928

Carretera General, s/n
E - 39130 PEDREÑA (Cantabria)

Office	Secretaría	(34) 942 - 500 001
Pro shop	Pro-shop	(34) 942 - 500 001
Fax	Fax	(34) 942 - 500 136
Web	www.realgolfdepedrena.com	
Situation	Situación	Santander, 24 km
Annual closure	Cierre anual	no
Weekly closure	Cierre semanal	no

Fees main season Precios tempor. alta — 18 holes

	Week days Semana	We/Bank holidays Fin de sem./fiestas
Individual Individual	€ 134	€ 134
Couple Pareja	€ 268	€ 268

* Member's guests only (Sólo invitados de socios)

Caddie Caddie on request **Electric Trolley** Carro eléctrico yes

Buggy Coche yes **Clubs** Palos yes

Credit cards Tarjetas de crédito no

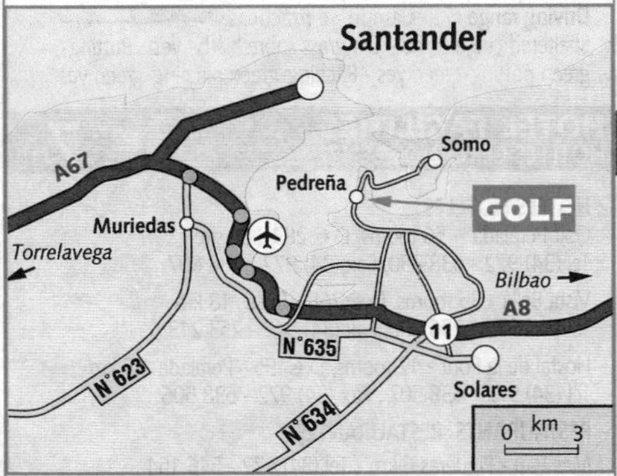

Access Acceso : Bilbao, N 634, N 635 → Santander.
Map 2 on page 1088 Plano 2 Página 1088

GOLF COURSE — RECORRIDO — 16/20

Site	Emplazamiento	
Maintenance	Mantenimiento	
Architect	Arquitecto	Harry S. Colt
Type	Tipo	seaside course, forest
Relief	Relieve	
Water in play	Agua	
Exp. to wind	Exp. al viento	
Trees in play	Arboles	

Scorecard Tarjeta	Chp. Campeonato	Mens Caballeros	Ladies Damas
Length Longitud	5764	5541	4764
Par	70	70	70
Slope system	131	124	122

Advised golfing ability Nivel de juego aconsejado — 0 12 24 36

Hcp required Handicap exigido — 28 Men, 36 Ladies

CLUB HOUSE & AMENITIES — CLUB HOUSE Y DEPENDENCIAS — 6/10

Pro shop Pro-shop
Driving range Campo de prácticas
Sheltered cubierto 5 mats - On grass sobre hierba yes - Putting-green putting-green yes - Pitching-green pitching-green no

HOTEL FACILITIES — HOTELES CERCANOS — 6/10

HOTELS HOTELES

Real - 123 rooms, D € 323- Santander 24 km
Tel (34) 942 - 272 550, Fax (34) 942 - 274 573

NH Ciudad de Santander - Santander 24 km
60 rooms, D € 174
Tel (34) 942 - 227 965, Fax (34) 942 - 217 303

Hotel Bemon Playa - 56 rooms, D € 107 - Somo 1 km
Tel (34) 942 - 510 708, Fax (34) 942 - 510 708

RESTAURANTS RESTAURANTES

La Sardina - Santander 24 km - Tel (34) 942 - 271 035
Mesón Segoviano - Santander 24 km - Tel (34) 942 - 311 010
Rhin - Santander 24 km - Tel (34) 942 - 273 034

Peralada

15 | 7 | 7

Un recorrido táctico. En primer lugar hay que sobrepasar los bunkers, saber evitarlos o quedarse corto: en cada par 4, un bunker de calle espera las caídas de drives imperfectos entre 190 y 240 metros desde las salidas de atrás. Hay además vías de agua que cruzan y flanquean las calles en los alrededores de varios greenes, por lo que es fundamental medir bien las distancias y saber de lo que uno es capaz en cada ocasión. Pero estas dificultades no menguan la franqueza de un recorrido en el que algunos dog-legs y varios fuera de límites ayudan a mantener la concentración. Poniendo empeño se puede cumplir el handicap. En todo caso, es un recorrido agradable para jugar en familia dejando que cada uno escoja el tee de salida que más le convenga. Al igual que las calles y los greenes (hay 8 con doble escalón), los roughs son densos, sembrados de olivos. En Peralada se pueden usar todos los palos de la bolsa y, probablemente, de diversa manera. Campo modélico en la protección ambiental y de las especies y no tanto en lo tocante a la urbanización que lo rodea que afecta en algunos hoyos a la concentración de los jugadores.

This is a tactical course. First of all you have to avoid the sand by either carrying the bunkers or laying up short. Because on each par 4, a fairway bunker lurks close to the drive landing zone, from 200 to 250 yards from the back-tees. But these difficulties (there are also a few dangerous water hazards) take absolutely nothing away from the course's openness, where a few gentle dog-legs and out-of-bounds help keep players focused. With a little concentration, you might even play to your handicap at Peralada. At all events, this is a pleasant course for all the family where everyone can choose the tees that suit them best. Like the fairways and the greens (8 of which have two tiers), the thick rough is dotted with olive trees. A model course for the protection of nature but a little less so in terms of surrounding buildings, which on some holes might affect your concentration.

Peralada Golf — 1993

Rocaberti s/n
E - 17491 PERALADA (Girona – Alto Ampurdan)

Office	Secretaria	(34) 972 - 538 287
Pro shop	Pro-shop	(34) 972 - 538 287
Fax	Fax	(34) 972 - 538 236
Web	www.golfperalada.com	
Situation	Situación	Figueras (pop. 35 301), 6 km
Annual closure	Cierre anual	no
Weekly closure	Cierre semanal	no
Fees main season	Precios tempor. alta	18 holes

	Week days Semana	We/Bank holidays Fin de sem./fiestas
Individual Individual	€ 70	€ 70
Couple Pareja	€ 140	€ 140

Caddie Caddie no — **Electric Trolley** Carro eléctrico no
Buggy Coche yes — **Clubs** Palos yes

Credit cards Tarjetas de crédito
VISA - Eurocard - MasterCard - AMEX

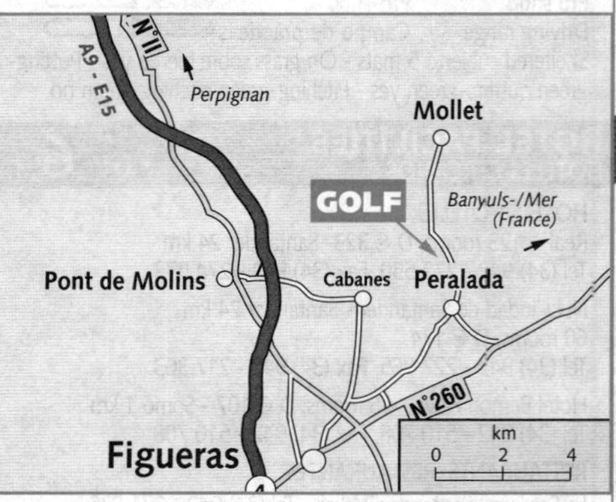

Access Acceso : A7 Perpignan-Barcelona, Exit (Salida) 4, N260 → Llança y Portbou, Golf on the left → Peralada
Map 3 on page 1091 Plano 3 Página 1091

GOLF COURSE — RECORRIDO — 15/20

Site	Emplazamiento	
Maintenance	Mantenimiento	
Architect	Arquitecto	Jorge Soler
Type	Tipo	open country
Relief	Relieve	
Water in play	Agua	
Exp. to wind	Exp. al viento	
Trees in play	Arboles	

Scorecard Tarjeta	Chp. Campeonato	Mens Caballeros	Ladies Damas
Length Longitud	5990	5716	4786
Par	71	71	71
Slope system	120	120	115

Advised golfing ability Nivel de juego aconsejado — 0 12 24 36
Hcp required Handicap exigido — 28 Men, 36 Ladies

CLUB HOUSE & AMENITIES — CLUB HOUSE Y DEPENDENCIAS — 7/10

Pro shop	Pro-shop
Driving range	Campo de prácticas

Sheltered cubierto no - On grass sobre hierba yes - Putting-green putting-green yes - Pitching-green pitching-green yes

HOTEL FACILITIES — HOTELES CERCANOS — 7/10

HOTELS HOTELES
Golf Peralada - 56 rooms, D € 283 - on site
Tel (34) 972 - 538 830, Fax (34) 972 - 538 807

Vista Bella - 35 rooms, D € 268 - Roses 18 km
Tel (34) 972 - 256 200, Fax (34) 942 - 253 213

Hostal de la Font - 12 rooms, D € 95 - Peralada 1,5 km
Tel (34) 972 - 538 507 , Fax (34) 972 - 538 506

RESTAURANTS RESTAURANTES
Mas Pau - Figueras 6 km - Tel (34) 972 - 546 [illegible]54
La Olivera - on site - Tel (34) 972 - 538 830
Cal Sagrista - Peralada 1 km - Tel (34) 972 - 538 301
El Bulli (Ferran Adria) - Cala Montjol - Tel (34) 972 150 457

PGA de Catalunya

18	7	7

Pocos kilómetros al sur de Girona y dentro de la zona de influencia turística de la Costa Brava, enriquece la oferta de buen golf en el noreste de España. El recorrido es bello, bueno y exigente, con excelentes vistas que llegan hasta los Pirineos. Las calles son anchas y onduladas, abiertas en un frondoso bosque de pinos y alcornoques, pero el rough es implacable, y los dos grandes lagos añaden dimensión y vistas escénicas al campo. Los greenes, muy defendidos tanto por la distancia como por bunkers, agua y accidentes del terreno, tienen unas dimensiones espléndidas y gran movimiento para el disfrute del buen pateador. Los desniveles y las distancias de green a tee demandan una buena preparación física del jugador que, sin duda, verá gratamente compensado su esfuerzo ante la inteligencia del diseño que premia el buen golpe. La inmediata puesta en juego de un nuevo recorrido de 18 hoyos, diseñado también por Neil Coles y Angel Gallardo, abrirá una etapa de obras de mejora de este soberbio campo.

The opening of this course has enhanced the bunch of great courses in this part of Spain, which boasts assets such as beaches and pine forests, a great tradition for culture and good food, superb landscapes and good communications. This course is at once good, beautiful and demanding, with some wonderful views over the Pyrenees. The fairways are wide and rolling, laid out in a forest thick with pine and cork-oak trees, but the rough is uncompromising and two large lakes add a scenic dimension to the whole layout. The greens, difficult to reach through sheer length and tightly guarded by sand-traps, water and sloping terrain, provide added interest for good putters. The hilly terrain and distance between green and tee-box are best suited to the fit golfer who, in return, will be rewarded for his or her effort by the intelligence of a layout which helps the best shots. A second 18-hole course will be fully operational by the Spring of 2006 along with a 150-room hotel.

PGA Golf de Catalunya — 1999

Ctra N-II, km 701
E - 17455 CALDES DE MALAVELLA (Girona)

Office	Secretaria	(34) 972 - 472 577
Pro shop	Pro-shop	(34) 972 - 472 577
Fax	Fax	(34) 972 - 470 493
Web	www.pgacatalunya.com	
Situation	Situación	Girona (pop. 71 000), 13 km
Annual closure	Cierre anual	no
Weekly closure	Cierre semanal	no

Fees main season Precios tempor. alta — 18 holes

	Week days / Semana	We/Bank holidays / Fin de sem./fiestas
Individual Individual	€ 75	€ 75
Couple Pareja	€ 150	€ 150

* Call before coming

Caddie Caddie no — **Electric Trolley** Carro eléctrico yes
Buggy Coche yes — **Clubs** Palos yes

Credit cards Tarjetas de crédito
VISA - Eurocard - MasterCard - AMEX

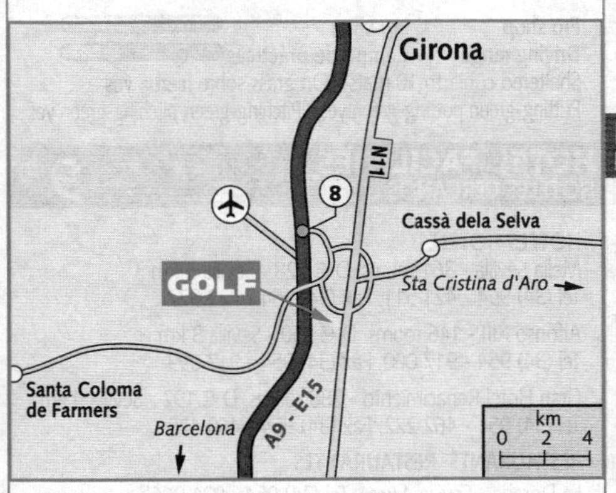

Access Acceso : Barcelona, A2 Exit (salida) 9. N2 → Girona. Golf after Km 701 point.
Map 3 on page 1091 Plano 3 Página 1091

GOLF COURSE — RECORRIDO — 18/20

Site	Emplazamiento	
Maintenance	Mantenimiento	
Architect	Arquitecto	Neil Coles, Angel Gallardo
Type	Tipo	parkland, forest
Relief	Relieve	
Water in play	Agua	
Exp. to wind	Exp. al viento	
Trees in play	Arboles	

Scorecard Tarjeta	Chp. Campeonato	Mens Caballeros	Ladies Damas
Length Longitud	6588	6226	5310
Par	72	72	72
Slope system	130	130	130

Advised golfing ability Nivel de juego aconsejado — 0 12 24 36
Hcp required Handicap exigido — 28 Men, 36 Ladies

CLUB HOUSE & AMENITIES — CLUB HOUSE Y DEPENDENCIAS — 7/10

Pro shop Pro-shop
Driving range Campo de prácticas
Sheltered cubierto no - On grass sobre hierba yes (100 places) - Putting-green putting-green yes - Pitching-green pitching-green yes

HOTEL FACILITIES — HOTELES CERCANOS — 7/10

HOTELS HOTELES
Balneario Vichy Catalan - Caldes de Malavella 5 km
82 rooms, D € 196
Tel (34) 972 - 470 000, Fax (34) 972 - 472 299

Carlemany - Girona 13 km - 87 rooms, D € 146
Tel (34) 972 - 211 212, Fax (34) 972 - 214 994

Park Hotel San Jorge - Playa de Aro 30 km - 104 rooms, D € 211
Tel (34) 972 - 652 311, Fax (34) 972 - 652 576

RESTAURANTS RESTAURANTES
La Roca Petita - Riudellots de la Selva 10 km
Tel (34) 972 - 477 132
Hostal de la Granota - Vidreras 6 km - Tel (34) 972 - 853 044
Vichy Catalán - Caldes de Malavella 5 km
Tel (34) 972 - 470 000

1181

Pineda

15 | 7 | 9

Se trata de un recorrido con todas las características de un Country Club, con actividades sociales y deportivas variadas (tenis, piscina, hípica, paddle) al lado de Sevilla, lo que le asegura una fuerte frecuentación. Esencialmente son los invitados de los socios quienes pueden jugar. Creado en 1939, el recorrido sólo tenía 9 hoyos, y ha habido que esperar hasta 1992 para verlo convertido en un 18 hoyos con una longitud respetable. Su estética es la de un verdadero parque con abundante vegetación, cosa bella y apreciable sobre todo en los veranos calurosos. Los hoyos están bien estructurados y el ritmo de juego es excelente. Hay que ser muy precisos en los segundos golpes ya que los greenes no son muy grandes. En realidad es un recorrido muy formador que ha facilitado excelentes jugadores a los equipos nacionales españoles.

Pineda is part of a real country-club concept with a wide variety of social and sporting activities (tennis, swimming-pool, horse-riding, paddle-tennis) at the gates of Seville. This makes it a busy course and explains why the majority of visitors are member guests. Created in 1939, Pineda originally had only 9 holes and was extended to 18 holes and a very respectable yardage only in 1992. This is a park-style course with lush vegetation which most will find pretty welcome, particularly on hot summer afternoons. The holes are neatly proportioned and the layout well-balanced, but your approach shots must be accurate to hit the smallish greens. This is in fact a very instructive course that has schooled many excellent players who have go on to play in the Spanish national teams.

Real Club Pineda de Sevilla — 1939

Avda. Jerez, s/n
E - 41012 SEVILLA

Office	Secretaria	(34) 954 - 611 400
Pro shop	Pro-shop	(34) 954 - 611 400
Fax	Fax	(34) 954 - 617 704
Web	www.rcpineda.com	
Situation	Situación	Sevilla (pop. 70 4857), 3 km
Annual closure	Cierre anual	no
Weekly closure	Cierre semanal	no

Fees main season Precios tempor. alta — 18 holes

	Week days / Semana	We/Bank holidays / Fin de sem./fiestas
Individual Individual	€ 78	*
Couple Pareja	€ 156	*

* Member's guests only (Sólo invitados de socios)

Caddie Caddie no — **Electric Trolley** Carro eléctrico no
Buggy Coche no — **Clubs** Palos no
Credit cards Tarjetas de crédito no

Sevilla
Canal de Alfonso XIII
Av. de la Paz
GOLF
SE 401
Av. de Jerez
Hipódromo
Utrera
SE30
Cádiz
A4
0 km 1

Access Acceso : CN IV Sevilla → Cadiz, in El Cortijo de Pineda
Map 8 on page 1101 Plano 8 Página 1101

GOLF COURSE — RECORRIDO — 15/20

Site	Emplazamiento	
Maintenance	Mantenimiento	
Architect	Arquitecto	R.& F. M. Benjumea, Luis Recasens
Type	Tipo	parkland
Relief	Relieve	
Water in play	Agua	
Exp. to wind	Exp. al viento	
Trees in play	Arboles	

Scorecard Tarjeta	Chp. Campeonato	Mens Caballeros	Ladies Damas
Length Longitud	6147	6037	5077
Par	72	72	72
Slope system	120	119	115

Advised golfing ability Nivel de juego aconsejado — 0 12 24 36
Hcp required Handicap exigido — 28 Men, 36 Ladies

CLUB HOUSE & AMENITIES — CLUB HOUSE Y DEPENDENCIAS — 7/10

Pro shop Pro-shop
Driving range Campo de prácticas
Sheltered cubierto 10 mats - On grass sobre hierba yes - Putting-green putting-green yes - Pitching-green pitching-green yes

HOTEL FACILITIES — HOTELES CERCANOS — 9/10

HOTELS HOTELES

Melia Sevilla - 361 rooms, D € 228 - Sevilla 5 km
Tel (34) 954 - 421 511, Fax (34) 954 - 422 977

Alfonso XIII - 146 rooms, D € 350 - Sevilla 3 km
Tel (34) 954 - 917 000, Fax (34) 954 - 917 099

Gran Hotel Renacimiento - 288 rooms, D € 192 - Sevilla 4 km
Tel (34) 954 - 462 222, Fax (34) 954 - 460 428

RESTAURANTS RESTAURANTES

La Dorada - Sevilla 4 km - Tel (34) 954 - 921 066
La Albahaca - Sevilla 4 km - Tel (34) 954 - 220 714
El Espigon - Sevilla 4 km - Tel (34) 954 - 626 851

Puerta de Hierro *Abajo*

18 | 8 | 9

Las nuevas vías rápidas de la periferia de Madrid afectaron al viejo campo "de abajo" de Puerta de Hierro que nunca había conseguido hacerse famoso. Robert Trent Jones Jr. recibió el encargo de recomponer estos otros 18 hoyos que el club necesita para sus dos mil jugadores activos y el resultado es un recorrido de considerable dificultad e innegable belleza. Encinas, pinos y monte bajo componen el marco de unas calles anchas que suben y bajan siguiendo el relieve del terreno. En la mayoría de los hoyos es preciso pegar largo y colocar el golpe de salida en el lugar preciso para poder atacar unos greenes amplísimos, bien defendidos por enormes bunkers, con acentuados movimientos y plataformas que obligan a medir muy bien los pats. Por todo ello hay que considerarlo un magnífico test para la más alta competición e incluso un campo muy interesante para jugarlo desde los tees alternativos.

The expressways around the city of Madrid have had their effect on the old "lower" course of Puerta de Hierro, which has lost quite a bit of its fame and appeal. Robert Trent Jones Jnr. was assigned with redesigning the 18 holes of the second course that the club needed for its 2,000 active members. The result is this extremely difficult but very beautiful course, where oak-trees, pines and little mounds line fairways, which hug the natural contours of the terrain. On most of the holes you need to be long and place your shot with considerable precision in order to attack the huge greens. These are well guarded by vast sand-traps, are sharply contoured and sometimes multi-tiered to make putting a trickier business than usual. Nonetheless, Puerta de Hierro Abajo is a magnificent test for the highest level tournaments and also a very interesting course for the lesser player hitting it from the front tees..

Real Club de la Puerta de Hierro — 1998

Avda. de Miraflores s/n. Ciudad Puerta de Hierro
E - 28035 MADRID

Office	Secretaría	(34) 913 - 161 745
Pro shop	Pro-shop	(34) 913 - 768 330
Fax	Fax	(34) 913 - 738 111
Web	www.realclubpuertadehierro.com	
Situation	Situación	Madrid, 4 km
Annual closure	Cierre anual	no
Weekly closure	Cierre semanal	no

Fees main season Precios tempor. alta	Week days Semana	We/Bank holidays Fin de sem./fiestas
	18 holes	
Individual Individual	€ 108	€ 226*
Couple Pareja	€ 216	€ 452*

* Member's guests only (sólo invitados de socios)

Caddie Caddie no — **Electric Trolley** Carro eléctrico yes
Buggy Coche yes — **Clubs** Palos no
Credit cards Tarjetas de crédito no

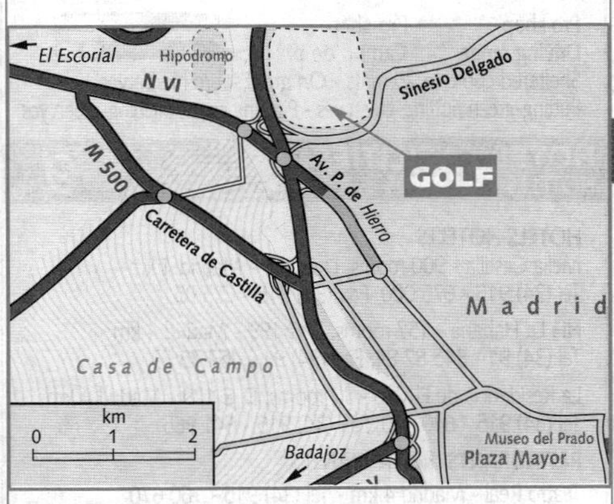

Access Acceso : Next to the Ciudad Universitaria, besides the Urbanización Puerta de Hierro
Map 4 on page 1092 Plano 4 Página 1092

GOLF COURSE — 18/20
RECORRIDO

Site	Emplazamiento	
Maintenance	Mantenimiento	
Architect	Arquitecto	R. Trent Jones Jr
Type	Tipo	parkland
Relief	Relieve	
Water in play	Agua	
Exp. to wind	Exp. al viento	
Trees in play	Arboles	

Scorecard Tarjeta	Chp. Campeonato	Mens Caballeros	Ladies Damas
Length Longitud	6504	6052	5114
Par	72	72	72
Slope system	130	124	123

Advised golfing ability Nivel de juego aconsejado — 0 12 24 36
Hcp required Handicap exigido — 28 Men/36 Ladies

CLUB HOUSE & AMENITIES — 8/10
CLUB HOUSE Y DEPENDENCIAS

Pro shop Pro-shop
Driving range Campo de prácticas
Sheltered cubierto 25 mats - On grass sobre hierba yes - Putting-green putting-green yes - Pitching-green pitching-green yes

HOTEL FACILITIES — 9/10
HOTELES CERCANOS

HOTELS HOTELES
Melia Castilla - 900 rooms, D € 240 - Madrid 4 km
Tel (34) 915 - 675 000, Fax (34) 915 - 675 051
NH La Habana - 157 rooms, D € 199 - Madrid 4 km
Tel (34) 91 - 345 82 84, Fax (34) 91 - 457 75 79
La Residencia de El Viso - Madrid 4 km
12 rooms, D € 129
Tel (34) 915 - 640 370, Fax (34) 915 - 641 965

RESTAURANTS RESTAURANTES
Teatro Real - Madrid 4 km - Tel (34) 915 - 160 670
La Trainera - Madrid 4 km - Tel (34) 915 - 760 575
Zalacain - Madrid 4 km - Tel (34) 915 - 614 840
Bocaito (tapas) - Madrid 4 km - Tel (34) 915 - 321 219

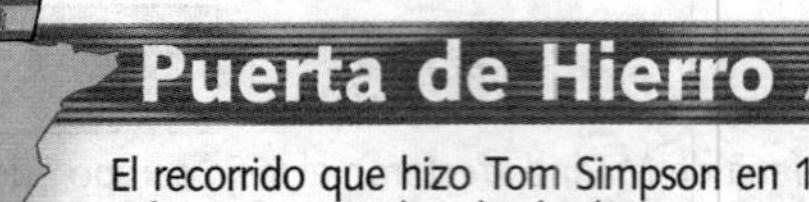

16	8	9

El recorrido que hizo Tom Simpson en 1904 ya fue remodelado en los años setenta; de las reformas que se han hecho los primeros años de este siglo son autores Robert Trent Jones Jr, y Kyle Philips, y han tenido como principal objetivo renovarlo y adaptarlo a las magnitudes del golf actual. Se han añadido pocos metros porque los arquitectos han preferido potenciar las características del campo, volviendo a poner en juego sus bunkers, sus cuestas, sus árboles y cuantos obstáculos y accidentes del terreno dibujan los hoyos y siempre han hecho del viejo Puerta de Hierro –probablemente el club más privado de España- un campo de precisión y estrategia. Ahora los greenes son más amplios, tienen diferentes planos, siguen siendo rápidos y de lectura muy delicada, lo cual pone al jugador visitante en desventaja cuando compite con uno local, y reciben el abrazo envenado de esos bunkers "marca de la casa" Trent Jones.

Designed in 1904 by Tom Simpson, this course was remodelled in the 1970s and again at the turn of this century particularly by Robert Trent Jones Jr. and Kyle Phillips in order to adapt it to modern-day golfing. This was done without lengthening the course too much so as to respect the spirit of the site with its hills and woods and constantly sloping landscape embracing the natural terrain. A very good tournament course which is not over-wide, Puerta de Hierro calls for extreme accuracy if you want to card a good score. But even mid-handicappers will not find this too troublesome because you can always play safe on every hole. There are no huge difficulties that force you to shape those delicate shots to make par or scrape a bogey. The greens really are huge and sometimes multi-tiered and their speed and contouring make for difficult reading. The members of this very prestigious and very private club (you'll need to be invited to play here) enjoy the advantage of knowing their own course and are perhaps better equipped to escape from the famous Trent Jones sand-traps.

Real Club de la Puerta de Hierro — 1904

Avda. de Miraflores s/n. Ciudad Puerta de Hierro
E - 28035 MADRID

Office	Secretaria	(34) 913 - 161 745
Pro shop	Pro-shop	(34) 913 - 768 330
Fax	Fax	(34) 913 - 738 111
Web	www.realclubpuertadehierro.com	
Situation	Situación	Madrid, 4 km
Annual closure	Cierre anual	no
Weekly closure	Cierre semanal	no

Fees main season Precios tempor. alta	Week days Semana	We/Bank holidays Fin de sem./fiestas
		18 holes
Individual Individual	€ 108	€ 226*
Couple Pareja	€ 216	€ 452*

* Member's guests only (sólo invitados de socios)

Caddie Caddie no — **Electric Trolley** Carro eléctrico yes

Buggy Coche yes — **Clubs** Palos no

Credit cards Tarjetas de crédito no

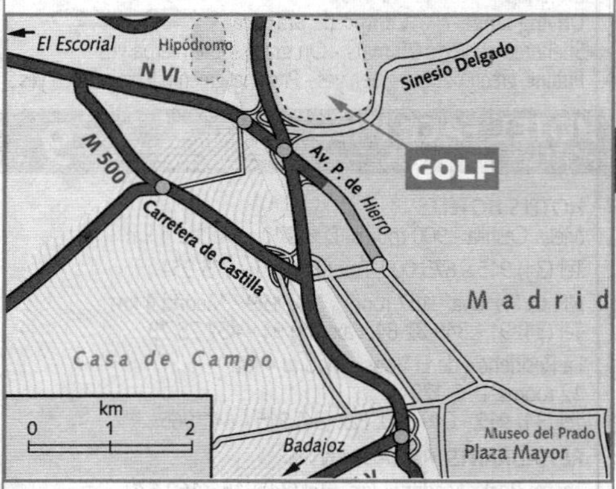

Access Acceso : Next to the Ciudad Universitaria, besides the Urbanización Puerta de Hierro

Map 4 on page 1092 Plano 4 Página 1092

GOLF COURSE — RECORRIDO 16/20

Site	Emplazamiento	
Maintenance	Mantenimiento	
Architect	Arquitecto	Tom Simpson, John Harris
Type	Tipo	parkland
Relief	Relieve	
Water in play	Agua	
Exp. to wind	Exp. al viento	
Trees in play	Arboles	

Scorecard Tarjeta	Chp. Campeonato	Mens Caballeros	Ladies Damas
Length Longitud	6375	5963	5045
Par	72	72	72
Slope system	124	121	120

Advised golfing ability Nivel de juego aconsejado — 0 12 24 36

Hcp required Handicap exigido — 28 Men, 36 Ladies

CLUB HOUSE & AMENITIES — CLUB HOUSE Y DEPENDENCIAS 8/10

Pro shop Pro-shop

Driving range Campo de prácticas

Sheltered cubierto 25 mats - On grass sobre hierba yes - Putting-green putting-green yes - Pitching-green pitching-green yes

HOTEL FACILITIES — HOTELES CERCANOS 9/10

HOTELS HOTELES

Melia Castilla - 900 rooms, D € 240 - Madrid 4 km
Tel (34) 915 - 675 000, Fax (34) 915 - 675 051

NH La Habana - 157 rooms, D € 199 - Madrid 4 km
Tel (34) 91 - 345 82 84, Fax (34) 91 - 457 75 79

La Residencia de El Viso - 12 rooms, D € 129 - Madrid 4 km
Tel (34) 915 - 640 370, Fax (34) 915 - 641 965

RESTAURANTS RESTAURANTES

Teatro Real - Madrid 4 km - Tel (34) 915 - 160 670

La Trainera - Madrid 4 km - Tel (34) 915 - 760 575

Zalacain - Madrid 4 km - Tel (34) 915 - 614 840

La Botilleria (tapas) - Madrid 4 km - Tel (34) 915 - 484 620

Pula

13 | 6 | 5

Con escasos desniveles, es un campo cómodo de andar aunque tiene varios greenes elevados que requieren aproches por alto bien controlados. La anchura de las calles da sensación de espacio, cosa que agradará a los pegadores, pero no hay que fiarse ya que algunos obstáculos no son muy visibles. El presidente y propietario del campo, Romeo Sala, está empeñado en hacer de Pula un campo de referencia para unas vacaciones de golf en Mallorca y promueve constantemente mejoras en su diseño y servicios, por ejemplo las reformas que se han hecho en los últimos meses, con la experiencia de juego, en ocasiones del más alto nivel, del recorrido. Por eso hay que seguir de cerca la evolución de este campo que está muy bien adaptado a los diferentes niveles de juego, con hoyos de diferentes exigencias en los que cualquier jugador tendrá ocasión de intentar golpes muy variados en cuanto a potencia y trayectoria de la bola. Bien integrado en un paisaje que ofrece magníficas vistas panorámicas sobre la montaña.

Only slightly hilly, the course is easy to walk but elevated greens call for controlled high approach shots. The width of the fairways gives a pleasant sensation of open space and will appeal to big-hitters, although they should watch out for a number of hazards that are not always clearly visible. The site's owner Romeo Sala has decided to make this the reference course for golfing vacations in Majorca by constantly looking to improve the layout and services, like for example the way the closing holes have been restyled taking account of the experience of top level golfers. This is why we will be keeping close tabs on this course which is suitable for all players. A number of holes present a variety of challenges where golfers always have the choice in terms of how far and along which line they should hit the ball. The layout also fits in beautifully with the landscape and offers fine views over the mountains.

Pula Golf 1995
Predio de Pula
E - 07550 SON SERVERA (Mallorca - Islas Baleares)

Office	Secretaria	(34) 971 - 817 034
Pro shop	Pro-shop	(34) 971 - 817 034
Fax	Fax	(34) 971 - 817 035
Web	www.pulagolf.com	
Situation	Situación	Palma (pop. 308 616), 70 km
Annual closure	Cierre anual	no
Weekly closure	Cierre semanal	no
Fees main season	Precios tempor. alta	18 holes

	Week days Semana	We/Bank holidays Fin de sem./fiestas
Individual Individual	€ 84	€ 84
Couple Pareja	€ 168	€ 168

Caddie Caddie no — **Electric Trolley** Carro eléctrico yes
Buggy Coche yes — **Clubs** Palos yes
Credit cards Tarjetas de crédito
VISA - Eurocard - MasterCard - AMEX - DC

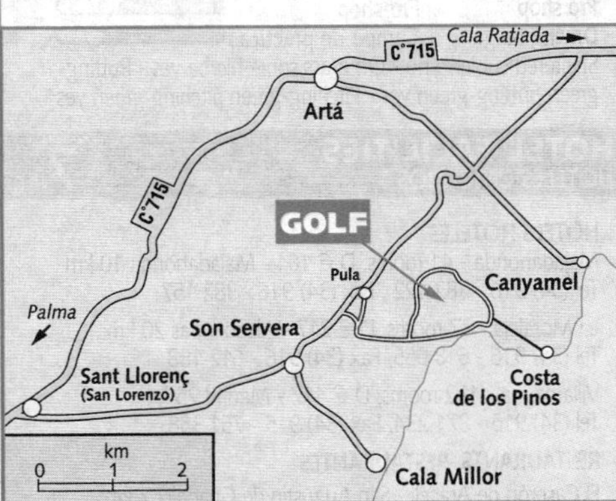

Access Acceso : Palma C715 → Manacor, → Son Servera, Pula Golf on left hand side → Capdepera
Map 1 on page 1087 Plano 1 Página 1087

GOLF COURSE
RECORRIDO — **13**/20

Site	Emplazamiento	
Maintenance	Mantenimiento	
Architect	Arquitecto	F.L. Segales
Type	Tipo	country
Relief	Relieve	
Water in play	Agua	
Exp. to wind	Exp. al viento	
Trees in play	Arboles	

Scorecard Tarjeta	Chp. Campeonato	Mens Caballeros	Ladies Damas
Length Longitud	6073	5676	5045
Par	70	72	72
Slope system	136	136	134

Advised golfing ability 0 12 24 36
Nivel de juego aconsejado
Hcp required Handicap exigido 28 Men, 36 Ladies

CLUB HOUSE & AMENITIES
CLUB HOUSE Y DEPENDENCIAS — **6**/10

Pro shop Pro-shop
Driving range Campo de prácticas
Sheltered cubierto 10 mats - On grass sobre hierba yes - Putting-green putting-green yes - Pitching-green pitching-green yes

HOTEL FACILITIES
HOTELES CERCANOS — **5**/10

HOTELS HOTELES
Eurotel Golf Punta Rotja - Son Servera 4 km
202 rooms, D € 194
Tel (34) 971 - 816 500, Fax (34) 971 - 816 525

Aguait - Cala Rajada 10 km
188 rooms, D € 132
Tel (34) 971 - 563 408, Fax (34) 971 - 565 106

Pula Suites Hotel - on site - 68 rooms, D € 240
Tel (34) 971 567 307, Fax (34) 971 568 053

RESTAURANTS RESTAURANTES
S'Era de Pula - Son Servera 7 km - Tel (34) 971 - 567 940
Son Floriana - Son Servera 10 km - Tel (34) 971 - 586 075

Real Sociedad Club de Campo *Norte* | 18 | 7 | 7

Construido en una pequeña colina, en un terreno muy típico de los alrededores de Madrid, este recorrido de la Real Sociedad Hípica Española Club de Campo ofrece una gran variedad de distancias y tipo de hoyos gracias a sus múltiples tees de salida. Nos encontramos con el afán de variedad de Robert von Hagge y su diseño bien característico: roughs espesos, calles de trazado muy variado y muy cuidadas en superficie, greens amplios con múltiples desniveles, constituyendo un recorrido destinado más bien a los buenos jugadores y que beneficia a los pegadores inteligentes porque hay que saber administrar la potencia y la precisión. Pero también los jugadores técnicos sabrán salvar un buen resultado si son diestros en el juego corto, en el que tendrán ocasión de lucirse con todo tipo de aproches: por alto, rodados, jugando con las caídas de los greenes y de sus contornos. El vecino circuito de velocidad resulta ruidoso cuando hay carreras o entrenamientos pero la categoría del campo compensa de largo este inconveniente.

Built on a little hill typical of the type of terrain found around Madrid, the new course belonging to the Real Sociedad Hípica Española de Club de Campo offers an amazing combination of distances and types of hole thanks to the many different tee-boxes. This reflects the emphasis on variety which is the trademark of Robert von Hagge (who also designed Empordà). Other distinctive features are the thick rough, highly contoured fairways and huge, multi-tiered greens which generally tend to make this a course for good players who think enough to know when power must be combined with accuracy. It is also intended for smart players and fine craftsmen who can save their card if their short game is on song. The club's ambition is clearly to host major international tournaments. Close to the Jarama circuit, this layout is a new addition to a region already spoilt for excellent courses (Jarama R.A.C.E., La Moraleja).

Real Sociedad Hipica Española Club de Campo — 1997

Carretera de Burgos, km. 26,4
E - 28709 SAN SEBASTIAN DE LOS REYES (Madrid)

Office	Secretaria	(34) 916 - 571 018
Pro shop	Pro-shop	(34) 916 - 571 018
Fax	Fax	(34) 916 - 571 022
Web	www.rshecc.es	
Situation	Situación	Madrid, 26 km
Annual closure	Cierre anual	no
Weekly closure	Cierre semanal	no

Fees main season Precios tempor. alta	18 holes	
	Week days Semana	We/Bank holidays Fin de sem./fiestas
Individual Individual	€ 100	*
Couple Pareja	€ 200	*

* Member's guests only (sólo invitados de socios)

Caddie Caddie no — **Electric Trolley** Carro eléctrico yes
Buggy Coche yes — **Clubs** Palos yes
Credit cards Tarjetas de crédito no

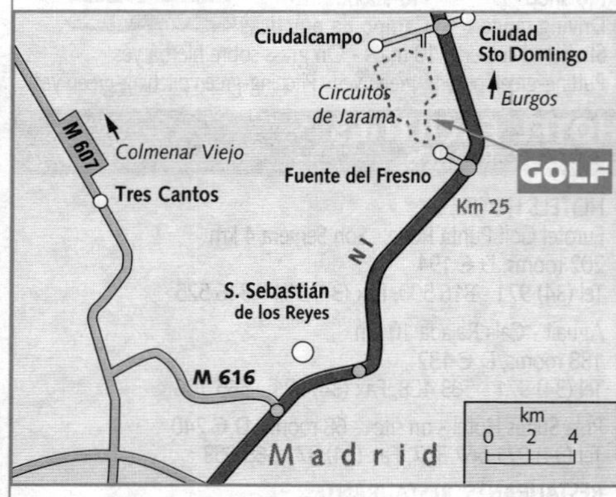

Access Acceso : CN I - Km 26,400
Map 4 on page 1092 Plano 4 Página 1092

GOLF COURSE RECORRIDO — 18/20

Site	Emplazamiento	
Maintenance	Mantenimiento	
Architect	Arquitecto	Robert von Hagge
Type	Tipo	forest, hilly
Relief	Relieve	
Water in play	Agua	
Exp. to wind	Exp. al viento	
Trees in play	Arboles	

Scorecard Tarjeta	Chp. Campeonato	Mens Caballeros	Ladies Damas
Length Longitud	6464	6071	5104
Par	72	72	72
Slope system	122	123	115

Advised golfing ability Nivel de juego aconsejado — 0 12 24 36
Hcp required Handicap exigido — 28 men, 32 ladies

CLUB HOUSE & AMENITIES CLUB HOUSE Y DEPENDENCIAS — 7/10

Pro shop Pro-shop
Driving range Campo de prácticas
Sheltered cubierto no - On grass sobre hierba yes - Putting-green putting-green yes - Pitching-green pitching-green yes

HOTEL FACILITIES HOTELES CERCANOS — 7/10

HOTELS HOTELES
Majadahonda - 41 rooms, D € 164 - Majadahonda 10 km
Tel (34) 916 - 382 122 , Fax (34) 916 - 382 157

La Moraleja - 37 rooms, D € 217 - Alcobendas 20 km
Tel (34) 916 - 618 055, Fax (34) 916 - 612 188

Villamagna - 182 rooms, D € 417 - Madrid 25 km
Tel (34) 915 - 871 234, Fax (34) 915 - 751 358

RESTAURANTS RESTAURANTES
El Caserón de Araceli - San Augustin de Guadalix 7 km
Tel (34) 918 - 418 531
Zalacain - Madrid 20 km - Tel (34) 915 - 614 840
La Trainera - Madrid 25 km - Tel (34) 915 - 760 575

Real Sociedad Club de Campo *Sur*

17	7	7

En un terreno mucho más escarpado que el campo Norte, Von Hagge ha hecho un segundo recorrido para "la Hípica", como se suele llamar ahora a este club de nombre tan largo fundado en 1928, perfectamente complementario del campo Norte. El Campo Sur es mucho más técnico, más corto pero más delicado de trazar en calles generalmente estrechas entre grandes bunkers que perfilan las calles y los greenes, y pequeños bunkers que hay que evitar a toda costa, algunos árboles que obligan mucho a colocar los golpes, dog-legs y cuestas pronunciadas que convierten varias veces unas medidas cortas en golpes mucho más importantes. Los greenes, siempre de tamaño grande, son de excelente calidad, algunos están en alto y varios tienen uno o dos escalones. Los pares 3 no son largos pero son un gran test de precisión. Es un gran campo para jugar en familia, ¡y todos agradecerán que sea en coche!, en el que cada uno podrá destacar en algún aspecto del juego.

Over terrain that is much hillier than the "Norte" course, Robert von Hagge has designed a second course for "la Hípica", the name of the club founded in 1928. Perfectly complementary to its neighbour, this layout is more technical in style and shorter as well, but the tee-shot is never easy to narrow fairways between large bunkers outlining the way to the greens. A number of small bunkers should be avoided at all costs and several trees call for the careful placing of shots. A number of dog-legs and sloping fairways sometimes make the shot to be played more crucial than it might look. The greens are nicely sized, of excellent quality and in some cases elevated or multi-tiered. The par 3s are not very long but do require extreme accuracy, as is always the case with this architect. A very amusing course to play with all the family – everyone will also appreciate a buggy – and one that lets each golfer shine in what he or she does best.

Real Sociedad Hípica Española Club de Campo — 2001

Carretera de Burgos, km. 26,4
E - 28709 SAN SEBASTIAN DE LOS REYES (Madrid)

Office	Secretaria	(34) 916 - 571 018
Pro shop	Pro-shop	(34) 916 - 571 018
Fax	Fax	(34) 916 - 571 022
Web	www.rshecc.es	
Situation	Situación	Madrid, 26 km
Annual closure	Cierre anual	no
Weekly closure	Cierre semanal	no
Fees main season	Precios tempor. alta	18 holes

	Week days Semana	We/Bank holidays Fin de sem./fiestas
Individual Individual	€ 100	*
Couple Pareja	€ 200	*

* Member's guests only (sólo invitados de socios)

Caddie Caddie no — **Electric Trolley** Carro eléctrico yes
Buggy Coche yes — **Clubs** Palos yes
Credit cards Tarjetas de crédito no

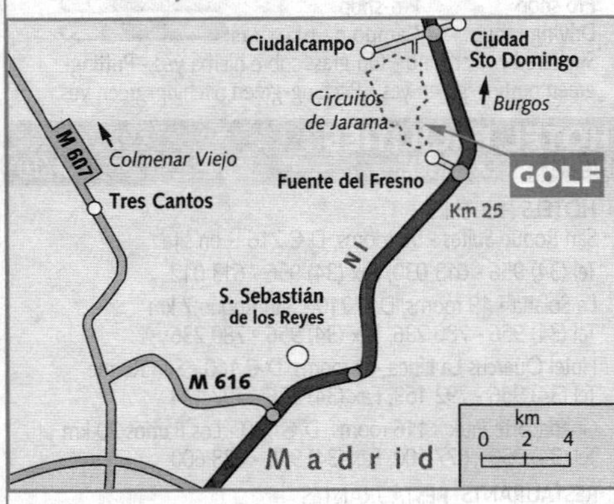

Access Acceso : CN I - Km 26,400
Map 4 on page 1092 Plano 4 Página 1092

GOLF COURSE — RECORRIDO — 17/20

Site	Emplazamiento	
Maintenance	Mantenimiento	
Architect	Arquitecto	Robert von Hagge
Type	Tipo	forest, hilly
Relief	Relieve	
Water in play	Agua	
Exp. to wind	Exp. al viento	
Trees in play	Arboles	

Scorecard Tarjeta	Chp. Campeonato	Mens Caballeros	Ladies Damas
Length Longitud	6121	5759	5001
Par	72	72	72
Slope system	126	123	120

Advised golfing ability Nivel de juego aconsejado: 0 12 24 36
Hcp required Handicap exigido: 28 Men, 32 Ladies

CLUB HOUSE & AMENITIES — CLUB HOUSE Y DEPENDENCIAS — 7/10

Pro shop Pro-shop
Driving range Campo de prácticas
Sheltered cubierto no - On grass sobre hierba yes - Putting-green putting-green yes - Pitching-green pitching-green yes

HOTEL FACILITIES — HOTELES CERCANOS — 7/10

HOTELS HOTELES

Zenit de Los Reyes - 72 rooms, D € 130 - S Sebastián 15 km
Tel (34) 916 - 591 600 , Fax (34) 916 - 591 601

La Moraleja - Alcobendas 20 km - 37 rooms, D € 217
Tel (34) 916 - 618 055, Fax (34) 916 - 612 188

Villamagna - Madrid 25 km - 182 rooms, D € 417
Tel (34) 915 - 871 234, Fax (34) 915 - 751 358

RESTAURANTS RESTAURANTES

El Caserón de Araceli - San Augustin de Guadalix 7 km
Tel (34) 918 - 418 531

Izamar - S. Sebastián 15 km - Tel (34) 916 - 583 893

Gaztelupe - S. Sebastián 15 km - Tel (34) 916 - 530 616

San Roque *Old Course*

17 | 8 | 8

San Roque gustará incluso a los que no es gustan los campos con urbanización. En primer lugar porque las casas y residencias que lo rodean son magníficas, y en segundo lugar porque están apartadas del recorrido. Por su relieve no es necesario alquilar un coche y está bien protegido por los árboles, excepto un tramo expuesto al viento, entre el 13 y el 15, que bordea la colina. Muy largo saliendo desde atrás y con una primera vuelta de calles muy estrechas, es más "humano" con los tees de salida adelantados para los jugadores con un handicap superior a 10. Exige ser un jugador completo, con mucho "feeling" para negociar los aproches a greenes con muchas caídas y que están perfectamente protegidos, así como una gran finura en el juego corto. Si a esto añadimos la calidad de las instalaciones y de su mantenimiento, entendemos que Tony Jacklin y Dave Thomas hicieron unc de los grandes recorridos de la Costa.

Golfers who don't like property development courses will love San Roque. Firstly because the villas and residences are magnificent, secondly because the course is some distance from them. The terrain is easy for walking and well protected by trees, except the 13th and 15th holes, laid out on the side of a hill and exposed to the wind. Very long off the back-tees, compounded by tight fairways on the front nine, the course is more "human" when played from the front-tees for players with handicaps in double figures. It demands an all-round game and a lot of feeling to negotiate the approach shots to greens that are very undulating and perfectly well-defended. A well-honed short game is also in order. Add to these compliments the quality of green-keeping and of the facilities and you will understand how Tony Jacklin and Dave Thomas have designed one of the coast's great courses. One minor criticism would be the course's difficulty for inexperienced players.

The San Roque Club — 1990

Urbanización San Roque – Carretera N-340, km. 127
E- 11360 SAN ROQUE (Cádiz)

Office	Secretaria	(34) 956 - 613 030
Pro shop	Pro-shop	(34) 956 - 613 030
Fax	Fax	(34) 956 - 613 012
Web	www.sanroqueclub.com	
Situation	Situación	San Roque, 6 km

Algeciras (pop. 101 556), 20 km

Annual closure	Cierre anual	no
Weekly closure	Cierre semanal	no
Fees main season	Precios tempor. alta	18 holes

	Week days Semana	We/Bank holidays Fin de sem./fiestas
Individual Individual	€ 155	€ 155
Couple Pareja	€ 310	€ 310

Caddie Caddie on request **Electric Trolley** Carro eléctrico no
Buggy Coche yes **Clubs** Palos yes
Credit cards Tarjetas de crédito
VISA - MasterCard - AMEX - DC

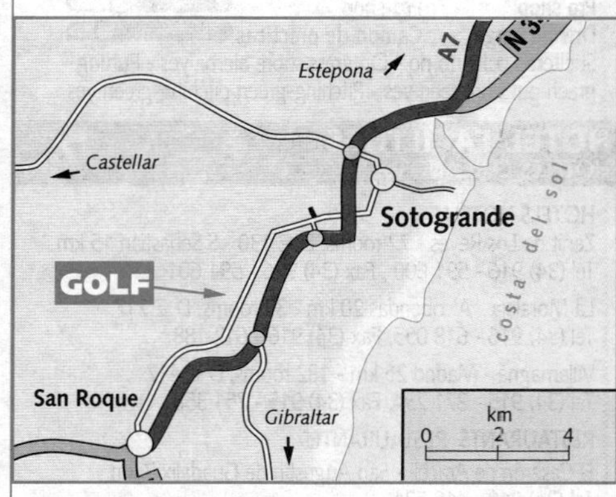

Access Acceso : N340 Estepona → Cádiz, km 126,5 turn right → Golf
Map 8 on page 1101 Plano 8 Página 1101

GOLF COURSE
RECORRIDO — 17/20

Site	Emplazamiento	
Maintenance	Mantenimiento	
Architect	Arquitecto	Dave Thomas Tony Jacklin
Type	Tipo	parkland
Relief	Relieve	
Water in play	Agua	
Exp. to wind	Exp. al viento	
Trees in play	Arboles	

Scorecard Tarjeta	**Chp.** Campeonato	**Mens** Caballeros	**Ladies** Damas
Length Longitud	6494	6134	5174
Par	72	72	72
Slope system	131	126	121

Advised golfing ability Nivel de juego aconsejado — 0 12 24 36
Hcp required Handicap exigido — 28 Men, 36 Ladies

CLUB HOUSE & AMENITIES
CLUB HOUSE Y DEPENDENCIAS — 8/10

Pro shop Pro-shop
Driving range Campo de prácticas
Sheltered cubierto no - On grass sobre hierba yes - Putting-green putting-green yes - Pitching-green pitching-green yes

HOTEL FACILITIES
HOTELES CERCANOS — 8/10

HOTELS HOTELES
San Roque Suites - 50 rooms, D € 216 - on site
Tel (34) 956 - 613 030, Fax (34) 956 - 613 012
La Solana - 19 rooms, D € 210 - San Roque 7 km
Tel (34) 956 - 780 236, Fax (34) 956 - 780 236
Hotel Quercus La Línea - 9 rooms, D € 160 - San Roque
Tel (34) 956 - 792 159, Fax (34) 956 - 797 144
Guadacorte Park - 116 rooms, D € 130 - Los Barrios 20 km
Tel (34) 956 - 677 500, Fax (34) 956 - 678 600

RESTAURANTS RESTAURANTES
Venta Toledo - Guadiaro 7 km - Tel (34) 956 - 614 248
Bolero - San Roque on site - Tel (34) 956 - 613 030
El Copo - Palmones 15 km - Tel (34) 956 - 677 710

San Roque *New Course*

18	8	8

Perry Dye ha hecho aquí un campo completo de última generación. Incluso aquellos para quienes este exigente recorrido les venga grande, disfrutarán con la amplísima variedad de elementos que retan al jugador, siempre con fair-play, a mover la bola en dirección y distancia para dibujar el recorrido. Bunkers de talud muy alto castigan los malos drives, en unas calles bastante estrechas; en pocos greenes, siempre muy defendidos por los lados, se puede llegar rodando; obstáculos de agua, alcornoques y monte bajo, pot bunkers, waste land, y desniveles que dan movimiento al recorrido componen la travesía de un golf moderno que requiere, además de pegada, una inteligente estrategia para escoger el golpe que cada uno es capaz de dar con probabilidades de éxito. Los greenes, muy amplios en los pares 3, son de movimiento suave pero total, lo que complica mucho los pats largos. Y para redondear el placer de jugar, el mantenimiento es excelente.

Perry Dye has produced here a course that is typical of new-age golf architecture designed primarily for scratch and low-handicap golfers. It is a real challenge for everyone, and to get around unscathed you will need skills in working the ball and a clear idea of how far you can hit each club. The deep bunkers immediately punish wayward drives, especially since the fairways could have been wider. The greens are generally well-defended each side but often leave a little scope for chipped shots up front. Water hazards, cork-oak trees, undergrowth, pot-bunkers and waste-bunkers are added complications to a course that is modern in every respect; you will need to strike the ball cleanly and have a sound sense of strategy to weigh up your own capabilities. The greens, which are huge on the par 3s, are slightly contoured but make long putts no laughing matter. Keep smiling, though, as the views all around are superb.

The San Roque Club — 2004

Urbanización San Roque – Carretera N-340, km. 127
E- 11360 SAN ROQUE (Cádiz)

Office Secretaria (34) 956 - 613 030
Pro shop Pro-shop (34) 956 - 613 030
Fax Fax (34) 956 - 613 012
Web www.sanroqueclub.com
Situation Situación San Roque, 6 km
Algeciras (pop. 101 556), 20 km

Annual closure Cierre anual — no
Weekly closure Cierre semanal — no
Fees main season Precios tempor. alta — 18 holes

	Week days / Semana	We/Bank holidays / Fin de sem./fiestas
Individual Individual	€ 126	€ 126
Couple Pareja	€ 252	€ 252

Caddie Caddie on request **Electric Trolley** Carro eléctrico no
Buggy Coche yes **Clubs** Palos yes
Credit cards Tarjetas de crédito
VISA - MasterCard - AMEX - DC

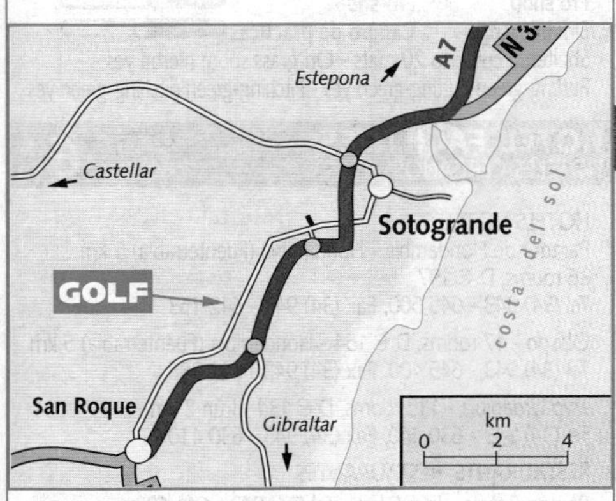

Access Acceso : N340 Estepona → Cádiz, km 126,5 turn right → Golf
Map 8 on page 1101 Plano 8 Página 1101

GOLF COURSE — RECORRIDO — 18/20

Site Emplazamiento
Maintenance Mantenimiento
Architect Arquitecto — Perry Dye
Type Tipo — parkland
Relief Relieve
Water in play Agua
Exp. to wind Exp. al viento
Trees in play Arboles

Scorecard / Tarjeta	Chp. / Campeonato	Mens / Caballeros	Ladies / Damas
Length Longitud	6497	6079	5010
Par	72	72	72
Slope system	135	129	127

Advised golfing ability Nivel de juego aconsejado — 0 12 24 36
Hcp required Handicap exigido — 28 Men, 36 Ladies

CLUB HOUSE & AMENITIES — CLUB HOUSE Y DEPENDENCIAS — 8/10

Pro shop Pro-shop
Driving range Campo de prácticas
Sheltered cubierto no - On grass sobre hierba yes - Putting-green putting-green yes - Pitching-green pitching-green yes

HOTEL FACILITIES — HOTELES CERCANOS — 8/10

HOTELS HOTELES

San Roque Suites - 50 rooms, D € 216 - on site
Tel (34) 956 - 613 030, Fax (34) 956 - 613 012

La Solana - 19 rooms, D € 210 - San Roque 7 km
Tel (34) 956 - 780 236, Fax (34) 956 - 780 236

Hotel Quercus La Línea - 9 rooms, D € 160 - San Roque
Tel (34) 956 - 792 159, Fax (34) 956 - 797 144

Guadacorte Park - 116 rooms, D € 130 - Los Barrios 20 km
Tel (34) 956 - 677 500, Fax (34) 956 - 678 600

RESTAURANTS RESTAURANTES

Venta Toledo - Guadiaro 7 km - Tel (34) 956 - 614 248
Bolero - San Roque on site - Tel (34) 956 - 613 030
El Copo - Palmones 15 km - Tel (34) 956 - 677 710

San Sebastián

14 | 6 | 6

Es la cuna y feudo del gran campeón español José María Olazábal, que vive en las inmediaciones y se entrena aquí además de en otros campos de la zona. El recorrido fue diseñado por el profesional francés Pierre Hirigoyen en un terreno con muchas cuestas y con una media docena de hoyos en una planicie bastante húmeda con algunos obstáculos de agua. La dificultad esencial, aparte de no salirse de la calle, radica en no ponerse nervioso ni desmoralizarse ante los muchos desniveles del terreno. Sin embargo, los obstáculos son visibles y se puede decir que es un recorrido claro con algunos greenes en alto dando lugar a situaciones muy variadas alrededor de los mismos, lo que explica la virtuosidad adquirida por Olazábal. Es muy difícil cumplir el handicap desde las salidas de atrás, aunque no sea excesivamente largo, por lo que es mejor escoger salidas más avanzadas. No es un recorrido que guste a todos, pero posee una personalidad incontestable. Las montañas del entorno son realmente muy bonitas...

It is the home course and fief of the top Spanish champion Olazábal, who can often be seen on the driving range, lives nearby and plays on the best courses in the region. The course was designed by the French pro Pierre Hirigoyen over very hilly terrain, although half a dozen holes are pretty flat, a little damp and protected by a few hazards. The essential difficulty here, apart from hitting your ball in the fairway, is keeping a cool head and not letting the steep slopes get the better of you. Luckily, the hazards are clearly in view and the course hides nothing, apart from a number of elevated greens. There is a variety of interesting situations around the greens, which might explain the virtuosity of Olazábal in this area developed out on the course. A good score is a tough proposition from the back tees but a distinct possibility when playing further forward. Not everyone loves this course but it does have definite character. And the mountains all around look simply beautiful.

Real Golf Club de San Sebastián — 1968

Chalet Borda Gain Apartado 6
E - 20280 HONDARRIBIA (Guipuzcoa – País Vasco)

Office	Secretaria	(34) 943 - 616 845
Pro shop	Pro-shop	(34) 943 - 616 845
Fax	Fax	(34) 943 - 611 491
Web		www.golfsansebastian.com
Situation	Situación	San Sebastián, 18 km

Irún (pop. 53 861), 3 km

Annual closure	Cierre anual	no
Weekly closure	Cierre semanal	no

Fees main season Precios tempor. alta	Week days Semana	We/Bank holidays Fin de sem./fiestas
	18 holes	
Individual Individual	€ 100	*
Couple Pareja	€ 200	*

* Member's guests only (sólo invitados de socios)

Caddie Caddie no — **Electric Trolley** Carro eléctrico yes
Buggy Coche yes — **Clubs** Palos no

Credit cards Tarjetas de crédito
VISA - Eurocard - MasterCard - AMEX - DC

Access Acceso : San Sebastián A8 → Irún, Biarritz.
Exit (Salida) 4 → Aeropuerto, Golf 3 km
St Jean de Luz → Irún, Golf 3 km → San Sebastián
Map 2 on page 1088 Plano 2 Página 1088

GOLF COURSE — RECORRIDO — 14/20

Site	Emplazamiento	
Maintenance	Mantenimiento	
Architect	Arquitecto	Pierre Hirigoyen
Type	Tipo	forest, hilly
Relief	Relieve	
Water in play	Agua	
Exp. to wind	Exp. al viento	
Trees in play	Arboles	

Scorecard Tarjeta	Chp. Campeonato	Mens Caballeros	Ladies Damas
Length Longitud	5962	5790	4883
Par	71	71	71
Slope system	134	133	125

Advised golfing ability Nivel de juego aconsejado — 0 12 24 36
Hcp required Handicap exigido — 28 Men, 36 Ladies

CLUB HOUSE & AMENITIES — CLUB HOUSE Y DEPENDENCIAS — 6/10

Pro shop Pro-shop
Driving range Campo de prácticas
Sheltered cubierto 20 mats - On grass sobre hierba yes - Putting-green putting-green yes - Pitching-green pitching-green yes

HOTEL FACILITIES — HOTELES CERCANOS — 6/10

HOTELS HOTELES

Parador de Hondarribia - Hondarribia (Fuenterrabia) 5 km
36 rooms, D € 197
Tel (34) 943 - 645 500, Fax (34) 943 - 642 153

Obispo - 17 rooms, D € 154 - Hondarribia (Fuenterrabia) 5 km
Tel (34) 943 - 645 400, Fax (34) 943 - 642 386

Tryp Urdanibia - 115 rooms, D € 134 - Irún 2 km
Tel (34) 943 - 630 440, Fax (34) 943 - 630 410

RESTAURANTS RESTAURANTES

Ramón Roteta - Irún 5 km - Tel (34) 943 - 641 693
Ibaiondo - Irún 2 km - Tel (34) 943 - 632 888
Jaizubia - Irún 2 km - Tel (34) 943 - 618 066

Sant Cugat

13 | 6 | 5

Es un campo urbano con algunos hoyos que tocan el bosque y ciertos desniveles acusados en una parte del recorrido. No es difícil lograr un buen resultado: las dificultades están a la vista, rara vez en la línea de juego, y las generalmente despejadas entradas en los greenes permiten desarrollar toda la amplia gama de golpes de aproach por alto y rodando y la bola. Los greenes son de buena calidad y el mantenimiento del campo nos hace sentir jugando en un parque donde todo parece estar a favor del jugador que sea preciso con la medida de cada golpe, más incluso con su distancia que con la línea. Algunos obstáculos de agua, algunos bunkers de green, árboles y bosque, son las mayores dificultades de este recorrido. Su escasa longitud permite no sólo cumplir el handicap fácilmente sino que lo hace muy agradable para jugar en match-play: pueden caer muchos birdies. Los buenos jugadores se explayarán a gusto y no dudarán en intentar llegar a green con el driver en ciertos pares 4. Los principiantes conseguirán sus primeros pares.

A residential course with a few holes on the edge of a forest and a part of the course running over some rather hilly terrain. It is not too difficult to shoot a good score, either. The hazards are clearly in view and seldom affect your game, to the extent that many greens can be approached with chip shots (beware overshooting the green!). The greens are good and general green-keeping of a pretty high standard, enough to make you feel as if you were in a park where everything is prepared for the accurate hitter who controls both distance and line. A few water hazards, green-side bunkers, trees and woods form the basic part of the course's difficulties. Being a short course, most players should play to their handicap without too much problem, and it is also fun for match-play with birdies perhaps more common than usual. Very good players will have lots of fun and won't think twice about going for the green on a number of short par 4s, while beginners should easily find their feet.

Club de Golf Sant Cugat — 1914

C/Villa, s/n
E - 08190 SANT CUGAT DEL VALLES (Barcelona)

Office	Secretaria	(34) 936 - 743 908
Pro shop	Pro-shop	(34) 936 - 743 958
Fax	Fax	(34) 936 - 755 152
Web		www.golfsantcugat.com
Situation	Situación	Barcelona, 20 km
Annual closure	Cierre anual	no
Weekly closure	Cierre semanal	no

Fees main season Precios tempor. alta	Week days Semana	We/Bank holidays Fin de sem./fiestas
		18 holes
Individual Individual	€ 150	€ 150
Couple Pareja	€ 300	€ 300

Caddie Caddie no — **Electric Trolley** Carro eléctrico yes
Buggy Coche yes — **Clubs** Palos yes
Credit cards Tarjetas de crédito no

Terrassa
Sabadell
A18
E 9
A7
Rubi
7-8
Cerdanyola
Tarragona
5
Sant Cugat del Vallès
A7
GOLF
E9
Molins de Rei
6
Tibidabo
A2
0 2 4 km
Barcelona

Access Acceso : Barcelona E9 → Sant Cugat del Vallès
Map 3 on page 1091 Plano 3 Página 1091

GOLF COURSE — RECORRIDO — 13/20

Site	Emplazamiento	
Maintenance	Mantenimiento	
Architect	Arquitecto	Harry S. Colt & others
Type	Tipo	hilly, residential parkland
Relief	Relieve	
Water in play	Agua	
Exp. to wind	Exp. al viento	
Trees in play	Arboles	

Scorecard Tarjeta	**Chp.** Campeonato	**Mens** Caballeros	**Ladies** Damas
Length Longitud	5050	5050	4430
Par	69	69	69
Slope system	121	121	118

Advised golfing ability Nivel de juego aconsejado: 0 12 24 36
Hcp required Handicap exigido: 28 Men, 36 Ladies

CLUB HOUSE & AMENITIES — CLUB HOUSE Y DEPENDENCIAS — 6/10

Pro shop Pro-shop
Driving range Campo de prácticas
Sheltered cubierto 15 mats - On grass sobre hierba yes - Putting-green putting-green yes - Pitching-green pitching-green yes

HOTEL FACILITIES — HOTELES CERCANOS — 5/10

HOTELS HOTELES
Novotel - 150 rooms, D € 131 - Sant Cugat 2 km
Tel (34) 935 - 894 141, Fax (34) 935 - 893 031

Sant Cugat Hotel - Sant Cugat del Vallès 2 km
97 rooms, D € 160
Tel (34) 935 - 441 448, Fax (34) 935 - 442 671

Neri - 22 rooms, D € 225 - Barcelona 20 km
Tel (34) 93 - 304 0655, Fax (34) 93 - 304 0337

RESTAURANTS RESTAURANTES
La Bolera - Sant Cugat 2 km - Tel (34) 936 - 741 675
Masía Can Atmetller - Sant Cugat 2 km
Tel (34) 936 - 749 151
Via Veneto - Barcelona 20 km - Tel (34) 932 - 007 244

Santa Ponsa *Santa Ponsa I*

14	6	7

En un denso complejo residencial en una de las zonas turísticas de Mallorca de mayor aglomeración, Santa Ponsa I, a pie de hotel, cumple bien su función de golf de vacaciones. El diseño de Folco Nardi es sobrio y convencional, con grandes espacios, pocos pero importantes obstáculos de agua y bunkers de intención. La longitud puede intimidar a los jugadores de tipo medio (dos pares 4 en la primera vuelta por encima de los 400 metros y el hoyo 10, par 5, de 590 metros desde las salidas largas) y a las señoras, así como varios greenes en alto que parecen más difíciles de alcanzar. Buen terreno para los pegadores, por tanto. Los greenes, de tamaño medio y superficie generalmente plana, son rápidos y suelen estar protegidos por los costados, con lo que una buena tarjeta aquí es un plus de las vacaciones. El complejo dispone de un segundo recorrido de 18 hoyos, Santa Ponsa II, obra de José Gancedo, reservado a los socios.

Within a residential and hotel resort lining one of the largest tourist areas of Majorca, Santa Ponsa I effectively fills its role as a holiday golf course. Folco Nardi's design is understated and conventional with wide open space and few water hazards and bunkers, even they do play an important part golf-wise. Yardage may deter senior players and the average hacker: two par 4s are in excess of 440 yards, the par 5 10th hole posts a cool 649 yards from the tips and many elevated greens look so difficult to reach. So advantage to the long-hitters. The greens are averagely-sized, generally flat, pretty quick and well protected by mounds; signing for a good score will certainly put you in good cheer for the evening ahead and the rest of your holiday. The resort boasts a second 18-hole course, the Santa Ponsa II, built by José Gancedo but reserved for members only.

Golf Santa Ponsa I — 1977

Avda. del Golf s/n. Urbanización Santa Ponsa
E - 07184 SANTA PONSA (Mallorca - Islas Baleares)

Office	Secretaría	(34) 971 - 690 211
Pro shop	Pro-shop	(34) 971 - 690 211
Fax	Fax	(34) 971 - 693 364
Web	www.habitatgolf.es	
Situation	Situación	Palma, 16 km
Annual closure	Cierre anual	no
Weekly closure	Cierre semanal	no

Fees main season Precios tempor. alta — 18 holes

	Week days / Semana	We/Bank holidays / Fin de sem./fiestas
Individual Individual	€ 70	€ 70
Couple Pareja	€ 140	€ 140

Caddie Caddie no — **Electric Trolley** Carro eléctrico no

Buggy Coche yes — **Clubs** Palos yes

Credit cards Tarjetas de crédito
VISA - MasterCard

Access Acceso : Palma PM1 → Andraix, Viejo Molino, turn left → Santa Ponsa, → Golf
Map 1 on page 1087 Plano 1 Página 1087

GOLF COURSE — RECORRIDO — 14/20

Site	Emplazamiento	
Maintenance	Mantenimiento	
Architect	Arquitecto	Folco Nardi
Type	Tipo	residential, open country
Relief	Relieve	
Water in play	Agua	
Exp. to wind	Exp. al viento	
Trees in play	Arboles	

Scorecard / Tarjeta	Chp. / Campeonato	Mens / Caballeros	Ladies / Damas
Length Longitud	6543	6106	5241
Par	72	72	72
Slope system	124	124	123

Advised golfing ability / Nivel de juego aconsejado: 0 12 24 36

Hcp required Handicap exigido: 28 Men, 36 Ladies

CLUB HOUSE & AMENITIES — CLUB HOUSE Y DEPENDENCIAS — 6/10

Pro shop Pro-shop
Driving range Campo de prácticas
Sheltered cubierto 10 mats - On grass sobre hierba yes - Putting-green putting-green yes - Pitching-green pitching-green yes

HOTEL FACILITIES — HOTELES CERCANOS — 7/10

HOTELS HOTELES

Golf Santa Ponsa - 12 rooms, D € 170 - Santa Ponsa 1 km
Tel (34) 971 - 697 133, Fax (34) 971 - 694 853

Hotel Port Adriano Marina Golf - El Toro 3 km
69 rooms, D € 315
Tel (34) 971 - 237 323, Fax (34) 971 - 237 070

Hesperia Playas de Mallorca - Santa Ponsa 3 km
212 rooms, D € 120
Tel (34) 971 - 693 366, Fax (34) 971 - 692 070

RESTAURANTS RESTAURANTES

Sa Masia - Santa Ponsa 2 km - Tel (34) 971 - 690 412
Utopia - El Toro 4 km - Tel (34) 971 232 425
Samanthas - Palma 15 km - Tel (34) 971 - 700 000

Sevilla

17 | 7 | 8

Con una gran preocupación por los detalles y la estrategia, José María Olazábal ha "firmado" este recorrido. Al limitar la talla de los greens, ha querido favorecer el juego corto, uno de sus puntos fuertes. Al ser un malabarista con la bola, ha creado un recorrido que necesita dominar perfectamente todos los efectos y trayectorias (altas y bajas). Hay un gran número de bunkers y obstáculos de agua en la línea de juego, completados por 12.000 árboles y matorrales plantados para lograr un recorrido más complejo... y no sólo para protegerse del sol en verano. Equilibrado en su conjunto se adapta bien a los diferentes niveles de juego y se complica a medida que se retroceden los tees de salida. Sede la Copa del Mundo en 2004, se alargó en doscientos metros y amplió la incidencia en el juego de varios obstáculos de agua. Franco y fácil de jugar sin coche, el Real Golf de Sevilla es una síntesis del estilo americano con algún vago recuerdo de links. Todo este conjunto de cualidades explican su éxito.

A course carrying the Olazábal "label" where a lot of attention has gone into the finest detail and strategy. By restricting the size of the greens, he has highlighted the short game, one of his own fortes. And because Olazábal is a worker of the ball, the course demands skills for every trajectory and for fashioning the ball both ways. The course has a large number of bunkers and water hazards, all very much in play, and these will be completed by the 12,000 trees and bushes that have been planted to make the course a little trickier... and not only to provide shade from the sun in summer. This is a finely balanced layout that adapts easily to different levels of skill and becomes more complex from the back-tees. Hosting the World Cup here in 2004 resulted in the course being lengthened and greater emphasis on the water hazards. Open and easy to walk, the Real Golf de Seville combines American and links style golf. Might this explain the course's success?

Real Club de Golf de Sevilla — 1991

Apartado de Correos 29
E - 41089 MONTEQUINTO (Sevilla)

Office	Secretaria	(34) 954 - 124 301
Pro shop	Pro-shop	(34) 954 - 124 301
Fax	Fax	(34) 954 - 124 229
Web	www.sevillagolf.com	
Situation	Situación	Sevilla, 10 km
Annual closure	Cierre anual	no
Weekly closure	Cierre semanal	no

Fees main season Precios tempor. alta — 18 holes

	Week days / Semana	We/Bank holidays / Fin de sem./fiestas
Individual Individual	€ 85	€ 116*
Couple Pareja	€ 170	€ 232*

* with members only (sólo con socios)

Caddie Caddie on request — **Electric Trolley** Carro eléctrico yes
Buggy Coche yes — **Clubs** Palos yes
Credit cards Tarjetas de crédito
VISA - Eurocard - MasterCard - AMEX

Access Acceso : A4 Sevilla - Utrera, km 3,2
Map 8 on page 1101 Plano 8 Página 1101

GOLF COURSE — RECORRIDO — 17/20

Site	Emplazamiento	
Maintenance	Mantenimiento	
Architect	Arquitecto	José María Olazábal
Type	Tipo	country
Relief	Relieve	
Water in play	Agua	
Exp. to wind	Exp. al viento	
Trees in play	Arboles	

Scorecard / Tarjeta	Chp. / Campeonato	Mens / Caballeros	Ladies / Damas
Length Longitud	6529	6185	5305
Par	72	72	72
Slope system	135	132	128

Advised golfing ability / Nivel de juego aconsejado — 0 12 24 36
Hcp required Handicap exigido — 28 Men, 36 Ladies

CLUB HOUSE & AMENITIES — CLUB HOUSE Y DEPENDENCIAS — 7/10

Pro shop Pro-shop
Driving range Campo de prácticas
Sheltered cubierto 10 mats - On grass sobre hierba yes - Putting-green putting-green yes - Pitching-green pitching-green yes

HOTEL FACILITIES — HOTELES CERCANOS — 8/10

HOTELS HOTELES
Hotel Ciudad de Sevilla - 95 rooms, D € 163 - Sevilla 3 km
Tel (34) 954 - 230 505, Fax (34) 954 - 238 539

Hotel Alfonso XIII - 127 rooms, D € 541 - Sevilla 3 km
Tel (34) 954 - 917 000, Fax (34) 954 - 917 099

Puerta de Triana - 65 rooms, D € 85 - Sevilla 8 km
Tel (34) 954 - 215 404, Fax (34) 954 - 215 401

RESTAURANTS RESTAURANTES
Taberna Alabardero - Sevilla 10 km - Tel (34) 954 - 560 637
La Albahaca - Sevilla 10 km - Tel (34) 954 - 220 714
Manolo Mayo - Los Palacios y Villafranca 8 km
Tel (34) 955 - 811 086

Sherry Golf

14	7	7

Tiene mérito haber sabido construir un campo entretenido en un terreno insulso. Gracias a los movimientos de tierra, a la colocación de muchos bunkers de intención y de ocho obstáculos de agua, Sherry Golf ofrece un campo largo (excepto para las señoras, que es marcadamente corto) y de riesgo. En la primera parte predominan las cuestas y desniveles y en la segunda, donde en terreno sigue siendo accidentado, domina el agua que obliga a dar golpes de gran precisión. 13, 14 y 16 son, en este sentido, los hoyos clave para elaborar el resultado. No es, en cambio, un campo largo de andar y, por sus múltiples elementos, será divertido para todo tipo de jugadores, que hallarán, en uno u otro hoyo, alicientes para salir satisfechos... o deseosos de volver a intentarlo. Como el campo es despejado, mejor evitarlo en época de calor y alternarlo con los atractivos de la ciudad que tiene su fama en las bodegas y los caballos (se recomienda la visita a la Escuela de Arte Ecuestre).

This course has the merit of being great fun despite being built across some rather bland terrain. With a lot of clever earthwork, very many bunkers and eight water hazards, Sherry Golf is a course that is both dangerous and long – except for the ladies, who will find it really short. The first part of the course is marked by steeply sloping terrain, but over the second half, although the slopes are still there, it is the water hazards that call for some accurate hitting. The key holes for a good card are N°s 13, 14, and 16. It is not a long course to walk and the variety of the layout will keep golfers of all levels happy… or make them want to come back and try their arm a second time. As the land on which the course was built was somewhat barren, you would be well advised not to play here in very hot weather, when time might be better spent exploring the attractions of a city well known for it wine-bars and horses (we recommend a visit to the School of Equestrian Arts).

Sherry Golf Jerez — **2004**
Autovía A-4 Jerez-Cádiz, Km. 642
E- 11407 JEREZ DE LA FRONTERA (Cádiz)

Office	Secretaria	(34) 956 - 088 330
Pro shop	Pro-shop	(34) 956 - 088 330
Fax	Fax	(34) 956 - 088 331
Web		www.sherrygolf.com
Situation	Situación	Jerez de la Frontera, 3 km
Annual closure	Cierre anual	no
Weekly closure	Cierre semanal	no
Fees main season	Precios tempor. alta	18 holes

	Week days Semana	We/Bank holidays Fin de sem./fiestas
Individual Individual	€ 55	€ 55
Couple Pareja	€ 110	€ 110

Caddie Caddie no — **Electric Trolley** Carro eléctrico yes
Buggy Coche yes — **Clubs** Palos yes
Credit cards Tarjetas de crédito
VISA - MasterCard - AMEX

Access Acceso : Motorway (Autovía) A-4 Jerez-Cádiz, exit at km 642
Map 7 on page 1098 Plano 7 Página 1098

GOLF COURSE 14/20
RECORRIDO

Site	Emplazamiento	
Maintenance	Mantenimiento	
Architect	Arquitecto	Blake Sterling Marco Martín
Type	Tipo	open country
Relief	Relieve	
Water in play	Agua	
Exp. to wind	Exp. al viento	
Trees in play	Arboles	

Scorecard Tarjeta	**Chp.** Campeonato	**Mens** Caballeros	**Ladies** Damas
Length Longitud	6572	6160	4093
Par	72	72	72
Slope system	129	127	123

Advised golfing ability 0 12 24 36
Nivel de juego aconsejado
Hcp required Handicap exigido — 24 Men, 36 Ladies

CLUB HOUSE & AMENITIES 7/10
CLUB HOUSE Y DEPENDENCIAS

Pro shop Pro-shop
Driving range Campo de prácticas
Sheltered cubierto no - On grass sobre hierba yes - Putting-green putting-green yes - Pitching-green pitching-green yes

HOTEL FACILITIES 7/10
HOTELES CERCANOS

HOTELS HOTELES
Sherry Park - 175 rooms, D € 150 - Jerez de la Frontera 5 km
Tel (34) 956 - 317 614, Fax (34) 956 - 311 300

Monasterio de San Miguel - El Puerto de Santa María 15 km
155 rooms, D € 150
Tel (34) 956 - 540 440, Fax (34) 956 - 542 604

G. H. Palmera Plaza - 48 rooms, D € 250 - Jerez de la F. 5 km
Tel (34) 956 - 031 500, Fax (34) 956 - 031 800

RESTAURANTS RESTAURANTES
Gaitan - Jerez de la Frontera 5 km - Tel (34) 956 - 168 021
Juanito - Jerez de la Frontera 5 km - Tel (34) 956 - 334 838
Casa Paco Ceballos (tapas) - El Puerto de Santa María 15 km
Tel (34) 956 - 542 908

Son Antem *Oeste*

16	8	8

Marriott ha hecho una fuerte inversión en su complejo de Son Antem, incluida la construcción de este segundo campo, que debe considerarse de gama alta y, sin embargo, el mantenimiento de ambos recorridos ha quedado muy por debajo de las expectativas. Por eso la baja nota que se adjudica en esta edición al "oeste" y la ausencia –esperamos, como todos los aficionados, breve- del recorrido "este" que últimamente ha sido recortado en más de cien metros. Con casi seis mil trescientos metros desde atrás, Son Antem Oeste disfruta de un bello emplazamiento para el placer de jugadores con experiencia que, además de pegar largo a la bola, lo hagan con un sólido control de la dirección porque las calles bordeadas de altos árboles se ven estrechas, porque tres lagos afectan directamente al juego de cinco hoyos y porque el moldeado del campo obliga a pensar los golpes para llevarlos al lugar más rentable para resolver la vuelta con éxito. Un campo tan interesante necesita, como el agua, el cuidado que se merece.

Marriott has invested a great deal in the Son Antem resort and in the building of this second course; the whole site is designed to form what should be an upscale golfing resort, yet overall green-keeping for both courses falls clearly below the standard we expected on arriving, at least it did when we played here. Whence a lower score for the course in this present edition and the omission – hopefully only temporary – of the "Este" course, which has recently been shortened by over 100 yards. Stretching some 6,900 yards, Son Antem Oeste is a good test for better golfers, who not only have to hit it a long way but also need to keep some control over where it goes, because the narrow fairways are lined with tall trees, the three lakes have a direct influence on play and the general design of the course calls for some careful thought if you want to keep your score in two-figures. This layout and its water hazards call for a lot of care and attention in every respect.

Mallorca Marriott Son Antem Golf Resort & Spa — 2001

Carretera de Llucmajor Km 3,4
E - 07620 LLUCMAJOR (Mallorca - Islas Baleares)

Office	Secretaria	(34) 971 - 129 200
Pro shop	Pro-shop	(34) 971 - 129 200
Fax	Fax	(34) 971 - 129 201
Web	www.marriotthotels.com/pmigs	
Situation	Situación	Palma, 20 km
Annual closure	Cierre anual	no
Weekly closure	Cierre semanal	no

Fees main season Precios tempor. alta	18 holes	
	Week days Semana	**We/Bank holidays** Fin de sem./fiestas
Individual Individual	€ 74	€ 74
Couple Pareja	€ 148	€ 148

Caddie Caddie no **Electric Trolley** Carro eléctrico yes

Buggy Coche yes **Clubs** Palos yes

Credit cards Tarjetas de crédito
VISA - MasterCard - AMEX

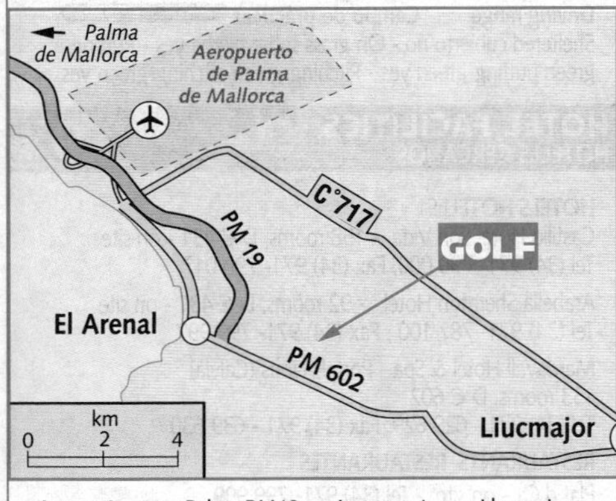

Access Acceso : Palma PM19 → Aeropuerto, → Llucmajor PM602, km 3,4 → Golf
Map 1 on page 1087 Plano 1 Página 1087

GOLF COURSE — RECORRIDO — 16/20

Site	Emplazamiento	
Maintenance	Mantenimiento	
Architect	Arquitecto	F. López Segales
Type	Tipo	inland
Relief	Relieve	
Water in play	Agua	
Exp. to wind	Exp. al viento	
Trees in play	Arboles	

Scorecard Tarjeta	**Chp.** Campeonato	**Mens** Caballeros	**Ladies** Damas
Length Longitud	6293	5913	5007
Par	72	72	72
Slope system	137	137	137

Advised golfing ability Nivel de juego aconsejado — 0 12 24 36

Hcp required Handicap exigido — 27 Men, 35 Ladies

CLUB HOUSE & AMENITIES — CLUB HOUSE Y DEPENDENCIAS — 8/10

Pro shop Pro-shop
Driving range Campo de prácticas
Sheltered cubierto yes - On grass sobre hierba yes - Putting-green putting-green yes - Pitching-green pitching-green yes

HOTEL FACILITIES — HOTELES CERCANOS — 8/10

HOTELS HOTELES
Mallorca Marriott - on site - 215 rooms, D € 225
Tel (34) 971- 129 100, Fax (34) 971- 129 103

Hotel Delta - Cala Blava 8 km
288 rooms, D € 220
Tel (34) 971- 741 000, Fax (34) 971- 741 000

Hotel Garonda - Can Pastilla 10 km
133 rooms, D € 124
Tel (34) 971- 262 200, Fax (34) 971- 262 109

RESTAURANTS RESTAURANTES
El Olivar - on site - Tel (34) 971- 129 100
Binicomprat - Algaida 10 km - Tel (34) 971- 125 411
Caís Cotxer - Can Pastilla 10 km - Tel (34) 971- 262 049

Son Muntaner

16 | 8 | 9

He aquí un campo comercial y sin embargo exclusivo: sólo pueden jugar las personas que estén alojadas en los hoteles del parque Son Vida, una exquisita ciudad de vacaciones con dos campos de golf, a 10 minutos del centro de Palma de Mallorca. Son Muntaner es un campo perfectamente integrado en su medio mediterráneo: almedros, algorrobos, pinos y olivos acompañan amablemente al jugador, enmarcando el vuelo de su bola (es de esperar); es uno de aquellos campos en que no es difícil recordar cada hoyo después de haberlo jugado por primera vez, y donde se pueden jugar todos los palos de la bolsa y varios tipos de chip. Es de distancias cómodas pero también tiene golpes muy exigentes, como por ejemplo la salida del 5 (un par 3 en subida de 205 metros) y todo el hoyo 15, que es el hoyo más largo del campo; junto al tee de salida de este hoyo hay un majestuoso olivo milenario de 9 metros de cuerda.

This is a commercial golf course reserved exclusively for guests staying at the two hotels in the Son Vida park, a lovely holiday village with two golf courses lying just 10 minutes away from Palma. Son Muntaner has been designed to fit in perfectly with its Mediterranean environment and is lined with almond trees, carobs, pine and olive trees which clearly outline and dictate the kind of shot you have to hit next. This is one of those courses where you easily remember the holes after just a single round and where you will need every club in your bag. It is not excessively long but certain holes suddenly appear to be very challenging, like the 5th, an uphill par 3 stretching some 225 yards, then the 15th, the longest hole on the course. Before driving, look around and admire the age-old olive tree: the circumference of the trunk measures more than 9 metres.

Son Muntaner Golf — 2000

Urbanización Son Vida
E - 07013 PALMA DE MALLORCA (Mallorca - Islas Baleares)

Office	Secretaria	(34) 971 - 783 036
Pro shop	Pro-shop	(34) 971 - 783 030
Fax	Fax	(34) 971 - 783 031
Web	www.sonmuntanergolf.com	
Situation	Situación	Palma de Mallorca, 2 km
Annual closure	Cierre anual	no
Weekly closure	Cierre semanal	no

Fees main season Precios tempor. alta	Week days Semana	We/Bank holidays Fin de sem./fiestas
	18 holes	
Individual Individual	€ 145	€ 145*
Couple Pareja	€ 290	€ 290*

* Only for guests (exclusivo para clienteles) at Son Vida, Arabella, Castillo Hotels

Caddy Caddy no — **Electric Trolley** Carro eléctrico yes

Buggy Coche yes — **Clubs** Palos yes

Credit cards Tarjetas de crédito
VISA - MasterCard

Access Acceso : From Palma, Ring Road (Vía de Cintura), Exit (salida) Son Rapinya, → Golf San Muntaner
Map 1 on page 1087 Plano 1 Página 1087

GOLF COURSE — RECORRIDO — 16/20

Site	Emplazamiento	
Maintenance	Mantenimiento	
Architect	Arquitecto	Kurt Rossknecht
Type	Tipo	parkland
Relief	Relieve	
Water in play	Agua	
Exp. to wind	Exp. al viento	
Trees in play	Arboles	

Scorecard Tarjeta	Chp. Campeonato	Mens Caballeros	Ladies Damas
Length Longitud	6347	6036	5205
Par	72	72	72
Slope system	129	127	126

Advised golfing ability Nivel de juego aconsejado — 0 12 24 36

Hcp required Handicap exigido — 27 Men, 35 Ladies

CLUB HOUSE & AMENITIES — CLUB HOUSE Y DEPENDENCIAS — 8/10

Pro shop Pro-shop

Driving range Campo de prácticas

Sheltered cubierto no - On grass sobre hierba yes - Putting-green putting-green yes - Pitching-green pitching-green yes

HOTEL FACILITIES — HOTELES CERCANOS — 9/10

HOTELS HOTELES

Castillo Hotel Son Vida - 158 rooms, D € 431 - on site
Tel (34) 971- 790 000, Fax (34) 971- 790 017

Arabella Sheraton Hotel - 92 rooms, D € 431 - on site
Tel (34) 971- 787 100 , Fax (34) 971- 799 997

Mardavall Hotel & Spa - Portals Nous (Calvià)
133 rooms, D € 602
Tel (34) 971 - 629 629, Fax (34) 971 - 639 630

RESTAURANTS RESTAURANTES

Plat d'Or - on site - Tel (34) 971- 799 999
El Pato - on site - Tel (34) 971- 791 500
La Lubina - Palma 2 km - Tel (34) 971- 723 350

Son Vida

14	6	9

F. W. Hawtree supo sacar muy buen partido de un terreno colgado de una ladera al pie del Castillo de Son Vida; casi cuarenta años más tarde el alemán Kurt Rossknecht ha dirigido unas importantes obras de remodelación que además de mejorar los sistemas de riego y drenaje y de rehacer varios greenes, que han ganado en velocidad y movimientos, han alargado el campo más de ochenta metros. Pinos, palmeras y almendros –precioso el espectáculo de los almendros en flor a principios de febrero- decoran el campo y la vez constituyen una referencia decisiva en este campo junto con los bunkers de green. Desde los tees pueden verse las calles estrechas, pero se ensanchan a la caída del drive y también es buen aliciente para los pegadores la tentación de acortar hacia green en los dog-legs. Unos hoyos finales, especialmente 14, 15 y 18, con buenas razones para decidir muchos partidos y la calidad de su mantenimiento nos mueven a aconsejarlo como una buena diversión para todo tipo de jugadores.

Hawtree squeezed everything he could out of terrain lying below the castle of Son Vida. Almost 40 years later, the German architect Kurt Rossknecht undertook extensive restyling work that has improved the watering and drainage systems, not to mention the re-laying of several greens that are now faster and more finely contoured. These works have lengthened the course by almost 90 yards. Pines, palm trees and almond trees – magnificent when blossoming in February – decorate the course and form the basic part of the difficulties here along with green-side bunkers. You can clearly see the narrow fairways from the tees and they tend to get wider where the ball should be landing, and on several dog-legs it is always tempting to cut corners and get a shorter second shot. The back nine holes, particularly the 14th, 15th and 18th, are the acid test on this course. Together with excellent green-keeping, these closing holes are a very good reason to come back for more of the same.

Son Vida Golf S.A. — 1964

Urbanización Son Vida
E - 07013 PALMA DE MALLORCA
(Mallorca - Islas Baleares)

Office	Secretaria	(34) 971 - 791 210
Pro shop	Pro-shop	(34) 971 - 791 210
Fax	Fax	(34) 971 - 791 127
Web	www.sonvidagolf.com	
Situation	Situación	Palma de Mallorca, 2 km
Annual closure	Cierre anual	no
Weekly closure	Cierre semanal	no
Fees main season	Precios tempor. alta	18 holes

	Week days Semana	We/Bank holidays Fin de sem./fiestas
Individual Individual	€ 70	€ 70
Couple Pareja	€ 140	€ 140

Caddy Caddy no — Electric Trolley Carro eléctrico yes
Buggy Coche yes — Clubs Palos yes
Credit cards Tarjetas de crédito
VISA - MasterCard

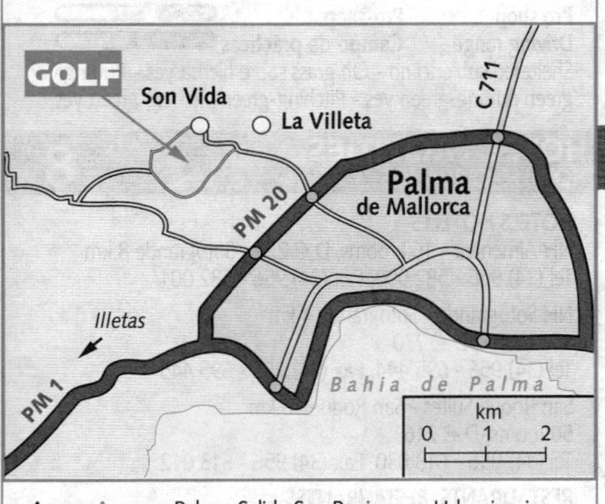

Access Acceso : Palma, Salida Son Rapinya → Urbanizacion Son Vida
Map 1 on page 1087 Plano 1 Página 1087

GOLF COURSE RECORRIDO — 14/20

Site	Emplazamiento	
Maintenance	Mantenimiento	
Architect	Arquitecto	F.W. Hawtree
Type	Tipo	parkland, residential
Relief	Relieve	
Water in play	Agua	
Exp. to wind	Exp. al viento	
Trees in play	Arboles	

Scorecard Tarjeta	Chp. Campeonato	Mens Caballeros	Ladies Damas
Length Longitud	5601	5601	4738
Par	71	71	71
Slope system	128	130	130

Advised golfing ability / Nivel de juego aconsejado: 0 12 24 36
Hcp required / Handicap exigido: 28 Men, 36 Ladies

CLUB HOUSE & AMENITIES CLUB HOUSE Y DEPENDENCIAS — 6/10

Pro shop — Pro-shop
Driving range — Campo de prácticas
Sheltered cubierto 10 mats - On grass sobre hierba yes - Putting-green putting-green yes - Pitching-green pitching-green yes

HOTEL FACILITIES HOTELES CERCANOS — 9/10

HOTELS HOTELES

Arabella Sheraton Golf Hotel - 92 rooms, D € 450 - on site
Tel (34) 971 - 787 100, Fax (34) 971 - 787 101

Castillo Hotel Son Vida - 158 rooms, D € 431 - on site
Tel (34) 971- 790 000, Fax (34) 971- 790 017

Saratoga - 187 rooms, D € 145 - Palma 6 km
Tel (34) 971 - 727 240, Fax (34) 971 - 727 312

RESTAURANTS RESTAURANTES

El Pato - Golf - Tel (34) 971 - 791 500
Diplomatic - Palma 6 km - Tel (34) 971 - 726 482

Sotogrande

18	8	8

Abierto en 1964, es uno de los clubs con más solera de la Costa del Sol y uno de sus mejores recorridos. La prioridad la tienen los socios y los visitantes se admiten con grandes restricciones. En un sitio muy tranquilo, rodeado de casas espléndidas, con variedad de árboles, es más duro de lo que uno quisiera y menos de lo que parece. Gracias en parte a la ausencia casi total de rough, lo que permite que los "pegadores" puedan expresarse con todas sus fuerzas sin más preocupación que la de evitar los numerosos obstáculos de agua concentrados sobre todo en los últimos hoyos. Los golfistas de diferentes niveles se deleitarán con esta armoniosa preparación del recorrido, a pesar de que los greens sean extensos, con muchas caídas y a menudo en ellos se destroce el resultado. Bien acompasado, con dificultades bien repartidas, Sotogrande es uno de los grandes ejemplos de la arquitectura de Trent Jones, y uno de los mejores recorridos de España, muchas veces eclipsado por su vecino Valderrama. Espléndido recorrido corto de par 28.

Opened in 1964, this is one of the coast's most select golf clubs and also one of the best courses. Members have priority and tough restrictions are placed on the admission of visitors. On a very quiet site, encircled by majestic houses and enhanced with numerous trees (pine, olive, oak, eucalyptus and palm trees), it is at once harder than you would like and easier than it looks. This is partly because of the virtual absence of rough, enabling long-hitters to open their shoulders with no worries other than avoiding the numerous water hazards, concentrated particularly over the last holes. But players of all levels will have fun with this friendly preparation, even though the greens are huge, very undulating and often murderous for the score card. Very well paced with difficulties evenly spread around the course, Sotogrande is one of the great examples of architecture à la Trent Jones and one of the best courses in Spain, a bit in the shadow of Valderrama.

Real Club de Golf Sotogrande — 1964

Paseo del Parque s/n
E - 11310 SOTOGRANDE (Cádiz)

Office	Secretaría	(34) 956 - 785 014
Pro shop	Pro-shop	(34) 956 - 785 012
Fax	Fax	(34) 956 - 795 029
Web	www.golfsotogrande.com	
Situation	Situación	Estepona, 30 km

Algeciras (pop. 101 556), 30 km

Annual closure	Cierre anual	no
Weekly closure	Cierre semanal	no

Fees main season Precios tempor. alta	**Week days** Semana	**We/Bank holidays** Fin de sem./fiestas
18 holes		
Individual Individual	€ 160	*
Couple Pareja	€ 320	*

* Member's guests only (sólo invitados de socios)

Caddie Caddie on request **Electric Trolley** Carro eléctrico yes

Buggy Coche yes **Clubs** Palos yes

Credit cards Tarjetas de crédito
VISA - MasterCard - AMEX

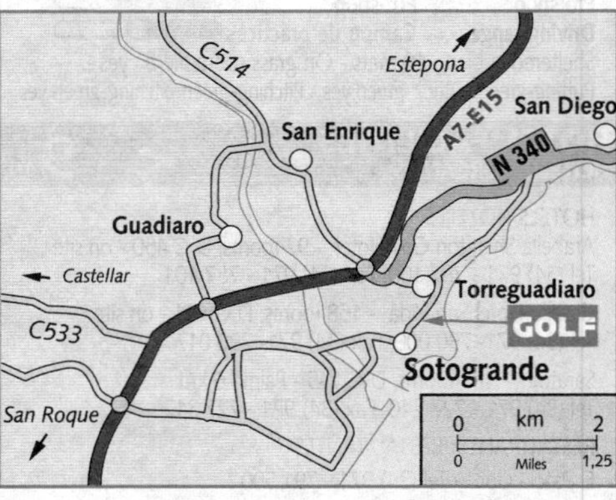

Access Acceso : N340 Estepona → Cádiz. Exit (salida) km 131 Sotogrande, Golf on the left
Map 8 on page 1101 Plano 8 Página 1101

GOLF COURSE — RECORRIDO — 18/20

Site	Emplazamiento	
Maintenance	Mantenimiento	
Architect	Arquitecto	Robert Trent Jones
Type	Tipo	seaside parkland
Relief	Relieve	
Water in play	Agua	
Exp. to wind	Exp. al viento	
Trees in play	Arboles	

Scorecard Tarjeta	**Chp.** Campeonato	**Mens** Caballeros	**Ladies** Damas
Length Longitud	6304	5874	5147
Par	72	72	72
Slope system	135	131	125

Advised golfing ability Nivel de juego aconsejado — 0 12 24 36

Hcp required Handicap exigido — 25 Men, 30 Ladies

CLUB HOUSE & AMENITIES — CLUB HOUSE Y DEPENDENCIAS — 8/10

Pro shop	Pro-shop
Driving range	Campo de prácticas

Sheltered cubierto no - On grass sobre hierba yes - Putting-green putting-green yes - Pitching-green pitching-green yes

HOTEL FACILITIES — HOTELES CERCANOS — 8/10

HOTELS HOTELES

NH Almenara - 160 rooms, D € 223 - Sotogrande 8 km
Tel (34) 956 - 582 000, Fax (34) 956 - 582 001

NH Sotogrande - Sotogrande 4 km
106 rooms, D € 270
Tel (34) 956 - 695 444, Fax (34) 956 - 695 445

San Roque Suites - San Roque 10 km
50 rooms, D € 216
Tel (34) 956 - 613 030, Fax (34) 956 - 613 012

RESTAURANTS RESTAURANTES

Los Remos - San Roque 15 km - Tel (34) 956 - 698 412
Pedro - San Roque 15 km - Tel (34) 956 - 698 453

Torremirona

13 | 7 | 7

Este campo se halla en el centro de una planicie con unas vistas espléndidas sobre las estribaciones de los Pirineos que han recogido en sus cuadros famosos pintores locales. Todavía le faltan años para que la vegetación plantada con él crezca y se asiente pero uno de los tesoros del emplazamiento es su luz y el colorido de la naturaleza que lo rodea. No es largo, aunque los pegadores podrán disfrutar en dos pares 4 exigentes, y permite jugar con cierta tranquilidad, aunque el recorrido sorprende gratamente de vez en cuando con tiros que merecen una gran concentración, como la salida del 10, un par 3 con agua a la izquierda, o la del 15, un par 3 con el green en alto. El campo, pues, es versátil porque los jugadores expertos pueden hallar en él ocasiones de plantearse el reto de dar el golpe precisamente indicado, y los jugadores de mayor handicap tienen muchas opciones para cubrir su recorrido sin excesivos riesgos. El hotel abierto junto al tee del 1 sugiere además que es un buen modelo de instalación para unas confortables vacaciones de golf.

This course lies at the centre of a plain giving some splendid views over the foothills of the Pyrenees, as illustrated by four famous local artists. Of course it will take years for the young plantation to grow and mature but the location of this layout already provides magnificent light and colours from the natural setting all around. This is a virtually flat and easy course to play. It is not wide, though, but big-hitters will enjoy two demanding par 4s in particular. It also has a few surprises in store when shots call for extra concentration, like at the 10th hole, a par 3 with water to the left, or the 15th, another par 3 with an elevated green. This is a versatile course in that skilled players have the chance to attack the pin if they play straight, while the higher-handicap golfer has a number of options open to him to get around the course without any excessive risk-taking. The hotel behind the first tee-box makes this a model resort for an enjoyable golf holiday.

Torremirona Golf Club — 1993

Ctra. N-260, Km 46
E - 17744 NAVATA (Girona – Alt Empordà)

Office	Secretaría	(34) 972 - 553 737
Pro shop	Pro-shop	(34) 972 - 553 737
Fax	Fax	(34) 972 - 553 716
Web	www.torremirona.com	
Situation	Situación	Figueras, 10 km
Annual closure	Cierre anual	no
Weekly closure	Cierre semanal	no
Fees main season	Precios tempor. alta	18 holes

	Week days Semana	We/Bank holidays Fin de sem./fiestas
Individual Individual	€ 72	€ 72
Couple Pareja	€ 144	€ 144

Caddie Caddie no — **Electric Trolley** Carro eléctrico yes

Buggy Coche yes — **Clubs** Palos yes

Credit cards Tarjetas de crédito
VISA - Eurocard - MasterCard - AMEX

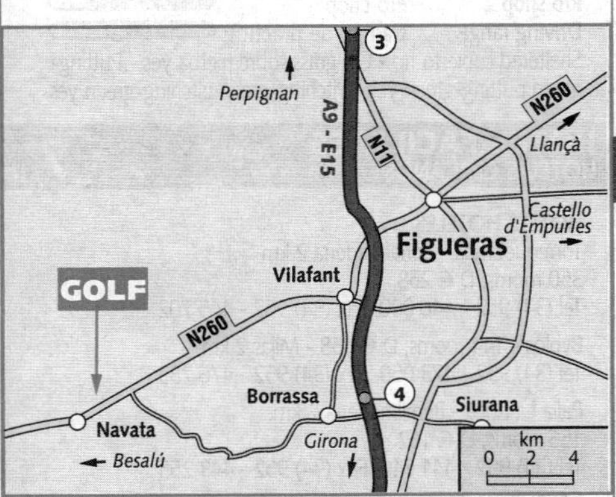

Access Acceso : Figueras, N260 → Olot, Km 46, turn right.
Map 2 on page 1091 Plano 2 Página 1091

GOLF COURSE — RECORRIDO — 13/20

Site	Emplazamiento	
Maintenance	Mantenimiento	
Architect	Arquitecto	Tecnoa, Eugenio Aguado
Type	Tipo	parkland, inland
Relief	Relieve	
Water in play	Agua	
Exp. to wind	Exp. al viento	
Trees in play	Arboles	

Scorecard Tarjeta	Chp. Campeonato	Mens Caballeros	Ladies Damas
Length Longitud	6232	5937	5124
Par	72	72	72
Slope system	129	125	120

Advised golfing ability Nivel de juego aconsejado: 0 12 24 36

Hcp required Handicap exigido: 28 Men, 36 Ladies

CLUB HOUSE & AMENITIES — CLUB HOUSE Y DEPENDENCIAS — 7/10

Pro shop Pro-shop
Driving range Campo de prácticas
Sheltered cubierto no - On grass sobre hierba yes (25 places) - Putting-green putting-green yes - Pitching-green pitching-green yes

HOTEL FACILITIES — HOTELES CERCANOS — 7/10

HOTELS HOTELES

Torremirona - 49 rooms, D € 232 - on site
Tel (34) 972 - 566 700, Fax (34) 972 - 566 767

Mas Falgarona - 9 rooms, D € 190 - Avinyonet 5 km
Tel (34) 972 - 546 628, Fax (34) 972 - 547 071

Empordá - 42 rooms, D € 135 - Figueras 11 km
Tel (34) 972 - 500 562, Fax (34) 972 - 509 358

RESTAURANTS RESTAURANTES

El Canigo - Figueras 11 km - Tel (34) 972 - 566 700
Mas Pau - Avinyonet 5 km - Tel (34) 972 - 546 154
Durán - Figueras 10 km - Tel (34) 972 - 501 250

Torrequebrada

14	7	7

En una de sus primeras obras, José Gancedo aplicó la filosofía que ha seguido fielmente en su carrera: adaptar el recorrido a la forma y entorno del terreno. El relieve de este campo pone incluso difícil jugar sin coche. Los golpes de salida son decisivos porque con una mala salida, se acabó el hoyo, tan escasas son las posibilidades de recuperación para acabar con un resultado que no emborrone la tarjeta. No hay que dejarse engañar por unas distancias que parecen muy fáciles, porque las dificultades y los obstáculos influyen tanto en el juego que hasta los golpes cortos tier en riesgos: árboles, bosque, rough, bunkers y obstáculos de agua se encuentran en la línea de juego. Se puede sufrir tanto con el descontrol de la bola, que ni la belleza del panorama lo compensará. Hasta que no se conozca un poco bien el campo olvídese de contarlas; si juega match-play se divertirá mucho más y jugará mucho más tranquilo... al menos hasta que se vaya quedando sin bolas.

With one of his first courses, architect José Gancedo has applied a philosophy that he would do well to pursue in the future, namely the art of adapting a course to the shape and topography of the terrain. This site is hilly enough to make walking rather too tiring so go for a buggy. Here, the tee-shot is of prime importance. A wild drive and all may be lost. And don't be fooled by the short yardage because the numerous hazards make even the shortest irons a tricky business. Trees, woods, rough, bunkers and water are all very much to the fore, and the beauty of the scenery is scant consolation should you lose your grip and your game. For the first couple of rounds, you are better off in match-play, in which case the course can be great fun (even on the few blind holes) except for the less experienced players, who will feel the pressure even more when they start running out of balls...

1200

Golf Torrequebrada — 1977

Apartado de Correos 120
E - 29630 BENALMADENA COSTA (Málaga – Costa del Sol)

Office	Secretaría	(34) 952 - 561 102
Pro shop	Pro-shop	(34) 952 - 561 102
Fax	Fax	(34) 952 - 561 129
Web	www.golftorrequebrada.com	
Situation	Situación	Torremolinos, 8 km

Fuengirola (pop. 43 048), 5 km

Annual closure	Cierre anual	no
Weekly closure	Cierre semanal	no
Fees main season	Precios tempor. alta	18 holes

	Week days Semana	We/Bank holidays Fin de sem./fiestas
Individual Individual	€ 90	€ 90
Couple Pareja	€ 180	€ 180

Caddie Caddie no — **Electric Trolley** Carro eléctrico yes
Buggy Coche yes — **Clubs** Palos yes
Credit cards Tarjetas de crédito
VISA - Mastercard

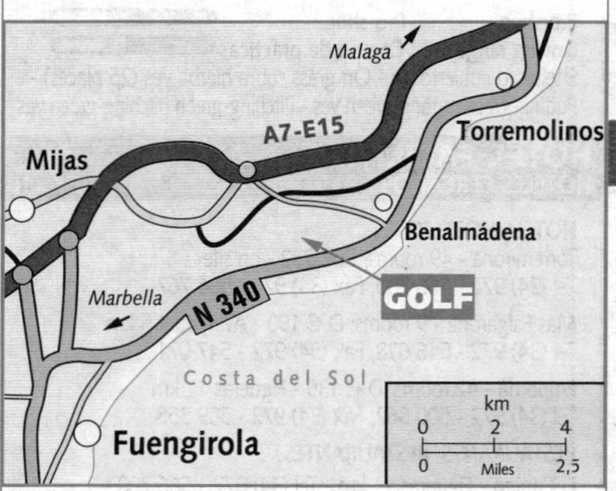

Access Acceso : CN-340 Málaga → Marbella. Exit (salida) km 220, between Torremolinos and Fuengirola.
Map 8 on page 1101 Plano 8 Página 1101

GOLF COURSE — RECORRIDO — 14/20

Site	Emplazamiento	
Maintenance	Mantenimiento	
Architect	Arquitecto	José Gancedo
Type	Tipo	hilly
Relief	Relieve	
Water in play	Agua	
Exp. to wind	Exp. al viento	
Trees in play	Arboles	

Scorecard Tarjeta	Chp. Campeonato	Mens Caballeros	Ladies Damas
Length Longitud	5852	5763	4881
Par	72	72	72
Slope system	134	133	122

Advised golfing ability Nivel de juego aconsejado — 0 12 24 36
Hcp required Handicap exigido — 28 Men, 36 Ladies

CLUB HOUSE & AMENITIES — CLUB HOUSE Y DEPENDENCIAS — 7/10

Pro shop Pro-shop
Driving range Campo de prácticas
Sheltered cubierto no - On grass sobre hierba yes - Putting-green putting-green yes - Pitching-green pitching-green yes

HOTEL FACILITIES — HOTELES CERCANOS — 7/10

HOTELS HOTELES

Torrequebrada - Benalmadena 2 km
350 rooms, D € 258
Tel (34) 952 - 446 000, Fax (34) 952 - 445 702

Byblos - 144 rooms, D € 358 - Mijas 2 km
Tel (34) 952 - 473 050, Fax (34) 952 - 476 783

Palia La Roca - Benalmadena 2 km
156 rooms, D € 162
Tel (34) 952 - 441 740, Fax (34) 952 - 443 255

RESTAURANTS RESTAURANTES

Mar de Alboran - Benalmadena 2 km - Tel (34) 952 - 446 427
Chef Alonso - Benalmadena 2 km - Tel (34) 952 - 443 435

Ulzama

16	6	6

Este campo discurre a 500 metros de altitud en un terreno accidentado en el que los jugadores en baja forma física acabarán agotados. La adaptación del recorrido al terreno es extraordinaria: se trata de una de las últimas obras del gran arquitecto Javier Arana, y Francisco López Segales. Toda la acción transcurre en medio de un inmenso y frondoso bosque. Aunque las calles no son muy estrechas, el jugador que no logre mantener la bola bien recta será "recompensado" a la altura de sus errores. Es un recorrido natural, con un paisaje análogo al de un parque con unos greenes de tamaño medio y bastante planos. Suerte que no hay muchos bunkers porque hay varios golpes de aproach ciegos. En efecto tiene muchos elementos propios que hacen preciso haberlo jugado previamente para poder hacer un buen resultado. Para el jugador de tipo medio es un recorrido de longitud asequible en el que los pares 3 son bastante largos exceptuando el hoyo 2.

At over 1500 ft. above sea-level, Ulzama unfolds over hilly terrain where the less fit player will probably feel the strain. But the way the course has been adapted to the lie of the land is quite remarkable, hardly a surprise when you learn that this is one of the latest courses by the great designer Javier Arana, with F. López Segales. The major visual feature is basically its layout in a majestic oak forest. With this said, the fairways are never too tight, which doesn't mean to say that players who make a mess of their tee-shot and don't hit it straight won't be penalised accordingly. This course is a very natural-looking layout in landscape reminiscent of park-land with average-sized, rather flat greens. Bunkers are limited in number, which is probably a good thing given the number of blind shots, and you need to know the course well before any hope of shooting a good score. For the average player, this is a course of reachable length but the par 3s are on the long side (except N° 2).

Club de Golf Ulzama — 1965/1990

E - 31799 GUERENDIAIN
(Valle de Ulzama-Navarra)

Office	Secretaria	(34) 948 - 305 162
Pro shop	Pro-shop	(34) 948 - 305 471
Fax	Fax	(34) 948 - 309 209
Web	www.golfulzama.com	
Situation	Situación	Pamplona, 22 km
Annual closure	Cierre anual	no
Weekly closure	Cierre semanal	no

Fees main season Precios tempor. alta	18 holes	
	Week days Semana	**We/Bank holidays** Fin de sem./fiestas
Individual Individual	€ 80	€ 100
Couple Pareja	€ 160	€ 200

Caddie Caddie no — **Electric Trolley** Carro eléctrico yes
Buggy Coche yes — **Clubs** Palos yes
Credit cards Tarjetas de crédito
VISA

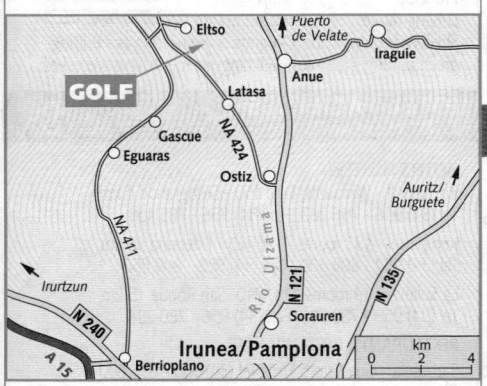

Access Acceso : Pamplona, N-121 → Irun.
Turn in Ostiz (km 15) → Lizaso (Valle Ulzama) after 6 km.
Map 2 on page 1089 Plano 2 Página 1089

GOLF COURSE — RECORRIDO — 16/20

Site	Emplazamiento	
Maintenance	Mantenimiento	
Architect	Arquitecto	Javier Arana F. López Segales
Type	Tipo	forest
Relief	Relieve	
Water in play	Agua	
Exp. to wind	Exp. al viento	
Trees in play	Arboles	

Scorecard Tarjeta	**Chp.** Campeonato	**Mens** Caballeros	**Ladies** Damas
Length Longitud	6259	6096	5170
Par	72	72	72
Slope system	130	1329	123

Advised golfing ability Nivel de juego aconsejado — 0 12 24 36
Hcp required Handicap exigido — 28 Men, 36 Ladies

CLUB HOUSE & AMENITIES — CLUB HOUSE Y DEPENDENCIAS — 6/10

Pro shop Pro-shop
Driving range Campo de prácticas
Sheltered cubierto no - On grass sobre hierba yes - Putting-green putting-green yes - Pitching-green pitching-green yes

HOTEL FACILITIES — HOTELES CERCANOS — 6/10

HOTELS HOTELES
Ventas Ulzama - Puerto Belate 8 km
15 rooms, D € 84
Tel (34) 948 - 305 138, Fax (34) 948 - 305 138

Lorentxo - 10 rooms, D € 44 - Olave 10 km
Tel (34) 948 - 332 486, Fax (34) 948 - 332 679

Aguirre - 12 rooms, D € 57 - Oricain 14 km
Tel (34) 948 - 330 375

RESTAURANTS RESTAURANTES
Josetxo - Pamplona 21 km - Tel (34) 948 - 222 097
La Chistera - Pamplona 21 km - Tel (34) 948 - 210 512
Castillo de Javier - Pamplona 21 km - Tel (34) 948 - 221 894

1201

Valderrama

19 | 8 | 8

No hay que perdérselo porque es un campo en condiciones de juego exquisitas, con la fama de haber acogido la Ryder Cup de 1997 y de grandes torneos del circuito europeo y mundial. Valderrama ha adquirido notoriedad internacional bajo la impulsión de su propietario Jaime Ortiz-Patiño, quien impuso no sólo modificaciones del recorrido original (sobre todo el 17) sino que ha exigido un mantenimiento del campo de excepcional calidad (hasta uno teme sacar chuletas, porque las calles son tan perfectas que parecen greenes). La dificultad estratégica del trazado, la omnipresencia de los alcornoques, la dimensión de los bunkers y algunos obstáculos de agua, obligan a estudiar muy bien cada golpe. Las caídas de los greenes aumentan aún más la presión. Es inútil pretender cumplir el handicap porque incluso a los grandes campeones les cuesta muchísimo acabar en par. Pero es una visita obligada, a pesar del precio y de las restricciones para socios y visitantes, ante la calidad del desafío y por veneración a un santuario.

Valderrama has gained international fame through the energy of proprietor Jaime Ortiz-Patiño, who not only insisted on making changes to the original layout but also demanded exceptional standards of course maintenance. But honestly, if the standards of green-keeping here were not quite as excellent, this sometimes controversial course would certainly not be rated as high as it is... Other courses elsewhere provide a little more variety in their layout. The strategic difficulty, omnipresent trees, the size of the bunkers and a few water hazards keep the player constantly on his toes at every stroke. And the pressure is made worse when it comes to reading the greens. Don't bother about playing to your handicap, as even the top champions find making par a tough enough task. For the excellence of the challenge and the impression of walking over hallowed terrain, Valderrama is essential visiting despite the green-fee and restrictions applying to both members and visitors.

Club de Golf Valderrama — 1975

Avenida de los Cortijos 1
E - 11310 SOTOGRANDE (Cádiz)

Office Secretaria (34) 956 - 791 200
Pro shop Pro-shop (34) 956 - 795 775
Fax Fax (34) 956 - 796 028
Web www.valderrama.com
Situation Situación Estepona, 30 km
Algeciras (pop. 101 556), 30 km
Annual closure Cierre anual no
Weekly closure Cierre semanal no

Fees main season Precios tempor. alta	18 holes	
	Week days Semana	**We/Bank holidays** Fin de sem./fiestas
Individual Individual	€ 260	€ 290
Couple Pareja	€ 520	€ 580

Mostly members & guests: book in advance

Caddie Caddie yes — **Electric Trolley** Carro eléctrico no
Buggy Coche yes — **Clubs** Palos yes
Credit cards Tarjetas de crédito VISA - AMEX

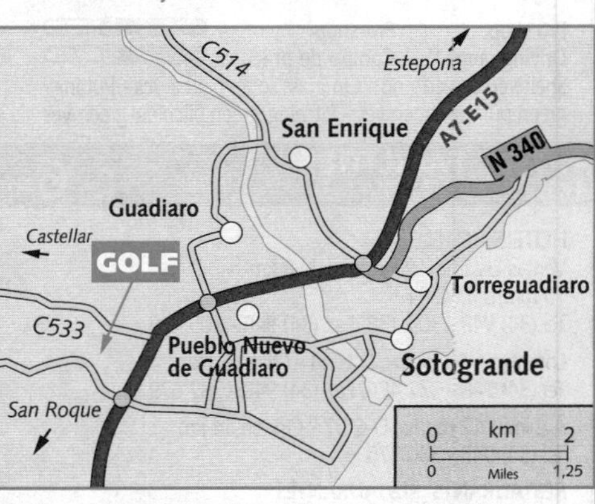

Access Acceso : N340 Estepona → Cadiz. Exit (salida) Km 132 Sotogrande, Golf on the right (opposite to the sea)
Map 8 on page 1101 Plano 8 Página 1101

GOLF COURSE — RECORRIDO — 19/20

Site Emplazamiento
Maintenance Mantenimiento
Architect Arquitecto Robert Trent Jones
Type Tipo parkland
Relief Relieve
Water in play Agua
Exp. to wind Exp. al viento
Trees in play Arboles

Scorecard Tarjeta	**Chp.** Campeonato	**Mens** Caballeros	**Ladies** Damas
Length Longitud	6356	5995	4873
Par	71	72	72
Slope system	146	142	133

Advised golfing ability Nivel de juego aconsejado 0 12 24 36
Hcp required Handicap exigido 24 Men, 36 Ladies

CLUB HOUSE & AMENITIES — CLUB HOUSE Y DEPENDENCIAS — 8/10

Pro shop Pro-shop
Driving range Campo de prácticas
Sheltered cubierto no - On grass sobre hierba yes - Putting-green putting-green yes - Pitching-green pitching-green yes

HOTEL FACILITIES — HOTELES CERCANOS — 8/10

HOTELS HOTELES
Royal Golf - 70 rooms, D € 150 - Sotogrande 4 km
Tel (34) 956 - 796 263, Fax (34) 956 - 785 159
Kempinski - 133 rooms, D € 425 - Estepona 30 km
Tel (34) 952 - 809 500 , Fax (34) 952 - 809 550
La Solana - 19 rooms, D € 210- San Roque 15 km
Tel (34) 956 - 780 236, Fax (34) 956 - 780 236

RESTAURANTS RESTAURANTES
Barbesula - Guadiaro 5 km - Tel (34) 956 - 695 600
Lido - Estepona 30 km - Tel (34) 952 - 794 345

Valle del Este

16	5	6

José Canales ha hecho en Valle del Este un recorrido de formidable calidad estética y técnica. Ha conservado la esencia de la naturaleza del lugar para hacer un recorrido de una belleza deslumbrante. Y, al mismo tiempo, un magnífico campo de golf donde las distancias vienen corregidas por cuestas pronunciadas. Las calles son amplias para la caída de las salidas, con bunkers bastante grandes y en claras posiciones de defensa de unos greenes que tienen amplias superficies no siempre en el mismo plano. Casi todos los hoyos tienen cuatro plataformas de tees y algunos hasta seis para poder jugar tanto con las distancias como con los ángulos. Como suelen estar en alto, producen unas panorámicas de gran espectacularidad. Es probable que algún jugador se queje porque tiene que jugar mucho cuesta arriba y tirar a banderas ciegas. Sin duda es un campo que tiene que disfrutarse más cuanto más se juegue y, la primera vez, es un excelente ejercicio de los recursos del jugador para golpes variados, no convencionales, de pensar en técnica y en estrategia.

José Canales has produced here a very stylish course which technically speaking is excellent. He has succeeded in preserving the very essence of the site's natural beauty to create a very handsome layout indeed. At the same time, this is an excellent golf course where distances can be deceiving owing to the topography. The fairways are wide where the drive should land and bunkers pretty vast and clearly located to defend large and differently contoured greens. Almost every hole has four tee-boxes and some even have six so that each player can adjust to the distances and angles he has to contend with. And as they are generally elevated, the view of the hole is clear and spectacular. Some people might complain that several holes are uphill or blind but this is a course you need to play several times. First time out will be an exercise in reconnoitering as the shots you play are not always text-book and call for clear strategy.

Valle del Este Golf Club

Urbanización Valle del Este Resort
E - 04620 VERA (Almería – Andalucía)

Office Secretaria (34) 950 - 398 743
Pro shop Pro-shop (34) 950 - 398 743
Fax Fax (34) 950 - 398 214
Web www.valledeleste.es
Situation Situación Almería, 100 km
Vera (pop. 6.000), 4 km

Annual closure Cierre anual no
Weekly closure Cierre semanal no

Fees main season Precios tempor. alta	18 holes	
	Week days Semana	**We/Bank holidays** Fin de sem./fiestas
Individual Individual	€ 65	€ 65
Couple Pareja	€ 130	€ 130

Caddie Caddie no — **Electric Trolley** Carro eléctrico yes
Buggy Coche yes — **Clubs** Palos yes
Credit cards Tarjetas de crédito
VISA - Eurocard - MasterCard

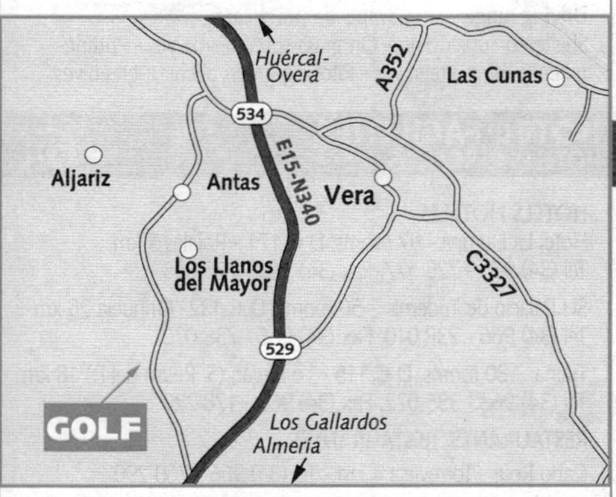

Access Acceso : N-340/E15. Exit (Salida) 529.
On A-352 turn right and U-turn right to the club
Map 9 on page 1103 Plano 9 Página 1103

GOLF COURSE — RECORRIDO 16/20

Site	Emplazamiento	
Maintenance	Mantenimiento	
Architect	Arquitecto	José Canales
Type	Tipo	desert, open space
Relief	Relieve	
Water in play	Agua	
Exp. to wind	Exp. al viento	
Trees in play	Arboles	

Scorecard Tarjeta	**Chp.** Campeonato	**Mens** Caballeros	**Ladies** Damas
Length Longitud	5717	5329	4882
Par	71	71	71
Slope system	135	130	132

Advised golfing ability Nivel de juego aconsejado — 0 12 24 36
Hcp required Handicap exigido — 28 Men, 36 Ladies

CLUB HOUSE & AMENITIES — CLUB HOUSE Y DEPENDENCIAS 5/10

Pro shop Pro-shop
Driving range Campo de prácticas
Sheltered cubierto no - On grass sobre hierba yes - Putting-green putting-green yes - Pitching-green pitching-green yes

HOTEL FACILITIES — HOTELES CERCANOS 6/10

HOTELS HOTELES

Hotel Valle del Este Golf, Spa - 142 rooms, D € 165 - on site
Tel (34) 950 - 548 600, Fax (34) 950 - 461 006

Parador de los Reyes Católicos - Mojácar 5 km
98 rooms, D € 141
Tel (34) 950 - 478 250, Fax (34) 950 - 478 183

Marina Playa - 335 rooms, D € 145 - Mojácar 5 km
Tel (34) 950 - 548 500, Fax (34) 950 - 548 545

RESTAURANTS RESTAURANTES

Terraza Carmona - Vera 2 km - Tel (34) 950 - 390 180
El Felipe - Mojácar 5 km - Tel (34) 950 - 478 202

1203

Villamartín

16	7	6

Es el primer campo (con Las Ramblas y La Finca) del Grupo inmobiliario Urbanizadora Villamartín. Sobre un terreno naturalmente accidentado Putman, con mucha imaginación, ha sabido adaptar a él su diseño haciendo un recorrido que es un reto para los mejores por distancia, sobre todo desde las salidas largas, y tiene el aliciente de que los jugadores medios ven la posibilidad de que su esfuerzo resulte premiado. Desniveles, agua, árboles al borde de las calles y greenes interesantes y agradecidos. Varios pares 4 más bien cortos permiten disfrutar un poquito. El agua, que tan poco gusta a los jugadores de tipo medio, se halla verdaderamente en línea de juego en tres hoyos (sobre todo en el 9), y preferirán admirar los árboles, raramente en línea de juego pero muy presentes. Los greenes son de buen tamaño, con ligeras ondulaciones y aguantan bien la bola aún cuando el golpe no sea perfecto. Es un recorrido adaptable fácilmente para jugar en familia y con jugadores de niveles diferentes, y en general muy bien cuidado.

With Las Ramblas and Finca, this is the first course from the Urbanizadora Villamartín group. Over hilly terrain and using loads of imagination, Putman has successfully adapted his design and built a course that is a real challenge to the better players through sheer length, especially from the back tees. It also has extra appeal in that the not-so-good player always has the chance to see his good shots aptly rewarded. The slopes, water, trees lining the fairways and greens are interesting and fair in the way they are laid out. A number of short par 4s are fun to play and water is only really in play on three holes (especially the 9th). High-handicappers, who tend not to like water, can preferably admire the trees, which although rarely in play are very much a part of the course. The greens are large, rolling and pitch well, even from slightly mis-hit shots. This is a most versatile and generally well-prepared course, easy to play with the family or with players of all different levels.

Campo de Golf Villamartín 1972

Apartado 28
E - 03189 ORIHUELA COSTA (Alicante)

Office Secretaría (34) 966 - 765 170
Pro shop Pro-shop (34) 966 - 765 170
Fax Fax (34) 966 - 765 170
Web www.golfvillamartin.com
Situation Situación Alicante, 50 km
Torrevieja (pop. 25 891), 7 km

Annual closure Cierre anual no

Weekly closure Cierre semanal no

Fees main season Precios tempor. alta 18 holes

	Week days Semana	We/Bank holidays Fin de sem./fiestas
Individual Individual	€ 60	€ 60
Couple Pareja	€ 120	€ 120

Caddie Caddie no — **Electric Trolley** Carro eléctrico no

Buggy Coche yes — **Clubs** Palos yes

Credit cards Tarjetas de crédito no

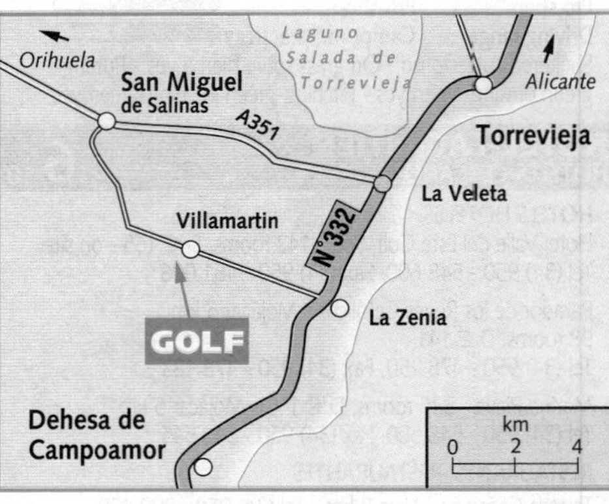

Access Acceso : N332 → Cartagena, 55 km S. de Alicante. Torrevieja → Golf

Map 7 on page 1099 Plano 7 Página 1099

GOLF COURSE — RECORRIDO 16/20

Site Emplazamiento
Maintenance Mantenimiento
Architect Arquitecto John Putman
Type Tipo country, hilly
Relief Relieve
Water in play Agua
Exp. to wind Exp. al viento
Trees in play Arboles

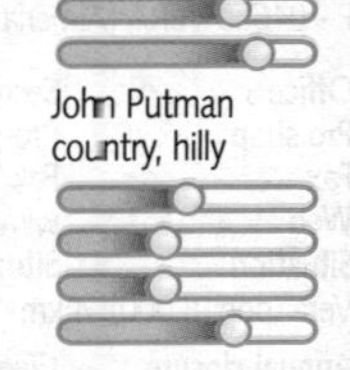

Scorecard Tarjeta	Chp. Campeonato	Mens Caballeros	Ladies Damas
Length Longitud	6132	6037	5259
Par	72	72	72
Slope system	135	134	129

Advised golfing ability Nivel de juego aconsejado 0 12 24 36

Hcp required Handicap exigido 28 Men, 36 Ladies

CLUB HOUSE & AMENITIES — CLUB HOUSE Y DEPENDENCIAS 7/10

Pro shop Pro-shop
Driving range Campo de prácticas
Sheltered cubierto no - On grass sobre hierba yes - Putting-green putting-green yes - Pitching-green pitching-green yes

HOTEL FACILITIES — HOTELES CERCANOS 6/10

HOTELS HOTELES

Hotel La Laguna - 97 rooms, D € 171 - Rojales 3 km
Tel (34) 965 - 725 577, Fax (34) 965 - 725 855

SH Palacio de Tudemir - 50 rooms, D € 132 - Orihuela 25 km
Tel (34) 966 - 738 010, Fax (34) 966 - 738 070

Traíña - 80 rooms, D € 115 - Lo Págan (S. Pedro del P.) 18 km
Tel (34) 968 - 335 022, Fax (34) 968 - 178 220

RESTAURANTS RESTAURANTES

Cabo Roig - Torrevieja 4 km - Tel (34) 966 - 760 290
Morales - Torrevieja 4 km - Tel (34) 966 - 721 293

Zaudín

16 | 7 | 6

Este campo es una buena muestra de la capacidad de evolución de una firma ilustre como la de Gary Player. Aquí se ve un recorrido diseñado con mucho detalle y las dificultades que tiene son variadas. Pero en definitiva es un campo noble y como todas las realizaciones del gran maestro, el campo deja jugar y permite lucirse con golpes de buen control, cortos y largos. Aparte de unos cuantos hoyos de ida y vuelta y de que hay demasiada distancia a veces de green a tee, Zaudín debe considerarse entre las buenas realizaciones del Sur de España. Palmeras, naranjos y grandes lagos hacen pensar en Florida, pero los olivos están tan presentes como en el panorama de Sevilla. Aquí, el drive de salida en los pares 4 y 5 no plantea grandes problemas pero los aproches son delicados (especialmente en el 17 y en el 18). Una vez en green, no hay sorpresas desagradables, no son inmensos ni tortuosos. La distancia razonable del recorrido y la calidad de las instalaciones hacen que sea una realización recomendable.

The architecture of Gary Player has evolved in 20 years: his courses are now much more intricate in the smaller details and offer a greater variety of difficulty. This is a very noble course and like all Player's designs it is enticing to play and rewards well-controlled shots with both long and short irons. If we exclude the large number of holes running parallel up and down and the sometimes long walk between holes, Zaudín is one of the great golfing achievements in southern Spain. The palm trees, orange trees and large lakes are reminiscent of Florida, but olive groves are as present as the views over Seville. The tee-shots on the par 4s and par 5s pose no real danger but approach shots are often tricky affairs (especially on the 17th and 18th holes). Once on the greens, there are no unpleasant surprises in store. They are not huge, but they are not too tortuous, either. The reasonable length of this course and the standard of facilities make this a most inviting location.

Club Zaudín — 1993

Ctra. Tomares-Mairena, km 1,5
E - 41940 TOMARES (Sevilla – Andalucía)

Office	Secretaria	(34) 954 - 154 159
Pro shop	Pro-shop	(34) 954 - 154 159
Fax	Fax	(34) 954 - 153 344
Web	www.zaudin.com	
Situation	Situación	Sevilla, 10 km
Annual closure	Cierre anual	no
Weekly closure	Cierre semanal	no
Fees main season	Precios tempor. alta	18 holes

	Week days Semana	We/Bank holidays Fin de sem./fiestas
Individual Individual	€ 50	€ 70
Couple Pareja	€ 100	€ 140

Caddie Caddie no **Electric Trolley** Carro eléctrico no

Buggy Coche yes **Clubs** Palos yes

Credit cards Tarjetas de crédito
VISA - Eurocard - MasterCard - AMEX - DC

Huelva
A49
4
Tomares
Sevilla
GOLF
Mairena del Aljarafe
Palomares del Río
Almensilla
SE 660
Coría del Rio
Guadalquivir
0 1 2 km

Access Acceso : SE 30 Mairena → Tomares, Km 1,5
Map 8 on page 1100 Plano 8 Página 1100

GOLF COURSE — RECORRIDO — 16/20

Site	Emplazamiento	
Maintenance	Mantenimiento	
Architect	Arquitecto	Gary Player
Type	Tipo	country, residential
Relief	Relieve	
Water in play	Agua	
Exp. to wind	Exp. al viento	
Trees in play	Arboles	

Scorecard Tarjeta	Chp. Campeonato	Mens Caballeros	Ladies Damas
Length Longitud	6192	5869	4967
Par	71	71	71
Slope system	120	118	112

Advised golfing ability Nivel de juego aconsejado: 0 12 24 36
Hcp required Handicap exigido: 28 Men, 36 Ladies

CLUB HOUSE & AMENITIES — CLUB HOUSE Y DEPENDENCIAS — 7/10

Pro shop Pro-shop
Driving range Campo de prácticas
Sheltered cubierto 10 mats - On grass sobre hierba yes - Putting-green putting-green yes - Pitching-green pitching-green no

HOTEL FACILITIES — HOTELES CERCANOS — 6/10

HOTELS HOTELES

Alcora - 401 rooms, D € 240 - S. Juan de Aznalfarache 500 m
Tel (34) 954 - 349 600, Fax (34) 954 - 170 128

Hacienda S. Ignacio - Castilleja de la Cuesta 3 km
18 rooms, D € 118
Tel (34) 954 - 169 290, Fax (34) 954 - 161 437

Vereda Real - Valencina de la Concepción 10 km
55 rooms, D € 102
Tel (34) 955 - 720 100, Fax (34) 955 - 728 383

RESTAURANTS RESTAURANTES

Egaña Oriza - Sevilla 15 km - Tel (34) 954 - 227 211
La Becerrita - Sevilla 10 km - Tel (34) 954 - 412 057
Robles Aljarafe - Castilleja de la Cuesta 3 km
Tel (34) 954 - 169 260

1205

SVERIGE

SWEDEN

Vidbynäs

SVERIGE

From May to September, southern Europeans can easily play golf in Sweden over long periods of daylight which often allow at least two rounds a day. With more than 560,000 players for almost 430 eighteen-hole courses, Sweden is one of the leading golf countries on the continent of Europe. Thanks to golf being considered above all else as a sport like soccer, tennis or skiing, and thanks finally to intelligent organization and media exposure, Sweden has produced an amazing number of champion golfers. Amongst the men, Jesper Parnevik, Per-Ulrik Johansson and Jarmo Sandelin are just three out of a whole bunch of good players. And as Sweden cultivates equality in sport and elsewhere, the output of top women players is equally impressive, with star players such as Helen Alfredsson, Sophie Gustafson, Carin Koch or the phenomenal Annika Sörenstam.

SWEDEN

Från maj till september är dagarna långa och fyllda av dagsljus. Ofta är det möjligt att hinna med två rundor om dagen. Med mer än 560.000 golfare fördelade på över 430 banor är Sverige en av de ledande golfnationerna i Europa.. Utvecklingen beror naturligtvis mycket på det stöd som spelet åtnjuter och att golf betraktas som vilken sport som helst, i jämnhöjd med fotboll, tennis och skidåkning. Detta har inneburit att Sverige har fått fram en rad stora golfspelare: Jesper Parnevik, Per-Ulrik Johansson och Jarmo Sandelin är bara tre av många exempel. Och eftersom Sverige är ett jämlikt land, såväl inom idrottens värld som inom övriga områden, är antalet kvinnliga stjärnor lika imponerande! Tänk bara på Helen Alfredsson, Sophie Gustafson, Carin Koch och den fenomenala Annika Sörenstam.

CLASSIFICATION OF GOLF COURSES

RANKNING AV BANOR

This classification gives priority consideration to the score awarded to the actual course.
Rankingen syftar endast på golfbanan.

Within each score, the ranking is purely alphabetical

Course score / Banans betyg				Page / Sid
18	8	6	Barsebäck Masters Course	1221
18	8	5	Falsterbo	1230
18	8	8	Halmstad	1238
18	8	6	Hills	1240
18	7	5	Ljunghusen	1251
17	7	6	Bro-Bålsta	1226
17	8	6	Kungsängen (European Tour Club)	1248
17	7	7	Kristianstad	1246
17	7	6	Lunds Akademiska	1252
17	7	6	Örebro	1254
17	7	7	Skövde Södra Banan	1259
17	7	8	Stenungsund	1261
17	8	7	Svartinge	1263
17	8	6	Ullna	1266
17	7	6	Varberg Västra	1267
17	8	6	Vidbynäs	1270
16	6	5	Åtvidaberg	1220
16	8	7	Båstad Old Course	1222
16	7	7	Bokskogen	1223
16	7	7	Bråviken	1225
16	7	5	Degeberga-Widtsköfle	1227
16	9	5	Fågelbro	1229
16	7	5	Flommen	1232
16	7	4	Forsbacka	1233
16	8	6	Frösåker	1234
16	7	5	Grönhögen	1237
16	8	6	Haninge	1239
16	6	7	Jönköping	1241
16	7	5	Mölle	1253
16	6	6	Österåker Västerled	1255
16	7	6	Saltsjöbaden	1257
16	7	7	Täby	1264
16	7	7	Vasatorp	1269
16	7	5	Visby	1271
15	6	6	Ängelholm	1218
15	7	6	Ängsö	1219
15	8	6	Drottningholm	1247
15	6	3	Fjällbacka	1231
15	6	7	Göteborg	1235
15	7	6	Gränna	1236
15	5	8	Kalmar	1242
15	7	6	Karlstad	1244
15	7	7	Knistad	1245
15	6	6	Kungsbacka	1249
15	8	7	Landskrona Gul Bana	1250
15	7	8	Rya	1256
15	7	5	Söderåsen	1260
15	8	9	Stockholm	1262
15	7	7	Torekov	1265
14	7	6	A 6	1217
14	7	6	Bosjökloster	1224
14	7	7	Ekerum Långe Jan	1228
14	6	6	Karlshamn Gamla Banan	1243
14	6	5	Skellefteå	1258
14	7	5	Värnamo	1268

HOTEL FACILITIES

HOTELL OMGIVNING

This classification gives priority consideration to the score awarded to the hotel facilities.
Rankingen syftar endast på hotellen.

		Hotel facility score / Hotell omgivning		Page / Sid
15	8	**9**	Stockholm	1262
18	8	**8**	Halmstad	1238
15	5	**8**	Kalmar	1242

HOTEL FACILITIES
HOTELL OMGIVNING

15	7	**8**	Rya	1256
17	7	**8**	Stenungsund	1261
16	8	**7**	Båstad Old Course	1222
16	7	**7**	Bokskogen	1223
16	7	**7**	Bråviken	1225
14	7	**7**	Ekerum Långe Jan	1228
15	6	**7**	Göteborg	1235
16	6	**7**	Jönköping	1241
15	7	**7**	Knistad	1245
17	7	**7**	Kristianstad	1246
15	8	**7**	Landskrona Gul Bana	1250
17	7	**7**	Skövde Södra Banan	1259
17	8	**7**	Svartinge	1263
16	7	**7**	Täby	1264
15	7	**7**	Torekov	1265
16	7	**7**	Vasatorp	1269
14	7	**6**	A 6	1217
15	6	**6**	Ängelholm	1218
15	7	**6**	Ängsö	1219
18	8	**6**	Barsebäck Masters Course	1221
14	7	**6**	Bosjökloster	1224
17	7	**6**	Bro-Bålsta	1226
15	8	**6**	Drottningholm	1247
16	8	**6**	Frösåker	1234
17	8	**6**	Kungsängen	1248
15	7	**6**	Gränna	1236
16	8	**6**	Haninge	1239
18	8	**6**	Hills	1240
14	6	**6**	Karlshamn Gamla Banan	1243
15	7	**6**	Karlstad	1244
15	6	**6**	Kungsbacka	1249
17	7	**6**	Lunds Akademiska	1252
17	7	**6**	Örebro	1254
16	6	**6**	Österåker Västerled	1255
16	7	**6**	Saltsjöbaden	1257
17	8	**6**	Ullna	1266
17	7	**6**	Varberg Västra	1267
17	8	**6**	Vidbynäs	1270
16	6	**5**	Åtvidaberg	1220
16	7	**5**	Degeberga-Widtsköfle	1227
16	9	**5**	Fågelbro	1229
18	8	**5**	Falsterbo	1230
16	7	**5**	Flommen	1232
16	8	**6**	Frösåker	1234
16	7	**5**	Grönhögen	1237
18	7	**5**	Ljunghusen	1251
16	7	**5**	Mölle	1253
14	6	**5**	Skellefteå	1258
15	7	**5**	Söderåsen	1260
14	7	**5**	Värnamo	1268
16	7	**5**	Visby	1271
16	7	**4**	Forsbacka	1233
15	6	**3**	Fjällbacka	1231

RECOMMENDED GOLFING STAY
REKOMMENDERAD GOLFVISTELSE

Barsebäck Masters Course	**18**	8	6	1221
Båstad Old Course	**16**	8	7	1222
Ekerum Långe Jan	**14**	7	7	1228
Falsterbo	**18**	8	5	1230
Halmstad	**18**	8	8	1238
Haninge	**16**	8	6	1239
Kalmar	**15**	5	8	1242
Kungsängen	**17**	8	8	1248
Ljunghusen	**18**	7	5	1251
Örebro	**17**	7	6	1254
Skövde Södra Banan	**17**	7	7	1259
Vasatorp	**16**	7	7	1269

RECOMMENDED HOLIDAYS
REKOMMENDERAD SEMESTERORT

Båstad Old Course	**16**	8	7	1222
Ekerum Långe Jan	**14**	7	7	1228
Falsterbo	**18**	8	5	1230
Fjällbacka	**15**	6	3	1231
Flommen	**16**	7	5	1232
Kungsbacka	**15**	6	6	1249
Ljunghusen	**18**	7	5	1251
Mölle	**16**	7	5	1253
Rya	**15**	7	8	1256
Torekov	**15**	7	7	1265

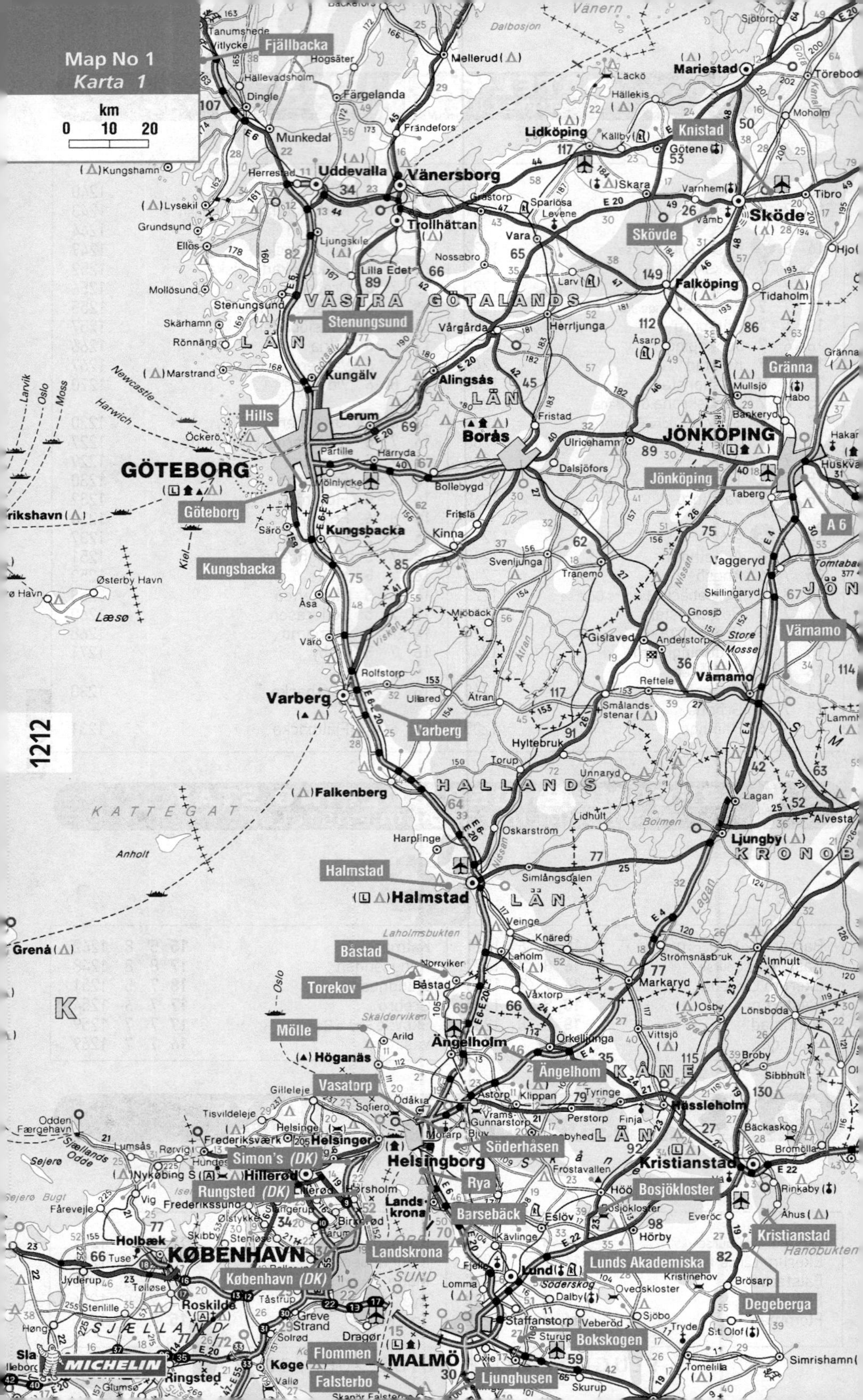
Map No 1
Karta 1
km
0 10 20
1212
Fjällbacka
Knistad
Skövde
Sköde
Stenungsund
Gränna
Hills
GÖTEBORG
Göteborg
Jönköping
JÖNKÖPING
A 6
Kungsbacka
Värnamo
Varberg
Halmstad
Båstad
Torekov
Mölle
Ängelhom
Ängelholm
Vasatorp
Söderhåsen
Simon's (DK)
Rungsted (DK)
Rya
Bosjökloster
Barsebäck
Landskrona
Kristianstad
Lunds Akademiska
København (DK)
KØBENHAVN
Degeberga
Bokskogen
Flommen
Falsterbo
Ljunghusen
MALMÖ
Helsingborg
Helsingør
Hillerød
Lund
Trollhättan
Vänersborg
Uddevalla
Borås
Alingsås
Kungälv
Lerum
Falköping
Lidköping
Mariestad
Ljungby
Markaryd
Hässleholm
Höganäs
Falkenberg
VÄSTRA GÖTALANDS LÄN
HALLANDS LÄN
KATTEGAT
Læsø
Anholt
MICHELIN

Askersund
Stjärnsund
Olshammar
Tjällmo
Finspång
Eriksberg
Runtuna
Trosa
Nynäshamn
Stigtomta
Jönåker
Nyköping
Oxelösund
Kolmården
Åby
Krokek
Bråviken
Lindö
Nävekvarn
Motala
Borensberg
Ljungsbro
Kimstad
Karlsborg
Vadstena
Roxen
Vreta Kloster
Kaga
Götakanal
NORRKÖPING
Skänninge
Malmslätt
Linghem
Söderköping
Vikingstad
LINKÖPING
Rök
Mantorp
Björsäter
Mjölby
ÖSTERGÖTLANDS
LÄN
Gdansk
Boxholm
Åtvidaberg
Valdemarsvik
Tranås
Sommen
Kisa
Överum
Aneby
Gamleby
Gudingen
Österbymo
Norra Kvill
Västervik
Eksjö
Vimmerby
Ankarsrum
Visby
Mariannelund
Storebro
Bodafors
Hultsfred
Sävsjö
Vetlanda
Kristdala
Fårbo
Hejde
Klintehamn
Korsberga
Virserum
Byxelkrok
Oskarshamn
Böda
Fågelfors
Blå Jungfrun
Åseda
Högsby
Löttorp
Emån
Rottne
Grönskåra
KALMAR
Mönsterås
Lenhovda
Helgasjön
Burgsvik
Okno
Vamlingbo
Växjö
Öland
Bäckebo
Borgholm
Köpingsvik
Orrefors
Ekerum
Hovmantorp
Nybro
Gärdslösa
Lessebo
Eriksmåle
Lindsdal
Kalmar
Smedby
Färjestaden
Åsnen
Emmaboda
Gårdby
Tingsryd
Urshult
Karlevi
Resmo
Mörbylånga
Söderåkra
Stora
Alvaret
Torsås
BLEKINGE
LÄN
Bräkne-Hoby
Kallinge
Rödeby
Grönhögen
Karlskrona
Ronneby
Nättraby
Jämjö
Karlshamn
Sölvesborg
Björketorp
Gdynia
1213
MICHELIN
d'après base de données au 1/1 500 000 - édition - 2005.
Autorisation n°0501023.

Map No 2
Karta 2
km
0
5
Bro-Bålsta
Kungsängen
Svartinge
Täby
Ullna
Österåker
Stockholm
Drottningholm
Salts öbaden
Karlstad
Örebro
Forsbacka
Märsta
Sigtuna
Frösunda
Markim
Orkesta
Norrsunda
Rosersberg
Skånela
Lindholmen
Vada
Skarven
Fysingen
Löwenströmska-
lasarettet
Hammarby
Ormsta
Gröndal
Karby
Össeby
Västra Ryd
Upplands-
Väsby
Frestaby
Bällsta
Angarn
Bro
Brunna
Ed
Vallentuna
Byle
Österåker
Säbyholm
Tibble
Bollstanäs
Vallentunasjön
Ullnasjön
Björknäs
Kungsängen
Rotebro
Norrviken
Näs
Bro
fjarden
Rydbo
Kallhäll
Edsberg
Ensta
Gorvaln
Täby
Östra Ryd
Sabysjon
Edsviken
Jakobsberg
Sollentuna
Enebyberg
Roslags-Nässby
Kungs-
berga
Viksjö
Helene-
lund
St Värtan
Vänthomen
Järfälla
Danderyd
Kista
Djursholm
Hilleshög
Barkarby
Ulriksdal
Mörby
Bogesund
Färentuna
Ricksättra
Spånga
Stock-
sund
Färingsö
Hasselby
Askrikefjärden
Vällingby
Sundbyberg
Lidingö
Solvalla
Haga
Sånga
Svartsjö
Bromma
Millesgården
Lambarfj.
Solna
Stenhamra
BROMMA
Brevik
Östermalm
Ångby
Skå
Lovö
Nockeby
Alvik
STOCKHOLM
Boo
Lång-
holmen
Skansen
Drottningholm
Essingen
Tureholm
Hammargården
Södermalm
Ekerön
Hägersten
Nacka
Älvnäs
Årsta
Mälarhöjden
Fisksätra
Närsta
Älvsjö
Enskede
Kaggeholm
Ekerö
Segeltorp
Saltsjöbaden
Skär-
holmen
Örby
Stureby
Skarpnäck
Sturehov
Vårby
Högdalen
Älta
Hallunda
Stuvsta
Sköndal
Fittja
Farsta
Tyresö
Botkyrka
Huddinge
Skrubba
Bornsjon
Alby
Magelungen
Trångsund
Salem
Skogås
Tullingesjon
Södertälje
Länna
Edane
Deje
Molkom
Storå
Ørje
Glava
Klässbol
Glafsfjorden
Kil
Karlstad
Forshaga
Storfors
Nora
Lindesberg
Årjäng
Skåre
Vålberg
Frövi
Långeserud
Nysäter
Grums
Skoghall
Kristinehamn
Karlskoga
ÖREBRO
Glanshammar
Garphyttan
Säffle
Degerfors
Örebro
Bengtsfors
Åmål
Svartå
LÄN
Ed
Dals
Långed
Gullspång
Laxå
Kumla
Pålsboda
Hallsberg
Bäckefors
Vänern
Skagern
Sjötorp
Askersund
Stjärnsund
Dalbosjön
Unden
Mellerud
MICHELIN
Mariestad
Olshammar
Töreboda
Läckö
E 18
E 4
E 20-E 4
E 20

Hassela
Norrfjärden
Gnarp
Bergsjö
Harmånger
Strömsbruk
Ljusnan
Ljusdal
N. Dellen
S. Dellen
Färila
Delsbo
Hälsingtuna
Malsta
Hälsingeleden
Järvsö
Forsa
Hudiksvall
ÄVLEBORGS
LÄN
Iggesund
Öjung
Mattsmyra
Vallsta
Enånger
Enhammarsfjärden
Arbrå
Tronö
Edsbyn
Ovanåker
Bollnäs
Alfta
Söderhamn
Sandarne
Kilafors
Ljusne
Skog
Lingbo
Bingsjö
Åmot
Norrsundet
Bergby
Ockelbo
Enviken
Bjursås
Svärdsjö
Grycksbo
Lumsheden
Järbo
Gavlebukten
Gävle
Falun
Sandviken
Valbo
Storvik
Hofors
Skutskär
Lovstabukten
Runn
Storsjön
Älvkarleby
Vika
Långshyttan
Stora Skedvi
Arsunda
Skarplinge
Öregrundsgrepen
Lövstabruk
Söderfors
Tierp
Öregrund
Säter
Garpenberg
Österfärnebo
Hedemora
Horndal
Gysinge
Hedesundaf.
UPPSALA
Månkarbo
Österbybruk
Östhammar
Storby
Eckerö
Gimo
Avesta
Dalälven
Östervåla
Vendel
Viksta
LÄN
Söderbärke
Norberg
Tenstaa
Salsta
Grisslehamn
Hallstavik
Fagersta
Björklinge
Vattholma
Väddö
Bälinge
Rasbo
Sala
Salbohed
Heby
Gåvsta
Edsbro
Virsbo
Skinnskatteberg
UPPSALA
Sävja
VÄSTMANLANDS
Fjärdhundra
Norrtälje
Örsundsbro
Skokloster
Rimbo
Kapellskär
Surahammar
Skultuna
Tillberga
Knivsta
Frösåker
Hallstahammar
Märsta
Arlanda
Ångsö
LÄN
Enköping
Kolsva
Sigtuna
Norrsunda
STOCKHOLMS
Kolbäck
VÄSTERÅS
Balsta
Upplands-Väsby
Köping
Vallentuna
Ängsö
Tidö
Bro
Åkersberga
Kungsör
Torshälla
Sollentuna
LÄN
Arboga
Jäder
Strängnäs
Vidbynäs
Täby
Österåker
Lidingö
Hjälmaren
Skogstorp
Eskilstuna
Drottningholm
Tallinn
Helsinki
Fågelbro
Alberga
Stora Sundby
Åkers styckebruk
Mariefred
Gripsholm
Sturehov
Boo
STOCKHOLM
Tumba
Tyresö
Nämndöfj.
Tullinge
SÖDERMANLANDS
Hälleforsnäs
Malmköping
Nykvarn
Södertälje
Jordbro
Vingåker
Flen
Stjärnhov
Järna
Västerhaninge
Haninge
Klaipeda
Gnesta
Sorunda
Baven
Mysingen
Katrineholm
LÄN
Tisnaren
Vagnhärad
Tullgarn
Ösmo
Eriksberg
Bettna
Runtuna
Nynäshamn
Yngaren
Trosa
Stigtomta
Gålö
BOTTENHAV
BOTTNISKA VIKEN
(GOLFE DE BO
1/ 1 670 000
MICHELIN

Map No 3
Karta 3
km
0 10 20
Malå
Jörn
Fallfors
Jävre
Kristineberg
Skellefteälven
Täme
Björksele
Byske
Norrby
Norsjö
Boliden
Kåge
Ruskséle
Bastuträsk
Skellefteå
Skelleftehamn
Kalvträsk
Skellefteå
Bureå
Latikberg
Lycksele
Kroksjö
Åmsele
Burträsk
Lövånger
Bygdsiljum
Lillögda
Hällnäs
Botsmark
Ånaset
Granön
Vindeln
Robertsfors
Åsele
Örträsk
Sjulsmark
Fredrika
Bygdeå
Vännäs
Sävar
Bjurholm
Sörfors
Holmön
UMEÅ
Rodvattnet
Sölberg
Nyåker
Obbola
Holmsund
Trehörningsjö
Hörnefors
Myckelgensjö
Nordmaling
Norra Kvarken
Björna
Rundvik
Merenkurkku
Bredbyn
Gideå
Norra Gloppet
Mellansel
Björköby
Degerfjärden
Replot
Skorped
Husum
Sidensjö
Överhörnäs
Vallgrund
Örnsköldsvik
Bjästa
VAASA
VASA
Köpmanholmen
Skuleskogen
Sundom
Docksta
Bergö
Bollstabruk
Ullånger
Mjällom
Skog
Malax
Maalahti
Kramfors
Nordingrå
Herrskog
Molpe
Ramvik
Korsnäs
Viksjö
Övermark
Härnösand
Närpes
Timrå
Haggdånger
Söråker
Alnö
Kaskinen
Kaskö
SUNDSVALL
Kristinestad
Kristiinankaupunki
Sundsvallsbukten
Njurundabommen
Härkmeri
Norrfjärden
Ömossa
Gnarp
Sideby
Harmånger
Merikarvia
MICHELIN

A 6

14 | 7 | 6

Om du är på väg norrut på E4 i det svindlande vackra landskapet rekommenderas ett besök på denna till namnet märkliga bana. Den är designad av Peter Nordwall, som här har ritat greener som ligger väl skyddade och som i varje fall för honom är förvånansvärt små, även i nyrenoverat skick. Nio av hålen har nyligen ändrats, och nya greener har tillkommit – lika knepiga att träffa som tidigare. Banan är relativt kuperad och bjuder på några ställen på en härlig utsikt. Detta innebär också att du under rundan kommer ställas inför några blinda slag, och dessutom skär en ravin in i spelet på flera hål och hotar att ställa till det för dig. Som på alla banor av den här typen krävs det några rundor innan du känner dig hemma. Försök att hålla huvudet kallt eller ännu bättre – lira en runda med en medlem som känner till alla problemen. Eller så struntar du helt enkelt i att föra scorekort! Vid sidan av 18-hålsbanan har ytterligare en 9-hålsslinga tillkommit, byggd mitt i ett förrädiskt skogsparti. Slutligen: Missa inte de fantastiska fiskrätterna i klubbhusrestaurangen.

This is one of the best courses on the south-east side of the wonderful lake Vättern. Before heading northward across the superb landscapes to be seen on the A4 motorway, this course going by the strange name A6 is well worth a round or two. It was designed by Peter Nordwall, who produced some well-guarded greens that are smaller than usual (for him) and so a little trickier to approach. 9 of the 18 holes have recently been altered, with new greens. The course is on the steep side, which gives a wild natural setting but also a number of blind shots and a dangerous ravine in play on several holes. It is difficult to get a clear idea of game strategy first time out. To tackle it with as cool a head as possible, try to play a round with a member or simply forget about keeping score. A further 9 holes have been added to the 18-hole course in the middle of some threatening trees. One last word for the delicious fish specialities in the club-house restaurant.

A 6 Golfklubb — 1989

Centralvägen
S - 553 05 JÖNKÖPING

Office	Sekretariat	(46) 036 - 308 130
Pro shop	Pro shop	(46) 036 - 719 105
Fax	Fax	(46) 036 - 308 140
Web	www.a6gk.se	
Situation	Läge	Jönköping, 3 km
Annual closure	Årlig stängning	no
Weekly closure	Daglig stängning	no

Fees main season Tariff hög säsong	Full day	
	Week days Veckodag	**We/Bank holidays** Lör/Söndag/Helgdag
Individual Individuellt	SKr 300	SKr 350
Couple Par	SKr 500	SKr 600

Juniors: – 50% / 2 Seniors, 2 Juniors (Familijegreenfee): SKr 700/800 (We)

Caddie Caddie no — **Electric Trolley** El vagn no
Buggy Golfbil no — **Clubs** Klubbor yes
Credit cards Kredit kort
VISA - AMEX

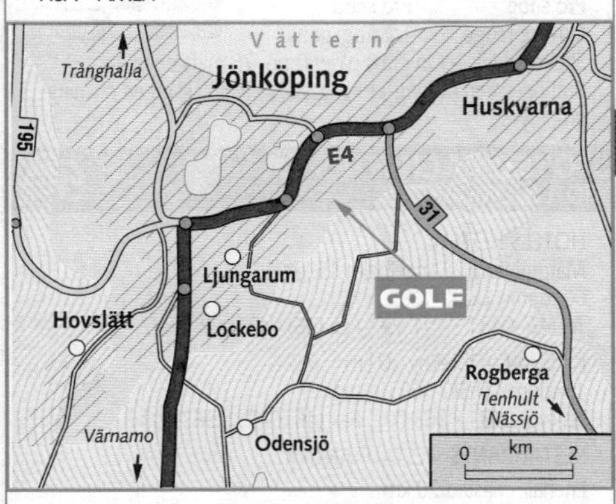

Access Tillfart : E4 Jönköping → Husqvarna. → "Nya A 6".
Map 1 on page 1212 Karta 1 se sid: 1212

GOLF COURSE — BANA — 14/20

Site	Läge	
Maintenance	Underhåll	
Architect	Arkitekt	Peter Nordwall
Type	Karaktär	forest, hilly
Relief	Nivåskillnader	
Water in play	Vatten på spelfältet	
Exp. to wind	Vindutsatt	
Trees in play	Träd på spelfältet	

Scorecard Scorekort	**Chp.** Back tees	**Mens** Herrtee	**Ladies** Damtee
Length Längd	6268	5668	4881
Par	72	72	72
Slope system	—	135	132

Advised golfing ability Rekommenderad spelnivå — 0 12 24 36
Hcp required Hcp erfordrad — 36

CLUB HOUSE & AMENITIES — KLUBBHUS OCH OMGIVNING — 7/10

Pro shop Pro shop
Driving range Träningsbana
Sheltered tak 10 mats - On grass på gräs yes - Putting-green putting-green yes - Pitching-green pitching-green yes

HOTEL FACILITIES — HOTELL OMGIVNING — 6/10

HOTELS HOTELL
John Bauer - Jönköping 4 km - 100 rooms, D SKr 1490 (with green fee)
Tel (46) 036 - 349 000
Comfort Home Hotel Victoria - Jönköping 5 km
90 rooms, D SKr 1395
Tel (46) 036 - 712 800, Fax (46) 036 - 715 050

RESTAURANTS RESTAURANGER
Restaurang Borgmästaren - Jönköping 3 km
Tel (46) 036 - 161 440
Restaurang Dragon - Jönköping 3 km
Tel (46) 036 - 172 800
Krogen Svarta Börsen - Jönköping 3 km
Tel (46) 036 - 712 222

Ängelholm

15 | **6** | **6**

En charmig liten bana i den djupaste av skogar… hm, det låter som den första textraden i en sång, men det är också det absolut bästa sättet att beskriva Ängelholm på. Den långtslående kanske inte är så förtjust i alla träden, ty detta är en bana som kräver försiktighet och premierar spelstrategi mer än långa drives. En del slag, som inspelet över vattnet på nionde hålet, är minst sagt utmanande, men generellt sett är detta en bana som framför allt kräver tålamod och självkontroll. Golfare av alla skicklighetsgrader trivs här, och som familjebana är den utomordentlig. Det viktigaste är att slå rakt, men den som har en bra bollträff och kan slå höga slag in mot greenerna och få bollen att stanna snabbt har en stor fördel. Ännu bättre om du är så duktig att du kan skruva den åt bägge hållen. Greenerna är medelstora men på inget vis lätthanterliga. Eller för att göra en snabb sammanfattning: För att spela den här banan sitter man gärna en extra timme i bilen.

A pretty little course down in the woods. This could be the first line of a song, but actually it is the first and most obvious way to describe the charm of Ängelholm. The wilder-hitters might not take too kindly to all these trees, but the caution required here will force them to think in terms more of game strategy than long drives. Some shots, like over the water on the 9th hole, are a little intimidating, but generally speaking this course plays with an open hand and simply has to be addressed with patience and self-restraint. Golfers of all levels soon get to like it, especially when playing with the family, as this is a course that also teaches you how to play. To play straight, of course, but also to strike the ball solidly on a layout that calls for target golf, balls hit high which stop quickly. If you can work the ball both ways, then so much the better. The greens are average in size and well enough designed to make putting more than just a formality. Put simply, it is well worth driving 30 or 40 miles out of your way to play Ängelholm.

Ängelholms GK — 1983

Box 117
S - 262 22 ÄNGELHOLM

Office	Sekretariat	(46) 0431 - 430 260
Pro shop	Pro shop	(46) 0431 - 12 27
Fax	Fax	(46) 0431 - 431 568
Web	www.golf.se/angelholmsgk/	
Situation	Läge	Ängelholm, 20 km
Annual closure	Årlig stängning	no
Weekly closure	Daglig stängning	no
Fees main season	Tariff hög säsong	18 holes

	Week days Veckodag	We/Bank holidays Lör/Söndag/Helgdag
Individual Individuellt	SKr 350	SKr 350
Couple Par	SKr 700	SKr 700

Caddie Caddie no — **Electric Trolley** El vagn no

Buggy Golfbil no — **Clubs** Klubbor no

Credit cards Kredit kort
VISA - Eurocard - MasterCard

Halmstad, Tassjö, Hillarp, Aggarp, Hunseröd, Rebbelberga, Ängelholm, E6-E20, Munka-Ljungby, GOLF, 13, Höja, Ossjö, Helsingborg, Landskrona, Malmö, Källna, E4, Starby, km 0 2 4

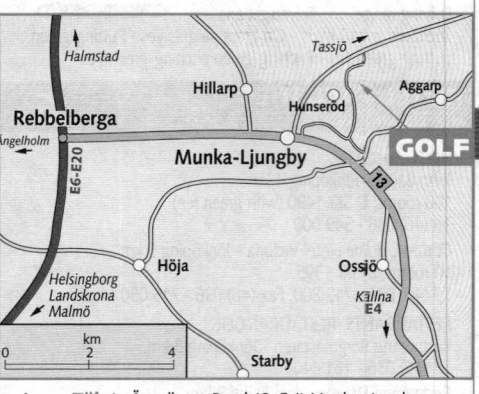

Access Tillfart : Ängelhom, Road 13. Exit Munka Ljungby, take Road 114 → Örkelljunga

Map 1 on page 1212 Karta 1 se sid: 1212

GOLF COURSE — BANA — 15/20

Site	Läge	
Maintenance	Underhåll	
Architect	Arkitekt	Jan Sederholm
Type	Karaktär	parkland
Relief	Nivåskillnader	
Water in play	Vatten på spelfältet	
Exp. to wind	Vindutsatt	
Trees in play	Träd på spelfältet	

Scorecard Scorekort	Chp. Back tees	Mens Herrtee	Ladies Damtee
Length Längd	5960	5760	4915
Par	72	72	72
Slope system	—	130	127

Advised golfing ability Rekommenderad spelnivå — 0 12 24 36

Hcp required Hcp erfordrad — 36

CLUB HOUSE & AMENITIES — KLUBBHUS OCH OMGIVNING — 6/10

Pro shop Pro shop
Driving range Träningsbana
Sheltered tak - On grass på gräs no, 25 mats open air - Putting-green putting-green yes (3) - Pitching-green pitching-green yes

HOTEL FACILITIES — HOTELL OMGIVNING — 6/10

HOTELS HOTELL

Margretetorp - Ängelholm 15 km
60 rooms, D SKr 1685
Tel (46) 0431 - 454 450, Fax (46) 0431 - 454 877

Kattegatt - Torekov 20 km
11 rooms, D SKr 1695
Tel (46) 0431 - 363 002, Fax (46) 0431 - 363 003

RESTAURANTS RESTAURANGER

Enehall - Båstad 20 km
Tel (46) 0431 - 750 15

Kattegatt - Torekov 20 km
Tel (46) 0431 - 363 002

Ängsö

15	7	6

En bana nära staden Västerås som helst ska besökas under den torra årstiden, blötan kan ställa till en del problem under våren. Sagt det, måste vi genast konstatera att närheten till Mälaren och landskapets skönhet nästan får dig att glömma bort själva spelet. Nivåskillnaderna är måttliga, men ett par upphöjda greener kan ge de svåraste flaggplaceringarna. Nyligen fick alla greener nytt gräs. Men innan du har nått så långt måste du handskas med resten av banan, med fairways som kan vara minst sagt lömska att träffa. På många hål frestas du att gena över doglegs, misslyckas du står det dig dyrt. Detta är en förrädisk bana eftersom den ser lite svårare ut än vad den egentligen är. Detta gäller från klubbtee, från backtee kan banan vara ett riktigt monster, och då finns det oftast bara ett sätt: långt och rakt. Och det är ju inget problem, eller hur? Ängsö är en härlig utmaning på en härlig plats. Kan man önska sig något mer? En vacker fontän att vila ögonen på ? Finns på 15 :e hålet !

The nearby magnificent Lake Mälaren and surrounding countryside almost make you forget you are here to play golf. The topography of the terrain is never excessive, but a few elevated greens sometimes lead to blind pin positions. Before getting that far, you will find some of the fairways a little deceptive in terms of view and distance, where the temptation to cut corners can prove fatal. The lush vegetation and number of hazards call for extreme accuracy off the tee and even an ability to flight the ball. In reality, this course looks more difficult than it actually is, so keep a cool head and do not be over-influenced by what you see. This is valid, of course, when playing from the normal tees, as the back-tees can sometimes turn the course into a real monster, where the only solution is to hit it very long and very straight. The way we all do, right? A great challenge and a great site. Who could ask for more? Looking for a (lucky) fountain? There is a beautiful one on the 15th hole.

Ängsö GK — 1984

Björnövägen 2
S - 721 30 VÄSTERÅS

Office	Sekretariat	(46) 0171 - 441 012
Pro shop	Pro shop	(46) 0171 - 441 041
Fax	Fax	(46) 0171 - 441 049
Web	www.angsogolf.org	
Situation	Läge	Västerås, 20 km
Annual closure	Årlig stängning	no
Weekly closure	Daglig stängning	no
Fees main season	Tariff hög säsong	18 holes

	Week days Veckodag	We/Bank holidays Lör/Söndag/Helgdag
Individual Individuellt	SKr 280	SKr 380
Couple Par	SKr 560	SKr 760

Juniors: – 50%

Caddie Caddie no — **Electric Trolley** El vagn no

Buggy Golfbil yes — **Clubs** Klubbor yes

Credit cards Kredit kort
VISA - Eurocard - MasterCard

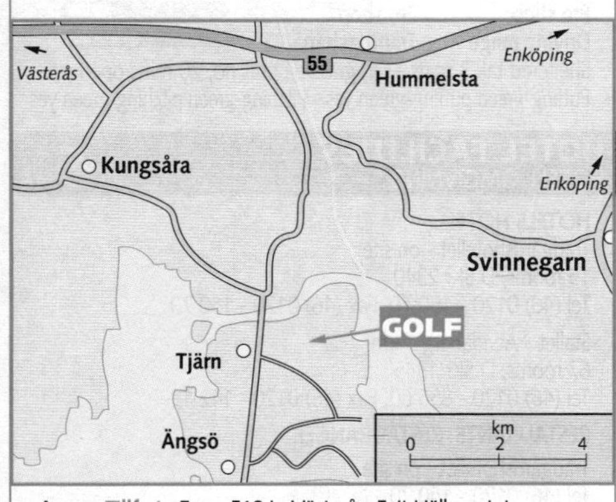

Access Tillfart : From E18 in Västerås, Exit Hällamotet.
→ Irsta. After 5 km, → Golf
Map 2 on page 1214 Karta 2 se sid: 1214

GOLF COURSE BANA — 15/20

Site	Läge	
Maintenance	Underhåll	
Architect	Arkitekt	Åke Hultström
Type	Karaktär	forest, parkland, open country
Relief	Nivåskillnader	
Water in play	Vatten på spelfältet	
Exp. to wind	Vindutsatt	
Trees in play	Träd på spelfältet	

Scorecard Scorekort	Chp. Back tees	Mens Herrtee	Ladies Damtee
Length Längd	6327	5880	5029
Par	72	72	72
Slope system	—	130	123

Advised golfing ability Rekommenderad spelnivå — 0 12 24 36

Hcp required Hcp erfordrad — 30 Men, 36 Ladies

CLUB HOUSE & AMENITIES KLUBBHUS OCH OMGIVNING — 7/10

Pro shop Pro shop
Driving range Träningsbana
Sheltered tak no - On grass på gräs no, 15 mats open air - Putting-green putting-green yes - Pitching-green pitching-green yes

HOTEL FACILITIES HOTELL OMGIVNING — 6/10

HOTELS HOTELL
Ängsö - 15 rooms, D SKr 799 (with dinner) - on site
Tel ((46) 0171 - 441 041

Radisson - Västerås 20 km
203 rooms, D SKr 1440
Tel (46) 021 - 101 010, Fax (46) 021 - 101 091

Stadshotellet - Västerås 20 km
137 rooms, D SKr 1320
Tel (46) 021 - 102 800, Fax (46) 021 - 102 810

RESTAURANTS RESTAURANGER
Lemone - Västerås 20 km
Tel (46) 021 - 410 60 75

Åtvidaberg

16 | 6 | 5

Banan i Åtvidaberg smälter in i landskapet mellan skogar och sjöar. I ett land med mängder av vattendrag hittar du naturligtvis också vattenhinder på banan. Det finns dock inget konstgjort amerikanskt över dessa, utan de är naturliga och typiska för sin omgivning. Initialt kanske du tycker att detta är en lätt bana, men skenet bedrar och om du inte passar dig hamnar du lätt i problem. Här finns massor med skog och även enskilda träd kommer i spel. Flera skarpa doglegs kräver att du är duktig på att manövrera bollen. Akta dig också för bunkrarna. Greenerna är mellanstora och ett par stycken är upphöjda. Allt som allt gör det att du behöver spela banan några gånger för att komma underfull med den. Hur som helst, en weekend på hotellet som ligger på banan är ett frestande förslag. Låt oss avsluta med att berömma det 11e hålet, en fantastisk par 5 som går utmed en sjö, framröstad av Golf Digest som ett av världens 500 bästa hål. Åtvidaberg är en charmerande upplevelse, som bara blir bättre. Peter Nordwall har framgångsrikt moderniserat banan utan att den förlorat i charm.

Typical of the surrounding countryside, this course is set amidst lakes and forests. In a land dotted with countless stretches of water, the water hazards here are very much Swedish style, not American. At first sight you might think this an easy course, but although playable by golfers of all abilities, it can also be dangerous. With the woods, a few isolated trees here and there, several dog-legs where skills in bending the ball will come in handy, a number of traps around the course, and average-sized and sometimes elevated greens, you will need to play several times to get to grips with this challenging layout. The now completed renewal work supervised by Peter Nordwall has helped to modernise the course without spoiling any of its charm. In a few words, special praise is in order for the excellent 11th hole, a beautiful par 5 alongside a lake voted by Golf Digest as one of the finest 500 holes in the world. A week-end's stay in the on-course hotel (with restaurant) will always be a tempting proposition.

Åtvidabergs Golfklubb — 1956

Box 180
S - 597 41 ÅTVIDABERG

Office	Sekretariat	(46) 0120 - 354 25
Pro shop	Pro shop	(46) 0120 - 126 95
Fax	Fax	(46) 0120 - 135 02
Web		www.golf.se/atvidabergsgk/
Situation	Läge	Åtvidaberg, 1 km
Annual closure	Årlig stängning	no
Weekly closure	Daglig stängning	no
Fees main season	Tariff hög säsong	18 holes

	Week days / Veckodag	We/Bank holidays / Lör/Söndag/Helgdag
Individual Individuellt	SKr 300	SKr 350
Couple Par	SKr 600	SKr 700

Juniors: SKr 200

Caddie Caddie no **Electric Trolley** El vagn no

Buggy Golfbil yes **Clubs** Klubbor yes

Credit cards Kredit kort
VISA - Eurocard - MasterCard - DC

Linköping
Grebo
GOLF
Ringarum
35
Bestorp
Åtvidaberg
134
Gamleby
Överum
Kisa
Oppeby
km
0 2 4

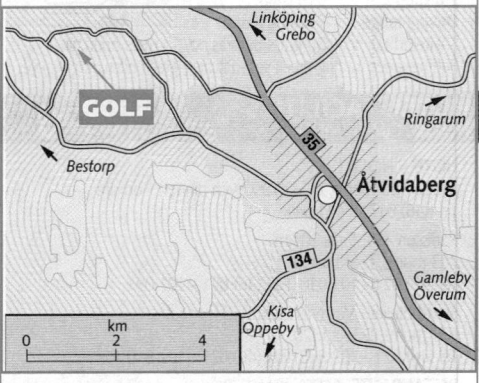

Access Tillfart : Linköping, R35 → Åtvidaberg, → Golf.
Map 1 on page 1213 Karta 1 se sid: 1213

GOLF COURSE — BANA — 16/20

Site	Läge	
Maintenance	Underhåll	
Architect	Arkitekt	Douglas Brasier Peter Nordwall
Type	Karaktär	forest
Relief	Nivåskillnader	
Water in play	Vatten på spelfältet	
Exp. to wind	Vindutsatt	
Trees in play	Träd på spelfältet	

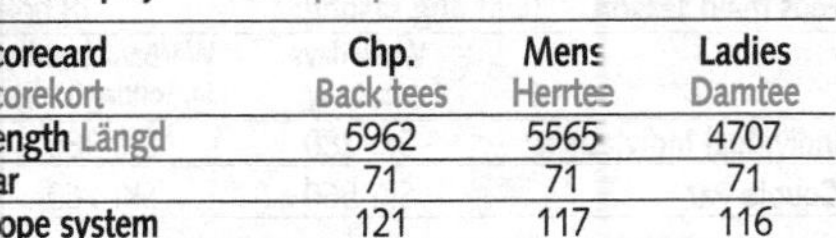

Scorecard Scorekort	Chp. Back tees	Mens Herrtee	Ladies Damtee
Length Längd	5962	5565	4707
Par	71	71	71
Slope system	121	117	116

Advised golfing ability Rekommenderad spelnivå — 0 12 24 36

Hcp required Hcp erfordrad — 36

CLUB HOUSE & AMENITIES — KLUBBHUS OCH OMGIVNING — 6/10

Pro shop Pro shop

Driving range Träningsbana

Sheltered tak 3 mats - On grass på gräs no, 20 mats open air - Putting-green putting-green yes - Pitching-green pitching-green yes

HOTEL FACILITIES — HOTELL OMGIVNING — 5/10

HOTELS HOTELL

Trädgårdshotellet - on site
15 rooms, D SKr 2340
Tel (46) 0120 - 150 70, Fax (46) 0120 - 150 70

Stallet - Åtvidaberg 1 km
67 rooms, D SKr 1345
Tel (46) 0120 - 855 00, Fax (46) 0120 - 142 19

RESTAURANTS RESTAURANGER

Trädgårdshotellet - on site
Tel (46) 0120 - 150 70

Bysjö Krog - Åtvidaberg 1 km
Tel (46) 0120 - 145 40

Barsebäck *Masters Course*

18 | 8 | 6

Från klubbhuset har du en fantastisk vy över Öresund som skiljer Sverige och Danmark åt. Träningsmöjligheterna är utomordentliga, och eftersom Mastersbanan rankas som en av de bästa i Sverige är en runda här ett måste. Masters-banan är en permanent sammanslagning med de bästa hålen från Barsebäcks två banor, varav Donald Steele är arkitekten bakom de nyare hålen. De första hålen vindlar genom tät skog, vilket kräver raka utslag samt en förmåga att manövrera bollen och att du är duktig på att rädda dig ur svåra lägen. Därefter når banan fram till vattnet och i stället för precisionsgolf blir det nu viktigt att kunna slå låga slag för att undgå vinden (en måttlig bris är dock vanligare än en kuling). För spelare som hoppas på ett lågt resultat är Barsebäck alltid en utmaning. Om inte annat får du glädja dig åt den omväxlande rundan som layouten bjuder. Den här banan kan du spela gång på gång utan att tröttna på den. Banan stod som värd för Solheim Cup år 2003.

The club-house here gives a splendid view over the Öresund, a large stretch of the North Sea which separates Sweden and Denmark. As the course rates as one of the best in Sweden, a round or two here is a must. This is the "Masters Course", subsequently supplemented by another Donald Steel 18-hole layout, some holes of which were successfully used to form a composite course for the Scandinavian Masters. This is now a permanent fixture. The first holes wind their way through thick but well-cleared woods, which require straight driving, an ability to bend the ball and skilled recovery shots. Then the course reaches the seaboard, where target golf has to give way to the ability to hit low, bump and run shots and take account of the always windy conditions. Although challenging for golfers looking for low scores, Barsebäck is still playable by the less skilled player, if only for experience in learning different styles of play. A superb course where the Solheim Cup has been played in 2003.

Barsebäck Golf & Country Club — 1969

S - 246 55 LÖDDEKÖPINGE

Office	Sekretariat	(46) 046 - 776 230
Pro shop	Pro shop	(46) 046 - 775 127
Fax	Fax	(46) 046 - 772 630
Web	www.barseback-golf.se	
Situation	Läge	Lund, 20 km
Annual closure	Årlig stängning	no
Weekly closure	Daglig stängning	no

Fees main season Tariff hög säsong — 18 holes

	Week days Veckodag	We/Bank holidays Lör/Söndag/Helgdag
Individual Individuellt	SKr 700	SKr 700
Couple Par	SKr 1400	SKr 1400

Juniors: – 50% / Full day: SKr 600

Caddie Caddie no — Electric Trolley El vagn yes

Buggy Golfbil yes — Clubs Klubbor yes

Credit cards Kredit kort
VISA - Eurocard - MasterCard - AMEX - DC

Hofterup
Landskrona
V. Karaby
GOLF
Kävlinge
Barsebäck
Hög
E6 - E20
Barsebäckshamn
Löddeköpinge
Malmö
Öresund
Vikhög
km
0 2 4
Malmö
Bjärred

Access Tillfart : E6 Malmö-Helsingborg: Exit Löddeköpinge. → Golfbana.

Map 1 on page 1212 Karta 1 se sid: 1212

GOLF COURSE BANA — 18/20

Site	Läge	
Maintenance	Underhåll	
Architect	Arkitekt	Ture Bruce
Type	Karaktär	seaside course, parkland
Relief	Nivåskillnader	
Water in play	Vatten på spelfältet	
Exp. to wind	Vindutsatt	
Trees in play	Träd på spelfältet	

Scorecard Scorekort	Chp. Back tees	Mens Herrtee	Ladies Damtee
Length Längd	6250	6020	5285
Par	72	72	72
Slope system	—	119	116

Advised golfing ability Rekommenderad spelnivå — 0 12 24 36

Hcp required Hcp erfordrad — 36

CLUB HOUSE & AMENITIES KLUBBHUS OCH OMGIVNING — 8/10

Pro shop — Pro shop
Driving range — Träningsbana
Sheltered tak 7 mats - On grass på gräs yes - Putting-green putting-green yes - Pitching-green pitching-green yes

HOTEL FACILITIES HOTELL OMGIVNING — 6/10

HOTELS HOTELL

Järavallen - 36 rooms, D SKr 1600 - on site
Tel (46) 046 - 777 050, Fax (46) 046 - 775 898

Grand Hotell - Lund 20 km
84 rooms, D SKr 1895
Tel (46) 046 - 280 61 00, Fax (46) 046 - 280 61 50

Lundia - Lund 20 km
97 rooms, D SKr 1375
Tel (46) 046 - 280 6500, Fax (46) 046 - 280 6510

RESTAURANTS RESTAURANGER

Grand Hotell - Lund 20 km - Tel (46) 046 - 280 61 00
Bantorget 9 - Lund 20 km - Tel (46) 046 - 320 200

Båstad *Old Course*

16 | 8 | 7

Banan designades på 30-talet av Hawtree och Taylor, och smälter på ett fint sätt in landskapet. Den rankas regelbundet bland de 20 bästa i Sverige. Initialt finansierades den av Ludvig Nobel (Alfreds brorson) för att attrahera engelska affärsmän. Banan är belägen på en halvö och har ett gammalt och mycket charmigt klubbhus. Den är ordentligt kuperad, vilket ger dig många intressanta lägen under din vandring. Detta gör bara layouten ännu bättre. Medelhandicaparen kommer att lära sig mycket under rundans gång, han behöver dock inte oroa sig över att bli av med särskilt många bollar. Största svårigheten är de ofta starkt ondulerade greenerna som tenderar att vara mycket snabba. Är du inte vän med din putter kan det stå dig riktigt dyrt. Flera av greenerna är också upphöjda, vilket kräver höga slag in mot dem. Varje hål är minnesvärt och skiljer sig från det föregående utan att harmonin störs. Den andra 18-hålsslingan på Båstad är inte lika charmig men är desto mer utmanande och kräver riktigt långa slag. Ett pittoreskt hotell bara några meter från första tee gör bilden komplett.

The natural-looking "Old Course" is regularly ranked in the country's top golf courses. It was financed by Ludvig Nobel (the nephew of Alfred) with the purpose of attracting British golfers. Located on a peninsula with an old-style club-house, all 18 holes involve a lot of climbing and provide all sorts of situations from where to play. This makes the layout all the more interesting... and instructive for mid-handicappers, who shouldn't have too much trouble with lost balls. One of the main difficulties lies with the greens, which are steeply contoured and often very slick. More, as some of the putting surfaces are elevated, high approach shots are the order of the day. Each hole is different and memorable, but this does nothing to deter from the overall impression of harmony and the measured layout of difficulties. The second course has not quite the same charm but is even more challenging, whence the need for some long-hitting. A beautiful hotel close to hole N°1 completes the picture.

Båstad Golfklubb — 1930

Boarp, Box 1037
S - 269 21 BÅSTAD

Office	Sekretariat	(46) 0431 - 783 70
Pro shop	Pro shop	(46) 0431 - 732 81
Fax	Fax	(46) 0431 - 733 31
Web	www.bgk.se	
Situation	Läge	Båstad, 4 km
Annual closure	Årlig stängning	no
Weekly closure	Daglig stängning	no

Fees main season Tariff hög säsong		Full day
	Week days Veckodag	**We/Bank holidays** Lör/Söndag/Helgdag
Individual Individuellt	SKr 500	SKr 500
Couple Par	SKr 1000	SKr 1000

Juniors: SKr 200 / Full week: SKr 2600

Caddie Caddie no — **Electric Trolley** El vagn no

Buggy Golfbil yes — **Clubs** Klubbor yes

Credit cards Kredit kort
VISA - Eurocard - MasterCard - AMEX - DC

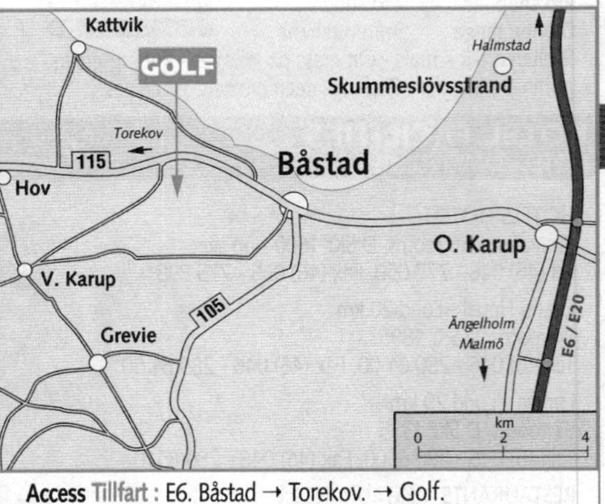

Access Tillfart : E6. Båstad → Torekov. → Golf.
Map 1 on page 1212 Karta 1 se sid: 1212

GOLF COURSE — BANA — 16/20

Site	Läge	
Maintenance	Underhåll	
Architect	Arkitekt	Hawtree & Taylor
Type	Karaktär	parkland
Relief	Nivåskillnader	
Water in play	Vatten på spelfältet	
Exp. to wind	Vindutsatt	
Trees in play	Träd på spelfältet	

Scorecard Scorekort	**Chp.** Back tees	**Mens** Herrtee	**Ladies** Damtee
Length Längd	5632	5526	4787
Par	71	71	71
Slope system	—	121	118

Advised golfing ability Rekommenderad spelnivå — 0 12 24 36

Hcp required Hcp erfordrad — 36

CLUB HOUSE & AMENITIES — KLUBBHUS OCH OMGIVNING — 8/10

Pro shop Pro shop
Driving range Träningsbana
Sheltered tak 4 mats - On grass på gräs no, 20 mats open air - Putting-green putting-green yes - Pitching-green pitching-green yes

HOTEL FACILITIES — HOTELL OMGIVNING — 7/10

HOTELS HOTELL

Clarencegården - 8 rooms, D SKr 1400 - on site
Tel (46) 0431 - 73 840

Skansen Hotell - Båstad 12 km
112 rooms, D SKr 1360
Tel (46) 0431 - 558 100, Fax (46) 0431 - 558 110

Kattegatt - Torekov 12 km
11 rooms, D SKr 1695
Tel (46) 0431 - 363 002, Fax (46) 0431 - 363 003

RESTAURANTS RESTAURANGER

Kattegatt - Båstad 8 km - Tel (46) 0431 - 363 002
Margretetorp - Båstad 11 km - Tel (46) 0431 - 454 450
Enehall - Båstad 10 km - Tel (46) 0431 - 750 15

Bokskogen

16	7	7

Den här banan arrangerade PLM Open under många år. Och inte undra på det! Banan är ett bra test, framför allt om du inte är så lång med drivern eller väljer att spela från backtee. Under sommaren är ruffarna tjocka och besvärliga, och fångar effektivt upp varje felriktat slag. Trots detta är vandringen mellan de höga bokarna så njutningsfylld att inte ens en liten vit boll kan förstöra din dag. Du behöver inte spela särskilt många rundor för att snabbt förstå att de flesta hinder ser du redan från tee. Banan är bredare än vad den verkar att vara. De största svårigheterna ligger i längden och några minst sagt knepiga greener. Allt detta gör Bokskogen till en bra värdemätare för hur du slår bollen. Även medelhandicapare kommer att ha stort utbyte av rundan om de inte förväntar sig underverk på scorekortet, vilket har blivit tuffare nu när greenerna och greenområdena har renoverats. Bokskogen ligger 20 kilometer från Malmö, och här finns förutom den nyss nämnda banan ytterligare en 18-hålare. Den senare är något kortare och mer lättspelad.

This course hosted the PLM Open for many a year and remains a very well maintained layout with no shortage of trouble if you play from the back tees or have a problem of length. In addition, the rough grows tall and thick in the summer and presents a serious threat to wayward shots. Despite this, the walk through a large forest of birch trees is so pleasant that even a little white ball can't really spoil your enjoyment. You don't need many rounds here to understand the layout, the course is wider than it looks and the main difficulty lies with reaching and successfully negotiating some pretty lively greens, which are often multi-tiered and elevated. All this makes Bokskogens a good yardstick for how well you are striking the ball, and a course playable by mid-handicappers if they don't look for miracle scores, a tougher proposition now that the greens and surrounds have been renovated. This is a fine golfing complex with a second and somewhat shorter 18 hole course for your enjoyment.

Bokskogens Golfklubb — 1964

Torrups Nygård
S - 230 40 BARA

Office	Sekretariat	(46) 040 - 406 900
Pro shop	Pro shop	(46) 040 - 481 153
Fax	Fax	(46) 040 - 406 929
Web	www.bokskogen.com	
Situation	Läge	Malmö, 20 km
Annual closure	Årlig stängning	no
Weekly closure	Daglig stängning	no
Fees main season	Tariff hög säsong	18 holes

	Week days Veckodag	We/Bank holidays Lör/Söndag/Helgdag
Individual Individuellt	SKr 500	SKr 500
Couple Par	SKr 1000	SKr 1000

Juniors: SKr 150

Caddie Caddie no — **Electric Trolley** El vagn no

Buggy Golfbil yes — **Clubs** Klubbor yes

Credit cards Kredit kort
VISA - Eurocard - MasterCard - AMEX - DC

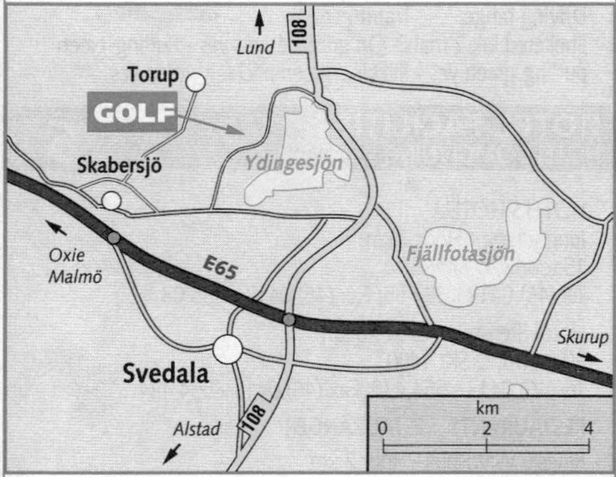

Lund
108
Torup
GOLF
Skabersjö
Ydingesjön
Oxie
Malmö
E65
Fjällfotasjön
Skurup
Svedala
Alstad
108
km
0 2 4

Access Tillfart : Malmö: E65 → Ystad. Exit Oxie, → Skabersjö, turn right at church, left at Torup, → Golf.

Map 1 on page 1212 Karta 1 se sid: 1212

GOLF COURSE — BANA — 16/20

Site	Läge	
Maintenance	Underhåll	
Architect	Arkitekt	Anders Amilon Jan Sederholm
Type	Karaktär	parkland
Relief	Nivåskillnader	
Water in play	Vatten på spelfältet	
Exp. to wind	Vindutsatt	
Trees in play	Träd på spelfältet	

Scorecard Scorekort	Chp. Back tees	Mens Herrtee	Ladies Damtee
Length Längd	6306	6006	5238
Par	72	72	72
Slope system	—	137	131

Advised golfing ability Rekommenderad spelnivå — 0 12 24 36

Hcp required Hcp erfordrad — 36

CLUB HOUSE & AMENITIES — KLUBBHUS OCH OMGIVNING — 7/10

Pro shop Pro shop
Driving range Träningsbana

Sheltered tak 3 mats - On grass på gräs yes - Putting-green putting-green yes - Pitching-green pitching-green no

HOTEL FACILITIES — HOTELL OMGIVNING — 7/10

HOTELS HOTELL

Mäster Johan - 69 rooms, D SKr 1995 - Malmö 20 km
Tel (46) 040 - 664 64 00, Fax (46) 040 - 664 64 01

Hilton Hotel - 210 rooms, D SKr 1933 - Malmö 20 km
Tel (46) 040 - 693 47 00, Fax (46) 040 - 693 47 11

Savoy Hotel - 109 rooms, D SKr 1450 - Malmö 20 km
Tel (46) 040 - 702 30, Fax (46) 040 - 664 48 50

Bokskogen - 1 cottage SKr 1200 - on site
Tel (46) 040 - 406 900

RESTAURANTS RESTAURANGER

Johan P Saluhallen - Malmö 20 km - Tel (46) 040 - 971 818
Årstiderna - Malmö 20 km - Tel (46) 040 - 230 910
Nyströms Gastronomi - Malmö 20 km - Tel (46) 040 - 305 303

Bosjökloster

14	7	6

Det här är en "gömd pärla" som är en utmaning för såväl den skicklige spelaren som höghandicaparen. Låt vara att vid första anblicken ser Bosjökloster rätt ordinär ut, men du får snart anledning att ändra dig. Från tee är banan ärlig, och kan du bara undvika ruffarna är den relativt bred. En gång i tiden var den till och med riktigt bred, men för varje år växer träden högre och fairways krymper. När vinden blåser gäller det att vara extra försiktig och tänka till lite extra över klubbvalen. Men svårigheterna tar inte slut där: Ju närmare green du kommer desto mer fantasi och känsla behöver du. Greenerna är inte bara knepiga att hitta rätt linje på, under sommaren är de även blixthala och då gäller det att slå inspelen med precision, och de blir bara bättre och snabbare för varje år. Om du behöver förbättra ditt närspel är detta en bra plats att vässa det på. När du har fått nog av att nöta pitchar kan du alltid ta en paus och beundra den vackra Ringsjön. Dock kan man få en smula magknip av några blinda utslag. Hur som helst, detta är en bana för alla, men du behöver arbeta hårt för en bra score.

This "hidden gem" is a good test for all players. Although at first sight this looks to be just an average course, you soon find yourself thinking otherwise. Off the tee it is an open proposition, as long as you keep out of the rough. And although once very wide open, it has tended to become narrower as the trees have grown taller. When the wind starts to blow, you need to be extra careful and think long and hard over club selection. But it does not end there, as the closer you get to the greens, the more imagination and "feel" you need. They are not only tricky when putting, they are also getting better and faster, every single year and so call for skilful short approach shots. If you need to sharpen up your short game, come and practice here. One minor gripe concerns the few blind tee-shots here (there is a periscope on the 6th hole!). When you have had enough, take time out to admire lake Ringsjön down below. A course for everyone, but you have to work hard for a good score.

Bosjökloster GK — 1974

S - 234 95 HÖÖR

Office	Sekretariat	(46) 0413 - 258 96
Pro shop	Pro shop	(46) 0413 - 258 60
Fax	Fax	(46) 0413 - 258 95
Web	www.golf.se/bosjoklostersgk/	
Situation	Läge	Höör, 5 km
Annual closure	Årlig stängning	no
Weekly closure	Daglig stängning	no
Fees main season	Tariff hög säsong	18 holes

	Week days Veckodag	We/Bank holidays Lör/Söndag/Helgdag
Individual Individuellt	SKr 300	SKr 300
Couple Par	SKr 600	SKr 600

Caddie Caddie no — Electric Trolley El vagn no

Buggy Golfbil yes — Clubs Klubbor yes

Credit cards Kredit kort

VISA - Eurocard - MasterCard

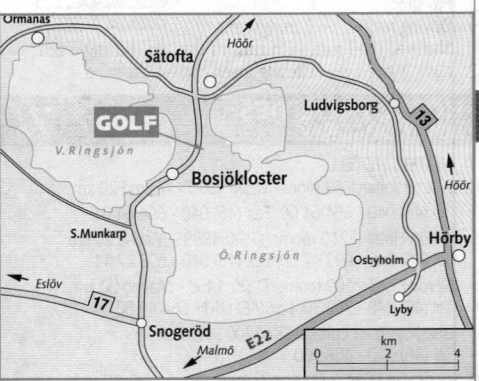

Access Tillfart : Malmö, E22 → Hässleholm. In Höör, Road 23 → Malmö, golf on left hand side

Map 1 on page 1212 Karta 1 se sid: 1212

GOLF COURSE — BANA 14/20

Site	Läge	
Maintenance	Underhåll	
Architect	Arkitekt	Douglas Brasier
Type	Karaktär	parkland, open country
Relief	Nivåskillnader	
Water in play	Vatten på spelfältet	
Exp. to wind	Vindutsatt	
Trees in play	Träd på spelfältet	

Scorecard Scorekort	Chp. Back tees	Mens Herrtee	Ladies Damtee
Length Längd	6135	5835	5010
Par	72	72	72
Slope system	—	132	128

Advised golfing ability / Rekommenderad spelnivå: 0 12 24 36

Hcp required — Hcp erfordrad: 30 Men, 36 Ladies

CLUB HOUSE & AMENITIES — KLUBBHUS OCH OMGIVNING 7/10

Pro shop	Pro shop
Driving range	Träningsbana

Sheltered tak 2 mats - On grass på gräs yes - Putting-green putting-green yes - Pitching-green pitching-green yes

HOTEL FACILITIES — HOTELL OMGIVNING 6/10

HOTELS HOTELL

Ringsjökrog - Höör 2 km
15 rooms, D SKr 950
Tel (46) 0413 - 332 55, Fax (46) 0413 - 335 03

Hotell Stensson - Eslöv 20 km
80 rooms, D SKr 1400
Tel (46) 0413 - 554 430, Fax (46) 0413 - 554 444

RESTAURANTS RESTAURANGER

Ringsjö Wärdshus - Höör 2 km
Tel (46) 0413 - 332 55
Medborgarhuset - Eslöv 20 km
Tel (46) 0413 - 106 64

Bråviken

16 | 7 | 7

Det är ett nöje att bara köra upp till klubbhuset och restaurangen som ryms i familjen Mannheims gamla herrgård. Banan ligger utlagd på mark som har skapat en högst varierande upplevelse: öppna landskap, parklandskap och skog borgar för variation hela vägen. Trots topografin har arkitekten Björn Magnusson lyckats bygga en bana med väl synliga hinder från tee, vilket gör det enklare för golfaren att hitta den bästa strategin. Bråviken kan vid första anblicken verka vara ganska vänlig, men du måste hela tiden vara på din vakt: misstag bestraffas snabbt och hårt. Framför allt måste du vara försiktig med alla de taggiga buskar som växer runt greenerna. Om din boll hamnar där är den ospelbar, och i värsta fall förlorad. Ett speciellt omnämnande till de stora fina utslagsplatserna (fem stycken på de flesta hålen), samt par 3-hålsbanan. Detta om detta, förutom banan vill vi även påpeka att atmosfären är vänlig och avslappnad, vilket bör få alla golfare att känna sig som hemma. Bråviken är väl värd att besöka.

The pleasure starts with the drive up to the club-house and restaurant, both located in the former manor of Mannheim. The estate over which the course has been laid out results in very different styles of hole: wide open space, parkland or forest mean variety all the way. Despite the topology, architect Björn Magnusson succeeded in never concealing the hazards from every tee-box. Bråvikens might appear very friendly at first sight, but watch out all the same: mistakes are quickly and severely punished. Be especially careful with the bramble bushes around the greens, where your ball will end up at best unplayable. What we can say is that the sanction is at least proportional to the mistake you make. A special word of praise should go to the excellence of tee-boxes (five on most holes) which help to modulate the difficulties at hand, and to the par-3 nine-hole course. Add to this the relaxed and friendly atmosphere here, and every golfer will feel confident about playing the course.

Bråvikens Golfklubb — 1992

Manheims Säteri
S - 605 91 NORRKÖPING

Office	Sekretariat	(46) 011 - 340 041
Pro shop	Pro shop	(46) 011 - 340 091
Fax	Fax	(46) 034 - 340 045
Web	www.bragk.se	
Situation	Läge	Norrköping, 8 km
Annual closure	Årlig stängning	no
Weekly closure	Daglig stängning	no
Fees main season	Tariff hög säsong	18 holes

	Week days Veckodag	We/Bank holidays Lör/Söndag/Helgdag
Individual Individuellt	SKr 350	SKr 400
Couple Par	SKr 700	SKr 800

Juniors: SKr 200/230 (We)

Caddie Caddie no — **Electric Trolley** El vagn no
Buggy Golfbil no — **Clubs** Klubbor yes

Credit cards Kredit kort
VISA - Eurocard - MasterCard - AMEX - JCB

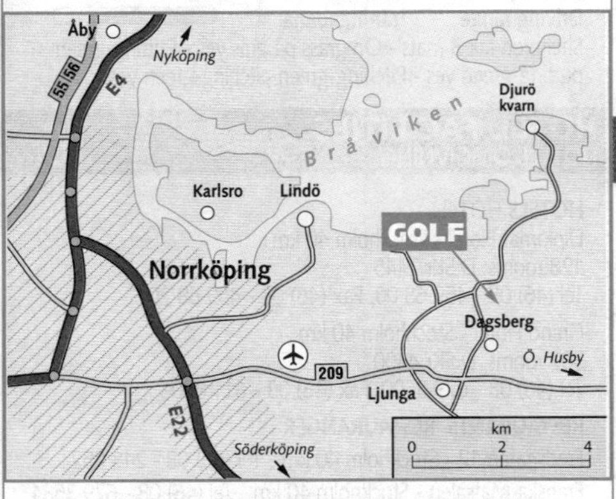

Access Tillfart : Norrköping, 209 → Airport (Flygplats). 881 → Djurön, → Golf
Map 1 on page 1213 Karta 1 se sid: 1213

GOLF COURSE — BANA — 16/20

Site	Läge	
Maintenance	Underhåll	
Architect	Arkitekt	Björn Magnusson
Type	Karaktär	forest, parkland
Relief	Nivåskillnader	
Water in play	Vatten på spelfältet	
Exp. to wind	Vindutsatt	
Trees in play	Träd på spelfältet	

Scorecard Scorekort	Chp. Back tees	Mens Herrtee	Ladies Damtee
Length Längd	6040	5635	5000
Par	72	72	72
Slope system	—	125	128

Advised golfing ability Rekommenderad spelnivå — 0 12 24 36
Hcp required Hcp erfordrad — 36

CLUB HOUSE & AMENITIES — KLUBBHUS OCH OMGIVNING — 7/10

Pro shop Pro shop
Driving range Träningsbana
Sheltered tak 5 mats - On grass på gräs no, 15 mats open air - Putting-green putting-green yes - Pitching-green pitching-green yes

HOTEL FACILITIES — HOTELL OMGIVNING — 7/10

HOTELS HOTELL
First Hotel - Norrköping 20 km
55 rooms, D SKr 649 w. GF
Tel (46) 011 - 197 220, Fax (46) 011 - 126 506

Mauritzbergs Slott - Vikbolandet 22 km
16 rooms, D SKr 2100
Tel (46) 0125 - 501 00, Fax (46) 0125 - 501 04

RESTAURANTS RESTAURANGER
Guskelov - Norrköping 8 km
Tel (46) 011 - 134 400
Bacchus - Norrköping 8 km
Tel (46) 011 - 100 740
O'Leary's - Norrköping 8 km - Tel (46) 011 - 105 107

Bro-Bålsta

17 | 7 | 6

Här är banan där Annika och Charlotta Sörenstam växte upp och lärde sig att spela, och med det i bakhuvudet förstår man varför bägge har blivit så duktiga med puttern. Peter Nordwall har designat greener med så skarpa konturer att en del är på gränsen till att vara orättvisa. De är också väldigt stora, så stora att bunkrar och vattenhinder knappast kommer i spel när du slår in mot dem. Från tee är det dock en helt annan historia, speciellt för de långtslående som kan råka i alla möjliga sorters svårigheter om utslaget blir snett. Med detta sagt kan vi konstatera att det är en mycket intelligent layout med väl synliga hinder från tee. Medelgolfaren, som inte slår så långt, kan sprida bollarna rätt rejält och ändå komma undan med det. Om vi dessutom tillägger att banan ligger i ett fantastiskt och böljande landskap, som en hyllning till de klassiska skotska banorna men anpassat för det nordiska klimatet så förstår du varför det utan vidare är värt att tillbringa en hel dag här. Och då menar vi en hel dag, driving rangen är öppen dygnet runt.

This is where Annika and Charlotta Sorenstam learned their trade and it is no wonder that both are good putters. These greens are very sharply contoured even to the extent of sometimes appearing almost unfair. They are also very large, even too large in relation to the type of shot you need to play. They are so big in fact that the bunkers and water hazards don't even come into play, although they definitely do for the tee-shot, particularly for the longer-hitters. With this said, the layout is plainly intelligent, hazards are clearly visible from the tee-box and strategy obvious enough. Moreover, the "average" player has all the room in the world to hit a bad shot and not really suffer the consequences. The site is one of pleasantly rolling terrain and set in a beautiful natural setting, like a tribute to the classical links courses in Scotland, adapted to suit the Nordic climate and landscape. This course is well worth a full day's golfing. And we mean a full day, as the driving range is open around the clock.

Bro-Bålsta Golfklubb — 1982

Ginnlögs väg
S - 197 91 BRO

Office	Sekretariat	(46) 08 - 582 413 00
Pro shop	Pro shop	(46) 08 - 582 413 05
Fax	Fax	(46) 08 - 582 400 06
Web	www.golf.se/brobalstagk/	
Situation	Läge	Stockholm, 40 km
Annual closure	Årlig stängning	no
Weekly closure	Daglig stängning	no

Fees main season / Tariff hög säsong	Week days / Veckodag	We/Bank holidays / Lör/Söndag/Helgdag
	Full day	
Individual Individuellt	SKr 400	SKr 400
Couple Par	SKr 800	SKr 800

Juniors: – 50%

Caddie Caddie no — Electric Trolley El vagn no

Buggy Golfbil no — Clubs Klubbor yes

Credit cards Kredit kort
VISA - Eurocard - MasterCard

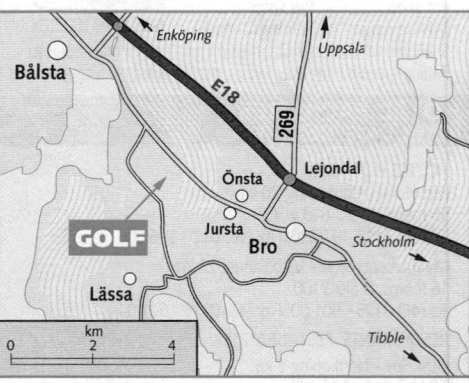

Access Tillfart : Stockholm E18 → Enköping.
Exit Bålsta. 1 km → Golf

Map 2 on page 1214 Karta 2 se sid: 1214

GOLF COURSE — BANA — 17/20

Site	Läge	
Maintenance	Underhåll	
Architect	Arkitekt	Peter Nordwall
Type	Karaktär	parkland, open country
Relief	Nivåskillnader	
Water in play	Vatten på spelfältet	
Exp. to wind	Vindutsatt	
Trees in play	Träd på spelfältet	

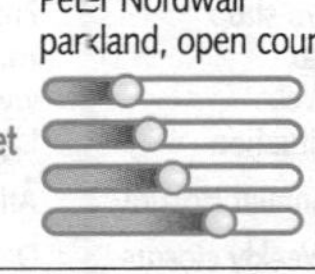

Scorecard / Scorekort	Chp. / Back tees	Mens / Herrtee	Ladies / Damtee
Length Längd	6505	5890	5160
Par	73	73	73
Slope system	—	128	126

Advised golfing ability / Rekommenderad spelnivå: 0 12 24 36

Hcp required / Hcp erfordrad: 30 Men, 32 Ladies

CLUB HOUSE & AMENITIES — KLUBBHUS OCH OMGIVNING — 7/10

Pro shop — Pro shop
Driving range — Träningsbana

Sheltered tak 3 mats - On grass på gräs yes - Putting-green putting-green yes - Pitching-green pitching-green yes

HOTEL FACILITIES — HOTELL OMGIVNING — 6/10

HOTELS HOTELL

Diplomat Hotel - Stockholm 40 km
128 rooms, D SKr 2445
Tel (46) 08 - 459 68 00, Fax (46) 08 - 459 68 20

Grand Hotel - Stockholm 40 km
307 rooms, D SKr 4400
Tel (46) 08 - 679 3500, Fax (46) 08 - 611 8606

RESTAURANTS RESTAURANGER

Fredsgatan 12 - Stockholm 40 km - Tel (46) 08 - 248 052
Franska Matsalen - Stockholm 40 km - Tel (46) 08 - 679 3584
Beirut Café - Stockholm 40 km - Tel (46) 08 - 212 025

Degeberga-Widtsköfle

16 | 7 | 5

Medan den skånska västkusten består av chica semesterbyar och klassisk linksgolf, så är sydöstsidan mer frekventerad av fotvandrare i nationalparken vid Stenshuvud och Simrishamnsfiskare som fångar torsk och sill utanför den lilla charmiga byn med sina gamla färgglada hus. Några kilometer därifrån, i ett vackert inlandslandskap, finns en gömd pärla, som bara har blivit bättre och bättre sedan den öppnade. Beroende på vinden varierar svårigheterna, men för den mindre erfarne golfaren bjuder den alltid motstånd. Banan är relativt kuperad och hinderna är väl synliga, framför allt de farliga greenbunkrarna. Ändå räcker det inte med att mata in höga slag mot greenerna, en och annan "chip'n'run" kan komma väl till pass, framför allt som sandjorden adderar en skotsk känsla. Det här är ett riktigt test av din kreativitet och ditt tålamod, samt din förmåga att hålla bollen i spel – framför allt om du hoppas på några par och birdies.

While the west coast of Scandia is the region of chic seaside resorts and classic links courses, the south-east coast is frequented more by hikers in the Stenshuvud national park and the herring and cod fishermen of Simrishamn, a pretty little town with old multi-coloured houses. A few kilometres up the road, set in beautiful inland landscape, lies this hidden gem, which has been growing better and better since it was first opened. Depending on the wind, it can play in all different ways but is never totally unforgiving for the less experienced golfer. Although relatively hilly, it does not hide its hazards, particularly the dangerous green-side bunkers. Yet pumping in high balls might not be enough here and bump 'n run approaches can come in very handy as the sandy soil adds to a distinctly Scottish flavour. A real test of creativity and patience, and accuracy too if you hope to land a few pars and birdies.

Degeberga-Widtsköfle Golfklubb — 1990

Box 71
S - 297 21 DEGEBERGA

Office	Sekretariat	(46) 044 - 355 035
Pro shop	Pro shop	(46) 044 - 355 024
Fax	Fax	(46) 044 - 355 075
Web	www.dwgolfklubb.com	
Situation	Läge	Kristianstad, 18 km
Annual closure	Årlig stängning	no
Weekly closure	Daglig stängning	no
Fees main season	Tariff hög säsong	18 holes

	Week days Veckodag	We/Bank holidays Lör/Söndag/Helgdag
Individual Individuellt	SKr 250	SKr 300
Couple Par	SKr 500	SKr 600

Juniors: SKr 100/120 (We)

Caddie Caddie no — **Electric Trolley** El vagn no

Buggy Golfbil no — **Clubs** Klubbor no

Credit cards Kredit kort
VISA - Eurocard - MasterCard - AMEX

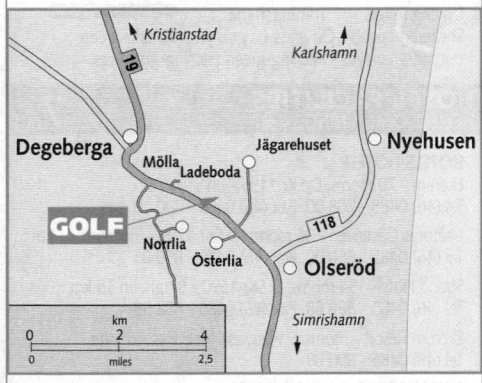

Kristianstad
19
Karlshamn
Degeberga
Jägarehuset
Nyehusen
Mölla
Ladeboda
GOLF
118
Norrlia
Österlia
Olseröd
km 0 2 4
0 miles 2,5
Simrishamn

Access Tillfart : On road 19 Kristianstad → Simrishamn-Ystad, after Degeberga
Map 1 on page 1212 Karta 1 se sid: 1212

GOLF COURSE — BANA — 16/20

Site	Läge	
Maintenance	Underhåll	
Architect	Arkitekt	Tommy Nordström
Type	Karaktär	heathland
Relief	Nivåskillnader	
Water in play	Vatten på spelfältet	
Exp. to wind	Vindutsatt	
Trees in play	Träd på spelfältet	

Scorecard Scorekort	Chp. Back tees	Mens Herrtee	Ladies Damtee
Length Längd	6302	5871	5066
Par	72	72	72
Slope system	—	130	133

Advised golfing ability Rekommenderad spelnivå — 0 12 24 36

Hcp required Hcp erfordrad — 36

CLUB HOUSE & AMENITIES — KLUBBHUS OCH OMGIVNING — 7/10

Pro shop Pro shop
Driving range Träningsbana
Sheltered tak yes - On grass på gräs yes - Putting-green putting-green yes - Pitching-green pitching-green yes

HOTEL FACILITIES — HOTELL OMGIVNING — 5/10

HOTELS HOTELL

Tomarp Gårdshotell - 12 rooms, D SKr 1800 - Tomarp 25 km
Tel (46) 044 - 93 118, Fax (46) 044 - 93 114

Hotel Svea - 59 rooms, D SKr 1090 - Simrishamn 20 km
Tel (46) 0414 - 411 720, Fax (46) 0414 - 143 41

Quality Grand Hotel - Kristianstad 18 km
148 rooms, D SKr 740
Tel (46) 044 - 284 800, Fax (46) 044 - 284 810

Kockska Gården - 18 rooms, D SKr 890 - Simrishamn 20 km
Tel (46) 0414 - 411 755, Fax (46) 0414 - 117 55

RESTAURANTS RESTAURANGER

Restaurant Hotel Svea - Simrishamn 20 km
Tel (46) 0414 - 411 720

Tomarp Gårdshotell - Tomarp 25 km - Tel (46) 044 - 93 118

Ekerum *Långe Jan*

14	7	7

Till Öland kommer man via den sex kilometer långa Ölandsbron. Här finns fyra golfbanor. Den bästa är Ekerum, en 36-hålsanläggning. Totalt är ön 12 mil lång, och består huvudsakligen av hedar där många intressanta växter och fåglar går att finna. En vandring eller en cykeltur över Stora Alvaret (på den södra delen av ön) är en ljuvlig upplevelse. Hotellet på golfbanan är en bra utgångspunkt, framför allt för barn-familjer. Att spela den här banan är också en upplevelse utöver det vanliga. Den sluttar ned mot havet, är lättpromenerad och inte alltför svår om du kan hålla dig borta från ruffen. Faktum är att varje gång du går ut här känns det som om du har en bra score på gång. Men att träffa greenerna på rätt antal slag är inte hela hemligheten. Greenerna är enorma, många av dem har platåer och är starkt ondulerade. Att hålla treputten borta är inte så lätt. Banans omgivningar höjer upplevelsen, för om vi ska vara ärlig är inte detta ett mästerverk, men du slösar definitivt inte bort din tid om du spelar här. Den andra 18-hålsslingan öppnade i början av 2003.

Now with 36 holes, this is the largest of the four golf clubs on the Island of Öland, linked by a 4 mile bridge to the south-eastern coast of mainland Sweden. The island, some 80 miles long, partly consists of vast moor-land which is home to some very interesting plants and birds. A walk or bicycle ride over the southern part of the island is a wonderful experience and the golf course hotel is an excellent base-camp for family expeditions. This course slopes down towards a stretch of sea, is easy to play walking and not too tough if you can keep out of some very thick rough. In fact, every time you play you feel you can card a very good score, but hitting the greens in regulation is not enough. The putting surfaces are huge, often multi-tiered, highly-contoured and very conducive to three-putting. The quality of the landscape "enhances" what is probably not an outstanding course, but you aren't wasting your time playing here. The whole complex is perhaps the finest "resort" in Sweden.

Ekerum Golfklubb & Resort — 1990

S - 387 92 BORGHOLM

Office	Sekretariat	(46) 0485 - 800 20
Pro shop	Pro shop	(46) 0485 - 808 77
Fax	Fax	(46) 0485 - 800 10
Web	www.ekerum.com	
Situation	Läge	Borgholm, 15 km

Kalmar, 27 km

Annual closure	Årlig stängning	no
Weekly closure	Daglig stängning	no
Fees main season	Tariff hög säsong	Full day

	Week days Veckodag	We/Bank holidays Lör/Söndag/Helgdag
Individual Individuellt	SKr 425	SKr 425
Couple Par	SKr 850	SKr 850

Juniors: SKr 145 / Full week: SKr 2125

Caddie Caddie no — **Electric Trolley** El vagn no

Buggy Golfbil yes — **Clubs** Klubbor yes

Credit cards Kredit kort

VISA - Eurocard - MasterCard - AMEX - DC

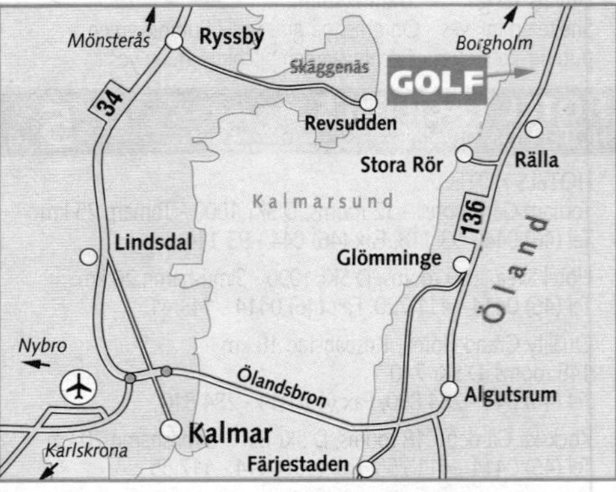

Access Tillfart : Kalmar → Ölandsbron. → Borgholm. Turn left → Ekerum Golf & Resort.

Map 1 on page 1213 Karta 1 se sid: 1213

GOLF COURSE — BANA — 14/20

Site	Läge	
Maintenance	Underhåll	
Architect	Arkitekt	Peter Nordwall
Type	Karaktär	parkland
Relief	Nivåskillnader	
Water in play	Vatten på spelfältet	
Exp. to wind	Vindutsatt	
Trees in play	Träd på spelfältet	

Scorecard Scorekort	Chp. Back tees	Mens Herrtee	Ladies Damtee
Length Längd	6465	5975	5034
Par	73	73	73
Slope system	—	127	130

Advised golfing ability Rekommenderad spelnivå: 0 12 24 36

Hcp required Hcp erfordrad: 36

CLUB HOUSE & AMENITIES — KLUBBHUS OCH OMGIVNING — 7/10

Pro shop	Pro shop
Driving range	Träningsbana

Sheltered tak no - On grass på gräs yes - Putting-green putting-green yes - Pitching-green pitching-green yes

HOTEL FACILITIES — HOTELL OMGIVNING — 7/10

HOTELS HOTELL

Ekerum - 70 rooms, D SKr 1195 - on site
Tel (46) 0485 - 808 00, Fax (46) 0485 - 800 10

Halltorps Gästgiveri - 36 rooms, D SKr 1200 - Borgholm 1 km
Tel (46) 0485 - 850 00, Fax (46) 0485 - 850 01

Strand Hotel- 134 rooms, D SKr 1590 - Borgholm 15 km
Tel (46) 0485 - 888 88, Fax (46) 0485 - 888 99

Ekerum Resort - rooms & villas, ask for prices - on site
Tel (46) 0485 - 800 08

RESTAURANTS RESTAURANGER

Halltorps Gästgiveri - Borgholm 1 km - Tel (46) 0485 - 850 00
Hotell Borgholm - Borgholm 15 km - Tel (46) 0485 - 770 60

Fågelbro

16 | 9 | 5

För att komma hit åker du genom ytterområdena av Skärgården, denna fantastiska värld med över 20 000 öar och klippor och som sträcker sig hela 140 kilometer ut i Östersjön. Många stockholmare har sommarhus i närheten, och under högsäsong är därför trycket hårt på Fågelbro. Paradoxalt nog ser du aldrig havet från banan, vilket dock inte förtar intrycket av att detta är en härlig naturupplevelse. Designen är mycket amerikansk, vilket märks sista nio där vatten kommer i spel på hela sex av hålen. Första nio är helt annorlunda och har mycket mer av parkbanekaraktär. Fågelbro är inte lång men har du problem med dina utslag kommer du snart att hamna i svårigheter. Även om ytorna vid sidan av fairways har rensats upp. Gränslinjen mellan en lyckad och en misslyckad score är synnerligen tunn. Här finns knappast ett enda hål där du kan slappna av, vilket höghandicapare inte kommer att uppskatta. Å andra sidan kommer belöningen efter rundan i klubbhuset som är ett av Sveriges charmigaste. Framför allt måste greenerna nämnas, de är i utmärkt kondition redan tidigt på våren. Så blir också Fågelbro bara bättre med åren.

To get here from Stockholm, you have to drive between land and water along the edge of an incredible archipelago of more than 20,000 islands and reefs stretching some 140 km into the Baltic Sea. This is the summer or week-end residence of many of the capital city's inhabitants and Fågelbro is one of the busiest courses. Paradoxically this is a wonderful natural setting where you never see the sea, but water is in play on six of the last nine holes, while the front nine looks more like a huge park. Fågelbro is not long but will pose big problems on days when your driving is not up to scratch. Fortunately, you can keep the driver in your bag on this narrow course where there is not a single hole where to relax. There is however the reward of the club-house, one of the most charming of its kind in Sweden. A special consideration for the greens, in superb condition in Summer.

Fågelbro Golf & Country Club — 1991

Fågelbro Säteri
S - 139 60 VÄRMDÖ

Office	Sekretariat	(46) 08 - 571 418 00
Pro shop	Pro shop	(46) 08 - 571 418 00
Fax	Fax	(46) 08 - 571 406 71
Web	www.fagelbrogolf.se	
Situation	Läge	Stockholm, 35 km
Annual closure	Årlig stängning	no
Weekly closure	Daglig stängning	no
Fees main season	Tariff hög säsong	full day

	Week days Veckodag	We/Bank holidays Lör/Söndag/Helgdag
Individual Individuellt	SKr 500	SKr 600
Couple Par	SKr 1000	SKr 1200

Juniors: SKr 300

Caddie Caddie no — **Electric Trolley** El vagn no

Buggy Golfbil yes — **Clubs** Klubbor yes

Credit cards Kredit kort
VISA - Eurocard - MasterCard - AMEX - DC

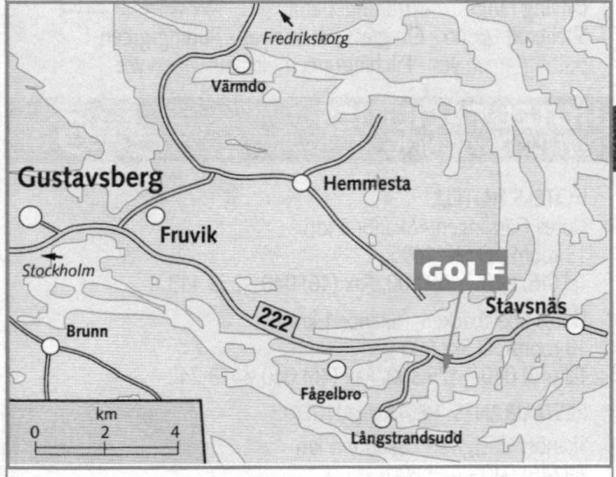

Access Tillfart : Stockholm, Väg 222 → Stavanäs/Djurö
Map 2 on page 1215 Karta 2 se sid: 1215

GOLF COURSE — BANA — 16/20

Site	Läge	
Maintenance	Underhåll	
Architect	Arkitekt	Björn Eriksson
Type	Karaktär	forest
Relief	Nivåskillnader	
Water in play	Vatten på spelfältet	
Exp. to wind	Vindutsatt	
Trees in play	Träd på spelfältet	

Scorecard Scorekort	Chp. Back tees	Mens Herrtee	Ladies Damtee
Length Längd	5974	5445	4535
Par	71	71	71
Slope system	—	130	124

Advised golfing ability Rekommenderad spelnivå — 0 12 24 36

Hcp required Hcp erfordrad — 24 Men, 30 Ladies

CLUB HOUSE & AMENITIES — KLUBBHUS OCH OMGIVNING — 9/10

Pro shop Pro shop
Driving range Träningsbana
Sheltered tak 2 mats - On grass på gräs no, 16 mats open air-
Putting-green putting-green yes - Pitching-green pitching-green no

HOTEL FACILITIES — HOTELL OMGIVNING — 5/10

HOTELS HOTELL
Fågelbrohus - 72 rooms, D SKr 1600 - on site
Tel (46) 08 - 571 401 00, Fax (46) 08 - 571 401 71

Grand Hotel - Stockholm 35 km
307 rooms, D SKr 4400
Tel (46) 08 - 679 3500, Fax (46) 08 - 611 8606

First Hotel Reisen - Stockholm 35 km
144 rooms, D SKr 2543
Tel (46) 08 - 223 260, Fax (46) 08 - 201 559

RESTAURANTS RESTAURANGER
Fågelbro - Stockholm 35 km - Tel (46) 08 - 759 0750
Fredsgatan 12 - Stockholm 35 km - Tel (46) 08 - 248 052
Franska Matsalen - Stockholm 35 km - Tel (46) 08 - 679 3584

Falsterbo

18 | 8 | 5

Detta är en av få linksbanor utanför Storbritannien där det känns som om du befinner dig på Skottlands östkust. Banan är omgärdad av vatten på tre sidor, och på första nio hålen finns också ett antal dammar. Övriga problem är den tjocka ruffen och bunkrar som lurar antingen på sidorna eller mitt i fairway. Greenerna kan man ofta närma sig med låga rullslag. De nyrenoverade greenerna har adderat en ny dimension till banan, och de små onduleringarna kan verkligen testa dig. Blåser det inte är banan i det närmaste ofarlig. Men de dagar när det friskar i, och det gör det nästan alltid, måste du ha god bollkontroll och kreativa lösningar. Spelare med bra känsla blir belönade, framför allt när det kommer till att rädda par runt greenerna. Några få rader av träd i banans ytterområde avskärmar Falsterbo från resten av omgivningen, och en gammal fyr mitt i området är ett pittoreskt inslag i en miljö som annars saknar starka färger. Längre söderut än så här kommer du inte i Sverige, och på våren är det här platsen att se de första gässen och änderna. Några väljer till och med att stanna och bygga bo i detta golfparadis. Vi förstår varför!

This is one of the pure links courses outside the British Isles where you feel as if you are in Scotland. Surrounded by water on three sides, there is also a number of ponds, particularly on the front nine. The other problems are the tall rough and bunkers, which lurk on either side and across the fairways, and beside greens which can often be reached with bump and run shots. The renovation of those greens has added a new dimension, and their small elevations can really test you. When the wind blows, you need good ball control and constant creativity. Players with good hands and touch are rewarded, particularly when it comes to saving par around the greens. A few rows of trees on the outskirts isolate the course from its surroundings and an old lighthouse adds a touch of colour to a rather bleak landscape. This is the southernmost part of Sweden where you first see the ducks and geese flying back to herald the first days of spring. Some even stop to nest alongside this little golfer's paradise, and understandably so.

Falsterbo Golfklubb — 1911

Fyrvägen
S - 239 40 FALSTERBO

Office	Sekretariat	(46) 040 - 470 078
Pro shop	Pro shop	(46) 040 - 470 078
Fax	Fax	(46) 040 - 472 722
Web	www.falsterbogk.com	
Situation	Läge	Malmö, 30 km
Annual closure	Årlig stängning	no
Weekly closure	Daglig stängning	no

Fees main season Tariff hög säsong	Full day	
	Week days Veckodag	We/Bank holidays Lör/Söndag/Helgdag
Individual Individuellt	SKr 600	SKr 600
Couple Par	SKr 1200	SKr 1200

Juniors: SKr 200

Caddie Caddie no — **Electric Trolley** El vagn no
Buggy Golfbil no — **Clubs** Klubbor yes
Credit cards Kredit kort
VISA - Eurocard - MasterCard - AMEX - DC

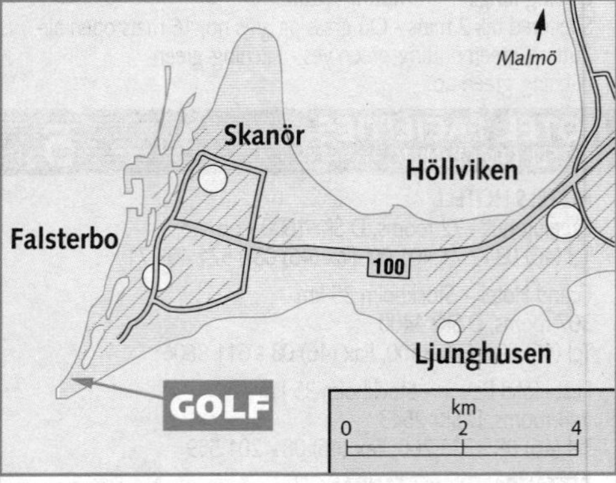

Access Tillfart : Malmö, E6 South (Syd). → Skanör/Falsterbo.
Map 1 on page 1212 Karta 1 se sid: 1212

GOLF COURSE — BANA — 18/20

Site	Läge	
Maintenance	Underhåll	
Architect	Arkitekt	Gunnar Bauer
Type	Karaktär	links, seaside course
Relief	Nivåskillnader	
Water in play	Vatten på spelfältet	
Exp. to wind	Vindutsatt	
Trees in play	Träd på spelfältet	

Scorecard Scorekort	Chp. Back tees	Mens Herrtee	Ladies Damtee
Length Längd	6065	5785	5040
Par	71	71	71
Slope system	—	127	126

Advised golfing ability Rekommenderad spelnivå — 0 12 24 36

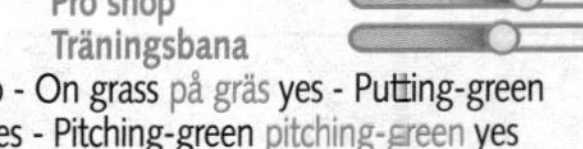

Hcp required Hcp erfordrad — 32

CLUB HOUSE & AMENITIES — KLUBBHUS OCH OMGIVNING — 8/10

Pro shop Pro shop
Driving range Träningsbana
Sheltered tak no - On grass på gräs yes - Putting-green putting-green yes - Pitching-green pitching-green yes

HOTEL FACILITIES — HOTELL OMGIVNING — 5/10

HOTELS HOTELL
Hotell Gässlingen - Skanör 5 km
13 rooms, D SKr 1495
Tel (46) 040 - 459 100, Fax (46) 040 - 359 113

Hotell Spelabäcken - Skanör 1 km
18 rooms, D SKr 900
Tel (46) 040 - 475 300, Fax (46) 040 - 473 242

RESTAURANTS RESTAURANGER
Skanörs Gästgiveri - Skanör 4 km
Tel (46) 040 - 475 690

Kaptensgården - Falsterbo 1 km - Tel (46) 040 - 470 750

Vellinge Gästgiveri - Vellinge 7 km - Tel (46) 040 - 424 865

Fjällbacka

15 | 6 | 3

Men platsen har sin berömmelse inte endast tack vare att Ingrid Bergman brukade åka hit på semestern: Detta är hummerns, krabbans och musslans huvudstad. Banan, som ritades av Erik Röös, öppnade 1967 och är resultatet av det arbete som visionären Harry Järund la ner. I dag är det en mycket välkänd bana belägen i ett ganska fantastiskt landskap, smala strängar av platt mark kantade av bergig terräng. Fairways vaktas på sina ställen av klippor, ungefär som på banorna i Arizona, enda skillnaden är att "öknen" här är grön och att en å rinner genom området och på flera ställen korsar banan. Fjällbaka är inte lång, men spelaren som kan manövrera bollen och då och då slå ett punchslag under vinden blir belönad därefter. Flera bunkrar har restaurerats och fått ny sand och ett par vattenhinder har tillkommit som gör att banan spelas avsevärt längre och bättre, inte minst tack vare det nya dräneringssystemet. Trots att detta är en inlandsbana är känslan av seasidegolf stark, framför allt när man måste spela klassiska rullslag.

Fjällbacka owes its reputation to the fact that Ingrid Bergman used to come here in summer, but also to its status as one of the northern capitals of lobster, crab and oysters. This layout, opened in 1967, has become a very well known course over a quite amazing site, a rocky region with patches of soil. It needed four years of work to treat the soil and miraculously improve the fairways as from Spring. The fairways are sort of guarded by the rocks, rather like on some of the courses in Arizona, the only difference being that the "desert" here is all green and crossed by a river that often comes into play. The course is not long, but players who can bend the ball, play knock-down shots or punch the ball will get their reward. With the new sand in bunkers and the addition of new water hazards, this course plays a bit longer and better because of the drainage system. Despite this being an inland course, there is still a seaside atmosphere, particularly when it comes to playing some good old bump and run shots.

Fjällbacka Golfklubb — 1967

PL 2005
S - 450 71 FJÄLLBACKA

Office	Sekretariat	(46) 0525 - 311 50
Pro shop	Pro shop	(46) 0525 - 315 60
Fax	Fax	(46) 0525 - 321 22
Web	www.fjallbacka.com/fjgk	
Situation	Läge	Fjällbacka, 2 km

Göteborg, 120 km

Annual closure	Årlig stängning	no
Weekly closure	Daglig stängning	no
Fees main season	Tariff hög säsong	18 holes

	Week days Veckodag	We/Bank holidays Lör/Söndag/Helgdag
Individual Individuellt	SKr 300	SKr 380
Couple Par	SKr 600	SKr 760

Juniors: – 50%

Caddie Caddie no — **Electric Trolley** El vagn no
Buggy Golfbil yes — **Clubs** Klubbor yes
Credit cards Kredit kort
VISA - Eurocard - MasterCard

Access Tillfart : Göteborg E6. Dingle, R163 → Fjällbacka. Golf 2 km north of Fjällbacka.
Map 1 on page 1212 Karta 1 se sid: 1212

GOLF COURSE — BANA — 15/20

Site	Läge	
Maintenance	Underhåll	
Architect	Arkitekt	Erik Röhs
Type	Karaktär	parkland, open country
Relief	Nivåskillnader	
Water in play	Vatten på spelfältet	
Exp. to wind	Vindutsatt	
Trees in play	Träd på spelfältet	

Scorecard Scorekort	Chp. Back tees	Mens Herrtee	Ladies Damtee
Length Längd	5935	5655	4985
Par	72	72	72
Slope system	—	119	118

Advised golfing ability Rekommenderad spelnivå — 0 12 24 36
Hcp required Hcp erfordrad 36

CLUB HOUSE & AMENITIES — KLUBBHUS OCH OMGIVNING — 6/10

Pro shop Pro shop
Driving range Träningsbana
Sheltered tak 6 mats - On grass på gräs yes - Putting-green putting-green yes - Pitching-green pitching-green yes

HOTEL FACILITIES — HOTELL OMGIVNING — 3/10

HOTELS HOTELL
Stora Hotellet - Fjällbacka 2 km
22 rooms, D SKr 1550
Tel (46) 0525 - 310 03, Fax (46) 0525 - 310 93

Oscar II - Fjällbacka 2 km
8 rooms, D SKr 995
Tel (46) 0525 - 322 10

RESTAURANTS RESTAURANGER
Restaurant Klassen - Fjällbacka 2 km
Tel (46) 0525 - 310 03
Storm - Fjällbacka 2 km
Tel (46) 0525 - 324 25

Flommen

16 | 7 | 5

Tillsammans med Falsterbo och Ljunghusen utgör Flommen en berömd trio, där Falsterbo, förstås, är den mest omtalade banan utanför Sverige. Vad gäller närheten till vatten så är det ett faktum som inte bara gör sig påmint för att Flommen ligger på en halvö – nix, här kommer vatten i spel på varje hål. Här finns inga träd, bara den eviga vinden, året om. För friluftsmänniskan är detta en mycket upphetsande bana, måhända lite mindre för golfaren som inte är i form eller som älskar att ströva i skogen. Hindrena syns tydligt från tee och är mycket farliga oavsett om vi talar om ruffen, bunkrarna eller vattnet (översvämningar kan vara ett problem). Några av greenerna är upphöjda, en del är svårlästa och knepiga att träffa. För matchspel är detta en idealisk bana eftersom ingenting kan tas för givet. Den modige har en fördel över den överdrivet försiktige. Om dina bollar tar slut får du ägna dig åt att tillsammans med alla fågelskådare studera det fantastiska naturlivet. Dammar och vattendrag har rensats ur och ser nu ut som under 1950-1960-talen, uppskattat inte minst av grodorna.

With Falsterbo and Ljunghusens, Flommens makes up a famous threesome of courses. This sort of peninsula gives you all the more the impression of being surrounded by water in that the stuff comes into play on virtually every hole. There are no trees here, just wind all year, so an exciting course for sports lovers, a little less so for golfers who prefer a stroll through the forest or who are not on top of their game. The hazards are visible enough and effectively dangerous, whether rough, bunkers or, of course, water. The greens are sometimes elevated (the terrain is subject to flooding on occasions), not always flat and difficult to approach. This is your ideal course for match-play, as here nothing is ever over: daring is sometimes more rewarding than extreme caution. Ponds and water hazards have been cleaned up and their 1950s/1960s look restored, a move much appreciated by the local frogs in a region where the wild-life is quite exceptional and attracts a good number of bird-watchers.

Flommens Golfklubb — 1935

Fädriften
S - 239 40 FALSTERBO

Office	Sekretariat	(46) 040 - 475 019
Pro shop	Pro shop	(46) 040 - 475 016
Fax	Fax	(46) 040 - 473 157
Web	www.flommensgk.se	
Situation	Läge	Malmö, 30 km

Höllviken, 8 km

Annual closure	Årlig stängning	no
Weekly closure	Daglig stängning	no
Fees main season	Tariff hög säsong	Full day

	Week days Veckodag	We/Bank holidays Lör/Söndag/Helgdag
Individual Individuellt	SKr 400	SKr 400
Couple Par	SKr 800	SKr 800

Juniors: SKr 150

Caddie Caddie no — **Electric Trolley** El vagn no

Buggy Golfbil no — **Clubs** Klubbor no

Credit cards Kredit kort
VISA - Eurocard - MasterCard - AMEX

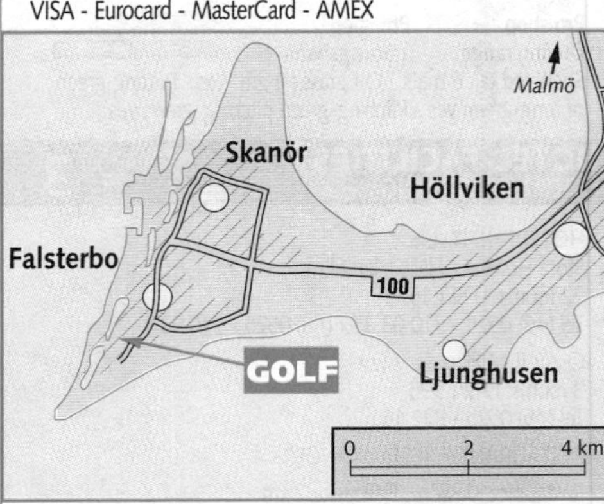

Access Tillfart : Malmö, E6 → Vellinge, → Skanör-Falsterbo, → Falsterbo. → Flommens Golfklubb.
Map 1 on page 1212 Karta 1 se sid: 1212

GOLF COURSE — BANA — 16/20

Site	Läge	
Maintenance	Underhåll	
Architect	Arkitekt	Stig Bergendorff Stig Kristersson
Type	Karaktär	seaside course, links
Relief	Nivåskillnader	
Water in play	Vatten på spelfältet	
Exp. to wind	Vindutsatt	
Trees in play	Träd på spelfältet	

Scorecard Scorekort	Chp. Back tees	Mens Herrtee	Ladies Damtee
Length Längd	6075	5797	5017
Par	72	72	72
Slope system	126	123	124

Advised golfing ability Rekommenderad spelnivå — 0 12 24 36

Hcp required Hcp erfordrad — 36

CLUB HOUSE & AMENITIES — KLUBBHUS OCH OMGIVNING — 7/10

Pro shop Pro shop
Driving range Träningsbana
Sheltered tak no - On grass på gräs yes - Putting-green putting-green yes - Pitching-green pitching-green yes

HOTEL FACILITIES — HOTELL OMGIVNING — 5/10

HOTELS HOTELL

Hotel Gässlingen - Skanör 4 km
13 rooms, D SKr 1495
Tel (46) 040 - 459 100, Fax (46) 040 - 359 113

Hotell Spelabäcken - Skanör 1 km
18 rooms, D SKr 900
Tel (46) 040 - 475 300, Fax (46) 040 - 473 242

RESTAURANTS RESTAURANGER

Skanörs Gästgiveri - Skanör 10 km
Tel (46) 040 - 475 690

Vellinge Gästgiveri - Vellinge 15 km
Tel (46) 040 - 424 865

Kaptensgården - Falsterbo 1 km - Tel (46) 040 - 470 750

Forsbacka

16	7	4

Många svenska banor är vackert infogade i naturen. Forsbacka är inget undantag. Banan ligger nära Åmål, en liten stad på Vätterns strand. Den är belägen i ett underbart landskap mellan sjöar och skog, ungefär som man föreställer sig ett svenskt vykort. Men eftersom den är ganska kuperad och här inte finns några golfbilar rekommenderar vi den endast till den som är i bra fysisk form och som inte är rädd för vatten, träd eller höga kullar. Som på de flesta kuperade banor vill man gärna veta vilka hinder som finns framför en, här finns dock inga gömda elakheter så länge du håller dig på fairway. De mest minnesvärda hålen är sjuan och nian, som bägge kräver långa slag och stor precision. Många golfare tycker att Forsbacka är en av Sveriges vackraste banor, andra kanske tycker att den är i väl förrädiska laget. Hur som helst, du måste spela här för att bilda dig en egen uppfattning. Bo över i Jägmästarflygeln, ett 1600-talshotell bara 20 meter från första tee.

Many Swedish courses are beautifully immersed in nature, and this is one of them. Forsbacka is close to Åmål, a small town on the shores of the Vänern, the largest lake in western Europe. The course offers a wonderful landscape of lakes and forests, rather like a postcard of Sweden, but being rather hilly and given the absence of carts we would recommend it only for golfers who are in good shape physically and for players for whom water, trees and slopes hold no fears. As with all hilly courses, we would like to see the hazards ahead, but here there are not really any hidden traps or unpleasant surprises in store. On this exciting course, perhaps the most memorable holes are from 7 to 9, where that hardest of combinations - length and accuracy - is a total and absolute necessity. For many golfers, Forsbacka is one of Sweden's most beautiful parkland courses, others might find it a little treacherous. You will judge for yourselves as you stay at the Jägmästarflygeln, a 17th century hotel just 20 metres from tee N° 1.

Forsbacka Golfklubb — 1971

Box 136
S - 662 23 ÅMÅL

Office	Sekretariat	(46) 0532 - 616 91
Pro shop	Pro shop	(46) 0532 - 616 94
Fax	Fax	(46) 0532 - 616 99
Web	www.golf.se/forsbackagk	
Situation	Läge	Åmål, 7 km Karlstad, 75 km
Annual closure	Årlig stängning	no
Weekly closure	Daglig stängning	no

Fees main season Tariff hög säsong	Full day	
	Week days Veckodag	**We/Bank holidays** Lör/Söndag/Helgdag
Individual Individuellt	SKr 250	SKr 300
Couple Par	SKr 500	SKr 600

Juniors: SKr 125/150 (We)

Caddie Caddie no **Electric Trolley** El vagn no

Buggy Golfbil yes **Clubs** Klubbor yes

Credit cards Kredit kort
VISA - Eurocard - MasterCard

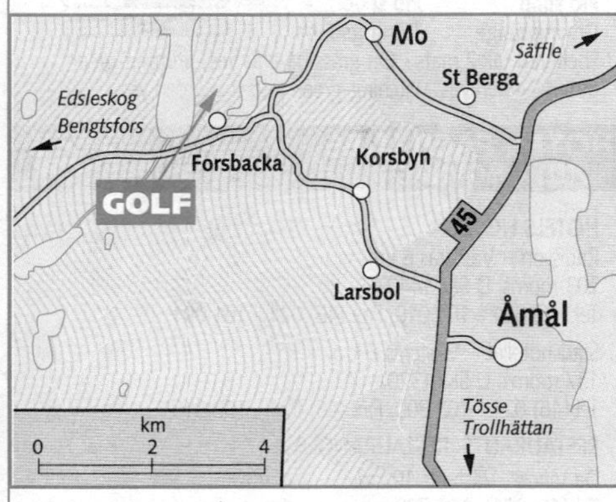

Access Tillfart : R45 Vänersborg-Karlstad.
Exit R164 → Bengtsfors. → Golf
Map 2 on page 1214 Karta 2 se sid: 1214

GOLF COURSE — BANA 16/20

Site	Läge	
Maintenance	Underhåll	
Architect	Arkitekt	Nils Sköld
Type	Karaktär	forest, parkland
Relief	Nivåskillnader	
Water in play	Vatten på spelfältet	
Exp. to wind	Vindutsatt	
Trees in play	Träd på spelfältet	

Scorecard Scorekort	**Chp.** Back tees	**Mens** Herrtee	**Ladies** Damtee
Length Längd	6040	5755	5050
Par	72	72	72
Slope system	128	125	118

Advised golfing ability Rekommenderad spelnivå — 0 12 24 36

Hcp required Hcp erfordrad 36

CLUB HOUSE & AMENITIES — KLUBBHUS OCH OMGIVNING 7/10

Pro shop Pro shop
Driving range Träningsbana
Sheltered tak 1 mat - On grass på gräs no, 12 mats open air - Putting-green putting-green yes - Pitching-green pitching-green no

HOTEL FACILITIES — HOTELL OMGIVNING 4/10

HOTELS HOTELL
Jägmästarflygeln - on site
13 rooms, D SKr 995
Tel (46) 0532 - 430 73, Fax (46) 0532 - 431 16

Dalhall - Åmål 10 km
20 rooms, D SKr 790
Tel (46) 0532 - 166 90, Fax (46) 0532 - 129 67

RESTAURANTS RESTAURANGER
Stadshotellet - Åmål 7 km
Tel (46) 0532 - 120 20
Barhörnan - Åmål 7 km
Tel (46) 0532 - 146 00

1233

Frösåker

16	8	6

Frösåker ligger mycket nära Västerås, där du bland sevärdheterna finner en sällsynt vacker kyrka och ett kvarter av gamla timmerhus. Även om detta är en relativt ny bana har den snabbt fått ett utomordentligt rykte. Inledningen är måhända lite tam, men sedan tar saker och ting fart och när du slutligen når 18e står du inför ett av Sveriges allra bästa hål. Hindrena på Frösåker kommer i alla former och harmonierar väl med landskapet i övrigt. Sista nio är betydligt mer utmanande än de första, och det är lätt att frestas att ta risker. Om du slår någorlunda rakt, förmår att hålla dig kall och har en hygglig teknik så har du alla möjligheter att komma in på ett bra resultat. För den som slår snett kan ruffen vålla stora problem, särskilt med tanke på att höga inspel med gott om bakskruv är ett måste på flera av hålen. En aning för svår för den inte fullt så erfarne golfaren, en njutning för alla andra. Med sikte på framtida stortävlingar pågår ett ständigt förbättringsarbete. Restaurangen är lika bra som alltid.

Frösåker is close to Västerås where you will find a very beautiful cathedral and an old district full of timber houses. This course has quickly built up an excellent reputation. Before reaching the magnificent 18th, one of the finest holes in the whole country, you start off with a few rather indifferent holes. Then things start to get more exciting in a much more attractive park landscape, where hazards of all shapes and sizes are brought into play, clearly and with a sense of harmony. The back 9 are even more demanding than the outward half and you will be tempted to take risks. If you are a reasonably straight hitter, can keep a cool head and have the proper technique to work the ball, you will come through with flying colours. For the more wayward hitters, the rough can be more than a handful, especially since approach shots to the greens are not easy and call for high shots. The club is seriously upgrading standards of maintenance. The restaurant is as good as ever.

Frösåker Golfklubb — 1989

Box 17015
S - 720 17 VÄSTERÅS

Office	Sekretariat	(46) 021 - 254 01
Pro shop	Pro shop	(46) 021 - 250 21
Fax	Fax	(46) 021 - 254 85
Web	www.fgcc.se	
Situation	Läge	Västerås, 20 km
Annual closure	Årlig stängning	no
Weekly closure	Daglig stängning	no

Fees main season Tariff hög säsong		18 holes
	Week days Veckodag	**We/Bank holidays** Lör/Söndag/Helgdag
Individual Individuellt	SKr 350	SKr 450
Couple Par	SKr 700	SKr 900

Juniors: SKr 120/180 (We) - Additional round SKr 150

Caddie Caddie no — **Electric Trolley** El vagn no

Buggy Golfbil yes — **Clubs** Klubbor yes

Credit cards Kredit kort
VISA - Eurocard - MasterCard - AMEX - DC

Access Tillfart : Stockholm E18 → Enköpping/Västerås. → Kärrbo.

Map 2 on page 1215 Karta 2 se sid: 1215

GOLF COURSE — BANA — 16/20

Site	Läge	
Maintenance	Underhåll	
Architect	Arkitekt	Sune Linde
Type	Karaktär	seaside course, parkland
Relief	Nivåskillnader	
Water in play	Vatten på spelfältet	
Exp. to wind	Vindutsatt	
Trees in play	Träd på spelfältet	

Scorecard Scorekort	**Chp.** Back tees	**Mens** Herrtee	**Ladies** Damtee
Length Längd	6400	5820	4950
Par	72	72	72
Slope system	—	130	124

Advised golfing ability Rekommenderad spelnivå — 0 12 24 36

Hcp required Hcp erfordrad — 36

CLUB HOUSE & AMENITIES — KLUBBHUS OCH OMGIVNING — 8/10

Pro shop Pro shop
Driving range Träningsbana
Sheltered tak 2 mats - On grass på gräs yes - Putting-green putting-green yes - Pitching-green pitching-green yes

HOTEL FACILITIES — HOTELL OMGIVNING — 6/10

HOTELS HOTELL

Radisson - Västerås 6 km
203 rooms, D SKr 1440
Tel (46) 021 - 101 010, Fax (46) 021 - 101 091

Stadshotellet - Västerås 6 km
137 rooms, D SKr 1320
Tel (46) 021 - 102 800, Fax (46) 021 - 102 810

RESTAURANTS RESTAURANGER

Da Vincis - Västerås 10 km
Tel (46) 021 - 188 220

Lemone - Västerås 10 km
Tel (46) 021 - 410 60 75

Göteborg

15 | 6 | 7

Detta är Sveriges äldsta bana, att få en starttid här på en helg är snudd på omöjligt. Den byggdes 1904, och träden som då planterades har nu hunnit växa sig stora och mäktiga vilket gör en del hål synnerligen knixiga. Här är du inte mycket hjälpt av råstyrka, betydligt bättre är att fokusera på precisionen. Men det ska du nog lyckas med eftersom banan är ganska kort och ligger i ett böljande landskap som inte är alltför fysiskt krävande. Dessutom är konditionen på banan nästan alltid i högsta klass, vilket gör att man gärna åker hit för att spela en vänskaplig match. Göteborg, eller i folkmun Hovås, kräver inte en gudabenådad talang, däremot ett hyggligt spel med fairwayträna och mellanjärnen samt de korta järnen. Detta är den första banan i Europa som har fått miljöcertifieringen ISO, och det är sannerligen perfekt plats att spela och ladda upp på inför tuffare uppgifter, eller som avslutning på en trevlig dag i staden, där det finns mycket att se.

This is the oldest course in Sweden where playing on week-ends is nigh on impossible. It was designed in 1904, and some of the oldest holes are all the narrower and trickier today in that the trees have grown upwards and outwards since they were first planted. It is on these holes in particular that brute force is best left in the locker room and replaced by emphasis on accuracy. This should not be too much of a handicap, though, as the course is short and set out over rolling terrain, which you can walk quite easily, especially since the grass and green-keeping in general are excellent. Indeed, the condition of the greens, bunkers and fairways makes the course even more pleasant to play and it can be great fun playing friendly matches here. Göteborg does not require any particular heaven-sent talent, just all-round skills for fairway woods and your medium and short irons. This course – the first in Europe to receive ISO-Environment certification – is perfect to hone your game before squaring up to more demanding challenges or after a pleasant visit to a city where there is much to see.

Göteborgs Golfklubb — 1904

Box 2056
S - 436 02 HOVÅS

Office	Sekretariat	(46) 031 - 282 444
Pro shop	Pro shop	(46) 031 - 286 159
Fax	Fax	(46) 031 - 685 333
Web	www.goteborgsgk.org	
Situation	Läge	Göteborg, 15 km
Annual closure	Årlig stängning	no
Weekly closure	Daglig stängning	no
Fees main season	Tariff hög säsong	18 holes

	Week days Veckodag	We/Bank holidays Lör/Söndag/Helgdag
Individual Individuellt	SKr 500	SKr 600
Couple Par	SKr 1000	SKr 1200

Juniors: – 50% / We: members only before 15:00

Caddie Caddie no — **Electric Trolley** El vagn no

Buggy Golfbil no — **Clubs** Klubbor no

Credit cards Kredit kort
VISA - Mastercard - AMEX

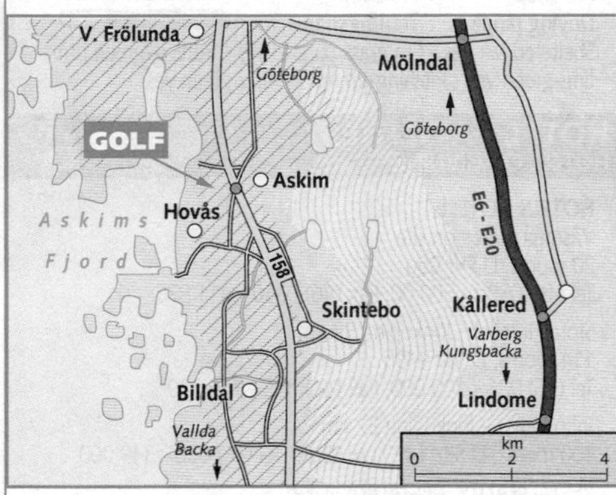

Access Tillfart : Göteborg, V 158 → Särö.
Map 1 on page 1212 Karta 1 se sid: 1212

GOLF COURSE
BANA — 15/20

Site	Läge	
Maintenance	Underhåll	
Architect	Arkitekt	Andrew Person
Type	Karaktär	parkland
Relief	Nivåskillnader	
Water in play	Vatten på spelfältet	
Exp. to wind	Vindutsatt	
Trees in play	Träd på spelfältet	

Scorecard Scorekort	Chp. Back tees	Mens Herrtee	Ladies Damtee
Length Längd	5575	5250	4630
Par	70	70	70
Slope system	—	125	123

Advised golfing ability Rekommenderad spelnivå — 0 12 24 36

Hcp required Hcp erfordrad — 30

CLUB HOUSE & AMENITIES
KLUBBHUS OCH OMGIVNING — 6/10

Pro shop Pro shop
Driving range Träningsbana
Sheltered tak 2 mats - On grass på gräs no (mats open air)
Putting-green putting-green yes - Pitching-green pitching-green no

HOTEL FACILITIES
HOTELL OMGIVNING — 7/10

HOTELS HOTELL

Quality Hotel 11 - Göteborg 15 km
133 rooms, D SKr 1750
Tel (46) 031 - 779 11 11, Fax (46) 031 - 779 11 10

Radissson - 333 rooms, D SKr 2100 - Göteborg 15 km
Tel (46) 031 - 758 50 00, Fax (46) 031 - 159 888

Victors - 44 rooms, D SKr 1700 - Göteborg 15 km
Tel (46) 031 - 174 180, Fax (46) 031 - 139 610

RESTAURANTS RESTAURANGER

Westra Piren - Göteborg 15 km - Tel (46) 031 - 519 555
Le Village - Göteborg 15 km - Tel (46) 031 - 242 003
Fiskekrogen - Göteborg 15 km - Tel (46) 031 - 101 005

Gränna

15	7	6

På den här banan finns inga omöjliga hinder som inte går att slå över med utslaget. Vad gäller medelhandicapare så kommer de också att trivas eftersom de sällan når hindrena som är så strategiskt placerade att de endast bekymrar de bättre spelarna (som på det fantastiska sista hålet). Från utslagsplatserna är det generella intrycket att fairways är mycket smala. Men detta är faktiskt en synvilla och mer ett psykologiskt problem än ett reellt, vilket kanske kan förklara att den som spelar här för första gången ofta är överdrivet försiktig. På Gränna kan man tydligt se banarkitekten Peter Nordwalls signum: Stora greener! Normalt innebär detta att de även blir aningen försvarslösa, men eftersom de på Gränna är starkt kuperade kommer du att inse att den viktigaste klubban i bagen är din putter. Bortsett från tre-fyra rätt ordinära hål är Gränna absolut värd ett besök, så är givetvis också stan med sina färgglada hus, och glöm för all del inte bort att äta en polkagris. Bo på Hotell Västanå, och utmana slottsspöket !

On this course, there are none of those impossible carries from the tee. Mid-handicappers like beginners will be happy, as the hazards out on the course are seldom in play for them, and the better players will be in their element, as the main hazards are reserved just for them (like on the wonderful last hole). From the tee-boxes you get the impression of the fairways here being very narrow. This is in fact an optical illusion and psychological trap, which explains why golfers playing here for the first time tend to be over-cautious. The course clearly carries the hallmarks of architect Peter Nordwall, i.e. very large greens, a feature that tends to blunt their defences, but as the contours are very pronounced, the putter once again will be the most important club in your bag. Excepting some ordinary holes, Gränna really is worth a visit, as is the village of the same name to see the coloured houses and taste the local barley sugar called polkagrisar. Hotel Västanå Slott is a must, even with its ghosts.

Gränna Golfklubb — 1989

Västanå Slott
S - 563 92 GRÄNNA

Office	Sekretariat	(46) 0390 - 100 30
Pro shop	Pro shop	(46) 0390 - 106 29
Fax	Fax	(46) 0390 - 100 34
Web	www.golf.se/grannagk	
Situation	Läge	Jönköping, 32 km
Annual closure	Årlig stängning	no
Weekly closure	Daglig stängning	no
Fees main season	Tariff hög säsong	full day

	Week days Veckodag	We/Bank holidays Lör/Söndag/Helgdag
Individual Individuellt	SKr 280	SKr 330
Couple Par	SKr 560	SKr 660

Juniors: SKr 120

Caddie Caddie no — **Electric Trolley** El vagn no

Buggy Golfbil yes — **Clubs** Klubbor yes

Credit cards Kredit kort
VISA - Eurocard - MasterCard - AMEX - DC

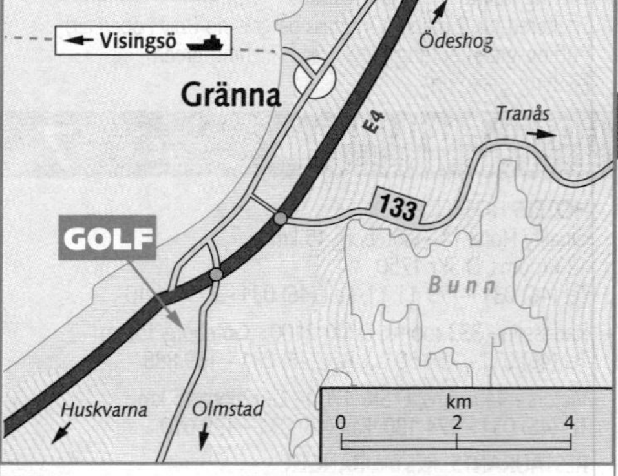

Access Tillfart : Gränna E4. 5 km Exit Gyllene Uttern. → Västanå Slott.
Map 1 on page 1212 Karta 1 se sid: 1212

GOLF COURSE — BANA — 15/20

Site	Läge	
Maintenance	Underhåll	
Architect	Arkitekt	Peter Nordwall
Type	Karaktär	parkland, open country
Relief	Nivåskillnader	
Water in play	Vatten på spelfältet	
Exp. to wind	Vindutsatt	
Trees in play	Träd på spelfältet	

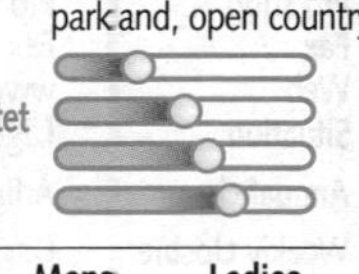

Scorecard Scorekort	Chp. Back tees	Mens Herrtee	Ladies Damtee
Length Längd	5967	5600	4741
Par	72	72	72
Slope system	—	132	128

Advised golfing ability Rekommenderad spelnivå — 0 12 24 36

Hcp required Hcp erfordrad — 36

CLUB HOUSE & AMENITIES — KLUBBHUS OCH OMGIVNING — 7/10

Pro shop Pro shop
Driving range Träningsbana
Sheltered tak yes - On grass på gräs yes - Putting-green putting-green yes - Pitching-green pitching-green yes

HOTEL FACILITIES — HOTELL OMGIVNING — 6/10

HOTELS HOTELL
Västanå Slott - on site
20 rooms, D SKr 950
Tel (46) 0390 - 500 00, Fax (46) 0390 - 411 875

Stora Hotellet - Jönköping 32 km
114 rooms, D SKr 1495
Tel (46) 036 - 100 000, Fax (46) 036 - 719 320

John Bauer - Jönköping 32 km
100 rooms, D SKr 1490 (w. GFee) Tel (46) 036 - 349 000

RESTAURANTS RESTAURANGER
Västanå Slott - on site - Tel (46) 0390 - 107 00
Esters Restaurang - Jönköping 32 km - Tel (46) 036 - 349 000
Trottoaren - Jönköping 32 km - Tel (46) 036 - 100 000

Grönhögen

16 | 7 | 5

Öland är som en stor gigantisk kalkstensskärva. Kanske är ön mest berömd för sina järnåldersfort, väderkvarnar, Alvaret, cyklingen eller orkidéerna. Och så golfen, förstås, med en sagolik linksbana tätt in på havet. Europatourgolfaren och banarkitekten Pierre Fulke ska verkligen äras för att han inte lät detta gå överbord. Det här är inte ett egocentriskt skrytbygge eller en enkel promenad längs havet – utan en riktig linksbana med buskar och ruff, ett och annat träd och 86 bunkrar, där ingen behöver gissa från vart sanden är tagen. Bunkrarna skapar ständiga överraskningar, men du kommer lära dig att ta dig ur dem. Och dubbelgreenen som finns här bara förstärker linkskänslan. Men detta är alls ingen plagiering av Skottland, utan en genuin bana, byggd med talang och omvårdnad. Men för att spela bra krävs det en smula tur med vinden, och att du har en inspirerad dag. Pegga upp på ettan, och sedan är det bara att hoppas… Du har en synnerligen oförutsägbar upplevelse framför dig!

The island of Öland is like a line of limestone whose specialities are plaice, Iron Age fortresses, windmills, moorland, cycling and orchids. And golf, with this amazing links very close to the sea. Much to his credit, the Swedish golfer Pierre Fulke has not gone overboard; this is neither a monument of self-satisfaction nor a simple stroll by the sea, rather a real links course in Sweden's pleasant land with bushes, rough, the odd tree you expect and 86 bunkers whose source of sand is obvious. Their presence sometimes comes as a surprise but you will eventually find your way out of them. And there is even the double green you would expect on a links course. Yet this is not a catalogue of Scottish products, rather a genuine, solid and testing course built with talent and obvious affection. Getting the better of it will depend on the wind, technique and inspiration. Start off at hole N° 1 and wait to see what happens by the time you get to the 18th green.

Grönhögen GK — 1996

S - 380 65 DEGERHAMN, ÖLAND

Office	Sekretariat	(46) 0485 - 665 990
Pro shop	Pro shop	(46) 0485 - 665 994
Fax	Fax	(46) 0485 - 665 999
Web	www.gronhogen.se	
Situation	Läge	Färjestaden, 50 km
Annual closure	Årlig stängning	no
Weekly closure	Daglig stängning	no
Fees main season	Tariff hög säsong	18 holes

	Week days / Veckodag	We/Bank holidays / Lör/Söndag/Helgdag
Individual Individuellt	SKr 300	SKr 350
Couple Par	SKr 600	SKr 700

Juniors: SKr 80

Caddie Caddie no — **Electric Trolley** El vagn no

Buggy Golfbil no — **Clubs** Klubbor no

Credit cards Kredit kort

VISA - Eurocard - MasterCard - AMEX - DC

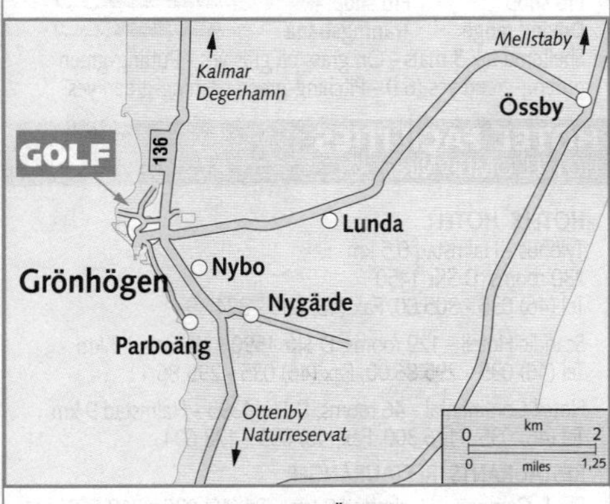

Access Tillfart : Kalmar, bridge to Öland. Road 136 for Ottenby. Golf 50 km

Map 1 on page 1213 Karta 1 se sid: 1213

GOLF COURSE — BANA — 16/20

Site	Läge	
Maintenance	Underhåll	
Architect	Arkitekt	Pierre Fulke
Type	Karaktär	links, seaside course
Relief	Nivåskillnader	
Water in play	Vatten på spelfältet	
Exp. to wind	Vindutsatt	
Trees in play	Träd på spelfältet	

Scorecard Scorekort	Chp. Back tees	Mens Herrtee	Ladies Damtee
Length Längd	6006	5802	5048
Par	72	72	72
Slope system	117	117	125

Advised golfing ability Rekommenderad spelnivå — 0 12 24 36

Hcp required Hcp erfordrad — 36

CLUB HOUSE & AMENITIES — KLUBBHUS OCH OMGIVNING — 7/10

Pro shop Pro shop

Driving range Träningsbana

Sheltered tak no - On grass på gräs yes - Putting-green putting-green yes - Pitching-green pitching-green yes

HOTEL FACILITIES — HOTELL OMGIVNING — 5/10

HOTELS HOTELL

Grönhögen - on site
10 rooms, D SKr 725
Tel (46) 0485 - 665 990, Fax (46) 0485 - 665 999

Hotell Kajutan - Mörbylånga 30 km
5 rooms, D SKr 890
Tel (46) 0485 - 408 10, Fax (46) 0485 - 348 04

Hotel Skansen - Färjestaden 50 km
31 rooms, D SKr 1290
Tel (46) 0485 - 305 30, Fax (46) 0485 - 348 04

RESTAURANTS RESTAURANGER

Wärdshuset - on site
Tel (46) 0485 - 661 131

1237

Halmstad

18 | 8 | 8

Banan ligger vid Tylösand, vilket är den populäraste stranden i staden. I övrigt rekommenderar vi att du besöker Stortorget och Miniland – det senare är ett Sverige uppbyggt i miniatyr. Efter detta ska du absolut ta dig tid för en runda golf på en av Sveriges allra bästa banor – utlagd i en tät tallskog och även om du inte kan se havet kan du på många ställen höra och känna det. Varje hål är kantat av träd, och därför finns det heller inget behov för ruff. Träden ger dig känslan av att hålen är längre och smalare än vad de verkligen är, och resultatet blir ofta att du spelar alltför försiktigt. Ett antal fairwaybunkers är extra luriga (framför allt på tvåan), för att inte tala om ån som rinner genom banan, och som lätt ställer till med problem på 12e och 16e hålen. I matchspel kan vad som helst hända där! Lyckligtvis är många av hindernа utom räckhåll för höghandicaparen – därför är också Halmstad relativt sett tuffare för den bättre spelaren. Är du inspirerad blir du dock belönad! Förutom mästerskapsbanan finns ytterligare en underbart, utmanande 18-hålsbana på området. Halmstad är ett måste, med landets bästa driving range och sex puttinggreener!

This course is at Tylösand, where essential visiting includes the "Miniland" attraction, a miniature Sweden with reduced-scale models of the finest landmarks and characters from legends of the country. Then move on and play one of the greatest courses in Sweden, laid out in a pine forest where you can always hear the sea without seeing it. Each hole is lined with trees, which are so dominant that there is no need for rough. A few fairway bunkers also lurk dangerously, as do a number of streams and ditches, like on the 12th and 16th holes. On the other hand, many of the hazards are out of reach for high-handicappers, meaning that Halmstad is a tough proposition for the better players, but one that rewards inspired play. With another shorter but beautiful and very challenging 18-hole course, the best driving range in Sweden and six putting-greens, Halmstad is a must.

Halmstad Golfklubb — 1938

Tylösand
S - 302 73 HALMSTAD

Office	Sekretariat	(46) 035 - 176 800
Pro shop	Pro shop	(46) 035 - 309 76
Fax	Fax	(46) 035 - 176 820
Web	www.hgk.se	
Situation	Läge	Halmstad, 9 km
Annual closure	Årlig stängning	no
Weekly closure	Daglig stängning	no
Fees main season	Tariff hög säsong	18 holes

	Week days Veckodag	We/Bank holidays Lör/Söndag/Helgdag
Individual Individuellt	SKr 600	SKr 600
Couple Par	SKr 1200	SKr 1200

Juniors: - 50% / Full day: SKr 900

Caddie Caddie no — **Electric Trolley** El vagn yes

Buggy Golfbil no — **Clubs** Klubbor yes

Credit cards Kredit kort
VISA - Eurocard - MasterCard - AMEX

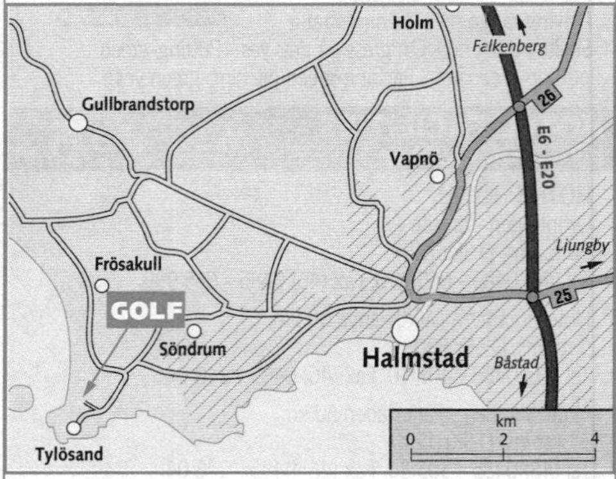

Holm, Falkenberg, Gullbrandstorp, Vapnö, E6 - E20, 26, Ljungby, Frösakull, GOLF, 25, Söndrum, Halmstad, Båstad, Tylösand, km 0 2 4

Access Tillfart : Halmstad, → Tylösand.
Map 1 on page 1212 Karta 1 se sid: 1212

GOLF COURSE — BANA — 18/20

Site	Läge	
Maintenance	Underhåll	
Architect	Arkitekt	Rafael Sundblom
Type	Karaktär	forest, parkland
Relief	Nivåskillnader	
Water in play	Vatten på spelfältet	
Exp. to wind	Vindutsatt	
Trees in play	Träd på spelfältet	

Scorecard Scorekort	Chp. Back tees	Mens Herrtee	Ladies Damtee
Length Längd	6317	5955	5116
Par	72	72	72
Slope system	—	133	129

Advised golfing ability Rekommenderad spelnivå — 0 12 24 36

Hcp required Hcp erfordrad — 24 Men, 32 Ladies

CLUB HOUSE & AMENITIES — KLUBBHUS OCH OMGIVNING — 8/10

Pro shop Pro shop
Driving range Träningsbana
Sheltered tak 3 mats - On grass på gräs yes - Putting-green putting-green yes (6 !) - Pitching-green pitching-green yes

HOTEL FACILITIES — HOTELL OMGIVNING — 8/10

HOTELS HOTELL
Tylöhus - Halmstad 0.5 km
230 rooms, D SKr 1450
Tel (46) 035 - 305 00, Fax (46) 035 - 324 39

Scandic Hotell - 129 rooms, D SKr 1590 - Halmstad 9 km
Tel (46) 035 - 295 86 00, Fax (46) 035 - 295 86 11

Hotell Continental - 46 rooms, D SKr 1395 - Halmstad 9 km
Tel (46) 035 - 176 300, Fax (46) 035 - 128 604

RESTAURANTS RESTAURANGER
Pio & Company - Halmstad 9 km - Tel (46) 035 - 210 669
Mårtensson - Halmstad 9 km - Tel (46) 035 - 177 575
Klosterköket - Halmstad 9 km - Tel (46) 035 - 124 050

Haninge

16	8	6

Strax söder om Stockholm ligger denna utomordentliga bana och med ett rykte om sig att vara en riktig mästerskapsanläggning. Detta ska dock inte avskräcka medelhandicaparen som kommer att ha en härlig runda framför sig, låt vara att han kanske inte blir alltför stolt över scoren. Men klubbhuset är någonting alldeles extra, ett slott från 1400-talet, och banan är en mix mellan öppna hål och parkbane-karaktär. Eftersom vatten kommer i spel på sju av hålen så kan man verkligen säga att detta är en komplett bana. Långtslående kan sträcka ut ordentligt då fyra av par 5-hålen är möjliga att nå på två slag. Det kan behövas eftersom det är lätt att scoren drar iväg på par 4-hålen och par 3-hålen. Greenerna är mycket bra designade, ganska stora och kuperade och med riktigt besvärliga lutningar på några ställen. De är dessutom väl skyddade bakom bunkrar och kullar som gör det eftersträvansvärt med höga inspel. Med en ny 9-hålsbana och en par 3-hålsbana samt utmärkta träningsmöjligheter är detta en suverän golfanläggning.

This excellent course has the reputation of being a fine championship test. This shouldn't deter mid-handicappers, who will have a lot of fun playing here, even though they might not be too proud of their card. Firstly, the club-house is a real picture, in an old 15th century castle. Then, the course itself mixes open holes with park-land and forest. And as water comes into play on seven holes, you could call this a complete course. Long-hitters can give it a real whack, probably reaching four of the par 5s in two and putting a few strokes in the bank in the process. They will need them on the par 3s and par 4s. The greens are well-designed, rather large and well contoured; some even have a number of very steep slopes. They are also well-guarded by bunkers and a series of mounds which call for high approach shots. A 9-hole course, a par 3 course and good practice facilities complete this great golfing complex.

Haninge Golfklubb — 1986

Årsta Slott
S - 136 91 HANINGE

Office	Sekretariat	(46) 08 - 500 328 58
Pro shop	Pro shop	(46) 08 - 500 328 55
Fax	Fax	(46) 08 - 500 328 51
Web	www.haningegk.se	
Situation	Läge	Stockholm, 30 km
Annual closure	Årlig stängning	no
Weekly closure	Daglig stängning	no

Fees main season Tariff hög säsong — Full day

	Week days Veckodag	We/Bank holidays Lör/Söndag/Helgdag
Individual Individuellt	SKr 400	SKr 450
Couple Par	SKr 800	SKr 900

Juniors: – 50% / Guests welcomed before 13:00 on week days and after 13:00 on week-ends

Caddie Caddie no — **Electric Trolley** El vagn no

Buggy Golfbil no — **Clubs** Klubbor yes

Credit cards Kredit kort
VISA - Eurocard - MasterCard

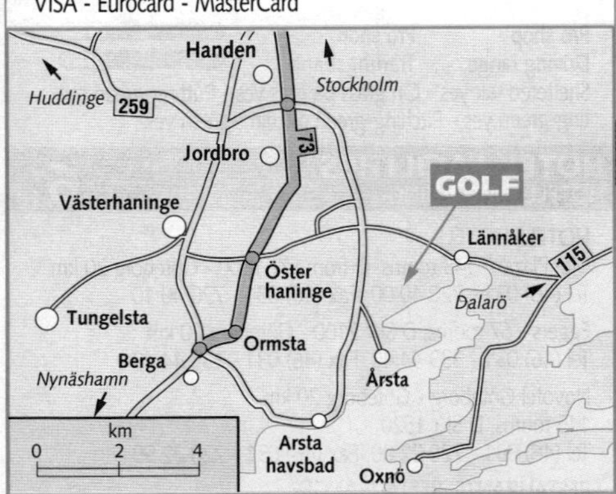

Access Tillfart : Stockholm, 73 → Nynäshamn. → Dalarö. → "Årsta Havsbad"
Map 2 on page 1215 Karta 2 se sid: 1215

GOLF COURSE — BANA — 16/20

Site	Läge	
Maintenance	Underhåll	
Architect	Arkitekt	Jan Sederholm
Type	Karaktär	forest, parkland
Relief	Nivåskillnader	
Water in play	Vatten på spelfältet	
Exp. to wind	Vindutsatt	
Trees in play	Träd på spelfältet	

Scorecard Scorekort	Chp. Back tees	Mens Herrtee	Ladies Damtee
Length Längd	6242	5874	5094
Par	73	73	73
Slope system	—	135	125

Advised golfing ability Rekommenderad spelnivå — 0 12 24 36

Hcp required Hcp erfordrad — 36

CLUB HOUSE & AMENITIES — KLUBBHUS OCH OMGIVNING — 8/10

Pro shop Pro shop
Driving range Träningsbana
Sheltered tak 2 mats - On grass på gräs yes - Putting-green putting-green yes (3) - Pitching-green pitching-green yes (2)

HOTEL FACILITIES — HOTELL OMGIVNING — 6/10

HOTELS HOTELL

Grand Hotel - 307 rooms, D SKr 4400 - Stockholm 20 km
Tel (46) 08 - 679 3500, Fax (46) 08 - 611 8606

First Hotel Reisen - Stockholm 20 km
144 rooms, D SKr 2543
Tel (46) 08 - 223 260, Fax (46) 08 - 201 559

City Hotel Slöjdgatan - Stockholm 20 km
292 rooms, D SKr 1900
Tel (46) 08 - 723 72 00, Fax (46) 08 - 723 72 09

RESTAURANTS RESTAURANGER

Paul and Norbert - Stockholm 20 km - Tel (46) 08 - 661 72 36
Franska Matsalen - Stockholm 20 km - Tel (46) 08 - 679 3584
Clas På Hörnet - Stockholm 20 km - Tel (46) 08 - 165 130

Hills

18 | 8 | 6

Detta är det dyraste golfbaneprojektet någonsin i Sverige, och då duger det inte med några halvdana lösningar. Ägarna kallade in Arthur Hills, en av de mest välmeriterade arkitekterna i USA, men som i Europa bara har ritat Oitavos i Portugal och den ännu inte öppnade Sands GC utanför Jönköping. Hills medarbetare Steve Forrest har varit en nyckelperson i arbetet med banan, som äar utlagd i en gigantisk tallskog, där träden tillsammans med ett antal klippor ständigt är i spel. Banan är relativt kuperad (golfbil rekommenderas), med väl synliga hinder från varje tee. Ofta är utslagsplatserna upphöjda över lågt placerade fairways, som sedan stiger högre och högre ju närmare greenen vi kommer – det här är amerikansk "målgolf" i den djupaste svenska skogen. Beroende på vilken tee du peggar upp på kan banan i princip göras ospelbar, men valmöjligheterna (sju utslagsplatser) gör också detta till ett väldigt underhållande test. En ovanlig men väldigt imponerande layout där den mindre skicklige golfaren bara kan hoppas att han en dag kommer bli bättre!

This course is the most expensive golfing venture ever undertaken in Sweden. The promoters called in Arthur Hills, one of today's most prominent architects in the United States but whose work in Europe has been Oitavos in Portugal and the future Sand GC at Jönköping. His collaborator Steve Forrest was the king-pin of this project laid out in a huge pine forest where the trees, together with a number of salient rocks are always in play. Rather hilly (buggy recommended), it clearly shows its difficulties from the tee that are often elevated and overlook a plunging fairway which then sweeps up to even higher greens, i.e. US-style target golf in a Swedish forest. Depending on the tees you play, this course is such a brute at times that it can prove virtually impossible, but the choice of tee-boxes (as many as 7 per hole) make it a versatile test of golf. An uncommon and impressive layout where the less experienced golfer can hope only to get better one day.

Hills Golf Club — 2005

Hills väg
S - 431 90 MÖLNDAL

Office	Sekretariat	(46) 031 - 873 636
Pro shop	Pro shop	(46) 031 - 873 636
Fax	Fax	(46) 031 - 873 635
Web	www.hillsgolfclub.se	
Situation	Läge	Mölndal, 8 km
Göteborg, 20 km		
Annual closure	Årlig stängning	no
Weekly closure	Daglig stängning	no

Fees main season Tariff hög säsong	18 holes	
	Week days Veckodag	**We/Bank holidays** Lör/Söndag/Helgdag
Individual Individuellt	SKr 675	SKr 875
Couple Par	SKr 1350	SKr 1750

Green-fee includes buggy /
Access limited for visitors (book in advance)

Caddie Caddie no — **Electric Trolley** El vagn no
Buggy Golfbil yes — **Clubs** Klubbor yes

Credit cards Kredit kort
VISA - Eurocard - MasterCard - AMEX

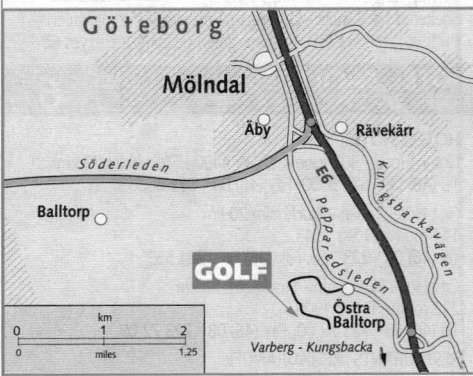

Access Tillfart : Göteborg, E20 South. Exit Torrekulamuttet. Follow signs towards Balltorp, turn left at second turnabout.
Map 1 on page 1212 Karta 1 se sid: 1212

GOLF COURSE — BANA — 18/20

Site	Läge	
Maintenance	Underhåll	
Architect	Arkitekt	Arthur Hills, Steve Forrest
Type	Karaktär	forest, parkland
Relief	Nivåskillnader	
Water in play	Vatten på spelfältet	
Exp. to wind	Vindutsatt	
Trees in play	Träd på spelfältet	

Scorecard Scorekort	**Chp.** Back tees	**Mens** Herrtee	**Ladies** Damtee
Length Längd	7071	6138	4711
Par	72	72	72
Slope system	—	—	—

Advised golfing ability Rekommenderad spelnivå — 0 12 24 36
Hcp required Hcp erfordrad — 32

CLUB HOUSE & AMENITIES — KLUBBHUS OCH OMGIVNING — 8/10

Pro shop Pro shop
Driving range Träningsbana
Sheltered tak yes - On grass på gräs yes - Putting-green putting-green yes - Pitching-green pitching-green yes

HOTEL FACILITIES — HOTELL OMGIVNING — 6/10

HOTELS HOTELL

Elite Plaza - 143 rooms, D from SKr 1800 - Göteborg 20 km
Tel (46) 031 - 720 40 00, Fax (46) 031 - 720 40 10

Eggers - 67 rooms, D SKr 2100 - Göteborg 20 km
Tel (46) 031 - 333 44 40, Fax (46) 031 - 333 44 49

Novotel Göteborg - Göteborg 20 km
145 rooms, D SKr 1520
Tel (46) 031 - 720 22 00, Fax (46) 031 - 720 22 99

RESTAURANTS RESTAURANGER

Sjömagasinet - Göteborg 20 km - Tel (46) 031 - 775 59 20
Hos Pelle - Göteborg 20 km - Tel (46) 031 - 121 031
Lilla London - Göteborg 20 km - Tel (46) 031 - 184 062

Jönköping

16 | 6 | 7

Staden är en bra start för en resa runt Vättern, Sveriges näst största sjö, berömd för sitt kalla, klara och för all del stormiga vatten när vinden ligger på. Bara några minuter söder om staden ligger banan i en kuperad terräng med ett charmerande klubbhus i centrum. Med dagens mått mätt är den ganska kort, och här kan faktiskt även vardagshackaren hoppas på att träffa parfyrorna på två slag. Problemet är att man sällan får ett rakt läge utan ständigt står i sluttningar. På så vis är Jönköping ingen lätt nöt att knäcka, framför allt som de flesta hinder finns runt de väldesignade och snabba greenerna. De spelare med bra teknik och ett smart huvud på axlarna har en stor fördel. Trevligt är också att alla spelare, oavsett skicklighet, kan spela med varandra och ha stort utbyte av rundan – vilket inte är så vanligt som man kanske tror. Jönköping är ett bra exempel på att längd faktiskt inte är allt. En hel del förändringar har gjorts med bunkrarna, vilket förenklat banan för höghandicaparen och gjort det svårare för den bättre spelaren.

This little town is the starting point for trips around the Vättern, Sweden's second largest lake known for its clear and cold water. Just a few minutes to the south of the town, this 18-hole course is laid out over hilly terrain around a charming club-house. Today it might be considered very short, where even the average hacker can hope to hit the longest par 4s in two. But like everyone else, they won't often find flat lies from where to hit the next shot. In fact, Jönköpings is all the more dangerous because of its shortness; most of the difficulties lie on and around the greens, which are excellent and well-designed putting surfaces given. The wily technicians and players with brawn and brain in good working order will probably score better than the rest. Players of all abilities can happily play together, a fun factor that is less frequent than one might think. Changes made to the very many bunkers here have made the course easier for high-handicappers and tougher for the better players.

Jönköpings Golfklubb — 1938

Kettilstorp
S - 556 27 JÖNKÖPING

Office Sekretariat (46) 036 - 765 67
Pro shop Pro shop (46) 036 - 763 90
Fax Fax (46) 036 - 765 11
Web www.golf.se/jonkopingsgk
Situation Läge Jönköping, 3 km
Annual closure Årlig stängning no
Weekly closure Daglig stängning no

Fees main season Tariff hög säsong	Full day	
	Week days Veckodag	We/Bank holidays Lör/Söndag/Helgdag
Individual Individuellt	SKr 300	SKr 350
Couple Par	SKr 600	SKr 700

Juniors: – 50% / Booking one day before play

Caddie Caddie no — **Electric Trolley** El vagn no
Buggy Golfbil no — **Clubs** Klubbor yes
Credit cards Kredit kort
VISA - Eurocard - MasterCard

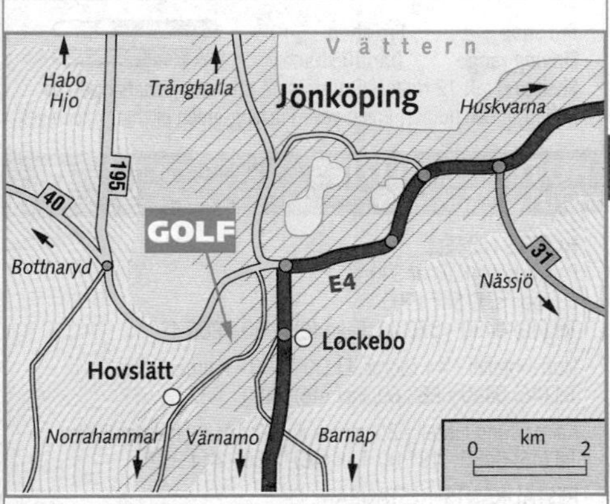

Access Tillfart : Jönköping R40 → Göteborg. Exit Kettilstorp.
Map 1 on page 1212 Karta 1 se sid: 1212

GOLF COURSE — BANA 16/20

Site Läge
Maintenance Underhåll
Architect Arkitekt Frank Dyer
Type Karaktär parkland
Relief Nivåskillnader
Water in play Vatten på spelfältet
Exp. to wind Vindutsatt
Trees in play Träd på spelfältet

Scorecard Scorekort	Chp. Back tees	Mens Herrtee	Ladies Damtee
Length Längd	5564	5313	4717
Par	70	70	70
Slope system	—	123	123

Advised golfing ability Rekommenderad spelnivå 0 12 24 36
Hcp required Hcp erfordrad 30 Men, 30 Ladies

CLUB HOUSE & AMENITIES — KLUBBHUS OCH OMGIVNING 6/10

Pro shop Pro shop
Driving range Träningsbana
Sheltered tak 15 mats - On grass på gräs no, 15 mats open air - Putting-green putting-green yes - Pitching-green pitching-green yes

HOTEL FACILITIES — HOTELL OMGIVNING 7/10

HOTELS HOTELL
Stora Hotellet - Jönköping 3 km
114 rooms, D SKr 1495
Tel (46) 036 - 100 000, Fax (46) 036 - 719 320

John Bauer - Jönköping 3 km
100 rooms, D SKr 1490 (w. GFee)
Tel (46) 036 - 349 000

RESTAURANTS RESTAURANGER
Trottoaren - Jönköping 3 km
Tel (46) 036 - 100 000

Esters Restaurang - Jönköping 3 km
Tel (46) 036 - 349 000

Kalmar

15	5	8

Bron mellan Öland och Kalmar betyder numera att du kan spela Ekerum och Kalmar på samma dag, eller varför inte trycka in två rundor i Kalmar? Här finns nämligen två utmärkta banor. Mästerskapsbanan är resultatet av elva hål från den gamla banan, byggd 1947, och sju hål från den nya banan som öppnade 1992. Låt vara att många tyckte det var ett helgerån att blanda nytt och gammalt när så gjordes, men bortsett från några av de nya greenerna har det blivit en lyckad mix. Hålen smälter perfekt in i varandra. Från klubbhuset tittar du ut över Östersjön, och på första hålet spelar du till och med över vattnet. Efter ettan får du vara beredd på att alla klubbor kommer i spel om du vill undvika hinderna, dit ett antal strategiskt placerade träd får räknas. På Kalmar gäller det att hålla sig borta från skogen. Av största betydelse är att tänka innan du slår och att använda dig av de resurser du har för dagen, en bra teknik skadar förstås inte heller. Eftersom de flesta hinder syns tydligt från tee får du leta efter en annan ursäkt för en misslyckad score! De problem som man för inte så länge sedan hade med greenerna är nu glömda och åtgärdade.

This championship course is in fact a mix of 11 holes from the old course, created in 1947, with seven holes from the new course opened in 1992. Some saw this as plain sacrilege, but you have to admit that the two go together well. Now, the holes blend into each other in a perfect match. The whole complex magnificently overlooks the Baltic and the first hole is in fact played over water. The rest of the programme calls for every club in your bag, if only to avoid the hazards, which include some very dangerous trees. Here more than usual, if you keep long and straight you will be literally out of the woods. Course management is vital using whatever resources you have on that particular day, and good golfing technique. As all the difficulties are clearly in view, you will have to find another excuse for a bad score. The recent problems with the greens now seem to be forgotten.

Kalmar Golfklubb — 1947

Box 278
S - 391 23 KALMAR

Office	Sekretariat	(46) 0480 - 472 111
Pro shop	Pro shop	(46) 0480 - 472 049
Fax	Fax	(46) 0480 - 472 314
Web	www.kalmargk.se	
Situation	Läge	Kalmar, 8 km
Annual closure	Årlig stängning	no
Weekly closure	Daglig stängning	no

Fees main season Tariff hög säsong — Full day

	Week days Veckodag	We/Bank holidays Lör/Söndag/Helgdag
Individual Individuellt	SKr 300	SKr 350
Couple Par	SKr 480	SKr 560

2 adults + 2 children: SKr 380 and 620 (We)/Juniors SKr 140

Caddie Caddie no — **Electric Trolley** El vagn no

Buggy Golfbil yes — **Clubs** Klubbor yes

Credit cards Kredit kort
VISA - Eurocard - MasterCard - DC

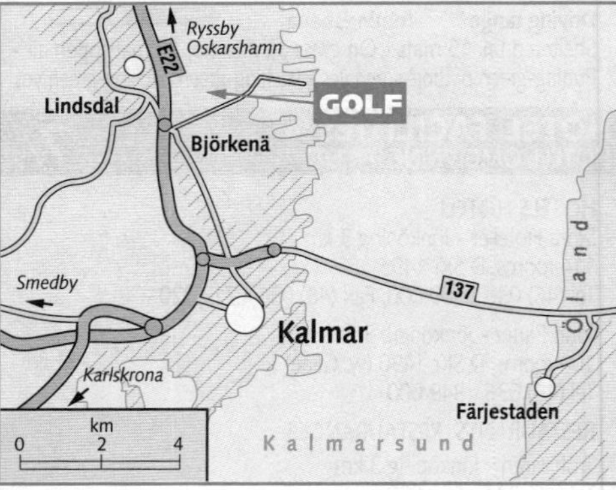

Access Tillfart : Kalmar E22 Exit Kalmar N/Lindsdal.
Map 1 on page 1213 Karta 1 se sid: 1213

GOLF COURSE — BANA — 15/20

Site	Läge	
Maintenance	Underhåll	
Architect	Arkitekt	Sundblom, Gierdsjö Nils Sköld, Sune Linde
Type	Karaktär	parkland
Relief	Nivåskillnader	
Water in play	Vatten på spelfältet	
Exp. to wind	Vindutsatt	
Trees in play	Träd på spelfältet	

Scorecard Scorekort	Chp. Back tees	Mens Herrtee	Ladies Damtee
Length Längd	6028	5685	4864
Par	72	72	72
Slope system	—	127	124

Advised golfing ability Rekommenderad spelnivå — 0 12 24 36

Hcp required Hcp erfordrad — 36

CLUB HOUSE & AMENITIES — KLUBBHUS OCH OMGIVNING — 5/10

Pro shop Pro shop
Driving range Träningsbana
Sheltered tak 12 mats - On grass på gräs no, 7 mats open air - Putting-green putting-green yes - Pitching-green pitching-green yes

HOTEL FACILITIES — HOTELL OMGIVNING — 8/10

HOTELS HOTELL
Packhuset - Kalmar 8 km
68 rooms, D SKr 1500
Tel (46) 0480 - 570 00, Fax (46) 0480 - 866 42

Slottshotellet - 44 rooms, D SKr 1590 - Kalmar 8 km
Tel (46) 0480 - 882 60, Fax (46) 0480 - 882 66

Kalmarsund Hotell - 85 rooms, D SKr 1415 - Kalmar 8 km
Tel (46) 0480 - 181 00, Fax (46) 0480 - 411 337

RESTAURANTS RESTAURANGER
Kalmar Hamnkrog - Kalmar 8 km - Tel (46) 0480 - 411 020
Matisse - Kalmar 8 km - Tel (46) 0480 - 272 86
Källaren Kronan - Kalmar 8 km - Tel (46) 0480 - 411 400

Karlshamn *Gamla Banan*

14	6	6

Detta är en historisk region, som har sett allt från en rysk ubåt stranda på klipporna till en 26 kilo tung lax fångas i Mörrum, kanske det mest välkända fiskecentret i Sverige. Banan är utlagd genom tät skog där det inte finns några som helst flyktvägar att hoppas på. Hemligheten är att ignorera träden, för faktum är att fairways är bredare än vad de verkar. Hur som helst, det har sin charm att rädda sig ur skogen, och det är även möjligt då ett stort arbete har lagts ned på att rensa undervegetationen. Nåväl, för den mer klaustrofobiske och snedslående golfaren är kanske inte "charm" det rätta ordet. Han kommer att få det svårt att slappna av och njuta av spelet. Men det är heller ingen idé att vara överdrivet försiktig från tee eftersom detta bara leder till långa andraslag in mot greener som på sina ställen vaktas av djupa och rymningssäkra bunkrar. Greenerna har också sin historia: Många är upphöjda eller ligger precis intill sluttningar vilket kräver ett taktiskt sinne då det inte alltid går att rulla in bollen. Det sägs att efter en runda här så drömmer du i veckor om stora, vackra träd. Ytterligare en 18-hålsbana har precis öppnat, men en hel del arbete återstår innan den är färdig.

Close to Mörrum, one of the great fishery centres in Sweden, this course was laid out through a forest, from which there is no escaping on virtually every hole. The secret is to try to ignore it, as the fairways are wider than they look. And anyway, it's such fun hitting recovery shots from out of the trees. The more claustrophobic golfer or wayward hitter will find it hard to relax and really hit the ball here. Being over-careful off the tee will often lead to a very long second shot, which will have to avoid some deep and distinctly inescapable greenside bunkers. The greens are often elevated or at the bottom of a hill; this calls for careful thinking and often rules out the bump and run shot. They say that after playing here you spend the next few weeks dreaming about big beautiful trees. Another 18-hole course has just been opened but has yet to achieve the challenge of this layout.

Karlshamns Golfklubb — 1966

Box 188
S - 374 23 KARLSHAMN

Office	Sekretariat	(46) 0454 - 500 85
Pro shop	Pro shop	(46) 0454 - 541 41
Fax	Fax	(46) 0454 - 501 60
Web	www.karlshamnsgk.com	
Situation	Läge	Karlshamn, 7 km
Annual closure	Årlig stängning	no
Weekly closure	Daglig stängning	no

Fees main season Tariff hög säsong	18 holes	
	Week days Veckodag	We/Bank holidays Lör/Söndag/Helgdag
Individual Individuellt	SKr 320	SKr 320
Couple Par	SKr 640	SKr 640

Juniors: – 50% / Full week: SKr 1600 (800 for juniors)

Caddie Caddie no — Electric Trolley El vagn no
Buggy Golfbil no — Clubs Klubbor yes
Credit cards Kredit kort
VISA - Eurocard - MasterCard

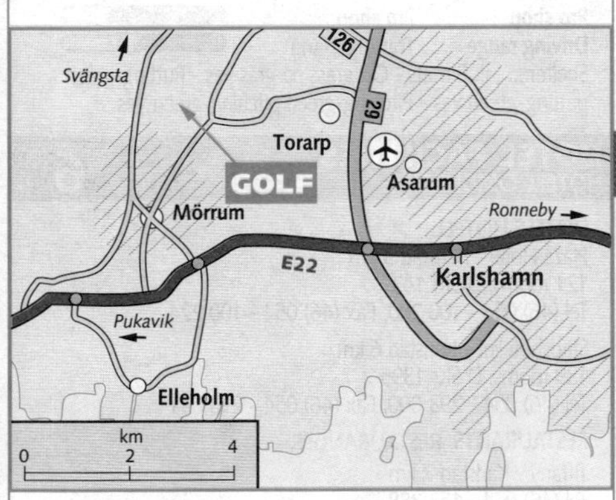

Access Tillfart : Karlshamn E22 → Kristianstad. Mörrum, R29. Golf north of Mörrum.
Map 1 on page 1213 Karta 1 se sid: 1213

GOLF COURSE — BANA — 14/20

Site	Läge	
Maintenance	Underhåll	
Architect	Arkitekt	Douglas Brasier
Type	Karaktär	forest, parkland
Relief	Nivåskillnader	
Water in play	Vatten på spelfältet	
Exp. to wind	Vindutsatt	
Trees in play	Träd på spelfältet	

Scorecard Scorekort	Chp. Back tees	Mens Herrtee	Ladies Damtee
Length Längd	6035	5703	4908
Par	72	72	72
Slope system	—	139	133

Advised golfing ability / Rekommenderad spelnivå: 0 12 24 36
Hcp required / Hcp erfordrad: 36

CLUB HOUSE & AMENITIES — KLUBBHUS OCH OMGIVNING — 6/10

Pro shop — Pro shop
Driving range — Träningsbana
Sheltered tak 2 mats - On grass på gräs yes - Putting-green putting-green yes - Pitching-green pitching-green no

HOTEL FACILITIES — HOTELL OMGIVNING — 6/10

HOTELS HOTELL
First Hotel Karlshamn - Karlshamn 7 km
132 rooms, D SKr 1353
Tel (46) 0454 - 890 00, Fax (46) 0454 - 891 50

Scandic Hotell Karlshamn - Karlshamn 7 km
132 rooms, D SKr 1500
Tel (46) 0454 - 588 700, Fax (46) 0454 - 588 711

RESTAURANTS RESTAURANGER
Lord Nelson - Karlshamn 7 km
Tel (46) 0454 - 845 35

Loch Ness - Karlshamn 7 km
Tel (46) 0454 - 126 00

Gourmet Grön - Karlshamn 7 km - Tel (46) 0454 - 164 40

1243

Karlstad

15 | 7 | 6

Detta är i hjärtat av Värmland – ett landskap av skogar, forsar, sjöar, små bondgårdar och härliga måltider. Det var också hemvist för Selma Lagerlöf, författaren till Nils Holgerssons underbara resor, som är en fantastisk hyllning till Sverige. Lagerlöfs hus ligger mindre än en timmes resa från banan, som vindlar genom lummig skog och är en njutning för den som gillar vildmarksliv, något som kan skänka tröst åt den som olyckligtvis inte har någon av sina bästa dagar, vilket är lätt hänt här om man inte driver bollen bra från tee. Banan är mycket lång, och på vår och höst är den ofta blöt och tung. Då är många av par 4-hålen svåra att nå även för den bättre spelaren. Men Karlstad är inte bara skog, det finns också relativt öppna partier, vilket vi är tacksamma för. Flertalet av greenerna är dock väldigt svårlästa, och troligen är banan relativt sett svårare för låghandicaparen än för höghandicaparen som inte behöver träffa varje green på rätt antal slag. Om du kan låta bli att stressa upp dig över resultatet så får du en ljuvlig och avslappnad dag på en bana som på ett väldigt fint sätt smälter in i omgivningarna. Och varför inte ta en lektion av Henry Reis, Annika Sörenstams tränare...? Och därefter avsluta med en massage i klubbhusets spa.

This is the capital of Värmland, a landscape of forests, streams, lakes, small farms and rich food (sausage, roast pork with oat mash). It is also the region of Selma Lagerlöf, the author of The Travels of Nils Holgersson. Karlstad runs through a forest and is a real treat for lovers of wildlife, which can offer some solace and compensation for the disappointing score they might have to settle for here, unless they are hitting their driver really well. The course is very long, wet outside summer, and some of the par 4s are hard to reach, even for the better player. Yet its openness works in its favour. In actual fact, the lower handicap golfer is more likely to suffer here than the lesser golfer. If you can keep your mind off worrying about carding a good score, you can enjoy a great round. Or take a lesson with the headpro, Henry Reis, Annika Sörenstam's teacher.

Karlstad Golfklubb — 1958

Höja 510
S - 655 92 KARLSTAD

Office	Sekretariat	(46) 054 - 86 6 353
Pro shop	Pro shop	(46) 054 - 866 270
Fax	Fax	(46) 054 - 866 478
Web	www.karlstadgk.com	
Situation	Läge	Karlstad, 8 km
Annual closure	Årlig stängning	no
Weekly closure	Daglig stängning	no
Fees main season	Tariff hög säsong	Full day

	Week days / Veckodag	We/Bank holidays / Lör/Söndag/Helgdag
Individual Individuellt	SKr 280	SKr 320
Couple Par	SKr 560	SKr 640

Juniors: – 50% / Booking two days in advance

Caddie Caddie no **Electric Trolley** El vagn no

Buggy Golfbil yes **Clubs** Klubbor yes

Credit cards Kredit kort
VISA - Eurocard - MasterCard - DC

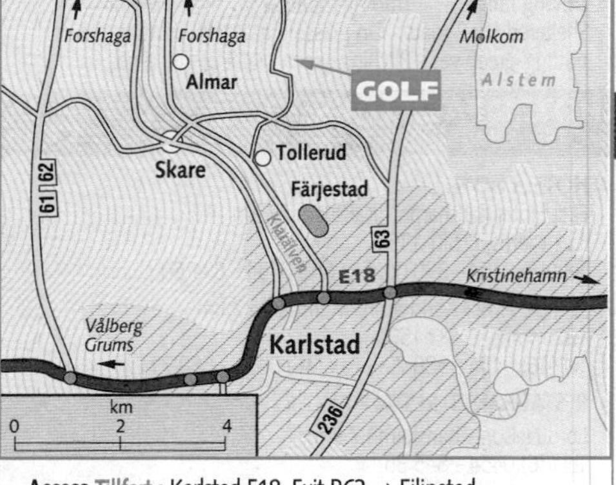

Access Tillfart : Karlstad E18. Exit R63 → Filipstad.
4 km → Golf

Map 2 on page 1214 Karta 2 se sid: 1214

GOLF COURSE — BANA — 15/20

Site	Läge	
Maintenance	Underhåll	
Architect	Arkitekt	Nils Sköld, Sune Linde
Type	Karaktär	forest, parkland
Relief	Nivåskillnader	
Water in play	Vatten på spelfältet	
Exp. to wind	Vindutsatt	
Trees in play	Träd på spelfältet	

Scorecard / Scorekort	Chp. / Back tees	Mens / Herrtee	Ladies / Damtee
Length Längd	6215	5985	5060
Par	72	72	72
Slope system	—	131	130

Advised golfing ability Rekommenderad spelnivå: 0 12 24 36

Hcp required Hcp erfordrad 36

CLUB HOUSE & AMENITIES — KLUBBHUS OCH OMGIVNING — 7/10

Pro shop Pro shop
Driving range Träningsbana
Sheltered tak 8 mats - On grass på gräs yes - Putting-green putting-green yes - Pitching-green pitching-green yes

HOTEL FACILITIES — HOTELL OMGIVNING — 6/10

HOTELS HOTELL

Plaza Hotel - Karlstad 5 km
121 rooms, D SKr 1439
Tel (46) 054 - 100 200, Fax (46) 054 - 100 224

Stadshotellet - Karlstad 6 km
139 rooms, D SKr 1395
Tel (46) 054 - 293 000, Fax (46) 054 - 293 031

RESTAURANTS RESTAURANGER

Tiffany - Karlstad 7 km
Tel (46) 054 - 153 388

Vivaldi - Karlstad 5 km
Tel (46) 054 - 100 200

Knistad

15	7	7

Alldeles intill "Sveriges bästa konferenshotell", och bokstavligen talat mitt emellan Vänern och Vättern, ligger Knistad i ett underbart, pittoreskt landskap. Banan är relativt kuperad, men är ändå lätt att promenera, vilket kan vara skönt att veta eftersom dina krafter behövs för att skicka bollen högt upp i luften för att komma åt de många upphöjda och trixiga greenerna. Fast målet med banans design var inte att bygga ett allt för svårt test, utan att göra en bana som är spelbar för alla, en familjebana. För att nå ett bra resultat är det en fördel om du inte gapar efter allt för mycket... 78 bunkrar och en besvärlig tjockruff bestraffar den som är vild från tee. Även om Knistad kanske saknar ett riktigt signaturhål är banan rolig och avkopplande att spela, och passar alla dem som har kommit hit för att också jobba och konferera en smula.

Virtually midway between the lakes of Vänern and Vättern, the Knistad course lies next to "the best seminar hotel in Sweden" in a wonderfully picturesque and romantic setting. It is rather hilly but never tiring, and so much the better because you will need all your strength to hit some high balls into a number of elevated greens that are invariably tricky and sharply contoured. Yet the goal here was not to build too tough a test and the course is playable by everyone, including the whole family. When it comes down to it, you are better off not being too greedy as 78 bunkers and wicked rough await any wildly-hit ball. Fun to play, Knistad maybe lacks a signature hole but is a pretty relaxing day's golf, which will suit all those who come here to do a bit of work.

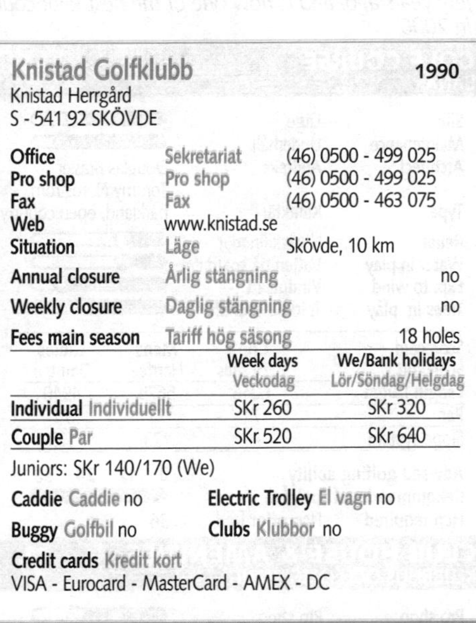

Knistad Golfklubb — 1990

Knistad Herrgård
S - 541 92 SKÖVDE

Office	Sekretariat	(46) 0500 - 499 025
Pro shop	Pro shop	(46) 0500 - 499 025
Fax	Fax	(46) 0500 - 463 075
Web	www.knistad.se	
Situation	Läge	Skövde, 10 km
Annual closure	Årlig stängning	no
Weekly closure	Daglig stängning	no

Fees main season / Tariff hög säsong	18 holes	
	Week days / Veckodag	We/Bank holidays / Lör/Söndag/Helgdag
Individual Individuellt	SKr 260	SKr 320
Couple Par	SKr 520	SKr 640

Juniors: SKr 140/170 (We)

Caddie Caddie no — Electric Trolley El vagn no

Buggy Golfbil no — Clubs Klubbor no

Credit cards Kredit kort
VISA - Eurocard - MasterCard - AMEX - DC

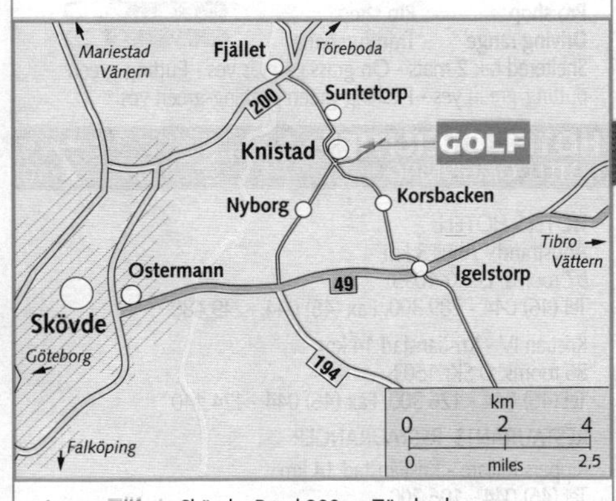

Access Tillfart : Skövde, Road 200 → Töreboda. Follow signs to golf

Map 1 on page 1212 Karta 1 se sid: 1212

GOLF COURSE — BANA — 15/20

Site	Läge	
Maintenance	Underhåll	
Architect	Arkitekt	Jeremy Turner
Type	Karaktär	parkland, hilly, open country
Relief	Nivåskillnader	
Water in play	Vatten på spelfältet	
Exp. to wind	Vindutsatt	
Trees in play	Träd på spelfältet	

Scorecard / Scorekort	Chp. / Back tees	Mens / Herrtee	Ladies / Damtee
Length Längd	6035	5745	4775
Par	72	72	72
Slope system	122	122	127

Advised golfing ability / Rekommenderad spelnivå: 0 12 24 36

Hcp required / Hcp erfordrad: 36

CLUB HOUSE & AMENITIES — KLUBBHUS OCH OMGIVNING — 7/10

Pro shop	Pro shop
Driving range	Träningsbana

Sheltered tak 14 mats - On grass på gräs yes - Putting-green putting-green yes - Pitching-green pitching-green yes

HOTEL FACILITIES — HOTELL OMGIVNING — 7/10

HOTELS HOTELL

Knistad Herrgård - 79 rooms, D SKr 1700 - on site
Tel (46) 0500 - 463 170, Fax (46) 0500 - 463 075

Mariestad Stadshotellet - Mariestad 45 km
29 rooms, D from SKr 850
Tel (46) 0501 - 138 00, Fax (46) 0501 - 776 40

Moholms Herrgård - 8 rooms, ask for prices - Moholm 28 km
Tel (46) 0506 - 220 500, Fax (46) 0506 - 220 60

RESTAURANTS RESTAURANGER

Moholms Herrgård - Moholm 28 km - Tel (46) 0506 - 220 500

Knistad Herrgård - on site
Tel (46) 0500 - 463 170

Kristianstad

17 | 7 | 7

Detta är jordbruksland i ett långsamt böljande landskap, och den topografin återspeglar sig också i banan. Kristianstad ligger inte långt från havet – sandjorden och layouten påminner också om en links-bana, fast i själva verket befinner vi oss i ett parklandskap. Många greener närmar man sig bäst med låga rullslag, framför allt de dagar när vinden ligger på. Banan ändrar gång på gång karaktär, såvä visuellt som rent strategiskt. Ibland är den vänlig, ibland direkt fientlig. Nyckelhålen är 14-16 – massor med vatten kommer i spel och en otålig själ riskerar att bestraffas hårt. De här hindema ska dock inte hindra höghandicaparen från att spela här. Banan genomgick för några år sedan en omfattande renovering, och utan tvekan till det bättre. Den är nu en av de konditionsmässigt bästa banorna i Sverige. En ny 18-hålsslinga kommer att öppna våren 2006.

Scania (Skåne) is the Swedish south, where there is a definite Danish influence, a logical enough state of affairs when you realize that Denmark only granted Sweden its natural maritime frontier in the early 18th century. Here, we are in farming country in a landscape of gently rolling valleys, and this course reflects the same topology. Located not far from the sea, the sandy soil and layout are reminiscent of a links course, although in reality the setting is one large park. The grass is wonderful and many of the greens can be reached with low running shots, a considerable advantage given how windy it can be here. The course changes faces time and time again, both visually and strategically, now friendly, now distinctly hostile. The key holes are 14 through 16, spectacular numbers with a lot of water where impatience can cost you dearly. These difficulties, however, should not prevent the higher-handicap golfers from playing here and rubbing shoulders with the better players. The course has been restyled a few years ago, and is now one of the best kept courses in Sweden. A second 18-hole course will be added in 2006.

Kristianstads Golfklubb — 1924

Box 41
S - 296 21 ÅHUS

Office	Sekretariat	(46) 044 - 247 656
Pro shop	Pro shop	(46) 044 - 247 429
Fax	Fax	(46) 044 - 247 635
Web	www.kristianstadsgk.com	
Situation	Läge	Kristianstad, 18 km
Annual closure	Årlig stängning	no
Weekly closure	Daglig stängning	no

Fees main season Tariff hög säsong		Full day
	Week days Veckodag	**We/Bank holidays** Lör/Söndag/Helgdag
Individual Individuellt	SKr 350	SKr 350
Couple Par	SKr 700	SKr 700

Juniors: SKr 200 / 36 holes: SKr 450

Caddie Caddie no **Electric Trolley** El vagn no

Buggy Golfbil yes **Clubs** Klubbor yes

Credit cards Kredit kort
VISA - Eurocard - MasterCard - AMEX - DC

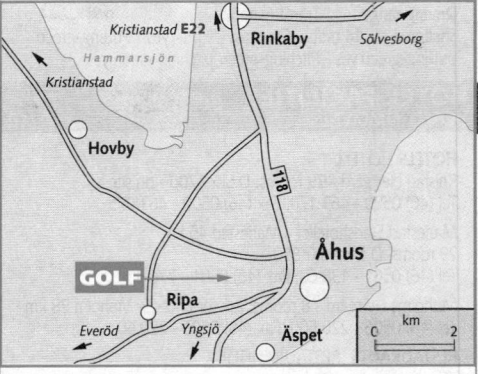

Access Tillfart : Malmö, E22 → Kristianstad. 118 → Åhus. Rondell i Åhus → Golf

Map 1 on page 1212 Karta 1 se sid: 1212

GOLF COURSE — BANA — 17/20

Site	Läge	
Maintenance	Underhåll	
Architect	Arkitekt	Douglas Brasier Tommy Nordström
Type	Karaktär	parkland, open country
Relief	Nivåskillnader	
Water in play	Vatten på spelfältet	
Exp. to wind	Vindutsatt	
Trees in play	Träd på spelfältet	

Scorecard Scorekort	**Chp.** Back tees	**Mens** Herrtee	**Ladies** Damtee
Length Längd	6046	5675	4940
Par	71	71	71
Slope system	—	123	123

Advised golfing ability Rekommenderad spelnivå — 0 12 24 36

Hcp required Hcp erfordrad 36

CLUB HOUSE & AMENITIES — KLUBBHUS OCH OMGIVNING — 7/10

Pro shop Pro shop

Driving range Träningsbana

Sheltered tak 2 mats - On grass på gräs yes - Putting-green putting-green yes - Pitching-green pitching-green yes

HOTEL FACILITIES — HOTELL OMGIVNING — 7/10

HOTELS HOTELL

Åhustrand - Åhus 3 km
57 rooms, D SKr 1095
Tel (46) 044 - 289 300, Fax (46) 044 - 249 480

Kristian IV - Kristianstad 14 km
86 rooms, D SKr 1503
Tel (46) 044 - 126 300, Fax (46) 044 - 124 140

RESTAURANTS RESTAURANGER

Kippers Källare - Kristianstad 14 km
Tel (46) 044 - 106 200

Kung Kristian - Kristianstad 14 km
Tel (46) 044 - 210 034

Kungliga Drottningholm

15	8	6

Drottningholms slott är arkitektoniskt en korsning mellan barock och neoklassisk stil, ett Versailles i miniatyr för en monarki som strävar mot enkelhet. På sommaren är teatern här en fantastisk plats för operauppsättningar. Kinaslottet och trädgårdarna är också värda ett besök. Nyligen har banan upphöjts till "Kunglig", men efter några rundor här så bjuds du inte på några nya överraskningar. Banan är en blandning av parkbanekaraktär och öppna landskap. Den är byggd av Sköld och Sundblom, och är en trevlig bekantskap för medelgolfaren och låghandicaparen. För den som hoppas på en riktigt bra score är Drottningholm en bra utmaning. Inte minst då en missad fairway omedelbart innebär ett besök i den tjocka ruffen eller i skogen. Vattenhinder kommer egentligen bara i spel på två av hålen, det femte och det 18e. Däremot är det viktigt att kunna skruva bollen från tee, framför allt på dogleghålen, om du inte vill ställas inför ett "blint" inspel. Några nya utslagsplatser har tillkommit, vilket kanske är en föraning om en större uppgradering. Spela här från midsommar och framåt när banan är i toppkondition.

Between Baroque and Neo-classical, Drottningholm Castle is a sort of unpretentious Château de Versailles for a monarchy that thrives on simplicity. In summer, the theatre here is a marvellous setting for operas, while the gardens are both well worth the visit. The course here has just recently been elevated to "Royal" seal status, but after a few rounds you will find nothing to really surprise you. The site is a blend of parkland and wide open space, as Swedish as the layout of Sköld and Sundblom. This course is pleasant to play for mid- and low-handicappers and a real challenge for golfers looking to card a low score, as a missed fairway can be very costly, especially on account of the trees and tall rough. The water hazards only really come into play on the 5 and 18th holes, while a number of tee-shots call for some bending of the ball, especially on the dog-leg holes (five of the par 4s), if you don't want to be left with a "blind" shot. Play here from mid-summer onwards when the course is in tip-top condition.

Kungliga Drottningholms Golfklubb — 1959

PL 183
S - 178 93 DROTTNINGHOLM

Office	Sekretariat	(46) 08 - 759 0085
Pro shop	Pro shop	(46) 08 - 759 0314
Fax	Fax	(46) 08 - 759 0851
Web	www.drgk.nu	
Situation	Läge	Stockholm, 25 km
Annual closure	Årlig stängning	no
Weekly closure	Daglig stängning	no

Fees main season Tariff hög säsong — Full day

	Week days Veckodag	We/Bank holidays Lör/Söndag/Helgdag
Individual Individuellt	SKr 450	SKr 450
Couple Par	SKr 900	SKr 900

Juniors: – 50%

Caddie Caddie no — **Electric Trolley** El vagn no

Buggy Golfbil no — **Clubs** Klubbor yes

Credit cards Kredit kort
VISA - Eurocard - MasterCard

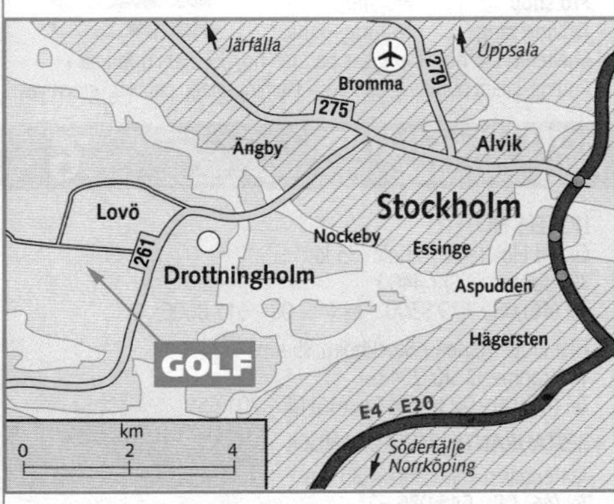

Access Tillfart : Stockholm, Drottningholmsvägen. → Slottet. Exit Lovö Kyrka. 300 m → Golf

Map 2 on page 1214 Karta 2 se sid: 1214

GOLF COURSE — BANA — 15/20

Site	Läge	
Maintenance	Underhåll	
Architect	Arkitekt	Rafael Sundblom Nils Sköld
Type	Karaktär	parkland
Relief	Nivåskillnader	
Water in play	Vatten på spelfältet	
Exp. to wind	Vindutsatt	
Trees in play	Träd på spelfältet	

Scorecard Scorekort	Chp. Back tees	Mens Herrtee	Ladies Damtee
Length Längd	6125	5745	5040
Par	71	71	71
Slope system	—	130	123

Advised golfing ability Rekommenderad spelnivå — 0 12 24 36

Hcp required Hcp erfordrad — 28 Men, 30 Ladies

CLUB HOUSE & AMENITIES — KLUBBHUS OCH OMGIVNING — 8/10

Pro shop Pro shop

Driving range Träningsbana

Sheltered tak yes - On grass på gräs no, 25 mats open air
Putting-green putting-green yes - Pitching-green pitching-green yes

HOTEL FACILITIES — HOTELL OMGIVNING — 6/10

HOTELS HOTELL

Grand Hotel - Stockholm 25 km
307 rooms, D SKr 4400
Tel (46) 08 - 679 3500, Fax (46) 08 - 611 8606

Diplomat Hotel - Stockholm 25 km
128 rooms, D SKr 2445
Tel (46) 08 - 459 68 00, Fax (46) 08 - 459 68 20

First Hotel Reisen - 144 rooms, D SKr 2543 - Stockholm 25 km
Tel (46) 08 - 223 260, Fax (46) 08 - 201 559

RESTAURANTS RESTAURANGER

Fredsgatan 12 - Stockholm 25 km - Tel (46) 08 - 248 052
Franska Matsalen - Stockholm 25 km - Tel (46) 08 - 679 3584
Operakällaren - Stockholm 25 km - Tel (46) 08 - 676 58 00

Kungsängen (European Tour Club) 17 | 8 | 6

Den här anläggningen, som också kallas för Kungsängen, består av 36 hål – den kortare slingan heter Queen's Course och den längre slingan heter King's Course, som vi avhandlar här. King's Course designades av Anders Forsbrand och målsättningarna var två: Dels skulle det bli en mästerskapsbana, dels skulle den vara spelbar för oss amatörer som i slutändan betalar kalaset. Detta är en mycket lång bana, kuperad och väldigt tekniskt krävande. King's är knappast en bana för den med ett högt handicap, du måste ha under 23, eller som bara spelar golf för att få gå ut och gå i naturen. Å andra sidan, golfare som letar efter en utmaning som testar deras tålamod och förmåga att scora väl ska definitivt åka hit. Några av hålen är rent layout-mässigt mindre lyckade, andra är helt magnifika. Landningsområdena, tidigare ordentligt kritiserade, har gjorts bredare, och banan har nu nått full mognad, en utveckling som naturligtvis är föranledd av att Scandinavian Masters spelas här när Europatouren kommer på besök till Stockholm. Fem nya utslagsplatser har adderat, och såväl klubbhus som restaurang har renoverats.

This golf comprises two courses, of which the Queen's Course is on the short side, and the King's the one we are reviewing here. It was designed by Anders Forsbrand with a view to becoming a championship course, but it shouldn't be forgotten that week in, week out, it is we amateurs who play and pay. This very long layout is technically demanding and very hilly: as there are neither carts nor caddies, it takes a fit golfer to enjoy playing here... and a handicap of lower than 23. However, the landing zone for drives have been enlarged. Golfers who look to test their patience and their ability to score well, work on their strategy or develop their technique, must play this course. While they may dispute the golfing spirit of some holes, others are simply excellent. This course is reaching full maturity and the regular hosting of the Scandinavian Masters when the European Tour comes to Stockholm has done a great deal to help its development. Five new tee-boxes have been opened and the clubhouse and restaurant have been renovated.

Kungsängen GC (European Tour Club) 1992

Box 133
S - 196 21 KUNGSÄNGEN

Office	Sekretariat	(46) 08 - 584 507 30
Pro shop	Pro shop	(46) 08 - 584 507 31
Fax	Fax	(46) 08 - 584 710 02
Web	www.kungsangengc.se	
Situation	Läge	Stockholm, 25 km
Annual closure	Årlig stängning	no
Weekly closure	Daglig stängning	no

Fees main season Tariff hög säsong	Full day	
	Week days Veckodag	We/Bank holidays Lör/Söndag/Helgdag
Individual Individuellt	SKr 600	SKr 600
Couple Par	SKr 1200	SKr 1200

Juniors: – 50%

Caddie Caddie no | **Electric Trolley** El vagn no
Buggy Golfbil yes | **Clubs** Klubbor yes

Credit cards Kredit kort
VISA - Eurocard - MasterCard - AMEX - DC

Access Tillfart : Stockholm, E18 → Enköping.
Exit Tibble/Brunna. → Golf
Map 2 on page 1214 Karta 2 se sid: 1214

GOLF COURSE 17/20
BANA

Site	Läge	
Maintenance	Underhåll	
Architect	Arkitekt	Anders Forsbrand
Type	Karaktär	forest, hilly
Relief	Nivåskillnader	
Water in play	Vatten på spelfältet	
Exp. to wind	Vindutsatt	
Trees in play	Träd på spelfältet	

Scorecard Scorekort	Chp. Back tees	Mens Herrtee	Ladies Damtee
Length Längd	6248	5784	4827
Par	72	72	72
Slope system	—	143	131

Advised golfing ability 0 12 24 36
Rekommenderad spelnivå
Hcp required Hcp erfordrad 22 Men/30 Ladies

CLUB HOUSE & AMENITIES 8/10
KLUBBHUS OCH OMGIVNING

Pro shop Pro shop
Driving range Träningsbana
Sheltered tak no - On grass på gräs no, 35 mats open air -
Putting-green putting-green yes - Pitching-green pitching-green yes

HOTEL FACILITIES 6/10
HOTELL OMGIVNING

HOTELS HOTELL
Grand Hotel - Stockholm 35 km
307 rooms, D SKr 4400
Tel (46) 08 - 679 3500, Fax (46) 08 - 611 8606

First Hotel Reisen - Stockholm 35 km
144 rooms, D SKr 2543
Tel (46) 08 - 223 260, Fax (46) 08 - 201 559

RESTAURANTS RESTAURANGER
Teatergrillen - Stockholm 35 km
Tel (46) 08 - 545 035 62
Ocean - Stockholm 35 km
Tel (46) 08 - 652 4090
Franska Matsalen - Stockholm 35 km - Tel (46) 08 - 679 3584

Kungsbacka

15 | 6 | 6

Banan öppnade 1974, arkitekten heter Frank Pennink, och det finns ingen som helst anledning varför du skulle spela dåligt här, inte med tanke på att här finns ett magnifikt övningsfält, tre puttinggreener och fyra pitchinggreener... Men, men – banan är en sällsynt tuff nöt att knäcka, med flera olika typer av golf. Till en början spelar vi i ett parklandskap, sedan övergår det till golf med seasidekänsla och därefter golf i tät, ogenomtränglig skog. Den trånga avslutningen där vinden torkar upp greenerna och gör dem hårda är en alldeles egen historia, inte minst med tanke på hur svårt det är att få bollen att stanna kvar på det finklippta. Svårigheten ligger alltså i att ställa om från att ha försökt lura vinden med låga slag till att spela klassisk målgolf med höga slag. Detta är ett riktigt nervtest! Två nya bäckar gör det inte lättare. För höghandicaparen kan det bli lite väl mycket av det goda, om han nu inte förmår att ta det med jämnmod och inse att han ännu har mycket att lära. Har han den distansen kan han mycket väl spela Kungsbacka. Sex av hålen har nya greenområden, med mindre bunkrar och brantare kanter. Ungefär som i Skottland, det blir roligare så !

Firstly you have to adjust to some abrupt changes of surroundings, from parkland to seaboard to forest. You start off over wide open space and end up down a narrow strait where the wind can twist and turn, dry the greens and make those approach shots even tougher. From the roll-on shots by the sea you then have to change modes to target golf. For the nerves, nothing is simple here, especially since the last section of the course is the most demanding. High-handicappers will be hard pushed to keep up with the better players, and two new creeks does not make it any easier, though. Yet if they can take it like a man and realize willingly that they still have much to learn, then there's no reason why they should not play here. On six holes the areas around the greens have been restyled with smaller bunkers and steeper mounds, just like in Scotland. More fun that way.

Kungsbacka Golfklubb — 1974

Hamra Gård 515
S - 429 44 SÄRÖ

Office	Sekretariat	(46) 031 - 938 181
Pro shop	Pro shop	(46) 031 - 938 189
Fax	Fax	(46) 031 - 938 170
Web	www.kbgk.org	
Situation	Läge	Göteborg, 25 km
Annual closure	Årlig stängning	no
Weekly closure	Daglig stängning	no

Fees main season Tariff hög säsong	18 holes	
	Week days Veckodag	**We/Bank holidays** Lör/Söndag/Helgdag
Individual Individuellt	SKr 400	SKr 400
Couple Par	SKr 800	SKr 800

Juniors: – 50% / We: visitors only after 14:00

Caddie Caddie no — **Electric Trolley** El vagn no
Buggy Golfbil yes — **Clubs** Klubbor yes
Credit cards Kredit kort
VISA - Eurocard - MasterCard

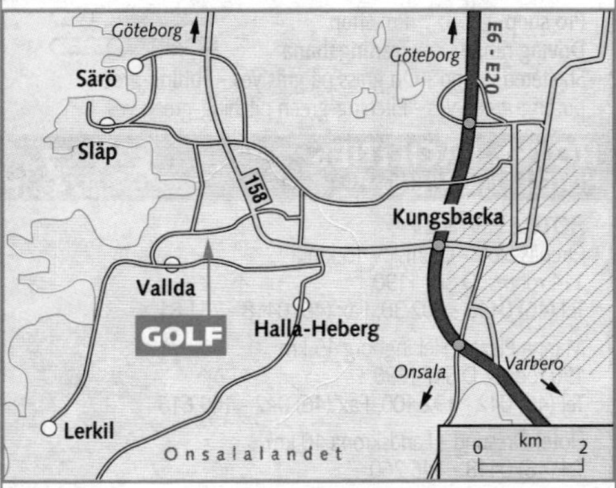

Access Tillfart : Göteborg, E6 → Kungsbacka. Exit 60 → Särö. 7 km → Golf
Map 1 on page 1212 Karta 1 se sid: 1212

GOLF COURSE — BANA — 15/20

Site	Läge	
Maintenance	Underhåll	
Architect	Arkitekt	Frank Pennink
Type	Karaktär	seaside course, parkland
Relief	Nivåskillnader	
Water in play	Vatten på spelfältet	
Exp. to wind	Vindutsatt	
Trees in play	Träd på spelfältet	

Scorecard Scorekort	**Chp.** Back tees	**Mens** Herrtee	**Ladies** Damtee
Length Längd	6096	5831	5030
Par	72	72	72
Slope system	—	137	136

Advised golfing ability Rekommenderad spelnivå — 0 12 24 36
Hcp required Hcp erfordrad — 36

CLUB HOUSE & AMENITIES — KLUBBHUS OCH OMGIVNING — 6/10

Pro shop Pro shop
Driving range Träningsbana
Sheltered tak 8 mats - On grass på gräs no, 22 mats open air - Putting-green putting-green ja - Pitching-green pitching-green ja

HOTEL FACILITIES — HOTELL OMGIVNING — 6/10

HOTELS HOTELL
Säröhus - Särö 4 km
83 rooms, D SKr 1220
Tel (46) 031 - 936 090, Fax (46) 031 - 936 185

Hotell Halland - Kungsbacka 12 km
30 rooms, D SKr 1195
Tel (46) 0300 - 775 30, Fax (46) 0300 - 162 25

RESTAURANTS RESTAURANGER
Hotell Halland - Kungsbacka 12 km
Tel (46) 0300 - 775 30

Pio Pepe - Kungsbacka 11 km
Tel (46) 0300 - 199 04

Kliv in Kök & Bar - Kungsbacka 11 km - Tel (46) 0300 - 199 04

Landskrona *Gul Bana*

15 | 8 | 7

Från det att du anländer så trivs du här, med klubbhuset, restaurangen och omklädningsrummen i den gamla gården. Här finns också ett golfmuseum. Mångfalden fortsätter ute på banan, som växlar mellan parklandskap och seaside och en härlig utsikt över Öresund. Men Landskrona är inte bara vacker, den är också en läcker bana att spela som från första till sista hålet överraskar dig. Den är inte så svår, men vinden kan göra det besvärligt och den är definitivt inte så kort som du först förleds att tro. Lyckligtvis är layouten ganska öppen, men du måste vara försiktig så du inte hamnar i någon av de många fairwaybunkrarna eller den tuffa ruffen som brukar dra till sig missriktade drives. För att ta dig runt banan måste du fatta vettiga beslut, framför allt runt greenen. Detta är en bana för alla, men den premierar den tänkande golfaren. Spela även den andra 18-hålsslingan, par 64, som bidrar till att göra den här platsen till en verklig njutning.

Things look good the moment you arrive here, with the club-house, restaurant and locker-rooms laid out inside old farm-buildings. There is also a golf museum. This is all the diversity of golf, which as it happens continues out on the course with parkland and inland styles alternating with seaside landscapes and views over the Öresund. Yet Landskrona is not only great to look at, it is also great to play, with a course that grabs you and amazes throughout. It is not all that difficult, but the wind can make it tricky and suddenly seem not as short as you thought. Fortunately the layout is very open with hazards clear to see, but you will need to be especially careful to avoid the fairway bunkers and rough, which is tough enough for wayward drivers to spend most of the day there. On the technical side, you need an all-round game and be able to go for the right option, especially with your short game. A course for everyone, especially golfers who can keep a clear mind. And the par-64 18-hole course makes this site even more enjoyable.

Landskrona GK — 1962

Erikstorp
S - 261 61 LANDSKRONA

Office	Sekretariat	(46) 0418 - 446 260
Pro shop	Pro shop	(46) 0418 - 159 75
Fax	Fax	(46) 0418 - 446 262
Web	www.landskronagk.se	
Situation	Läge	Landskrona, 3 km
Annual closure	Årlig stängning	no
Weekly closure	Daglig stängning	no
Fees main season	Tariff hög säsong	18 holes

	Week days Veckodag	We/Bank holidays Lör/Söndag/Helgdag
Individual Individuellt	SKr 300	SKr 320
Couple Par	SKr 600	SKr 640

Juniors: – 50%

Caddie Caddie no — Electric Trolley El vagn no
Buggy Golfbil no — Clubs Klubbor no
Credit cards Kredit kort
VISA - Eurocard - MasterCard

Access Tillfart : E6 Malmö → Helsingborg, Exit Landskrona N., → Borstahusen
Map 1 on page 1212 Karta 1 se sid: 1212

GOLF COURSE BANA — 15/20

Site	Läge	
Maintenance	Underhåll	
Architect	Arkitekt	Ture Bruce, Åke Persson
Type	Karaktär	seaside course, parkland
Relief	Nivåskillnader	
Water in play	Vatten på spelfältet	
Exp. to wind	Vindutsatt	
Trees in play	Träd på spelfältet	

Scorecard Scorekort	Chp. Back tees	Mens Herrtee	Ladies Damtee
Length Längd	5730	5585	4850
Par	71	71	71
Slope system	123	123	123

Advised golfing ability / Rekommenderad spelnivå: 0 12 24 36
Hcp required / Hcp erfordrad: 36

CLUB HOUSE & AMENITIES KLUBBHUS OCH OMGIVNING — 8/10

Pro shop / Pro shop
Driving range / Träningsbana
Sheltered tak no - On grass på gräs yes - Putting-green putting-green yes - Pitching-green pitching-green yes

HOTEL FACILITIES HOTELL OMGIVNING — 7/10

HOTELS HOTELL

Örenäs Slott - Glumslöv 15 km
114 rooms, D SKr 1190
Tel (46) 0418 - 702 30, Fax (46) 0418 - 731 81

Marina Plaza - Helsingborg 15 km
190 rooms, D SKr 1690
Tel (46) 042 - 192 100, Fax (46) 042 - 149 616

Hotel Öresund - Landskrona 10 km,
Tel (46) 0418 - 446 260

RESTAURANTS RESTAURANGER

Oskar Trapp - Helsingborg 15 km
Tel (46) 042 - 146 044

Ljunghusen

18 | 7 | 5

Några tips innan du slår ut: När du begraver bollen i tjock ljung (vilket du kommer att göra), så försök att ta dig därifrån så fort som möjligt, även om detta innebär att du bara hackar bollen några meter till höger eller vänster. En annan sak: När du har en nedförsputt i medvind så behöver du...äsch, glöm det! För att scora väl på den här banan måste du ha stor fantasi och hela tiden befinna dig på rätt sida om flaggan. På den här typen av seaside-bana räcker det alltså inte med att ha tränat som en galning på övningsfältet. Här krävs andra kunskaper! Du måste kunna manövrera bollen åt bägge hållen. På sätt och vis är detta klassisk linksgolf, även om du inte kommer se några gigantiska sandklitter som du kan göra på Irland. Vad som däremot finns här är ljung – tjock och ogenomtränglig på sommaren. Därför verkar också fairways från utslagsplatserna vara löjligt smala. Men detta är faktiskt inte riktigt sant, och spelare av alla skicklighetsgrader kan verkligen ha ett fint utbyte av en runda här. I varje fall så länge som du är villig att eftertänksamt ta dig an varje slag, ett i taget. En del tycker till och med att banan är bättre än närbelägna Falsterbo.

When you bury your ball in the heather, get back into the fairway at all costs, even if it means hacking the ball just a few yards. When faced with a downhill putt with the wind behind you, well, forget it. To score well, you must be on the right side of the pin and show creativity from tee to green. You won't find the spectacular sights of huge Irish-style dunes here, but you will be confronted with each and every feature of links play (with a few recent bunkers to boot). With the addition of heather, you get the impression that the fairways are ridiculously narrow. This is not really true, as Ljunghusens is a course for golfers of all abilities, as long as they review their strategy at each shot. Your reward will be to contemplate with a positive eye this huge stretch of purple, yellow and green, which really comes to life in the summer twilight.

Ljunghusens Golfklubb — 1932

Kinells väg
S - 236 42 HÖLLVIKEN

Office Sekretariat (46) 040 - 458 000
Pro shop Pro shop (46) 040 - 452 561
Fax Fax (46) 040 - 454 265
Web www.ljgk.se
Situation Läge Malmö, 30 km; Falsterbo, 1 km
Annual closure Årlig stängning no
Weekly closure Daglig stängning no

Fees main season Tariff hög säsong	Full day	
	Week days Veckodag	**We/Bank holidays** Lör/Söndag/Helgdag
Individual Individuellt	SKr 480	SKr 480
Couple Par	SKr 960	SKr 960

We 05 → 09 & every day in 07: limitation of Green fees
Juniors: – 50%

Caddie Caddie no **Electric Trolley** El vagn no
Buggy Golfbil yes **Clubs** Klubbor yes
Credit cards Kredit kort
VISA - Eurocard - MasterCard - AMEX - DC

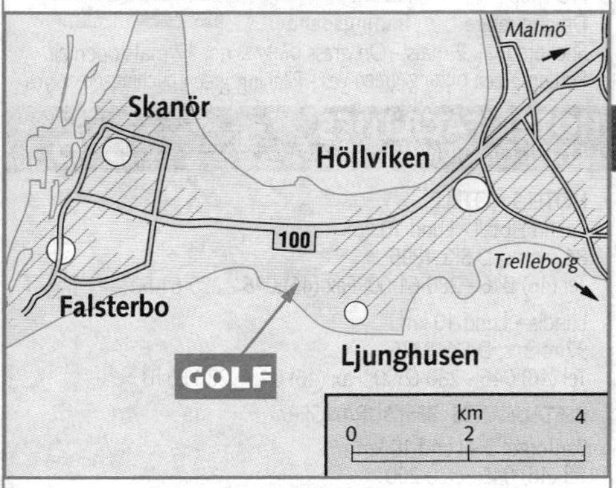

Access Tillfart : Malmö: E6 → Falsterbo.
Map 1 on page 1212 Karta 1 se sid: 1212

GOLF COURSE — BANA 18/20

Site Läge
Maintenance Underhåll
Architect Arkitekt Douglas Brasier
Type Karaktär seaside course
Relief Nivåskillnader
Water in play Vatten på spelfältet
Exp. to wind Vindutsatt
Trees in play Träd på spelfältet

Scorecard Scorekort	**Chp.** Back tees	**Mens** Herrtee	**Ladies** Damtee
Length Längd	6115	5895	5120
Par	72	72	72
Slope system	—	133	132

Advised golfing ability Rekommenderad spelnivå 0 12 24 36
Hcp required Hcp erfordrad 36

CLUB HOUSE & AMENITIES — KLUBBHUS OCH OMGIVNING 7/10

Pro shop Pro shop
Driving range Träningsbana
Sheltered tak 2 mats - On grass på gräs yes - Putting-green putting-green yes - Pitching-green pitching-green yes

HOTEL FACILITIES — HOTELL OMGIVNING 5/10

HOTELS HOTELL
Hotell Gässlingen - Skanör 8 km
13 rooms, D SKr 1495
Tel (46) 040 - 459 100, Fax (46) 040 - 359 113

Hotell Spelabäcken - Skanör 6 km
18 rooms, D SKr 900
Tel (46) 040 - 475 300, Fax (46) 040 - 473 242

RESTAURANTS RESTAURANGER
Skanörs Gästgiveri - Skanör 10 km
Tel (46) 040 - 475 690

Vellinge Gästgiveri - Vellinge 15 km
Tel (46) 040 - 424 865

Kaptensgården - Falsterbo 1 km - Tel (46) 040 - 470 750

Lunds Akademiska

17 | 7 | 6

Lund är en härlig plats att besöka, bubblande av liv, vilket kanske inte är så konstigt med tanke på att det är Sveriges näst största universitetsstad. Ett av många utflyktsmål vi rekommenderar att besöka är den stora domkyrkan. I en nationalpark några kilometer österut från själva staden ligger en bana ritad 1936 av Morrison, vars namn är förknippat med många av Europas bästa banor. Under sommaren växer ruffen tjock och vild, och straffar sneda drives obarmhärtigt. Första nio är som en vandring genom en lummig park. Andra nio ligger öppnare och är svårare. Helt logiskt kommer banans klimax i avslutningen. På hålen 16-18 förenar sig ruffen, vattnet och skogen i ett gemensamt försök att förstöra din score. Om du klarar detta så kan du spela var som helst, och sedan uppskatta det nya klubbhuset! Alla älskar den här charmerande platsen, men det är troligen en utmaning som uppskattas mer av den bättre spelaren, och kanske än mer nu när samtliga greener har blivit omgjorda. Men se dig för, fairways kantas av gamla vikingagravar, och i klubbhuset kan du få en broschyr över alla sällsynta blommor som växer här.

Several miles to the east of Lund lies a national park and a golf course designed in 1936 by Morrison, whose name is linked with many of the top courses in Europe. Here in summer, the rough grows high and thick and punishes wild driving unrelentlessly. The outward nine are like a walk through a huge tree-strewn park, the back nine are laid out over more open space, but are tougher to play. Quite logically the climax comes over the finishing holes, 16 through 18, where water, rough and trees join forces to ruin your card. If you can resist this treatment, you can play just about everywhere and appreciate the new club-house. Everyone loves this charming spot, but its challenge is probably better appreciated and accepted by the more proficient players, even more so now that the greens have been re-laid. Watch out, as here you are stepping back in history with ancient Viking tombs lining the fairways, and taking a lesson in nature too with the rare flowers described in a special brochure.

Lunds Akademiska Golfklubb 1936

Kungsmarken
S - 225 92 LUND

Office	Sekretariat	(46) 046 - 990 04
Pro shop	Pro shop	(46) 046 - 990 96
Fax	Fax	(46) 046 - 991 46
Web	www.lagk.se	
Situation	Läge	Lund, 10 km
Annual closure	Årlig stängning	no
Weekly closure	Daglig stängning	no

Fees main season Tariff hög säsong — Full day

	Week days Veckodag	We/Bank holidays Lör/Söndag/Helgdag
Individual Individuellt	SKr 350	SKr 450
Couple Par	SKr 700	SKr 900

Juniors: SKr 150/180 (We)

Caddie Caddie no — **Electric Trolley** El vagn no

Buggy Golfbil yes — **Clubs** Klubbor yes

Credit cards Kredit kort
VISA - Eurocard - MasterCard - AMEX - DC

Access Tillfart : Lund, E22 1 km, → S. Sandby. 3 km → "Kungsmarken."

Map 1 on page 1212 Karta 1 se sid: 1212

GOLF COURSE
BANA — 17/20

Site	Läge	
Maintenance	Underhåll	
Architect	Arkitekt	John Morrison S. Böstrom
Type	Karaktär	parkland
Relief	Nivåskillnader	
Water in play	Vatten på spelfältet	
Exp. to wind	Vindutsatt	
Trees in play	Träd på spelfältet	

Scorecard Scorekort	Chp. Back tees	Mens Herrtee	Ladies Damtee
Length Längd	6040	5705	5030
Par	72	72	72
Slope system	—	133	129

Advised golfing ability Rekommenderad spelnivå — 0 12 24 36

Hcp required Hcp erfordrad — 36

CLUB HOUSE & AMENITIES
KLUBBHUS OCH OMGIVNING — 7/10

Pro shop Pro shop
Driving range Träningsbana
Sheltered tak 2 mats - On grass på gräs no, 17 mats open air
Putting-green putting-green yes - Pitching-green pitching-green yes

HOTEL FACILITIES
HOTELL OMGIVNING — 6/10

HOTELS HOTELL
Grand Hotell - Lund 10 km
84 rooms, D SKr 1895
Tel (46) 046 - 280 61 00, Fax (46) 046 - 280 61 50

Lundia - Lund 10 km
97 rooms, D SKr 1375
Tel (46) 046 - 280 6500, Fax (46) 046 - 280 6510

RESTAURANTS RESTAURANGER
Bantorget 9 - Lund 10 km
Tel (46) 046 - 320 200
Grand Hotell - Lund 10 km
Tel (46) 046 - 280 61 00

Mölle

16 | 7 | 5

Vägen upp till Kullaberg förbi Höganäs är med alla sina fiskelägen vacker som ett vykort. Detta är Sveriges keramik-centrum, och väl framme i Mölle kan du begrunda det faktum att du nu är på platsen där män och kvinnor för första gången fick sola och bada tillsammans. Golfbanan ligger högre upp i en nationalpark, och att den är belägen där förklarar också varför antalet bunkrar är begränsat på banan (endast elva stycken). Nåväl, de flesta greener är små, ligger väl skyddade uppbyggda på platåer och är snabbast i landet. Du behöver kunna slå höga inspel här, men många hål kräver också att du behärskar låga rullslag. Banan är kraftigt kuperad, vilket kan vara slitsamt (det finns inga golfbilar). Om du ska kunna klara dig runt här och träffa greenerna måste du ha ett brett register av olika typer av slag, framför allt med mellanjärnen och de korta järnen. Eftersom banan inte är särskilt lång kan du gott lämna drivern hemma. Layouten bör passa de flesta spelarkategorier, men vi varnar för vinden, den kan vara riktigt besvärlig: Här finns inte ett tråkigt hål eller slag på hela banan.

The road along the Kullen peninsula is as pretty as a picture with fishing villages and the town of Höganäs, the centre of the Swedish ceramics and sandstone pottery industry on the way to Mölle, the first seaside resort in Sweden where men and women were able to bathe together. The golf course is higher up in a national park, a fact that limited the number of bunkers (11 green-side traps). No matter, many of the greens are small, elevated, well-guarded (only one is really blind) and the fastest in the whole country. You need to hit the ball high here, of course, but approach shots hit along the ground are often a better solution. Hilly enough to deter tired legs, Mölle requires all sorts of shots to hit the greens. This is not really a long course and the driver can easily stay in the bag all day. Over a layout that is well suited to all playing abilities, the wind can be the most bothersome element to distract from the pleasure of playing here: there is not a single boring hole or shot on the course.

Mölle Golfklubb — 1944

Box 44
S - 260 42 MÖLLE

Office	Sekretariat	(46) 042 - 347 520
Pro shop	Pro shop	(46) 042 - 347 012
Fax	Fax	(46) 042 - 347 523
Web	www.mollegk.se	
Situation	Läge	Mölle, 3 km Helsingborg, 30 km
Annual closure	Årlig stängning	no
Weekly closure	Daglig stängning	no

Fees main season Tariff hög säsong	Full day	
	Week days Veckodag	We/Bank holidays Lör/Söndag/Helgdag
Individual Individuellt	SKr 350	SKr 350
Couple Par	SKr 700	SKr 700

Juniors: SKr 150

Caddie Caddie no — Electric Trolley El vagn no
Buggy Golfbil yes — Clubs Klubbor yes

Credit cards Kredit kort
VISA - Eurocard - MasterCard

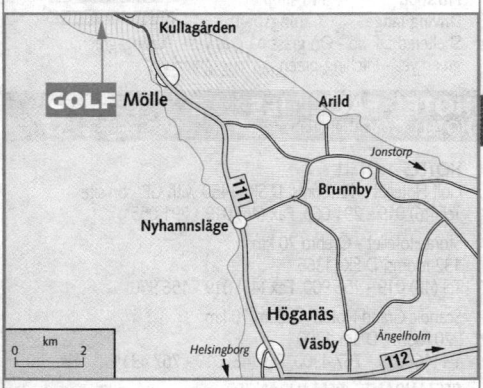

Access Tillfart : Helsingborg, R111 → Höganäs/Mölle. Mölle, → Kullens Fyr.
Map 1 on page 1212 Karta 1 se sid: 1212

GOLF COURSE — BANA 16/20

Site	Läge	
Maintenance	Underhåll	
Architect	Arkitekt	Ture Bruce
Type	Karaktär	parkland, hilly
Relief	Nivåskillnader	
Water in play	Vatten på spelfältet	
Exp. to wind	Vindutsatt	
Trees in play	Träd på spelfältet	

Scorecard Scorekort	Chp. Back tees	Mens Herrtee	Ladies Damtee
Length Längd	5467	5312	4627
Par	70	70	70
Slope system	—	131	125

Advised golfing ability / Rekommenderad spelnivå: 0 12 24 36
Hcp required — Hcp erfordrad — 32 Men, 36 Ladies

CLUB HOUSE & AMENITIES — KLUBBHUS OCH OMGIVNING 7/10

Pro shop — Pro shop
Driving range — Träningsbana
Sheltered tak no - On grass på gräs yes - Putting-green putting-green yes - Pitching-green pitching-green yes

HOTEL FACILITIES — HOTELL OMGIVNING 5/10

HOTELS HOTELL

Kullabergs Värdshus - on site
89 rooms, D SKr 2040 with dinner
Tel (46) 042 - 185 390, Fax (46) 042 - 149 616

Grand Hotel - Mölle 4 km
42 rooms, D SKr 1650
Tel (46) 042 - 362 230, Fax (46) 042 - 362 231

RESTAURANTS RESTAURANGER

Le Petit - Helsingborg 30 km
Tel (46) 042 - 219 727

Oskar Trapp - Helsingborg 30 km
Tel (46) 042 - 146 044

Gastro - Helsingborg 30 km - Tel (46) 042 - 243 470

Örebro

17 | 7 | 6

Trots att den inte är monsterlång räknas Örebro som en av de bästa banorna i Sverige. Det är en trevlig plats att besöka med ett charmigt klubbhus och ett övningsfält som är bland det bästa vi kan erbjuda här i landet. Pitch- och puttbanan är också en höjdare! När du väl har värmt upp kan du börja fundera över att attackera banrekordet som innehas av Joakim Haeggman och Pierre Fulke på 63 slag. Båda spelarna är kända för sin skicklighet med drivern, och det kommer du också behöva. Detta gäller framför allt för första nio där träden är mer i spel än på sista nio. Dessutom skadar det inte att vara utrustad med en stor portion tålamod och ta chanserna när de dyker upp. Du måste också vara smart när du attackerar greenerna, av vilka flera ligger på platåer. Örebro är en härlig utmaning där en sund teknik är att föredra framför muskler. Och du – tycker du det blir för svårt är det inte nödvändigt att spela från backtee. En ny niohåls parkbana öppnade sommaren 2003.

Örebro is generally considered to be one of the very best courses in Sweden. It is a pleasant spot, the clubhouse very agreeable, the driving range is one of the best in the country and there is a pitch and putt course that is great fun. When nicely warmed up, you can start to think about getting out there and trying to beat the course record of 63 set by Joakim Haeggman and Pierre Fulke. Both players are straight drivers and you will need the same accuracy, at least on the front nine, where the forest poses more of a threat than on the inward nine. You need to be patient here and grasp the right opportunities provided by your own talent or any luck that comes your way. You also need to be smart to appreciate some of the approach shots to greens that are sometimes elevated but never oversized. Örebro is a mighty challenge but places emphasis more on technique than power, an asset for golfers who always look to their swing (or change of club) to hit the ball 20 yards further. A new parkland 9-hole course was opened in the summer of 2003.

Örebro Golfklubb — 1962

Lanna
S - 719 93 VINTROSA

Office	Sekretariat	(46) 019 - 164 070
Pro shop	Pro shop	(46) 019 - 291 045
Fax	Fax	(46) 019 - 164 075
Web	www.orebrogk.com	
Situation	Läge	Örebro, 20 km
Annual closure	Årlig stängning	no
Weekly closure	Daglig stängning	no

Fees main season Tariff hög säsong		Full day
	Week days Veckodag	We/Bank holidays Lör/Söndag/Helgdag
Individual Individuellt	SKr 380	SKr 400
Couple Par	SKr 760	SKr 800

Juniors: SKr 150/200 (We)

Caddie Caddie no **Electric Trolley** El vagn no

Buggy Golfbil yes **Clubs** Klubbor yes

Credit cards Kredit kort
VISA - Eurocard - MasterCard - AMEX - DC

Tysslingen
Arboga
Hjälmaren
GOLF
Karlskoga
Vintrosa
Örebro
E18
E20
Hidinge
Fjugesta
Hallsberg
km 0 2 4

Access Tillfart : Örebro, E18 → Oslo. 20 km, → "Lanna"
Map 2 on page 1214 Karta 2 se sid: 1214

GOLF COURSE — BANA — 17/20

Site	Läge	
Maintenance	Underhåll	
Architect	Arkitekt	Flera
Type	Karaktär	forest, parkland
Relief	Nivåskillnader	
Water in play	Vatten på spelfältet	
Exp. to wind	Vindutsatt	
Trees in play	Träd på spelfältet	

Scorecard Scorekort	Chp. Back tees	Mens Herrtee	Ladies Damtee
Length Längd	6160	5860	5065
Par	71	71	71
Slope system	–	130	123

Advised golfing ability Rekommenderad spelnivå — 0 12 24 36

Hcp required Hcp erfordrad — 36

CLUB HOUSE & AMENITIES — KLUBBHUS OCH OMGIVNING — 7/10

Pro shop Pro shop
Driving range Träningsbana
Sheltered tak no - On grass på gräs yes - Putting-green putting-green yes - Pitching-green pitching-green yes

HOTEL FACILITIES — HOTELL OMGIVNING — 6/10

HOTELS HOTELL
Golf Hotellet - 12 rooms, D SKr 1450 with GF - on site
Tel (46) 019 - 291 065, Fax (46) 019 - 291 055

Stora Hotellet - Örebro 20 km
132 rooms, D SKr 1365
Tel (46) 019 - 156 900, Fax (46) 019 - 156 950

Scandic Grand Hotel - Örebro 20 km
220 rooms, D SKr 1790
Tel (46) 019 - 767 4300, Fax (46) 019 - 767 4311

RESTAURANTS RESTAURANGER
Slottskällaren - Örebro 20 km - Tel (46) 019 - 156 900
Babar - Örebro 20 km - Tel (46) 019 - 101 900
Tulins - Örebro 20 km - Tel (46) 019 - 132 530

Österåker Västerled

16 | 6 | 6

Österåker är inget undantag från den här trenden som har sitt upphov i dagens nya teknologi som har gett oss järnklubbor som går allt högre och wedgar som får mer och mer loft. Många av greenerna vaktas av ett stort antal hinder, de är dessutom relativt hårda vilket gör att du måste slå höga pitch-slag mot dem för att få bollen att stanna. Om du har en lobbwedge – stoppa den i bagen! Du behöver dessutom långa, raka utslag – framför allt under sommaren då ruffen växer hög. En tuff utmaning, framför allt de nio första som är betydligt trixigare än andra nio som är längre men inte fullt så krävande. Om du har en dålig svingdag får du förlita dig på ditt närspel, men eftersom detta är något förunnat låghandicapare så kan spelare med högre handicap få det besvärligt. För att göra saken än mer problematisk så är vatten i spel på åtta av hålen. Av rundan kommer du framför allt att minnas de spektakulära par 3-hålen. Här har Europatouren för damer kommit på besök, och över de senaste åren har en rad tees och greener uppgraderats. Har du tid, stanna och spela den andra 18-hålsslingan här (Österled), med en fantastisk layout i ett relativt öppet landskap som gör den här anläggningen komplett.

A lot of the greens here are guarded at the front by a number of hazards, and as they are also pretty firm you have to hit high pitches and be able to stop the ball on the putting surface. If you have a lob-wedge, use it. Otherwise, what with the tall rough in summer, you need some straight driving as well, a tough proposition early in the day because the front nine are a good deal trickier than the back nine. If your swing is off-colour, your short game should help you out, but it is not always the forte of high-handicappers. To top it all, some fearsome water is in play on eight holes. The holes to remember on this course are the spectacular par 3s. Over the last few years, quite a few of tees and greens have been remodeled. If you have the time, play the other 18-hole course as well (Österled), a great layout over heathland which beautifully completes what is an excellent resort.

Österåkers Golfklubb 1990

Hagby 1:1
S - 184 92 ÅKERSBERGA

Office	Sekretariat	(46) 08 - 540 851 90
Pro shop	Pro shop	(46) 08 - 540 684 49
Fax	Fax	(46) 08 - 540 668 32
Web	www.ostgk.se	
Situation	Läge	Stockholm, 20 km
Annual closure	Årlig stängning	no
Weekly closure	Daglig stängning	no

Fees main season Tariff hög säsong — Full day

	Week days Veckodag	We/Bank holidays Lör/Söndag/Helgdag
Individual Individuellt	SKr 400	SKr 450
Couple Par	SKr 800	SKr 900

Juniors: SKr 220
GF before 15:00 (week days) and after 14:00 (We)

Caddie Caddie no — **Electric Trolley** El vagn no
Buggy Golfbil no — **Clubs** Klubbor yes
Credit cards Kredit kort
VISA - Eurocard - MasterCard - AMEX - DC

Access Tillfart : Stockholm, E18 → Norrtälje. → Åkersberga, → Waxholm
Map 2 on page 1214 Karta 2 se sid: 1214

GOLF COURSE BANA 16/20

Site	Läge	
Maintenance	Underhåll	
Architect	Arkitekt	Sven Tumba, Jan Sederholm
Type	Karaktär	parkland
Relief	Nivåskillnader	
Water in play	Vatten på spelfältet	
Exp. to wind	Vindutsatt	
Trees in play	Träd på spelfältet	

Scorecard Scorekort	Chp. Back tees	Mens Herrtee	Ladies Damtee
Length Längd	6145	5790	5010
Par	72	72	72
Slope system	—	141	138

Advised golfing ability Rekommenderad spelnivå — 0 12 24 36
Hcp required Hcp erfordrad — 24 Men, 30 Ladies

CLUB HOUSE & AMENITIES KLUBBHUS OCH OMGIVNING 6/10

Pro shop Pro shop
Driving range Träningsbana
Sheltered tak 6 mats - On grass på gräs no, 30 mats open air - Putting-green putting-green yes - Pitching-green pitching-green yes

HOTEL FACILITIES HOTELL OMGIVNING 6/10

HOTELS HOTELL
Clarion Hotel - Stockholm 17 km
532 rooms, D SKr 2495
Tel (46) 08 - 462 10 00, Fax (46) 08 - 462 10 99

First Hotel Reisen - Stockholm 20 km
144 rooms, D SKr 2543
Tel (46) 08 - 223 260, Fax (46) 08 - 201 559

Victory - Stockholm 20 km - 45 rooms, D SKr 3500
Tel (46) 08 - 143 090, Fax (46) 08 - 202 177

RESTAURANTS RESTAURANGER
Eriks - Stockholm 20 km - Tel (46) 08 - 238 500
Annakahn - Stockholm 17 km - Tel (46) 08 - 440 30 00
Den Gyldene Freden - Stockholm 20 km - Tel (46) 08 - 249 760

Rya

15 | 7 | 8

Även nu när bron mellan Malmö och Köpenhamn har byggts kan man fortfarande tura mellan Helsingborg och Helsingør, den kortaste vägen mellan Sverige och Danmark. Från Rya, strax söder om Helsingborg, ser man inte bara Öresund utan även Danmark på andra sidan sundet. Bortsett från fem ganska kuperade hål är resten av banan platt och varierar i stil mellan links och parkbanekaraktär. På några hål kommer träd i spel, annars är det vattenhinder som är de största hoten, framför allt på det fjärde och det åttonde, som kan vara svåra för höghandicaparen. Nåja, det åttonde hålet ställer till med problem för alla – ett vattenhinder skär igenom fairway precis framför greenen på detta par 5-hål som måste räknas vara ett av de bästa i hela landet. 16e är också minnesvärt – en par 3 med sundet och Danmark i bakgrunden. Efter rundan kan du ta med dig barnen till stranden (50 meter bort), gå till bastun (40 meter bort) eller återvända till klubbhuset (som är nyrenoverat).

Even when the motorway-train link from Malmö to København is open, there will still be the ferry link between Helsingborg and Helsingør, the shortest way of getting from one country to the other. From the Rya course, to the south of Helsingborg, you can see not only the Öresund strait but also Denmark on the other side. Aside from five rather hilly holes, the rest of the course is flat with a style varying from links to parkland. Trees are in play only on a few holes, otherwise the hazards that are present are very dangerous, particularly on holes 4 and 8, where water will cause trouble for the high-handicap golfers. In fact, hole N° 8 will cause problems for everyone, with water crossing the fairway next to the green of this superb par 5, which has to rate as one of the finest holes in the whole country. The 16th, too, is a great hole, a short par 3 with the sea and Denmark in the background. At the end of your round, you can take the children to the beach (less than 60 yards away), go to the sauna (40 yards) or return to the clubhouse (refurbished).

Rya Golfklubb — 1935

PL 5500
S - 255 92 HELSINGBORG

Office	Sekretariat	(46) 042 - 220 182
Pro shop	Pro shop	(46) 042 - 221 688
Fax	Fax	(46) 042 - 220 394
Web	www.ryagolf.se	
Situation	Läge	Helsingborg, 10 km
Annual closure	Årlig stängning	no
Weekly closure	Daglig stängning	no

Fees main season Tariff hög säsong	Week days Veckodag	We/Bank holidays Lör/Söndag/Helgdag
	18 holes	
Individual Individuellt	SKr 450	SKr 500
Couple Par	SKr 900	SKr 1000

GF full week day: SKr 500 / Juniors: – 50%

Caddie Caddie no — **Electric Trolley** El vagn no
Buggy Golfbil no — **Clubs** Klubbor yes
Credit cards Kredit kort
VISA - Eurocard - MasterCard

Access Tillfart : Malmö E6 → Helsingborg. → Rydebäck. → Golf
Map 1 on page 1212 Karta 1 se sid: 1212

GOLF COURSE — BANA — 15/20

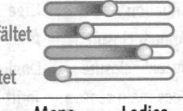

Site	Läge	
Maintenance	Underhåll	
Architect	Arkitekt	Rafael Sundblom
Type	Karaktär	seaside course, parkland
Relief	Nivåskillnader	
Water in play	Vatten på spelfältet	
Exp. to wind	Vindutsatt	
Trees in play	Träd på spelfältet	

Scorecard Scorekort	Chp. Back tees	Mens Herrtee	Ladies Damtee
Length Längd	5857	5558	4846
Par	71	71	71
Slope system	—	124	126

Advised golfing ability Rekommenderad spelnivå — 0 12 24 36
Hcp required Hcp erfordrad — 32 Men, 34 Ladies

CLUB HOUSE & AMENITIES — KLUBBHUS OCH OMGIVNING — 7/10

Pro shop Pro shop
Driving range Träningsbana
Sheltered tak yes - On grass på gräs yes - Putting-green putting-green yes - Pitching-green pitching-green yes

HOTEL FACILITIES — HOTELL OMGIVNING — 8/10

HOTELS HOTELL
Marina Plaza - Helsingborg 7 km
190 rooms, D SKr 1690
Tel (46) 042 - 192 100, Fax (46) 042 - 149 616

Grand Hotell - Helsingborg 7 km
116 rooms, D SKr 1395
Tel (46) 042 - 380 400, Fax (46) 042 - 380 404

RESTAURANTS RESTAURANGER
Le Petit - Helsingborg 7 km
Tel (46) 042 - 219 727
Oskar Trapp - Helsingborg 7 km - Tel (46) 042 - 146 044
Niklas - Helsingborg 7 km - Tel (46) 042 - 280 050

Saltsjöbaden

16	7	6

Allt som allt finns 24 000 öar i skärgården, gömda i ett vattenlandskap som oftast ser lugnt ut men snabbt kan förvandlas till ett rytande. Precis i början av detta finner man Saltsjöbaden, vars layout och stil påminner mycket om en brittisk parkbana, detta trots sitt skärgårdsläge nära vattnet. Långtslående spelare, vana vid öppna ytor, finner kanske banan väl smal, men då den spelas ganska kort brukar ett långt järn från utslaget mer än väl räcka. Terrassgreener, små och svårlästa, kräver precision i inspelen och ett kallt huvud då banan har mer än sin beskärda del av hinder. I stället för råstyrka premieras finlir, särskilt på de vackra sluthålen. Hela familjen kommer att ha glädje av att spela här, då banan inte är för svår för motionsgolfaren. Dröm dock inte om allt för låga scorer, det är lätt att tappa slag här i en alarmerande hastighet. Renoveringen av banan med fyra helt nya hål och ett antal omgjorda greener har blivit en stor framgång.

This parkland course has a very British flavour to it, lying at the heart of the seaside resort of Saltsjöbaden in the Stockholm group of islands. There are some 24,000 of these in all with landscapes that look peaceful but can turn wild at a moment's notice. Big-hitters used to wide open spaces might find the course on the narrow side but the moderate yardage should prompt them and others to prefer a long iron to the driver, especially since flighting the ball here is more than useful. The elevated greens, smallish but with some tricky contours to read, call for accuracy and a cool head as the course has more than its fair share of hazards. Rather than brute strength, you should try a little finesse to get around this course, especially since the closing holes are real beauties. All the family can play this layout which is not too intimidating for the average golfer. Just don't dream too much about low scoring, as strokes slip away at an alarming rate. The renewal of the course with four new holes and a number of re-laid greens has been a great success.

Saltsjöbadens GK — 1929

Kvarntorpsvägen, Box 51
S - 133 21 SALTSJÖBADEN

Office	Sekretariat	(46) 08 - 717 01 25
Pro shop	Pro shop	(46) 08 - 717 10 35
Fax	Fax	(46) 08 - 556 167 39
Web	www.saltsjobadensgk.se	
Situation	Läge	Stockholm, 30 km
Annual closure	Årlig stängning	no
Weekly closure	Daglig stängning	no
Fees main season	Tariff hög säsong	18 holes

	Week days Veckodag	We/Bank holidays Lör/Söndag/Helgdag
Individual Individuellt	SKr 420	SKr 420*
Couple Par	SKr 840	SKr 840*

Juniors: SKr 200 / * We: visitors after 14:00

Caddie Caddie no — **Electric Trolley** El vagn no

Buggy Golfbil no — **Clubs** Klubbor yes

Credit cards Kredit kort
VISA - Eurocard - MasterCard - AMEX - DC

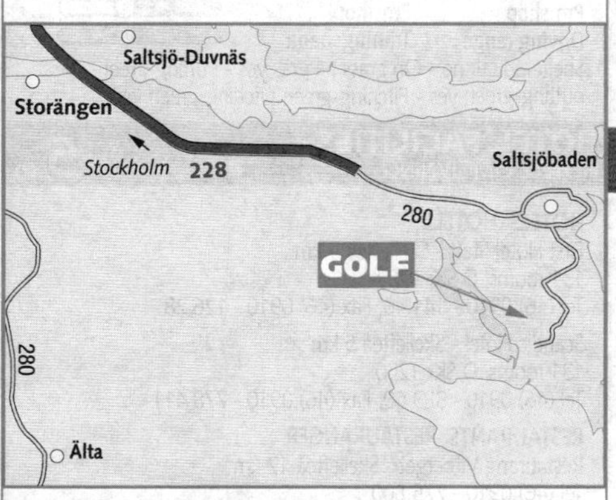

Access Tillfart : Stockholm, 222/228 → Saltsjöbaden.
At stop lights turn right at Saltsjöbaden Center.
Follow signs to Golf.
Map 2 on page 1214 Karta 2 se sid: 1214

GOLF COURSE — BANA — 16/20

Site	Läge	
Maintenance	Underhåll	
Architect	Arkitekt	Douglas Brasier
Type	Karaktär	inland, parkland
Relief	Nivåskillnader	
Water in play	Vatten på spelfältet	
Exp. to wind	Vindutsatt	
Trees in play	Träd på spelfältet	

Scorecard Scorekort	Chp. Back tees	Mens Herrtee	Ladies Damtee
Length Längd	5809	5430	4527
Par	71	71	71
Slope system	—	128	121

Advised golfing ability Rekommenderad spelnivå — 0 12 24 36

Hcp required Hcp erfordrad — 36

CLUB HOUSE & AMENITIES — KLUBBHUS OCH OMGIVNING — 7/10

Pro shop Pro shop
Driving range Träningsbana
Sheltered tak no - On grass på gräs yes - Putting-green putting-green yes - Pitching-green pitching-green yes

HOTEL FACILITIES — HOTELL OMGIVNING — 6/10

HOTELS HOTELL

Clarion Hotel - 532 rooms, D SKr 2495 - Stockholm 30 km
Tel (46) 08 - 462 10 00, Fax (46) 08 - 462 10 99

Stockholm Plaza - Stockholm 30 km
147 rooms, D SKr 2095
Tel (46) 08 - 566 22 000, Fax (46) 08 - 566 22 020

Grand Hotel - 307 rooms, D SKr 4400 - Stockholm 30 km
Tel (46) 08 - 679 3500, Fax (46) 08 - 611 8606

RESTAURANTS RESTAURANGER

Stallmästaregården - Stockholm 30 km
Tel (46) 08 - 610 13 00

Annakahn - Stockholm 30 km - Tel (46) 08 - 440 30 00

Fredsgatan 12 - Stockholm 30 km - Tel (46) 08 - 248 052

Skellefteå

14 | 6 | 5

Skellefteå ligger i ett ingenmansland mellan norr och söder i Sverige. Ändå finns polcirkeln på ett relativt nära avstånd, och här kan sommardagarna kännas oändliga. Om du är tillräckligt vältränad kan du spela flera banor om dagen och ändå hinna njuta av var och en av dem. Banan är ganska flack och från utslagsplatserna kan du se de flesta av hindren. Fairway kantas av träd, och dessa undviker du bäst genom en smula klokskap förenat med skicklighet: Spela försiktigt när du behöver det, slå en kontrollerad fade, och så vidare. Till sist besegrar sunt förnuft ren råstyrka. Fyra talangfulla arkitekter har byggt denna bana i omgångar mellan 1970-1995, vilket kan få en att tro att detta skulle ge en splittrad helhetsbild, men så är det inte. Skellefteå är utan vidare den bästa banan i den här regionen. För lite extra inspiration inför nästa runda rekommenderas ett besök i gamla stan.

This is not yet the great North, but it is not the south either; the Polar Circle is not so far away and summer days can seem endless. If you are fit enough, you will have the time to play several courses in a day and fully appreciate the difficulties of each one. From the tees on this relatively flat and tree-strewn terrain, you can see most of the hazards, which are most effectively avoided with a little skill and thought, i.e. playing short here, fading the ball there, and so forth. At the final count, using your head is more important than physical strength. Four talented architects helped to design this course between 1970 and 1995, which has still nonetheless retained a certain unity. All in all, this is a good and the most impressive course to be found in this part of Sweden. Spare a little time to see the old Parish village of Bonnstan, you might find a little extra inspiration for your next round.

Skellefteå Golfklubb — 1970

Roönnbäcken
S - 931 92 SKELLEFTEÅ

Office	Sekretariat	(46) 0910 - 779 866
Pro shop	Pro shop	(46) 0303 - 779 866
Fax	Fax	(46) 0303 - 779 933
Web	www.skelleftegolf.nu	
Situation	Läge	Skellefteå, 5 km
Annual closure	Årlig stängning	no
Weekly closure	Daglig stängning	no
Fees main season	Tariff hög säsong	Full day

	Week days Veckodag	We/Bank holidays Lör/Söndag/Helgdag
Individual Individuellt	SKr 300	SKr 300
Couple Par	SKr 600	SKr 600

Juniors: – 50% / Full week: SKr 1400

Caddie Caddie no — **Electric Trolley** El vagn no

Buggy Golfbil no — **Clubs** Klubbor yes

Credit cards Kredit kort
VISA - Eurocard - MasterCard - AMEX - DC

Access Tillfart : E4 → Skellefteå. V 364 → Burträsk. 5 km → Golf, Rönnbäcken.
Map 3 on page 1216 Karta 3 se sid: 1216

GOLF COURSE BANA — 14/20

Site	Läge	
Maintenance	Underhåll	
Architect	Arkitekt	Sköld, Karlsson Nordwall, Larsson
Type	Karaktär	forest
Relief	Nivåskillnader	
Water in play	Vatten på spelfältet	
Exp. to wind	Vindutsatt	
Trees in play	Träd på spelfältet	

Scorecard Scorekort	Chp. Back tees	Mens Herrtee	Ladies Damtee
Length Längd	6187	5801	4971
Par	72	72	72
Slope system	—	131	124

Advised golfing ability Rekommenderad spelnivå — 0 12 24 36

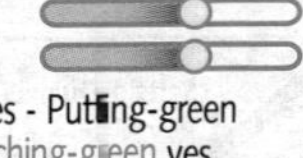

Hcp required Hcp erfordrad — no

CLUB HOUSE & AMENITIES KLUBBHUS OCH OMGIVNING — 6/10

Pro shop Pro shop
Driving range Träningsbana
Sheltered tak no - On grass på gräs yes - Putting-green putting-green yes - Pitching-green pitching-green yes

HOTEL FACILITIES HOTELL OMGIVNING — 5/10

HOTELS HOTELL

First Hotel Statt - Skellefteå 3 km
131 rooms, D SKr 1253
Tel (46) 0910 - 141 40, Fax (46) 0910 - 126 28

Scandic Hotel - Skellefteå 5 km
131 rooms, D SKr 1250
Tel (46) 0910 - 383 00, Fax (46) 0910 - 778 411

RESTAURANTS RESTAURANGER

Restaurang Vitberget - Skellefteå 12 km
Tel (46) 0910 - 775 800

Nordanågårdens Värdshus - Skellefteå 5 km
Tel (46) 0910 - 533 50

Carl Victor - Skellefteå 5 km - Tel (46) 0910 - 100 29

Skövde *Södra Banan*

17	7	7

Besök exempelvis Mariestad, där kan du ta en sväng runt den magnifika kyrkan eller bara strosa runt bland de vackra trähusen. Ungefär fem mil därifrån hittar du ett välkomnande klubbhus byggt högst upp på en kulle med utsikt över ettan och 18e, och för att ta sig dit krävs nästan lika mycket energi som att spela banan (alla med dålig kondition är härmed varnade). Genom att studera greenernas storlek förstår man snabbt vem som har designat banan: Peter Nordwall, förstås. Han har lagt ut en lång och svår bana, där bra bollträff är ett måste. På Skövde är allting stort, från utslagsplatserna till amerikansk-inspirerade fairways. För faktum är att de är bredare än vad de verkar vara vid första anblicken. Tur är det, för första gången ser du bara hinder – skog och tjock ruff. En av banans stora förtjänster är att den är så omväxlande, vilket verkligen kräver att du kan använda alla klubbor i bagen. Även höghandicapare kommer dock ha en kul dag på banan – även om den kanske blir lite längre än vanligt. Niohålaren strax intill är också en frestande rekommendation.

On the shores of the Lake Vänern, you will find the little town of Mariestad and visit the cathedral and old wooden houses. At about fifty kilometres from there, a welcoming club-house stands atop a hill, overlooking holes 1 and 18, which requires about as much stamina to reach as the course does to play. The size of the greens are a good clue to who designed this course, Peter Nordwall, who has laid out a long and difficult course, where the ball needs to be hit crisp and clean. Everything is big here, from the tee-boxes to the rather American style fairways. In fact, the holes are wider than you think and all you see are the hazards of trees and tall rough. One of the qualities of this course is the variety of holes and of the shots you need to play. High-handicappers will have fun working their way around this course, but it may take them a little longer than usual to get home safely. Skövde has been elected as "the best course built in the 90's in Sweden". And the 9-holer is an exciting proposition.

Skövde Golfklubb — 1991

Box 269
S - 541 26 SKÖVDE

Office	Sekretariat	(46) 0500 - 411 535
Pro shop	Pro shop	(46) 0500 - 412 537
Fax	Fax	(46) 0500 - 410 116
Web	www.skovdegk.nu	
Situation	Läge	Skövde, 5 km
Annual closure	Årlig stängning	no
Weekly closure	Daglig stängning	no

Fees main season Tariff hög säsong		Full day
	Week days Veckodag	**We/Bank holidays** Lör/Söndag/Helgdag
Individual Individuellt	SKr 270	SKr 340
Couple Par	SKr 540	SKr 680

Juniors: SKr 170/220 (We) / Family (2 adults, 2 juniors): SKr 530/640 (We)

Caddie Caddie no — **Electric Trolley** El vagn no
Buggy Golfbil no — **Clubs** Klubbor no
Credit cards Kredit kort
VISA - Eurocard - MasterCard - AMEX - DC

Lerdala
Mariestad
48
Töreboda
Skara
Skövde
Tibro
49
49
Vämb
GOLF
Skultorp
km
0 2 4
48
46
Falköping

Access Tillfart : Jönköping R47/48 → Skövde. R49 → Skara. Cementa/Rockwool, → Simsjön. Golf 2 km
Map 1 on page 1212 Karta 1 se sid: 1212

GOLF COURSE — BANA — 17/20

Site	Läge	
Maintenance	Underhåll	
Architect	Arkitekt	Peter Nordwall
Type	Karaktär	parkland
Relief	Nivåskillnader	
Water in play	Vatten på spelfältet	
Exp. to wind	Vindutsatt	
Trees in play	Träd på spelfältet	

Scorecard Scorekort	**Chp.** Back tees	**Mens** Herrtee	**Ladies** Damtee
Length Längd	6215	5740	4885
Par	72	72	72
Slope system	—	136	127

Advised golfing ability Rekommenderad spelnivå — 0 12 24 36
Hcp required Hcp erfordrad — 36

CLUB HOUSE & AMENITIES — KLUBBHUS OCH OMGIVNING — 7/10

Pro shop Pro shop
Driving range Träningsbana
Sheltered tak 5 mats - On grass på gräs yes - Putting-green putting-green yes - Pitching-green pitching-green yes

HOTEL FACILITIES — HOTELL OMGIVNING — 7/10

HOTELS HOTELL
Billingehus - Skövde 3 km
240 rooms, D SKr 1403
Tel (46) 0500 - 445 700, Fax (46) 0500 - 483 880

Billingen - Skövde 4 km
106 rooms, D SKr 1650
Tel (46) 0500 - 410 790, Fax (46) 0500 - 417 310

RESTAURANTS RESTAURANGER
Skafferiet - Skövde 5 km
Tel (46) 0500 - 411 177
Parnassen - Skövde 5 km
Tel (46) 0500 - 411 912
Orient Palace - Skövde 5 km - Tel (46) 0500 - 489 883

Söderåsen

15	7	5

Sista biten upp mot klubbhuset är magnifik med träd på bägge sidor. Detta är ett typiskt skånskt landskap, och tankarna går till dignande smörgåsbord med lax, sill, ål och mycket mer. Banan kan dock lätt trycka ned din positivism med all skog, tjock ruff och strategiskt utplacerade diken. Var kylig: Det viktigaste är att ha ett bra huvud och förmåga att anpassa sig när saker inte riktigt går som det är tänkt. Sedan skadar det förstås inte heller med en smula ödmjukhet! Om du tycker om att spela banor som utvecklar dig som golfare kommer du älska att spela här. Även höghandicapare klarar sig runt om de inte överskattar sin egen kapacitet, vill säga. Greenerna är relativt små, och ofta väldigt snabba. Många är upphöjda och kräver ett delikat närspel – särskilt många greenträffar på rätt antal slag kan du nämligen inte räkna med. Detta gäller framför allt på par 4-hålen som är tuffa att nå på två slag.

The drive to this course set amidst an ocean of trees is simply splendid, the same goes for the typical countryside of Skåne, the country's southernmost province, famous for its smörgåsbord, a sort of huge brunch based on fish (salmon, herring and eels in season) and meat (particularly duck and goose). A forest, tall rough and a few very well located ditches can easily wear down the optimism of any golfer here. The basic requirements are good game strategy, the ability to adapt when things don't go quite the way you planned and a certain degree of humility. You will love playing here if you appreciate courses which help make you become a better golfer. High-handicappers, as long as they don't overestimate their playing ability, will get by without too much damage. The greens are rather small, frequently fast and slick, often elevated and always requiring a lot of touch to stop the ball when your approach has missed its target. Many holes stick in the mind, particularly the 2nd, a par 4 which is tough to reach in two shots and a good yardstick for gauging the shape of your game.

Söderåsens Golfklubb — 1972

Box 41
S - 260 50 BILLESHOLM

Office	Sekretariat	(46) 042 - 733 37
Pro shop	Pro shop	(46) 042 - 724 45
Fax	Fax	(46) 042 - 739 63
Web	www.golf.se/soderasensgk/	
Situation	Läge	Helsingborg, 20 km
Annual closure	Årlig stängning	no
Weekly closure	Daglig stängning	no

Fees main season Tariff hög säsong		Full day
	Week days Veckodag	We/Bank holidays Lör/Söndag/Helgdag
Individual Individuellt	SKr 320	SKr 380
Couple Par	SKr 640	SKr 760

Juniors: - 50% / Booking possible 5 days in advance

Caddie Caddie no — **Electric Trolley** El vagn no
Buggy Golfbil yes — **Clubs** Klubbor yes
Credit cards Kredit kort
VISA - Eurocard - MasterCard - AMEX - DC

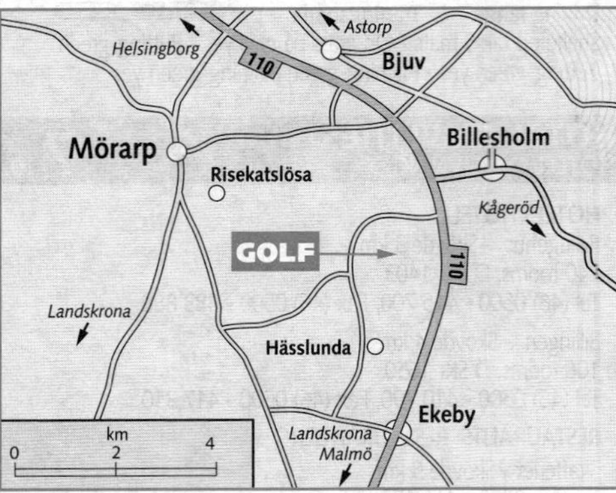

Access Tillfart : Malmö, E6. R110. → Golf
Map 1 on page 1212 Karta 1 se sid: 1212

GOLF COURSE — BANA — 15/20

Site	Läge	
Maintenance	Underhåll	
Architect	Arkitekt	Ture Bruce
Type	Karaktär	forest, parkland
Relief	Nivåskillnader	
Water in play	Vatten på spelfältet	
Exp. to wind	Vindutsatt	
Trees in play	Träd på spelfältet	

Scorecard Scorekort	Chp. Back tees	Mens Herrtee	Ladies Damtee
Length Längd	6050	5657	4879
Par	71	71	71
Slope system	—	134	128

Advised golfing ability Rekommenderad spelnivå: 0 12 24 36
Hcp required Hcp erfordrad 36

CLUB HOUSE & AMENITIES — KLUBBHUS OCH OMGIVNING — 7/10

Pro shop Pro shop
Driving range Träningsbana
Sheltered tak 2 mats - On grass på gräs yes - Putting-green putting-green yes - Pitching-green pitching-green yes

HOTEL FACILITIES — HOTELL OMGIVNING — 5/10

HOTELS HOTELL
Marina Plaza - Helsingborg 20 km
190 rooms, D SKr 1690
Tel (46) 042 - 192 100, Fax (46) 042 - 149 6‑6

Grand Hotell - Helsingborg 20 km
116 rooms, D SKr 1395
Tel (46) 042 - 380 400, Fax (46) 042 - 380 404

RESTAURANTS RESTAURANGER
Gastro - Helsingborg 20 km - Tel (46) 042 - 243 470
Le Petit - Helsingborg 20 km - Tel (46) 042 - 219 727
Oskar Trapp - Helsingborg 20 km
Tel (46) 042 - 146 044

Stenungsund

17	7	8

Utsikten med alla fjordar och öar går inte av för hackor. Från banan kan du skymta havet, men i grunden är detta en inlandsbana. Peter Nordwall har ritat på sitt speciella sätt, med andra ord: allting är stort. Anråseå, som skär genom banan, har han dock inte lyckats förvandla till en ocean. Hur som helst, atmosfären är en skotsk seaside-känsla, och layouten fordrar att du kan slå flera typer av slag med hygglig bollträff. Banan är ung med en gammal, mogen känsla. Skötseln är tipp-topp, med ett suveränt underhållningsarbete från banpersonalen, framför allt ska storleken och konditionen på utslagsplatserna nämnas. Dessutom är jordmånen utmärkt, vilket bidrar till att banan är i god kondition redan tidigt på våren. Detta är en riktig mästerskapsbana, vilket innebär att alla hinder finns åtminstone 200 meter från tee – höghandicapare kan därmed lugnt andas ut. Fast på greenerna kommer de att mötas av samma problem som de bättre spelarna – här är det känsla och fantasi som gäller.

From the Stenungsund course, you can make out the sea in the distance, although this is very much an inland course. Here again, Peter Nordwall has done everything in his own, oversized style, and while he has brought the Anräseå river into play, at least he was unable to transform it into an ocean. All the same, you still find a sort of Scottish seaside course atmosphere here, a layout which requires the full range of shots and some solid striking of the ball. Still very young, the course looks much older, especially thanks to maintenance and green-keeping. Of particular note are the size and excellent condition of the tee-boxes. The great soil has something to do with it, and the course is in good condition from early spring. A real championship course indeed, but as all the hazards are at least 220 yards (200 metres) from the tee, mid- and high-handicappers can breathe easily. They will however be on an equal footing with the better players when tackling the huge greens, where touch and feel count for much more than long game technique.

Stenungsund Golfklubb — 1993

PL Lundby 7480
S - 444 93 STENUNGSUND

Office	Sekretariat	(46) 0303 - 778 470
Pro shop	Pro shop	(46) 0303 - 778 188
Fax	Fax	(46) 0303 - 778 350
Web	www.stenungsundgk.se	
Situation	Läge	Göteborg, 45 km
Annual closure	Årlig stängning	no
Weekly closure	Daglig stängning	no

Fees main season Tariff hög säsong — 18 holes

	Week days Veckodag	We/Bank holidays Lör/Söndag/Helgdag
Individual Individuellt	SKr 340	SKr 340
Couple Par	SKr 680	SKr 680

Juniors: – 50%

Caddie Caddie no — **Electric Trolley** El vagn no
Buggy Golfbil yes — **Clubs** Klubbor yes
Credit cards Kredit kort no

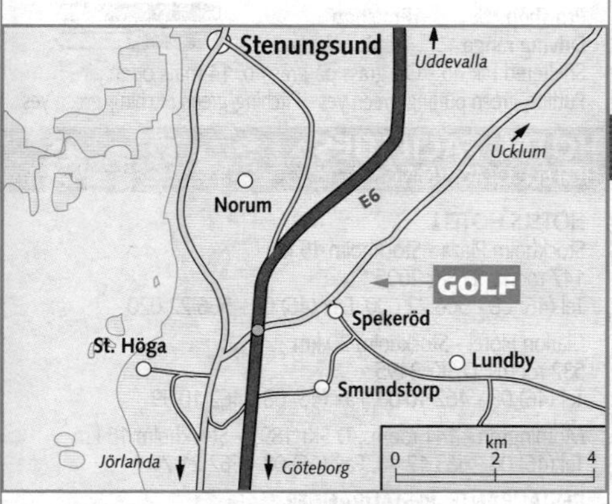

Access Tillfart : Göteborg, E6 → "Stora Höga-motet". → Ucklum. 1,5 km Golf
Map 1 on page 1212 Karta 1 se sid: 1212

GOLF COURSE — BANA — 17/20

Site	Läge	
Maintenance	Underhåll	
Architect	Arkitekt	Peter Nordwall
Type	Karaktär	parkland, open country
Relief	Nivåskillnader	
Water in play	Vatten på spelfältet	
Exp. to wind	Vindutsatt	
Trees in play	Träd på spelfältet	

Scorecard Scorekort	Chp. Back tees	Mens Herrtee	Ladies Damtee
Length Längd	6238	5825	4936
Par	72	72	72
Slope system	136	131	128

Advised golfing ability Rekommenderad spelnivå — 0 12 24 36
Hcp required Hcp erfordrad — 36

CLUB HOUSE & AMENITIES — KLUBBHUS OCH OMGIVNING — 7/10

Pro shop Pro shop
Driving range Träningsbana
Sheltered tak no - On grass på gräs yes - Putting-green putting-green yes - Pitching-green pitching-green yes

HOTEL FACILITIES — HOTELL OMGIVNING — 8/10

HOTELS

Stenungsbaden Yacht Club - Stenungsund 5 km
200 rooms, D SKr 1990
Tel (46) 0303 - 726 800, Fax (46) 0303 - 726 399

Solliden - 13 rooms, D SKr 995 - Stenungsund 5 km
Tel (46) 0303 - 698 70, Fax (46) 0303 - 870 00

Hotel Reis - 17 rooms, D SKr 595 - Stenungsund 5 km
Tel (46) 0303 - 770 011, Fax (46) 0303 - 824 72

RESTAURANTS RESTAURANGER

Bara Kök och Bar - Stenungsund 5 km
Tel (46) 0303 - 654 50

Sjökanten - Stenungsund 5 km - Tel (46) 0303 - 770 040

Stenungsbaden - Stenungsund 5 km - Tel (46) 0303 - 831 00

Stockholm

15	8	9

Layouten har en skotsk känsla, framför allt i hur bunkrarna har lagts ut. Detta är inget att förvånas över då såväl Morrison som Nicholson har varit inblandade i banbygget. Greenerna ligger väl skyddade bakom hinder, de är svåra att läsa, många har branta sluttningar och i en del fall ställs man dessutom inför ett blint inspel. De blinda slagen är dock ett mindre problem för de långtslående. Naturen är relativt kuperad, och med tanke på hur nära banan ligger staden är det förvånansvärt tyst och stilla. Träden ser inte bara till att dämpa oväsendet runt omkring de är dessutom en ständig oroskälla för oss golfare, inte minst på banans sex dogleg-hål. Om du ska göra en bra score här måste du ha ordning på spelet. Par är 69, och eftersom det finns få par 5-hål är birdiemöjligheterna begränsade. Banan är sällsynt charmig och oftast i excellent kondition. Se bara till att vara ute i god tid om du vill boka en starttid. Synd bara att man för något år sedan tvingades sälja mark till kommunen, nu är Kevinge i kortaste laget och hänger tyvärr inte riktigt med när man ser till utvecklingen av utrustningen och golfarnas uppskruvade krav.

The layout has a certain Scottish flavour to it, particularly in the way the bunkers are laid out. This is hardly surprising, as Morrison had a lot to do with the design; greens that are already tough to read, sharply contoured and sometimes blind are also very well guarded. The blind shots are perhaps less of a problem for long hitters, as the layout is rather hilly and strangely quiet for a city course. The trees dampen the surrounding noise but are also a major hazard, especially on the dog-legs. To score here, you simply have to play very well, especially since there are few par 5s to bring that welcome birdie or two. A charming course in superb condition, it is not easy to play, but if you have enough patience to secure a tee-off time, you will be well rewarded. Unfortunately the course is now really short and somewhat outdated.

Stockholms Kolfklubb — 1932

Kevingestrand 20
S - 182 57 DANDERYD

Office	Sekretariat	(46) 08 - 544 907 15
Pro shop	Pro shop	(46) 08 - 544 907 11
Fax	Fax	(46) 08 - 544 907 12
Web	www.sgk.nu	
Situation	Läge	Stockholm, 7 km
Annual closure	Årlig stängning	no
Weekly closure	Daglig stängning	no
Fees main season	Tariff hög säsong	Full day

	Week days / Veckodag	We/Bank holidays / Lör/Söndag/Helgdag
Individual Individuellt	SKr 500	SKr 600
Couple Par	SKr 1000	SKr 1200

Juniors: – 50%

Caddie Caddie no — **Electric Trolley** El vagn no
Buggy Golfbil no — **Clubs** Klubbor yes
Credit cards Kredit kort
VISA - Eurocard - MasterCard

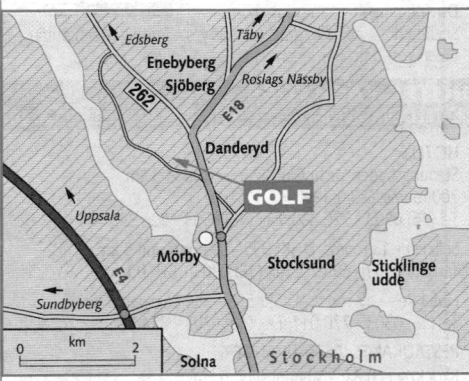

Access Tillfart : E18 → Norrtälje → "Danderyd Kyrka", 262 → Sollentuna, → Golf
Map 2 on page 1214 Karta 2 se sid: 1214

GOLF COURSE — BANA — 15/20

Site	Läge	
Maintenance	Underhåll	
Architect	Arkitekt	John Morrison, M. Nicholson
Type	Karaktär	parkland
Relief	Nivåskillnader	
Water in play	Vatten på spelfältet	
Exp. to wind	Vindutsatt	
Trees in play	Träd på spelfältet	

Scorecard Scorekort	Chp. Back tees	Mens Herrtee	Ladies Damtee
Length Längd	5437	5164	4552
Par	69	69	69
Slope system	124	121	122

Advised golfing ability Rekommenderad spelnivå — 0 12 24 36
Hcp required Hcp erfordrad — 24 Men, 30 Ladies

CLUB HOUSE & AMENITIES — KLUBBHUS OCH OMGIVNING — 8/10

Pro shop Pro shop
Driving range Träningsbana
Sheltered tak no - On grass på gräs no, 14 mats open air - Putting-green putting-green yes - Pitching-green pitching-green yes

HOTEL FACILITIES — HOTELL OMGIVNING — 9/10

HOTELS HOTELL
Stockholm Plaza - Stockholm 15 km
147 rooms, D SKr 2095
Tel (46) 08 - 566 22 000, Fax (46) 08 - 566 22 020

Clarion Hotel - Stockholm 20 km
532 rooms, D SKr 2495
Tel (46) 08 - 462 10 00, Fax (46) 08 - 462 10 99

Mornington - 141 rooms, D SKr 1895 - Stockholm 15 km
Tel (46) 08 - 663 12 40, Fax (46) 08 - 662 21 79

RESTAURANTS RESTAURANGER
Fredsgatan 12 - Stockholm 15 km - Tel (46) 08 - 248 052
Operakällaren - Stockholm 15 km - Tel (46) 08 - 676 58 01
Vassa Eggen - Stockholm 15 km - Tel (46) 08 - 21 61 69

Svartinge

17 | 8 | 7

Det är lätt att missa denna bana nordväst om Stockholm, dels för att den är mycket privat, dels för att den på ett vykortsvackert vis sjunker in i landskapet. Trots att den öppnade för bara något år sedan är den förbluffande mogen och kvalitetsmässigt redan en av landets bästa. Arkitekten har inte gjort någon hemlighet av att han eftersträvar att göra en så modern layout som möjligt, med stora utslagsplatser och greener, samt massor med hinder. Dessutom kantas smala fairways (åtminstone ser de smala ut) av tjock ruff. Den smarte golfaren kommer att få belöning för sitt tålamod, medan den djärve kanske känner att hinderna ser farligare ut än vad de i själva verket är och kommer undan med en och annan chansning. Svartinge har en bra harmoni och balans, framför allt gillade vi de fyra avslutningshålen som kommer kräva all din koncentration och skicklighet. Längs hela vänstersidan på det 18:e vaktar vatten. Ett nytt klubbhus har uppförts, en blandning av modernism och klassism – lite som banan själv, faktiskt.

Happy and hidden, this course is in any case very private and tucked away in a landscape of countryside and woods that would make a great postcard from Sweden. Opened recently, the course's maturity already makes this one of the country's finest. The architect made no bones about going for distinctly modern styling with large tee-boxes and greens and the widespread presence of hazards, all dangerous and calling for careful consideration. What's more, the tall rough makes for some narrow fairways. The wise golfer will see his patience rewarded while the bolder player might also feel that the dangers are less real than they look and come through largely unscathed. On a well-balanced course, we especially liked the four closing holes where your last ounces of strength will come in handy to stay out of trouble, especially on the par-5 18th with water on the left. The new club-house is a blend of modernism and classicism, much like the course itself.

Svartinge Golf — 2001

Svartinge Gård
S - 192 77 SOLLENTUNA

Office	Sekretariat	(46) 08 - 594 822 50
Pro shop	Pro shop	(46) 08 - 594 822 50
Fax	Fax	(46) 08 - 754 31 40
Web	www.svartingegolf.se	
Situation	Läge	Stockholm, 45 km
Annual closure	Årlig stängning	no
Weekly closure	Daglig stängning	no

Fees main season Tariff hög säsong	Week days Veckodag	We/Bank holidays Lör/Söndag/Helgdag
	18 holes	
Individual Individuellt	SKr 400	SKr 600
Couple Par	SKr 800	SKr 1200

Full day: SKr 600/800 (We) - Only members' guests

Caddie Caddie no — **Electric Trolley** El vagn no

Buggy Golfbil no — **Clubs** Klubbor no

Credit cards Kredit kort
VISA - Eurocard - MasterCard - AMEX - DC

Upplands Väsby
E4
GOLF
Holmb-od-avägen
Norrviken
Kungsängen
östra Järvafältets Naturreservat
Stockholm
Sollentuna
km 0 1 2

Access Tillfart : Stockholm, E4 North → Upplands Väsby. At Rotebro, turn left → Stäket. After 1 km, at Bisslinge, turn right.
Map 2 on page 1214 Karta 2 se sid: 1214

GOLF COURSE — BANA — 17/20

Site	Läge	
Maintenance	Underhåll	
Architect	Arkitekt	Peter Nordwall
Type	Karaktär	inland, parkland
Relief	Nivåskillnader	
Water in play	Vatten på spelfältet	
Exp. to wind	Vindutsatt	
Trees in play	Träd på spelfältet	

Scorecard Scorekort	Chp. Back tees	Mens Herrtee	Ladies Damtee
Length Längd	6363	5852	4946
Par	72	72	72
Slope system	—	—	—

Advised golfing ability Rekommenderad spelnivå — 0 12 24 36

Hcp required Hcp erfordrad — 36

CLUB HOUSE & AMENITIES — KLUBBHUS OCH OMGIVNING — 8/10

Pro shop Pro shop
Driving range Träningsbana
Sheltered tak 2 mats - On grass på gräs yes - Putting-green putting-green yes - Pitching-green pitching-green yes

HOTEL FACILITIES — HOTELL OMGIVNING — 7/10

HOTELS HOTELL
Clarion Hotel - 532 rooms, D SKr 2495 - Stockholm 35 km
Tel (46) 08 - 462 10 00, Fax (46) 08 - 462 10 99

Stockholm Plaza - 147 rooms, D SKr 2095 - Stockholm 25 km
Tel (46) 08 - 566 22 000, Fax (46) 08 - 566 22 020

Grand Hotel - 307 rooms, D SKr 4400 - Stockholm 30 km
Tel (46) 08 - 679 3500, Fax (46) 08 - 611 8606

RESTAURANTS RESTAURANGER
Edsbacka Bistro - Stockholm 10 km
Tel (46) 08 - 631 00 34
Stallmästaregården - Stockholm 30 km
Tel (46) 08 - 610 13 00
Annakahn - Stockholm 30 km - Tel (46) 08 - 440 30 00

Täby

16 | 7 | 7

Klubbhuset ligger i en gammal herrgård i trä. Från verandan njuter du av dagens vedermödor och blickar ut över 18e greenen. När du tänker tillbaka på din runda kan du reflektera en stund över att det var här som Jesper Parnevik lärde sig spela golf. Då förstår man varför han blev den mästare som han är på att manövrera och kontrollera bollen. På Täby kommer nämligen alla klubbor i bagen till användning. Du kommer definitivt råka ut för några rejäla överraskningar. Banan ligger i ett kuperat skogsområde, och det är sällan som du får ett platt läge (vilket kan vara knepigt för höghandicaparen). På 14e kliver du plötsligt ut ur skogen och på de fyra följande hålen ändrar banan karaktär. Nu är det seaside-golf som gäller! Fast havet heter här Vallentunasjön. På Täby, som på så många andra banor, är det viktigt att kunna skruva bollen från tee för att få ett så bra inspelsläge som möjligt (om du nu inte behärskar att slå bollen spikrakt, vilket är det svåraste slaget i golf). Om du bara har en dag över för golfspel så spela Ullna på förmiddagen och Täby på eftermiddagen, och du kommer få uppleva fantastiskt greenkeeper-arbete i en underbar miljö alldeles nära Stockholm.

When looking back over your round, you might well remember that Jesper Parnevik learned his trade here. No wonder he became such a good worker of the ball. At Täby, you need every club in your bag and every shot in the book. Expect a few surprises too, as the holes are laid out in the middle of a forest over hilly terrain, meaning that you are hardly ever playing the ball from a flat lie (not easy for high-handicappers). Suddenly, when playing holes 14 through 17, you are in a whole change of scenery, similar to a seaside course except that here the course unwinds alongside lake Vallentunasjön. At Täby as elsewhere, astute placing of the drive is essential off the tee, fading and drawing the ball. If you only have one day, play Ullna in the morning and Täby in the afternoon to make the most of superb green-keeping and a magnificent location so close to Stockholm.

Täby Golfklubb — 1968

Skålhamra Gård
S - 187 70 TÄBY

Office	Sekretariat	(46) 08 - 510 232 61
Pro shop	Pro shop	(46) 08 - 510 232 61
Fax	Fax	(46) 08 - 510 234 41
Web	www.taby-gk.com	
Situation	Läge	Stockholm, 25 km
Annual closure	Årlig stängning	no
Weekly closure	Daglig stängning	no

Fees main season Tariff hög säsong	Week days Veckodag	Full day We/Bank holidays Lör/Söndag/Helgdag
Individual Individuellt	SKr 450	SKr 450
Couple Par	SKr 900	SKr 900

Juniors: – 50% / Maximum of three players before 8:00

Caddie Caddie no — **Electric Trolley** El vagn no
Buggy Golfbil yes — **Clubs** Klubbor yes
Credit cards Kredit kort
VISA - Eurocard - MasterCard

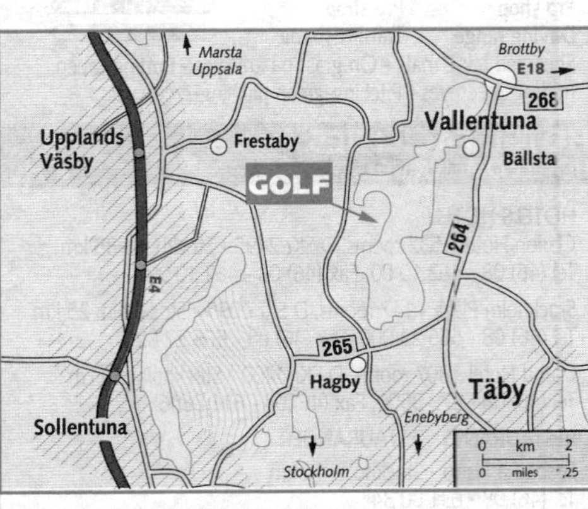

Access Tillfart : Stockholm, E18 → Vallentuna, "Danderyds Kyrka". 3 km → "Skålhamra 7"
Map 2 on page 1214 Karta 2 se sid: 1214

GOLF COURSE — BANA — 16/20

Site	Läge	
Maintenance	Underhåll	
Architect	Arkitekt	Nils Sköld
Type	Karaktär	seaside course, parkland
Relief	Nivåskillnader	
Water in play	Vatten på spelfältet	
Exp. to wind	Vindutsatt	
Trees in play	Träd på spelfältet	

Scorecard Scorekort	Chp. Back tees	Mens Herrtee	Ladies Damtee
Length Längd	6105	5812	5036
Par	72	72	72
Slope system	132	129	129

Advised golfing ability Rekommenderad spelnivå — 0 12 24 36
Hcp required Hcp erfordrad — 30 Men, 34 Ladies

CLUB HOUSE & AMENITIES — KLUBBHUS OCH OMGIVNING — 7/10

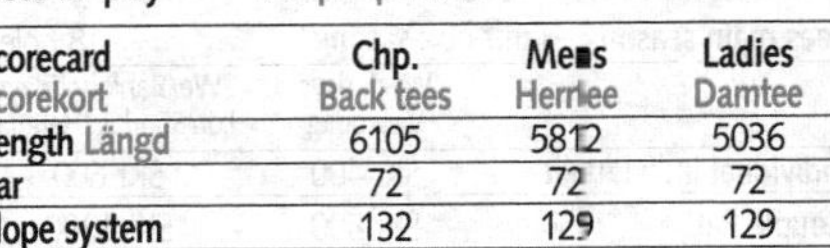

Pro shop Pro shop
Driving range Träningsbana
Sheltered tak 3 mats - On grass på gräs no, 24 mats open air - Putting-green putting-green yes - Pitching-green pitching-green yes

HOTEL FACILITIES — HOTELL OMGIVNING — 7/10

HOTELS HOTELL

Radisson SAS Royal Park - Stockholm 20 km
184 rooms, D SKr 2420
Tel (46) 08 - 624 55 00, Fax (46) 08 - 858 566

First Hotel Reisen - Stockholm 25 km
144 rooms, D SKr 2543
Tel (46) 08 - 223 260, Fax (46) 08 - 201 559

Lady Hamilton - 34 rooms, D SKr 1790 - Stockholm 25 km
Tel (46) 08 - 506 401 00, Fax (46) 08 - 506 401 10

RESTAURANTS RESTAURANGER

Edsbacka Krog - Sollentuna 15 km - Tel (46) 08 - 850 815
Stallmästaregården - Stockholm 25 km
Tel (46) 08 - 610 13 00

Torekov

15 | 7 | 7

Torekov ligger längst ute på Bjärehalvön, en halvö norr om Helsingborg. Det här är Sveriges Brighton. Banan öppnade redan 1925 men byggdes om i början av 90-talet av Nils Sköld. Vi kan tillägga att han lyckades väl. Klimatet och sandjorden gör det i princip möjligt att spela året om här. Banan är kort, men kräver bra drives eller långa järnslag från tee för att ge dig möjlighet att spela in mot greenerna med ett mellanjärn eller ett kort järn. Det är i varje fall vad du kan hoppas på de dagar det är vindstilla, vilket händer ungefär två gånger om året. De andra 363 dagarna får du plocka fram ditt skotska spel och studsa och rulla bollen upp på greener som ofta är hårda och snabba. Det finns definitivt bättre golfbanor än denna, men få har en större charm och ett sådant lugnt behagligt tempo. Några monsterhål finns inte så detta är en perfekt bana för hela familjen att åka till. Dessutom, har du bra bollträff finns möjligheten till en låg runda. Du kommer inte att vara ensam – att spela här är en övning i "kändis-spaning".

Torekov is situated at the tip of a peninsula to the north of Malmö and Helsingborg. This is the Swedish Brighton. The course was altered in the early 1990s by Nils Sköld, for the better we might add. The climate and largely sandy soil make this course playable virtually all year. A very short layout, it calls for some excellent driving or long irons off the tee to end up with a short or medium iron going into the green, at least if the wind is quiet. This is the case about two days a year. For the other 363 days, you will have to call on all your Scottish flair when selecting the right club to play and master the low shots to hit greens that are often firm and slick. There are certainly better courses than this, but few have greater charm and such an easy pace and tempo. There are few high-risk holes, so this is an ideal course for family holidays, where the pleasure of playing together counts for more than carding a great score. You won't be alone, as playing here is an exercise in "celebrity spotting".

Torekovs Golfklubb — 1925

Box 81
S - 260 93 TOREKOV

Office	Sekretariat	(46) 0431 - 449 844
Pro shop	Pro shop	(46) 0431 - 449 847
Fax	Fax	(46) 0431 - 364 916
Web	www.togk.se	
Situation	Läge	Båstad, 15 km
Annual closure	Årlig stängning	no
Weekly closure	Daglig stängning	no

Fees main season Tariff hög säsong	Week days Veckodag	We/Bank holidays Lör/Söndag/Helgdag
		Full day
Individual Individuellt	SKr 400	SKr 450
Couple Par	SKr 800	SKr 900

Juniors: – 50% / We: GF after 12:00

Caddie Caddie no — **Electric Trolley** El vagn yes
Buggy Golfbil yes — **Clubs** Klubbor yes
Credit cards Kredit kort
VISA - Eurocard - MasterCard - AMEX

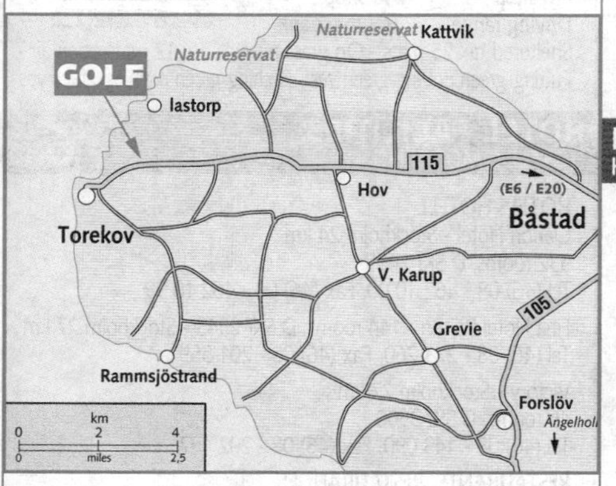

Access Tillfart : Båstad R115.
Map 1 on page 1212 Karta 1 se sid: 1212

GOLF COURSE — BANA — 15/20

Site	Läge	
Maintenance	Underhåll	
Architect	Arkitekt	Nils Sköld
Type	Karaktär	seaside course, open country
Relief	Nivåskillnader	
Water in play	Vatten på spelfältet	
Exp. to wind	Vindutsatt	
Trees in play	Träd på spelfältet	

Scorecard Scorekort	Chp. Back tees	Mens Herrtee	Ladies Damtee
Length Längd	5707	5707	5027
Par	72	72	72
Slope system	—	133	128

Advised golfing ability Rekommenderad spelnivå — 0 12 24 36
Hcp required Hcp erfordrad — 36

CLUB HOUSE & AMENITIES — KLUBBHUS OCH OMGIVNING — 7/10

Pro shop Pro shop
Driving range Träningsbana
Sheltered tak 1 mat - On grass på gräs no, 14 mats open air - Putting-green putting-green ja - Pitching-green pitching-green ja

HOTEL FACILITIES — HOTELL OMGIVNING — 7/10

HOTELS HOTELL

Kattegatt - 11 rooms, D SKr 1695 - Torekov 5 km
Tel (46) 0431 - 363 002, Fax (46) 0431 - 363 003

Margretetorp - 60 rooms, D SKr 1685 - Ängelholm 20 km
Tel (46) 0431 - 454 450, Fax (46) 0431 - 454 877

Hemmeslöv - 90 rooms, D SKr 800 - Båstad 20 km
Tel (46) 0431 - 742 65, Fax (46) 0431 - 748 88

RESTAURANTS RESTAURANGER

Kattegatt - Torekov 5 km
Tel (46) 0431 - 363 002
Enehall - Båstad 10 km
Tel (46) 0431 - 750 15
Margretetorp - Båstad 20 km - Tel (46) 0431 - 454 450

Ullna

17	8	6

En dag på Ullna måste börja med att blicka ut över Ullnasjön och se solen reflektera i vattnet. Vatten kommer i spel på tolv av hålen och tredje hålet är en kort och oförglömlig par 3:a med en ögreen. För att leverera en bra score här är det nödvändigt att du är i absolut toppform. Ullna är en väldigt ärlig bana som inte gömmer sina hinder – de syns tydligt från tee. Den är dessutom nästan helt platt, och sammantaget är den ett av de finaste exempel på "targetgolf" som finns i Sverige. De duktiga spelarna kommer säkert göra en eller annan birdie för att kompensera för oundvikliga bogeys. Sven Tumba, banarkitekten, har dock inte gjort livet lätt för höghandicaparen, som kommer att tvingas plocka upp bollen på många hål (om han har några kvar, vill säga). Ullna är spektakulär, konstgjord och välmanikyrerad, och en högst oförglömlig upplevelse. Och då inte bara för hål 4 och 17, som är bland de bästa som man kan finna i Sverige. Intressant är också det nybyggda 11 hålet, en fin par 3a över vatten. Det här är en bana för konnässörer och skickliga spelare som kan slå bollen högt och med precision mot fantastiska greener.

Water is almost everywhere, coming into play on 12 holes: you will need to be on top of your game to card a good score. This is a very forthright course which clearly shows it hand in terms of hazards; it is also virtually flat and one of the finest examples of target golf in the whole of Sweden. All the same, while the best players should come through unscathed and find a few birdies to make up for the inevitable bogeys, architect Sven Tumba did not spare too many thoughts for the higher-handicappers, who will spend a lot of time picking up their balls (if they have any left). Spectacular, artificial and finely contoured, Ullna is a memorable course, and not only for holes 4 and 17, two of the finest in the country, but also for the new number 11, a pretty par 3 full of water. This is a course for connoisseurs and skilled players who can hit high, accurate shots into excellent greens.

Ullna Golf & Country Club — 1981

Rosenkälla
S - 184 94 Åkersberga

Office	Sekretariat	(46) 08 - 514 412 30
Pro shop	Pro shop	(46) 08 - 514 412 30
Fax	Fax	(46) 08 - 510 260 68
Web	www.ullnagolf.se	
Situation	Läge	Stockholm, 27 km
Annual closure	Årlig stängning	no
Weekly closure	Daglig stängning	no

Fees main season Tariff hög säsong	Week days Veckodag	We/Bank holidays Lör/Söndag/Helgdag
		Full day
Individual Individuellt	SKr 600	SKr 600
Couple Par	SKr 1200	SKr 1200

Members' guests: SKr 450
Maximum handicap in a group: 72

Caddie Caddie no — Electric Trolley El vagn no
Buggy Golfbil yes — Clubs Klubbor yes

Credit cards Kredit kort
VISA - Eurocard - MasterCard - AMEX - DC

1266

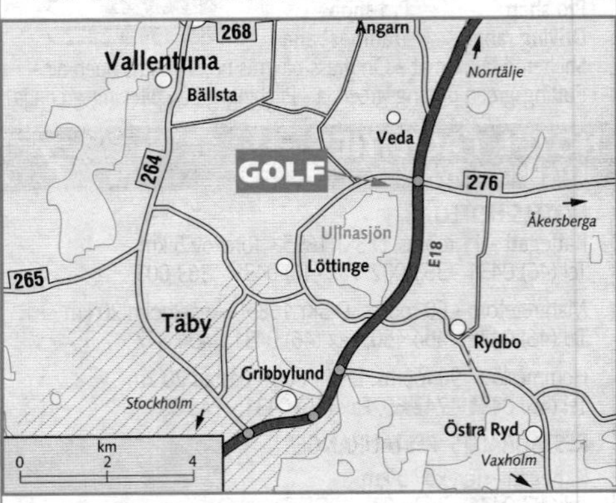

Access Tillfart : Stockholm, E 18 → Norrtälje. → Åkersberga, → Gribbylund, → Golf
Map 2 on page 1214 Karta 2 se sid: 1214

GOLF COURSE / BANA — 17/20

Site	Läge	
Maintenance	Underhåll	
Architect	Arkitekt	Sven Tumba
Type	Karaktär	parkland
Relief	Nivåskillnader	
Water in play	Vatten på spelfältet	
Exp. to wind	Vindutsatt	
Trees in play	Träd på spelfältet	

Scorecard Scorekort	Chp. Back tees	Mens Herrtee	Ladies Damtee
Length Längd	6210	5750	4915
Par	72	72	72
Slope system	—	136	131

Advised golfing ability / Rekommenderad spelnivå: 0 12 24 36
Hcp required / Hcp erfordrad: 24 Men, 30 Ladies

CLUB HOUSE & AMENITIES / KLUBBHUS OCH OMGIVNING — 8/10

Pro shop — Pro shop
Driving range — Träningsbana
Sheltered tak 25 mats - On grass på gräs no, 12 mats open air - Putting-green putting-green yes - Pitching-green pitching-green yes

HOTEL FACILITIES / HOTELL OMGIVNING — 6/10

HOTELS HOTELL
Clarion Hotel - Stockholm 24 km
532 rooms, D SKr 2495
Tel (46) 08 - 462 10 00, Fax (46) 08 - 462 10 99

First Hotel Reisen - 144 rooms, D SKr 2543 - Stockholm 27 km
Tel (46) 08 - 223 260, Fax (46) 08 - 201 559

Victory - Stockholm 27 km
45 rooms, D SKr 3500
Tel (46) 08 - 143 090, Fax (46) 08 - 202 177

RESTAURANTS RESTAURANGER
Eriks - Stockholm 27 km - Tel (46) 08 - 238 500
Annakahn - Stockholm 27 km - Tel (46) 08 - 440 30 00
Den Gyldene Freden - Stockholm - Tel (46) 08 - 249 760

Varberg *Västra* 17 | 7 | 6

Den här klubben, som också äger ytterligare en 18-hålsbana (Varberg Östra, några kilometer längre bort) frågade arkitekten Tommy Nordström om han inte kunde designa en tekniskt krävande bana som skulle flyta in i landskapsbilden. Resultatet blev en blandning av en brittisk parkbana, inte olik Belfry, och en amerikansk anläggning med stora, härliga greener. Och just »stort«, det är vad man förknippar layouten med. Här är allting "XL", vilket ger en berusande frihetskänsla från utslagsplatsen. Men akta dig för att tappa koncentrationen, ruffen är ruggig och diken och dammar är ofta i spel. De stora greenerna gör dock det lätt att hålla undan från greenbunkrarna. En poäng med layouten är att den gynnar den sämre golfaren som från tee inte når många av hinderna. Varberg är en bra och modern bana som kräver en god bollträff, en het putter och ett kallt huvud för att du ska nå klubbhuset utan alltför många missöden. Hade banan legat närmare en storstad hade den garanterat fått större uppmärksamhet.

Very close to the fortified town of Varberg, this club, which also owns a second separate 18 hole course (Östra, a few miles down the road), asked Nordström to design a technically challenging course to blend in with the countryside. The end-impression is that of a parkland course in the Belfry vein with the quality of the greens reminiscent of American courses. Everything is outsized here, whence the feeling of freedom on the tee. Watch out though, as the rough can be a shocker and ditches and ponds very often come into play. This is not so with a number of greenside bunkers, owing to the size of the greens. Let it be said in passing that the main hazards are within the reach of better players and tend to spare the mid-handicappers. A fine modern course which demands some good ball-striking, a hot putter and a clear head to see you home. People would almost certainly talk more about this course if it were close to a major city.

Varbergs GK — 1992

Himle
S - 430 10 TVÅÅKER

Office	Sekretariat	(46) 0340 - 480 380
Pro shop	Pro shop	(46) 0340 - 43 448
Fax	Fax	(46) 0340 - 480 388
Web	www.varbergsgk.com	
Situation	Läge	Varberg, 8 km
Annual closure	Årlig stängning	no
Weekly closure	Daglig stängning	no

Fees main season Tariff hög säsong		18 holes
	Week days Veckodag	We/Bank holidays Lör/Söndag/Helgdag
Individual Individuellt	SKr 380	SKr 380
Couple Par	SKr 760	SKr 760

Full dai: SKr 480 / Juniors: – 50%

Caddie Caddie no — **Electric Trolley** El vagn no

Buggy Golfbil yes — **Clubs** Klubbor yes

Credit cards Kredit kort
VISA - Eurocard - MasterCard - AMEX - DC

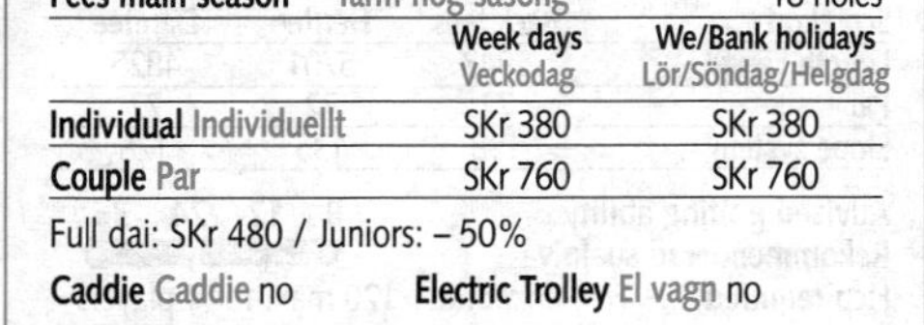

Göteborg
Varberg
Hunnestad
A6
Spannarp
GOLF
Himle
Träslövsläge
Ås
Tvååker
Falkenberg
København
km 0 2 4
miles 0 1,25

Access Tillfart : Varberg, E6 South, Exit → "Golfbana"
Map 1 on page 1212 Karta 1 se sid: 1212

GOLF COURSE — BANA 17/20

Site	Läge	
Maintenance	Underhåll	
Architect	Arkitekt	Tommy Nordström
Type	Karaktär	parkland
Relief	Nivåskillnader	
Water in play	Vatten på spelfältet	
Exp. to wind	Vindutsatt	
Trees in play	Träd på spelfältet	

Scorecard Scorekort	Chp. Back tees	Mens Herrtee	Ladies Damtee
Length Längd	6435	5755	4855
Par	72	72	72
Slope system	141	135	130

Advised golfing ability Rekommenderad spelnivå — 0 12 24 36

Hcp required Hcp erfordrad — 36

CLUB HOUSE & AMENITIES — KLUBBHUS OCH OMGIVNING 7/10

Pro shop Pro shop
Driving range Träningsbana
Sheltered tak 5 mats - On grass på gräs yes - Putting-green putting-green yes - Pitching-green pitching-green yes

HOTEL FACILITIES — HOTELL OMGIVNING 6/10

HOTELS HOTELL

Comfort Hotel Fregatten - Varberg 10 km
93 rooms, D SKr 765
Tel (46) 0340 - 677 000, Fax (46) 0340 - 611 121

Best Western Varberg Stadshote - Varberg 10 km
123 rooms, D SKr 1375
Tel (46) 0340 - 690 100, Fax (46) 0340 - 690 101

Grand Hotel Falkenberg - Falkenberg 15 km
71 rooms, D from SKr 970
Tel Tel (46) 0346 - 144 , Fax (46) 0346 - 829 25

RESTAURANTS RESTAURANG

Lundkvistahahuset - Varberg 10 km - Tel (46) 0340 - 14 390
Café & Krog Stadt - Varberg 10 km - Tel (46) 0340 - 690 100

Värnamo

14	7	5

Tack vare E 4 ligger banan perfekt till för dig som färdas från Malmö till Stockholm, eller tvärtom. Ändå kan Värnamo, i en positiv mening, kännas som att komma till världens ände. Att släntra upp till klubbhuset en tidig morgon och titta ut över sjön Hindsen är en magisk upplevelse. Som så många andra svenska banor är Värnamo byggd på en romantisk, nästan teatralisk plats. Klarar du av par 3-hålen är du på väg mot en bra score. Fast den riktiga utmaningen finns i de något upphöjda greenerna som inte är alldeles lätta att läsa. Missar du en green skadar det inte om du har en vass lobbwedge i bagen. På Värnamo finns inga riktiga monsterhinder som avskräcker höghandicaparen, medan det för den bättre spelaren gäller att undvika skogen om han vill briljera inför släkt och vänner och visa vad han kan göra med en golfklubba. Olyckligtvis förstörde stormen 2005 ett stort antal träd, och bestal banan från några av dess mest dramatiska upplevelser.

A very reachable course, which is close to the motorway running across the country from Malmö to Stockholm. But it is still far enough for the golfer to feel as if he were playing at the ends of the earth. Arriving early morning at the club-house built on a small hill overlooking Lake Hindsen is a magic experience. Like many Swedish courses, this has a romantic, theatrical setting, but that is only the beginning. It might be on the short side, but start off by getting the better of the par 3s and you can think about carding a good score. Here, the real challenge lies with the slightly elevated greens, which are sharply contoured and tough to read. You will also need a lot of touch. A missed green cries out for a lob-wedge, if you have one. There are no excessive hazards to deter the high-handicapper, while the better players will have to come to terms with the trees before showing friends and family what he or she can do with a golf club. Unfortunately, the storms of 2005 destroyed a large number of trees and deprived the course of some of its more "dramatic" moments.

Värnamo Golfklubb 1962

Box 146
S - 331 21 VÄRNAMO

Office	Sekretariat	(46) 0370 - 239 91
Pro shop	Pro shop	(46) 0370 - 239 93
Fax	Fax	(46) 0370 - 239 92
Web	www.varnamogk.com	
Situation	Läge	Jönköping, 70 km

Värnamo, 7 km

Annual closure	Årlig stängning	no
Weekly closure	Daglig stängning	no
Fees main season	Tariff hög säsong	Full day

	Week days Veckodag	We/Bank holidays Lör/Söndag/Helgdag
Individual Individuellt	SKr 300	SKr 350
Couple Par	SKr 475	SKr 525

Juniors: SKr 130/160 (We)

Caddie Caddie no — **Electric Trolley** El vagn no

Buggy Golfbil yes — **Clubs** Klubbor yes

Credit cards Kredit kort
VISA - Eurocard - MasterCard - DC

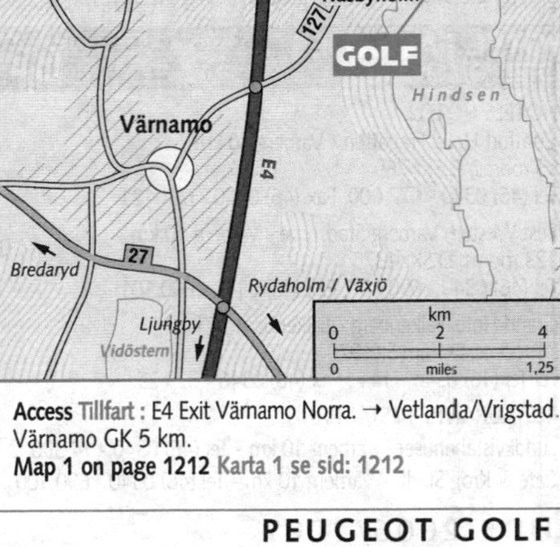

Access Tillfart : E4 Exit Värnamo Norra. → Vetlanda/Vrigstad. Värnamo GK 5 km.
Map 1 on page 1212 Karta 1 se sid: 1212

GOLF COURSE 14/20
BANA

Site	Läge	
Maintenance	Underhåll	
Architect	Arkitekt	Nils Sköld
Type	Karaktär	forest, parkland
Relief	Nivåskillnader	
Water in play	Vatten på spelfältet	
Exp. to wind	Vindutsatt	
Trees in play	Träd på spelfältet	

Scorecard Scorekort	**Chp.** Back tees	**Mens** Herrtee	**Ladies** Damtee
Length Längd	5943	5701	4825
Par	72	72	72
Slope system	138	135	126

Advised golfing ability 0 12 24 36
Rekommenderad spelnivå
Hcp required Hcp erfordrad 120 max. for 4 players

CLUB HOUSE & AMENITIES 7/10
KLUBBHUS OCH OMGIVNING

Pro shop Pro shop
Driving range Träningsbana
Sheltered tak 2 mat - On grass på gräs no, 22 mats open air
Putting-green putting-green yes - Pitching-green pitching-green yes

HOTEL FACILITIES 5/10
HOTELL OMGIVNING

HOTELS HOTELL
Park Inn - Värnamo 7 km
125 rooms, D SKr 1395
Tel (46) 0370 - 656 600, Fax (46) 0370 - 656 609

Tre Liljor - Värnamo 7 km
39 rooms, D SKr 1400
Tel (46) 0370 - 473 00, Fax (46) 0370 - 168 90

RESTAURANTS RESTAURANGER
Harrys - Värnamo 7 km
Tel (46) 0370 - 498 00

Napoli - Värnamo 7 km
Tel (46) 0370 - 120 60

Vasatorp

16 | 7 | 7

Vasatorps golfbana gömmer inga obehagliga överraskningar: Slå rakt och håll dig på fairway, och du kommer att göra en bra score (svårare än så är inte golf). Trots den täta skogen är banan förhållandevis bred – även för Ballesteros, som när han vann SEO här spred sina drives både till höger och vänster. Om du ska ha en chans att nå på rätt antal slag och få bra inspelsvinklar måste du välja drivern från tee. Många greener är omgärdade av kullar, vilket ställer höga krav på dina inspel. Greenerna är relativt stora och kan bjuda på en stor variation vad gäller flaggplaceringarna, något som kan inverka högst påtagligt på ditt resultat. Här är det amerikansk målgolf som gäller – höga inspel är att föredra framför att rulla in bollen. För höghandicaparen är det bäst att spela här på sommaren då marken är torr och bollen rullar långt. Sagt det kan vi konstatera att Vasatorp kan bli ganska blöt, framför allt på våren. Den andra 18-hålsbanan som finns här måste också nämnas… precis som en helt ny niohålsbana.

This course has no traps in store: hit it straight, keep in the fairway and you will card a good score (golf is that simple). Despite the trees, the whole complex is wide, enough so for Ballesteros to have won here even though he sprayed his drives left and right into the undergrowth. Quite simply, here you have to hit the driver if you want to reach the long holes in regulation and approach the greens from the right angle. A number of sandhills and mounds can complicate your approach shots. The greens are pretty huge, with many different pin positions that can seriously damage your card, especially since here you have to play target golf rather than bump and run shots. High-handicappers are best advised to play Vasatorps in summer, when the ground is dry and affords welcome roll for added length. With this said, this course can get rather wet, especially in the Spring. One last word for the excellent second 18-hole course here... and a brand new 9-hole layout.

Vasatorps Golfklubb — 1973

Box 13035
S - 250 13 HELSINGBORG

Office	Sekretariat	(46) 042 - 235 058
Pro shop	Pro shop	(46) 042 - 235 045
Fax	Fax	(46) 042 - 235 135
Web	www.vasatorpsgk.se	
Situation	Läge	Helsingborg, 7 km
Annual closure	Årlig stängning	no
Weekly closure	Daglig stängning	no

Fees main season Tariff hög säsong — 18 holes

	Week days Veckodag	We/Bank holidays Lör/Söndag/Helgdag
Individual Individuellt	SKr 340	SKr 380
Couple Par	SKr 680	SKr 760

Juniors: – 50% / Full day 510/570 (We)

Caddie Caddie no — **Electric Trolley** El vagn yes
Buggy Golfbil no — **Clubs** Klubbor yes
Credit cards Kredit kort
VISA - Eurocard - MasterCard - AMEX - DC

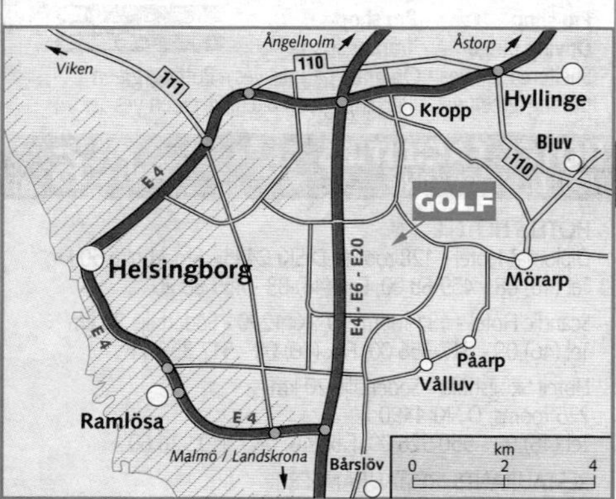

Access Tillfart : Kelsingborg, E4 West (Österut) → "Höganäsrondellen". → Råå. Turn left at traffic lights (Trafiklij, vä). 500 m → Kropp.
Map 1 on page 1212 Karta 1 se sid: 1212

GOLF COURSE — BANA — 16/20

Site	Läge	
Maintenance	Underhåll	
Architect	Arkitekt	Ture Bruce
Type	Karaktär	forest, parkland
Relief	Nivåskillnader	
Water in play	Vatten på spelfältet	
Exp. to wind	Vindutsatt	
Trees in play	Träd på spelfältet	

Scorecard Scorekort	Chp. Back tees	Mens Herrtee	Ladies Damtee
Length Längd	6165	5895	5510
Par	72	72	72
Slope system	136	133	128

Advised golfing ability Rekommenderad spelnivå — 0 12 24 36
Hcp required Hcp erfordrad — 36

CLUB HOUSE & AMENITIES — KLUBBHUS OCH OMGIVNING — 7/10

Pro shop Pro shop
Driving range Träningsbana
Sheltered tak 7 mats - On grass på gräs no, 30 mats open air
Putting-green putting-green yes - Pitching-green pitching-green yes

HOTEL FACILITIES — HOTELL OMGIVNING — 7/10

HOTELS HOTELL
Marina Plaza - Helsingborg 7 km
190 rooms, D SKr 1690
Tel (46) 042 - 192 100, Fax (46) 042 - 149 616

Grand Hotell - Helsingborg 7 km
116 rooms, D SKr 1395
Tel (46) 042 - 380 400, Fax (46) 042 - 380 404

RESTAURANTS RESTAURANGER
Oskar Trapp - Helsingborg 7 km
Tel (46) 042 - 146 044
Niklas - Helsingborg 7 km
Tel (46) 042 - 280 050

Vidbynäs

17 | 8 | 6

Amerikanen Curley (från Schmidt-Curley) fick förtroendet att rita Axa-banan, den första av två banor i denna ambitiösa satsning. Tillsammans med partnern Schmidt är han van vid att hantera mastodontprojekt, som exempelvis Mission Hills i Kina. Så känns också deras professionalism igen i varje kontur på fairways och greener, bunkrarnas placering, fokuset på formerna, balansen mellan skogsbana och hedlandskap och däremellan några vattenhål. Det är slående hur väl avvägt som träd och vattenhinder tas in i spelet. Arkitektens digra kunskap om spelet märks i kraven; här gäller det att behärska bollflyktslagarna och ha ett smart huvud. Detta är en spännande bana, och finns det någon rättvisa kan man i varje fall konstatera att här belönas bra slag. En rad olika utslagsplatser gör det också möjligt att variera svårigheterna så att alla spelare har utbyte av rundan. Antingen faller du handlös för denna upplevelse eller så är du lite mer avvaktande, men är du på väg söderut från Stockholm ska du absolut ta chansen att stanna här och se med egna ögon.

This was an ambitious project assigned to the American Brian Curley, whose present Axa Course is the first of two 18-hole courses. With his partner Lee Schmidt, they are accustomed to handling mammoth projects, that of Landmark Golf in earlier times and Mission Hills in China today. Their professionalism can be felt here in lavish proportions on the fairways, greens, bunkering, the focus on shapes, the balance between forest, open country and lake-side holes and the way trees, salient rocks and stretches of water have been usefully brought into play. The need to flight the ball and use your brains also testifies to excellent knowledge of the game of golf and golfers. An exciting course to play where there is some justice in that it rewards good shots. And there will be some for everybody because the number of tee-boxes makes it possible to vary the difficulties. You may or may not like it, but you cannot afford to miss it when coming from Stockholm.

Vidbynäs GC — 2004

Vidbynäs Gård
S - 155 91 NYKVARN

Office	Sekretariat	(46) 08 - 554 906 00
Pro shop	Pro shop	(46) 08 - 554 906 06
Fax	Fax	(46) 08 - 554 906 29
Web	www.vidbynasgolf.se	
Situation	Läge	Södertälje, 20 km
Annual closure	Årlig stängning	nc
Weekly closure	Daglig stängning	nc

1270

Fees main season Tariff hög säsong	Week days Veckodag	We/Bank holidays Lör/Söndag/Helgdag
		18 holes
Individual Individuellt	SKr 500	SKr 600
Couple Par	SKr 1000	SKr 1200

Juniors: SKr 200/300 (We)

Caddie Caddie no — **Electric Trolley** El vagn no

Buggy Golfbil no — **Clubs** Klubbor no

Credit cards Kredit kort
VISA - Eurocard - MasterCard - AMEX

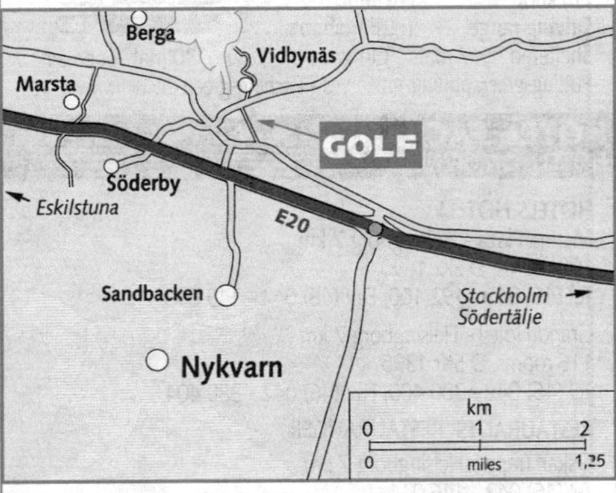

Access Tillfart : Stockholm, E20 → Göteborg. Exit after Södertälje → Nykvarn. Follow signs, golf 1,5 km

Map 2 on page 1215 Karta 2 se sid: 1215

GOLF COURSE — BANA — 17/20

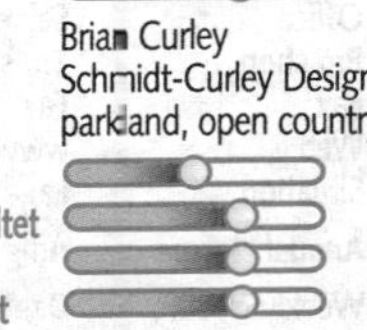

Site	Läge	
Maintenance	Underhåll	
Architect	Arkitekt	Brian Curley Schmidt-Curley Design
Type	Karaktär	parkland, open country
Relief	Nivåskillnader	
Water in play	Vatten på spelfältet	
Exp. to wind	Vindutsatt	
Trees in play	Träd på spelfältet	

Scorecard Scorekort	Chp. Back tees	Mens Herrtee	Ladies Damtee
Length Längd	6630	5877	4846
Par	72	72	72
Slope system	—	—	—

Advised golfing ability Rekommenderad spelnivå — 0 12 24 36

Hcp required Hcp erfordrad — 30 Men, 36 Ladies

CLUB HOUSE & AMENITIES — KLUBBHUS OCH OMGIVNING — 8/10

Pro shop Pro shop
Driving range Träningsbana
Sheltered tak yes - On grass på gräs yes - Putting-green putting-green yes - Pitching-green pitching-green yes

HOTEL FACILITIES — HOTELL OMGIVNING — 6/10

HOTELS HOTELL

Diplomat Hotel - 128 rooms, D SKr 2445 - Stockholm 50 km
Tel (46) 08 - 459 68 00, Fax (46) 08 - 459 68 20

Scandic Hotel - 131 rooms, D SKr 1290 - Södertälje 20 km
Tel (46) 08 - 517 356 00, Fax (46) 08 - 517 356 11

Hotell Skogshöjd - Södertälje 20 km
225 rooms, D SKr 1490
Tel (46) 08 - 550 926 00, Fax (46) 08 - 550 926 60

RESTAURANTS RESTAURANGER

The Osprey - on site
Tel (46) 08 - 554 906 03

Restaurang Skogshöjd - Södertälje 20 km
Tel (46) 08 - 550 926 00

Visby

16 | 7 | 5

Bli inte skrämd av Gotlands geografiska läge! Klimatet är milt och på sommaren flockas turisterna här. Precis som handelsmännen gjorde under medeltiden. Faktum är att Visby har så många avtryck från den här perioden att Unesco har satt staden på sin lista över kulturminnesmärkta platser. Kustlinjen är något alldeles extra, och nästan halva banan är också utlagd nära denna, resten av hålen vindlar fram i ett skogsparti. Det finns ingen hejd på alla hinder och det krävs att du inte släpper på koncentrationen. Även greenerna är lagom knepiga. De som byggdes 1959 är små och förrädiska, medan de som byggdes i början av 90-talet är större och mer kuperade. Som du kanske förstår är vinden här en avgörande faktor, något som du kommer att känna direkt på första hålet: Längs hela högersidan lurar vatten. För att ta dig till Gotland väntar en färjetur på 4–8 timmar (beroende på vilket bolag du åker med), så en bra idé är att stanna här i några dagar och spela banan flera gånger (samt niohålsbanan som ligger på området). Beställ "Dagens fisk" i restaurangen, njut av den och den magnifika utsikten.

On the isle of Gotland, the climate is very mild and the area is a famous holiday destination. Visby has so many vestiges of the Middle Ages that it is on the Unesco world heritage list of historical sites. This course is laid out half beside the sea, half amidst trees. There is no shortage of hazards to keep you on your toes, and the greens, too, can cause their share of problems. Those built in 1959 are small and treacherous, the others, built in the 1990s, are larger and contoured. Obviously, the wind here is a decisive factor, as you will see and feel straightaway on hole number one. Here, your brushes with water begin down the right-hand side of the fairway. Getting here involves a four to eight-hour trip (depending if you go by ferry or the new catamaran), so a good idea is to stay for several days, play the course a number of times (this and the adjacent seaside and forest nine-hole layout), and enjoy your dinner with the fish of the day and a great view over the sea.

Visby Golfklubb — 1959

Kronholmen Västergarn
S - 620 020 KLINTEHAMN

Office	Sekretariat	(46) 0498 - 200 930
Pro shop	Pro shop	(46) 0498 - 200 939
Fax	Fax	(46) 0498 - 200 932
Web	www.visbygk.com	
Situation	Läge	Visby , 25 km
Annual closure	Årlig stängning	no
Weekly closure	Daglig stängning	no

Fees main season Tariff hög säsong	18 holes	
	Week days Veckodag	**We/Bank holidays** Lör/Söndag/Helgdag
Individual Individuellt	SKr 400	SKr 400
Couple Par	SKr 800	SKr 800

Full day GF: SKr 600 / Juniors: – 50%

Caddie Caddie no — **Electric Trolley** El vagn no
Buggy Golfbil yes — **Clubs** Klubbor yes
Credit cards Kredit kort
VISA - Eurocard - MasterCard - AMEX

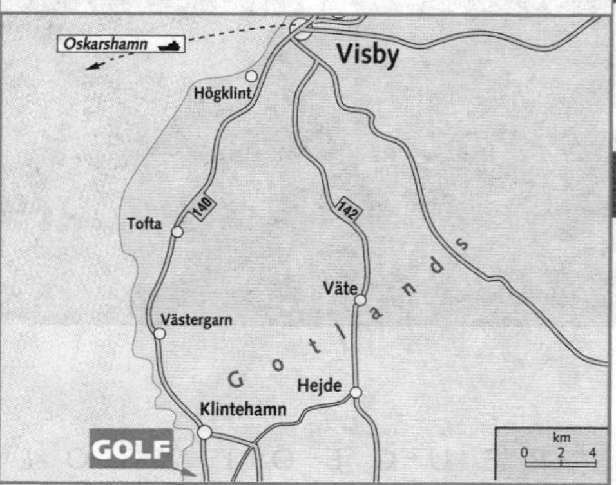

Access Tillfart : Stockholm, R79 → Nynäshamn. Ferry → Visby. R140 → Klintehamn. 25 km, → Golf
Map 1 on page 1213 Karta 1 se sid: 1213

GOLF COURSE — BANA — 16/20

Site	Läge	
Maintenance	Underhåll	
Architect	Arkitekt	Nils Sköld, Peter Nordwall
Type	Karaktär	seaside course, parkland
Relief	Nivåskillnader	
Water in play	Vatten på spelfältet	
Exp. to wind	Vindutsatt	
Trees in play	Träd på spelfältet	

Scorecard Scorekort	**Chp.** Back tees	**Mens** Herrtee	**Ladies** Damtee
Length Längd	6066	5843	5046
Par	72	72	72
Slope system	122	119	120

Advised golfing ability Rekommenderad spelnivå — 0 12 24 36
Hcp required Hcp erfordrad — 36

CLUB HOUSE & AMENITIES — KLUBBHUS OCH OMGIVNING — 7/10

Pro shop Pro shop
Driving range Träningsbana
Sheltered tak 2 mats - On grass på gräs yes - Putting-green putting-green yes - Pitching-green pitching-green yes

HOTEL FACILITIES — HOTELL OMGIVNING — 5/10

HOTELS HOTELL
Kronholmens Gård - Klintehamn 1km
4 rooms, D SKr 600
Tel (46) 0498 - 245 004, Fax (46) 0498 - 245 023

Visby Hotell - Visby 30 km
134 rooms, D SKr 1520
Tel (46) 0498 - 204 000, Fax (46) 0498 - 211 320

RESTAURANTS RESTAURANG
Lindgården - Visby 30 km
Tel (46) 0498 - 218 700

Visby Hotell - Visby 30 km
Tel (46) 0498 - 204 000

SUISSE SCHWEIZ SVIZZERA

SWITZERLAND

Ascona

GUIDE 2006/2007

SWITZERLAND

As in other European countries, the majority of courses featured here are private but open to the general public with a few restrictions or limited access on week-ends. The best idea is to make enquiries and book in advance, and remember that a letter of introduction from your own club is always a good idea. With 46,500 players and 59 18-hole courses, Switzerland is not a top golfing country but the courses here are very good and often set amidst some fabulous landscapes. A number of environmental restrictions (more or less well-founded) have hampered development of the game somewhat and the number of new courses being opened is still inadequate. The course at Vuissens makes a first appearance here, as does the Zuoz Madulain at the Engadin Golf Club, and a special mention is made of the now transformed course at Montreux.

SUISSE

Comme dans les autres pays d'Europe, la majeure partie des golfs présentés ici sont privés, mais ouverts au public avec quelques restrictions ou difficultés d'accès en week-end. Il convient donc de s'informer et de réserver à l'avance, et une lettre d'introduction de votre club ne sera jamais inutile. Avec 46.500 joueurs, et 59 parcours de 18 trous, la Suisse n'est pas un très grand pays golfique, mais ses parcours sont de qualité et souvent situés dans des paysages superbes. Certaines contraintes environnementales (plus ou moins fondées) entravent quelque peu son développement et le nombre d'ouverture de parcours reste insuffisant. Celui de Vuissens fait son entrée ici, tout comme le "Zuoz Madulain" du golf d'Engadin, avec une mention aussi pour la métamorphose de Montreux.

SCHWEIZ

Wie auch in anderen europäischen Ländern sind die meisten Golfplätze privat, aber der Öffentlichkeit bis auf gewisse Einschränkungen an den Wochenenden zugänglich. Es ist daher empfehlenswert, sich vorher zu informieren oder zu reservieren, und ein Empfehlungsschreiben Ihres Clubs ist ebenfalls nützlich. Mit 46'500 Golfern und 59 18-Loch-Plätzen zählt die Schweiz sicherlich nicht zu den typischen Golfländern, aber dafür sind die Plätze sehr gut und landschaftlich außerordentlich reizvoller eingebettet. Hohe Umweltschutzauflagen behindern nach wie vor die Entwicklung der Golfplätze. Einer der neu vorgestellten Plätze ist Vuissens ebenso wie Zuoz Mandulain im Engadin und eine besondere Erwähnung findet der umgestaltete Kurs von Montreux .

Map No 1
Carte 1
km
0 10 20
Largue (La) (F)
Bâle Hagenthal (F)
Wylihof
Les Bois
Neuchâtel
Vuissens
Lausanne
Blumisberg
La Gruyère
Domaine Impérial
Montreux
Crans-sur-Sierre
Divonne (F)
Genève
Evian (F)
Maison Blanche (F)
Esery (F)
Chamonix (F)
MULHOUSE
BASEL
Belfort
Vesoul
Montbéliard
BESANÇON
DOUBS
JURA
Solothurn
Biel/Bienne
BERN
Neuchâtel
Fribourg
Pontarlier
LAUSANNE
SUISSE
VAUD
Montreux
Évian
Thonon
GENÈVE
Annemasse
ANNECY
Chamonix-Mont-Blanc
Sion
Sierre
Martigny
MICHELIN

Todtnau
Altglashütten
Blumberg
Überlingen
Salem
Feldberg
Schluchsee
Bonndorf
Bodman-Ludwigshafen
Birnau
Bernau-im Schwarzwald
St. Blasien
Radolfzell
Markdorf
Meckenbeuren
Schönau
Stühlingen
Singen
Allensbach
Meersburg
Schaffhausen
Horn
Konstanz
Friedrichshafen
Todtmoos
Neuhausen
Stein
Steckborn
Immenstaad
Kreuzlingen
Bodensee
Waldshut-Tiengen
Langenargen
Wehr
Weinfelden
Romanshorn
Bad Säckingen
Zurzach
Rhein
Breitenloo
Frauenfeld
Arbon
Rheinfelden (Baden)
Laufenburg
Amriswil
Rorschach
Bülach
Wängi
Bischofszell
Rheinfelden
Brugg
Winterthur
Wil
St. Gallen
Sissach
Baden
Kloten
Teufen
Gossau
Altstätten
Pfäffikon
Herisau
Aarau
Lenzburg
Dietikon
ZÜRICH
Olten
Wohlen
Uster
Wetzikon
Wattwil
Urnäsch
Appenzell
Zurich Zumikon
Wald
Rüti
Säntis
2502
Aarburg
AARGAU
Küsnacht
Thalwil
Meilen
Kulm
Horgen
Wädenswil
Kaltbrunn
Gams
Muri
Unterwasser
Reinach
Ennetsee-Holzhäusern
Rapperswil
Buchs
Langenthal
Hochdorf
Zug
Walensee
Walenstadt
Sursee
Schönenberg
Einsiedeln
Näfels
Flums
Küssnacht
Sattel
Sargans
Sempachersee
Ruswil
Arth
Glarus
LUZERN
Rigi
Vitznau
Schwyz
Bad Ragaz
Weggis
Gersau
Bächistock
2914
Kriens
Entlebuch
Stansstad
Brunnen
Sumiswald
Luzern
Seelisberg
Linthal
Piz Sardona
3056
Pilatus
Beckenried
06-2005
Flüelen
Langnau
Sarnen
Stans
Altdorf
Flims Waldhaus
Reichenau
Flühli
1948
Klausenpass
SCHWEIZ
GRA
Engelberg
UNTERWALDEN
URI
Ilanz
Lungern
Titlis
3239
2350
Brünigpass
Vorderrhein
Brienz
1007
Meiringen
2259
Wassen
Oberalppass
Disentis/Mustèr
Interlaken-Unterseen
Gunten
2681
Sustenpass
2044
2998
Göschenen
SVIZZ
Spiez
Interlaken
Aare
3630
Hospental
Andermatt
3211
Piz Medel
Hinterrhein
Grindelwald
Pso del Lucomagno
Splügen
Kiental
Wengen
Lauterbrunnen
Grimselpass
2431
Furkapass
2108
Pso d. S. Gottardo
Airolo
1916
Olivone
Pso del S. Bernardino
2065
Splügenpass
Pso dello Spluga
2113
Mürren
Finsteraarhorn
2165
3402
S. Bernardino
Rheinwaldhorn
4158
4274
Jungfrau
Münster
Nufenenpass
Ticino
2478
Mesocco
Madesimo
4195
Aletschhorn
Kandersteg
Peccia
Rotten (Rhône)
Lötschbergtunnel
Formazza
Sonogno
Biasca
Bignasco
TICINO
Moesa
Goppenstein
Maggia
Brig
2593
Visp
Baceno
Toce
A 13-E 43
Bellinzona
Ascona
Locarno
Simplonpass
2005
Ascona
Brissago
Gravedona
Grächen
Iselle
S. Maria Maggiore
Lugano
St Niklaus
Bognanco
Cannobio
Menaggio
4023
Domodossola
Cannero Riv.
LUGANO
Cadenabbia
Varenna
Villadossola
Tremezzo
Bellagio
4505
Saas-Fee
Luino
Gandria
Täsch
Lago Maggiore
Ponte Tresa
Campione
Zermatt
Mergozzo
Verbania-Pallanza
M. Generoso
1703
4478
Anzola d'Ossola
MONTE ROSA
4634
Macugnaga
Baveno
Gravellona-Toce
1491
Valtournenche
Omegna
Nonio
Gressoney-la-Trinite
Alagna Valsesia
Meina
Champoluc
Varallo
Orta S. Giulio
Arona
1277
MICHELIN
d'après base de données au 1/1 000 000 - édition 2005
Autorisation n°0501023.

Map No 2
Carte 2
km
0 10 20
1278
Ravensburg
Kempten
Wangen
Isny
Tettnang
Friedrichshafen
Lindenberg
Deutsche Alpenstraße
Immenstadt
Sonthofen
Langenargen
Lindau
Lindau-
Bad Schachen (D)
Bregenz
Dornbirn
Lustenau
Hohenems
Götzis
Rankweil
Feldkirch
Bodensee
Romanshorn
Arbon
Amriswil
Rorschach
Bischofszell
Wil
St. Gallen
Gossau
Herisau
Teufen
Altstätten
Appenzell
Urnäsch
Wattwil
Säntis
2502
Weinfelden
Mittelberg
Wertach
Pfronten
Oberjoch-P.
Hindelang
Tannheim
Reutte
Füssen
Roßhaupten
Steingaden
Weißenbach
Berwang
Fernpaß
Nassereith
Imst
Fischen
Balderschwang
Nebelhorn
2224
Oberstdorf
Riezlern
Hirschegg
Kleinwalsertal
Baad
Mittelberg
Elbigenalp
Holzgau
Steeg
Lech
Egg
Bizau
Schoppernau
Hochtannbergpaß
Warth
Schröcken
Lech
Zürs
Flexenpaß
1773
Klösterle
St. Anton
Arlbergpaß
Arlberg-Straßentunnel
Parseierspitze
3036
Landeck
VORARLBERG
Thüringen
Bludenz
Nenzing
Brand
Schruns
Lünersee
2964
St. Gallenkirch
Gaschurn
Partenen
Gargellen
Bielerhöhe
2036
Piz Buin
3312
Silvrettagruppe
Ischgl
Galtür
Trisanna
Serfaus
Ried
Pfunds
Nauders
Martina
Reschenpaß/
Pso di Resia
1507
Vaduz
LIECHTENSTEIN
Buchs
Gams
Unterwasser
Kaltbrunn
Walensee
Walenstadt
Näfels
Flums
Sargans
Glarus
Maienfeld
Bad Ragaz
Schiers
Landquart
Küblis
Klosters
Piz Sardona
3056
Linthal
Flims
Waldhaus
Reichenau
Chur
Weissfluhgipfel
2844
Davos
GRAUBÜNDEN
Arosa
Lenzerheide
Valbella
Ilanz
Thusis
Tiefencastel
Bergün/
Bravuogn
Albulapass
2312
Piz Kesch
3418
Flüelapass
2383
Susch
Zernez
Ardez
Scuol
S. Valentino alla
St. Valentin a. d.
Malles Ven. / Mals
Sluderno/
Ofenpass/
Pass dal Fuorn
2149
Tubre/
Taufers i. M.
Müstair
Pass Umbrail
2502
Trafoi
Pso d. Stelvio/
Stilfserjoch
2757
Solda/
Sulden
M. Cevedale / Zufall
3769
Bormio
Sta Caterina
Valfurva
Pso di Gavia
2621
Zuoz
Livigno
Pso di Foscagno
2291
Samedan
Engadin
Pontresina
St-Moritz
Julierpass
2284
Savognin
3378
Silvaplana
Sils/Segl Maria
Maloja
1815
Piz Bernina
4049
Pso del Bernina
2330
3302
3439
Poschiavo
Grosio
Ponte di Legno
1883
VIZZERA
Splügen
2113
Splügenpass
Pso dello Spluga
Hinterrhein
Pso del S. Bernardino
2065
S. Bernardino
Rheinwaldhorn
3402
Olivone
Madesimo
Cresta
Soglio
Mesocco
Castasegna
Chiavenna
Chiesa in Valmalenco
3678
M. Disgrazia
Biasca
Tirano
Edolo
Aprica
1181
Tresenda
Sondrio
Bagni del Masino
M. Adamello
3554
Bellinzona
Gravedona
Colico
Morbegno
Alpi Orobie
3052
Pso di Coca
Pso del Vivione
1828
Schilpario
Valbondione
Dezzo
Pso d. Presolana
1297
Breno
Pso di Croce Domini
1892
2070
Darfo-Boario Terme
Bagolino
Lugano
LUGANO
Menaggio
Bellano
Varenna
Bellagio
Cadenabbia
Tremezzo
Gandria
Campione
M. Generoso
1703
Morcote
Mendrisio
Gerola Alta
1985
Foppolo
Pso S. Marco
2554
Piazza Brembana
Barzio
Clusone
Lovere
Pisogne
"L'Albenza"
Bergamo (I)
Villa d'Este (I)
Monticello (I)
Carimate (I)
Como
Cernobbio
Chiasso
Varese
Erba
Lecco
Calolziocorte
Oggiono
Cantu
S. Pellegrino Terme
Selvino
Albino
Gandino
Trescore Balneario
Sarnico
Iseo
Collio
Vestone
Gardone Val Trompia
Idro
LOMBARDIA
Bergamo
Seriate
Merate
Lago d'Iseo
MICHELIN

CLASSIFICATION OF GOLF COURSES
CLASSEMENT DES PARCOURS EINTEILUNG DER GOLFPLÄTZE

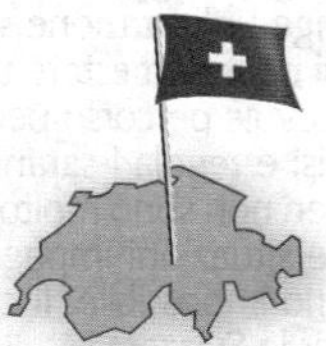

This classification gives priority consideration to the score awarded to the actual course.

Ce classement donne priorité à la note attribuée au parcours.

Diese Einteilung berücksichtigt in erster Linie die dem Golfplatz erteilte Note.

Within each score, the ranking is purely alphabetical

Course score / Note du parcours / Note für den Golfplatz — **Page / Seite**

Course score				Page
18	8	6	Domaine Impérial	1285
17	7	8	Genève	1288
16	7	7	Lausanne	1291
16	8	7	Sempachersee West + Ost	1298
16	1	6	Vuissens	1299
15	7	7	Ascona	1280
15	7	6	Blumisberg	1282
15	7	6	Les Bois	1292
15	7	8	Lugano	1293
15	6	6	Montreux	1295
15	7	6	Zumikon	1301
15	7	7	Engadin Zuoz Madulain	1286
14	7	8	Crans-sur-Sierre	1284
14	7	6	Gruyère (La)	1289
14	6	6	Interlaken	1290
14	7	7	Neuchâtel	1296
14	7	6	Schönenberg	1297
14	7	6	Wylihof	1300
13	7	6	Bad Ragaz	1281
13	7	6	Breitenloo	1283
13	7	6	Ennetsee-Holzhäusern	1287
13	6	7	Luzern	1294

HOTEL FACILITIES
ENVIRONNEMENT HOTELIER
EINTEILUNG DES HOTELANGEBOTS DER UMGEBUNG

This classification gives priority consideration to the score awarded to the hotel facilities.

Ce classement donne priorité à la note attribuée à l'environnement hôtelier.

Diese Klassifikation berücksichtigt in erster Linie die Bewertung für das Hotelangebot.

Hotel facility score / Note de l'environnement hotelier / Note für das Hotelangebot der Umgebung — **Page / Seite**

		Hotel facility score		Page
14	7	8	Crans-sur-Sierre	1284
17	7	8	Genève	1288
15	7	8	Lugano	1293
15	7	7	Ascona	1280
10	7	7	Engadin Zuoz Madulain	1286
16	7	7	Lausanne	1291
13	6	7	Luzern	1294
14	7	7	Neuchâtel	1296
16	8	7	Sempachersee West + Ost	1298
13	7	6	Bad Ragaz	1281
15	7	6	Blumisberg	1282
13	7	6	Breitenloo	1283
18	8	6	Domaine Impérial	1285
13	7	6	Ennetsee-Holzhäusern	1287
14	7	6	Gruyère (La)	1289
14	6	6	Interlaken	1290
15	7	6	Les Bois	1292
15	6	6	Montreux	1295
14	7	6	Schönenberg	1297
16	1	6	Vuissens	1299
14	7	6	Wylihof	1300
15	7	6	Zumikon	1301

Ascona

15 | 7 | 7

Sulle rive dello splendido Lago Maggiore, in uno dei più bei luoghi di villeggiatura della Svizzera, il Patriziale aggiunge un'attrazione supplementare alla regione in quanto pianeggiante, e senza insidie nascoste. I molti alberi danno in estate un' ombra gradita, senza che il sottobosco ne sia penalizzato. Lo si puo considerare un piacevole percorso per giocare con tutta la famiglia, ma è anche un ottimo banco di prova dove i giocatori precisi e regolari saranno a loro agio anche se dovranno impiegare tutte le risorse nel gioco corto, in quanto i green non sono molto grandi ma molto ben difesi e sovente sopraelevati. Il percorso è corto ma offre parecchie situazioni impegnative e anche se lo spazio non consente di allungarlo l'intenzione non è quella di renderlo impossibile. Il clima mite e la natura del terreno permettono di giocare quasi tutto l'anno, fatto insolito per la Svizzera

Alongside the beautiful Lake Maggiore, one of the prettiest Swiss holiday sites, the "Patriziale" adds extra charm to the region, all the more so in that the course is flat with no hidden traps. The very many trees bring welcome shade in summer, and the undergrowth is never too penalizing. This is what might be considered to be a very pleasant holiday course, for playing with all the family with little at stake, but also a cleverly worked out test of golf where straight and consistent players will feel at home. They will, nonetheless, need a finely tuned short game, because the greens are not enormous, are well-defended and often come with several tiers. The layout is short, for sure, but it offers some pretty stiff resistance. And anyway, space is far too limited to lengthen the course and the objective has never been to turn it into a monster. The pleasant climate and the nature of the terrain mean being able to play here most of the year, a feature that is not all that common in Switzerland.

Golf Club Patriziale Ascona — 1928

Via al Lido 81
CH - 6612 ASCONA

Office	Segreteria	(41) 091 - 791 21 32
Pro shop	Pro shop	(41) 091 - 792 14 36
Fax	Fax	(41) 091 - 791 07 06
Web	www.golf.ascona.ch	
Situation	Località'	Locarno, 3 km
Annual closure	Chiusura annuale	no
Weekly closure	Chiusura settimanale	no

Fees main season Tariffe alta stagione — 18 holes

	Week days / Settimana	We/Bank holidays / Feriale/Festivo
Individual Individuale	CHF 100	CHF 110
Couple Coppia	CHF 200	CHF 220

Under 18: CHF 50

Caddie Caddie no — **Electric Trolley** Carello elettrico yes

Buggy Car no — **Clubs** Bastoni yes

Credit cards Carte di credito
VISA - Eurocard - Mastercard - AMEX

Access Itinerario : Locarno → Ascona, → Via Lido, Golf
Map 1 on page 1277 Carta 1 Pagina 1277

GOLF COURSE — PERCORSO — 15/20

Site	Paesaggio	
Maintenance	Manutenzione	
Architect	Architetto	Harry S. Colt, C. Alison, C.K. Cotton
Type	Tipologia	parkland
Relief	Relievo terreno	
Water in play	Acqua in gioco	
Exp. to wind	Esposto al vento	
Trees in play	Alberi in gioco	

Scorecard / Carta-score	Chp. / Camp.	Mens / Uomini	Ladies / Donne
Length Lunghezza	5933	5569	4918
Par	71	71	71
Slope system	126	118	119

Advised golfing ability / Livello di gioco consigliato: 0 12 24 36

Hcp required Handicap richiesto 30

CLUB HOUSE & AMENITIES — CLUB HOUSE E SERVIZI — 7/10

Pro shop — Pro shop
Driving range — Campo pratica
Sheltered coperto 40 mats - On grass in erba yes - Putting-green Putting-green yes (2) - Pitching-green Green-pratica yes

HOTEL FACILITIES — ALBERGHI — 7/10

HOTELS ALBERGHI
Castello-Seeschloss - Ascona 1 km
45 rooms, D from CHF 300
Tel (41) 091 - 791 01 61, Fax (41) 091 - 791 18 04
Castello del Sole - 83 rooms, D CHF 600 - Ascona 1 km
Tel (41) 091 - 791 02 02, Fax (41) 091 - 792 11 18
Casa Berno - 62 rooms, D from CHF 400 - Ascona 1 km
Tel (41) 091 - 791 32 32, Fax (41) 091 - 792 11 14

RESTAURANTS RISTORANTE
Aphrodite - Ascona 1 km - Tel (41) 091 - 785 88 88
Osteria Dell'Enoteca - Losone 3 km - Tel (41) 091 - 791 78 17
Centenario - Locarno 3 km - Tel (41) 091 - 743 82 22
Hostaria San Pietro - Ascona 1 km - Tel (41) 091 - 791 39 76

Bad Ragaz

13 | 7 | 6

Wie viele andere Schweizer Plätze stammt auch dieser Parcours aus der Feder Donald Harradines, einem der begnadeten Architekten, der die Natur gekonnt in seine Arbeit einbezieht. Das Bergpanorama und die bewaldete Gegend verleihen Bad Ragaz einen besonderen Charme. Gestaltung und Platzcharakter bergen keine Überraschungen, aber der Kurs verspricht dank seiner der wenig ausgeprägten Geländeformen und der vernünftigen Länge Spielfreude für jede Handicapklasse. Ein wenig schade ist höchstens, dass der Fluss, der durch die Anlage führt, zu wenig im Spiel ist, aber der Architekt wollte sich nicht auf künstliche Eingriffe einlassen. Er arbeitete mit der Natur, wie sie sich ihm bot, und ihm lag auch nicht daran, die Besucher dieser wundervollen Parklandschaft zu frustrieren. Einzig das Gelände könnte ein wenig mehr onduliert sein. Die eher schmalen Fairways der ersten neun Loch verlangen präzise Bälle. Longhitter spielen ihre Trümpfe daher eher auf der zweiten Platzhälfte aus. In Bad Ragaz bietet sich die Chance für schmeichelhafte Scores. Warum auch nicht?

Like many Swiss courses, Bad Ragaz was designed by Donald Harradine, a generally academic architect who willingly lets nature keep the upper hand. Moreover, the setting for Bad Ragaz is a very pleasant site in a forest surrounded by mountains. The course itself has very little in the way of stylish surprises or outstanding personality, but it is pleasant to play for its flattish relief and very reasonable length. It is a pity that the river crossing the course was not brought into play in a more imaginative way, but the architect refused to be drawn by artificial expedients. He worked with what he had and the goal was certainly not to scare off holiday visitors in this very beautiful park. The only real regret would be a certain lack of relief in the way the terrain has been contoured. The front nine are rather tight and call for precision play, while the back nine give greater scope to the long-hitters. A round of golf here is perhaps the opportunity to sign for a flattering score, but why not, after all?

Bad Ragaz Golf Club — 1957

Hans Albrecht Strasse
CH - 7310 BAD RAGAZ

Office Sekretariat (41) 081 - 303 37 17
Pro shop Pro shop (41) 081 - 303 37 15
Fax Fax (41) 081 - 303 37 27
Web www.resortragaz.ch
Situation Lage Bad Ragaz (pop. 4 757)
Chur (pop. 30 800), 24 km
Annual closure Jährliche Schliessung 8/12→18/1
Weekly closure Wöchentliche Schliessung no

Fees main season Preisliste hochsaison — Full day

	Week days Woche	We/Bank holidays We/Feiertag
Individual Individuell	CHF 100	CHF 120
Couple Ehepaar	CHF 200	CHF 240

Juniors under 21, Sudents under 25: – 50%

Caddie Caddie no **Electric Trolley** Elektrokarren yes
Buggy Elektrischer Wagen medical reasons
Clubs Leihschläger yes

Credit cards Kreditkarten
VISA - Eurocard - MasterCard - AMEX - DC

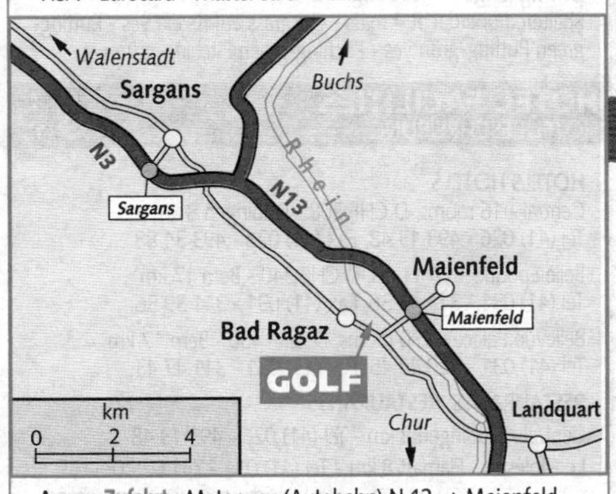

Access Zufahrt : Motorway (Autobahn) N 13 → Maienfeld → Bad Ragaz → Golf
Map 2 on page 1278 Karte 2 Seite 1278

GOLF COURSE — PLATZ 13/20

Site Lage
Maintenance Instandhaltung
Architect Architekt Donald Harradine
Type Typ forest, parkland
Relief Begehbarkeit
Water in play Platz mit Wasser
Exp. to wind Wind ausgesetzt
Trees in play Platz mit Bäumen

Scorecard Scorekarte	Chp. Chp.	Mens Herren	Ladies Damen
Length Länge	5700	5490	4860
Par	70	70	70
Slope system	125	117	115

Advised golfing ability Empfohlene Spielstärke 0 12 24 36
Hcp required Min. Handicap 30

CLUB HOUSE & AMENITIES — KLUBHAUS UND NEBENGEBÄUDE 7/10

Pro shop Pro shop
Driving range Übungsplatz
Sheltered überdacht 20 mats - On grass auf Rasen 12 mats
open air - Putting-green Putting-grün yes - Pitching-green Pitching-grün yes

HOTEL FACILITIES — HOTEL BESCHREIBUNG 6/10

HOTELS HOTELS
Grand Hotel Hof Ragaz - Bad Ragaz
133 rooms, D CHF 520
Tel (41) 081 - 303 30 30, Fax (41) 081 - 303 30 33

Quellenhof - Bad Ragaz
106 rooms, D CHF 730
Tel (41) 081 - 303 30 30, Fax (41) 081 - 303 30 33

Tamina - 44 rooms, D CHF 300 - Bad Ragaz
Tel (41) 081 - 302 81 51, Fax (41) 081 - 302 23 08

RESTAURANTS RESTAURANTS
Aebtestube - Bad Ragaz - Tel (41) 081 - 303 30 30
Löwen - Bad Ragaz - Tel (41) 081 - 302 13 06

Blumisberg

15	7	6

Blumisberg mit Aussicht auf den Jura und die Alpen liegt in coupiertem Gelände mit stolzem Baumbestand, der vor allem die ersten neun Loch prägt. Die Anlage lässt sich aber trotzdem zu Fuss gut bewältigen. Die Mehrheit der Holes bietet gut sichtbare Hindernisse, hauptsächlich Grünbunker. Die Grüns sind von mittlerer Grösse, gut verteidigt und relativ wellig. Obwohl nicht schwer zu erreichen erlauben einige Etagengrüns abwechslungsreiche, und herausfordernde Fahnenpositionen. Schon mittlere Handicaps können hier aber zu einem guten Spielrhythmus finden und geniessen die vernünftige Länge der eher breiten Fairways, obwohl man vor allem einige Bahnen der ersten Neun nicht unterschätzen sollte. Gute Golfer legen ihr Ballkönnen vor allem auf verschiedenen, schräg abfallenden Fairways in die Waagschale und haben alle Möglichkeiten, den Ball zu shapen. Platzpflege und Greenkeeping sind gut.

With the Jura mountains on one side and the Alps on the other, Blumisberg is hilly and woody (especially the front nine), but walkable if you settle for just the 18 holes. Although a few holes require a little explanation, the vast majority hide nothing with clearly visible hazards, basically green-side bunkers. The greens are average in size, well-defended and sloping, with a number of two-tiered surfaces which make for some interesting pin positions. They are not too difficult to reach, either, as the fairways are pretty wide, but some of the slopes on the outward nine may make life difficult for the more careless players. By and large, players can get a good rhythm going and the length of the course is reasonable enough to suit all players of decent ability. The best will be in their element here, working the ball both ways in order to card a good score. This is important, especially to handle some of the sloping fairways. Green-keeping and general maintenance are good.

Golf & Country Club Blumisberg — 1959

CH - 3184 WÜNNEWIL

Office	Sekretariat	(41) 026 - 496 34 38
Pro shop	Pro shop	(41) 026 - 496 17 27
Fax	Fax	(41) 026 - 496 35 23
Web	www.swissgolfnetwork.ch	
Situation	Lage	Bern, 17 km
Annual closure	Jährliche Schliessung	15/11→15/3
Weekly closure	Wöchentliche Schliessung	no

Monday (Montag): Restaurant

Fees main season Preisliste hochsaison		Full day
	Week days Woche	**We/Bank holidays** We/Feiertag
Individual Individuell	CHF 100	CHF 100*
Couple Ehepaar	CHF 200	CHF 200*

* We: only with members (nur in Mitgliederbegleitung) from 05 → 09.

Caddie Caddie no — **Electric Trolley** Elektrokarren yes

Buggy Elektrischer Wagen on request

Clubs Leihschläger yes

Credit cards Kreditkarten no

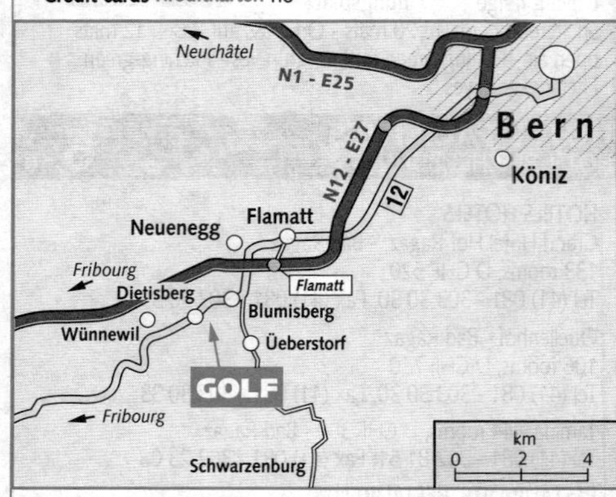

Access Zufahrt : Motorway (Autobahn) E 25 Freiburg-Bern → Flamatt, 6 km → Freiburg. 4,5 km left → Dietisberg. → Golf

Map 1 on page 1276 Karte 1 Seite 1276

GOLF COURSE — PLATZ — 15/20

Site	Lage	
Maintenance	Instandhaltung	
Architect	Architekt	B. von Limburger
Type	Typ	forest, open country
Relief	Begehbarkeit	
Water in play	Platz mit Wasser	
Exp. to wind	Wind ausgesetzt	
Trees in play	Platz mit Bäumen	

Scorecard Scorekarte	**Chp.** Chp.	**Mens** Herren	**Ladies** Damen
Length Länge	6011	5687	4977
Par	72	72	72
Slope system	129	126	125

Advised golfing ability Empfohlene Spielstärke — 0 12 24 36

Hcp required Min. Handicap 30

CLUB HOUSE & AMENITIES — KLUBHAUS UND NEBENGEBÄUDE — 7/10

Pro shop Pro shop

Driving range Übungsplatz

Sheltered überdacht 4 mats - On grass auf Rasen yes - Putting-green Putting-grün yes - Pitching-green Pitching-grün yes

HOTEL FACILITIES — HOTEL BESCHREIBUNG — 6/10

HOTELS HOTELS

Central - 16 rooms, D CHF 208 - Düdingen 8 km
Tel (41) 026 - 493 13 48, Fax (41) 026 - 493 34 88

Belle Epoque - 17 rooms, D CHF 340 - Bern 17 km
Tel (41) 031 - 311 43 36, Fax (41) 031 - 311 39 36

Bellevue Palace - 130 rooms, D CHF 450 - Bern 17 km
Tel (41) 031 - 320 45 45, Fax (41) 031 - 311 47 43

RESTAURANTS RESTAURANTS

Central - Düdingen 8 km - Tel (41) 026 - 493 13 48

Le Moléson - Flamatt 8 km - Tel (41) 031 - 741 02 40

Schultenheissenstube - Bern 17 km - Tel (41) 031 - 326 80 80

Wein und Sein - Bern 17 km - Tel (41) 031 - 311 98 44

Breitenloo

13	7	6

Ein kleiner Flecken im Eggwald über den Anhöhen zwischen Kloten und Winterthur mit Aussichten auf das umliegende Glattal und die Alpen. Donald Harradine hat diesen Platz (wie viele Schweizer Kurse) in britischem Stil in eine hügelige Landschaft gezeichnet. Das Gelände wird auf den zweiten neun Loch etwas flacher. Mit einigen Out of Bounds und kleinen Wasserhindernissen sind die Schwierigkeiten nicht allzu zahlreich, aber der Ball muss auf den Fairways an den richtigen Positionen plaziert werden, damit die Greens angreifbar werden - Präzision im Umgang mit dem kleinen Ball kann sich als nützlich erweisen. Longhitter sollten gut aufpassen, denn der Platz ist lang, aber nicht so verzeihend, wie man es sich manchmal wünschen würde. In jedem Fall lässt sich dieser gut gepflegte Platz unter Golfern verschiedener Spielstärke mit viel Spass spielen - vor allem im Sommer, wenn der Ball gut rollt.

A little patch of remote forest – the Eggwald - in the countryside, with wide spaces opening onto the surrounding region, particularly the Glatt valley, the Alps and the hills close to Winterthur. Another Harradine course, Breitenloo has a clearly British style to it and is laid out over a gently hilly terrain (even though the back nine are flatter). Despite a number of out-of-bounds and small water hazards, the difficulties are few and far between, are evenly spread and clearly visible. Some of the greens need a carefully placed tee-shot for an easier second shot, and fading or drawing the ball can, as always, prove helpful. At all events, this well-manicured course is easily playable by all the family or with players of varying ability. The bigger-hitters should watch out, because the layout is rather long and is not as forgiving as they might like. All good fun anyway, especially in summer when the ball rolls a long way.

Golf Club Breitenloo — 1966

Untere Zaüne 9
CH - 8309 OBERWIL b. NÜRENSDORF

Office	Sekretariat	(41) 01 - 836 40 80
Pro shop	Pro shop	(41) 01 - 836 46 14
Fax	Fax	(41) 01 - 837 10 85
Web	www.swissgolfnetwork.ch	
Situation	Lage	Zürich, 22 km
Annual closure	Jährliche Schliessung	15/11→15/3
Weekly closure	Wöchentliche Schliessung	no

Fees main season Preisliste hochsaison	18 holes	
	Week days Woche	We/Bank holidays We/Feiertag
Individual Individuell	CHF 100	*
Couple Ehepaar	CHF 200	*

* We: with members only (nur in Mitgliederbegleitung)

Caddie Caddie on request **Electric Trolley** Elektrokarren yes

Buggy Elektrischer Wagen no **Clubs** Leihschläger yes

Credit cards Kreditkarten no

Access Zufahrt : Zürich-Kloten → Kloten → Bassersdorf → Birchwil-Oberwil, in Oberwil (Restaurant Linde) → Golf
Map 1 on page 1277 Karte 1 Seite 1277

GOLF COURSE PLATZ — 13/20

Site	Lage	
Maintenance	Instandhaltung	
Architect	Architekt	Donald Harradine Frank Pennink
Type	Typ	parkland
Relief	Begehbarkeit	
Water in play	Platz mit Wasser	
Exp. to wind	Wind ausgesetzt	
Trees in play	Platz mit Bäumen	

Scorecard Scorekarte	Chp. Chp.	Mens Herren	Ladies Damen
Length Länge	6320	5760	5144
Par	72	72	72
Slope system	133	127	128

Advised golfing ability Empfohlene Spielstärke 0 12 24 36

Hcp required Min. Handicap 30

CLUB HOUSE & AMENITIES KLUBHAUS UND NEBENGEBÄUDE — 7/10

Pro shop Pro shop
Driving range Übungsplatz
Sheltered überdacht 6 mats - On grass auf Rasen yes - Putting-green Putting-grün yes - Pitching-green Pitching-grün yes

HOTEL FACILITIES HOTEL BESCHREIBUNG — 6/10

HOTELS HOTELS

Renaissance Hotel - Glattbrugg 14 km
204 rooms, D CHF 345
Tel (41) 01 - 874 50 00, Fax (41) 01 - 874 50 01

Widder - 49 rooms, D CHF 640 - Zurich 14 km
Tel (41) 01 - 224 25 26, Fax (41) 01 - 224 24 24

Ermitage am See - Küsnacht-Zurich 12 km
26 rooms, D CHF 360
Tel (41) 01 - 914 42 42, Fax (41) 01 - 914 42 43

RESTAURANTS RESTAURANTS

Zum Bären - Nürensdorf 4 km - Tel (41) 01 - 838 36 36
Sonnenberg - Zürich 22 km - Tel (41) 01 - 266 97 97
Rössli - Lindau 6 km - Tel (41) 0523 - 451 151

Crans-sur-Sierre

14	7	8

C'est le plus célèbre parcours de Suisse, grâce aux efforts de son président Gaston Barras pour y accueillir depuis des années l'European Masters. Il n'est jamais vraiment intimidant : ses obstacles sont bien visibles, modérément en jeu, la difficulté principale reste le choix de club en fonction des dénivellations. Assez accidenté, il est d'ailleurs fatigant à jouer à pied. La splendeur du panorama sur les Alpes (Cervin, Mont Blanc, Alpes bernoises) est parfois à couper le souffle et console des petites désillusions golfiques. En altitude, les balles volant loin, quelques drives peuvent être flatteurs. Un bon parcours de vacances, avec un entretien dépendant de la durée de l'hiver. Quelques remodelages de ce tracé ont été effectués par Seve Ballesteros, qui a introduit des modifications au 15 et au 17, devenus plus esthétiques et délicats à aborder. D'autres trous ont été allongés, quelques greens retravaillés, le tout par petites touches.

This is the most famous of Swiss courses thanks to the work put in by club chairman Gaston Barras to stage the European Masters here over the past few years. The course is never really intimidating, the hazards are clearly in view and not always directly in play. The main problem is the choice of club to offset the steep gradients. It is a hilly course which can be tiring to cover on foot. The beautiful scenery of the Alps (Cervin, Mont Blanc) is quite breath-taking and enough to make up for the mishaps that can so easily mess up your card. At altitude, the ball travels further and a number of drives will prove flattering. A good holiday course where green-keeping is dependent upon the weather. A little restyling work has been carried out by Seve Ballesteros, who has made a few changes to the 15th and 17th holes, both now more attractive and trickier. Other holes have been lengthened and a few greens re-laid, all the work being carried out in stages.

Golf Club de Crans-sur-Sierre — 1907

CH - 3953 CRANS-SUR-SIERRE

Office	Secrétariat	(41) 027 - 485 97 97
Pro shop	Pro-shop	(41) 027 - 481 40 61
Fax	Fax	(41) 027 - 481 97 98
Web	www.swissgolfnetwork.ch	
Situation	Situation	Sierre, 15 km
Annual closure	Fermeture annuelle	31/10→30/4
Weekly closure	Fermeture hebdomadaire	no

Fees main season Tarifs haute saison	Week days Semaine	We/Bank holidays We/Férié
		18 holes
Individual Individuel	CHF 125	CHF 125
Couple Couple	CHF 250	CHF 250

Caddie Caddie on request **Electric Trolley** Chariot électrique yes

Buggy Voiturette yes **Clubs** Clubs yes

Credit cards Cartes de crédit

VISA - Eurocard - MasterCard - AMEX - DC

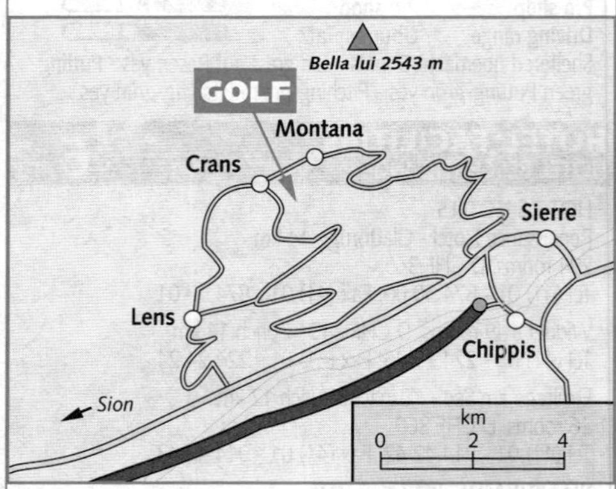

Access Accès : Lausanne → Montreux. In Sierre → Crans

Map 1 on page 1276 Carte 1 Page 1276

GOLF COURSE — PARCOURS 14/20

Site	Site	
Maintenance	Entretien	
Architect	Architecte	M. Nicholson Seve Ballesteros
Type	Type	mountain, parkland
Relief	Relief	
Water in play	Eau en jeu	
Exp. to wind	Exposé au vent	
Trees in play	Arbres en jeu	

Scorecard Carte de score	Chp. Chp.	Mens Mess.	Ladies Da.
Length Long.	6341	5916	5059
Par	72	72	72
Slope system	138	130	136

Advised golfing ability Niveau de jeu recommandé: 0 12 24 36

Hcp required Handicap exigé 36

CLUB HOUSE & AMENITIES — CLUB-HOUSE ET ANNEXES 7/10

Pro shop Pro-shop

Driving range Practice

Sheltered couvert 9 mats - On grass sur herbe no, 30 mats open air - Putting-green putting-green yes - Pitching-green pitching green yes

HOTEL FACILITIES — ENVIRONNEMENT HOTELIER 8/10

HOTELS HÔTELS

Grand Hôtel du Golf - 80 rooms, D CHF 500 - Crans-sur-Sierre
Tel (41) 027 - 485 42 42, Fax (41) 027 - 485 42 43

Alpina et Savoy - 40 rooms, D CHF 400 - Crans-sur-Sierre
Tel (41) 027 - 485 09 00, Fax (41) 027 - 485 09 99

Alpha - 25 rooms, D CHF 210 - Crans-sur-Sierre
Tel (41) 027 - 484 24 00, Fax (41) 027 - 484 24 10

RESTAURANTS RESTAURANTS

Le Bistrot des Ours - Crans -sur-Sierre
Tel (41) 027 - 485 93 33

Cervin - Vermala 4 km - Tel (41) 027 - 481 21 80

L'Atelier Gourmand - Sierre 13 km - Tel (41) 027 - 455 13 51

Domaine Impérial

18	8	6

Par son esthétique et la stratégie de jeu, ce parcours est le plus nettement américain des golfs suisses, bien que son architecte Pete Dye n'ait pas détruit la nature ! En bordure du Lac Léman, avec de belles perspectives sur le Jura et les Alpes, il se joue sans fatigue physique, mais les fairways bien travaillés, les profonds bunkers, la diversité des obstacles (arbres, obstacles d'eau) et l'intelligence de leur placement en font un défi permanent, constamment renouvelé : on joue ici tous les clubs de son sac, et de multiples façons. On notera en particulier l'excellent rythme du parcours, la subtilité des par 3, de longueur pourtant fort raisonnable, et le modelage de greens très défendus, qu'il faut savoir "rater du bon côté". Techniquement impressionnant, il se laisse apprivoiser si l'on ajoute la réflexion à la maîtrise du jeu. L'entretien est généralement de très bonne qualité, tous les détails sont soignés, et les greens sont souvent rapides, ce qui va bien dans la logique du dessin.

In style and game strategy, this is clearly the most American of all Swiss courses, although Pete Dye has clearly refrained from meddling with nature. On the banks of lake Geneva with fine views over the Jura mountains and the Alps, it is an easily walkable course, but the well-designed fairways, the deep bunkers, the variety of hazards (trees and water) and the intelligence deployed in placing them make this course a permanent challenge which will never lie down. You play every club in the bag, and in different ways. In particular, this is a good course for quick play with subtle but reasonable-length par 3s and well-designed, well-defended greens which, if you are going to miss, should not be missed on the wrong side. Although technically very impressive, you can keep your head above water by playing with skill and brains. Green-keeping is excellent overall; every detail is carefully tended and the greens are fast... matching the standard of the whole layout.

Domaine Impérial — 1987

Villa Prangins
CH - 1196 GLAND

Office	Secrétariat	(41) 022 - 999 06 00
Pro shop	Pro-shop	(41) 022 - 999 06 80
Fax	Fax	(41) 022 - 999 06 06
Web	www.golfdomaineimperial.com	
Situation	Situation	Nyon, 3 km
Annual closure	Fermeture annuelle	15/12→1/2
Weekly closure	Fermeture hebdomadaire	Monday

(lundi): Restaurant

Fees main season Tarifs haute saison	18 holes	
	Week days Semaine	**We/Bank holidays** We/Férié
Individual Individuel	CHF 150	*
Couple Couple	CHF 300	*

* We & Monday (lundi): members only (membres seulement) - Week days: before 12:00

Caddie Caddie on request **Electric Trolley** Chariot électrique yes

Buggy Voiturette medical reasons only **Clubs** Clubs yes

Credit cards Cartes de crédit
VISA - Eurocard - MasterCard - AMEX

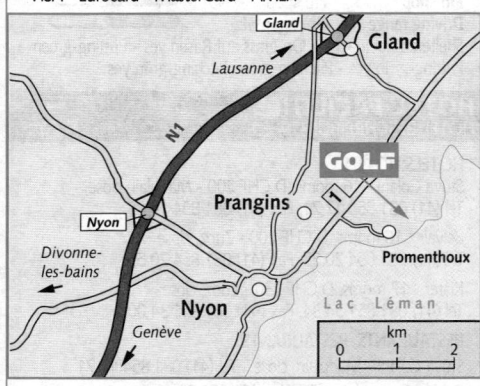

Gland
Lausanne
N1
GOLF
Prangins
Nyon
Divonne-les-bains
Promenthoux
Lac Léman
Genève
km 0 1 2

Access Accès : Genève-Lausanne → Gland, "Route Suisse" → Genève, 400 m on left hand side

Map 1 on page 1276 Carte 1 Page 1276

GOLF COURSE — PARCOURS — 18/20

Site	Site	
Maintenance	Entretien	
Architect	Architecte	Pete Dye
Type	Type	forest, country
Relief	Relief	
Water in play	Eau en jeu	
Exp. to wind	Exposé au vent	
Trees in play	Arbres en jeu	

Scorecard Carte de score	**Chp.** Chp.	**Mens** Mess.	**Ladies** Da.
Length Long.	6336	5913	5023
Par	72	72	72
Slope system	129	122	121

Advised golfing ability Niveau de jeu recommandé — 0 12 24 36

Hcp required Handicap exigé — 30

CLUB HOUSE & AMENITIES — CLUB-HOUSE ET ANNEXES — 8/10

Pro shop Pro-shop
Driving range Practice

Sheltered couvert 10 mats - On grass sur herbe no, 30 mats open air - Putting-green putting-green oui - Pitching-green pitching green oui

HOTEL FACILITIES — ENVIRONNEMENT HOTELIER — 6/10

HOTELS HÔTELS

de la Plage - 10 rooms, D CHF 120 - Gland 4 km
Tel (41) 022 - 364 10 35, Fax (41) 022 - 364 34 81

Beau Rivage - 50 rooms, D CHF 320 - Nyon 5 km
Tel (41) 022 - 365 41 41, Fax (41) 022 - 365 41 65

La Barcarolle - 39 rooms, D CHF 290 - Prangins 4 km
Tel (41) 022 - 365 78 78, Fax (41) 022 - 365 78 00

RESTAURANTS RESTAURANTS

Restaurant du Golf - on site - Tel (41) 022 - 999 06 00
Café du Marché - Nyon 5 km - Tel (41) 022 - 362 35 00
Auberge du Soleil - Bursins 10 km - Tel (41) 021 - 824 13 44
La Barcarolle - Prangins 4 km - Tel (41) 022 - 365 78 78

Engadin *Zuoz Madulain*

15	7	7

Auch wenn der Golfplatz nur für fünf Monate im Jahr geöffnet ist, bereitet es eine enorme Freude und ist es ein einzigartiges Erlebnis, sich auf diesem im Hochengadin gelegenen Golfplatz aufzuhalten, der weit oberhalb des glamourösen St. Moritz und inmitten der historischen und landestypischen Dörfer Zuoz, Madulain oder La Punt liegt. Der den natürlichen Gegebenheiten angepasste und in einem relativ kleinen Stück Land angelegte Parcours erstreckt sich über eine Schleife, die erst mit dem 18. Loch zum Clubhaus zurückkehrt. Trotz der topographischen und ökologischen Einschränkungen gelang es Les Furber, einen höchst interessanten Kurs zu gestalten, auf dem sehr gute Spieler viel Spaß bei dem Versuch haben werden, einige der kurzen Par 4-Löcher mit dem ersten Schlag zu erreichen. In Zuoz-Madulain müssen sie sich einer zeitgemäßeren Herausforderung stellen als auf dem deutlich britischer angehauchten Nachbarn in Samedan, der trotz seines hohen Alters nach wie vor nichts von seiner Attraktivität verloren hat.

This course is open only for five months of the year but it is such fun, and so different, to find yourself in the Haute-Engadine, over and beyond the glitter of Saint Moritz and amidst the historical and typical villages of Zuoz, Madulain or La Punt. Close to the Swiss National Park, one of Europe's richest for wildlife, here is a great excuse to get back into shape with some fresh farm produce and hikes across the foothills. This course has been slotted into a rather narrow strip of land, following the natural slopes over a single loop that does not return to the club-house (except at the 18th, of course). Les Furber has laid out a most interesting course despite the topographic and ecological restrictions and the best players will have fun trying to drive the greens on a number of rather par 4s. Here they will find a more modern challenge than on its more British neighbour of Samedan, still as pleasant as ever despite its "grand old age".

Engadin Golf AG Zuoz-Madulain — 1998

A l'En 14
CH - 7503 SAMEDAN

Office	Sekretariat	(41) 081 851 35 80
Pro shop	Pro shop	(41) 081 854 08 06
Fax	Fax	(41) 081 851 35 89
Web	www.engadin-golf.com	
Situation	Lage	St Moritz, 8 km
Annual closure	Jährliche Schliessung	15/10→15/5
Weekly closure	Wöchentliche Schliessung	no

Fees main season Preisliste hochsaison — 18 holes

	Week days / Woche	We/Bank holidays / We/Feiertag
Individual Individuell	CHF 100	CHF 100
Couple Ehepaar	CHF 200	CHF 200

Juniors CHF 60

Caddie Caddie no — **Electric Trolley** Elektrokarren yes

Buggy Elektrischer Wagen yes (medical reason)

Clubs Leihschläger yes

Credit cards Kreditkarten
VISA - CB - Eurocard - MasterCard - AMEX - DC

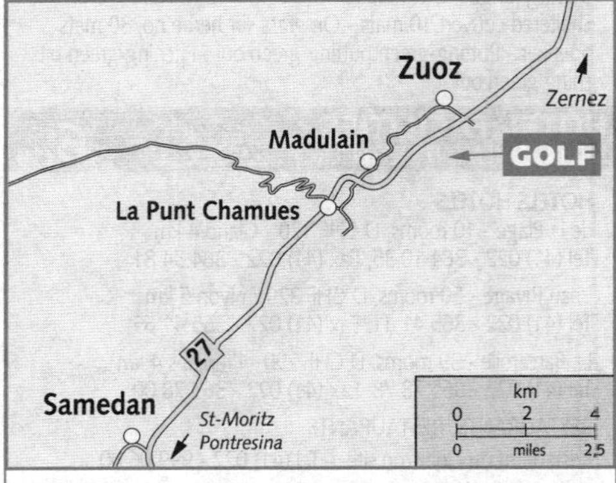

Access Zufahrt : Saint Moritz → Zernez, Scuol.
Golf on the left after Samedan
Map 2 on page 1278 Karte 2 Seite 1278

GOLF COURSE / PLATZ — 15/20

Site	Lage	
Maintenance	Instandhaltung	
Architect	Architekt	Les Furber
Type	Typ	open country, mountain
Relief	Begehbarkeit	
Water in play	Platz mit Wasser	
Exp. to wind	Wind ausgesetzt	
Trees in play	Platz mit Bäumen	

Scorecard / Scorekarte	Chp. / Chp.	Mens / Herren	Ladies / Damen
Length Länge	6007	5609	4543
Par	72	72	72
Slope system	142	132	128

Advised golfing ability Empfohlene Spielstärke — 0 12 24 36

Hcp required Min. Handicap — 28

CLUB HOUSE & AMENITIES / KLUBHAUS UND NEBENGEBÄUDE — 7/10

Pro shop Pro shop
Driving range Übungsplatz
Sheltered überdacht - On grass auf Rasen yes - Putting-green Putting-grün yes - Pitching-green Pitching-grün yes

HOTEL FACILITIES / HOTEL BESCHREIBUNG — 7/10

HOTELS HOTELS

Stüva Colani - 16 rooms, D CHF 200 - Madulain close
Tel (41) 081 854 17 71, Fax (41) 081 854 14 35

Belvair - 16 rooms, D CHF 200 - Zuoz, close
Tel (41) 081 854 20 23, Fax (41) 081 854 20 55

Klarer - 17 rooms, D CHF 230 - Zuoz, close
Tel (41) 081 851 34 34, Fax (41) 081 851 34 00

RESTAURANTS RESTAURANTS

Stüva Colani - Madulain, close - Tel (41) 081 854 17 71
Dorta - Zuoz, close - Tel (41) 081 854 20 40
Jöhri's Talvo - Champfer 11 km - Tel (41) 081 - 833 44 55

Ennetsee-Holzhäusern

13	7	6

1995 war es soweit: der erste öffentliche Golfplatz der Schweiz wurde eröffnet. Er liegt in einer wenig schmeichelnden Industriezone, doch dieses Manko könnte mit einem soliden Bepflanzungsprogramm behoben werden. Angelegt mit dem Ziel Golfer auszubilden und eine erschwingliche Alternative zu den Privatclubs zu bieten, wartet der Kurs nicht mit extra golferischen Schwierigkeiten auf (es sind kaum Wasserhindernisse im Spiel), was sehr gute Spieler enttäuschen mag. Es ist schade, dass die Grüns und Bunker nicht vielseitiger gestaltet wurden. Der sonst angenehm zu spielende Platz würde so mehr fürs Auge bieten und dem Stammspieler zu technisch vielseitigere Herausforderungen entgegensetzen. Die Anlage offeriert nebst dem 27-Loch-Golfplatz grosszügig angelegte Trainingsmöglichkeiten, einschließlich eines 6-Loch-Übungsplatzes und gewährt auch noch teils herrliche Aussicht auf den Zuger See.

This is at last Switzerland's first truly public golf course, opened in 1995. It has been laid out on an industrial site which is still a little unattractive but it could easily grow into something much better with a good plantation programme. The aim here is to coach golfers and offer an economical alternative to the private courses. As a result, there was no deliberate quest for difficulty (for example, there are very few water hazards in play), so the better players might feel disappointed. It is though a shame that the greens and bunkers weren't given more careful thought - they would have added a little more style and pleasure to a course which elsewhere makes for a pleasant round of golf - and that there is not more technical variety for the people who play here regularly. The whole complex also includes a 9 hole course, a six-hole course and huge practice facilities, plus a few wonderful views of Lake Zug.

Golfpark Holzhäusern — 1995

Katharinenhof
CH - 6343 ROTKREUZ

Office	Sekretariat	(41) 041 - 799 70 10
Pro shop	Pro shop	(41) 041 - 799 06 19
Fax	Fax	(41) 041 - 799 70 15
Web	www.golfpark-holzhaeusern.ch	
Situation	Lage	Luzern, 20 km

Zug (pop. 22 366), 10 km

Annual closure	Jährliche Schliessung	no
Weekly closure	Wöchentliche Schliessung	no
Fees main season	Preisliste hochsaison	18 holes

	Week days Woche	We/Bank holidays We/Feiertag
Individual Individuell	CHF 60	CHF 80
Couple Ehepaar	CHF 120	CHF 160

Caddie Caddie no — **Electric Trolley** Elektrokarren yes

Buggy Elektrischer Wagen no — **Clubs** Leihschläger yes

Credit cards Kreditkarten no

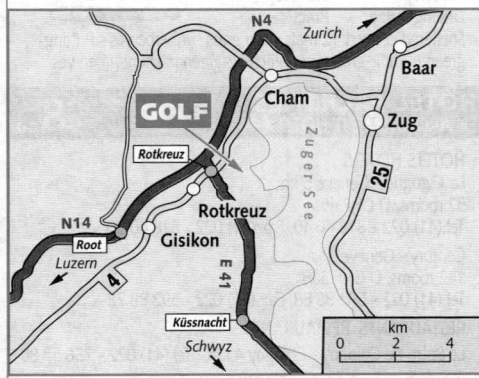

N4
Zurich
Baar
Cham
GOLF
Zug
Rotkreuz
Zuger See
25
Rotkreuz
N14
Gisikon
Root
Luzern
4
E 41
Küssnacht
Schwyz
km
0 2 4

Access Zufahrt : Motorway (Autobahn) N4 or N14 → Rotkreuz → Industrie Ost → "Golfpark"

Map 1 on page 1277 Karte 1 Seite 1277

GOLF COURSE — PLATZ — 13/20

Site	Lage	
Maintenance	Instandhaltung	
Architect	Architekt	Mario Verdieri
Type	Typ	open country
Relief	Begehbarkeit	
Water in play	Platz mit Wasser	
Exp. to wind	Wind ausgesetzt	
Trees in play	Platz mit Bäumen	

Scorecard Scorekarte	Chp. Chp.	Mens Herren	Ladies Damen
Length Länge	5882	5702	4991
Par	70	70	70
Slope system	127	125	122

Advised golfing ability Empfohlene Spielstärke — 0 12 24 36

Hcp required Min. Handicap 35

CLUB HOUSE & AMENITIES — KLUBHAUS UND NEBENGEBÄUDE — 7/10

Pro shop	Pro shop
Driving range	Übungsplatz

Sheltered überdacht 40 mats - On grass auf Rasen yes - Putting-green Putting-grün yes - Pitching-green Pitching-grün yes

HOTEL FACILITIES — HOTEL BESCHREIBUNG — 6/10

HOTELS HOTELS

Waldheim - Risch 2 km
34 rooms, D CHF 280
Tel (41) 041 - 799 70 70, Fax (41) 041 - 799 70 79

Parkhotel - Zug 10 km
110 rooms, D CHF 390
Tel (41) 041 - 727 48 48, Fax (41) 041 - 727 48 49

RESTAURANTS RESTAURANTS

Rathauskeller - Zug 10 km - Tel (41) 041 - 711 00 58
Hecht - Zug 10 km - Tel (41) 041 - 729 81 46
Raben - Cham 4 km - Tel (41) 041 - 780 13 12
Carpe Diem - Steinhausen 6 km - Tel (41) 041 - 748 81 18

Genève

17	7	8

Un des parcours suisses les plus intéressants, et bien que ce soit le grand club des Genevois, on a tout loisir d'en jouer le parcours en semaine. Sa qualité n'étonnera pas : Robert Trent Jones en est l'auteur. Dans un site magnifique surplombant le Lac Léman, il a une fois de plus signé un dessin très imaginatif et d'une grande intelligence stratégique. La multiplicité des départs et des positions de drapeaux permet de l'adapter à tous les niveaux, même si les joueurs très moyens auront du mal à y scorer. Les greens sont vastes (un double green aux 9 et 18), très dessinés, ce qui rend essentielle une bonne maîtrise du petit jeu et du putting... même si l'on réussit à bien travailler la balle au grand jeu, notamment sur les nombreux dog-legs. Une consolation pour ceux dont le swing n'est pas exceptionnel : si certains arbres peuvent poser problème, il y a peu d'obstacles d'eau (8, 16 et 17). Un grand classique toujours bien entretenu.

One of the most interesting Swiss courses, and although this is the place to play golf in Geneva, you can easily get a tee-off time during the week. Its excellence hardly comes as a surprise as it was designed by a one Robert Trent Jones. In a magnificent setting overlooking Lake Geneva, Jones has once again come up with a very imaginative layout calling for considerable strategic intelligence. The many different tees and pin positions make this a course for players of all abilities, even though your average hacker will find scoring a tough proposition. The greens are huge (the 9th and 18th have a double green) and well designed, thus calling for good putting skills and a sharp short game, even if your long game is on tune with the ball moving both ways, particularly on the very many dog-legs. There is one consolation for duffers, namely that although a few trees may cause problems, there are few water hazards (on the 8th, 16th and 17th holes only). Green-keeping is always very good.

Golf Club de Genève — 1972

70, route de la Capite
CH - 1233 COLOGNY

Office	Secrétariat	(41) 022 - 707 48 00
Pro shop	Pro-shop	(41) 022 - 707 48 15
Fax	Fax	(41) 022 - 707 48 20
Web	www.swissgolfnetwork.ch	
Situation	Situation	Genève, 5 km
Annual closure	Fermeture annuelle	15/12→5/3
Weekly closure	Fermeture hebdomadaire	monday (lundi)

Fees main season Tarifs haute saison	18 holes	
	Week days Semaine	**We/Bank holidays** We/Férié
Individual Individuel	CHF 150	*
Couple Couple	CHF 300	*

* Non members: only Tuesday morning (Mardi matin) → Friday morning (Vendredi)

Caddie Caddie yes (mandatory/obligatoire)

Electric Trolley Chariot électrique yes

Buggy Voiturette medical reasons **Clubs** Clubs yes

Credit cards Cartes de crédit no

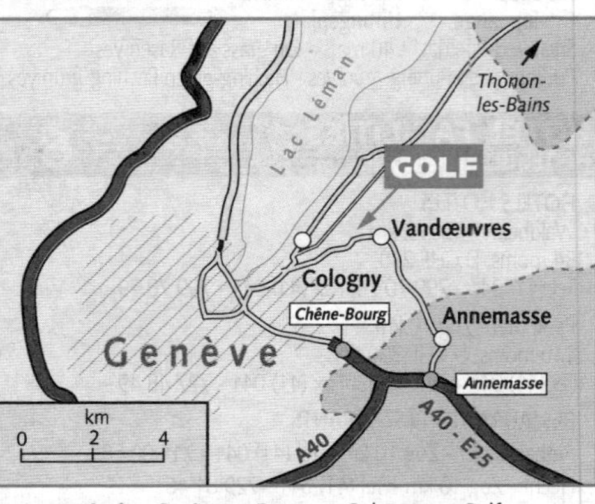

Access Accès : Genève → Evian, → Cologny, → Golf
Map 1 on page 1276 Carte 1 Page 1276

GOLF COURSE — PARCOURS — 17/20

Site	Site	
Maintenance	Entretien	
Architect	Architecte	Robert Trent Jones
Type	Type	parkland
Relief	Relief	
Water in play	Eau en jeu	
Exp. to wind	Exposé au vent	
Trees in play	Arbres en jeu	

Scorecard Carte de score	**Chp.** Chp.	**Mens** Mess	**Ladies** Da.
Length Long.	6152	5898	5152
Par	72	72	72
Slope system	125	124	125

Advised golfing ability Niveau de jeu recommandé: 0 12 24 36

Hcp required Handicap exigé 28

CLUB HOUSE & AMENITIES — CLUB-HOUSE ET ANNEXES — 7/10

Pro shop Pro-shop
Driving range Practice
Sheltered couvert 12 mats - On grass sur herbe yes - Putting-green putting-green yes - Pitching-green pitching green yes

HOTEL FACILITIES — ENVIRONNEMENT HOTELIER — 8/10

HOTELS HÔTELS

La Cigogne - Genève 5 km
52 rooms, D CHF 455
Tel (41) 022 - 818 40 40, Fax (41) 022 - 818 40 50

Century - Genève 5 km
142 rooms, D CHF 308
Tel (41) 022 - 592 88 88, Fax (41) 022 - 592 88 78

RESTAURANTS RESTAURANTS

Le Bistro de Cologny - Cologny 4 km - Tel (41) 022 - 736 57 80
Auberge du Lion d'Or - Cologny 4 km
Tel (41) 022 - 736 44 32
Le Béarn - Genève 6 km - Tel (41) 022 - 321 00 28
La Closerie - Cologny 3 km - Tel (41) 022 - 736 13 55

Gruyère (La)

14	7	6

Il n'est pas très habituel de conseiller des parcours courts, mais celui-ci, avec son par 68, est des plus amusants. Evidemment, les golfeurs du plus haut niveau n'y seront pas à l'aise, mais ils sont une minorité ! En premier lieu, Jeremy Pern a tiré un parti remarquable d'un terrain difficile à adapter au golf, et mis l'accent sur la précision, dans tous les secteurs du jeu. Qu'il s'agisse du drive, du second coup, des approches vers des greens très défendus ou du putting, cet aspect ludique est à la fois intéressant et formateur. Le parcours est assez physique, mais les fairways (étroits) sont assez plats, ce qui ne rend pas la marche trop ardue. L'imagination et l'intelligence de l'architecte en font une réussite, même s'il n'a pas eu l'espace pour s'exprimer pleinement. La qualité de l'entretien et la facilité relative pour y scorer en font une bonne adresse, relevée encore par un environnement magnifique au bord du lac de Gruyère. Et l'on s'y reposera agréablement au restaurant du club-house.

It is not every day that we recommend short courses, but this one is most amusing. The most proficient golfers will obviously not feel too excited about it, but they are a minority anyway. Firstly, Jeremy Pern has done a remarkable job with terrain that was difficult to harness for golf and has placed emphasis on precision in every department of the game. Whether for the drive, the second shot, approaches to very well-guarded greens or putting, this fun aspect is both interesting and educational. The course is pretty hilly, although the actual fairways are rather flat (and narrow), which means easy walking. The architect's imagination and intelligence have made this a class course, even though space was restricted. The standard of green-keeping and the relative ease of scoring make this a good address, enhanced by a magnificent setting on the banks of Lake Gruyère and a very pleasant club-house restaurant where you can relax after your round.

Golf de la Gruyère — 1993

Le Château
CH - 1649 PONT-LA-VILLE

Office	Secrétariat	(41) 026 - 414 94 60
Pro shop	Pro-shop	(41) 026 - 414 94 60
Fax	Fax	(41) 026 - 414 94 20
Web	www.golfgruyere.ch	
Situation	Situation	Fribourg, 12 km
Annual closure	Fermeture annuelle	2/1→1/3
Weekly closure	Fermeture hebdomadaire	no

Fees main season / Tarifs haute saison	Week days / Semaine	We/Bank holidays / We/Férié
		18 holes
Individual Individuel	CHF 80	CHF 100
Couple Couple	CHF 160	CHF 200

Juniors: 40%

Caddie Caddie no — Electric Trolley Chariot électrique no

Buggy Voiturette yes — Clubs Clubs yes

Credit cards Cartes de crédit
VISA - Eurocard - MasterCard - AMEX - DC

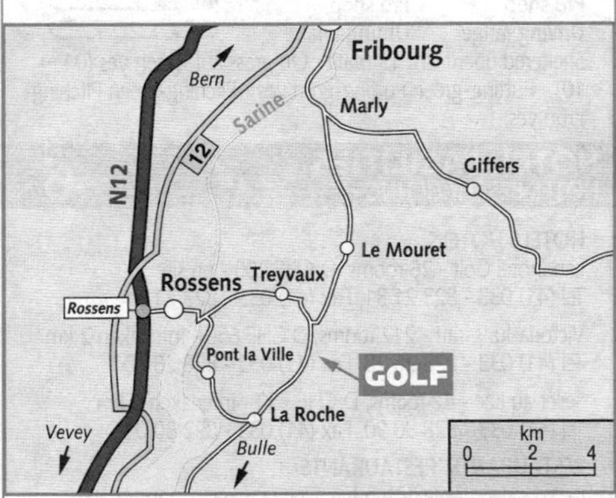

Access Accès : E25 Fribourg-Vevey → Rossens → Pont-la-Ville
Map 1 on page 1276 Carte 1 Page 1276

GOLF COURSE — PARCOURS — 14/20

Site	Site	
Maintenance	Entretien	
Architect	Architecte	Jeremy Pern
Type	Type	country
Relief	Relief	
Water in play	Eau en jeu	
Exp. to wind	Exposé au vent	
Trees in play	Arbres en jeu	

Scorecard / Carte de score	Chp. / Chp.	Mens / Mess.	Ladies / Da.
Length Long.	5058	4758	4093
Par	68	68	68
Slope system	122	116	117

Advised golfing ability / Niveau de jeu recommandé: 0 12 24 36

Hcp required — Handicap exigé — 36

CLUB HOUSE & AMENITIES — CLUB-HOUSE ET ANNEXES — 7/10

Pro shop — Pro-shop
Driving range — Practice

Sheltered couvert 3 mats (+ indoor) - On grass sur herbe yes (in summer) - Putting-green putting-green yes - Pitching-green pitching green yes

HOTEL FACILITIES — ENVIRONNEMENT HOTELIER — 6/10

HOTELS HÔTELS

Hôtel Restaurant du Golf - 12 rooms, D CHF 250 - on site
Tel (41) 026 - 414 94 00, Fax (41) 026 - 414 94 20

Hostellerie Saint Georges - Gruyères 12 km
14 rooms, D CHF 180
Tel (41) 026 - 921 83 00, Fax (41) 026 - 921 83 39

Hôtel Cailler - 50 rooms, D CHF 220 - Charmey 15 km
Tel (41) 026 - 927 62 62, Fax (41) 026 - 927 62 63

RESTAURANTS RESTAURANTS

Au Lion d'Or - Hauteville 12 km - Tel (41) 026 - 915 15 51
Restaurant de la Tour - Bulle 15 km - Tel (41) 026 - 912 74 70
Restaurant des Trois Tours - Bourguillon (Fribourg) 13 km
Tel (41) 026 - 322 30 69

Interlaken

14	6	6

Vom Thunerseeufer nur durch eine Naturschutzzone getrennt, bietet der Interlakner Golfplatz je nach Wasserstand des Sees und Regenmenge recht feuchte Bedingungen, doch er gibt ein gutes Beispiel für das Miteinander von Golf und Ökologie ab – oder in anderen Worten: er fügt sich perfekt in die Landschaft ein. Die recht flache Anlage steht in einem faszinierenden Kontrast zu den umliegenden Berner Alpengipfeln. Der Spielrhythmus ist ansprechend, doch die ersten fünf Loch können - bedingt durch ihre beträchtliche Länge - eine gute Scorekarte schon zu Beginn der Runde gefährden. Die gut und vielseitig gestalteten Grüns fordern einige interessante Annäherungsschläge. Moderate Schwierigkeiten bestimmen den Gesamteindruck dieses Kurses, der sich für eine angenehme Familienrunde eignet. Einige Fairways mögen vor allem aus Sicht des hintersten Abschlags schmal erscheinen. Einem Abschlag übrigens, den man bei Regen lieber ignorieren sollte.

Not far from Lake Thun, from which the course is separated by a protected natural expanse of land, this can be a very wet course when it rains but forms a good example of coexistence with ecological requirements. This is another way of saying that it blends perfectly with its natural environment. In contrast with the impressive mountain setting, the course is rather flat and can be played at a good pace, even though the first five holes are a tough proposition in terms of length and can spoil any hope of returning a good card. The greens are well cut out, rather varied and make for some interesting approach shots. The overriding impression is that of a course where difficulties have been kept to a reasonable minimum for a pleasant round of golf with all the family. Having said that, some holes can look decidedly tight, especially from the back tees, which should be unashamedly forgotten whenever it rains.

Golf-Club Interlaken-Unterseen 1966

Postfach 110
CH - 3800 INTERLAKEN

Office	Sekretariat	(41) 033 - 823 60 16
Pro shop	Pro shop	(41) 033 - 822 79 70
Fax	Fax	(41) 033 - 823 42 03
Web	www.interlakengolf.ch	
Situation	Lage	Interlaken, 2 km
Annual closure	Jährliche Schliessung	15/11→31/3
Weekly closure	Wöchentliche Schliessung	no
Fees main season	Preisliste hochsaison	18 holes

	Week days Woche	We/Bank holidays We/Feiertag
Individual Individuell	CHF 90	CHF 105
Couple Ehepaar	CHF 180	CHF 210

Caddie Caddie no — Electric Trolley Elektrokarren yes

Buggy Elektrischer Wagen no — Clubs Leihschläger yes

Credit cards Kreditkarten
VISA - Eurocard - MasterCard - AMEX

Brientz
GOLF
Interlaken
Thun
Brientzersee
Unterseen
Interlaken
N8
Thunersee
wilderswil
Unterseen
N8
Därligen
Spiez
km
0 2 4

Access Zufahrt : Motorway (Autobahn) N8.
Exit Unterseen → Thunersee, Golf
Map 1 on page 1277 Karte 1 Seite 1277

GOLF COURSE PLATZ 14/20

Site	Lage	
Maintenance	Instandhaltung	
Architect	Architekt	Donald Harradine
Type	Typ	parkland, open country
Relief	Begehbarkeit	
Water in play	Platz mit Wasser	
Exp. to wind	Wind ausgesetzt	
Trees in play	Platz mit Bäumen	

Scorecard Scorekarte	Chp. Chp.	Mens Herren	Ladies Damen
Length Länge	5864	5534	4694
Par	72	72	72
Slope system	131	130	121

Advised golfing ability 0 12 24 36
Empfohlene Spielstärke
Hcp required Min. Handicap 36

CLUB HOUSE & AMENITIES KLUBHAUS UND NEBENGEBÄUDE 6/10

Pro shop Pro shop
Driving range Übungsplatz
Sheltered überdacht 13 mats - On grass auf Rasen yes (04 → 10) - Putting-green Putting-grün yes - Pitching-green Pitching-grün yes

HOTEL FACILITIES HOTEL BESCHREIBUNG 6/10

HOTELS HOTELS
Landhotel Golf - 26 rooms, D CHF 200 - on site
Tel (41) 033 - 823 21 31, Fax (41) 033 - 823 21 91

Victoria Jungfrau - 212 rooms, D CHF 650 - Interlaken 2 km
Tel (41) 033 - 828 28 28, Fax (41) 033 - 828 28 80

Seiler au Lac - 42 rooms, D CHF 350 - Interlaken 5 km
Tel (41) 033 - 828 90 90, Fax (41) 033 - 822 30 01

RESTAURANTS RESTAURANTS
La Terrasse - Interlaken 3 km - Tel (41) 033 - 828 28 28
Stocker's Degusta - Interlaken 3 km - Tel (41) 033 - 822 00 29
Alpenblick - Oberdorf/Wilderswil 3 km
Tel (41) 033 - 828 35 50

Lausanne

16 | 7 | 7

Un parcours séduisant et tranquille à première vue, mais dont les nombreuses difficultés se révèlent peu à peu dans ce site très boisé, et les scores peuvent vite se révéler frustrants ! Bien rythmé dans son enchaînement, il est souvent étroit, assez vallonné, mais sans vraiment de pièges cachés. Le remodelage des greens par Jeremy Pern a rajeuni ce parcours classique de façon spectaculaire, et oblige plus encore à réfléchir avant de jouer, d'autant que les bunkers de green, également retravaillés, amènent à porter souvent la balle au lieu de la faire rouler. Les joueurs moyens, qui ont souvent du mal à le faire, auront tout intérêt à jouer des départs avancés. Très agréable à jouer en été quand le terrain est sec, Lausanne était autrefois plus difficile dans des conditions humides, le placement de la balle au drive devenant alors encore plus crucial, mais le résultat des travaux a nettement amélioré cet aspect des choses, sans que le cachet du parcours en soit modifié. Un bel endroit et une véritable réussite, où la vitesse des greens peut être déterminante.

At first view, an appealing and quiet golf course, but one where the numerous difficulties gradually emerge in a very woody site. With nicely paced continuity, the fairways are often tight and rather hilly, but with no real hidden traps. Recent restyling by architect Jeremy Pern has spectacularly rejuvenated this classic course which now requires more careful thought before each shot, especially since the green-side bunkers, which have also been redesigned, often call for a high lob shot instead of the easier chip into the green. Average players, who often have problems with this kind of approach, will be better off playing from the front tees. Very pleasant to play in summer when the terrain is dry, Lausanne can prove to be a tougher proposition in wet conditions, when placing the ball off the tee becomes even more crucial. However, work has been carried out and has distinctly improved this side of things without affecting the course's cachet. A definite winner.

Golf Club de Lausanne — 1931

3, route du Golf
CH - 1000 Lausanne 25

Office	Secrétariat	(41) 021 - 784 84 84
Pro shop	Pro-shop	(41) 021 - 784 84 74
Fax	Fax	(41) 021 - 784 84 80
Web	www.swissgolfnetwork.ch	
Situation	Situation	Lausanne, 5 km
Annual closure	Fermeture annuelle	15/12→15/3
Weekly closure	Fermeture hebdomadaire	no

Fees main season Tarifs haute saison	18 holes	
	Week days Semaine	**We/Bank holidays** We/Férié
Individual Individuel	CHF 100	CHF 130
Couple Couple	CHF 200	CHF 260

Under 21: – 50%

Caddie Caddie on request **Electric Trolley** Chariot électrique yes
Buggy Voiturette yes(medical reasons) **Clubs** Clubs yes
Credit cards Cartes de crédit
VISA - MasterCard - AMEX

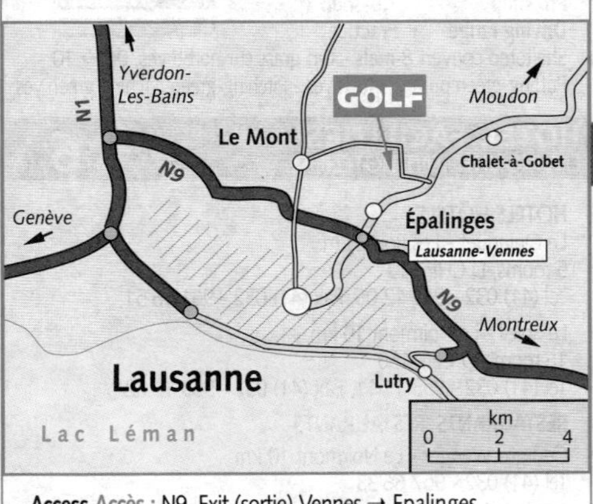

Access Accès : N9, Exit (sortie) Vennes → Epalinges. Chalet-à-Gobet, → Le Mont, Golf
Map 1 on page 1276 Carte 1 Page 1276

GOLF COURSE — PARCOURS — 16/20

Site	Site	
Maintenance	Entretien	
Architect	Architecte	Narbel Jeremy Pern
Type	Type	parkland
Relief	Relief	
Water in play	Eau en jeu	
Exp. to wind	Exposé au vent	
Trees in play	Arbres en jeu	

Scorecard Carte de score	**Chp.** Chp.	**Mens** Mess.	**Ladies** Da.
Length Long.	6197	5793	5139
Par	72	72	72
Slope system	135	128	129

Advised golfing ability Niveau de jeu recommandé — 0 12 24 36
Hcp required Handicap exigé — 28

CLUB HOUSE & AMENITIES — CLUB-HOUSE ET ANNEXES — 7/10

Pro shop Pro-shop
Driving range Practice
Sheltered couvert 4 mats - On grass sur herbe yes - Putting-green putting-green yes - Pitching-green pitching green yes

HOTEL FACILITIES — ENVIRONNEMENT HOTELIER — 7/10

HOTELS HÔTELS

Les Chevreuils - Vers-chez-les-Blancs 5 km
30 rooms, D CHF 234
Tel (41) 021 - 784 20 21, Fax (41) 021 - 784 15 45

Beau Rivage Palace - 169 rooms, D CHF 470 - Lausanne 6 km
Tel (41) 021 - 613 33 33, Fax (41) 021 - 613 33 34

Victoria - 55 rooms, D CHF 320 - Lausanne 6 km
Tel (41) 021 - 342 02 02, Fax (41) 021 - 342 02 22

RESTAURANTS RESTAURANTS

Hôtel de Ville (Rochat) - Crissier 10 km
Tel (41) 021 - 634 05 05

La Grappe d'Or - Lausanne 6 km - Tel (41) 021 - 323 07 60

A la Pomme de Pin - Lausanne 6 km - Tel (41) 021 - 323 46 56

Les Bois

15 | 7 | 6

Le Golf Club Les Bois se trouve au milieu de la région des Franches Montagnes, typique du Jura Suisse. Un vrai et superbe décor d'opérette. Le terrain est accidenté, mais acceptable sur le plan physique (chariot électrique ou voiturette pour les moins solides). Il a été construit en deux temps, mais la différence entre les greens est presque insensible. Le parcours mélange les trous en forêt et les trous en espace plus ouvert, l'ensemble étant harmonieux et très bien équilibré. Certes, on ne voit pas tous les obstacles, et l'on ne peut concevoir une bonne stratégie de jeu avant d'avoir joué plusieurs fois, mais sachez au moins que ce parcours est aussi franc qu'on le devine, et qu'il n'est pas vraiment nécessaire de travailler la balle. En revanche, il faut savoir lire ces greens, pas du tout évidents. Pour finir, vous garderez en particulier le souvenir des trous 14 à 16 au milieu des sapins, qui peuvent figurer parmi les plus beaux trous de Suisse. Un golf de très bon niveau, et jouable par tous.

The Golf Club Les Bois is located amidst the region of Franches Montagnes that is typical of the Swiss Jura mountains. A superb decor in true operetta style. The terrain is hilly but not over-demanding physically (think about an electric trolley or buggy for the less able). It was built in two phases, which is now not evident at all. The course is a mixture of holes through a forest and holes in more open space, all harmoniously put together with clever balance. You definitely do not see all the hazards and effective game strategy is not possible before playing the course several times. Suffice it to say that this layout is as open and honest as you might guess and you don't really need to bend or flight the ball. What you do need to know is how to read the greens here, which are anything but straightforward. The holes you will remember are 14 through 16 in the middle of pine trees, which might rank as some of the finest holes of golf in the whole of Switzerland. A first rate course, playable by everyone.

Golf Club Les Bois — 1995

Les Murs, Case Postale 26
CH - 2336 LES BOIS

Office	Secrétariat	(41) 032 - 961 10 03
Pro shop	Pro-shop	(41) 032 - 961 19 44
Fax	Fax	(41) 032 - 961 10 17
Web	www.swissgolfnetwork.ch	
Situation	Situation	La Chaux-de-Fonds, 12 km
Annual closure	Fermeture annuelle	1/11→1/4
Weekly closure	Fermeture hebdomadaire	no

Fees main season Tarifs haute saison	18 holes	
	Week days Semaine	We/Bank holidays We/Férié
Individual Individuel	CHF 80	CHF 100
Couple Couple	CHF 160	CHF 200

Juniors under 21: – 50%

Caddie Caddie no — **Electric Trolley** Chariot électrique yes

Buggy Voiturette yes — **Clubs** Clubs yes

Credit cards Cartes de crédit
VISA - Eurocard - MasterCard - AMEX - DC

Access Accès : Genève, Lausanne, Bern : A1 → Neuchâtel. N20 → La Chaux-de-Fonds. Road 18 → Saignelégier.

Map 1 on page 1276 Carte 1 Page 1276

GOLF COURSE — PARCOURS — 15/20

Site	Site	
Maintenance	Entretien	
Architect	Architecte	Jeremy Pern
Type	Type	forest, country
Relief	Relief	
Water in play	Eau en jeu	
Exp. to wind	Exposé au vent	
Trees in play	Arbres en jeu	

Scorecard Carte de score	Chp. Chp.	Mens Mess.	Ladies Da.
Length Long.	6053	5768	4879
Par	72	72	72
Slope system	128	126	126

Advised golfing ability Niveau de jeu recommandé — 0 12 24 36

Hcp required Handicap exigé — 54

CLUB HOUSE & AMENITIES — CLUB-HOUSE ET ANNEXES — 7/10

Pro shop	Pro-shop
Driving range	Practice

Sheltered couvert 8 mats - On grass sur herbe yes, 06 → 10 - Putting-green putting-green yes - Pitching-green pitching green yes

HOTEL FACILITIES — ENVIRONNEMENT HOTELIER — 6/10

HOTELS HÔTELS

Le Quinquet - Les Bois 2 km
5 rooms, D CHF 140
Tel (41) 032 - 961 12 06, Fax (41) 032 - 961 16 51

Le Soleil - Le Noirmont 10 km
16 rooms, D CHF 150
Tel (41) 032 - 953 11 11, Fax (41) 032 - 953 11 62

RESTAURANTS RESTAURANTS

Georges Wenger - Le Noirmont 10 km
Tel (41) 032 - 957 66 33

Hôtel de la Gare et du Parc - Saignelégier 20 km
Tel (41) 032 - 951 11 21

Auberge de l'Ours - Les Bois 2 km - Tel (41) 032 - 961 14 45

Lugano

15 | 7 | 8

Fondato nel 1926, il percorso é stato rimodellato successivamente da Donald Harradine e Cabell Robinson che ha aggiunto qualche laghetto al corso d'acqua esistente (La Magliasina), ma non ha potuto allungarlo per mancanza di spazio. I green sono ben difesi e questo ridimensiona il desiderio di grandi performance. E' molto franco e non bisogna giocarci dieci volte per capire la strategia di gioco. La vegetazione mitiga il disegno delle buche che sono una a fianco all'altra e obbliga i giocatori lunghi a drivare con l'effetto per avere un approccio ideale al green. Gli altri giocatori possono rifarsi con la precisione, in quanto il percorso non é molto lungo. In un posto molto piacevole di una magnifica regione, é un buon percorso di villeggiatura ma la sua manutenzione deve essere migliorata per potergli attribuire un voto migliore.

Opened in 1926, the course has been successively reshaped by Donald Harradine and Cabell Robinson, who added several lakes to the existing river Magliasina but were not allowed to lengthen the course owing to lack of space. The greens are nonetheless well defended, which may cut short any desire to go for the performance. You don't need to play this very honest course ten times to understand what it is about, because you will have a clear vision of the best strategy. The vegetation reduces the impression of up and down holes suggested by the layout, and forces long-hitters to fade or draw the ball to get a good approach into the green. Good and not so good players can get along well together here, where lack of precision is offset by short yardage. In a very pleasant setting and wonderful region, this is a good holiday course, but to get a better score, green-keeping and maintenance must be kept to the highest possible standards.

Golf Club Lugano — 1926

Via Boett
CH - 6983 MAGLIASO

Office Segreteria (41) 091 - 606 15 57
Pro shop Pro shop (41) 091 - 606 46 76
Fax Fax (41) 091 - 606 65 58
Web www.golflugano.ch
Situation Località Lugano, 5 km
Annual closure Chiusura annuale no
Weekly closure Chiusura settimanale no

Fees main season Tariffe alta stagione	18 holes	
	Week days Settimana	**We/Bank holidays** Feriale/Festivo
Individual Individuale	CHF 90	CHF 110
Couple Coppia	CHF 180	CHF 220

Under 21: – 50%

Caddie Caddie no — **Electric Trolley** Carello elettrico no
Buggy Car medical reasons — **Clubs** Bastoni yes
Credit cards Carte di credito
VISA - Eurocard

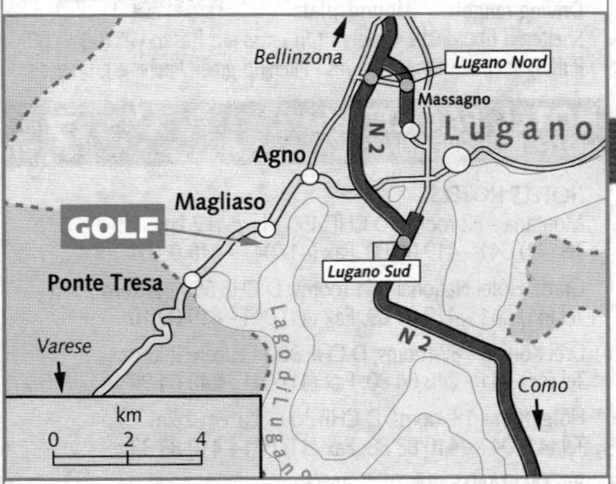

Access Itinerario : Lugano, → Ponte Tresa, → Magliaso, Golf
Map 1 on page 1277 Carta 1 Pagina 1277

GOLF COURSE — PERCORSO — 15/20

Site Paesaggio
Maintenance Manutenzione
Architect Architetto: Donald Harradine, Cabell B. Robinson
Type Tipologia: parkland
Relief Relievo terreno
Water in play Acqua in gioco
Exp. to wind Esposto al vento
Trees in play Alberi in gioco

Scorecard Carta-score	**Chp.** Camp.	**Mens** Uomini	**Ladies** Donne
Length Lunghezza	5575	5258	4629
Par	71	71	71
Slope system	125	122	124

Advised golfing ability Livello di gioco consigliato: 0 12 24 36
Hcp required Handicap richiesto 36

CLUB HOUSE & AMENITIES — CLUB HOUSE E SERVIZI — 7/10

Pro shop Pro shop
Driving range Campo pratica
Sheltered coperto 9 mats - On grass in erba no - Putting-green Putting-green yes - Pitching-green Green-pratica yes

HOTEL FACILITIES — ALBERGHI — 8/10

HOTELS ALBERGHI
Villa Magliasina - Magliaso 500 m
27 rooms, D CHF 350
Tel (41) 091 - 611 29 29, Fax (41) 091 - 611 29 20

Principe Leopoldo - Lugano 7 km
37 rooms, D CHF 600
Tel (41) 091 - 985 88 55, Fax (41) 091 - 985 88 25

Gardenia - 21 rooms, D CHF 300 - Caslano 1 km
Tel (41) 091 - 611 82 11, Fax (41) 091 - 611 82 10

RESTAURANTS RISTORANTE
Locanda Esterel - Caslano 1 km - Tel (41) 091 - 611 21 20
Santabbondio - Sorengo 4 km - Tel (41) 091 - 993 23 88
Al Portone - Lugano 7 km - Tel (41) 091 - 923 55 11

Luzern

13	6	7

1925 erbaut und seither mehrfach verändert, vor allem Anfang der 90er Jahre, bietet dieser Parcours verschiedene abwechslungsreiche Aussichten auf den Vierwaldstättersee, auf Hügellandschaften und auf schneebedeckte Berge. Die betonten Geländeformen mit teils erheblichen Steigungen wurden geschickt einbezogen, denn die grossen Höhenunterschiede liegen meist zwischen den Bahnen. Die meisten Bahnen sind gerade - Doglegs sind wenige zu finden -, aber oft schmal und von Bäumen gesäumt und verlangen nach geraden Schlägen. Das Auf und Ab ist ein wenig schade, aber anders hätte man den Platz nicht in die Landschaft fügen können, ohne das ganze Gelände zu zerstören. Da es nur ein Wasserhindernis zu überwinden gilt, haben gute Spieler sicher Chancen auf niedrige Scores, obwohl Annäherungen auf entweder tiefer oder höher gelegene Grüns Gefühl für die Distanz und solide Schläge verlangen. Uns gefiel der Charme dieser Anlage mit ihrem traditionellen Platzkonzept und auch die Umgebung – sie machen Luzern zum lohnenden Golfabstecher.

This course has been restyled since its opening, particularly so in the early 1990s to improve the safety of walkers. There are pretty views over Lake Lucerne, the hills and the snow-capped mountains. The terrain is steep and rather hilly but has been well utilized, as the steepest slopes are to be found primarily between holes. There are few dog-legs but most holes are straight and require straight shots, skirting the trees. This up and down layout of holes is a bit of a pity but it was difficult to plan otherwise without demolishing the whole site. With a single water hazard, skilled players will doubtless find this an easy course to score on, even though care is called for when attacking the greens, which are rarely on the same level as the fairway (elevated or in a hollow). We liked the charm of the site and a certain idea of old-style golf courses, without the difficulties found on many modern courses.

Luzern Golf Club — 1925

Dietschiberg
CH - 6006 LUZERN

Office	Sekretariat	(41) 041 - 420 97 87
Pro shop	Pro shop	(41) 041 - 420 97 86
Fax	Fax	(41) 041 - 420 82 48
Web	www.golfclubluzern.ch	
Situation	Lage	Luzern, 2 km
Annual closure	Jährliche Schliessung	31/10→1/4
Weekly closure	Wöchentliche Schliessung	no

Restaurant closed on Monday (Montag)

Fees main season Preisliste hochsaison — 18 holes

	Week days Woche	We/Bank holidays We/Feiertag
Individual Individuell	CHF 110	CHF 130
Couple Ehepaar	CHF 220	CHF 260

Juniors under 21: – 50%

Caddie Caddie no **Electric Trolley** Elektrokarren yes

Buggy Elektrischer Wagen medical reasons only

Clubs Leihschläger yes

Credit cards Kreditkarten
Club: Mastercard - Pro shop: VISA - MasterCard - AMEX

Access Zufahrt : Luzern → "Dreilinden", → Trachtenmuseum, Dietschibergstrasse

Map 1 on page 1277 Karte 1 Seite 1277

GOLF COURSE PLATZ — 13/20

Site	Lage	
Maintenance	Instandhaltung	
Architect	Architekt	Ruzzo Reuss
Type	Typ	forest, hilly
Relief	Begehbarkeit	
Water in play	Platz mit Wasser	
Exp. to wind	Wind ausgesetzt	
Trees in play	Platz mit Bäumen	

Scorecard Scorekarte	Chp. Chp.	Mens Herren	Ladies Damen
Length Länge	6067	5744	5017
Par	73	73	73
Slope system	128	124	124

Advised golfing ability Empfohlene Spielstärke — 0 12 24 36

Hcp required Min. Handicap — 30

CLUB HOUSE & AMENITIES KLUBHAUS UND NEBENGEBÄUDE — 6/10

Pro shop Pro shop
Driving range Übungsplatz
Sheltered überdacht 4 mats - On grass auf Rasen yes (06 → 09)
Putting-green Putting-grün yes - Pitching-green Pitching-grün yes

HOTEL FACILITIES HOTEL BESCHREIBUNG — 7/10

HOTELS HOTELS

Montana - 62 rooms, D CHF 450 - Luzern 2 km
Tel (41) 041 - 419 00 00, Fax (41) 041 - 419 00 01

Grand Hôtel National - 41 rooms, D CHF 650 - Luzern 2 km
Tel (41) 041 - 419 09 09, Fax (41) 041 - 419 09 10

Drei Könige - 67 rooms, D CHF 300 - Luzern 2 km
Tel (41) 041 - 248 04 80, Fax (41) 041 - 248 04 90

Hofgarten - 18 rooms, D CHF 300 - Luzern 2 km
Tel (41) 041 - 410 88 88, Fax (41) 041 - 410 83 33

RESTAURANTS RESTAURANTS

Rössli - Adlingenswil 2 km - Tel (41) 041 - 370 10 30
Old Swiss House - Luzern 2 km - Tel (41) 041 - 410 61 71
Galliker - Luzern 2 km - Tel (41) 041 - 240 10 02

Montreux

15	6	6

La beauté du panorama sur les Alpes n'a pas changé, c'est une qualité si commune aux parcours suisses qu'on pourrait la négliger. On était heureux de l'environnement sublime, avec une vue spectaculaire sur les Dents du Midi, pour pimenter un parcours plaisant et élégant, mais assez banal, on aura plus de mal à lever la tête après une telle métamorphose. Il ne suffit plus d'éviter les arbres pour ramener une bonne carte, l'Américain Ronald Fream a mené brillamment le travail de rénovation demandé par le club, notamment avec quatre nouveaux trous. On connaît son goût des formes, on les retrouvera dans le remodelage de l'ensemble des greens, de leur environnement immédiat et des bunkers. De plus, trois lacs ont été créés qui interviennent sur cinq trous, tout comme de nouveaux bunkers de fairway. Autrement dit, le golf de Montreux a voulu entrer dans son second siècle d'existence en frappant un grand coup. Et même 18 !

The beautiful panorama over the Alps never changes and is an attribute so common on Swiss courses that it tends to be sometimes overlooked. They were lucky here to benefit from such magnificent surroundings with a quite spectacular view over the Dents du Midi, if only to add a little spice to a course that until recently was a pleasant, elegant but rather plain course. Now, though, players will have their minds more on a genuinely transformed layout. There is no more question of just avoiding the trees to card a good score, as American architect Ronald Fream has brilliantly carried out the renovation work requested by the club, most notably with four completely new holes. We know all about his penchant for shaping and he has employed it here to remodel all the greens, the areas immediately around them and the bunkers. In addition, he has dug three lakes, which come into play on five holes, and some new fairway bunkers. In other words Montreux has set out to mark its second century of existence with a bang, which resonates over all 18 holes.

Golf Club Montreux — 1900

Route d'Evian 54
CH - 1860 AIGLE

Office	Secrétariat	(41) 024 - 466 46 16
Pro shop	Pro-shop	(41) 024 - 466 14 64
Fax	Fax	(41) 024 - 466 60 47
Web	www.swissgolfnetwork.ch	
Situation	Situation	Montreux, 15 km
Annual closure	Fermeture annuelle	no
Weekly closure	Fermeture hebdomadaire	no

Fees main season Tarifs haute saison — 18 holes

	Week days / Semaine	We/Bank holidays / We/Férié
Individual Individuel	CHF 80	CHF 100
Couple Couple	CHF 160	CHF 200

Under 21: CHF 50 - CHF 60 (We)

Caddie Caddie no — **Electric Trolley** Chariot électrique yes
Buggy Voiturette yes — **Clubs** Clubs yes
Credit cards Cartes de crédit
VISA - Eurocard - Mastercard - AMEX - DC

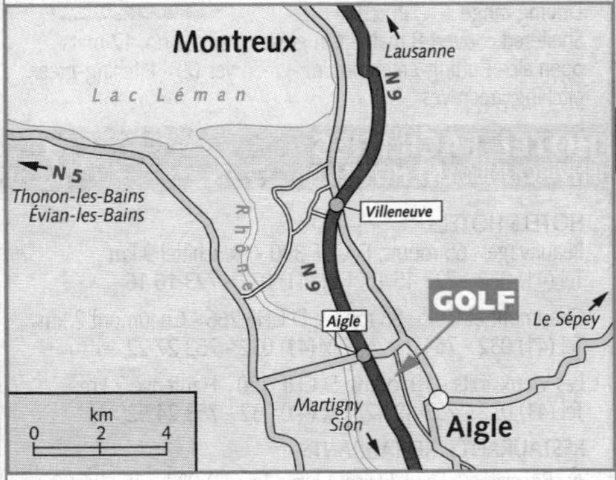

Access Accès : N9 Montreux-Martigny, Exit (sortie) Aigle, turn right, then right → Golf
Map 1 on page 1276 Carte 1 Page 1276

GOLF COURSE — PARCOURS — 15/20

Site	Site	
Maintenance	Entretien	
Architect	Architecte	Donald Harradine Ronald Fream (2005)
Type	Type	parkland
Relief	Relief	
Water in play	Eau en jeu	
Exp. to wind	Exposé au vent	
Trees in play	Arbres en jeu	

Scorecard Carte de score	Chp. Chp.	Mens Mess.	Ladies Da.
Length Long.	6099	5782	5083
Par	72	72	72
Slope system	122	122	121

Advised golfing ability Niveau de jeu recommandé — 0 12 24 36
Hcp required Handicap exigé 36

CLUB HOUSE & AMENITIES — CLUB-HOUSE ET ANNEXES — 6/10

Pro shop Pro-shop
Driving range Practice
Sheltered couvert 6 mats - On grass sur herbe yes - Putting-green putting-green yes - Pitching-green pitching green yes

HOTEL FACILITIES — ENVIRONNEMENT HOTELIER — 6/10

HOTELS HÔTELS

Le Montreux Palace - Montreux 25 km
235 rooms, D CHF 640
Tel (41) 021 - 962 12 12, Fax (41) 021 - 962 17 17

Villa Toscane - 50 rooms, D CHF 260 - Montreux 25 km
Tel (41) 021 - 966 88 88, Fax (41) 021 - 966 88 00

Nord - 19 rooms, D CHF 150 - Aigle 3 km
Tel (41) 024 - 468 10 55, Fax (41) 024 - 468 10 56

RESTAURANTS RESTAURANTS

Le Pont de Brent - Montreux-Brent 30 km
Tel (41) 021 - 964 52 30
L'Hôtel de Ville - Ollon 10 km - Tel (41) 024 - 499 19 22
Auberge de Vouvry - Vouvry 10 km - Tel (41) 024 - 481 12 21

Neuchâtel

14 | 7 | 7

Ce parcours accidenté, mais sans excès, a été dessiné dans une ancienne zone agricole au pied du Jura par l'un des architectes les plus constamment présents dans les golfs suisses. L'absence d'arrosage automatique peut être problématique en temps de forte sécheresse, mais les précipitations naturelles permettent de le maintenir généralement en bon état. Les obstacles sont rarement très dangereux (quelques hors-limites), et la longueur raisonnable pour la plupart des joueurs permet d'offrir pas mal d'occasions de birdie (ou de pars pour les joueurs moyens). Pas de pièges ici ni de complications artificielles : ce parcours a été coulé dans la nature, à l'intention évidente des familles, ou de ceux qui ne souhaitent pas trop se compliquer la vie sur un parcours (ils sont nombreux). Autrement dit, c'est une œuvre utile. Mais il y a si peu d'obstacles dangereux que l'on peut se laisser surprendre par le seul obstacle d'eau, au 9.

This is a rather hilly course laid out over a former farming region at the foot of the Jura mountains by one of Switzerland's more prominent course architects. There being no automatic sprinklers, it is not a course to be recommended during a drought, but natural rainfall generally tends to keep it in good condition. The hazards are rarely very dangerous (a few out-of-bounds) and the reasonable length can produce more than one opportunity to catch an elusive birdie (or the equally elusive par for lesser players). There are no traps or artificial complications here, as this course was cast in natural land, evidently intended for families or golfers who prefer not to make life any more complicated than it often can be on a golf course (and there are a lot of those). In other words, this is a pretty useful course where there are so few dangerous hazards that you may be caught unaware by the single stretch of water on the 9th hole.

Golf & Country Club Neuchâtel — 1975

Hameau de Voëns
CH - 2072 SAINT-BLAISE

Office	Secrétariat	(41) 032 - 753 55 50
Pro shop	Pro-shop	(41) 032 - 753 70 84
Fax	Fax	(41) 032 - 753 29 40
Web	www.swissgolfnetwork.ch	
Situation	Situation	Neuchâtel, 5 km
Annual closure	Fermeture annuelle	15/11→15/3
Weekly closure	Fermeture hebdomadaire	no

Fees main season Tarifs haute saison	18 holes	
	Week days Semaine	**We/Bank holidays** We/Férié
Individual Individuel	CHF 90	CHF 110
Couple Couple	CHF 180	CHF 220

Juniors: – 50%

Caddie Caddie no — **Electric Trolley** Chariot électrique no

Buggy Voiturette medical reasons **Clubs** Clubs yes

Credit cards Cartes de crédit
VISA - Eurocard - Mastercard - AMEX - DC

Lignières
Biel
Enges
GOLF
La Chaux-de-Fonds
Cornaux
Thielle
St-Blaise
Bern
Marin
Lausanne
Neuchâtel
km 0 2 4
Lac de Neuchâtel

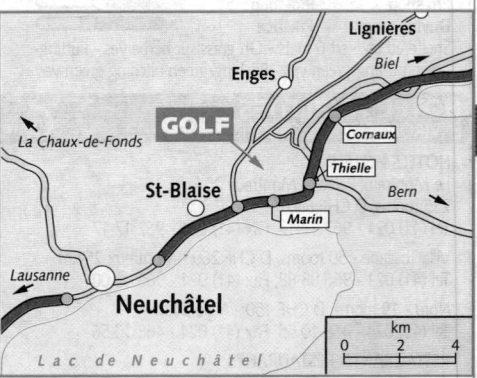

Access Accès : A1 Bâle-Payerne, Exit (sortie) Neuchâtel. In Kerzers → Neuchâtel to St Blaise, → Lignières. 3 km, Voëns, golf on the left.

Map 1 on page 1276 Carte 1 Page 1276

GOLF COURSE — PARCOURS — 14/20

Site	Site	
Maintenance	Entretien	
Architect	Architecte	Donald Harradine
Type	Type	parkland
Relief	Relief	
Water in play	Eau en jeu	
Exp. to wind	Exposé au vent	
Trees in play	Arbres en jeu	

Scorecard Carte de score	**Chp.** Chp.	**Mens** Mess.	**Ladies** Da.
Length Long.	5917	5618	4825
Par	71	71	71
Slope system	129	125	121

Advised golfing ability Niveau de jeu recommandé: 0 12 24 36

Hcp required Handicap exigé 36

CLUB HOUSE & AMENITIES — CLUB-HOUSE ET ANNEXES — 7/10

Pro shop Pro-shop
Driving range Practice
Sheltered couvert 8 mats - On grass sur herbe no, 12 mats open air - Putting-green putting-green yes (2) - Pitching-green pitching green yes

HOTEL FACILITIES — ENVIRONNEMENT HOTELIER — 7/10

HOTELS HÔTELS

Beaurivage - 65 rooms, D CHF 390 - Neuchâtel 9 km
Tel (41) 032 - 723 15 15, Fax (41) 032 - 723 16 16

Chaumont et Golf - 88 rooms, D CHF 266 - Chaumont 2 km
Tel (41) 032 - 754 21 75, Fax (41) 032 - 753 27 22

Les Vieux Toits - 10 rooms, D CHF 150 - Hauterive 2 km
Tel (41) 032 - 753 42 42, Fax (41) 032 - 753 24 52

RESTAURANTS RESTAURANTS

Au Boccalino - Saint-Blaise 4 km - Tel (41) 032 - 753 36 80
Auberge d'Hauterive - Hauterive 2 km
Tel (41) 032 - 753 17 98
Hôtel DuPeyrou - Neuchâtel 9 km - Tel (41) 032 - 725 11 83

Schönenberg

14 | 7 | 6

Die Lage des Platzes auf einem schmalen Terrain von 2 km x 300m entlang des Flüsschens Krebs erklärt die zahlreichen aber nicht allzu spielbestimmenden Out of Bounds und auch den feuchten Torfboden. Donald Harradine machte das Beste aus den interessanten Gegebenheiten. Auf viel Erdbewegung musste ohnehin aus Gründen des Naturschutzes verzichtet werden. Von den hintersten Abschlägen gespielt ist der Platz recht lang, Bäume, Bunker und zahlreiche Wasserflächen sind Anziehungspunkte für von der Ziellinie abweichende Bälle und machen die Aufgaben heikel. Spielstrategie wird ist auf jedem Loch gefordert – das macht das Spiel hier vielfältig und interessant. Auch ohne golfarchitektonische Sonderleistungen ist Schönenberg eine ausserordentliche Anlage und dank der naturrechtlich geschützten Zonen auch ein gutes Beispiel für das Nebeneinander von Golf und Natur.

A lay-out on a narrow strip of terrain (2 km x 300 m) along the river Krebs explains both the many OBs (although not too many in play) and the wetness of the soil, which is basically peat. Donald Harradine squeezed the very best out of this very interesting site without resorting to any excessive shifting of earth – the tight ecological restrictions here made sure of that. Reasonable from the normal tees, it gets much longer from the back-tees, especially since the bunkers and many water hazards easily collect balls hit off-target. Each hole requires definite strategy, but this and especially the variety of holes make it a pleasant course to play. Without displaying any exceptional imagination on the part of the architect, Schönenberg is a very attractive course and again shows a good example of ecology and golf living easily side by side (several areas are natural trust land). This is always a thorny problem in Switzerland.

Golf & Country Club Schönenberg — 1968

CH - 8824 SCHÖNENBERG

Office Sekretariat (41) 01 - 788 90 40
Pro shop Pro shop (41) 01 - 788 90 55
Fax Fax (41) 01 - 788 90 45
Web www.swissgolfnetwork.ch
Situation Lage
Zürich (pop. 336 821), 25 km
Annual closure Jährliche Schliessung yes 15/11→1/3
Weekly closure Wöchentliche Schliessung no

Fees main season Preisliste hochsaison	18 holes	
	Week days Woche	We/Bank holidays We/Feiertag
Individual Individuell	CHF 120	*
Couple Ehepaar	CHF 240	*

* We: members only (nur Mitglieder)

Caddie Caddie no — **Electric Trolley** Elektrokarren yes
Buggy Elektrischer Wagen no — **Clubs** Leihschläger yes
Credit cards Kreditkarten
VISA - Eurocard - Mastercard - AMEX

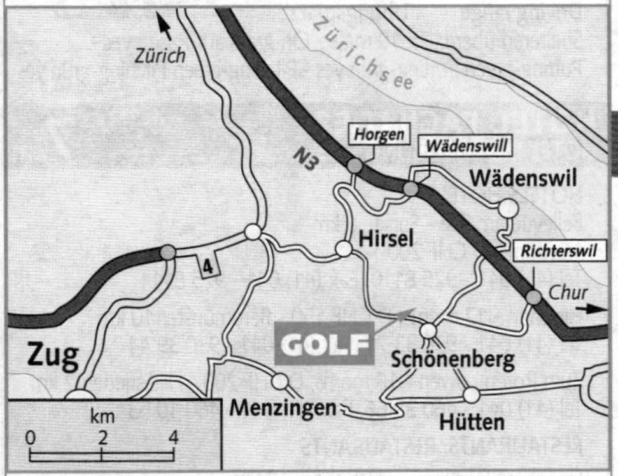

Access Zufahrt : Autobahn Zürich-Chur → Horgen oder Wädenswil, → Zug, Hirsel → Schönenberg, Golf 1,5 km.
Map 1 on page 1277 Karte 1 Seite 1277

GOLF COURSE — PLATZ 14/20

Site Lage
Maintenance Instandhaltung
Architect Architekt — Donald Harradine
Type Typ — country
Relief Begehbarkeit
Water in play Platz mit Wasser
Exp. to wind Wind ausgesetzt
Trees in play Platz mit Bäumen

Scorecard Scorekarte	Chp. Chp.	Mens Herren	Ladies Damen
Length Länge	6205	5650	4847
Par	72	72	72
Slope system	137	131	129

Advised golfing ability Empfohlene Spielstärke — 0 12 24 36
Hcp required Min. Handicap — 30

CLUB HOUSE & AMENITIES — KLUBHAUS UND NEBENGEBÄUDE 7/10

Pro shop Pro shop
Driving range Übungsplatz
Sheltered überdacht 4 mats - On grass auf Rasen yes (04-10) - Putting-green Putting-grün yes - Pitching-green Pitching-grün yes

HOTEL FACILITIES — HOTEL BESCHREIBUNG 6/10

HOTELS HOTELS

Seehotel Meierhof - Horgen 15 km
107 rooms, D CHF 235
Tel (41) 01 - 728 91 91, Fax (41) 01 - 728 92 92

Panorama - Feusisberg 5 km
116 rooms, D CHF 280
Tel (41) 01 - 786 00 00, Fax (41) 01 - 786 00 99

Schitt - Pfäffikon 6 km - 29 rooms, D CHF 195
Tel (41) 055 - 416 17 18, Fax (41) 055 - 416 17 19

RESTAURANTS RESTAURANTS

Zur Faktorei - Bäch 6 km - Tel (41) 01 - 784 03 16
Eichmühle - Wädenswil 5 km - Tel (41) 01 - 780 34 44
Seeli - Bäch 6 km - Tel (41) 01 - 784 03 07

Sempachersee *West/Ost*

16	8	7

Die Gegend ist eher flach, bietet aber dennoch eine wunderschöne Sicht auf den Sempachersee, man befindet sich hier übrigens in der Nähe eines der bekannten Schlachtfelder des Mittelalters. Wer diesen Platz spielen will, tut gut gut daran, seine Tücken vorher zu studieren. Er bietet einiges an Schwierigkeiten, die man entweder umgehen oder mit einigem Risiko auch direkt angreifen kann. Dabei kann man durchaus angenehme Überraschungen erleben und stellt fest, dass der Platz gar nicht so ungastlich ist. Die Fairways sind angenehm breit, denn die Bäume müssen noch wachsen, bevor der Platz seinen wahren Charakter zeigen kann. Im Moment gilt es vor allem bei den Abschlägen auf das hohe Rough zu achten, ebenso wie auf Wasser, das ebenfalls ins Spiel kommt. Die Grüns sind mittelgroß aber schön gezeichnet, und je nach Fahnenposition kann der Schwierigkeitsgrad recht stark variieren. In dieser wunderschönen Gegend wird der insgesamt unterhaltsam und intelligent angelegte Platz im Laufe der nächsten Jahre noch einiges an Qualität gewinnen. Der Club hat kürzlich zudem einen weiteren Platz in Kemptthal in der Nähe von Winterthur eröffnet.

The site provides an outstanding view over the Sempachersee, close to a famous battlefield. Battling is the right word when it comes to contending with these 18 holes, with careful study of your opponent's strengths required before going on the offensive. The course conceals some of its difficulties but you can get around them, or take risks and "take 'em by surprise". If you succeed, it won't be such a hostile proposition after all. The area is nicely wide open and the trees will have to grow before Sempachersee shows its true colours. For the time being, watch out for the tall rough, which threatens many a tee-shot, and several water hazards that are laid out in a rather classic and effective style. Greens are well-designed and provide a good number of different pin positions to make the golfer's life a little more difficult. The club has recently opened another course at Kemptthal, close to Winterthur.

Golf Sempachersee — 1996

CH - 6024 HILDISRIEDEN

Office	Sekretariat	(41) 041 - 462 71 71
Pro shop	Pro shop	(41) 041 - 462 71 75
Fax	Fax	(41) 041 - 462 71 72
Web	www.golf-sempachersee.ch	
Situation	Lage	Luzern, 20 km
Annual closure	Jährliche Schliessung	no
Weekly closure	Wöchentliche Schliessung	no

Fees main season Preisliste hochsaison	Week days Woche	We/Bank holidays We/Feiertag
		18 holes
Individual Individuell	CHF 140	*
Couple Ehepaar	CHF 280	*

* We: with members only (nur in Mitgliederbegleitung)
ASG members, CHF 90/110

Caddie Caddie on request — **Electric Trolley** Elektrokarren yes

Buggy Elektrischer Wagen yes — **Clubs** Leihschläger yes

Credit cards Kreditkarten
VISA - Eurocard - AMEX

Rothbach
Schopfen
Beromünster
GOLF
Länkenhof
Basel
Hildisrieden
Eich
A2
Sempach
Sempacher See
Emmen Luzern
km 0 1 2

Access Zufahrt : Luzern, N2 → Basel. → Sempach. Hildisrieden.

Map 1 on page 1277 Karte 1 Seite 1277

GOLF COURSE — PLATZ — 16/20

Site	Lage	
Maintenance	Instandhaltung	
Architect	Architekt	Kurt Rossknecht
Type	Typ	open country, forest
Relief	Begehbarkeit	
Water in play	Platz mit Wasser	
Exp. to wind	Wind ausgesetzt	
Trees in play	Platz mit Bäumen	

Scorecard Scorekarte	Chp. Chp.	Mens Herren	Ladies Damen
Length Länge	6161	5863	5102
Par	72	72	72
Slope system	127	122	125

Advised golfing ability — Empfohlene Spielstärke: 0 12 24 36

Hcp required — Min. Handicap: 30

CLUB HOUSE & AMENITIES — KLUBHAUS UND NEBENGEBÄUDE — 8/10

Pro shop — Pro shop
Driving range — Übungsplatz

Sheltered überdacht 10 mats - On grass auf Rasen yes - Putting-green Putting-grün yes - Pitching-green Pitching-grün yes

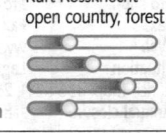

HOTEL FACILITIES — HOTEL BESCHREIBUNG — 7/10

HOTELS HOTELS

Bellevue am See - Sursee 6 km
16 rooms, D CHF 200
Tel (41) 041 - 925 8110, Fax (41) 041 - 925 8111

Hirschen - 12 rooms, D CHF 150 - Beromünster 10 km
Tel (41) 041 - 930 33 71, Fax (41) 041 - 930 39 44

Zum Roten Löwen - 16 rooms, D CHF 200 - Hildisrieden 2 km
Tel (41) 041 - 460 33 66, Fax (41) 041 - 460 10 53

RESTAURANTS RESTAURANTS

Herlisberg Wirtshaus - Herlisberg 10 km
Tel (41) 041 - 930 12 80

Vogelsang - Vogelsang 5 km - Tel (41) 041 - 462 66 66

Schlössli Utenberg - Luzern 16 km - Tel (41) 041 - 420 00 22

Vuissens

16	1	6

Dans cette région de la campagne fribourgeoise appelée Le Gros de Vaud, ce golf a été construit dans un site agréablement vallonné arrosé par la Petite Glâne, qui a permis la création d'une vingtaine de lacs et de biotopes. Plus de 6.000 arbres (35 essences) ont été plantés, ajoutant au charme campagnard des lieux. Ouvert depuis 2001, le parcours devrait enfin s'accompagner d'un club-house digne de ce nom début 2006, aménagé dans la vénérable grange d'un château du XIIIè siècle. On n'en sera pas étonné, le dessin de Jeremy Pern est de première qualité, avec la singularité de cinq pars 5 et cinq pars 3. Il a joué habilement de la topographie, mais aussi apporté des mouvements au terrain, avec des formes qui ne sont pas sans évoquer les links, les roughs parfois hauts venant renforcer cette parenté. Quelques obstacles d'eau apportent quelques touches de modernisme, sans que rien ne soit exagéré, pas même les reliefs des excellents greens. On ajoute la beauté des points de vue au plaisir de jouer ce tracé intelligent.

In this region of the Fribourg countryside, this course lies over a pleasantly rolling site crossed by the Petite Glâne river, which led to the creation of around twenty lakes and biotopes. More than 6,000 trees (35 varieties) were planted, adding to the site's country charm. Opened in 2001, the course should at long last be given a club-house worthy of the name sometime in early 2006 (fitted inside the venerable barn of a 13th century castle). Not surprisingly, this Jeremy Pern layout is top-notch with the singularity of five par 5s and five par 3s. He has very cleverly played around with topography but also moved quite a bit of earth to create shapes somewhat reminiscent of your standard links, with some tall rough. A few water hazards add a dash or two of modernism, but without ever going overboard. The same goes for the contouring of the excellent greens. Playing this intelligent layout is enhanced by the beauty of the surrounding views.

Golf Club Vuissens — 2001

CH - 1486 VUISSENS

Office Secrétariat (41) 024 - 433 33 00
Pro shop Pro-shop —
Fax Fax (41) 024 - 433 33 04
Web www.golfvuissens.ch
Situation Situation Yverdon-les-Bains, 17 km
Annual closure Fermeture annuelle no
Weekly closure Fermeture hebdomadaire

Fees main season Tarifs haute saison	18 holes	
	Week days Semaine	We/Bank holidays We/Férié
Individual Individuel	CHF 90	CHF 100
Couple Couple	CHF 180	CHF 200

Juniors under 21: – 50%

Caddie Caddie no — **Electric Trolley** Chariot électrique no
Buggy Voiturette yes — **Clubs** Clubs yes
Credit cards Cartes de crédit
VISA - Eurocard - MasterCard

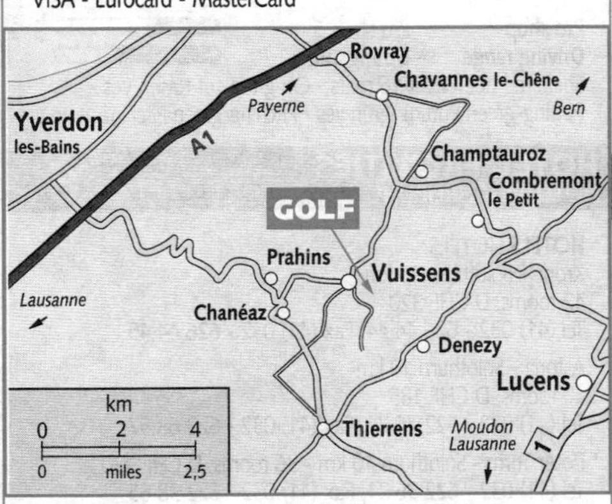

Access Accès : Lausanne A1 → Yverdon-les-Bains, Exit Yverdon-Sud, → Mouddon-Thierrens. After Prahins, turn left → Vuissens. Bern A1 → Lausanne, Exit Estavayer-le-Lac, → Murist, Champtauroz, Vuissens
Map 1 on page 1276 Carte 1 Page 1276

GOLF COURSE — PARCOURS 16/20

Site Site
Maintenance Entretien
Architect Architecte Jeremy Pern
Type Type parkland, open country
Relief Relief
Water in play Eau en jeu
Exp. to wind Exposé au vent
Trees in play Arbres en jeu

Scorecard Carte de score	Chp. Chp.	Mens Mess.	Ladies Da.
Length Long.	6009	5521	4869
Par	72	72	72
Slope system	131	125	124

Advised golfing ability Niveau de jeu recommandé 0 12 24 36
Hcp required Handicap exigé

CLUB HOUSE & AMENITIES — CLUB-HOUSE ET ANNEXES 1/10

Pro shop Pro-shop
Driving range Practice
Sheltered couvert - On grass sur herbe yes - Putting-green putting-green yes - Pitching-green pitching green yes

HOTEL FACILITIES — ENVIRONNEMENT HOTELIER 6/10

HOTELS HÔTELS
Grand Hôtel des Bains - Yverdon-les-Bains 17 km
125 rooms, D CHF 350
Tel (41) 024 - 424 64 64, Fax (41) 024 - 424 64 65

La Prairie - Yverdon-les-Bains 17 km - 36 rooms, D CHF 245
Tel (41) 024 - 425 19 19, Fax (41) 024 - 425 00 79

RESTAURANTS RESTAURANTS
La Gerbe d'Or - Estavayer-le-Lac 15 km
Tel (41) 026 - 663 11 81

Auberge de Vers-chez-Perrin - Payerne/Vers-chez-Perrin 12 km - Tel (41) 026 - 660 58 46

Le Pavillon (Hôtel des Bains) - Yverdon-les-Bains 17 km
Tel (41) 024 - 424 64 64

Wylihof

14 | 7 | 6

Wylihof ist ein noch junger Platz, der aber schon gut gereift ist und bereits Gastgeber für etliche gute Turniere war. Wenn man allein auf die Länge des Platzes schaut erscheint er sehr schwierig, aber trotzdem ist kein Loch übertrieben. In diesem offenen, flachen Gelände kommen an einigen Bahnen Bäume ins Spiel, an einem anderen halben Dutzend Löcher ist es dagegen Wasser. Dazu ist das Rough hoch und dicht, so dass, wer darin landet, sich wünscht, er wäre auf dem Kurzgemähten geblieben. Glücklicherweise sind die Fairways relativ breit und die Bunker nicht zu tief, so dass auf diesem Platz niemand über Gebühr leiden muss. Der Architekt war sichtbar von britischen Links Courses beeinflusst und wohl auch von modernem amerikanischen Design. Insgesamt hätten wir uns ein wenig mehr Erdbewegung und einen Touch mehr Pfiff in der Konzeption gewünscht. Die Spielstrategie ist leicht auszumachen, alle Schwierigkeiten sind vom Abschlag zu sehen. Ein schönes Clubhaus, gute Übungseinrichtungen und ein herrlicher Blick über die Berge des Jura vervollständigen das Bild.

Wylihof is maturing nicely enough to have already hosted some good tournaments. Looking at its length it might seem a tough proposition but no one hole could ever really be qualified as over the top. Over a very open and flat site, trees come into play on several holes, water hazards appear on half a dozen others and the rough is tough enough to wish you had stayed on the straight and narrow. Luckily the fairways are wide and the bunkers none too deep so that average players should not suffer unduly. The architect was inspired by links courses and US style modernism, but we would have liked to see a little more shifting of earth or a touch more imagination to add a little spice to the course's overall conception. Game strategy is pretty obvious as the difficulties are there to be seen. A fine club-house, good facilities and beautiful views over the Jura mountains complete the picture.

Golf Club Wylihof — 1995

Wylihof 12
CH - 4708 LUTERBACH

Office	Sekretariat	(41) 032 - 682 28 28
Pro shop	Pro shop	(41) 032 - 682 65 11
Fax	Fax	(41) 032 - 682 65 17
Web	www.golfclub.ch	
Situation	Lage	Solothurn, 8 km
Annual closure	Jährliche Schliessung	15/11→15/3
Weekly closure	Wöchentliche Schliessung	no
Fees main season	Preisliste hochsaison	18 holes

	Week days Woche	We/Bank holidays We/Feiertag
Individual Individuell	CHF 120	CHF 120*
Couple Ehepaar	CHF 240	CHF 240*

* We: only with members (nur in Mitgliederbegleitung).

Caddie Caddie no — **Electric Trolley** Elektrokarren no

Buggy Elektrischer Wagen medical reasons only

Clubs Leihschläger yes

Credit cards Kreditkarten VISA - Eurocard - MasterCard

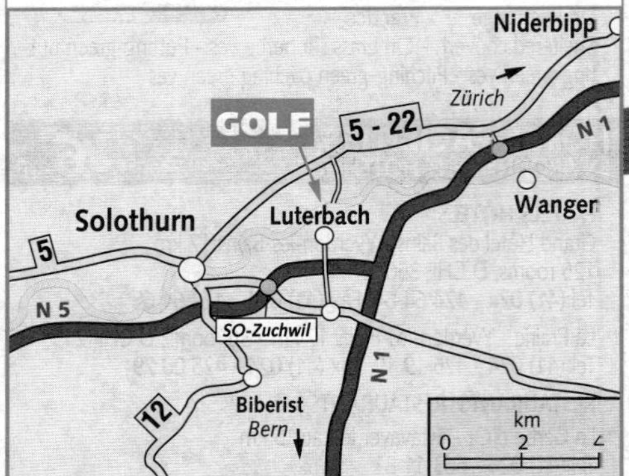

Access Zufahrt : Motorway (Autobahn) N1→ Wangen A/Aar, → Solothurn, → Koppingen, after bridge over Aar river (Aarbrücke), turn left → Golf

Map 1 on page 1276 Karte 1 Seite 1276

GOLF COURSE — PLATZ — 14/20

Site	Lage	
Maintenance	Instandhaltung	
Architect	Architekt	Ruzzo Reuss
Type	Typ	open country
Relief	Begehbarkeit	
Water in play	Platz mit Wasser	
Exp. to wind	Wind ausgesetzt	
Trees in play	Platz mit Bäumen	

Scorecard Scorekarte	Chp. Chp.	Mens Herren	Ladies Damen
Length Länge	6584	6093	5286
Par	73	73	73
Slope system	138	130	128

Advised golfing ability Empfohlene Spielstärke — 0 12 24 36

Hcp required Min. Handicap 36

CLUB HOUSE & AMENITIES — KLUBHAUS UND NEBENGEBÄUDE — 7/10

Pro shop Pro shop

Driving range Übungsplatz

Sheltered überdacht 16 mats - On grass auf Rasen yes - Putting-green Putting-grün yes - Pitching-green Pitching-grün yes

HOTEL FACILITIES — HOTEL BESCHREIBUNG — 6/10

HOTELS HOTELS

Krone - Solothurn 10 km
42 rooms, D CHF 320
Tel (41) 032 - 626 44 44, Fax (41) 032 - 626 44 45

Astoria - Solothurn 10 km
40 rooms, D CHF 185
Tel (41) 032 - 622 75 71, Fax (41) 032 - 623 68 57

Roter Turm - Solothurn 10 km - 36 rooms, D CHF 230
Tel (41) 032 - 622 96 21, Fax (41) 032 - 622 98 65

RESTAURANTS RESTAURANTS

Zum Alten Stephan - Solothurn 10 km
Tel (41) 032 - 622 11 09

Chutz - Langendorf 8 km - Tel (41) 032 - 622 34 71

Zumikon

15 | 7 | 6

Vergleichbar mit dem Top-Club Genf im Westen der Schweiz ist Zumikon der Jagdgrund der wohlhabenden Zürcher. Gäste sind nur unter der Woche willkommen, auf Einhaltung der Kleiderordnung wird geachtet. Die ersten neun Loch in Zumikon sind recht flach, aber sehr lang. Der Weg zurück ist mit einigen Schräglagen und Hängen wesentlich coupierter und kann Senioren Mühe bereiten. Dieser Nachteil wird aber durch kürzere Spielbahnen kompensiert. Die gut platzierten Hindernisse stören vor allem gute Golfer, beeinflussen aber das Spiel höherer Handicaps wenig. Zumikon ist daher auch ein guter Test des golferischen Könnens und häufig auch Austragungsort von Turnieren, lässt aber in seinem Design das gewisse Etwas an Originalität vermissen. Trotzdem langweilt sich hier niemand, und das ist für Golfer jedes Handicaps ein wichtiger Punkt. Der Pflegezustand ist dem hohen Standard angemessen.

Just as Geneva is the top private club to the west of Switzerland, this is the traditional hunting ground for the good people of Zurich and is open on week days only (with dress code). The front nine at Zumikon are pretty flat but very long. The back nine are much hillier with a number of dangerous slopes in all directions, often a problem for senior players but one that is offset by the shorter length of holes. The hazards are generally well sited and tend to bother the better players more than the rest. Reassuring for the latter, at least. Zumikon is a very respectable test of golf and often a venue for tournaments, but we were sorry to see a little lack of originality and stamina in a very reasonable layout, and greens in a fair condition. All this still places the course a little way behind the very best to be found in Switzerland. However, there is never a dull moment here, and golfers of all levels will appreciate that.

Golf & Country Club Zurich — 1929

CH - 8126 ZUMIKON

Office Sekretariat (41) 01 - 288 10 88
Pro shop Pro shop (41) 01 - 288 10 83
Fax Fax (41) 01 - 288 10 78
Web www.swissgolfnetwork.ch
Situation Lage Zürich, 7 km
Annual closure Jährliche Schliessung 31/10→1/4
Weekly closure Wöchentliche Schliessung Monday (Montag)

Fees main season Preisliste hochsaison 18 holes

	Week days Woche	We/Bank holidays We/Feiertag
Individual Individuell	CHF 150	*
Couple Ehepaar	CHF 300	*

* We: members only (nur Mitglieder)

Caddie Caddie on request **Electric Trolley** Elektrokarren yes
Buggy Elektrischer Wagen no **Clubs** Leihschläger yes
Credit cards Kreditkarten no

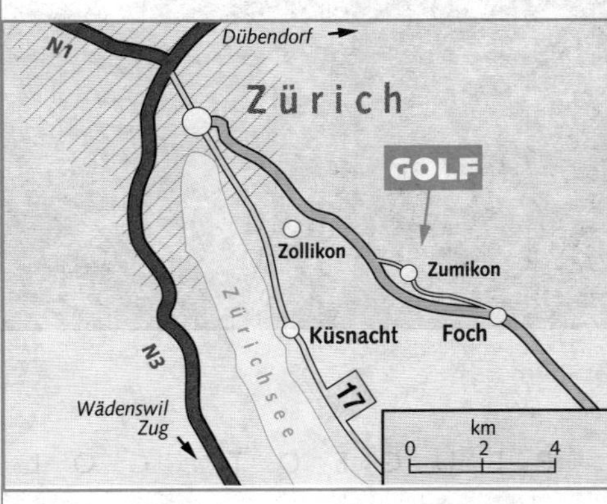

Access Zufahrt : Zürich → Forch, Zumikon → Dorfplatz → Strubenacher Strasse
Map 1 on page 1277 Karte 1 Seite 1277

GOLF COURSE — PLATZ 15/20

Site Lage
Maintenance Instandhaltung
Architect Architekt Donald Harradine
Type Typ parkland
Relief Begehbarkeit
Water in play Platz mit Wasser
Exp. to wind Wind ausgesetzt
Trees in play Platz mit Bäumen

Scorecard Scorekarte	Chp. Chp.	Mens Herren	Ladies Damen
Length Länge	6350	5867	5186
Par	72	72	72
Slope system	130	128	124

Advised golfing ability Empfohlene Spielstärke 0 12 24 36
Hcp required Min. Handicap 24

CLUB HOUSE & AMENITIES — KLUBHAUS UND NEBENGEBÄUDE 7/10

Pro shop Pro shop
Driving range Übungsplatz
Sheltered überdacht 4 mats - On grass auf Rasen yes - Putting-green Putting-grün yes - Pitching-green Pitching-grün yes

HOTEL FACILITIES — HOTEL BESCHREIBUNG 6/10

HOTELS HOTELS

Wassberg - 15 rooms, D CHF 255 - Forch 6 km
Tel (41) 01 - 980 43 00, Fax (41) 01 - 980 43 03

Ermitage am See - 26 rooms, D CHF 350 - Küsnacht 5 km
Tel (41) 01 - 914 42 42, Fax (41) 01 - 914 42 43

Sonne - 40 rooms, D CHF 300 - Küsnacht 5 km
Tel (41) 01 - 914 18 18, Fax (41) 01 - 914 18 00

RESTAURANTS RESTAURANTS

Ermitage am See - Küsnacht 5 km - Tel (41) 01 - 914 42 42

Petermann's Kunststuben - Küsnacht 2 km
Tel (41) 01 - 910 07 15

Vorderer Sternen - Zürich 6 km - Tel (41) 01 - 251 49 49

AUTRES PAYS

OTHER COUNTRIES

Gloria Golf Resort

OTHER COUNTRIES

Cyprus - Russia
Czech Republic
Turkey - Slovenia

Golf in Europe is broadening its frontiers eastwards and to the south. To the east, the Czech Republic has a golfing heritage rich enough to produce several excellent courses for more than 19,000 local players and a number of others now under development look promising indeed. Even Russia now has one superb 18-hole course, which will soon be joined by others. Slovenia has rejuvenated and even expanded the "old" course at Bled. Further south, golf is an important asset for tourism and courses are beginning to spring up, for the time being catering more to foreign golfers in search of sunnier climes than to local players. Turkey is one country which has systematically been building some good courses in the seaside areas of Belek and Antalya, where a new 36-hole resort - the Antalya Golf Club - is now completed. Cyprus also made a conspicuous appearance two years ago with the very fine Aphrodite Hills course, which is as excellent as ever. New golfing countries have now emerged, such as Poland and Hungary, but harsh climatic conditions notwithstanding, they will need to maintain consistent standards of green-keeping to become a permanent viable proposition for golf-trotters.

AUTRES PAYS

En Europe, le golf élargit ses frontières et gagne vers l'Est et vers le sud. A l'est, la République Tchèque possède un passé golfique assez riche pour avoir plusieurs bons parcours et plus de 19.000 joueurs, et certains en construction sont prometteurs. Même la Russie possède aujourd'hui un superbe parcours de 18 trous, auquel d'autres vont s'ajouter très vite. La Slovénie a rajeuni son "vieux" parcours de Bled. Plus au sud, le golf est un important atout pour le tourisme et les parcours commencent à sortir de terre, pour l'instant davantage destinés aux joueurs étrangers avides de soleil qu'aux joueurs locaux. La Turquie est l'un de ces pays à avoir systématiquement construit de bons parcours autour des importantes stations balnéaires de Belek et Antalya, où un nouveau resort avec 36 trous, l'Antalya Golf Club a pris tout de suite sa place et entre dans ce guide avec le "Sultan". Chypre encore, dont le très beau Aphrodite Hills a fait une entrée remarquée il y a deux ans et a su maintenir sa qualité. De nouveaux pays golfiques ont fait leur apparition, comme la Pologne ou la Hongrie, mais ils devront malgré des climats parfois difficiles maintenir une qualité d'entretien élevée pour séduire les visiteurs de manière constante.

CLASSIFICATION OF COURSES
CLASSEMENT DES PARCOURS

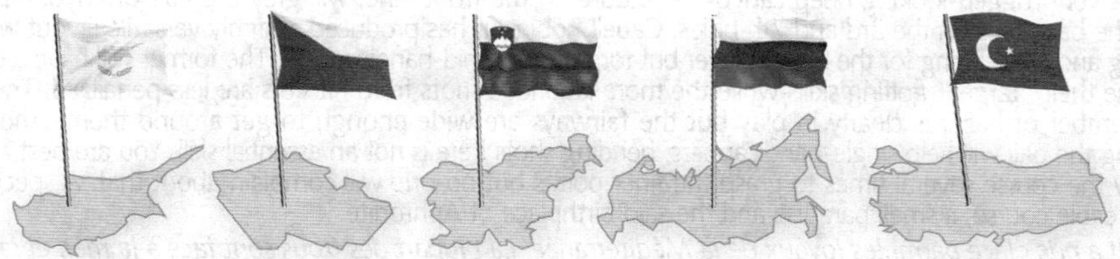

This classification gives priority consideration to the score awarded to the actual course.

Ce classement donne priorité à la note attribuée au parcours.

CYP Cyprus - **Cz** Czech Republic - **RU** Russia - **SLO** Slovenia - **TR** Turkey

Within each score, the ranking is purely alphabetical

Course score / Note du parcours					Page
17	7	7	Antalya GC Sultan	TR	1312
17	7	7	Aphrodite Hills	CYP	1306
17	7	6	Moscow	RU	1310
17	7	7	National GC	TR	1314
17	8	6	Robinson	TR	1315
15	7	8	Bled King's Course	SLO	1311
15	7	7	Gloria Golf Resort	TR	1313
15	7	6	Karlovy Vary	CZ	1307
15	6	7	Praha Karlstejn	CZ	1309
14	7	6	Mariánské Lázne	CZ	1308

HOTEL FACILITIES
ENVIRONNEMENT HOTELIER

This classification gives priority consideration to the score awarded to the hotel facilities.

Ce classement donne priorité à la note attribuée à l'environnement hôtelier.

		Hotel facility score / Note de l'environnement hôtelier			Page
15	7	**8**	Bled King's Course	SLO	1311
15	6	**7**	Praha Karlstejn	CZ	1309
17	7	**7**	Antalya GC Sultan	TR	1312
17	7	**7**	Aphrodite Hills	CYP	1306
15	7	**7**	Gloria Golf Resort	TR	1313
17	7	**7**	National GC	TR	1314
17	7	**6**	Moscow	RU	1310
17	8	**6**	Robinson	TR	1315
15	7	**6**	Karlovy Vary	CZ	1307
14	7	**6**	Mariánské Lázne	CZ	1308

Aphrodite Hills

17	7	7

This course is ranked amongst the very best around the Mediterranean. Most of the holes are facing the sea and the vegetation – carob, olive and lentisk trees - add delightful local colour while a very rugged-looking deep canyon, a feature on the front nine, will grey the hair of anyone playing from the back tees on the 3rd and 7th holes. Cabell Robinson has produced a highly versatile layout which is exciting and challenging for the better player but forgiving for mid-handicappers. The former will have a chance to hone their "target" golfing skills while the more laborious shots from hackers are less penalized. There are any number of hazards clearly in play but the fairways are wide enough to get around them. And while flighting the ball will help single-handicappers, bending shots here is not an essential skill. You are best advised to play the course several times to grasp the finer points but no-one will complain about that. A spectacular and likeable course, a small paradise and the said birthplace of Aphrodite.

Ce golf a pris place parmi les joyaux de la Méditerranée. La plupart des trous sont face à la mer, et la végétation – caroubiers, oliviers, lentisques – donne une saveur locale, l'aspect sauvage étant offert par un profond canyon qui donnera des cheveux blancs à ceux qui jouent "du fond" sur le 3 et le 7. Cabell Robinson a livré un parcours très varié dans son déroulement, excitant et exigeant pour les meilleurs, mais bien plus indulgent pour les joueurs moyens. Les premiers joueront en "target golf", mais les balles plus laborieuses des seconds seront peu pénalisées. Les obstacles sont nombreux, bien en jeu, mais les fairways sont assez larges pour les contourner, et s'il n'est pas indispensable de travailler la balle, les virtuoses s'en trouveront avantagés. Il vaut mieux jouer ici plusieurs fois pour en distinguer les nuances, mais ce ne sera pas une corvée ! En résumé, un parcours spectaculaire et attachant, le petit paradis où Aphrodite est née.

Aphrodite Hills Golf — 2002

Aphrodite Hills, Nr. Kouklia - P.O. Box 8500
CYP - PAPHOS (Cyprus)

Office	Secrétariat	(357) 26 - 818 700
Pro shop	Pro-shop	(357) 26 - 818 700
Fax	Fax	(357) 26 - 818 701
Web	www.aphroditehills.com	
Situation	Situation	Paphos, 17 km
Annual closure	Fermeture annuelle	no
Weekly closure	Fermeture hebdomadaire	no

Fees main season Tarifs haute saison	18 holes	
	Week days Semaine	We/Bank holidays We/Férié
Individual Individuel	C£ 64	C£ 64
Couple Couple	C£ 128	C£ 128

Green fee includes buggy C£ 45 23/05 → 12/09

Caddie Caddie no — Electric Trolley Chariot électrique no

Buggy Voiturette yes — Clubs Clubs yes

Credit cards Cartes de crédit
VISA - Eurocard - MasterCard - AMEX - DC

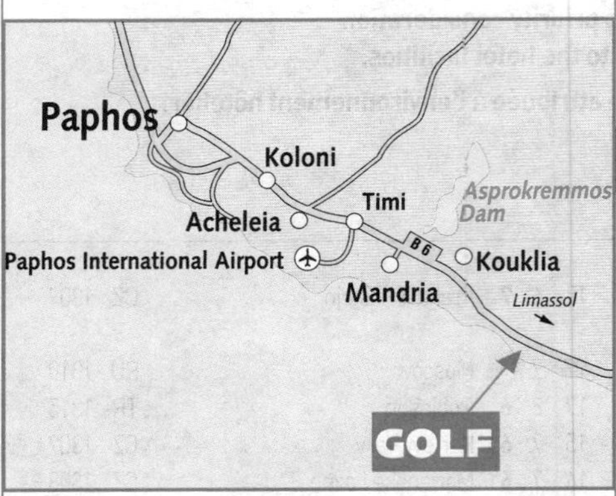

Access Accès : On the coastal road Paphos to Limassol.

GOLF COURSE PARCOURS — 17/20

Site	Site	
Maintenance	Entretien	
Architect	Architecte	Cabell B. Robinson
Type	Type	seaside course, residential
Relief	Relief	
Water in play	Eau en jeu	
Exp. to wind	Exposé au vent	
Trees in play	Arbres en jeu	

Scorecard Carte de score	Chp. Chp.	Mens Mess.	Ladies Da.
Length Long.	6270	5720	4850
Par	71	70	70
Slope system	—	—	—

Advised golfing ability 0 12 24 36
Niveau de jeu recommandé

Hcp required Handicap exigé no

CLUB HOUSE & AMENITIES CLUB HOUSE ET ANNEXES — 7/10

Pro shop Pro-shop
Driving range Practice
Sheltered couvert - On grass sur herbe yes - Putting-green putting-green yes - Pitching-green pitching green yes

HOTEL FACILITIES ENVIRONNEMENT HOTELIER — 7/10

HOTELS HÔTELS

Intercontinental Hotel - 290 rooms, from C£ 120 - on site
Tel (357) 26 - 818 700 - Fax (357) 26 - 818 701

Paphos Amathus Beach - Paphos 20 km
278 rooms, D C£ 220
Tel (357) 26 - 964 300, Fax (357) 26 - 964 222

Athena Beach Hotel - Paphos 20 km - 400 rooms, D C£ 130
Tel (357) 26 - 965 300, Fax (357) 26 - 965 400

Imperial Hotel - Paphos 20 km - 242 rooms, D C£ 100
Tel (357) 26 - 964 293, Fax (357) 26 - 964 293

RESTAURANTS RESTAURANTS

Archontariki Restaurant - Paphos 20 km - Tel (357) 06 - 321 328
Piasta Greeka Taverna - Paphos 20 km - Tel (357) 06 - 233 311

Karlovy Vary

15 | 7 | 6

Formerly known by its Austrian name of Karlsbad, Karlovy Vary was one of the great spas much visited by the aristocracy for several centuries. Goethe and Beethoven were some of the more prestigious visitors who came to treat their ills and, so they would have us believe, their love stories as well. As in many spas, golf was played here from a very early period, from 1904 in fact, but a new layout was designed in 1933 before being altered and improved upon thanks to the endeavours of the Golf Resort Company, two of whose shareholders are the impressive Grandhotel Pupp and the extravagant Hotel Imperial. This rather hilly course (but never too much of a climb) is of a very respectable length for players of all abilities without any insurmountable hazards. As water is not often in play (except on the 4th hole), trees and bunkers are the main obstacles likely to shatter your golfing ambitions. This classic layout – with a new club-house – boasts some unique touches of natural romanticism and Slav charm that are simply irresistible.

Autrefois connue sous le nom de Carlsbad, Karlovy Vary a été l'une des grandes stations thermales de l'aristocratie. Goethe et Beethoven en ont été parmi les plus prestigieux visiteurs, pour leurs maux, et quelques aventures discrètes, croit-on. Comme dans beaucoup de villes d'eau, le golf a été pratiqué très tôt dans cette superbe vallée romantique, dès 1904, mais le nouveau tracé de 1933 a été modifié et amélioré depuis, grâce aux efforts des actionnaires, dont l'impressionnant Grandhotel Pupp et l'extravagant Hotel Imperial. Le parcours assez accidenté, mais sans exagération, est d'une longueur très respectable pour tous les niveaux, mais sans que personne n'ait d'obstacle insurmontable à franchir. L'eau étant assez peu en jeu, ce sont les arbres et bunkers qui peuvent contrer vos ambitions. Ce tracé classique – avec un nouveau club-house – réserve ces touches de romantisme naturel et de charme slave que l'on ne peut qu'aimer.

Golf Resort Karlovy Vary a.s. — 1933

Prazska 125
CZ - 360 01 Karlovy Vary

Office	Secrétariat	(420) 353 - 333 1101
Pro shop	Pro-shop	(420) 353 - 331 001
Fax	Fax	(420) 353 - 331 001
Web	www.golfresort.cz	
Situation	Situation	Karlovy Vary, 6 km

Praha (pop. 1 203 230), 120 km

Annual closure	Fermeture annuelle	01/12 → 31/03
Weekly closure	Fermeture hebdomadaire	no
Fees main season	Tarifs haute saison	18 holes

	Week days Semaine	We/Bank holidays We/Férié
Individual Individuel	CZK 1650/€ 54	CZK 1650/€ 54
Couple Couple	CZK 3300/€ 108	CZK 3300/€ 108

Special fees for Grandhotel Pupp guests / Juniors: CZK 1100

Caddie Caddie no — **Electric Trolley** Chariot électrique yes

Buggy Voiturette yes — **Clubs** Clubs yes

Credit cards Cartes de crédit
VISA - Eurocard - MasterCard - AMEX

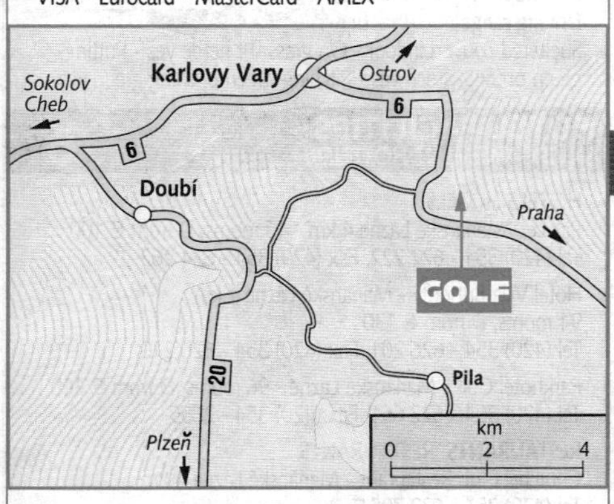

Access Accès : Praha, E48 → Karlovy Vary.
700 m before Olsová Vrata and airport, turn right → Golf.
Map 4 on page 355 Carte 4 Page 355

GOLF COURSE — PARCOURS — 15/20

Site	Site	
Maintenance	Entretien	
Architect	Architecte	C. Noskowski
Type	Type	parkland, forest
Relief	Relief	
Water in play	Eau en jeu	
Exp. to wind	Exposé au vent	
Trees in play	Arbres en jeu	

Scorecard Carte de score	Chp. Chp.	Mens Mess.	Ladies Da.
Length Long.	6167	5731	5034
Par	72	72	72
Slope system	137	133	136

Advised golfing ability Niveau de jeu recommandé — 0 12 24 36

Hcp required Handicap exigé — 36

1307

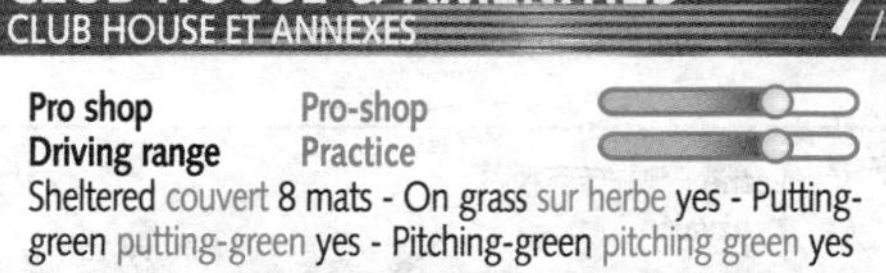

CLUB HOUSE & AMENITIES — CLUB HOUSE ET ANNEXES — 7/10

Pro shop Pro-shop
Driving range Practice
Sheltered couvert 8 mats - On grass sur herbe yes - Putting-green putting-green yes - Pitching-green pitching green yes

HOTEL FACILITIES — ENVIRONNEMENT HOTELIER — 6/10

HOTELS HÔTELS

Grandhotel Pupp - Karlovy Vary 4 km
112 rooms, D from € 200
Tel (420) 353 - 109 111, Fax (420) 353 - 226 638

Hotel Dvorák - Karlovy Vary 4 km
106 rooms, D € 170
Tel (420) 353 - 102 111, Fax (420) 353 - 102 119

RESTAURANTS RESTAURANTS

Golf restaurant - on site - Tel (420) 17 333 1101

Vinárna Karel IV - Karlovy Vary 4 km
Tel (420) 353 - 227 255

Grand Restaurant - Karlovy Vary 4 km
Tel (420) 353 - 109 111

14	7	6

The former Marienbad was the other major spa town frequented by the aristocracy of all the countries of Europe up until World War I. At an altitude of 600 metres, the nobility and the "grand bourgeoisie" would come here to treat any number of affections. Today, the town is enjoying a new lease of life and golfers can come and "treat" their swing in the crisp air and deep forests of Bohemia on what is the country's oldest course. There is a chance, certainly, that you might find the design of this grand parkland layout a little outmoded, but it oozes inimitable charm and presents a tougher challenge than you might expect, especially from the back tees and on some of the long par 4s like holes N° 6, 11 or 18. Water hazards are infrequent but dangerous every time, while two or three complex greens will help add to your score. With this said, reasonable players will make hay before resting their weary bones in the tastefully restored Belle Epoque style clubhouse. This centenary golf club has been given a 'Royal' accolade by H.M. the Queen Elisabeth II.

L'ancienne Marienbad est l'autre grande station thermale de l'aristocratie des pays d'Europe jusqu'avant la Première Guerre Mondiale. La noblesse et la grande bourgeoisie venaient y soigner leurs affections. La ville retrouve aujourd'hui une nouvelle jeunesse, et les golfeurs pourront y soigner leurs swings dans l'air vif et les forêts profondes de Bohême sur le plus ancien parcours du pays. Certes, on pourra trouver l'architecture de golf de ce grand parc un peu démodée, mais il y a ici un charme inimitable, et un challenge plus difficile qu'on pourrait s'y attendre, en tout cas des départs arrière, en particulier sur quelques longs par 4 comme le 6, le 11 ou le 18. Les obstacles d'eau ne sont pas nombreux, mais tous dangereux, et deux ou trois greens un peu complexes contribuent aussi à alourdir les scores. Cependant, les joueurs raisonnables tireront sans mal leur épingle du jeu, avant de se reposer dans un club-house Belle Epoque restauré avec goût. Un beau centenaire célébré par un titre 'Royal'.

Royal Mariánské Lázne — 1905

P.O. Box 47
CZ - 353 01 MARIANSKE LAZNE

Office	Secrétariat	(420) 354 - 624 300
Pro shop	Pro-shop	(420) 354 - 620 251
Fax	Fax	(420) 354 - 625 195
Web		
Situation	Situation	Mariánské Lázne, 2 km

Praha (pop. 1 203 230), 160 km

Annual closure	Fermeture annuelle	1/11→31/3
Weekly closure	Fermeture hebdomadaire	no
Fees main season	Tarifs haute saison	18 holes

	Week days Semaine	We/Bank holidays We/Férié
Individual Individuel	CZK 1450/€ 50	CZK 1650/€ 54
Couple Couple	CZK 2900/€ 100	CZK 3300/€ 108

Caddie Caddie on request **Electric Trolley** Chariot électrique no

Buggy Voiturette yes **Clubs** Clubs yes

Credit cards Cartes de crédit
VISA - Eurocard - MasterCard - DC - AMEX

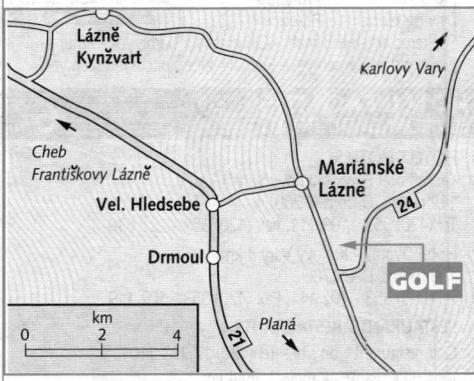

Lázně Kynžvart
Karlovy Vary
Cheb
Františkovy Lázně
Vel. Hledsebe
Mariánské Lázně
24
Drmoul
GOLF
km
0 2 4
21
Planá

Access Accès : Turn off the main road to Karlovy Vary opposite Hotel Golf
Map 4 on page 355 Carte 4 Page 355

GOLF COURSE — PARCOURS — 14/20

Site	Site	
Maintenance	Entretien	
Architect	Architecte	unknown
Type	Type	parkland
Relief	Relief	
Water in play	Eau en jeu	
Exp. to wind	Exposé au vent	
Trees in play	Arbres en jeu	

Scorecard Carte de score	**Chp.** Chp.	**Mens** Mess.	**Ladies** Da.
Length Long.	6135	5935	5285
Par	72	72	72
Slope system	125	123	130

Advised golfing ability Niveau de jeu recommandé — 0 12 24 36

Hcp required Handicap exigé 36

CLUB HOUSE & AMENITIES — CLUB HOUSE ET ANNEXES — 7/10

Pro shop Pro-shop
Driving range Practice

Sheltered couvert indoor - On grass sur herbe yes - Putting-green putting-green yes - Pitching-green pitching green yes

HOTEL FACILITIES — ENVIRONNEMENT HOTELIER — 6/10

HOTELS HÔTELS

Palace - Mariánské Lázne 4 km - 45 rooms, D from € 100
Tel (420) 354 - 622 222, Fax (420) 354 - 624 262

Hotel Villa Butterfly - Mariánské Lázne 4 km
94 rooms, D from € 130
Tel (420) 354 - 626 201, Fax (420) 354 - 626 210

Parkhotel Golf - Mariánské Lázne - 96 rooms, D from € 100
Tel (420) 354 - 622 651, Fax (420) 354 - 2655

RESTAURANTS RESTAURANTS

Churchill Club Restaurant - Mariánské Lázne 4 km
Tel (420) 354 - 622 705

Hotel Koliba Restaurant - Mariánské Lázne 4 km
Tel (420) 354 - 625 169

Fontaine - Mariánské Lázne 4 km - Tel (420) 354 - 626 201

Praha Karlstejn

15 | 6 | 7

There is no point in trying to describe the riches of Prague in a few lines, except to rate it amongst the "world's most beautiful cities"... Simply treat yourself to a stop-off on the Plzen road (Plzen is a beer centre and a 1 hour drive) to play this course on the edge of the superb valley of Berounka, at the foot of Hrad Karlstejn, the castle built by Charles IV and magnificently restored in the 19th century. This course has very quickly made a name for itself, appealing to golfers not only for the site but also for being a very intelligent layout. It is also very modern in its careful bunkering, the bringing into play of natural contours and the variety of holes. Water comes into play only on a few holes, but the profile of the many doglegs, one or two elevated greens and the variety of shots you need to shape make this a rather tricky challenge that golfers will only start to master after several outings. The architects set out to achieve the eternal Trent Jones project of "easy bogey, tough birdie", and they succeeded. Shooting par is no easy feat.

Il serait aussi vain de tenter de décrire les richesses de Prague, que d'autres "plus belles villes du monde"... Offrez-vous simplement une halte sur la route de Plzen, capitale de la bière (1 heure de route), pour jouer ce parcours au bord de la superbe vallée de la Berounka, à l'ombre de Hrad Karlstejn, la château construit par Charles IV et magnifiquement restauré au XIXè siècle. Ce golf s'est vite bâti une réputation, il a séduit par son site, mais aussi son parcours très intelligent. Il est aussi très moderne par son bunkering soigné, la mise en jeu des reliefs, la variété des trous. L'eau n'est vraiment en jeu que sur quelques trous, mais le profil des nombreux doglegs, un ou deux greens très en hauteur, la variété des coups à jouer en font un challenge délicat, que l'on ne maîtrise pas en une seule fois. Les architectes ont voulu réaliser l'éternel projet de Trent Jones "bogey facile, birdie difficile". Ils ont réussi : même le par n'est pas simple..

Praha Karlstejn Golf Klub 1993
P.O. Box 280
CZ - 267 27 LITEN

Office	Secrétariat	(420) 0311 - 604 991
Pro shop	Pro-shop	(420) 0311 - 604 991
Fax	Fax	(420) 0311 - 684 717
Web	www.karlstejn-golf.cz	
Situation	Situation	Praha, 30 km
Annual closure	Fermeture annuelle	1/12→31/3
Weekly closure	Fermeture hebdomadaire	no

Fees main season Tarifs haute saison	18 holes	
	Week days Semaine	**We/Bank holidays** We/Férié
Individual Individuel	CZK 2000/€ 65	CZK 3000/€ 98
Couple Couple	CZK 4000/€ 130	CZK 6000/€ 196

under 18 years old: – 50%

Caddie Caddie on request **Electric Trolley** Chariot électrique no

Buggy Voiturette yes **Clubs** Clubs yes

Credit cards Cartes de crédit
VISA - Eurocard - MasterCard - AMEX

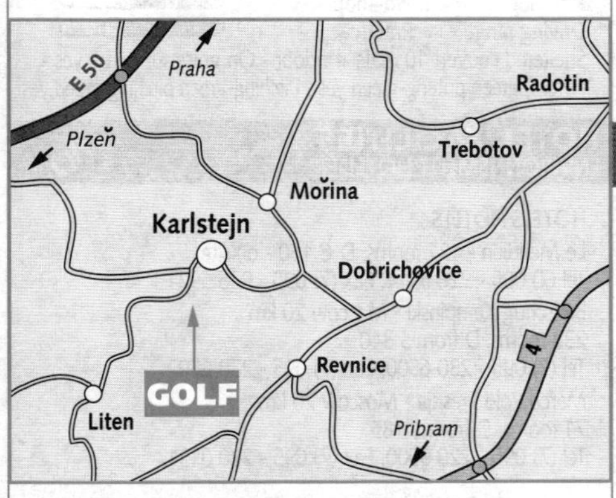

Access Accès : Praha, D5 → Plzen. Exit → Lodenice, Buhovice, Morina, Karlstejn.

GOLF COURSE
PARCOURS 15/20

Site	Site	
Maintenance	Entretien	
Architect	Architecte	Les Furber Jim Eremko
Type	Type	forest, hilly
Relief	Relief	
Water in play	Eau en jeu	
Exp. to wind	Exposé au vent	
Trees in play	Arbres en jeu	

Scorecard Carte de score	**Chp.** Chp.	**Mens** Mess.	**Ladies** Da.
Length Long.	6304	5880	4876
Par	72	72	72
Slope system	131	126	119

Advised golfing ability 0 12 24 36
Niveau de jeu recommandé
Hcp required Handicap exigé 36

CLUB HOUSE & AMENITIES
CLUB HOUSE ET ANNEXES 6/10

Pro shop Pro-shop
Driving range Practice
Sheltered couvert 10 mats - On grass sur herbe yes - Putting-green putting-green yes - Pitching-green pitching green yes

HOTEL FACILITIES
ENVIRONNEMENT HOTELIER 7/10

HOTELS HÔTELS
Grand Hotel Bohemia - Praha 30 km - 78 rooms, D from € 330
Tel (420) 0234 - 608 111, Fax (420) 0222 - 329 545

Hoffmeister - Praha 30 km - 38 rooms, D from € 280
Tel (420) 0251 - 017 111, Fax (420) 0251 - 017 120

U Krále Karla - Praha 30 km - 19 rooms, D from € 200
Tel (420) 0257 - 532 869, Fax (420) 0257 - 533 591

RESTAURANTS RESTAURANTS
U Modre Kachnicky - Praha 30 km - Tel (420) 0257 - 320 308
Vinárna V Zátiší - Praha 30 km
Tel (420) 0222 - 221 155
U medvídku (Pub & Restaurant) - Praha 30 km
Tel (420) 0224 - 211 916

Moscow

17	7	6

Russia had to wake up to golf one day or another, and although for the time being the majority of golfers are Western businessmen or diplomats, it is surely only a matter of time before we see a Russian champion. At least they have a great course to play on. Built over a 120 hectare estate, this layout also boasts a hotel and modern houses that reminded us of the little dachas in Doctor Zhivago. This is a Trent Jones Jr. course through and through, looking like a little corner of America. But failing a Russian style of golf architecture, the landscape of birch-trees and lakes adds considerable local colour. Actually, through its strategic intelligence, the loving care that went into every detail of the design, the layout and balance of course difficulties and for sheer golfing excellence, this course is a must. With a number of different tee-boxes, it is also playable by everyone. The standard of accommodation makes this a top-notch week-end golf-course, albeit not necessarily within the means of your average "Moujik" on the street.

La Russie devait bien s'éveiller un jour au golf... et même si pour l'instant les diplomates et businessmen occidentaux forment le gros des pratiquants ici, il y aura sans doute un jour de grands joueurs russes. Au moins ont-ils ici un grand parcours ! Construit à l'intérieur d'un domaine de 120 hectares, il s'accompagne d'un hôtel et de maisons modernes réminiscentes des "datchas" du Docteur Jivago. Ce parcours de Trent Jones Jr. est en droite ligne de toutes ses créations, comme un petit coin d'Amérique. Néanmoins, à défaut d'une style "russe" d'architecture de golf, le paysage de bouleaux et de lacs est là pour donner la couleur locale. Par son intelligence stratégique, le soin apporté au dessin des moindres détails, la disposition et l'équilibre des difficultés, ce parcours est un "must", à la portée de tous (ou presque) par l'étagement des départs. La qualité du "réceptif" en fait un lieu de week-end de grande qualité... mais pas à la portée du "moujik" moyen.

Le Meridien Moscow Country Club — 1993

Nakhabino, Krasnogorsky District
143 430 RUSSIAN FEDERATION

Office	Secrétariat	(7) 095 - 926 5911
Pro shop	Pro-shop	(7) 095 - 926 5910
Fax	Fax	(7) 095 - 926 5921
Web	www.lemeridien-mcc.com	
Situation	Situation	Moscow, 15 km
Annual closure	Fermeture annuelle	no
Weekly closure	Fermeture hebdomadaire	monday

Fees main season Tarifs haute saison — 18 holes

	Week days / Semaine	We/Bank holidays / We/Férié
Individual Individuel	US$ 75	US$ 100
Couple Couple	US$ 150	US$ 200

Caddie Caddie on request **Electric Trolley** Chariot électrique no

Buggy Voiturette medical reasons **Clubs** Clubs yes

Credit cards Cartes de crédit
VISA - MasterCard - AMEX - JCB

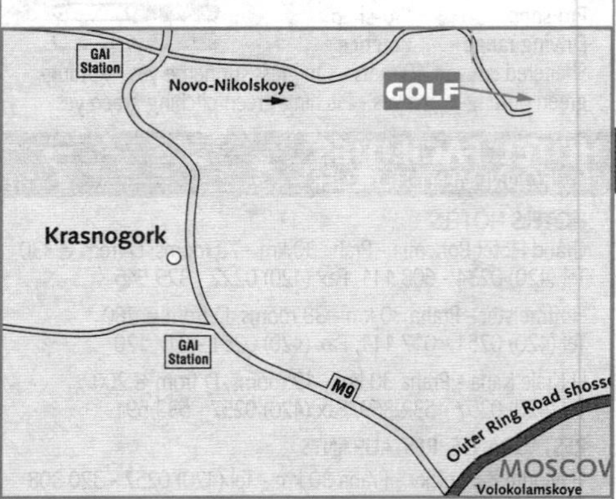

Access Accès : Moscow, Volokolamskoye Shosde. Gai Station, turn right → Krasnogorsk and Novo-Nikolskoye. Gai Station, right turn at sign "Moscow Country Club, 2.6 km"

GOLF COURSE — PARCOURS — 17/20

Site	Site	
Maintenance	Entretien	
Architect	Architecte	R. Trent Jones Jr.
Type	Type	forest
Relief	Relief	
Water in play	Eau en jeu	
Exp. to wind	Exposé au vent	
Trees in play	Arbres en jeu	

Scorecard Carte de score	Chp. Chp.	Mens Mess.	Ladies Da.
Length Long.	6390	5953	5248
Par	72	72	72
Slope system	—	—	—

Advised golfing ability Niveau de jeu recommandé — 0 12 24 36

Hcp required Handicap exigé 36

CLUB HOUSE & AMENITIES — CLUB HOUSE ET ANNEXES — 7/10

Pro shop Pro-shop
Driving range Practice
Sheltered couvert 10 mats + indoor - On grass sur herbe yes - Putting-green putting-green yes - Pitching-green pitching green yes

HOTEL FACILITIES — ENVIRONNEMENT HOTELIER — 6/10

HOTELS HÔTELS

Le Meridien - 131 rooms, D € 160 - on site
Tel (7) 095 - 926 5911, Fax (7) 095 - 926 5921

Baltschug Kempinski - Moscow 20 km
232 rooms, D from $ 340
Tel (7) 095 - 230 6500, Fax (7) 095 - 230 6502

Marco Polo Presnja - Moscow 20 km
71 rooms, D from $ 185
Tel (7) 095 - 220 0000, Fax (7) 095 - 220 0131

Bled King's Course

15 | 7 | 8

If you are holidaying in the south of Austria or in north-eastern Italy, you are only a short drive away from the Bled golf course in Slovenia, in a mountainous region where the beauty of the landscape with a spectacular lake is second to none. The present 18-hole layout was designed in 1937 then restyled by Donald Harradine before being re-opened in 1972. But the real development is ongoing, with an additional 9-hole course due to be upgraded to 18 holes in the next future. Although this is a mountainous region, the actual course is none too hilly and hazards are clearly visible on what is a classic layout. Many golfers will be reassured by the absence of water, but that doesn't mean you can hit it just anywhere, as thick trees line the fairways and from the back-tees yardage is more than respectable. Add to this a large and comfortable club-house sporting local architecture (with rooms) and very good hotels nearby, and you see why Bled is a pretty destination off the beaten track. The appeal of the course is a good reason for a visit here.

Wer im Süden von Österreich oder im Nordosten von Italien Urlaub macht, ist nur eine kurze Autofahrt von Bled in Slowenien entfernt. Der Platz liegt in einer der reizvollsten Alpenlandschaften Europas mit einem zauberhaften See. Der 18-Loch-Platz wurde 1937 erbaut und 1972 von Donald Harradine überarbeitet. Weitere neun Löcher sind bereits fertiggestellt, und es bestehen Pläne für einen weiteren Ausbau der Anlage. Obwohl der Platz von herrlichen Bergen umgeben, ist der 18-Loch-Meisterschaftsplatz trotz einiger Höhenunterschiede, die den Reiz etlicher Löcher dieses klassischen Designs ausmachen, kein "Bergziegenplatz", sondern gut begehbar. Viele Golfer werden es schätzen, dass im Gegensatz zu den neuen neun Löcher auf dem alten Platz keine Wasserhindernisse lauern. Aber das bedeutet nicht, dass man hier nach Belieben streuen kann, da die Spielbahnen von dichtem Wald umgeben sind. Von den hinteren Meisterschaftsabschlägen weist der Platz eine ordentliche Länge auf. Das reizvolle Clubhaus mit etlichen Zimmern und einige vorzügliche Hotels machen Bled zu einem Geheimtip.

Bled Golf & Country Club — 1937

Kidriceva 10 c.
SLO - 4260 BLED

Office Sekretariat (386) 0453 - 77 711
Pro shop Pro shop (386) 0453 - 77 711
Fax Fax (386) 0453 - 77 722
Web www.s5.net/golf-bled
Situation Lage Ljubljana, 25 km
Lece, 3 km
Annual closure Jährliche Schliessung 1/12→1/3
Weekly closure Wöchentliche Schliessung no
Fees main season Preisliste hochsaison 18 holes

	Week days Woche	We/Bank holidays We/Feiertag
Individual Individuell	€ 51	€ 62
Couple Ehepaar	€ 102	€ 124

Caddie Caddie on request **Electric Trolley** Elektrokarren no
Buggy Elektrischer Wagen yes **Clubs** Leihschläger yes
Credit cards Kreditkarten VISA - Eurocard - MasterCard

Access Zufahrt : Ljubljana → München/Salzburg
Map 2 on page 925 Karte 2 Seite 925

GOLF COURSE — PLATZ 15/20

Site Lage
Maintenance Instandhaltung
Architect Architekt D. Harradine
Type Typ mountain, parkland
Relief Begehbarkeit
Water in play Platz mit Wasser
Exp. to wind Wind ausgesetzt
Trees in play Platz mit Bäumen

Scorecard Scorekarte	Chp. Chp.	Mens Herren	Ladies Damen
Length Länge	6339	5982	5403
Par	73	73	73
Slope system	—	—	—

Advised golfing ability Empfohlene Spielstärke 0 12 24 36
Hcp required Min. Handicap 36

CLUB HOUSE & AMENITIES — KLUBHAUS UND NEBENGEBÄUDE 7/10

Pro shop Pro shop
Driving range Übungsplatz
Sheltered überdacht 12 mats - On grass auf Rasen yes - Putting-green Putting-grün yes (2) - Pitching-green Pitching-grün yes (3)

HOTEL FACILITIES — HOTEL BESCHREIBUNG 8/10

HOTELS HOTELS
Club House Hotel Bled - on site
13 rooms, D from € 80
Tel (386) 0453 - 78 300, Fax (386) 0453 - 78 327

Hotel-Villa Bled - 30 rooms, D from € 190 - Bled 5 km
Tel (386) 0457 - 91 500, Fax (386) 0457 - 41 320

Grand Hotel Toplice - 90 rooms, D rom € 150 - Bled 3 km
Tel (386) 0457 - 91 000, Fax (386) 0457 - 41 841

RESTAURANTS RESTAURANTS
King's Club House - on site - Tel (386) 0453 - 78 300
Villa Bled - Bled 5 km - Tel (386) 0457 - 91 500
Gostilna Kunstelj - Radovljica 5 km - Tel (386) 0445 - 304

Antalya GC *Sultan*

17 | 7 | 7

The site chosen for the "Pacha" course and this "Sultan" championship layout was anything but easy terrain. In a forest of pine and eucalyptus trees lined with swamps – since transformed into a multitude of lakes – European Golf Design and David Jones have laid out two demanding courses. The Sultan is the prettiest and the most exciting. Any number of dangerous bunkers add to the natural difficulties – the ability to bend the ball is a must to escape from, or to avoid, the most heavily wooded areas – and these are compounded by water hazards on nearly one half of the course. The fairways, though, are pretty wide and the well-contoured greens big enough to forgive a few errors of judgment. Particularly impressive are the very long 12th hole, a narrow par 4, and the testing 18th after a breath-taking moment on the 17th where the view down to the green is most impressive. Very long from the tips, the course is not the monster you might think and the pleasant climate makes for a good day's golfing. A successful venture.

In einem Wald, in dem vor allem Pinien und Eukalyptusbäume beheimatet sind, und dessen Moore mittlerweile zu vielen Wasserhindernissen Jones zwei anspruchsvolle Plätze angelegt. Der "Sultan" ist dabei der Schönere und Aufregendere von beiden. Ganz gleich wie viele tückische Bunker zu den natürlichen Schwierigkeiten hinzukommen – man sollte den Ball gut manövrieren können, um den stark bewaldeten Zonen des Platzes zu entkommen oder sie gar komplett zu vermeiden. Hinzu kommt noch, dass fast auf der Hälfte aller Löcher Wasserhindernisse auf die Spieler warten. Dennoch sind die Spielbahnen relativ breit und die grosszügig angelegten Grüns verzeihen auch den ein oder anderen nicht ganz präzisen Annäherungsschlag. Besonders beeindruckend sind unter anderem das sehr lange 12. Loch, ein sehr schmales Par 4, und das herausfordernde Schlussloch nach dem atemberaubenden 17. Loch, das einen absolut unvergesslichen Blick hinab zum Grün bietet.

Antalya Golf Club — 2002

Belek Turizm Merzeki
TR - 07500 ANTALYA

Office	Sekretariat	(90) 242 - 725 5970
Pro shop	Pro shop	(90) 242 - 725 5970
Fax	Fax	(90) 242 - 725 5971
Web	www.antalyagolfclub.com.tr	
Situation	Lage	Antalya, 35 km
Annual closure	Jährliche Schliessung	no
Weekly closure	Wöchentliche Schliessung	no

Fees main season Preisliste hochsaison — 18 holes

	Week days Woche	We/Bank holidays We/Feiertag
Individual Individuell	€ 95	€ 95
Couple Ehepaar	€ 190	€ 190

Caddie Caddie no — **Electric Trolley** Elektrokarren yes
Buggy Elektrischer Wagen yes — **Clubs** Leihschläger yes

Credit cards Kreditkarten
VISA - Eurocard - MasterCard - AMEX - DC

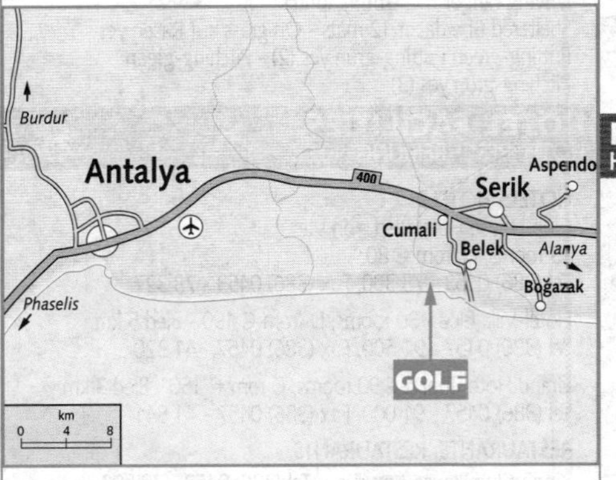

Access Zufahrt : Antalya → Belek → Antalya Golf Club

GOLF COURSE — PLATZ — 17/20

Site	Lage	
Maintenance	Instandhaltung	
Architect	Architekt	David Jones, European Golf Design
Type	Typ	parkland, forest
Relief	Begehbarkeit	
Water in play	Platz mit Wasser	
Exp. to wind	Wind ausgesetzt	
Trees in play	Platz mit Bäumen	

Scorecard Scorekarte	Chp. Chp.	Mens Herren	Ladies Damen
Length Länge	6411	5958	5003
Par	71	71	72
Slope system	142	135	130

Advised golfing ability Empfohlene Spielstärke — 0 12 24 36
Hcp required Min. Handicap — 24 Men, 28 Ladies

CLUB HOUSE & AMENITIES — KLUBHAUS UND NEBENGEBÄUDE — 7/10

Pro shop Pro shop
Driving range Übungsplatz
Sheltered überdacht yes - On grass auf Rasen yes - Putting-green putting-grün yes - Pitching-green pitching grün yes

HOTEL FACILITIES — HOTEL BESCHREIBUNG — 7/10

HOTELS HÔTELS

Sirene - 436 rooms, Seasonal price (ask) - Belek, close
Tel (90) 242 - 725 4844, Fax (90) 242 - 725 4842

The Dome Kempinski - 160 rooms, D from € 300 - Belek, close
Tel (90) 242 - 710 1300, Fax (90) 242 - 725 5575

Talya Hoteli - 204 rooms, D € 160 - Antalya 35 km
Tel (90) 242 - 248 6800, Fax (90) 242 - 241 5400

RESTAURANTS RESTAURANTS

5 restaurants Sirene Hotel - Tel (90) 242 - 725 4844 - close

Restaurants The Dome Hotel - Belek close
Tel (90) 242 - 710 1300

Gloria Golf Resort

15 | 7 | 7

As everywhere else in this region, the Gloria course is rather flat and the very many trees bring some welcome shade when you hit your ball slightly off-target. There is little tall rough to speak of, so getting back on the "short stuff" is no real problem. Only slightly trickier are the one or two huge fairway bunkers, which are more in play for the mid-handicapper than they are for the better player. You might even find them too large, but they serve to add visual appeal and to clearly outline each hole. The green-side bunkers are no big hazard either, a reassuring thought when approaching the greens with bump and run shots... hit deliberately or otherwise. We couldn't help thinking that the design of Michel Gayon might have made more of this site, but the course is very pleasant to play during the holidays for players of all abilities. Here, visitors will find excellent practice facilities, a few practice holes, a beach hotel and a beach to ensure sunny holidays.

Wie alle anderen Plätze in dieser klimatisch so angenehmen Gegend ist auch der Platz von Gloria flach. Die vielen Bäume (es gibt sehr viele Pinien) spenden etwas Schatten, wenn man den Ball leicht verzieht. Es gibt kaum hohes Rough, so dass man den Ball leicht wieder auf kurz gemähten Rasen zurückspielen kann. Etwas schwieriger sind ein oder zwei riesige Fairwaybunker, die allerdings mehr für mittlere Handicaps als für bessere Golfer ins Spiel kommen. Diese Bunker mögen vielen als zu groß erscheinen, aber sie stellen einen optischen Reiz dar und geben den Löchern Kontur. Die Grünbunker stellen ebenfalls kein allzu großes Hindernis dar, selbst wenn man die Grüns mit "bump 'n run"-Schlägen, absichtlich oder unabsichtlich, anspielt. Vielleicht hätte der Architekt Michel Gayon mehr aus dem Gelände machen können. Trotzdem entstand ein Urlaubsplatz, der für alle Spielstärken reizvoll ist. Besucher finden vorzügliche Übungseinrichtungen, ein paar Übungslöcher, ein Strandhotel und einen Strand ohne viel Schatten.

Gloria Golf Resort — 1997

Acisu Mevkii, Belek Mail Box 27 Serik
TR - BELEK, ANTALYA (Türkiye)

Office	Sekretariat	(90) 242 - 715 1520
Pro shop	Pro shop	(90) 242 - 715 1520
Fax	Fax	(90) 242 - 715 1635
Web	www.gloriagolf.com	
Situation	Lage	Antalya, 45 km
Annual closure	Jährliche Schliessung	no
Weekly closure	Wöchentliche Schliessung	no

Fees main season Preisliste hochsaison	18 holes	
	Week days Woche	We/Bank holidays We/Feiertag
Individual Individuell	€ 80	€ 80
Couple Ehepaar	€ 160	€ 160

Seasonal special fees (ask for details)
Juniors (–18): – 50 % / Special fees

Caddie Caddie yes — **Electric Trolley** Elektrokarren no
Buggy Elektrischer Wagen yes — **Clubs** Leihschläger yes
Credit cards Kreditkarten
VISA - Eurocard - MasterCard - AMEX

GOLF COURSE — PLATZ — 15/20

Site	Lage	
Maintenance	Instandhaltung	
Architect	Architekt	Michel Gayon
Type	Typ	forest, parkland
Relief	Begehbarkeit	
Water in play	Platz mit Wasser	
Exp. to wind	Wind ausgesetzt	
Trees in play	Platz mit Bäumen	

Scorecard Scorekarte	Chp. Chp.	Mens Herren	Ladies Damen
Length Länge	6296	5900	5200
Par	72	72	72
Slope system	—	—	—

Advised golfing ability Empfohlene Spielstärke: 0 12 24 36
Hcp required Min. Handicap: 28 Men/36 Ladies

CLUB HOUSE & AMENITIES — KLUBHAUS UND NEBENGEBÄUDE — 7/10

Pro shop Pro shop
Driving range Übungsplatz
Sheltered überdacht 48 mats - On grass auf Rasen no - Putting-green Putting-grün yes - Pitching-green Pitching-grün yes (2)

HOTEL FACILITIES — HOTEL BESCHREIBUNG — 7/10

HOTELS HOTELS
Gloria Golf Resort Hotel - on site
402 rooms, D from € 150
Tel (90) 242 - 715 1520, Fax (90) 242 - 715 1525

RESTAURANTS RESTAURANTS
4 restaurants - on site - Tel (90) 242 - 715 1520
Other restaurants in town

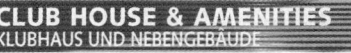

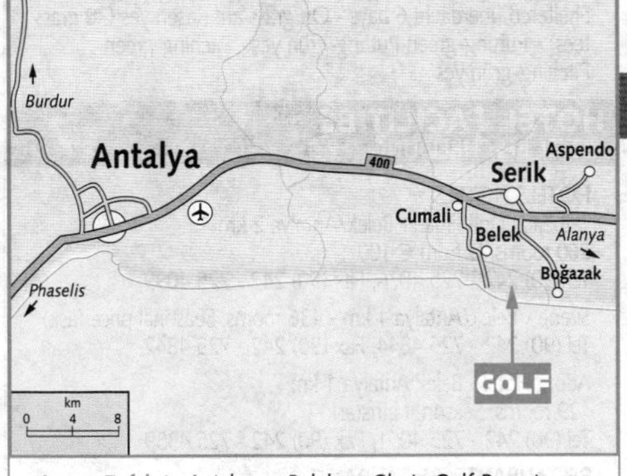

Access Zufahrt : Antalya → Belek → Gloria Golf Resort

1313

National GC 17 | 7 | 7

In a superb setting, this top-notch course was laid out by David Jones and David Feherty, one of the more colourful and interesting characters in today's world of professional golf. We might also have expected a little more "fantasy" from Feherty, but while the style is a clever blend of American and British features, the constraints involved in building a course that is playable for everyone might have dampened his enthusiasm in this respect. Although the course is perfectly playable and even fun for the less experienced or reasonable golfer, it is still a tricky proposition for the low handicapper as the fairways get very narrow when winding between the pines and eucalyptus trees. Hazards are well located but always in view, which is probably a good thing because strategy is important here and skills in bending the ball something of a necessity to avoid a few isolated and carefully positioned trees.

Die Einfahrt, der Garten und das Clubhaus machen das Verweilen vor oder nach der Runde zum Vergnügen. Der Platz wurde von David Jones und David Feherty, einem der schillerndsten Charaktere des Profigolfs, entworfen. Bei diesen "Vätern" hätten wir etwas mehr Fantasie erwartet, aber die Beschränkung, einen Platz für alle Spielstärken zu bauen, hat Fehertys Kreativität wohl ein wenig gedämpft. Entstanden ist eine Mischung aus amerikanischen und englischen Design-Elementen. Obwohl der Platz auch für schwächere Spieler zu empfehlen ist, spielt sich der Platz für niedrige Handicaps schwierig, weil die engen Fairways sich zwischen Pinien und Eukalyptus-Bäumen schlängeln. Die Hindernisse sind gut platziert und immer sichtbar, was auf einem strategischen Platz von Vorteil ist. Die Fähigkeit, den Ball mit unterschiedlichen Flugkurven auf die Reise zu schicken, hilft, einzeln und sorgfältig positionierte Bäume zu umspielen. Dies ist ein wirklicher Spitzenplatz in herrlicher Umgebung mit Schnee bedeckten Gipfeln im Hintergrund.

National Golf Club — 1994

Belek Turizm Merkezi
TR - 07500 SERIK, ANTALYA (Türkiye)

Office	Sekretariat	(90) 242 - 725 4620
Pro shop	Pro shop	(90) 242 - 725 4620
Fax	Fax	(90) 242 - 725 4623
Web	www.nationalturkey.com	
Situation	Lage	Antalya, 35 km
Annual closure	Jährliche Schliessung	no
Weekly closure	Wöchentliche Schliessung	no

Fees main season Preisliste hochsaison — 18 holes

	Week days / Woche	We/Bank holidays / We/Feiertag
Individual Individuell	€ 88	€ 88
Couple Ehepaar	€ 176	€ 176

US$ or Euros. Seasonal tariffs (ask for details).

Caddie Caddie on request **Electric Trolley** Elektrokarren no

Buggy Elektrischer Wagen yes **Clubs** Leihschläger yes

Credit cards Kreditkarten
VISA - Eurocard - MasterCard - AMEX

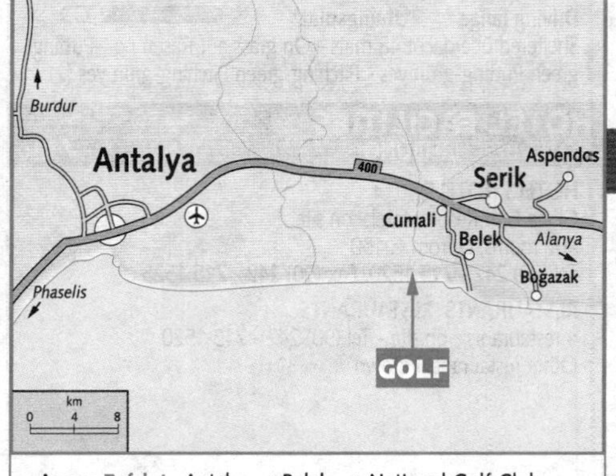

Access Zufahrt : Antalya → Belek. → National Golf Club

GOLF COURSE — PLATZ — 17/20

Site	Lage	
Maintenance	Instandhaltung	
Architect	Architekt	David Feherty David Jones
Type	Typ	forest
Relief	Begehbarkeit	
Water in play	Platz mit Wasser	
Exp. to wind	Wind ausgesetzt	
Trees in play	Platz mit Bäumen	

Scorecard Scorekarte	Chp. Chp.	Mens Herren	Ladies Damen
Length Länge	6172	5410	4886
Par	72	72	72
Slope system	—	—	—

Advised golfing ability Empfohlene Spielstärke — 0 12 24 36

Hcp required Min. Handicap — 28 Men/36 Ladies

CLUB HOUSE & AMENITIES — KLUBHAUS UND NEBENGEBÄUDE — 7/10

Pro shop Pro shop
Driving range Übungsplatz
Sheltered überdacht 6 bays - On grass auf Rasen yes (30 grass tees) - Putting-green Putting-grün yes - Pitching-green Pitching-grün yes

HOTEL FACILITIES — HOTEL BESCHREIBUNG — 7/10

HOTELS HOTELS
Tatbeach Golf Hotel - Belek/Antalya 2 km
260 rooms, D from € 100
Tel (90) 242 - 725 4076, Fax (90) 242 - 725 4099

Sirene - Belek/Antalya 1 km - 436 rooms, Seasonal price (ask)
Tel (90) 242 - 725 4844, Fax (90) 242 - 725 4842

Adora Hotel - Belek Antalya 1 km
429 rooms, Season. tariffs(ask)
Tel (90) 242 - 725 4051, Fax (90) 242 - 725 4359

RESTAURANTS RESTAURANTS
Meridiana Restaurant - on site - Tel (90) 242 - 725 4620
In the Hotels - Belek Antalya - Tel

Robinson

17	8	6

When approaching, you will notice the very pleasant landscape, with holes laid out amidst a pine forest along the river Acisu. Off the tee, the course is relatively easy; the problems begin with the second shot and are more apparent for the more proficient birdie-hunting golfer than for the mid-handicapper. The greens are very well defended by often deep but visible bunkers, which are well shaped in the tradition of architect Dave Thomas. The secret is simple: place your drive for an easier approach, and work on bending the ball, it will come in useful. You still have all the time and leisure to focus on your game though, as there is little hilly relief to speak of, there are no blind shots and only the greens are elevated. Water is not too much of a danger here and is rarely frontal. If we also throw in the leisure facilities courtesy of the Robinson group which runs the place, "Nobilis" has become a great holiday destination.

Schon wenn man sich dem Platz nähert, erkennt man die Schönheit der Landschaft. Der Platz liegt inmitten eines Pinienwaldes am Fluss Acisu. Vom Abschlag erscheint der Platz leicht, die Schwierigkeiten beginnen erst beim Anspielen der Grüns, und das ganz besonders für auf Birdies Jagd machende bessere Spieler. Die Grüns sind sehr gut verteidigt, die Bunker sind tief und – wie bei Dave Thomas üblich – gut gestaltet. Das Geheimnis ist einfach: Man muss den Drive so platzieren, dass man einen einfacheren Schlag zum Grün hat. Wer dazu den Ball mit Fade oder Draw spielen kann, ist im Vorteil. Der Platz ist bis auf die erhöhten Grüns vollkommen flach, es gibt keine blinden Schläge, und auch das Wasser stellt keine allzu große Gefahr da, zumal es nur wenige frontale Wasserhindernisse gibt. Da der Platz über eine vorzügliche Driving Range verfügt und der Robinson Club, der die Anlage führt, Bungalows verschiedener Größen am 8. und 9.

Robinson Club Nobilis — 1998

Acisu Mevkii / Belek, PK 56 - Serik
TR - 07500 ANTALYA (Türkiye)

Office	Sekretariat	(90) 242 - 715 1987
Pro shop	Pro shop	(90) 242 - 715 1987
Fax	Fax	(90) 242 - 715 1985
Web	www.nobilis.com.tr	
Situation	Lage	Antalya, 45 km
Annual closure	Jährliche Schliessung	no
Weekly closure	Wöchentliche Schliessung	no

Fees main season Preisliste hochsaison — 18 holes

	Week days / Woche	We/Bank holidays / We/Feiertag
Individual Individuell	€ 74	€ 74
Couple Ehepaar	€ 148	€ 148

under 18: - 50% - Seasonal tariffs. / Hotel guests: € 59

Caddie Caddie on request **Electric Trolley** Elektrokarren no

Buggy Elektrischer Wagen yes **Clubs** Leihschläger yes

Credit cards Kreditkarten
VISA - Eurocard - MasterCard

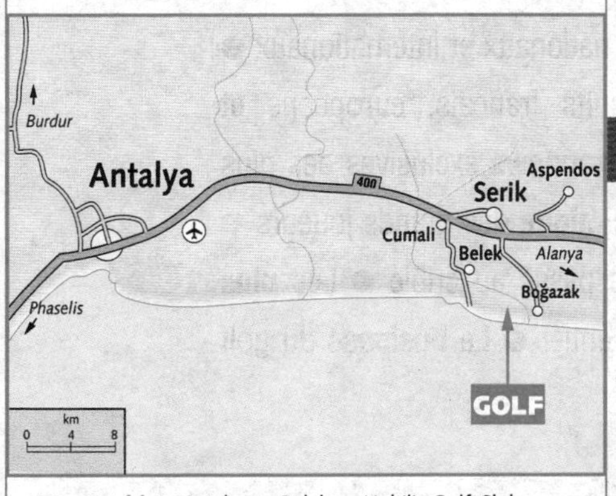

Access Zufahrt : Antalya → Belek → Nobilis Golf Club

GOLF COURSE / PLATZ — 17/20

Site	Lage	
Maintenance	Instandhaltung	
Architect	Architekt	Dave Thomas
Type	Typ	forest, parkland
Relief	Begehbarkeit	
Water in play	Platz mit Wasser	
Exp. to wind	Wind ausgesetzt	
Trees in play	Platz mit Bäumen	

Scorecard Scorekarte	Chp. / Chp.	Mens / Herren	Ladies / Damen
Length Länge	6312	5877	5103
Par	72	72	72
Slope system	—	—	—

Advised golfing ability Empfohlene Spielstärke — 0 12 24 36

Hcp required Min. Handicap — 28 Men/36 Ladies

CLUB HOUSE & AMENITIES / KLUBHAUS UND NEBENGEBÄUDE — 8/10

Pro shop Pro shop
Driving range Übungsplatz
Sheltered überdacht no - **On grass** auf Rasen yes - **Putting-green** Putting-grün yes - **Pitching-green** Pitching-grün yes

HOTEL FACILITIES / HOTEL BESCHREIBUNG — 6/10

HOTELS HOTELS

Nobilis Villas - on site
406 rooms, from € 700 (week)
Tel (90) 242 - 715 1987, Fax (90) 242 - 715 1985

Gloria Golf Resort Hotel - Gloria Golf Resort 5
402 rooms, D from € 150
Tel (90) 242 - 715 1520, Fax (90) 242 - 715 1525

RESTAURANTS RESTAURANTS

Club house - Nobilis Golf Club, on site
Tel (90) 242 - 715 1987

4 restaurants - Gloria Golf Resort, on site
Tel (90) 242 - 715 1520

Classement alphabétique et aéroports
Alphabetische Einteilung und Flughafen
I alfabetisk ordning och närmaste flygplatser
Clasificación alfabética y aeropuertos
Ordine alfabetico e aeroporti più vicini

Golf courses / Parcours / Golfplatz / Golfbaner / Reccoridos / Percorso — ✈ — Page / Page / Seite / Side / Página / Pagina

A

Golf course		Airport	Page
A 6	S	Jönköping, 8 km	1217
Abenberg	D	Nürnberg, 30 km	366
Aberdovey	WAL	Cardiff, 140 km	779
Ableiges	F	Charles-de-Gaulle, 48 km	201
Aboyne	SCO	Aberdeen, 45 km	676
Acaya	I	Brindisi, 20 km	934
Adare	IRL	Shannon, 20 km	817
Ailette (L')	F	Charles-de-Gaulle, 109 km	202
Aisses (Les)	F	Orly, 145 km	203
Albarella	I	Venezia, 50 km	935
Albi	F	Toulouse, 65 km	204
Alcaidesa	E	Gibraltar, 10 km	1107
Alcanada	E	Palma de Mallorca, 60 km	1108
Aldeburgh	ENG	Stansted, 140 km	500
Alhaurín	E	Malaga, 30 km	1109
Alicante	E	Alicante, 15 km	1110
Alloa	SCO	Edinburgh, 50 km	677
Almenara	E	Málaga, 100 km	1111
Almerimar	E	Almería, 48 km	1112
Aloha	E	Malaga, 60 km	1113
Alwoodley (The)	ENG	Leeds, 7 km	501
Alyth	SCO	Edinburgh, 96 km	678
Am Alten Fliess	D	Köln-Bonn, 30 km	367
Amarilla	E	Tenerife, 4 km	1114
Ambrosiano	I	Milano, 75 km	936
Amirauté (L')	F	Charles-de-Gaulle, 200 km	205
Amsterdam	NL	Amsterdam, 10 km	992
Anderstein	NL	Amsterdam, 60 km	993
Ängelholm	S	Malmö, 120 km	1218
Ängsö	S	Arlanda, 70 km	1219
Antalya GC	TR	Antalya, 30 km	1312
Antwerp	B	Antwerpen, 15 km	96
Aphrodite Hills	CYP	Paphos, 17 km	1306
Apremont	F	Charles-de-Gaulle, 34 km	206
Arcachon	F	Bordeaux, 66 km	207
Arcangues	F	Biarritz-Parme, 3 km	208
Ardglass	NIR	Belfast, 65 km	901
Arendal	N	Kristiansand, 80 km	1030
Aroeira	P	Lisboa, 11 km	1052
Arras	F	Charles-de-Gaulle, 150 km	209
Arzaga	I	Verona, 45 km	937
Ascona	CH	Lugano, 40 km	1280
Ashburnham	WAL	Cardiff, 90 km	780
Ashridge	ENG	Heathrow, 48 km	502
Asolo	I	Venezia, 66 km	938
Athlone	IRL	Dublin, 125 km	818
Åtvidaberg	S	Linköping, 35 km	1220
Augerville	F	Orly, 70 km	210
Ayr (Belleisle)	SCO	Glasgow, 55 km	679

B

Golf course		Airport	Page
Baberton	SCO	Edinburgh, 8 km	680
Bad Abbach-Deutenhof	D	München, 90 km	368
Bad Bevensen	D	Hamburg, 100 km	369
Bad Griesbach	D	München, 180 km	370/371/372
Bad Ragaz	CH	Zürich, 100 km	1281
Baden	F	Lorient, 45 km	211
Bâle-Hagenthal	F	Bâle-Mulhouse, 8 km	212
Ballater	SCO	Dyce, 35 km	681
Ballybunion	IRL	Shannon, 88 km	819/820
Ballykisteen	IRL	Shannon, 50 km	821
Ballyliffin	IRL	Belfast, 160 km	822/823
Bamberg	D	Nürnberg, 40 km	373
Bamburgh Castle	ENG	Newcastle, 50 km	503
Banchory	SCO	Aberdeen, 32 km	682
Bangor	NIR	Belfast, 40 km	902
Barbaroux	F	Toulon-Hyères, 51 km	213
Barlassina	I	Milano, 35 km	939
Barsebäck	S	Malmö, 50 km	1221
Båstad	S	Halmstad, 30 km	1222
Bath	ENG	Bristol, 20 km	504
Batouwe	NL	Amsterdam, 80 km	994
Bearna	IRL	Galway, 20 km	824
Beau Desert	ENG	Birmingham, 30 km	505
Belas	P	Lisboa, 15 km	1053
Bélesbat	F	Orly, 40 km	214
Belle-Dune	F	Le Touquet, 25 km	215
Belmullet (Carne)	IRL	Sligo, 115 km	825

Belvoir Park	NIR	Belfast, 12 km	903
Bercuit	B	Bruxelles (Brussel), 30 km	97
Bergamo	I	Bergamo, 18 km	940
Bergisch Land Wuppertal	D	Düsseldorf, 20 km	374
Berkhamsted	ENG	Heathrow, 48 km	506
Berkshire (The)	ENG	Heathrow, 25 km	507/508
Berlin-Wannsee	D	Berlin, 40 km	375
Berwick/Tweed	ENG	Newcastle, 60 km	509
Béthemont	F	Charles-de-Gaulle, 55 km	216
Beuerberg	D	München, 80 km	376
Biarritz	F	Biarritz, 3 km	217
Biella - Le Betulle	I	Torino, 75 km	941
Bitburger Land	D	Luxembourg, 55 km	377
Bitche	F	Strasbourg, 80 km	218
Blackmoor	ENG	Heathrow, 65 km	510
Blairgowrie	SCO	Edinburgh, 90 km	683/684
Bled	SLO	Ljubljana, 25 km	1311
Blumisberg	CH	Genève, 135 km	1282
Boat of Garten	SCO	Inverness, 45 km	685
Bogogno	I	Milano, 33 km	942/943
Bokskogen	S	Malmö, 7 km	1223
Bologna	I	Bologna, 6 km	944
Bolton Old Links	ENG	Manchester, 25 km	511
Bonalba	E	Alicante, 15 km	1115
Bondues	F	Lille, 20 km	219/220
Bonmont	E	Barcelona, 140 km	1116
Bordes (Les)	F	Orly, 130 km	221
Borre	N	Oslo, 75 km	1031
Bosjökloster	S	Malmö, 70 km	1224
Boulie (La)	F	Orly, 20 km	222
Bovey Castle	ENG	Exeter, 30 km	512
Bowood (Cornwall)	ENG	Plymouth, 65 km	513
Bowood G&CC	ENG	Bristol, 50 km	514
Brampton	ENG	Glasgow, 160 km	515
Brancepeth Castle	ENG	Newcastle, 20 km	516
Bråviken	S	Norrköping, 5 km	1225
Breitenloo	CH	Zürich, 8 km	1283
Bresse (La)	F	Lyon-Saint Exupéry, 62 km	223
Brest Iroise	F	Brest, 20 km	224
Bretesche (La)	F	Nantes, 61 km	225
Brigode	F	Lille, 15 km	226
Bro-Bålsta	S	Stockholm, 35 km	1226
Broadstone	ENG	Bournemouth, 17 km	517
Broekpolder	NL	Rotterdam, 15 km	995
Brokenhurst Manor	ENG	Southampton, 16 km	518
Brora	SCO	Inverness, 92 km	686
Bruntsfield	SCO	Edinburgh, 10 km	687
Buchanan Castle	SCO	Glasgow, 33 km	688
Buckinghamshire	ENG	Heathrow, 16 km	519
Bude & North Cornwall	ENG	Exeter, 70 km	520
Bundoran	IRL	Sligo, 45 km, Belfast, 176 km	826
Burnham & Berrow	ENG	Bristol, 38 km	521
Burntisland	SCO	Edinburgh, 27 km	689
Buxtehude	D	Hamburg, 60 km	378

C

Cairndhu	NIR	Belfast, 40 km	904
Caldy	ENG	Liverpool, 38 km	522
Camberley Heath	ENG	Heathrow, 50 km	523
Came Down	ENG	Exeter, 53 km	524
Campoamor	E	Alicante, 50 km	1117
Cannes Mandelieu	F	Nice, 38 km	227
Cannes-Mougins	F	Nice, 18 km	228
Canyamel	E	Palma, 68 km	1118
Cap d'Agde	F	Béziers, 25 km	229
Carden Park	ENG	Manchester, 50 km	525
Cardiff	WAL	Cardiff, 16 km	781
Cardigan	WAL	Cardiff, 140 km	782
Cardrona	SCO	Edinburgh, 50 km	690
Cardross	SCO	Glasgow, 25 km	691
Carlisle	ENG	Glasgow, 160 km	526
Carlow	IRL	Dublin, 100 km	827
Carmarthen	WAL	Cardiff, 100 km	783
Carnoustie	SCO	Edinburgh, 100 km	692/693
Carton House	IRL	Dublin, 30 km	828/829
Carvoeiro	P	Faro, 42 km	1054
Castelconturbia	I	Milano, 30 km	945
Castelgandolfo	I	Roma Fiumicino, 53 km	946
Castello di Tolcinasco	I	Milano, 50 km	947
Castillo de Gorraiz	E	Pamplona, 8 km	1119
Castleknock	IRL	Dublin, 13 km	830
Castlerock	NIR	Belfast, 80 km	905
Castletown	ENG	Ronaldsway, 4 km	527
Cavendish	ENG	Manchester, 20 km	528
Celtic Manor	WAL	Cardiff, 30 km	784
Cély	F	Orly, 40 km	230
Cerdaña	E	Barcelona, 150 km	1120
Cervia	I	Bologna, 96 km	948
Chailly (Château de)	F	Dijon-Bourgogne, 66 km	231
Chambon-sur-Lignon (Le)	F	Lyon-Saint Exupéry, 145 km	232
Chamonix	F	Genève, 80 km	233
Champ de Bataille	F	Orly, 150 km	234
Chantaco	F	Biarritz, 15 km	235
Chantilly	F	Charles-de-Gaulle, 21 km	236
Charleville	IRL	Cork, 60 km	831
Charmeil	F	Grenoble, 15 km	237
Chart Hills	ENG	Gatwick, 50 km	529
Château de la Chouette	F	Charles-de-Gaulle, 45 km	238
Château de la Tournette	B	Bruxelles, 45 km	98
Château de Preisch	F	Luxembourg, 20 km	239
Chaumont-en-Vexin	F	Charles-de-Gaulle, 60 km	240
Cheverny	F	Tours, 70 km	241
Chiberta	F	Biarritz, 5 km	242
Citywest	IRL	Dublin, 20 km	832
Clandeboye	NIR	Belfast, 35 km	906
Claux Amic	F	Nice, 37 km	243
Clitheroe	ENG	Manchester, 60 km	530

Club de Campo	E	Madrid, 20 km	1121
Club zur Vahr (Garlstedt)	D	Bremen, 30 km	379
Cochrane Castle	SCO	Glasgow, 9 km	694
Cognac	F	Angoulème, 44 km	244
Collingtree Park	ENG	Luton, 45 km	531
Colony Club	A	Wien, 20 km	68
Connemara	IRL	Galway, 100 km	833
Conwy	WAL	Manchester, 180 km	785
Copt Heath	ENG	Birmingham, 15 km	532
Cork GC	IRL	Cork, 10 km	834
Cosmopolitan	I	Pisa, 15 km	949
Costa Ballena	E	Jerez, 40 km	1122
Costa Brava	E	Barcelona, 100 km	1123
Costa Dorada	E	Barcelona, 100 km	1124
County Louth	IRL	Dublin, 36 km	835
County Sligo	IRL	Sligo, 15 km	836
County Tipperary	IRL	Cork, 90 km	837
Courson	F	Orly, 20 km	245/246
Courtown	IRL	Dublin, 105 km	838
Coxmoor	ENG	East Midlands, 40 km	533
Crail	SCO	Edinburgh, 85 km	695
Crans-sur-Sierre	CH	Genève, 200 km	1284
Crieff	SCO	Edinburgh, 70 km	696
Cromstrijen	NL	Rotterdam, 35 km	996
Cruden Bay	SCO	Aberdeen, 38 km	697
Cumberwell Park	ENG	Bristol, 40 km	534

D

Dalmahoy	SCO	Edinburgh, 5 km	698
Dartmouth	ENG	Plymouth, 60 km	535
De Pan	NL	Amsterdam, 65 km	997
Degeberga-Widtsköfle	S	Kristianstad, 15 km	1227
Deinster Mühle	D	Hamburg, 50 km	380
Delamere Forest	ENG	Manchester, 40 km	536
Dellach	A	Graz, 130 km	69
Denham	ENG	Heathrow, 16 km	537
Desert Springs	E	Almería, 100 km	1125
Dieppe-Pourville	F	Charles-de-Gaulle, 200 km	247
Dinard	F	Rennes 75 km	248
Dingle Links (Ceann Sibeal)	IRL	Cork, 160 km	839
Disneyland Paris	F	Orly, 40 km - Roissy, 28 km	249
Divonne	F	Genève, 15 km	250
Domaine Impérial	CH	Genève, 25 km	1285
Domangère (La)	F	Nantes, 67 km	251
Domtal-Mommenheim	D	Frankfurt, 40 km	381
Donegal	IRL	Belfast, 160 km, Sligo, 45 km	840
Dooks	IRL	Cork, 115 km	841
Doonbeg	IRL	Shannon, 85 km	842
Downfield	SCO	Edinburgh, 80 km	699
Drente	NL	Groningen, 30 km	998
Dromoland Castle	IRL	Shannon, 15 km	843
Drottningholm	S	Stockholm, 75 km	1247
Druids Glen	IRL	Dublin, 40 km	844/845
Duddingston	SCO	Edinburgh, 12 km	700
Duff House Royal	SCO	Aberdeen, 75 km	701
Duke's St Andrews	SCO	Edinburgh, 80 km	702
Dumfries & County	SCO	Edinburgh/Glasgow, 115 km	703
Dunbar	SCO	Edinburgh, 48 km	704
Dundalk	IRL	Dublin, 80 km	846
Dundonald	SCO	Glasgow, 50 km	705
Dunfermline	SCO	Edinburgh, 25 km	706
Düsseldorfer	D	Düsseldorf, 8 km	382

E

East Devon	ENG	Exeter, 10 km	538
East Renfrewshire	SCO	Glasgow, 20 km	707
East Sussex N.	ENG	Gatwick, 35 km	539
Edzell	SCO	Aberdeen, 60 km	708
Efteling	NL	Eindhoven, 40 km	999
Eichenheim	A	München, 120 km	70
Eindhoven	NL	Eindhoven, 12 km	1000
Ekerum	S	Kalmar, 27 km	1228
El Bosque	E	Valencia, 5 km	1126
El Cortijo	E	Las Palmas, 25 km	1127
El Prat	E	Barcelona, 35 km	1128/1129
El Puerto	E	Jerez, 20 km	1130
El Saler	E	Valencia, 16 km	1131
Elfrather Mühle	D	Düsseldorf, 30 km	383
Elgin	SCO	Aberdeen, 100 km	709
Elie	SCO	Edinburgh, 80 km	710
Emporda	E	Barcelona 120 km	1132
Engadin Zuoz	CH	Zurich, 225 km	1286
Ennetsee-Holzhäusern	CH	Zürich, 45 km	1287
Enniscrone	IRL	Sligo, 55 km	847
Esbjerg	DK	Billund, 70 km	124
Escorpion	E	Valencia, 10 km	1133
Esery	F	Genève,16 km	252
Esker Hills	IRL	Dublin, 100 km	848
Espoo	FIN	Helsinki, 25 km	144
Essener Oefte	D	Düsseldorf, 25 km	384
Estela	P	Porto, 40 km	1055
Estérel	F	Nice, 60 km	253
Etiolles Colonial	F	Orly, 15 km	254
Etretat	F	Le Havre-Octeville, 20 km	255
European (The)	IRL	Dublin, 90 km	849
Kungsängen (European Tour Club)	S	Stockholm, 30 km	1248
Evian	F	Genève, 52 km	257

F

Fågelbro	S	Stockholm, 75 km	1229
Fairhaven	ENG	Manchester, 100 km	540
Faithlegg	IRL	Cork, 135 km	850
Falkenstein	D	Hamburg, 30 km	385
Falkirk Tryst	SCO	Edinburgh, 32 km	711
Falnuée	B	Charleroi, 25 km	99

Golf	Country	Airport	Page
Falsterbo	S	Malmö, 45 km	1230
Fanø	DK	Esbjerg, 10 km	125
Feldafing	D	München, 80 km	386
Felixstowe Ferry	ENG	Stansted, 120 km	541
Ferndown	ENG	Bournemouth, 7 km	542
Feucherolles	F	Orly, 30 km	258
Firenze - Ugolino	I	Firenze, 16 km	950
Five Nations	B	Bruxelles, 80 km	100
Fjällbacka	S	Göteborg, 130 km	1231
Fleesensee	D	Berlin, 145 km	387
Flommen	S	Malmö, 45 km	1232
Fontainebleau	F	Orly, 40 km	259
Fontana	A	Wien, 45 km	71
Fontanals	E	Perpignan, 110 km	1134
Fontcaude	F	Montpellier, 15 km	260
Fontenailles	F	Orly, 55 km	261
Fontenelles (Les)	F	Nantes, 70 km	262
Forest of Arden	ENG	Birmingham, 6 km	543
Forest Pines	ENG	Humberside, 11 km	544
Forfar	SCO	Edinburgh, 120 km	712
Formby	ENG	Manchester, 80 km	545
Forsbacka	S	Karlstad, 70 km	1233
Fortrose & Rosemarkie	SCO	Inverness, 40 km	713
Fota Island	IRL	Cork, 18 km	851
Four Seasons Provence (Terre Blanche)	F	Nice, 58 km	263/264
Franciacorta	I	Bergamo, 30 km	951
Frankfurter GC	D	Frankfurt, 5 km	388
Fränkische Schweiz	D	Nürnberg, 45 km	389
Frégate	F	Toulon, 50 km	265
Frilford Heath	ENG	Heathrow, 75 km	546
Frösåker	S	Stockholm, 80 km	1234
Fulford	ENG	Leeds, 35 km	547
Fürstlicher GC Bad Waldsee	D	Stuttgart, 140 km	390

G

Golf	Country	Airport	Page
Galway Bay	IRL	Galway, 6 km	852
Ganton	ENG	Leeds, 60 km	548
Gardagolf	I	Bergamo, 73 km	952
Garlenda	I	Genova, 75 km	953
Garmisch-Partenkirchen	D	München, 110 km	391
Gelpenberg	NL	Eelde, 50 km	1001
Gendersteyn	NL	Eindhoven, 10 km	1002
Genève	CH	Genève, 10 km	1288
Glamorganshire	WAL	Cardiff, 13 km	786
Glasson	IRL	Dublin, 120 km	853
Gleidingen	D	Hannover, 40 km	392
Glen	SCO	Edinburgh, 30 km	714
Glen of the Downs	IRL	Dublin, 40 km	854
Gleneagles	SCO	Edinburgh, 70 km	715/716/717
Gloria Golf Resort	TR	Antalya, 42 km	1313
Goes	NL	Rotterdam, 80 km	1003
Gog Magog	ENG	Stansted, 48 km	549
Golf Barrière Deauville	F	Charles-de-Gaulle, 200 km	266
Golf Barrière La Baule	F	Nantes, 60 km	267
Golf d'Aro	E	Girona, 25 km	1135
Golf del Sur	E	Tenerife, 2 km	1136
Golf Parc Nantilly	F	Charles-de-Gaulle, 85 km	268
Golfpark Gut Häusern	D	München 42 km	393
Golfresort Haugschlag	A	Wien, 160 km	72
Golspie	SCO	Inverness, 90 km	718
Göteborg	S	Göteborg, 25 km	1235
Gouverneur (Le)	F	Lyon-Saint Exupéry, 40 km	269
Graafschap	NL	Amsterdam, 110 km	1004
Granada	E	Granada, 15 km	1137
Grand Ducal de Luxembourg	L	Luxembourg, 1 km	116
Grande Bastide (La)	F	Nice, 26 km	270
Grande-Motte (La)	F	Montpellier, 10 km	271
Grange	IRL	Dublin, 20 km	855
Gränna	S	Jönköping, 40 km	1236
Grantown on Spey	SCO	Inverness, 56 km	719
Granville	F	Rennes, 80 km	272
Green Eagle	D	Hamburg, 60 km	394
Grenoble Bresson	F	Grenoble, 50 km	273
Grönhögen	S	Stockholm, 400 km	1237
Gruyère (La)	CH	Genève, 120 km	1289
Guadalhorce	E	Málaga, 4 km	1138
Guadalmina	E	Málaga, 64 km	1139
Gujan-Mestras	F	Bordeaux-Mérignac, 50 km	274
Gullane	SCO	Edinburgh, 50 km	720
Gut Altentann	A	Salzburg, 17 km	73
Gut Grambek	D	Hamburg, 50 km	395
Gut Kaden	D	Hamburg, 20 km	396
Gut Lärchenhof	D	Köln-Bonn, 35 km	397
Gut Ludwigsberg	D	München, 70 km	398
Gut Thailing	D	München, 65 km	399
Gütersloh (Westfälischer GC)	D	Paderborn, 30 km	400

H

Golf	Country	Airport	Page
Haagsche	NL	Amsterdam, 45 km	1005
Hadley Wood	ENG	Heathrow, 48 km	550
Haggs Castle	SCO	Glasgow, 9 km	721
Hainaut	B	St-Ghislain, 10 km	101
Hallamshire-	ENG	Leeds, 25 km	551
Halmstad	S	Göteborg, 160 km	1238
Hamburg-Ahrensburg	D	Hamburg, 20 km	401
Hanau-Wilhelmsbad	D	Frankfurt, 25 km	402
Hanbury Manor	ENG	Heathrow, 60 km	552
Haninge	S	Stockholm, 70 km	1239
Hankley Common	ENG	Heathrow, 50 km	553
Hannover	D	Hannover, 12 km	403
Hardelot	F	Lille, 153 km	275

Hardenberg	D	Hannover, 120 km	404
Harrogate	ENG	Leeds, 25 km	554
Haut-Poitou	F	Poitiers 25 km	276
Hawkstone Park	ENG	Manchester, 65 km	555
Hayling	ENG	Southampton, 45 km	556
Headfort	IRL	Dublin, 55 km	856
Hechingen-Hohenzollern	D	Stuttgart, 50 km	405
Helsinki	FIN	Helsinki, 19 km	145
Heritage (The)	IRL	Dublin, 70 km	857
Herkenbosch	NL	Maastricht, 35 km	1006
Hermitage	IRL	Dublin, 10 km	858
Hertfordshire	ENG	Heathrow, 55 km	557
Hever	ENG	Gatwick, 25 km	558
High Post	ENG	Heathrow, 130 km	559
Hills	S	Göteborg, 20 km	1240
Hillside	ENG	Manchester, 80 km	560
Hilversum	NL	Amsterdam, 40 km	1007
Himmerland	DK	Aalborg, 50 km	126
Hindhead	ENG	Heathrow, 55 km	561
Hof Trages	D	Frankfurt, 45 km	406
Hoge Kleij	NL	Amsterdam, 50 km	1008
Hohenpähl	D	München, 73 km	407
Holstebro	DK	Århus, 100 km	127
Holyhead	WAL	Manchester, 220 km	787
Hossegor	F	Biarritz, 28 km	277
Houtrak	NL	Amsterdam, 20 km	1009
Hubbelrath	D	Düsseldorf, 18 km	408
Huddersfield (Fixby)	ENG	Leeds Bradford, 25 km	562
Hunstanton	ENG	Stansted, 150 km	563
Huntercombe	ENG	Heathrow, 65 km	564

I

I Roveri	I	Torino, 7 km	954
ICL (Le Lys-Chantilly)	F	Charles-de-Gaulle, 25 km	278
Iffeldorf	D	München, 70 km	409
Ilkley	ENG	Leeds, 15 km	565
Interlaken	CH	Bern, 59 km	1290
Inverness	SCO	Glasgow, 256 km	722
Ipswich (Purdis Heath)	ENG	Stansted, 84 km	566
Is Arenas	I	Cagliari, 110 km	955
Is Molas	I	Cagliari, 35 km	956
Islantilla	E	Faro (Portugal), 69 km	1140
Isle Adam (L')	F	Charles-de-Gaulle, 23 km	279
Isle of Purbeck	ENG	Bournemouth, 16 km	567

J

Jakobsberg	D	Frankfurt, 100 km	410
Jarama R.A.C.E.	E	Madrid, 20 km	1141
John O'Gaunt	ENG	Luton 28 km	568
Jönköping	S	Jönköping, 2 km	1241
Joyenval	F	Orly, 32 km	281/282
Jura Golf Park	D	Nürnberg, 50 km	411

K

K Club	IRL	Dublin, 44 km	859/860
Kalmar	S	Kalmar, 5 km	1242
Karlovy Vary	CZ	Karlovy Vary, 1 km	1307
Karlshamn	S	Kristianstad, 60 km	1243
Karlstad	S	Karlstad, 6 km	1244
Kempferhof (Le)	F	Strasbourg, 14 km	283
Kennemer	NL	Amsterdam, 20 km	1010
Kikuoka	L	Luxembourg, 10 km	117
Kilkea Castle	IRL	Dublin, 70 km	861
Killarney	IRL	Cork, 105 km	863
Kilmarnock (Barassie)	SCO	Glasgow, 50 km	723
King's Lynn	ENG	Stansted, 75 km	569
Kingsbarns	SCO	Edinburgh, 80 km	724
Kingussie	SCO	Inverness, 70 km	725
Kirkistown Castle	NIR	Belfast, 55 km	907
Klagenfurt-Seltenheim	A	Klagenfurt, 3 km	74
Knistad	S	Göteborg, 180 km	1245
Knock	NIR	Belfast, 21 km	908
København	DK	København, 30 km	128
Köln (Refrath)	D	Köln-Bonn, 25 km	412
Krefelder	D	Düsseldorf, 30 km	413
Kristianstad	S	Malmö, 90 km	1246
Kungsbacka	S	Göteborg, 30 km	1249
Kytäjä	FIN	Helsinki, 60 km	146

L

La Cala	E	Málaga, 35 km	1142/1143
La Dehesa	E	Madrid, 35 km	1144
La Finca	E	Alicante, 40 km	1145
La Herreria	E	Madrid, 60 km	1146
La Manga	E	Alicante, 110 km	1147/1148
La Moraleja	E	Madrid, 15 km	1149/1150
La Moye	ENG	Jersey, 3 km	570
La Quinta	E	Málaga, 64 km	1151
La Reserva	E	Málaga, 120 km	1152
La Sella	E	Valencia, 70 km	1153
Lacanau	F	Bordeaux, 55 km	284
Ladybank	SCO	Edinburgh, 56 km	726
Lage Vuursche	NL	Amsterdam, 65 km	1011
Lahinch	IRL	Shannon, 55 km	864
Lanark	SCO	Edinburgh, 48 km	727
Landskrona	S	Malmö, 45 km	1250
Langland Bay	WAL	Cardiff, 65 km	788
Largue (La)	F	Bâle-Mulhouse, 35 km	285
Larvik	N	Oslo, 120 km	1032
Las Américas	E	Tenerife, 15 km	1155
Las Brisas	E	Málaga, 60 km	1156
Las Palmas	E	Las Palmas, 20 km	1157
Læsø Seaside	DK	Aalborg, 100 km	129
Lauro	E	Málaga, 10 km	1158
Lausanne	CH	Genève, 60 km	1291
Laval-Changé	F	Nantes, 100 km	286

Le Pavoniere	I	Firenze, 15 km	957
Le Querce	I	Roma, 95 km	958
Le Robinie	I	Milano, 9 km	959
Lee Valley	IRL	Cork, 14 km	865
Lerma	E	Madrid, 200 km	1159
Les Bois	CH	Genève, 140 km	1292
Letham Grange	SCO	Edinburgh, 110 km	728
Leven	SCO	Edinburgh, 56 km	729
Lichtenau-Weickershof	D	Nürnberg, 40 km	414
Lignano	I	Venezia, 108 km	960
Limburg	B	Bruxelles, 75 km	102
Limère	F	Orly, 130 km	287
Limerick County	IRL	Shannon, 40 km	866
Lindau-Bad Schachen	D	Zürich, 130 km	415
Linden Hall	ENG	Newcastle, 40 km	571
Lindenhof	D	Frankfurt, 16 km	416
Lindrick	ENG	Leeds, 40 km	572
Liphook	ENG	Gatwick, 48 km	573
Lisburn	NIR	Belfast, 14 km	909
Little Aston	ENG	Birmingham, 25 km	574
Ljunghusen	S	Malmö, 45 km	1251
Llandudno (Maesdu)	WAL	Manchester, 160 km	789
Llanymynech	WAL	Manchester, 120 km	790
Loch Lomond	SCO	Glasgow, 32 km	730
London Golf Club	ENG	Gatwick, 58 km	575
Longniddry	SCO	Edinburgh, 30 km	731
Los Arqueros	E	Málaga, 65 km	1160
Los Naranjos	E	Málaga, 62 km	1161
Losby	N	Oslo, 36 km	1033
Lübeck-Travemünder	D	Hamburg, 90 km	417
Luffenham Heath	ENG	Birmingham, 70 km	576
Luffness New	SCO	Edinburgh, 30 km	732
Lugano	CH	Lugano, 2 km	1293
Lundin	SCO	Edinburgh, 55 km	733
Lunds Akademiska	S	Malmö, 25 km	1252
Luttrellstown	IRL	Dublin, 10 km	867
Luzern	CH	Zürich, 70 km	1294

M

Machrie	SCO	Islay Airport, 5 km	734
Machrihanish	SCO	Glasgow (+ ferry or air)	735
Main-Taunus	D	Frankfurt, 20 km	418
Maison Blanche	F	Genève, 10 km	288
Makila Golf Club	F	Biarritz, 4 km	289
Málaga	E	Málaga, 3 km	1162
Malahide	IRL	Dublin, 7 km	868
Malone	NIR	Belfast, 16 km	910
Manchester	ENG	Manchester, 20 km	577
Mannings Heath	ENG	Gatwick, 18 km	578
Manor House (Castle Combe)	ENG	Bristol, 45 km	579
Marbella	E	Málaga, 51 km	1163
Marco Simone	I	Roma, 73 km	961
Margara	I	Torino, 109 km	962
Mariánské Lázne	CZ	Praha, 160 km	1308
Märkischer Potsdam	D	Berlin, 45 km	419
Marriott St Pierre	WAL	Cardiff, 45 km	791
Masia Bach	E	Barcelona, 40 km	1164
Maspalomas	E	Las Palmas, 30 km	1165
Massane-Montpellier	F	Montpellier, 14 km	290
Massereene	NIR	Belfast, 7 km	911
Master	FIN	Helsinki, 25 km	147
Mediterraneo	E	Valencia-Manises, 70 km	1166
Médoc	F	Bordeaux, 20 km	291/292
Meland	N	Bergen, 60 km	1034
Memmingen Gut Westerhart	D	München, 140 km	420
Mendip	ENG	Bristol, 30 km	580
Meon Valley	ENG	Southampton, 16 km	581
Mere	ENG	Manchester, 8 km	582
Mijas	E	Málaga, 20 km	1167
Miklagard	N	Oslo, 10 km	1035
Milano	I	Milano, 70 km	963
Mittelrheinischer	D	Frankfurt, 100 km	421
Modena	I	Bologna, 40 km	964
Moliets	F	Biarritz, 50 km	293
Mölle	S	Malmö, 110 km	1253
Møn	DK	København, 120 km	130
Monifieth	SCO	Edinburgh, 96 km	736
Mont-Garni	B	Bruxelles, 70 km	103
Montanya	E	Barcelona, 80 km	1169
Monte Carlo (Mont Agel)	F	Nice, 20 km	295
Monte Mayor	E	Málaga, 65 km	1170
Montecastillo	E	Jerez, 7 km	1171
Montecchia	I	Venezia, 95 km	965
Montenmedio	E	Jerez, 70 km	1172
Monticello	I	Milano, 30 km	966
Montreux	CH	Genève, 85 km	1295
Montrose	SCO	Aberdeen, 72 km	737
Moor Allerton	ENG	Leeds Bradford, 15 km	583
Moor Park	ENG	Heathrow, 16 km	584
Moortown	ENG	Leeds, 10 km	585
Moray	SCO	Inverness, 60 km	738
Morfontaine	F	Charles-de-Gaulle, 25 km	297
Morgado do Reguengo	P	Faro, 65 km	1056
Moscow	RU	Moscow, 35 km	1310
Moss & Rygge	N	Oslo, 40 km	1036
Motzener See	D	Berlin, 45 km	422
Mount Juliet	IRL	1Dublin, 136 km	869
Mount Wolseley	IRL	Dublin, 93 km	870
Muirfield	SCO	Edinburgh, 40 km	739
Mullingar	IRL	Dublin, 90 km	871
Mullion	ENG	Exeter, 160 km	586
München-Riedhof	D	München, 90 km	423
Münchner-Strasslach	D	München, 80 km	424
Murcar	SCO	Aberdeen, 12 km	740
Murrayshall	SCO	Edinburgh, 72 km	741

ALPHABETICAL ORDER AND CLOSEST AIRPORTS

N

Golf	Country	Airport	Page
Nahetal	D	Frankfurt, 90 km	425
Nairn	SCO	Inverness, 9 km	742
Nairn Dunbar	SCO	Inverness, 15 km	743
National	F	Orly, 32 km	298
National GC	TR	Antalya, 32 km	1314
Nefyn & District	WAL	Manchester, 180 km	792
Neguri	E	Bilbao, 12 km	1173
Neuchâtel	CH	Genève, 125 km	1296
Neusiedlersee-Donnerskirchen	A	Wien, 38 km	75
New Zealand	ENG	Heathrow, 22 km	587
Newbury & Crookham	ENG	Heathrow, 80 km	588
Newport	WAL	Cardiff, 30 km	793
Newtonmore	SCO	Inverness, 72 km	744
Nîmes-Campagne	F	Nîmes, 2 km	299
Noordwijk	NL	Amsterdam, 35 km	1012
Nordcenter	FIN	Helsinki, 75 km	148
Nordvestjysk	DK	Aalborg, 70 km	131
North Berwick	SCO	Edinburgh, 50 km	745
North Hants	ENG	Heathrow, 40 km	589
North Wales (Llandudno)	WAL	Manchester, 160 km	794
Northamptonshire	ENG	Luton, 55 km	590
Northop Country Park	WAL	Manchester, 70 km	795
Notts (Hollinwell)	ENG	Birmingham, 69 km	591
Novo Sancti Petri	E	Jerez, 50 km	1174
Nunspeet	NL	Amsterdam, 85 km	1013

O

Golf	Country	Airport	Page
Oberfranken	D	Nürnberg, 80 km	426
Oberschwaben Bad Waldsee	D	Stuttgart, 140 km	427
Oitavos	P	Lisboa, 30 km	1057
Old Head	IRL	Cork, 20 km	872
Old Thorns	ENG	Gatwick, 49 km	592
Olgiata	I	Roma, 25 km	967
Oliva Nova	E	Valencia, 76 km	1175
Omaha Beach	F	Orly, 220 km	300
Oostende	B	Brussel/Bruxelles, 115 km	104
Oosterhout	NL	Amsterdam, 100 km	1014
Orchardleigh	ENG	Bristol, 32 km	593
Örebro	S	Örebro, 15 km	1254
Öschberghof	D	Stuttgart, 100 km	428
Oslo	N	Oslo, 10 km	1037
Österåker	S	Stockholm, 40 km	1255
Oudenaarde	B	Brussel/Bruxelles, 85 km	105
Ozoir-la-Ferrière	F	Charles-de-Gaulle, 47 km	301

P

Golf	Country	Airport	Page
Padova	I	Venezia, 40 km	968
Palheiro	P	Funchal, 16 km	1058
Palmares	P	Faro, 75 km	1059
Pals (Platja de Pals)	E	Barcelona, 120 km	1177
Panmure	SCO	Edinburgh, 100 km	746
Pannal	ENG	Leeds, 20 km	594
Panoramica	E	Valencia, 150 km	1178
Paradiso del Garda	I	Verona, 14 km	969
Parco di Roma	I	Roma, 25 km	970
Paris International	F	Charles-de-Gaulle, 15 km	302
Parkstone	ENG	Bournemouth, 12 km	595
Pau	F	Pau, 5 km	303
Pedreña	E	Santander, 7 km	1179
Penha Longa	P	Lisboa, 25 km	1060
Penina	P	Faro, 60 km	1061
Pennard	WAL	Cardiff, 50 km	796
Peralada	E	Perpignan (France), 60 km	1180
Perranporth	ENG	Plymouth, 80 km	596
Pevero	I	Olbia, 30 km	971
PGA de Catalunya	E	Barcelona, 133 km	1181
PGA National	IRL	Dublin, 30 km	873
Pickala	FIN	Helsinki, 60 km	149
Pineda	E	Sevilla, 15 km	1182
Pinheiros Altos	P	Faro, 12 km	1062
Pinnau	D	Hamburg, 25 km	429
Pitlochry	SCO	Edinburgh, 105 km	747
Pleasington	ENG	Manchester, 45 km	597
Pléneuf-Val-André	F	Rennes, 80 km	304
Ploemeur Océan	F	Lorient, 4 km	305
Poggio dei Medici	I	Firenze, 28 km	972
Pont Royal	F	Marseille, 50 km	306
Porcelaine (La)	F	Limoges, 15 km	307
Pornic	F	Nantes, 41 km	308
Portal	ENG	Manchester, 30 km	598
Portmarnock	IRL	Dublin, 8 km	874
Portmarnock Links	IRL	Dublin, 8 km	875
Portpatrick (Dunskey)	SCO	Glasgow, 150 km	748
Portsalon	IRL	Belfast, 160 km	876
Portstewart	NIR	Belfast, 64 km	912
Powerscourt	IRL	Dublin, 20 km	877/878
Powfoot	SCO	Glasgow, 130 km	749
Praha Karlstejn	CZ	Praha/Prag, 50 km	1309
Praia d'El Rey	P	Lisboa, 75 km	1063
Prestbury	ENG	Manchester, 15 km	599
Prestwick	SCO	Glasgow, 55 km	750
Prestwick St Nicholas	SCO	Glasgow, 55 km	751
Prieuré (Le)	F	Charles-de-Gaulle, 70 km	309
Prince de Provence	F	Nice, 100 km	310
Prince's	ENG	Gatwick, 145 km	600
Puerta de Hierro	E	Madrid, 15 km	1183/1184
Pula	E	Palma, 63 km	1185
Punta Ala	I	Firenze, 140 km	973
Purmerend	NL	Amsterdam, 25 km	1015
Pyle & Kenfig	WAL	Cardiff, 25 km	797

Q

Golf	Country	Airport	Page
Quinta da Marinha	P	Lisboa, 28 km	1064
Quinta da Ria	P	Faro, 39 km	1065

Quinta de Cima	P	Faro, 39 km	1066
Quinta do Brinçal	P	Lisboa, 55 km	1067
Quinta do Lago	P	Faro, 10 km	1069
Quinta do Peru	P	Lisboa, 46 km	1070

R

Rapallo	I	Genova, 59 km	974
Raray (Château de)	F	Charles-de-Gaulle, 34 km	311
Rathcore	IRL	Dublin, 30 km	879
Rathsallagh	IRL	Dublin, 80 km	880
Ravenstein	B	Bruxelles, 12 km	106
Real Sociedad Club de Campo	E	Madrid, 20 km	1186/1187
Rebetz	F	Charles-de-Gaulle, 67 km	312
Reddish Vale	ENG	Manchester, 12 km	601
Reichsstadt Bad Windsheim	D	Nürnberg, 50 km	430
Reichswald-Nürnberg	D	Nürnberg, 2 km	431
Rethmar	D	Hannover, 25 km	432
Rheine/Mesum	D	Münster/Osnabrück, 18 km	433
Rheinhessen	D	Frankfurt, 55 km	434
Ribagolfe	P	Lisboa, 64 km	1071/1072
Rigenée	B	Bruxelles, 35 km	107
Rijk van Nijmegen	NL	Eindhoven, 65 km	1016
Rimini	I	Rimini, 10 km	975
Ring of Kerry	IRL	Cork, 75 km	881
Rinkven	B	Antwerpen, 30 km	108
Rittergut Birkhof	D	Düsseldorf, 20 km	435
Riva dei Tessali	I	Bari, 128 km	976
Robinson	TR	Antalya, 42 km	1315
Rochefort	F	Orly, 35 km	313
Roganstown	IRL	Dublin, 8 km	882
Rolls of Monmouth	WAL	Cardiff, 65 km	798
Roma - Acquasanta	I	Roma, 30 km	977
Roncemay	F	Orly, 135 km	314
Rosapenna	IRL	Sligo, 150 km	883/884
Rosendael	NL	Amsterdam, 90 km	1017
Ross-on-Wye	ENG	Birmingham, 95 km	602
Rosslare	IRL	Dublin, 160 km	885
Roxburghe (The)	SCO	Edinburgh, 90 km	752
Royal Aberdeen	SCO	Aberdeen, 10 km	753
Royal Ashdown Forest	ENG	Gatwick, 20 km	603
Royal Belfast	NIR	Belfast, 30 km	913
Royal Birkdale	ENG	Manchester, 80 km	604
Royal Burgess	SCO	Edinburgh, 4 km	754
Royal Cinque Ports	ENG	Gatwick, 145 km	605
Royal County Down	NIR	Belfast, 48 km	914
Royal Cromer	ENG	Stansted, 120 km	606
Royal Dornoch	SCO	Inverness, 82 km	755
Royal Dublin	IRL	Dublin, 13 km	886
Royal Guernsey	ENG	Guernsey, 8 km	607
Royal Jersey	ENG	Jersey, 10 km	608
Royal Latem	B	Bruxelles, 65 km	109
Royal Liverpool (Hoylake)	ENG	Liverpool, 35 km	609
Royal Lytham & St Anne's	ENG	Manchester, 100 km	610
Royal Mid-Surrey	ENG	Heathrow, 17 km	611
Royal Mougins	F	Nice, 29 km	315
Royal Musselburgh	SCO	Edinburgh, 20 km	756
Royal North Devon (Westward Ho!)	ENG	Plymouth, 90 km	612
Royal Oak	DK	Billund, 60 km	132
Royal Porthcawl	WAL	Cardiff, 25 km	799
Royal Portrush	NIR	Belfast, 80 km	915/916
Royal St David's	WAL	Manchester, 120 km	800
Royal St George's	ENG	London Gatwick, 145 km	613
Royal Troon	SCO	Glasgow, 50 km	757
Royal West Norfolk (Brancaster)	ENG	Stansted, 150 km	614
Royal Wimbledon	ENG	Heathrow, 40 km	615
Royal Zoute	B	Brussel (Bruxelles), 108 km	110
Rudding Park	ENG	Leeds, 20 km	616
Rungsted	DK	København, 40	133
Ruuhikoski	FIN	Seinäjoki, 30 km	150
Rya	S	Malmö, 120 km	1256
Rye	ENG	London Gatwick, 50 km	617

S

S. Lourenço	P	Faro, 12 km	1073
Sablé-Solesmes	F	Orly, 250 km	316
Saint Donat	F	Nice, 37 km	318
Saint-Cloud	F	Orly, 25 km	317
Saint-Endréol	F	Nice, 70 km	319
Saint-Germain	F	Orly, 30 km	320
Saint-Jean-de-Monts	F	Nantes, 68 km	321
Saint-Laurent	F	Lorient, 40 km	322
Saint-Nom-la-Bretèche	F	Orly, 30 km	323/324
Sainte-Baume (La)	F	Marseille-Marignane, 73 km	325
Sainte-Maxime	F	Toulon, 55 km	326
Saltsjöbaden	S	Stockholm, 40 km	1257
Samsø	DK	Århus, 50 km	134
San Domenico	I	Brindisi, 45 km	978
San Roque	E	Gibraltar, 15 km	1188/1189
San Sebastián	E	Biarritz (France), 20 km	1190
Sand Moor	ENG	Leeds, 10 km	618
Sandiway	ENG	Manchester, 35 km	619
Sant Cugat	E	Barcelona, 35 km	1191
Santa Ponsa	E	Palma, 26 km	1192
Santo da Serra	P	Funchal, 6 km	1074
Sarfvik	FIN	Helsinki, 25 km	151
Sart-Tilman	B	Liège, 20 km	111
Saunton	ENG	Plymouth, 90 km	620/621
Savenay	F	Nantes, 40 km	327
Schloss Braunfels	D	Frankfurt, 85 km	436
Schloss Ebreichsdorf	A	Wien, 15 km	76
Schloss Egmating	D	München, 55 km	437
Schloss Klingenburg	D	München, 150 km	438
Schloss Langenstein	D	Stuttgart, 150 km	439
Schloss Lüdersburg	D	Hamburg, 50 km	440

ALPHABETICAL ORDER AND CLOSEST AIRPORTS

Golf	Country	Closest airport	Page
Schloss Myllendonk	D	Düsseldorf, 25 km	441
Schloss Nippenburg	D	Stuttgart, 35 km	442
Schloss Schönborn	A	Wien, 55 km	77
Schloss Wilkendorf	D	Berlin, 50 km	443
Schönenberg	CH	Zürich, 30 km	1297
Schwanhof	D	Nürnberg, 85 km	444
Scotscraig	SCO	Edinburgh, 95 km	758
Sct. Knuds	DK	Odense, 30 km	135
Seacroft	ENG	Humberside, 80 km	622
Seafield	IRL	Dublin, 100 km	887
Seapoint	IRL	Dublin, 48 km	888
Seascale	ENG	Manchester, 200 km	623
Seaton Carew	ENG	Teesside, 20 km	624
Seddiner See	D	Berlin, 50 km	445
Seignosse	F	Biarritz, 39 km	328
Semlin am See	D	Berlin, 70 km	446
Sempachersee	CH	Zürich, 120 km	1298
Senne	D	Paderborn, 43 km	447
Servanes	F	Marseille, 57 km	329
Sevilla	E	Sevilla, 10 km	1193
Shanklin & Sandown	ENG	Southampton, 65 km	625
Sherborne	ENG	Bristol, 45 km	626
Sheringham	ENG	Stansted, 120 km	627
Sherry Golf	E	Jerez, 15 km	1194
Sherwood Forest	ENG	East Midlands, 40 km	628
Shiskine (Blackwaterfoot)	SCO	Glasgow	759
Silloth-on-Solway	ENG	Glasgow, 200 km	629
Simon's	DK	København, 40 km	136
Sint Nicolaasga	NL	Amsterdam, 120 km	1018
Skellefteå	S	Skellefteå, 10 km	1258
Skövde	S	Jönköping, 90 km	1259
Slaley Hall	ENG	Newcastle, 35 km	630
Slieve Russell	IRL	Dublin, 128 km	889
Söderåsen	S	Malmö, 120 km	1260
Son Antem	E	Palma, 10 km	1195
Son Muntaner	E	Palma, 15 km	1196
Son Vida	E	Palma, 15 km	1197
Sorknes	N	Oslo, 165 km	1038
Sotogrande	E	Málaga, 120 km	1198
Soufflenheim	F	Strasbourg, 50 km	330
South County	IRL	Dublin, 25 km	890
Southerndown	WAL	Cardiff, 36 km	801
Southerness	SCO	Glasgow, 155 km	760
Southport & Ainsdale	ENG	Manchester, 80 km	631
Spa (Les Fagnes)	B	Liège, 25 km	112
Spérone	F	Figari, 27 km	331
Spiegelven	B	Maastricht, 25 km	113
Sporting-Club Berlin	D	Berlin, 80 km	448/449/450
St Andrews	SCO	Edinburgh, 80 km	761/764
St Andrews Bay	SCO	Edinburgh, 80 km	765/766
St Enodoc	ENG	Plymouth, 80 km	632
St George's Hill	ENG	Heathrow, 28 km	633
St Helen's Bay	IRL	Dublin, 160 km	891
St Margaret's	IRL	Dublin, 6 km	892
St Mellion	ENG	Plymouth, 16 km	634
St. Dionys	D	Hamburg, 60 km	451
St. Eurach	D	München, 70 km	452
St. Leon-Rot	D	Frankfurt, 100 km	454/455
Stavanger	N	Stavanger, 10 km	1039
Steiermärkischer Murhof	A	Graz, 20 km	78
Stenungsund	S	Göteborg, 65 km	1261
Stockholm	S	Stockholm, 33 km	1262
Stoke Park	ENG	Heathrow, 24 km	635
Stolper Heide	D	Berlin, 10 km	455
Stoneham	ENG	Southampton, 4 km	636
Strasbourg Illkirch	F	Strasbourg, 12 km	332
Strathaven	SCO	Glasgow, 35 km	767
Stuttgarter Solitude	D	Stuttgart, 25 km	456
Sunningdale	ENG	Heathrow, 20 km	636/637
Svartinge	S	Stockholm, 20 km	1263
Swinley Forest	ENG	Heathrow, 20 km	639
Sybrook	NL	Enschede Twente, 5 km	1019
Sylt	D	Westerland, 5 km	457

T

Golf	Country	Closest airport	Page
Täby	S	Stockholm, 30 km	1264
Tadmarton Heath	ENG	Heathrow, 80 km	640
Tain	SCO	Inverness, 65 km	768
Talma	FIN	Helsinki,	152
Taulane	F	Nice, 75 km	333
Tawast	FIN	Helsinki, 60 km	153
Taymouth Castle	SCO	Edinburgh, 125 km	769
Tegernseer Bad Wiessee	D	München, 85 km	458
Tenby	WAL	Cardiff, 75 km	802
The Belfry	ENG	Birmingham, 15 km	641/642
The Country Club (Tullnerfeld)	A	Wien, 50 km	79
The Grove	ENG	London Heathrow, 20 km	643
The Island	IRL	Dublin, 8 km	893
Thetford	ENG	Stansted, 90 km	644
Thorndon Park	ENG	Stansted, 37 km	645
Thornhill	SCO	Edinburgh, Glasgow, 109 km	770
Thorpeness	ENG	Stansted, 145 km	646
Thurlestone	ENG	Plymouth, 50 km	647
Torekov	S	Halmstad, 30 km	1265
Torino - La Mandria	I	Torino, 7 km	979
Torremirona	E	Barcelona, 150 km	1199
Torrequebrada	E	Málaga, 15 km	1200
Toulouse Palmola	F	Toulouse, 40 km	334
Touquet (Le)	F	Lille, 151 km	336
Toxandria	NL	Eindhoven, 40 km	1020
Tralee	IRL	Cork, 120 km	894
Trevose	ENG	Plymouth, 80 km	648
Troia	P	Lisboa, 42 km	1075
Tulfarris	IRL	Dublin, 50 km	895
Turnberry	SCO	Glasgow, 80 km	771/772
Tutzing	D	München, 80 km	459
Twente	NL	Enschede Twente, 15 km	1021

U

Course	Country	Airport	Page
Ullna	S	Stockholm, 40 km	1266
Ulzama	E	Pamplona, 28 km	1201

V

Course	Country	Airport	Page
Val de Sorne	F	Lyon, 134 km	337
Val Queven	F	Lorient, 3 km	338
Valderrama	E	Málaga, 120 km	1202
Vale do Lobo	P	Faro, 18 km	1077
Vale Hotel, Golf & Spa (Vale of Glamorgan)	WAL	Cardiff, 30 km	803
Valle del Este	E	Alicante, 90 km	1203
Varberg	S	Göteborg, 80 km	1267
Varese	I	Milano, 25 km	980
Värnamo	S	Jönköping, 70 km	1268
Vasatorp	S	Malmö, 85 km	1269
Vaucouleurs (La)	F	Orly, 71 km	339
Vejle	DK	Billund, 40 km	137
Venezia	I	Venezia, 13 km	981
Verona	I	Verona, 5 km	982
Vidbynäs	S	Stockholm, 140 km	1270
Vila Sol	P	Faro, 22 km	1078
Vilamoura	P	Faro, 22 km	1079/1080/1081
Villa d'Este	I	Milano, 37 km	983
Villamartin	E	Alicante, 50 km	1204
Villette d'Anthon	F	Lyon-Saint Exupéry, 12 km	340
Visby	S	Visby, 30 km	1271
Volcans (Les)	F	Clermont-Ferrand, 19 km	341
Vuissens	CH	Genève, 110 km	1299

W

Course	Country	Airport	Page
Walddörfer	D	Hamburg, 20 km	460
Wallasey	ENG	Liverpool, 35 km	649
Walton Heath	ENG	Gatwick, 15 km	650
Wantzenau (La)	F	Strasbourg, 27 km	342
Warrenpoint	NIR	Belfast, 75 km	917
Warwickshire	ENG	Birmingham, 30 km	652
Wasserburg Anholt	D	Düsseldorf, 80 km	461
Waterford Castle	IRL	Cork, 130 km	896
Waterloo	B	Bruxelles, 20 km	114/115
Waterville	IRL	Cork, 150 km	897
Wendlohe	D	Hamburg, 10 km	462
Wentworth	ENG	Heathrow, 20 km	653/654
West Berkshire	ENG	Heathrow, 80 km	655
West Cornwall	ENG	Plymouth, 120 km	656
West Hill	ENG	Heathrow, 44 km	657
West Kilbride	SCO	Glasgow, 50 km	773
West Lancashire	ENG	Manchester, 80 km	658
West Surrey	ENG	Gatwick, 15 km	659
West Sussex	ENG	Gatwick, 40 km	660
Western Gailes	SCO	Glasgow, 50 km	774
Weston-Super-Mare	ENG	Bristol, 25 km	661
Westport	IRL	Knock, 50 km	898
Whitekirk	SCO	Edinburgh, 50 km	775
Whittington Heath	ENG	Birmingham, 20 km	662
Wilmslow	ENG	Manchester, 6 km	663
Wimereux	F	Lille-Lesquin, 143 km	343
Winnerod	D	Frankfurt, 80 km	463
WinstonGolf	D	Hamburg, 120 km	464
Wittelsbacher	D	München, 80 km	465
Woburn	ENG	Heathrow, 70 km	664/665
Woking	ENG	Heathrow, 38 km	666
Woodbridge	ENG	Stansted, 120 km	667
Woodbrook	IRL	Dublin, 30 km	899
Woodbury Park	ENG	Exeter, 10 km	668
Woodenbridge	IRL	Dublin, 88 km	900
Woodhall Spa	ENG	Humberside, 70 km	669
Woodsome Hall	ENG	Manchester, 40 km	670
Worplesdon	ENG	Heathrow, 39 km	671
Wouwse Plantage	NL	Eindhoven, 70 km	1022
Wylihof	CH	Zurich-Kloten, 110 km	1300

Z

Course	Country	Airport	Page
Zaudín	E	Sevilla, 15 km	1205
Zuid Limburg	NL	Maastricht, 25 km	1023
Zumikon	CH	Zurich-Kloten, 30 km	1301

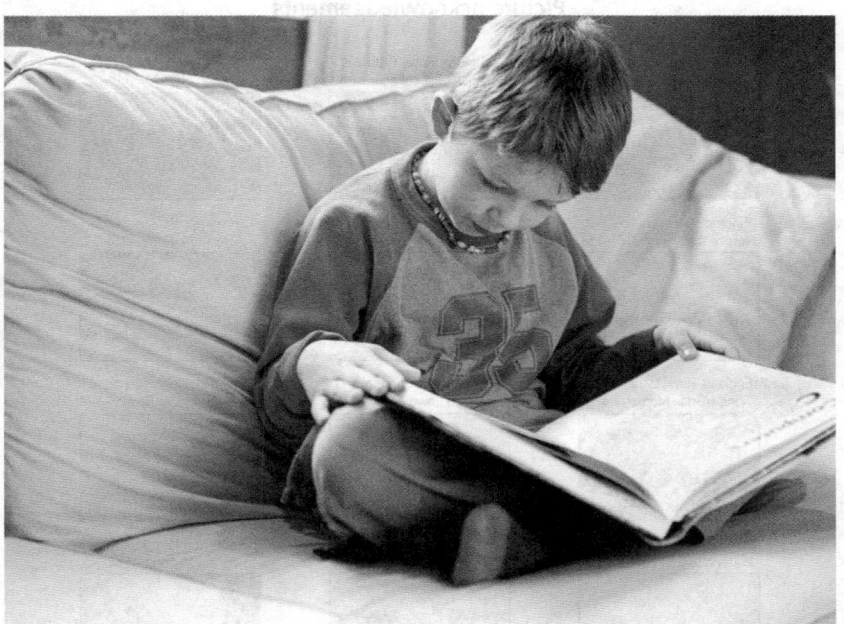

Picture acknowledgements

Austria: Gut Altentann
Brian Morgan - 70

Belgium: Royal Club des
Fagnes/G.C LesFagnes - 80

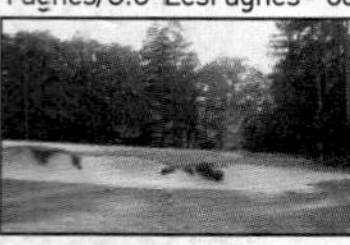

Denmark: Royal Oak
Brian Morgan - 118

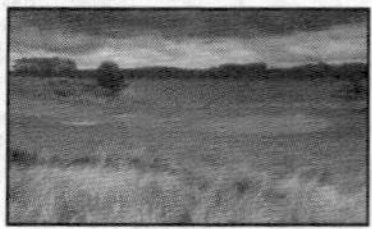

Finland: Nordcenter-Benz
Nordcenter Golf & CC - 138

France: Seignosse
Jean-François Lefèvre - 154

Germany: Sporting Club
Berlin/A-Rosa - 344

England: Royal Lytham & St
Anne's/Brian Morgan - 496

Scotland: Dundonald
Ian Lowe - 672

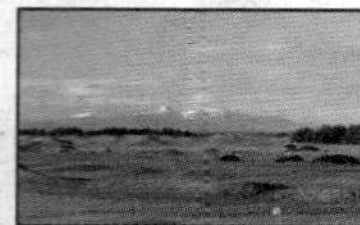

Wales: Celtic Manor
The Celtic Manor Resort - 776

Ireland: Waterville
Waterville Golf Links - 904

Italy: Pevero
Jean-François Lefèvre - 918

Netherlands: Kennemer
Brian Morgan - 984

Norway: Evje
Torsten Pamp - 1024

Portugal: Vilamoura - Victoria
Stefan von Stengel - 1040

Spain: PGA de Catalunya
GolfSpain - 1082

Sweden: Vidbynäs
Peter Frick - 1206

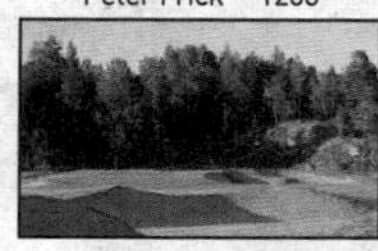

Switzerland: Ascona
Brian Morgan - 1272

Turkey: Gloria Resort
Brian Morgan - 1302

© Editions Mourgue d'Algue

Golf Européen Holding, 16 Chemin du Golf, F-78860 Saint-Nom-La-Bretèche

www.peugeotgolfguide.com

Despite every effort, a number of errors may have crept in here and there when entering our information; we apologize for any such errata and will be glad to hear from you in order to eliminate them from the next edition.

En dépit de nos efforts, certaines erreurs ont pu se glisser dans la saisie et le report des informations recueillies.
Nous prions nos lecteurs de nous en excuser et de nous en informer afin de pouvoir les rectifier dans la prochaine édition.

Data base design & Layout: François GARRY - Printing works: Imprimerie MAURY